TRAVELING WITH YOUR PET
THE AAA PETBOOK®

The AAA guide to more than 13,000
pet-friendly, AAA Approved® hotels
and restaurants across
the United States and Canada.

19th Edition

AAA PUBLISHING

AAA thanks the following organization for its assistance:
Veterinary Emergency & Critical Care Society

Cover Photos

Front: Editors' Pick - Tanner at Arches National Park, Moab, Utah
Submitted by owner Cynthia B. Lytle
Back: 1st place Photo Contest Winner: Jackie in the Painted Desert, Petrified Forest National Park,
Arizona
Submitted by owner Christine Jones
Spine: 2nd place Photo Contest Winner: Orvis at Ocean Park, Oak Bluffs, Martha's Vineyard,
Massachusetts
Submitted by owners Arthur & Linda Everly

Published by AAA Publishing
1000 AAA Drive, Heathrow, Florida 32746

Nineteenth Edition Copyright © 2017 AAA Publishing. All rights reserved.
ISBN: 978-1-59508-592-4 Stock Number 552217
Printed in the USA by Dickinson Press, Inc.

About This Book

Welcome to the 19th edition of *Traveling With Your Pet: The AAA PetBook*®, an indispensable, easy-to-use resource for travelers with pets. This comprehensive book provides all the information needed to take your four-legged friends on the road, from activity planning and trip preparation to finding a place to stay or eat.

Recreational Resources

- Dog parks where you and your furry friends can play, exercise or just relax.
- Popular attractions that allow pets or offer kennel service.
- Recreation information for U.S. and Canadian national public lands that allow pets.

Practical Considerations

- An extensive list of emergency animal clinics for unexpected situations en route and at your destination, compiled by the Veterinary Emergency & Critical Care Society.
- Procedures and tips for crossing the U.S./Canadian border in either direction with pets.
- Policies pertaining to service animals.

Detailed Listings

- More than 12,000 AAA Approved and Diamond Rated hotels, with specific pet policy details: deposits and fees, size restrictions, housekeeping and pet care services, designated rooms and other guidelines. Plus, facility details including room rates, highway directions, amenities, recreation, dining and accessibility.
- About 1,000 AAA Approved and Diamond Rated restaurants that allow pets in outside dining areas. Also, in the Hotels section, page numbers for nearby pet-friendly restaurants are cross-referenced.

Meet the AAA PetBook® Cover Models!

Every so often, we get an entry that's so compelling our editors decide to use it on the book's front cover — separate from the placements designated for our first- and second-place contest winners. This year the honor was awarded to Tanner, a stunning Shetland sheepdog from Arizona.

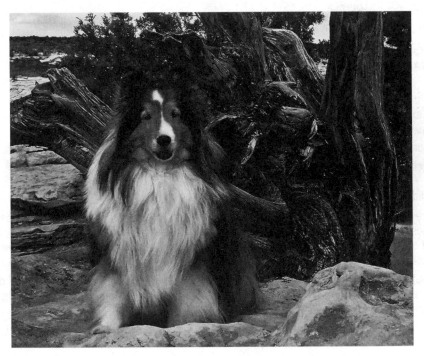

Editors' Pick — Tanner

Tanner is shown here relaxing at Arches National Park in Moab, Utah. On this particular road trip, which his owner says he enjoys, he also traveled to Colorado. Tanner is a certified therapy dog and loves to visit patients at the local cancer center.

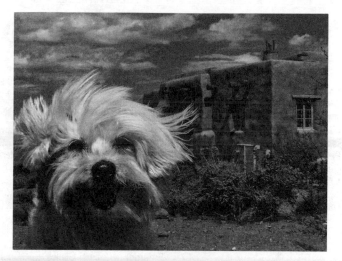

1st place winner — Jackie

Jackie, a Coton de Tulear, poses in the Painted Desert in Petrified Forest National Park, Ariz. This was her family's third 8-week cross-country road trip, and she has now been to all 48 contiguous states. Jackie's family loves seeing her smile and prance from the mountain trails of Idyllwild, Calif., to the dog-friendly beaches of Sanibel Island, Fla.

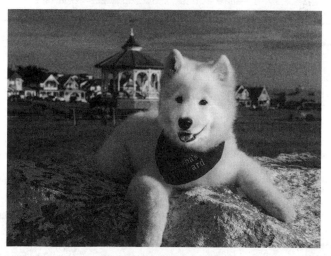

2nd place winner — Orvis

Orvis, a Samoyed, is pictured here resting after an early morning walk through Ocean Park on Martha's Vineyard, Mass. His family likes to plan vacations where they can all be active together. Dog-friendly places and hiking trails around New England are always high on their list of places to go.

Turn to Page p. 321 to view a sampling of more highlights from the last photo contest.

TABLE OF CONTENTS

AAA PetBook® Photo Contest

Traveling With Pets

Pet-Friendly Places

Pet-Friendly Hotels & Restaurants

U.S. Hotels

Canadian Hotels

Restaurants

Many people view their pets as full-fledged members of the family. Spot and Snowball often have their own beds, premium-quality foods, a basketful of toys and a special place in their humans' hearts.

Until it's time to go on vacation, that is. Then the family dog or cat is consigned to "watching the fort" at home while everyone else experiences the joy of traveling. Many animal lovers hesitate to take their pet with them because they don't think they'll be able to find accommodations that accept four-legged guests. Others aren't sure how — or if — their furry friends will adapt.

The truth is, including a pet in the family vacation is fairly easy, so long as you plan ahead. Most pets respond well to travel, a fact that isn't lost on the tourism industry. More than 13,000 AAA Approved hotels and restaurants from coast to coast are pet-friendly, and airline bookings for pet passengers are on the rise. Great companions at home, pets are earning their stripes on the road, too.

So if you've been longing to hit the trail with a canine or feline companion, read the tips on the following pages. You may find that a getaway can be far more enjoyable with than without your pet.

Should Your Pet Travel?

❧ **Rule 1: Pets who are very young, very old, pregnant, sick, injured, prone to biting or excessive vocalizing, or who cannot follow basic obedience commands should not travel.**

Before you make reservations, determine if your pet is able to travel. Most animals can and do make the most of the experience, but a small percentage simply are not cut out for traveling. Illness, physical condition and temperament are important factors, as is your pet's ability to adjust to such stresses as changes to his environment and routine. When in doubt, check with your veterinarian. If you feel your pet isn't up to the trip, it's better for everyone if he stays home.

❧ **Rule 2: If your pet can't actively participate in the trip, she should stay home.**

Even if Spot and Snowball are seasoned travelers, take into account the type of vacation and activities you have planned. No pet is going to be happy (or safe) cooped up in a car or hotel room. Likewise, the family dog may love camping and hiking, but the family cat may not. Putting a little thought toward your animal's needs and safety will pay off in a more enjoyable vacation for everyone.

❧ **Rule 3: Be specific when making travel plans that include your pet. Nobody wants unpleasant surprises on vacation.**

Most of the information in this book pertains to cats and dogs. If you own a bird, hamster, pig, ferret, lizard or other exotic creature, remember that unusual animals are not always accepted as readily as more conventional pets. Always specify the type of pet you have when making arrangements. Check if the municipalities you are traveling through and staying within have breed-specific regulations, i.e. certain dogs not allowed on the premises or even in the municipality. City or county resources should be referenced, as establishments may be unaware of their local restrictions.

Also check states' animal policies. **Hawaii** imposes a 120-day quarantine for all imported dogs, cats and other carnivores to prevent the importation of rabies. In some cases, the quarantine period may be reduced to 5 days or less if a pet meets various pre- and post-arrival requirements. Guide dogs and service dogs are exempt from the quarantine provided they have: a standard health certificate issued within 30 days prior to arrival; a current rabies vaccination with documentation of the product name, lot number and lot expiration date; a successful result of an OIE-FAVN rabies blood test conducted after 1 year of age; and an electronic identification microchip implanted and operational. Upon arrival, guide dogs and service dogs still must be examined for external parasites. For additional details, obtain the Hawaii Rabies Quarantine Information Brochure from the Hawaii Department of Agriculture, Animal Quarantine Station, 99-951 Halawa Valley St., Aiea, HI 96701-5602; phone (808) 483-7151, e-mail rabiesfree@hawaii.gov. Further information also is available from the department's web site: www.hdoa.hawaii.gov/ai/aqs.

North Carolina has stringent restrictions regarding pets in hotels. Make certain you understand an accommodation's specific policies before making reservations.

❧ **Rule 4: Never leave your pet with someone you don't trust.**

If Spot and Snowball stay behind, leave them in good hands while you're gone. **Family, friends and neighbors** make good sitters (provided they're willing), especially if they know your pet and can care for him in your home. Provide detailed instructions for feeding, exercise and medication, as well as phone numbers for your destination, your veterinarian and your local animal emergency clinic.

Professional pet sitters offer a range of services, from feeding and walking your pet daily to full-time house sitting while you are gone. Interview several candidates, and always check credentials and references. For additional information, contact the National Association of Professional Pet Sitters or Pet Sitters International. *(See sidebars on p. 8 and p. 9.)*

Kennels board many animals simultaneously and generally are run by professionals who will provide food and exercise according to your instructions. Pets usually are kept in a run (dogs) or cage (cats and small dogs) and may not get the same level of human interaction as at home. Veterinary clinics also board pets and may be the best choice if yours is sick, injured or needs special medical care.

Veterinarians, fellow pet owners and professional associations are a good source of referrals for sitters and kennels.

Traveling With Service Animals

Individuals with disabilities who own service animals to assist them with everyday activities undoubtedly face challenges, but traveling should not be one of them. Service animals (the accepted term for animals trained to help people with disabilities) are not pets and thus are not subject to many of the laws or policies pertaining to pets.

The Americans With Disabilities Act (ADA) defines a service animal as "any guide dog, signal dog or other animal individually trained to provide assistance to an individual with a disability." ADA regulations stipulate that public accommodations are required to modify policies, practices and procedures to permit the use of a service animal by an individual with a disability.

The purpose of these regulations is to provide equal access opportunities for people with disabilities and to ensure that they are not separated from their service animals. A tow truck operator, for example, must allow a service animal to ride in the truck with her owner rather than in the towed vehicle.

Public accommodations may charge a fee or deposit to an individual who has a disability — provided that fee or deposit is required of all customers — but no fees or deposits may be charged for the service animal, even those normally charged for pets.

CHOOSING A PET SITTER

Before hiring a pet sitter, ask:
- Is he or she insured (for commercial liability) and bonded?
- What is included in the fee?
- Does the sitter require that your pet have a current vaccination?
- What kind of animals does the sitter typically care for?
- How will a medical, weather or home emergency be handled?
- Does he or she fully understand your pet's medical or dietary needs?
- How much time will be spent with your pet?

The pet sitter should:
- Have a polished, professional attitude.
- Provide references.
- Have a standard contract outlining terms of service.
- Have experience in caring for animals.
- Insist on current vaccinations.
- Ask about your pet's health, temperament, schedule and needs.
- Visit and interact with your pet before you leave.
- Devote time and attention to your pet.
- Be affiliated with pet care organizations.

Be sure you:
- Explain your pet's personality — favorite toys, good and bad habits, hiding spots, general health, etc.
- Leave care instructions, keys, food and water dishes, extra supplies (food, medication, etc.), and phone numbers for your veterinarian and an emergency contact.
- Bring pets inside before leaving.

CHOOSING A KENNEL

Before reserving a kennel, ask:
- What is included in the fee?
- Are current vaccinations required?
- What kind of animals do they board?
- How will a medical or weather emergency be handled?
- Will your pet be kept in a cage or run?
- Will your pet receive daily exercise?
- Does the kennel fully understand your pet's medical or dietary needs?
- How and how often will staff interact with your pet?

The kennel should:
- Require proof of current vaccinations.
- Be clean, well-ventilated and offer adequate protection from the elements.
- Have separate areas for dogs, cats and other animals, with secure fencing and caging.
- Clean and disinfect facilities daily.
- Give your pet his regular food on his regular schedule.
- Provide soft bedding in runs/cages.
- Understand your pet's medical needs.
- Provide or obtain veterinary care if necessary.
- Offer sufficient supervision.
- Have a friendly, animal-loving staff.

Be sure you:
- Notify staff of behavior quirks (dislike of other animals, children, etc.).
- Provide food and medication.
- Leave a familiar object with your pet.
- Leave phone numbers for your veterinarian and an emergency contact.
- Spend time with your pet before boarding him.

The handler/owner is responsible for the animal's care and behavior; if the dog creates an altercation or poses a direct threat, the handler may be required to remove it from the premises and pay for any resulting damages.

Pet Partners, an organization devoted to companion and service animals, has information about laws that affect people and service animals in public accommodations. Phone (425) 679-5500 for more information, or visit www.petpartners.org.

Preparing Your Pet for Travel

Happily, many vacations can be planned to include fun activities for pets. Trips to parks, nature trails, the ocean or lakes offer exposure to the world beyond the window or fence at home, as well as the chance to explore new sights and sounds. Even the streets of an unfamiliar city can provide a smorgasbord of discoveries for your animal friend to enjoy.

Once you decide Spot and Snowball are ready to hit the road, plan accordingly:

❧ **Get a clean bill of health from the veterinarian.** Update your pet's vaccinations, check his general physical condition and obtain a health certificate showing proof of up-to-date inoculations, particularly rabies, distemper and kennel cough. Such documentation will be necessary if you cross state or country lines, and also may come in handy in the unlikely event your pet gets lost and must be retrieved from the local shelter. Don't forget to ask the doctor about potential health risks at your destination (Lyme disease, heartworm infection) and the necessary preventive measures.

If your pet is taking prescribed medicine, pack a sufficient supply plus a few days' extra. Also take the prescription in case you need a refill. Be prepared for emergencies by getting the names and numbers of clinics or doctors at your destination from your veterinarian or the American Animal Hospital Association. **Hint:** Obtain these references before you leave and keep them handy throughout the trip.

Make sure your pet is in good physical shape overall, especially if you are planning an active vacation. If your animal is primarily sedentary or overweight, he may not be up to lengthy hikes through the woods.

Note: Some owners believe a sedated animal will travel more easily than one that is fully aware, but this is rarely the case. In fact, tranquilizing an animal can make travel much more stressful. Always consult a veterinarian about what is best for your pet, and administer sedatives only under the doctor's direction. In addition, never give an animal medication that is specifically prescribed for humans. The dosage may be too high for an animal's much smaller body mass, or may cause dangerous side effects.

❧ **Acclimate your pet to car travel.** Even if you're flying, your pet will have to ride in the car to get to the airport or terminal, and you don't want any unpleasant surprises before departure.

Some animals are used to riding in the car and even enjoy it. But most associate the inside of the carrier or the car with one thing only: the annual visit to the V-E-T. Considering that these visits usually end with a jab from a sharp needle, it's no wonder that some pets forget their training and act up in the car. If this is your situation, you will have to re-train your animal to view a drive as a reward, not a punishment.

CONTACT INFORMATION

The following organizations offer information, tips, brochures and other travel materials designed to help you and your pet enjoy a happy and safe vacation.

American Animal Hospital Association
12575 W. Bayaud Ave., Lakewood, CO 80228-2021
(303) 986-2800 — www.aaha.org

American Society for the Prevention of Cruelty to Animals
424 E. 92nd St., New York, NY 10128-6804
(212) 876-7700 — www.aspca.org

American Veterinary Medical Association
1931 N. Meacham Rd., Suite 100
Schaumburg, IL 60173-4360
(800) 248-2862 — www.avma.org

The Humane Society of the United States
1255 23rd St. N.W., Suite 450
Washington, DC 20037-1560
(202) 452-1100 — www.humanesociety.org

National Association of Professional Pet Sitters
1120 Rte. 73, Suite 200
Mt. Laurel, NJ 08054-5113
(856) 439-0324 — www.petsitters.org

Pet Sitters International
201 E. King St., King, NC 27021-9161
(336) 983-9222 — www.petsit.com

USDA-APHIS-Center for Animal Welfare
Beacon Facility Mailstop 1180, 9240 Troost Ave., Kansas City, MO 64131-3055
(816) 737-4200 —
www.aphis.usda.gov/aphis/ourfocus/animalwelfare

Begin by allowing your pet to become used to the car without actually going anywhere. Then take short trips to places that are fun for animals, such as the park or the drive-through window at a fast-food restaurant. (Keep those indulgent snacks to a minimum!) Be sure to praise her for good behavior with words, petting and healthy treats. It shouldn't take long before you and your furry friend are enjoying leisurely drives without incident. *(See Traveling by Car, p. 12.)*

❀ **Brush up on behavior.** Will Snowball make a good travel companion? Or will he be an absolute terror on the road? Don't wait until the vacation is already under way to find out; review general behavioral guidelines with respect to your animal, keeping in mind that the unfamiliarity of travel situations may test the temperament of even the most well-behaved pet.

It's a good idea to socialize Spot by exposing her to other people and animals (especially if she normally stays inside). You're likely to encounter both on your trip, and it is important that she learns to behave properly in the company of strangers. Make her introduction to the outside world gradual, such as a walk in a new neighborhood or taking her along while you run errands. Exposure to new situations will help reduce fear of the unknown and result in more socially acceptable behavior.

Is your pet housebroken? How is he around children? Does he obey vocal commands? Be honest about your animal's ability to cope in unfamiliar surroundings. Depending on the length and nature of the trip and your pet's level of command response, an obedience refresher course might be a good idea.

❀ **Learn about your destination.** Check into quarantines or other restrictions well in advance, and make follow-up calls as your departure date approaches. Find out what types of documentation will be required — not just en route, but on the way home as well.

Be aware of potential safety or health risks where you're going, and plan accordingly. For example, the southeastern United States — particularly Florida — is home to alligators and heartworm-carrying mosquitoes, and many mountainous and wooded areas may harbor ticks that transmit Lyme disease.

Confirm all travel plans within a few days of your departure, especially with hotels and airlines; their policies may have changed after you made the reservations. If you plan to visit state parks or attractions that accept pets on the premises, obtain their animal regulations in advance.

❀ **Determine the best mode of transportation.** Most people traveling with pets drive. Many airlines do accept animals in the passenger cabin or cargo hold, and as more people choose to fly with their pet airlines are becoming more pet-conscious. Restrictions vary as to the type and number of pets an airline will carry, however, so inquire about animal shipping and welfare policies before making reservations. If your pet must travel in the cargo hold, heed the cautionary advice in the Traveling by Air section. *(See p. 13.)*

WHAT TO TAKE

❑ Carrier or crate. *(See Selecting a Carrier or Crate, p. 11, for specifications.)*
❑ Nylon or leather collar or harness, license tag, ID tag(s) and leash. All should be sturdy and should fit your pet properly.
❑ Food and water dishes.
❑ Can opener and spoon (for canned food).
❑ An ample supply of food, plus a few days' extra.
❑ Bottled water from home. (Many animals are finicky about their drinking water.)
❑ Cooler with ice.
❑ Healthy treats.
❑ Medications, if necessary.
❑ Health certificate and other required documents.
❑ A blanket or other bedding. (If your pet is used to sleeping on the furniture, bring an old blanket or sheet to place on top of the hotel's bedding.)
❑ Litter supplies (for cats or other small animals), a scooper and plastic bags (for dogs).
❑ Favorite toys.
❑ Carpet deodorizer.
❑ Chewing preventative.

❑ A recent photograph and a written description including name, breed, gender, height, weight, coloring and distinctive markings.
❑ Grooming supplies:
   comb/brush
   nail clippers
   shampoo
   cloth and paper towels
   cotton balls/tissues
❑ First-aid kit:
   gauze, bandages and adhesive tape
   hydrogen peroxide
   rubbing alcohol
   ointment
   muzzle
   scissors
   tweezers (for removing ticks, burrs, splinters, etc.)
   local emergency phone numbers
   first-aid guide (such as *Pet First Aid: Cats & Dogs*, published by The Humane Society of the United States and the American Red Cross)

Flying is really the only major alternative to car travel. Greyhound and other interstate bus lines do not accept pets. Select Amtrak routes do allow dogs and cats. **Note:** Seeing-eye dogs and other service animals are exempt from the regulations prohibiting pets on Amtrak and interstate bus lines. Local rail and bus companies may allow pets in small carriers, but this is an exception rather than a rule.

The only cruise ship that currently permits pets is the Cunard Line's *Queen Mary 2* (on trans-Atlantic crossings only); kennels are provided, but animals are accepted on a very limited basis. Some small charter and sightseeing boat companies permit pets onboard, however.

A word of advice: Never try to sneak your pet onto any mode of public transportation where she is not permitted. You may face legal action or fines, and the animal may be confiscated if discovered.

✤ **Pack as carefully for your pet as you do for yourself.** *(See What To Take, p. 10.)* Make sure she has a collar with a license tag and ID tag(s) listing her name and yours, along with your address and phone number. As an added precaution, some owners outfit their dog with a second tag listing the name and number of a contact person at home. Popular backup identification methods are to have your animal tattooed with an ID number (usually a social security number) or to implant a microchip under her skin.

If your pet requires medication, make sure that is specified on his tag. This helps others understand your animal's needs and also may prevent people from keeping a found pet or from stealing one to sell.

Note: Choke chains, collars that tighten when they are pulled, may be useful during training sessions, but they do not make good full-time collars. If the chain catches on something, your pet could choke herself trying to pull free. For regular wear, use a harness or a conventional collar made of nylon or leather.

Selecting a Carrier or Crate

This is one of the most important steps in ensuring your pet's safety when traveling. A good-quality carrier not only contains your pet during transit, it also gives him a safe, reassuring place to stay when confinement is necessary at your destination. Acclimate the animal before the trip so he views the crate as a cozy den, not a place of exile.

If you plan to travel by car, a carrier will confine your pet en route, and also may come in handy if Spot or Snowball must stay in the room unsupervised. A secured crate will prevent your pet from escaping from the room when the cleaning staff arrives, or at night if camping in the open. *(See At Your Destination, p. 15.)*

Some airlines allow small pets to travel in the passenger cabin as carry-on luggage. There are no laws dictating the type of carrier to use, but remember that it must be small

enough to fit under a standard airplane seat and should generally not exceed 45 linear inches (length + width + height), or roughly **21.5 by 15.5 by 9 inches.** Depending on the airline, carrier size limits may be even smaller. If your pet will be flying in the cargo hold, you must use a carrier that meets U.S. Department of Agriculture Animal and Plant Health Inspection Service (USDA-APHIS) specifications. *(See Traveling by Air, p. 13.)*

Crates are available at pet supply stores; some airlines also sell carriers. Soft-sided travel bags are handy for flyers with small pets. Before you make the investment, make sure your carrier is airline-approved.

Even if you never take to the skies, these common-sense guidelines provide a good rule of thumb in selecting a crate for other uses. When transporting live animals in airline baggage holds, USDA-APHIS rules stipulate the following:

✤ The crate must be enclosed, but with ventilation openings occupying at least 16 percent of total wall space on two opposing walls, at least one-third of which must be located on the top half of the kennel. A three-quarter-inch lip or rim must surround the exterior to prevent air holes from being blocked.

✤ The crate must open easily, but must be sufficiently strong to hold up during normal cargo transit procedures (loading, unloading, etc.).

✤ The floor must be solid and leakproof, and must be covered with an absorbent lining or material (such as an old towel or litter).

✤ The crate must be just large enough to allow the animal to turn freely while standing, and to have a full range of normal movement while standing or lying down.

✤ The crate must offer exterior grips or handles so that handlers do not have to place their hands or fingers inside.

✤ Food and water dishes must be securely attached and accessible without opening the kennel.

Ventilation openings

Live animal label

Spacer bar

Name and address label

Food and water dishes

HEATSTROKE AND HYPOTHERMIA

The best way to treat heatstroke or hypothermia is to prevent it. Do not leave pets unattended in a car, even if only for a few minutes. Also heed airlines' restrictions on pet travel, and carefully investigate animal welfare policies to make certain the airline has safeguards to protect your pet from both conditions.

Other preventive measures are to avoid strenuous exercise — including such activities as hiking and "fetch" — when the sun is strongest (10 a.m.-2 p.m.), and to provide your pet access to clean, fresh drinking water at all times.

Following are the warning signs and basic first aid for heatstroke and hypothermia. Always be alert to your pet's physical condition and watch for symptoms — immediate attention to the situation may mean the difference between life and death. If your pet is struck with either disorder, take him to an animal hospital or veterinarian as fast as safely possible.

HEATSTROKE

Symptoms
- rapid, shallow breathing
- excessive salivation
- heavy panting
- hot to the touch
- glazed eyes
- unsteadiness, dizziness
- deep red or purple tongue or gums
- vomiting
- body temperature of 104 F or higher

First Aid
- place pet in the shade
- quickly dampen with cool water, especially on the head and neck
- give small amounts of water

HYPOTHERMIA

Symptoms
- shivering
- weakness
- lethargy
- cold to the touch
- body temperature of 95 F or lower

First Aid
- place in a warm area
- wrap in towels or a blanket
- quickly warm by gently massaging the head, chest and extremities

* If the carrier has wheels, they must be removed or immobilized prior to loading.

* One-inch lettering stating "Live Animals" must be placed visibly on the top and on one or more sides and must be accompanied by directional arrows showing the crate's proper orientation. It also is a good idea to label the crate with your name, home address and home phone number, as well as an address and phone number where you can be reached during the trip. **Hint:** Use an adhesive label or an indelible marker and write directly on the crate, as paper may be ripped off accidentally in transit.

* Attach a list of care instructions (feeding, watering, etc.) for a 24-hour period to the exterior of the carrier. This will help airport workers care for your pet if he is sent to the wrong destination.

* If you are traveling with multiple pets, note that crates may contain only one animal whose weight exceeds 20 pounds. Smaller animals may travel together under the following guidelines: one species to a crate, except compatible dogs and cats of similar size; two puppies or kittens under 6 months of age; 15 guinea pigs or rabbits; 50 hamsters. **Note:** These are federal limits; airlines may impose more stringent regulations.

Traveling by Car

The first step in ensuring your pet's well-being during a vacation is to train her to ride in the car. AAA recommends that you restrain your pet in the back seat of the vehicle to avoid distractions as well as to protect the animal and other passengers in the event of a collision. The front airbag can be deadly to a pet during a crash, even if the pet is restrained. Options for restraints include harnesses and crates that can be strapped down. Visit AAA.com/PetBook for additional information about traveling safely with your pet.

To help prevent car sickness, feed your pet a light meal 4 to 6 hours before departing. Do not give an animal food or water in a moving vehicle.

Never allow your pet to ride in the bed of a pickup truck. It's illegal in some states; he also can jump out or be thrown, endangering himself and others on the road. Harnessing or leashing him to the truck bed is not advisable either: If he tries to jump out, he could be dragged along the road or the restraint could become a noose. Avoid placing animals in campers or trailers as well. **If your pet cannot ride in the car with you, leave him at home.**

Don't let your dog stick her head out the window, no matter how enjoyable it seems. Road debris and other flying objects can injure delicate eyes and ears, and the animal is at greater risk for severe injury if the vehicle should stop suddenly or be struck. If it is hot outside, run the air conditioner instead of opening the windows, and be sure that the air flow is reaching your pet.

AAA recommends that drivers stop every 2 hours to stretch their legs and take a quick break from driving. Your pet will appreciate the same break. Plan to visit a rest stop every 4 hours or so to let him have a drink and a chance to answer the call of nature. (Cat owners should bring along a litter box; dog owners should clean up afterward.)

Be sure your pet is leashed before opening the car door. This is not merely a courtesy to fellow travelers; it will prevent her from unexpectedly breaking free and running away. Keep in mind that even the most obedient pet may become disoriented during travel or in strange places and set off for home. **Hint:** If your pet is not used to traveling, use a harness instead of a collar; it is more difficult for an animal to wriggle out of a harness.

NEVER leave an animal in a parked car, even if the windows are partially open. Even on pleasant days the temperature inside a car can soar to well over 100 degrees in less than 10 minutes, placing your pet at risk for heatstroke and possibly death. On very cold days, hypothermia is a risk. Also, animals left unattended in parked cars can be stolen.

Traveling by Air

(Service animals are normally exempt from most of the regulations and fees specified in this section. Check policies with the airline when making reservations.)

Opinion is divided as to whether air travel is truly safe for pets. Statistically, it is less dangerous than being a passenger in a car, but some experts warn of potentially deadly conditions for animals. The truth lies somewhere in between: Most pets arrive at their destination in fine condition, but death or injury is always a possibility. Before you decide to fly, know the risk factors and the necessary precautions to keep your pet safe.

❧ **Determine whether your pet is fit to fly.** The Animal Welfare Act (AWA), administered by USDA-APHIS, specifies that dogs and cats must be at least 8 weeks old and weaned at least 5 days before air travel. Animals that are very young, very old, pregnant, ill or injured should not fly at all. Cats, snub-nosed dogs (pugs, boxers, etc.) and long-nosed dogs (shelties, collies, etc.) are prone to severe respiratory difficulties in an airplane's poorly ventilated cargo hold and should travel only in the passenger cabin (if size allows) with their owner. Some airlines will not accept snub-nosed breeds if the temperature exceeds 75 degrees anywhere in the routing. A few airlines may not allow snub-nosed breeds in the cargo hold at any time of year.

❧ **Decide where your pet will fly.** Most animals fly in the hold as checked baggage when traveling with their owners, or as cargo when they are unaccompanied. The AWA was enacted to ensure animals traveling in this manner are treated humanely and are not subjected to dangerous or life-threatening conditions. For specific requirements pertaining to your animal, check with the airline in advance, as policies vary. Some airlines will not ship dogs as checked baggage, and others will only accept dogs shipped as cargo from "known shippers"; i.e., commercial shippers or licensed pet breeders.

Items classified as "dangerous goods" (dry ice or toxic chemicals, for example) must be transported in a different part of the hold from where live animals are carried. Some planes are designed to have separate hold areas, but so-called "people mover" airlines that are primarily interested in getting human passengers from one point to another as quickly as possible may not give priority to this feature. Check your airline's specific baggage policies so you know exactly where in the hold your pet will be traveling.

Small pets may be taken into the passenger cabin with you as carry-on luggage on most airlines. This places the animal's welfare squarely in your hands but is feasible only if he is very well-behaved and fits comfortably in a container that meets standard carry-on regulations. *(See Selecting a Carrier or Crate, p. 11.)* Keep in mind that the carrier — with the animal inside — must be kept under the seat in front of you throughout the flight. Most airlines charge a fee (anywhere from $50-$125 each way) for carry-on pets. **Note:** AWA regulations do not apply to animals traveling in the cabin.

PET INSURANCE

Just like their owners, pets can experience major medical problems at some point in their lifetime — even those that live indoors. And if illness strikes while you're on the road, it may be necessary to obtain care quickly. As a result, more and more people who travel with their devoted companion are considering pet health insurance.

Insurance plans run the gamut from basic coverage and routine care for illness and injury to comprehensive health maintenance, vaccinations and exams. Annual premiums range from less than $100 to more than $700, depending on the type of pet and plan. When choosing your plan, consider the following:

- What are the enrollment guidelines (age, breed, specific restrictions, etc.)?
- Which expenses are covered and which are excluded?
- What is the plan's policy concerning existing health problems?
- Does the plan allow you to use your own veterinarian?
- How are veterinary fees paid?
- Is a multiple pet discount offered?

❧ **Do your homework.** Investigate the airline's animal transport and welfare policies, especially if you are flying with a small or commuter airline. All airlines are subject to basic AWA regulations, but specific standards of care vary greatly from one company to another. Do your research well in advance and confirm the information 24-48 hours before departing.

The more information an airline provides, the better care your pet is likely to receive. Beware of companies that have vague animal welfare guidelines, or none at all. All major airlines provide information about pet transport on their Web sites. Also talk to fellow travelers and pet owners about their experiences. Finally, keep in mind that airlines are not required to transport live animals and can refuse to carry them for any reason.

❧ **Protect your investment.** Most people think of their pets as part of the family, but the legal system assigns them the same value as a piece of luggage. Inquire about insurance — an airline that won't insure animals in its care may not be the right one for your pet. (Always read the fine print before purchasing any insurance policy.) Also ask if the airline's workers are trained to handle animals. Few are, but it doesn't hurt to check. Remember, it's up to you to choose an airline that values pets and will treat yours with care.

❧ **Understand the potential hazards.** Because a plane's cargo hold is neither cooled nor heated until take-off, the most dangerous time for your pet is that spent on the ground in this unventilated compartment. In summer the space absorbs heat while the plane sits on the tarmac; the reverse is true in winter, when it is no warmer inside the hold than outside. Both instances expose pets to the possibility of serious injury or death from heatstroke or hypothermia. **Note:** The latter also may be a concern during flight if the hold's heater is disabled or turned off, allowing the temperature to drop to near-freezing levels.

To minimize these risks, USDA-APHIS rules prohibit animals from being kept in the hold or on the tarmac for more than 45 minutes when temperatures are above 85 F or below 45 F. Some airlines impose even tighter temperature restrictions and may not permit animals to fly on planes going to cities where the ground temperatures may exceed these limits during certain months of the year. (Exceptions may be made for animals whose veterinarians certify they are acclimated to colder temperatures, but never warmer.)

❧ **Make stress-free travel arrangements.** Once you decide to fly, reserve space for Spot or Snowball when you arrange your own tickets, preferably well in advance of your travel date. Airlines accept only a limited number of animals per flight — usually two to four in the passenger cabin and one pet per passenger — on a first-come, first-served basis. More animals are generally allowed in the cargo hold.

Prepare to pay a fee each way; the cost is often greater for large animals traveling on a flight without their owner. Always reconfirm your reservations and flight information 24-48 hours before departure.

If your pet will be flying in the hold, travel on the same plane and reserve a nonstop flight. This not only reduces the danger of heatstroke or hypothermia during layovers, it also eliminates the possibility that she will be placed on the wrong connecting flight. In summer, fly during the early morning or late evening when temperatures are cooler. Because of large crowds and the chance of heavy air traffic causing delays, avoid holiday travel whenever possible.

Additional precautions may be necessary when traveling outside the United States and Canada. Other countries may impose lengthy quarantines, and airline workers outside North America may not be bound by animal welfare laws. *(See International Travel, p. 17.)*

❧ **Play an active role in your pet's well-being.** Flying safely with your pet requires careful planning and attention to his welfare. See the veterinarian within 10 days of departure for a health certificate (required by most airlines) and a pre-flight check-up.

Address any concerns you have about your pet traveling by air, especially if you are considering tranquilization. Sedation usually is not recommended for cats and dogs, regardless of whether they fly in the cabin or in the hold. Exposure to increased altitude pressure can create respiratory and cardiovascular problems; animals with short,

---

AIRLINE CONTACT INFORMATION

Following is a list of the major North American airlines and their toll-free reservation numbers.

Web site addresses include information about flying with animals. **Hint:** Look under links for baggage, cargo or special travel needs, or do a site search for "pets."

Air Canada . . . .(888) 247-2262
www.aircanada.com

Alaska Airlines . . . .(800) 252-7522
www.alaskaair.com

American Airlines . . . .(800) 433-7300
www.aa.com

Delta Air Lines . . . .(800) 221-1212
www.delta.com

JetBlue Airways . . . .(800) 538-2583
www.jetblue.com

Southwest Airlines . . . .(800) 435-9792
www.southwest.com

United Airlines . . . .(800) 864-8331
www.united.com

wide heads are particularly susceptible to disorientation and possible injury. Sedation should never be administered without your veterinarian's approval.

Obtain an airline-approved carrier and acclimate your pet to its presence by leaving it open with a familiar object inside. A sturdy, well-ventilated crate adds an additional measure of protection.

Because animals are classified as luggage, they may be loaded on the plane via conveyor belt. If the crate falls off the belt, your pet could be injured or released. Ask that she be hand-carried on and off the plane, and that you be permitted to watch both procedures. Also ask about "counter-to-counter" shipping, in which the animal is loaded immediately before departure and unloaded immediately after arrival. There usually is an additional fee for this service.

Make sure you will have access to your pet if there is a lengthy layover or delay. Think twice about flying on an airline that won't allow you to check on your animal under such circumstances.

❀ **Prepare for the flight.** Keep in mind that traveling with an animal will require additional pre-flight time and preparation on your part. Exercise your pet before the flight, and arrive at least 2 but not more than 4 hours before departure. If he is traveling as carry-on luggage, check-in is normally at the passenger terminal; if he is traveling as checked baggage or as cargo in the cargo hold, proceed to the airline's cargo terminal, which is often in a different location. Find this out when making reservations and again when confirming flight information.

Make sure your animal's crate is properly labeled and secured, but do not lock it in case airline personnel have to provide emergency care. Include an ice pack for extra comfort on a hot day or a hot water bottle on a cold day. **Hint:** Wrap in a towel to prevent leaking.

Do not feed your pet less than 4 hours before departure, but provide water up until boarding. **Hint:** Freeze water in the bowl so that it melts throughout the trip, providing a constant drinking source.

Spot or Snowball should wear a sturdy collar (breakaway collars are recommended for cats) and two identification tags marked with your name, home address and phone number, and travel address and phone number. It's also a good idea to clip your pet's nails before departure so they won't accidentally get caught on any part of the carrier.

Note: You may be required to take your pet out of the carrier as you pass through security on your way to the gate. Make sure the animal is wearing a collar and leash or harness.

Attach food and water dishes inside the carrier so that airline workers can reach them without opening the door. If the trip will take longer than 12 hours, also attach a plastic bag with at least one meal's worth of dry food. Animals under 16 weeks of age must be fed every 12 hours, adult animals every 24 hours. Water must be provided at least every 12 hours, regardless of the animal's age.

Allow your pet to answer the call of nature before boarding, but do not take her out of the carrier while in the terminal. As a courtesy, wait until you are outside and away from fellow travelers. Keep her leash with you — do not leave it inside or attached to the kennel.

If your pet is traveling as carry-on luggage, let the passenger sitting next to you know. Someone with allergies may want to change seats.

Perhaps the most important precaution is to alert the flight crew and the captain that your pet is aboard. The pilot must activate the heater for the cargo hold; make sure this is done once you are in the air. If there are layovers or delays, ask the flight crew to be sure your pet has adequate shelter and/or ventilation; better yet, ask them to allow you to check in-person.

If you have arranged to watch your pet being unloaded, ask a flight attendant to call the baggage handlers and let them know you are on the way. Above all, do not hesitate to voice any concerns you have for your pet's welfare — it is your responsibility to do so.

❀ **Be prepared for emergencies.** In the unlikely event your pet gets lost en route, contact the airline, local humane shelters, animal control agencies or USDA-APHIS. Many airlines can trace a pet that was transferred to the wrong flight. If your pet is injured in transit, proceed to the nearest animal hospital; register any complaints with USDA-APHIS. **Hint:** Carry a list of emergency contact numbers and a current photograph of your pet in your wallet or purse, just in case.

At Your Destination

How well you and your companion behave on the road directly affects the way future furry travelers will be treated. Always clean up after your pet and keep him under your control. This is not only a courtesy to fellow human travelers; it's the surest way to enjoy a safe and happy vacation

Inquire about pet policies before making hotel reservations. Properties may impose restrictions on the type or size of pet allowed, or they may designate only certain rooms, such as smoking rooms, for travelers with animals. If you have a dog, get a room on the first floor with direct access outside, preferably near a walking area; keep her leashed on any excursion.

Hotels may have supervision policies requiring that pets be crated when unattended or that they may not be left alone at all. Allow your pet only in designated exercise or animal-approved areas; never take him into such off-limits places as the lobby, pool area, patio or restaurant. Prepare to receive limited housekeeping service, or none at all.

Expect to pay some type of additional charge, which may be per room or per pet and may include any of the following: refundable deposit, non-refundable deposit, daily fee, weekly fee.

If staying with friends or relatives, make certain your pet is a welcome guest. Know and respect their "house rules," especially if they have small children or pets of their own.

Once in the room, check for such hazards as chemically treated toilet water, hiding spaces and electrical cords before freeing your pet. Give her time to adjust to her new surroundings under your supervision.

Above all, practice good "petiquette":

❧ Try not to leave your pet alone, but if you must, crate or otherwise confine her.

❧ Crate at night as well.

❧ To keep your pet and the housekeeper from having an unexpected encounter, leave the "Do Not Disturb" sign on the door when you go out without him.

❧ Barking dogs make poor hotel neighbors — keep your pet quiet.

❧ Don't allow your pet on the furniture. If she insists on sleeping on the bed, bring a bedspread or sheet from home and place that on top of the hotel bedding.

❧ Clean up after your pet immediately — inside the room and out — and leave no trace of him behind when checking out.

❧ Dispose of litter and other "accidents" properly — check with housekeeping.

❧ Notify the management immediately if something is damaged, and be ready to pay for repairs.

❧ Add a little extra to the housekeeping tip.

❧ When you take your pet out of the room, keep her leashed, especially in wilderness areas and around small children. No matter how obedient she is at home, new stimuli and distractions may cause her to forget or ignore vocal commands. Know and obey animal policies at parks, beaches and other public areas. Check before arriving to make certain animals still are welcome, even if you've been there before — the rules may have changed.

❧ Look for outdoor cafes when selecting restaurants. For health reasons, pets are not permitted inside eating establishments, but many restaurants allow animals to sit quietly with their owners at outdoor tables *(see Pet-Friendly Restaurants, p. 593)*. Drive-through restaurants are another alternative.

In Case of Emergency

Be prepared for any turn of events by knowing how to get to the nearest animal hospital. *(See Emergency Animal Clinics, p. 56.)* Also have the name and number of a local animal shelter and a local veterinarian handy — ask your veterinarian for a recommendation. Take first-aid supplies with you and know how to use them. An animal in pain may become aggressive, so exercise caution at all times.

Emergency evacuation shelters do not accept pets, and domesticated animals do not fare well if left to weather an emergency on their own, especially when far from home. Avert a potential tragedy by planning in advance where you will go with your pet in case of evacuation. Use the listings in this book to find other hotels willing to take you and your pet. Above all, don't wait for disaster to strike. Leave as soon as the evacuation order is announced, and take your animal with you.

The Great Outdoors

Travelers planning an active or camping vacation should make some additional preparations. Check in advance to be sure your pet is permitted at campgrounds, parks, beaches, trails and anywhere else you will be visiting. If there are restrictions — and there usually are — follow them. Remember that pets other than service animals usually are not allowed in public buildings.

Note: It is not advisable to take animals other than dogs into wilderness areas. For example, bringing a pet is not recommended at some national parks in Alaska. Also keep in mind that rural areas often have few veterinarians and even fewer boarding kennels.

Use common sense. Clean up after your pet, do not allow excessive vocalizing and keep her under your control. If the property requires your pet to be leashed or crated at all times, do so. Few parks or natural areas will allow a pet to be unattended, even when chained — the risk of disagreeable encounters with other travelers or wildlife is too great. The National Park Service may confiscate pets that harm wildlife or other visitors.

If camping, crate your pet at night to protect him from the elements and predators. (Chaining confines the animal but won't keep him from becoming a midnight snack.)

When hiking, stick to the trail and keep your pet on a short leash. It is all too easy for an unleashed pet to wander off and get lost or fall prey to a larger animal. Keep an eye out for such wildlife as alligators, bears, big cats, porcupines and skunks, and avoid other dogs and small children. Be aware of indigenous poisonous plants, such as English ivy and oleander, or those causing physical injury, such as cactus, poison ivy or stinging nettle. Your veterinarian or local poison control center should be able to give you a full list of hazardous flora.

Before setting out on the trail, make sure both of you are in good physical shape. An animal that rarely exercises at home will not suddenly be ready for a 10-mile trek across uneven terrain. Plan a hike well within the limits of your pet's endurance, and don't push — remember, if Spot gets too tired to make it back on her own, you'll have to carry her.

Carry basic first-aid supplies, including a first-aid guide. *(See What To Take, p. 10.)* Also carry fresh drinking water for both of you — "found" water may contain harmful germs or toxins. Drink often, not just when thirst strikes, and have your pet do the same. Watch for signs of dehydration, leg or foot injuries, heat exhaustion or heatstroke. Stop immediately and return home or to camp if any of these occur.

Note: Dogs can carry their own backpacks (check your local pet store for specially designed packs), but should never carry more than one-third of their body weight. Train the dog to accept the pack beforehand, and only use it with a strong, healthy animal in excellent physical condition.

No matter where or how you spend your vacation, visit the veterinarian when you return home to check for injuries, parasites and general health.

Traveling Between the United States and Canada

Traveling across the international border with your pet — either from the United States into Canada or from Canada into the United States — should prove largely hassle-free, although some basic regulations need to be kept in mind. All U.S. and Canadian citizens traveling between the United States and Canada are required to show a passport or other accepted secure document. For additional information about secure documents visit www.travel.state.gov or phone (877) 487-2778.

U.S. citizens taking pet cats and dogs 3 months of age and older into Canada must carry a rabies vaccination certificate signed by a licensed veterinarian that describes the animal, provides proof of rabies vaccination and includes documentation of the product name, lot number and lot expiration date. Collar tags are not sufficient proof of immunization. The certificate also is needed to bring a pet dog back into the United States; make sure the vaccination doesn't expire while you're in Canada. **Note:** Pit bulls are not permitted to be taken into Ontario.

Service animals are exempt from import restrictions. Also exempt are puppies and kittens under 3 months old; obtain a certificate of health from your veterinarian indicating that the animal is too young to vaccinate. **Note:** For details on pet imports, contact the Canadian Food Inspection Agency (CFIA); phone (800) 442-2342 or visit the Web site at www.inspection.gc.ca. If you need assistance while in Canada, contact the Embassy of the United States of America, 490 Sussex Dr., Ottawa, ON, Canada K1N 1G8; phone (613) 688-5335.

Canadian travelers may take pet cats and dogs into the United States with no restrictions, but U.S. Customs requires that dogs have proof of rabies vaccination no less than 30 days before arrival. For additional information on U.S. regulations, contact the USDA-APHIS National Center for Import & Export, (301) 734-8364.

International Travel

If you plan to travel abroad with Spot or Snowball, prepare for a lengthy flight and at least a short quarantine period. Be aware that airline and animal workers in other countries may not be bound by the same animal welfare laws that exist in the United States and Canada. Contact the embassy or consulate at your destination for information about documentation and quarantine requirements, animal control laws and animal welfare regulations.

As with any trip, have your pet checked by your regular veterinarian within 10 days of departure to obtain a health certificate showing proof of rabies and other inoculations. If you are traveling with an animal other than a domesticated dog or cat, check with USDA-APHIS for restrictions or additional documentation required.

The booklet "Bringing Pets and Wildlife into the United States: Licensing and Health Requirements" has general information about traveling abroad with animals; visit www.cbp.gov.

Note: Island nations such as Australia and the United Kingdom, which are rabies-free, have adopted the Pet Travel Scheme (PETS) to allow entry for dogs, cats and ferrets from the U.S. and Canada without the usual 6-month quarantine. Pets must be tested and vaccinated for rabies at least 21 days prior to travel, be implanted with microchip identification (prior to the rabies vaccination) and receive a certificate of treatment from an official government veterinarian or have a pet passport. For information, visit www.gov.uk/take-pet-abroad. Hawaii, which has a standard 120-day quarantine for all imported animals except guide dogs, has adopted a similar expedited program of 5 days or less; a pet must have been vaccinated at least *twice* for rabies in its lifetime.

Loss Prevention Tips

Searching the woods or an unfamiliar town for a missing pet is easily prevented by following these helpful tips:

🐾 Have your pet wear a sturdy nylon or leather collar with current ID and rabies tags firmly attached. Be sure the ID tag includes the phone number of an emergency contact. Consider having your pet implanted with microchip identification; it's a simple procedure similar to a vaccination.

🐾 Keep your pet on a leash or harness. Even trained animals can become agitated or disoriented in unfamiliar surroundings and fail to obey vocal commands.

🐾 Attach the leash or harness while your pet is still inside the closed car or crate.

🐾 Do not leave your pet unattended at any time, anywhere. A stolen pet is extremely difficult to recover.

🐾 Escape-proof your hotel room by crating your pet and asking hotel management to make certain no one enters your room while you are gone. (Inform the property that you're traveling with an animal when making reservations.)

❖ Take along a recent picture and a detailed written description of your pet.

If your pet gets lost these steps will improve your chances of recovery:

❖ If your pet is lost in transit, contact the airline immediately. Ask to trace the animal via the airline's automated baggage tracking system.

❖ Contact local police, animal control, animal shelters, humane organizations and veterinary clinics with a description and a recent photograph. Stay in contact until your pet is found, and provide your home and destination phone numbers.

❖ Post signs and place an ad in the local newspaper so that anyone who comes across your pet knows she is lost and how to reach you.

The Last Word

You are ultimately responsible for your pet's welfare and behavior while traveling. Since animals cannot speak for themselves, it is up to you to focus on your pet's well-being every step of the way. It also is important to make sure he conducts himself properly so that other pets will be welcome visitors in the future. Following the common-sense information in this book will help ensure that both you and your animal companion have a safe and happy trip.

Pet-Friendly Places

in the United States and Canada

Dog Parks
Attractions
National Public Lands
Emergency Animal Clinics

DOG PARKS

A dog park is a place where people and their dogs can play together. These places offer dogs an area to play, exercise and socialize with other dogs while their owners enjoy the park-like setting. Dog park size and features vary greatly from location to location, from several hundred square feet in urban areas to several hundred acres in the suburbs and rural locations. Dog owners should remember to always keep their animal leashed until they reach the dog park entrance, to maintain voice control of their animal at all times, to bring their own supply of bags for picking up after their pet (and to be diligent in doing so), and to always have fresh water available for their dog. Please observe all dog park rules. The dog parks listed here welcome people who travel with their dogs; private parks or parks requiring local residency are not included. **Note:** Fence types and heights vary, and some areas have no fencing at all, requiring that the dog be under firm voice control.

United States

ALABAMA

Cahaba Beach Dog Park - Birmingham
www.cbdogpark.com, (205) 397-3647
3555 Cahaba Beach Rd., 35242.
Daily 8-8, May-Oct.; 8-6, rest of year.
Fenced, 2.5 acres, trees, trails, streams, dog beach, staffed, separate areas for large and small dogs.

Loch Haven Dog Park - Hoover
www.hooveralabama.gov/index.aspx?nid=667,
(205) 444-7500
3469 Loch Haven Dr., 35216.
Daily dawn-dusk.
Fenced, 17 acres, obstacle course, .4-mile walking track, picnic area.

Moss Rock Preserve - Hoover
www.hooveralabama.gov/index.aspx?nid=214,
(205) 823-1641
616 Preserve Pkwy., 35226.
Daily dawn-dusk.
Fenced, rocks for climbing, trees, trails. Dogs must be leashed.

ARIZONA

Echo Mountain Off-Leash Area - Phoenix
www.phoenix.gov/parks/parks/dog-parks, (602) 262-6696
17447 N. 20th St., 85022.
Daily dawn-dusk.
Fenced, 2.3 acres, grass surface, separate areas for large and small dogs, disposal bags and trash cans, drinking fountains in both areas, double-gated entryways.

Hance Dog Park - Phoenix
www.friendsofhancedogpark.com, (623) 850-4716
323 W. Culver St., 85003.
Daily 6:30 a.m.-9 p.m.
Fenced, 1 acre, drinking fountains with integrated water bowls, benches, sound buffer, trees.

Petsmart Dog Park at Washington Park - Phoenix
www.phoenix.gov/parks/parks/dog-parks, (602) 262-6971
6503 N. 21st Ave., 85015.
Daily 6:30 a.m.-10 p.m.
Fenced, 2.65 acres, separate areas for large and small dogs, two double-gated entryways, grass surface, drinking fountains, benches, disposal bags and trash cans.

RJ Dog Park at Pecos Park - Phoenix
www.phoenix.gov/parks/parks/dog-parks/pecos-dog-park,
(602) 534-5252
17010 48th St., 85048.
Daily 6 a.m.-11 p.m.
Fenced, 2 acres, separate areas for large and small dogs, double-gated entryways, drinking fountain, lighted, disposal bags and trash cans.

Rose Mofford Sports Complex Dog Park - Phoenix
www.phoenix.gov/parks/parks/dog-parks/mofford-dog-park,
(602) 261-8011
9833 N. 25th Ave., 85021.
Daily 6:30 a.m.-10 p.m.
Fenced, 2.5 acres, separate areas for large and small dogs, double-gated entryways, drinking fountains, benches, trees, disposal bags and trash cans.

Steele Indian School Park - Phoenix
www.phoenix.gov/parks/parks/dog-parks/steele-dog-park,
(602) 495-0739
300 E. Indian School Rd., 85012.
Daily 6 a.m.-10 p.m.
Fenced, 1.63 acres, separate areas for large and small dogs, double-gated entryways, drinking fountain, cement pathways, grass surface.

Christopher Columbus Park - Tucson
www.tucsonaz.gov/parks/dog-parks, (520) 791-5909
4600 N. Silverbell Rd., 85745.
Daily dawn-dusk.
Fenced, less than 1 acre, lighted, drinking fountain, agility equipment, shade, covered pavilion, disposal scoop and trash cans.

Jacobs Park - Tucson
www.tucsonaz.gov/parks/dog-parks, (520) 791-5909
3300 N. Fairview Ave., 85705.
Daily dawn-dusk.
Fenced, less than 1 acre, grass and cement surface, picnic area, disposal bags and trash cans.

Miko's Corner Playground at Reid Park - Tucson
www.tucsonaz.gov/parks/dog-parks, (520) 791-4873
900 S. Randolph Way, 85716.
Daily 7 a.m.-10 p.m.
Fenced, 2 acres, double-gated entryway, lighted, separate areas for large and small dogs, drinking fountains, covered pavilion with picnic area.

Palo Verde Park - Tucson
www.tucsonaz.gov/parks/dog-parks, (520) 791-5930
300 S. Mann Ave., 85710.
Daily 6 a.m.-10:30 p.m.
Fenced, less than 1 acre, separate areas for large and small dogs, lighted, picnic areas, double-gated entryway, disposal scoops and trash cans, drinking fountains.

Purple Heart Park - Tucson
www.tucsonaz.gov/parks/dog-parks, (520) 791-4873
10050 E. Rita Rd., 85747.
Daily 7 a.m.-10 p.m.
Fenced, 1 acre, separate areas for large and small dogs, double-gated entryway, walking path, drinking fountains, trees, benches, granite gravel surface, lighted.

Sixth Avenue Dog Park - Tucson
www.tucsonaz.gov/parks/dog-parks, (520) 791-5909
2075 N. 6th Ave., 85705.
Daily dawn-dusk.
Fenced, grass and gravel surface, covered pavilion, dog wash area, picnic area, double-gated entryway.

Udall Park - Tucson
www.tucsonaz.gov/parks/dog-parks, (520) 791-4931
7290 E. Tanque Verde Rd., 85715.
Daily 6 a.m.-10 p.m.
Fenced, less than 1 acre, gravel and artificial turf surface, benches, drinking fountains.

CALIFORNIA

Wildcatters Dog Park - Brea
www.ci.brea.ca.us, (714) 671-4437
3450 E. Santa Fe Rd., 92821.
Fri.-Wed. 7 a.m.-dusk, Thurs. noon-dusk.
Benches, dog water fountains, picnic tables, double-entry gates, grass turf, separate areas for large and small dogs, dog waste clean-up stations.

Fullerton Pooch Park - Fullerton
www.fullertondogparkfoundation.org, (714) 738-6575
210 S. Basque Ave., 92832.
Thurs.-Tues. 7 a.m.-8 p.m.
Fenced, three areas for large and small dogs, grass, wood chip surface, disposal bags and trash cans.

Huntington Dog Beach - Huntington Beach
www.dogbeach.org, (714) 841-8644
100 Goldenwest St., 92648.
Daily 6 a.m.-10 p.m. Parking: $1.50/hour.
One-mile stretch of beach, disposal bags and trash cans, restrooms, lifeguard station.

Laguna Beach Dog Park - Laguna Beach
www.lagunabeachdogpark.com, (949) 910-9947
20672 Laguna Canyon Rd., 92651.
Thurs.-Tues. dawn-dusk.
Fenced, 2 acres, grass, separate areas for large and small dogs, drinking fountains, benches, shade.

Arroyo Seco Dog Park at Hermon Park - Los Angeles
www.laparks.org, (323) 255-0370
5568 Via Marisol, 90042.
Daily dawn-dusk.
Fenced, 1.3 acres, benches, drinking fountains, restrooms, separate areas for large and small dogs, lighted.

Barrington Dog Park - Los Angeles
www.laparks.org/dogpark/barrington, (310) 476-4866
333 S. Barrington Ave., 90049.
Wed.-Mon. 5 a.m.-10:30 p.m., Tues. 10 a.m.-10:30 p.m.
Fenced, 1.5 acres, separate areas for large and small dogs, benches, drinking fountain, three-dog limit, mulch surface.

Griffith Dog Park - Los Angeles
www.laparks.org/dogpark/griffith, (323) 913-4688
4701 Zoo Dr., 90027.
Daily dawn-dusk.
Fenced, 1.5 acres, separate areas for large and small or timid dogs, picnic tables, drinking troughs, drinking fountain, restrooms.

Laurel Canyon Dog Park - Los Angeles
www.laparks.org/dogpark/laurel-canyon, (818) 769-4415
8260 Mulholland Dr., 90046.
Sat.-Thurs. 6 a.m.-dusk, Fri. 11-dusk.
Fenced, 3 acres, separate areas for large and small or timid dogs, grass, wash station, restrooms.

Runyon Canyon Dog Park - Los Angeles
www.laparks.org/dogpark/runyon-canyon, (323) 666-5046
2000 N. Fuller Ave., 90046.
Daily dawn-dusk.
Fenced, 90 acres, hiking and walking trails.

Silverlake Dog Park - Los Angeles
www.laparks.org/dogpark/silverlake, (323) 644-3946
1850 W. Silver Lake Dr., 90026.
Thurs.-Tues. 6 a.m.-10 p.m., Wed. 8:30 a.m.-10 p.m.
Fenced, 1.25 acres, separate areas for large and small dogs, gravel surface, lighted.

Canine Commons at Alston Park - Napa
www.cityofnapa.org, (707) 257-9529
2099 Dry Creek Rd., 94558.
Daily dawn-dusk.
39 acres, agility equipment, dog water fountain, double-gated entry, disposal bags.

Whitnall Off-Leash Dog Park - North Hollywood
www.laparks.org, (818) 756-8190
5801 Whitnall Hwy., 91601.
Daily dawn-dusk.
Fenced, 3 acres, separate areas for large and small dogs, grass, drinking fountains, lighted, disposal bags and trash cans, water bowls, common tennis balls.

Alice Frost Kennedy Dog Park - Pasadena
pasadenapooch.org, (626) 577-8738
3026 E. Orange Grove Blvd., 91107.
Daily 6 a.m.-10 p.m.
Fenced, 2.5-acre grassy area, separate areas for large dogs and small and special-needs dogs, trees, benches, drinking fountains.

Cadman Community Park - San Diego
www.sandiego.gov/park-and-recreation/parks/dogs/leashfree, (619) 525-8213
4280 Avati Dr., 92117.
Daily 7-9:30, 5-7. Phone ahead to confirm schedule.
Fenced, trees, shade, grass surface, restrooms.

Capehart Park - San Diego
www.sandiego.gov/park-and-recreation/parks/dogs/leashfree, (619) 221-8901
4747 Soledad Mountain Rd., 92109.
Daily 24 hours.
Fenced, 1 acre, separate areas for large and small dogs, drinking fountains, picnic tables, benches.

Doyle Community Park - San Diego
www.sandiego.gov/park-and-recreation/parks/dogs/leashfree, (619) 525-8213
8175 Regents Rd., 92122.
Daily 24 hours.
Fenced, separate areas for large and small dogs, drinking fountains, grass surface.

Kearny Mesa Community Park - San Diego
www.sandiego.gov/park-and-recreation/parks/dogs/leashfree, (619) 525-8212
3170 Armstrong St., 92111.
Daily 6:30 a.m.-10 p.m.
Fenced, 1 acre, lighted, drinking fountains, separate areas for large and small dogs, disposal bags and trash cans, restrooms, trees.

Maddox Neighborhood Park - San Diego
www.sandiego.gov/park-and-recreation/parks/dogs/leashfree, (619) 525-8213
7815 Flanders St., 92126.
Daily dawn-dusk.
Fenced, less than 1 acre, artificial turf surface, drinking fountain.

Nate's Point Dog Park at Balboa Park - San Diego
www.npdog.org/park.html, (619) 325-5620
2500 Balboa Dr., 92103.
Daily 24 hours.
Fenced, trees, benches, picnic area, disposal bags and trash cans, drinking fountains, grass surface.

Rancho Peñasquitos Park - San Diego
www.sandiego.gov/park-and-recreation/parks/dogs/leashfree, (619) 525-8213
13292 Salmon River Rd., 92129.
Daily dawn-dusk.
Fenced, 1 acre, double-gated entryway, separate areas for large and small dogs, benches, drinking fountains, artificial turf surface.

Alamo Square Dog Play Area - San Francisco
sfrecpark.org/parks-open-spaces/dog-play-areas-program, (415) 218-0259
1012 Hayes St., 94117.
Daily dawn-dusk.
10 acres, open grass field, shaded slopes, bushes, city views, picnic tables, dog play area.

Alta Plaza Park - San Francisco
sfrecpark.org/parks-open-spaces/dog-play-areas-program, (415) 292-2012
Jackson & Steiner sts., 94115.
Daily dawn-dusk.
Fenced, less than 1 acre, grass surface, restrooms, paved pathways.

Bernal Heights Dog Park - San Francisco
sfrecpark.org/parks-open-spaces/dog-play-areas-program, (415) 831-2084
3458 Folsom St., 94110.
Daily dawn-dusk.
39 acres, city views, disposal bags and trash cans, gravel trails, drinking fountains, benches.

Buena Vista Park - San Francisco
sfrecpark.org/parks-open-spaces/dog-play-areas-program, (415) 831-2084
1106 Haight St., 94117.
Daily dawn-dusk.
35 acres, paved and dirt paths, trees, shade, bench, grass.

Corona Heights Dog Play Area - San Francisco
sfrecpark.org/parks-open-spaces/dog-play-areas-program, (415) 819-2699
Roosevelt & Museum Way, 94114.
Daily dawn-dusk.
Fenced, double-gated entryway, drinking fountains, mulch surface.

Douglass Dog Play Area - San Francisco
sfrecpark.org/parks-open-spaces/dog-play-areas-program, (415) 970-8063
26th & Douglass sts., 94131.
Daily dawn-dusk.
Fenced, 1.6 acres, hills, drinking fountains, benches, trees, disposal bags and trash cans, walking path.

Eureka Valley Dog Play Area - San Francisco
sfrecpark.org/parks-open-spaces/dog-play-areas-program, (415) 831-6810
100 Collingwood St., 94114.
Daily 6 a.m.-10 p.m.
Fenced, less than 1 acre, trash cans, shade, benches, double-gated entryway, sand surface.

Head & Brotherhood Dog Play Area - San Francisco
sfrecpark.org/parks-open-spaces/dog-play-areas-program, (415) 831-2700
Head St. & Brotherhood Way, 94122.
Daily dawn-dusk.
Less than 1 acre, grass surface, trees, disposal bags and trash cans.

Lafayette Park Dog Play Area - San Francisco
sfrecpark.org/parks-open-spaces/dog-play-areas-program, (415) 831-2700
Washington & Laguna sts., 94109.
Daily dawn-dusk.
Fenced, less than 1 acre, drinking fountains, disposal bags and trash cans, mulch surface, restrooms, picnic area.

McKinley Square - San Francisco
sfrecpark.org/parks-open-spaces/dog-play-areas-program, (415) 831-6358
2301 20th St., 94107.
Daily dawn-dusk.
Less than 1 acre, grass surface, walking trails.

Mission Dolores Park Dog Play Areas - San Francisco
sfrecpark.org/parks-open-spaces/dog-play-areas-program, (415) 831-2700
568 Dolores St., 94110.
Daily dawn-dusk.
Grass surface, two off-leash play areas, hills, benches, covered pavilions.

St. Mary's Dog Park - San Francisco
sfrecpark.org/parks-open-spaces/dog-play-areas-program, (415) 695-5006
95 Justin Dr., 94112.
Daily dawn-dusk.
Fenced, trees, grass surface, shade, benches, drinking fountains.

Roy M. Butcher Dog Park - San Jose
www.sanjoseca.gov/facilities/Facility/Details/19, (408) 535-3500
3950 Camden Ave., 95109.
Daily dawn-1 hour after dusk.
Fenced, 10 acres, separate areas for large and small dogs, benches, restrooms.

Selma Olinder Park - San Jose
www.sanjoseca.gov/facilities/Facility/Details/123, (408) 535-3500
848 E. Williams St., 95116.
Daily dawn-1 hour after dusk.
Fenced, separate areas for large and small dogs, mulch surface, double-gated entryway, drinking fountain, shade, benches.

Sepulveda Basin Off-Leash Dog Park - Van Nuys
www.laparks.org/dogpark/sepulveda, (818) 756-7667
17550 Victory Blvd., 91406.
Daily dawn-dusk.
Fenced, 5 acres, separate areas for large and small or timid dogs, grass, shade, drinking fountains with water bowls, picnic tables.

Westminster Dog Park - Venice
www.laparks.org/dogpark/westminster, (310) 396-6794
1234 Pacific Ave., 90291.
Wed.-Mon. dawn-dusk, Tues. 10-dusk.
Fenced, less than 1 acre, separate areas for large and small dogs, mulch.

COLORADO

Cheyenne Meadows Dog Park - Colorado Springs
coloradosprings.gov/dogparks, (719) 385-5940
1560 Charmwood Dr., 80906.
Daily dawn-dusk.
Fenced, grass, benches, disposal bags.

Garden of the Gods Dog Run - Colorado Springs
www.gardenofgods.com/parkinfo/index_109.cfm,
(719) 634-6666
1805 N. 30th St., 80904.
Daily 5 a.m.-11 p.m., May-Oct.; 5 a.m.-9 p.m., rest of year.
Less than 1 acre, benches, walking and hiking trails, trash cans.

Palmer Park Ute Crest Dog Run - Colorado Springs
coloradosprings.gov/dogparks, (719) 385-5940
3650 Maizeland Rd., 80909.
Daily 5 a.m.-11 p.m., May-Oct.; 5 a.m.-9 p.m., rest of year.
Fenced area for small dogs, picnic area, walking and hiking trails.

Rampart Dog Park - Colorado Springs
coloradosprings.gov/dogparks, (719) 385-5940
8270 Lexington Dr., 80920.
Daily 5 a.m.-11 p.m., May-Oct.; 5 a.m.-9 p.m., rest of year.
Fenced, drinking fountains, water bowls, benches, shade, agility course, trash can.

Red Rock Canyon Open Space - Colorado Springs
www.redrockcanyonopenspace.org/recreation/maps,
(719) 385-5940
3550 W. High St., 80904.
Daily 5 a.m.-11 p.m., May-Oct.; 5 a.m.-9 p.m., rest of year.
Two off-leash areas, 5/8 mile in length, walking and hiking trails.

Chatfield State Park Dog Off-Leash Area (DOLA) - Littleton
cpw.state.co.us/off-leash, (303) 791-7275
11500 N. Roxborough Park Rd., 80125.
Daily 5 a.m.-10 p.m. $2.
69 acres, paved and unpaved trails, two ponds.

DISTRICT OF COLUMBIA

Gage-Eckington Dog Park - Washington, D.C.
www.dpr.dc.gov/page/dog-parks, (202) 673-7647
286 V St. N.W., 20001.
Daily dawn-dusk.
Fenced, less than 1 acre, grass surface, disposal bags and trash cans.

Guy Mason Dog Park - Washington, D.C.
www.dogsofguymason.wordpress.com, (202) 673-7647
3600 Calvert St. N.W., 20008.
Mon.-Fri. 9 a.m.-10 p.m., Sat. 9-5.
Fenced, double-gated entryway, drinking fountain, disposal bags and trash cans, benches, shade, restrooms.

Langdon Dog Park - Washington, D.C.
www.langdondogpark.org, (202) 673-7647
2901 20th St. N.E., 20018.
Daily dawn-dusk.
Fenced, gravel surface, drinking fountains, separate areas for large and small dogs, disposal bags and trash cans.

Newark Street Dog Park - Washington, D.C.
www.newarkstdogpark.wordpress.com, (202) 673-7647
3878 Newark St. N.W., 20008.
Mon.-Fri. 7-dusk, Sat.-Sun. 8-dusk, Apr.-Oct.; Mon.-Fri. 7 a.m.-7:30 p.m., Sat.-Sun. 8-7:30, rest of year.
Fenced, double-gated entryway, benches, shade, covered pavilion, granite gravel surface, separate areas for large and small dogs, disposal bags and trash cans, common tennis balls.

Shaw Dog Park - Washington, D.C.
www.shawdogs.org, (330) 737-1364
1673 11th St. N.W., 20001.
Mon.-Fri. 7 a.m.-10 p.m., Sat.-Sun. 8 a.m.-10 p.m.
Fenced, separate areas for large and small or senior dogs, common water and water bowls, gravel surface, lighted.

S Street Dog Park - Washington, D.C.
www.dpr.dc.gov/page/dog-parks, (202) 673-7647
1706 S St. N.W., 20009.
Mon.-Fri. 7 a.m.-8 p.m., Sat.-Sun. 8-8.
Fenced, double-gated entryway, artificial turf surface, drinking fountain, benches, trees, shade.

Upshur Dog Park - Washington, D.C.
www.dpr.dc.gov/page/dog-parks, (202) 576-6842
4300 Arkansas Ave. N.W., 20011.
Mon.-Fri. 7 a.m.-9 pm., Sat.-Sun. 8 a.m.-9 p.m.
Fenced, double-gated entryway, disposal bags and trash cans, drinking fountains, gravel surface.

Walter Pierce Dog Park - Washington, D.C.
www.dpr.dc.gov/page/dog-parks, (202) 673-7647
2700 Adams Mill Rd. N.W., 20009.
Daily dawn-dusk.
Fenced, double-gated entryway, sand surface, trees, shade.

FLORIDA

Crest Lake Dog Park - Clearwater
www.clearwater-fl.com/gov/depts/parksrec, (727) 562-4800
201 S. Glenwood Ave., 33755.
Daily 6 a.m.-9 p.m.
Fenced, 1.75 acres, double-gated entryway, benches, disposal bags and trash cans, drinking fountains, water bowls, leash holders, wash station.

Enterprise Dog Park - Clearwater
www.myclearwater.com, (727) 562-4800
2671 Enterprise Rd. E., 33761.
Daily dawn-dusk.
Fenced, drinking fountains, dog wash station, agility equipment, benches, disposal bags and trash cans, covered picnic areas.

Gemini Springs Dog Park - Debary
www.volusia.org, (386) 668-3810
37 Dirksen Dr., 32713.
Daily dawn-dusk.
Fenced, 4.5 acres, separate areas for larger dogs (over 25 lbs.) and smaller dogs, shaded areas, dog wash stations, water fountains, benches.

Canine Beach - Fort Lauderdale
www.fortlauderdale.gov/departments/parks-recreation,
(954) 564-4521
3109 E. Sunrise Blvd., 33304.
Fri.-Sun. 3-7, Nov.-Feb.; Fri.-Sun. 5-9, rest of year.
Park ranger on duty, disposal bags and trash cans, beach showers, drinking fountains.

Snyder Park - Fort Lauderdale
www.fortlauderdale.gov/departments/parks-recreation,
(954) 828-4341
3299 S.W. 4th Ave., 33315.
Daily 7-7, Mar.-Oct.; 7-6, rest of year. Sat.-Sun. $5 per day, $1 per hour; Mon.-Fri. free.
Fenced, separate areas for large and small dogs, agility course, drinking fountains, disposal bags and trash cans, benches, trees, dog beach.

Riviera Oaks Dog Park - Holly Hill
www.rivieraoaksdogpark.org, (832) 596-4048
980 Alabama Ave., 32117.
Daily dawn-dusk.
Benches, covered pavilion, separate areas for large and small dogs, water stations, restrooms.

Confederate Park Dog Park - Jacksonville
www.visitjacksonville.com/directory/confederate-park-dog-park,
(904) 630-2489
956 Hubbard St., 32206.
Mon.-Fri. 8 a.m.-10 p.m.
Fenced, 3 acres, disposal bags and trash cans, covered
pavilions, drinking fountain.

Higgs Beach Dog Park - Key West
www.monroecounty-fl.gov, (305) 295-4385
Atlantic Blvd., 33040.
Daily 6 a.m.-11 p.m.
Separate areas for large and small dogs, water fountains,
picnic tables, disposal bags.

Amelia Earhart Bark Park - Miami
www.miamidade.gov/parks, (305) 685-8389
401 E. 65th St., 33138.
Daily dawn-dusk. Parking: Sat.-Sun. $7 per private vehicle.
Fenced, 5 acres, separate areas for large and small dogs,
shade, cement and grass surfaces, benches, picnic areas,
drinking fountains, disposal bags and trash cans.

Blanche Park - Miami
www.miamigov.com, (305) 960-2946
3045 Shipping Ave., 33133.
Daily dawn-dusk.
Fenced, turf and grass surfaces, trees, shade, drinking
fountains, disposal bags and trash cans, benches.

Perrine Wayside Park - Miami
www.palmettobay-fl.gov/node/95, (305) 259-1234
16425 S. Dixie Hwy., 33157.
Daily 8-8.
Fenced, 3 acres, separate areas for large and small dogs,
disposal bags and trash cans, dog pond, grass, walking
trails, wash station, drinking fountains, trees, benches, picnic
tables, two entrances.

West Kendall District Park - Miami
www.miamidade.gov/parks/facilities-dog-parks.asp,
(305) 386-0227
11255 S.W. 157th Ave., 33196.
Daily 9-6.
Fenced, 6.5 acres, agility courses, separate areas for large
and small dogs, drinking fountain, water sprays, shade,
picnic areas, disposal bags and trash cans, benches,
restrooms.

Flamingo Bark Park - Miami Beach
web.miamibeachfl.gov/parksandrecreation, (305) 673-7766
1200 Meridian Ave., 33139.
Daily 7 a.m.-9 p.m.
Fenced, less than 1 acre, double-gated entrance, benches,
shade, separate areas for large and small dogs, grass,
drinking fountains, disposal bags and trash cans.

North Shore Open Space Park - Miami Beach
web.miamibeachfl.gov/parksandrecreation, (305) 861-3616
8101 Collins Ave., 33141.
Daily dawn-dusk.
Fenced, 1 acre, double-gated entrance, separate areas for
large and small dogs, drinking fountains, dog bowls, walking
paths, benches, disposal bags and trash cans, beach
access.

Pinetree Bark Park - Miami Beach
web.miamibeachfl.gov/parksandrecreation, (305) 673-7730
4400 Pinetree Dr., 33140.
Daily dawn-dusk.
Double-gated entry, grass, benches, drinking fountains,
disposal bags and trash cans.

South Pointe Park - Miami Beach
web.miamibeachfl.gov/parksandrecreation, (305) 673-7766
1 Washington Ave., 33109.
Daily dawn-7 p.m.
Fenced, less than 1 acre, double-gated entrance, drinking
fountains, picnic tables, benches.

Washington Avenue Bark Park - Miami Beach
web.miamibeachfl.gov/parksandrecreation, (305) 673-7766
201 2nd St., 33139.
Daily dawn-dusk.
Fenced, disposal bags and trash cans, trees, double-gated
entry, shade, grass surface, drinking fountains, wash station,
benches.

East Greynolds Dog Park - North Miami Beach
www.miamidade.gov/parks/facilities-dog-parks.asp,
(305) 945-3425
16700 Biscayne Blvd., 33160.
Daily dawn-dusk. Parking: $7.
Fenced, 2 acres, separate areas for large and small
dogs, drinking fountains, wash stations, walkways, shade,
grass.

Barber Park - Orlando
www.ocfl.net/CultureParks/DogParks.aspx, (407) 254-6860
3701 Gatlin Ave., 32812.
Daily 8-8, in summer; 8-6, rest of year.
Fenced, shade, covered pavilion, drinking fountain, common
water bowls, grass and cement surface, disposal bags and
trash cans, benches, separate areas for large and small
dogs.

Barnett Park - Orlando
www.ocfl.net/CultureParks/DogParks.aspx, (407) 836-6248
4801 W. Colonial Dr., 32808.
Mon.-Sat. 8-8, Sun. 1-8.
Fenced, benches, grass surface, disposal bags and trash
cans.

Downey Dog Park - Orlando
www.ocfl.net/CultureParks/DogParks.aspx, (407) 254-9180
10107 Flowers Ave., 32825.
Daily 8-8, in summer; 8-6, rest of year.
Fenced, benches, separate areas for large and small dogs,
grass surface, wash station.

Dr. Phillips Dog Park - Orlando
www.ocfl.net/CultureParks/DogParks.aspx, (407) 254-9045
8249 Buenavista Woods Blvd., 32836.
Daily 8-8, in summer; 8-6, rest of year.
Fenced, separate areas for large and small dogs, grass and
mulch surface, splash area, benches, trees, disposal bags
and trash cans.

Meadow Woods Dog Park - Orlando
www.ocfl.net/CultureParks/DogParks.aspx, (407) 858-4725
1751 Rhode Island Woods Cir., 32824.
Daily 8-8, in summer; 8-6, rest of year.
Fenced, separate areas for large and small dogs, benches,
grass, drinking fountains, walking paths.

Park of the Americas - Orlando
www.cityoforlando.net/parks/park-americas, (407) 246-2283
201 Andes Ave., 32807.
Daily 8 a.m.-30 minutes before dusk.
Fenced, separate areas for large and small dogs, grass,
shade, drinking fountain, covered pavilion, benches, disposal
bags and trash cans.

Yucatan Park - Orlando
www.ocfl.net/CultureParks/DogParks.aspx, (407) 254-9160
6400 Yucatan Dr., 32807.
Daily 8-8, in summer; 8-6, rest of year.
Fenced, separate areas for large and small dogs, benches,
trees, covered pavilion, drinking fountain.

Veterans Park Dog Park - Saint Johns
www.co.st-johns.fl.us/recreation/parks/Veterans.aspx,
(904) 209-0655
1332 Veterans Pkwy., 32259.
Daily dawn-dusk.
Fenced, 3 acres, separate areas for large and small dogs,
drinking fountains, picnic areas, disposal bags and trash
cans.

Paw Park - Sanford
www.pawparksanford.org, (407) 688-5103
427 S. French Ave., 32771.
Daily 8-dusk.
Fenced, shade, drinking fountains, grass and cement
surface, dog wash station, disposal bags and trash cans,
benches, agility equipment, separate areas for large and
small dogs, lighted.

Paws Dog Park at Treaty Park - St. Augustine
www.co.st-johns.fl.us/Recreation/Parks/TreatyDogPark.aspx,
(904) 209-0655
1595 Wildwood Dr., 32086.
Daily dawn-dusk.
Fenced, drinking fountain, separate areas for large and
small dogs, shade, benches.

Coquina Key Dog Park - St. Petersburg
www.stpeteparksrec.org, (727) 893-7441
3595 Locust St. S.E., 33705.
Daily dawn-dusk.
Fenced, drinking fountains, shade, trees, agility equipment,
disposal bags and trash cans, wash station.

Crescent Lake Dog Park - St. Petersburg
www.stpeteparksrec.org, (727) 893-7335
1320 5th St. N., 33704.
Daily dawn-dusk.
Fenced, double-gated entryway, separate areas for large
and small dogs, grass and gravel surface, benches, drinking
fountain, disposal bags and trash cans.

Kenwood Dog Park - St. Petersburg
www.stpeteparksrec.org/dog-parks.html, (727) 893-7441
401 20th St. N., 33713.
Daily dawn-dusk.
Fenced, 3 acres, dog wash area, double-gated entryway,
separate areas for large and small dogs, grass surface,
trees, picnic area, benches.

Lake Vista Dog Park - St. Petersburg
www.stpeteparksrec.org/dog-parks.html, (727) 893-7441
1401 62nd Ave. S., 33705.
Daily dawn-dusk.
Fenced, double-gated entryway, separate areas for large
and small dogs, gravel and grass surfaces, trees, benches.

North Shore Dog Park - St. Petersburg
www.stpeteparksrec.org/dog-parks.html, (727) 893-7335
901 N. Shore Dr. N.E., 33701.
Daily dawn-dusk.
Fenced, separate areas for large and small dogs, trees,
shade, benches, wash station, disposal bags and trash
cans.

Walter Fuller Dog Park - St. Petersburg
www.stpeteparksrec.org/dog-parks.html, (727) 893-7441
7891 26th Ave. N., 33710.
Daily dawn-dusk.
Fenced, double-gated entryway, separate areas for large
and small dogs, gravel and grass surfaces, drinking fountain.

Curtis Hixon Waterfront Dog Park - Tampa
www.tampagov.net/parks-and-recreation, (813) 274-8211
600 N. Ashley Dr., 33602.
Daily dawn-10 p.m. Parking: $5.
Fenced, drinking fountains, artificial turf surface, separate
areas for large and small dogs, lighted.

Davis Islands Dog Beach - Tampa
www.tampagov.net/parks-and-recreation, (813) 274-8615
1002 Severn Ave., 33606.
Daily dawn-dusk.
Beach access, wash station, picnic areas, trees, disposal
bags and trash cans.

Gadsden Dog Park - Tampa
www.tampagov.net/parks-and-recreation, (813) 274-8211
6901 S. MacDill Ave., 33611.
Daily dawn-dusk.
Fenced, double-gated entryway, separate areas for large
and small dogs, shade, benches, trees, disposal bags and
trash cans.

Giddens Dog Park - Tampa
www.tampagov.net/parks-and-recreation, (813) 231-5284
5202 N. 12th St., 33603.
Daily dawn-dusk.
Fenced, grass surface, shade, benches, trees.

James Urbanski Dog Park at Al Lopez Park - Tampa
www.tampagov.net/parks-and-recreation, (813) 274-8211
4810 N. Himes Ave., 33614.
Daily dawn-dusk.
Fenced, 1.5 acres, separate areas for large and small dogs,
drinking fountains, benches, picnic area, grass surface,
disposal bags and trash cans, trees.

Palma Ceia Dog Park - Tampa
www.tampagov.net/parks-and-recreation, (813) 274-8615
2200 S. Marti St., 33629.
Mon.-Fri. 8-dusk, Sat.-Sun. 9-dusk.
Fenced, less than 1 acre, drinking fountains, shade, trees,
grass surface.

Rowlett Dog Park - Tampa
www.tampagov.net/parks-and-recreation, (813) 274-8211
2501 E. River Hills Dr., 33604.
Daily dawn-dusk.
Fenced, trees, covered pavilions, separate areas for large
and small dogs, grass surface, agility equipment.

Washington Street Dog Park - Tampa
www.tampagov.net/parks-and-recreation, (813) 274-8211
118 N. 12th St., 33602.
Daily dawn-dusk.
Fenced, artificial turf surface, shade, trees, benches, drinking
fountain, covered pavilion.

Vero Beach Dog Park - Vero Beach
www.verodogpark.org, (772) 234-2824
3449 Indian River Dr. E., 32963.
Daily dawn-dusk.
Fenced, 5 acres, separate areas for large and small dogs,
grass, shade, drinking fountains, benches, dog wash area,
covered pavilion, double-gated entryway, restrooms, disposal
bags and trash cans.

West Orange Park - Winter Garden
www.ocfl.net/CultureParks/DogParks.aspx, (407) 656-3299
12400 Marshall Farms Rd., 34787.
Daily 8-8, in summer; 8-6, rest of year.
Fenced, separate areas for large and small dogs, mulch and
concrete surface, trees, drinking fountains, disposal bags
and trash cans, benches, picnic tables.

Lake Baldwin Dog Park - Winter Park
cityofwinterpark.org/departments/parks-recreation/parks,
(407) 599-3399
2000 S. Lakemont Ave., 32789.
Daily 8-dusk.
Fenced, lake access, dog beach, trees, trails, wash stations,
drinking stations, disposal bags and trash cans, water bowls,
picnic tables.

Hound Ground - Winter Springs
www.winterspringsfl.org/EN/web/dept/pr/dogpark.htm,
(407) 327-6599
900 Hicks Ave., 32708.
Thurs.-Tues. dawn-dusk.
Fenced, covered pavilion, drinking fountains, common water
bowls, grass and cement surface, disposal bags and trash
cans, benches, agility equipment, separate areas for large
and small dogs.

GEORGIA

Piedmont Park - Atlanta
www.piedmontpark.org, (404) 875-7275
1320 Monroe Dr. N.E., 30306.
Daily 6 a.m.-11 p.m.
Fenced, 3 acres, separate areas for large and small dogs,
benches, restrooms.

South Bend Park - Atlanta
www.atlantaga.gov, (404) 546-6788
1955 Compton Dr. S.E., 30315.
Daily 6 a.m.-11 p.m.
Fenced, 74 acres, trees, shade.

HAWAII

Hawaii Kai Dog Park - Honolulu
www.hui-ilio.org, (808) 396-5225
234 Keahole St., 96825.
Wed.-Mon. dawn-dusk, Tues. noon-dusk.
Fenced, separate areas for large and small dogs, benches,
drinking fountain, trees, picnic tables.

Moanalua Dog Park - Honolulu
www.hawaiianhumane.org/Dog-Friendly-Parks.html,
(808) 768-4385
2900 Moanalua Park Rd., 96819.
Wed.-Mon. dawn-dusk; Tues. noon-dusk.
Fenced, drinking fountain, picnic tables, restrooms, shade.

Mililani Dog Park - Mililani
www.hawaiianhumane.org/Dog-Friendly-Parks.html,
(808) 946-2187
95-1069 Ukuwai St., 96789.
Thurs.-Tues. dawn-dusk; Wed. noon-dusk.
Fenced, drinking fountain with water bowls, trees, disposal
bags and trash cans.

ILLINOIS

Grant Bark Park - Chicago
www.southloopdogpac.org/south-loop-dog-parks
/grant-bark-park, (312) 264-5630
900 S. Columbus Dr., 60605.
Fenced, less than 1 acre, drinking fountain, disposal bags
and trash cans, asphalt, pea gravel.

Montrose Dog Beach - Chicago
www.chicagoparkdistrict.com/facilities/dog-friendly-areas,
(312) 742-5121
4400 N. Lake Shore Dr., 60640.
Daily dawn-9 p.m.
Separate fenced area, 4 acres, dog beach, boat launch,
trash cans.

Noethling Playlot Park ("Wiggly Field") - Chicago
www.chicagoparkdistrict.com/parks/Noethling-Playlot-Park,
(312) 742-7816
2645 N. Sheffield Ave., 60614.
Daily 6 a.m.-11 p.m.
Fenced, less than 1 acre, drinking fountain.

Pottawattomie Park - Chicago
www.chicagoparkdistrict.com/parks/Pottawattomie-Park,
(773) 262-5835
7403-27 N. Wolcott, 60626.
Daily 6 a.m.-11 p.m.
Less than 1 acre, separate areas for large and small dogs,
drinking fountain.

Puptown at Margate Park Fieldhouse - Chicago
www.chicagoparkdistrict.com/facilities/dog-friendly-areas,
(312) 742-7522
4900 N. Marine Dr., 60640.
Daily 6 a.m.-11 p.m.
Fenced, less than 1 acre, asphalt, pea gravel, disposal bags
and trash cans, dog water fountain.

INDIANA

Smock Dog Park - Greenwood
www.indy.gov, (317) 888-0070
4200 E. County Line Rd., 46143.
Daily dawn-dusk. $5.
Fenced, 4 acres, benches.

Broad Ripple Park - Indianapolis
www.broadripplepark.org, (317) 327-7161
1550 Broad Ripple Ave., 46220.
Mon.-Thurs. 9-8:30, Fri. 9-5, Sat. 9-1. $5.
Fenced, grass, drinking fountain, disposal bags and trash
cans, restrooms, benches.

Eagle Creek Bark Park - Indianapolis
eaglecreekpark.org/park-activities, (317) 327-7116
6515 Delong Rd., 46278.
Daily 8-7. $5.
Fenced, grass and gravel surface.

Paul Ruster Bark Park - Indianapolis
www.indy.gov, (317) 327-0143
11300 E. Prospect St., 46239.
Daily 7 a.m.-8 p.m. $5.
Fenced, grass and gravel surfaces, disposal bags and trash
cans, benches.

KANSAS

Shawnee Mission Park Off-Leash Dog Park - Shawnee
www.jcprd.com/parks_facilities/shawnee_mission.cfm,
(913) 888-4713
7900 Renner Rd., 66219.
Daily 5 a.m.-11 p.m., Mar.-Oct.; 6 a.m.-8 p.m., rest of year.
53 acres, wood chip surface, trails, restrooms, dog beach,
disposal bags and trash cans, drinking fountains.

KENTUCKY

The Barklands of Beckley Creek Park - Louisville
www.louisvilledogs.com, (502) 584-0350
1310 S. Beckley Station Rd., 40245.
Daily dawn-dusk.
Fenced, 4 acres, divided into three areas for resting, small
and all dogs. Email info@louisvilledogs.com before visiting
and bring a copy of vaccination records for entrance to the
park.

Champions Dog Run at Champions Park - Louisville
www.louisvilledogs.com, (502) 456-8100
2930 River Rd., 40206.
Daily 6 a.m.-11 p.m.
Fenced, 3.6 acres, separate area for small dogs, drinking
fountain. Email info@louisvilledogs.com before visiting and
bring a copy of vaccination records for entrance to the park.

Cochran Hill Dog Run at Cherokee Park - Louisville
www.louisvilledogs.com, (502) 456-8100
745 Cochran Hill Rd., 40206.
Daily dawn-dusk.
Fenced, 2 acres, separate areas for large and small dogs,
disposal bags and trash cans, benches, trees, shade. Email
info@louisvilledogs.com before visiting and bring a copy of
vaccination records for entrance to the park.

**Sawyer Dog Park at E.P. "Tom" Sawyer State Park -
Louisville**
www.louisvilledogs.com, (502) 429-3280
3111 Freys Hill Rd., 40241.
Daily dawn-dusk.
Fenced, 6 acres, separate area for small dogs, shade,
benches, drinking fountains, walking paths, common toys
and tennis balls, dog pool, disposal bags and trash cans.

Vettiner Dog Run - Louisville
www.louisvilledogs.com, (502) 456-8100
5550 Charlie Vettiner Park Rd., 40299.
Daily dawn-dusk.
Fenced, 2 acres, gated, separate areas for large and small
dogs. Email info@louisvilledogs.com before visiting and bring
a copy of vaccination records for entrance to the park.

LOUISIANA

Bonnabel Boat Launch BarkPark - Metairie
www.bonnabelboatlaunch.com/barkpark-dog-park
-bonnabel-metairie-la.htm, (504) 658-4000
1599 Bonnabel Blvd., 70005.
Daily dawn-dusk.
Fenced, double-gated entryway, agility courses, grass
surface, disposal bags and trash cans, drinking fountain.
Maximum of two dogs per person.

NOLA City Bark - New Orleans
www.nolacitybark.org, (504) 483-9377
30 Zachary Taylor Dr., 70124.
Wed.-Mon. 5:30 a.m.-9 p.m., Tues. 1-9. $10 (three-day
permit).
Fenced, 4.6 acres, .25-mi. walking trail, separate areas for
large and small dogs, restrooms, drinking fountain, splash
area, disposal bags and trash cans. Purchase permits online
or in person Mon.-Fri. between 8 a.m. and 5 p.m.

MAINE

Quarry Run Dog Park - Portland
(207) 808-5400
1026 Ocean Ave., 04103.
Daily 6:30 a.m.-10 p.m.
Fenced, 10 acres, dirt trails, disposal bags.

MARYLAND

Canton Dog Park - Baltimore
cantoncommunity.org/content.php?page=Canton_Dog_Park,
(410) 342-0900
1285 S. Bouldin St., 21224.
Daily dawn-dusk.
Fenced, separate areas for large and small or older dogs,
shade, parking, water source, disposal bags.

Locust Point Dog Park - Baltimore
www.locustpointdogpark.org, (410) 396-7900
1627 E. Fort Ave., 21230.
Daily dawn-dusk.
Fenced, trees, benches, hours for small and older dogs in
the morning and afternoon, water station, artificial turf
surface, water slide.

Patterson Dog Park - Baltimore
www.pattersondogpark.org, (410) 276-3676
27 S. Patterson Park Ave., 21231.
Daily dawn-dusk.
Fenced, trees, benches, rocks for climbing, drinking fountain
and hose bibb, disposal stations, artificial turf surface.

MASSACHUSETTS

Peters Park Dog Run - Boston
www.peterspark.org, (617) 635-4500
1277 Washington St., 02118.
Daily dawn-dusk.
Fenced, less than 1 acre, separate areas for large and
small dogs, benches.

Danehy Park - Cambridge
www.cambridgema.gov/CDD/parks/osplanning/offleash.aspx,
(617) 349-4800
168 New St., 02238.
Daily dawn-dusk.
Fenced, separate areas for large and small dogs, gravel
surface, drinking water, disposal bags, benches.

Fresh Pond Reservation - Cambridge
www.cambridgema.gov/Water/freshpondreservation.aspx,
(617) 349-4770
250 Fresh Pond Pkwy., 02138.
Daily dawn-dusk.
Partially fenced, trees, shade, trash cans, beach, disposal
bags.

Falmouth Dog Park - Falmouth
www.falmouthdogpark.com, (508) 331-2929
257 Brick Kiln Rd., 02541.
Daily dawn-dusk.
Fenced, 1.6 acres, separate areas for large and small dogs,
benches, water fountains, waste disposal cans.

MINNESOTA

**Franklin Terrace Off-Leash Recreation Area -
Minneapolis**
www.minneapolisparks.org, (612) 230-6400
925 Franklin Terr., 55406.
Daily 6 a.m.-10 p.m. $5.
Fenced, 1.37 acres, double-gated entryway, mulch surface,
disposal bags and trash cans, trees, shade.

**Lake of the Isles Off-Leash Recreation Area -
Minneapolis**
www.minneapolisparks.org, (612) 230-6400
2845 Lake of the Isles Pkwy. W., 55405.
Daily 6 a.m.-10 p.m. $5.
Fenced 1.87 acres, separate areas for large and small dogs,
mulch surface, water bowls, benches.

Loring Park Off-Leash Dog Park - Minneapolis
www.minneapolisparks.org, (612) 230-6400
1382 Willow St., 55403.
Daily 6 a.m.-10 p.m. $5.
Fenced, less than 1 acre, agility course, grass, double-gated
entryway, water bowls, gravel surface.

Lyndale Farmstead Off-Leash Recreation Area - Minneapolis
www.minneapolisparks.org, (612) 230-6400
3845 Dupont Ave. S., 55409.
Daily 6 a.m.-10 p.m. $5.
Fenced, less than 1 acre, crushed granite surface, benches, covered pavilion.

Minnehaha Off-Leash Recreation Area - Minneapolis
www.minneapolisparks.org, (612) 230-6400
5399 S. Minnehaha Park Dr., 55417.
Daily 6 a.m.-10 p.m. $5.
Fenced, 6.58 acres, walking trails, woods, river access, dog beach.

St. Anthony Parkway Off-Leash Recreation Area - Minneapolis
www.minneapolisparks.org, (612) 230-6400
700 St. Anthony Pkwy., 55418.
Daily 6 a.m.-10 p.m. $5.
Fenced, 2.17 acres, mulch surface, disposal bags and trash cans.

Victory Prairie Off-Leash Recreation Area - Minneapolis
www.minneapolisparks.org, (612) 230-6400
4701 Russell Ave. N., 55412.
Daily 6 a.m.-10 p.m. $5.
Fenced, 2.62 acres, grass, common tennis balls, disposal bags and trash cans, water bowls.

MISSOURI

Elmo & Rosalea Marrs Memorial Dog Park at Stockstill Park - Branson
www.bransonparksandrecreation.com, (417) 335-2368
524 Stockstill Ln., 65615.
Daily dawn-dusk. $5 day pass, $2 each additional dog.
Fenced, 1.5 acres, separate areas for large and small dogs, pavilion, picnic tables, benches, play equipment. Maximum of two dogs per person.

Penn Valley Off-Leash Dog Park - Kansas City
www.kcparks.org/parks/dog-park, (816) 513-7500
2927 Wyandotte St., 64111.
Daily dawn-dusk.
Fenced, 2.7 acres, separate areas for large and small dogs, drinking fountains, disposal bags and trash cans.

Swope Park Off-Leash Dog Park - Kansas City
www.kcparks.org/parks/dog-park, (816) 513-7500
4701 E. Gregory Blvd., 64132.
Daily dawn-one hour after dusk.
Fenced, 5 acres, separate areas for large and small dogs, drinking fountains, trees.

Wayside Waifs Bark Park - Kansas City
www.waysidewaifs.org, (816) 761-8151
3901 Martha Truman Rd., 64137.
Daily 24 hours. $3.
Fenced, 5 acres, separate areas for large and small dogs, trees, shade, covered pavilions, park benches, lighted, time-out kennels, drinking fountains, restrooms.

DuSable Dog Park - St. Charles
www.stcharlesparks.com, (636) 949-3372
2598 N. Main St., 63301.
Daily dawn-10 p.m.
Fenced, 2.5 acres, separate areas for large and small dogs, covered pavilion, shade, trees, grass surface, restrooms.

Lister Dog Park - St. Louis
apamo.org/st-louis-dog-parks, (314) 289-5300
4597 Olive St., 63108.
Daily dawn-dusk.
Fenced, 2.5 acres, mulch surface.

NEVADA

All American Park - Las Vegas
www.lasvegasnevada.gov, (702) 229-6011
1309 S. Buffalo Dr., 89117.
Daily dawn-dusk.
Fenced, restrooms, picnic areas.

Barkin' Basin Park - Las Vegas
www.lasvegasnevada.gov, (702) 229-6011
7351 W. Alexander Blvd., 89129.
Daily dawn-9 p.m.
Fenced, 7.75 acres, separate areas for large and small dogs, shaded benches, drinking fountains, water stations, lighted walking trails, grass, restrooms.

Centennial Hills Park - Las Vegas
www.lasvegasnevada.gov, (702) 229-6718
7101 N. Buffalo Dr., 89131.
Mon.-Wed. and Fri.-Sun. dawn-dusk, Thurs. 3-dusk.
Fenced, separate areas for large and small dogs, grass, benches, shade, covered pavilion, disposal bags and trash cans.

Charlie Kellogg and Joe Zaher Sports Complex - Las Vegas
www.lasvegasnevada.gov, (702) 229-2100
7901 W. Washington Ave., 89128.
Fri.-Wed. dawn-dusk, Thurs. 3-dusk.
Fenced, separate areas for large and small dogs, drinking fountain, walking trails, disposal bags and trash cans, benches, restrooms, shade.

Children's Memorial Park Dog Park - Las Vegas
www.lasvegasnevada.gov, (702) 229-6718
6601 W. Gowan Rd., 89108.
Daily dawn-dusk.
Fenced, less than 1 acre, separate areas for large and small dogs, drinking fountains, shade trees.

Justice Myron E. Leavitt Family Park - Las Vegas
www.lasvegasnevada.gov, (702) 229-6718
2329 S. Eastern Ave., 89104.
Daily dawn-dusk.
Fenced, separate areas for large and small dogs, picnic areas, walking trails, drinking fountain, agility course, disposal bags and trash cans.

Police Memorial Park - Las Vegas
www.lasvegasnevada.gov, (702) 229-6011
3250 Metro Academy Way, 89129.
Daily dawn-dusk.
Fenced, separate areas for large and small dogs, shade, drinking fountain, disposal bags and trash cans.

Woofter Dog Park - Las Vegas
www.lasvegasnevada.gov, (702) 229-2330
1682 N. Rock Springs Dr., 89128.
Daily dawn-dusk.
Fenced, separate areas for large and small dogs, benches, trees, restrooms.

Whitaker Dog Park - Reno
www.reno.gov/government/departments/parks-recreation
-community-services/parks-trails/dogs-dog-parks,
(775) 334-2270
550 University Terr., 89503.
Fenced, less than 1 acre, double-gated entries, shade, disposal bags.

NEW MEXICO

Coronado Dog Park - Albuquerque
www.cabq.gov/parksandrecreation/parks/dog-parks,
(505) 768-5300
301 McKnight Ave. N.W., 87102.
Daily 6 a.m.-10 p.m.
Fenced, picnic areas, benches, trees, disposal bags and trash cans.

North Domingo Baca Dog Park - Albuquerque
www.cabq.gov/parksandrecreation/parks/dog-parks,
(505) 768-5305
7520 Corona Ave. N.E., 87113.
Daily 6 a.m.-10 p.m.
Fenced, separate areas for large and small dogs, disposal bags and trash cans, two levels, covered picnic areas, benches, mulch surface.

Skyline Dog Park - Albuquerque
www.cabq.gov/parksandrecreation/parks/dog-parks,
(505) 768-5300
12700 Montgomery Blvd. N.E., 87111.
Daily 6 a.m.-10 p.m.
Fenced, sand surface, disposal bags and trash cans.

Frank Ortiz Park Off-Leash Area - Santa Fe
www.santafenm.gov, (505) 955-2100
160 Camino de Las Crucitas, 87501.
Daily dawn-dusk.
Walking trails, water bowls, disposal bags and trash cans, sand surface.

Salvador Perez Park - Santa Fe
www.santafenm.gov/salvador_perez_park, (505) 955-2510
601 Alta Vista St., 87505.
Daily 6 a.m.-8 p.m.
Fenced, grass surface, drinking fountain, disposal bags and trash cans, benches.

NEW YORK

Amherst Paw Park - Amherst
www.amherst.ny.us, (716) 631-7000
500 Smith Rd., 14051.
Daily dawn-dusk.
Fenced, separate areas for large and small dogs, grass surface, disposal bags and trash cans.

The Barkyard - Buffalo
www.thebarkyard.org, (716) 218-0303
D A R Dr., 14202.
Daily dawn-dusk.
Fenced, 1.6 acres, separate areas for large and small dogs, double-gated entryway, lighted, drinking fountains, benches, covered pavilions.

Madison Square Park Dog Run - New York
www.nycgovparks.org/parks/madison-square-park,
(212) 538-1884
2 E. 23rd St., 10010.
Daily dawn-midnight.
Fenced, double-gated entryway, benches, disposal bags and trash cans, separate areas for large and small dogs, wash station, drinking fountain, gravel surface.

Peter Detmold Park Dog Run - New York
www.nycgovparks.org/parks/peter-detmold-park,
(212) 639-9675
454 E. 51st St., 10022.
Daily dawn-midnight.
Fenced, brick surface, disposal bags and trash cans, common tennis balls and toys, lighted, trees, shade, picnic area.

Sir William's Dog Run at Ft. Tryon Park - New York
www.nycgovparks.org/parks/fort-tryon-park, (212) 795-1388
689 Fort Washington Ave., 10032.
Daily dawn-dusk.
Fenced, 1.5 acres, shade, benches, separate areas for timid and friendly dogs, mulch and grass surfaces.

Union Square Dog Run - New York
www.nycgovparks.org/parks/union-square-park,
(212) 639-9675
40 E. 14th St., 10003.
Daily 6 p.m.-midnight.
Fenced, double-gated entryway, trees, benches, disposal bags and trash cans.

Washington Square Park Dog Run - New York
www.nycgovparks.org/parks/washington-square-park,
(212) 639-9675
1 Washington Square E., 10011.
Daily dawn-midnight. Free.
Fenced, separate areas for large and small dogs, drinking fountain, lighted, benches, trees, shade, dog splash area, common toys and tennis balls.

NORTH CAROLINA

Barkingham Park at Reedy Creek Park - Charlotte
charmeck.org, (704) 336-3854
2900 Rocky River Rd., 28215.
Daily 7:30 a.m.-dusk.
Fenced, 4 acres, grass, trees, shade, benches.

Davie Dog Park - Charlotte
charmeck.org, (704) 554-0402
4635 Pineville-Matthews Rd., 28277.
Daily 7:30 a.m.-dusk.
Fenced, 5 acres, separate areas for large and small dogs, trails, dog pool, benches, disposal bags and trash cans, drinking fountain.

Frazier Park - Charlotte
charmeck.org, (704) 432-4280
1201 W. 4th St., 28202.
Daily 7:30 a.m.-dusk.
Fenced, 1.3 acres, separate areas for large and small dogs, drinking fountains.

Ray's Fetching Meadow - Charlotte
charmeck.org, (704) 643-5725
8711 Monroe Rd., 28212.
Daily 7:30 a.m.-dusk.
Fenced, 1 acre, walking trails.

Shuffletown Park - Charlotte
charmeck.org, (704) 336-8869
9500 Bellhaven Blvd., 28214.
Daily 7:30 a.m.-dusk.
Fenced, separate areas for large and small dogs, walking path, disposal bags and trash cans, water stations, trees, benches.

Swaney Pointe K-9 Park - Cornelius
www.charmeck.org/mecklenburg/county/ParkandRec/Parks/DogParks/Pages/default.aspx, (704) 336-8869
18441 Nantz Rd., 28078.
Daily 7:30 a.m.-dusk.
Fenced, 4 acres, separate areas for large and small dogs, picnic area.

OHIO

Mt. Airy Forest Dog Park - Cincinnati
www.cincinnatiparks.com/mt-airy-forest, (513) 352-4080
3006 Westwood Northern Blvd., 45211.
Daily 6 a.m.-10 p.m.
Fenced, 2 acres, separate areas for large and small dogs,
trees, drinking fountain, benches, obstacle course, wash
station. No disposal bags available.

Otto Armleder Dog Park - Cincinnati
www.cincinnatiparks.com/river-parks/otto-armleder-park,
(513) 521-7275
5057 Wooster Pike, 45226.
Daily 6 a.m.-10 p.m.
Fenced, 10 acres, separate areas for large and small dogs,
grass, drinking fountains, wash station, disposal bags and
trash cans.

Washington Park - Cincinnati
www.washingtonpark.org, (513) 621-4400
1230 Elm St., 45202.
Daily 6 a.m.-11:00 p.m.
Fenced, less than 1 acre, climbing rocks, benches, drinking
fountain, splash area, artificial turf surface, pea gravel.

Clark Field Dog Park - Cleveland
(216) 575-0920
1095 Clark Ave., 44113.
Daily 8 a.m.-9 p.m.
Separate areas for large and small dogs, gravel, drinking
fountain, trees, disposal bags and trash cans, hand sanitizer,
benches.

Lakewood Dog Park - Cleveland
www.lakewooddogpark.com, (216) 364-7274
1699 Valley Pkwy., 44107.
Daily 8 a.m.-9 p.m.
Gravel and grass surfaces, trees, shade, drinking fountain,
toys, water bowls, disposal bags and trash cans, 50-foot
gated area for smaller or less-social dogs.

Big Walnut Dog Park - Columbus
www.columbus.gov/recreationandparks/dog-parks
/All-Dog-Parks, (614) 645-3300
5000 E. Livingston Ave., 43227.
Daily 7 a.m.-11 p.m.
Fenced, 3 acres, two entrances, lighted, pond access,
separate areas for large and small dogs.

Godown Dog Park - Columbus
www.worthingtondogpark.com, (614) 349-6630
6099 Godown Rd., 43235.
Daily dawn-dusk.
Fenced, 4.5-acre large dog area, 1-acre small dog area, two
entrances, paved pathways, wash station, disposal bags and
trash cans, information pavilion, hills, trees, benches,
drinking fountains.

Three Creeks Dog Park - Columbus
www.columbus.gov/recreationandparks/dog-parks
/All-Dog-Parks, (614) 645-3300
2648 Spangler Rd., 43207.
Daily 8 a.m.-dusk.
Fenced, 5 acres, separate areas for large and small dogs,
walking trails, drinking fountains.

Wheeler Dog Park - Columbus
www.columbus.gov/recreationandparks/dog-parks
/All-Dog-Parks, (614) 645-3300
725 Thurber Dr. W., 43215.
Daily 7 a.m.-11 p.m.
Fenced, 1.5 acres, benches, disposal bags and trash cans,
close to neighboring parks, lighted, walking paths, drinking
fountain.

Woodland Dog Park - Eastlake
www.eastlakeohio.com, (440) 951-1416
35576 Lake Shore Blvd., 44095.
Daily dawn-dusk.
Fenced, less than 1 acre, picnic tables, shade, water bowls,
disposal bags and trash cans.

Memorial Dog Park - Medina
www.medinaoh.org/government/departments/parks
/memorial-park, (330) 721-6950
349 E. Homestead St., 44256.
Daily dawn-dusk.
Fenced, less than 1 acre, separate areas for large and
small dogs, benches, grass, trees, disposal bags and trash
cans, drinking fountain.

OKLAHOMA

Fred Quinn Happy Tails Dog Park - Oklahoma City
www.midwestcityok.org, (405) 739-1293
8700 E. Reno Ave., 73110.
Daily 5 a.m.-11 p.m.
Fenced, splash pond, benches, lighted, common toys and
tennis balls, disposal bags and trash cans, covered
pavilions, separate areas for large and small dogs.

Paw Park at Lake Hefner - Oklahoma City
www.pawok.com, (405) 949-7293
3303 N.W. Grand Blvd., 73116.
Daily dawn-dusk.
Fenced, 2 acres, separate areas for large and small dogs,
double-gated entryway, drinking fountains, swimming pond,
benches, shade, disposal bags and trash cans. Children
under 10 are not allowed in the dog park.

Biscuit Acres Dog Park - Tulsa
www.biscuitacres.com, (918) 596-7275
5804 E. 91st St., 74137.
Daily 5 a.m.-9 p.m.
Fenced, 2.5 acres, separate areas for large and small dogs,
drinking fountains, fire hydrant, shade, disposal bags and
trash cans, double-gated entryways.

Joe Station Dog Park - Tulsa
www.cityoftulsa.org/culture--recreation/tulsa-parks.aspx,
(918) 596-2100
2279 Charles Page Blvd., 74127.
Daily 5 a.m.-11 p.m.
Fenced, grass surface, drinking fountain, separate areas for
large and small dogs, lighted.

OREGON

L.L. Stub Stewart State Park - Buxton
www.oregonstateparks.org/park_255.php, (503) 324-0606
30380 N.W. Hwy. 47, 97109.
Daily dawn-dusk.
Fenced, less than 1 acre, double-gated entryway, drinking
fountain, disposal bags and trash cans, benches.

Alberta Park - Portland
www.portlandoregon.gov/parks/39523, (503) 823-3647
2187 N.E. Killingsworth St., 97211.
Daily 5 a.m.-midnight.
1.32 acres, trees, disposal bags and trash cans, drinking
fountains, restrooms.

Brentwood Park Off-Leash Area - Portland
www.portlandoregon.gov/parks/article/91310, (503) 823-3647
6100 S.E. Duke St., 97206.
Daily 5 a.m.-midnight.
Fenced, drinking fountain, benches, disposal bags and trash
cans.

Chimney Park - Portland
www.portlandoregon.gov/parks/39523, (503) 823-7529
9360 N. Columbia Blvd., 97203.
Daily 5 a.m.-midnight.
Fenced, 5.52 acres, disposal bags and trash cans, trees,
grass surface, double-gated entryway, common water bowls,
drinking fountains.

Couch Park - Portland
www.portlandoregon.gov/parks/39523, (503) 823-3647
2004 N.W. Glisan St., 97209.
Daily 5 a.m.-midnight.
Less than 1 acre, disposal bags and trash cans, trees,
grass surface, drinking fountain.

Delta Park - Portland
www.portlandoregon.gov/parks/39523, (503) 823-3647
10774 N. Union Ct., 97217.
Daily 5 a.m.-midnight.
Fenced, 1.81 acres, trees, picnic area, trash cans.

East Holladay Park - Portland
www.portlandoregon.gov/parks/39523, (503) 823-3647
12999 N.E. Holladay St., 97230.
Daily 8 a.m.-9 p.m., June 15-Sept. 1; Mon.-Fri. 6-7:30 a.m.
and 4-9 p.m., Sat.-Sun. 8 a.m.-9 p.m., rest of year.
Fenced, 5.59 acres, grass surface, walking paths, trees.

Gabriel Park - Portland
www.portlandoregon.gov/parks/39523, (503) 823-2525
6820 S.W. 45th Ave., 97219.
Daily 5 a.m.-midnight.
Fenced, 1.75 acres, grass surface, walking trails, drinking
fountains, trees, disposal bags and trash cans, benches.

Lynchwood Park - Portland
www.portlandoregon.gov/parks/39523, (503) 823-7529
16982 S.E. Haig St., 97236.
Daily 5 a.m.-midnight.
Fenced, 1.18 acres, grass surface, picnic areas, benches,
trees.

Mt. Tabor Park - Portland
www.portlandoregon.gov/parks/39523, (503) 823-3647
1204 S.E. 60th Ave., 97215.
Daily 7 a.m.-9 p.m.
Partially fenced, 4.19 acres, three double-gated entryways,
trees, drinking fountains, trash cans.

Normandale Park - Portland
www.portlandoregon.gov/parks/39523, (503) 823-7529
1282 N.E. 57th Ave., 97213.
Daily 5 a.m.-midnight.
Fenced, 1.62 acres, separate areas for large and small
dogs, trees, drinking fountains, disposal bags and trash
cans.

Wallace Park - Portland
www.portlandoregon.gov/parks/39523, (503) 823-3647
2595 N.W. Raleigh St., 97210.
Daily 5 a.m.-midnight.
Fenced, less than 1 acre, drinking fountain, trash cans,
trees, shade.

Ash Avenue Dog Park - Tigard
www.tigard-or.gov/community/dogparks.php, (503) 639-4171
9025 S.W. Burnham St., 97223.
Daily dawn-dusk.
Fenced, covered shelter, wood fiber surface, drinking
fountains, dog wash station.

Potso Dog Park - Tigard
www.tigard-or.gov/community/dogparks.php, (503) 639-2931
13200 S.W. Wall St., 97223.
Daily dawn-dusk.
Fenced, 1.55 acres, drinking fountain, disposal bags and
trash cans, covered picnic area, walking path, separate
areas for large and small dogs, grass surface.

Summerlake Park Dog Park - Tigard
www.tigard-or.gov/community/dogparks.php, (503) 639-2931
11450 S.W. Winter Lake Dr., 97223.
Daily dawn-dusk.
Fenced, less than 1 acre, drinking fountains, disposal bags
and trash cans, covered picnic areas, trees, double-gated
entryway.

PENNSYLVANIA

Grove Park Dog Run - Abington
www.abington.org/departments/parks-recreation/parks-facilities,
(215) 576-5213
1436 Easton Rd., 19001.
Daily dawn-dusk.
Fenced, 2 acres, separate areas for large and small dogs,
grass surface, trees, benches, drinking fountains, disposal
bags and trash cans.

Curtis Dog Park - Elkins Park
www.cheltenhamtownship.org, (215) 887-6200
1250 W. Church Rd., 19027.
Daily dawn-dusk.
Fenced, more than 1 acre, trees, benches, mulch surface,
separate areas for large and small dogs, disposal bags and
trash cans.

MonDaug Bark Park - Fort Washington
www.upperdublin.net/departments/parks-recreation/,
(215) 643-1600
1130 Camp Hill Rd., 19034.
Daily dawn-dusk.
Fenced, 1 acre, separate areas for large and small dogs,
three double-gated entryways, walking trails, stream,
disposal bags and trash cans, grass surface.

Horsham Dog Park at Kohler Park - Horsham
www.horshamdogpark.com, (215) 290-1917
1013 Horsham Rd., 19044.
Daily dawn-dusk.
Fenced, 1.5 acres, separate areas for large and small dogs,
benches, grass surface, disposal bags and trash cans,
restrooms, trees, water bowls.

Columbus Square Dog Park - Philadelphia
www.mycolumbussquare.org/about/dog-park/, (215) 685-1890
1200 Wharton St., 19147.
Daily 7 a.m.-9 p.m.
Fenced, trees, agility equipment, benches, wash station,
common toys and water bowls, gravel surface.

Schuylkill River Dog Run - Philadelphia
www.phillyfido.org, (215) 686-1776
2500 Lombard St., 19103.
Daily dawn-dusk.
Fenced, separate areas for large and small dogs, gravel,
artificial turf and brick surface, trees, benches, drinking
fountain, water bowls, wash station.

Seger Dog Run - Philadelphia
www.segerdogrun.org, (215) 686-1780
1020 Lombard St., 19105.
Daily dawn-dusk. Donations.
Fenced, 2 acres, double-gated entryway, drinking fountain,
disposal bags and trash cans, mulch surface, benches.

Allegheny Commons Park - Pittsburgh
www.alleghenycommons.org, (412) 330-2569
11 Children's Way, 15212.
Daily 6 a.m.-11 p.m.
Grass surface, trees, benches, pond access, walking paths.

Bernard Dog Run - Pittsburgh
www.bernarddogrun.org, (412) 255-2539
3 Rivers Heritage Trail System, 15201.
Daily dawn-dusk.
Fenced, drinking fountains, separate areas for large and
small dogs, disposal bags and trash cans, common water
bowls, trees.

Frick Park Dog Park - Pittsburgh
pittsburghpa.gov/citiparks/off-leash-areas, (412) 682-7275
6750 Forbes Ave., 15221.
Daily 6 a.m.-11 p.m.
Fenced, drinking fountains, disposal bags and trash cans,
pond access, benches, two separate play areas.

Riverview Park Dog Park - Pittsburgh
www.pittsburghpa.gov/citiparks/off-leash-areas,
(412) 255-2539
1 Riverview Ave., 15214.
Daily dawn-dusk.
Fenced, separate areas for large and small dogs, grass and
mulch surface.

RHODE ISLAND

Dexter Training Ground Dog Park - Providence
www.providenceri.com/parks-and-rec, (401) 421-2489
73 Dexter St., 02909.
Daily dawn-dusk.
Fenced, mulch surface, separate areas for large and small
dogs.

Gano Street Dog Park - Providence
www.providenceri.com/parks-and-rec, (401) 785-9450
123 Gano St., 02906.
Daily dawn-dusk.
Fenced, separate areas for large and small dogs,
double-gated entryway, benches, disposal bags and trash
cans, gravel surface, common water bowls.

SOUTH CAROLINA

James Island County Park - Charleston
www.ccprc.com, (843) 795-7275
871 Riverland Dr., 29412.
Daily 8-dusk, Mar.-Apr. and day after Labor Day-Oct. 31;
8-8, May-Labor Day; 8-5, rest of year.
Fenced, separate areas for large and small dogs, dog
beach, benches, shade, restrooms.

Sesquicentennial State Park - Columbia
www.southcarolinaparks.com/sesqui/introduction.aspx,
(803) 788-2706
9564 Two Notch Rd., 29223.
Daily 8 a.m.-6 p.m. Dog permit $4. Park admission $5;
$3.25 (ages 65+); $3 (ages 6-15).
Fenced, 2 acres, lake access, grass surface, disposal bags
and trash cans.

**Mount Pleasant Palmetto Islands County Park - Mount
Pleasant**
www.ccprc.com, (843) 884-0832
444 Needlerush Pkwy., 29464.
Daily dawn-dusk.
Fenced, separate areas for large and small dogs, benches,
shade, restrooms, picnic areas.

**North Charleston Wannamaker County Park - North
Charleston**
www.ccprc.com, (843) 762-5585
8888 University Blvd., 29406.
Tues.-Sun. 8 a.m.-dusk, Mon. 10-dusk. $2.
Fenced, separate areas for large and small dogs, benches,
shade, restrooms, drinking fountain, dog wash station.

TENNESSEE

Nutro Dog Park - Brentwood
www.brentwood-tn.org, (615) 371-0060
1 Heritage Way, 37027.
Daily 8 a.m.-dusk.
Fenced, 1.5-acre large dog area, .65-acre small dog area,
benches, fire hydrants, trees, shade, drinking fountains.

Freedom Run Dog Park at Liberty Park - Franklin
www.franklintn.gov/government/parks/facilities-and-parks
/dogs-dog-parks, (615) 791-3217
2098 Turning Wheel Ln., 37067.
Daily dawn-dusk.
Fenced, 1 acre, separate areas for large and small dogs,
shade, disposal bags and trash cans. Dogs must be older
than 4 months.

K-9 Korral Dog Park - Franklin
www.franklintn.gov/government/parks/facilities-and-parks
/dogs-dog-parks, (615) 550-6948
239 Franklin Rd., 37064.
Daily dawn-dusk.
Fenced, double-gated entryway, disposal bags and trash
cans, grass surface, common tennis balls and toys.

The Outback at Shelby Farms Park - Memphis
www.shelbyfarmspark.org, (901) 767-7275
500 N. Pine Lake Dr., 38134.
Daily 6 a.m.-8 p.m., Mar. 15-Oct. 31; 6-6, Nov. 15-Mar. 14.
More than 100 acres, separate areas for large and small
dogs, disposal bags and trash cans, benches, lakes for
swimming, drinking fountains, wash station.

Centennial Dog Park - Nashville
www.nashville.gov/Parks-and-Recreation/Parks/Dog-Parks.aspx,
(615) 862-8400
2500 West End Ave., 37210.
Daily dawn-8 p.m.
Fenced, double-gated entryway, separate areas for large
and small dogs, grass and mulch surfaces, drinking fountain,
benches, picnic tables, common tennis balls and toys,
disposal bags and trash cans.

Shelby Dog Park - Nashville
www.nashville.gov/Parks-and-Recreation/Parks/Dog-Parks.aspx,
(615) 862-8750
2001 Boscobel St., 37206.
Daily dawn-8 p.m.
Fenced, grass surface, drinking fountain, common tennis
balls, disposal bags and trash cans, benches.

Warner Dog Park - Nashville
www.nashville.gov/Parks-and-Recreation/Parks/Dog-Parks.aspx,
(615) 862-8750
50 Vaughn Rd., 37221.
Daily dawn-dusk.
Fenced, double-gated entryway, grass surface, trees,
common tennis balls, drinking fountain, benches.

TEXAS

Red Bud Isle Dog Park - Austin
www.austintexas.gov/page/park-directory, (512) 974-6700
3401 Red Bud Tr., 78703.
Daily dawn-dusk.
17.49 acres, loop trail, several swimming areas.

Bark Park Central in Deep Ellum Park - Dallas
www.dallasparks.org/Facilities, (214) 670-4100
2530 Commerce St., 75226.
Tues.-Sun. 5 a.m.-midnight.
Fenced, 1.2 acres, drinking fountains, disposal bags and
trash cans, grass, benches, tennis balls, vending machines
with pet items, canine artwork.

NorthBark Dog Park - Dallas
www.dallasparks.org/Facilities, (214) 670-1923
4899 Gramercy Oaks Dr., 75287.
Wed.-Mon. dawn-dusk.
Fenced, 21 acres, lawn, walking trails, pavilion, dog beach,
benches, drinking fountain, shade, separate areas for large
and small dogs, wash station.

Wagging Tail Dog Park - Dallas
www.waggingtaildogpark.org, (214) 670-1589
5841 Keller Springs Rd., 75248.
Tues.-Sat. dawn-dusk.
Fenced, 7 acres, separate areas for large and small dogs,
.25-mi. walking trail, drinking fountains, benches.

White Rock Dog Park - Dallas
www.whiterockdogpark.org, (214) 670-4100
8000 E. Mockingbird Ln., 75218.
Tues.-Sun. 5 a.m.-11 p.m.
Fenced, 3 acres, swimming area, separate areas for large
and small dogs, benches, drinking fountain, picnic tables.

Ervan Chew - Houston
www.houstontx.gov/parks/dogparks.html, (832) 395-7000
4502 Dunlavy St., 77006.
Daily dawn-dusk.
Fenced, less than 1 acre, shade, benches, dog splash area,
2 dog per person limit.

Levy Park - Houston
www.houstontx.gov/parks/dogparks.html, (713) 524-8000
3801 Eastside St., 77098.
Daily dawn-dusk.
Fenced, trees, benches, picnic tables, designated dog run.

Maxey Park - Houston
www.houstontx.gov/parks/dogparks.html, (713) 837-0311
601 Maxey Rd., 77013.
Daily dawn-dusk.
Fenced, 12 acres, drinking fountains, separate areas for
large and small dogs, wash station, disposal bags and trash
cans, benches, trees.

Tanglewood Park - Houston
www.houstontx.gov/parks/dogparks.html, (832) 395-7000
5801 Woodway Dr., 77057.
Daily dawn-dusk.
Fenced, less than 1 acre, picnic tables, drinking fountain,
lighted, benches, mulch surface, tennis balls, trash cans.

T.C. Jester Park - Houston
www.houstontx.gov/parks/dogparks.html, (832) 395-7000
4201 W. T.C. Jester Blvd., 77018.
Daily 6 a.m.-11 p.m.
Fenced, 1 acre, separate areas for large and small dogs,
benches, drinking fountains, disposal bags and trash cans,
dog pool.

West Webster Park - Houston
www.houstontx.gov/parks/dogparks.html, (832) 395-7000
1502 W. Webster St., 77019.
Daily dawn-dusk.
Fenced, less than 1 acre, drinking fountain, wash station,
disposal bags and trash cans, trees.

Madison Square Park Dog Park - San Antonio
www.sanantonio.gov/ParksAndRec/ParksFacilities.aspx,
(210) 207-8480
400 Lexington Ave., 78215.
Daily 5 a.m.-11 p.m.
Fenced, less than 1 acre, disposal bags and trash cans,
drinking fountain, benches.

McAllister Park Dog Park - San Antonio
www.sanantonio.gov/ParksAndRec/ParksFacilities.aspx,
(210) 207-8480
13102 Jones Maltsberger Rd., 78247.
Daily 5 a.m.-11 p.m.
Fenced, 1.5 acres, exercise equipment, picnic area,
benches, walking trail.

Pearsall Dog Park - San Antonio
www.sanantonio.gov/ParksAndRec/ParksFacilities.aspx,
(210) 207-8480
4700 Old Pearsall Rd., 78242.
Daily 5 a.m.-11 p.m.
Fenced, 1.5 acres, picnic areas, trash cans, agility
equipment.

Phil Hardberger Park East Dog Park - San Antonio
www.sanantonio.gov/ParksAndRec/ParksFacilities.aspx,
(210) 207-8480
13203 Blanco Rd., 78216.
Daily 7:30 a.m.-dusk.
Fenced, 1.8 acres, separate areas for large and small dogs,
dog playhouse, grass surface.

Phil Hardberger Park West Dog Park - San Antonio
www.sanantonio.gov/ParksAndRec/ParksFacilities.aspx,
(210) 207-8480
8400 N.W. Military Hwy., 78231.
Daily 7:30 a.m.-dusk.
Fenced, 1.5 acres, agility equipment, separate areas for
large and small dogs.

Tom Slick Dog Park - San Antonio
www.sanantonio.gov/ParksAndRec/ParksFacilities.aspx,
(210) 207-8480
7400 Hwy. 151, 78227.
Daily 5 a.m.-11 p.m.
Fenced, 1 acre, separate areas for large and small dogs,
benches, picnic area, drinking fountain, dog wash area,
shade.

UTAH

Millrace Park - Salt Lake City
www.taylorsvilleut.gov/parks_rec.dogpark.html,
(385) 468-1800
1150 W. 5400 S., 84123.
Mon. and Wed.-Fri. 7 a.m.-10 p.m., Sat. 8-4, Sun. 4-10,
Apr.-Oct.; Mon. and Wed.-Fri. 8-7, Sat. 8-4, Sun. 4-7, rest
of year. $10.
Fenced.

West Jordan Off-Leash Dog Park - West Jordan
www.slco.org/recreation/parks/WestJordanDog/index.html,
(385) 468-1800
5982 W. New Bingham Hwy., 84081.
Daily dawn-dusk.
Fenced, 3.77 acres, separate areas for large and small
dogs, drinking fountains.

VIRGINIA

Shirlington Park - Arlington
parks.arlingtonva.us/parksfacilities/dog-parks,
(703) 228-6525
2601 S. Arlington Mill Dr., 22206.
Daily 6 a.m.-8 p.m.
Fenced, double-gated entryway, splash area, trees,
separate areas for large and small dogs, dog wash area.

Barker Field at Byrd Park - Richmond
www.barkerfield.org, (804) 646-5733
Shirley Ln., 23220.
Daily dawn-dusk.
Fenced, double-gated entryway, benches, grass surface,
shade, trees, disposal bags and trash cans.

Church Hill Dog Park - Richmond
www.richmondgov.com/parks/parkChimborazo.aspx,
(804) 447-6205
3200 E. Broad St., 23223.
Daily dawn-dusk.
Fenced, separate areas for large and small dogs, drinking
fountains.

Waller Mill Dog Park - Williamsburg
www.williamsburgva.gov/index.aspx?page=353,
(757) 259-3778
Route 645, Airport Rd., 23185.
Daily dawn-dusk. $2 per dog.
Fenced, 1.5 acres, separate areas for large and small dogs.

WASHINGTON

Blue Dog Pond - Seattle
www.seattle.gov/parks, (206) 684-4075
1520 26th Ave. S., 98144.
Daily 4 a.m.-11:30 p.m.
Fenced, less than 1 acre, drinking fountains.

Denny Park - Seattle
www.seattle.gov/parks, (206) 684-4075
100 Dexter Ave. N., 98109.
Daily 4 a.m.-11:30 p.m.
Fenced, trees, benches, lighted, double-gated entryway,
grass and gravel surface.

Dr. Jose Rizal Park - Seattle
www.seattle.gov/parks, (206) 684-4075
1008 12th Ave. S., 98144.
Daily 4 a.m.-11:30 p.m.
Fenced, 4 acres, drinking fountains, gravel surface.

Genesee Park and Playfield - Seattle
www.seattle.gov/parks, (206) 684-4075
4316 S. Genesee St., 98118.
Daily 4 a.m.-11:30 p.m.
Fenced, 2.5 acres, double-gated entryway, gravel surface,
drinking fountain.

Golden Gardens Park - Seattle
www.seattle.gov/parks, (206) 684-4075
8498 Seaview Pl. N.W., 98117.
Daily 4 a.m.-11:30 p.m.
Less than 1 acre, mulch surface, trees, picnic areas,
covered pavilion, restrooms.

Kinnear Park - Seattle
www.seattle.gov/parks, (206) 684-4075
899 W. Olympic Pl., 98119.
Daily 6 a.m.-dusk.
Fenced, double-gated entry way, less than 1 acre, mulch
surface, agility equipment, benches, trees, shade.

Magnolia Manor Park Off-Leash Area - Seattle
www.seattle.gov/parks, (206) 684-4075
3500 28th Ave. W., 98199.
Daily 4 a.m.-11:30 p.m.
Fenced, less than 1 acre, drinking fountain, agility
equipment, picnic areas, benches, walking paths.

Northacres Park - Seattle
www.seattle.gov/parks, (206) 684-4075
12718 1st Ave. N.E., 98125.
Daily 6 a.m.-10 p.m.
Fenced, less than 1 acre, trails, shade, trees, benches,
restrooms, picnic areas.

Regrade Park - Seattle
www.seattle.gov/parks, (206) 684-4075
2251 3rd Ave., 98121.
Daily 6 a.m.-10 p.m.
Fenced, less than 1 acre, double-gated entryway, drinking
fountains.

Warren G. Magnuson Park - Seattle
www.seattle.gov/parks, (206) 684-4946
7400 Sand Point Way N.E., 98115.
Daily 4 a.m.-11:30 p.m.
Fenced, 9 acres, drinking fountains, trails, gravel surface,
separate areas for large and small or shy dogs.

Westcrest Park - Seattle
www.seattle.gov/parks, (206) 684-4075
9000 8th Ave. S.W., 98106.
Daily 6 a.m.-10 p.m.
Fenced, 4 acres, walking paths, drinking fountain, shade,
trees, benches, restrooms, picnic areas, lighted, separate
areas for large and small or shy dogs.

Woodland Park - Seattle
www.seattle.gov/parks, (206) 684-4075
1000 N. 50th St., 98103.
Daily 4 a.m.-11:30 p.m.
Fenced, less than 1 acre, benches, drinking fountain.

Sequim Dog Park - Sequim
www.sequimdogparks.org, (360) 681-5373
202 N. Blake Rd., 98382.
Double-gated entry, separate areas for large and small dogs,
agility equipment.

Dakota Memorial Off-Leash Dog Park - Vancouver
www.clark.wa.gov/public-works/dog-parks, (888) 899-0025
1502 N.E. 164th Ave., 98684.
Daily dawn-dusk.
Fenced, 8 acres, separate areas for large and small dogs,
double-gated entryway, mulch walking path, grass surface,
drinking fountains, agility area, trees and shade, benches.

Hazel Dell "Ross" Dog Park - Vancouver
clarkdogpaw.org/dog-parks/hazel-dell-ross, (888) 899-0025
5274 N.E. 18th Ave., 98663.
Daily dawn-dusk.
Fenced, 8 acres, separate areas for large and small dogs,
double-gated entryway, walking trails, benches.

Kane Memorial Dog Park - Vancouver
www.clark.wa.gov/public-works/dog-parks, (888) 899-0025
10910 N.E. 172nd Ave., 98682.
Daily dawn-dusk.
Fenced, 2.5 acres, double-gated entryway, walking trail,
drinking fountains.

Lucky Memorial Dog Park (Brush Prairie) - Vancouver
www.clark.wa.gov/public-works/dog-parks, (888) 899-0025
10102 N.E. 149th St., 98662.
Daily dawn-dusk.
Fenced, 7.5 acres, separate areas for large and small dogs,
walking path, double-gated entryways, agility course, water
available, disposal bags and trash cans.

WISCONSIN

Currie Park - Milwaukee
county.milwaukee.gov/Dogs9203/DogExerciseAreas.htm,
(414) 464-8400
3535 N. Mayfair Rd., 53222.
Daily 5 a.m.-10 p.m. $5.
Fenced, 1.5 acres, trees, benches, dog bowls, grass and mulch surfaces.

Estabrook Park - Milwaukee
county.milwaukee.gov/Dogs9203/DogExerciseAreas.htm,
(414) 964-0064
4400 N. Estabrook Ln., 53211.
Daily 5 a.m.-10 p.m. Parking: $5.
Fenced, 3 acres, separate areas for large and small dogs, trees, benches, picnic area, restrooms.

Granville Park - Milwaukee
county.milwaukee.gov/Dogs9203/DogExerciseAreas.htm,
(414) 257-7275
11718 W. Good Hope Pl., 53224.
Daily 5 a.m.-10 p.m. $5.
10 acres, hills, woods, grass, river access, walking trails, disposal bags and trash cans.

Warnimont Dog Exercise Area - Milwaukee
county.milwaukee.gov/Dogs9203/DogExerciseAreas.htm,
(414) 678-9364
5400 S. Lake Dr., 53217.
Daily 5 a.m.-10 p.m. $5.
Fenced, 5 acres, woods, trails, separate areas for large and small dogs, restrooms, benches, disposal bags and trash cans.

Runway Dog Exercise Area - Oak Creek
county.milwaukee.gov/Dogs9203/DogExerciseAreas.htm,
(414) 762-1550
1214 E. Rawson Ave., 53154.
Daily 5 a.m.-10 p.m. $5.
Fenced, 26 acres, separate areas for large and small dogs, wood-chipped walking trails, covered pavilion with picnic tables, water bowls, disposal bags and trash cans.

Canada

ALBERTA

Bowmont Off-Leash Area - Calgary
www.calgary.ca/CSPS/Parks/Pages/Locations
/Off-leash-area-locations.aspx, (403) 268-2489
85th St. N.W. & 48th Ave. N.W., T3L 1S4.
Daily dawn-dusk.
Fenced, disposal bags and trash cans, grass surface, benches, trees.

Edworthy Off-Leash Area - Calgary
www.calgary.ca/CSPS/Parks/Pages/Locations
/SW-parks/Edworthy-Park.aspx, (403) 268-3800
5050 Spruce Dr. S.W., T3C 3B2.
Daily 5 a.m.-11 p.m.
Trees, grass surface, benches, walking paths, disposal bags and trash cans, hills.

River Park - Calgary
www.calgary.ca/CSPS/Parks/Pages/Locations
/Off-leash-area-locations.aspx, (403) 268-2489
5139 14th St. S.W., T3E 1P1.
Daily dawn-dusk.
Trees, shade, grass surface, river, beach access, disposal bags and trash cans.

Tom Campbell's Hill - Calgary
www.calgary.ca/CSPS/Parks/Pages/Locations
/Off-leash-area-locations.aspx, (403) 268-2489
25 St. Georges Dr. N.E., T2E 5E4.
Daily 5 a.m.-11 p.m.
Trees, hills, shade, grass surface.

Jackie Parker Recreation Area - Edmonton
www.edmonton.ca/activities_parks_recreation
/parks_rivervalley/jackie-parker-park.aspx, (780) 442-5311
4540 50th St. N.W., T6L 6B6.
Daily 5 a.m.-11 p.m.
Walking paths, river access, trees, shade, restrooms, disposal bags and trash cans.

Terwillegar Park - Edmonton
www.edmonton.ca/terwillegarpark, (780) 442-5311
10 Rabbit Hill Rd. N.W., T6R 0J3.
Daily 5 a.m.-11 p.m.
Trees, benches, picnic area, walking trails, river access, disposal bags and trash cans, restrooms.

BRITISH COLUMBIA

Andy Livingstone Dog Park - Vancouver
vancouver.ca/parks-recreation-culture/
dog-off-leash-areas.aspx, (604) 257-8400
89 Expo Blvd., V6B 1R1.
Daily 6 a.m.-10 p.m.
Fenced, grass surface.

Charleson Dog Park - Vancouver
vancouver.ca/parks-recreation-culture/
dog-off-leash-areas.aspx, (604) 257-8400
999 Charleson St., V5Z 4A2.
Daily 6 a.m.-10 p.m.
Fenced, splash area, benches, grass surface, disposal bags and trash cans.

Coopers Park Dog Park - Vancouver
vancouver.ca/parks-recreation-culture/
dog-off-leash-areas.aspx, (604) 873-7000
1020 Marinaside Cres., V6Z 2W9.
Daily 6 a.m.-10 p.m.
Grass surface, trees, hedges, disposal bags and trash cans, benches.

Devonian Harbour Park Dog Park - Vancouver
vancouver.ca/parks-recreation-culture/
dog-off-leash-areas.aspx, (604) 873-7000
1929 W. Georgia St., V6G 2W9.
Daily 6 a.m.-10 p.m.
Fenced, grass surface, benches, lake access, walking paths, trees, shade.

Dusty Greenwell Park Dog Park - Vancouver
vancouver.ca/parks-recreation-culture/
dog-off-leash-areas.aspx, (604) 873-7000
2799 Wall St., V5K 1A9.
Daily 5-10 and 5-10.
Grass surface, benches, disposal bags and trash cans, walking paths, hills, trees, shade.

Emery Barnes Park Dog Park - Vancouver
vancouver.ca/parks-recreation-culture/
dog-off-leash-areas.aspx, (604) 873-7000
1188 Seymour St., V6B 3M7.
Daily 6 a.m.-10 p.m.
Fenced, benches, picnic areas, gravel surface, drinking
fountains, restrooms, disposal bags and trash cans.

Fraserview Dog Park - Vancouver
vancouver.ca/parks-recreation-culture/
dog-off-leash-areas.aspx, (604) 873-7000
8101 Kerr St., V5S 2C8.
Daily 5-10 and 5-10.
Partially fenced, walking trails, trees, hills, shade, disposal
bags and trash cans, grass and mulch surface.

Hadden Park Dog Park - Vancouver
vancouver.ca/parks-recreation-culture/
dog-off-leash-areas.aspx, (604) 873-7000
1905 Ogden Ave., V6J 1A3.
Daily 6 a.m.-10 p.m., Oct.-Apr.; 6-10 and 5-10, rest of year.
Beach access, disposal bags and trash cans, trees.

Portside Dog Park at Crab Park - Vancouver
vancouver.ca/parks-recreation-culture/
dog-off-leash-areas.aspx, (604) 873-7000
101 E. Waterfront Rd., V6A 4K3.
Daily 6-10 and 5-10.
Grass surface, benches, trees, hedges, disposal bags and
trash cans.

ONTARIO

**Niagara Falls Dog Park in Fireman's Park - Niagara
Falls**
www.niagarafalls.ca/city-hall/recreation/parks/dog-park.aspx,
(905) 356-1355
2275 Dorchester Rd., L2J 4L6.
Daily dawn-dusk.
Separate areas for large and small dogs, disposal bags,
benches, shade.

Jack Purcell Dog Park - Ottawa
www.ottawa.ca/en/residents/parks-and-recreation,
(613) 564-1050
320 Jack Purcell Ln., K2P 2J5.
Daily 24 hours.
Fenced, gravel and grass surface, drinking fountain,
separate areas for large and small dogs.

Bickford Park - Toronto
www.toronto.ca/parks/prd/facilities/complex/295,
(416) 338-5058
400 Grace St., M6G 3A8.
Daily 6 a.m.-11:59 p.m.
Grass surface, trees, water bowls, benches, hills, lighted.

Carlaw Parkette - Toronto
www.toronto.ca/parks/prd/facilities/complex/50,
(416) 338-5058
855 Gerrard St. E., M4M 1Y7.
Daily dawn-dusk.
Fenced, mulch surface, drinking fountain, disposal bags and
trash cans.

Coronation Dog Park - Toronto
www.toronto.ca/parks/prd/facilities/complex/467/index.htm,
(416) 338-5058
711 Lake Shore Blvd. W., M5V 3T7.
Daily dawn-dusk.
Fenced, trees, double-gated entryway, walking paths,
disposal bags and trash cans.

High Park Off-Leash Area - Toronto
www.toronto.ca/parks/prd/facilities/complex/77/index.htm,
(416) 392-2489
1873 Bloor St. W., M6P 3K7.
Daily 8 a.m.-dusk.
Walking trails, grass surface, disposal bags and trash cans,
trees, shade, drinking fountains, restrooms.

Orphan's Greenspace Dog Park - Toronto
www.toronto.ca/parks, (416) 338-5058
51 Power St., M5A 3Y7.
Daily dawn-dusk.
Fenced, double-gated entryway, picnic areas, benches,
mulch surface, trees.

Riverdale Park West - Toronto
www.toronto.ca/parks/prd/facilities/complex/344/,
(416) 338-5058
375 Sumach St., M5A 3P7.
Daily dawn-dusk.
Grass surface, hills, walking trails, trees, shade, benches,
drinking fountains.

QUEBEC

Parc Lafontaine - Montréal
www.montreal.com/parks/lafontaine.html, (514) 872-6381
3933 Avenue du Parc La Fontaine, H2L 3A8.
Daily 6 a.m.-7 p.m.
Fenced, splash area, grass surface, disposal bags and
trash cans.

Pente Douce Dog Park - Québec
www.pets.ca/dogs/dog-parks/quebec/quebec-city,
(418) 641-6010
600 Avenue Belvedere, G1N 2J7.
Daily 8 a.m.-11 p.m.
Fenced, gravel surface, picnic areas, trees.

Pointe-aux-Lievres Dog Park - Québec
www.ville.quebec.qc.ca, (418) 641-6345
25 Rue de la Pointe-aux-Lievres, G1K 2L1.
Daily 8 a.m.-11 p.m.
Fenced, benches, double-gated entryway, gravel surface,
disposal bags and trash cans.

ATTRACTIONS
United States

CALIFORNIA

◆ Disneyland® Resort

(714) 781-4400, 1313 Harbor Blvd., is off I-5 Disneyland Dr. and Disney Way exits at 1313 Harbor Blvd., Anaheim
Two theme parks—Disneyland and Disney California Adventure Park—as well as the shopping, dining and entertainment area Downtown Disney and three hotels comprise this popular Southern California resort. Indoor kennels are available for a fee on a first-come, first-served basis at Disneyland Kennel Club, located to the right of the main Disneyland park entrance; overnight boarding is not available. Pets are permitted to ride on resort trams but not on buses running to and from Toy Story Parking Lot. Pets must have proof of current vaccinations. Both theme parks are open daily with extended hours during the summer, on some holidays and on weekends. Cost: One-day, one-park ticket $97-$124; $91-$118 (ages 3-9). Two-day $199; $187 (ages 3-9). Three-day $270; $258 (ages 3-9). Four-day $290; $275 (ages 3-9). Five-day $305; $290 (ages 3-9). One-day Disneyland® Resort Park Hopper® ticket $157-$174; $151-$168 (ages 3-9). Two-day $244; $232 (ages 3-9). Three-day $315; $303 (ages 3-9). Four-day $335; $320 (ages 3-9). Five-day $350; $335 (ages 3-9). Validity periods for Park Hopper tickets vary according to ticket type. Select theme park tickets are available at participating AAA/CAA Travel offices. Parking: $20 (autos or motorcycles); $25 (RVs or oversize vehicles). Disneyland.com

◆ Mendocino Coast Botanical Gardens

(707) 964-4352, 18220 N. SR 1, 1 mi. s. on SR 1, Fort Bragg
This 47-acre facility is one of the few gardens located directly on an ocean shore. Pathways wind past succulents, camellias, rhododendrons, rose and dahlia gardens, and a coastal forest of pines, magnolias and ferns that leads to bluffs overlooking the Pacific. Pets on leash are permitted. Daily 9-5, Mar.-Oct.; 9-4, rest of year. Closed first Sat. in Aug. (except for those attending the Art in the Gardens fundraiser), the Sat. after Labor Day, Thanksgiving and Christmas. Cost: $14; $10 (ages 65+); $5 (ages 5-17). Electric carts are available for a fee. www.gardenbythesea.org

◆ SeaWorld San Diego

(800) 257-4268, 500 SeaWorld Dr., 500 SeaWorld Dr., off I-5 on Mission Bay's south shore, San Diego
The 189-acre park features shows, up-close animal encounters, attractions and rides. Outdoor kennels are available for a fee on a first-come, first-served basis; overnight boarding is not available. Opens daily at 9 or 10; closing times vary. Hours may be extended during summer and holiday periods. Phone ahead for show schedules. Cost: $93; $83 (ages 3-9). Combination 7-day ticket with San Diego Zoo and San Diego Zoo Safari Park $165; $135 (ages 3-9). Rates may vary; phone ahead. Parking: $16; $11 (motorcycles); $21 (RVs and preferred). seaworldparks.com/en/seaworld-sandiego

◆ Six Flags Magic Mountain

(661) 255-4111, 26101 Magic Mountain Pkwy., 26101 Magic Mountain Pkwy., Valencia
This 260-acre theme park boasts 18 roller coasters and more than 100 other rides, games and attractions for all ages. Free kennel facilities are available in the main parking lot. Opens daily at 10:30, late Mar.-Labor Day; Fri.-Sun. at 10:30, day after Labor Day-Oct. 31; Sat.-Sun. and holidays at 10:30, rest of year. Closing times vary. Cost: $79.99; $54.99 (under 48 inches tall); free (ages 0-2). Prices may vary; phone ahead. Parking: $20. www.sixflags.com

DISTRICT OF COLUMBIA

◆ Washington Monument

(877) 444-6777, 15th St. & Constitution Ave. N.W., near the center of the National Mall; the grounds extend from 14th to 17th sts. and from Constitution to Independence aves. N.W., Washington, D.C.
This instantly recognizable 555-foot marble obelisk commemorates our nation's first president and is surrounded by expansive grounds. Pets on leash are permitted. www.nps.gov/wamo

FLORIDA

◆ Busch Gardens Tampa

(888) 800-5447, 3000 E. Busch Blvd., 3000 E. Busch Blvd. (SR 580), 2 mi. e. of jct. I-275 exit 50 or 2 mi. w. of I-75 exit 265, Tampa
The 335-acre adventure park features thrilling rides, live shows, shopping, dining and a major zoo with more than 2,000 animals. Indoor kennels are available for a fee on a first-come, first-served basis; overnight boarding is not available. Proof of current vaccinations is required. Generally opens daily between 9 and 10; closing times vary. Cost: $102.99; free (ages 0-2). Admission includes a second visit within 7 days of first visit. Serengeti Safari Tour $29-$39. Discounted tickets are available in advance through the attraction's website. Parking: $18; $24 (RVs and preferred). www.buschgardens.com

◆ Kennedy Space Center Visitor Complex

(321) 449-4444, SR 405 & SR 3, 11 mi. e. of I-95 on SR 405, Kennedy Space Center
Built in 1967, the modern facility explores the past, present and future of the U.S. space program. Free kennel facilities are available. Complex open daily at 9; closing times vary. Bus tours depart daily every 15 minutes beginning at 10; last tour departs at 2:30. Cost: (includes all shows, exhibits, 3-D films, KSC bus tour, Shuttle Launch Experience and Heroes and Legends Featuring the U.S. Astronaut Hall of Fame) $50; $40 (ages 3-11). Phone ahead to verify prices. Parking: $10; $5 (motorcycle); $15 (RV). www.kennedyspacecenter.com

SeaWorld Orlando

(888) 800-5447, 7007 SeaWorld Dr., at jct. I-4 and SR 528 (Beachline Expwy.), Orlando
This marine life adventure park has themed shows; up-close animal encounters; attractions; and rides, including the face-down flying coaster Manta, the floorless coaster Kraken and the water coaster Journey to Atlantis. Air-conditioned kennels are available for a fee on a first-come, first-served basis. Proof of current vaccinations is required. Opens daily at 9; closing times vary. Cost: $99; free (ages 0-2). There is an additional fee for VIP tours. Dine with Shamu reservations are required; visit Guest Relations for details.
Discounted theme park tickets are available in advance through the attraction's website. Parking: $18 (private vehicles and motorcycles); $22 (RVs, trailers, semitrucks and preferred); $35 (valet). www.seaworld.com/orlando

Universal Orlando™ Resort

(407) 363-8000, 1000 Universal Studios Plaza, off I-4 exit 75A (eastbound) or 74B (westbound), following signs to the parking garages at 6000 Universal Blvd., Orlando
The resort brings movies and games to life through rides and shows at Universal Studios Florida, visits the universe of myths, legends and superheroes at Universal's Islands of Adventure, and offers Universal CityWalk for shopping, dining and nighttime entertainment. Kennels are available for a fee on a first-come, first-served basis; overnight boarding is not available. Proof of current vaccinations is required. Follow signs to RV and Camper parking lot for kennel access. The theme parks generally open daily at 9 a.m.; closing times vary by season. Universal CityWalk™ is open daily 11 a.m.-2 a.m. Theme park and CityWalk™ hours may vary; phone ahead. Cost: A 1-Day Park-to-Park ticket, which allows same-day access to both Universal Studios Florida™ and Universal's Islands of Adventure™, is $169; $164 (ages 3-9). A 2-Day Park-to-Park ticket, which allows same-day access to both parks over two days, is $254.99; $244.99 (ages 3-9). A 3-Day Park-to-Park ticket, which allows same-day access to both parks over three days, is $274.99; $264.99 (ages 3-9). All multi-day park tickets include admission to select live entertainment venues at Universal CityWalk™. Special advance purchase discount tickets are available at participating AAA/CAA offices. Members who pre-purchase admission through their AAA/CAA branch will receive discounts at select restaurant and merchandise locations within the resort (excludes purchases at food or merchandise carts and purchases of alcohol, tobacco, candy, film, collectibles, sundry items, tattoos and services). Phone ahead to confirm admission and schedule. Parking: $20; $22 (RV or bus); free (after 10 p.m.; not valid during Halloween Horror Nights and Eve). Preferred $30. Valet parking $15-$45. www.universalorlando.com

Walt Disney World® Resort

(407) 824-4321, 3111 World Dr., accessible from Florida's Tpke., US 192, Osceola Pkwy. and several exits off I-4 s. of Orlando, Lake Buena Vista
The expansive complex includes Magic Kingdom® Park, Epcot®, Disney's Hollywood Studios®, Disney's Animal Kingdom® Theme Park, two water parks, more than 20 resort hotels and numerous entertainment, shopping and dining facilities.
With the exception of service dogs, pets are not permitted in theme parks, resort hotels or buses. Best Friends Pet Care offers air-conditioned accommodations for pets at 2510 Bonnet Creek Pkwy. Reservations are recommended but not required. Disney Resort hotel reservations do not guarantee space for pets. Proof of current vaccinations is required. Phone (877) 4 WDW-PETS for information and reservations.
Theme parks open daily generally at 9, with earlier openings for guests staying at a Disney resort hotel; closing times vary. Cost: One-Day Base Magic Kingdom® Park $107-$124; $101-$118 (ages 3-9). 1-Day Base Epcot® or Disney's Hollywood Studios® or Disney's Animal Kingdom® Theme Park $99-$119; $93-$113 (ages 3-9). Prices vary by season. Two-day ticket $199; $187 (ages 3-9). Three-day ticket $289; $271 (ages 3-9). Four-day ticket $350; $330 (ages 3-9). Five-day ticket $370; $350 (ages 3-9). Six-day ticket $390; $370 (ages 3-9). Seven-day ticket $410; $390 (ages 3-9). Eight-day ticket $420; $400 (ages 3-9). Nine-day ticket $430; $410 (ages 3-9). Ten-day ticket $440; $420 (ages 3-9). **Park Hopper® Option** $50-$60 more with the purchase of a 2-to-3-day base ticket; $75 more with a 4-to-10-day base ticket.
Ticket options for additional fees include admission to other entertainment areas and "hopping" between theme parks. Prices do not include tax. Tickets and options are non-transferable, non-refundable and expire 14 days from first use. Passes are non-transferable, non-refundable and expire one year from date of issue. All parks, attractions and entertainment may be changed, canceled or discontinued without notice and without liability. Select theme park tickets are available at participating AAA/CAA Travel offices. Parking: $20; $22 (camper); $25 (bus or tractor-trailer); free (Disney resort guests with valid resort ID). The fee allows parking for that entire day.
Disneyworld.com

GEORGIA

Six Flags Over Georgia

(770) 948-9290, 275 Riverside Pkwy., 275 Riverside Pkwy. S.W., Austell
Six Flags has more than 100 acres where visitors of all ages can experience thrilling rides, games and live shows. Kennels are available for a fee at the main entrance; overnight boarding is not available. Proof of current vaccinations is required. Opens daily at 10:30, late May-early Aug.; Sat.-Sun. at 10:30, early Mar.-late May and early Aug.-late Sept. Closing times vary. The park also is open select days in Oct. for Fright Fest and select days Nov.-Jan. for Holiday in the Park. Cost: All-inclusive 1-day (including Hurricane Harbor) $65.99; $45.99 (children under 48 inches tall); free (ages 0-2). Prices may vary; phone ahead. AAA members save on select services and merchandise. See Guest Relations for details. Parking: $20. www.sixflags.com/overgeorgia

IOWA

Pella Historical Village

(641) 620-9463, jct. E. First and Franklin sts., Pella
A country store, log cabin, wooden shoe workshop, windmill, smithy and other buildings are reminders of this town's Dutch heritage. Leashed pets are permitted but are not allowed in the windmill. Mon.-Fri. 10-5, Sat. 10-4, mid-Mar. through Dec. 31. Early closing some holidays; phone ahead. Cost: $10; $6 (ages 12+ and college students with ID); $2 (ages 5-11); free (military with ID, Memorial Day-Labor Day). www.pellahistorical.org

MASSACHUSETTS

Bunker Hill Monument

(617) 242-7275, Address not available, in Monument Square in Charlestown, Boston
Part of Boston National Historical Park, this 221-foot-tall granite obelisk commemorates the site of the Battle of Bunker Hill, which occurred on June 17, 1775. Leashed pets are permitted on the grounds but not inside the monument. Daily 9-5, mid-Mar. through Nov. 30; Mon.-Fri. 1-5, Sat.-Sun. 9-5, rest of year. Last admission 30 minutes before closing. Cost: Free.
www.nps.gov/bost/historyculture/bhm.htm

MISSOURI

The Gateway Arch

(314) 982-1410, Memorial Dr. and Market St. within Jefferson National Expansion Memorial park, St. Louis
This curved, stainless steel monument soars 630 feet high and symbolizes the gateway to the West. A tram ride takes visitors to an observation deck. Pets on leashes are permitted on the grounds. Arch tram departures daily 8 a.m.-10 p.m., Memorial Day weekend-Labor Day; 9-6, rest of year. Ticket center at The Old Courthouse open daily 7:30 a.m.-8 p.m., Memorial Day weekend-Labor Day; 9-5, rest of year. Cost: (includes entrance to the Arch and movie) $3; free (ages 0-15). Journey to the Top (includes entrance to the Arch, movie and tram ride to the Arch observation room) $13; $10 (ages 3-15). www.nps.gov/jeff

Six Flags St. Louis

(636) 938-5300, 4900 Six Flags Rd., off I-44 at 4900 Six Flags Rd., Eureka
Themed areas showcase a variety of shows, rides and attractions; kids will have a ball exploring Bugs Bunny National Park. Free kennels are available in the parking lot; see toll plaza attendant for details. Pets cannot be kept overnight and must have current vaccinations and registration tags. Park open early Apr.-late Oct.; days and hours vary. Hurricane Harbor open Memorial Day weekend-Labor Day; days and hours vary. Cost: (Includes Hurricane Harbor) $63.99; $48.99 (children under 48 inches tall); free (ages 0-2). Prices may vary; phone ahead. AAA members save on select services. See guest relations for details. Parking: $20; $25 (preferred). www.sixflags.com/stlouis

NORTH CAROLINA

Biltmore

(828) 225-1333, 1 Lodge St., on US 25, 3 blks. n. of I-40 exit 50 or 50B to 1 Lodge St., Asheville
Self-guiding tours of George Washington Vanderbilt's spectacular 250-room, French Renaissance-style château include the upstairs and downstairs, 75 acres of formal gardens, the conservatory and Antler Hill Village. Pets on leash are permitted on estate grounds, but not in buildings. Outdoor kennels are available on a first-come, first-served basis; inquire at the parking lot upon arrival. Estate admission gate open daily 8:30-6:30, Apr.-Dec. Phone for schedule rest of year. Last admission is 2 hours before closing. Winery open Mon.-Thurs. 10-8, Fri.-Sat. 10-9, Sun. noon-8. Cost: All-inclusive admission $60-$75; $30-$37.50 (ages 10-16); free (ages 0-9 with paying adult). Rates may be slightly higher on peak weekends and during seasonal celebrations. Phone ahead to confirm admission. Audio guide $10.98. Guided tours $19. Member discounts are available; tickets can be purchased at the AAA Carolinas office in Asheville (1000 Merrimon Ave., Suite B). www.biltmore.com

Carowinds Amusement and Water Park

(704) 588-2600, 14523 Carowinds Blvd., 10 mi. s. on I-77 to exit 90, is on the North Carolina/South Carolina border at 14523 Carowinds Blvd., Charlotte
Covering 398 acres, the park features more than 50 rides, shows and attractions, including 13 roller coasters—Intimidator is the tallest, fastest and longest in the Southeast. Free climate-controlled kennels are available on a first-come, first-served basis. Overnight boarding is not available. Park opens daily at 10, late May to mid-Aug.; Sat.-Sun. at 10, late Mar.-late May and mid-Aug. to early Sept.; closing times vary but are either 8 or 10 p.m. The park is also open Sat.-Sun., early Sept.-late Oct.; phone for hours. Cost: $65; $44 (ages 62+ or under 48 inches tall); $34 (after 4 p.m.); free (ages 0-2). Season passes also are available. Parking: $15. www.carowinds.com

OHIO

💎 Cedar Point

(419) 627-2350, 1 Cedar Point Dr., off US 6, 10 mi. n. of Ohio Tpke. exit 118 at 1 Cedar Point Dr., Sandusky
This 364-acre amusement/theme park offers more than 70 rides, including 17 roller coasters and more than a dozen thrill rides. Kennels are available for a fee on a first-come, first-served basis at Pet Chek, located across from the bus lot. Overnight boarding is not available. Cedar Point opens daily at 10 (closing times are between 8 p.m. and midnight), mid-May through Labor Day; open Fri. 6 p.m.-midnight, Sat.-Sun. all day for HalloWeekends (park opens at 11 and closes between 8 p.m. and midnight), mid-Sept. to late Oct. Cost: $67; $45 (ages 62+ and under 48 inches tall in shoes); free (ages 0-2). Reduced admission is available after 4 p.m. Multiday combination tickets with Cedar Point Shores are available. Fast Lane wristbands may be purchased to help minimize wait times at certain rides. Phone ahead to verify all rates. Parking: $15-$20 (varies by date).
www.cedarpoint.com

PENNSYLVANIA

💎 Hersheypark

(800) 437-7439, 100 W. Hersheypark Dr., just off SR 743 and US 422, Hershey
Founded in 1907 as a recreational gathering place for employees of Milton S. Hershey's chocolate company, Hersheypark today has more than 70 rides and attractions—including 13 roller coasters—plus live entertainment. Kennels are available mid-May to mid-Sept. for a fee on a first come, first-served basis; overnight boarding is not available. Proof of current vaccinations is required. Open daily at 10, Memorial Day-Labor Day; some Sat.-Sun. at 10, day after Labor Day-Sept. 30. Closing times vary; phone ahead. Phone for Springtime in the Park and Christmas Candylane schedules. Cost: (includes ZooAmerica North American Wildlife Park) $62.95; $39.95 (ages 3-8 and 55-69); $25.95 (ages 70+). Sunset admission (after 3 when park closes at 6, after 4 when park closes at 8, after 5 when park closes at 10 and 11) $29.95; $25.95 (ages 3-8 and 55-69); $17.95 (ages 70+). Other admission packages, including multiday options, are available.
www.hersheypark.com

TENNESSEE

💎 Dollywood

(865) 428-9488, 1020 Dollywood Ln., 1 mi. n.e. off US 441 at 1020 Dollywood Ln., Pigeon Forge
Conceived and operated by Dolly Parton, the theme park evokes the traditions of the Smoky Mountains with craft demonstrations, entertainment, seasonal festivals and more than 40 rides and attractions. Indoor kennel facilities are available for a fee by reservation and on a first-come, first-served basis at Doggywood, located near the front entrance. Overnight boarding is not available. Proof of current vaccinations is required. Phone (865) 428-9826 for information and reservations. Park open daily 10-10, mid-June to early Aug.; Wed.-Mon. 10-7, late Mar. to mid-June and early Aug.-Aug. 31; Wed.-Mon. 10-6, in Sept. SkyZip open late Mar.-late Oct. Cost: Park $67; $62 (ages 60+); $54 (ages 4-11). SkyZip $39. Combination ticket is available with Dollywood's Splash Country. Prices may vary; phone ahead to confirm admission and schedule. Parking: $12.
www.dollywood.com

TEXAS

💎 Caverns of Sonora

(325) 387-3105, 1711 Private Rd. 4468, 8 mi. w. off I-10 exit 392 and 7 mi. s. on Cavern Rd. (Ranch Rd. 1989), Sonora
A 1.75-mile trail winds through the cave, where the temperature is a constant 70 degrees F with 98 percent humidity. Stalagmites, stalactites and helictites cover the walls, ceiling and floor of the cave, exhibiting a wide range of natural colors. Free kennels are available. Daily 8-6, Mar. 1-Labor Day; 9-5, rest of year. Cost: Crystal Palace tour $20; $16 (ages 4-11). Prices may vary.
www.cavernsofsonora.com

💎 SeaWorld San Antonio

(800) 700-7786, 10500 SeaWorld Dr., 10500 SeaWorld Dr., San Antonio
This marine life adventure park entertains and educates with shows, up-close animal encounters, attractions and rides. Free outdoor kennels are located off the main parking lot; overnight boarding is not available. Opens daily at 9 or 10, late May-late Aug.; days and hours vary rest of year. Cost: $68. Combination ticket with Aquatica, SeaWorld's Waterpark $99. Admission and parking prices may vary; phone ahead. Parking: $20; $25 (preferred).
seaworldparks.com/en/seaworld-sanantonio

Six Flags Fiesta Texas

(210) 697-5050, 17000 I-10W, 17000 I-10W, San Antonio
Housed in a former rock quarry, the park celebrates Texas and the Southwest with thrill and family-style rides, live entertainment and themed areas. Kennels are located to the right of the main entrance; overnight boarding is not available. Proof of current vaccinations and registration tags is required. Park open daily, late May-late Aug. (also in mid-Mar. for spring break); open Sat.-Sun. and some weekdays, late Apr.-late May; open Sat.-Sun., Mar. 1 to mid-Mar. and late Mar.-late Apr.; open select days, early Sept.-early Jan. Water park open daily, early June-late Aug. Park and water park hours vary. Cost: $73.99; $57.99 (under 48 inches tall); free (ages 0-2). Rates may vary; phone ahead. AAA members save on select services and merchandise. See guest relations for details. Rides, shows and attractions are subject to change without notice. Parking: $20. www.sixflags.com

Six Flags Over Texas

(817) 640-8900, 2201 Road to Six Flags, 2201 Road to Six Flags, Arlington
The 205-acre theme park depicts Texas under the flags of France, Mexico, the Republic of Texas, the Old South, Spain and the United States. Air-conditioned kennels are available next to the picnic area. Daily, late May-early Aug.; Sat.-Sun., Mar. 1-late May, mid-Aug. through Oct. 31 and day after Thanksgiving-Dec. 31. Hours vary. Cost: $68.99; $53.99 (under 48 inches tall); free (ages 0-2). Rates may vary; phone ahead. AAA members save on select services and merchandise. See guest relations for details. Parking: $20. www.sixflags.com

VIRGINIA

Busch Gardens Williamsburg

(800) 343-7946, 1 Busch Gardens Blvd., 1 Busch Gardens Blvd., Williamsburg
This 100-acre adventure park features thrill rides, animal attractions and shows, and shops and eateries set amid various European-themed villages. Kennel facilities are available for a fee in the England parking lot. Open Mar.-Dec.; days and hours vary. Cost: $80; $70 (ages 3-9). Multiday and combination tickets with Water Country USA are available. Parking: $15. seaworldparks.com/en/buschgardens-williamsburg/

Kings Dominion

(804) 876-5000, 16000 Theme Park Dr., .5 mi. e. off I-95 exit 98 at 16000 Theme Park Dr., Doswell
A 300-foot replica of the Eiffel Tower stands at the gates to this 400-acre theme park, which features live shows, thrill and family rides, and a water park. Kennels are available for a fee outside the front gate; overnight boarding is not available. Parks open daily, Memorial Day-Labor Day. Schedules vary rest of year; phone ahead. Cost: (includes Soak City in season) $67; $45 (ages 62+ and under 48 inches tall); free (ages 0-2). Dinosaurs Alive! additional $5. Prices may vary. Parking: $15. www.kingsdominion.com

Water Country USA

(800) 343-7946, 176 Water Country Pkwy., 176 Water Country Pkwy., Williamsburg
Pools, water rides, lazy rivers and a high-dive show are just some of the attractions offered at this water park. Kennel facilities are available for a fee and are located in the England parking lot at Busch Gardens Williamsburg. Opens daily at 10, Memorial Day-Labor Day. Days and closing times vary. Cost: $54; $47 (ages 3-9). Multiday and combination tickets with Busch Gardens Williamsburg are available. Rates may vary; phone ahead. Parking: $15. watercountryusa.com/wc/

Canada

ONTARIO

◆ Canada's Wonderland

(905) 832-7000, off Hwy. 400, Rutherford Rd. exit northbound or Major MacKenzie Dr. E. exit southbound at 9580 Jane St., Vaughan

This 121-hectare (365-acre) theme park has more than 200 attractions and 65 rides, in addition to a water park and participative play areas for children. Air-conditioned kennels are available for a fee; overnight boarding is not permitted. Daily 10-10, late July-Aug. 31; Sat.-Sun. and Labour Day 10-8, in Sept.; Sat.-Sun. 10-5, Oct. 1-Nov. 1. Hours are subject to change without notice; phone to verify schedule and admission prices. Cost: Passport for grounds and most rides $64; $37.99 (under 48" tall and ages 60+). Concerts are available at an extra charge. Height restrictions apply to some rides. Parking: $17.70. www.canadaswonderland.com

◆ Upper Canada Village

(613) 543-4328, 13740 CR 2, 11 km (7 mi.) e. on CR 2 off Hwy. 401, Morrisburg

Upper Canada Village re-creates life during the 1860s through a working community of artisans and costumed interpreters who perform chores typical of the era. Guide dogs and other service animals are permitted. All other pets must be kept on a leash and may not enter historic buildings. Daily 9:30-5, early May-Labour Day; Wed.-Sun. 9:30-5, day after Labour Day through mid-Sept. Cost: Village $19; $18 (ages 65+); $12 (ages 6-12); free (ages 0-5). Rates, including those for special events, may vary; phone ahead. www.uppercanadavillage.com

NATIONAL PUBLIC LANDS

The National Public Lands listed below permit pets on a leash. Keep in mind that animals may be prohibited from entering public buildings and even some areas outdoors, particularly those that are ecologically sensitive. Where swimming is permitted, there are usually no lifeguards on duty; people and pets swim at their own risk. Specific pet policies vary from park to park and are subject to change. Always check in advance regarding any applicable regulations and to confirm that pets are still permitted where you are going.

Be aware of dangers to your pet in natural areas, including snakes, ticks and fast-moving currents in rivers and streams. An unleashed dog may chase after a wild animal and become separated from its owner, increasing the risk of loss or injury. Never leave your pet unattended. Keep him leashed or crated at all times. Follow park guidelines faithfully, and monitor your pet's behavior; the National Park Service may confiscate pets that harm wildlife or other visitors. *For additional information on outdoor vacations, see The Great Outdoors, p. 16.*

United States

ALABAMA
Conecuh National Forest
On the Alabama-Florida border.
(334) 222-2555
🚴 🏕 🥾 ⛱ 🏊

Horseshoe Bend National Military Park
12 mi. n. of Dadeville on SR 49.
(256) 234-7111
🥾 ⛱ 🏊 🏛

Talladega National Forest
In central Alabama.
(256) 362-2909
🚴 🏕 🥾 ⛱ 🏊

Tuskegee National Forest
Northeast of Tuskegee.
(334) 727-2652
🚴 🏕 🥾 ⛱

William B. Bankhead National Forest
In northwestern Alabama.
(205) 489-5111
🚴 🏕 🥾 ⛱ 🏊

ALASKA
Chugach National Forest
Along the Gulf of Alaska from Cape Suckling to Seward.
(907) 743-9500
🚴 🏕 🥾 ⛱ 🏛

Denali National Park and Preserve
In south-central Alaska.
(907) 683-2294
🏕 🥾 ⛱ 🏛 🍽

Glacier Bay National Park and Preserve
North of Cross Sound to the Canadian border.
(907) 697-2230
🏕 🥾 🏛 🍽

Kenai Fjords National Park
Southeastern side of the Kenai Peninsula.
(907) 224-7500 or (907) 224-2132
🏕 🥾 ⛱ 🏛

Lake Clark National Park and Preserve
In southern Alaska.
(907) 644-3626
🏕 🥾 🏛

Tongass National Forest
In southeastern Alaska.
(907) 228-6220
🚴 🏕 🥾 ⛱ 🏊 🏛

Wrangell-St. Elias National Park and Preserve
In southeastern Alaska, northwest of Tongass National Forest.
(907) 822-7250
🏕 🥾 ⛱ 🏛

ARIZONA
Apache-Sitgreaves National Forests
In east-central Arizona.
(928) 333-4301
🚴 🏕 🥾 ⛱ 🏛 🍽

Coconino National Forest
In north-central Arizona.
(928) 527-3600
🚴 🏕 🥾 ⛱ 🏊 🍽

Coronado National Forest
In southeastern Arizona and southwestern New Mexico.
(520) 388-8300
🚴 🏕 🥾 ⛱ 🏛

Glen Canyon National Recreation Area
In northern Arizona and Southern Utah.
(928) 608-6200
🚴 🏕 🥾 ⛱ 🏊 🏛 🍽

Grand Canyon National Park
In northwestern Arizona.
(928) 638-2901
🏕 🥾 ⛱ 🏛 🍽

Kaibab National Forest
In north-central Arizona.
(928) 643-7298
🚴 🏕 🥾 ⛱ 🏛 🍽

🚴 Bicycling Trails   🏕 Camping   🥾 Hiking Trails   ⛱ Picnic Facilities
🏊 Swimming   🏛 Visitor Center   🍽 Food Service

Petrified Forest National Park
In east-central Arizona, east of Holbrook.
(928) 524-6228
🏄 ⛱ 🛖 🍽

Prescott National Forest
In central Arizona.
(928) 443-8000
🔺 🏄 ⛱ 🍽

Saguaro National Park
Two districts, 15 mi. east and west of Tucson.
(520) 733-5153
🚲 🔺 🏄 ⛱ 🛖

Tonto National Forest
In central Arizona.
(602) 225-5200
🚲 🔺 🏄 ⛱ 🛝 🍽

ARKANSAS
Buffalo National River
In northwestern Arkansas.
(870) 439-2502
🔺 🏄 ⛱ 🛝 🛖 🍽

Hot Springs National Park
In western Arkansas.
(501) 620-6715
🔺 🏄 ⛱ 🛖

Ouachita National Forest
In west-central Arkansas and southeastern Oklahoma.
(501) 321-5202
🚲 🔺 🏄 ⛱ 🛝 🛖

Ozark National Forest
In northwestern Arkansas.
(479) 964-7200
🚲 🔺 🏄 ⛱ 🛝 🛖

St. Francis National Forest
In east-central Arkansas.
(479) 964-7200
🔺 🏄 ⛱ 🛝 🛖

CALIFORNIA
Angeles National Forest
In southern California.
(626) 574-5200
🚲 🔺 🏄 ⛱ 🛝 🛖 🍽

Cleveland National Forest
In southwestern California.
(858) 673-6180
🚲 🔺 🏄 ⛱ 🛖 🍽

Death Valley National Park
Along the Nevada border in east-central California.
(760) 786-3200
🚲 🔺 🏄 ⛱ 🛝 🛖

Eldorado National Forest
In central California.
(530) 644-6048
🚲 🔺 🏄 ⛱ 🛝 🛖 🍽

Golden Gate National Recreation Area
North of the Golden Gate Bridge and in northern and western San Francisco.
(415) 561-4700
🚲 🔺 🏄 ⛱ 🛝 🛖 🍽

Inyo National Forest
In east-central California.
(760) 873-2400
🚲 🔺 🏄 ⛱ 🛝 🛖 🍽

King Range National Conservation Area
In northwestern California.
(707) 825-2300
🚲 🔺 🏄 ⛱ 🛝 🛖 🍽

Klamath National Forest
In northern California.
(530) 842-6131
🚲 🔺 🏄 ⛱ 🛝 🛖

Lassen National Forest
In northeastern California.
(530) 257-2151
🚲 🔺 🏄 ⛱ 🛝 🛖 🍽

Lassen Volcanic National Park
In northeastern California.
(530) 595-4444
🔺 🏄 ⛱ 🛝 🛖 🍽

Los Padres National Forest
In southern California.
(805) 968-6640
🚲 🔺 🏄 ⛱ 🛝 🛖

Mendocino National Forest
In northwestern California.
(530) 934-2350
🚲 🔺 🏄 ⛱ 🛝 🛖 🍽

Modoc National Forest
In northeastern California.
(530) 233-5811
🚲 🔺 🏄 ⛱ 🛝 🛖

Mojave National Preserve
Between I-15 and I-40 in southeastern California.
(760) 252-6108
🔺 🏄 ⛱ 🛖 🍽

Plumas National Forest
In northern California.
(530) 283-2050
🚲 🔺 🏄 ⛱ 🛝 🛖 🍽

Point Reyes National Seashore
Along the California coast just north of San Francisco.
(415) 464-5100
🚲 🔺 🏄 ⛱ 🛖 🍽

Redwood National and State Parks
On the northern California coast.
(707) 465-7765
🚲 🔺 🏄 ⛱ 🛝 🛖 🍽

🚲 Bicycling Trails   🔺 Camping   🏄 Hiking Trails   ⛱ Picnic Facilities
🛝 Swimming   🛖 Visitor Center   🍽 Food Service

San Bernardino National Forest
In southern California.
(909) 382-2600
🚴 🔺 🏍 🎋 🛶 🏕 🍴

Santa Monica Mountains National Recreation Area
West from Griffith Park in Los Angeles past the Ventura
County line.
(805) 370-2301
🚴 🔺 🏍 🎋 🛶 🏕 🍴

Sequoia and Kings Canyon National Parks
In east-central California.
(559) 565-3341
🔺 🏍 🎋 🏕

Sequoia National Forest
In south-central California.
(559) 784-1500
🚴 🔺 🏍 🎋 🛶 🏕 🍴

Shasta-Trinity National Forests
In northern California.
(530) 226-2500
🚴 🔺 🏍 🎋 🛶 🏕 🍴

Sierra National Forest
In central California.
(559) 297-0706
🚴 🔺 🏍 🎋 🛶 🏕 🍴

Six Rivers National Forest
In northwestern California.
(707) 442-1721
🚴 🔺 🏍 🎋 🛶 🏕 🍴

Smith River National Recreation Area
Within Six Rivers National Forest in northwestern
California.
(707) 457-3131
🚴 🔺 🏍 🎋 🛶

Stanislaus National Forest
Within Six Rivers National Forest in northwestern
California.
(707) 457-3131
🚴 🔺 🏍 🎋 🛶 🍴

Tahoe National Forest
In north-central California.
(530) 265-4531
🔺 🏍 🎋 🛶 🏕 🍴

Whiskeytown-Shasta-Trinity National Recreation Area
North and west of Redding.
(530) 242-3400
🚴 🔺 🏍 🎋 🛶 🏕 🍴

Yosemite National Park
In central California.
(209) 372-0200
🚴 🔺 🏍 🎋 🛶 🏕 🍴

COLORADO
Arapaho and Roosevelt National Forests and Pawnee National Grassland
In north-central Colorado.
(970) 295-6700
🚴 🔺 🏍 🎋 🛶 🏕

Arapaho National Recreation Area
In north-central Colorado.
(970) 887-4100
🚴 🔺 🏍 🎋 🛶 🏕

Black Canyon of The Gunnison National Park
In western Colorado.
(970) 249-1914
🔺 🏍 🎋 🏕

Curecanti National Recreation Area
In south-central Colorado between Gunnison and
Montrose, paralleling US 50.
(970) 641-2337
🔺 🏍 🎋 🛶 🏕 🍴

Dinosaur National Monument
In northeast Utah and northwest Colorado.
(435) 781-7700
🚴 🔺 🏍 🎋 🏕

Grand Mesa—Uncompahgre—Gunnison National Forests
In west-central Colorado.
(970) 874-6600
🚴 🔺 🏍 🎋 🏕 🍴

Great Sand Dunes National Park and Preserve
Northeast of Alamosa.
(719) 378-6399
🔺 🏍 🎋 🏕

Mesa Verde National Park
In southwestern Colorado.
(970) 529-4465
🔺 🏍 🎋 🏕

Pikes Peak and Pike National Forest
In south-central Colorado.
(719) 553-1400
🚴 🔺 🏍 🎋 🏕 🍴

Rio Grande National Forest
In south-central Colorado.
(719) 852-5941
🚴 🔺 🏍 🎋 🛶 🏕

Rocky Mountain National Park
In north-central Colorado.
(970) 586-1206
🔺 🏍 🎋 🏕

Routt National Forest
In northwestern Colorado.
(970) 638-4516
🚴 🔺 🏍 🎋 🛶 🏕

San Isabel National Forest
In central Colorado.
(719) 553-1400
🚴 🔺 🏍 🎋 🏕 🍴

San Juan National Forest
In southwestern Colorado.
(970) 247-4874
🚴 🔺 🏍 🎋 🏕 🍴

White River National Forest
In west-central Colorado.
(970) 945-2521
🚴 🔺 🏍 🎋 🛶 🏕 🍴

FLORIDA
Apalachicola National Forest
In northwestern Florida.
(850) 926-3561
[icons]

Biscayne National Park
In southeast Florida.
(305) 230-7275
[icons]

Ocala National Forest
In north-central Florida.
(352) 236-0288
[icons]

Ocala National Forest (Alexander Springs Recreation Area)
13 mi. n.e. of Umatilla via SR 19 and CR 445.
(352) 669-3522
[icons]

Ocala National Forest (Juniper Springs Recreation Area)
28 mi. e. of Ocala on SR 40.
(352) 625-3147
[icons]

Ocala National Forest (Lake Dorr Recreation Area)
5 mi. n. of Umatilla on SR 19.
(352) 236-0288
[icons]

Osceola National Forest
Near the Georgia border.
(386) 752-2577
[icons]

Osceola National Forest (Olustee Beach Recreation Area)
.25 mi. n. of Olustee on CR 231 (Pine Street).
(904) 487-1462
[icons]

GEORGIA
Chattahoochee and Oconee National Forests
In central and northern Georgia.
(770) 297-3000
[icons]

Chattahoochee River National Recreation Area
North of Atlanta.
(678) 538-1200
[icons]

IDAHO
Boise National Forest
In southwestern Idaho.
(208) 373-4007
[icons]

Caribou-Targhee National Forest
In southeastern Idaho.
(208) 524-7500
[icons]

Clearwater National Forest
In northeastern Idaho.
(208) 476-4541
[icons]

Idaho Panhandle National Forests
In northern and northwestern Idaho.
(208) 765-7223
[icons]

Nez Perce National Forest
In northwestern Idaho.
(208) 983-1950
[icons]

Payette National Forest
In west-central Idaho.
(208) 634-0700
[icons]

Salmon-Challis National Forest
In east-central Idaho.
(208) 756-5100
[icons]

Sawtooth National Forest
In south-central Idaho.
(208) 737-3200
[icons]

Sawtooth National Recreation Area
In south-central Idaho.
(208) 727-5013
[icons]

ILLINOIS
Shawnee National Forest
In southern Illinois.
(618) 253-7114
[icons]

INDIANA
Hoosier National Forest
In southern Indiana.
(812) 275-5987
[icons]

Indiana Dunes National Lakeshore
On the southern shore of Lake Michigan.
(219) 926-7561
[icons]

KENTUCKY
Daniel Boone National Forest
Five districts in eastern and southeastern Kentucky.
(859) 745-3100
[icons]

Daniel Boone National Forest (Laurel River Lake)
Off I-75 west of Corbin.
(606) 864-4163
[icons]

    Bicycling Trails   Camping   Hiking Trails   Picnic Facilities
    Swimming   Visitor Center   Food Service

Daniel Boone National Forest (Red River Gorge Geological Area)
Off SR 15.
(606) 663-8100
▲ 林 ⇱ ⋔

Daniel Boone National Forest (Rockcastle)
22 mi. southwest of London via SR 192/3497.
(606) 864-4163
▲ 林 ⇱ ⋤

Daniel Boone National Forest (Sawyer)
5 mi. west of Cumberland Falls on SR 90, then 7 mi. north on SR 896 following signs.
(606) 376-5323
▲ 林 ⇱

Daniel Boone National Forest (S-Tree)
.5 mi. west of McKee on US 421, 3 mi. south on SR 89, 1 mi. west on FR 43, then south on FR 20 following signs.
(606) 864-4163
▲ 林 ⇱

Daniel Boone National Forest (Turkey Foot)
3 mi. north of McKee on SR 89, then east on FR 4 following signs for 3 mi.
(606) 864-4163
▲ 林 ⇱

Land Between The Lakes National Recreation Area
In western Kentucky and Tennessee.
(270) 924-2000
⑤ ▲ 林 ⇱ ⋤ ⋔

Mammoth Cave National Park
In south-central Kentucky 10 mi. west of Cave City.
(270) 758-2180
⑤ ▲ 林 ⇱ ⋔

LOUISIANA
Bayou Sauvage National Wildlife Refuge
Within the New Orleans city limits.
(985) 882-2000
⑤ 林 ⇱

Black Bayou Lake National Wildlife Refuge
In northeastern Louisiana.
(318) 387-1114
⑤ 林 ⋔

Kisatchie National Forest
In central and northern Louisiana.
(318) 473-7160
⑤ ▲ 林 ⇱ ⋤

Sabine National Wildlife Refuge
In southwestern Louisiana.
(337) 762-3816
林

Tensas River National Wildlife Refuge
In northeastern Louisiana.
(318) 574-2664
⑤ 林 ⇱ ⋔

MAINE
Acadia National Park
Along the Atlantic coast southeast of Bangor.
(207) 288-3338

⑤ ▲ 林 ⇱ ⋤ ⋔ ⋈

MICHIGAN
Hiawatha National Forest
In Michigan's Upper Peninsula.
(906) 786-4062
⑤ ▲ 林 ⇱ ⋤ ⋔

Huron-Manistee National Forests
In the northern part of the Lower Peninsula.
(231) 775-2421
⑤ ▲ 林 ⇱ ⋤ ⋔

Ottawa National Forest
In Michigan's Upper Peninsula.
(906) 932-1330
⑤ ▲ 林 ⇱ ⋤ ⋔

Pictured Rocks National Lakeshore
Along Lake Superior in Michigan's Upper Peninsula.
906-387-3700
▲ 林 ⇱ ⋤ ⋔

Sleeping Bear Dunes National Lakeshore
Along Lake Michigan in the northwestern part of the Lower Peninsula.
(231) 326-5134
▲ 林 ⇱ ⋤ ⋔

MINNESOTA
Chippewa National Forest
In north-central Minnesota.
(218) 335-8600
⑤ ▲ 林 ⇱ ⋤ ⋔ ⋈

Superior National Forest
In northeastern Minnesota.
(218) 626-4300
⑤ ▲ 林 ⇱ ⋤ ⋔ ⋈

MISSISSIPPI
Bienville National Forest
In central Mississippi.
(601) 469-3811
▲ 林 ⇱ ⋤ ⋔

Delta National Forest
In west-central Mississippi.
(662) 873-6256
⑤ ▲ 林 ⇱ ⋔

De Soto National Forest
In southeastern Mississippi.
(601) 528-6160
⑤ ▲ 林 ⇱ ⋤ ⋔

Gulf Islands National Seashore
Along the Gulf of Mexico in southern Mississippi.
(228) 875-9057
▲ 林 ⇱ ⋔

Holly Springs National Forest
In north-central Mississippi.
(662) 236-6550
▲ 林 ⇱ ⋤ ⋔

Homochitto National Forest
In the southwestern corner of Mississippi.
(601) 384-5876
⑤ ▲ 林 ⇱ ⋤ ⋔

Tombigbee National Forest
In east-central Mississippi.
(662) 285-3264
🚴 🏕 🥾 🍽 🛆 👥

MISSOURI
Mark Twain National Forest
Southern Missouri.
(573) 364-4621
🚴 🏕 🥾 🍽

Mark Twain National Forest (Big Bay Recreation Area)
1 mi. southeast of Shell Knob on SR 39, then 3 mi. southeast on CR YY.
(573) 364-4621
🏕 🍽 🛆

Mark Twain National Forest (Crane Lake Recreation Area)
12 mi. south of Ironton off SR 49 and CR E.
(573) 364-4621
🚴 🥾 🍽 🛆

Mark Twain National Forest (Fourche Lake Recreation Area)
18 mi. west of Doniphan on US 160.
(573) 364-4621
🥾 🍽

Mark Twain National Forest (Noblett Lake Recreation Area)
8 mi. west of Willow Springs on SR 76, then 1.4 mi. south on SR 181, 3 mi. southeast on CR AP and 1 mi. southwest on CR 857.
(573) 364-4621
🚴 🏕 🥾 🍽

Mark Twain National Forest (Pinewoods Lake Recreation Area)
2 mi. west of Ellsinore on SR 60.
(573) 364-4621
🚴 🥾 🍽 🛆

Mark Twain National Forest (Red Bluff Recreation Area)
1 mi. east of Davisville on CR V, then 1 mi. north on FR 2011.
(573) 364-4621
🏕 🥾 🍽 🛆

Ozarks and Ozark National Scenic Riverways
In southeastern Missouri.
(573) 323-4236
🏕 🥾 🍽 🛆 👥

MONTANA
Beaverhead-Deerlodge National Forest
In southwestern Montana.
(406) 683-3900
🚴 🏕 🥾 🍽 🛆

Bighorn Canyon National Recreation Area
In southern Montana and northern Wyoming.
(406) 666-2412
🏕 🥾 🍽 🛆 👥 🍴

Bitterroot National Forest
In western Montana.
(406) 363-7100
🚴 🏕 🥾 🍽 🛆 👥

Custer National Forest
In southeastern Montana.
(406) 255-1400
🚴 🏕 🥾 🍽 🛆 🍴

Flathead National Forest
In northwestern Montana.
(406) 758-5204
🚴 🏕 🥾 🍽 🛆 👥

Gallatin National Forest
In south-central Montana.
(406) 522-2520
🚴 🏕 🥾 🍽 🛆 👥 🍴

Glacier National Park
In northwestern Montana.
(406) 888-7800
🏕 🥾 🍽 🛆 👥 🍴

Helena National Forest
In west-central Montana.
(406) 449-5201
🏕 🥾 🍽 🛆

Kootenai National Forest
In northwestern Montana.
(406) 293-6211
🚴 🏕 🥾 🍽 🛆 👥 🍴

Lewis and Clark National Forest
In central Montana.
(406) 791-7700
🏕 🥾 🍽 🛆

NEVADA
Great Basin National Park
In central Nevada, 5 mi. west of Baker near the Nevada-Utah border.
(775) 234-7331
🚴 🏕 🥾 🍽 👥

Humboldt-Toiyabe National Forest
In central, western, northern and southern Nevada and eastern California.
(775) 331-6444
🚴 🏕 🥾 🍽

Lake Mead National Recreation Area
In northwestern Arizona and southeastern Nevada.
(702) 293-8990
🚴 🏕 🥾 🍽 🛆 👥 🍴

NEW HAMPSHIRE
White Mountains and White Mountain National Forest
In northern New Hampshire.
(603) 528-8721
🚴 🏕 🥾 🍽 🛆 👥

🚴 Bicycling Trails   🏕 Camping   🥾 Hiking Trails   🍽 Picnic Facilities
🛆 Swimming   👥 Visitor Center   🍴 Food Service

NEW JERSEY
Gateway National Recreation Area (Sandy Hook Unit)
In northeastern New Jersey.
(732) 872-5970

NEW MEXICO
Carson National Forest
In north-central New Mexico.
(575) 758-6200

Chaco Culture National Historical Park
In northwestern New Mexico.
(505) 786-7014

Cibola National Forest
In central New Mexico.
(505) 856-7325

El Malpais National Conservation Area
23 mi. south of I-40 via SRs 53 and 117.
(505) 783-4774

Gila National Forest
In southwestern New Mexico.
(575) 388-8201

Lincoln National Forest
In south-central New Mexico.
(575) 434-7200

Santa Fe National Forest
In north-central New Mexico between the Jemez Mountains and the Sangre de Cristo Mountains.
(505) 438-5300

NEW YORK
Finger Lakes National Forest
In south-central New York on a ridge between Seneca and Cayuga lakes, via I-90, I-81 and SR 17.
(607) 546-4470

Gateway National Recreation Area (Jamaica Bay Unit)
In Brooklyn and Queens boroughs in New York City.
(718) 338-3799

Gateway National Recreation Area (Staten Island Unit)
On Staten Island borough in New York City.
(718) 354-4500

NORTH CAROLINA
Cape Hatteras National Seashore
In eastern North Carolina along the Outer Banks.
(252) 473-2111

Croatan National Forest
In southeastern North Carolina.
(252) 638-5628

Croatan National Forest (Cedar Point)
1.25 mi. north jct. SRs 24 and 58, 3 mi. southeast of Swansboro.
(252) 638-5628

Nantahala National Forest
At North Carolina's southwestern tip.
(828) 257-4200

Nantahala National Forest (Hanging Dog)
21 acres 5 mi. northwest of Murphy on SR 1326.
(828) 837-5152

Nantahala National Forest (Jackrabbit Mountain)
10 mi. northeast of Hayesville via US 64, SR 175 and SR 1155.
(828) 524-6441

Nantahala National Forest (Standing Indian Mountain)
9 mi. west of Franklin on US 64, 2 mi. east on old US 64, then 2 mi. south on FR 67.
(828) 524-6441

Pisgah National Forest
In western North Carolina.
(828) 257-4200

Pisgah National Forest (Lake Powhatan)
7 mi. southwest of Asheville on SR 191 and FR 3484.
(828) 670-5627

Pisgah National Forest (Rocky Bluff)
3 mi. south of Hot Springs on SR 209.
(828) 682-6146

Uwharrie National Forest
In central North Carolina.
(910) 576-6391

Uwharrie National Forest (Badin Lake)
10 mi. north of Troy on SR 109.
(910) 576-6391

NORTH DAKOTA
Theodore Roosevelt National Park (North Unit)
In western North Dakota.
(701) 842-2333

Theodore Roosevelt National Park (South Unit)
In western North Dakota.
(701) 623-4466

OHIO
Cuyahoga Valley National Park
In northeastern Ohio.
(800) 257-9477
🚴 ⛺ 🥾 ⛱ 🏠 🍴

OKLAHOMA
Black Kettle National Grassland
Off SR 283 in Cheyenne.
(580) 497-2143
⛺ 🥾 ⛱ 🏠 🍴

Chickasaw National Recreation Area
In south-central Oklahoma.
(580) 622-7234
🚴 ⛺ 🥾 ⛱ 🏠 🏠

OREGON
Crater Lake National Park
On the crest of the Cascade Range off SR 62.
(541) 594-3100
🚴 ⛺ 🥾 ⛱ 🏠 🍴

Deschutes National Forest
In central Oregon 6 mi. south of Bend via US 97.
(541) 383-5300
🚴 ⛺ 🥾 ⛱ 🏠 🏠 🍴

Fremont-Winema National Forest
In south-central Oregon.
(541) 947-2151
🚴 ⛺ 🥾 ⛱ 🏠 🏠 🍴

Hells Canyon National Recreation Area
In northeastern Oregon and western Idaho.
(509) 758-0616
🚴 ⛺ 🥾 ⛱ 🏠

Malheur National Forest
In eastern Oregon.
(541) 575-3000
🚴 ⛺ 🥾 ⛱ 🏠

Mt. Hood and Mt. Hood National Forest
In northwestern Oregon.
(888) 622-4822
🚴 ⛺ 🥾 ⛱ 🏠 🏠 🍴

Ochoco National Forest
In central Oregon off US 26.
(541) 416-6500
🚴 ⛺ 🥾 ⛱ 🏠

Oregon Dunes National Recreation Area
Between North Bend and Florence.
(541) 750-7000
⛺ 🥾 ⛱ 🏠 🏠

Rogue River–Siskiyou National Forest
In southwestern Oregon off I-5 from Medford.
(541) 858-2200
🚴 ⛺ 🥾 ⛱ 🏠 🏠

Siuslaw National Forest
In western Oregon.
(541) 750-7000
🚴 ⛺ 🥾 ⛱ 🏠 🏠

Umatilla National Forest
In northeastern Oregon.
(541) 278-3716
🚴 ⛺ 🥾 ⛱ 🏠 🏠

Umpqua National Forest
In southwestern Oregon 33 mi. east of Roseburg on SR 138.
(541) 672-6601
🚴 ⛺ 🥾 ⛱ 🏠 🏠 🍴

Wallowa-Whitman National Forest
In northeastern Oregon.
(541) 523-6391
⛺ 🥾 ⛱ 🏠

Willamette National Forest
In western Oregon.
(541) 225-6300
🚴 ⛺ 🥾 ⛱ 🏠 🍴

PENNSYLVANIA
Allegheny National Forest
In northwestern Pennsylvania.
(814) 723-5150
🚴 ⛺ 🥾 ⛱ 🏠 🏠 🍴

Delaware Water Gap National Recreation Area
In eastern Pennsylvania and northwestern New Jersey.
(570) 426-2457
🚴 ⛺ 🥾 ⛱ 🏠 🏠

SOUTH CAROLINA
Congaree National Park
Southeast of Hopkins.
(803) 776-4396
⛺ 🥾 ⛱ 🏠

Francis Marion National Forest
On the Coastal Plain north of Charleston.
(803) 561-4000
🚴 ⛺ 🥾 ⛱ 🏠

Sumter National Forest
In western South Carolina.
(803) 561-4000
🚴 ⛺ 🥾 ⛱ 🏠

SOUTH DAKOTA
Badlands National Park
In southwestern South Dakota.
(605) 433-5361
⛺ 🥾 ⛱ 🏠 🍴

Black Hills National Forest
In southwestern South Dakota.
(605) 673-9200
🚴 ⛺ 🥾 ⛱ 🏠 🏠 🍴

🚴 Bicycling Trails   ⛺ Camping   🥾 Hiking Trails   ⛱ Picnic Facilities
⛳ Swimming   🏠 Visitor Center   🍴 Food Service

Wind Cave National Park
In southwestern South Dakota.
(605) 745-4600

TENNESSEE
Big South Fork National River and Recreation Area
In northeastern Tennessee and southeastern Kentucky.
(423) 286-7275

Cherokee National Forest
In eastern Tennessee.
(423) 476-9700

TEXAS
Amistad National Recreation Area
Northwest of Del Rio via US 90.
(830) 775-7491

Angelina National Forest
In east Texas.
(936) 897-1068

Big Bend National Park
In southwest Texas.
(432) 477-2251

Davy Crockett National Forest
In east Texas.
(936) 655-2299

Lake Meredith National Recreation Area
45 mi. northeast of Amarillo and 9 mi. west of Borger via SR 136.
(806) 857-3151

Padre Island National Seashore
On Padre Island near Corpus Christi.
(361) 949-8068

Sabine National Forest
In east Texas.
(409) 625-1940

Sam Houston National Forest
40 mi. north of Houston in east Texas.
(936) 344-6205

UTAH
Arches National Park
In eastern Utah.
(435) 719-2100

Ashley National Forest
In northeastern Utah.
(435) 789-1181

Bryce Canyon National Park
In southwestern Utah.
(435) 834-5322

Canyonlands National Park
In southeastern Utah.
(435) 719-2313

Capitol Reef National Park
10 mi. east of Torrey on SR 24.
(435) 425-3791

Dixie National Forest
In southwestern Utah.
(435) 865-3700

Fishlake National Forest
In south-central Utah.
(435) 896-9233

Flaming Gorge National Recreation Area
In northeastern Utah on the Wyoming-Utah border.
(435) 784-3445

Manti-La Sal National Forest
In southeastern Utah.
(435) 637-2817

Uinta National Forest
In north-central, central and northeastern Utah.
(801) 342-5100

Wasatch-Cache National Forest
In northeastern and north-central Utah.
(801) 342-5100

Zion National Park
In southwestern Utah.
(435) 772-3256

VERMONT
Green Mountains and Green Mountain National Forest
In south-central Vermont.
(802) 747-6700

VIRGINIA
George Washington and Jefferson National Forests
In western Virginia and the eastern edge of West Virginia.
(540) 265-5100

Mount Rogers National Recreation Area
In southwestern Virginia.
(276) 783-5196

Shenandoah National Park
In northwestern Virginia.
(540) 999-3500
▲ 𝟙 ⅌ 👥 🍽

WASHINGTON
Colville National Forest
In northeastern Washington.
(509) 684-7000
🚲 ▲ 𝟙 ⅌ ⚊

Gifford Pinchot National Forest
In southwestern Washington.
(360) 891-5000
🚲 ▲ 𝟙 ⅌ ⚊ 👥 🍽

Gifford Pinchot National Forest (Goose Lake)
13 mi. west of Trout Lake via SR 141, FR 24 and FR 60.
(509) 395-3400
▲ ⅌ ⚊

Gifford Pinchot National Forest (Takhlakh Lake)
32 mi. southeast of Randle via SR 131, FR 23 and FR 2329.
(360) 497-1100
▲ 𝟙 ⅌ ⚊

Lake Chelan National Recreation Area
In north-central Washington.
(509) 682-1900
▲ 𝟙 ⅌ 👥 🍽

Lake Roosevelt National Recreation Area
In northeastern Washington.
(509) 633-9441
▲ ⅌ ⚊ 👥 🍽

Mount Baker-Snoqualmie National Forest
2 mi. east of Glacier on SR 542.
(425) 783-6000
🚲 ▲ 𝟙 ⅌ ⚊ 👥 🍽

Mount Baker-Snoqualmie National Forest (Douglas Fir)
2 mi. east of Glacier on SR 542.
(425) 783-6000
▲ 𝟙 ⅌

Mount Baker-Snoqualmie National Forest (Horseshoe Cove)
14 mi. north of Concrete on Baker Lake.
(360) 599-2714
▲ 𝟙 ⚊

Mount Baker-Snoqualmie National Forest (Shannon Creek)
24 mi. north of Concrete on Baker Lake.
(360) 599-2714
▲ 𝟙 ⅌ ⚊

Mount Rainier National Park
In west-central Washington.
(360) 569-2211
🚲 ▲ 𝟙 ⅌ 👥 🍽

Okanogan-Wenatchee National Forest
In north-central Washington.
(509) 826-3275
🚲 ▲ 𝟙 ⅌ ⚊ 👥 🍽

Okanogan-Wenatchee National Forest (Bonaparte Lake)
7 mi. northwest of Wauconda via SR 20 and CR 4953.
(509) 664-9200
▲ ⅌ ⚊

Okanogan-Wenatchee National Forest (Bumping Lake)
3 mi. south of Goose Prairie.
(509) 664-9200
▲ ⅌ ⚊

Okanogan-Wenatchee National Forest (Kachess Lake)
15 mi. north of Easton via I-90 and FR 49.
(509) 852-1100
🚲 ▲ 𝟙 ⅌ ⚊

Okanogan-Wenatchee National Forest (Lost Lake)
17 mi. northwest of Wauconda via SR 20, CR 4953, FR 32 and FR 33.
(509) 852-1100
▲ ⅌ ⚊

Okanogan-Wenatchee National Forest (Rimrock Lake Area)
At Rimrock off US 12.
(509) 653-1401
▲ ⅌ ⚊

Olympic National Forest
In northwestern Washington.
(360) 956-2402
🚲 ▲ 𝟙 ⅌ ⚊ 👥 🍽

Olympic National Forest (Falls Creek)
3 mi. east of US 101 on Quinault Lake.
(360) 956-2402
▲ 𝟙 ⅌ ⚊

Olympic National Forest (Willaby)
2 mi. east of US 101 on Quinault Lake.
(360) 956-2402
▲ 𝟙 ⅌ ⚊

Olympic National Forest (Wynoochee Lake-Coho)
1 mi. west of Montesano on US 12, then 37 mi. north on FR 22 (Old Wynoochee Valley Rd.).
(360) 956-2402
🚲 ▲ 𝟙 ⅌ ⚊

Olympic National Park
In the Olympic peninsula in northwestern Washington.
(360) 565-3130
▲ 𝟙 ⅌ ⚊ 👥 🍽

Ross Lake National Recreation Area
Between the north and south sections of North Cascades National Park.
(360) 854-7200
▲ 𝟙 ⅌ 👥 🍽

🚲 Bicycling Trails   ▲ Camping   𝟙 Hiking Trails   ⅌ Picnic Facilities
⚊ Swimming   👥 Visitor Center   🍽 Food Service

WEST VIRGINIA
Monongahela National Forest
In eastern West Virginia.
(304) 636-1800

Monongahela National Forest (Lake Sherwood)
11 mi. northeast of Neola on SR 14.
(304) 636-1800

New River Gorge National River
Between Fayetteville and Hinton.
(304) 465-0508

Spruce Knob-Seneca Rocks National Recreation Area
In east-central West Virginia.
(304) 257-4488

WISCONSIN
Apostle Islands National Lakeshore
Off northern Wisconsin's Bayfield Peninsula in Lake Superior.
(715) 779-3397

Chequamegon-Nicolet National Forest
In north-central and northeastern Wisconsin.
(715) 362-1300

St. Croix National Scenic Riverway
Running 252 mi. from Cable to Prescott.
(715) 483-2274

WYOMING
Bighorn National Forest
In north-central Wyoming.
(307) 674-2600

Devils Tower National Monument
Between Sundance and Hulett.
(307) 467-5283

Grand Teton National Park
In northwestern Wyoming.
(307) 739-3300

Medicine Bow National Forest
In southeastern Wyoming.
(307) 745-2300

Shoshone National Forest
In northwestern Wyoming.
(307) 527-6241

Yellowstone National Park
In northwestern Wyoming.
(307) 344-7381

Canada

ALBERTA
Banff National Park
In southwestern Alberta, west of Calgary.
(403) 762-1550
🚴 🅰 🏃 ⛱ 🏊 👥 🍽

Elk Island National Park
In central Alberta, east of Edmonton.
(780) 992-2950
🅰 🏃 ⛱ 👥 🍽

Jasper National Park
In west-central Alberta along the British Columbia border.
(780) 852-3858
🚴 🅰 🏃 ⛱ 🏊 👥 🍽

Waterton Lakes National Park
In Alberta's southwestern corner.
(403) 859-2224
🚴 🅰 🏃 ⛱ 🏊 👥 🍽

BRITISH COLUMBIA
Glacier National Park
In southeastern British Columbia.
(250) 837-7500
🚴 🅰 🏃 ⛱ 👥 🍽

Gulf Islands National Park Reserve
Off the southeast coast of Vancouver Island.
(250) 654-4000
🅰 🏃 ⛱ 🏊

Kootenay National Park
In southeastern British Columbia.
(250) 343-6783
🚴 🅰 🏃 ⛱ 🏊 👥 🍽

Mount Revelstoke National Park
In southeastern British Columbia.
(250) 837-7500
🚴 🅰 🏃 ⛱

Pacific Rim National Park Reserve
On the southwestern coast of Vancouver Island.
(250) 726-7721
🅰 🏃 ⛱ 🏊 👥

Yoho National Park
On the British Columbia-Alberta border.
(250) 343-6783
🚴 🅰 🏃 ⛱ 👥 🍽

MANITOBA
Riding Mountain National Park
In southwestern Manitoba.
(204) 848-7275
🚴 🅰 🏃 ⛱ 🏊 👥 🍽

NEW BRUNSWICK
Fundy National Park
On Hwy. 114, 130 km. southwest of Moncton.
(506) 887-6000
🚴 🅰 🏃 ⛱ 🏊 👥 🍽

Kouchibouguac National Park
On Hwy. 134, north of Moncton.
(506) 876-2443
🚴 🅰 🏃 ⛱ 🏊 👥

NEWFOUNDLAND AND LABRADOR
Gros Morne National Park
On Newfoundland's western coast.
(709) 458-2417
🅰 🏃 ⛱ 🏊 👥

Terra Nova National Park
In eastern Newfoundland.
(709) 533-2801
🅰 🏃 ⛱ 🏊 👥 🍽

NORTHWEST TERRITORIES
Wood Buffalo National Park
On the Northwest Territories-Alberta border.
(867) 872-7900
🅰 🏃 ⛱ 🏊 👥

NOVA SCOTIA
Cape Breton Highlands National Park
5 km. northeast of Chéticamp on Cabot Tr.
(902) 224-2306
🅰 🏃 ⛱ 🏊 👥

Kejimkujik National Park and National Historic Site
In southwestern Nova Scotia off Hwy. 8 at Maitland Bridge.
(902) 682-2772
🚴 🅰 🏃 ⛱ 🏊 👥 🍽

ONTARIO
Bruce Peninsula National Park
In southwestern Ontario.
(519) 596-2233
🅰 🏃 ⛱ 🏊

Fathom Five National Marine Park
Off the northern tip of the Bruce Peninsula in southern Ontario.
(519) 596-2233
🅰 🏃 ⛱ 🏊 👥

Georgian Bay Islands National Park
Along the southeastern portion of Georgian Bay.
(705) 526-9804
🚴 🅰 🏃 ⛱ 🏊 👥

Point Pelee National Park
South of Leamington.
(519) 322-2365
🚴 🏃 ⛱ 🏊 👥 🍽

Pukaskwa National Park
On the north shore of Lake Superior.
(807) 229-0801
🅰 🏃 ⛱ 🏊 👥

🚴 Bicycling Trails   🅰 Camping   🏃 Hiking Trails   ⛱ Picnic Facilities
🏊 Swimming   👥 Visitor Center   🍽 Food Service

Thousand Islands National Park
In the St. Lawrence River between Kingston and Brockville.
(613) 923-5261
🅰 🏕 🎋 ⚓ 🚻

PRINCE EDWARD ISLAND
Prince Edward Island National Park
Along the island's northern shore.
(902) 672-6350
🚴 🅰 🏕 🎋 ⚓ 🚻 🍴

QUEBEC
Forillon National Park
20 km. northeast of Gaspé via Hwy. 132.
(418) 368-5505
🚴 🅰 🏕 🎋 ⚓ 🚻 🍴

La Mauricie National Park
North of Trois-Rivières via Hwy. 55.
(819) 538-3232
🚴 🅰 🏕 🎋 ⚓ 🚻 🍴

SASKATCHEWAN
Grasslands National Park
Between Val Marie and Killdeer in southern Saskatchewan.
(306) 298-2257
🅰 🏕 🎋 🚻

Prince Albert National Park
In central Saskatchewan.
(306) 663-4522
🚴 🅰 🏕 🎋 ⚓ 🚻 🍴

This list of emergency animal clinics in the United States and Canada is provided by the Veterinary Emergency & Critical Care Society (VECCS) as a service to the community for information purposes only. This is not to be construed as a certification or an endorsement of any clinic listed. For further information, contact the society at (210) 698-5575 or online at www.veccs.org. Note: Hours frequently change, and not all clinics are open 24 hours or in the evening. In addition, not all facilities listed here are emergency clinics. In non-emergency situations, it's best to call first.

If you are traveling to an area not covered in this list, be prepared for an emergency by asking your regular veterinarian to recommend a clinic or veterinarian at your destination. The American Animal Hospital Association also can recommend veterinary clinics that meet the association's high standards for veterinary care. For additional information contact the association at (303) 986-2800.

United States

ALABAMA

Bailey Small Animal Teaching Hospital, Auburn University
1220 Wire Rd., Auburn
(334) 844-4690

Animal Medical Center
2864 Acton Rd., Birmingham
(205) 967-7389

Emergency Pet Care
4524 Southlake Pkwy., Suite 28, Birmingham
(205) 988-5988

Southern Regional Veterinary Emergency Services
301 Westgate Pkwy., Dothan
(334) 699-7787

Animal Emergency Clinic of North Alabama
2112 Memorial Pkwy. S., Huntsville
(256) 533-7600

Animal Emergency & Referral Center of Mobile, LLC
2573 Government Blvd., Mobile
(251) 706-0890

Emergency Pet Care
7299 Gadsden Hwy., Trussville
(205) 205-2273

ALASKA

Pet Emergency Treatment, Inc.
2320 E. Dowling Rd., Anchorage
(907) 274-5636

After Hours Veterinary Emergency Clinic
8 Bonnie Ave., Fairbanks
(907) 479-2700

Southeast Alaska Animal Medical Center
8231 Glacier Hwy., Juneau
(907) 789-7551

ARIZONA

Emergency Animal Clinic, PLC
13034 W. Rancho Santa Fe Blvd., Suite 101, Avondale
(623) 385-4555

Animal Health Services
37555 N. Cave Creek Rd., Cave Creek
(480) 488-6181

First Regional Animal Hospital
1233 W. Warner Rd., Chandler
(480) 732-0335

Canyon Pet Hospital
1054 E. Old Canyon Ct., Flagstaff
(928) 774-5197

Emergency Animal Clinic, PLC
86 W. Juniper Ave., Gilbert
(480) 497-0222

1st Emergency Pet Care
1423 S. Higley Rd., Suite 102, Mesa
(408) 924-1123

Mesa Veterinary Hospital
858 N. Country Club Dr., Mesa
(480) 833-7330

Emergency Animal Clinic
9875 W. Peoria Ave., Peoria
(623) 974-1520

Emergency Animal Clinic, PLC
2260 W. Glendale Ave., Phoenix
(602) 995-3757

North Valley Animal Emergency Center
3134 W. Carefree Hwy., Suite A-2, Phoenix
(623) 516-8571

Sonora Veterinary Specialists
4015 E. Cactus Rd., Phoenix
(602) 765-3700

Ironwood Animal Hospital
85 W. Combs Rd., Suite 116, San Tan Valley
(480) 888-2299

Emergency Animal Clinic
22595 N. Scottsdale Rd., Suite 10, Scottsdale
(480) 949-8001

Paradise Valley Emergency Animal Clinic
6969 E. Shea Blvd., Suite 225, Scottsdale
(480) 991-1848

Arizona Veterinary Surgery
4131 E. Speedway Blvd., Tucson
(520) 795-9955

Ina Road Animal Hospital
7320 N. La Cholla Blvd., Suite 114, Tucson
(520) 544-7700

Pima Pet Clinic / Animal Emergency Service
4832 E. Speedway Blvd., Tucson
(520) 327-5624

Southern Arizona Veterinary Specialty and Emergency Center
141 E. Fort Lowell Rd., Tucson
(520) 888-3177

Southern Arizona Veterinary Specialty and Emergency Center
7474 E. Broadway Blvd., Tucson
(520) 888-3177

Valley Animal Hospital, P.C.
4984 E. 22nd St., Tucson
(520) 748-0331

Veterinary Specialty Center of Tucson
4909 N. La Canada Dr., Tucson
(520) 795-9955

ARKANSAS
Ft. Smith Animal Emergency Clinic
4301 Regions Park Dr., Suite 3, Fort Smith
(479) 649-3100

Pulaski County Veterinary Emergency Clinic
801 John Barrow Rd., Suite 6, Little Rock
(501) 224-3784

After Hours Animal Hospital
290 Smokey Ln., North Little Rock
(501) 955-0911

Animal Emergency & Specialty Clinic
8735 Sheltie Dr., Suite G, North Little Rock
(501) 224-3784

Animal Emergency Clinic of Northwest Arkansas
1110 Mathias Dr., Suite E, Springdale
(501) 927-0007

CALIFORNIA
East Bay Veterinary Emergency
1312 Sunset Dr., Antioch
(925) 754-5001

Central Coast Pet Emergency Clinic
1558 W. Branch St., Arroyo Grande
(805) 489-6573

Atascadero Pet Hospital and Emergency Center
9575 El Camino Real, Atascadero
(805) 466-3880

Animal Emergency & Urgent Care
4300 Easton Dr., Suite 1, Bakersfield
(661) 322-6019

Pet Emergency Treatment & Specialty (PETS) Referral Center
1048 University Ave., Berkeley
(510) 548-6684

East of the River Veterinary Emergency Clinic
222 Boston Tpke., Bolton
(860) 647-0264

Sage Centers for Veterinary Specialty and Emergency Care
907 Dell Ave., Campbell
(408) 343-7243

United Veterinary Specialty & Emergency
905 Dell Ave., Campbell
(408) 371-6252

Pacific Veterinary Specialists and Emergency Critical Care Center
1980 41st Ave., Capitola
(831) 476-2584

VCA Sacramento Animal Medical Group
4990 Manzanita Ave., Carmichael
(916) 331-7460

North Valley Emergency Veterinary Clinic
2500 Zanella Way, Suite A, Chico
(530) 899-1720

Sage Centers for Veterinary Specialty and Emergency Care
1410 Monument Blvd., Concord
(925) 627-7243

VCA Aacacia Animal Hospital
939 W. 6th St., Corona
(951) 371-1002

ACCESS Specialty Animal Hospital - Los Angeles
9599 Jefferson Blvd., Culver City
(310) 558-6100

UC Davis Veterinary Medical Teaching Hospital - Small Animal Emergency and Critical Care Service
1 Garrod Dr., Davis
(530) 752-1393

Pet Specialists of Monterey
451 Canyon Del Rey Blvd., Del Rey Oaks
(831) 899-7387

SAGE Centers for Veterinary Specialty & Emergency Care
7121 Amador Plaza Rd., Dublin
(925) 771-5630

Vetcare Emergency & Specialty Care Center
7660 Amador Valley Blvd., Dublin
(925) 556-1234

Emergency Pet Clinic of San Gabriel Valley
3254 Santa Anita Ave., El Monte
(626) 579-4550

North Coast Veterinary and Emergency
414 Encinitas Blvd., Encinitas
(760) 632-1072

Animal Urgent Care
2430 S. Escondido Blvd., Escondido
(760) 738-9600

Animal Emergency Center
3954 Jacobs Ave., Suite A, Eureka
(707) 443-2776

Solano-Napa Pet Emergency Clinic
4437 Central Pl., Fairfield
(707) 864-1444

VCA All-Care Animal Referral Center
18440 Amistad St., Suite E, Fountain Valley
(714) 963-0909

Ohlone Veterinary Emergency Clinic
1618 Washington Blvd., Fremont
(510) 657-6620

Fresno Pet Emergency & Referral Center, Inc.
7375 N. Palm Bluffs Ave., Fresno
(559) 437-3766

Fresno Veterinary Specialty and Emergency Center
6606 N. Blackstone Ave., Fresno
(559) 451-0800

Veterinary Emergency Service, Inc.
1639 N. Fresno St., Fresno
(559) 486-0520

Orange County Emergency Pet Clinic
12750 Garden Grove Blvd., Garden Grove
(714) 537-3032

eMash, Inc. Emergency & Mobile Animal Services Hospital
10825 Watsonville Rd., Gilroy
(408) 847-1122

Pet Medical Center - Chatoak
17659 Chatsworth St., Granada Hills
(818) 363-7444

Animal Emergency Clinic
12022 La Crosse Ave., Grand Terrace
(909) 825-9350

Crossroads Animal Emergency
18364 Beach Blvd., Huntington Beach
(714) 794-6900

Irvine Regional Animal Emergency Hospital
1371 Reynolds Ave., Irvine
(949) 833-9020

North Orange County Emergency Pet Clinic
1474 S. Harbor Blvd., La Habra
(714) 441-2925

Pet Emergency and Specialty Center
5232 Jackson Dr., Suite 105, La Mesa
(619) 462-4800

Animal Emergency Clinic
1055 W. Avenue M, Suite 101, Lancaster
(661) 723-3959

Animal Specialty Group
4641 Colorado Blvd., Los Angeles
(818) 244-7977

Animal Surgical and Emergency Center
1535 S. Sepulveda Blvd., Los Angeles
(310) 473-5906

Eagle Rock Emergency Pet Clinic
4254 Eagle Rock Blvd., Los Angeles
(323) 254-7382

VCA West Los Angeles Animal Hospital
1818 S. Sepulveda Blvd., Los Angeles
(310) 473-2951

Animal Urgent Care
2805 Hillcrest, Mission Viejo
(949) 364-6228

Portola Plaza Veterinary Hospital
27752 Santa Margarita Pkwy., Mission Viejo
(949) 859-2101

Veterinary Emergency Clinic
1800 Prescott Rd., Suite E, Modesto
(209) 527-8844

Monterey Peninsula Veterinary Emergency & Specialty Center
20 Lower Ragsdale Dr., Suite 150, Monterey
(831) 373-7374

All Creatures Emergency Center
22722 Lyons Ave., Suite 5, Newhall
(661) 291-1121

Central Orange County Emergency Animal Clinic
3720 Campus Drive, Suite D, Newport Beach
(949) 261-7979

Crossroads Animal Emergency and Referral Clinic
11057 E. Rosecrans Ave., Norwalk
(562) 863-2522

Orange Veterinary Hospital
1100 W. Chapman Ave., Orange
(714) 997-8200

Extraordinary Veterinary Services
5714 Los Coyotes Dr., Palm Springs
(760) 202-8710

South Peninsula Veterinary Emergency Clinic
3045 Middlefield Rd., Palo Alto
(650) 494-1461

Animal Emergency Clinic of Pasadena
2121 E. Foothill Blvd., Pasadena
(626) 564-0704

Animal Emergency Clinic of San Diego
12775 Poway Rd., Poway
(858) 748-7387

Animal Care Center
6470 Redwood Dr., Rohnert Park
(707) 584-4343

Atlantic Street Veterinary Hospital and Pet Emergency Center, Inc.
1100 Atlantic St., Roseville
(916) 783-4655

El Camino Veterinary Hospital
4000 El Camino Ave., Sacramento
(916) 488-6878

Mueller Animal Hospital
6420 Freeport Blvd., Sacramento
(916) 428-9202

Vista Veterinary Specialists
7425 Greenhaven Dr., Sacramento
(916) 231-4445

VCA Sacramento Veterinary Referral Center
9801 Old Winery Pl., Sacramento
(916) 362-3111

San Carlos Pet Emergency Hospital
718 El Camino Real, San Carlos
(650) 591-5718

Animal ER of San Diego
5610 Kearny Mesa Rd., Suite A, San Diego
(858) 569-0600

VCA Emergency Animal Hospital and Referral Center
2317 Hotel Cir. S., San Diego
(619) 299-2400

Veterinary Specialty Hospital
10435 Sorrento Valley Rd., San Diego
(858) 875-7500

All Animals Emergency Hospital
1333 Ninth Ave., San Francisco
(415) 566-0531

Pets Unlimited
2343 Fillmore St., San Francisco
(415) 563-6700

San Francisco Veterinary Specialists
600 Alabama St., San Francisco
(415) 401-9200

Emergency Animal Clinic of South San Jose
5440 Thornwood Dr., Suite E, San Jose
(408) 578-5622

Silicon Valley Veterinary Specialists
7160 Santa Teresa Blvd., San Jose
(408) 649-7070

South Bay Animal Hospital & Pet Resort
5188 Moorpark Ave., San Jose
(408) 899-4791

Veterinary Medical and Surgical Group - Orange County
31896 Plaza Dr., Suite C1, San Juan Capistrano
(949) 201-4100

Bay Area Veterinary Emergency Clinic
14790 Washington Ave., San Leandro
(510) 352-6080

California Veterinary Specialists
100 N. Rancho Santa Fe Rd., San Marcos
(760) 734-4433

North Peninsula Veterinary Emergency Clinic, Inc.
227 N. Amphlett Blvd., San Mateo
(650) 348-2575

Sage Centers for Veterinary Specialty and Emergency
251 N. Amphlett Blvd., San Mateo
(650) 417-7243

The Pet Emergency and Specialty Center of Marin
901 E. Francisco Blvd., Suite C, San Rafael
(415) 456-7372

Advanced Veterinary Specialists
414 E. Carrillo St., Santa Barbara
(805) 729-4460

VCA Care Specialty and Emergency Animal Hospital
301 E. Haley St., Santa Barbara
(805) 899-2273

Pacific Emergency Pet Hospital, Inc.
2963 State St., Santa Barbara
(805) 682-5120

Santa Cruz Veterinary Hospital
2585 Soquel Dr., Santa Cruz
(831) 475-5400

North Bay Animal Emergency Hospital
1304 Wilshire Blvd., Santa Monica
(310) 451-8962

Emergency Animal Hospital of Santa Rosa
1946 Santa Rosa Ave., Santa Rosa
(707) 544-1647

PetCare Veterinary Hospital
2425 Mendocino Ave., Santa Rosa
(707) 579-3900

PetCare Veterinary Hospital
1370 Fulton Rd., Santa Rosa
(707) 579-5900

Beverly Oaks Animal Hospital and Emergency Animal Clinic
14302 Ventura Blvd., Sherman Oaks
(818) 788-7860

TLC Pet Medical Centers - South Pasadena
1412 Huntington Dr., South Pasadena
(626) 441-8555

Associated Veterinary Emergency Services
3008 E. Hammer Ln., Suite 115, Stockton
(209) 952-8387

Animal Emergency Centre
11740 Ventura Blvd., Studio City
(818) 760-3882

Emergency Pet Clinic of Temecula
27443 Jefferson Ave., Temecula
(951) 695-5044

Conejo Valley Veterinary Hospital
1850 E. Thousand Oaks Blvd., Thousand Oaks
(805) 495-4671

Pet Emergency Clinic
2967 N. Moorepark Rd., Thousand Oaks
(805) 492-2436

Animal Emergency Medical Center
3511 Pacific Coast Hwy., Suite A, Torrance
(310) 325-3000

Emergency Pet Clinic of South Bay
2325 Torrance Blvd., Torrance
(310) 320-8300

Monte Vista Small Animal Hospital
901 E. Monte Vista Ave., Turlock
(209) 634-0023

Advanced Critical Care & Internal Medicine
2965 Edinger Ave., Tustin
(949) 654-8950

Inland Valley Emergency Pet Clinic
10 W. 7th St., Upland
(909) 931-7871

Pet Emergency Clinic
2301 S. Victoria Ave., Ventura
(805) 642-8562

Veterinary Medical and Surgical Group
2199 Sperry Ave., Ventura
(805) 339-2290

Animal Emergency Clinic
15532 Bear Valley Rd., Victorville
(760) 962-1122

Pinnacle Veterinary Service, Inc.
2300 S. Divisadero St., Visalia
(559) 732-8000

Tulare Kings Veterinary Emergency Service
4240 W. Mineral King, Visalia
(559) 739-7054

Coastal Emergency Animal Hospital
1900 Hacienda Dr., Vista
(760) 630-6343

TLC Pet Medical Centers - West Hollywood
8725 Santa Monica Blvd., West Hollywood
(310) 859-4852

ACCESS Specialty Animal Hospital - San Fernando Valley
20051 Ventura Blvd., Woodland Hills
(818) 887-2262

VCA Veterinary Specialists of the Valley
22123 Ventura Blvd., Woodland Hills
(818) 883-8387

COLORADO

Animal Urgent Care, Inc.
7851 Indiana St., Arvada
(303) 420-7387

Aurora Veterinary Emergency Center
18511 E. Hampden Ave., Aurora
(303) 699-1665

Seven Hills Veterinary Hospital
18325 E. Girard Ave., Aurora
(303) 699-1600

Valley Emergency Pet Care
180 Fiou Ln., Suite 101, Basalt
(970) 927-5066

Alpenglow Veterinary Specialty & Emergency Center
3640 Walnut St., Boulder
(303) 443-4569

Animal Emergency & Referral Center
1480 W. Midway Blvd., Boulder
(303) 464-7744

Boulder Emergency Pet Clinic
1658 30th St., Boulder
(303) 440-7722

VCA Douglas County Animal Hospital
531 Jerry St., Castle Rock
(303) 688-2480

Animal Emergency Care Centers, Inc.
3775 Airport Rd., Colorado Springs
(719) 578-9300

Animal Emergency Care Centers - North
5520 N. Nevada Ave., Colorado Springs
(719) 299-3323

Animal Emergency Care, Inc.
5752 N. Academy Blvd., Colorado Springs
(719) 260-7141

Alameda East Veterinary Hospital
9770 E. Alameda Ave., Denver
(303) 366-2639

Central Veterinary Emergency Services
3550 S. Jason St., Englewood
(303) 874-7387

Pets Emergency Hospital
3629 23rd Ave., Evans
(970) 339-8700

Fort Collins Veterinary Emergency and Rehabilitation Hospital
816 S. Lemay Ave., Fort Collins
(970) 484-8080

James L. Voss Veterinary Teaching Hospital - Colorado State University
300 W. Drake Rd., Fort Collins
(970) 221-4535

Grand Valley Veterinary Emergency Center
1660 North Ave., Grand Junction
(970) 255-1911

Animal Hospital Center
5640 County Line Pl., Suite 1, Highlands Ranch
(303) 740-9595

Animal Critical Care & Emergency Services, Inc.
1597 Wadsworth Blvd., Lakewood
(303) 239-1200

Animal E.R.
221 W. County Line Rd., Littleton
(720) 283-9348

Columbine Animal Hospital & Emergency Clinic
5546 W. Canyon Tr., Littleton
(303) 929-4040

Animal Emergency & Critical Care
104 S. Main St., Longmont
(303) 678-8844

Animal Emergency Services of Northern Colorado
201 W. 67th Ct., Loveland
(970) 663-5760

Animal Emergency & Urgent Care
17701 Cottonwood Dr., Parker
(720) 842-5050

Emergency Animal Hospital of Pueblo
472 S. Joe Martinez Blvd., Pueblo
(719) 229-7030

Pueblo Area Pet Emergency Hospital
712 Fortino Blvd., Pueblo
(719) 544-7788

Community Pet Hospital
12311 Washington St., Thornton
(303) 451-1333

Northside Emergency Pet Clinic, P.C.
945 W. 124th Ave., Westminster
(303) 252-7722

Wheat Ridge Animal Hospital / Wheat Ridge Veterinary Specialists
3695 Kipling St., Wheat Ridge
(303) 424-3325

CONNECTICUT
Farmington Valley Veterinary Emergency Hospital
9 Avonwood Rd., Avon
(860) 674-1886

Veterinary Emergency Center
135 Dowd Ave., Canton
(860) 693-6992

Cheshire Veterinary Hospital
1572 S. Main St., Cheshire
(203) 271-1577

V-E-T-S (Veterinary Emergency Treatment Services)
114 Westbrook Rd., Essex
(860) 444-8870

New Haven Hospital for Veterinary Medicine, Inc.
843 State St., New Haven
(203) 865-0878

Newtown Veterinary Specialists
52 Church Hill Rd., Newtown
(203) 270-8387

Veterinary Referral & Emergency Center
123 W. Cedar St., Norwalk
(203) 854-9960

Animal Emergency Hospital of Central Connecticut
588 Cromwell Ave., Rocky Hill
(860) 563-4447

VCA Shoreline Veterinary Referral and Emergency Center
895 Bridgeport Ave., Shelton
(203) 929-8600

Cornell University Veterinary Specialists
880 Canal St., Stamford
(203) 595-2777

Shoreline Animal Emergency Clinic
7365 Main St., Stratford
(203) 375-6500

Connecticut Veterinary Center
470 Oakwood Ave., West Hartford
(860) 233-8564

Veterinary Specialists of CT
933 N. Main St., West Hartford
(860) 236-3273

DELAWARE
VCA Newark Animal Hospital
1360 Marrows Rd., Newark
(302) 737-8100

Veterinary Emergency Center of Delaware
1212 E. Newport Pike, Wilmington
(302) 691-3647

Windcrest Animal Emergency Hospital
3705 Lancaster Pike, Wilmington
(302) 998-2995

DISTRICT OF COLUMBIA
Friendship Hospital for Animals
4105 Brandywine St., Washington
(202) 363-7300

FLORIDA
Boca Veterinary Emergency Center
5030 Champion Blvd., Boca Raton
(861) 443-3699

Southwest Florida Veterinary Specialists
28400 Old 41 Rd., Suite 1, Bonita Springs
(239) 992-8387

PetPB Animal Emergency & Advanced Imaging
2246 N. Congress Ave., Boynton Beach
(561) 752-3232

Bradenton Veterinary Emergency
2910 Manatee Ave. W., Bradenton
(941) 748-0202

Veterinary Emergency Center
3915 Cortez Rd. W., Bradenton
(941) 896-9420

Animal Emergency Clinic of Brandon
693 W. Lumsden Rd., Brandon
(813) 684-3013

Animal ER of Southwest Florida, Inc.
1327 N.E. Pine Island Rd., Suite 110, Cape Coral
(239) 673-7426

Veterinary Emergency Clinic of Central Florida - Seminole County
195 Concord Dr., Casselberry
(407) 644-4449

Animal Emergency and Critical Care Services of S. Florida
9410 Stirling Rd., Cooper City
(954) 432-5611

Coral Springs Animal Hospital
2160 N. University Dr., Coral Springs
(954) 753-1800

Doral Centre Animal Hospital
9400 N.W. 58th St., Doral
(305) 598-1234

Florida Veterinary Referral Center & 24 Hour Emergency & Critical Care
9220 Estero Park Commons Blvd., Suite 7, Estero
(239) 992-8878

Animal Emergency Trauma Center
2200 W. Oakland Park Blvd., Fort Lauderdale
(954) 731-4228

Emergency Veterinary Clinic, Inc.
2045 Collier Ave., Fort Myers
(239) 939-5542

Specialized Veterinary Services
9500 Marketplace Rd., Fort Myers
(239) 947-0588

Animal Emergency and Referral Center
3984 S. US 1, Fort Pierce
(772) 466-3441

Affiliated Pet Emergency Services
7314 W. University Ave., Gainesville
(352) 373-4444

University of Florida Small Animal Hospital
2089 S.W. 16th Ave., Gainesville
(352) 392-2235

Hollywood Animal Hospital
2864 Hollywood Blvd., Hollywood
(954) 920-3556

Affiliated Veterinary Emergency Center
3444 Southside Blvd., Suite 101, Jacksonville
(904) 642-5911

Emergency Pet Care, LLC
14185 Beach Blvd., Suite 7, Jacksonville
(904) 223-8000

Emergency Pet Care of Jupiter
300 Central Blvd., Jupiter
(561) 746-0555

Tampa Bay Veterinary Emergency Service
1501 S. Belcher Rd., Suite 1A, Largo
(727) 531-5752

Veterinary Emergency Clinic of Central Florida - Lake County Facility
33040 Professional Dr., Leesburg
(352) 728-4440

Animal Emergency and Critical Care Center of Brevard
2281 W. Eau Gallie Blvd., Melbourne
(321) 725-5365

Animal Emergency Clinic of South Florida
12683 S. Dixie Hwy., Miami
(305) 251-2096

Knowles Animal Clinic - Snapper Creek Emergency Clinic
9933 Sunset Dr., Miami
(305) 279-2323

Miami Pet Emergency
11774 N. Kendall Dr., Miami
(305) 273-8100

Miami Veterinary Specialists
8601 Sunset Dr., Miami
(305) 665-2820

The Pet Emergency Room
6394 S. Dixie Hwy., Miami
(305) 666-4142

Animal Specialty Hospital of Florida (ASH)
10130 Market St., Suite 1, Naples
(239) 263-0480

Emergency Pet Hospital of Collier Co.
6530 Dudley Dr., Naples
(941) 263-8010

Ocala Animal Emergency Hospital
1815 N.E. Jacksonville Rd., Ocala
(352) 840-0044

University of Florida Pet Emergency Treatment Services
3200 S.W. 27th Ave., Ocala
(352) 294-0886

Clay Duval Pet Emergency Clinic
275 Corporate Way, Suite 200, Orange Park
(904) 264-8281

Animal Emergency Center
7313 Lake Underhill Rd., Orlando
(407) 273-3336

Veterinary Emergency Clinic of Central Florida - Orange County
2080 Principal Row, Orlando
(407) 438-4449

Pet Emergency and Critical Care Clinic
3816 Northlake Blvd., Palm Beach Gardens
(561) 691-9999

A.A. Animal ER Center, LLC
36401 US 19N, Palm Harbor
(727) 787-5402

Animal Emergency & Urgent Care
30610 US 19N, Palm Harbor
(727) 786-5755

St. Francis Emergency Animal Hospital
6602 Pines Blvd., Pembroke Pines
(954) 962-0300

Veterinary Emergency Referral Center
4800 N. Davis Hwy., Pensacola
(850) 477-3914

The Veterinary Emergency Clinic
17829 Murdock Cir., Port Charlotte
(941) 255-5222

Animal Specialty and Emergency Hospital
5775 Schenck Ave., Rockledge
(321) 752-7600

Critical Care and Veterinary Specialists of Sarasota
4937 S. Tamiami Tr., Sarasota
(941) 929-1818

Sarasota Veterinary Emergency Hospital
7414 S. Tamiami Tr., Sarasota
(941) 923-7260

Animal Emergency Clinic of St. Petersburg
3165 22nd Ave. N., St. Petersburg
(727) 323-1311

Noah's Animal Hospital and 24 Hour Emergency
2050 62nd Ave. N., St. Petersburg
(727) 522-6640

Pet Emergency & Critical Care Clinic, Inc.
2239 S. Kanner Hwy., Stuart
(772) 781-3302

Allied Veterinary Emergency Hospital
2324 Centerville Rd., Tallahassee
(850) 222-0123

FVS (Florida Veterinary Specialists)
3000 Busch Lake Blvd., Tampa
(813) 933-8944

Tampa Bay Veterinary Emergency Service
238 E. Bearss Ave., Tampa
(813) 265-4043

Animal E.R.
8237 Cooper Creek Blvd., University Park
(941) 355-2884

Animal Emergency Clinic
3425 Forest Hill Blvd., West Palm Beach
(561) 433-2244

Palm Beach Veterinary Specialists
3884 Forest Hill Blvd., West Palm Beach
(561) 434-5700

VCA Cabrera Animal Hospital
6390 S.W. 8th St., West Miami
(305) 261-2374

GEORGIA

All Pets Emergency and Referral Center, P.C.
6460 Hwy. 9N, Alpharetta
(678) 366-2125

University of Georgia - Vet Teaching Hospital
College of Veterinary Medicine, Athens
(706) 542-3221

Animal Emergency Center of Sandy Springs
228 Sandy Springs Pl. N.E., Atlanta
(404) 252-7881

Georgia Veterinary Specialists and Emergency Care
455 Abernathy Rd. N.E., Atlanta
(404) 459-0963

Mountain Emergency Animal Center
1163 Windy Ridge Rd., Blue Ridge
(706) 632-7879

Brunswick Pet ER
208 Scranton Connector, Suite 122, Brunswick
(912) 275-8246

North Georgia Veterinary Specialists
1328 Buford Hwy., Building 200, Buford
(678) 835-3300

East Metro Animal Emergency Clinic, LLC
6225 Hwy. 278 N.W., Covington
(678) 212-0300

PetFirst 24 Hour Animal Hospital
4075 Pleasant Hill Rd., Duluth
(678) 745-1262

Southern Crescent Animal Emergency
1270 Hwy. 54 E., Fayetteville
(770) 460-8166

An-Emerge
275 Pearl Nix Pkwy., Suite 3, Gainesville
(770) 534-2911

Eastside Animal Medical Center
1835 Grayson Hwy., Grayson
(678) 958-5530

Atlanta Veterinary Specialists
7350 McGinnis Ferry Rd., Johns Creek
(770) 407-3000

Animal Emergency Center of Gwinnett
1956 Lawrenceville-Suwanee Rd., Lawrenceville
(770) 277-3220

Cobb Emergency Veterinary Clinic
630 Cobb Pkwy. N., Suite C, Marietta
(770) 424-9157

Animal Emergency Center of North Fulton
900 Mansell Rd., Suite 19, Roswell
(770) 594-2266

Savannah Veterinary Emergency Clinic
317 Eisenhower Dr., Savannah
(912) 355-6113

DeKalb-Gwinnett Animal Emergency Clinic
6430 Lawrenceville Hwy., Tucker
(770) 491-0661

Cherokee Emergency Veterinary Clinic
7800 Hwy. 92, Woodstock
(678) 238-0700

HAWAII

Veterinary Emergency + Referral Center of Hawaii
1347 Kapiolani Blvd., Suite 103, Honolulu
(808) 735-7735

IDAHO

Mountain View Animal Hospital / Pet ER
3435 N. Cole Rd., Boise
(208) 375-0251

WestVet 24 Hour Animal Emergency Hospital and Specialty Center
5019 N. Sawyer Ave., Garden City
(208) 375-1600

Idaho Falls Veterinary Emergency Clinic
3151 McNeil Dr., Idaho Falls
(208) 552-0662

All Valley Animal Care Center
2326 E. Cinema Dr., Meridian
(208) 888-0818

WestVet Animal Emergency
3085 E. Magic View Dr., Suite. 110, Meridian
(208) 288-0400

North Idaho Pet Emergency
2700 E. Seltice Way, Suite 12, Post Falls
(208) 777-2707

ILLINOIS

Animal E.R. of Arlington Heights
1195 E. Palatine Rd., Arlington Heights
(847) 394-6049

VCA Aurora Animal Hospital
2600 W. Galena Blvd., Aurora
(630) 896-8541

Animal Emergency Clinic of McLean County
2505 E. Oakland Ave., Bloomington
(309) 665-5020

Veterinary Specialty Center
1515 Busch Pkwy., Buffalo Grove
(847) 459-7535

Animal Emergency Clinic of Champaign County
1713 S. State St., Unit 4, Champaign
(217) 359-1977

Chicago Veterinary Emergency & Specialty Center
3123 N. Clybourne Ave., Chicago
(773) 281-7110

Premier Veterinary Group - Chicago
3927 W. Belmont Ave., Chicago
(773) 516-5800

Animal Emergency Center
2005 Mall St., Collinsville
(618) 346-1898

Countryside Veterinary Center
9823 W. 55th St., Countryside
(708) 469-6050

Emergency Veterinary Care South Assoc.
13715 S. Cicero Ave., Crestwood
(708) 388-3771

Companion Animal Specialty & Emergency Hospital
1095 Pingree Rd., Suite 120, Crystal Lake
(815) 479-9119

Arboretum View Animal Hospital
2551 Warrenville Rd., Downers Grove
(630) 963-0424

Dundee Animal Hospital
199 Penny Ave., Dundee
(847) 428-6114

Elmhurst Animal Care Center
850 S. Riverside Dr., Elmhurst
(630) 530-1900

Midwest Animal Emergency Hospital
7510 W. North Ave., Elmwood Park
(708) 453-4755

VCA Franklin Park Animal Hospital
9846 W. Grand Ave., Franklin Park
(847) 455-4922

Hawthorne Animal Hospital
5 Cougar Dr., Glen Carbon
(618) 288-3971

Wheaton Animal Hospital
266 Roosevelt Rd., Glen Ellyn
(630) 665-1500

Premier Veterinary Group
1810 E. Belvidere Rd., Grayslake
(847) 548-5300

Emergency Veterinary Services
820 Ogden Ave., Lisle
(630) 960-2900

Animal Emergency of Mokena
19110 S. 88th Ave., Mokena
(708) 326-4800

Naperville Animal Hospital
1023 E. Ogden Ave., Naperville
(630) 355-5300

Springbrook Animal Care Center
2759 Forgue Dr., Naperville
(630) 428-0500

Animal Emergency Clinic of McLeon County
704-B S. Main St., Normal
(309) 454-8802

Animal Emergency and Critical Care Center
1810 Frontage Rd., Northbrook
(847) 564-5775

Tri-County Animal Emergency Clinic
1800 N. Sterling Ave., Peoria
(309) 672-1565

CARE Animal Emergency Services
14411 S. Rte. 59, Plainfield
(877) 859-7387

Animal Emergency Clinic of Rockford
4236 Maray Dr., Rockford
(815) 229-7791

Emergency Veterinary Services of St. Charles
530 Dunham Rd., St. Charles
(630) 584-7447

Animal 911
3735 W. Dempster St., Skokie
(847) 673-9110

Animal Emergency Clinic of Springfield
1333 W. Wabash Ave., Springfield
(617) 698-0870

University of Illinois College of Veterinary Medicine
1008 W. Hazelwood Dr., Urbana
(217) 333-5300

INDIANA
VCA Northwood Animal Hospital
3255 N. SR 9, Anderson
(765) 649-5218

St. Francis Family Pet Health Care
822 W. Plymouth St., Bremen
(574) 546-9005

Circle City Veterinary Specialty and Emergency Hospital
9650 Mayflower Park Dr., Carmel
(317) 872-8387

Northeast Indiana Veterinary Emergency & Specialty Hospital
5818 Maplecrest Rd., Fort Wayne
(260) 426-1062

Airport Animal Emergi-Center, P.C.
5235 W. Washington St., Indianapolis
(317) 248-0832

Animal Emergency Center of Indianapolis
8250 Bash St., Indianapolis
(317) 849-4925

Indianapolis Veterinary Emergency Center
5425 Victory Dr., Indianapolis
(317) 782-4484

Noah's Animal Hospital, P.C.
5510 Millersville Rd., Indianapolis
(317) 253-1327

VCA West 86th Street Animal Hospital
4030 W. 86th St., Indianapolis
(317) 872-0200

Animal Emergency Clinic of Tippecanoe County
1343 Sagamore Pkwy. N., Lafayette
(765) 449-2001

Animal Emergency Clinic
2324 Grape Rd., Mishawaka
(574) 259-8387

Lincolnway Veterinary Clinic, LLC
4043 Lincolnway E., Mishawaka
(574) 256-1871

Calumet Emergency Veterinary Clinic
216 W. Lincoln Hwy., Schererville
(219) 865-0970

IOWA

Iowa State University, Veterinary Clinical Sciences Teaching Hospital
1800 Christensen Dr., Ames
(515) 294-4900

Animal Emergency Center of the Quad Cities
1510 State St., Bettendorf
(563) 344-9599

Eastern Iowa Veterinary Specialty Center
755 Capital Dr. S.W., Cedar Rapids
(319) 841-5161

Iowa Veterinary Specialties
6110 Creston Ave., Des Moines
(515) 280-3100

KANSAS

Kansas State University Vet. Med. Teaching Hospital
1800 Denison Ave., Manhattan
(785) 532-4100

VCA Mission Animal Referral & Emergency Center
5914 Johnson Dr., Mission
(913) 722-5566

Veterinary Specialty & Emergency Center
11950 W. 110th St., Overland Park
(913) 642-9563

Central Kansas Veterinary Center
515 W. Blanchard Ave., South Hutchinson
(620) 663-8387

Emergency Animal Clinic of Topeka
839 S.W. Fairlawn Rd., Topeka
(785) 272-2926

Veterinary Emergency and Specialty Hospital of Wichita
727 S. Washington St., Wichita
(316) 262-5321

KENTUCKY

Bluegrass Veterinary Specialists & Animal Emergency
1591 Winchester Rd., Suite 106, Lexington
(859) 268-7604

MetVet Lexington
150 Dennis Dr., Lexington
(859) 276-2505

Jefferson Animal Hospital and Regional Emergency Center
4504 Outer Loop, Louisville
(502) 966-4104

Louisville Veterinary Specialty and Emergency Services
13160 Magisterial Dr., Louisville
(502) 244-3036

Greater Cincinnati Veterinary Specialists & Emergency Services
11 Beacon Dr., Wilder
(859) 572-0560

LOUISIANA

Animal Emergency Clinic of Baton Rouge
7353 Jefferson Hwy., Baton Rouge
(225) 927-8800

Baton Rouge Pet Emergency Hospital
1514 Cottondale Dr., Baton Rouge
(225) 925-5566

Sherwood South Animal Emergency & Critical Care Center
3803 S. Sherwood Forest Blvd., Baton Rouge
(225) 293-6440

Louisiana Veterinary Referral Center
2611 Florida St., Mandeville
(985) 626-4862

Metairie Small Animal Hospital
101 Metairie Rd., Metairie
(504) 835-4266

Southeast Veterinary Emergency and Critical Care
3409 Division St., Metairie
(504) 219-0444

MAINE

Eastern Maine Emergency Veterinary Clinic
15 Dirigo Dr., Brewer
(207) 989-6267

Animal Emergency Clinic of Mid-Maine
37 Strawberry Ave., Lewiston
(207) 777-1110

Animal Emergency Clinic
739 Warren Ave., Portland
(207) 878-3121

Maine Veterinary Referral Center
1500 Technology Way, Scarborough
(207) 885-1290

MARYLAND

Anne Arundel Veterinary Emergency Clinic
808 Bestgate Rd., Annapolis
(410) 224-0331

Falls Road Animal Hospital
6314 Falls Rd., Baltimore
(410) 825-9100

Animal Emergency Hospital
807B Belair Rd., Bel Air
(410) 420-7297

Harford Emergency Veterinary Services
526 Underwood Ln., Bel Air
(410) 420-8000

Emergency Veterinary Clinic, Inc.
32 Mellor Ave., Catonsville
(410) 788-7042

Emergency Animal Hospital of Ellicott City
10270 Baltimore National Pike (US 40W), Ellicott City
(410) 750-1177

Crossroads Animal Referral and Emergency
1080 W. Patrick St., Frederick
(301) 662-2273

Frederick Emergency Animal Hospital
434 Prospect Blvd., Frederick
(301) 662-6622

VCA Veterinary Referral Associates
500 Perry Pkwy., Gaithersburg
(301) 926-3300, ext. 140

Mountain View Animal Emergency
17747 Virginia Ave., Hagerstown
(301) 733-7339

Rocky Gorge Animal Hospital
7515 Brooklyn Bridge Rd., Laurel
(301) 776-7744

Hope Advanced Veterinary Center
1 Taft Ct., Rockville
(301) 637-3228

Metropolitan Emergency Animal Clinic
12106 Nebel St., Rockville
(301) 770-5226

Pets ER
329 Tilghman Rd., Suite 100, Salisbury
(410) 543-8400

PET + ER
1209 Cromwell Bridge Rd., Towson
(410) 252-8387

Southern Maryland Veterinary Referral Center
3485 Rockefeller Ct., Waldorf
(301) 638-0988

Central Carroll Animal Emergency
1030 Baltimore Blvd., Suite 180, Westminster
(410) 871-9001

**Westminster Veterinary Hospital and Emergency/
Trauma Center**
269 W. Main St., Westminster
(410) 848-3363

MASSACHUSETTS
Animal Emergency Care
164 Great Rd., Acton
(978) 263-1742

Angell Animal Medical Center
350 S. Huntington Ave., Boston
(617) 522-7282

Cape Cod Veterinary Specialists Emergency Service
230 Main St., Buzzards Bay
(508) 759-5125

Wignall Animal Hospital
1837 Bridge St., Dracut
(978) 454-8272

Fall River Animal Hospital, Inc.
33 18th St., Fall River
(508) 675-6374

MetroWest Veterinary Referral Hospital
5 Strathmore Rd., Natick
(508) 319-2117

Essex County Veterinary Emergency Hospital
247 Chickering Rd., North Andover
(978) 725-5544

Tufts University School of Veterinary Medicine
200 Westboro Rd., North Grafton
(508) 839-7826

Animal ER
1634 W. Housatonic St., Pittsfield
(413) 997-3425

Veterinary Emergency & Specialty Hospital
141 Greenfield Rd., South Deerfield
(413) 665-4911

**Cape Cod Veterinary Specialists 24 Hour Emergency
& Critical Care**
79 Theophilus Smith Rd., South Dennis
(508) 398-7575

VCA South Shore Animal Hospital
595 Columbian St., South Weymouth
(781) 337-6622

Angell Animal Medical Center - Western New England
171 Union St., Springfield
(413) 785-1221

Boston Road Animal Hospital
1235 Boston Rd., Springfield
(413) 783-1203

Mass-RI Veterinary ER
477 Milford Rd., Swansea
(508) 730-1112

BluePearl Veterinary Partners - Waltham
180 Bear Hill Rd., Waltham
(781) 684-8387

New England Animal Medical Center
595 W. Center St., West Bridgewater
(508) 580-2515

Wachusett Animal Hospital
29 Theodore Dr., Westminster
(978) 874-4100

Massachusetts Veterinary Referral Hospital
20 Cabot Rd., Woburn
(781) 932-5802

Woburn Animal Hospital
373 Russell St., Woburn
(718) 933-0170

MICHIGAN
Affiliated Veterinary Emergency Service, P.C.
15220 Southfield Rd., Allen Park
(313) 389-1700

Animal Emergency Clinic
4126 Packard Rd., Ann Arbor
(734) 971-8774

Ann Arbor Animal Hospital Emergency
2150 W. Liberty St., Ann Arbor
(734) 662-4474

Emergency Veterinary Hospital
5245 Jackson Rd., Ann Arbor
(734) 369-6446

Michigan Veterinary Specialists
3412 E. Walton Blvd., Auburn Hills
(248) 371-3713

Oakland Veterinary Referral Services
1400 S. Telegraph Rd., Bloomfield Hills
(248) 334-6877

Animal ER Center
1120 Welch Rd., Commerce
(248) 960-7200

Veterinary Emergency Service - West
24400 Ford Rd., Dearborn Heights
(313) 274-3300

Michigan State University, Veterinary Teaching Hospital
736 Wilson Rd., East Lansing
(517) 353-5420

Animal Emergency Hospital
1007 S. Ballenger Hwy., Flint
(810) 238-7557

Animal Emergency Hospital
3260 Plainfield Ave. N.E., Grand Rapids
(616) 361-9911

Michigan Veterinary Specialists
1425 Michigan St. N.E., Suite F, Grand Rapids
(616) 284-5300

Southwest Michigan Animal Emergency Hospital
3301 S. Burdick St., Kalamazoo
(616) 381-5228

Lansing Veterinary Urgent Care
3276 E. Jolly Rd., Lansing
(517) 393-9200

Animal Emergency Hospital of Macomb
45245 Romeo Plank Rd., Macomb
(586) 307-3730

Veterinary Emergency Service East
28223 John R Rd., Madison Heights
(248) 547-4677

Veterinary Care Specialists
205 Rowe Rd., Milford
(248) 684-0468

Animal Emergency Center
24360 Novi Rd., Novi
(248) 348-1788

Veterinary Emergency Service West
40850 Ann Arbor Rd., Plymouth
(734) 207-8500

Animal Emergency Center
265 E. 2nd St., Rochester
(248) 651-1788

Great Lakes Pet Emergencies
1221 Tittabawassee Rd., Saginaw
(989) 752-1960

BluePearl Southfield
29080 Inkster Rd., Southfield
(248) 354-6640

MINNESOTA
South Metro Animal Emergency Care
14690 Pennock Ave., Apple Valley
(952) 953-3737

Affiliated Emergency Veterinary Service - Blaine
11850 Aberdeen St. N.E., Blaine
(763) 754-5000

Affiliated Emergency Veterinary Hospital
1615 Coon Rapids Blvd., Coon Rapids
(763) 754-9434

Affiliated Emergency Veterinary Service - Duluth
2314 W. Michigan St., Duluth
(218) 302-8000

Affiliated Emergency Veterinary Service - Eden Prairie
7717 Flying Cloud Dr., Eden Prairie
(952) 942-8272

Affiliated Emergency Veterinary Service - Golden Valley
4708 Hwy. 55, Golden Valley
(763) 529-6560

Animal Emergency Clinic
1163 Helmo Ave. N., Oakdale
(651) 501-3766

Affiliated Emergency Veterinary Service - Rochester
121 23rd Ave. S.W., Rochester
(507) 424-3976

Affiliated Emergency Veterinary Service - St. Cloud
4180 Thielman Ln., Suite 120, St. Cloud
(320) 258-3481

Animal Emergency Clinic
301 University Ave., St. Paul
(651) 293-1800

University of Minnesota College of Veterinary Medicine - Veterinary Medical Center
1365 Gortner Ave., St. Paul
(612) 626-8387

MISSISSIPPI
Gulf Coast Veterinary Emergency Hospital, Pa.
13095 Hwy. 67, Biloxi
(228) 392-7474

MISSOURI
DBA Animal Emergency Clinic
7095 Metropolitan Blvd., Suite G, Barnhart
(636) 464-2846

DBA Animal Emergency Clinic
12501 Natural Bridge Rd., Bridgeton
(314) 739-1500

University of Missouri Veterinary Health Center
900 E. Campus Dr., Columbia
(573) 882-7821

Animal Emergency Center
8141 N. Oak Trfy., Kansas City
(816) 455-5430

Animal Emergency & Referral Hospital
3495 N.E. Ralph Powell Rd., Lee's Summit
(816) 554-4990

VSS Emergency Center
1021 Howard George Dr., Manchester
(636) 227-6100

Animal Emergency Clinic
334 Fort Zumwalt Sq., O'Fallon
(636) 240-5496

DBA Animal Emergency Clinic
9937 Big Bend Blvd., St. Louis
(314) 822-7600

Animal Emergency Center Inc.
3257 E. Outer Rd., Scott City
(573) 334-3400

Emergency Veterinary Clinic of Southwest Missouri
400 S. Glenstone Ave., Springfield
(417) 890-1600

Animal Emergency & Referral Center
16457 Village Plaza View Dr., Wildwood
(636) 458-1777

MONTANA
Pet Emergency and Trauma Service
1103 Reeves Rd. W., Bozeman
(406) 587-3996

Pet Emergency Center
1914 S. Reserve St., Missoula
(406) 829-9300

NEBRASKA
United Vet Emergency Treatment Services
3700 S. 9th St., Lincoln
(402) 489-6800

Animal Emergency Clinic
9664 Mockingbird Dr., Omaha
(402) 339-6232

NEVADA
Animal Emergency Center of Las Vegas
3340 E. Patrick Ln., Las Vegas
(702) 457-8050

Las Vegas Animal Emergency Hospital
5231 W. Charleston Blvd., Las Vegas
(702) 822-1045

Veterinary Emergency and Critical Care
8650 W. Tropicana Ave., Suite B-104, Las Vegas
(702) 262-7070

Animal Emergency Center of Reno
6425 S. Virginia St., Reno
(775) 851-3600

NEW HAMPSHIRE
Capital Area Veterinary Emergency Service
1 Intervale Rd., Concord
(603) 227-1199

Small Animal Veterinary Emergency Service
63 Evans Dr., Lebanon
(603) 306-0007

Veterinary Emergency Center of Manchester
336 Abby Rd., Manchester
(603) 666-6677

Meredith Place Veterinary Emergency Hospital
8 Maple St., Suite 2, Meredith
(603) 279-1117

Animal Hospital of Nashua
168 Main Dunstable Rd., Nashua
(603) 880-3034

Veterinary Emergency, Critical Care & Referral Center
15 Piscataqua Dr., Newington
(603) 431-3600

Port City Veterinary Referral Hospital
215 Commerce Way, Suite 100, Portsmouth
(603) 433-0056

Rockingham Emergency Veterinary Hospital
3 Cobbetts Pond Rd., Windham
(603) 870-9770

NEW JERSEY
Ocean View Veterinary Hospital
2033 Rt. 9, Cape May Court House
(609) 486-5025

Garden State Veterinary Specialists
643 Rt. 27, Iselin
(732) 283-3535

Jersey Shore Veterinary Emergency Service
1000 Rt. 70, Lakewood
(732) 363-3200

Crown Veterinary Specialists
23 Blossom Hill Rd., Lebanon
(908) 236-4120

Red Bank Veterinary Hospital Linwood
535 Maple Ave., Linwood
(609) 926-5300

North Jersey Veterinary Emergency Services, LLC
724 Ridge Rd., Lyndhurst
(201) 438-7122

Animal Emergency Service of South Jersey
220 Mount Laurel Rd., Mount Laurel
(856) 727-1332

Newton Veterinary Hospital
116 Hampton House Rd., Newton
(973) 383-4321

Oradell Animal Hospital
580 Winters Ave., Paramus
(201) 262-0010

Alliance Emergency Veterinary Clinic
540 Rt. 10 W., Randolph
(973) 328-2844

Animerge
21 Rt. 206 N., Raritan
(908) 707-9077

NorthStar VETS
315 Robbinsville-Allentown Rd., Robbinsville
(609) 259-8300

Garden State Veterinary Specialists
1 Pine St., Tinton Falls
(732) 922-0011

Red Bank Veterinary Hospital
197 Hance Ave., Tinton Falls
(732) 747-3636

Animal Emergency and Referral Center
647 Bloomfield Ave., West Caldwell
(973) 226-3282

Saint Francis Veterinary Center
392 Kings Hwy, Woolwich Township
(856) 467-0050

NEW MEXICO
Staley's Veterinary Medical Clinic
1407 Indian Wells Rd., Alamogordo
(505) 437-3063

ABQ Petcare Hospital
9032 Montgomery Blvd. N.E., Albuquerque
(505) 299-8387

Albuquerque Animal Emergency Clinic
4000 Montgomery Blvd. N.E., Albuquerque
(505) 884-3433

Veterinary Emergency & Specialty Center of Santa Fe
2001 Vivigen Way, Santa Fe
(505) 984-0625

NEW YORK
Greater Buffalo Veterinary Emergency Services
4949 Main St., Amherst
(716) 839-4044

Veterinary Emergency & Critical Care Center
2115 Downer Street Rd., Baldwinsville
(315) 638-3500

Katonah Bedford Veterinary Center
546 N. Bedford Rd., Bedford Hills
(914) 241-7700

Atlantic Coast Veterinary Specialists
3250 Veterans Memorial Hwy., Bohemia
(631) 285-7780

Veterinary Emergency and Referral Group
318 Warren St., Brooklyn
(718) 522-9400

Animal Emergency Service
6230-C Jericho Tpke., Commack
(631) 462-6044

Veterinary Medical Center of Central New York
5841 Bridge St., Suite 200, East Syracuse
(315) 446-7933

New York Veterinary Specialty / Animal Emergency Services
2233 Broadhollow Rd., Farmingdale
(631) 694-3400

Northway Animal Emergency Clinic
35 Fawn Rd., Gansevoort
(518) 761-2602

Natural Vet For Pets, P.C.
585 Warburton Ave., Hastings-on-Hudson
(914) 478-4100

Animal Emergency Clinic of the Hudson Valley
1112 Morton Blvd., Kingston
(845) 336-0713

Capital District Animal Emergency Clinic
222 Troy Schenectady Rd., Latham
(518) 785-1094

Orange County Animal Emergency Service
517 Rt. 211 E., Middletown
(845) 692-0260

The Veterinary Referral Center of Ultravet Diagnostics
220 E. Jericho Tpke., Mineola
(516) 294-6680

Flannery Animal Hospital
789 Little Britain Rd., New Windsor
(845) 565-7387

Animal Medical Center
510 E. 62nd St., New York
(212) 838-8100

BluePearl Midtown West
410 W. 55th St., New York
(212) 767-0099

Fifth Avenue Veterinary Specialists
1 W. 15th St., New York
(212) 924-3311

Manhattan Veterinary Group
240 E. 80th St., New York
(212) 988-1000

Orchard Park Veterinary Medical Center
3930 N. Buffalo Rd., Orchard Park
(716) 662-6660

Long Island Veterinary Specialists / Animal Emergency & Critical Care Center
163 S. Service Rd., Plainview
(516) 501-1700

Animal Emergency Clinic of Hudson Valley
84 Patrick Ln., Poughkeepsie
(845) 471-8242

East End Veterinary Emergency Center
67 Commerce Dr., Riverhead
(631) 369-4513

Animal Hospital of Pittsford (Monroe Emergency Service)
2816 Monroe Ave., Rochester
(716) 271-7700

Animal Emergency Services
825 White Spruce Blvd., Rochester
(585) 424-1277

Animal Hospital of the Rockaways
114-10 Beach Channel Dr., Rockaway Park
(718) 474-0500

Animal Emergency Service
280-L Middle Country Rd., Selden
(631) 698-2225

Valley Cottage Animal Hospital
202 Rt. 303, Valley Cottage
(845) 268-9263

Central Veterinary Associates
73 W. Merrick Rd., Valley Stream
(516) 825-3066

The Center for Specialized Veterinary Care
609-5 Cantiague Rock Rd., Westbury
(516) 420-0000

Nassau Animal Emergency Clinic
740 Old Country Rd., Westbury
(516) 333-6262

Veterinary Medical Center of Long Island
75 Sunrise Hwy., West Islip
(631) 587-0800

The Veterinary Emergency Group
193 Tarrytown Rd., White Plains
(914) 949-8779

Animal Specialty Center
9 Odell Plaza, Yonkers
(914) 457-4000

NORTH CAROLINA
Small Animal Emergency Services
1335 N. Sandhills Blvd., Aberdeen
(910) 944-0405

Regional Emergency Animal Care Hospital (R.E.A.C.H.)
677 Brevard Rd., Asheville
(828) 665-4399, ext. 107

Animal Emergency Clinic of the High Country, PLLC
1126 Blowing Rock Rd., Suite A, Boone
(828) 268-2833

Animal Emergency Clinic of Cary
220 High House Rd., Cary
(919) 462-8989

Veterinary Specialty Hospital of the Carolinas
6405 Tryon Rd., Cary
(919) 233-4911

Animal Medical Hospital
3832 Monroe Rd., Charlotte
(704) 334-4684

Carolina Veterinary Specialists - Animal Emergency and Trauma Center
2225 Township Rd., Charlotte
(704) 504-9608

Triangle Pet Emergency Treatment Service
608 Morreene Rd., Durham
(919) 489-0615

Animal Urgent Care
3635 Sycamore Dairy Rd., Fayetteville
(910) 864-2844

Western Carolina Regional Animal Hospital and Veterinary Emergency Hospital
205 N. Highland Lake Rd., Flat Rock
(828) 697-7767

After Hours Veterinary Emergency Clinic
5505 W. Friendly Ave., Greensboro
(336) 851-1990

Carolina Veterinary Specialists - Animal Emergency & Trauma Center
501 Nicholas Rd., Greensboro
(336) 632-0605

Happy Tails Veterinary Emergency Clinic
2936 Battleground Ave., Greensboro
(336) 288-2688

Pet Emergency Clinic of Pitt County
2207 Evans St., Greenville
(252) 321-1521

Veterinary Referral Hospital of Hickory
126 Hwy. 321 S.W., Hickory
(828) 328-2660

Triangle Veterinary Referral Hospital of Holly Springs
2120 Werrington Dr., Suite 201, Holly Springs
(919) 973-5620

Carolina Veterinary Specialists - Huntersville
12117 Statesville Rd., Huntersville
(704) 949-1100

Cabarrus Emergency Veterinary Clinic
1317 S. Cannon Blvd., Kannapolis
(704) 932-1182

Charlotte Veterinary Emergency & Trauma Services
2440 Plantation Center Dr., Matthews
(704) 844-6440

Carolina Veterinary Specialists - Matthews
4099 Campus Ridge Rd., Matthews
(704) 815-3939

After Hours Small Animal Emergency Clinic
409 Vick Ave., Raleigh
(919) 781-5145

North Carolina State University, Small Animal Emergency Service
4700 Hillsborough St., Raleigh
(919) 513-6130

Quail Corners Animal Hospital & 24 Hour Emergency Care
1613 E. Millbrook Rd., Raleigh
(919) 876-0739

Thomasville Veterinary Hospital, P.A.
303 National Hwy., Thomasville
(336) 475-9119

Animal Emergency & Trauma Hospital of Wilmington
50 Greenville Ave., Wilmington
(910) 790-1070

Eastern Carolina Veterinary Emergency Treatment Service
4935 Raleigh Road Pkwy. W., Wilson
(252) 265-9920

Carolina Veterinary Specialists - Animal Emergency & Trauma Center
1600 Hanes Mall Blvd., Winston-Salem
(336) 896-0902

NORTH DAKOTA
Red River Animal Emergency Clinic
1401 Oak Manor Ave. S., Suite 2, Fargo
701-478-9299

OHIO
Akron Veterinary Referral & Emergency Center
1321 Centerview Cir., Akron
(330) 665-4996

Animal Emergency Clinic West
2101 N. Cleveland-Massillon Rd., Akron
(216) 362-6001

Metropolitan Veterinary Hospital
1053 S. Cleveland-Massillon Rd., Akron
(330) 666-2976

Stark County Veterinary Emergency Clinic, LLC
2705 Fulton Dr. N.W., Canton
(330) 452-5117

Cincinnati Animal Referral and Emergency Care Center
6995 E. Kemper Rd., Cincinnati
(513) 530-0911

Capital Veterinary Referral & Emergency Clinic
5230 Renner Rd., Columbus
(614) 870-0480

Ohio State University Veterinary Hospital
601 Vernon Tharp St., Columbus
(614) 293-3551

Dayton Care Center
6405 Clyo Rd., Dayton
(937) 428-0911

Dayton Emergency Veterinary Clinic
2714 Springboro W., Dayton
(937) 293-2714

Ohio State University, Veterinary Medical Center at Dublin
5020 Bradenton Ave., Dublin
(614) 889-8070

After Hours Animal Emergency Clinic, Inc.
2680 W. Liberty St., Girard
(330) 530-8387

Animal Emergency Critical Care Center, Inc.
5152 Grove Ave., Lorain
(440) 240-1400

Aaron Animal Clinic and Emergency Hospital
7640 Broadview Rd., Parma
(216) 901-9980

Animal Emergency & Critical Care Center of Toledo, Inc.
2921 Douglas Rd., Toledo
(419) 473-0328

Green Animal Medical Center
1620 Corporate Woods Cir., Uniontown
(330) 896-4040

VCA Great Lakes Veterinary Specialists
4760 Richmond Rd., Warrensville Heights
(216) 831-6789

Cleveland Road Animal Hospital
2752 Cleveland Rd., Wooster
(330) 345-6063

MedVet Associates, Ltd.
300 E. Wilson Bridge Rd., Worthington
(800) 890-9010

OKLAHOMA
Animal Emergency Center
2121 McKown Dr., Norman
(405) 360-7828

Animal Emergency Center
931 S.W. 74th St., Oklahoma City
(405) 631-7828

Neel Veterinary Hospital
2700 N. MacArthur Blvd., Oklahoma City
(405) 947-8387

Veterinary Emergency and Critical Care Hospital
1800 W. Memorial Rd., Oklahoma City
(405) 749-6989

Animal Emergency Center
4055 S. 102nd E. Ave., Tulsa
(918) 665-0508

OREGON
Animal Emergency Center of Central Oregon
1245 S.E. 3rd St., Suite C3, Bend
(541) 385-9110

Cascade Animal Emergency Clinic
425 N.E. Windy Knolls, Suite 4, Bend
(541) 318-5829

Northwest Veterinary Specialists Emergency Service
16756 S.E. 82nd Dr., Clackamas
(503) 656-3999

Willamette Veterinary Hospital
1562 S.W. 3rd St., Corvallis
(541) 753-2223

Lake Oswego Veterinary Emergency
3996 Douglas Way, Lake Oswego
(503) 850-6296

Southern Oregon Veterinary Specialty Center
3265 Biddle Rd., Medford
(541) 282-7711

Dove Lewis Emergency Animal Hospital
1945 N.W. Pettygrove St., Portland
(503) 228-7281

VCA Southeast Portland Animal Hospital
13830 S.E. Stark St., Portland
(503) 255-8139

Umpqua Emergency Veterinary Hospital
545 W. Umpqua St., Suite 1, Roseburg
(541) 440-6320

Salem Veterinary Emergency Clinic
3215 Market St. N.E., Salem
(503) 588-8082

Emergency Veterinary Hospital
103 W. Q St., Springfield
(541) 746-0112

Emergency Veterinary Clinic of Tualatin
19314 S.W. Mohave Ct., Tualatin
(503) 691-7922

PENNSYLVANIA
Veterinary Referral and Emergency Center
318 Northern Blvd., Clarks Summit
(570) 587-7777

Northwest Pennsylvania Pet Emergency Center
429 W. 38th St., Erie
(814) 866-5920

Keystone Veterinary Emergency and Referral
1200 W. Chester Pike, Havertown
(484) 454-5412

Center for Animal Referral and Emergency Services
2010 Cabot Blvd. W., Suite D, Langhorne
(215) 750-2774

Gwynedd Veterinary Hospital
1615 W. Point Pike, Lansdale
(215) 699-9294

Veterinary Specialty and Emergency Center
301 Veterans Hwy., Levittown
(215) 750-7884

Hope Veterinary Specialists
40 Three Tun Rd., Malvern
(610) 296-2099

Rossmoyne Animal Emergency Trauma Center
4930 Ritter Rd., Suite 101, Mechanicsburg
(717) 796-2334

Allegheny Veterinary Emergency Trauma & Specialty
4224 Northern Pike, Monroeville
(412) 373-4200

Matthew J. Ryan Veterinary Hospital at the University of Pennsylvania
3900 Delancey St., Philadelphia
(215) 898-4680

VCA Castle Shannon Animal Hospital Service
3610 Library Rd., Pittsburgh
(412) 885-2500

Veterinary Emergency Clinic
882 Butler St., Pittsburgh
(412) 492-9855

Pennsylvania Veterinary Specialty and Emergency Associates - Hickory Veterinary Hospital
2303 Hickory Rd., Plymouth Meeting
(610) 828-3054

Creature Comforts Veterinary Service
Old Rt. 115, Saylorsburg
(570) 992-0400

Central Pennsylvania Emergency Treatment Services
1522 Martin St., State College
(814) 237-4670

Metzger Animal Hospital
1044 Benner Pike, State College
(814) 237-5333

Metropolitan Emergency Service
2626 Van Buren Ave., Valley Forge
(610) 666-1050

Bucks County Veterinary Emergency Trauma Service
978 Easton Rd., Warrington
(215) 918-2200

Animal Emergency Center
395 Susquehanna Tr., Watsontown
(570) 742-7400

Valley Central Veterinary Referral Center
210 Fullerton Ave., Whitehall
(610) 435-5588

Animal Emergency & Referral Center of York 24HR Care
1640 S. Queen St., York
(717) 767-5355

RHODE ISLAND
Ocean State Veterinary Specialists
1480 S. County Tr., East Greenwich
(401) 886-6787

SOUTH CAROLINA
Charleston Veterinary Referral Center
3484 Shelby Ray Ct., Charleston
(843) 614-8387

Palmetto Regional Emergency Hospital for Animals
10298 Two Notch Rd., Columbia
(803) 865-1418

South Carolina Veterinary Emergency Care
132 Stonemark Ln., Columbia
(803) 798-3837

South Carolina Veterinary Specialists & Emergency Care
3924 Fernandina Rd., Columbia
(803) 561-0015

Animal Emergency Clinic
393 Woods Lake Rd., Greenville
(864) 232-1878

Mt. Pleasant Emergency Veterinary Hospital
930B Pine Hollow Rd., Mt. Pleasant
(843) 216-7554

Animal Emergency Hospital of the Strand
303 Hwy. 15, Suite 1, Myrtle Beach
(843) 445-9797

Veterinary Specialty Care - North Charleston
3163 W. Montague Ave., North Charleston
(843) 744-3372

Spartanburg Veterinary Emergency Clinic
1291 Asheville Hwy., Spartanburg
(864) 591-1923

SOUTH DAKOTA
Veterinary Emergency Hospital
3508 S. Minnesota Ave., Suite 104, Sioux Falls
(605) 977-6200

TENNESSEE
Midland Pet Emergency Center, Inc.
235 Calderwood St., Alcoa
(865) 982-1007

Airport Pet Emergency Clinic
2436 Hwy. 75, Blountville
(423) 279-0574

Regional Institute for Veterinary Emergencies and Referrals
2132 Amnicola Hwy., Chattanooga
(423) 698-4612

Animal Emergency Clinic of Maury County, LLC
1900 Shady Brook St., Suite B, Columbia
(931) 380-1929

PetMed Emergency Center, LLC
830 N. Germantown Pkwy., Suite 105, Cordova
(901) 624-9002

Jackson Pet Emergency Clinic, LLC
2815 N. Highland Ave., Suite D, Jackson
(731) 660-4343

Knoxville Pet Emergency Clinic
1819 Ailor Ave., Knoxville
(865) 637-0114

University of Tennessee Veterinary Medical Center
2407 River Dr., Knoxville
(865) 974-8387

Animal Medical Center
234 River Rock Blvd., Murfreesboro
(615) 867-7575

Nashville Pet Emergency Clinic
2000 12th Ave. S., Nashville
(615) 383-2600

Nashville Veterinary Specialists
2971 Sidco Dr., Nashville
(615) 386-0107

TEXAS

I-20 Animal Medical Center
5820 W. I-20, Arlington
(817) 478-9238

AM/PM Animal Hospital
2239 S. Lamar Blvd., Austin
(512) 448-2676

Austin Vet Care - Central
4106 N. Lamar Blvd., Austin
(512) 961-3059

Emergency Animal Hospital of Northwest Austin
12034 Research Blvd., Suite 8, Austin
(512) 331-6121

Emergency Animal Hospital of Northwest Austin - South Branch
4434 Frontier Tr., Austin
(512) 899-0955

White Angel Animal Hospital
1901 RR 620 N., Austin
(512) 266-7838

Southeast Texas Animal Emergency Clinic
3420 W. Cardinal Dr., Beaumont
(409) 842-3239

Burleson Animal Emergency Hospital
805 N.E. Alsbury Blvd., Burleson
(817) 447-9194

North Texas Emergency Pet Clinic
1712 W. Frankford Rd., Suite 108, Carrolton
(972) 323-1310

Texas A&M University Veterinary Teaching Hospital
4475 TAMU, College Station
(979) 845-3541

Heritage Veterinary Hospital
3930 Glade Rd., Suite 120, Colleyville
(817) 358-0404

Emergency Animal Clinic
12101 Greenville Ave., Suite 118, Dallas
(972) 994-9110

The E-Clinic, Inc.
3337 Fitzhugh Ave., Dallas
(214) 520-8388

Grayson County Animal Emergency Clinic
3301 Woodlawn Blvd., Denison
(903) 337-0898

Denton County Animal Emergency Room
4145 S. I-35E, Suite 101, Denton
(940) 271-1200

El Paso Animal Emergency Center
1220 Airway Blvd., El Paso
(915) 203-0818

Airport Freeway Animal Emergency Clinic
411 N. Main St., Euless
(817) 571-2088

DFW North Emergency Veterinary Clinic
2311 Cross Timbers, Suite 319, Flower Mound
(469) 464-2964

Fort Worth Animal Emergency Hospital
4631 Citylake Blvd. W., Fort Worth
(817) 263-2900

Metro West Emergency Veterinary Center
3201 Hulen St., Fort Worth
(817) 731-3734

Frisco Emergency Pet Care
10150 Legacy Dr., Suite 500, Frisco
(469) 287-6767

Animal Emergency Hospital of North Texas
2700 W. Hwy. 114, Grapevine
(817) 410-2273

Animal Emergency Center of West Houston
4823 Hwy. 6N, Houston
(832) 593-8387

Animal Emergency Clinic SH 249
18707 SH 249, Houston
(281) 890-8875

Animal Emergency Clinic Southeast
10331 Gulf Frwy., Houston
(713) 941-8460

Gulf Coast Animal Emergency Hospital
1111 W. Loop S., Suite 200, Houston
(713) 693-1100

Gulf Coast Veterinary Specialists
1111 W. Loop S., Suite 140, Houston
(713) 693-1111

NHVS Animal Emergency & Specialty - Katy
19450 Katy Frwy., Suite 200, Houston
(281) 675-6000

NHVS Animal Emergency & Specialty - Willowbrook
19311 SH 249, Houston
(281) 890-8875

Veterinary Emergency Referral Group, Inc.
8921 Katy Frwy., Houston
(713) 932-9589

I-20 Animal Hospital
3713 Fort Worth Hwy., Hudson Oaks
(817) 341-3331

Animal Emergency Clinic North East
10205 Birchridge Dr., Humble
(281) 446-4900

VCA Metroplex Animal Hospital & Pet Lodge
700 W. Airport Frwy., Irving
(972) 438-7113

All Pets Animal Hospital & 24 Hour Emergency Service
24221 Kingsland Blvd., Katy
(281) 392-7387

After Hours Veterinary Services
2501 S. W.S. Young, Suite 413, Killeen
(254) 628-5017

VCA Animal Emergency Hospital Southeast Calder Road
1108 Gulf Frwy. S., Suite 280, League City
(281) 332-1678

Animal Emergency Hospital of Mansfield
301 N. Hwy. 287, Mansfield
(817) 473-7838

Animal Medical Center of McAllen, Pet Doctor 911
7017 N. 10th St., McAllen
(956) 683-7387

Veterinary Referral Center of East Dallas
4651 N. Belt Line Rd., Mesquite
(972) 226-3377

Animal Emergency & Urgent Care Center of The Woodlands
27870 I-45 N., Oak Ridge North
(281) 367-5444

Pearland 288 Animal Emergency Clinic
10100 Broadway St., Suite 102, Pearland
(713) 482-4592

Emergency Pet Care of Round Rock
301 Chisholm Tr., Round Rock
(512) 961-5200

Angel of Mercy Animal Critical Care, Inc.
8734 Grissom Rd., San Antonio
(210) 684-2105

Animal Emergency Room
4315 Fredericksburg Rd., Suite 2, San Antonio
(210) 737-7380

Emergency Pet Center
8503 Broadway St., Suite 105, San Antonio
(210) 822-2873

Emergency Pet Center
503 E. Sonterra Blvd., San Antonio
(210) 404-2873

Mission Pet Emergency
8202 N. Loop 1604 W., San Antonio
(210) 691-0900

Northeast Emergency Animal Clinic
8365 Perrin Beitel, San Antonio
(210) 650-3141

NHVS Animal Emergency & Specialty - Spring
1646 Spring Cypress Rd., Suite 100, Spring
(832) 616-5000

Animal Emergency Clinic - Sugar Land
9920 Hwy. 90A, Suite 100C, Sugar Land
(281) 340-8387

Southwest Freeway Animal Hospital & Emergency Center
15575 Southwest Frwy., Sugar Land
(281) 491-8387

Sugar Land Veterinary Specialists and Emergency Center
1515 Lake Pointe Pkwy., Sugar Land
(281) 491-7800

Premier Veterinary Hospital
6001 S. Broadway Ave., Tyler
(903) 617-6072

Texas Animal Medical Center
4900 Steinbeck Bend, Waco
(254) 753-0901

UTAH
Utah Veterinary Center
308 W. 7200 S., Midvale
(801) 871-0600

Advanced Veterinary Care
1021 E. 3300 S., Salt Lake City
(801) 942-3951

Central Emergency Animal Hospital
55 E. Miller Ave., Salt Lake City
(801) 487-1325

Pet E.R. - The Pet Emergency Room
6360 S. Highland Dr., Salt Lake City
(801) 278-3367

Animal Emergency Center
2465 N. Main St., Suite 5, Sunset
(801) 776-8118

VERMONT
Burlington Emergency & Veterinary Specialists
200 Commerce St., Williston
(802) 863-2387

VIRGINIA
VCA Alexandria Veterinary Animal Hospital
2660 Duke St., Alexandria
(703) 823-3601

Artemis Veterinary Emergency & Specialty Services
7951 Gainesford Ct., Suite 115, Bristow
(703) 722-9159

Greenbrier Emergency Animal Hospital
370 Greenbrier Dr., Suite A2, Charlottesville
(434) 202-1616

Veterinary Emergency Treatment Services & Specialty
1540 Airport Rd., Charlottesville
(434) 973-3519

Greenbrier Veterinary Emergency Center
1100 Eden Way N., Suite 101B, Chesapeake
(757) 366-9000

SouthPaws Veterinary Referral Center
8500 Arlington Blvd., Fairfax
(703) 752-9100

Fredericksburg Regional Veterinary Emergency Center, LLC
2301 1/2 Jefferson Davis Hwy., Fredericksburg
(540) 372-3470

Animal Emergency Critical Care Associates
165 Fort Evans Rd. N.E., Leesburg
(703) 777-5755

Animal Emergency & Critical Care of Lynchburg
3432 Odd Fellows Rd., Lynchburg
(434) 846-1504

Veterinary Referral & Critical Care (VRCC)
1596 Hockett Rd., Manakin Sabot
(804) 784-8722

Prince William Emergency Veterinary Clinic
8610 Centreville Rd., Manassas
(703) 361-8287

Animal Emergency Care
12501 Hull Street Rd., Midlothian
(804) 744-9800

Blue Ridge Veterinary Associates
120 E. Cornwell Ln., Purcellville
(540) 338-7387

Dogwood Veterinary Emergency and Specialty Center
5918 W. Broad St., Richmond
(804) 716-4700

Veterinary Emergency Center, Inc.
3312 W. Cary St., Richmond
(804) 353-9000

Emergency Veterinary Services of Roanoke
4902 Frontage Rd. N.W., Roanoke
(540) 563-8575

Regional Veterinary Referral Center
6651 Backlick Rd., Springfield
(703) 451-8900

The Cove - Center of Veterinary Expertise
6550 Hampton Roads Pkwy., Suite 113, Suffolk
(757) 935-9111

Veterinary Emergency Services
465 Lee Hwy., Verona
(540) 248-1051

Hope Advanced Veterinary Center
140 Park St. S.E., Vienna
(703) 281-5121

Beach Veterinary Emergency Clinic
1124 Lynnhaven Pkwy., Virginia Beach
(757) 468-4900

Tidewater Veterinary Emergency and Critical Care Center
364 S. Independence Blvd., Virginia Beach
(757) 499-5463

Valley Emergency Veterinary Clinic, LLC
164-4 Garber Ln., Winchester
(540) 662-7811

Woodbridge Animal Hospital
2703 Caton Hill Rd., Woodbridge
(703) 897-5665

Animal Emergency Center
5007 Victory Blvd., Suite D2, Yorktown
(757) 234-0461

Peninsula Emergency Veterinary Clinic
1120 George Washington Memorial Hwy., Yorktown
(757) 874-8115

WASHINGTON

Auburn Veterinary Hospital
718 Auburn Way N., Auburn
(253) 939-6272

Animal Emergency Care
317 Telegraph Rd., Bellingham
(360) 758-2200

Veterinary Emergency Relief Services
702 Kentucky St., Suite 445, Bellingham
(360) 318-3985

Animal Emergency Clinic of Everett
3625 Rucker Ave., Everett
(425) 258-4466

Alpine Animal Hospital
888 N.W. Sammamish Rd., Issaquah
(425) 392-8888

Animal Emergency & Specialty
12305 120th Ave. N.E., Suite K, Kirkland
(425) 827-8727

Seattle Veterinary Specialists
11814 115th Ave. N.E., Suite 102, Kirkland
(425) 823-9111

Agape Pet Emergency Center
16418 7th Pl. W., Lynnwood
(425) 741-2688

Veterinary Specialty Center
20115 44th Ave. W., Lynnwood
(425) 697-6106

Pet Emergency Center
14434 Avon Allen Rd., Mount Vernon
(360) 848-5911

Mid-Columbia Pet Emergency Services
8913 Sandifur Pkwy., Pasco
(509) 547-3577

Animal Emergency & Trauma Center
320 Lindvig Way, Poulsbo
(360) 697-7771

VCA Central Kitsap Animal Hospital
10310 Central Valley Rd. N.E., Poulsbo
(360) 692-6162

Washington State University - Veterinary Teaching Hospital
100 Grimes Way, Pullman
(509) 335-8771

Animal Emergency Hospital of Redmond
16421 Cleveland St., Suite H, Redmond
(425) 250-7090

BluePearl Veterinary Partners - Renton
4208 Lind Ave. S.W., Renton
(205) 364-1660

BluePearl Veterinary Partners - Seattle
11536 Lake City Way N.E., Seattle
(206) 364-1660

Emerald City Emergency Clinic
4102 Stone Way N., Seattle
(206) 634-9000

Five Corners Veterinary Hospital
15707 1st Ave. S., Seattle
(206) 243-2982

Animal Medical Center of Seattle
14810 15th Ave N.E., Shoreline
(206) 204-3366

P.S.C.V.M. Small Animal Emergency and Critical Care Center
11308 92nd St. S.E., Snohomish
(360) 563-5300

Pet Emergency Clinic
21 E. Mission Ave., Spokane
(509) 326-6670

The Animal Emergency Clinic - Puget Sound Veterinary Referral Center, PLLC
5608 S. Durango St., Tacoma
(253) 474-0791

Summit Veterinary Referral Center
2505 S. 80th St., Tacoma
(253) 983-1114

Columbia River Veterinary Specialists
6818 N.E. Fourth Plain Blvd., Suite C, Vancouver
(360) 694-3007

St. Francis 24 Hr. Animal Hospital
12010 N.E. 65th St., Vancouver
(360) 253-5446

Yakima Pet Emergency Service
510 W. Chestnut Ave., Yakima
(509) 452-4138

WEST VIRGINIA
Kanawha Valley Animal Emergency Clinic
5304 MacCorkle Ave. S.W., Charleston
(304) 768-2911

Animal Urgent Care, Inc.
4201 Wood St., Wheeling
(304) 233-0002

WISCONSIN
Fox Valley Animal Referral Center
4706 New Horizons Blvd., Appleton
(920) 993-9193

Lakeshore Veterinary Hospital
2100 W. Silver Spring Dr., Glendale
(414) 540-6710

WVRC - Grafton
1381 N. Port Washington Rd., Grafton
(262) 546-0249

Green Bay Animal Emergency Center
933 Anderson Dr., Suite F, Green Bay
(920) 494-9400

Crawford Animal Hospital
4607 S. 108th St., Greenfield
(414) 543-3499

Emergency Clinic for Animals
229 W. Beltline Hwy., Madison
(608) 274-7772

University of Wisconsin, Veterinary Teaching Hospital
2015 Linden Dr., Madison
(608) 263-7600

Veterinary Emergency Service
4902 E. Broadway, Madison
(608) 222-2455

Veterinary Emergency Service
1612 N. High Point Rd., Middleton
(608) 831-1101

Central Wisconsin Animal Emergency Center
1420 Kronenwetter Dr., Mosinee
(715) 693-6934

Lakeshore Veterinary Specialists
207 W. Seven Hills Rd., Port Washington
(262) 268-7800

WVRC - Racine
4333 S. Green Bay Rd., Racine
(262) 553-9223

WVRC - Waukesha
360 Bluemound Rd., Waukesha
(262) 542-3241

Canada

ALBERTA

Calgary Animal Referral and Emergency Centre
7140 12th St. S.E., Calgary
(403) 520-8387

Calgary North Veterinary Hospital and Emergency Service
4204 4th St. N.W., Calgary
(403) 277-0135

McKnight 24 Hour Veterinary Hospital
34-5010 4th St. N.E., Calgary
(403) 457-0911

Western Veterinary Specialist and Emergency Centre
1802 10th Ave. S.W., Calgary
(403) 770-1340

Edmonton South Animal Hospital
3823 99th St. N.W., Edmonton
(780) 666-7374

Edmonton Veterinarians Emergency Clinic
11104 102nd Ave., Edmonton
(780) 433-9505

Guardian Veterinary Centre
5620 99th St. N.W., Edmonton
(780) 436-5880

BRITISH COLUMBIA

Animal Critical Care Group
1410 Boundary Rd., Burnaby
(604) 473-4882

Central Animal Emergency Clinic
812 Roderick Ave., Coquitlam
(604) 931-1911

Animal Emergency Clinic of the Fraser Valley
6325 204th St., Suite 306, Langley
(604) 514-1711

Mainland Animal Emergency Clinic
15338 Fraser Hwy., Surrey
(604) 588-4000

Canada West Veterinary Specialists
1988 Kootenay St., Vancouver
(604) 473-4882

Intercity Animal Emergency Clinic
580 S.E. Marine Dr., Vancouver
(604) 321-8080

Vancouver Animal Emergency Clinic, Ltd.
1590 W. 4th St., Vancouver
(604) 734-5104

Central Victoria Veterinary Hospital
760 Roderick St., Victoria
(250) 475-2495

MANITOBA

Winnipeg Animal Emergency Clinic
400 Pembina Hwy., Winnipeg
(204) 452-9427

NEW BRUNSWICK

Oaks Veterinary Medical & Emergency Referral Center
565 Mapleton Rd., Moncton
(506) 854-6257

NOVA SCOTIA

Metro Animal Emergency Clinic
201 Brownlow Ave., Unit 9, Dartmouth
(902) 468-0674

ONTARIO

Veterinary Emergency Clinic of York Region
14879 Yonge St., Aurora
(905) 713-2323

Huronia Veterinary Emergency Clinic
4-130 Bell Farm Rd., Barrie
(705) 722-0377

Pet Hospital of Prince Edward and Hastings Counties
5529 Hwy. 62 S., Belleville
(613) 968-9956

Emergency Veterinary Clinic
1 Wexford Rd., Brampton
(905) 495-9907

North Town Veterinary Hospital
496 Main St. N., Brampton
(905) 451-2000

Burgess Veterinary Emergency Clinic
775 Woodview Rd., Burlington
(905) 637-8111

Alta Vista Animal Health
2616 Bank St., Gloucester
(613) 731-9911

Halton-Wentworth Emergency Vet Clinic
505 King St. W., Hamilton
(905) 529-1004

London Veterinary Emergency Clinic
41 Adelaide St. N., Unit 43, London
(519) 432-7341

Mississauga-Oakville Veterinary Emergency Hospital
2285 Bristol Cir., Oakville
(905) 829-9444

Vaughan-Richmond Hill Veterinary Emergency Clinic
10303 Yonge St., Richmond Hill
(905) 884-1832

Niagara Veterinary Emergency Clinic
2F Tremont Dr., Unit 1, St. Catharines
(905) 641-3185

Veterinary Emergency Clinic
920 Yonge St., Suite 117, Toronto
(416) 920-2002

Veterinary Emergency Hospital of West Toronto
150 Norseman St., Toronto
(416) 239-3453

VETS Toronto
1025 Kingston Rd., Toronto
(416) 690-0625

Animal Emergency Clinic
1910 Dundas St. E., Unit 122, Whitby
(905) 576-3031

QUEBEC
Centre Veterinaire Laval
4530 Hwy. 440, Laval
(450) 781-1200

Centre Veterinaire DMV
2300 54e Ave., Montréal
(514) 633-8888

Centre Veterinaire Daubigny
3349 Boul. Wilfrid-Hamel, Québec
(418) 872-5355

University of Montreal Veterinary Hospital
3200 Sicotte St., Saint-Hyacinthe
(450) 778-8111

Pet-Friendly Hotels & Restaurants

How to Use the Listings

U.S. Hotels

Canadian Hotels

Restaurant Listings

Some 13,000 AAA Approved hotels and restaurants across North America accept traveling pets. This guide provides listings for those lodgings and restaurants in the United States and Canada that roll out the welcome mat for pets as well as the people who love them.

For the purpose of this book, "pets" are domestic cats or dogs. If you are planning to travel with any other kind of animal — particularly such exotic pets as birds or reptiles — check with the property before making definite plans. Expect to keep nontraditional pets crated at all times.

Hotel Listings

Hotels are listed alphabetically under the city or town in which they physically are located or under the nearest recognized city or town. U.S. properties are shown first, followed by Canadian properties. Each hotel listing provides the following information (see sample listing below):

❶ 🅰🅰🅰 or 🅲🅰🅰 logos distinguish establishments that participate in the AAA/CAA logo licensing program.

❷ Diamond Rating

❸ Property name

❹ Hotel classification
(see next page for descriptions)

❺ Special amenities offered. These properties provide an additional benefit to pets, such as treats, toys or gifts, pet sitting and/or walking, a pet menu, food/water dishes, pet sheets or pillows, pet beds or other extras.

❻ Telephone number

❼ Two-person (2P) rate year-round, and cancellation notice validity period (if more than 48 hours). Rates listed are daily. **Note:** Most establishments accept credit cards, but a small number require cash, so please call ahead to verify. "Call for rates" indicates rates were not available at time of printing. Please contact property for current rate information.

❽ Physical address and/or highway location, if available

❾ Exterior or interior corridors

❿ Pet policies. If the phrase "pets accepted" appears, the property does accept pets but specific information was unavailable at press time. Otherwise, pet-specific policies are denoted as follows:

Size. "Very small" denotes pets weighing up to 10 pounds; "small," up to 25 pounds; "medium," up to 50 pounds; and "large," up to 100 pounds. If no size is specified, the property accepts pets of all sizes.

Species. "Other" indicates the property accepts animals other than dogs and cats. Always call ahead and specify the type of pet you plan to bring.

Deposits and fees. Includes the dollar amount, the type of charge (refundable deposit or nonrefundable fee), the frequency of the charge and whether the charge is per pet or per room.

Designated rooms. Guests with pets are placed in certain rooms, often smoking rooms or those on the ground floor.

Housekeeping service. The phrase "service with restrictions" denotes properties that require the pet to be crated, removed or attended by the owner during housekeeping service.

Supervision. The pet is required to be supervised at all times.

Crate. The pet must be crated when the owner is not present.

⓫ Member values, services and facilities:

🆂🅰🆅🅴 Discounted standard room rate or lowest public rate available at time of booking for dates of stay

🅴🅲🅾 Indicates hotels that have been certified by well-established government and/or private eco-certification organizations. For more information about these organizations and their programs, visit AAA.com/eco.

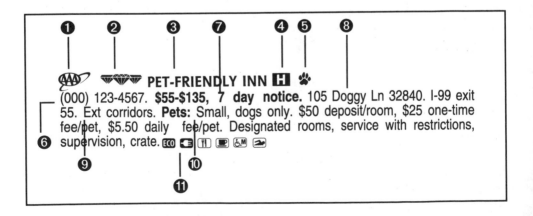

■ Electric vehicle charging station on premises. Station locations are provided by Department of Energy.

📶 Free Wireless Internet service on premises

📶 No Wireless Internet service on premises

📶 Wireless Internet service on premises for a fee

⊠ Smoke-free premises

♿ Accessible features
(call property for available services and amenities)

🔲 Refrigerator

☕ Coffee maker

🍴 Restaurant on premises

🏊 Pool

🏐 Recreational activities

❄ No air conditioning

📺 No TV

☎ No telephones

Please note: Some in-room amenities represented by the icons in the listings may be available only in selected rooms, and may incur an extra fee. Please inquire when making your reservations.

To avoid fines, always inform the management that you are traveling with an animal. Many properties require guests with pets to sign a waiver or release form and to pay for the room with a credit card. Whether you pay in cash or by credit card, you will be held liable for any damages caused by your pet, even if the property does not charge a deposit or pet fee. It is not a good idea to leave your pet unattended in the room, but if you must, crate him and notify management. When in public areas, keep your pet leashed and do not allow him to disturb other guests.

It is important to remember that animal policies do change; always confirm restrictions and fees when making reservations and again 1-2 days before departure.

Listing information is subject to change. All listing information was accurate at press time. Hotel rates and policies change and the publisher cannot be held liable for changes occurring after publication. AAA cannot guarantee the safety of guests or their pets at any facility.

AAA Hotel Diamond Ratings

Before a property is listed by AAA, it must satisfy a set of minimum standards regarding basic lodging needs as identified by AAA members. If a property meets those requirements (determined during an unannounced evaluation by a AAA inspector), it is assigned a Diamond Rating.

Once an establishment becomes AAA Approved, it is then assigned a rating of one to five Diamonds, indicating the extensiveness of its facilities, amenities and services, from basic to moderate to luxury. The Diamond Ratings guide members in selecting establishments appropriately matched to their needs and expectations.

◆ Budget-oriented, offering basic comfort and hospitality.

◆◆ Affordable, with modestly enhanced facilities, décor and amenities.

◆◆◆ Distinguished, multifaceted with enhanced physical attributes, amenities and guest comforts.

◆◆◆◆ Refined, stylish with upscale physical attributes, extensive amenities and a high degree of hospitality, service and attention to detail.

◆◆◆◆◆ Ultimate luxury, sophistication and comfort with extraordinary physical attributes, meticulous personalized service, extensive amenities and impeccable standards of excellence.

Hotel Classifications

BB Bed & Breakfast: Typically owner-operated with a high degree of personal touches. Guests are encouraged to interact during evening and breakfast hours. A continental or full, hot breakfast is included in the room rate.

CA Cabin/Cottage: Vacation-oriented, typically small-scale, freestanding units with simple construction, homey design and basic décor. Often located in wooded, rural or waterfront locations. As a rule, essential cleaning supplies, kitchen utensils and complete bed and bath linens are supplied.

CO Condominium: Apartment-style accommodations of varying design or décor, units often contain one or more bedrooms, a living room, full kitchen and an eating area. As a rule, essential cleaning supplies, kitchen utensils and complete bed and bath linens are supplied.

CI Country Inn: Although similar in definition to a bed and breakfast, country inns are usually larger in scale with spacious public areas and offer a dining facility that serves breakfast and dinner.

H Hotel: Typically a multistory property with interior room entrances and a variety of guest unit styles. The magnitude of the public areas is determined by the overall theme, location and service level, but may include a variety of facilities such as a restaurant, shops, a fitness center, a spa, a business center and meeting rooms.

VH House: Freestanding units of varying home-style design. Typically larger scale, often containing two or more bedrooms, a living room, a full kitchen, a dining room and multiple bathrooms. As a rule, essential cleaning supplies, kitchen utensils and complete bed and bath linens are supplied.

M Motel: A one- or two-story roadside property with exterior room entrances and drive up parking. Public areas and facilities are often limited in size and/or availability.

RA Ranch: Typically a working ranch featuring an obvious rustic, Western theme, equestrian-related activities and a variety of guest unit styles.

Restaurant Listings

Restaurants are listed alphabetically under the city or town in which they physically are located or under the nearest recognized city or town. U.S. properties are shown first, followed by Canadian establishments.

Note: Call first before taking your pet to a restaurant, as pet policies may change. Each listing provides the following information (see sample listing below):

❶ 🐾 or 🐾 logos distinguish establishments that participate in the AAA/CAA logo licensing program.

❷ Diamond Rating

❸ Restaurant name

❹ Telephone number

❺ Cuisine type identifies the predominant food style and classification represents the overall restaurant

❻ Prices represent the minimum and maximum entrée cost per person

❼ Physical address and/or highway location

❽ Restaurant icons:
  🔌 Electric vehicle charging station on premises.

  B Breakfast

  L Lunch

  D Dinner

  24 Open 24 hours

  LATE Open after 11 p.m.

  &M Accessible features (call property for available

services and amenities)

  ✗ No air conditioning

  ◎ Designated smoking section

Listing information, including pet policies, is subject to change; always confirm pricing, policies and restrictions with the restaurant before your visit as the publisher cannot be held liable for changes occurring after publication. In addition, AAA cannot guarantee the safety of guests or their pets at any facility.

AAA Restaurant Diamond Ratings

Before a restaurant is listed by AAA, it must satisfy a set of minimum standards regarding basic restaurant needs as identified by AAA members. If an establishment meets those requirements (determined during an unannounced evaluation by a AAA inspector) and is recommended for AAA Approval, it is then assigned a rating of one to five Diamonds.

♦ Simple, economical food, often quick-serve, in a functional environment.

♦♦ Familiar food, often cooked to order, served in casual surroundings.

♦♦♦ Trendy cuisine, skillfully prepared and served, with expanded beverage options, in an enhanced setting.

♦♦♦♦ Distinctive fine-dining. Creative preparations, skillfully served, often with wine steward, amid upscale ambience.

♦♦♦♦♦ Leading-edge cuisine of the finest ingredients, uniquely prepared by an acclaimed chef, served by expert service staff led by maître d' in extraordinary surroundings.

---

❶   ❷   ❸   ❹   ❻   ❼

🐾   ♦♦♦♦♦ **PET-FRIENDLY RESTAURANT**
SEAFOOD. FINE DINING. (000) 123-4567. **$11-$59.**, 236 Perimeter Center Pkwy 30346. I-285 exit 26 eastbound, 0.5 mi to Hammond Dr, then 0.6 mi e; exit 28 westbound, just n to Hammond Dr, then just e. L D

❺

❽

United States Hotels

ALABAMA

ABBEVILLE
◆◆ **Abbeville Inn** M
(334) 585-5060. **Call for rates.** 1237 US Hwy 431 S 36310. Jct SR 27. Ext corridors. **Pets:** Accepted.

ALABASTER
◆◆ **Candlewood Suites Alabaster** H
(205) 620-0188. **Call for rates.** 1004 Balmoral Dr 35007. I-65 exit 238, just e. Int corridors. **Pets:** Accepted.

ALBERTVILLE
◆◆ **Microtel Inn & Suites by Wyndham Albertville** H
(256) 894-4000. **$69-$82.** 220 Hwy 75 N 35951. Jct US 431 and SR 75, just ne. Int corridors. **Pets:** Medium, other species. $10 daily fee/pet. Designated rooms, service with restrictions, crate.

ALEXANDER CITY
◆◆ **Days Inn** M
(256) 234-6311. **$69-$89.** 3146 US Hwy 280 35010. Jct US 280 and SR 22. Ext corridors. **Pets:** Small. $10 daily fee/pet. Designated rooms, service with restrictions, supervision.

ANDALUSIA
◆◆ **Econo Lodge** M
(334) 222-7511. **$60-$70.** 1421 Dr MLK Jr Expwy 36420. On US 84 Bypass. Ext corridors. **Pets:** Medium. $20 daily fee/pet. Designated rooms, no service, supervision.

ATHENS
◆◆ **Best Western Athens Inn** H
(256) 233-4030. **$80-$130.** 1329 US Hwy 72 E 35611. I-65 exit 351, just w. Ext corridors. **Pets:** Accepted.

◆◆ **Sleep Inn Athens** H
(256) 232-4700. **$72-$109.** 1115 Audubon Ln 35611. I-65 exit 351, just nw. Int corridors. **Pets:** Accepted.

AUBURN
◆◆◆ **The Crenshaw Guest House** BB
(334) 821-1131. **Call for rates.** 371 N College St 36830. Just w of downtown; in historic district. Ext/int corridors. **Pets:** Accepted.

◆◆ **The Hotel at Auburn University & Dixon Conference Center** H
(334) 821-8200. **Call for rates.** 241 S College St 36830. Just e of downtown. Int corridors. **Pets:** Accepted.

◆◆ **Quality Inn** M
(334) 734-1002. **$60-$289.** 1212 Mall Pkwy 36831. 2 mi w of US 280 on SR 14/15 (Pepperell Pkwy). Ext corridors. **Pets:** Accepted.

BESSEMER
◆◆◆ **Best Western Plus Bessemer Hotel & Suites** H
(205) 481-1950. **$90-$170.** 5041 Academy Ln 35022. I-20/59 exit 108, just sw. Int corridors. **Pets:** Accepted.

Comfort Inn H
(205) 428-3999. **$75-$200.** 5051 Academy Ln 35022. I-20/59 exit 108, just sw. Int corridors. **Pets:** Accepted.

◆◆ **Quality Inn** M
(205) 428-3194. **$69-$120.** 5021 Academy Ln 35022. I-20/59 exit 108, just sw. Ext corridors. **Pets:** Accepted.

◆◆ **Sleep Inn** H
(205) 424-0000. **$70-$200.** 1259 Greenmor Dr 35022. I-459 exit 6, just s, then just w. Int corridors. **Pets:** Small. $20 daily fee/pet. Designated rooms, service with restrictions, supervision.

BIRMINGHAM *(Restaurants p. 593)*
◆◆◆ **Drury Inn & Suites-Birmingham Southeast** H
(205) 967-2450. **$89-$154.** 3510 Grandview Pkwy 35243. I-459 exit 19 (US 280 E), just e. Int corridors. **Pets:** Accepted.

◆◆ **Embassy Suites by Hilton Birmingham** H
(205) 879-7400. **$109-$209.** 2300 Woodcrest Pl 35209. Just n of jct US 31 and 280 exit 21st Ave southbound, 0.3 mi s. Int corridors. **Pets:** Accepted.

◆◆◆ **The Hotel Highland at Five Points South, an Ascend Collection Hotel Member** H
(205) 933-9555. **$120-$205.** 1023 20th 35205. Jct University Blvd and 20th St S, 0.3 mi s. Int corridors. **Pets:** Accepted.

◆◆ **La Quinta Inn Birmingham/Cahaba Park South** H
(205) 995-9990. **$67-$196.** 513 Cahaba Park Cir 35242. I-459 exit 19 (US 280), 1.2 mi e. Int corridors. **Pets:** Accepted.

◆◆ **Residence Inn by Marriott Birmingham Downtown @ UAB** H
(205) 731-9595. **$110-$203.** 821 20th St S 35205. Jct University Blvd, just s; corner of 8th Ct S. Int corridors. **Pets:** Medium. $100 one-time fee/room. Service with restrictions, crate.

◆◆ **Residence Inn by Marriott Birmingham Inverness** H
(205) 991-8686. **$86-$159.** 3 Greenhill Pkwy 35242. I-459 exit 19 (US 280), 2 mi e. Ext corridors. **Pets:** Accepted.

◆◆ **Sheraton Birmingham Hotel** H
(205) 324-5000. **Call for rates.** 2101 Richard Arrington Jr Blvd N 35203. I-20/59 exit 22nd St, just n. Int corridors. **Pets:** Accepted.

◆◆◆ **The Westin Birmingham** H
(205) 307-3600. **Call for rates.** 2221 Richard Arrington Jr Blvd N 35203. I-20/59 exit 125 westbound; exit 125A eastbound. Int corridors. **Pets:** Accepted.

CALERA
◆◆ **Quality Inn** H
(205) 668-3641. **$86-$96.** 357 Hwy 304 35040. I-65 exit 231, just se. Ext corridors. **Pets:** Other species. $20 daily fee/room. Service with restrictions, supervision.

CLANTON

AAA ♦♦♦ **Best Western Inn** H
(205) 280-1006. **$80-$120.** 801 Bradberry Ln 35046. I-65 exit 205, 0.5 mi e. Ext corridors. **Pets:** Small, dogs only. $10 daily fee/pet. Designated rooms, service with restrictions, supervision.
⟦SAVE⟧ ⟦⟧ ⟦⟧ ⟦⟧ ⟦⟧

CULLMAN *(Restaurants p. 593)*

AAA ♦♦♦ **Best Western Fairwinds Inn** M
(256) 737-5009. **$80-$90.** 1917 Commerce Ave NW 35055. I-65 exit 310, just e. Ext corridors. **Pets:** Dogs only. $10 daily fee/pet. Designated rooms, service with restrictions, crate. ⟦SAVE⟧ ⟦⟧ ⟦⟧ ⟦⟧ ⟦⟧

♦♦ **Sleep Inn & Suites** H
(256) 734-6166. **$85-$160.** 2050 Old Hwy 157 35057. I-65 exit 310, just ne. Int corridors. **Pets:** Accepted. ⟦⟧ ⟦⟧ ⟦⟧ ⟦⟧

DAPHNE

♦♦♦♦ **Hampton Inn Mobile-East Bay Daphne** H
(251) 626-2220. **$99-$229.** 29451 US Hwy 98 36526. I-10 exit 35A eastbound; exit 35 westbound, just s. Int corridors. **Pets:** Accepted.
⟦⟧ ⟦⟧ ⟦⟧ ⟦⟧ ⟦⟧

♦♦♦♦ **Hilton Garden Inn** H
(251) 625-0020. **$129-$189.** 29546 N Main St 36526. I-10 exit 35B eastbound; exit 35 westbound, just s. Int corridors. **Pets:** Accepted.
⟦⟧ ⟦⟧ ⟦⟧ ⟦⟧ ⟦⟧ ⟦⟧

♦♦♦♦ **Homewood Suites by Hilton Mobile East Bay/Daphne** H
(251) 621-0100. **$149-$289.** 29474 N Main St 36526. I-10 exit 35A eastbound; exit 35 westbound, just s. Int corridors. **Pets:** Accepted.
⟦⟧ ⟦⟧ ⟦⟧ ⟦⟧ ⟦⟧

DECATUR *(Restaurants p. 593)*

AAA ♦♦ **Best Western River City Hotel** H
(256) 301-1006. **$90-$110.** 1305 Front Ave SW 35603. I-65 exit 334, 8 mi nw. Int corridors. **Pets:** Accepted.
⟦SAVE⟧ ⟦⟧ ⟦⟧ ⟦⟧ ⟦⟧ ⟦⟧

♦♦♦ **Microtel Inn & Suites by Wyndham** H
(256) 301-9995. **$59-$90, 3 day notice.** 2226 Beltline Rd SW (SR 67) 35601. SR 67, 4 mi w of jct US 31. Int corridors. **Pets:** Accepted.
⟦⟧ ⟦⟧ ⟦⟧ ⟦⟧ ⟦⟧ ⟦⟧

♦♦ **Quality Inn** H
(256) 355-2229. **$64-$80.** 2120 Jameson Pl SW 35603. SR 67, 1.6 mi s of jct US 72A; 3.9 mi n of jct US 31. Ext corridors. **Pets:** Accepted.
⟦⟧ ⟦⟧ ⟦⟧ ⟦⟧

DEMOPOLIS

AAA ♦♦♦ **Best Western Plus Two Rivers Hotel & Suites** H
(334) 289-2611. **$99-$110.** 662 US Hwy 80 W 36732. Jct US 43, 0.8 mi w. Int corridors. **Pets:** Accepted. ⟦SAVE⟧ ⟦⟧ ⟦⟧ ⟦⟧ ⟦⟧ ⟦⟧ ⟦⟧

DOTHAN

♦♦♦♦ **Comfort Suites** H
(334) 792-9000. **$89-$129.** 1650 Westgate Pkwy 36303. 0.7 mi n of jct US 231 and 431, just e. Int corridors. **Pets:** Medium. $45 one-time fee/room. Service with restrictions, crate. ⟦⟧ ⟦⟧ ⟦⟧ ⟦⟧ ⟦⟧ ⟦⟧

♦♦♦ **La Quinta Inn & Suites-Dothan** H
(334) 793-9090. **$79-$159.** 3593 Ross Clark Cir 36303. Just w of jct US 231; northwest end of town. Int corridors. **Pets:** Accepted.
⟦⟧ ⟦⟧ ⟦⟧ ⟦⟧ ⟦⟧

AAA ♦♦♦ **Residence Inn by Marriott Dothan** H
(334) 793-1030. **$113-$186.** 186 Hospitality Ln 36303. On US 231, 1.7 mi n of Ross Clark Cir Bypass. Int corridors. **Pets:** Accepted.
⟦SAVE⟧ ⟦⟧ ⟦⟧ ⟦⟧ ⟦⟧ ⟦⟧

ENTERPRISE

AAA ♦♦♦ **Americas Best Value Inn & Suites** M
(334) 348-2378. **$60-$70.** 101 Access Dr 36330. Jct US 84 and SR 167, 0.5 mi w. Ext corridors. **Pets:** $15 daily fee/pet. Designated rooms, no service, supervision. ⟦SAVE⟧ ⟦⟧ ⟦⟧ ⟦⟧ ⟦⟧ ⟦⟧

EVERGREEN

♦♦♦ **Econo Lodge Inn & Suites** M
(251) 578-2100. **$64-$129.** 215 Hwy 83 36401. I-65 exit 96, just w. Ext corridors. **Pets:** Accepted. ⟦⟧ ⟦⟧ ⟦⟧

♦♦♦ **Sleep Inn & Suites** H
(251) 578-9590. **$89-$113.** 78 Liberty Hill Pl 36401. I-65 exit 96, just ne. Int corridors. **Pets:** Accepted. ⟦⟧ ⟦⟧ ⟦⟧ ⟦⟧ ⟦⟧ ⟦⟧

FLORENCE

AAA ♦♦♦♦ **Marriott Shoals Hotel & Spa** H
(256) 246-3600. **$123-$209.** 10 Hightower Pl 35630. Jct US 43/72 and SR 133 (Cox Creek Pkwy S), 1.5 mi s; just n of Wilson Dam. Int corridors. **Pets:** Dogs only. $75 one-time fee/pet. Designated rooms, service with restrictions, crate. ⟦SAVE⟧ ⟦⟧ ⟦⟧ ⟦⟧ ⟦⟧ ⟦⟧ ⟦⟧ ⟦⟧

FORT PAYNE

♦♦ **Days Inn** M
(256) 845-2085. **$66-$99, 3 day notice.** 1416 Glenn Blvd SW 35968. I-59 exit 218, just w. Ext corridors. **Pets:** Accepted. ⟦⟧ ⟦⟧ ⟦⟧ ⟦⟧

♦♦ **Quality Inn Fort Payne** H
(256) 845-2950. **$75-$136.** 102 Drinkard Dr NW 35967. I-59 exit 222, 1 mi se, then n on Gault Ave NW. Int corridors. **Pets:** Large, dogs only. $10 daily fee/pet. Designated rooms, service with restrictions, supervision. ⟦⟧ ⟦⟧ ⟦⟧

FULTONDALE

AAA ♦♦♦ **Holiday Inn Express & Suites Birmingham-Fultondale** H
(205) 439-6300. **Call for rates.** 1733 Fulton Rd 35068. I-65 exit 267, just e. Int corridors. **Pets:** Accepted. ⟦SAVE⟧ ⟦⟧ ⟦⟧ ⟦⟧ ⟦⟧ ⟦⟧

GADSDEN

♦♦♦ **Comfort Suites of Gadsden** H
(256) 538-5770. **$89-$190.** 96 Walker St 35904. I-59 exit 181, just n. Int corridors. **Pets:** Accepted. ⟦⟧ ⟦⟧ ⟦⟧ ⟦⟧ ⟦⟧

GENEVA

♦♦ **Briarwood Inn of Geneva** M
(334) 684-7715. **Call for rates.** 1503 W Magnolia Ave 36340. On SR 52, 0.3 mi w of jct SR 196. Ext corridors. **Pets:** Small, dogs only. $20 daily fee/pet. Designated rooms, service with restrictions, supervision.
⟦⟧ ⟦⟧ ⟦⟧ ⟦⟧ ⟦⟧

GREENVILLE

AAA ♦♦ **Best Western Inn** M
(334) 382-9200. **$65-$150.** 56 Cahaba Rd 36037. I-65 exit 130, just n on SR 185. Ext corridors. **Pets:** Very small. $20 daily fee/pet. Designated rooms, no service, supervision. ⟦SAVE⟧ ⟦⟧ ⟦⟧ ⟦⟧ ⟦⟧

♦♦ **Comfort Inn** H
(334) 383-9595. **$79-$194.** 1029 Fort Dale Rd 36037. I-65 exit 130, just n on SR 185. Int corridors. **Pets:** Accepted. ⟦⟧ ⟦⟧ ⟦⟧ ⟦⟧ ⟦⟧

GULF SHORES

▼▼▼ Staybridge Suites-Gulf Shores 🅷
(251) 975-1030. **Call for rates.** 3947 Gulf Shores Pkwy 36542. On SR
59, 3.1 mi n of jct SR 180. Int corridors. **Pets:** Accepted.
🔣 🛁 🛜 ✕ 🔋 💻

GUNTERSVILLE

▼▼▼ Wyndham Garden Lake Guntersville 🅷
(256) 582-2220. **$90-$110.** 2140 Gunter Ave 35976. Jct US 431 (Gunter
Ave) and SR 79. Ext corridors. **Pets:** $20 daily fee/room. Service with
restrictions, crate. 🍴 🔣 🛁 ✕ 🛜 ✕ 🔋 💻

HOMEWOOD *(Restaurants p. 593)*

⟨⟨⟨⟩ ▼▼▼ Aloft Birmingham Soho Square 🅷
(205) 874-8055. **$149-$224.** 1903 29th Ave S 35209. I-59/20 exit 126A,
3.5 mi s on US 31, then just w; corner of 19th St S; jct Montgomery
Pkwy and Oxmoor Rd/Hollywood Blvd, just w; downtown. Int corridors.
Pets: Accepted. 🅂🄰🅅🄴 🍴 🔣 🛁 🛜 ✕ 🔋 💻

⟨⟨⟨⟩ ▼▼▼ Best Western Plus Carlton Suites 🅷
(205) 940-9990. **$90-$170.** 140 State Farm Pkwy 35209. I-65 exit 255,
just w to Wildwood Pkwy, then just n. Int corridors. **Pets:** Accepted.
🅂🄰🅅🄴 🔣 🛁 🛜 ✕ 🔋 💻

▼▼▼ Candlewood Suites Birmingham-Homewood 🅷
(205) 769-9777. **Call for rates.** 400 Commons Dr 35209. I-65 exit 255,
0.7 mi w to John Carroll intersection, then s along frontage road. Int
corridors. **Pets:** Accepted. 🔣 🛜 ✕ 🔋 💻

▼▼▼ Drury Inn & Suites-Birmingham Southwest 🅷
(205) 940-9500. **$99-$184.** 160 State Farm Pkwy 35209. I-65 exit 255,
0.5 mi on northwest frontage road. Int corridors. **Pets:** Accepted.
🍴 🔣 🛁 🛜 ✕ 🔋 💻

⟨⟨⟨⟩ ▼▼▼ Residence Inn by Marriott Birmingham
Homewood 🅷
(205) 943-0044. **$101-$179.** 50 State Farm Pkwy 35209. I-65 exit 255,
just e on Lakeshore Pkwy, just n on Wildwood Pkwy, then 0.8 mi along
frontage road. Int corridors. **Pets:** Accepted.
🅂🄰🅅🄴 🔣 🛁 🛜 ✕ 🔋 💻

▼▼▼ TownePlace Suites by Marriott Birmingham
Homewood 🅷
(205) 943-0114. **$84-$122.** 500 Wildwood Cir N 35209. I-65 exit 255,
0.6 mi w, then just n. Int corridors. **Pets:** Accepted.
🄴🄲🄾 🔣 🛁 🛜 ✕ 🔋 💻

HOOVER

⟨⟨⟨⟩ ▼▼▼ Days Inn at the Galleria 🅷
(205) 985-7500. **$69-$119.** 1800 Riverchase Dr 35244. I-459 exit 13,
0.5 mi s on US 31, then 0.4 mi w on SR 150. Ext corridors.
Pets: Medium, other species. $25 daily fee/pet. Service with restrictions,
crate. 🅂🄰🅅🄴 🛁 🛜 🔋 💻

▼▼▼ Homewood Suites Birmingham-SW/Riverchase
Galleria 🅷
(205) 637-2900. **$109-$289.** 121 Riverchase Pkwy E 35244. I-65 exit
247, just sw on Valleydale Rd, then just n. Int corridors.
Pets: Accepted. 🍴 🔣 🛁 🛜 ✕ 🔋 💻

▼▼▼ Homewood Suites by Hilton-Birmingham
South 🅷
(205) 995-9823. **$109-$189.** 215 Inverness Center Dr 35242. I-459 exit
19 (US 280), 1.8 mi e, then just s. Int corridors. **Pets:** Accepted.
🔣 🛁 🛜 ✕ 🔋 💻

⟨⟨⟨⟩ ▼▼▼ Hyatt Place Birmingham/Hoover 🅷
(205) 988-8444. **$79-$169.** 2980 John Hawkins Pkwy 35244. I-459 exit
13, 0.5 mi s on US 31, then 0.8 mi w on SR 150. Int corridors.
Pets: Accepted. 🅂🄰🅅🄴 🔣 🛁 🛜 ✕ 🔋 💻

⟨⟨⟨⟩ ▼▼▼ Hyatt Place Birmingham/Inverness 🅷
(205) 995-9242. **$89-$209.** 4686 US Hwy 280 E 35242. I-459 exit 19
(US 280), 1.7 mi e, then just s to Inverness Pkwy. Int corridors.
Pets: Accepted. 🅂🄰🅅🄴 🍴 🔣 🛁 🛜 ✕ 🔋 💻

⟨⟨⟨⟩ ▼▼▼ Hyatt Regency Birmingham-The Wynfrey
Hotel 🅷
(205) 705-1234. **$99-$349.** 1000 Riverchase Galleria 35244. I-459 exit
13, just s. Int corridors. **Pets:** Accepted.
🅂🄰🅅🄴 🍴 🔣 🛁 🛰 ✕ 🔋 💻

▼▼▼ La Quinta Inn & Suites Birmingham Hoover 🅷
(205) 403-0096. **$67-$207.** 120 Riverchase Pkwy E 35244. I-65 exit
247, just sw on Valleydale Rd, then just n. Int corridors.
Pets: Accepted. 🔣 🛁 🛜 ✕ 🔋 💻

▼▼▼ Residence Inn by Marriott
Birmingham/Hoover 🅷
(205) 733-1655. **$104-$177.** 2725 John Hawkins Pkwy 35244. I-459 exit
13A (Galleria Blvd/SR 150), 0.5 mi se to SR 150, then 1.5 mi s. Int
corridors. **Pets:** Accepted. 🔣 🛁 🛜 ✕ 🔋 💻

HUNTSVILLE *(Restaurants p. 593)*

▼▼ Extended Stay America Huntsville-U.S. Space and
Rocket Center 🅷
(256) 830-9110. **$60-$70.** 4751 Governors House Dr 35805. I-565 exit
17A, just s, then 0.5 mi w. Ext corridors. **Pets:** Accepted.
🔣 🛜 🔋

▼▼▼ Home2 Suites by Hilton 🅷 🐾
(256) 971-1667. **$99-$149.** 7010 Cabela Dr 35806. I-565 exit 14, 0.6 mi
n, 0.3 mi w, then 0.3 mi s. Int corridors. **Pets:** Other species. $75 one-
time fee/room. Service with restrictions, crate.
🍴 🔣 🛜 ✕ 🔋 💻

▼▼▼ La Quinta Inn Huntsville (Research Park) 🅷
(256) 830-2070. **$67-$103.** 4870 University Dr NW 35816. I-565 exit
14B, 2.6 mi n on SR 255 (Research Park Blvd), then 1.1 mi e on US
72. Ext/int corridors. **Pets:** Accepted. 🛁 🛜 🔋 💻

⟨⟨⟨⟩ ▼▼▼ Microtel Inn & Suites by Wyndham Huntsville 🅷
(256) 859-6655. **$59-$75.** 1820 Chase Creek Row 35811. Jct US 72
and Shields Rd, just n, just w. Int corridors. **Pets:** Other species. $15
one-time fee/pet. Designated rooms, service with restrictions, supervision. 🔣 🛁 🛜 🔋 💻

▼▼▼ Quality Inn & Suites 🅷
(256) 837-7412. **$75-$121.** 6200 Torok Cir 35806. I-565 exit 14B, 2.6
mi n on SR 255 (Research Park Blvd), then 0.6 mi w on US 72. Int
corridors. **Pets:** Accepted. 🔣 🛁 🛜 ✕ 🔋 💻

▼▼▼ TownePlace Suites by Marriott Huntsville 🅷
(256) 971-5277. **$84-$133.** 1125 McMurtrie Dr 35806. I-565 exit 14B,
2.6 mi n on SR 255 (Research Park Blvd), 0.8 mi w on US 72, then
just s. Int corridors. **Pets:** Accepted. 🔣 🛁 🛜 ✕ 🔋 💻

⟨⟨⟨⟩ ▼▼▼▼ The Westin Huntsville 🅷
(256) 428-2000. **Call for rates.** 6800 Governors West NW 35806. I-565
exit 14A, 0.5 mi n on SR 255 (Research Park Blvd), just w on Madison
Pike, then 0.5 mi n. Int corridors. **Pets:** Accepted.
🅂🄰🅅🄴 🍴 🔣 🛁 ✕ 🛜 ✕ 🔋 💻

IRONDALE *(Restaurants p. 593)*

▼▼▼ Holiday Inn Express Hotel & Suites Birmingham
East 🅷
(205) 957-0555. **Call for rates.** 811 Old Grants Mill Rd 35210. I-20 exit
133, just s on Kilgore Memorial Hwy. Int corridors. **Pets:** Accepted.
🍴 🔣 🛁 🛜 ✕ 🔋 💻

LEEDS

AAA ▼▼▼ **Best Western Plus Bass Hotel & Suites** H
(205) 640-5300. **$77-$90.** 1949 Village Dr 35094. I-20 exit 144A westbound; exit 144B eastbound, just ne. Int corridors. **Pets:** Accepted.
SAVE 🏷 🏊 📶 🛗 💳

LUVERNE

▼▼ **Rutledge Inn** H
(334) 335-3050. **$65-$75.** 1701 Montgomery Hwy 36049. Jct US 331 and SR 10. Int corridors. **Pets:** Other species. $20 one-time fee/room.
🏷 🏊 📶 🛗 💳

MADISON

AAA ▼▼▼ **Best Western Plus Madison-Huntsville Hotel** H
(256) 772-7170. **$79-$139.** 9035 Madison Blvd 35758. I-565 exit 9, just nw. Ext/int corridors. **Pets:** Accepted.
SAVE 🍴 🏷 🏊 📶 🛗 💳

◆◆◆ **Country Inn & Suites By Carlson/Huntsville Airport** H
(256) 325-0007. **$75-$200.** 101 Westchester Dr 35758. I-565 exit 9, just n to jct Madison Blvd and SR 20, then just w. Int corridors. **Pets:** Large. $15 daily fee/pet. Designated rooms, no service, supervision. 🏷 🏊 📶 ✖ 🛗 💳

MOBILE *(Restaurants p. 593)*

◆◆◆ **Candlewood Suites Downtown** H
(251) 690-7818. **Call for rates.** 121 N Royal St 36602. Corner of St. Louis St; downtown; parking and rear entrance on St. Joseph St. Int corridors. **Pets:** Accepted. 🏷 🏊 📶 ✖ 🛗 💳

▼▼▼ **Drury Inn-Mobile** H
(251) 344-7700. **$89-$129.** 824 W I-65 Service Rd S 36609. I-65 exit 3 (Airport Blvd), just w, then just s. Int corridors. **Pets:** Accepted.
🏷 🏊 📶 ✖ 🛗 💳

AAA ▼▼▼ **Holiday Inn Mobile West I-10** H
(251) 666-5600. **$85-$169.** 5465 Hwy 90 W 36619. I-10 exit 15B, just e on US 90, then just s on Coca Cola Rd. Int corridors. **Pets:** Service with restrictions, supervision. SAVE 🍴 🏊 📶 ✖ 🛗 💳

▼▼▼ **Homewood Suites Mobile I-65/Airport Blvd** H
(251) 304-1142. **$109-$189.** 1388 W I-65 Service Rd S 36609. I-65 exit 3 southbound, 1.1 mi s; exit 1 northbound, just n on w frontage road. Int corridors. **Pets:** Accepted. 🏷 📶 ✖ 🛗 💳

AAA ▼▼▼ ▼▼ **Renaissance-The Battle House Mobile Hotel & Spa** H 🐾
(251) 338-2000. **$141-$208.** 26 N Royal St 36602. I-10 exit 26B (Water St) eastbound, just w on Government St, then just n. Int corridors. **Pets:** Other species. $75 one-time fee/room. Service with restrictions. SAVE 🍴 🏷 🏊 ✖ 📶 ✖ 🛗 💳

◆◆ **Residence Inn by Marriott Mobile** H
(251) 304-0570. **$107-$181.** 950 W I-65 Service Rd S 36609. I-65 exit 3 (Airport Blvd), just w, then 0.4 mi s. Int corridors. **Pets:** Accepted.
🏷 🏊 📶 ✖ 🛗 💳

▼▼▼ **TownePlace Suites by Marriott Mobile** H
(251) 345-9588. **$94-$150.** 1075 Montlimar Dr 36609. I-65 exit 3 (Airport Blvd), 0.5 mi w, then 0.5 mi s. Int corridors. **Pets:** Other species. $85 one-time fee/room. Service with restrictions.
🏊 📶 ✖ 🛗 💳

MONROEVILLE

AAA ▼▼ ▼▼ **Best Western Inn** M
(251) 575-9999. **$81-$90.** 4419 S Alabama Ave 36460. On SR 21, 0.5 mi n of jct US 84. Ext corridors. **Pets:** Medium. $10 daily fee/room. Service with restrictions, crate. SAVE 🍴 🏊 📶 🛗 💳

◆◆ **Mockingbird Inn & Suites** M
(251) 743-3297. **Call for rates.** 4389 S Alabama Ave 36460. On SR 21, 0.5 mi n of jct US 84. Ext corridors. **Pets:** Medium. $10 daily fee/room. Service with restrictions, crate. 🍴 🏊 📶 🛗 💳

MONTGOMERY *(Restaurants p. 593)*

▼▼ **Baymont Inn & Suites** M
(334) 277-4442. **$49-$70.** 5837 Monticello Dr 36117. I-85 exit 6, just n, then just e. Ext corridors. **Pets:** Accepted. 🏊 📶 🛗 💳

▼▼ **Baymont Inn & Suites Montgomery South** H
(334) 288-8844. **$54-$64.** 4273 Troy Hwy 36116. 1 mi s of jct US 80 and 231 (Troy Hwy). Int corridors. **Pets:** Accepted.
🍴 🏷 🏊 📶 ✖ 🛗 💳

▼▼▼ **Candlewood Suites at EastChase** H
(334) 277-0677. **Call for rates.** 9151 Boyd Cooper Pkwy 36117. I-85 exit 11, just sw. Int corridors. **Pets:** Accepted. 🏷 📶 ✖ 🛗 💳

▼▼▼ **Drury Inn & Suites-Montgomery** H
(334) 273-1101. **$94-$139.** 1124 Eastern Blvd 36117. I-85 exit 6, just n. Int corridors. **Pets:** Accepted. 🏷 🏊 📶 🛗 💳

◆◆ **Embassy Suites by Hilton Montgomery-Hotel & Conference Center** H
(334) 269-5055. **$164-$194.** 300 Tallapoosa St 36104. Between Molton and Commerce sts; downtown. Int corridors. **Pets:** Accepted.
🍴 🏷 🏊 🏊 ✖ 🛗 💳

AAA ◆◆ **Homewood Suites by Hilton** H
(334) 272-3010. **$89-$289.** 1800 Interstate Park Dr 36109. I-85 exit 4, just n on Perry Hill Rd, then just e. Int corridors. **Pets:** $75 one-time fee/room. Service with restrictions, supervision.
SAVE 🍴 🏷 🏊 📶 🛗 💳

AAA ◆◆ **Microtel Inn & Suites by Wyndham Montgomery** H
(334) 649-4465. **$60-$100.** 100 Gibbons Dr 36117. I-85 exit 11, just nw. Int corridors. **Pets:** Medium. $10 daily fee/pet. Service with restrictions, crate. SAVE 🍴 🏷 📶 🛗 💳

▼▼ **Quality Inn Airport South** H
(334) 280-0306. **$80-$85.** 7731 Slade Plaza Blvd 36105. I-65 exit 164, just s. Int corridors. **Pets:** Accepted. 🏷 🏊 📶 🛗 💳

AAA ◆◆ **Residence Inn by Marriott Montgomery** H
(334) 270-3300. **$112-$179.** 1200 Hilmar Ct 36117. I-85 exit 6, just s on Eastern Blvd, then just e. Ext corridors. **Pets:** Accepted.
SAVE 🍴 🏊 📶 ✖ 🛗 💳

▼▼▼ **Sleep Inn & Suites** H
(334) 387-1004. **$75-$170.** 5005 Carmichael Rd 36106. I-85 exit 6, just s. Int corridors. **Pets:** Accepted. 🏷 🏊 📶 🛗 💳

▼▼▼ **Staybridge Suites-EastChase** H
(334) 277-9383. **$134-$169, 3 day notice.** 7800 EastChase Pkwy 36117. I-85 exit 9 (Taylor Rd), just s, then 1 mi e; in The Shoppes of EastChase. Int corridors. **Pets:** Accepted. 🏷 🏊 📶 🛗 💳

OPELIKA

▼▼▼ **Holiday Inn Express & Suites** H
(334) 749-5250. **Call for rates.** 1801 Capps Landing 36804. I-85 exit 58, just e, then just s. Int corridors. **Pets:** Accepted.
🏷 📶 ✖ 🛗 💳

OXFORD

▼▼▼ **Hampton Inn & Suites** H
(256) 831-8958. **$104-$154.** 210 Colonial Dr 36203. I-20 exit 188, just n, then w. Int corridors. **Pets:** Accepted. 🏷 🏊 📶 ✖ 🛗 💳

▼▼▼ Holiday Inn Express & Suites
Anniston/Oxford H
(256) 835-8768. Call for rates. 160 Colonial Dr 36203. I-20 exit 188, just n, then w. Int corridors. Pets: Accepted.
🚭♿M ⤳ 📶 ✕ 🔒 💻

OZARK
♦♦♦ ▼♦ Baymont Inn & Suites Ozark M
(334) 774-0233. $59-$70. 1360 US Hwy 231 S 36360. 0.3 mi s of jct SR 249. Ext corridors. Pets: Accepted.
SAVE 🍽 ♿M ⤳ 📶 🔒 💻

♦♦♦ ▼▼▼ Microtel Inn & Suites by Wyndham
Ozark H
(334) 774-2771. $65-$79. 1140 US Hwy 231 N 36360. Jct SR 27, 1 mi n. Int corridors. Pets: $15 daily fee/pet. Service with restrictions, supervision. SAVE 🍽 ⤳ 📶 ✕ 🔒 💻

PRATTVILLE (Restaurants p. 593)
▼▼ Baymont Inn & Suites Prattville H
(334) 361-6463. $59-$74. 104 Jameson Ct 36067. I-65 exit 179, 1.4 mi w. Ext corridors. Pets: Accepted. ⤳ 📶 🔒 💻

▼♦♦♦ La Quinta Inn & Suites H
(334) 358-5454. $86-$196. 261 Interstate Commercial Park Loop 36066. I-65 exit 181, just w. Int corridors. Pets: Accepted.
♿M ⤳ 📶 ✕ 🔒 💻

▼▼ Quality Inn H
(334) 365-6003. $74-$114. 797 Business Park Dr 36067. I-65 exit 181, just w, then just n. Int corridors. Pets: Medium. $10 daily fee/pet. Designated rooms, service with restrictions, supervision.
⤳ 📶 🔒 💻

PRICEVILLE
▼▼ Comfort Inn H
(256) 355-1037. $80-$149. 3239 Point Mallard Pkwy 35603. I-65 exit 334, just w. Int corridors. Pets: Accepted. ⤳ 📶 ✕ 🔒 💻

SARALAND
▼▼ Microtel Inn & Suites by Wyndham Saraland/North
Mobile H
(251) 675-5045. $70-$90. 1124 Shelton Beach Rd 36571. I-65 exit 13, just e, then just n. Int corridors. Pets: Medium, other species. $50 deposit/room, $25 one-time fee/room. Designated rooms, service with restrictions, crate. ♿M 📶 🔒 💻

SCOTTSBORO
▼▼▼ Comfort Inn & Suites H
(256) 259-8700. $80-$159. 25775 John T Reid Pkwy 35768. Jct US 72 and SR 35/279, 1.2 mi ne, just e on CR 33. Int corridors. Pets: Small, other species. $20 one-time fee/pet. Designated rooms, service with restrictions, supervision. ♿M ⤳ 📶 ✕ 🔒 💻

▼▼ Quality Inn H
(256) 574-6666. $55-$90. 208 Micah Way 35769. On US 72, just s of jct SR 35. Ext corridors. Pets: Accepted. ⤳ 📶 🔒 💻

SYLACAUGA
▼▼ Quality Inn M
(256) 245-4141. $79-$159. 89 Gene Stewart Blvd 35151. Jct US 280, just s. Ext corridors. Pets: Accepted. ⤳ 📶 🔒 💻

TUSCALOOSA (Restaurants p. 593)
♦♦♦ ▼▼▼ Best Western Park Plaza Motor Inn H
(205) 556-9690. $95-$140. 3801 McFarland Blvd 35405. I-59/20 exit 73, just ne on US 82. Ext corridors. Pets: Accepted.
SAVE ⤳ 📶 🔒 💻

▼▼ Centerstone Inn H
(205) 556-3232. Call for rates. 4700 Doris Pate Dr 35405. I-59/20 exit 76, just n. Int corridors. Pets: Accepted. ⤳ 📶 ✕ 🔒 💻

▼▼ Microtel Inn & Suites by Wyndham
Tuscaloosa H
(205) 553-4095. $70-$390. 1417 Veterans Memorial Pkwy 35404. I-59/20 exit 73, 1.8 mi n on US 82 W, then 0.5 mi e. Int corridors.
Pets: Accepted. 📶 ✕ 🔒 💻

▼▼▼ Wingate by Wyndham Tuscaloosa H
(205) 553-5400. $79-$289. 4918 Skyland Blvd E 35405. I-59/20 exit 76, just n. Int corridors. Pets: Accepted. ♿M ⤳ 📶 🔒 💻

TUSCUMBIA
▼▼ Microtel Inn & Suites by Wyndham Tuscumbia/
Muscle Shoals H
(256) 248-0055. $62-$95. 1852 Hwy 72 E 35674. Just w of jct US 72 and 43. Int corridors. Pets: Accepted.
🍽 ♿M ⤳ 📶 ✕ 🔒 💻

VANCE
▼▼ Greystone Inn & Suites H
(205) 556-3606. Call for rates. 11170 Will Walker Rd 35490. I-59/20 exit 89 northbound, 0.8 mi n on Mercedes Dr, 0.3 mi w, then just s; exit southbound, just s. Int corridors. Pets: Accepted.
🍽 ♿M 📶 ✕ 🔒 💻

ALASKA

ANCHORAGE
▼▼▼ Home2 Suites by Hilton Anchorage Midtown H
(907) 561-5618. $109-$339. 4700 Union Square Dr 99503. SR 1 (Seward Hwy) exit Tudor Rd, 0.8 mi w, U-turn at C St, then just s on Union Square Dr. Int corridors. Pets: Accepted.
♿M 📶 ✕ 🔒 💻

▼▼▼ The Lakefront Anchorage H 🐾
(907) 243-2300. Call for rates. 4800 Spenard Rd 99517. Jct International Airport Rd, just n. Int corridors. Pets: $30 daily fee/pet. Designated rooms, service with restrictions, supervision.
🍽 ♿M 📶 ✕ 🔒 💻

▼▼ My Place Hotel Anchorage Midtown H
(907) 929-3500. $165-$175. 729 E 40th Ave 99503. Jct Old Seward Hwy (SR 1) and E 40th Ave. Int corridors. Pets: Accepted.
🍽 ♿M 📶 ✕ 🔒 💻

▼▼▼ Residence Inn by Marriott H 🐾
(907) 563-9844. $136-$265. 1025 E 35th Ave 99508. Corner of SR 1 (Seward Hwy) and 36th Ave. Int corridors. Pets: $100 one-time fee/room. Service with restrictions, supervision.
♿M ⤳ 📶 ✕ 🔒 💻

WWWW **Sheraton Anchorage Hotel & Spa** H
(907) 276-8700. **$159-$449.** 401 E 6th Ave 99501. Jct 6th Ave and Denali St. Int corridors. **Pets:** Accepted. SAVE ▯▯ ⊛ ⊠ ▤ �(▯

WWW **TownePlace Suites by Marriott Anchorage Midtown** H
(907) 334-8000. **$110-$294.** 600 E 32nd Ave 99503. Just e of Denali and E 32nd Ave. Int corridors. **Pets:** Accepted.
⌖▯ ⊛ ⊠ ▤ ▯

WWW **The Voyager Inn** H
(907) 277-9501. **Call for rates.** 501 K St 99501. At K St and 5th Ave. Int corridors. **Pets:** Accepted. SAVE ⊛ ⊠ ▤ ▯

CANTWELL

W **Backwoods Lodge** M
(907) 987-0960. **Call for rates.** Denali Hwy MP 133.8 99729. SR 3 (Denali Hwy), just e of jct SR 8 (George Parks Hwy). Ext corridors.
Pets: Accepted. ▯▯ ⊛ ⊠ ▯(▤ ▯

FAIRBANKS

WWWW **Pike's Waterfront Lodge** H
(907) 456-4500. **Call for rates.** 1850 Hoselton Dr 99709. Jct Airport Way and Hoselton Dr. Ext/int corridors. **Pets:** Dogs only. $25 daily fee/pet. Designated rooms, service with restrictions, supervision.
SAVE ▯▯ ⊠ ⊛ ⊠ ▤ ▯

HAINES

WW **Aspen Suites Hotel** H
(907) 766-2211. **Call for rates.** 409 Main St 99827. Downtown. Int corridors. **Pets:** Accepted. ⌖▯ ⊛ ⊠ ▤ ▯

WWW W **Captain's Choice Motel** M
(907) 766-3111. **$155.** 108 2nd Ave N 99827. Jct 2nd Ave and Dalton St. Ext corridors. **Pets:** Accepted. SAVE ⊛ ⊠ ▯(▤ ▯

HOMER

WWWW **Best Western Bidarka Inn** H ✿
(907) 235-8148. **$100-$200.** 575 Sterling Hwy 99603. Just n of Pioneer Ave on SR 1 (Sterling Hwy). Ext/int corridors. **Pets:** Large, other species. $15 daily fee/pet. Designated rooms, service with restrictions, supervision. SAVE ▯▯ ⌖▯ ⊛ ▯(▤ ▯

KETCHIKAN

WWWW **Cape Fox Lodge** H
(907) 225-8001. **Call for rates.** 800 Venetia Way 99901. Above Creek St (tramway from Creek St). Ext/int corridors. **Pets:** $15 daily fee/pet. Designated rooms, service with restrictions, crate.
SAVE ▯▯ ⌖▯ ⊛ ⊠ ▯(▤ ▯

WWWW **The Landing Hotel** H ✿
(907) 225-5166. **$164-$270.** 3434 Tongass Ave 99901. Across from Alaska Marine Hwy ferry terminal. Ext/int corridors. **Pets:** Large, other species. $50 deposit/pet, $10 daily fee/pet. Designated rooms, service with restrictions, supervision. SAVE ▯▯ ⌖▯ ⊛ ⊠ ▤ ▯

KODIAK

WWWW **Best Western Kodiak Inn & Convention Center** H
(907) 486-5712. **$106-$235.** 236 W Rezanof Dr 99615. Just w of ferry terminal; downtown. Ext/int corridors. **Pets:** Medium. $35 one-time fee/pet. Designated rooms, service with restrictions, supervision.
SAVE ▯▯ ⌖▯ ⊠ ▯(▤ ▯

MOOSE PASS

W **Trail Lake Lodge** M
(907) 288-3101. **Call for rates.** 33654 Depot Rd 99631. US 9 (Seward Hwy) at MM 29.5. Ext corridors. **Pets:** Accepted. ▯▯ ⊛ ⊠ ▯(

SEWARD

WW **Harbor 360 Hotel** H
(907) 865-6224. **Call for rates.** 1412 4th Ave 99664. Adjacent to Small Boat Harbor. Int corridors. **Pets:** Accepted.
⌖▯ ⊇ ⊛ ⊠ ▤ ▯

WWWW **Hotel Seward** H
(907) 224-8001. **$59-$399, 3 day notice.** 221 5th Ave 99664. Downtown; just n of Alaska SeaLife Center. Int corridors. **Pets:** Medium, dogs only. $25 daily fee/pet. Designated rooms, supervision.
SAVE ▯▯ ⌖▯ ⊠ ⊛ ⊠ ▯(▤ ▯

SITKA

WW **Super 8-Sitka** H
(907) 747-8804. **$139-$172.** 404 Sawmill Creek Rd 99835. Corner of Lake St and Halibut Point Rd/Sawmill Creek Rd, just e. Int corridors.
Pets: Accepted. ▯▯ ⌖▯ ⊛ ▤ ▯

WW **Totem Square Hotel & Marina** H
(907) 747-3693. **Call for rates.** 201 Katlian St 99835. In Totem Square Complex near municipal office. Int corridors. **Pets:** Accepted.
▯▯ ⌖▯ ⊛ ⊠ ▯(▤ ▯

WW **Westmark Sitka** H
(907) 747-6241. **$189-$230.** 330 Seward St 99835. Center. Int corridors.
Pets: Accepted. ▯▯ ⌖▯ ⊛ ⊠ ▯(▤ ▯

SKAGWAY

WW **Westmark Inn Skagway** M
(907) 983-6000. **$119-$199.** 3rd Ave & Spring St 99840. Jct 3rd Ave and Spring St; downtown. Ext/int corridors. **Pets:** Accepted.
▯▯ ⌖▯ ⊛ ⊠ ▯(▤ ▯

TOK

WW **Cleft of the Rock Bed & Breakfast** BB
(907) 883-4219. **$115-$170, 3 day notice.** 0.5 Sundog Tr 99780. Jct SR 1 and 2 (Alaskan Hwy), 2.5 mi w on SR 2 (Alaskan Hwy) to Sundog Tr, 0.5 mi n. Int/int corridors. **Pets:** Accepted.
▯▯ ⊛ ⊠ ▯(▯ ⊘ ▤ ▯

TRAPPER CREEK

WW **Gate Creek Cabins** CA
(907) 733-1393. **$150, 10 day notice.** 21800 Townes Pl 99683. George Parks Hwy (SR 3), Milepost 114, 10.5 mi w at Petersville Rd. Ext corridors. **Pets:** Dogs only. $25 one-time fee/pet. Designated rooms, no service, supervision. ⊠ ⊛ ⊠ ▯(▯ ▤ ▯

W **Trapper Creek Inn & RV Park** M
(907) 733-2302. **Call for rates.** Mile 114.6 Parks Hwy 99683. George Parks Hwy (SR 3), Milepost 114. Ext corridors. **Pets:** Accepted.
▯▯ ⊛ ⊠ ▯(▯ ▤ ▯

VALDEZ

WWW **Best Western Valdez Harbor Inn** H
(907) 835-3434. **$99-$249.** 100 N Harbor Dr 99686. Just s at Meals Ave. Int corridors. **Pets:** Small, dogs only. $250 deposit/room, $10 daily fee/pet. Designated rooms, service with restrictions, supervision.
SAVE ▯▯ ⌖▯ ⊛ ▯(▤ ▯

WASILLA

WWWW **Best Western Lake Lucille Inn** H
(907) 373-1776. **$100-$300.** 1300 W Lake Lucille Dr 99654. SR 3 (George Parks Hwy), just w on Hallea Ln; center. Int corridors.
Pets: $20 daily fee/pet. Service with restrictions, crate.
SAVE ⊠ ⊛ ⊠ ▯(▤ ▯

ARIZONA

AJO

▼ **La Siesta Motel & RV Resort** Ⓜ
(520) 387-6569. **Call for rates.** 2561 N Ajo-Gila Bend Hwy 85321. On SR 85, 1.8 mi n of town plaza. Ext corridors. **Pets:** Accepted.
🏊 🛜 ✖ ⬛ 🖵

AMADO

▼▼▼ **Amado Territory Bed & Breakfast** ⒷⒷ
(520) 398-8684. **Call for rates.** 3001 E Frontage Rd 85645. I-19 exit 48, just e, then just s. Int corridors. **Pets:** Accepted.
🛜 ✖ Ⓦ ⓩ

ANTHEM

▼▼▼ **Hampton Inn Anthem** Ⓗ
(623) 465-7979. **$99-$239.** 42415 N 41st Dr 85086. I-17 exit 229 (Anthem Way), just w. Int corridors. **Pets:** Accepted.
🅟Ⓜ 🏊 🛜 ✖ ⬛ 🖵

APACHE JUNCTION

⒜⒜⒜ ▼ **Apache Junction Motel** Ⓜ
(480) 982-7702. **$49-$89, 3 day notice.** 1680 W Apache Tr 85120. US 60 exit 195, 2 mi n, then just w. Ext corridors. **Pets:** Small, dogs only. $20 one-time fee/pet. Designated rooms, service with restrictions, supervision. 🆂🅰🆅🅴 🛜 ✖ ⬛

BELLEMONT

▼ **Days Inn Bellemont** Ⓗ
(928) 556-9599. **$75-$180.** 12380 I-40 86015. I-40 exit 185, just n. Int corridors. **Pets:** Other species. $15 daily fee/pet. Service with restrictions, supervision. 🅟Ⓜ 🛜 ✖ 🖵

BENSON

⒜⒜⒜ ▼▼▼ **Best Western Quail Hollow Inn** Ⓗ
(520) 586-3646. **$75-$115.** 699 N Ocotillo Rd 85602. I-10 exit 304 (Ocotillo Rd), just s. Ext corridors. **Pets:** Other species. $10 daily fee/pet. Designated rooms. 🆂🅰🆅🅴 🏊 🛜 ⬛ 🖵

BISBEE

▼▼▼ **Audrey's Inn** ⒸⓄ
(520) 227-6120. **Call for rates.** 20 Brewery Ave 85603. Just ne of Main St; in historic district. Int corridors. **Pets:** Accepted. 🛜 ✖ ⬛ 🖵

BULLHEAD CITY

▼▼ **Days Inn Bullhead City Inn** Ⓗ 🐾
(928) 754-3000. **$70-$85.** 1126 Hwy 95 86429. 1.8 mi s of Laughlin Bridge. Ext corridors. **Pets:** Medium, dogs only. $15 daily fee/pet. Designated rooms, service with restrictions, supervision.
🏊 🛜 ⬛ 🖵

▼ **Lake Mohave Marina** Ⓜ
(928) 754-3245. **Call for rates.** 2690 E Katherine Spur Rd 86429. Jct SR 95, 1.5 mi e on SR 68, 1 mi n, then 5.4 mi e; at Katherine Landing; in Lake Mead National Recreation Area. Ext corridors. **Pets:** Medium, other species. $50 deposit/pet, $10 daily fee/pet. Service with restrictions, crate. ✖ 🛜 ⬛ 🖵

CAMERON

⒜⒜⒜ ▼▼▼ **Cameron Trading Post Motel, Restaurant & Gift Shop** Ⓜ
(928) 679-2231. **Call for rates.** 466 N Hwy 89 86020. 1 mi from east gate turn off. Ext corridors. **Pets:** $25 one-time fee/pet. Designated rooms, no service, crate. 🆂🅰🆅🅴 🍽 🛜 ✖ ⬛ 🖵

CAMP VERDE

⒜⒜⒜ ▼▼▼ **The Lodge** Ⓗ
(928) 567-6611. **Call for rates.** 333 Middle Verde Rd 86322. I-17 exit 289, 0.4 mi se. Ext corridors. **Pets:** Accepted.
🆂🅰🆅🅴 🍽 🏊 🛜 ✖ ⬛ 🖵

CAREFREE

▼▼▼▼ **Boulders Resort & Spa, Curio Collection by Hilton** Ⓗ
(480) 488-9009. **$199-$599.** 34631 N Tom Darlington Dr 85377. Jct Scottsdale and Bell rds, 11 mi n. Ext corridors. **Pets:** Accepted.
🍽 🅟Ⓜ 🏊 ✖ 🛜 ✖ ⬛ 🖵

⒜⒜⒜ ▼▼▼ **Carefree Resort & Conference Center** Ⓗ
(480) 488-5300. **Call for rates.** 37220 Mule Train Rd 85377. SR 101 exit 36 (Pima Rd), 12.2 mi n to Cave Creek Rd, 1 mi w, then 0.4 mi n. Ext/int corridors. **Pets:** Accepted.
🆂🅰🆅🅴 🍽 🏊 ✖ 🛜 ✖ ⬛ 🖵

CASA GRANDE

⒜⒜⒜ ▼▼▼ **Holiday Inn Express & Suites Casa Grande** Ⓗ
(520) 509-6333. **$99-$159.** 805 N Cacheries Ct 85122. I-10 exit 194 (SR 287), 0.6 mi w. Int corridors. **Pets:** Accepted.
🆂🅰🆅🅴 🅟Ⓜ 🏊 🛜 ✖ ⬛ 🖵

⒜⒜⒜ ▼▼▼ **Holiday Inn Hotel Casa Grande** Ⓗ
(520) 426-3500. **Call for rates.** 777 N Pinal Ave 85122. I-10 exit 194 (SR 287), 3.9 mi w. Int corridors. **Pets:** Other species. $50 one-time fee/pet. Designated rooms, service with restrictions, supervision.
🆂🅰🆅🅴 🍽 🏊 🛜 ✖ ⬛ 🖵

▼▼▼ **MainStay Suites Casa Grande** Ⓗ
(520) 426-1177. **$50-$100.** 851 N Henness Rd 85222. I-10 exit 194 (SR 287), 1 mi w, then just n. Int corridors. **Pets:** Accepted.
🛜 ✖ ⬛ 🖵

⒜⒜⒜ ▼▼▼ **Quality Inn** Ⓗ
(520) 836-1600. **Call for rates.** 665 N Via del Cielo Rd 85222. I-10 exit 194 (SR 287), 1 mi w. Ext corridors. **Pets:** Accepted.
🆂🅰🆅🅴 🏊 🛜 ✖ ⬛ 🖵

⒜⒜⒜ ▼▼▼ **Super 8** Ⓗ
(520) 836-8800. **$59-$71.** 2066 E Florence Blvd 85222. I-10 exit 194 (SR 287), 0.6 mi w. Int corridors. **Pets:** Accepted.
🆂🅰🆅🅴 🏊 🛜 ⬛ 🖵

CATALINA

▼▼ **Catalina Inn** Ⓗ
(520) 818-9500. **Call for rates.** 15691 N Oracle Rd 85739. 4.6 mi n of Tangerine Rd. Ext/int corridors. **Pets:** Accepted.
🏊 🛜 ✖ ⬛ 🖵

CHANDLER

⒜⒜⒜ ▼▼▼ **Comfort Inn Chandler-Phoenix South** Ⓗ
(480) 857-4969. **$70-$210.** 7400 W Boston St 85226. I-10 exit 160 (Chandler Blvd), just e, then just s on Southgate Dr. Int corridors. **Pets:** Medium, dogs only. $20 daily fee/pet. Designated rooms, service with restrictions, supervision. 🆂🅰🆅🅴 🅟Ⓜ 🏊 🛜 ✖ ⬛ 🖵

⒜⒜⒜ ▼▼▼ **Crowne Plaza San Marcos Golf Resort** Ⓗ
(480) 812-0900. **Call for rates.** 1 N San Marcos Pl 85225. Jct Chandler Blvd, just s on Arizona Ave, then just w on Buffalo St; in historic downtown. Ext corridors. **Pets:** Other species. $25 one-time fee/pet. Service with restrictions, crate. 🆂🅰🆅🅴 🍽 🅟Ⓜ 🏊 ✖ 🛜 ✖ ⬛ 🖵

▼▼ **Hawthorn Suites by Wyndham-Chandler** H
(480) 705-8881. **$75-$150.** 5858 W Chandler Blvd 85226. I-10 exit 160 (Chandler Blvd), 1.5 mi e. Int corridors. **Pets:** Accepted.

▼▼▼ **Hilton Phoenix Chandler** H
(480) 899-7400. **$109-$329.** 2929 W Frye Rd 85224. SR 202 exit 50B (Price Rd), 0.4 mi n, then just e. Int corridors. **Pets:** Accepted.

▼▼▼▼ **Home2 Suites by Hilton Phoenix Chandler** H
(480) 659-2090. **Call for rates.** 249 W Queen Creek Rd 85248. I-10 exit 164 (Queen Creek Rd), 3.8 mi e. Int corridors. **Pets:** Accepted.

▼▼▼ **Homewood Suites by Hilton Phoenix-Chandler** H
(480) 753-6200. **$90-$300.** 7373 W Detroit St 85226. I-10 exit 160 (Chandler Blvd), 0.4 mi e, n on 54th St, then just w. Int corridors. **Pets:** Accepted.

▼▼▼▼ **Homewood Suites by Hilton-Phoenix/Chandler Fashion Center** H
(480) 963-5700. **$99-$299.** 1221 S Spectrum Blvd 85286. SR 202 exit 50B (Price Rd), just s. Int corridors. **Pets:** Accepted.

(AAA) ▼▼▼▼ **Hyatt Place Phoenix Chandler-Fashion Center** H
(480) 812-9600. **$89-$299.** 3535 W Chandler Blvd 85226. I-10 exit 160 (Chandler Blvd), 4 mi e. Int corridors. **Pets:** Medium, dogs only. $75 one-time fee/room. Service with restrictions, crate.

(AAA) ▼▼▼▼ **Radisson Phoenix-Chandler** H
(480) 961-4444. **Call for rates.** 7475 W Chandler Blvd 85226. I-10 exit 160 (Chandler Blvd), just e, then just s on Southgate Dr. Int corridors. **Pets:** Medium, dogs only. $75 one-time fee/room. Service with restrictions.

(AAA) ▼▼▼▼ **Residence Inn by Marriott-Chandler Fashion Center** H
(480) 782-1551. **$100-$209.** 200 N Federal St 85226. I-10 exit 160 (Chandler Blvd), 4.2 mi e, just n on N Metro Blvd, then just e. Int corridors. **Pets:** Accepted.

(AAA) ▼▼▼▼ **Sheraton Grand at Wild Horse Pass** H
(602) 225-0100. **$99-$648, 3 day notice.** 5594 W Wild Horse Pass Blvd 85226. I-10 exit 162, 2.4 mi w. Int corridors. **Pets:** Accepted.

CHINO VALLEY

(AAA) ▼▼▼ **Days Inn Chino Valley** H
(928) 636-0311. **$76-$155.** 688 Fletcher Ct 86323. Center. Int corridors. **Pets:** Dogs only. $10 daily fee/pet. Designated rooms, service with restrictions, supervision.

COTTONWOOD

▼▼▼ **AZ Pines Motel** M 🐾
(928) 634-9975. **$75-$159.** 920 S Camino Real 86326. Jct SR 260, just nw on SR 89A, then just s. Ext corridors. **Pets:** Dogs only. $20 one-time fee/room, $5 daily fee/room. Designated rooms, service with restrictions, supervision.

(AAA) ▼▼▼ **Best Western Cottonwood Inn** H
(928) 634-5575. **$110-$180.** 993 S Main St 86326. On SR 89A, at SR 260. Ext corridors. **Pets:** Small, dogs only. $20 daily fee/pet. Designated rooms, service with restrictions, supervision.

(AAA) ▼▼ **The View Motel** M
(928) 634-7581. **$59-$150.** 818 S Main St 86326. On SR 89A, 0.4 mi nw of jct SR 260. Ext corridors. **Pets:** Accepted.

EAGAR

(AAA) ▼▼▼ **Best Western Sunrise Inn** M
(928) 333-2540. **$103-$165.** 128 N Main St 85925. Jct SR 260, just n; jct US 60, 1.5 mi s. Ext corridors. **Pets:** Accepted.

EHRENBERG

(AAA) ▼▼▼ **Best Western Desert Oasis** H
(928) 923-9711. **$85-$230.** Exit 1 S Frontage Rd 85334. I-10 exit 1, just s; 0.5 mi e of Colorado River. Int corridors. **Pets:** Other species. $10 daily fee/pet. Designated rooms, service with restrictions, supervision.

ELOY

▼▼ **Motel 6 #1263** M
(520) 836-3323. **$45-$69.** 4965 S Sunland Gin Rd 85231. I-10 exit 200, just w. Ext corridors. **Pets:** Accepted.

FLAGSTAFF

(AAA) ▼▼▼ **Best Western Pony Soldier Inn & Suites** H
(928) 526-2388. **$74-$299.** 3030 E Route 66 86004. I-40 exit 201, just n, then 1 mi w. Int corridors. **Pets:** Accepted.

▼▼▼ **Comfort Inn I-17/I-40** H
(928) 774-2225. **$90-$210.** 2355 S Beulah Blvd 86001. I-40 exit 195, just n to Forest Meadows St, then 1 blk w. Int corridors. **Pets:** Accepted.

(AAA) ▼▼▼ **Days Hotel Flagstaff** H
(928) 779-6944. **$56-$255.** 2200 E Butler Ave 86004. I-40 exit 198 (Butler Ave), just n. Int corridors. **Pets:** Accepted.

(AAA) ▼▼▼ **Days Inn & Suites** H
(928) 527-1477. **$63-$250.** 3601 E Lockett Rd 86004. I-40 exit 201, 0.5 mi w on I-40 business loop, then just n on Fanning Dr. Int corridors. **Pets:** $25 one-time fee/room, $5 daily fee/room. Designated rooms, service with restrictions, supervision.

(AAA) ▼▼▼▼ **DoubleTree by Hilton Flagstaff** H
(928) 773-8888. **$129-$229.** 1175 W Route 66 86001. I-40 exit 195, 1.5 mi n on SR 89A (Milton Rd), then 0.5 mi w. Int corridors. **Pets:** Accepted.

▼▼▼▼ **Drury Inn & Suites-Flagstaff** H
(928) 773-4900. **$119-$289.** 300 S Milton Rd 86001. I-40 exit 195, 1.8 mi n on SR 89A (Milton Rd). Int corridors. **Pets:** Accepted.

(AAA) ▼▼▼ **GreenTree Inn Flagstaff** H
(928) 773-1111. **$70-$160.** 2755 S Woodlands Village Blvd 86001. I-40 exit 195, just n to Forest Meadows St, w to Beulah Blvd, just s, then w. Ext corridors. **Pets:** Medium. $15 daily fee/pet. Service with restrictions, crate.

(AAA) ▼▼▼▼ **Sonesta ES Suites Flagstaff** H
(928) 526-5555. **Call for rates.** 1400 N Country Club Dr 86004. I-40 exit 201, 0.5 mi s. Ext/int corridors. **Pets:** Accepted.

▼▼▼▼ **SpringHill Suites by Marriott** H
(928) 774-8042. **$113-$221.** 2455 S Beulah Blvd 86001. I-40 exit 195, just n to Forest Meadows St, then 1 blk w. Int corridors. **Pets:** Accepted.

▼▼▼▼ Starlight Pines, A Bed & Breakfast BB
(928) 527-1912. **$159-$179, 14 day notice.** 3380 E Lockett Rd 86004.
I-40 exit 201, 0.5 mi w on I-40 business loop, then just n. Int corridors.
Pets: Accepted. 🔊 ⊠ 🕷 🗷

▲▲▲ ▼▼◆ Super 8 Flagstaff H
(928) 526-0818. **$50-$320.** 3725 N Kasper Ave 86004. I-40 exit 201,
just n, 0.5 mi w on I-40 business loop, then just n. Int corridors.
Pets: Accepted. SAVE 🔊 ⊠ 🕆 🖵

FLORENCE
▼▼▼▼ GreenTree Inn & Suites Florence H
(520) 868-9900. **Call for rates.** 240 W Hwy 287 85132. Just w of jct
SR 79 and 287. Int corridors. **Pets:** Accepted.
🔁 🔊 ⊠ 🕆 🖵

▼▼▼▼ Rancho Sonora Inn CI
(520) 868-8000. **Call for rates.** 9198 N Hwy 79 85232. 5 mi s of SR
287. Ext corridors. **Pets:** $10 daily fee/pet. Designated rooms, service
with restrictions, crate. 🔁 🔊 ⊠ 🗷 🕆 🖵

FOREST LAKES
▲▲▲ ▼ Forest Lakes Lodge M 🐾
(928) 535-4727. **Call for rates.** 2823 SR 260 85931. Between MM 288
and 289. Ext corridors. **Pets:** Small, other species. $15 one-time fee/
room. Service with restrictions, supervision. SAVE 🍴 🔊 🐾 🕆

FOUNTAIN HILLS
▼◆◆◆ Inn at Eagle Mountain H
(480) 816-3000. **Call for rates.** 9800 N Summer Hill Blvd 85268. Loop
101 exit 41, 7.3 mi e on Shea Blvd, 0.3 mi e on Eagle Mountain Pkwy,
then just w. Ext corridors. **Pets:** Accepted.
🍴 🔁 ⊠ 🔊 ⊠ 🕆 🖵

GILA BEND
▲▲▲ ▼▼◆ Best Western Space Age Lodge M
(928) 683-2273. **$110-$170.** 401 E Pima St 85337. Business Loop I-8;
center. Ext corridors. **Pets:** Accepted.
SAVE 🍴 🔁 🔊 ⊠ 🕆 🖵

GILBERT
▲▲▲ ▼▼▼◆ Hyatt Place Phoenix/Gilbert H
(480) 899-5900. **$69-$229.** 3275 S Market St 85297. Loop 202 exit 42
(Val Vista Dr), just n, then just e. Int corridors. **Pets:** Accepted.
SAVE 🍴 🔊M 🔁 🔊 ⊠ 🕆 🖵

▼▼▼▼ Residence Inn by Marriott Phoenix Gilbert H
(480) 699-4450. **$118-$276.** 3021 E Banner Gateway Dr 85234. US 60
exit 186 (Higley Rd), just s, then just w. Int corridors. **Pets:** Accepted.
🔊M 🔁 🔊 ⊠ 🕆 🖵

GLENDALE
**▼▼▼▼ Comfort Suites Glendale University of Phoenix
     Stadium Area** H
(623) 271-9005. **$109-$459.** 9824 W Camelback Rd 85305. SR 101 exit
5 (Camelback Rd), just w to 99th St, then just n. Int corridors.
Pets: Large. $25 one-time fee/room. Designated rooms, service with
restrictions, crate. 🔊M 🔁 🔊 ⊠ 🕆 🖵

▼▼▼▼ Renaissance Glendale Hotel & Spa H
(623) 937-3700. **$120-$278.** 9495 W Coyotes Blvd 85305. SR 101 exit
7 (Glendale Ave), just e to N 95th Ave, just n, then just e. Int corridors.
Pets: Accepted. 🍴 🔊M 🔁 ⊠ 🔊 ⊠ 🕆 🖵

**▼▼▼▼ Residence Inn by Marriott Phoenix Glendale Sports
     & Entertainment District** H
(623) 772-8900. **$111-$237.** 7350 W Zanjero Blvd 85305. SR 101 exit 7
(Glendale Ave), then e. Int corridors. **Pets:** Accepted.
🔊M 🔁 🔊 ⊠ 🕆 🖵

▼▼▼▼ Staybridge Suites Phoenix/Glendale H
(623) 842-0000. **Call for rates.** 9340 W Cabela Dr 85305. SR 101 exit
7 (Glendale Ave), 0.6 mi e to N Zanjero Blvd, then just n. Int corridors.
Pets: Accepted. 🔊M 🔁 🔊 ⊠ 🕆 🖵

GOODYEAR
▲▲▲ ▼▼◆ Best Western Phoenix Goodyear Inn H
(623) 932-3210. **$80-$210.** 55 N Litchfield Rd 85338. I-10 exit 128, 0.8
mi s. Ext/int corridors. **Pets:** Accepted. SAVE 🔁 🔊 ⊠ 🕆 🖵

▼▼▼▼ Comfort Suites Goodyear H 🐾
(623) 266-2884. **$100-$340.** 15575 W Roosevelt St 85338. I-10 exit
126, just s on Estrella Pkwy, then just n. Int corridors. **Pets:** Large,
other species. $25 one-time fee/pet. Designated rooms, service with
restrictions, supervision. 🔊M 🔁 🔊 ⊠ 🕆 🖵

▼▼▼▼ Hampton Inn & Suites Goodyear H
(623) 536-1313. **$109-$229.** 2000 N Litchfield Rd 85395. I-10 exit 128,
0.5 mi n. Int corridors. **Pets:** Accepted. 🔊M 🔁 🔊 ⊠ 🕆 🖵

▼▼▼▼ Holiday Inn & Suites Goodyear H
(623) 547-1313. **Call for rates.** 1188 N Dysart Rd 85395. I-10 exit 129
(Dysart Rd), just n. Int corridors. **Pets:** Accepted.
🍴 🔊M 🔁 🔊 ⊠ 🕆 🖵

**▼▼◆ Lexington Inn & Suites - Goodyear/West
     Phoenix** H
(623) 535-1313. **Call for rates.** 1313 N Litchfield Rd 85395. I-10 exit
128, just n. Int corridors. **Pets:** Accepted.
🔊M 🔁 🔊 ⊠ 🕆 🖵

▼▼◆ Quality Inn & Suites Goodyear H 🐾
(623) 932-9191. **$80-$190.** 950 N Dysart Rd 85338. I-10 exit 129 (Dysart Rd), just s. Ext corridors. **Pets:** Other species. $20 deposit/pet, $20
daily fee/pet. Service with restrictions, supervision.
🍴 🔁 🔊 🕆 🖵

▼▼▼▼ Residence Inn by Marriott H
(623) 866-1313. **$107-$213.** 2020 N Litchfield Rd 85395. I-10 exit 128,
0.6 mi n. Int corridors. **Pets:** Accepted. 🔊M 🔁 🔊 ⊠ 🕆 🖵

**▼▼▼▼ TownePlace Suites by Marriott
     Phoenix/Goodyear** H
(623) 535-5009. **$83-$202.** 13971 W Celebrate Life Way 85338. I-10
exit 128, just s, then just w. Int corridors. **Pets:** Accepted.
🔊M 🔁 🔊 ⊠ 🕆 🖵

GRAND CANYON NATIONAL PARK - SOUTH RIM
▲▲▲ ▼▼◆ Grand Canyon Plaza Hotel H 🐾
(928) 638-2673. **Call for rates.** 406 Canyon Plaza Ln 86023. On SR
64; 2 mi s of South Rim entrance. Ext/int corridors. **Pets:** $50 one-time
fee/pet. Service with restrictions, crate.
SAVE 🍴 🔊M 🔁 🔊 ⊠ 🕆 🖵

▲▲▲ ▼▼◆ Red Feather Lodge H
(928) 638-2414. **$75-$350.** 300 SR 64 86023. 1 mi s of South Rim
entrance. Ext/int corridors. **Pets:** Other species. $40 deposit/pet, $25
daily fee/pet. Designated rooms, supervision.
SAVE 🍴 🔊M 🔁 🔊 🕆 🖵

▼▼◆ Yavapai Lodge M 🐾
(928) 638-4001. **Call for rates.** South Rim 86023. 1 mi e of Grand
Canyon Village South Rim. Ext/int corridors. **Pets:** $25 one-time fee/pet.
Designated rooms, service with restrictions, supervision.
🍴 🔊M 🔊 ⊠ 🕆 🖵

GREEN VALLEY
▲▲▲ ▼▼▼◆ Best Western Green Valley Inn H
(520) 625-2250. **$84-$149.** 111 S La Canada Dr 85614. I-19 exit 65,
just w, then just s. Int corridors. **Pets:** $20 daily fee/pet. Service with
restrictions, supervision. SAVE 🍴 🔁 🔊 ⊠ 🕆 🖵

AAA ▽▽ Comfort Inn H
(520) 399-3736. **$69-$119.** 90 W Esperanza Blvd 85614. I-19 exit 65, just w. Int corridors. **Pets:** $25 daily fee/pet. Designated rooms, service with restrictions, supervision. [SAVE] ⊇ ◉ ⊠ ⊟ ▣

▽▽ Vagabond Inn Executive H
(520) 625-0900. **Call for rates.** 19200 S I-19 Frontage Rd 85614. I-19 exit 69 (Duval Mine Rd), west side of interstate, then just s. Int corridors. **Pets:** Accepted. ⊇ ◉ ⊠ ⊟ ▣

AAA ▽▽▽ Wyndham Canoa Ranch Resort CO
(520) 382-0450. **$92-$219, 3 day notice.** 5775 S Camino Del Sol 85622. I-19 exit 56 (Canoa Rd), just w, 0.5 mi n on Frontage Rd to Calle Tres, just w, then 1 mi s. Int corridors. **Pets:** Other species. $25 daily fee/pet. Service with restrictions, crate.
[SAVE] ❚❚ ⊇ ⊠ ◉ ⊠ ⊟ ▣

HEBER

AAA ▽▽ Best Western Sawmill Inn H
(928) 535-5053. **$70-$200.** 1877 Hwy 260 85928. 0.5 mi e of center. Ext corridors. **Pets:** Accepted. [SAVE] [ECO] ◉ ⊟ ▣

HOLBROOK

AAA ▽▽ Best Western Arizonian Inn H
(928) 524-2611. **$80-$210.** 2508 Navajo Blvd 86025. I-40 exit 289, 0.5 mi w. Ext corridors. **Pets:** Accepted. [SAVE] ⊇ ◉ ⊠ ⊟ ▣

▽▽ Days Inn M
(928) 524-6949. **$60-$83.** 2601 Navajo Blvd 86025. I-40 exit 289, 0.3 mi w. Ext corridors. **Pets:** Accepted. [ECO] ⊇ ◉ ⊟ ▣

AAA ▽▽▽ Howard Johnson H
(928) 524-2566. **$59-$77.** 2608 E Navajo Blvd 86025. I-40 exit 289, just w. Ext corridors. **Pets:** Accepted. [SAVE] ⊇ ◉ ⊟ ▣

AAA ▽▽▽ Quality Inn H
(928) 524-6131. **$75-$99.** 2602 Navajo Blvd 86025. I-40 exit 289, just w. Ext corridors. **Pets:** Accepted. [SAVE] ⊇ ◉ ⊠ ⊟ ▣

JEROME

▽▽ Connor Hotel of Jerome H
(928) 634-5006. **Call for rates.** 160 S Main St 86331. Center. Int corridors. **Pets:** Accepted. ◉ ⊠ ⊟ ▣

KAYENTA

▽▽▽ Hampton Inn of Kayenta H
(928) 697-3170. **$89-$129.** Hwy 160 86033. Just w of US 163. Int corridors. **Pets:** Medium. Service with restrictions, supervision.
❚❚ ◐M ⊇ ◉ ⊠ ▣

KINGMAN

AAA ▽▽▽ Best Western Plus A Wayfarer's Inn & Suites H
(928) 753-6271. **$110-$149.** 2815 E Andy Devine Ave 86401. I-40 exit 53, 0.5 mi w on Route 66. Ext corridors. **Pets:** Medium, dogs only. $10 one-time fee/room. Supervision. [SAVE] ◐M ⊇ ◉ ⊟ ▣

AAA ▽▽▽ Best Western Plus King's Inn & Suites H ❁
(928) 753-6101. **$95-$117.** 2930 E Andy Devine Ave 86401. I-40 exit 53, just w on Route 66. Ext corridors. **Pets:** Small, other species. $10 daily fee/room. Designated rooms, service with restrictions, supervision.
[SAVE] ◐M ⊇ ◉ ⊟ ▣

▽▽ Comfort Inn H
(928) 718-1717. **$84-$139.** 3129 E Andy Devine Ave 86401. I-40 exit 53, just w on Route 66. Int corridors. **Pets:** Accepted.
◐M ⊇ ◉ ⊠ ⊟ ▣

▽▽▽ Holiday Inn Express Hotel & Suites H
(928) 718-4343. **Call for rates.** 3031 E Andy Devine Ave 86401. I-40 exit 53, just w on Route 66. Int corridors. **Pets:** Accepted.
◐M ⊇ ◉ ⊠ ⊟ ▣

AAA ▽▽▽ SpringHill Suites by Marriott H
(928) 753-8766. **$123-$166.** 3101 E Andy Devine Ave 86401. I-40 exit 53, just w on Route 66. Int corridors. **Pets:** Accepted.
[SAVE] ◐M ⊇ ◉ ⊠ ⊟ ▣

LAKE HAVASU CITY *(Restaurants p. 594)*

▽▽▽ Hampton Inn Lake Havasu H
(928) 855-4071. **$129-$239.** 245 London Bridge Rd 86403. 0.5 mi n of London Bridge. Ext/int corridors. **Pets:** Accepted.
⊇ ⊠ ◉ ⊠ ⊟ ▣

▽▽ Island Suites H
(928) 855-7333. **Call for rates.** 236 S Lake Havasu Ave 86403. Just s of jct McCulloch Blvd. Int corridors. **Pets:** Accepted.
⊇ ◉ ⊟ ▣

▽▽ The Nautical Beachfront Resort H
(928) 855-2141. **$89-$359, 3 day notice.** 1000 McCulloch Blvd N 86403. 1.4 mi w of London Bridge, follow signs. Ext corridors. **Pets:** Accepted. ❚❚ ⊇ ◉ ⊠ ⊟ ▣

▽▽ Quality Inn & Suites H
(928) 855-1111. **$75-$190.** 271 S Lake Havasu Ave 86403. SR 95, just e on Swanson Ave, just s. Ext corridors. **Pets:** Other species. $20 daily fee/pet. Service with restrictions, crate. ❚❚ ⊇ ◉ ⊟ ▣

LITCHFIELD PARK

AAA ▽▽▽▽ The Wigwam H
(623) 935-3811. **$129-$499, 3 day notice.** 300 E Wigwam Blvd 85340. I-10 exit 128 (Litchfield Rd), 2.4 mi n, then 0.4 mi e. Ext corridors. **Pets:** Accepted. [SAVE] ❚❚ ◐M ⊇ ⊠ ◉ ⊠ ⊟ ▣

MARANA

▽▽▽ La Quinta Inn & Suites NW Tucson Marana H
(520) 572-4235. **$81-$291.** 6020 W Hospitality Rd 85743. I-10 exit 246 (Cortaro Rd), just w, then just n. Int corridors. **Pets:** Accepted.
◐M ⊇ ◉ ⊠ ⊟ ▣

AAA ▽▽▽▽ The Ritz-Carlton, Dove Mountain H
(520) 572-3000. **Call for rates.** 15000 N Secret Springs Dr 85658. I-10 exit 240 (Tangerine Rd), 5 mi e to Dove Mountain Dr, then 4.5 mi n, follow signs. Int corridors. **Pets:** Accepted.
[SAVE] ❚❚ ◐M ⊇ ⊠ ◉ ⊠ ⊟ ▣

MARICOPA

▽▽▽ Harrah's Ak-Chin Casino Resort H
(480) 802-5000. **Call for rates.** 15406 Maricopa Rd 85239. Jct SR 238, 4.5 mi s on SR 347. Ext/int corridors. **Pets:** Accepted.
❚❚ ◐M ⊇ ◉ ⊟ ▣

MESA

AAA ▽▽▽ Best Western Plus Mesa H
(480) 926-3600. **$69-$229.** 1563 S Gilbert Rd 85204. US 60 (Superstition Frwy) exit 182 (Gilbert Rd), just n. Int corridors. **Pets:** Accepted.
[SAVE] ⊇ ◉ ⊠ ▣

AAA ▽▽▽ Best Western Superstition Springs Inn H
(480) 641-1164. **$81-$200.** 1342 S Power Rd 85206. Just n of US 60 (Superstition Frwy) exit 188 (Power Rd); northwest corner of Power Rd and Hampton Ave. Ext corridors. **Pets:** Accepted.
[SAVE] ⊇ ◉ ⊟ ▣

▽▽ Days Hotel Mesa Near Phoenix H
(480) 844-8900. **$66-$180.** 333 W Juanita Ave 85210. US 60 (Superstition Frwy) exit 179 (Country Club Dr), just s, then just e. Int corridors. **Pets:** Accepted. ⊇ ◉ ⊠ ⊟ ▣

▼◆◆ Days Inn-East Mesa H
(480) 981-8111. **$55-$120.** 5531 E Main St 85205. 0.4 mi e of Higley Rd. Ext corridors. **Pets:** Medium, dogs only. $10 daily fee/pet. Designated rooms, service with restrictions. 🏊 📶 🛁 💻

◈ ▼◆◆ Four Points by Sheraton at Phoenix Mesa Gateway Airport H
(480) 579-2100. **$68-$160.** 6850 E Williams Field Rd 85212. SR 202 exit 36 (Power Rd); 1.5 mi s, then just e. Int corridors. **Pets:** Accepted.
SAVE 🍴 ⓜ 📶 ✕ 🛁 💻

◈ ▼◆◆ Hilton Phoenix/Mesa H
(480) 833-5555. **$79-$269.** 1011 W Holmes Ave 85210. US 60 (Superstition Frwy) exit 178 (Alma School Rd), just n, then just e. Int corridors. **Pets:** Accepted. SAVE 🍴 ⓜ 🏊 📶 ✕ 🛁 💻

▼◆◆◆ Holiday Inn & Suites Phoenix-Mesa/Chandler H
(480) 964-7000. **Call for rates.** 1600 S Country Club Dr 85210. US 60 (Superstition Frwy) exit 179 (Country Club Dr), just s. Ext/int corridors. **Pets:** Accepted. 🍴 ⓜ 🏊 📶 ✕ 🛁 💻

◈ ▼◆◆ Hyatt Place Phoenix/Mesa H
(480) 969-8200. **$89-$299.** 1422 W Bass Pro Dr 85201. Loop 202 exit 10 (Dobson Rd), just s, then just e. Int corridors. **Pets:** Accepted.
SAVE 🍴 ⓜ 🏊 📶 ✕ 🛁 💻

▼◆◆◆ La Quinta Inn & Suites Mesa Superstition Springs H
(480) 654-1970. **$95-$587.** 6530 E Superstition Springs Blvd 85206. US 60 (Superstition Frwy) exit 187 (Superstition Springs Blvd) eastbound, just se; exit 188 (Power Rd) westbound, just sw. Int corridors.
Pets: Accepted. ⓜ 🏊 📶 ✕ 🛁 💻

▼◆ La Quinta Inn & Suites Phoenix Mesa West H
(480) 844-8747. **$67-$246.** 902 W Grove Ave 85210. US 60 (Superstition Frwy) exit 178 (Alma School Rd), just n, then just e. Int corridors. **Pets:** Accepted. 🏊 📶 ✕ 🛁 💻

◈ ▼◆◆ Residence Inn by Marriott Phoenix Mesa H
(480) 610-0100. **$86-$299.** 941 W Grove Ave 85210. US 60 (Superstition Frwy) exit 178 (Alma School Rd), just n, then just e. Int corridors. **Pets:** Medium, other species. $100 one-time fee/room. Service with restrictions, crate. SAVE ⓜ 🏊 📶 ✕ 🛁 💻

◈ ▼◆◆ Sheraton Mesa Hotel at Wrigleyville West H 🐾
(480) 664-1221. **$99-$329.** 860 N Riverview 85201. SR 202 exit 10 (Dobson Rd), just s to Cubs Way, then just w. Int corridors. **Pets:** Large, dogs only. Service with restrictions, supervision.
SAVE 🍴 ⓜ ✕ 📶 ✕ 🛁 💻

NOGALES

▼◆◆ Candlewood Suites H
(520) 281-1111. **$99-$159.** 875 N Frank Reed Rd 85621. I-19 exit 4, just w to Frank Reed Rd, then just nw. Int corridors. **Pets:** Accepted.
📶 ✕ 🛁 💻

▼◆◆ Holiday Inn Express Hotel Nogales H
(520) 281-0123. **$99-$249.** 850 W Shell Rd 85621. I-19 exit 4, just w to Frank Reed Rd, then just nw. Int corridors. **Pets:** Accepted.
🏊 ✕ 📶 ✕ 🛁 💻

ORO VALLEY

◈ ▼◆◆◆ Hilton Tucson El Conquistador Golf & Tennis Resort H
(520) 544-5000. **$99-$399.** 10000 N Oracle Rd 85704. I-10 exit 248 (Ina Rd); jct Ina Rd, 4.4 mi n. Ext/int corridors. **Pets:** Accepted.
SAVE ECO 🍴 ⓜ 🏊 ✕ 📶 ✕ 🛁 💻

PAGE

◈ ▼◆◆ Courtyard by Marriott H
(928) 645-5000. **$84-$269.** 600 Clubhouse Dr 86040. On Loop 89, jct US 89. Int corridors. **Pets:** Accepted.
SAVE 🍴 ⓜ 🏊 📶 ✕ 🛁 💻

◈ ▼◆◆ Lake Powell Days Inn & Suites H
(928) 645-2800. **$70-$355.** 961 N Hwy 89 86040. On US 89, just s. Int corridors. **Pets:** Medium, other species. $25 daily fee/pet. Designated rooms, service with restrictions, supervision.
SAVE ⓜ 🏊 📶 ✕ 🛁 💻

▼◆ Lake Powell Resort and Marina H
(928) 645-2433. **Call for rates.** 100 Lakeshore Dr 86040. 4 mi n of Glen Canyon Dam via US 89. Int corridors. **Pets:** Accepted.
🍴 🏊 📶 ✕ 🛁 💻

PARADISE VALLEY

◈ ▼◆◆◆ Hermosa Inn H
(602) 955-8614. **$179-$549, 7 day notice.** 5532 N Palo Cristi Rd 85253. 1 mi s of Lincoln Dr; corner of Stanford Dr. Ext corridors.
Pets: Accepted. SAVE 🍴 ⓜ 🏊 ✕ 📶 ✕ 🛁 💻

◈ ▼◆◆◆ Omni Scottsdale Resort & Spa at Montelucia H
(480) 627-3200. **Call for rates.** 4949 E Lincoln Dr 85253. Southeast corner of Lincoln Dr and Tatum Blvd, enter from Lincoln Dr. Ext/int corridors. **Pets:** Accepted. SAVE 🍴 ⓜ 🏊 ✕ 📶 ✕ 🛁 💻

◈ ▼◆◆◆ Sanctuary Camelback Mountain H 🐾
(480) 948-2100. **$269-$999, 14 day notice.** 5700 E McDonald Dr 85253. SR 101 exit McDonald Dr, 3.9 mi w; 1.8 mi w of jct Scottsdale Rd. Ext corridors. **Pets:** Medium. $100 one-time fee/room. Service with restrictions, crate. SAVE 🍴 ⓜ 🏊 ✕ 📶 ✕ 🛁 💻

PARKER

◈ ▼◆◆ Best Western Parker Inn H
(928) 669-6060. **$100-$220.** 1012 Geronimo Ave 85344. Jct SR 95, just e. Int corridors. **Pets:** Accepted. SAVE 🏊 📶 ✕ 🛁 💻

PAYSON

▼◆◆ Quality Inn Payson H
(928) 474-3241. **$85-$300.** 801 N Beeline Hwy 85541. SR 87, 0.6 mi n of SR 260. Ext corridors. **Pets:** Accepted.
✕ 🏊 📶 ✕ 🛁 💻

▼◆◆ Wooden Nickel Cabins CA
(928) 478-4519. **$149-$229.** 165 S Hunter Creek Dr 85541. SR 87, 22 mi e on SR 260, 0.7 mi n; just w of MM 275. Ext corridors.
Pets: Accepted. 🍴 📶 ✕ 🐾 🛁 💻

PEACH SPRINGS

◈ ▼◆◆ Hualapai Lodge H
(928) 769-2230. **Call for rates.** 900 Route 66 86434. Center. Int corridors. **Pets:** Accepted. SAVE 🍴 ⓜ 🏊 📶 ✕ 🛁 💻

PEORIA

▼◆ Comfort Suites by Choice Hotels/Peoria Sports Complex H
(623) 334-3993. **$64-$219.** 8473 W Paradise Ln 85382. SR 101 exit 14 (Bell Rd), just e to 83rd Ave, just s, then just w. Int corridors.
Pets: Accepted. 🏊 📶 ✕ 🛁 💻

▼◆ Days Hotel Peoria Glendale Area H
(623) 979-7200. **$53-$135.** 8955 W Grand Ave 85345. SR 101 N exit 11 (Grand Ave), 0.5 mi e. Int corridors. **Pets:** Accepted.
🍴 🏊 📶 ✕ 🛁 💻

▼▼ **Extended Stay America Peoria** H
(623) 487-0020. **$60-$115.** 7345 W Bell Rd 85382. SR 101 exit 14 (Bell Rd), 1.2 mi e. Int corridors. **Pets:** Accepted. 🛜 ⊠ 🖥

▼▼ **Holiday Inn Express Hotel & Suites Peoria North-Glendale** H
(623) 853-1313. **Call for rates.** 16771 N 84th Ave 85382. SR 101 exit 14 (Bell Rd), just w, then just s. Int corridors. **Pets:** Accepted.
🔥M 🛩 🛜 ⊠ 🖥 🖥

▼▼▼ **La Quinta Inn & Suites Phoenix West/Peoria** H
(623) 487-1900. **$79-$499.** 16321 N 83rd Ave 85382. SR 101 exit 14 (Bell Rd), just e, then just s. Int corridors. **Pets:** Accepted.
🔥M 🛩 🛜 ⊠ 🖥 🖥

▼▼▼ **Residence Inn by Marriott Glendale/Peoria** H
(623) 979-2074. **$103-$264.** 8435 W Paradise Ln 85382. SR 101 exit 14 (Bell Rd), just e to 83rd Ave, just s, then just w. Int corridors. **Pets:** Other species. $100 one-time fee/room. Service with restrictions.
🔥M 🛩 🛜 ⊠ 🖥 🖥

PHOENIX *(Restaurants p. 594)*

◢◢◣ ▼▼▼ **Aloft Phoenix Airport Hotel** H
(602) 275-6300. **$79-$279.** 4450 E Washington St 85034. SR 143 exit Washington St, just w. Int corridors. **Pets:** Accepted.
SAVE 🔥M 🛩 🛜 ⊠ 🖥 🖥

◢◢◣ ▼▼▼ ▼▼▼ **Arizona Biltmore, A Waldorf Astoria Resort** H 🐾
(602) 955-6600. **$119-$449.** 2400 E Missouri Ave 85016. Jct Camelback Rd, 0.5 mi n on 24th St, then 0.4 mi e. Ext/int corridors. **Pets:** Other species. $50 deposit/room, $50 one-time fee/room. Service with restrictions. SAVE ECO 🍴 🔥M 🛩 ⊠ 🛜 🖥 🖥

◢◢◣ ▼▼▼ ▼▼▼ **Best Western InnSuites Phoenix Hotel & Suites** H
(602) 997-6285. **$99-$149.** 1615 E Northern Ave 85020. SR 51 exit 7, 0.6 mi w. Ext corridors. **Pets:** Accepted. SAVE 🛩 🛜 ⊠ 🖥 🖥

◢◢◣ ▼▼▼ ▼▼▼ **The Camby, Autograph Collection** H 🐾
(602) 468-0700. **$233-$395.** 2401 E Camelback Rd 85016. Southeast corner of Camelback Rd and 24th St. Int corridors. **Pets:** Small, other species. $100 one-time fee/pet. Service with restrictions, supervision.
SAVE 🍴 🔥M 🛩 🛜 ⊠ 🖥 🖥

▼▼ **Candlewood Suites Phoenix** H
(602) 861-4900. **Call for rates.** 11411 N Black Canyon Hwy 85029. I-17 exit 208 (Peoria Ave), just e, then 0.4 mi n. Int corridors.
Pets: Accepted. 🛩 🛜 ⊠ 🖥 🖥

◢◢◣ ▼▼▼ **Country Inn & Suites By Carlson Phoenix Airport** H
(480) 829-0700. **$69-$238.** 4702 E University Dr 85034. I-10 exit 151 (University Dr), 2 mi n, then e. Int corridors. **Pets:** $20 daily fee/room. Designated rooms, service with restrictions, supervision.
SAVE 🔥M 🛩 🛜 ⊠ 🖥 🖥

◢◢◣ ▼▼▼ **Crowne Plaza Phoenix Airport** H
(602) 273-7778. **$79-$249.** 4300 E Washington St 85034. SR 202 exit 2 (44th St), 0.7 mi s. Int corridors. **Pets:** Accepted.
SAVE 🍴 🛩 🛜 ⊠ 🖥 🖥

◢◢◣ ▼▼▼ **DoubleTree Suites by Hilton Phoenix** H
(602) 225-0500. **$99-$469.** 320 N 44th St 85008. SR 202 exit 2 (44th St), 0.5 mi s. Ext corridors. **Pets:** Accepted.
SAVE 🍴 🔥M 🛩 🛜 ⊠ 🖥 🖥

▼▼▼ **Drury Inn & Suites Phoenix Airport** H
(602) 437-8400. **$84-$269.** 3333 E University Dr 85034. I-10 exit 151 (University Dr), just e, then just s on Elwood St. Int corridors.
Pets: Accepted. 🍴 🛩 🛜 ⊠ 🖥 🖥

▼▼▼ **Drury Inn & Suites Phoenix Happy Valley** H
(623) 879-8800. **$84-$269.** 2335 W Pinnacle Peak Rd 85027. I-17 exit 217 (Pinnacle Peak Rd), just e. Int corridors. **Pets:** Accepted.
🔥M 🛩 🛜 ⊠ 🖥 🖥

◢◢◣ ▼▼▼ **Embassy Suites by Hilton Phoenix Airport at 24th St** H
(602) 957-1910. **$84-$269.** 2333 E Thomas Rd 85016. SR 51 exit 2 (44th St), just e. Ext corridors. **Pets:** Accepted.
SAVE 🍴 🛩 🛝 🖥 🖥

◢◢◣ ▼▼▼ **Embassy Suites by Hilton Phoenix Biltmore** H
(602) 955-3992. **$119-$329.** 2630 E Camelback Rd 85016. Just n of Camelback Rd, on 26th St. Int corridors. **Pets:** Accepted.
SAVE 🍴 🛩 🛝 ⊠ 🖥 🖥

▼▼ ▼ **Extended Stay America Phoenix-Biltmore** H
(602) 265-6800. **$70-$115.** 5235 N 16th St 85016. Jct SR 51, just w on Camelback Rd, then just n. Int corridors. **Pets:** Accepted.
🛩 🛜 ⊠ 🖥

▼▼ ▼ **Extended Stay America-Phoenix-Chandler** H
(480) 785-0464. **$60-$110.** 14245 S 50th St 85044. I-10 exit 159, just w on Ray Rd, just s, then just e. Int corridors. **Pets:** Accepted.
🔥M 🛜 ⊠ 🖥

▼▼ ▼ **Extended Stay America Phoenix-Chandler-E Chandler Blvd** H
(480) 753-6700. **$55-$105.** 5035 E Chandler Blvd 85048. I-10 exit 160 (Chandler Blvd), just w. Ext corridors. **Pets:** Accepted.
🛩 🛜 ⊠ 🖥

▼▼ ▼ **Extended Stay America Phoenix-Deer Valley** H
(623) 879-6609. **$55-$115.** 20827 N 27th Ave 85027. I-17 exit 215A, just w. Int corridors. **Pets:** Accepted. 🛜 ⊠ 🖥

◢◢◣ ▼▼▼ **Four Points by Sheraton Phoenix North** H
(602) 943-2341. **$59-$219.** 2532 W Peoria Ave 85029. I-17 exit 208 (Peoria Ave), just e, then just n on 25th Ave. Int corridors.
Pets: Accepted. SAVE 🍴 🔥M 🛩 🛜 ⊠ 🖥 🖥

◢◢◣ ▼▼▼ **Four Points by Sheraton Phoenix South Mountain** H
(480) 893-3000. **Call for rates.** 10831 S 51st St 85044. I-10 exit 157 (Elliott Rd), just w, then just s. Int corridors. **Pets:** Accepted.
SAVE 🍴 🔥M ⊠ 🛜 ⊠ 🖥 🖥

▼▼▼ **Hilton Phoenix Suites** H 🐾
(602) 222-1111. **$89-$310.** 10 E Thomas Rd 85012. Just e of Central Ave; in Phoenix Plaza. Int corridors. **Pets:** $25 one-time fee/room. Service with restrictions, crate. 🍴 🔥M 🛩 🛝 🖥 🖥

◢◢◣ ▼▼▼ **Holiday Inn & Suites Phoenix Airport North** H
(602) 244-8800. **$119-$419.** 1515 N 44th St 85008. SR 202 exit 2 (44th St), 0.3 mi n. Ext corridors. **Pets:** Small. $50 one-time fee/pet. Designated rooms, service with restrictions, supervision.
SAVE 🍴 🔥M 🛩 🛜 ⊠ 🖥 🖥

▼▼▼ **Holiday Inn North Phoenix** H
(602) 548-6000. **$69-$289.** 12027 N 28th Dr 85029. I-17 exit 209 (Cactus Rd), just w, then just s. Int corridors. **Pets:** Accepted.
🍴 🔥M 🛩 🛜 ⊠ 🖥 🖥

▼▼▼ **Homewood Suites by Hilton Phoenix-Biltmore** H
(602) 508-0937. **$99-$329.** 2001 E Highland Ave 85016. Just e of 20th St. Int corridors. **Pets:** Accepted. 🛩 🛜 🖥 🖥

▼▼▼ **Homewood Suites by Hilton Phoenix Metrocenter** H
(602) 674-8900. **$89-$199.** 2536 W Beryl Ave 85021. I-17 exit 208 (Peoria Ave), just e, just s on 25th Ave, then just w. Int corridors.
Pets: Accepted. ⬛Ⓜ ➡ 🛜 ✖ 🖥 💻

▼▼▼ **Homewood Suites Phoenix North/Happy Valley** H
(623) 580-1800. **$99-$329.** 2470 W Charlotte Dr 85085. I-17 exit 217 (Pinnacle Peak Rd), 0.6 mi n on Frontage Rd. Int corridors.
Pets: Accepted. ⬛Ⓜ ➡ 🛜 ✖ 🖥 💻

⬥⬥⬥ ▼▼ ▼▼ **Hotel Palomar Phoenix-CityScape** H
(602) 253-6633. **Call for rates.** 2 E Jefferson St 85004. Northeast corner of Central Ave and Jefferson St. Int corridors. **Pets:** Accepted.
SAVE ⍾⍾ ⬛Ⓜ 🛜 ✖ 🖥

⬥⬥⬥ ▼▼▼ **Hyatt Place Phoenix-North** H
(602) 997-8800. **$64-$229.** 10838 N 25th Ave 85029. I-17 exit 208 (Peoria Ave), just e, then 0.3 mi n. Int corridors. **Pets:** Accepted.
SAVE ⍾⍾ ➡ 🛜 ✖ 🖥 💻

▼▼▼▼ **La Quinta Inn & Suites Phoenix Chandler** H
(480) 961-7700. **$67-$240.** 15241 S 50th St 85044. I-10 exit 160 (Chandler Blvd), just w, then just n. Int corridors. **Pets:** Accepted.
⬛Ⓜ ➡ ✖ 🖥 💻

▼▼▼ **La Quinta Inn & Suites Phoenix I-10 West** H
(602) 595-7601. **$79-$295.** 4929 W McDowell Rd 85035. I-10 exit 139 (51st Ave), just n, then just e. Int corridors. **Pets:** Accepted.
➡ 🛜 ✖ 🖥 💻

▼▼ **La Quinta Inn Phoenix North** H
(602) 993-0800. **$67-$361.** 2510 W Greenway Rd 85023. I-17 exit 211, just e. Ext corridors. **Pets:** Accepted. ➡ 🛜 ✖ 🖥 💻

⬥⬥⬥ ▼▼▼ **Pointe Hilton Squaw Peak Resort** H
(602) 997-2626. **$139-$369.** 7677 N 16th St 85020. SR 51 exit Glendale Ave, 0.4 mi w, then 0.6 mi n. Ext corridors. **Pets:** Accepted.
SAVE ⍾⍾ ➡ ✖ 🛜 ✖ 🖥 💻

⬥⬥⬥ ▼▼▼ **Pointe Hilton Tapatio Cliffs Resort** H
(602) 866-7500. **$139-$369.** 11111 N 7th St 85020. I-17 exit 207 (Dunlap Ave), 3 mi e, then 2 mi n. Ext corridors. **Pets:** Accepted.
SAVE ECO ⊟ ⍾⍾ ⬛Ⓜ ➡ ✖ 🛜 ✖ 🖥 💻

⬥⬥⬥ ▼▼ **Quality Inn Phoenix Airport** H
(480) 893-3900. **$56-$110.** 5121 E La Puenta Ave 85044. I-10 exit 157 (Elliot Rd), just w, just n on 51st St, then just e. Ext corridors.
Pets: Accepted. SAVE ➡ 🛜 ✖ 🖥 💻

⬥⬥⬥ ▼▼ **Quality Inn Phoenix North I-17** H
(602) 864-6233. **$59-$189.** 8101 N Black Canyon Hwy 85021. I-17 exit 206 (Northern Ave), just e, then just n; on east side of freeway. Ext corridors. **Pets:** Accepted. SAVE ➡ 🛜 🖥 💻

▼▼▼▼ **Radisson Hotel Phoenix North** H
(602) 997-5900. **Call for rates.** 10220 N Metro Pkwy E 85051. I-17 exit 208 (Peoria Ave), 0.3 mi w to 28th Dr, just s, then just e. Int corridors.
Pets: Accepted. ⍾⍾ ➡ 🛜 ✖ 🖥 💻

⬥⬥⬥ ▼▼ **Red Roof PLUS+ Phoenix West** H
(602) 233-8004. **$50-$126.** 5215 W Willetta St 85043. I-10 exit 139 (51st Ave), just n, just e on McDowell Rd, then just s. Int corridors.
Pets: Accepted. SAVE ⬛Ⓜ ➡ 🛜 ✖ 🖥 💻

▼▼▼▼ **Residence Inn by Marriott Phoenix** H
(602) 864-1900. **$90-$201.** 8242 N Black Canyon Hwy 85051. I-17 exit 207 (Dunlap Ave), just w, then 0.8 mi s; on frontage road. Ext/int corridors. **Pets:** Accepted. ➡ 🛜 ✖ 🖥 💻

▼▼▼▼ **Residence Inn by Marriott Phoenix North/Happy Valley** H
(623) 580-8833. **$87-$240.** 2035 W Whispering Wind Dr 85085. I-17 exit 128 (Happy Valley Rd), 0.4 mi e to 23rd Ave, just s, then just e. Int corridors. **Pets:** Accepted. ➡ 🛜 ✖ 🖥 💻

⬥⬥⬥ ▼▼▼ **Residence Inn Phoenix Desert View at Mayo Clinic** H ❀
(480) 563-1500. **$99-$293, 3 day notice.** 5665 E Mayo Blvd 85054. SR 101 exit 32 (56th St), just s, just e. Int corridors. **Pets:** Medium, other species. $100 one-time fee/room. Service with restrictions, crate.
SAVE ⍾⍾ ⬛Ⓜ ➡ 🛜 ✖ 🖥 💻

⬥⬥⬥ ▼▼▼ **Royal Palms Resort and Spa** H
(602) 840-3610. **$179-$1499, 7 day notice.** 5200 E Camelback Rd 85018. Just e of 52nd St. Ext/int corridors. **Pets:** Accepted.
SAVE ECO ⊟ ⍾⍾ ⬛Ⓜ ➡ ✖ 🛜 ✖ 🖥 💻

⬥⬥⬥ ▼▼▼ **Sheraton Crescent Hotel** H
(602) 943-8200. **$69-$299.** 2620 W Dunlap Ave 85021. I-17 exit 207 (Dunlap Ave), just e. Int corridors. **Pets:** Accepted.
SAVE ⍾⍾ ⬛Ⓜ ➡ ✖ 🛜 ✖ 🖥 💻

⬥⬥⬥ ▼▼▼ **Sheraton Grand Phoenix** H
(602) 262-2500. **$89-$499.** 340 N 3rd St 85004. I-10 exit 145A (7th St), 0.5 mi s to Fillmore St, just w, then just s. Int corridors. **Pets:** Accepted.
SAVE ECO ⍾⍾ ⬛Ⓜ ➡ 🛜 ✖ 🖥 💻

▼▼▼ **Sleep Inn Phoenix Airport** H
(480) 967-7100. **$65-$175.** 2621 S 47th Pl 85034. I-10 exit 151 (University Dr), 2 mi n, then just w. Int corridors. **Pets:** Accepted.
➡ 🛜 ✖ 🖥 💻

⬥⬥⬥ ▼▼▼ **Sleep Inn Phoenix North** H
(602) 504-1200. **$63-$129.** 18235 N 27th Ave 85053. I-17 exit 214A (Union Hills Dr), just w, then just s. Int corridors. **Pets:** Small. $100 deposit/room, $15 daily fee/pet. Designated rooms, service with restrictions, supervision. SAVE ⬛Ⓜ ➡ 🛜 ✖ 🖥 💻

⬥⬥⬥ ▼▼▼ **Super 8-Downtown Phoenix/Convention Center** M
(602) 252-6823. **$63-$153.** 965 E Van Buren St 85006. I-10 exit 145 (7th St), just s, then just e. Ext corridors. **Pets:** Accepted.
SAVE ➡ 🛜 ✖ 🖥 💻

▼▼▼▼ **TownePlace Suites by Marriott Phoenix North** H
(602) 943-9510. **$61-$166.** 9425 N Black Canyon Frwy 85021. I-17 exit 207 (Dunlap Ave), just e, then 0.3 mi n. Int corridors. **Pets:** Accepted.
⬛Ⓜ ➡ 🛜 ✖ 🖥 💻

▼▼▼▼ **The Westin Phoenix Downtown** H
(602) 429-3500. **$89-$499.** 333 N Central Ave 85004. Northeast corner of Central Ave and Van Buren St. Int corridors. **Pets:** Accepted.
SAVE ⍾⍾ ⬛Ⓜ ➡ 🛜 ✖ 🖥 💻

PINETOP-LAKESIDE *(Restaurants p. 594)*

▼▼ **Antlers Inn** M
(928) 367-4146. **$60-$125.** 1023 E White Mountain Blvd 85935. On SR 260; east end of town. Ext corridors. **Pets:** Small, dogs only. $10 daily fee/room. Designated rooms, supervision. 🛜 ✖ 🖥 💻

⬥⬥⬥ ▼▼▼ **Best Western Inn of Pinetop** M
(928) 367-6667. **$79-$170.** 404 E White Mountain Blvd 85935. On SR 260, east end of town. Ext corridors. **Pets:** Accepted.
SAVE 🛜 🖥 💻

⬥⬥⬥ ▼▼▼ **Hon-Dah Resort Casino and Conference Center** H
(928) 369-0299. **$129-$199.** 777 Hwy 260 85935. Jct SR 260 and 73; east end of town. Int corridors. **Pets:** $50 one-time fee/room. Service with restrictions, supervision. SAVE ⍾⍾ ⬛Ⓜ ➡ ✖ 🛜 🖥 💻

Northwoods Resort CA
(928) 367-2966. **Call for rates.** 165 E White Mountain Blvd 85935. On SR 260, MM 352. Ext corridors. **Pets:** Accepted.

Quality Inn Pinetop M
(928) 367-3636. **$71-$260.** 458 E White Mountain Blvd 85935. On SR 260; east end of town. Ext corridors. **Pets:** Accepted.

PRESCOTT

Best Western Prescottonian M
(928) 445-3096. **$85-$160.** 1317 E Gurley St 86301. On SR 89, just s of jct SR 69. Ext corridors. **Pets:** Accepted.

Hassayampa Inn H
(928) 778-9434. **$89-$289, 3 day notice.** 122 E Gurley St 86301. Jct Marina St; downtown. Int corridors. **Pets:** Medium. Designated rooms, service with restrictions, supervision.

La Quinta Inn & Suites H
(928) 777-0770. **$75-$224.** 4499 E SR 69 86301. 3.6 mi e of jct SR 89. Int corridors. **Pets:** Accepted.

Prescott Cabin Rentals-Lynx Creek Farm CA
(928) 710-5029. **Call for rates.** 5555 Onyx Dr 86303. Jct SR 89, 5 mi e on SR 69, 0.4 mi s on dirt/gravel road. Ext corridors. **Pets:** Other species. $10 daily fee/pet. No service, crate.

Quality Inn M
(928) 776-1282. **$84-$229.** 1105 E Sheldon St 86301. 0.4 mi e of jct SR 89. Int corridors. **Pets:** Accepted.

Residence Inn by Marriott H
(928) 775-2232. **$115-$208.** 3599 Lee Cir 86301. Jct SR 69, just n on Lee Blvd, then just e. Int corridors. **Pets:** Accepted.

SpringHill Suites by Marriott H
(928) 776-0998. **$98-$187.** 200 E Sheldon St 86301. On SR 89; at Marina St. Int corridors. **Pets:** Accepted.

PRESCOTT VALLEY

Americas Best Value Inn H
(928) 772-2200. **$59-$155.** 8383 E SR 69 86314. Just w of N Navajo Dr. Int corridors. **Pets:** Medium, dogs only. $10 daily fee/pet. Designated rooms, service with restrictions, supervision.

Arizona Inn of Prescott Valley H
(928) 772-8600. **$69-$125.** 7875 E Hwy 69 86314. Corner of Windsong Rd. Ext corridors. **Pets:** Other species. $15 daily fee/room. Service with restrictions, crate.

Comfort Suites Prescott Valley H
(928) 771-2100. **$84-$239.** 2601 N Crownpointe Dr 86314. Just w on SR 69, just n on Market St. Int corridors. **Pets:** Medium. $40 one-time fee/room. Designated rooms, service with restrictions, supervision.

QUARTZSITE

Super 8-Quartzsite M
(928) 927-8080. **$70-$120, 3 day notice.** 2050 Dome Rock Rd 85359. I-10 exit 17, just s to Frontage Rd, then 0.6 mi w. Int corridors. **Pets:** Other species. $20 daily fee/pet. No service, supervision.

SAFFORD

Best Western Desert Inn M
(928) 428-0521. **$76-$85.** 1391 W Thatcher Blvd 85546. US 191, 1 mi w on US 70. Ext corridors. **Pets:** Accepted.

SCOTTSDALE *(Restaurants p. 594)*

Aloft Scottsdale H ❖
(480) 253-3700. **$89-$409.** 4415 N Civic Center Plaza 85251. Scottsdale Rd, just e on Camelback Rd, just s on 75th St. Int corridors. **Pets:** Medium, dogs only. Service with restrictions, supervision.

Best Western Plus Scottsdale Thunderbird Suites H
(480) 951-4000. **$99-$279.** 7515 E Butherus Dr 85260. 0.5 mi e of jct Scottsdale Rd. Ext/int corridors. **Pets:** Accepted.

Best Western Plus Sundial H
(480) 994-4170. **$90-$380.** 7320 E Camelback Rd 85251. Just e of Scottsdale Rd. Ext corridors. **Pets:** Accepted.

The Canyon Suites at The Phoenician, A Luxury Collection Resort, Scottsdale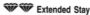
(480) 423-2880. **Call for rates.** 6000 E Camelback Rd 85251. 0.5 mi w of 64th St; in The Phoenician, A Luxury Collection Resort, Scottsdale. Int corridors. **Pets:** Accepted.

Comfort Suites Old Town H
(480) 946-1111. **$72-$239.** 3275 N Drinkwater Blvd 85251. N of Thomas Rd; just e of Scottsdale Rd. Int corridors. **Pets:** Accepted.

Country Inn & Suites By Carlson H
(480) 314-1200. **Call for rates.** 10801 N 89th Pl 85260. SR 101 exit 41 (Shea Blvd), just e, then just n. Int corridors. **Pets:** Accepted.

Courtyard by Marriott Scottsdale at Mayo Clinic H
(480) 860-4000. **$93-$274.** 13444 E Shea Blvd 85259. SR 101 exit 41 (Shea Blvd), 5.8 mi e. Int corridors. **Pets:** Accepted.

DoubleTree Resort by Hilton Paradise Valley-Scottsdale H 🐾
(480) 947-5400. **$79-$489.** 5401 N Scottsdale Rd 85250. Just n of Chaparral Rd; on east side of Scottsdale Rd. Ext corridors. **Pets:** Medium, dogs only. $50 one-time fee/pet. Service with restrictions, supervision.

Extended Stay America Phoenix-Scottsdale H
(480) 483-1333. **$60-$145.** 10660 N 69th St 85254. Jct Scottsdale Rd, just w on Shea Blvd, then just n. Int corridors. **Pets:** Accepted.

Extended Stay America-Phoenix-Scottsdale-North H
(480) 607-3767. **$65-$150.** 15501 N Scottsdale Rd 85254. SR 101 exit 38 (Frank Lloyd Wright Blvd), 2 mi w, 0.5 mi s on Scottsdale Rd, then just e on Tierra Buena Ln. Ext corridors. **Pets:** Accepted.

Extended Stay America-Phoenix-Scottsdale-Old Town M
(480) 994-0297. **$60-$150.** 3560 N Marshall Way 85251. Just w of Scottsdale Rd on Goldwater Blvd, just s. Ext corridors. **Pets:** Accepted.

Fairmont Scottsdale Princess H
(480) 585-4848. **$169-$3299, 7 day notice.** 7575 E Princess Dr 85255.
SR 101 exit 34 (Scottsdale Rd), 0.8 mi s, then just e; 0.6 mi n of Bell
Rd. Ext/int corridors. **Pets:** Accepted.

**Four Seasons Resort Scottsdale at
Troon North** H
(480) 515-5700. **$159-$839, 7 day notice.** 10600 E Crescent Moon Dr
85262. SR 101 exit 36 (Pima Rd), 4.7 mi n, 2 mi e on Happy Valley
Rd, then 1.5 mi n on Alma School Rd. Ext corridors. **Pets:** Accepted.

Gainey Suites Hotel H
(480) 922-6969. **$129-$289.** 7300 E Gainey Suites Dr 85258. Just e of
Scottsdale Rd. Int corridors. **Pets:** Small, dogs only. $50 one-time fee/
room. Service with restrictions, supervision.

Hampton Inn & Suites Scottsdale Riverwalk H
(480) 270-5393. **$79-$309.** 9550 E Talking Stick Way 85256. SR 101
exit 44 (Indian Bend Rd), just e. Int corridors. **Pets:** $50 one-time fee/
pet. Designated rooms, service with restrictions, supervision.

**Hilton Scottsdale Resort &
Villas** H
(480) 948-7750. **$89-$509.** 6333 N Scottsdale Rd 85250. SR 101 exit
45, 2.1 mi w on McDonald Dr, then 0.3 mi n. Int corridors.
Pets: Medium, other species. $50 one-time fee/room. Service with
restrictions, supervision.

Holiday Inn Express Scottsdale North H
(480) 596-6559. **$79-$349.** 7350 E Gold Dust Ave 85258. Just e of
Scottsdale Rd; just s of Shea Blvd; on north side of Gold Dust Ave. Int
corridors. **Pets:** Accepted.

**Homewood Suites by Hilton
Phoenix/Scottsdale** H
(480) 368-8705. **$59-$399.** 9880 N Scottsdale Rd 85253. 0.5 mi s of
Shea Blvd. Int corridors. **Pets:** Accepted.

Hotel Valley Ho H
(480) 248-2000. **$149-$499.** 6850 E Main St 85251. 0.4 mi w of Scottsdale Rd, just s of Indian School Rd; on north side of Main St. Ext/int
corridors. **Pets:** Accepted.

Hyatt House Scottsdale/Old Town H
(480) 946-7700. **$79-$399.** 4245 N Drinkwater Blvd 85251. 0.3 mi e of
Scottsdale Rd. Ext corridors. **Pets:** Accepted.

Hyatt Place Scottsdale/Old Town H
(480) 423-9944. **$89-$249.** 7300 E 3rd Ave 85251. Just e of Scottsdale
Rd. Int corridors. **Pets:** Medium, dogs only. $75 one-time fee/room.
Service with restrictions.

**Hyatt Regency Scottsdale Resort & Spa
at Gainey Ranch** H
(480) 444-1234. **$140-$605, 3 day notice.** 7500 E Doubletree Ranch
Rd 85258. SR 101 exit 43, 2.6 mi w on Via de Ventura. Ext/int corridors. **Pets:** Medium. $15 one-time fee/room. Designated rooms, service
with restrictions, supervision.

**JW Marriott Camelback Inn Resort &
Spa** H
(480) 948-1700. **$134-$474, 3 day notice.** 5402 E Lincoln Dr 85253.
0.5 mi e of Tatum Blvd; on north side of Lincoln Dr. Ext corridors.
Pets: Accepted.

La Quinta Inn & Suites Phoenix Scottsdale H
(480) 614-5300. **$75-$372.** 8888 E Shea Blvd 85260. SR 101 exit 41
(Shea Blvd); northeast corner. Int corridors. **Pets:** Accepted.

The McCormick Scottsdale H
(480) 948-5050. **Call for rates.** 7401 N Scottsdale Rd 85253. 0.8 mi n
of Indian Bend Rd. Ext/int corridors. **Pets:** Accepted.

Motel 6 Scottsdale #29 M
(480) 946-2280. **$55-$105.** 6848 E Camelback Rd 85251. Just w of
Scottsdale Rd. Ext corridors. **Pets:** Accepted.

**The Phoenician, A Luxury Collection
Resort, Scottsdale** H
(480) 941-8200. **$249-$999.** 6000 E Camelback Rd 85251. 0.5 mi w of
64th St. Ext/int corridors. **Pets:** Medium, other species. $175 one-time
fee/room. Service with restrictions, crate.

Residence Inn by Marriott Scottsdale North H
(480) 563-4120. **$99-$350.** 17011 N Scottsdale Rd 85255. SR 101 exit
34 (Scottsdale Rd), 1.1 mi s; northeast corner of Frank Lloyd Wright
Blvd and Scottsdale Rd. Int corridors. **Pets:** Accepted.

**Residence Inn by Marriott, Scottsdale/
Paradise Valley** H
(480) 948-8666. **$99-$317.** 6040 N Scottsdale Rd 85253. Just n of
McDonald Dr. Ext/int corridors. **Pets:** Accepted.

The Scott Resort & Spa H
(480) 945-7666. **$109-$419, 3 day notice.** 4925 N Scottsdale Rd
85251. Southeast corner of Scottsdale and Chaparral rds. Int corridors.
Pets: Accepted.

**Scottsdale Marriott at McDowell
Mountains** H
(480) 502-3836. **$134-$365.** 16770 N Perimeter Dr 85260. SR 101 exit
36 (Princess Dr/Pima Rd), just w to N Perimeter Dr, then 0.6 mi s. Int
corridors. **Pets:** Accepted.

Scottsdale Resort & Athletic Club H
(480) 344-0600. **Call for rates.** 8235 E Indian Bend Rd 85250. 1.5 mi
e of Scottsdale Rd. Ext corridors. **Pets:** Accepted.

**The Scottsdale Resort at McCormick
Ranch** H
(480) 991-9000. **$89-$399, 3 day notice.** 7700 E McCormick Pkwy
85258. Just w of Hayden Rd; 0.7 mi e of Scottsdale Rd. Ext/int corridors. **Pets:** Accepted.

**SpringHill Suites by Marriott-Scottsdale
North** H
(480) 922-8700. **$71-$282.** 17020 N Scottsdale Rd 85255. Just n of
Frank Lloyd Wright Blvd. Int corridors. **Pets:** Accepted.

**TownePlace Suites by Marriott
Scottsdale** H
(480) 551-1100. **$82-$307.** 10740 N 90th St 85260. SR 101 exit 41
(Shea Blvd), just e to 90th St, then just n. Int corridors. **Pets:** Other
species. $114 one-time fee/room. Service with restrictions.

We-Ko-Pa Resort and Conference Center H
(480) 789-5300. **$79-$269.** 10438 N Ft. McDowell Rd 85264. Jct Shea Blvd, 1.6 mi ne on SR 87. Int corridors. **Pets:** Accepted.

The Westin Kierland Resort & Spa H
(480) 624-1000. **$139-$779, 7 day notice.** 6902 E Greenway Pkwy 85254. 0.5 mi w of Scottsdale Rd. Int corridors. **Pets:** Accepted.

W Scottsdale H
(480) 970-2100. **$149-$909.** 7277 E Camelback Rd 85251. Just e of Scottsdale Rd. Int corridors. **Pets:** Medium. $100 one-time fee/room, $25 daily fee/room. Service with restrictions, supervision.

SEDONA *(Restaurants p. 594)*

Amara Resort and Spa, a Kimpton Hotel H
(928) 282-4828. **$199-$509, 3 day notice.** 100 Amara Ln 86336. Jct SR 179, 0.4 mi ne; center. Int corridors. **Pets:** Other species. Service with restrictions.

Andante Inn of Sedona H
(928) 282-1533. **$80-$210.** 2545 W Hwy 89A 86336. Jct SR 179, 2.4 mi w. Int corridors. **Pets:** Medium, dogs only. $25 one-time fee/room. Designated rooms, service with restrictions, supervision.

Arroyo Pinion Hotel, an Ascend Hotel Collection Member H
(928) 204-1146. **$129-$279.** 3119 W Hwy 89A 86336. Jct SR 179, 3 mi w. Ext corridors. **Pets:** Medium, other species. $20 daily fee/pet. Designated rooms, service with restrictions, supervision.

Best Western Plus Arroyo Roble Hotel & Creekside Villas H
(928) 282-4001. **$199-$409.** 400 N SR 89A 86336. Jct SR 179, 0.5 mi ne. Ext corridors. **Pets:** Large, dogs only. $20 daily fee/room. Designated rooms, service with restrictions, supervision.

Best Western Plus Inn of Sedona H
(928) 282-3072. **$149-$279.** 1200 W SR 89A 86336. Jct SR 179, 1.2 mi w. Ext corridors. **Pets:** Other species. $20 one-time fee/room. Service with restrictions, crate.

El Portal Sedona Hotel H
(928) 203-9405. **$299-$499, 15 day notice.** 95 Portal Ln 86336. Jct SR 89A, just s on SR 179, just w. Ext/int corridors. **Pets:** Other species. Service with restrictions, supervision.

Hilton Sedona Resort at Bell Rock H
(928) 284-4040. **Call for rates.** 90 Ridge Trail Dr 86351. Jct SR 89A, 7.3 mi s on SR 179. Int corridors. **Pets:** Large, other species. $50 one-time fee/room. Designated rooms, service with restrictions, supervision.

L'Auberge de Sedona Inn and Spa H
(928) 282-1661. **Call for rates.** 301 L'Auberge Ln 86336. Jct SR 179, just n on SR 89A, then ne; down the hill. Ext/int corridors. **Pets:** Dogs only. $50 daily fee/pet. Designated rooms, service with restrictions, supervision.

The Lodge at Sedona BB
(928) 204-1942. **Call for rates.** 125 Kallof Pl 86336. Jct SR 179, 1.8 mi w on SR 89A, then just s. Ext/int corridors. **Pets:** Accepted.

Matterhorn Inn M
(928) 282-7176. **$119-$209.** 230 Apple Ave 86336. Jct SR 179, just ne on SR 89A; uptown. Ext corridors. **Pets:** Accepted.

Orchards Inn of Sedona H
(928) 282-2405. **Call for rates.** 254 N SR 89A 86336. Jct SR 179, just ne. Ext corridors. **Pets:** Accepted.

Poco Diablo Resort H
(928) 282-7333. **$149-$299.** 1752 State Route 179 86336. Jct SR 179, 2 mi s of SR 89A. Ext corridors. **Pets:** Dogs only. $25 daily fee/room. Designated rooms, service with restrictions, supervision.

Sedona Real Inn & Suites H
(928) 282-1414. **$99-$240.** 95 Arroyo Pinon Dr 86336. Jct SR 179, 3.4 mi w on SR 89A, just sw. Ext corridors. **Pets:** Medium, other species. $30 one-time fee/pet. Designated rooms, service with restrictions, supervision.

Sedona Rouge Hotel & Spa H
(928) 203-4111. **$209-$279, 3 day notice.** 2250 W Hwy 89A 86336. Jct SR 179, 2 mi w. Ext/int corridors. **Pets:** Medium, dogs only. $50 one-time fee/pet. Designated rooms, service with restrictions, supervision.

Sedona Village Lodge M
(928) 284-3626. **$69-$119, 3 day notice.** 105 Bell Rock Plaza 86351. Jct SR 179, just w. Ext/int corridors. **Pets:** Accepted.

Sky Ranch Lodge M
(928) 282-6400. **$120-$349.** 1105 Airport Rd 86336. Jct SR 179, 1 mi w on SR 89A, then 1 mi s. Ext corridors. **Pets:** Accepted.

Southwest Inn at Sedona H
(928) 282-3344. **Call for rates.** 3250 W Hwy 89A 86336. Jct SR 179, 3.5 mi w. Ext corridors. **Pets:** Medium. $20 daily fee/pet. Designated rooms, service with restrictions, supervision.

SELIGMAN

Deluxe Inn Motel M
(928) 422-3244. **$62-$80.** 22295 Old Hwy 66 86337. I-40 exit 121 eastbound, 1 mi n, then 0.7 mi e; exit 123 westbound, just ne on I-40 business loop, then 2.4 mi w. Ext corridors. **Pets:** Medium, other species. $15 one-time fee/pet. Designated rooms, service with restrictions, supervision.

SHOW LOW

Best Western Paint Pony Lodge M
(928) 537-5773. **$90-$170.** 581 W Deuce of Clubs Ave 85901. On US 60 and SR 260. Ext corridors. **Pets:** Accepted.

Days Inn M
(928) 537-4356. **$68-$130.** 480 W Deuce of Clubs Ave 85901. On US 60 and SR 260. Ext/int corridors. **Pets:** Large, other species. $10 daily fee/pet. Service with restrictions, crate.

K C Motel M
(928) 537-4433. **$59-$79.** 60 W Deuce of Clubs Ave 85901. On US 60 and SR 260. Ext corridors. **Pets:** Accepted.

Kiva Motel M
(928) 537-4542. **$58-$68, 3 day notice.** 261 E Deuce of Clubs 85901. On US 60 and SR 260; center. Ext corridors. **Pets:** Accepted.

SIERRA VISTA

Candlewood Suites H ❁
(520) 439-8200. **$110-$149.** 1904 S Hwy 92 85635. Jct SR 90 and 92, 1.4 mi s. Int corridors. **Pets:** Other species. $15 one-time fee/pet. Designated rooms, service with restrictions. 🐾 🛜 ✕ 🖥 💻

Days Inn H
(520) 458-8500. **$69-$80.** 3460 E Fry Blvd 85635. Just w of jct SR 90 and 92. Ext corridors. **Pets:** Accepted. 🔥M 🐾 🛜 ✕ 🖥 💻

Gateway Studio Suites H
(520) 458-5555. **Call for rates.** 203 S Garden Ave 85635. Just s of Fry Blvd; just e of main gate to Fort Huachuca. Int corridors. **Pets:** Accepted. 🐾 🛜 ✕ 🖥 💻

Holiday Inn Express H
(520) 439-8800. **$99-$199.** 1902 S Hwy 92 85635. Jct SR 90 and 92, 1.4 mi s. Int corridors. **Pets:** Accepted. 🐾 🛜 ✕ 🖥 💻

Quality Inn H
(520) 458-7900. **$49-$99.** 1631 S Hwy 92 85635. On SR 92, 1 mi s of jct SR 90. Int corridors. **Pets:** Small. $10 daily fee/pet. Designated rooms, service with restrictions, supervision. SAVE 🐾 🛜 🖥 💻

Sun Canyon Inn H
(520) 226-8894. **Call for rates.** 260 N Garden Ave 85635. Just n of Fry Blvd; just e of main gate to Fort Huachuca. Int corridors. **Pets:** Accepted. 🐾 🛜 ✕ 🖥 💻

TownePlace Suites by Marriott H
(520) 515-9900. **$116-$208.** 3399 Rodeo Dr 85635. Jct SR 90, 1.5 mi s on SR 92, just w on Avenida Cochise, just s on Oakmont Dr, then just e. Int corridors. **Pets:** $100 one-time fee/room.
🐾 ✕ 🖥 💻

SURPRISE

Comfort Inn & Suites Surprise-Peoria H
(623) 544-6874. **$70-$175.** 13337 W Grand Ave 85374. Jct Bell Rd, 0.4 mi se. Int corridors. **Pets:** Medium. $20 daily fee/pet. Service with restrictions, supervision. SAVE 🔥M 🐾 🛜 ✕ 🖥 💻

Days Inn & Suites Surprise H
(623) 933-4000. **$44-$80.** 12477 W Bell Rd 85374. US 60 (Grand Ave), 1.2 mi e. Int corridors. **Pets:** Accepted. 🐾 🛜 ✕ 🖥 💻

Hampton Inn & Suites by Hilton Surprise H
(623) 537-9122. **$89-$299.** 14783 W Grand Ave 85374. Jct Bell Rd, 2 mi nw. Int corridors. **Pets:** Accepted.
SAVE 🔥M 🐾 🛜 ✕ 🖥 💻

Quality Inn & Suites of Sun Cities H
(623) 583-3500. **$61-$138.** 16741 N Greasewood St 85374. US 60 (Grand Ave), 1.2 mi e on Bell Rd, then just s. Int corridors. **Pets:** Accepted. 🐾 🛜 ✕ 🖥 💻

Residence Inn by Marriott Phoenix NW Surprise H
(623) 249-6333. **$112-$245.** 16418 N Bullard Ave 85374. Jct US 60 (Grand Ave), 1.4 mi w on Bell Rd, then just s. Int corridors. **Pets:** Accepted. 🔥M 🐾 🛜 ✕ 🖥 💻

Windmill Suites in Surprise H ❁
(623) 583-0133. **$79-$239.** 12545 W Bell Rd 85378. US 60 (Grand Ave), 1 mi e. Int corridors. **Pets:** Medium. Designated rooms, service with restrictions, crate. SAVE 🐾 🛜 ✕ 🖥 💻

TAYLOR

Rodeway Inn-Silver Creek Inn M
(928) 536-2600. **$63-$75.** 825 N Main St 85939. On SR 77. Ext corridors. **Pets:** Medium. $100 deposit/room, $15 daily fee/pet. Service with restrictions, supervision. SAVE 🍴 🛜 🖥 💻

TEMPE *(Restaurants p. 594)*

Aloft Hotel Tempe H
(480) 621-3300. **$99-$389.** 951 E Playa Del Norte Dr 85281. SR 202 (Red Mountain Frwy) exit 7 (Rural Rd), just s on Scottsdale Rd, then just e. Int corridors. **Pets:** Accepted.
SAVE ECO 🔥M 🐾 🛜 ✕ 🖥 💻

Baymont Inn & Suites Tempe Phoenix Airport H
(480) 858-9898. **$80-$150.** 808 N Scottsdale Rd 85281. SR 202 (Red Mountain Frwy) exit 7 (Rural Rd S), just n. Int corridors. **Pets:** Accepted. 🔥M 🐾 🛜 ✕ 🖥 💻

Best Western Inn of Tempe H ❁
(480) 784-2233. **$80-$200.** 670 N Scottsdale Rd 85281. SR 202 (Red Mountain Frwy) exit 7 (Rural Rd S), just s. Int corridors. **Pets:** Large. $10 daily fee/pet. Designated rooms, service with restrictions, crate.
SAVE 🛜 ✕ 🖥 💻

Best Western Plus Tempe by the Mall H
(480) 820-7500. **$90-$260.** 5300 S Priest Dr 85283. I-10 exit 155 (Baseline Rd), 0.4 mi e, then just s. Int corridors. **Pets:** Large. $25 daily fee/pet. Designated rooms, service with restrictions, supervision. SAVE 🐾 🛜 ✕ 🖥 💻

Days Inn & Suites H
(480) 345-8585. **$69-$70.** 1660 W Elliot Rd 85284. I-10 exit 157, just e. Ext corridors. **Pets:** Accepted. 🐾 🛜 🖥 💻

DoubleTree by Hilton Phoenix-Tempe H
(480) 967-1441. **$89-$289.** 2100 S Priest Dr 85282. I-10 exit 153 (Broadway Rd), 0.5 mi e. Ext corridors. **Pets:** Accepted.
SAVE 🍴 🐾 ✕ 🛜 ✕ 🖥 💻

Drury Inn & Suites Phoenix Tempe H
(480) 940-3700. **$84-$269.** 1780 W Ranch Rd 85284. I-10 exit 158 (Warner Rd), Just e, then just s. Int corridors. **Pets:** Accepted.
🔥M 🛜 ✕ 🖥 💻

Extended Stay America-Phoenix/Airport/Tempe H
(480) 557-8880. **$60-$105.** 2165 W 15th St 85281. I-10 exit 153B (Broadway Rd), 0.3 mi ne, just nw on S 52nd St, then just w. Int corridors. **Pets:** Accepted. 🐾 🛜 🖥

Hawthorn Suites by Wyndham H
(480) 633-2744. **$55-$150.** 2301 E Southern Ave 85282. SR 101 exit 54 (Southern Ave/Baseline Rd); at southeast corner. Int corridors. **Pets:** Accepted. SAVE ECO 🔥M 🐾 🛜 ✕ 🖥 💻

Hotel Tempe Phoenix Airport InnSuites Hotel & Suites H
(480) 897-7900. **Call for rates.** 1651 W Baseline Rd 85283. I-10 exit 155 (Baseline Rd), just e. Ext corridors. **Pets:** Accepted.
🐾 ✕ 🛜 🖥 💻

Hyatt Place Tempe/Phoenix Airport H
(480) 804-9544. **$69-$259.** 1413 W Rio Salado Pkwy 85281. Just w of Priest Dr. Int corridors. **Pets:** Accepted.
SAVE 🍴 🔥M 🐾 🛜 ✕ 🖥 💻

La Quinta Inn Phoenix Sky Harbor Airport South H
(480) 967-4465. **$67-$372.** 911 S 48th St 85281. I-10 exit 153B (Broadway Rd) eastbound; exit 153A (University Dr) westbound, 0.8 mi n; on south side of University Dr; east side of SR 143 (Hohokam Expwy). Ext/int corridors. **Pets:** Accepted. 🐾 🛜 ✕ 🖥 💻

Red Lion Inn & Suites Phoenix/Tempe - ASU H
(480) 675-9799. **$79-$199.** 1429 N Scottsdale Rd 85281. SR 202 Loop (Red Mountain Frwy) exit 7 (Rural Rd S), 0.5 mi n. Int corridors. **Pets:** Accepted. 🔥M 🐾 🛜 ✕ 🖥 💻

◇◇◇◇ ▼▼◇ Red Roof PLUS+ Tempe-Phoenix Airport 🅷
(480) 449-3205. **$54-$123.** 2135 W 15th St 85281. I-10 exit 153B (Broadway Rd), just nw on S 52nd St, then just w. Int corridors. **Pets:** Accepted. ⟨SAVE⟩ ⇄ 📶 ⊠ 🔋 🖵

▼▼◇◇ Residence Inn by Marriott Tempe 🅷
(480) 756-2122. **$91-$228.** 5075 S Priest Dr 85282. I-10 exit 155 (Baseline Rd), 0.4 mi e, then just n. Ext/int corridors. **Pets:** Accepted.
⟨&M⟩ 🏊 📶 ⊠ 🔋 🖵

◇◇◇◇ ▼▼◇◇ Residence Inn by Marriott Tempe Downtown/University 🅷
(480) 967-2300. **$115-$315.** 510 S Forest Ave 85281. Jct University Dr, just n on Mill Ave, just e; downtown. Int corridors. **Pets:** Accepted.
⟨SAVE⟩ ⟨&M⟩ 📶 ⊠ 🔋 🖵

◇◇◇ ▼▼◇ Sheraton Phoenix Airport Hotel Tempe 🅷
(480) 967-6600. **$79-$289.** 1600 S 52nd St 85281. I-10 exit 153B (Broadway Rd) westbound; exit 153A (48th St) eastbound, 0.3 mi ne. Int corridors. **Pets:** Accepted. ⟨SAVE⟩ 🍽 ⟨&M⟩ ⇄ ⊠ 📶 ⊠ 🔋 🖵

◇◇◇ ▼▼▼◇ Tempe Mission Palms Hotel & Conference Resort 🅷
(480) 894-1400. **Call for rates.** 60 E 5th St 85281. Jct University Dr, just n on Mill Ave, just e. Int corridors. **Pets:** Small. $100 deposit/pet, $25 one-time fee/pet. Service with restrictions, supervision.
⟨SAVE⟩ ⟨ECO⟩ 🍽 ⟨&M⟩ ⇄ ⊠ 📶 ⊠ 🔋 🖵

▼▼▼◇ TownePlace Suites by Marriott Tempe at Arizona Mills Mall 🅷 🐾
(480) 345-7889. **$78-$187.** 5223 S Priest Dr 85283. I-10 exit 155 (Baseline Rd), southeast corner of Baseline Rd and Priest Dr. Int corridors. **Pets:** Medium, dogs only. $75 one-time fee/room. Service with restrictions, supervision. ⟨&M⟩ ⇄ 📶 ⊠ 🔋 🖵

TOLLESON

◇◇◇◇ ▼▼◇ Best Western Tolleson-Phoenix Hotel 🅷
(623) 936-6000. **$100-$139.** 8421 W McDowell Rd 85353. I-10 exit 135 (83rd Ave), just n, then just w. Int corridors. **Pets:** Accepted.
⟨SAVE⟩ ⇄ 📶 ⊠ 🔋 🖵

▼▼◇ Premier Inns 🅷
(623) 533-4660. **Call for rates.** 8399 W Lynwood St 85353. I-10 exit 135 (83rd Ave), just n, then just w. Ext corridors. **Pets:** Accepted.
⇄ 📶 🔋

TOMBSTONE

◇◇◇◇ ▼▼◇ Landmark Lookout Lodge 🅷 🐾
(520) 457-2223. **$99-$139.** 781 N Hwy 80 85638. On SR 80, 1 mi n of center. Ext corridors. **Pets:** Medium. $10 daily fee/pet. Designated rooms, service with restrictions, supervision.
⟨SAVE⟩ ⇄ 📶 ⊠ 🔋 🖵

TUBAC

◇◇◇◇ ▼▼◇◇ Tubac Golf Resort & Spa 🅷 🐾
(520) 398-2211. **$119-$219, 5 day notice.** 1 Otero Rd 85646. I-19 exit 40 (Chavez Siding Rd), on east side, then 2 mi s. Ext corridors. **Pets:** $25 daily fee/room. Designated rooms, no service, supervision.
⟨SAVE⟩ ⟨ECO⟩ 🍽 ⇄ ⊠ 📶 ⊠ 🔋 🖵

TUBA CITY

◇◇◇◇ ▼▼▼ Quality Inn Navajo Nation 🅷
(928) 283-4545. **$125-$259.** 10 N Main St 86045. 1 mi n of US 160. Int corridors. **Pets:** Medium, other species. $10 daily fee/pet. Service with restrictions, supervision. ⟨SAVE⟩ 🍽 ⟨&M⟩ 📶 🔋 🖵

TUCSON *(Restaurants p. 594)*

◇◇◇◇ ▼▼▼◇ Aloft Tucson University 🅷
(520) 908-6800. **$89-$409.** 1900 E Speedway Blvd 85719. Southeast corner of Speedway Blvd and Campbell Ave. Int corridors.
Pets: Accepted. ⟨SAVE⟩ 🍽 ⟨&M⟩ 📶 ⊠ 🔋 🖵

◇◇◇◇ ▼▼▼ Americas Best Value Inn-Tucson 🅷
(520) 884-5800. **$43-$120.** 810 E Benson Hwy 85713. I-10 exit 262, just s. Ext corridors. **Pets:** Medium. $25 deposit/pet. Service with restrictions, supervision. ⟨SAVE⟩ ⟨&M⟩ ⇄ 📶 🔋

◇◇◇◇ ▼▼▼ Arizona Riverpark Inn 🅷
(520) 239-2300. **$89-$199, 3 day notice.** 777 W Cushing St 85745. I-10 exit 258 (Broadway Blvd/Congress St), just w, then 0.4 mi s. Ext/int corridors. **Pets:** Medium. $35 one-time fee/room. Service with restrictions, supervision. ⟨SAVE⟩ 🍽 ⇄ ⊠ 📶 🔋 🖵

◇◇◇◇ ▼▼▼▼ Best Western InnSuites Tucson Foothills Hotel & Suites 🅷 🐾
(520) 297-8111. **$72-$109.** 6201 N Oracle Rd 85704. I-10 exit 250 (Orange Grove Rd), 4 mi e, then just s. Ext corridors. **Pets:** Large. $20 one-time fee/room. Service with restrictions, supervision.
⟨SAVE⟩ ⇄ 📶 🔋 🖵

◇◇◇◇ ▼▼▼▼ Best Western Plus Tucson Int'l Airport Hotel & Suites 🅷
(520) 746-3932. **$79-$149.** 6801 S Tucson Blvd 85756. Just n of Tucson International Airport. Int corridors. **Pets:** Accepted.
⟨SAVE⟩ ⇄ 📶 ⊠ 🔋 🖵

◇◇◇◇ ▼▼▼▼ Best Western Royal Sun Inn & Suites 🅷 🐾
(520) 622-8871. **$59-$225.** 1015 N Stone Ave 85705. I-10 exit 257 (Speedway Blvd), 0.8 mi e, then just s. Ext corridors. **Pets:** Designated rooms, supervision. ⟨SAVE⟩ ⟨ECO⟩ 🍽 ⇄ 📶 ⊠ 🔋 🖵

◇◇◇◇ ▼▼▼▼ Candlewood Suites Tucson 🅷 🐾
(520) 373-5799. **$69-$209.** 1995 W River Rd 85704. I-10 exit 250 (Orange Grove Rd), 0.4 mi e to River Rd, then 2.7 mi se. Int corridors. **Pets:** Medium, dogs only. $15 daily fee/pet. Service with restrictions, crate. ⟨SAVE⟩ ⟨&M⟩ 📶 ⊠ 🔋 🖵

▼▼◇◇ Catalina Park Inn Bed and Breakfast 🅱🅱
(520) 792-4541. **$125-$190, 14 day notice.** 309 E 1st St 85705. I-10 exit 257 (Speedway Blvd), 1 mi e to 5th Ave, just s, then just e; in West University Historic District. Ext/int corridors. **Pets:** Medium, dogs only. Designated rooms, supervision. 🍽 📶 ⊠

▼▼◇◇ Comfort Suites at Sabino Canyon 🅷
(520) 298-2300. **$64-$149.** 7007 E Tanque Verde Rd 85715. Jct Grand Rd, 0.4 mi ne. Ext corridors. **Pets:** Medium, other species. $50 daily fee/pet. Designated rooms, supervision. ⇄ 📶 ⊠ 🔋 🖵

▼▼◇◇ Comfort Suites at Tucson Mall 🅷
(520) 888-6676. **$79-$209.** 515 W Auto Mall Dr 85705. I-10 exit 254 (Prince Rd), 1.9 mi e, then 1.2 mi n. Int corridors. **Pets:** Medium, other species. $25 one-time fee/room. Service with restrictions.
⇄ 📶 ⊠ 🔋 🖵

◇◇◇◇ ▼▼◇◇ Country Inn & Suites By Carlson-Tucson Airport 🅷
(520) 741-9000. **Call for rates.** 6681 S Tucson Blvd 85756. 0.4 mi n of Tucson International Airport entrance. Int corridors. **Pets:** Dogs only. $25 one-time fee/room. Designated rooms, service with restrictions, supervision. ⟨SAVE⟩ ⟨&M⟩ ⇄ 📶 🔋 🖵

◇◇◇◇ ▼▼◇◇ Country Inn & Suites By Carlson-Tucson City Center 🅷
(520) 867-6200. **$89-$199.** 705 N Freeway 85745. I-10 exit 257 (Speedway Blvd), just w, then just s. Int corridors. **Pets:** Accepted.
⟨SAVE⟩ ⇄ 📶 ⊠ 🔋 🖵

AAA ◆◆◆ Desert Diamond Casino & Hotel H
(520) 342-3100. **$99-$209.** 7350 S Nogales Hwy 85756. I-19 exit 95 (Valencia Rd), 1.4 mi e, then 1 mi s. Int corridors. **Pets:** Medium. $100 deposit/room. Service with restrictions, crate.
[SAVE] [▯] [♿M] [≈] [奈] [✕] [☎] [▯]

AAA ◆◆◆ DoubleTree Suites by Hilton Tucson Airport H
(520) 225-0800. **$79-$299.** 7051 S Tucson Blvd 85756. At entrance to Tucson International Airport. Ext corridors. **Pets:** Other species. $50 one-time fee/room. Service with restrictions, supervision.
[SAVE] [▯] [♿M] [≈] [奈] [✕] [☎] [▯]

◆ Econo Lodge University M
(520) 622-6714. **$48-$88.** 1136 N Stone Ave 85705. I-10 exit 257 (Speedway Blvd) eastbound, just e, then just n. Ext corridors.
Pets: Accepted. [≈] [奈] [☎]

◆◆ Extended Stay America-Tucson Grant Road H
(520) 795-9510. **$70-$80.** 5050 E Grant Rd 85712. 0.5 mi e of Swan Rd. Ext corridors. **Pets:** Accepted. [奈] [✕] [☎]

◆◆◆ Hampton Inn Tucson North H
(520) 206-0602. **$79-$179.** 1375 W Grant Rd 85745. I-10 exit 256 (Grant Rd), just w. Int corridors. **Pets:** Accepted.
[♿M] [≈] [奈] [✕] [☎] [▯]

◆◆◆ Holiday Inn Express Tucson Airport H
(520) 889-6600. **$119-$219, 14 day notice.** 2548 E Medina Rd 85756. 0.5 mi n of Tucson International Airport entrance. Int corridors.
Pets: Other species. $25 one-time fee/pet. Designated rooms, service with restrictions, crate. [♿M] [≈] [奈] [✕] [☎] [▯]

AAA ◆◆◆ Homewood Suites by Hilton Tucson/St. Philip's Plaza/University H
(520) 577-0007. **$105-$250.** 4250 N Campbell Ave 85718. I-10 exit 254 (Prince Rd), 4 mi e, then 1 mi n. Int corridors. **Pets:** Accepted.
[SAVE] [≈] [✕] [奈] [✕] [☎] [▯]

AAA ◆◆◆ Hyatt Place Tucson Airport H
(520) 295-0405. **$69-$199.** 6885 S Tucson Blvd 85756. Just n of Tucson International Airport. Int corridors. **Pets:** Accepted.
[SAVE] [▯] [♿M] [≈] [奈] [✕] [☎] [▯]

◆◆◆ La Posada Lodge & Casitas H
(520) 887-4800. **$89-$119.** 5900 N Oracle Rd 85704. 0.5 mi s of Orange Grove Rd. Ext corridors. **Pets:** Accepted.
[▯] [≈] [奈] [✕] [☎] [▯]

◆◆◆ La Quinta Inn & Suites Tucson Airport H
(520) 573-3333. **$67-$295.** 7001 S Tucson Blvd 85706. Just n of Tucson International Airport. Int corridors. **Pets:** Accepted.
[♿M] [≈] [奈] [☎] [▯]

◆◆◆ La Quinta Inn & Suites Tucson Reid Park H
(520) 795-0330. **$67-$290.** 102 N Alvernon Way 85711. Jct Broadway Rd; just n. Ext/int corridors. **Pets:** Accepted. [奈] [✕] [☎] [▯]

AAA ◆◆◆ The Lodge at Ventana Canyon H ☙
(520) 577-1400. **$95-$799, 7 day notice.** 6200 N Clubhouse Ln 85750. I-10 exit 256 (Grant Rd), 8.6 mi e, 0.6 mi e on Tanque Verde Rd, 2 mi n on Sabino Canyon Rd, then 3.2 mi n on Kolb Rd. Ext/int corridors.
Pets: Dogs only. $100 one-time fee/room. Designated rooms, service with restrictions. [SAVE] [▯] [♿M] [≈] [✕] [奈] [✕] [☎] [▯]

◆◆◆ Lodge on the Desert H
(520) 320-2000. **$99-$329, 3 day notice.** 306 N Alvernon Way 85711. I-10 exit 258 (Broadway Blvd/Congress St), 4 mi e, then just n. Ext corridors. **Pets:** Accepted. [▯] [≈] [奈] [✕] [☎] [▯]

AAA ◆◆◆ Loews Ventana Canyon Resort H ☙
(520) 299-2020. **$129-$349, 3 day notice.** 7000 N Resort Dr 85750. I-10 exit 256 (Grant Rd), 8.6 mi e, 0.6 mi ne on Tanque Verde Rd, 2 mi n on Sabino Canyon Rd, then 3.5 mi n on Kolb Rd. Ext/int corridors.
Pets: Medium. $100 one-time fee/room. Designated rooms, service with restrictions, supervision.
[SAVE] [ECO] [▯] [♿M] [≈] [✕] [奈] [✕] [☎] [▯]

◆ Motel 6 Tucson North #1127 H
(520) 744-9300. **$55-$65.** 4630 W Ina Rd 85741. I-10 exit 248 (Ina Rd), just e to Camino de Oeste, then just n. Int corridors. **Pets:** Accepted.
[≈] [奈] [☎]

◆◆◆ Omni Tucson National Resort H
(520) 297-2271. **Call for rates.** 2727 W Club Dr 85742. I-10 exit 246 (Cortaro Rd), 3.5 mi e, then just n on Shannon Rd. Ext corridors.
Pets: Small. $100 one-time fee/room. Designated rooms, service with restrictions, crate. [▯] [♿M] [≈] [✕] [奈] [✕] [☎] [▯]

AAA ◆◆◆ Quality Inn Tucson Airport H
(520) 294-2500. **$70-$80.** 2803 E Valencia Rd 85706. 1 mi ne of Tucson International Airport; just e of Tucson Blvd. Ext/int corridors.
Pets: Small. $10 daily fee/pet. Service with restrictions, supervision.
[SAVE] [≈] [奈] [☎] [▯]

AAA ◆◆◆ Radisson Suites Tucson H
(520) 721-7100. **Call for rates.** 6555 E Speedway Blvd 85710. Just e of Wilmot Rd. Ext corridors. **Pets:** Medium. $75 one-time fee/pet. Designated rooms, service with restrictions, supervision.
[SAVE] [▯] [≈] [奈] [☎] [▯]

AAA ◆◆◆ Red Lion Inn & Suites Tucson North H
(520) 575-9255. **$69-$219.** 7411 N Oracle Rd 85704. SR 77 (Oracle Rd), just n of Ina Rd. Ext corridors. **Pets:** Medium. $15 one-time fee/pet. Designated rooms, service with restrictions, supervision.
[SAVE] [♿M] [≈] [奈] [✕] [☎] [▯]

AAA ◆◆◆ Red Roof Inn-Tucson South H
(520) 571-1400. **$39-$120.** 3704 E Irvington Rd 85714. I-10 exit 264 westbound; exit 264B eastbound. Ext corridors. **Pets:** Accepted.
[SAVE] [≈] [奈] [✕] [☎] [▯]

◆◆◆ Residence Inn by Marriott Tucson Airport H
(520) 294-5522. **$81-$140.** 2660 E Medina Rd 85756. 0.5 mi n of airport entrance on Tucson Blvd, just e. Int corridors. **Pets:** Accepted.
[≈] [奈] [✕] [☎] [▯]

◆◆◆ Residence Inn by Marriott Williams Centre H
(520) 790-6100. **$123-$205.** 5400 E Williams Cir 85711. Jct Campbell Ave, 3.8 mi e on Broadway Blvd, just s, then just e on Williams Blvd. Int corridors. **Pets:** Large, other species. $250 one-time fee/room. Service with restrictions, supervision. [♿M] [≈] [奈] [✕] [☎] [▯]

AAA ◆◆◆ Sheraton Tucson Hotel & Suites H
(520) 323-6262. **$89-$289.** 5151 E Grant Rd 85712. Jct Campbell Ave, 3.6 mi e. Ext/int corridors. **Pets:** Accepted.
[SAVE] [▯] [♿M] [≈] [奈] [✕] [☎] [▯]

AAA ◆◆◆ Sonesta ES Suites Tucson H ☙
(520) 721-0991. **Call for rates.** 6477 E Speedway Blvd 85710. Just e of Wilmot Rd. Ext corridors. **Pets:** Small. $150 one-time fee/room. Designated rooms, service with restrictions, crate. [SAVE] [≈] [奈] [✕] [☎] [▯]

◆◆◆ Staybridge Suites Tucson Airport H
(520) 807-1004. **$109-$189.** 2705 E Executive Dr 85756. 0.7 mi n of Tucson International Airport. Int corridors. **Pets:** Accepted.
[♿M] [≈] [奈] [✕] [☎] [▯]

◆◆ Studio 6 Extended Stay #6002 M
(520) 746-0030. **$53-$103.** 4950 S Outlet Center Dr 85706. I-10 exit 264A eastbound; exit 264B westbound, just s, then just nw on Julian Dr. Ext corridors. **Pets:** Other species. $10 daily fee/room. Service with restrictions, supervision. [≈] [奈] [☎] [▯]

▼▼▼▼ **TownePlace Suites by Marriott Tucson** 🄷
(520) 292-9697. **$74-$164.** 405 W Rudasill Rd 85704. Jct Orange Grove Rd, 0.5 mi s on Oracle Rd, then just e. Int corridors. **Pets:** Accepted. 🔲🄼 🛜 ⊠ 🔋 🖥

▼▼▼▼ **TownePlace Suites by Marriott Tucson Airport** 🄷
(520) 294-6677. **$71-$138.** 6595 S Bay Colony Dr 85756. 0.7 mi n of Tucson International Airport. Int corridors. **Pets:** Other species. $100 one-time fee/room. Service with restrictions, supervision.
🄼 🔲🄼 🛜 ⊠ 🔋 🖥

▼▼▼▼ **TownePlace Suites by Marriott Tucson Williams Centre** 🄷
(520) 747-0720. **$82-$142.** 384 S Williams Blvd 85711. Jct Campbell Ave, 3.8 mi e on Broadway Blvd, just s. Int corridors. **Pets:** Accepted.
🄼 🔲🄼 🛜 ⊠ 🔋 🖥

⚠ ▼▼ ▼▼ **Viscount Suite Hotel** 🄷
(520) 745-6500. **$79-$199, 3 day notice.** 4855 E Broadway Blvd 85711. Just e of Swan Rd. Int corridors. **Pets:** Medium. Service with restrictions, crate. SAVE 🍴 🄼 🔲🄼 🛜 ⊠ 🔋 🖥

⚠ ▼▼▼▼ **The Westin La Paloma Resort & Spa** 🄷
(520) 742-6000. **$79-$399, 7 day notice.** 3800 E Sunrise Dr 85718. SR 77 (Oracle Rd), 4.6 mi e on Ina Rd via Skyline and Sunrise drs, then just s on Via Palomita. Ext corridors. **Pets:** Accepted.
SAVE ECO ◀🔌 🍴 🄼 🔲🄼 ⊠ 🛜 ⊠ 🔋 🖥

⚠ ▼▼▼▼ **Westward Look Wyndham Grand Resort & Spa** 🄷
(520) 297-1151. **$119-$459, 7 day notice.** 245 E Ina Rd 85704. I-10 exit 248 (Ina Rd), 6 mi e, then left on Westward Look Dr. Ext corridors.
Pets: Accepted. SAVE ECO 🍴 🄼 🔲🄼 ⊠ 🛜 ⊠ 🔋 🖥

WELLTON

▼▼▼▼ **Microtel Inn & Suites by Wyndham Wellton** 🄷
(928) 785-3777. **$67.** 28784 Commerce Way 85356. I-8 exit 30, just s. Int corridors. **Pets:** Accepted. 🔲🄼 🛜 ⊠ 🔋 🖥

WICKENBURG

⚠ ▼▼ ▼▼ **Best Western Rancho Grande** 🄷
(928) 684-5445. **$68-$125.** 293 E Wickenburg Way 85390. On US 60; center. Ext corridors. **Pets:** Accepted. SAVE 🔲🄼 🛜 ⊠ 🔋 🖥

▼▼ ▼▼ **Quality Inn Wickenburg** 🄷
(928) 684-5461. **$74-$110.** 850 E Wickenburg Way 85390. 1.3 mi se on US 60. Int corridors. **Pets:** Medium. $15 daily fee/pet. Designated rooms, service with restrictions, supervision. 🔲🄼 🛜 ⊠ 🔋 🖥

⚠ ▼▼▼ **Super 8 Wickenburg** 🄼
(928) 684-0808. **$50-$130.** 1021 N Tegner St 85390. 1 mi n of jct US 60 and 93. Ext/int corridors. **Pets:** Other species. $10 daily fee/pet. Service with restrictions, supervision. SAVE 🛜 ⊠ 🔋 🖥

WILLCOX

⚠ ▼▼ ▼▼ **Days Inn** 🄼
(520) 384-4222. **$55-$73.** 724 N Bisbee Ave 85643. I-10 exit 340, just s. Ext corridors. **Pets:** Medium. $10 daily fee/pet. Service with restrictions, supervision. SAVE 🔲🄼 🛜 🔋 🖥

▼▼▼▼ **Holiday Inn Express & Suites Willcox** 🄷
(520) 384-5333. **Call for rates.** 1251 N Virginia Ave 85643. I-10 exit 340, just n. Int corridors. **Pets:** Accepted.
🄼 🔲🄼 🛜 ⊠ 🔋 🖥

WILLIAMS *(Restaurants p. 594)*

⚠ ▼▼▼▼ **Best Western Plus Inn of Williams** 🄷
(928) 635-4400. **$110-$251.** 2600 W Route 66 86046. I-40 exit 161, south on Route 66. Int corridors. **Pets:** Small. $25 daily fee/pet. Designated rooms, service with restrictions, supervision.
SAVE 🍴 🄼 🔲🄼 🛜 ⊠ 🔋 🖥

▼▼▼ **Days Inn of Williams** 🄼
(928) 635-4051. **$70-$254.** 2488 W Route 66 86046. I-40 exit 161, just e. Int corridors. **Pets:** Accepted. 🔲🄼 🛜 ⊠ 🔋 🖥

⚠ ▼▼ **Knights Inn** 🄼
(928) 635-1412. **$100-$150.** 750 N Grand Canyon Blvd 86046. I-40 exit 163, just s. Int corridors. **Pets:** Accepted. SAVE 🛜 ⊠ 🔋

⚠ ▼▼ **Travelodge Williams** 🄼
(928) 635-2651. **$60-$180.** 430 E Route 66 86046. I-40 exit 163, 0.5 mi s, then just e. Ext corridors. **Pets:** Accepted.
SAVE 🄼 🔲🄼 🛜 🔋 🖥

WINDOW ROCK

⚠ ▼▼ ▼▼ **Quality Inn Navajo Nation Capital** 🄷
(928) 871-4108. **$79-$165.** 48 W Hwy 264 86515. Center. Ext corridors. **Pets:** Medium. $50 deposit/room. Service with restrictions, crate.
SAVE 🛜 🔋 🖥

WINSLOW

▼▼▼▼ **La Posada Hotel** 🄷
(928) 289-4366. **$119-$169, 7 day notice.** 303 E 2nd St 86047. I-40 exit 253, 1 mi s to Route 66 (2nd St), then just e; in historic downtown. Int corridors. **Pets:** Accepted. ◀🔌 🍴 🄼 🛜 ⊠ 🆉

YOUNGTOWN

⚠ ▼▼ ▼▼ **Sun City Inn & Suites** 🄷
(623) 933-8211. **$79-$300.** 11201 Grand Ave 85363. On US 60, just se of 113th Ave. Ext/int corridors. **Pets:** Accepted.
SAVE 🔲🄼 🛜 🔋 🖥

YUMA

⚠ ▼▼ ▼▼ **Best Western InnSuites Yuma Mall Hotel & Suites** 🄷
(928) 783-8341. **$74-$129.** 1450 Castle Dome Ave 85365. I-8 exit 2 (16th St/US 95), just e to Yuma Palms Pkwy, just n, then just w. Ext corridors. **Pets:** Accepted. SAVE 🍴 🔲🄼 🛜 🔋 🖥

▼▼▼▼ **Candlewood Suites** 🄷
(928) 726-2800. **Call for rates.** 2036 S Ave 3 E 85365. I-8 exit 3, just n, then just w on Frontage Rd. Int corridors. **Pets:** Accepted.
🄼 🛜 ⊠ 🔋 🖥

⚠ ▼▼ ▼▼ **Days Inn Yuma** 🄼
(928) 329-7790. **$60-$99.** 1671 E 16th St 85365. I-8 exit 2 (16th St/US 95), just e. Int corridors. **Pets:** Accepted.
SAVE 🄼 🔲🄼 🛜 ⊠ 🔋 🖥

⚠ ▼▼ ▼▼ **Historic Coronado Motor Hotel** 🄷
(928) 783-4453. **$80-$140.** 233 4th Ave 85364. I-8 exit 172 (4th Ave) eastbound, 0.5 mi s; exit 1 (Harold C. Giss Pkwy) westbound, 1 mi w. Ext corridors. **Pets:** Accepted. SAVE 🍴 🔲🄼 🛜 ⊠ 🔋 🖥

▼▼▼ **Holiday Inn Express & Suites** 🄷
(928) 317-1400. **Call for rates.** 2044 S Ave 3 E 85365. I-8 exit 3, just n, then just w on Frontage Rd. **Pets:** Other species. $15 daily fee/pet. Designated rooms, service with restrictions, supervision.
🄼 🔲🄼 🛜 ⊠ 🔋 🖥

▼▼▼▼ **Homewood Suites by Hilton Yuma** 🄷
(928) 782-4100. **$85-$159.** 1955 E 16th St 85365. I-8 exit 2 (16th St/US 95), 0.4 mi e. Int corridors. **Pets:** Accepted.
🄼 🔲🄼 🛜 🔋 🖥

La Fuente Inn & Suites [H]
(928) 329-1814. **Call for rates.** 1513 E 16th St 85365. I-8 exit 2 (16th St/US 95), just e. Ext corridors. **Pets:** Accepted.

Radisson Hotel Yuma [H]
(928) 783-8000. **Call for rates.** 1501 S Redondo Center Dr 85365. I-8 exit 2 (16th St/US 95), just w, then just n. Int corridors. **Pets:** Accepted.

TownePlace Suites by Marriott [H]
(928) 783-6900. **$93-$177.** 1726 S Sunridge Dr 85365. I-8 exit 2 (16th St/US 95), just e to Sunridge Dr, then just s. Int corridors. **Pets:** Accepted.

Yuma Cabana Motel [M]
(928) 783-8311. **Call for rates.** 2151 S 4th Ave 85364. I-8 exit 2 (16th St/US 95), 1 mi w, then 0.5 mi s. Int corridors. **Pets:** Accepted.

ARKANSAS

ALMA

Quality Inn & Suites [H]
(479) 632-4141. **$66-$116.** 439 Hwy 71 N 72921. I-40 exit 13, just n. Ext/int corridors. **Pets:** Accepted.

ARKADELPHIA

Quality Inn [M] ❀
(870) 246-5592. **$75-$109.** 136 Valley St 71923. I-30 exit 78, just e. Ext corridors. **Pets:** Large. $10 daily fee/pet. Designated rooms, service with restrictions, supervision.

BATESVILLE

Super 8-Batesville [M]
(870) 793-5888. **$62-$72.** 1287 N St. Louis St 72501. 1 mi n on US 167. Int corridors. **Pets:** Accepted.

BENTON

Best Western Benton Inn [M]
(501) 778-9695. **$75-$85.** 17036 I-30 72019. I-30 exit 117 westbound; exit 118 eastbound; on northwest service road. Ext corridors. **Pets:** Accepted.

BENTONVILLE

21C Museum Hotel [H]
(479) 286-6500. **Call for rates.** 200 NE A St 72712. Just n of jct Central Ave; downtown. Int corridors. **Pets:** Accepted.

La Quinta Inn & Suites Bentonville [H]
(479) 271-7555. **$75-$196.** 1001 SE Walton Blvd 72712. I-49 exit 85, 0.7 mi w. Int corridors. **Pets:** Accepted.

TownePlace Suites by Marriott Bentonville/Rogers [H]
(479) 621-0202. **$86-$144.** 3100 SE 14th St 72712. I-49 exit 86, just e. Int corridors. **Pets:** Accepted.

Wingate by Wyndham [H]
(479) 418-5400. **$74-$200.** 7400 SW Old Farm Blvd 72712. 7.4 mi w of jct Walton and SW Regional Airport blvds. Int corridors. **Pets:** Other species. $50 one-time fee/room. Service with restrictions, supervision.

BLYTHEVILLE

Comfort Inn & Suites [H]
(870) 763-0900. **$102-$184.** 1510 E Main St 72315. I-55 exit 67, just w. Int corridors. **Pets:** Medium, other species. $15 one-time fee/room. Designated rooms, service with restrictions, supervision.

Hampton Inn by Hilton [H]
(870) 763-5220. **$119-$149.** 301 N Service Rd 72315. I-55 exit 67, just nw. Int corridors. **Pets:** Accepted.

Quality Inn [H]
(870) 763-7081. **$79-$88.** 1520 E Main St 72315. I-55 exit 67, just w. Ext corridors. **Pets:** Accepted.

BRYANT

Americas Best Value Inn [M]
(501) 653-7800. **$60-$200.** 407 W Commerce St 72022. I-30 exit 123, just n on SR 183, then just w. Ext corridors. **Pets:** Accepted.

Comfort Inn & Suites [H]
(501) 653-4000. **$87-$169.** 209 W Commerce St 72022. I-30 exit 123, just n on SR 183, then just w. Int corridors. **Pets:** Medium. $10 daily fee/pet. Designated rooms, service with restrictions, supervision.

La Quinta Inn & Suites Bryant [H]
(501) 847-9494. **$97-$186.** 408 W Commerce St 72022. I-30 exit 123, just n on SR 183, then just w. Int corridors. **Pets:** Accepted.

Super 8 [M]
(501) 847-7888. **$55-$160.** 201 Dell Dr 72022. I-30 exit 123, just s on SR 183, then just e. Ext corridors. **Pets:** Accepted.

CABOT

Days Inn & Suites-Cabot [H]
(501) 605-1810. **$80-$110.** 1302 W Locust St 72023. US 67/167 exit 19, just e, then just n. Int corridors. **Pets:** Medium. $10 daily fee/pet. Service with restrictions, supervision.

CLARKSVILLE

Best Western Sherwood Inn [H]
(479) 754-7900. **$75-$89.** 1207 S Rogers Ave 72830. I-40 exit 58, just n. Ext corridors. **Pets:** Accepted.

Quality Inn & Suites [H]
(479) 754-3000. **$63-$120.** 1167 S Rogers Ave 72830. I-40 exit 58, just n. Ext corridors. **Pets:** Small. $20 daily fee/room. Designated rooms, service with restrictions, supervision.

CONWAY

Best Western Conway [M]
(501) 329-9855. **$65-$109.** 816 E Oak St 72032. I-40 exit 127, just e on US 64. Ext/int corridors. **Pets:** Other species. $20 daily fee/room. Designated rooms, service with restrictions, crate.

Candlewood Suites [H] ❀
(501) 329-8551. **$59-$149.** 2360 Sanders St 72032. I-40 exit 125, just s on US 65 business route, then just e. Int corridors. **Pets:** Medium. Designated rooms, service with restrictions, crate.

La Quinta Inn & Suites [H]
(501) 328-5100. **$81-$174.** 2350 Sanders St 72032. I-40 exit 125, just s on US 65 business route, then just e. Int corridors. **Pets:** Accepted.

▼▼ **Microtel Inn & Suites by Wyndham Conway** 🄷
(501) 327-0898. **$60-$80.** 2475 Sanders St 72032. I-40 exit 125, just s on US 65 business route, then just e. Int corridors. **Pets:** Accepted.
🛜 ⊠ 🔋 💻

▼▼ **Quality Inn** Ⓜ
(501) 329-0300. **$56-$95.** 150 Skyline Dr N 72032. I-40 exit 125, just n. Ext corridors. **Pets:** $20 daily fee/pet. Designated rooms, service with restrictions. 🛌 🛜 🔋 💻

▼▼ **Super 8-Conway** 🄷
(501) 505-8880. **$60.** 2430 Sanders St 72032. I-40 exit 125, just s on US 65 business route, then just e. Int corridors. **Pets:** Accepted.
🛌 🛜 🔋 💻

EL DORADO
▼▼ **La Quinta Inn El Dorado** 🄷
(870) 863-6677. **$82-$176.** 2303 Junction City Rd 71730. Jct US 167, just e on US 82 business route. Int corridors. **Pets:** Accepted.
🍴 🛌 🛜 🔋 💻

EUREKA SPRINGS *(Restaurants p. 595)*
▼▼▼ **1886 Crescent Hotel & Spa** 🄷 🐾
(479) 253-9766. **Call for rates.** 75 Prospect Ave 72632. Jct SR 23, 1.3 mi w on US 62B Historic Loop. Int corridors. **Pets:** $25 daily fee/pet. Designated rooms, service with restrictions.
🍴 🛌 🛜 ⊠ 🔋 💻

▼▼▼ **Arsenic & Old Lace B&B** 🄱🄱 🐾
(479) 253-5454. **$159-$329, 15 day notice.** 60 Hillside Ave 72632. Jct US 62, 1.2 mi n on SR 23, just sw; downtown. Ext/int corridors. **Pets:** Dogs only. $15 daily fee/pet. Designated rooms, service with restrictions, crate. 🍽 🍴 🛜 ⊠ 🎦 🔋 💻

▼▼ **Basin Park Hotel** 🄷 🐾
(479) 253-7837. **Call for rates.** 12 Spring St 72632. Jct US 62, 0.7 mi n on SR 23, then just nw; downtown. Int corridors. **Pets:** $25 one-time fee/pet. Designated rooms, service with restrictions.
🍴 🛜 ⊠ 🔋 💻

🆊 ▼▼▼ **Best Western Eureka Inn** 🄷
(479) 253-9551. **$80-$149.** 101 E Van Buren St 72632. Jct SR 23 and US 62. Ext/int corridors. **Pets:** Medium, dogs only. $25 daily fee/pet. Designated rooms, service with restrictions, crate.
🆂🅰🆅🅴 🛌 ⊠ 🛜 ⊠ 🔋 💻

🆊 ▼▼▼ **Best Western Inn of the Ozarks** 🄷
(479) 253-9768. **$89-$129, 3 day notice.** 207 W Van Buren St 72632. Jct SR 23 N, 0.5 mi w on US 62. Ext corridors. **Pets:** Medium, dogs only. $10 daily fee/pet. Designated rooms, service with restrictions, crate. 🆂🅰🆅🅴 🍴 🅶🅼 🛌 ⊠ 🛜 ⊠ 🔋 💻

▼▼ **Red Bud Valley Resort** 🄲🄰
(479) 253-9028. **$99-$273, 30 day notice.** 369 CR 340 72632. Jct SR 23, 2.3 mi e on US 62, 0.6 mi s on CR 302, just w. Ext corridors.
Pets: Accepted. 🍴 🎦 ⊠ 🎦 🔋 💻

FAYETTEVILLE
🆊 ▼▼▼ **Best Western Windsor Suites** 🄷
(479) 301-2882. **$84-$159.** 1122 S Futrall Dr 72701. I-49 exit 62, just se. Ext corridors. **Pets:** Accepted. 🆂🅰🆅🅴 🛌 🛜 🔋 💻

▼▼▼ **The Chancellor Hotel** 🄷
(479) 442-5555. **Call for rates.** 70 N East Ave 72701. Center of downtown. Int corridors. **Pets:** Accepted. 🍴 🛌 🛜 ⊠ 🔋 💻

▼▼ **Comfort Inn & Suites** 🄷
(479) 571-5177. **$79-$220.** 1234 Steamboat Dr 72704. I-49 exit 64, just nw. Int corridors. **Pets:** Accepted. 🅶🅼 🛌 🛜 ⊠ 🔋 💻

▼▼▼ **La Quinta Inn & Suites Fayetteville** 🄷
(479) 587-8600. **$86-$356.** 720 E Millsap Rd 72703. I-49 exit 67, 1.5 mi e, then just s on US 71B. Int corridors. **Pets:** Accepted.
🛌 🛜 ⊠ 🔋 💻

▼▼ **Sleep Inn by Choice Hotels** 🄷
(479) 587-8700. **$77-$210.** 728 E Millsap Rd 72703. I-49 exit 67, 1.5 mi e, then just s on US 71B. Int corridors. **Pets:** Other species. $25 one-time fee/room. Designated rooms, service with restrictions, crate.
🛜 🔋 💻

▼▼▼ **Staybridge Suites** 🄷 🐾
(479) 695-2400. **$99-$299.** 1577 W 15th St 72701. Just w of jct Razorback Rd. Int corridors. **Pets:** Medium. $15 daily fee/room. Service with restrictions, crate. 🅶🅼 🛌 🛜 🔋 💻

FORDYCE
▼▼ **Days Inn** Ⓜ
(870) 352-2400. **$77-$90.** 2500 W 4th St 71742. US 79/167, 1 mi w. Ext/int corridors. **Pets:** Medium. $10 daily fee/pet. Service with restrictions, supervision. 🍴 🛌 🛜 🔋 💻

FORREST CITY
▼▼ **Colony Inn** Ⓜ
(870) 633-0870. **$72-$84.** 2333 N Washington St 72335. I-40 exit 241A, just s. Ext corridors. **Pets:** Large. $20 daily fee/pet. Service with restrictions, crate. 🛌 🛜 🔋 💻

▼▼▼ **Days Inn Forrest City** 🄷
(870) 633-6300. **$85-$125.** 200 Holiday Dr 72335. I-40 exit 241B, just n. Ext corridors. **Pets:** Medium, other species. $15 daily fee/pet. Service with restrictions, supervision. 🍴 🛌 🛜 🔋 💻

FORT SMITH
▼▼▼ **Beland Manor Bed & Breakfast** 🄱🄱 🐾
(479) 782-3300. **$115-$185, 5 day notice.** 1320 S Albert Pike 72903. I-49 exit 8A (Rogers Ave), 1.3 mi w. Int corridors. **Pets:** Dogs only. Designated rooms, service with restrictions, crate. 🍴 🛜 ⊠

🆊 ▼▼▼ **Best Western Aspen** 🄷
(479) 452-9000. **$89-$129.** 2900 S 68th St 72903. I-49 exit 8B (Rogers Ave), just e, then just s. Int corridors. **Pets:** Other species. $25 one-time fee/pet. Designated rooms, service with restrictions, crate.
🆂🅰🆅🅴 🛌 🛜 ⊠ 🔋 💻

▼▼▼ **Courtyard by Marriott Downtown Fort Smith** 🄷
(479) 783-2100. **$101-$154.** 900 Rogers Ave 72901. I-49 exit 8A (Rogers Ave), 3.9 mi w; downtown. Int corridors. **Pets:** Accepted.
🍴 🅶🅼 🛌 🛜 ⊠ 🔋 💻

▼▼▼ **Hampton Inn** 🄷 🐾
(479) 452-2000. **$104-$199.** 6201-C Rogers Ave 72903. I-49 exit 8B (Rogers Ave), just ne. Int corridors. **Pets:** Medium. $50 one-time fee/room. Designated rooms, service with restrictions, supervision.
🛌 🛜 ⊠ 🔋 💻

▼▼▼ **Holiday Inn Express** 🄷
(479) 452-7500. **Call for rates.** 6813 Phoenix Ave 72903. I-49 exit 8B (Rogers Ave), 0.6 mi e, then 0.5 mi s on 70th St. Int corridors.
Pets: Accepted. 🛌 🛜 ⊠ 🔋 💻

▼▼▼ **Home2 Suites by Hilton-Fort Smith** 🄷
(479) 452-2100. **$109-$149.** 7400 Phoenix Ave 72903. I-49 exit 8B (Rogers Ave), 0.8 mi e, then just s on 74th st. Ext corridors.
Pets: Small. $125 one-time fee/pet. Designated rooms, service with restrictions, supervision. 🍴 🅶🅼 🛜 ⊠ 🔋 💻

▼▼▼ **Residence Inn by Marriott** 🄷
(479) 478-8300. **$93-$153.** 3005 S 74th St 72903. I-49 exit 8B (Rogers Ave), 0.8 mi e, then just n. Int corridors. **Pets:** Medium, other species. $75 one-time fee/room. Service with restrictions, supervision.
🛌 🛜 ⊠ 🔋 💻

HARDY

AAA⧸ ▼▼💎 Best Western Village Inn M
(870) 856-2176. **$78-$93.** 3587 Hwy 62/412 72542. 2 mi sw. Ext corridors. **Pets:** Small, dogs only. $25 daily fee/pet. Designated rooms, service with restrictions, supervision. [SAVE] [¶] [≈] [🛜] [🔒] [💻]

HARRISON

▼▼💎 Holiday Inn Express Hotel & Suites H
(870) 741-3636. **Call for rates.** 117 Hwy 43 E 72601. Jct US 62/65/412, just e. Int corridors. **Pets:** Small. $25 one-time fee/pet. Service with restrictions, supervision. [≈] [✕] [🛜] [✕] [🔒] [💻]

▼▼💎 Quality Inn H
(870) 741-7676. **$90-$115.** 1210 Hwy 62/65 N 72601. Jct SR 43, 0.4 mi w on US 62/65/412. Ext/int corridors. **Pets:** Medium. $25 one-time fee/pet. Service with restrictions, supervision. [≈] [🛜] [🔒] [💻]

HOPE

AAA⧸ ▼▼💎 Best Western of Hope H 🐾
(870) 777-9222. **$74-$89.** 1800 Holiday Dr 71801. I-30 exit 30, just nw. Ext corridors. **Pets:** Other species. $10 daily fee/room. Service with restrictions, crate. [SAVE] [≈] [🛜] [🔒] [💻]

HOT SPRINGS

AAA⧸ ▼▼💎 Best Western Winners Circle Inn M 🐾
(501) 624-2531. **$89-$169.** 2520 Central Ave 71901. Jct US 70/270, 1.3 mi n on SR 7. Ext/int corridors. **Pets:** Small, dogs only. $25 one-time fee/room. Service with restrictions, supervision.
[SAVE] [ᴋM] [≈] [🛜] [🔒] [💻]

AAA⧸ ▼▼💎 Clarion Resort H
(501) 525-1391. **$99-$249.** 4813 Central Ave 71913. Jct US 70/270, 2.6 mi s on SR 7. Int corridors. **Pets:** Medium, other species. $20 daily fee/pet. Service with restrictions, crate.
[SAVE] [¶] [ᴋM] [≈] [✕] [🛜] [🔒] [💻]

▼▼💎 Embassy Suites by Hilton Hot Springs-Hotel & Spa H
(501) 624-9200. **$139-$199.** 400 Convention Blvd 71901. Jct US 70/270 business route, just n on SR 7, then just e. Int corridors.
Pets: Accepted. [¶] [ᴋM] [≈] [✕] [🛜] [🔒] [💻]

AAA⧸ ▼▼💎 Staybridge Suites H 🐾
(501) 525-6500. **$99-$199.** 103 Lookout Cir 71913. US 70/270 exit 5A, 3.9 mi s on SR 7. Int corridors. **Pets:** Large, other species. $75 one-time fee/room. Service with restrictions, crate.
[SAVE] [ᴋM] [≈] [🛜] [✕] [🔒] [💻]

JACKSONVILLE

AAA⧸ ▼▼💎 Best Western Jacksonville Inn M
(501) 982-8181. **$69-$195.** 1600 John Harden Dr 72076. US 67/167 exit 11, just s on west service road. Ext corridors. **Pets:** Accepted.
[SAVE] [≈] [🛜] [🔒] [💻]

▼▼ Super 8 M
(501) 982-9219. **$65-$70.** 1850 John Harden Dr 72076. US 67/167 exit 11, just s on west service road. Ext corridors. **Pets:** Small, dogs only. $10 one-time fee/pet, $10 daily fee/pet. Designated rooms, service with restrictions, supervision. [≈] [🛜] [🔒] [💻]

JOHNSON

▼▼▼ TownePlace Suites by Marriott Fayetteville North/Springdale H
(479) 966-4400. **$88-$135.** 5437 S 48th St 72741. I-49 exit 69, just se. Int corridors. **Pets:** Accepted. [ᴋM] [≈] [🛜] [✕] [🔒] [💻]

LITTLE ROCK

AAA⧸ ▼▼▼ Comfort Inn & Suites Little Rock Airport H 🐾
(501) 376-2466. **$80-$130.** 4301 E Roosevelt Rd 72206. I-440 exit 3, just n. Int corridors. **Pets:** Other species. $25 one-time fee/pet. Service with restrictions, supervision. [SAVE] [¶] [ᴋM] [≈] [✕] [🔒] [💻]

▼▼▼ Comfort Inn & Suites Presidential H
(501) 687-7700. **$79-$1000.** 707 I-30 72202. I-30 exit 140A, just e. Int corridors. **Pets:** Accepted. [¶] [ᴋM] [≈] [🛜] [✕] [🔒] [💻]

AAA⧸ ▼▼💎 Days Inn & Suites Airport M
(501) 490-2010. **$60.** 3200 Bankhead Dr 72206. I-440 exit 3, just s. Ext corridors. **Pets:** Accepted. [SAVE] [≈] [🛜] [🔒] [💻]

▼▼💎 Embassy Suites Hotel Little Rock H
(501) 312-9000. **$99-$169.** 11301 Financial Centre Pkwy 72211. I-430 exit 5, 1 mi n on Shackleford Rd, then 0.4 mi w. Int corridors.
Pets: Medium, other species. $75 one-time fee/room. Designated rooms, service with restrictions, crate.
[¶] [ᴋM] [≈] [✕] [🛜] [🔒] [💻]

AAA⧸ ▼▼▼ ▼▼▼ The Empress of Little Rock BB
(501) 374-7966. **$139-$329, 7 day notice.** 2120 S Louisiana St 72206. I-630 exit 1B, 0.6 mi s. Int corridors. **Pets:** Medium, dogs only. $25 one-time/pet. Designated rooms, service with restrictions, crate.
[SAVE] [¶] [🛜] [✕]

AAA⧸ ▼▼▼ Holiday Inn Airport Conference Center H
(501) 490-1000. **$94-$149.** 3201 Bankhead Dr 72206. I-440 exit 3, just s. Int corridors. **Pets:** Accepted. [SAVE] [¶] [≈] [🛜] [✕] [🔒] [💻]

▼▼▼ Holiday Inn Express Airport H
(501) 490-4000. **$92-$132.** 3121 Bankhead Dr 72206. I-440 exit 3, just s. Int corridors. **Pets:** Accepted. [ᴋM] [≈] [🛜] [✕] [🔒] [💻]

▼▼▼ Holiday Inn Express Hotel & Suites H
(501) 224-2600. **Call for rates.** 4900 Talley Rd 72204. I-430 exit 4, just e. Int corridors. **Pets:** Medium. $30 daily fee/room. Service with restrictions, supervision. [ᴋM] [≈] [🛜] [✕] [🔒] [💻]

▼▼💎 Holiday Inn-Financial Centre Parkway H
(501) 225-1075. **Call for rates.** 10920 Financial Centre Pkwy 72211. I-430 exit 5, 1 mi n on Shackleford Rd, then just w. Int corridors.
Pets: Accepted. [¶] [ᴋM] [≈] [🛜] [✕] [🔒] [💻]

AAA⧸ ▼▼▼ Home2 Suites by Hilton H 🐾
(501) 588-3000. **$99-$149.** 2710 S Shackleford Rd 72205. I-430 exit 5, 6 mi s. Int corridors. **Pets:** Large, other species. $125 one-time fee/pet. Designated rooms, service with restrictions, crate.
[SAVE] [¶] [ᴋM] [🛜] [✕] [🔒] [💻]

▼▼💎 Homewood Suites by Hilton Little Rock H
(501) 375-4663. **$149-$209.** 400 River Market Ave 72201. I-30 exit 141A, just w on 2nd St, then just s; downtown. Int corridors.
Pets: Accepted. [¶] [ᴋM] [🛜] [✕] [🔒] [💻]

▼▼💎 Residence Inn by Marriott H
(501) 312-0200. **$96-$176.** 1401 S Shackleford Rd 72211. I-430 exit 5, just n. Int corridors. **Pets:** Accepted. [≈] [🛜] [✕] [🔒] [💻]

▼▼💎 Residence Inn by Marriott -Downtown H
(501) 376-7200. **$107-$171.** 219 River Market Ave 72201. I-30 exit 141A, just w on 2nd St, then just s; downtown. Int corridors.
Pets: Other species. $75 one-time fee/room. Service with restrictions.
[ᴋM] [🛜] [✕] [🔒] [💻]

▼▼💎 TownePlace Suites by Marriott-Little Rock H
(501) 225-6700. **$72-$108.** 12 Crossings Ct 72205. I-430 exit 5, 0.6 mi e on Shackleford Rd, then just w. Int corridors. **Pets:** Accepted.
[ᴋM] [≈] [🛜] [✕] [🔒] [💻]

LONOKE

Best Western Plus Lonoke Hotel H
(501) 676-8880. **$99-$103.** 102 Dee Dee Ln 72086. I-40 exit 175, just n. Int corridors. **Pets:** Accepted. SAVE ⎷M ⊇ ⎗ ✕ 🔒 ▣

Days Inn H
(501) 676-5138. **$70-$75.** 105 Dee Dee Ln 72086. I-40 exit 175, just n. Ext corridors. **Pets:** Accepted. ⊇ ⎗ 🔒 ▣

Holiday Inn Express Hotel & Suites H
(501) 676-7800. **$114-$139.** 104 Dee Dee Ln 72086. I-40 exit 175, just n. Int corridors. **Pets:** Accepted. ⎷M ⊇ ⎗ ✕ 🔒 ▣

MAUMELLE

Holiday Inn Express & Suites-Maumelle H
(501) 851-4422. **Call for rates.** 200 Holiday Dr 72113. I-40 exit 142, just s. Int corridors. **Pets:** Accepted. ⎷M ⊇ ⎗ ✕ 🔒 ▣

MCGEHEE

Super 8 McGehee M
(870) 222-3564. **$80-$100.** 1202 Hwy 65 N 71654. Center. Ext corridors. **Pets:** Small, dogs only. $20 daily fee/room. Designated rooms, service with restrictions, supervision. ⏹ ⊇ ⎗ ✕ 🔒 ▣

MONTICELLO

Days Inn M
(870) 367-1881. **$52-$70.** 317 Hwy 425 N 71655. Jct US 278, just n. Ext corridors. **Pets:** Accepted. SAVE ⊇ ⎗ 🔒 ▣

MOUNTAIN HOME

Comfort Inn H
(870) 424-9000. **$93-$189.** 1031 Highland Cir 72653. Jct US 412/62, 1.8 mi w on US 62 business route. Ext/int corridors. **Pets:** Small, dogs only. $35 one-time fee/room. Service with restrictions, supervision.
SAVE ⎷M ⊇ ⎗ ✕ 🔒 ▣

Teal Point Resort CA
(870) 492-5145. **$83-$110, 60 day notice.** 715 Teal Point Rd 72653. Jct US 62 business route, 3.5 mi e on US 412/62, 0.6 mi n on CR 406. Ext corridors. **Pets:** Other species. $10 daily fee/pet. No service, crate.
SAVE ⏹ ⊇ ✕ ⎗ ✕ ⊠ 🔒 ▣

MOUNTAIN VIEW

Econo Lodge M
(870) 269-2828. **Call for rates.** 601 Sylamore Ave 72560. Jct Main St, 1 mi n on SR 5/9/14. Ext corridors. **Pets:** Accepted.
⊇ ⎗ 🔒 ▣

NORTH LITTLE ROCK

Best Western Plus JFK Inn & Suites H
(501) 246-3300. **$91-$146.** 2500 Main St 72114. I-40 exit 153A, just s on JFK Blvd. Int corridors. **Pets:** Medium, other species. $20 one-time fee/room. Designated rooms, service with restrictions, supervision.
SAVE ⎷M ⊇ ⎗ ✕ 🔒 ▣

La Quinta Inn & Suites North Little Rock-McCain Mall H
(501) 945-0808. **$75-$170.** 4311 Warden Rd 72116. US 67/167 exit 1 southbound; exit 2 northbound, just s on west service road. Int corridors. **Pets:** Accepted. ⎷M ⊇ ⎗ 🔒 ▣

Red Roof Inn-North Little Rock H
(501) 945-0080. **$49-$90.** 5711 Pritchard Dr 72117. I-40 exit 157, just s, then just w. Int corridors. **Pets:** Accepted. ⏹ ⊇ ⎗ 🔒 ▣

Red Roof Inn North Little Rock-JFK/City Center H
(501) 758-1851. **$49-$90.** 120 W Pershing Blvd 72114. I-40 exit 153A, just s on JFK Blvd, then just w. Int corridors. **Pets:** Accepted.
⏹ ⎷M ⊇ ⎗ ✕ 🔒 ▣

Residence Inn by Marriott-North H
(501) 945-7777. **$93-$140.** 4110 Healthcare Dr 72117. I-40 exit 156, just n, then just w. Int corridors. **Pets:** Accepted.
⎷M ⊇ ⎗ ✕ 🔒 ▣

PINE BLUFF

Holiday Inn Express Hotel & Suites H
(870) 879-3800. **Call for rates.** 3620 Camden Rd 71603. I-530 exit 39, just sw. Int corridors. **Pets:** Accepted. ⎷M ⊇ ⎗ ✕ 🔒 ▣

Presidential Hotel & Suites H
(870) 535-6300. **$71-$79.** 3104 Market St 71601. I-530 exit 46, just n on US 65 business route. Int corridors. **Pets:** Accepted.
⊇ ⎗ 🔒 ▣

Quality Inn & Suites Pine Bluff H
(870) 535-5300. **$64-$130.** 2809 Pines Mall Dr 71601. I-530 exit 46, just n on Harding Ave. Int corridors. **Pets:** $10 daily fee/pet. Service with restrictions, supervision. ⊇ ⎗ 🔒 ▣

POCAHONTAS

Days Inn & Suites H
(870) 892-9500. **$86-$89.** 2805 Hwy 67 S 72455. Jct US 62, 1.7 mi s. Int corridors. **Pets:** Other species. $10 daily fee/pet. Service with restrictions, supervision. ⎗ ✕ 🔒 ▣

ROGERS

Aloft Rogers-Bentonville H ❀
(479) 268-6799. **$89-$289.** 1103 S 52nd St 72758. I-49 exit 83, just nw. Int corridors. **Pets:** Medium. Designated rooms, service with restrictions, supervision. SAVE ⊇ ⎗ ✕ 🔒 ▣

Candlewood Suites H
(479) 636-2783. **Call for rates.** 4601 W Rozell St 72757. I-49 exit 85, 0.5 mi n on 46th St. Int corridors. **Pets:** Accepted. ⊇ ⎗ 🔒 ▣

Country Inn & Suites By Carlson H
(479) 633-0055. **$89-$199.** 4304 W Walnut St 72756. I-49 exit 85, just e. Int corridors. **Pets:** Accepted. ⊇ ⎗ ✕ 🔒 ▣

Embassy Suites Northwest Arkansas H 🐾
(479) 254-8400. **$139-$269.** 3303 Pinnacle Hills Pkwy 72758. I-49 exit 83, just w, then 0.6 mi s. Int corridors. **Pets:** Large. $50 one-time fee/room. Designated rooms, service with restrictions.
⏹ ⎷M ⊇ ✕ ⎗ ✕ 🔒 ▣

Homewood Suites by Hilton H
(479) 636-5656. **$99-$229.** 4302 W Walnut St 72756. I-49 exit 85, just e. Int corridors. **Pets:** Accepted. ⎷M ⊇ ⎗ ✕ 🔒 ▣

Hyatt Place Rogers/Bentonville H
(479) 633-8555. **$89-$299.** 4610 W Walnut St 72756. I-49 exit 85, just e. Int corridors. **Pets:** Medium, dogs only. $75 one-time fee/room. Service with restrictions, crate. SAVE ⊇ ⎗ ✕ 🔒 ▣

Microtel Inn & Suites by Wyndham Rogers H
(479) 636-5551. **$50-$136.** 909 S 8th St 72756. 0.5 mi s of jct Walnut St. Int corridors. **Pets:** Accepted. ⎗ 🔒 ▣

Residence Inn by Marriott H ❀
(479) 636-5900. **$104-$203.** 4611 W Locust St 72756. I-49 exit 85, 0.4 mi n on 46th St. Int corridors. **Pets:** Other species. $75 one-time fee/room. Service with restrictions, crate. ⎷M ⊇ ⎗ ✕ 🔒 ▣

Staybridge Suites Rogers-Bentonville H ❖
(479) 845-5701. Call for rates. 1801 S 52nd St 72758. I-49 exit 83, just nw. Int corridors. Pets: Other species. $75 one-time fee/room. Service with restrictions, crate.

RUSSELLVILLE
La Quinta Inn & Suites H
(479) 967-2299. $93-$196. 111 E Harrell Dr 72802. I-40 exit 81, just e, then just n. Int corridors. Pets: Accepted.

Quality Inn M
(479) 967-7500. $74-$83. 3019 E Parkway Dr 72802. I-40 exit 84, just s, then just w. Ext corridors. Pets: Medium. $15 daily fee/pet. Service with restrictions, supervision.

Super 8 Russellville H
(479) 968-8898. $63-$78. 2404 N Arkansas Ave 72802. I-40 exit 81, just s. Int corridors. Pets: Accepted.

SEARCY
Best Western Plus Searcy Inn H
(501) 279-9191. $90-$159. 501 Willow St 72143. US 67/167 exit 46, just w, then just n. Int corridors. Pets: $15 daily fee/pet. Designated rooms, service with restrictions, supervision.

Microtel Inn & Suites by Wyndham H
(501) 268-1555. $55-$100. 3668 Ferren Tr 72143. US 67/167 exit 46, just e, then just n. Int corridors. Pets: Accepted.

SPRINGDALE
Hampton Inn & Suites H ❖
(479) 756-3500. $99-$284. 1700 S 48th St 72762. I-49 exit 72, just e. Int corridors. Pets: Large, other species. Designated rooms, service with restrictions.

Holiday Inn Northwest AR Hotel & Convention Center H
(479) 751-8300. $89-$339. 1500 S 48th St 72762. I-49 exit 72, just e. Int corridors. Pets: Accepted.

La Quinta Inn & Suites Springdale H
(479) 751-2626. $86-$187. 1300 S 48th St 72764. I-49 exit 72, just e. Int corridors. Pets: Accepted.

Residence Inn by Marriott H
(479) 872-9100. $104-$172. 1740 S 48th St 72762. I-49 exit 72, just e to 48th St, then just s. Int corridors. Pets: Other species. $75 one-time fee/room. Service with restrictions.

STAR CITY
Americas Best Value Inn & Suites Star City H
(870) 628-6883. $66-$125. 1308 N Lincoln Ave 71667. Just n on US 425. Int corridors. Pets: Very small, dogs only. $5 daily fee/pet. Service with restrictions, supervision.

VAN BUREN
Best Western Van Buren Inn H ❖
(479) 474-8100. $100-$149. 1903 N 6th St 72956. I-40 exit 5, just n, then just e. Ext corridors. Pets: Small, other species. $20 daily fee/pet. Designated rooms, service with restrictions, supervision.

Sleep Inn & Suites H ❖
(479) 262-6776. $73-$121. 1633 N 12th Ct 72956. I-40 exit 5, just s on Fayetteville Rd, 0.6 mi e on Pointer Tr, then just n. Int corridors. Pets: $15 daily fee/pet. Service with restrictions, supervision.

WEST MEMPHIS
Days Inn West Memphis H
(870) 735-8600. $53-$90. 1100 Ingram Blvd 72301. I-40 exit 279A, just n. Ext corridors. Pets: Other species. $10 daily fee/pet. Service with restrictions, crate.

CALIFORNIA

AGOURA HILLS (Restaurants p. 595)
Sheraton Agoura Hills Hotel H
(818) 707-1220. $159-$309. 30100 Agoura Rd 91301. US 101 exit 38 (Reyes Adobe Rd), just w, then just s. Int corridors. Pets: Accepted.

ALAMEDA
Marina Village Inn H
(510) 523-9450. Call for rates. 1151 Pacific Marina 94501. I-880 exit Broadway W, through Webster Tube, s on Atlantic Ave, then just e on Triumph St. Ext/int corridors. Pets: Accepted.

ALHAMBRA
Super 8 Los Angeles/Alhambra M
(323) 225-2310. $65-$105. 5350 S Huntington Dr 90032. I-10 exit 22 (Fremont Ave), 2.5 mi n, then 0.5 mi w. Ext corridors. Pets: $20 daily fee/pet. Designated rooms, service with restrictions.

ALPINE
Ayres Lodge Alpine M
(619) 445-5800. $119-$249. 1251 Tavern Rd 91901. I-8 exit 30 (Tavern Rd), just s. Ext corridors. Pets: Other species. $45 one-time fee/pet. Designated rooms, service with restrictions, supervision.

ALTURAS
Best Western Trailside Inn M
(530) 233-4111. $110-$130. 343 N Main St 96101. Just s of jct US 395/SR 299 and Main St; jct W 4th St. Ext corridors. Pets: Medium, dogs only. $20 daily fee/pet. Designated rooms, service with restrictions, supervision.

AMERICAN CANYON
Holiday Inn Express & Suites-Napa Valley American Canyon H
(707) 552-8100. Call for rates. 5001 Main St 94503. I-80 exit 36 (American Canyon Rd), 3.1 mi sw, 1.1 mi n on SR 29 (Broadway St), just e on Eucalyptus Dr, then just s. Int corridors. Pets: Small. $50 one-time fee/room. Designated rooms, service with restrictions, supervision.

ANAHEIM

▼▼▼▼ Anaheim Holiday Inn Hotel & Suites H
(714) 535-0300. **$69-$699.** 1240 S Walnut St 92802. I-5 exit 110 (Harbor Blvd/Ball Rd) northbound; exit 110A (Harbor Blvd) southbound, just n, 0.5 mi w on Ball Rd, then just s. Int corridors. **Pets:** Accepted.
[icons]

▼▼▼ The Anaheim Hotel H
(714) 772-5900. **Call for rates.** 1700 S Harbor Blvd 92802. I-5 exit 110 (Harbor Blvd/Ball Rd) northbound; exit 110A (Harbor Blvd) southbound, 0.6 mi s. Ext corridors. **Pets:** Accepted.
[icons]

▼▼▼▼ Anaheim Majestic Garden Hotel H ❀
(714) 778-1700. **$119-$269.** 900 S Disneyland Dr 92802. I-5 exit 110 (Harbor Blvd/Ball Rd) northbound; exit 110A (Harbor Blvd) southbound, just n, just w on Ball Rd, then just n. Int corridors. **Pets:** Medium. $50 one-time fee/room. Designated rooms, service with restrictions, supervision. [icons]

▼▼▼ Anaheim TownePlace Suites by Marriott M
(714) 939-9700. **$116-$200.** 1730 S State College Blvd 92806. I-5 exit 109 (Katella Ave/Disney Way) northbound; exit 109A (Katella Ave/Orangewood Ave) southbound, 0.7 mi e, then just n. Int corridors.
Pets: Accepted. [icons]

▼▼▼ Candlewood Suites Anaheim-Resort Area H
(714) 635-5555. **Call for rates.** 1733 S Anaheim Blvd 92805. I-5 exit 109 (Katella Ave/Disney Way) northbound; exit 109A (Katella Ave/Orangewood Ave) southbound, just w, then just n. Int corridors.
Pets: Accepted. [icons]

▼▼▼ Clarion Hotel Anaheim Resort H
(714) 750-3131. **$100-$309.** 616 Convention Way 92802. I-5 exit 109 (Katella Ave/Disney Way) northbound; exit 109A (Katella Ave/Orangewood Ave) southbound, 0.8 mi w to Harbor Blvd, just s, then just w. Int corridors. **Pets:** Accepted.
[icons]

▼▼ Extended Stay America-Orange County-Anaheim Convention Center M
(714) 502-9988. **$100-$130.** 1742 S Clementine St 92802. I-5 exit 109 (Katella Ave/Disney Way) northbound; exit 109A (Katella Ave/Orangewood Ave) southbound, just w, then just n. Int corridors.
Pets: Accepted. [icons]

▼▼▼▼ Four Points by Sheraton-Anaheim H
(714) 758-0900. **$99-$299.** 1221 S Harbor Blvd 92805. I-5 exit 110 (Harbor Blvd/Ball Rd) northbound; exit 110A (Harbor Blvd) southbound, just n. Ext corridors. **Pets:** Accepted.
[icons]

▼▼▼ Hotel Indigo Anaheim M
(714) 772-7755. **Call for rates.** 435 W Katella Ave 92802. I-5 exit 109 (Katella Ave/Disney Way) northbound; exit 109A (Katella Ave/Orangewood Ave) southbound, 0.6 mi w. Int corridors. **Pets:** Accepted.
[icons]

▼▼▼ Motel 6 Anaheim-Maingate #1066 M
(714) 520-9696. **$65-$145.** 100 W Disney Way 92802. I-5 exit 109 (Katella Ave/Disney Way) northbound; exit 109B (Disney Way/Anaheim Blvd) southbound, just w, just n on Anaheim Blvd, then just w. Ext corridors. **Pets:** Accepted. [icons]

▼▼▼ Red Lion Hotel Anaheim Resort H
(714) 750-2801. **Call for rates.** 1850 S Harbor Blvd 92802. I-5 exit 109 (Katella Ave/Disney Way) northbound; exit 109A (Katella Ave/Orangewood Ave) southbound, 0.8 mi w, then just s. Int corridors.
Pets: Accepted. [icons]

▼▼▼ Residence Inn by Marriott Anaheim Maingate H ❀
(714) 533-3555. **$176-$301.** 1700 S Clementine St 92802. I-5 exit 109 (Katella Ave/Disney Way) northbound; exit 109A (Katella Ave/Orangewood Ave) southbound, just w, just n. Int corridors. **Pets:** Medium. $100 one-time fee/room. Service with restrictions.
[icons]

▼▼▼▼ Sheraton Park Hotel at the Anaheim Resort H
(714) 750-1811. **$139-$489, 3 day notice.** 1855 S Harbor Blvd 92802. I-5 exit 109 (Katella Ave/Disney Way) northbound; exit 109A (Katella Ave/Orangewood Ave) southbound, 0.8 mi w, then just s. Int corridors.
Pets: Medium, dogs only. Designated rooms, service with restrictions, supervision. [icons]

▼▼▼ SpringHill Suites by Marriott at Anaheim Resort /Convention Center H
(714) 533-2101. **$137-$263.** 1801 S Harbor Blvd 92802. I-5 exit 109 (Katella Ave/Disney Way) northbound; exit 109A (Katella Ave/Orangewood Ave) southbound 0.8 mi w, then just s. Int corridors.
Pets: Accepted. [icons]

▼▼▼ Staybridge Suites-Anaheim Resort H
(714) 748-7700. **$129-$249.** 1855 S Manchester Ave 92802. I-5 exit 109 (Katella Ave/Disney Way) northbound; exit 109A (Katella Ave/Orangewood Ave) southbound, just w, then 0.3 mi s; adjacent to west side of freeway. Int corridors. **Pets:** Accepted.
[icons]

ANDERSON

▼▼▼▼ Best Western Anderson Inn H
(530) 365-2753. **$100-$180.** 2688 Gateway Dr 96007. I-5 exit 668 (Central Anderson/Lassen Nat'l Park) northbound, just e on Balls Ferry Rd, then just s; exit southbound, just e, just s on McMurry Dr, just e on Balls Ferry Rd, then just s. Ext corridors. **Pets:** Medium, other species. $20 daily fee/pet. Designated rooms, service with restrictions, supervision. [icons]

▼▼▼▼ Gaia Hotel & Spa Redding, an Ascend Hotel Collection Member H
(530) 365-7077. **$99-$239.** 4125 Riverside Pl 96007. I-5 exit 670 (Riverside Ave), just e, then just n. Ext corridors. **Pets:** Medium. $25 one-time fee/pet. Designated rooms, service with restrictions, supervision.
[icons]

ANGELS CAMP

▼▼▼▼ Best Western Cedar Inn & Suites H
(209) 736-4000. **$79-$199, 3 day notice.** 444 S Main St 95222. On SR 49; center. Ext/int corridors. **Pets:** Accepted.
[icons]

▼ Jumping Frog Motel M
(209) 736-2191. **Call for rates.** 330 Murphys Grade Rd 95222. Just e of jct SR 49; center. Ext corridors. **Pets:** Accepted.
[icons]

▼▼▼ Travelodge Angels Camp H
(209) 736-4242. **$69-$189.** 600 N Main St 95222. On SR 49; north end of town. Ext corridors. **Pets:** Dogs only. $10 daily fee/pet. Service with restrictions, supervision. [icons]

ARCADIA

▼▼ Extended Stay America-Los Angeles-Arcadia H
(626) 446-6422. **$105-$140.** 401 E Santa Clara St 91006. I-210 exit 33 (Huntington Dr), just w to 5th Ave, just n, then just w. Int corridors.
Pets: Accepted. [icons]

▼▼▼ Residence Inn by Marriott Pasadena Arcadia H
(626) 446-6500. **$171-$252.** 321 E Huntington Dr 91006. I-210 exit 33 (Huntington Dr), 0.5 mi w, then just n on Gateway Dr. Ext corridors.
Pets: Accepted. [icons]

ARCATA

▼▼▼ Best Western Arcata Inn M ❀
(707) 826-0313. **$87-$92.** 4827 Valley West Blvd 95521. US 101 exit Giuntoli Ln/Janes Rd, just e, then just s. Ext corridors. **Pets:** Dogs only. $20 one-time fee/room. Designated rooms, service with restrictions, crate. [icons]

▼▼ **Days Inn & Suites Arcata** Ⓜ

(707) 826-2827. **$90-$155.** 4701 Valley West Blvd 95521. US 101 exit Giuntoli Ln/Janes Rd, just e, then just s. Ext corridors. **Pets:** Accepted.

🔥ᴹ 🛎 📶 🛄 💻

▼▼ **Hotel Arcata** Ⓗ

(707) 826-0217. **$97-$167.** 708 9th St 95521. Corner of G St; downtown; in plaza. Int corridors. **Pets:** Accepted. 🍽 📶 🐾 💻

ARNOLD

▼▼ **Arnold Meadowmont Lodge** Ⓜ

(209) 795-1394. **Call for rates.** 2011 Hwy 4 95223. On SR 4; south end of town. Ext corridors. **Pets:** Accepted. 🔥ᴹ 📶 🖂 🛄 💻

ARROYO GRANDE (Restaurants p. 595)

🔺 ▼▼▼ **Best Western Casa Grande Inn** Ⓜ

(805) 481-7398. **$110-$270.** 850 Oak Park Blvd 93420. US 101 exit 188 (Oak Park Blvd), just e. Ext/int corridors. **Pets:** Accepted.

🆂🅰🆅🅴 🛎 🖂 📶 🖂 🛄 💻

ATASCADERO

▼▼▼ **Carlton Hotel** Ⓗ

(805) 461-5100. **Call for rates.** 6005 El Camino Real 93422. US 101 exit Traffic Way, just e. Int corridors. **Pets:** Accepted.

🔥ᴹ 📶 🖂 🛄 💻

AUBURN

🔺 ▼▼▼ **Best Western Golden Key** Ⓗ 🐾

(530) 885-8611. **$99-$184.** 13450 Lincoln Way 95603. I-80 exit 121 (Foresthill Rd/Auburn Ravine Rd), just e, then just n. Ext corridors. **Pets:** $20 one-time fee/room. Designated rooms, service with restrictions, supervision. 🆂🅰🆅🅴 🔥ᴹ 🛎 📶 🛄 💻

▼▼▼ **Holiday Inn Auburn** Ⓗ 🐾

(530) 887-8787. **$160-$250.** 120 Grass Valley Hwy 95603. I-80 exit 119B (SR 49), just nw. Int corridors. **Pets:** Small, dogs only. $30 one-time fee/pet. Service with restrictions, crate.

🅴🅲🅾 🍽 🔥ᴹ 🛎 📶 🖂 🛄 💻

BAKERSFIELD

🔺 ▼▼▼ **Best Western Heritage Inn** Ⓜ

(661) 764-6268. **$85-$105.** 253 Trask St 93314. I-5 exit 253 (Stockdale Hwy), just e. Ext corridors. **Pets:** Accepted.

🆂🅰🆅🅴 🔥ᴹ 🛎 📶 🛄 💻

🔺 ▼▼▼ **Best Western Plus Hill House** Ⓗ

(661) 327-4064. **$110-$140.** 700 Truxtun Ave 93301. SR 99 exit 25 (California Ave), 1.2 mi e, 0.4 mi n on Chester Ave, then 0.4 mi e. Int corridors. **Pets:** Small. $20 daily fee/pet. Designated rooms, service with restrictions, supervision. 🆂🅰🆅🅴 🍽 🔥ᴹ 🛎 📶 🛄 💻

▼▼ **Extended Stay Deluxe Bakersfield-Chester Lane** Ⓗ

(661) 328-8181. **$75-$100.** 3600 Chester Ln 93309. SR 99 exit 25 (California Ave), just w to Real Rd, just s, then just w. Int corridors. **Pets:** Accepted. 🔥ᴹ 📶 🛄 💻

▼▼▼▼ **La Quinta Inn & Suites Bakersfield North** Ⓗ

(661) 393-7775. **$88-$301.** 8858 Spectrum Park Way 93308. SR 99 exit 30 (SR 65) northbound, just e to Merle Haggard Dr, just n to Spectrum Park Way, then just s; exit 31 (7th Standard Rd) southbound, just e, then just s. Int corridors. **Pets:** Accepted. 🛎 📶 🛄 💻

▼▼▼ **La Quinta Inn Bakersfield South** Ⓜ

(661) 325-7400. **$68-$163.** 3232 Riverside Dr 93308. SR 99 exit 26A (SR 58 W/Rosedale Hwy) southbound, just e, then just n; exit 26B (Buck Owens Blvd) northbound, just s. Ext corridors. **Pets:** Accepted.

🔥ᴹ 🛎 📶 🛄 💻

▲▲▲ ▼▼▼▼ **The Padre Hotel** Ⓗ

(661) 427-4900. **$119-$259.** 1702 18th St 93301. SR 58 exit 26A (Rosedale Hwy), 1.5 mi e, 0.3 mi s on F St, then 0.3 mi s. Int corridors. **Pets:** $50 one-time fee/pet. No service, supervision.

🆂🅰🆅🅴 🍽 🔥ᴹ 📶 🖂 🛄 💻

▲▲▲ ▼▼▼ **Red Lion Bakersfield** Ⓗ

(661) 327-9651. **Call for rates.** 2620 Buck Owens Blvd 93308. SR 99 exit 26B (Buck Owens Blvd) northbound, just s; exit 26 (SR 58 W/SR 178 E) southbound, just e, then just n. Ext/int corridors. **Pets:** Accepted. 🆂🅰🆅🅴 🍽 🔥ᴹ 🛎 📶 🛄 💻

▼▼▼▼ **Residence Inn by Marriott** Ⓗ 🌺

(661) 321-9800. **$112-$174.** 4241 Chester Ln 93309. SR 99 exit 25 (California Ave), 0.5 mi w, then just n. Ext corridors. **Pets:** Other species. $100 one-time fee/room. Service with restrictions, crate.

🅴🅲🅾 🔥ᴹ 🛎 📶 🖂 🛄 💻

▲▲▲ ▼▼▼ **Super 8** Ⓜ

(661) 833-1000. **$50-$78.** 3620 Wible Rd 93309. SR 99 exit 21 (White Ln), 0.3 mi w, then just n. Ext corridors. **Pets:** Medium. $5 daily fee/pet. Service with restrictions, supervision. 🆂🅰🆅🅴 🔥ᴹ 🛎 📶 🛄 💻

▼▼ **Super 8 Bakersfield** Ⓜ

(661) 322-1012. **$55-$75.** 901 Real Rd 93309. SR 99 exit 25 (California Ave), just w, then just s. Ext corridors. **Pets:** Medium, dogs only. $10 daily fee/pet. Designated rooms, service with restrictions, supervision.

🔥ᴹ 🛎 📶 🛄 💻

▲▲▲ ▼▼▼ **Travelodge of Bakersfield** Ⓜ

(661) 325-0772. **$50-$80.** 1011 Oak St 93304. SR 99 exit 25 (California Ave), just e, then just s. Ext/int corridors. **Pets:** Other species. $15 daily fee/pet. Designated rooms, service with restrictions, supervision.

🆂🅰🆅🅴 🛎 📶 🛄 💻

BANNING

▼▼ **Banning Travelodge** Ⓜ

(951) 849-1000. **$60-$140.** 1700 W Ramsey St 92220. I-10 exit 99 (22nd St), just n, then 0.4 mi e. Ext corridors. **Pets:** Accepted.

🔥ᴹ 🛎 📶 🛄 💻

▼▼▼ **Days Inn Banning** Ⓜ

(951) 849-0092. **$70-$130.** 2320 W Ramsey St 92220. I-10 exit 99 (22nd St), just n, then just w. Ext corridors. **Pets:** Accepted.

🔥ᴹ 🛎 📶 🛄 💻

▼▼▼▼ **Hampton Inn & Suites by Hilton Banning Beaumont** Ⓗ

(951) 922-1000. **$119-$299.** 6071 Joshua Palmer Way 92220. I-10 exit 96 (Highland Springs Ave), just n, then just e. Int corridors. **Pets:** Medium. $25 daily fee/pet. Designated rooms, service with restrictions, supervision. 🔥ᴹ 🛎 📶 🛄 💻

▼▼▼ **Quality Inn-Banning** Ⓜ

(951) 849-8888. **$75-$189.** 1690 W Ramsey St 92220. I-10 exit 99 (22nd St), just n, then 0.4 mi e. Int corridors. **Pets:** Accepted.

🔥ᴹ 🛎 📶 🖂 🛄 💻

BARSTOW

▼▼▼ **Ayres Hotel Barstow** Ⓗ

(760) 307-3121. **$99-$199.** 2812 Lenwood Rd 92311. I-15 exit 178 (Lenwood Rd), just se, then just s. Int corridors. **Pets:** Accepted.

🔌 🔥ᴹ 🛎 📶 🖂 🛄 💻

▲▲▲ ▼▼▼ **California Inn** Ⓜ 🐾

(760) 256-0661. **$55-$69.** 1431 E Main St 92311. I-15 N exit 184B (Main St), 0.7 mi e. Int corridors. **Pets:** $12 daily fee/pet. Designated rooms, service with restrictions, supervision. 🆂🅰🆅🅴 🛎 📶 🛄 💻

▼▼▼ **Comfort Suites** Ⓗ

(760) 253-3600. **$94-$164.** 2571 Fisher Blvd 92311. I-15 exit 178 (Lenwood Rd), just ne; north of Barstow Outlets. Int corridors.
Pets: Accepted. 🔥ᴹ 🛎 📶 🖂 🛄 💻

Days Inn Barstow M
(760) 256-1737. **$50-$75.** 1590 Coolwater Ln 92311. I-15 exit 184B (E Main St) northbound; exit 184 (E Main St/I-40 E/Needles) southbound, just w, then just s; I-40 exit 1 (E Main St) westbound, 0.7 mi w, then just s. Ext corridors. **Pets:** Medium. $10 daily fee/pet. Designated rooms, service with restrictions, supervision.

Days Inn South at Lenwood M
(760) 253-2121. **$80-$100.** 2551 Commerce Pkwy 92311. I-15 exit 178 (Lenwood Rd), 0.3 mi w, then just 0.8 mi n; s of downtown. Ext corridors. **Pets:** Accepted.

Hampton Inn & Suites H
(760) 253-2600. **$99-$189.** 2710 Lenwood Rd 92311. I-15 exit 178 (Lenwood Rd), just se, then 0.5 mi s. Int corridors. **Pets:** Accepted.

Holiday Inn Express Hotel & Suites H
(760) 253-9200. **Call for rates.** 2700 Lenwood Rd 92311. I-15 exit 178 (Lenwood Rd), just se, then 0.5 mi s. Int corridors. **Pets:** Accepted.

Quality Inn M
(760) 256-6891. **$75-$115.** 1520 E Main St 92311. I-15 exit 184B (E Main St) northbound; exit 184 (E Main St/I-40 E/Needles) southbound, 0.3 mi w. Ext corridors. **Pets:** Small. $25 one-time fee/room. Designated rooms, no service.

Sleep Inn on Historic Route 66 M
(760) 256-1300. **Call for rates.** 1861 W Main St 92311. I-15 exit 181 (L St), 0.5 mi n, then just e. Int corridors. **Pets:** Other species. $20 one-time fee/room. No service, supervision.

Stardust Inn M
(760) 256-7116. **$45-$65.** 901 E Main St 92311. I-15 exit 183 (Barstow Rd), 0.8 mi n, then 0.4 mi e. Ext corridors. **Pets:** Small, dogs only. $10 daily fee/pet. Designated rooms, service with restrictions, supervision.

BASS LAKE

The Pines Resort CA
(559) 642-3121. **Call for rates.** 54432 Rd 432 93604. SR 41 and 49, 3.5 mi ne on SR 41, 6 mi se on CR 222/274, then just s on CR 432; in Oakhurst. Ext/int corridors. **Pets:** Accepted.

BELMONT

Hyatt House Belmont/Redwood Shores H
(650) 591-8600. **$129-$499.** 400 Concourse Dr 94002. US 101 exit 412 (Ralston Ave), just e, then 0.3 mi n on Island Pkwy. Ext corridors. **Pets:** Accepted.

BENICIA *(Restaurants p. 595)*

Best Western Plus Heritage Inn H
(707) 746-0401. **$130-$299.** 1955 E 2nd St 94510. I-780 exit Central Benicia/E 2nd St, just ne. Ext/int corridors. **Pets:** Small. $20 daily fee/pet. Designated rooms, service with restrictions, supervision.

BERKELEY *(Restaurants p. 595)*

Americas Best Value Golden Bear Inn M
(510) 525-6770. **$85-$160.** 1620 San Pablo Ave 94702. I-80 exit 12 (Gilman St), 0.5 mi e, then just s. Ext corridors. **Pets:** Other species. $15 one-time fee/pet. Service with restrictions, supervision.

Claremont Club & Spa, A Fairmont Hotel H
(510) 843-3000. **$249-$519.** 41 Tunnel Rd 94705. SR 24 exit SR 13, 0.8 mi n; I-80 exit 11 (University Ave), just e, 1.5 mi s on San Pablo Ave, 2.6 mi e on Ashby Ave, then just e. Int corridors. **Pets:** Large. $99 one-time fee/room. Service with restrictions, supervision.

DoubleTree by Hilton Berkeley Marina H
(510) 548-7920. **$149-$549.** 200 Marina Blvd 94710. I-80 exit 11 (University Ave), 0.5 mi w; on Berkeley Marina. Int corridors. **Pets:** Dogs only. $50 one-time fee/room. Designated rooms, service with restrictions, supervision.

Hotel Durant H
(510) 845-8981. **Call for rates.** 2600 Durant Ave 94704. I-80 exit 11 (University Ave), 2 mi e to Oxford St, 0.3 mi s, then 0.5 mi e; jct Bowditch St. Int corridors. **Pets:** Accepted.

Hotel Shattuck Plaza H
(510) 845-7300. **Call for rates.** 2086 Allston Way 94704. I-80 exit 11 (University Ave), 2 mi e, just s on Shattuck Ave, then just w. Int corridors. **Pets:** Accepted.

BEVERLY HILLS *(Restaurants p. 595)*

The Beverly Hills Hotel and Bungalows H
(310) 276-2251. **$525-$1095.** 9641 Sunset Blvd 90210. I-405 exit 57 (Sunset Blvd), 3.7 mi e. Ext/int corridors. **Pets:** Other species. $35 daily fee/pet. Supervision.

The Beverly Hilton H
(310) 274-7777. **Call for rates.** 9876 Wilshire Blvd 90210. I-405 exit 55 (Wilshire Blvd), 2.2 mi e. Int corridors. **Pets:** Accepted.

Beverly Wilshire A Four Seasons Hotel H
(310) 275-5200. **Call for rates.** 9500 Wilshire Blvd 90212. I-405 exit 55 (Wilshire Blvd), 4.5 mi e. Int corridors. **Pets:** Accepted.

Montage Beverly Hills H
(310) 860-7800. **Call for rates.** 225 N Canon Dr 90210. I-405 exit 55A (Santa Monica Blvd), 3.4 mi e, then 0.4 mi s. Int corridors. **Pets:** Accepted.

The Peninsula Beverly Hills H
(310) 551-2888. **$595-$10000.** 9882 S Santa Monica Blvd 90212. I-405 exit 55A (Santa Monica Blvd), 2.2 mi e, at Wilshire Blvd. Ext/int corridors. **Pets:** $35 daily fee/pet.

SLS Hotel, A Luxury Collection Hotel, Beverly Hills H
(310) 247-0400. **$349-$899.** 465 S La Cienega Blvd 90048. I-10 exit 7A (La Cienega Blvd), 2.5 mi n. Int corridors. **Pets:** Accepted.

Viceroy L'Ermitage Beverly Hills H
(310) 278-3344. **$399-$1299.** 9291 Burton Way 90210. I-10 exit 6 (Robertson Blvd), 3.1 mi n, then just w. Int corridors. **Pets:** Medium. $50 daily fee/room. Service with restrictions, supervision.

BIG BEAR LAKE *(Restaurants p. 595)*

▼▼▼ Bay Meadows Resort CA
(909) 866-4666. **$79-$369, 5 day notice.** 39756 Big Bear Blvd 92315. SR 18, 1 mi w of Village. Ext corridors. **Pets:** Dogs only. $20 one-time fee/pet. Designated rooms, service with restrictions, supervision.
⊤⊤ ⑤M ➔ ✕ 🛜 ✕ ⅄ 🖥 🖵

ΔΔΔ ▼▼▼ Best Western Big Bear Chateau H
(909) 866-6666. **$99-$379.** 42200 Moonridge Rd 92315. SR 18, 1.5 mi e of Pine Knot Ave, 0.5 mi s. Int corridors. **Pets:** $40 one-time fee/room. Designated rooms, service with restrictions, crate.
SAVE ⑤M ➔ ✕ 🛜 ✕ ⅄ 🖥 🖵

▼▼ Eagle's Nest Bed & Breakfast BB ✿
(909) 866-6465. **$115-$185, 5 day notice.** 41675 Big Bear Blvd 92315. SR 18, 1 mi e of Pine Knot Ave. Ext/int corridors. **Pets:** Other species. $10 daily fee/pet. Designated rooms, service with restrictions, supervision. 🛜 ✕ 🕿 🖥 🖵

▼▼ Golden Bear Cottages CA
(909) 866-2010. **Call for rates.** 39367 Big Bear Blvd 92315. SR 18, 2 mi w of village. Ext corridors. **Pets:** Accepted.
⑤M ➔ ✕ 🛜 ✕ ⅄ 🖥 🖵

ΔΔΔ ▼▼▼ Grey Squirrel Resort CA
(909) 866-4335. **$100-$575, 30 day notice.** 39372 Big Bear Blvd 92315. SR 18, 2 mi w of village. Ext corridors. **Pets:** Accepted.
SAVE ⑤M ➔ ✕ 🛜 ✕ ⅄ 🖥 🖵

▼▼ Pine Knot Guest Ranch CA
(909) 866-6500. **Call for rates.** 908 Pine Knot Ave 92315. Just s of SR 18 and downtown area. Ext corridors. **Pets:** Accepted.
🛜 ✕ 🖥 🖵

▼▼ Sleepy Forest Cottages CA
(909) 866-7444. **$79-$299, 15 day notice.** 400 S Eureka Dr 92315. SR 18, 0.7 mi e of Pine Knot Ave, just n. Ext corridors. **Pets:** Accepted.
⊤⊤ ⑤M 🛜 ✕ 🖥 🖵

BIG PINE

▼ Bristlecone Motel M
(760) 938-2067. **Call for rates.** 101 N Main St 93513. On US 395. Ext corridors. **Pets:** Accepted. 🛜 ✕ 🖥 🖵

BISHOP *(Restaurants p. 595)*

ΔΔΔ ▼▼▼ Best Western Bishop Lodge M
(760) 873-3543. **$120-$299.** 1025 N Main St 93514. On US 395. Ext/int corridors. **Pets:** $20 daily fee/room. Designated rooms, service with restrictions, supervision. SAVE ⑤M ➔ 🛜 🖥 🖵

ΔΔΔ ▼▼▼ Comfort Inn M
(760) 873-4284. **$100-$155.** 805 N Main St 93514. On US 395. Ext corridors. **Pets:** $15 daily fee/pet. Designated rooms, service with restrictions, supervision. SAVE ⑤M ➔ 🛜 🖥 🖵

▼▼▼ Holiday Inn Express Hotel & Suites H
(760) 872-2423. **Call for rates.** 636 N Main St 93514. On US 395. Int corridors. **Pets:** Small, dogs only. $25 daily fee/pet. Designated rooms, service with restrictions, supervision.
⑤M ➔ ✕ 🛜 ✕ 🖥 🖵

▼▼▼▼ Joseph House Inn BB
(760) 872-3389. **$168-$200, 14 day notice.** 376 W Yaney St 93514. 0.3 mi w of US 395. Int corridors. **Pets:** Dogs only. Designated rooms, service with restrictions, supervision. 🛜 ✕ 🕿

▼▼ Travelodge M
(760) 872-1771. **$79-$220.** 155 E Elm St 93514. On US 395, just e. Ext corridors. **Pets:** Other species. $15 daily fee/pet. Designated rooms, service with restrictions, supervision. ⑤M ➔ 🛜 ✕ 🖥 🖵

▼▼ Vagabond Inn M
(760) 873-6351. **Call for rates.** 1030 N Main St 93514. On US 395. Ext corridors. **Pets:** Accepted. ⑤M ➔ 🛜 🖥 🖵

BLYTHE *(Restaurants p. 595)*

ΔΔΔ ▼▼▼ Best Western Sahara M
(760) 922-7105. **$84-$159.** 825 W Hobsonway 92225. I-10 exit 239 (Lovekin Blvd), just n, then just w. Ext corridors. **Pets:** Medium. $10 daily fee/room. Service with restrictions, supervision.
SAVE ⑤M ➔ 🛜 🖥 🖵

▼▼ Clarion Inn M
(760) 922-9000. **$79-$154.** 900 W Hobsonway 92225. I-10 exit 239 (Lovekin Blvd), just n, then just w. Ext corridors. **Pets:** Medium. $20 daily fee/room. Designated rooms, service with restrictions, supervision.
⑤M ➔ 🛜 🖥 🖵

BORREGO SPRINGS

ΔΔΔ ▼▼▼▼ La Casa del Zorro Resort & Spa H ✿
(760) 767-0100. **$129-$399, 4 day notice.** 3845 Yaqui Pass Rd 92004. 5.5 mi se on CR S3; jct Yaqui Pass and Borrego Springs rds. Ext corridors. **Pets:** Dogs only. $50 one-time fee/room. Designated rooms, service with restrictions, supervision.
SAVE ⊤⊤ ⑤M ➔ ✕ 🛜 ✕ 🖥 🖵

BRAWLEY

ΔΔΔ ▼▼▼▼ Best Western Plus Main Street Inn M
(760) 351-9800. **$94-$150.** 1562 E Main St 92227. On SR 78 and 111. Ext/int corridors. **Pets:** Other species. $20 daily fee/pet. Service with restrictions, supervision. SAVE ⑤M ➔ ✕ 🖥 🖵

ΔΔΔ ▼▼▼ Brawley Inn Hotel & Conference Center M
(760) 344-1199. **Call for rates.** 575 W Main St 92227. On SR 86 and 78. Ext/int corridors. **Pets:** Accepted.
SAVE ⊤⊤ ⑤M ➔ 🛜 🖥 🖵

BREA

▼▼▼ Chase Suite Hotels M
(714) 579-3200. **$109-$299.** 3100 E Imperial Hwy 92821. SR 57 exit 9 (SR 90), 1.5 mi e. Ext corridors. **Pets:** Medium. $250 deposit/room, $75 one-time fee/pet. Designated rooms, service with restrictions, supervision. ➔ 🛜 ✕ 🖥 🖵

BRIDGEPORT

ΔΔΔ ▼▼▼ Redwood Motel M ✿
(760) 932-7060. **$69-$250, 3 day notice.** 425 Main St 93517. On US 395; on north side of town. Ext corridors. **Pets:** $10 daily fee/pet. Designated rooms, service with restrictions, supervision.
SAVE 🛜 🖥 🖵

ΔΔΔ ▼▼ Ruby Inn M
(760) 932-7241. **$125-$250.** 333 Main St 93517. On US 395; center. Ext corridors. **Pets:** Medium. Service with restrictions, supervision.
SAVE 🛜 ✕ 🖥 🖵

ΔΔΔ ▼▼▼ Silver Maple Inn M ✿
(760) 932-7383. **$80-$150.** 310 Main St 93517. On US 395; center. Ext corridors. **Pets:** Other species. Service with restrictions, supervision.
SAVE 🛜 ✕ ⅄ 🖥 🖵

▼▼ Virginia Creek Settlement Motel and Cabins M
(760) 932-7780. **Call for rates.** 70847 US 395 93517. On US 395, 5 mi s. Ext corridors. **Pets:** Other species. Service with restrictions, crate.
⊤⊤ 🛜 ⅄ 🕿 🖥 🖵

ΔΔΔ ▼▼▼ Walker River Lodge M
(760) 932-7021. **$85-$230.** 100 Main St 93517. On US 395; at south end of town. Ext corridors. **Pets:** Accepted. SAVE ➔ 🛜 🖥 🖵

BUELLTON

Quality Inn Santa Ynez Valley M
(805) 688-0022. **$71-$239.** 630 Ave of the Flags 93427. US 101 exit 140B (Ave of the Flags) southbound, just s; exit 140A (SR 246) northbound, just w, then just n. Ext/int corridors. **Pets:** $25 one-time fee/pet. Supervision.

Santa Ynez Valley Marriott H
(805) 688-1000. **$128-$279, 3 day notice.** 555 McMurray Rd 93427. US 101 exit 140A (SR 246), just e, then just n. Int corridors. **Pets:** Accepted.

BURBANK (Restaurants p. 595)

Hotel Amarano Burbank H
(818) 842-8887. **Call for rates.** 322 N Pass Ave 91505. SR 134 exit 2 (Hollywood Way) westbound, just w on Alameda Ave, then 0.5 mi n; exit 2 (Pass Ave) eastbound, 0.5 mi n. Ext corridors. **Pets:** Accepted.

Los Angeles Marriott Burbank Airport Hotel H
(818) 843-6000. **$162-$279.** 2500 N Hollywood Way 91505. I-5 exit 149 (Hollywood Way), 1 mi s. Int corridors. **Pets:** Accepted.

Residence Inn by Marriott Los Angeles Burbank/Downtown H
(818) 260-8787. **$179-$280.** 321 Ikea Way 91502. I-5 exit 146A (Olive Ave) northbound, just e on Angeleno Ave, then just s; exit 146A (Verdugo Ave) southbound, just s on Front St, just e on Verdugo Ave, then just n. Int corridors. **Pets:** Accepted.

The Safari Inn M
(818) 845-8586. **$139-$269.** 1911 W Olive Ave 91506. I-5 exit 146A (Olive Ave), 1.3 mi sw. Ext corridors. **Pets:** Other species. $300 deposit/room, $25 daily fee/pet. Service with restrictions, supervision.

BURLINGAME

Crowne Plaza San Francisco Airport H
(650) 342-9200. **$109-$999.** 1177 Airport Blvd 94010. US 101 exit Broadway-Burlingame or Old Bayshore Hwy, just e. Int corridors. **Pets:** Accepted.

DoubleTree by Hilton Hotel San Francisco Airport H
(650) 344-5500. **$129-$499.** 835 Airport Blvd 94010. US 101 exit Broadway-Burlingame or Anza Blvd, just e. Int corridors. **Pets:** Accepted.

Embassy Suites San Francisco Airport - Waterfront H
(650) 342-4600. **$169-$559.** 150 Anza Blvd 94010. US 101 exit Broadway-Burlingame, just e. Int corridors. **Pets:** Large. $75 one-time fee/pet. Designated rooms, service with restrictions, supervision.

Hilton San Francisco Airport Bayfront H
(650) 340-8500. **Call for rates.** 600 Airport Blvd 94010. US 101 exit Broadway-Burlingame or Anza Blvd, 0.3 mi e. Int corridors. **Pets:** Accepted.

Hyatt Regency San Francisco Airport H
(650) 347-1234. **$139-$509.** 1333 Bayshore Hwy 94010. US 101 exit Broadway-Burlingame, just e. Int corridors. **Pets:** Accepted.

Red Roof PLUS+ San Francisco Airport M
(650) 342-7772. **$79-$199.** 777 Airport Blvd 94010. US 101 exit Broadway-Burlingame or Anza Blvd; just s of airport. Ext corridors. **Pets:** Accepted.

San Francisco Airport Marriott Waterfront H
(650) 692-9100. **$153-$371.** 1800 Old Bayshore Hwy 94010. US 101 exit Millbrae Ave, just e. Int corridors. **Pets:** Accepted.

BURNEY

Charm Motel M
(530) 335-3300. **$70-$100.** 37363 Main St 96013. 0.5 mi ne on SR 299; jct Roff Way. Ext corridors. **Pets:** $15 daily fee/pet. Service with restrictions, crate.

Green Gables Motel M
(530) 335-3300. **$70-$100.** 37385 Main St 96013. 0.5 mi ne on SR 299; jct Roff Way. Ext corridors. **Pets:** $15 daily fee/pet. Service with restrictions, crate.

CALABASAS (Restaurants p. 595)

The Anza-A Calabasas Hotel H
(818) 222-5300. **$99-$299.** 23627 Calabasas Rd 91302. US 101 exit 29 (Valley Cir/Mulholland Dr), just w, then 0.6 mi n. Int corridors. **Pets:** Dogs only. $25 daily fee/pet. Designated rooms, service with restrictions.

CALEXICO

Best Western John Jay Inn H
(760) 768-0442. **$80-$150.** 2421 Scaroni Ave 92231. I-8 exit 118A (SR 111 S), 5.5 mi s, just w on W Cole Rd, then just n. Int corridors. **Pets:** Accepted.

CALIFORNIA CITY

Best Western California City Inn & Suites H
(760) 373-1369. **$90-$140.** 10386 California City Blvd 93505. SR 14 exit 73 (California City Blvd), 10 mi e. Int corridors. **Pets:** Medium, other species. $20 daily fee/pet. Designated rooms, service with restrictions, supervision.

CALIMESA

Calimesa Inn Motel M
(909) 795-2536. **Call for rates.** 1205 Calimesa Blvd 92320. I-10 exit 88 (Calimesa Blvd), just ne. Ext corridors. **Pets:** Accepted.

CALISTOGA

Chelsea Garden Inn BB
(707) 942-0948. **$165-$400, 14 day notice.** 1443 2nd St 94515. Just n of jct Lincoln Ave and Fair Way. Ext/int corridors. **Pets:** Accepted.

Cottage Grove Inn CA
(707) 942-8400. **Call for rates.** 1711 Lincoln Ave 94515. On SR 29; at Wapoo Ave. Ext corridors. **Pets:** Accepted.

Solage Calistoga H
(707) 226-0800. **$400-$1290, 14 day notice.** 755 Silverado Tr 94515. Jct SR 29, 0.5 mi se. Ext corridors. **Pets:** Accepted.

CAMARILLO (Restaurants p. 595)

Best Western Camarillo Inn M
(805) 987-4991. **$100-$140.** 295 E Daily Dr 93010. US 101 N exit 55 (Las Posas Rd), just n, then just e. Ext corridors. **Pets:** $25 daily fee/room. Designated rooms, service with restrictions, supervision.

♨ ▼▼▼▼ Residence Inn by Marriott Camarillo 🅷
(805) 388-7997. **$132-$236.** 2912 Petit St 93012. US 101 exit 53A
(Flynn Rd) northbound, 0.8 mi n, then just w; exit Dawson Dr southbound, just w. Int corridors. **Pets:** Medium, other species. $100 one-
time fee/room. Service with restrictions, crate.

SAVE 🅜 ⛶ 🗙 📶 🗙 🛎 💻

CAMBRIA *(Restaurants p. 595)*

▼▼ Bluebird Inn Ⓜ
(805) 927-4634. **$90-$300.** 1880 Main St 93428. SR 1 exit Main St
northbound, 1.9 mi ne; exit Cambria Dr southbound, 0.5 mi se. Ext
corridors. **Pets:** Large, dogs only. $20 daily fee/pet. Designated rooms,
service with restrictions, supervision. 📶 🗙 🅺 🛎 💻

▼▼▼ The Burton Inn 🅷
(805) 927-5125. **Call for rates.** 4022 Burton Dr 93428. SR 1 exit Burton Dr, 1 mi ne. Ext/int corridors. **Pets:** Accepted.

🅜 📶 🗙 🛎 💻

▼▼▼ Cambria Shores Inn Ⓜ ☙
(805) 927-8644. **$209-$389, 7 day notice.** 6276 Moonstone Beach Dr
93428. SR 1 northbound exit Windsor Ave, just w, then 0.5 mi n. Ext
corridors. **Pets:** Dogs only. $15 daily fee/pet. Service with restrictions,
supervision. 📶 🗙 🛎 💻

▼▼▼ Fireside Inn On Moonstone Beach Ⓜ
(805) 927-8661. **Call for rates.** 6700 Moonstone Beach Dr 93428. SR
1 exit Weymouth St northbound, just w, then just n. Ext/int corridors.
Pets: Accepted. ⛶ 📶 🗙 🅺 🛎 💻

▼▼▼ Fog Catcher Inn Ⓜ
(805) 927-1400. **Call for rates.** 6400 Moonstone Beach Dr 93428. SR
1 exit Weymouth St northbound, just w, then just n. Ext corridors.
Pets: Accepted. ⛶ 📶 🗙 🅺 🛎 💻

▼▼ Sea Otter Inn Ⓜ ☙
(805) 927-5888. **Call for rates.** 6656 Moonstone Beach Dr 93428. SR
1 exit Moonstone Beach Dr southbound, just w, then 0.5 mi s. Ext corridors. **Pets:** $25 daily fee/room. Designated rooms, service with restric-
tions, supervision. 🄴 🍽 🅜 ⛶ 🗙 🅺 🛎 💻

▼▼ White Water Inn Ⓜ
(805) 927-1066. **$169-$449, 7 day notice.** 6790 Moonstone Beach Dr
93428. SR 1 exit Moonstone Beach Dr northbound, just w, then 0.4 mi
n. Ext corridors. **Pets:** Accepted. 🍽 🅜 📶 🗙 🅺 🛎

CAMPBELL *(Restaurants p. 596)*

♨ ▼▼▼ Larkspur Landing Campbell 🅷
(408) 364-1514. **Call for rates.** 550 W Hamilton Ave 95008. SR 17 exit
Hamilton Ave, 1 mi w. Int corridors. **Pets:** Accepted.

SAVE 🄴🄲🄾 🍽 🅜 📶 🗙 🛎 💻

**▼▼▼▼ Residence Inn by Marriott-San
Jose/Campbell** 🅷
(408) 559-1551. **$136-$299.** 2761 S Bascom Ave 95008. SR 17 exit
Camden Ave E, just n. Ext corridors. **Pets:** Accepted.
🍽 🅜 ⛶ 📶 🗙 🛎 💻

**▼▼▼ TownePlace Suites by Marriott-San
Jose/Campbell** 🅷 ☙
(408) 370-4510. **$137-$330.** 700 E Campbell Ave 95008. SR 17 exit
Hamilton Ave E, 0.3 mi to Bascom Ave, 0.3 mi s, then 0.3 mi w. Int
corridors. **Pets:** Small, other species. $150 one-time fee/room. Desig-
nated rooms, service with restrictions, crate. 🅜 📶 🗙 🛎 💻

CARDIFF-BY-THE-SEA

▼▼▼▼ Holiday Inn Express Encinitas Cardiff Beach 🅷
(760) 944-0427. **Call for rates.** 1661 Villa Cardiff Dr 92007. I-5 exit 40
(Birmingham Dr), just e, then just n. Int corridors. **Pets:** Accepted.
🅜 ⛶ 📶 🗙 🛎 💻

CARLSBAD *(Restaurants p. 596)*

**♨ ▼▼▼▼ Cape Rey Carlsbad, A Hilton
Resort** 🅷
(760) 602-0800. **$229-$289.** 1 Ponto Rd 92011. I-5 exit 45 (Poinsettia
Ln/Aviara Pkwy), just s on Carlsbad Blvd, 0.4 mi w, then just w. Int
corridors. **Pets:** Accepted. SAVE 🍽 🅜 🗙 📶 🗙 🛎 💻

▼▼▼▼ Carlsbad by the Sea Resort 🅷
(760) 438-7880. **Call for rates.** 850 Palomar Airport Rd 92011. I-5 exit
47 (Palomar Airport Rd), just e. Ext corridors. **Pets:** Accepted.
🅜 ⛶ 📶 🗙 🛎 💻

♨ ▼▼▼▼ Hyatt House San Diego/Carlsbad 🅷 ☙
(760) 929-8200. **$139-$429.** 5010 Avenida Encinas 92008. I-5 exit 48
(Cannon Rd), just w, then just s. Int corridors. **Pets:** Other species. $75
one-time fee/pet. Service with restrictions, supervision.
SAVE 🅜 ⛶ 📶 🗙 🛎 💻

▼▼▼▼ La Quinta Inn & Suites San Diego Carlsbad Ⓜ
(760) 438-2828. **$81-$328.** 760 Macadamia Dr 92011. I-5 exit 45 (Poinsettia Ln/Aviara Pkwy), just w to Ave Encinas, just n, then just e. Ext
corridors. **Pets:** Accepted. 🅜 ⛶ 📶 🗙 🛎 💻

**♨ ▼▼▼▼ Park Hyatt Aviara Resort, Golf Club &
Spa** 🅷
(760) 448-1234. **$195-$579, 7 day notice.** 7100 Aviara Resort Dr
92011. I-5 exit 45 (Poinsettia Ln/Aviara Pkwy), 1 mi e on Poinsettia Ln,
1 mi s on Aviara Pkwy, then just sw. Int corridors. **Pets:** Accepted.
SAVE 🍽 🅜 ⛶ 🗙 📶 🗙 🛎 💻

▼▼▼▼ West Inn & Suites 🅷 ☙
(760) 448-4500. **$159-$399, 3 day notice.** 4970 Avenida Encinas
92008. I-5 exit 48 (Cannon Rd), just w, then just n. Int corridors.
Pets: $75 daily fee/room. Designated rooms, service with restrictions,
supervision. 🍽 🅜 ⛶ 📶 🗙 🛎 💻

CARMEL-BY-THE-SEA *(Restaurants p. 596)*

▼▼▼▼ Adobe Inn 🅷
(831) 624-3933. **Call for rates.** Dolores St & 8th Ave 93921. Just s off
Ocean Ave. Ext corridors. **Pets:** Accepted.
🍽 ⛶ 📶 🗙 🅺 🛎 💻

♨ ▼▼▼▼ Briarwood Inn 🄱🄱 ☙
(831) 626-9056. **$115-$490, 3 day notice.** San Carlos St 93921. 3 blks
n of Ocean Ave; at 4th Ave. Ext corridors. **Pets:** Small, dogs only. $25
daily fee/pet. Designated rooms, supervision.
SAVE 📶 🗙 🅺 🛎 💻

▼▼▼ Carmel Country Inn 🄱🄱
(831) 625-3263. **Call for rates.** Dolores St & 3rd Ave 93921. 4 blks n
of Ocean Ave. Ext corridors. **Pets:** Accepted.
🍽 📶 🗙 🅺 🛎 💻

**♨ ▼▼▼ Carmel Fireplace Inn Bed &
Breakfast** 🄱🄱 ☙
(831) 624-4862. **$99-$395, 3 day notice.** San Carlos St & 4th Ave
93921. 3 blks n of Ocean Ave. Ext corridors. **Pets:** Small, dogs only.
$25 daily fee/pet. Designated rooms, supervision.
SAVE 📶 🗙 🅺 🛎 💻

▼▼▼ Carmel Garden Inn 🄱🄱 ☙
(831) 624-6926. **$209-$349, 3 day notice.** 4th Ave & Torres St 93921.
3 blks n of Ocean Ave. Ext corridors. **Pets:** Dogs only. $25 daily fee/
pet. Designated rooms, service with restrictions, supervision.
🍽 📶 🗙 🅺 🛎 💻

▼▼ Carmel Lodge Ⓜ
(831) 624-1255. **$189-$695, 3 day notice.** San Carlos St & 5th Ave
93921. 2 blks n of Ocean Ave. Ext/int corridors. **Pets:** Accepted.
🍽 📶 🗙 🅺 🛎 💻

▼▼▼ Carmel Mission Inn 🅷

(831) 624-1841. **$99-$599.** 3665 Rio Rd 93923. 1 mi s on SR 1. Ext/int corridors. **Pets:** $40 one-time fee/pet. Designated rooms, service with restrictions, crate. 🔳 🍽 🕭 🏊 ⊠ 🤶 ⊠ 🔋 🖳

▼▼▼ Coachman's Inn 🅷 🐾

(831) 624-6421. **$245-$399, 3 day notice.** San Carlos St at 7th Ave 93921. Just s of Ocean Ave on San Carlos St; between 7th and 8th aves. Ext corridors. **Pets:** Dogs only. $20 daily fee/pet. Designated rooms, service with restrictions, supervision. 🍽 🤶 ⊠ 🦮 🔋 🖳

▼▼▼ Cypress Inn 🅷 🐾

(831) 624-3871. **Call for rates.** Lincoln & 7th Ave 93921. Just s of Ocean Ave. Ext/int corridors. **Pets:** Other species. $30 daily fee/pet. Supervision. 🍽 🤶 ⊠ 🔋

▼▼▼ The Hideaway Inn 🅷

(831) 625-5222. **Call for rates.** Junipero St & 8th Ave 93921. S of Ocean Ave; between 7th and 8th aves. Ext/int corridors. **Pets:** Accepted. 🍽 🤶 ⊠ 🦮 🔋

◆◆◆ ▼▼▼ Hofsas House 🅷 🐾

(831) 624-2745. **$135-$400, 3 day notice.** 2 NW of 4th Ave on San Carlos St 93921. 3 blks n of Ocean Ave; between 3rd and 4th aves. Ext corridors. **Pets:** Dogs only. $30 daily fee/pet. Service with restrictions, supervision. (SAVE) 🍽 🏊 🤶 ⊠ 🦮 🔋 🖳

▼▼▼ Horizon Inn & Ocean View Lodge 🅷

(831) 624-5327. **Call for rates.** 3rd Ave & Junipero Ave 93921. 4 blks n of Ocean Ave. Ext corridors. **Pets:** Accepted. 🕭 🤶 ⊠ 🦮 🔋 🖳

◆◆◆ ▼▼▼ Svendsgaard's Inn 🅷 🐾

(831) 624-1511. **$189-$309, 3 day notice.** 4th Ave & San Carlos St 93921. 3 blks n of Ocean Ave. Ext corridors. **Pets:** $25 daily fee/pet. Designated rooms, supervision. (SAVE) 🏊 🤶 ⊠ 🦮 🔋 🖳

CARMEL VALLEY

◆◆◆ ▼▼▼▼ Bernardus Lodge & Spa 🅷 🐾

(831) 658-3400. **Call for rates.** 415 W Carmel Valley Rd 93924. 9.5 mi e of SR 1; just e of Los Laureles Grade. Ext corridors. **Pets:** Medium, dogs only. $150 one-time fee/pet. Service with restrictions. (SAVE) 🔳 🍽 🕭 🏊 🏋 ⊠ 🤶 ⊠ 🔋 🖳

▼▼▼ Carmel Valley Ranch 🅷

(831) 625-9500. **Call for rates.** One Old Ranch Rd 93923. 6.3 mi e of SR 1 via Carmel Valley Rd to Robinson Canyon Rd exit, follow signs. Ext corridors. **Pets:** Accepted. 🍽 🕭 🏊 ⊠ 🤶 ⊠ 🔋 🖳

CARPINTERIA

▼▼▼▼ Holiday Inn Express & Suites 🅷

(805) 566-9499. **Call for rates.** 5606 Carpinteria Ave 93013. US 101 exit 86A (Casitas Pass Rd), just s, then just e. Int corridors. **Pets:** Accepted. 🔳 🕭 🏊 🤶 ⊠ 🔋 🖳

CARSON

▼▼▼▼ DoubleTree by Hilton Hotel Carson 🅷

(310) 830-9200. **$159-$229.** 2 Civic Plaza Dr 90745. I-405 exit 34 (Carson St), just w, then just n. Int corridors. **Pets:** Accepted. 🍽 🏊 🤶 🔋 🖳

▼▼ Extended Stay America-Los Angeles/Carson 🅷

(310) 323-2080. **$90-$150.** 401 E Albertoni St 90746. SR 91 exit 7B (Avalon Blvd), just s, then just w. Int corridors. **Pets:** Accepted. 🤶 🔋

CASTRO VALLEY

▼▼ Comfort Inn Castro Valley 🅷

(510) 538-9501. **$115-$245.** 2532 Castro Valley Blvd 94546. I-580 exit Castro Valley Blvd, 0.3 mi n. Int corridors. **Pets:** Small, other species. $10 daily fee/pet. Service with restrictions, supervision. 🕭 🏊 🤶 ⊠ 🔋 🖳

CATHEDRAL CITY (Restaurants p. 596)

◆◆◆ ▼▼▼▼ DoubleTree by Hilton Golf Resort Palm Springs 🅷

(760) 322-7000. **Call for rates.** 67967 Vista Chino 92234. I-10 exit 126 (Date Palm Dr), 0.5 mi s, then 1 mi w. Int corridors. **Pets:** Accepted. (SAVE) 🍽 🕭 🏊 🤶 ⊠ 🤶 ⊠ 🔋 🖳

CAYUCOS

▼▼ Cayucos Beach Inn Ⓜ

(805) 995-2828. **$85-$195, 3 day notice.** 333 S Ocean Ave 93430. On SR 1 business route. Ext corridors. **Pets:** Accepted. 🕭 🤶 ⊠ 🔋 🖳

▼▼▼ Pier View Suites 🅷

(805) 995-0014. **$249-$349.** 12 N Ocean Ave 93430. On SR 1 business route. Ext/int corridors. **Pets:** Designated rooms, service with restrictions. 🕭 🤶 ⊠ 🦮 🔋 🖳

▼▼ Shoreline Inn On The Beach Ⓜ 🐾

(805) 995-3681. **Call for rates.** 1 Ocean 93430. On SR 1 business route. **Pets:** Other species. $45 one-time fee/pet. Service with restrictions, supervision. 🤶 🦮 🔋 🖳

CEDARVILLE

◆◆◆ ◇ Sunrise Motel Ⓜ

(530) 279-2161. **$69-$79, 7 day notice.** 62271 Hwy 299 W 96104. Jct SR 299 and CR 1, 0.6 mi w on CR 1. Ext corridors. **Pets:** Medium. $20 daily fee/pet. Designated rooms, service with restrictions, supervision. (SAVE) 🍽 🤶 ⊠ 📶 🔋 🖳

CERRITOS

◆◆◆ ▼▼▼ Sheraton Cerritos Hotel at Towne Center 🅷 🐾

(562) 809-1500. **$149-$269.** 12725 Center Court Dr 90703. SR 91 exit 19B (Artesia/Bloomfield Dr), just s to Town Center Dr, just e, then just s. Int corridors. **Pets:** Medium. $25 one-time fee/pet. Designated rooms, service with restrictions, supervision. (SAVE) 🍽 🏊 🍴 ⊠ 🖳

CHATSWORTH

◆◆◆ ▼▼ Ramada 🅷

(818) 998-5289. **$76-$139.** 21340 Devonshire St 91311. SR 118 exit 35 (De Soto Ave) eastbound, 1.5 mi s, then 0.5 mi w. Int corridors. **Pets:** Medium. $20 daily fee/pet. Designated rooms, service with restrictions, supervision. (SAVE) 🕭 🏊 🤶 🔋 🖳

▼▼▼ Staybridge Suites 🅷

(818) 773-0707. **Call for rates.** 21902 Lassen St 91311. SR 118 exit 34 (Topanga Canyon Blvd) eastbound, 2 mi s, then just e. Ext/int corridors. **Pets:** Accepted. 🕭 🏊 🤶 ⊠ 🔋 🖳

CHESTER

◆◆◆ ▼▼▼ Best Western Rose Quartz Inn 🅷

(530) 258-2002. **$100-$170.** 306 Main St 96020. 0.3 mi w of center on SR 36. Ext/int corridors. **Pets:** Accepted. (SAVE) 🕭 🤶 ⊠ 🔋 🖳

CHICO

◆◆◆ ▼▼▼ Best Western Heritage Inn - Chico 🅷

(530) 894-8600. **$99-$199.** 25 Heritage Ln 95926. SR 99 exit 387A (Mangrove Ave/Cohasset Rd), just n. Int corridors. **Pets:** Accepted. (SAVE) 🕭 🏊 🤶 🔋 🖳

AAA ▼▼▼▼ Oxford Suites Chico H
(530) 899-9090. **Call for rates.** 2035 Business Ln 95928. SR 99 exit 384 (E 20th St), just e, then just s. Int corridors. **Pets:** Accepted.
[SAVE] [⊟] [🛇M] [🛆] [✕] [📶] [✕] [🔋] [💻]

▼▼▼▼ Residence Inn by Marriott Chico H
(530) 894-5500. **$135-$202.** 2485 Carmichael Dr 95928. SR 99 exit 383 (Skyway/Park Ave), just w, then just n. Int corridors. **Pets:** Accepted.
[🛇M] [🛆] [📶] [✕] [🔋] [💻]

AAA ▼▼▼ Super 8 H
(530) 345-2533. **$57-$325.** 655 Manzanita Ct 95926. SR 99 exit 387A (Mangrove Ave/Cohasset Rd) just s, then just e. Int corridors. **Pets:** Medium. $12 daily fee/pet. Designated rooms, service with restrictions, supervision. [SAVE] [🛇M] [🛆] [📶] [🔋] [💻]

CHOWCHILLA

▼▼▼ Days Inn Gateway to Yosemite M
(559) 665-4821. **$59-$129.** 220 E Robertson Blvd 93610. SR 99 exit 170 (Robertson Blvd), just w. Ext corridors. **Pets:** Medium, other species. $40 daily fee/pet. No service, supervision.
[🛇M] [🛆] [📶] [🔋] [💻]

▼▼▼▼ Holiday Inn Express & Suites Gateway to Yosemite H
(559) 665-3300. **Call for rates.** 309 Prosperity Blvd 93610. SR 99 exit 170 (Robertson Blvd), just w, just s on Chowchilla Blvd, then just e. Int corridors. **Pets:** Medium, other species. $40 daily fee/pet. No service, supervision. [🍴] [🛇M] [🛆] [📶] [✕] [🔋] [💻]

CHULA VISTA *(Restaurants p. 596)*

▼▼▼ La Quinta Inn San Diego Chula Vista M
(619) 691-1211. **$90-$383.** 150 Bonita Rd 91910. I-805 exit 7C (E St/Bonita Rd), just w. Ext/int corridors. **Pets:** Accepted.
[🛇M] [🛆] [📶] [🔋] [💻]

CLAREMONT *(Restaurants p. 596)*

▼▼▼▼ Hotel Casa 425 H
(909) 624-2272. **$215-$400.** 425 W 1st St 91711. I-10 exit 47 (Indian Hill Blvd), 1.2 mi n, then just w. Ext corridors. **Pets:** Accepted.
[🛇M] [📶] [✕] [🔋] [💻]

▼▼ Motel 6 Claremont M
(909) 621-4831. **$69-$199, 3 day notice.** 840 S Indian Hill Blvd 91711. I-10 exit 47 (Indian Hill Blvd), just s; enter on Auto Center Dr. Ext corridors. **Pets:** Accepted. [🛇M] [🛆] [📶] [🔋]

CLEARLAKE

▼▼▼ Clear Lake Cottages and Marina CA
(707) 995-5253. **Call for rates.** 13885 Lakeshore Dr 95422. SR 53 exit Lakeshore Dr, 2.1 mi w. Ext corridors. **Pets:** Accepted.
[🍴] [🛆] [✕] [📶] [✕] [🔋] [🔋] [💻]

CLEARLAKE OAKS

AAA ▼▼▼ Lake Point Lodge M
(707) 998-4350. **$69-$199.** 13470 E Hwy 20 95423. Jct SR 20 and 53, 2.7 mi w. Ext corridors. **Pets:** Accepted. [SAVE] [🛆] [📶] [🔋] [💻]

CLOVERDALE

AAA ▼▼▼ Auberge on the Vineyard BB
(707) 894-5956. **Call for rates.** 29955 River Rd 95425. US 101 exit Citrus Fair Dr, just e, 0.5 mi n on Asti Rd, 0.8 mi e on Crocker Rd, then just s. Ext/int corridors. **Pets:** Accepted.
[SAVE] [🍴] [📶] [✕] [🔋] [🔋] [💻]

▼▼▼ Old Crocker Inn BB
(707) 894-4000. **Call for rates.** 1126 Old Crocker Inn Rd 95425. US 101 exit Citrus Fair Dr, just e, 0.5 mi n on Asti Rd, 0.8 mi e on First St, 3.8 mi s on River Rd, 1.1 mi e on Asti Ridge Rd, then just n. Ext corridors. **Pets:** Dogs only. $20 one-time fee/pet. Designated rooms, service with restrictions, supervision. [🍴] [🛆] [📶] [✕] [🔋] [🔋]

CLOVIS

▼▼▼▼ Hampton Inn & Suites Clovis-Airport North H
(559) 348-0000. **$99-$199.** 855 Gettysburg Ave 93612. SR 99 exit SR 180 (Sequoia-Kings Canyon/Airport) 6.8 mi e, 3.4 mi n on Clovis Ave, then just e. Int corridors. **Pets:** Medium, other species. Service with restrictions, supervision. [🛇M] [📶] [✕] [🔋] [💻]

▼▼▼▼ Homewood Suites by Hilton Fresno Airport/Clovis, CA H
(559) 292-4004. **$109-$239.** 835 Gettysburg Ave 93612. SR 99 exit SR 180 (Sequoia-Kings Canyon/Airport) 6.8 mi e, 3.4 mi n on Clovis Ave, then just e. Int corridors. **Pets:** Large, other species. $75 one-time fee/room. Service with restrictions, crate. [🍴] [🛇M] [📶] [🔋] [💻]

COALINGA

AAA ▼▼▼ Best Western Big Country Inn M ☘
(559) 935-0866. **$114-$170.** 25020 W Dorris Ave 93210. I-5 exit 334, just w. Ext corridors. **Pets:** Medium. $20 one-time fee/pet. Designated rooms, service with restrictions, supervision.
[SAVE] [⊟] [🛇M] [🛆] [📶] [🔋] [💻]

AAA ▼▼▼▼ The Inn at Harris Ranch H
(559) 935-0717. **$169-$499.** 24505 W Dorris Ave 93210. I-5 exit 334, just e. Ext/int corridors. **Pets:** Dogs only. $20 one-time fee/pet. Designated rooms, service with restrictions, supervision.
[SAVE] [⊟] [🍴] [🛇M] [🛆] [📶] [✕] [🔋] [💻]

COLTON

▼▼ Holiday Inn Express Colton-Riverside North H
(951) 788-9900. **Call for rates.** 2830 S Iowa Ave 92324. I-215 exit 37 (La Cadena Dr) northbound; exit 37 (Iowa Ave) southbound, just se. Int corridors. **Pets:** Accepted. [🛇M] [🛆] [📶] [✕] [🔋] [💻]

COLUMBIA

▼▼ Columbia Gem Motel M
(209) 532-4508. **$99-$159.** 22131 Parrots Ferry Rd 95370. 1.1 mi s of center; 3.2 mi n of downtown Sonora. Ext corridors. **Pets:** Dogs only. Service with restrictions, supervision. [📶] [✕] [🔋] [🔋] [💻]

CONCORD

AAA ▼▼▼▼ Crowne Plaza Hotel Concord/Walnut Creek H
(925) 825-7700. **Call for rates.** 45 John Glenn Dr 94520. I-680 exit 62 (Concord Ave), just e. Int corridors. **Pets:** Accepted.
[SAVE] [🍴] [🛇M] [🛆] [📶] [✕] [🔋] [💻]

AAA ▼▼▼▼ Hilton Concord H ☘
(925) 827-2000. **$99-$289.** 1970 Diamond Blvd 94520. I-680 exit 51 (Willow Pass Rd), just e, then just nw. Int corridors. **Pets:** Other species. $250 deposit/room, $50 one-time fee/pet. Service with restrictions, crate. [SAVE] [ECO] [🍴] [🛇M] [🛆] [📶] [✕] [🔋] [💻]

CORNING

AAA ▼▼▼▼ Best Western Plus Corning Inn H
(530) 824-5200. **$99-$169.** 910 Hwy 99 W 96021. I-5 exit 631 (Central Corning), just se. Int corridors. **Pets:** Medium. $15 daily fee/pet. Designated rooms, service with restrictions, supervision.
[SAVE] [🛇M] [🛆] [📶] [🔋] [💻]

AAA ▼▼▼ The Inn at Rolling Hills H
(530) 824-8300. **$129-$189.** 2645 Everett Freeman Way 96021. I-5 exit 628 (Liberal Ave/SR 99), just w, then just s. Int corridors.
Pets: Accepted. [SAVE] [🛇M] [🛆] [📶] [🔋] [💻]

CORONA *(Restaurants p. 596)*

▼▼▼ Ayres Suites Corona West H
(951) 738-9113. **$159-$179.** 1900 Frontage Rd 92882. SR 91 exit 48 (Maple St/W 6th St) eastbound; exit Maple St westbound, just sw. Ext/int corridors. **Pets:** Other species. $75 one-time fee/room. Designated rooms, service with restrictions, crate. [⊟] [🛇M] [🛆] [📶] [🔋] [💻]

Best Western Corona M
(951) 734-4241. **$106-$114.** 1084 Pomona Rd 92882. SR 91 exit 49 (Lincoln Ave), just ne. Ext corridors. **Pets:** Accepted.

Residence Inn by Marriott Corona H
(951) 371-0107. **$128-$193.** 1015 Montecito Dr 92879. I-15 exit 95 (Magnolia Ave), just e, just n on El Camino, just w on Carly Way, then just n. Int corridors. **Pets:** Accepted.

CORONADO (Restaurants p. 596)
Crown City Inn M
(619) 435-3116. **$100-$300.** 520 Orange Ave 92118. I-5 exit 14A (Coronado Bridge), 2.4 mi nw, then just sw. Ext corridors. **Pets:** Other species. $8 daily fee/pet. Designated rooms, service with restrictions, supervision.

Hotel del Coronado H
(619) 435-6611. **Call for rates.** 1500 Orange Ave 92118. I-5 exit 14A (Coronado Bridge), 2.4 mi nw, then 1.6 mi sw. Ext/int corridors. **Pets:** Medium. $125 one-time fee/room. Service with restrictions, crate.

Loews Coronado Bay Resort H
(619) 424-4000. **$209-$439, 3 day notice.** 4000 Loews Coronado Bay Rd 92118. I-5 exit 14A (Coronado Bridge), 2.4 mi nw to Orange Ave, 1 mi sw to Silver Strand Blvd, 4.5 mi s to Coronado Cays, then just e. Int corridors. **Pets:** Medium. $100 one-time fee/room. Service with restrictions.

CORTE MADERA
Marin Suites Hotel H
(415) 924-3608. **$139-$359, 3 day notice.** 45 Tamal Vista Blvd 94925. US 101 exit Lucky Dr southbound, just w on Fifer Ave, then 0.4 mi s; exit Tamalpais Rd/Paradise Dr northbound, 0.5 mi n on Madera Blvd (which becomes Tamal Vista Blvd). Ext corridors. **Pets:** Medium. $25 daily fee/pet. Designated rooms, service with restrictions, crate.

COSTA MESA (Restaurants p. 596)
Costa Mesa Marriott H
(714) 957-1100. **$100-$241.** 500 Anton Blvd 92626. I-405 exit 9B (Bristol St), just n, then 0.3 mi e. Int corridors. **Pets:** Accepted.

Crowne Plaza Costa Mesa Orange County H
(714) 557-3000. **$129-$399.** 3131 S Bristol St 92626. I-405 exit 9B (Bristol St), just s. Int corridors. **Pets:** Accepted.

Hilton Orange County/Costa Mesa H
(714) 540-7000. **$139-$279.** 3050 Bristol St 92626. I-405 exit 9B (Bristol St), just s. Int corridors. **Pets:** Accepted.

Ramada Inn & Suites H
(949) 645-2221. **$89-$219.** 1680 Superior Ave 92627. SR 55, just w of Newport Blvd at 17th St. Ext corridors. **Pets:** Accepted.

Residence Inn by Marriott Costa Mesa Newport Beach H
(714) 241-8800. **$146-$230.** 881 W Baker St 92626. SR 55 exit 5B (Baker St), just w. Int corridors. **Pets:** Accepted.

The Westin South Coast Plaza Hotel H
(714) 540-2500. **$149-$299.** 686 Anton Blvd 92626. I-405 exit 9B (Bristol St), just n, then just e. Int corridors. **Pets:** Accepted.

CULVER CITY
Four Points by Sheraton LA Westside H
(310) 641-7740. **$399-$499.** 5990 Green Valley Cir 90230. I-405 exit 49 (Slauson Ave/Sepulveda Blvd), just ne. Int corridors. **Pets:** Small. $25 daily fee/pet. Service with restrictions, crate.

CUPERTINO
Aloft Cupertino H
(408) 766-7000. **Call for rates.** 10165 N De Anza Blvd 95014. I-280 exit Sunnyvale-Saratoga Rd, just s. Int corridors. **Pets:** Accepted.

Cupertino Hotel H
(408) 996-7700. **$149-$669.** 10889 N De Anza Blvd 95014. I-280 exit Sunnyvale-Saratoga Rd, just n. Ext/int corridors. **Pets:** Dogs only. $35 daily fee/pet. Designated rooms, service with restrictions, supervision.

Juniper Hotel Cupertino, Curio Collection by Hilton H
(408) 253-8900. **Call for rates.** 10050 S De Anza Blvd 95014. I-280 exit De Anza Blvd, 0.7 mi s. Int corridors. **Pets:** Accepted.

CYPRESS
Hyatt House Cypress/Anaheim H
(714) 828-4000. **$139-$309.** 5905 Corporate Ave 90630. I-605 exit 1D (Katella Ave) southbound; exit 1B (Katella Ave/Willow St) northbound, 3 mi e, 0.4 mi n on Valley View Ave, then just w. Int corridors. **Pets:** Accepted.

DANA POINT
Best Western Plus Marina Shores Hotel H
(949) 248-1000. **$129-$279.** 34280 Pacific Coast Hwy 92629. I-5 exit 79 (Beach Cities Dr) northbound; exit 79 (Pacific Coast Hwy) southbound, 0.6 mi w, then 0.5 mi n. Ext/int corridors. **Pets:** Medium, other species. $20 daily fee/room. Service with restrictions, supervision.

Blue Lantern Inn BB
(949) 661-1304. **$195-$625.** 34343 Street of Blue Lantern 92629. I-5 exit 79 (Pacific Coast Hwy) southbound; exit Beach Cities Dr northbound, 1.5 mi n on Pacific Coast Hwy, then just w. Int corridors. **Pets:** Accepted.

DoubleTree Suites by Hilton Doheny Beach-Dana Point H
(949) 661-1100. **$159-$399.** 34402 Pacific Coast Hwy 92629. I-5 exit 79 (Beach Cities Dr) northbound; exit 79 (Pacific Coast Hwy) southbound, 0.6 mi w, U-turn at Doheny Park Plaza Dr, then 0.5 mi s. Int corridors. **Pets:** Accepted.

Monarch Beach Resort H
(949) 234-3200. **$375-$895, 3 day notice.** One Monarch Beach Resort 92629. I-5 exit 79 (Pacific Coast Hwy) northbound, 3 mi n, then 0.5 mi e on Niguel Rd; exit 86 (Crown Valley Pkwy) southbound, 3 mi w, 1 mi s on Pacific Coast Hwy, then 0.5 mi e on Niguel Rd. Int corridors. **Pets:** Accepted.

The Ritz-Carlton, Laguna Niguel H
(949) 240-2000. **$459-$4000, 7 day notice.** One Ritz-Carlton Dr 92629. I-5 exit 79 (Pacific Coast Hwy) northbound, 3 mi n, then just w; exit 86 (Crown Valley Pkwy) southbound, 3 mi w, 1 mi s on Pacific Coast Hwy, then just w. Int corridors. **Pets:** Accepted.

DANVILLE

Best Western Danville Sycamore Inn **H** ❖
(925) 855-8888. **$129-$229.** 803 Camino Ramon 94526. I-680 exit 38 (Sycamore Valley Rd), just e, then just s. Ext/int corridors. **Pets:** Other species. $20 daily fee/room. Designated rooms, service with restrictions, supervision. [SAVE] [icons]

DAVIS (Restaurants p. 596)

Best Western University Lodge **M**
(530) 756-7890. **$124-$160.** 123 B St 95616. I-80 exit 72B (Richards Blvd) westbound; exit 72 eastbound, just nw to 1st St, just w to B St, then just n; at 2nd and B sts. Ext corridors. **Pets:** Small. $100 one-time fee/pet. Service with restrictions, supervision.
[SAVE] [icons]

Hyatt Place UC Davis **H**
(530) 756-9500. **$129-$269.** 173 Old Davis Rd Ext 95616. I-80 exit 71 (UC Davis), 0.6 mi ne; just n of jct Alumni Ln; follow signs for Mondavi Center. Int corridors. **Pets:** Large, dogs only. $75 one-time fee/room. Service with restrictions, crate.
[SAVE] [icons]

University Park Inn & Suites **H** ❖
(530) 756-0910. **$129-$269, 3 day notice.** 1111 Richards Blvd 95616. I-80 exit 72B (Richards Blvd) westbound; exit 72 eastbound, just nw. Ext corridors. **Pets:** Medium, dogs only. $15 daily fee/pet. Supervision.
[SAVE] [icons]

DELANO

Best Western Liberty Inn **M**
(661) 725-0976. **$100-$150.** 14394 County Line Rd 93215. SR 99 exit 58 (County Line Rd), just e, then just n on Girard St. Int corridors. **Pets:** Accepted. [SAVE] [icons]

Rodeway Inn **M**
(661) 725-1022. **$75-$105.** 2211 Girard St 93215. SR 99 exit 58 (County Line Rd), just e, then just s. Ext corridors. **Pets:** Small, dogs only. $10 daily fee/pet. Designated rooms, service with restrictions, supervision. [SAVE] [icons]

DEL MAR (Restaurants p. 596)

Hilton San Diego Del Mar **H** ❖
(858) 792-5200. **$129-$429.** 15575 Jimmy Durante Blvd 92014. I-5 exit 36 (Via de la Valle), just w, then just s. Int corridors. **Pets:** Large, other species. $75 one-time fee/pet. Designated rooms, service with restrictions, supervision. [SAVE] [icons]

Hotel Indigo Del Mar **M** ❖
(858) 755-1501. **$129-$309, 3 day notice.** 710 Camino Del Mar 92014. I-5 exit 34 (Del Mar Heights Rd), 1 mi w, then just n. Ext corridors. **Pets:** $75 one-time fee/room. Service with restrictions.
[SAVE] [icons]

L'Auberge Del Mar **H**
(858) 259-1515. **$295-$720, 14 day notice.** 1540 Camino Del Mar 92014. I-5 exit 34 (Del Mar Heights Rd), 1 mi w, then 1 mi n. Int corridors. **Pets:** Accepted.
[SAVE] [icons]

DIAMOND BAR (Restaurants p. 596)

Ayres Suites Diamond Bar **H**
(909) 860-6290. **$159-$199.** 21951 Golden Springs Dr 91765. SR 57/60 exit 24B (Grand Ave), just s, then 0.5 mi w. Int corridors.
Pets: Accepted. [icons]

DINUBA

Holiday Inn Express Hotel & Suites Dinuba **H**
(559) 595-1500. **Call for rates.** 375 S Alta Ave 93618. SR 99 exit 112 (SR 201/Sierra St), 9 mi e, then 1 mi n. Int corridors. **Pets:** Accepted.
[icons]

DIXON

Best Western Plus Inn Dixon **H**
(707) 678-1400. **$94-$300.** 1345 Commercial Way 95620. I-80 exit 64 (Pitt School Rd), just s, just e on Stratford Ave, then just n. Ext/int corridors. **Pets:** Accepted. [SAVE] [icons]

DORRIS

Golden Eagle Motel **M**
(530) 397-3114. **$39-$289.** 100 W 1st St 96023. US 97; center. Ext corridors. **Pets:** Dogs only. $10 daily fee/pet. Designated rooms, service with restrictions, supervision. [SAVE] [icons]

DOWNIEVILLE

Riverside Inn **M**
(530) 289-1000. **$90-$185, 3 day notice.** 206 Commercial St (SR 49) 95936. On SR 49; center. Ext corridors. **Pets:** Other species. $15 one-time fee/pet. No service, supervision.
[icons]

DUBLIN

Holiday Inn Dublin **H**
(925) 828-7750. **Call for rates.** 6680 Regional St 94568. I-580 exit 44A, just ne. Int corridors. **Pets:** Accepted.
[icons]

Hyatt Place Dublin/Pleasanton **H**
(925) 828-9006. **$94-$369.** 4950 Hacienda Dr 94568. I-580 exit 46 (Hacienda Dr), just n; in Hacienda Crossing Shopping Center. Int corridors. **Pets:** Accepted. [SAVE] [icons]

DUNSMUIR

Oak Tree Inn **H**
(530) 235-4100. **Call for rates.** 4000 Siskiyou Ave 96025. I-5 exit 732 (Siskiyou Ave), just e. Int corridors. **Pets:** Accepted.
[icons]

EAST PALO ALTO

Four Seasons Hotel Silicon Valley at East Palo Alto **H**
(650) 566-1200. **Call for rates.** 2050 University Ave 94303. US 101 exit University Ave. Int corridors. **Pets:** Accepted.
[icons]

EL CAJON

Best Western Courtesy Inn **M**
(619) 440-7378. **$80-$156.** 1355 E Main St 92021. I-8 exit 19 (2nd St), 0.5 mi s, then just e. Ext corridors. **Pets:** Other species. $20 daily fee/room. Service with restrictions, supervision.
[SAVE] [icons]

EL CENTRO

TownePlace Suites by Marriott **H**
(760) 370-3800. **$104-$177.** 3003 S Dogwood Rd 92243. I-8 exit 116 (Dogwood Rd), 0.5 mi s. Int corridors. **Pets:** Accepted.
[icons]

ELK

Elk Cove Inn & Spa **CI** ❖
(707) 877-3321. **$125-$395, 14 day notice.** 6300 S Hwy 1 95432. On SR 1, 6.3 mi s of jct SR 128; just s of center. Ext/int corridors. **Pets:** Dogs only. Designated rooms, service with restrictions, supervision. [icons]

ELK GROVE

Fairfield Inn & Suites by Marriott Sacramento Elk Grove H

(916) 681-5400. **$115-$175.** 8058 Orchard Loop Ln 95624. SR 99 exit 289 (Cosumnes River Blvd/Calvine Rd), just se. Int corridors. **Pets:** Accepted. ⬛ ⬛ ⬛ ⬛ ⬛ ⬛ ⬛ ⬛

Holiday Inn Express & Suites H

(916) 478-4000. **Call for rates.** 2460 Maritime Dr 95758. I-5 exit 506 (Elk Grove Blvd), just e to Harbour Point Dr, just n, then just w. Int corridors. **Pets:** Accepted. ⬛ ⬛ ⬛ ⬛ ⬛ ⬛

Holiday Inn Express Hotel & Suites H

(916) 478-9000. **Call for rates.** 9175 W Stockton Blvd 95758. SR 99 exit 287 (Laguna Blvd), just w, then just n; in Laguna Gateway Shopping Center. Int corridors. **Pets:** Accepted.
⬛ ⬛ ⬛ ⬛ ⬛ ⬛

EL MONTE

Americas Best Value Inn & Suites M

(626) 442-8354. **$100-$160.** 12040 Garvey Ave 91732. I-10 exit 30 (Garvey Ave) westbound, just w; exit 29A (Peck Rd) eastbound, just s to Garvey Ave, then 0.6 mi e. Ext corridors. **Pets:** Small. $25 deposit/pet, $25 daily fee/pet. Designated rooms, service with restrictions, supervision. ⬛ ⬛ ⬛ ⬛ ⬛ ⬛ ⬛

EL SEGUNDO (Restaurants p. 596)

Aloft El Segundo Los Angeles Airport H

(424) 290-5555. **$129-$399.** 475 N Sepulveda Blvd 90245. I-105 exit 1B (Sepulveda Blvd) westbound; exit 1 eastbound, just s. Int corridors. **Pets:** Accepted. ⬛ ⬛ ⬛ ⬛ ⬛ ⬛

Hyatt House Los Angeles LAX/El Segundo H

(310) 725-0100. **$109-$299.** 810 S Douglas St 90245. I-405 exit 43 (Rosecrans Ave), 0.5 mi e, then just n. Ext corridors. **Pets:** Accepted.
⬛ ⬛ ⬛ ⬛ ⬛ ⬛

Hyatt Place Los Angeles/LAX/El Segundo H

(310) 322-2880. **$99-$289.** 750 N Nash St 90245. I-105 exit Nash St, just s. Int corridors. **Pets:** Accepted.
⬛ ⬛ ⬛ ⬛ ⬛ ⬛ ⬛

Residence Inn by Marriott-LAX/El Segundo H

(310) 333-0888. **$139-$260.** 2135 E El Segundo Blvd 90245. I-405 exit 44 (El Segundo Blvd), 1.4 mi w. Int corridors. **Pets:** Accepted.
⬛ ⬛ ⬛ ⬛ ⬛ ⬛

EMERYVILLE

Hyatt House Emeryville/San Francisco Bay Area H

(510) 601-5880. **$179-$419.** 5800 Shellmound St 94608. I-80 exit Powell St, just e. Int corridors. **Pets:** Accepted.
⬛ ⬛ ⬛ ⬛ ⬛ ⬛ ⬛

ENCINITAS (Restaurants p. 596)

Best Western Encinitas Inn & Suites at Moonlight Beach H

(760) 942-7455. **$120-$150.** 85 Encinitas Blvd 92024. I-5 exit 41B (Encinitas Blvd), just w. Ext corridors. **Pets:** Small, other species. $20 daily fee/pet. Designated rooms, service with restrictions, supervision.
⬛ ⬛ ⬛ ⬛ ⬛

Econo Lodge Moonlight Beach Encinitas M

(760) 436-4999. **$75-$249.** 410 N Coast Hwy 101 92024. I-5 exit 41B (Encinitas Blvd), 0.6 mi w, then 0.6 mi n. Ext/int corridors. **Pets:** Small, other species. $25 deposit/pet. Designated rooms, service with restrictions, supervision. ⬛ ⬛ ⬛ ⬛ ⬛ ⬛

Quality Inn Encinitas Near Legoland M

(760) 944-3800. **$69-$349.** 607 Leucadia Blvd 92024. I-5 exit 43 (Leucadia Blvd), just e. Ext corridors. **Pets:** Other species. $35 one-time fee/pet. Designated rooms, service with restrictions, supervision.
⬛ ⬛ ⬛ ⬛ ⬛ ⬛ ⬛

ESCONDIDO (Restaurants p. 596)

Best Western Escondido Hotel H ☙

(760) 740-1700. **$84-$119.** 1700 Seven Oaks Rd 92026. I-15 exit 33 (El Norte Pkwy), just e, then just n. Int corridors. **Pets:** Small, other species. $25 deposit/pet. Designated rooms, service with restrictions, supervision. ⬛ ⬛ ⬛ ⬛ ⬛ ⬛

Escondido Lodge M

(760) 743-9733. **Call for rates.** 2650 S Escondido Blvd 92025. I-15 exit 29 (Felicita Rd/Citracado Pkwy), 0.8 mi e on Citracado Pkwy, then just s; on frontage road, just past Centre City Pkwy. Ext corridors. **Pets:** Accepted. ⬛ ⬛ ⬛ ⬛ ⬛ ⬛

EUREKA

Best Western Plus Bayshore Inn H ☙

(707) 268-8005. **$100-$200.** 3500 Broadway 95503. Jct US 101 and Truesdale St; south end of town. Ext corridors. **Pets:** Dogs only. $20 daily fee/room. Designated rooms, service with restrictions, supervision.
⬛ ⬛ ⬛ ⬛ ⬛ ⬛ ⬛

Eureka Town House Motel M

(707) 443-4536. **$65-$195.** 933 4th St 95501. On US 101 southbound at K St. Ext corridors. **Pets:** Medium, dogs only. $12 daily fee/pet. Service with restrictions, supervision. ⬛ ⬛ ⬛ ⬛ ⬛ ⬛

Quality Inn Eureka M

(707) 443-1601. **$75-$220.** 1209 4th St 95501. On US 101 southbound; between M and N sts. Ext corridors. **Pets:** Small, dogs only. $15 daily fee/pet. Designated rooms, service with restrictions, supervision.
⬛ ⬛ ⬛ ⬛ ⬛ ⬛ ⬛

Red Lion Hotel Eureka H

(707) 445-0844. **Call for rates.** 1929 4th St 95501. On US 101 southbound; between T and V sts. Int corridors. **Pets:** Accepted.
⬛ ⬛ ⬛ ⬛ ⬛ ⬛ ⬛

FAIRFIELD

Staybridge Suites Fairfield-Napa Valley Area H

(707) 863-0900. **Call for rates.** 4775 Business Center Dr 94534. I-80 exit 41 (Green Valley Rd/Suisun Valley Rd), sw on Green Valley Rd, then just ne. Int corridors. **Pets:** Accepted.
⬛ ⬛ ⬛ ⬛ ⬛ ⬛ ⬛

FALL RIVER MILLS

Himont Motel M ☙

(530) 336-5541. **$69-$129.** 43021 Bridge St 96028. 0.4 mi sw on SR 299; jct SR 299 E and Bridge St. Ext corridors. **Pets:** Other species. $25 daily fee/pet. Designated rooms, service with restrictions, supervision. ⬛ ⬛ ⬛ ⬛ ⬛ ⬛

FILLMORE

Best Western La Posada Motel M

(805) 524-0440. **$116-$124.** 827 Ventura St 93015. On SR 126. Ext corridors. **Pets:** Accepted. ⬛ ⬛ ⬛ ⬛ ⬛ ⬛

FIREBAUGH

Best Western Apricot Inn H

(559) 659-1444. **$95-$125.** 46290 W Panoche Rd 93622. I-5 exit 368, just w. Ext corridors. **Pets:** Medium, other species. $20 one-time fee/room. Service with restrictions, supervision.
⬛ ⬛ ⬛ ⬛ ⬛ ⬛

FISH CAMP

AAA ◆◆◆ **The Cottages at Tenaya Lodge** **H**
(559) 683-6555. **$159-$455, 7 day notice.** 1122 Hwy 41 93623. 2 mi from Yosemite National Park South Gate. Ext corridors. **Pets:** Accepted.

◆◆ **The Narrow Gauge Inn** **CI**
(559) 683-7720. **$79-$369, 4 day notice.** 48571 Hwy 41 93623. SR 41, 4 mi from Yosemite National Park South Gate. Ext corridors.
Pets: Accepted.

AAA ◆◆◆ **Tenaya Lodge at Yosemite** **H**
(559) 683-6555. **$149-$450, 7 day notice.** 1122 Hwy 41 93623. 2 mi from Yosemite National Park South Gate. Int corridors. **Pets:** Accepted.

FOLSOM *(Restaurants p. 597)*

AAA ◆◆◆ **Lake Natoma Inn Hotel & Conference Center** **H**
(916) 351-1500. **$89-$169.** 702 Gold Lake Dr 95630. US 50 exit Folsom Blvd, 3 mi n, then 0.5 mi e on Riley St; behind The Lakes Specialty Shopping Center. Int corridors. **Pets:** $45 one-time fee/room, $15 daily fee/pet. Designated rooms, service with restrictions, crate.

AAA ◆◆◆ **Larkspur Landing Folsom** **H**
(916) 355-1616. **$169-$269.** 121 Iron Point Rd 95630. US 50 exit 23 (Folsom Blvd), 0.5 mi n to Iron Point Rd, then just e. Int corridors. **Pets:** Medium, dogs only. $75 one-time fee/room. Designated rooms, service with restrictions, crate.

◆◆◆ **Residence Inn by Marriott** **H**
(916) 983-7289. **$131-$189.** 2555 Iron Point Rd 95630. US 50 exit 27 (E Bidwell St), just n, then just w. Int corridors. **Pets:** Accepted.

◆◆◆ **Staybridge Suites Sacramento-Folsom** **H**
(916) 983-7885. **$129-$255.** 1745 Cavitt Dr 95630. US 50 exit 27 (E Bidwell St), 0.5 mi n, just ne on Iron Point Rd, then just se. Int corridors. **Pets:** Accepted.

FORT BRAGG *(Restaurants p. 597)*

AAA ◆◆◆ **Beachcomber Motel and Spa by the Sea** **M** ❀
(707) 964-2402. **$119-$299, 3 day notice.** 1111 N Main St 95437. 1 mi n on SR 1. Ext/int corridors. **Pets:** Other species. $20 daily fee/pet. Designated rooms, supervision.

AAA ◆◆◆ **Beach House Inn** **M** ❀
(707) 961-1700. **$89-$249, 3 day notice.** 100 Pudding Creek Rd 95437. 0.7 mi n on SR 1. Int corridors. **Pets:** Other species. $20 daily fee/pet. Designated rooms, supervision.

AAA ◆◆◆ **Emerald Dolphin Inn & Mini Golf** **H** ❀
(707) 964-6699. **$74-$245, 7 day notice.** 1211 S Main St 95437. On SR 1; at Harbor View Dr. Ext corridors. **Pets:** Dogs only. $20 daily fee/room. Designated rooms, service with restrictions, supervision.

AAA ◆◆◆ **Holiday Inn Express** **H**
(707) 964-1100. **$124-$199.** 250 Hwy 20 95437. On SR 20, just e of jct SR 1. Ext/int corridors. **Pets:** Accepted.

◆◆◆ **North Cliff Hotel** **H** ❀
(707) 962-2500. **$189-$305.** 1005 S Main St 95437. On SR 1; jct Noyo Point Rd; north end of Noyo River Bridge. Ext corridors. **Pets:** Other species. $25 daily fee/pet. Designated rooms, service with restrictions, supervision.

◆◆◆ **Super 8 Fort Bragg** **M** ❀
(707) 964-4003. **$75-$135.** 888 S Main St 95437. 0.5 mi s on SR 1; north end of Noyo River Bridge. Ext corridors. **Pets:** $10 daily fee/pet. Designated rooms, service with restrictions, supervision.

AAA ◆◆◆ **Surf & Sand Lodge** **M** ❀
(707) 964-9383. **$109-$349, 3 day notice.** 1131 N Main St 95437. 1 mi n on SR 1. Int corridors. **Pets:** Other species. $20 daily fee/pet. Designated rooms, supervision.

AAA ◆◆◆ **Surf Motel & Gardens** **M** ❀
(707) 964-5361. **Call for rates.** 1220 S Main St 95437. On SR 1; jct Oceanview Dr. Ext corridors. **Pets:** $12 daily fee/pet. Designated rooms, supervision.

◆◆ **Weller House Inn** **BB**
(707) 964-4415. **$95-$310, 15 day notice.** 524 Stewart St 95437. Just w of SR 1 on Pine St, just n. Ext/int corridors. **Pets:** Accepted.

FORTUNA

AAA ◆◆◆ **Best Western Country Inn** **M**
(707) 725-6822. **$90-$160.** 2025 Riverwalk Dr 95540. US 101 exit 687 (Kenmar Rd), just w. Ext corridors. **Pets:** Large, dogs only. $20 daily fee/room. Designated rooms, service with restrictions, supervision.

◆◆◆ **Fortuna Super 8** **M**
(707) 725-2888. **$80-$190.** 1805 Alamar Way 95540. US 101 exit 687 (Kenmar Rd), just w, then just n. Ext corridors. **Pets:** Accepted.

◆◆ **The Redwood Fortuna Riverwalk Hotel** **H**
(707) 725-5500. **Call for rates.** 1859 Alamar Way 95540. US 101 exit 687 (Kenmar Rd), just w, then just n. Ext corridors. **Pets:** Accepted.

FOUNTAIN VALLEY

AAA ◆◆◆ **Residence Inn by Marriott** **H**
(714) 965-8000. **$155-$240.** 9930 Slater Ave 92708. I-405 exit 14 (Brookhurst St), just n, then just w. Ext corridors. **Pets:** Other species. $100 one-time fee/room. Service with restrictions.

FREMONT *(Restaurants p. 597)*

AAA ◆◆◆ **Best Western Plus Garden Court Inn** **H**
(510) 792-4300. **$99-$329.** 5400 Mowry Ave 94538. I-880 exit Mowry Ave, just e. Int corridors. **Pets:** Accepted.

◆◆◆ **Comfort Inn Silicon Valley East** **H**
(510) 490-2900. **$89-$199.** 47031 Kato Rd 94538. I-880 exit Warren Ave/Mission Blvd E, just e. Int corridors. **Pets:** Accepted.

AAA ◆◆◆ **Hyatt Place Fremont/Silicon Valley** **H**
(510) 623-6000. **$99-$309.** 3101 W Warren Ave 94538. I-880 exit Warren Ave, just w. Int corridors. **Pets:** Medium. $75 one-time fee/pet. Service with restrictions, crate.

◆◆◆ **La Quinta Inn & Suites Fremont** **H**
(510) 445-0808. **$97-$262.** 46200 Landing Pkwy 94538. I-880 exit Fremont Blvd/Cushing Pkwy, just w. Int corridors. **Pets:** Accepted.

◆◆◆ **Residence Inn by Marriott Fremont Silicon Valley** **H**
(510) 794-5900. **$130-$286.** 5400 Farwell Pl 94536. I-880 exit Mowry Ave, just e. Ext corridors. **Pets:** Accepted.

FRESNO

⊘ ▼▼▼ **Best Western Village Inn** H ❖
(559) 226-2110. **$90-$150.** 3110 N Blackstone Ave 93703. SR 41 exit 130 (Shields Ave), just w; jct Shields and Blackstone aves. Int corridors. **Pets:** Other species. $20 one-time fee/room. Designated rooms, service with restrictions, crate. 🗚 ⚞ 🛜 ⌧ 🔌 💻

▼▼▼ **La Quinta Inn & Suites Fresno Northwest** H
(559) 275-3700. **$86-$224.** 5077 N Cornelia Ave 93722. SR 99 exit 140 (Shaw Ave), just e, then just n. Int corridors. **Pets:** Accepted.
🍴 🔌 ⚞ 🛜 ⌧ 🔌 💻

⊘ ▼▼▼ **La Quinta Inn & Suites Fresno Riverpark** H
(559) 449-0928. **$97-$317.** 330 E Fir Ave 93720. SR 41 exit Herndon Ave, just e, just n on Fresno St, then just w. Int corridors.
Pets: Accepted. 🗚 ⚞ 🔌 ⚞ 🛜 ⌧ 🔌 💻

▼▼ **Piccadilly Inn-Shaw** H
(559) 348-5520. **$109-$189.** 2305 W Shaw Ave 93711. SR 99 exit 140 (Shaw Ave), 3 mi e; jct Sequoia Dr. Ext/int corridors. **Pets:** Small, dogs only. $15 daily fee/room. Designated rooms, service with restrictions, supervision. 🔌 ⚞ 🛜 🔌 💻

▼▼▼ **Residence Inn by Marriott** H
(559) 222-8900. **$128-$190.** 5322 N Diana St 93710. SR 41 exit 132 (Shaw Ave), 0.3 mi w, 0.5 mi n on Blackstone Ave, just e on Barstow Ave, then just s. Int corridors. **Pets:** Accepted.
🌿 🍴 🔌 ⚞ 🛜 ⌧ 🔌 💻

▼▼▼ **TownePlace Suites by Marriott** H
(559) 435-4600. **$123-$172.** 7127 N Fresno St 93720. SR 41 exit Herndon Ave, just e, then just n. Int corridors. **Pets:** Accepted.
🔌 ⚞ 🛜 ⌧ 🔌 💻

FULLERTON

⊘ ▼▼▼ **Fullerton Marriott Hotel at California State University** H
(714) 738-7800. **$109-$192.** 2701 E Nutwood Ave 92831. SR 57 exit 7 (Nutwood Ave) northbound; exit 7 (Nutwood Ave/Chapman Ave) southbound, just w. Int corridors. **Pets:** Medium, dogs only. $100 one-time fee/room. Designated rooms, service with restrictions, supervision.
🗚 🌿 🍴 ⚞ 🛜 ⌧ 🔌 💻

GARBERVILLE *(Restaurants p. 597)*

▼▼▼ **Benbow Historic Inn** H
(707) 923-2124. **Call for rates.** 445 Lake Benbow Dr 95542. US 101 exit 636 (Benbow Lake Rd), just w. Ext/int corridors. **Pets:** $30 one-time fee/room. Designated rooms, service with restrictions, supervision.
🍴 ⚞ ⌧ 🛜 ⌧ 🔌 💻

⊘ ▼▼▼ **Best Western Plus Humboldt House Inn** M ❖
(707) 923-2771. **$135-$195.** 701 Redwood Dr 95542. US 101 exit Garberville, just e. Ext corridors. **Pets:** Medium, dogs only. $20 one-time fee/pet. Designated rooms, service with restrictions, supervision.
🗚 🔌 ⚞ 🛜 🔌 💻

GARDEN GROVE

▼▼▼ **Anaheim Marriott Suites** H
(714) 750-1000. **$118-$208.** 12015 Harbor Blvd 92840. I-5 exit 107B (Chapman Ave) northbound, 1.5 mi w, then just s; exit 107C (State College/The City Dr) southbound, just s on State College Blvd, 1.5 w on Chapman Ave, then just s. Int corridors. **Pets:** Accepted.
🍴 🔌 ⚞ 🔌 ⌧ 🔌 💻

⊘ ▼▼▼ **Hyatt Regency Orange County** H
(714) 750-1234. **$89-$279.** 11999 Harbor Blvd 92840. I-5 exit 107B (Chapman Ave) northbound, 1.5 mi w, then just s; exit 107C (State College Blvd/The City Dr) southbound, just s on State College Blvd, then 1.5 mi w on Chapman Ave. Int corridors. **Pets:** Accepted.
🗚 🌿 🍴 ⚞ ⌧ 🛜 ⌧ 🔌 💻

▼▼▼ **Residence Inn by Marriott Anaheim Resort Area** H
(714) 591-4000. **$158-$269.** 11931 Harbor Blvd 92840. I-5 exit 107B (Chapman Ave) northbound, 1.5 mi w, then just n; exit 107C (State College Blvd/The City Dr) southbound, just s on State College Blvd, 1.5 mi w on Chapman Ave, then just n. Int corridors. **Pets:** Accepted.
🔌 ⚞ ⌧ 🛜 ⌧ 🔌 💻

⊘ ▼▼▼ **Sheraton Garden Grove Anaheim South** H
(714) 703-8400. **$99-$329.** 12221 Harbor Blvd 92840. I-5 exit 110 (Harbor Blvd/Ball Rd), 2.2 mi s. Int corridors. **Pets:** Accepted.
🗚 🍴 ⚞ 🔌 ⌧ 🔌 💻

GEYSERVILLE

⊘ ▼▼▼ **Geyserville Inn** H ❖
(707) 857-4343. **$109-$499, 3 day notice.** 21714 Geyserville Ave 95441. US 101 exit E Canyon Rd, just s. Ext/int corridors. **Pets:** Dogs only. $25 daily fee/pet. Designated rooms, service with restrictions, supervision. 🗚 🍴 🔌 ⚞ 🛜 ⌧ 🔌 💻

GILROY

⊘ ▼▼▼ **Best Western Plus Forest Park Inn** H
(408) 848-5144. **$109-$199.** 375 Leavesley Rd 95020. US 101 exit Leavesley Rd, just w. Int corridors. **Pets:** $20 daily fee/pet. Designated rooms, service with restrictions, supervision.
🗚 🔌 ⚞ ⌧ 🛜 ⌧ 🔌 💻

⊘ ▼▼▼ **Quality Inn & Suites** H
(408) 847-5500. **$109-$249.** 8430 Murray Ave 95020. US 101 exit Leavesley Rd, just w. Ext corridors. **Pets:** Small. $10 daily fee/pet. Designated rooms, service with restrictions, crate.
🗚 ⚞ 🛜 ⌧ 🔌 💻

GLENDALE

▼▼▼ **Hilton Los Angeles North/Glendale** H
(818) 956-5466. **$159-$319.** 100 W Glenoaks Blvd 91202. SR 134 exit 7B (Brand Blvd), just n, then just w. Int corridors. **Pets:** Accepted.
🌿 🍴 🔌 ⚞ ⌧ 🔌 ⌧ 💻

GLEN ELLEN

▼▼▼ **Gaige House, A Four Sisters Inn** BB
(707) 935-0237. **$275-$625, 7 day notice.** 13540 Arnold Dr 95442. SR 12 exit Arnold Dr, 0.5 mi w. Ext/int corridors. **Pets:** Accepted.
⚞ 🛜 ⌧ 🔌 💻

GOLETA *(Restaurants p. 597)*

⊘ ▼▼▼ **The Goodland** H
(805) 964-6241. **Call for rates.** 5650 Calle Real 93117. 7 mi nw of town center via US 101, exit 104A (Patterson Ave), just e, then 0.7 mi n. Ext corridors. **Pets:** Accepted. 🗚 🍴 🔌 ⚞ 🛜 ⌧

GRASS VALLEY

⊘ ▼▼▼ **Best Western Gold Country Inn** M
(530) 273-1393. **$109-$199.** 972 Sutton Way 95945. SR 20 and 49 exit 183B (Brunswick Rd), just e, then just n; midway between Grass Valley and Nevada City. Ext corridors. **Pets:** Accepted.
🗚 🔌 ⚞ 🛜 🔌 💻

▼▼▼ **The Gold Miners Inn Holiday Inn Express & Suites** H ❖
(530) 477-1700. **$109-$269.** 121 Bank St 95945. SR 49 exit 182A (northbound) just n on Auburn St, then just e; (southbound) continue sw on Tinloy St, then just w. Int corridors. **Pets:** Large, other species. $60 one-time fee/room. Service with restrictions, crate.
🔌 🛜 ⌧ 🔌 💻

▼▼▼ Grass Valley Courtyard Suites Spa & Conference Center H
(530) 272-7696. **$153-$309.** 210 N Auburn St 95945. SR 49 exit 182A (SR 174/Colfax Ave/Central Grass Valley) southbound, just nw on Bennett St to N Auburn St, then just n; northbound, just n. Ext corridors.
Pets: Accepted.

GUALALA

◊◊◊ ▼▼▼ Gualala Country Inn M
(707) 884-4343. **$83-$200, 3 day notice.** 47975 Center St 95445. Just n of jct Old State Hwy; on SR 1. Ext/int corridors. **Pets:** Other species. $10 one-time fee/pet. Service with restrictions, supervision.

▼▼ North Coast Country Inn BB
(707) 884-4537. **$195-$245, 3 day notice.** 34591 S Hwy 1 95445. On SR 1, 4.5 mi n; jct Fish Rock Rd. Ext corridors. **Pets:** Accepted.

◊◊◊ ▼▼▼ Surf Inn M
(707) 884-3571. **Call for rates.** 39170 S Hwy 1 95445. Center. Ext corridors. **Pets:** Accepted.

GUERNEVILLE

▼▼▼ Applewood Inn, Restaurant & Spa CI
(707) 869-9093. **Call for rates.** 13555 Hwy 116 95446. 0.5 mi s of River Rd. Ext corridors. **Pets:** Accepted.

▼▼ Cottages on River Road CA 🐾
(707) 869-3848. **Call for rates.** 14880 River Rd 95446. 1.6 mi ne of jct SR 116. Ext corridors. **Pets:** Small, dogs only. $25 daily fee/pet. Designated rooms, service with restrictions, supervision.

◊◊◊ ▼▼▼ Ferngrove Cottages CA
(707) 869-8105. **Call for rates.** 16650 River Rd 95446. Just w of downtown. Ext corridors. **Pets:** Accepted.

▼▼ West Sonoma Inn & Spa CA
(707) 869-2874. **Call for rates.** 14100 Brookside Ln 95446. Just n of SR 116; on west end of downtown. Ext corridors. **Pets:** Accepted.

HALF MOON BAY *(Restaurants p. 597)*

▼▼ Coastside Inn Half Moon Bay H
(650) 726-3400. **Call for rates.** 230 S Cabrillo Hwy 94019. On SR 1, just s of SR 92. Ext corridors. **Pets:** Accepted.

▼▼▼ Half Moon Bay Lodge H
(650) 726-9000. **Call for rates.** 2400 Cabrillo Hwy S 94019. 2.5 mi s of jct SR 1 and 92, just w. Ext corridors. **Pets:** Accepted.

▼▼▼ The Oceanfront Hotel H
(650) 726-6642. **$290-$590, 7 day notice.** 211 Mirada Rd 94019. 3 mi n of jct SR 1 and 92 to Medio Ave, just w, then just n. Int corridors. **Pets:** Accepted.

◊◊◊ ▼▼▼▼ The Ritz-Carlton, Half Moon Bay H
(650) 712-7000. **$545-$4500, 3 day notice.** 1 Miramontes Point Rd 94019. 2.5 mi s of jct SR 1 (Cabrillo Hwy S) and 92, 0.8 mi w. Int corridors. **Pets:** Accepted.

HANFORD

◊◊◊ ▼▼ Sequoia Inn H
(559) 582-0338. **$86-$130.** 1655 Mall Dr 93230. SR 198 exit 85 (12th Ave), just n, then just e. Int corridors. **Pets:** Other species. $30 one-time fee/room. Service with restrictions.

HAWTHORNE

▼▼▼ Candlewood Suites LAX Hawthorne H
(310) 973-3331. **Call for rates.** 11410 Hawthorne Blvd 90250. I-105 exit 3 (Hawthorne Blvd/Prairie Ave), 0.6 mi s. Int corridors. **Pets:** Large, other species. $150 deposit/pet. Service with restrictions, crate.

◊◊◊ ▼▼▼ TownePlace Suites by Marriott Los Angeles LAX/Manhattan Beach M
(310) 725-9696. **$124-$194.** 14400 Aviation Blvd 90250. I-405 exit 43 (Rosecrans Ave), 0.4 mi w. Int corridors. **Pets:** Accepted.

HAYWARD

▼▼▼ La Quinta Inn & Suites Oakland - Hayward H
(510) 732-6300. **$86-$339.** 20777 Hesperian Blvd 94541. I-880 exit A St, 0.5 mi w, then just s. Int corridors. **Pets:** Accepted.

HEALDSBURG *(Restaurants p. 597)*

◊◊◊ ▼▼▼ Best Western Dry Creek Inn H 🐾
(707) 433-0300. **$99-$349.** 198 Dry Creek Rd 95448. US 101 exit Dry Creek Rd, just se. Ext corridors. **Pets:** $50 daily fee/room. Service with restrictions, supervision.

HEMET *(Restaurants p. 597)*

◊◊◊ ▼▼▼▼ Best Western Plus Diamond Valley Inn H
(951) 658-2281. **$89-$129.** 3510 W Florida Ave 92545. 3 mi w of SR 79 N (San Jacinto St) on SR 74/79. Int corridors. **Pets:** Accepted.

◊◊◊ ▼▼▼▼ Quality Inn M
(951) 766-1902. **$79-$145.** 1201 W Florida Ave 92543. 1.5 mi w of SR 79 N (San Jacinto St) on SR 74/79. Ext corridors. **Pets:** Small. $20 daily fee/pet. Designated rooms, service with restrictions, supervision.

HESPERIA *(Restaurants p. 597)*

▼▼ Econo Lodge M
(760) 949-1515. **$65-$139.** 11976 Mariposa Rd 92345. I-15 exit 147 (Bear Valley Rd), just e, then just s. Ext corridors. **Pets:** Small, dogs only. $10 daily fee/pet. Service with restrictions, supervision.

▼▼ La Quinta Inn & Suites H
(760) 949-9900. **$81-$185.** 12000 Mariposa Rd 92345. I-15 exit 147 (Bear Valley Rd), just e, then just s. Int corridors. **Pets:** Accepted.

HOLLYWOOD

◊◊◊ ▼▼▼ Hollywood Hotel H 🐾
(323) 315-1800. **$99-$349.** 1160 N Vermont Ave 90029. US 101 exit 6A (Vermont Ave), 0.5 mi n. Int corridors. **Pets:** Large. $50 daily fee/pet. Service with restrictions, supervision.

▼▼▼ ▼▼▼ Loews Hollywood H 🐾
(323) 856-1200. **Call for rates.** 1755 N Highland Ave 90028. US 101 exit 9B (Highland Ave) northbound; exit 9C southbound, 0.6 mi s. Int corridors. **Pets:** Medium. $25 daily fee/pet. Designated rooms.

▼▼ Motel 6 Los Angeles - Hollywood #4044 M
(323) 464-6006. **Call for rates.** 1738 N Whitley Ave 90028. US 101 exit 9C southbound, just s, just w, then just s. Int corridors. **Pets:** Accepted.

W Hollywood H

(323) 798-1300. **$329-$699.** 6250 Hollywood Blvd 90028. US 101 exit 8B (Hollywood Blvd), 0.5 mi w. Int corridors. **Pets:** Accepted.

SAVE ECO ⊟ ¶¶ 🏊 ⊠ 📶 ⊠ 🛏 🖵

HUNTINGTON BEACH

Hyatt Regency Huntington Beach Resort & Spa H

(714) 698-1234. **$179-$499, 3 day notice.** 21500 Pacific Coast Hwy 92648. I-405 exit 16 (Beach Blvd), 6.5 mi s, then just w. Ext/int corridors. **Pets:** Accepted.

SAVE ECO ⊟ ¶¶ 🔥M 🏊 ⊠ 📶 ⊠ 🛏 🖵

The Waterfront Beach Resort, A Hilton Hotel H 🐾

(714) 845-8000. **$219-$499.** 21100 Pacific Coast Hwy 92648. I-405 exit 16 (Beach Blvd), 6.5 mi s, then just w. Int corridors. **Pets:** Medium. $50 one-time fee/pet. Service with restrictions, crate.

SAVE ECO ¶¶ 🔥M 🏊 ⊠ 📶 ⊠ 🛏 🖵

IDYLLWILD *(Restaurants p. 597)*

Woodland Park Manor CA

(951) 659-2657. **$99-$215, 10 day notice.** 55350 S Circle Dr 92549. From SR 243 and town center, 1.5 mi ne. Ext corridors. **Pets:** Dogs only. $15 one-time fee/pet. Supervision. 🏊 📶 ⊠ 🐾 🛏 🖵

INDIAN WELLS *(Restaurants p. 597)*

Hyatt Regency Indian Wells Resort & Spa H

(760) 776-1234. **$99-$429, 3 day notice.** 44-600 Indian Wells Ln 92210. I-10 exit 134 (Cook St), 4.4 mi s, 1.5 mi e on SR 111, then just n. Ext/int corridors. **Pets:** Accepted.

SAVE ECO ⊟ ¶¶ 🔥M 🏊 ⊠ 📶 ⊠ 🛏 🖵

Miramonte Resort & Spa, Curio Collection by Hilton H

(760) 341-2200. **Call for rates.** 45000 Indian Wells Ln 92210. I-10 exit 134 (Cook St), 4.4 mi s, 1.5 mi e on SR 111, then just s. Ext/int corridors. **Pets:** Accepted.

SAVE ECO ⊟ ¶¶ 🔥M 🏊 ⊠ 📶 ⊠ 🛏 🖵

INDIO

Best Western Date Tree Hotel M 🐾

(760) 347-3421. **$80-$260.** 81-909 Indio Blvd 92201. I-10 exit 139 (Jefferson St/Indio Blvd), 2.5 mi se. Int corridors. **Pets:** $15 daily fee/pet. Service with restrictions. SAVE ⊟ ¶¶ 🔥M 🏊 📶 ⊠ 🛏 🖵

Indian Palms Country Club & Resort H

(760) 775-4444. **$69-$400.** 48-630 Monroe St 92201. I-10 exit 142 (Monroe St), 3 mi s. Ext corridors. **Pets:** Accepted.

SAVE ¶¶ 🔥M 🏊 ⊠ 📶 ⊠ 🛏 🖵

Indio Super 8 & Suites M

(760) 342-0264. **$79-$189.** 81-753 Hwy 111 92201. I-10 exit 142 (Monroe St), 1.5 mi s, then 0.5 mi w. Ext corridors. **Pets:** Small, dogs only. $100 deposit/room, $25 daily fee/pet. Designated rooms, service with restrictions, supervision. SAVE 🔥M 🏊 📶 ⊠ 🛏 🖵

INDUSTRY *(Restaurants p. 597)*

Pacific Palms Resort H

(626) 810-4455. **$235-$1699, 3 day notice.** One Industry Hills Pkwy 91744. SR 60 exit 18 (Azusa Ave), 1.3 mi n, then 0.5 mi w. Int corridors. **Pets:** Medium. $35 daily fee/pet. Supervision.

ECO ⊟ ¶¶ 🔥M 🏊 ⊠ 📶 ⊠ 🖵

IRVINE *(Restaurants p. 597)*

Hilton Irvine/Orange County Airport H

(949) 833-9999. **$109-$249.** 18800 MacArthur Blvd 92612. I-405 exit 8 (MacArthur Blvd/John Wayne Airport), 0.5 mi s. Int corridors. **Pets:** Accepted. ECO ¶¶ 🏊 📶 ⊠ 🛏 🖵

Hotel Irvine H

(949) 230-4452. **$119-$299.** 17900 Jamboree Rd 92614. I-405 exit 7 (Jamboree Rd), just ne. Int corridors. **Pets:** Accepted.

SAVE ECO ¶¶ 🏊 ⊠ 📶 🛏 🖵

Residence Inn by Marriott Irvine John Wayne Airport H

(949) 261-2020. **$128-$264.** 2855 Main St 92614. I-405 exit 7 (Jamboree Rd), just n, then just e. Int corridors. **Pets:** Accepted.

SAVE 🏊 📶 ⊠ 🛏 🖵

Residence Inn by Marriott-Irvine Spectrum H

(949) 380-3000. **$155-$250.** 10 Morgan St 92618. I-5 exit 94 (Alton Pkwy) southbound; exit 94B northbound, 2 mi e, then just se. Ext corridors. **Pets:** Other species. $100 one-time fee/pet. Designated rooms, service with restrictions. SAVE ECO ¶¶ 🏊 📶 ⊠ 🛏 🖵

Wyndham Irvine-Orange County Airport H

(949) 863-1999. **$89-$299, 3 day notice.** 17941 Von Karman Ave 92614. I-405 exit 7 (Jamboree Rd), 0.3 mi n to Main St, 0.5 mi w, then just sw. Int corridors. **Pets:** Small. $55 one-time fee/room. Service with restrictions, supervision. SAVE ¶¶ 🏊 📶 ⊠ 🖵

JACKSON

Best Western Amador Inn H

(209) 223-0211. **$99-$129.** 200 S Hwy 49 95642. Just se of jct SR 49 and 88. Int corridors. **Pets:** Medium. $15 daily fee/pet. Designated rooms, service with restrictions, supervision.

SAVE 🔥M 🏊 📶 ⊠ 🛏 🖵

JAMESTOWN

Country Inn Sonora M

(209) 984-0315. **Call for rates.** 18730 Hwy 108 95327. SR 108, 1 mi e of town. Ext corridors. **Pets:** Accepted. ¶¶ 🔥M 🏊 📶 🛏 🖵

National Hotel & Restaurant CI 🐾

(209) 984-3446. **$140-$160, 3 day notice.** 18183 Main St 95327. In historic downtown. Int corridors. **Pets:** Medium. $25 deposit/pet. Service with restrictions, supervision. SAVE ¶¶ 📶 ⊠ 🅦 🐾

JULIAN *(Restaurants p. 597)*

Julian Lodge B & B Mountain Inn M

(760) 765-1420. **Call for rates.** 2720 C St 92036. Just s of Main St on SR 78 and 79. Ext/int corridors. **Pets:** Accepted.

SAVE 🔥M 📶 ⊠ 🐾 🛏 🖵

JUNE LAKE

Double Eagle Resort and Spa CA

(760) 648-7004. **$199-$669, 30 day notice.** 5587 Hwy 158 93529. 3 mi w of village. Ext corridors. **Pets:** $50 one-time fee/pet. Designated rooms, service with restrictions, supervision.

SAVE ¶¶ 🔥M 🏊 ⊠ 📶 ⊠ 🅜 🛏 🖵

June Lake Motel M

(760) 648-7547. **Call for rates.** 2716 Hwy 158 93529. US 395 exit SR 158 northbound, 2.7 mi s. Ext corridors. **Pets:** Accepted.

📶 ⊠ 🐾 🛏 🖵

June Lake Villager M

(760) 648-7712. **$80-$310.** 640 Hwy 158 93529. On SR 158; center of village. Ext corridors. **Pets:** $10 daily fee/pet. Designated rooms, service with restrictions, crate. 📶 🅜 🐾 🛏 🖵

KERNVILLE *(Restaurants p. 597)*

▼▼ ▼▼ Barewood Inn & Suites M
(760) 376-1910. **$92-$375, 3 day notice.** 7013 Wofford Blvd 93285. In Wofford Heights. Ext corridors. **Pets:** Large. $10 one-time fee/pet. Service with restrictions, supervision. 📶 ⊠ 🗎 💻

▼▼ ▼▼ River View Lodge M
(760) 376-6019. **Call for rates.** 2 Sirretta St 93238. On Kernville Rd; at bridge. Ext corridors. **Pets:** Accepted. 📶 ⊠ 📼 🗎

KETTLEMAN CITY

⬨⬨⬨ ▼▼ ▼▼ Best Western Kettleman City Inn & Suites M
(559) 386-0804. **$116-$180.** 33410 Powers Dr 93239. I-5 exit 309 (SR 41), just n, just w on Bernard Dr, then just s. Ext corridors. **Pets:** $15 daily fee/pet. Designated rooms, service with restrictions, supervision.
SAVE 🆓 ➰ 📶 ⊠ 🗎 💻

KLAMATH

⬨⬨⬨ ▼▼ Motel Trees M
(707) 482-3152. **$75-$150.** 15495 Hwy 101 N 95548. On US 101, 4.5 mi n of Klamath. Ext corridors. **Pets:** $10 daily fee/pet. Designated rooms, service with restrictions, supervision.
SAVE 🍴 📶 🆓 🗎 💻

LAGUNA BEACH *(Restaurants p. 597)*

▼▼ ▼▼ Art Hotel-Laguna Beach M
(949) 494-6464. **$129-$214, 3 day notice.** 1404 N Coast Hwy 92651. SR 133 to Coast Hwy, 1.1 mi n on SR 1. Ext corridors. **Pets:** Designated rooms, service with restrictions. 🍴 ➰ 📶 ⊠ 🗎 💻

⬨⬨⬨ ▼▼ ▼▼ Capri Laguna on the Beach, a Boutique Hotel H
(949) 494-6533. **$184-$700, 3 day notice.** 1441 S Coast Hwy 92651. SR 33, 1 mi s on SR 1. Ext corridors. **Pets:** Accepted.
SAVE 🍴 ➰ 📶 ⊠ 🆓 🗎 💻

▼▼▼▼ Casa Laguna Inn & Spa BB
(949) 494-2996. **Call for rates.** 2510 S Coast Hwy 92651. SR 133 to Coast Hwy, 1.3 mi s on SR 1. Ext corridors. **Pets:** Accepted.
🍴 ➰ 📶 ⊠ 🗎 💻

▼▼▼▼ Holiday Inn Laguna Beach H
(949) 494-1001. **$159-$499.** 696 S Coast Hwy 92651. SR 133 to Coast Hwy, 0.5 mi s on SR 1. Ext corridors. **Pets:** Accepted.
🍴 ➰ 📶 ⊠ 🗎 💻

⬨⬨⬨ ▼▼▼▼ Montage Laguna Beach H
(949) 715-6000. **Call for rates.** 30801 S Coast Hwy 92651. SR 133 to Coast Hwy, 3 mi s on SR 1. Ext/int corridors. **Pets:** Accepted.
SAVE 🆓 📧 🍴 ➰ ⊠ 📶 ⊠ 🗎

⬨⬨⬨ ▼▼▼▼ Surf & Sand Resort H
(949) 497-4477. **Call for rates.** 1555 S Coast Hwy 92651. SR 133, 1 mi s. Ext corridors. **Pets:** Accepted.
SAVE 📧 🍴 🆓 ➰ ⊠ 🆓 ⊠ 🗎 💻

▼▼ ▼▼ The Tides Laguna Beach M
(949) 494-2494. **$129-$429, 3 day notice.** 460 N Coast Hwy 92651. SR 133 to Coast Hwy, 0.5 mi n on SR 1. Ext corridors. **Pets:** Accepted.
➰ 📶 ⊠ 🗎 💻

LAGUNA HILLS

▼▼▼▼ The Hills Hotel, an Ascend Hotel Collection Member H
(949) 586-5000. **$105-$489.** 25205 La Paz Rd 92653. I-5 exit 89 (La Paz Rd), just w. Int corridors. **Pets:** Accepted.
🍴 🆓 ➰ 📶 ⊠ 🗎 💻

LA JOLLA *(Restaurants p. 598)*

⬨⬨⬨ ▼▼ ▼▼ Empress Hotel of La Jolla H ✿
(858) 454-3001. **$129-$499.** 7766 Fay Ave 92037. I-5 exit 28 (La Jolla Village Dr) southbound, 0.7 mi w to Torrey Pines Rd, 2.5 mi sw to Prospect St, 0.8 mi sw, then just s; exit 26A (La Jolla Pkwy) northbound, 1.5 mi n to Torrey Pines Rd, 1 mi sw to Prospect St, 0.8 mi sw, then just s. Int corridors. **Pets:** Medium. $75 one-time fee/room. Designated rooms, service with restrictions, supervision.
SAVE 🆓 🍴 🆓 📶 ⊠ 🗎 💻

⬨⬨⬨ ▼▼▼▼ Estancia La Jolla Hotel & Spa H
(858) 550-1000. **Call for rates.** 9700 N Torrey Pines Rd 92037. I-5 exit 28 (La Jolla Village Dr), 0.7 mi w, then 1 mi n. Ext/int corridors.
Pets: Accepted. SAVE 🍴 🆓 ➰ ⊠ 📶 ⊠ 🗎 💻

⬨⬨⬨ ▼▼▼▼ Holiday Inn Express La Jolla M
(858) 454-7101. **$109-$289.** 6705 La Jolla Blvd 92037. I-5 exit 28 (La Jolla Village Dr) southbound, 0.7 mi w to Torrey Pines Rd, 3 mi sw to Girard Ave, just s to Pearl St, 0.4 mi w, then 0.6 mi s; exit 26A (La Jolla Pkwy) northbound, 1.5 mi n to Torrey Pines Rd, 1.5 mi sw to Girard Ave, just s to Pearl St, 0.4 mi w, then 0.6 mi s. Ext corridors.
Pets: Accepted. SAVE ➰ 📶 ⊠ 🗎 💻

⬨⬨⬨ ▼▼▼▼▼ Hyatt Regency La Jolla H
(858) 552-1234. **$99-$349, 3 day notice.** 3777 La Jolla Village Dr 92122. I-5 exit 28 (La Jolla Village Dr), just e. Int corridors.
Pets: Accepted.
SAVE 🆓 📧 🍴 🆓 ➰ ⊠ 🆓 ⊠ 🗎 💻

⬨⬨⬨ ▼▼▼▼▼ La Valencia Hotel H
(858) 454-0771. **$279-$795, 3 day notice.** 1132 Prospect St 92037. I-5 exit 26A (La Jolla Pkwy) northbound, 1.5 mi n to Torrey Pines Rd, 1 mi sw to Prospect St, then 0.6 mi sw; exit 28 (La Jolla Village Dr) southbound, 0.7 mi w to Torrey Pines Rd, 2.5 mi sw to Prospect St, then 0.6 mi sw. Ext/int corridors. **Pets:** Accepted.
SAVE 🍴 🆓 ➰ ⊠ 📶 ⊠ 💻

⬨⬨⬨ ▼▼▼▼ The Lodge at Torrey Pines H
(858) 453-4420. **$325-$875, 3 day notice.** 11480 N Torrey Pines Rd 92037. I-5 exit 29 (Genesee Ave), 0.8 mi w, then just n. Int corridors. **Pets:** Medium, dogs only. $75 one-time fee/pet. Service with restrictions, supervision. SAVE 🆓 🍴 🆓 ➰ ⊠ 📶 ⊠ 💻

⬨⬨⬨ ▼▼▼▼ Residence Inn by Marriott San Diego La Jolla H
(858) 587-1770. **$140-$265.** 8901 Gilman Dr 92037. I-5 exit 27 (Gilman Dr), 1.3 mi nw. Ext corridors. **Pets:** Accepted.
SAVE 🆓 ➰ 📶 ⊠ 🗎 💻

▼▼▼▼ San Diego Marriott La Jolla H
(858) 587-1414. **$133-$327.** 4240 La Jolla Village Dr 92037. I-5 exit 28 (La Jolla Village Dr), 0.8 mi e. Int corridors. **Pets:** Accepted.
🍴 🆓 ➰ 🆓 ⊠ 🗎 💻

⬨⬨⬨ ▼▼▼▼ Sheraton La Jolla Hotel H ✿
(858) 453-5500. **$149-$394.** 3299 Holiday Ct 92037. I-5 exit 28 (La Jolla Village Dr), just w to Villa La Jolla Dr, just s, then just e. Ext/int corridors. **Pets:** Medium, dogs only. $75 one-time fee/room. Designated rooms, service with restrictions, supervision.
SAVE 🆓 🍴 🆓 ➰ 📶 ⊠ 🗎 💻

LAKE ARROWHEAD

▼▼▼▼ Arrowhead Saddleback Inn CI
(909) 336-3571. **$137-$648, 7 day notice.** 300 S SR 173 92352. On SR 173; jct SR 189. Ext/int corridors. **Pets:** Other species. $15 daily fee/pet. Designated rooms, service with restrictions, supervision.
🍴 🆓 📶 ⊠ 🗎 💻

⬨⬨⬨ ▼▼ ▼▼ Arrowhead Tree Top Lodge M
(909) 337-2311. **$109-$189, 7 day notice.** 27992 Rainbow Dr 92352. 0.3 mi s of Lake Arrowhead Village on SR 173. Ext corridors.
Pets: Accepted. SAVE 🍴 ➰ 📶 📼 🗎 💻

▼▼◆ Bracken Fern Manor **BB** ❀
(909) 336-5000. **$100-$150, 7 day notice.** 815 Arrowhead Villa Rd 92352. 0.8 mi n of SR 18, 0.4 mi e of jct SR 173. Int corridors. **Pets:** Large, other species. $100 deposit/room. Designated rooms, no service. 🤝 ✕ 🦮 📶 ☎

◢◣ ▼◆▼◆ Lake Arrowhead Resort and Spa, Autograph Collection **H**
(909) 336-1511. **$152-$285, 3 day notice.** 27984 Hwy 189 92352. Just w of SR 173; in Lake Arrowhead Village. Int corridors. **Pets:** Accepted. 🆂🅰🆅🅴 🍴 ♿ 🛄 ✕ 📶 ✕ 🛗 🖥

LAKE FOREST *(Restaurants p. 598)*

◢◣ ▼◆▼◆ Best Western Plus Irvine Spectrum Hotel **M**
(949) 380-9888. **$89-$299.** 23192 Lake Center Dr 92630. I-5 exit Lake Forest Dr, just e, just s on Rockfield Blvd, just w on Boeing, then just s. Ext corridors. **Pets:** Accepted. 🆂🅰🆅🅴 🍴 🛄 🤝 🛗 🖥

◢◣ ▼◆▼◆ The Prominence Hotel and Suites **H**
(949) 900-1288. **$95-$205.** 20768 Lake Forest Dr 92630. I-5 exit 92A (Lake Forest Dr) northbound; exit 92 (Bake Pkwy/Lake Forest Dr) southbound, 4 mi e. Int corridors. **Pets:** Accepted. 🆂🅰🆅🅴 🛄 🤝 ✕ 🛗 🖥

▼◆ ▼◆ Quality Inn & Suites Irvine Spectrum **H**
(949) 458-1900. **$89-$239.** 23702 Rockfield Blvd 92630. I-5 exit 92A (Lake Forest Dr) northbound; exit 92 (Bake Pkwy/Lake Forest Dr) southbound, 0.5 mi e on Lake Forest Dr, then just s. Int corridors. **Pets:** Medium, other species. $100 deposit/pet, $35 daily fee/pet. Designated rooms, no service, supervision. 🍴 🛄 🤝 🛗 🖥

▼◆▼◆ Staybridge Suites Irvine East/Lake Forest **H**
(949) 462-9500. **$119-$249.** 2 Orchard Rd 92630. I-5 exit 92B (Bake Pkwy) northbound; exit 92 (Bake Pkwy/Lake Forest Dr) southbound, 4.7 mi e on Bake Pkwy, just n on Rancho Pkwy S, then just w. Int corridors. **Pets:** Accepted. 🍴 🛄 🤝 ✕ 🛗 🖥

LA MIRADA

▼◆▼◆ Residence Inn by Marriott **H**
(714) 523-2800. **$144-$196.** 14419 Firestone Blvd 90638. I-5 exit 118 (Valley View Ave), just n, then 0.5 mi e. Ext corridors. **Pets:** Accepted. 🛄 🤝 ✕ 🛗 🖥

LANCASTER

◢◣ ▼◆▼◆ Americas Best Value Inn & Suites of Lancaster **M**
(661) 945-8771. **$75-$85.** 44131 Sierra Hwy 93534. SR 14 exit 42 (Ave K), 2 mi e, then just n. Ext corridors. **Pets:** Other species. $250 deposit/pet, $20 daily fee/pet. Designated rooms, service with restrictions, supervision. 🆂🅰🆅🅴 🛄 🤝 🛗 🖥

▼◆ ▼◆ Comfort Inn & Suites **H**
(661) 723-2001. **$99-$179.** 1825 W Ave J-12 93534. SR 14 exit 43 (Ave J) northbound; exit 20th St southbound, just s, then just e. Int corridors. **Pets:** $30 daily fee/pet. Service with restrictions, supervision. ♿ 🛄 ✕ 🤝 🖥

▼◆▼◆ Homewood Suites Lancaster **H**
(661) 723-8040. **$129-$199.** 2320 W Double Play Way 93536. SR 14 exit 44 (Ave I), just w, s on Valley Central Way, then just e. Int corridors. **Pets:** Accepted. ♿ 🛄 🤝 ✕ 🛗 🖥

◢◣ ▼◆▼◆ Oxford Inn & Suites Lancaster **H**
(661) 949-3423. **Call for rates.** 1651 W Ave K 93534. SR 14 exit 42 (Ave K), just w. Int corridors. **Pets:** Accepted. 🆂🅰🆅🅴 ♿ 🛄 🤝 ✕ 🛗 🖥

▼◆▼◆ TownePlace Suites by Marriott **H**
(661) 723-6709. **$96-$177.** 2024 W Ave, J-8 93536. SR 14 exit 43 (Ave I), just w. Int corridors. **Pets:** Accepted. ♿ 🤝 ✕ 🛗 🖥

LA PALMA

▼◆▼◆ La Quinta Inn & Suites Buena Park **H**
(714) 670-1400. **$104-$185.** 3 Centerpointe Dr 90623. SR 91 exit 21 (Orangethorpe Ave/Valley View St) eastbound; exit 22 westbound, just n. Int corridors. **Pets:** Accepted. 🛄 🤝 ✕ 🛗 🖥

LA QUINTA

▼◆▼◆ La Quinta Resort & Club, A Waldorf Astoria Resort **H**
(760) 564-4111. **Call for rates.** 49-499 Eisenhower Dr 92253. I-10 exit 137 (Washington St), 4.7 mi s, then 1 mi sw. Ext corridors. **Pets:** Accepted. 🍴 ♿ 🛄 ✕ 🤝 ✕ 🛗 🖥

LEBEC

▼◆▼◆ Holiday Inn Express Frazier Park/Lebec **H**
(661) 248-1600. **$115-$209.** 612 Wainright Ct 93243. I-5 exit 205 (Frazer Mountain Rd), just n. Int corridors. **Pets:** Accepted. ◀ ♿ 🛄 🤝 ✕ 🛗 🖥

▼◆▼◆ Ramada Limited Grapevine **M**
(661) 248-1530. **$79-$117.** 9000 Countryside Ct 93243. I-5 exit 215 (Grapevine Rd), just w. Ext corridors. **Pets:** Accepted. ♿ 🛄 🤝 🛗 🖥

LEE VINING *(Restaurants p. 598)*

◢◣ ▼◆◆ Murphey's Motel **M**
(760) 647-6316. **$58-$163.** 51493 Hwy 395 93541. Jct Lee Vining Ave and US 395; in town. Ext corridors. **Pets:** Dogs only. $15 daily fee/room. Service with restrictions, supervision. 🆂🅰🆅🅴 🤝 ✕ 🛗 🖥

LEGGETT

◢◣ ▼◆ Redwoods River Resort **CA**
(707) 925-6249. **$75-$133, 14 day notice.** 75000 Hwy 101 95585. 6.5 mi n of jct SR 1. Ext corridors. **Pets:** Accepted. 🆂🅰🆅🅴 🍴 🛄 📶 ✕ ☎ 🛗 🖥

LINCOLN

▼◆▼◆ Holiday Inn Express Hotel & Suites **H**
(916) 644-3440. **$125-$190.** 155 Ferrari Ranch Rd 95648. SR 65 exit 315 (Ferrari Ranch Rd), just e; jct Groveland Ln. Int corridors. **Pets:** Accepted. ♿ 🛄 🤝 ✕ 🛗 🖥

LITTLE RIVER *(Restaurants p. 598)*

▼◆▼◆ Little River Inn **CI** ❀
(707) 937-5942. **Call for rates.** 7901 N Hwy 1 95456. On SR 1, just s of Van Damme State Park entrance. Ext/int corridors. **Pets:** Large, other species. $25 daily fee/pet. Service with restrictions, supervision. ◀ 🍴 ♿ 🛄 🤝 ✕ 🦮 🛗 🖥

LIVERMORE

▼◆▼◆ Holiday Inn Express Hotel & Suites-Livermore **H**
(925) 961-9600. **Call for rates.** 3000 Constitution Dr 94551. I-580 exit 50 (Airway Blvd/Collier Canyon Rd), just n, just e on N Canyons Pkwy, then just s. Int corridors. **Pets:** Accepted. ♿ 🛄 🤝 ✕ 🛗 🖥

▼◆▼◆ La Quinta Inn Livermore **H**
(925) 373-9600. **$67-$185.** 7700 Southfront Rd 94551. I-580 exit Greenville Rd, just s, then just w; jct Mountain Vista Pkwy. Int corridors. **Pets:** Accepted. 🍴 ♿ 🛄 🤝 ✕ 🛗 🖥

▼◆▼◆ Residence Inn by Marriott **H**
(925) 373-1800. **$151-$305.** 1000 Airway Blvd 94551. I-580 exit 50 (Airway Blvd/Collier Canyon Rd), just n. Ext corridors. **Pets:** Other species. $150 one-time fee/room. Service with restrictions. ♿ 🛄 🤝 ✕ 🛗 🖥

LODI

▼▼▼ Holiday Inn Express H
(209) 210-0150. **Call for rates.** 1337 E Kettleman Ln 95240. SR 99 exit Kettleman Ln, 0.4 mi e. Int corridors. **Pets:** Accepted.
🍽 ⌖M ⊇ 📶 ✕ 🖥 💻

🔺🔺 ▼▼▼ Microtel Inn & Suites by Wyndham H
(209) 367-9700. **$69-$95.** 6428 W Banner St 95242. I-5 exit 485 (SR 12), just e, then just s. Int corridors. **Pets:** Medium, dogs only. $15 daily fee/pet. Designated rooms, service with restrictions, supervision.
SAVE ⌖M ⊇ 📶 ✕ 🖥 💻

▼▼▼ Wine & Roses Hotel Spa and Restaurant H
(209) 334-6988. **Call for rates.** 2505 W Turner Rd 95242. I-5 exit Turner Rd, 5 mi e; SR 99 exit Turner Rd, 2.4 mi w. Ext corridors.
Pets: Accepted. 🍽 ⌖M ⊇ ✕ 📶 ✕ 🖥 💻

LOMA LINDA

▼▼ Loma Linda Inn M
(909) 583-2500. **Call for rates.** 24532 University Ave 92354. I-10 exit 74 (Tippecanoe Ave), 1 mi s, just w on Stewart St, just s on Campus, then just w. Ext corridors. **Pets:** Accepted. ⌖M 📶 ✕ 🖥 💻

LONE PINE

🔺🔺 ▼▼▼ Best Western Plus Frontier Motel M
(760) 876-5571. **$89-$149.** 1008 S Main St 93545. On US 395. Ext corridors. **Pets:** Medium, other species. Designated rooms, service with restrictions, supervision. SAVE ⊇ 📶 ✕ 🖥 💻

🔺🔺 ▼▼▼ Comfort Inn M 🐾
(760) 876-8700. **$90-$215.** 1920 S Main St 93545. US 395, 1.5 mi s of town. Int corridors. **Pets:** Medium. $20 daily fee/pet. Designated rooms, service with restrictions, supervision.
SAVE ⌖M ⊇ 📶 ✕ 🖥 💻

🔺🔺 ▼▼▼ Dow Villa Motel M
(760) 876-5521. **$82-$176.** 310 S Main St 93545. On US 395; center. Ext corridors. **Pets:** Other species. $100 deposit/room. Designated rooms, service with restrictions, supervision.
SAVE 🍽 ⌖M ⊇ 📶 ✕ 🖥 💻

🔺🔺 ▼ Timberline Motel M
(760) 876-4555. **Call for rates.** 215 E Post St 93545. US 395, just e. Ext corridors. **Pets:** Dogs only. $10 daily fee/pet. Designated rooms, service with restrictions, supervision. SAVE 📶 ☎ 🖥 💻

LONG BEACH (Restaurants p. 598)

▼▼ Extended Stay America-Los Angeles-Long Beach Airport H
(562) 989-4601. **$110-$145.** 4105 E Willow St 90815. I-405 exit 27 (Lakewood Blvd), just s, then 0.3 mi w. Int corridors. **Pets:** Accepted.
🍽 ⌖M 📶 ✕ 🖥

🔺🔺 ▼▼▼ Hilton Long Beach H
(562) 983-3400. **$149-$309.** 701 W Ocean Blvd 90831. I-710 exit Downtown/Broadway, just e to Daisy Ave, just s to Ocean Blvd, then just w. Int corridors. **Pets:** Accepted.
SAVE ECO 🍽 ⌖M ⊇ ✕ 📶 ✕ 🖥 💻

▼▼▼ Hotel Current M
(562) 597-1341. **Call for rates.** 5325 E Pacific Coast Hwy 90804. I-405 exit 23 (SR 22/Long Beach) northbound, 2 mi nw; exit 27 (Lakewood Blvd) southbound, 2 mi se on SR 1. Ext corridors. **Pets:** $50 one-time fee/room. Designated rooms, service with restrictions, crate.
ECO 🍽 ⌖M ⊇ 📶 ✕ 🖥 💻

▼▼▼ Hotel Maya - a DoubleTree by Hilton H 🐾
(562) 435-7676. **$189-$419.** 700 Queensway Dr 90802. I-710 exit 1A (Harbor Scenic Dr/Queen Mary), 1.3 mi s, then just e. Ext corridors. **Pets:** Medium. $50 one-time fee/pet. Service with restrictions, supervision. ECO 🍽 ⊇ ✕ 📶 ✕ 🖥 💻

🔺🔺 ▼▼▼ Hyatt Centric H
(562) 432-1234. **$99-$429.** 285 Bay St 90802. I-710 exit 1C (Shoreline Dr/Downtown), 1 mi se, just n on Aquarium Way, then just w. Int corridors. **Pets:** Accepted. SAVE 🍽 ⊇ 📶 ✕ 🖥 💻

🔺🔺 ▼▼▼▼ Hyatt Regency Long Beach H 🐾
(562) 491-1234. **$89-$389.** 200 S Pine Ave 90802. I-710 exit 1C (Shoreline Dr/Downtown), 1 mi s. Int corridors. **Pets:** Medium, dogs only. $100 one-time fee/room. Service with restrictions, supervision.
SAVE ECO ⊟ 🍽 ⌖M ⊇ 📶 ✕ 🖥 💻

🔺🔺 ▼▼▼ Residence Inn by Marriott Long Beach H
(562) 595-0909. **$149-$222.** 4111 E Willow St 90815. I-405 exit 27 (Lakewood Blvd), just s, then just w. Ext corridors. **Pets:** Accepted.
SAVE ECO ⌖M ⊇ 📶 ✕ 🖥 💻

🔺🔺 ▼▼▼ Residence Inn by Marriott Long Beach Downtown H
(562) 495-0700. **$170-$245.** 600 Queensway Dr 90802. I-710 exit 1A (Harbor Scenic Dr/Queen Mary), 1.3 mi s, then just w. Int corridors. **Pets:** Other species. $100 one-time fee/room. Service with restrictions.
SAVE ⊇ 📶 ✕ 🖥 💻

LOS ALAMITOS

🔺🔺 ▼▼▼ Residence Inn by Marriott-Cypress/Los Alamitos H 🐾
(714) 484-5700. **$147-$227.** 4931 Katella Ave 90720. I-605 exit 1D (Katella Ave) southbound; exit 1B (Katella Ave/Willow St) northbound, 1.9 mi e. Int corridors. **Pets:** Medium, other species. $100 one-time fee/room. Service with restrictions, crate.
SAVE ECO ⊇ 📶 ✕ 🖥 💻

LOS ALTOS

▼▼▼ Residence Inn by Marriott-Palo Alto/Los Altos H
(650) 559-7890. **$146-$369.** 4460 El Camino Real 94022. US 101 exit San Antonio Rd, 2 mi w to SR 82, then just n. Int corridors.
Pets: Accepted. ⌖M ⊇ 📶 ✕ 🖥 💻

LOS ANGELES (Restaurants p. 598)

🔺🔺 ▼▼ Best Western Plus Dragon Gate Inn H
(213) 617-3077. **$159-$399.** 818 N Hill St 90012. US 101 exit 2C (Broadway/Spring St), 0.6 mi n to Alpine St, just e, then just n. Ext corridors. **Pets:** Accepted. SAVE 📶 ✕ 🖥 💻

🔺🔺 ▼▼▼ The Concourse Hotel at Los Angeles Airport – A Hyatt Affiliate H
(310) 670-9000. **$99-$399, 3 day notice.** 6225 W Century Blvd at Sepulveda Blvd 90045. I-405 exit 46 (Century Blvd), 1.6 mi w. Int corridors. **Pets:** Accepted. SAVE ECO 🍽 ⊇ 📶 ✕ 🖥 💻

▼▼▼ Extended Stay America-Los Angeles/LAX Airport H
(310) 568-9337. **$145-$220.** 6531 S Sepulveda Blvd 90045. I-405 exit 49 (Howard Hughes Pkwy), 0.9 mi w, then just n. Int corridors.
Pets: Accepted. ⌖M 📶 🖥

🔺🔺 ▼▼▼ Four Points by Sheraton LAX H
(310) 645-4600. **$119-$300.** 9750 Airport Blvd 90045. I-405 exit 46 (Century Blvd), 1.5 mi w, then just n. Int corridors. **Pets:** Accepted.
SAVE 🍽 ⊇ 📶 ✕ 🖥 💻

▼▼▼ Four Seasons Hotel Los Angeles at Beverly Hills H
(310) 273-2222. **Call for rates.** 300 S Doheny Dr 90048. I-10 exit 6 (Robertson Blvd), 3 mi n to Burton Way, then just w. Int corridors.
Pets: Accepted. 🍽 ⊇ ✕ 📶 ✕ 🖥 💻

Hilton Checkers Los Angeles H

(213) 624-0000. **$179-$529.** 535 S Grand Ave 90071. SR 110 exit 23B (4th St), merge to the right up ramp to Hope St, then just s. Int corridors. **Pets:** Accepted.

Hotel Bel-Air H

(310) 472-1211. **$565-$1075.** 701 Stone Canyon 90077. I-405 exit 57 (Sunset Blvd). Ext corridors. **Pets:** Accepted.

Hotel Palomar Los Angeles Beverly Hills H

(310) 475-8711. **Call for rates.** 10740 Wilshire Blvd 90024. I-405 exit 55B (Wilshire Blvd), 1 mi w; in Westwood. Int corridors. **Pets:** Accepted.

The Hotel Wilshire H

(323) 852-6000. **Call for rates.** 6317 Wilshire Blvd 90048. I-10 exit 7B (Washington Blvd) westbound, 3 mi n, then just w. Int corridors. **Pets:** Accepted.

InterContinental Los Angeles Century City H

(310) 284-6500. **Call for rates.** 2151 Avenue of the Stars 90067. I-10 exit 6 (Robertson Blvd), 2.7 mi n to Olympic Blvd, 1.9 mi w, then just n. Int corridors. **Pets:** Accepted.

La Quinta Inn & Suites LAX H

(310) 645-2200. **$101-$302.** 5249 W Century Blvd 90045. I-405 exit 46 (Century Blvd), just w. Int corridors. **Pets:** Accepted.

The Line Hotel H

(213) 381-7411. **Call for rates.** 3515 Wilshire Blvd 90010. I-10 exit 11 (Normandie Ave), 1.8 mi n. Int corridors. **Pets:** Accepted.

Luxe City Center Hotel H

(213) 748-1291. **$199-$799, 3 day notice.** 1020 S Figueroa St 90015. SR 110 exit 22 (9th St), just e to Flower St, just s to 11th St, just w, then just n. Int corridors. **Pets:** Accepted.

Luxe Sunset Boulevard Hotel H

(310) 476-6571. **$259-$1500.** 11461 Sunset Blvd 90049. I-405 exit 57 (Sunset Blvd), just w. Int corridors. **Pets:** Accepted.

Omni Los Angeles Hotel at California Plaza H

(213) 617-3300. **Call for rates.** 251 S Olive St 90012. SR 110 exit 23B (4th St), just n. Int corridors. **Pets:** Small. $50 one-time fee/pet. Service with restrictions, supervision.

The Orlando Hotel H

(323) 658-6600. **$389-$1500.** 8384 W 3rd St 90048. I-10 exit 7A (La Cienega Blvd), 2.3 mi n, then just e. Int corridors. **Pets:** Small, other species. $50 daily fee/pet. Designated rooms, service with restrictions, supervision.

Radisson Hotel Midtown Los Angeles at USC H

(213) 748-4141. **Call for rates.** 3540 S Figueroa St 90007. SR 110 exit 20B (Exposition Blvd), just w, then just n. Int corridors. **Pets:** Accepted.

Residence Inn by Marriott-Beverly Hills H

(310) 228-4100. **$213-$344.** 1177 S Beverly Dr 90035. I-10 exit 6 (Robertson Blvd), 1.6 mi n to Pico Blvd, then 0.6 mi w. Int corridors. **Pets:** Accepted.

Residence Inn by Marriott Los Angeles L.A. Live H

(213) 443-9200. **$211-$398.** 901 W Olympic Blvd 90015. SR 110 exit 22 (9th St), s on Flower St, then just w. Int corridors. **Pets:** $100 one-time fee/pet. Service with restrictions.

Residence Inn by Marriott Los Angeles LAX/Century Blvd H

(310) 568-7700. **$152-$246.** 5933 W Century Blvd 90045. I-405 exit 46 (Century Blvd), 1.2 mi w; between Airport Blvd and Avion Dr. Ext corridors. **Pets:** Accepted.

Sheraton Gateway, Los Angeles H

(310) 642-1111. **Call for rates.** 6101 W Century Blvd 90045. I-405 exit 46 (Century Blvd), 1.3 mi w. Int corridors. **Pets:** Accepted.

Sheraton Grand Los Angeles H

(213) 488-3500. **$169-$659.** 711 S Hope St 90017. SR 110 exit 22 (9th St), 0.4 mi s, then just w. Int corridors. **Pets:** Accepted.

Sofitel Los Angeles at Beverly Hills H

(310) 278-5444. **Call for rates.** 8555 Beverly Blvd 90048. I-10 exit 7A (La Cienega Blvd), 2.5 mi n. Int corridors. **Pets:** Accepted.

Travelodge Hotel at Lax H 🐾

(310) 649-4000. **$84-$199.** 5547 W Century Blvd 90045. I-405 exit 46 (Century Blvd), 0.5 mi w. Ext/int corridors. **Pets:** Medium. $25 daily fee/pet. Designated rooms, service with restrictions, crate.

The Westin Bonaventure Hotel & Suites H

(213) 624-1000. **$260-$550, 3 day notice.** 404 S Figueroa St 90071. SR 110 exit 22 (9th St), just e, then 0.5 mi n. Int corridors. **Pets:** Accepted.

The Westin Los Angeles Airport H

(310) 216-5858. **$159-$279.** 5400 W Century Blvd 90045. I-405 exit 46 (Century Blvd), just w. Int corridors. **Pets:** Accepted.

W Los Angeles-West Beverly Hills H

(310) 208-8765. **$300-$600.** 930 Hilgard Ave 90024. I-405 exit 55B (Wilshire Blvd), 0.6 mi e to Glendon Ave, just n, then just e. Int corridors. **Pets:** Accepted.

LOS BAÑOS

Best Western Executive Inn H

(209) 827-0954. **$90-$132.** 301 W Pacheco Blvd 93635. 1.2 mi w of jct SR 152 and 165. Int corridors. **Pets:** Medium, dogs only. $20 daily fee/pet. Designated rooms, service with restrictions, supervision.

La Quinta Inn & Suites H

(209) 827-4677. **$67-$174.** 20 W Pacheco Blvd 93635. 1 mi w of jct SR 165 and 152. Int corridors. **Pets:** Accepted.

LOS OSOS

Sea Pines Golf Resort H 🐾

(805) 528-5252. **$109-$184.** 1945 Solano St 93402. SR 1 exit Los Osos/Baywood Park, 4 mi s on S Bay Blvd, 1.6 mi w on Los Osos Valley Rd, 0.3 mi n on Pecho Rd, then just w on Skyline Dr. Ext corridors. **Pets:** Dogs only. $25 daily fee/room. Designated rooms, service with restrictions, supervision.

MAMMOTH LAKES (Restaurants p. 598)

▼▼▼ The Mammoth Creek Inn Ⓜ
(760) 934-6162. Call for rates. 663 Old Mammoth Rd 93546. Just s of SR 203. Int corridors. Pets: Accepted. ⊠ 🛜 ⊠ 🅺 🔋 🖵

▼▼▼ Mammoth Mountain Inn Ⓗ
(760) 934-2581. Call for rates. 1 Minaret Rd 93546. 5 mi w of town on SR 203. Int corridors. Pets: Accepted.
🍴 👥 👥 ⊠ 🛜 ⊠ 🅺 🔋 🖵

ⒶⒶⒶ ▼▼▼ Sierra Lodge Ⓜ
(760) 934-8881. $79-$199. 3540 Main St 93546. On SR 203, 0.6 mi w of Old Mammoth Rd. Int corridors. Pets: Accepted. ⓢ🛜 🅺 🔋

▼▼▼ Sierra Nevada Resort & Spa Ⓗ
(760) 934-2515. $99-$409. 164 Old Mammoth Rd 93546. Just s of SR 203. Ext/int corridors. Pets: Large, dogs only. $25 daily fee/pet. Designated rooms, supervision. 🍴 👥 ⊠ 🛜 🔋 🖵

ⒶⒶⒶ ▼▼▼ ▼▼▼ The Westin Monache Resort Ⓒ
(760) 934-0400. $199-$359, 7 day notice. 50 Hillside Dr 93546. SR 203, 1 mi w to Minaret Rd, 0.3 mi n to Forest Tr, just w, then just nw. Int corridors. Pets: Accepted.
ⓢ 🔌 🍴 👥 👥 ⊠ 🛜 ⊠ 🔋 🖵

MANHATTAN BEACH

▼▼▼ Manhattan Beach Marriott Ⓗ
(310) 546-7511. $132-$340. 1400 Parkview Ave 90266. I-405 exit 43 (Rosecrans Ave), 1 mi w, then just s. Int corridors. Pets: Accepted.
🄴 🔌 🍴 👥 ⊠ 💿 ⊠ 🖵

ⒶⒶⒶ ▼▼▼ Residence Inn by Marriott Ⓗ
(310) 421-3100. $160-$260. 1700 N Sepulveda Blvd 90266. I-405 exit 43B (Rosecrans Ave), 1.5 mi w, then 1 mi s on SR 1. Ext corridors.
Pets: Accepted. ⓢ 👥 👥 🛜 ⊠ 🔋 🖵

MANTECA

ⒶⒶⒶ ▼▼▼ Best Western Plus Executive Inn & Suites Ⓗ
(209) 825-1415. $80-$150. 1415 E Yosemite Ave 95336. SR 99 exit 242, just w. Ext/int corridors. Pets: Accepted.
ⓢ 👥 👥 🛜 ⊠ 🔋 🖵

MARINA

ⒶⒶⒶ ▼▼▼ The Sanctuary Beach Resort Ⓗ 🐾
(831) 883-9478. Call for rates. 3295 Dunes Dr 93933. SR 1 exit Reservation Rd, just w. Ext corridors. Pets: Other species. $50 daily fee/room. Service with restrictions, crate.
ⓢ 🍴 👥 👥 🛜 ⊠ 🅺 🔋 🖵

MARINA DEL REY (Restaurants p. 598)

ⒶⒶⒶ ▼▼▼ HOTEL MDR - A DoubleTree by Hilton Ⓗ
(310) 822-8555. $199-$399. 13480 Maxella Ave 90292. SR 90 (Marina Frwy), just n on Lincoln Blvd (SR 1). Int corridors. Pets: Accepted.
ⓢ 🄴 🍴 👥 👥 🛜 ⊠ 🔋 🖵

ⒶⒶⒶ ▼▼▼ ▼▼▼ The Ritz-Carlton, Marina del Rey Ⓗ 🐾
(310) 823-1700. $329-$899. 4375 Admiralty Way 90292. SR 90 (Marina Frwy), just s on Lincoln Blvd (SR 1), then just w on Bali Way. Int corridors. Pets: Small, dogs only. $125 daily fee/room. Supervision.
ⓢ 🍴 👥 👥 ⊠ 💿 ⊠ 🖵

MARIPOSA

ⒶⒶⒶ ▼▼▼ Americas Best Value Inn-Mariposa Lodge Ⓜ
(209) 966-3607. $69-$179, 3 day notice. 5052 Hwy 140 95338. Center. Ext corridors. Pets: Accepted. ⓢ 👥 👥 🛜 ⊠ 🔋 🖵

ⒶⒶⒶ ▼▼▼ Best Western Plus Yosemite Way Station Motel Ⓗ
(209) 966-7545. $119-$219. 4999 Hwy 140 95338. SR 140 at SR 49 S. Ext corridors. Pets: Accepted. ⓢ 👥 👥 🛜 ⊠ 🔋 🖵

MARTINEZ

ⒶⒶⒶ ▼▼▼ Best Western Plus John Muir Inn Ⓗ
(925) 229-1010. $99-$179. 445 Muir Station Rd 94553. Jct I-680 and SR 4, 2.3 mi w on SR 4 exit 10 (Pine St/Center Ave), then just s. Int corridors. Pets: Accepted. ⓢ 👥 👥 🛜 🔋 🖵

MARYSVILLE (Restaurants p. 598)

ⒶⒶⒶ ▼▼▼ Comfort Suites Ⓗ
(530) 742-9200. $89-$194. 1034 N Beale Rd 95901. SR 70 northbound exit 20A, just e, then just n; exit 20B southbound, just se. Int corridors. Pets: Medium, other species. $10 one-time fee/pet. Designated rooms, service with restrictions, supervision.
ⓢ 👥 👥 🛜 ⊠ 🔋 🖵

MCCLOUD

ⒶⒶⒶ ▼▼▼ McCloud Hotel ⒷⒷ
(530) 964-2822. Call for rates. 408 Main St 96057. I-5 exit 736 (SR 89/McCloud), 9 mi e; jct SR 89 and W Minnesota Ave, 0.3 mi ne on W Minnesota Ave to Main St, then just n. Int corridors. Pets: Accepted.
ⓢ 🍴 👥 🛜 ⊠ 🎬 🌀

▼▼▼ McCloud Mercantile Hotel ⒷⒷ 🐾
(530) 964-2330. $129-$250, 10 day notice. 241 Main St 96057. I-5 exit 736 (SR 89/McCloud), 9 mi e; jct SR 89 and W Minnesota Ave, 0.3 mi ne on W Minnesota Ave to Main St, then just n. Ext/int corridors. Pets: Large, dogs only. $25 daily fee/pet. Designated rooms, service with restrictions, supervision. 🍴 🛜 ⊠ 🌀

MENDOCINO (Restaurants p. 598)

▼▼▼ Agate Cove Inn ⒸⒶ
(707) 937-0551. $189-$379, 14 day notice. 11201 N Lansing St 95460. Just w on Little Lake Rd from jct SR 1, then 0.6 mi n. Ext corridors.
Pets: Accepted. 🔌 🍴 👥 🛜 ⊠ 🅺 🌀 🔋 🖵

ⒶⒶⒶ ▼▼▼ ▼▼▼ Stanford Inn by the Sea Eco-Resort Ⓒ 🐾
(707) 937-5615. $250-$475, 7 day notice. 44850 Comptche-Ukiah Rd 95460. SR 1 exit Comptche-Ukiah Rd, just e. Ext corridors. Pets: Other species. $45 one-time fee/pet. Supervision.
ⓢ 🄴 🔌 🍴 👥 👥 ⊠ 🛜 ⊠ 🔋 🖵

MENLO PARK

▼▼▼ Red Cottage Inn & Suites Ⓜ
(650) 326-9010. Call for rates. 1704 El Camino Real 94025. US 101 exit 406 (Marsh Rd), 0.4 mi s on Middlefield Rd, 0.6 mi w on Encinal Ave, then just n. Ext corridors. Pets: Accepted.
👥 👥 🛜 ⊠ 🔋 🖵

ⒶⒶⒶ ▼▼▼ Residence Inn by Marriott Palo Alto Menlo Park Ⓗ 🐾
(650) 327-2000. $144-$386. 555 Glenwood Ave 94025. US 101 exit 406 (SR 84 E/Marsh Rd), 1.1 mi w on Marsh Rd, 0.6 mi s on Middlefield Rd, then 0.5 mi w. Int corridors. Pets: Other species. $100 one-time fee/room. Designated rooms, service with restrictions, crate.
ⓢ 👥 🛜 ⊠ 🔋 🖵

MERCED

ⒶⒶⒶ ▼▼▼ Best Western Inn Ⓗ 🐾
(209) 723-2163. $100-$175. 1033 Motel Dr 95341. SR 99 exit SR 140, just e, then just s. Ext corridors. Pets: Other species. $15 daily fee/room. Designated rooms, service with restrictions, crate.
ⓢ 👥 👥 🛜 🔋 🖵

MILLBRAE

Aloft San Francisco Airport H
(650) 443-5500. **Call for rates.** 401 E Millbrae Ave 94030. US 101 exit Millbrae Ave, just e. Int corridors. **Pets:** Medium, dogs only. Designated rooms, service with restrictions, supervision.

The Westin San Francisco Airport H
(650) 692-3500. **Call for rates.** 1 Old Bayshore Hwy 94030. Just e of US 101 exit Millbrae Ave. Int corridors. **Pets:** Medium, dogs only. Service with restrictions, supervision.

MILL VALLEY

Acqua Hotel H
(415) 380-0400. **Call for rates.** 555 Redwood Hwy 94941. US 101 exit Seminary Dr. Ext/int corridors. **Pets:** Dogs only. $30 daily fee/room. Designated rooms, service with restrictions, supervision.

Holiday Inn Express Mill Valley/San Francisco Area H
(415) 332-5700. **Call for rates.** 160 Shoreline Hwy 94941. US 101 exit Stinson Beach southbound, just nw; exit Mill Valley/SR 1/Stinson Beach northbound, 0.4 mi nw. Int corridors. **Pets:** Accepted.

Mill Valley Inn H
(415) 389-6608. **$189-$589, 14 day notice.** 165 Throckmorton Ave 94941. Center. Ext/int corridors. **Pets:** Accepted.

MILPITAS

Best Western Plus Brookside Inn H
(408) 263-5566. **$229-$349.** 400 Valley Way 95035. I-880 exit Calaveras Blvd (SR 237), just e. Ext/int corridors. **Pets:** Accepted.

Crowne Plaza San Jose-Silicon Valley H
(408) 321-9500. **Call for rates.** 777 Bellew Dr 95035. SR 237 exit McCarthy Blvd, just s, then just e. Int corridors. **Pets:** Accepted.

Larkspur Landing Milpitas H
(408) 719-1212. **$99-$409, 3 day notice.** 40 Ranch Dr 95035. SR 237 exit McCarthy Blvd, just n. Int corridors. **Pets:** Accepted.

Residence Inn by Marriott Milpitas Silicon Valley H
(408) 941-9222. **$116-$351.** 1501 California Cir 95035. I-880 exit Dixon Landing Rd E, just s. Int corridors. **Pets:** Accepted.

Sheraton San Jose Hotel H
(408) 943-0600. **$89-$699.** 1801 Barber Ln 95035. 4 mi n of San Jose International Airport; 0.3 mi nw of I-880 and Montague Expwy. Ext/int corridors. **Pets:** Accepted.

Sonesta Silicon Valley H
(408) 943-9080. **$99-$399.** 1820 Barber Ln 95035. I-880 exit Montague Expwy, just w, then just n on McCarthy Blvd, just e. Int corridors. **Pets:** Accepted.

TownePlace Suites by Marriott Milpitas H
(408) 719-1959. **$149-$279.** 1428 Falcon Dr 95035. I-680 exit Montague Expwy W, just n. Int corridors. **Pets:** Accepted.

MIRANDA

Miranda Gardens Resort CA
(707) 943-3011. **Call for rates.** 6766 Ave of the Giants 95553. US 101 exit 650, 0.3 mi e on Maple Hills Rd, then 1.5 mi nw. Ext corridors. **Pets:** Small, dogs only. $35 daily fee/pet. Designated rooms, supervision.

MI-WUK VILLAGE

Christmas Tree Inn M
(209) 586-1005. **$89-$150, 3 day notice.** 24685 Hwy 108 95346. On SR 108, 15 mi e of Sonora. Ext corridors. **Pets:** Medium, dogs only. $25 one-time fee/room. Designated rooms, service with restrictions, supervision.

MODESTO

Baymont Inn & Suites Modesto Salida M
(209) 543-9000. **$68-$119.** 4100 Salida Blvd 95358. SR 99 exit Pelandale Ave, just w, then just s. Ext corridors. **Pets:** Accepted.

Best Western Palm Court Inn H
(209) 521-9000. **$115-$165.** 2001 W Orangeburg Ave 95350. SR 99 exit 229 (Briggsmore Ave), just e, then just s. Ext corridors. **Pets:** Accepted.

Best Western Town House Lodge H
(209) 524-7261. **$105-$145.** 909 16th St 95354. Between I and J sts; downtown. Ext corridors. **Pets:** Medium. $20 daily fee/room. Designated rooms, service with restrictions, crate.

DoubleTree by Hilton Hotel Modesto H
(209) 526-6000. **Call for rates.** 1150 9th St 95354. SR 99 exit 226 (Central Modesto) northbound; exit 226B (Maze Blvd) southbound, 0.7 mi ne; between K and L sts. Int corridors. **Pets:** Accepted.

Microtel Inn & Suites by Wyndham Modesto Ceres H
(209) 538-6466. **$65-$94.** 1760 Herndon Rd 95307. SR 99 exit Hatch Rd E, 0.5 mi s; jct Evans Rd. Int corridors. **Pets:** Accepted.

MOJAVE

Best Western Desert Winds M
(661) 824-3601. **$99-$109.** 16200 Sierra Hwy 93501. On SR 14 and 58; center. Ext corridors. **Pets:** Medium. $10 daily fee/pet. Service with restrictions, supervision.

Executive Inn H
(661) 824-1015. **Call for rates.** 2201 Hwy 58 93501. Just e of SR 14. Ext corridors. **Pets:** Accepted.

Mariah Country Inn & Suites H
(661) 824-4980. **$92-$142.** 1385 Hwy 58 93501. SR 14 exit 172 (SR 58), 1.5 mi e. Int corridors. **Pets:** Medium. $10 daily fee/pet. Service with restrictions, supervision.

MONTECITO

Four Seasons Resort The Biltmore Santa Barbara H
(805) 969-2261. **$495-$1520, 3 day notice.** 1260 Channel Dr 93108. US 101 exit 94A (Olive Mill Rd), 0.3 mi s. Ext/int corridors. **Pets:** Other species. Designated rooms, service with restrictions, supervision.

MONTEREY (Restaurants p. 599)

◇◇ ▼▼▼ Bay Park Hotel H
(831) 649-1020. Call for rates. 1425 Munras Ave 93940. SR 1 exit Soledad Dr/Munras Ave, just w. Int corridors. Pets: Accepted.

SAVE ▯ ▯ ▯ ▯ ▯ ▯ ▯

◇◇ ▼▼▼▼ Best Western Plus Victorian Inn H
(831) 373-8000. $119-$509, 3 day notice. 487 Foam St 93940. SR 1 exit Monterey, 3.4 mi w. Ext/int corridors. Pets: Accepted.

SAVE ECO ▯ ▯ ▯ ▯ ▯ ▯

◇◇ ▼▼▼▼ Casa Munras Garden Hotel & Spa H
(831) 375-2411. $109-$600, 3 day notice. 700 Munras Ave 93940. SR 1 exit Soledad Dr/Munras Ave, 0.8 mi w. Ext/int corridors. Pets: Accepted. SAVE ECO ▯ ▯ ▯ ▯ ▯ ▯ ▯

◇◇ ▼▼▼ Comfort Inn-Monterey Bay H
(831) 373-3081. $79-$469. 2050 N Fremont St 93940. SR 1 exit Fremont St or Casa Verde Way, 0.3 mi e. Ext corridors. Pets: Accepted.

SAVE ▯ ▯ ▯ ▯ ▯

◇◇ ▼▼▼ Comfort Inn-Monterey by the Sea H
(831) 372-2908. $79-$549. 1252 Munras Ave 93940. SR 1 exit Soledad Dr/Munras Ave, just s. Ext corridors. Pets: Accepted.

SAVE ECO ▯ ▯ ▯ ▯ ▯ ▯

◇◇ ▼▼▼ Hotel Pacific H
(831) 373-5700. $159-$599, 3 day notice. 300 Pacific St 93940. SR 1 exit Del Monte Ave, 2.2 mi w. Ext/int corridors. Pets: Accepted.

SAVE ▯ ▯ ▯ ▯ ▯ ▯

◇◇ ▼▼▼▼ Hyatt Regency Monterey Hotel & Spa H ❀
(831) 372-1234. $139-$779, 3 day notice. 1 Old Golf Course Rd 93940. SR 1 exit Aguajito Rd northbound; exit Monterey southbound, just e. Int corridors. Pets: Medium. $100 one-time fee/room. Service with restrictions, supervision.

SAVE ECO ▯ ▯ ▯ ▯ ▯ ▯ ▯ ▯

◇◇ ▼▼▼▼ InterContinental The Clement Monterey H
(831) 375-4500. $199-$899. 750 Cannery Row 93940. Between Prescott and David aves. Int corridors. Pets: Other species. $150 deposit/room, $75 one-time fee/room. Designated rooms, service with restrictions, supervision. SAVE ▯ ▯ ▯ ▯ ▯ ▯ ▯ ▯

▼▼▼▼ Mariposa Inn & Suites H
(831) 649-1414. $109-$409, 3 day notice. 1386 Munras Ave 93940. SR 1 exit Soledad Dr/Munras Ave, just w. Ext/int corridors. Pets: Dogs only. $40 daily fee/pet. Designated rooms, service with restrictions, supervision. ▯ ▯ ▯ ▯ ▯ ▯ ▯

◇◇ ▼▼▼▼ Monterey Tides, a Joie de Vivre Hotel H ❀
(831) 394-3321. $139-$379. 2600 Sand Dunes Dr 93940. SR 1 exit Del Rey Oaks, just w. Ext corridors. Pets: Medium, other species. $50 daily fee/pet. Service with restrictions, supervision.

SAVE ▯ ▯ ▯ ▯ ▯ ▯ ▯

◇◇ ▼▼▼ Pacific Inn Monterey M ❀
(831) 373-2445. $59-$700, 3 day notice. 2332 N Fremont St 93940. SR 1 exit Del Rey Oaks or Fremont St, 0.7 mi e. Ext corridors. Pets: $30 daily fee/pet. Designated rooms, supervision.

SAVE ▯ ▯ ▯ ▯ ▯

◇◇ ▼▼▼ Portola Hotel & Spa H ❀
(831) 649-4511. $159-$1599. 2 Portola Plaza 93940. 2 mi w of SR 1 exit Del Monte or Munras aves; downtown. Int corridors. Pets: $50 one-time fee/room, $25 daily fee/room. Designated rooms, service with restrictions, supervision.

SAVE ECO ▯ ▯ ▯ ▯ ▯ ▯ ▯ ▯

MONTE RIO

▼▼▼ Rio Villa Beach Resort M
(707) 865-1143. Call for rates. 20292 Hwy 116 95462. Center. Ext corridors. Pets: Accepted. ▯ ▯ ▯ ▯ ▯

MORENO VALLEY

◇◇ ▼▼▼▼ La Quinta Inn & Suites H
(951) 486-9000. $92-$196. 23090 Sunnymead Blvd 92553. SR 60 exit 60 (Frederick St/Pigeon Pass Rd), just s, then just e. Int corridors. Pets: Accepted. SAVE ▯ ▯ ▯ ▯ ▯ ▯

MORGAN HILL

▼▼▼ Residence Inn by Marriott H
(408) 782-8311. $143-$266. 18620 Madrone Pkwy 95037. US 101 exit Cochrane W, just n. Int corridors. Pets: Accepted.

▯ ▯ ▯ ▯ ▯ ▯ ▯

MORRO BAY (Restaurants p. 599)

▼▼▼▼ 456 Embarcadero Inn & Suites M ❀
(805) 772-2700. $149-$599, 3 day notice. 456 Embarcadero Blvd 93442. SR 1 exit Morro Bay Blvd, 0.7 mi w to Main St, 0.3 mi s to Marina St, just w, then just s. Ext corridors. Pets: Medium, dogs only. $20 daily fee/pet. Designated rooms, service with restrictions, supervision. ▯ ▯ ▯ ▯ ▯

▼▼▼▼ Beach Bungalow Inn & Suites M
(805) 772-9700. Call for rates. 1050 Morro Ave 93442. SR 1 exit Morro Bay Blvd northbound, 0.8 mi w, then just n. Ext corridors. Pets: Accepted. ▯ ▯ ▯ ▯ ▯

◇◇ ▼▼▼ Best Western El Rancho M
(805) 772-2212. $89-$299. 2460 Main St 93442. SR 1 exit Morro Bay Blvd, 0.5 mi n. Ext corridors. Pets: Accepted.

SAVE ▯ ▯ ▯ ▯ ▯

◇◇ ▼▼▼ Inn at Morro Bay H
(805) 772-5651. $99-$425. 60 State Park Rd 93442. SR 1 exit Morro Bay Blvd westbound, 0.7 mi w, then 1 mi s on Main St. Ext corridors. Pets: Accepted. SAVE ▯ ▯ ▯ ▯ ▯ ▯ ▯ ▯

◇◇ ▼▼▼▼ La Serena Inn H
(805) 772-5665. $69-$319, 3 day notice. 990 Morro Ave 93442. SR 1 exit Morro Bay Blvd northbound, 0.7 mi w, then just n. Int corridors. Pets: Accepted. SAVE ▯ ▯ ▯ ▯

◇◇ ▼▼▼ Morro Bay Sandpiper Inn M
(805) 772-7503. $50-$299, 3 day notice. 540 Main St 93442. SR 1 exit Morro Bay Blvd, 0.7 mi w, then 0.4 mi s. Ext corridors. Pets: Accepted.

SAVE ▯ ▯ ▯ ▯ ▯

MOUNTAIN VIEW (Restaurants p. 599)

▼▼▼ Extended Stay America-San Jose, Mountain View H
(650) 962-1500. $170-$265. 190 E El Camino Real 94040. SR 82, just w of SR 85. Ext corridors. Pets: Accepted. ▯ ▯ ▯ ▯ ▯

▼▼▼ Residence Inn by Marriott-Palo Alto/Mountain View H
(650) 940-1300. $134-$362, 3 day notice. 1854 W El Camino Real 94040. US 101 exit 399 (Shoreline Blvd/Mountain View), 2 mi to SR 82, then 0.5 mi n. Int corridors. Pets: Accepted.

▯ ▯ ▯ ▯ ▯

MOUNT SHASTA

◇◇ ▼▼▼▼ Best Western Plus Tree House H ❀
(530) 926-3101. $140-$250. 111 Morgan Way 96067. I-5 exit 738 (Central Mount Shasta), just e. Ext/int corridors. Pets: Large, other species. $20 daily fee/room. Service with restrictions, supervision.

SAVE ▯ ▯ ▯ ▯ ▯ ▯ ▯

◆ Cold Creek Inn **M** ❖
(530) 926-9851. **$79-$149.** 724 N Mount Shasta Blvd 96067. I-5 exit
738 (Central Mount Shasta), 0.5 mi ne on W Lake St, then 0.5 mi nw.
Ext corridors. **Pets:** Other species. $25 daily fee/pet. Designated rooms,
service with restrictions, supervision. 🐾 ✕ 🅿 💻

◆◆◆ Mount Shasta Resort **CA**
(530) 926-3030. **$119-$349, 14 day notice.** 1000 Siskiyou Lake Blvd
96067. I-5 exit 738 (Central Mount Shasta), 0.4 mi w on Lake St (which
becomes Hatchery Ln), just s on S Old Stage Rd; at split follow sign
for resort, 1.4 mi s on W A Barr Rd, then just se. Ext corridors.
Pets: Accepted. 🍴 ♿ ✕ 🐾 ✕ 🅿 💻

MURRIETA

◆◆◆ Residence Inn by Marriott Temecula Murrieta **H**
(951) 698-6300. **$119-$201.** 25407 Madison Ave 92562. I-15 exit 64
(Murrieta Hot Springs Rd), just s. Int corridors.
Pets: Other species. $150 one-time fee/pet, $20 daily fee/pet. Service
with restrictions. 🍴 ♿ 🐾 ✕ 🅿 💻

MYERS FLAT

◆◆◆ ◆◆ Myers Inn **BB**
(707) 943-3259. **Call for rates.** 12913 Ave of the Giants 95554. US
101 exit Myers Flat, just w. Int corridors. **Pets:** Accepted.
[SAVE] 🍴 🐾 ✕ 🐾 🗹

NAPA

◆◆◆ ◆◆◆ Andaz Napa **H** ❖
(707) 687-1234. **$199-$629, 3 day notice.** 1450 1st St 94559. SR 29
exit SR 221, 2.6 mi n on SR 221, 1.2 mi nw on Soscol Ave, then just
w on 1st St. Int corridors. **Pets:** Medium, dogs only. $150 one-time
fee/pet. Service with restrictions. [SAVE] 🍴 ♿ 🐾 ✕ 🅿 💻

◆◆◆◆ Blackbird Inn **BB**
(707) 226-2450. **$195-$325, 7 day notice.** 1755 1st St 94559. SR 29
exit 1st St, 0.5 mi e to Jefferson St, then just n. Int corridors.
Pets: Medium, dogs only. $65 daily fee/room. Designated rooms, ser-
vice with restrictions, supervision. ♿ 🐾 ✕

◆◆◆ ◆◆◆ Embassy Suites Napa Valley **H**
(707) 253-9540. **Call for rates.** 1075 California Blvd 94559. SR 29 exit
1st St, just ne. Ext/int corridors. **Pets:** Accepted.
[SAVE] [ECO] 🍴 ♿ 🐾 ✕ 🐾 ✕ 🅿 💻

◆◆◆ ◆◆◆ The Inn on First **BB** ❖
(707) 253-1331. **$175-$525, 30 day notice.** 1938 1st St 94559. SR 29
exit 1st St, just n on California Blvd, just e via Clay St, just s on Warren St, then just w. Ext/int corridors. **Pets:** Dogs only. $50 one-time
fee/room. Designated rooms, service with restrictions, crate.
[SAVE] [ECO] ♿ 🐾 ✕ 🐾 🅿 💻

◆◆◆ ◆◆◆ The Meritage Resort and Spa **H** ❖
(707) 251-1900. **Call for rates.** 875 Bordeaux Way 94558. 0.5 mi n of
jct SR 29 and 121; SR 121 N, follow Downtown Napa/Lake Berryessa,
w on Napa Valley Corporate Way, then just s. Int corridors. **Pets:** Other
species. $50 one-time fee/pet. Service with restrictions, supervision.
[SAVE] 🍴 ♿ 🐾 ✕ 🐾 ✕ 🅿 💻

◆◆◆◆ The Napa Inn **BB**
(707) 257-1444. **Call for rates.** 1137 Warren St 94559. SR 29 exit 1st
St, just n on California Blvd, just e on Clay st, then just n. Ext/int corridors. **Pets:** Accepted. 🍴 🐾 ✕ 🅿 💻

◆◆◆◆ Napa River Inn **H**
(707) 251-8500. **$199-$799, 3 day notice.** 500 Main St 94559. Jct 5th
St; downtown. Int corridors. **Pets:** Accepted.
🅿 ♿ 🐾 ✕ 🅿 💻

◆◆◆ ◆◆◆ Napa Winery Inn, an Ascend Hotel
Collection Member **H**
(707) 257-7220. **$109-$499, 3 day notice.** 1998 Trower Ave 94558. SR
29 exit Trower Ave, just e. Int corridors. **Pets:** Accepted.
[SAVE] ♿ 🐾 ✕ 🅿 💻

◆◆◆ ◆◆◆ ◆◆◆ The Westin Verasa Napa **H** ❖
(707) 257-1800. **$189-$599.** 1314 McKinstry St 94559. Jct Soscol Ave;
behind the Napa Valley Wine Train parking area. Int corridors.
Pets: Medium, other species. Service with restrictions, supervision.
[SAVE] [ECO] 🍴 ♿ 🐾 ✕ 🐾 ✕ 🅿 💻

NATIONAL CITY

◆◆◆ ◆◆◆ Best Western Plus Marina Gateway
Hotel **H** ❖
(619) 259-2800. **$109-$209.** 800 Bay Marina Dr 91950. I-5 exit 10 (Bay
Marina Dr), just w. Int corridors. **Pets:** Medium. $25 daily fee/pet. Des-
ignated rooms, service with restrictions, supervision.
[SAVE] 🍴 ♿ 🐾 ✕ 🅿 💻

NEEDLES *(Restaurants p. 599)*

◆◆◆ ◆◆ Best Western Colorado River Inn **M** ❖
(760) 326-4552. **$120-$130.** 2371 W Broadway 92363. I-40 exit 141 (W
Broadway/River Rd), 0.3 mi se; on Business Loop I-40. Ext corridors.
Pets: Other species. $15 daily fee/room. Designated rooms, service
with restrictions, crate. [SAVE] ♿ 🐾 ✕ 🅿 💻

◆◆◆ ◆◆◆ Rio del Sol Inn **M**
(760) 326-5660. **$99-$169, 3 day notice.** 1111 Pashard St 92363. I-40
exit 141 (W Broadway/River Rd), just sw. Ext corridors. **Pets:** Other
species. $15 daily fee/room. Service with restrictions, crate.
[SAVE] ♿ 🐾 ✕ 🅿 💻

NEWARK

◆◆◆ ◆◆◆ Aloft Silicon Valley **H**
(510) 494-8800. **$100-$499.** 8200 Gateway Blvd 94560. SR 84 exit
Thornton Ave, just s. Int corridors. **Pets:** Accepted.
[SAVE] [ECO] 🍴 ♿ 🐾 ✕ 🐾 ✕ 🅿 💻

◆◆◆◆ Chase Suite Hotel **H**
(510) 795-1200. **Call for rates.** 39150 Cedar Blvd 94560. I-880 exit
Mowry Ave, just w, then 0.3 mi s. Ext corridors. **Pets:** Accepted.
♿ 🐾 ✕ 🅿 💻

◆◆◆◆ DoubleTree by Hilton Newark/Fremont **H**
(510) 490-8390. **Call for rates.** 39900 Balentine Dr 94560. I-880 exit
Stevenson Blvd, just w. Int corridors. **Pets:** Accepted.
🍴 ♿ 🐾 ✕ 🅿 💻

◆◆◆◆ Homewood Suites by Hilton **H**
(510) 791-7700. **$259-$310.** 39270 Cedar Blvd 94560. I-880 exit Mowry
Ave, w to Cedar Blvd, then 0.3 mi s. Int corridors. **Pets:** Medium. $75
one-time fee/room. Service with restrictions, crate.
♿ 🐾 ✕ 🅿 💻

◆◆◆◆ Residence Inn by Marriott Newark/Silicon
Valley **H**
(510) 739-6000. **$124-$297.** 35466 Dumbarton Ct 94560. SR 84 exit
Newark Blvd, just s. Int corridors. **Pets:** Accepted.
[ECO] ♿ 🐾 ✕ 🅿 💻

NEWPORT BEACH *(Restaurants p. 599)*

◆◆◆ ◆◆◆ Balboa Bay Resort **H**
(949) 645-5000. **Call for rates.** 1221 W Coast Hwy 92663. SR 73 exit
15 (Jamboree Rd), 3.5 mi s, then just w. Int corridors. **Pets:** Accepted.
[SAVE] 🍴 🐾 ✕ 🅿 💻

◆◆◆ Extended Stay America-Orange County/John Wayne
Airport **H**
(949) 851-2711. **$110-$150.** 4881 Birch St 92660. I-405 exit 8 (MacArthur Blvd), 0.8 mi s, then just e. Int corridors. **Pets:** Accepted.
🍴 ♿ 🐾 🅿

◆◆◆ ◆◆◆ Fairmont Newport Beach **H** ❖
(949) 476-2001. **$129-$299.** 4500 MacArthur Blvd 92660. I-405 exit 8
(MacArthur Blvd), 1 mi s. Int corridors. **Pets:** Other species. $50 one-
time fee/pet. Service with restrictions, crate.
[SAVE] [ECO] 🍴 🐾 ✕ 🐾 ✕ 🅿 💻

Hyatt Regency Newport Beach H
(949) 729-1234. **$99-$319.** 1107 Jamboree Rd 92660. SR 73 exit 15 (Jamboree Rd), 3 mi s. Ext/int corridors. **Pets:** Medium, dogs only. $100 one-time fee/room. Designated rooms, service with restrictions, supervision.

Island Hotel Newport Beach H
(949) 759-0808. **Call for rates.** 690 Newport Center Dr 92660. SR 73 exit 14 (MacArthur Blvd) northbound, 3 mi s to San Joaquin Hills Rd, then 0.5 mi w; exit 15 (Jamboree Rd) southbound, 2.5 mi s to San Joaquin Hills Rd, then 0.5 mi e. Int corridors. **Pets:** Medium, dogs only. $150 one-time fee/room. Designated rooms, service with restrictions.

Newport Beach Marriott Bayview Hotel H
(949) 854-4500. **$145-$292.** 500 Bayview Cir 92660. SR 73 exit 15 (Jamboree Rd), just s, just w on Bayview Pl, then just n. Int corridors. **Pets:** Accepted.

NICE

Featherbed Railroad Co. BB
(707) 274-8378. **$150-$220, 3 day notice.** 2870 Lakeshore Blvd 95464. 0.5 mi s of SR 20. Ext corridors. **Pets:** Accepted.

NIPOMO

Kaleidoscope Inn & Gardens B&B BB
(805) 929-5444. **$140-$160, 7 day notice.** 130 E Dana St 93444. US 101 exit 179 (Tefft St), 0.7 mi e, just s on Thompson Rd, then just e. Ext/int corridors. **Pets:** Other species. $10 one-time fee/room. Designated rooms, no service.

NORTH HOLLYWOOD

The Garland H
(818) 980-8000. **Call for rates.** 4222 Vineland Ave 91602. US 101 exit 12C (Vineland Ave), just n. Int corridors. **Pets:** Accepted.

NORTHRIDGE

Extended Stay America-Los Angeles/Northridge H
(818) 734-1787. **$120-$150.** 19325 Londelius St 91324. SR 118 exit 37 (Tampa Ave), 3 mi s. Int corridors. **Pets:** Accepted.

NOVATO

Inn Marin M
(415) 883-5952. **$119-$329.** 250 Entrada Dr 94949. US 101 exit Ignacio Blvd, just w, just n on Enfrente Rd, then just e. Ext corridors. **Pets:** Other species. $30 one-time fee/room. Service with restrictions, crate.

OAKHURST *(Restaurants p. 599)*

Best Western Plus Yosemite Gateway Inn H
(559) 683-2378. **$99-$275.** 40530 Hwy 41 93644. SR 41 and 49, 0.8 mi n. Ext corridors. **Pets:** Accepted.

Château du Sureau CI
(559) 683-6860. **$445-$585, 14 day notice.** 48688 Victoria Ln 93644. Just w of jct SR 41 and 49. Ext/int corridors. **Pets:** Very small, dogs only. $85 one-time fee/room. Designated rooms, service with restrictions, supervision.

Comfort Inn Yosemite Area M
(559) 683-8282. **$90-$400.** 40489 Hwy 41 93644. SR 41 and 49, 0.6 mi n. Ext corridors. **Pets:** Other species. $25 daily fee/pet. Designated rooms, service with restrictions, supervision.

OAKLAND

Hilton Oakland Airport H
(510) 635-5000. **$119-$399.** 1 Hegenberger Rd 94621. I-880 exit Hegenberger Rd, 1 mi w; 1.3 mi e of Metropolitan Oakland International Airport. Int corridors. **Pets:** Accepted.

Homewood Suites by Hilton Oakland Waterfront H
(510) 663-2700. **Call for rates.** 1103 Embarcadero 94606. I-880 exit 16th Ave/Embarcadero southbound; exit 5th Ave/Embarcadero northbound, just w. Int corridors. **Pets:** Accepted.

La Quinta Inn Oakland Airport Coliseum H
(510) 632-8900. **$92-$246.** 8465 Enterprise Way 94621. I-880 exit Hegenberger Rd, just e. Int corridors. **Pets:** Accepted.

Waterfront Hotel, a Joie de Vivre hotel H
(510) 836-3800. **Call for rates.** 10 Washington St 94607. I-880 exit Broadway, 0.5 mi w. Int corridors. **Pets:** Accepted.

OAKLEY

Best Western Plus Delta Hotel H
(925) 755-1222. **$170-$236.** 5549 Bridgehead Rd 94561. SR 160 exit 1A (Main St), just e, then just n. Int corridors. **Pets:** Large, dogs only. $20 daily fee/room. Designated rooms, service with restrictions, supervision.

OAK VIEW

Oakridge Inn M
(805) 649-4018. **$75-$160, 3 day notice.** 780 N Ventura Ave 93022. 4 mi s on SR 33; 2 mi e of Lake Casitas; in Oak View. Ext corridors. **Pets:** Medium. $15 daily fee/pet. Designated rooms, supervision.

OCCIDENTAL

Occidental Hotel M
(707) 874-3623. **$95-$210, 3 day notice.** 3610 Bohemian Hwy 95465. In the village. Ext corridors. **Pets:** Small. $30 daily fee/pet. Designated rooms, service with restrictions, supervision.

OCEANO *(Restaurants p. 599)*

Oceano Inn M
(805) 473-0032. **Call for rates.** 1252 Pacific Blvd 93445. On SR 1. Ext corridors. **Pets:** Accepted.

OCEANSIDE *(Restaurants p. 599)*

La Quinta Inn San Diego Oceanside M
(760) 450-0730. **$67-$489.** 937 N Coast Hwy 92054. I-5 exit 54B (Coast Hwy/Oceanside) southbound; exit 54B (Camp Pendleton) northbound, just w. Int corridors. **Pets:** Accepted.

OJAI *(Restaurants p. 599)*

Blue Iguana Inn M
(805) 646-5277. **$369, 7 day notice.** 11794 N Ventura Ave 93023. 2.5 mi w of town on SR 33. Ext corridors. **Pets:** Dogs only. $100 deposit/pet, $20 daily fee/pet. Designated rooms, service with restrictions, supervision.

Casa Ojai Inn M
(805) 646-8175. **$120-$240.** 1302 E Ojai Ave 93023. 0.8 mi e on SR 150. Ext corridors. **Pets:** Accepted.

▼▼▼▼▼ Ojai Valley Inn & Spa 🄷
(805) 646-1111. **Call for rates.** 905 Country Club Rd 93023. 1 mi w on SR 150, just s. Ext/int corridors. **Pets:** Accepted.
(SAVE) ⊟ 🍴 &M 🛋 ✕ 📶 ✕ 🛗 📠 📺

OLYMPIC VALLEY
▼▼▼▼ PlumpJack Squaw Valley Inn 🄷
(530) 583-1576. **Call for rates.** 1920 Squaw Valley Rd 96146. I-80 exit SR 89, 8.3 mi s, then 2.2 mi sw. Int corridors. **Pets:** Accepted.
🍴 &M 🛋 ✕ 📶 ✕ 🛗 📺

ONTARIO
▼▼▼▼ Best Western Plus InnSuites Ontario Airport Hotel & Suites 🄷
(909) 466-9600. **$129-$189.** 3400 Shelby St 91764. I-10 exit 56 (Haven Ave), just n to Inland Empire Blvd, just w, then just se. **Pets:** Dogs only. $20 daily fee/pet. Designated rooms, service with restrictions, supervision. (SAVE) 🍴 &M 🛋 📶 🛗 📺

▼▼▼ Country Inn Ontario Ⓜ
(909) 923-1887. **$69-$109.** 2359 S Grove Ave 91761. SR 60 exit 36 (Grove Ave), just n. Ext corridors. **Pets:** Very small. $10 daily fee/pet. Designated rooms, service with restrictions, supervision.
(SAVE) &M 📶 🛗 📺

▼▼▼ DoubleTree by Hilton Ontario Airport 🄷
(909) 937-0900. **$94-$194.** 222 N Vineyard Ave 91764. I-10 exit 54 (Vineyard Ave), 0.4 mi s. Int corridors. **Pets:** Accepted.
(ECO) 🍴 &M 🛋 📶 ✕ 🛗 📺

▼▼▼ Hyatt Place Ontario/Rancho Cucamonga 🄷
(909) 980-2200. **$89-$249.** 4760 E Mills Cir 91764. I-10 exit 57 (Milliken Ave), just n, 0.5 mi e on Ontario Mills Pkwy, just n on Ontario Mills Dr, then just e. Int corridors. **Pets:** Accepted.
(SAVE) 🍴 &M 🛋 📶 ✕ 🛗 📺

▼▼▼ Ontario Airport Hotel & Conference Center 🄷
(909) 980-0400. **$79-$179.** 700 N Haven Ave 91764. I-10 exit 56 (Haven Ave), just n. Int corridors. **Pets:** Large, other species. $20 daily fee/pet. Service with restrictions.
(SAVE) (ECO) ⊟ 🍴 &M 🛋 📶 ✕ 🛗 📺

▼▼▼ Quality Inn Ontario Airport Convention Center Ⓜ
(909) 937-2999. **$79-$169.** 514 N Vineyard Ave 91764. I-10 exit 54 (Vineyard Ave), just s. Ext corridors. **Pets:** Accepted.
&M 🛋 📶 🛗 📺

▼▼▼ Residence Inn by Marriott Ontario-Airport 🄷
(909) 937-6788. **$114-$175.** 2025 Convention Center Way 91764. I-10 exit 54 (Vineyard Ave), just s, then 1 blk e. Ext corridors. **Pets:** Accepted. &M 🛋 ✕ 📶 🛗 📺

▼▼▼ Sheraton Ontario Airport Hotel 🄷
(909) 937-8000. **Call for rates.** 429 N Vineyard Ave 91764. I-10 exit 54 (Vineyard Ave), just s. Int corridors. **Pets:** Accepted.
(SAVE) 🍴 &M 🛋 📶 ✕ 📺

ORANGE
▼▼▼ ALO Hotel 🄷
(714) 978-9168. **$169-$219.** 3737 W Chapman Ave 92868. I-5 exit 107B (W Chapman Ave) northbound, just w; exit 107C (State College/The City Dr) southbound, just s on State College Blvd, then just w. Int corridors. **Pets:** Accepted. ⊟ 🍴 &M 🛋 📶 ✕ 🛗 📺

▼▼▼ DoubleTree by Hilton Hotel Anaheim - Orange County 🄷
(714) 634-4500. **$119-$299.** 100 The City Dr 92868. I-5 exit 107B (W Chapman Ave) northbound. just w; exit 107C (State College Blvd/The City Dr) southbound, just s on State College Blvd, then just w. Int corridors. **Pets:** Accepted. 🍴 &M 🛋 ✕ 📶 ✕ 🛗 📺

ORICK
▼▼▼ Elk Meadow Cabins 🄲🄰
(707) 488-2222. **$200-$300, 30 day notice.** 7 Valley Green Camp Rd 95555. US 101, milepost 124. Ext corridors. **Pets:** Accepted.
🍴 ✕ 📶 ✕ 🎾 🛗 📺

ORLAND
▼▼◇ Orland Inn Ⓜ 🐾
(530) 865-7632. **$79-$99.** 1052 South St 95963. I-5 exit 618 (CR 16/South St), just ne; in Stony Creek Square Shopping Center. Ext corridors. **Pets:** Other species. $11 daily fee/pet. Service with restrictions, crate. (SAVE) &M 🛋 📶

OXNARD (Restaurants p. 599)
▼▼▼ Best Western Oxnard Inn Ⓜ
(805) 483-9581. **$120-$299.** 1156 S Oxnard Blvd 93030. US 101 exit 61 (Rose Ave) northbound, 3 mi s, then 1 mi se; exit 62B (Oxnard Blvd) southbound, 3.5 mi s. Ext corridors. **Pets:** Accepted.
(SAVE) &M 🛋 📶 🛗 📺

▼▼▼▼ Residence Inn by Marriott at River Ridge 🄷
(805) 278-2200. **$133-$197.** 2101 W Vineyard Ave 93036. US 101 exit 62A (Vineyard Ave), 1.8 mi w. Ext corridors. **Pets:** Accepted.
(SAVE) &M 🛋 ✕ 📶 ✕ 🛗 📺

PACIFIC GROVE
▼▼▼ Bide-A-Wee Inn & Cottages Ⓜ
(831) 372-2330. **$79-$399, 7 day notice.** 221 Asilomar Ave 93950. 1 mi n of SR 68. Ext corridors. **Pets:** Accepted.
(SAVE) 🍴 📶 ✕ 🎾 🛗 📺

▼▼▼ Butterfly Grove Inn Ⓜ
(831) 250-8191. **$129-$299, 3 day notice.** 1073 Lighthouse Ave 93950. Just w of Seventeen Mile Dr. Ext/int corridors. **Pets:** Accepted.
(SAVE) 🍴 🛋 📶 ✕ 🎾 🛗 📺

▼▼▼ Centrella Inn 🄱🄱 🐾
(831) 372-3372. **$119-$499, 3 day notice.** 612 Central Ave 93950. At 17th St; center. Ext/int corridors. **Pets:** Medium, dogs only. $35 daily fee/pet. Designated rooms, service with restrictions, supervision.
🍴 📶 ✕ 🎾 🛗

▼▼▼ Deer Haven Inn Ⓜ
(831) 373-7784. **Call for rates.** 750 Crocker Ave 93950. Just e of SR 68 via Sinex Ave. Ext corridors. **Pets:** Accepted.
🍴 📶 ✕ 🎾 🛗 📺

▼▼▼ Gosby House Inn 🄱🄱
(831) 375-1287. **$125-$315, 7 day notice.** 643 Lighthouse Ave 93950. Downtown. Ext/int corridors. **Pets:** Accepted. 📶 ✕ 🎾 🛗

▼▼▼ Green Gables Inn 🄱🄱
(831) 375-2095. **$165-$350, 7 day notice.** 301 Ocean View Blvd 93950. At 5th St. Ext/int corridors. **Pets:** Dogs only. $65 one-time fee/room. Designated rooms, service with restrictions, supervision.
🍴 📶 ✕ 🎾 🛗 📺

▼▼◇ Pacific Gardens Inn 🄷
(831) 646-9414. **$99-$248, 7 day notice.** 701 Asilomar Blvd 93950. Just n of SR 68. Ext corridors. **Pets:** Large, dogs only. Service with restrictions. 🍴 📶 ✕ 🎾 🛗

▼▼▼ Sea Breeze Inn and Cottages Ⓜ
(831) 372-7771. **Call for rates.** 1100 Lighthouse Ave 93950. Just w of Seventeen Mile Dr; jct Lighthouse and Grove Acre aves. Ext/int corridors. **Pets:** Dogs only. $30 daily fee/pet. Designated rooms, service with restrictions, supervision. 📶 ✕ 🎾 🛗 📺

PALMDALE

Best Western Plus John Jay Inn & Suites H
(661) 575-9322. **$99-$179.** 600 W Palmdale Blvd 93551. SR 14 exit 35 (Palmdale Blvd), just w. Int corridors. **Pets:** Accepted.

Hampton Inn & Suites-Palmdale H
(661) 265-7400. **$119-$179.** 39428 Trade Center Dr 93551. SR 14 exit 37 (Rancho Vista Blvd/Ave P), just w, then just s to Trade Center Dr. Int corridors. **Pets:** Accepted.

Holiday Inn Palmdale-Lancaster H
(661) 947-8055. **$89-$249.** 38630 5th St W 93551. SR 14 exit 35 (Palmdale Blvd), 0.5 mi w. Int corridors. **Pets:** Accepted.

Residence Inn by Marriott H
(661) 947-4204. **$109-$182.** 514 W Ave P 93551. SR 14 exit 37 (Rancho Vista Blvd/Ave P), just e. Int corridors. **Pets:** Accepted.

Staybridge Suites H
(661) 947-9300. **$109-$239.** 420 W Park Dr 93551. SR 14 exit 35 (Palmdale Blvd), 0.5 mi w. Int corridors. **Pets:** Accepted.

PALM DESERT (Restaurants p. 599)

Best Western Plus Palm Desert Resort H
(760) 340-4441. **$79-$249.** 74-695 Hwy 111 92260. I-10 exit 134 (Cook St), 4.4 mi s, then 0.3 mi w. Ext corridors. **Pets:** Accepted.

Comfort Suites I-10 H
(760) 360-3337. **$75-$449.** 39585 Washington St 92211. I-10 exit 137 (Washington St), just n. Int corridors. **Pets:** Accepted.

Homewood Suites by Hilton-Palm Desert H
(760) 568-1600. **$94-$379.** 36-999 Cook St 92211. I-10 exit 134 (Cook St), 0.5 mi s; in The Village at University Park. Int corridors. **Pets:** Medium, other species. $75 one-time fee/room. Service with restrictions, supervision.

The Inn at Deep Canyon M
(760) 346-8061. **$59-$219, 3 day notice.** 74470 Abronia Tr 92260. I-10 exit 134 (Cook St), 4.4 mi s to SR 111, 0.5 mi w, then just s on Deep Canyon Rd. Ext corridors. **Pets:** Accepted.

Residence Inn by Marriott H
(760) 776-0050. **$104-$213.** 38-305 Cook St 92211. I-10 exit 134 (Cook St), 0.8 mi s. Ext corridors. **Pets:** Accepted.

PALM SPRINGS (Restaurants p. 600)

A Place In The Sun Garden Hotel M
(760) 325-0254. **Call for rates.** 754 E San Lorenzo Rd 92264. Just e of Palm Canyon Dr on Mesquite Ave, just n on Random Rd, then just e. Ext corridors. **Pets:** Accepted.

Best Western Inn At Palm Springs M
(760) 325-9177. **$79-$200.** 1633 S Palm Canyon Dr 92264. 1.3 mi s of Tahquitz Canyon Way. Ext corridors. **Pets:** Very small. $20 daily fee/room. Designated rooms, service with restrictions, supervision.

Hilton Palm Springs H
(760) 320-6868. **Call for rates.** 400 E Tahquitz Canyon Way 92262. Just e of Indian Canyon Dr. Int corridors. **Pets:** Accepted.

Hyatt Palm Springs H ❖
(760) 322-9000. **$109-$399, 3 day notice.** 285 N Palm Canyon Dr 92262. Downtown. Ext/int corridors. **Pets:** Dogs only. $50 one-time fee/room. Designated rooms, service with restrictions, supervision.

Parker Meridien Palm Springs H
(760) 770-5000. **Call for rates.** 4200 E Palm Canyon Dr 92264. I-10 exit 123 (Gene Autry Trl), 6.2 mi s, just w on E Palm Canyon Dr, then just n. Ext/int corridors. **Pets:** Accepted.

Renaissance Palm Springs Hotel H
(760) 322-6000. **$104-$257.** 888 Tahquitz Canyon Way 92262. 0.4 mi e of Indian Canyon Dr. Int corridors. **Pets:** Medium, dogs only. $100 one-time fee/room. Designated rooms, service with restrictions, supervision.

Skylark Hotel M
(760) 322-2267. **$149-$189, 3 day notice.** 1466 N Palm Canyon Dr 92262. 1.5 mi n of E Tahquitz Canyon Way. Ext corridors.
Pets: Accepted.

Triada Palm Springs H
(760) 844-7000. **Call for rates.** 640 N Indian Canyon Dr 92262. I-10 exit 120 (Indian Canyon Dr), 5 mi s. Ext corridors. **Pets:** Accepted.

PALO ALTO

Comfort Inn Palo Alto/Stanford Area M
(650) 493-3141. **$80-$380.** 3945 El Camino Real 94306. US 101 exit Oregon Expwy/Page Mill Rd, 1 mi s on SR 82. Ext corridors. **Pets:** $20 daily fee/pet. Designated rooms, service with restrictions, supervision.

Crowne Plaza Cabana Hotel H 🐾
(650) 857-0787. **Call for rates.** 4290 El Camino Real 94306. US 101 exit San Antonio Rd, 2 mi s, then 0.4 mi n on SR 82. Ext/int corridors. **Pets:** Small, dogs only. $50 one-time fee/room. Designated rooms, service with restrictions, supervision.

Dinah's Garden Hotel H 🐾
(650) 493-2844. **$109-$800.** 4261 El Camino Real 94306. US 101 exit San Antonio Rd, 2 mi s, then 0.4 mi n on SR 82. Ext/int corridors. **Pets:** Dogs only. $50 one-time fee/room. Designated rooms, service with restrictions, supervision.

Homewood Suites Palo Alto by Hilton H
(650) 559-8700. **$149-$479.** 4329 El Camino Real 94306. US 101 exit San Antonio Rd, 2 mi w to SR 82, then 1 mi n. Int corridors.
Pets: Accepted.

Sheraton Palo Alto Hotel H
(650) 328-2800. **$129-$549.** 625 El Camino Real 94301. US 101 exit 402 (Embarcadero Rd/Oregon Expwy), 1.8 mi w, then just n on SR 82. Int corridors. **Pets:** Accepted.

The Westin Palo Alto H
(650) 321-4422. **$149-$659.** 675 El Camino Real 94301. US 101 exit 402 (Embarcadero Rd/Oregon Expwy), 1.8 mi w, then just n on SR 82. Int corridors. **Pets:** Accepted.

PARADISE

Paradise Lodge H
(530) 876-0191. **$89-$130.** 5475 Clark Rd 95969. SR 191 (Skyway Rd), 1.1 mi e on Pearson Rd, 0.3 mi s. Int corridors. **Pets:** Dogs only. $20 daily fee/pet. Designated rooms, service with restrictions, supervision.

▼▼ Ponderosa Gardens Motel **M** ❖
(530) 872-9094. **Call for rates.** 7010 Skyway 95969. 2 blks e; center. Ext corridors. **Pets:** Other species. $200 deposit/room, $20 daily fee/pet. Designated rooms, service with restrictions, supervision.
(&M) (⌐) (⌂) (🖪) (💻)

PASADENA *(Restaurants p. 600)*

◈◈ ▼▼ Saga Motor Hotel **M**
(626) 795-0431. **$102-$106.** 1633 E Colorado Blvd 91106. I-210 exit 27 (Hill Ave), just s, then just e. Ext/int corridors. **Pets:** Medium, dogs only. $35 one-time fee/room. Designated rooms, service with restrictions, crate. (SAVE) (⌐) (⌂) (🗙) (🖪)

◈◈ ▼▼▼ Sheraton Pasadena Hotel **H** ❖
(626) 449-4000. **$179-$499.** 303 E Cordova St 91101. I-210 exit 26B (Lake Ave), 0.7 mi s, then just w. Int corridors. **Pets:** Medium, dogs only. Designated rooms, service with restrictions, supervision.
(SAVE) (ECO) (¶¶) (⌐) (⌂) (🗙) (🖪) (💻)

▼▼ Super 8 **M**
(626) 449-3020. **$69-$175.** 2863 E Colorado Blvd 91107. I-210 exit 29A (San Gabriel Blvd), just s, then just e. Ext corridors. **Pets:** Very small. $25 daily fee/pet. Designated rooms, no service, supervision.
(⌐) (⌂) (🖪) (💻)

◈◈ ▼▼▼ The Westin-Pasadena **H** ❖
(626) 792-2727. **Call for rates.** 191 N Los Robles Ave 91101. I-210 exit Los Robles Ave, just s; in Plaza Las Fuentes. Int corridors. **Pets:** Medium. Service with restrictions, supervision.
(SAVE) (ECO) (¶¶) (&M) (⌐) (🗙) (Sᵒ) (🗙) (🖪) (💻)

PASO ROBLES

▼▼▼ Holiday Inn Express Hotel & Suites **H** ❖
(805) 238-6500. **$109-$299.** 2455 Riverside Ave 93446. US 101 exit 231B (SR 46 E), just w, then just n. Int corridors. **Pets:** Dogs only. $35 one-time fee/room. Designated rooms, service with restrictions, supervision. (&M) (⌐) (⌂) (🗙) (🖪) (💻)

▼▼▼ La Quinta Inn & Suites Paso Robles **H**
(805) 239-3004. **$108-$405.** 2615 Buena Vista Dr 93446. US 101 exit 234 northbound; exit 231B (SR 46 E) southbound, 0.3 mi e, then just n. Int corridors. **Pets:** Accepted. (¶¶) (⌐) (⌂) (🗙) (🖪) (💻)

◈◈ ▼▼▼ The Oaks Hotel & Suites **H**
(805) 237-8700. **$129-$369.** 3000 Riverside Ave 93446. US 101 exit 231B (SR 46 E), just w, then 0.4 mi n. Int corridors. **Pets:** Dogs only. $40 one-time fee/pet. Designated rooms, service with restrictions, supervision. (SAVE) (⊑) (¶¶) (&M) (⌂) (🗙) (🖪) (💻)

PATTERSON

◈◈ ▼▼▼ Best Western Plus Villa Del Lago Inn **H** ❖
(209) 892-5300. **$121-$161.** 2959 Speno Dr 95363. I-5 exit 434 (Sperry Ave), just ne. Int corridors. **Pets:** Large. $20 daily fee/room. Designated rooms, service with restrictions, supervision.
(SAVE) (¶¶) (&M) (⌐) (🗙) (⌂) (🗙) (🖪) (💻)

PEBBLE BEACH

▼▼▼ The Lodge at Pebble Beach **H**
(831) 624-3811. **Call for rates.** 1700 Seventeen Mile Dr 93953. Off SR 1, follow signs. Ext/int corridors. **Pets:** Accepted.
(¶¶) (&M) (⌐) (🗙) (⌂) (🗙) (🗙) (💻)

PETALUMA

◈◈ ▼▼▼ Best Western Petaluma Inn **M**
(707) 763-0994. **$90-$280.** 200 S McDowell Blvd 94954. US 101 exit Washington St, just e. Ext corridors. **Pets:** Accepted.
(SAVE) (&M) (⌐) (⌂) (🗙) (🖪) (💻)

◈◈ ▼▼ Quality Inn-Petaluma **H** ❖
(707) 664-1155. **$89-$339.** 5100 Montero Way 94954. US 101 exit Old Redwood Hwy-Penngrove northbound; exit Petaluma Blvd N-Penngrove southbound (east side), just n on N McDowell Blvd, then just e. Ext/int corridors. **Pets:** Other species. $15 daily fee/room. Service with restrictions, supervision. (SAVE) (&M) (⌐) (⌂) (🗙) (🖪) (💻)

◈◈ ▼▼▼ Sheraton Sonoma County-Petaluma **H**
(707) 283-2888. **$109-$759.** 745 Baywood Dr 94954. US 101 exit SR 116 (Lakeville Hwy), just se. Int corridors. **Pets:** Accepted.
(SAVE) (⊑) (¶¶) (&M) (⌐) (🗙) (⌂) (🗙) (🖪) (💻)

PHELAN

◈◈ ▼▼▼ Best Western Cajon Pass **M**
(760) 249-6777. **$69-$149.** 8317 Hwy 138 92371. I-15 exit 131 (SR 138/Palmdale), just w. Ext corridors. **Pets:** Accepted.
(SAVE) (¶¶) (&M) (⌐) (⌂) (🖪) (💻)

PISMO BEACH *(Restaurants p. 600)*

▼▼▼ The Cliffs Resort **H**
(805) 773-5000. **$159-$575, 3 day notice.** 2757 Shell Beach Rd 93449. US 101 exit 193 (Spyglass Dr) northbound; exit 193 (Shell Beach Rd) southbound, just w, then just n. Int corridors. **Pets:** Accepted.
(¶¶) (⌐) (🗙) (⌂) (🗙) (🖪) (💻)

◈◈ ▼▼▼ Dolphin Bay Resort & Spa **CO** ❖
(805) 773-4300. **$355-$1270, 3 day notice.** 2727 Shell Beach Rd 93449. US 101 exit 193 (Spyglass Dr) northbound; exit 193 (Shell Beach Rd) southbound, just w, then just n; in Shell Beach area. Ext corridors. **Pets:** Dogs only. $65 daily fee/room. Designated rooms, service with restrictions, crate.
(SAVE) (¶¶) (&M) (⌐) (🗙) (⌂) (🗙) (🗙) (🖪) (💻)

▼▼ Edgewater Inn & Suites **M** ❖
(805) 773-4811. **$100-$325.** 280 Wadsworth Ave 93449. US 101 exit 191A (Wadsworth Ave) northbound, just w; exit 191B (Price St) southbound, just w, then 0.4 mi s on Dolliver St. Ext corridors. **Pets:** Service with restrictions, supervision. (¶¶) (&M) (⌐) (⌂) (🗙) (🖪) (💻)

▼▼ Inn at the Cove **M**
(805) 773-3511. **$179-$459, 3 day notice.** 2651 Price St 93449. US 101 exit 191B (Shell Beach Rd) northbound, just w, then 0.3 mi n; exit 191B (Price St) southbound, just w, then 0.4 mi n. Ext corridors. **Pets:** Accepted. (⊑) (&M) (⌐) (⌂) (🗙) (🖪) (💻)

◈◈ ▼▼▼ Oxford Suites Pismo Beach **H** ❖
(805) 773-3773. **Call for rates.** 651 Five Cities Dr 93449. US 101 exit 189 (4th St), just w, then just s. Ext corridors. **Pets:** $25 one-time fee/pet. Designated rooms, service with restrictions, supervision.
(SAVE) (⌐) (⌂) (🖪) (💻)

▼▼▼ Pismo Lighthouse Suites **M**
(805) 773-2411. **Call for rates.** 2411 Price St 93449. US 101 exit 191B (Price St) northbound, just w, then 0.5 mi s; exit southbound, just w, then just s. Ext corridors. **Pets:** Medium, dogs only. $50 daily fee/pet. Designated rooms, service with restrictions, supervision.
(⊑) (&M) (⌐) (🗙) (⌂) (🗙) (🗙) (🖪) (💻)

▼▼▼ SeaCrest OceanFront Hotel **M**
(805) 773-4608. **Call for rates.** 2241 Price St 93449. US 101 exit 191B (Shell Beach Rd) northbound, just w, then 0.5 mi s; exit 191B (Price St) southbound, just w, then just s. Ext/int corridors. **Pets:** Accepted.
(⌐) (⌂) (🗙) (🖪) (💻)

▼▼▼ Sea Gypsy Motel **M**
(805) 773-1801. **$80-$320.** 1020 Cypress St 93449. US 101 exit 191A (Wadsworth Ave) northbound, 0.3 mi w to Cypress St, then just s; exit 191A (SR 1) southbound, just w on Wadsworth Ave, then just s. Ext/int corridors. **Pets:** Other species. $15 daily fee/pet. Service with restrictions, supervision. (⌐) (⌂) (🗙) (🖪) (💻)

▼▼▼ **Shell Beach Inn** Ⓜ ❀
(805) 773-4373. **$65-$225.** 653 Shell Beach Rd 93449. US 101 exit 191B (Shell Beach Rd) northbound, just w, then 1.2 mi s; exit 191B (Price St) southbound, just w, then 1 mi n; in Shell Beach area. Ext corridors. **Pets:** Dogs only. $25 one-time fee/pet. No service, supervision. ⊜ 🖧 🛜 ✕ 🗲 🖵

ⒶⒶⒶ ▼▼▼ **Shore Cliff Lodge** Ⓗ
(805) 773-4671. **$99-$180.** 2555 Price St 93449. US 101 exit 191B (Shell Beach Rd) northbound; exit 191B (Price St) southbound, just w. Ext/int corridors. **Pets:** Accepted.
⟨SAVE⟩ 🖬 🗲ᴹ 🖧 🛜 ✕ 🗲 🖵

PLACENTIA

ⒶⒶⒶ ▼▼▼ **Residence Inn by Marriott Anaheim Placentia/Fullerton** Ⓗ
(714) 996-0555. **$130-$208.** 700 W Kimberly Ave 92870. SR 57 exit 6 (Orangethorpe Ave) southbound; exit 6A northbound, just w, just n on Placentia Ave, then just e. Ext corridors. **Pets:** Accepted.
⟨SAVE⟩ 🖧 🛜 ✕ 🗲 🖵

PLACERVILLE

ⒶⒶⒶ ▼▼▼ **Best Western Plus Placerville Inn** Ⓗ
(530) 622-9100. **$99-$169.** 6850 Green Leaf Dr 95667. US 50 exit 44A (Missouri Flat Rd S), just se. Ext/int corridors. **Pets:** Other species. $20 daily fee/pet. Designated rooms, service with restrictions, crate.
⟨SAVE⟩ 🗲ᴹ 🖧 🛜 ✕ 🗲 🖵

ⒶⒶⒶ ▼▼▼▼ **Eden Vale Inn** ⒷⒷ ❀
(530) 621-0901. **$208-$448, 15 day notice.** 1780 Springvale Rd 95667. US 50 exit 37 (Ponderosa Rd), just n, 4 mi ne on N Shingle Rd (which becomes Green Valley Rd/Lotus Rd), follow Lotus Rd 1.9 mi, then just nw; from SR 49, 4.7 mi sw on Lotus Rd, then just nw. Ext/int corridors. **Pets:** Dogs only. $25 daily fee/pet. ⟨SAVE⟩ 🍴 🗲ᴹ 🛜 ✕

PLEASANT HILL

ⒶⒶⒶ ▼▼▼ **Hyatt House Pleasant Hill** Ⓗ ❀
(925) 934-3343. **$94-$399.** 2611 Contra Costa Blvd 94523. I-680 exit Pleasant Hill/Contra Costa Blvd northbound, just n, then w; exit Monument Blvd southbound, just w, then just s; jct Boyd Rd. Int corridors. **Pets:** Medium. $175 one-time fee/room. Designated rooms, service with restrictions, crate. ⟨SAVE⟩ 🗲ᴹ 🖧 🛜 ✕ 🗲 🖵

▼▼▼ **Residence Inn by Marriott-Pleasant Hill** Ⓗ
(925) 689-1010. **$181-$307.** 700 Ellinwood Way 94523. I-680 exit 51, just w, just s on Contra Costa Blvd, just e on Ellinwood Dr, then just n. Ext/int corridors. **Pets:** Accepted. ⟨ECO⟩ 🗲ᴹ 🖧 🛜 ✕ 🗲 🖵

PLEASANTON

ⒶⒶⒶ ▼▼▼ **Best Western Plus Pleasanton Inn** Ⓗ
(925) 463-1300. **$120-$180.** 5375 Owens Ct 94588. I-580 exit 45 (Hopyard Rd/Dougherty Rd), just s on Hopyard Rd, just e on Owens Dr, then just n. Ext corridors. **Pets:** Medium, dogs only. $100 deposit/room, $35 daily fee/pet. Designated rooms, service with restrictions, supervision. ⟨SAVE⟩ 🗲ᴹ 🖧 🛜 🗲 🖵

▼▼▼ **DoubleTree by Hilton Pleasanton at the Club** Ⓗ
(925) 463-8000. **$109-$339.** 7050 Johnson Dr 94588. I-580 exit 45 (Hopyard Rd/Dougherty Rd), just s on Hopyard Rd, just w on Owens Dr, then 0.8 mi nw. Int corridors. **Pets:** Large, other species. $50 one-time fee/room. Service with restrictions, crate.
🍴 🗲ᴹ 🖧 ✕ 🖭 ✕ 🗲 🖵

ⒶⒶⒶ ▼▼▼ **Hyatt House Pleasanton** Ⓗ
(925) 730-0070. **$99-$349.** 4545 Chabot Dr 94588. I-580 exit 45 (Hopyard Rd/Dougherty Rd), 1 mi s on Hopyard Rd, just e on Stoneridge Dr, then just s. Ext corridors. **Pets:** Medium. $75 one-time fee/room. Service with restrictions. ⟨SAVE⟩ 🗲ᴹ 🖧 🛜 ✕ 🗲 🖵

ⒶⒶⒶ ▼▼▼ **Larkspur Landing Pleasanton** Ⓗ
(925) 463-1212. **$125-$499.** 5535 Johnson Dr 94588. I-580 exit 45 (Hopyard Rd/Dougherty Rd), just s on Hopyard Rd, just w on Owens Dr, then just n. Int corridors. **Pets:** Accepted.
⟨SAVE⟩ ⟨ECO⟩ 🗲ᴹ 🛜 ✕ 🗲 🖵

ⒶⒶⒶ ▼▼▼ **Pleasanton Marriott** Ⓗ
(925) 847-6000. **$97-$315.** 11950 Dublin Canyon Rd 94588. I-580 exit 44A (San Ramon Rd/Foothill Rd), just s, then just w. Int corridors.
Pets: Accepted. ⟨SAVE⟩ 🍴 🗲ᴹ 🖧 🛜 ✕ 🗲 🖵

ⒶⒶⒶ ▼▼▼ **Residence Inn by Marriott** Ⓗ
(925) 227-0500. **$98-$271.** 11920 Dublin Canyon Rd 94588. I-580 exit 44A (San Ramon Rd/Foothill Rd), just s, then just w. Int corridors.
Pets: Accepted. ⟨SAVE⟩ 🗲ᴹ 🖧 🛜 ✕ 🗲 🖵

PLYMOUTH

▼▼▼ **Shenandoah Inn** Ⓗ
(209) 245-4491. **Call for rates.** 17674 Village Dr 95669. On SR 49, south end of town. Ext corridors. **Pets:** Other species. $20 daily fee/pet. Designated rooms, service with restrictions, supervision.
🗲ᴹ 🖧 🛜 ✕ 🗲 🖵

POLLOCK PINES

ⒶⒶⒶ ▼▼▼ **Best Western Stagecoach Inn** Ⓜ
(530) 644-2029. **$129-$169.** 5940 Pony Express Tr 95726. US 50 exit 57 (Pollock Pines) eastbound, just n, then 1 mi e; exit Sly Park Rd westbound, just n, then 1 mi w. Ext corridors. **Pets:** Accepted.
⟨SAVE⟩ 🗲ᴹ 🖧 🛜 🗲 🖵

POMONA

▼▼ **Comfort Inn Near FairPlex** Ⓜ
(909) 620-0099. **$84-$144.** 1421 S Garey Ave 91766. I-10 exit 45B (Garey Ave), 2 mi s. Int corridors. **Pets:** Accepted.
🗲ᴹ 🛜 ✕ 🗲 🖵

ⒶⒶⒶ ▼▼▼ **Sheraton Fairplex Hotel & Conference Center** Ⓗ
(909) 622-2220. **$159-$269.** 601 W McKinley Ave 91768. I-10 exit 45A (White Ave) eastbound, 0.5 mi n, then just w; exit 43 (Fairplex Dr) westbound, 1 mi n, then 0.7 mi e. Int corridors. **Pets:** Accepted.
⟨SAVE⟩ 🍴 🗲ᴹ 🖧 ✕ 🖭 ✕ 🗲 🖵

PORTERVILLE

ⒶⒶⒶ ▼▼ **Best Western Porterville Inn** Ⓗ
(559) 781-7411. **$119-$229.** 350 W Montgomery Ave 93257. SR 65, 0.8 mi e on SR 190, just s on Jaye St, then just e. Int corridors.
Pets: Accepted. ⟨SAVE⟩ 🗲ᴹ 🖧 🛜 🗲 🖵

POWAY

ⒶⒶⒶ ▼▼▼ **Best Western Poway San Diego Hotel** Ⓜ ❀
(858) 748-6320. **$99-$299.** 13845 Poway Rd 92064. I-15 exit 18 (Poway Rd), 4.5 mi e. Ext corridors. **Pets:** Large. $15 daily fee/pet. Designated rooms, service with restrictions, supervision.
⟨SAVE⟩ ⟨ECO⟩ 🗲ᴹ 🖧 🛜 🗲 🖵

RAMONA

ⒶⒶⒶ ▼▼▼ **Ramona Valley Inn** Ⓜ
(760) 789-6433. **Call for rates.** 416 Main St 92065. SR 78, 0.5 mi e of jct SR 67. Ext corridors. **Pets:** Accepted.
⟨SAVE⟩ 🗲ᴹ 🖧 🛜 ✕ 🖭 🗲

RANCHO BERNARDO

ⒶⒶⒶ ▼▼▼ **Rancho Bernardo Inn** Ⓗ
(858) 675-8500. **$184-$409, 3 day notice.** 17550 Bernardo Oaks Dr 92128. I-15 exit 24 (Rancho Bernardo Rd), 1 mi e, then 1 mi n. Ext/int corridors. **Pets:** Accepted.
⟨SAVE⟩ 🖬 🍴 🗲ᴹ 🖧 ✕ 🛜 ✕ 🗲 🖵

RANCHO CORDOVA

Best Western Plus Rancho Cordova Inn H
(916) 631-7500. **$99-$149.** 10713 White Rock Rd 95670. US 50 exit 17 (Zinfandel Dr), just s, then just w. Ext/int corridors. **Pets:** Accepted.
SAVE 🏊 📶 🔀 🛗 💻

Fairfield Inn & Suites by Marriott H
(916) 858-8680. **$82-$151.** 10745 Gold Center Dr 95670. US 50 exit 17 (Zinfandel Dr), just se. Int corridors. **Pets:** Accepted.
🏊 📶 🔀 🛗 💻

Hawthorn Suites by Wyndham Rancho Cordova/Folsom H
(916) 351-9192. **$59-$209.** 12180 Tributary Point Dr 95670. US 50 exit 21 (Hazel Ave), just nw. Int corridors. **Pets:** Dogs only. $15 daily fee/pet. Service with restrictions, crate. SAVE 🏊 📶 🔀 🛗 💻

Hyatt Place Sacramento/Rancho Cordova H
(916) 635-4799. **$69-$189.** 10744 Gold Center Dr 95670. US 50 exit 17 (Zinfandel Dr), just s, just e on White Rock Rd, just n on Prospect Park Dr, then just w. Int corridors. **Pets:** Accepted.
SAVE 🍴 🏊 📶 🔀 🛗 💻

Residence Inn by Marriott H
(916) 851-1550. **$117-$176.** 2779 Prospect Park Dr 95670. US 50 exit 17 (Zinfandel Dr), just se. Int corridors. **Pets:** Accepted.
🏊 📶 🔀 🛗 💻

RANCHO CUCAMONGA
(Restaurants p. 600)

Aloft Ontario-Rancho Cucamonga H
(909) 484-2018. **$105-$239.** 10480 4th St 91730. I-10 exit 59 (Haven Ave), 0.3 mi n, then just w. Int corridors. **Pets:** Accepted.
SAVE 🏊 📶 🔀 🛗 💻

Four Points by Sheraton Ontario Rancho Cucamonga H
(909) 204-6100. **$104-$191.** 11960 Foothill Blvd 91739. I-15 exit 112 (Foothill Blvd), 0.8 mi w. Int corridors. **Pets:** Medium, other species. $75 one-time fee/room. Designated rooms, service with restrictions, supervision. SAVE 🍴 🏊 📶 🔀 🛗 💻

Homewood Suites by Hilton H
(909) 481-6480. **$139-$279.** 11433 Mission Vista Dr 91730. I-15 exit 110 (4th St), just w to Richmond Pl, just n, then just w. Int corridors. **Pets:** Accepted. 🏊 📶 🔀 🛗 💻

TownePlace Suites by Marriott H
(909) 466-1100. **$112-$175.** 9625 Milliken Ave 91730. I-10 exit 57 (Milliken Ave), 0.6 mi n. Int corridors. **Pets:** Large, other species. $100 one-time fee/room. Designated rooms, service with restrictions, supervision. 🏊 📶 🔀 🛗 💻

RANCHO MIRAGE *(Restaurants p. 600)*

The Ritz-Carlton, Rancho Mirage H
(760) 321-8282. **$179-$499, 7 day notice.** 68-900 Frank Sinatra Dr 92270. I-10 exit 130 (Bob Hope Dr), 3.3 mi s, then 3.2 mi w. Int corridors. **Pets:** Accepted. 🍴 🏊 🔀 🛗 💻

The Westin Mission Hills Golf Resort & Spa H
(760) 328-5955. **$109-$599, 3 day notice.** 71-333 Dinah Shore Dr 92270. I-10 exit 130 (Ramon Rd/Bob Hope Dr), 1 mi s on Bob Hope Dr, then 0.6 mi w. Ext corridors. **Pets:** Medium, dogs only. $100 deposit/room. Service with restrictions, supervision.
SAVE 🍴 🏊 🔀 🔀 🛗 💻

RANCHO PALOS VERDES

Terranea Resort H
(310) 265-2800. **$325-$4750, 7 day notice.** 100 Terranea Way 90275. I-110 exit Gaffey St, 1.5 mi s, 6.5 mi w on 25th St (which becomes Palos Verdes Dr S), then just sw. Ext/int corridors. **Pets:** Accepted.
🍴 🏊 🔀 🔀 🛗 💻

RANCHO SANTA FE *(Restaurants p. 600)*

The Inn at Rancho Santa Fe H
(858) 756-1131. **$199-$499, 7 day notice.** 5951 Linea del Cielo 92067. I-5 exit 37 (Lomas Santa Fe Dr), 4 mi e on CR S-8. Ext/int corridors.
Pets: Accepted. 🍴 🏊 🔀 📶 🔀 🛗 💻

Rancho Valencia Resort and Spa H 🐾
(858) 756-1123. **$496-$1452, 7 day notice.** 5921 Valencia Cir 92067. I-5 exit 36 (Via de la Valle), 1.3 mi e, 0.5 mi s on El Camino Real, 2.5 mi e on San Dieguito Rd, just e on Rancho Diegueno Rd, 1 mi ne on Rancho Valencia, then just e at main gate. Ext corridors. **Pets:** $150 one-time fee/room. Service with restrictions, crate.
SAVE 🍴 🏊 🏊 🔀 📶 🔀 🛗 💻

RED BLUFF

Best Western Antelope Inn H 🐾
(530) 527-8882. **$100-$150.** 203 Antelope Blvd 96080. I-5 exit 649 (SR 36), just e. Int corridors. **Pets:** Large, other species. $17 daily fee/pet. Designated rooms, service with restrictions, supervision.
SAVE 🍴 🏊 📶 🔀 🛗 💻

Comfort Inn H
(530) 529-7060. **$89-$134.** 90 Sale Ln 96080. I-5 exit 649 (SR 36), 0.3 mi e. Int corridors. **Pets:** Accepted. 🏊 📶 🛗 💻

Holiday Inn Express & Suites Red Bluff-South Redding Area H 🐾
(530) 528-1600. **$95-$170.** 2810 Main St 96080. I-5 exit 650 (Adobe Rd), just w, then just n. Int corridors. **Pets:** Other species. $35 daily fee/room. Designated rooms, service with restrictions, supervision.
🍴 🏊 📶 🔀 🛗 💻

REDCREST

Redcrest Resort CA 🐾
(707) 722-4208. **$100-$300, 14 day notice.** 26459 Ave of the Giants 95569. US 101 exit 667 (Redcrest), just e, then just n. Ext corridors. **Pets:** Large. $10 daily fee/pet. Designated rooms, service with restrictions, supervision. SAVE 🍴 📶 🔀 🔀 🔀 🛗 💻

REDDING *(Restaurants p. 600)*

Baymont Inn & Suites Redding H
(530) 722-9100. **$79-$160.** 2600 Larkspur Ln 96002. I-5 exit 677 (Cypress Ave), just e, then just s. Int corridors. **Pets:** Accepted.
SAVE 🏊 📶 🔀 🛗 💻

Best Western Plus Hilltop Inn H
(530) 221-6100. **$100-$139.** 2300 Hilltop Dr 96002. I-5 exit 677 (Cypress Ave), just e, then just n. Ext corridors. **Pets:** Medium, dogs only. $20 one-time fee/pet. Designated rooms, service with restrictions, supervision. SAVE 🍴 🍴 🏊 📶 🔀 🛗 💻

Best Western Plus Twin View Inn & Suites H
(530) 241-5500. **$95-$179.** 1080 Twin View Blvd 96003. I-5 exit 681 (Twin View Blvd), just w. Int corridors. **Pets:** $20 one-time fee/pet. Designated rooms, service with restrictions, supervision.
SAVE 🏊 📶 🔀 🛗 💻

Bridge Bay at Shasta Lake Lodge M
(530) 275-3021. **Call for rates.** 10300 Bridge Bay Rd 96003. I-5 exit 690 (Bridge Bay Rd), just w. Ext corridors. **Pets:** Other species. $10 daily fee/pet. Service with restrictions.
🍴 🏊 🔀 📶 🔀 🛗 💻

◆◆◆ ▼▼▼ Comfort Inn H
(530) 221-4472. **$104-$144.** 850 Mistletoe Ln 96002. I-5 exit 677 (Cypress Ave), 0.8 mi n on Hilltop Dr, then just e. Int corridors. **Pets:** Other species. $10 daily fee/pet. Designated rooms, service with restrictions, supervision. [SAVE] [≈] [📶] [✕] [🔒] [💻]

▼▼▼ Comfort Suites Redding H
(530) 246-8100. **$104-$159.** 1195 Grand Ave 96003. I-5 exit 681 (Twin View Blvd) northbound; exit 681B southbound, just w, then just n. Int corridors. **Pets:** Accepted. [✓M] [📶] [✕] [🔒] [💻]

▼▼▼ Fairfield Inn & Suites by Marriott H ✿
(530) 243-3200. **$106-$156.** 5164 Caterpillar Rd 96003. I-5 exit 681 (Twin View Blvd) northbound; exit 681B southbound, just w, then just n. Int corridors. **Pets:** Other species. $40 one-time fee/room. Designated rooms, service with restrictions, supervision.
[✓M] [≈] [📶] [✕] [🔒] [💻]

▼▼▼ Fawndale Lodge & RV Resort M
(530) 275-8000. **Call for rates.** 15215 Fawndale Rd 96003. I-5 exit 689 (Fawndale Rd), just e, then 0.3 mi s; 10 mi n of town; 1 mi s of Shasta Lake. Ext corridors. **Pets:** Accepted. [🍴] [≈] [📶] [✕] [🔒] [💻]

◆◆◆ ▼▼▼ Oxford Suites Redding H
(530) 221-0100. **Call for rates.** 1967 Hilltop Dr 96002. I-5 exit 677 (Cypress Ave), just e, then just n. Ext/int corridors. **Pets:** Accepted.
[SAVE] [✓M] [📶] [✕] [🔒] [💻]

◆◆◆ ▼▼▼ Redding Travelodge H
(530) 243-5291. **$62-$110.** 540 N Market St 96003. I-5 exit 680 (Lake Blvd) northbound, 0.5 mi w to Market St, then 0.5 mi s; exit Market St southbound, 2 mi s. Ext corridors. **Pets:** Other species. $8 daily fee/pet. Designated rooms, service with restrictions, supervision.
[SAVE] [✓M] [≈] [📶] [✕] [🔒] [💻]

▼▼▼ Red Lion Hotel Redding H
(530) 221-8700. **$99-$225.** 1830 Hilltop Dr 96002. I-5 exit 677 (Cypress Ave), just e, then 0.6 mi n. Int corridors. **Pets:** Dogs only. $15 one-time fee/room. Service with restrictions. [🍴] [✓M] [≈] [📶] [✕] [🔒] [💻]

◆◆◆ ▼▼▼ TownePlace Suites by Marriott H
(530) 223-0690. **$123-$173.** 2180 Larkspur Ln 96002. I-5 exit 677 (Cypress Ave), just e, just n on Hilltop Dr, just e on Industrial St, then just n. Int corridors. **Pets:** Accepted.
[SAVE] [✓M] [≈] [📶] [✕] [🔒] [💻]

REDLANDS

▼▼▼ Ayres Hotel Redlands H
(909) 335-9024. **$159-$189.** 1015 W Colton Ave 92374. I-10 exit 77B (Tennessee St) westbound; exit 77C eastbound, just s, then just e. Ext corridors. **Pets:** Accepted.
[ECO] [⊟] [✓M] [≈] [✕] [📶] [✕] [🔒] [💻]

▼▼▼ Country Inn & Suites By Carlson, San Bernardino (Redlands) H
(909) 792-7913. **Call for rates.** 1650 Industrial Park Ave 92374. I-10 E exit 77A (Alabama St), just s, then just w. Int corridors. **Pets:** Accepted.
[✓M] [≈] [📶] [✕] [🔒] [💻]

REDONDO BEACH

◆◆◆ ▼▼▼ Residence Inn by Marriott Los Angeles Redondo Beach H ✿
(310) 725-0108. **$124-$240.** 2420 Marine Ave 90278. I-405 exit 42B (Inglewood Ave), just n, then just w. Int corridors. **Pets:** Other species. $100 one-time fee/room. Service with restrictions, crate.
[SAVE] [📶] [✕] [🔒] [💻]

REDWOOD CITY

◆◆◆ ▼▼▼▼ Pullman San Francisco Bay Hotel H ✿
(650) 598-9000. **Call for rates.** 223 Twin Dolphin Dr 94065. US 101 exit Ralston Ave E, 0.5 mi s at jct Shoreline Dr. Int corridors. **Pets:** Very small, dogs only. Designated rooms, service with restrictions, supervision. [SAVE] [ECO] [🍴] [✓M] [≈] [📶] [✕] [🔒] [💻]

▼▼▼▼ TownePlace Suites by Marriott Redwood City/ Redwood Shores H
(650) 593-4100. **$134-$323.** 1000 Twin Dolphin Dr 94065. US 101 exit Redwood Shores Pkwy, 0.3 mi e, then just s. Int corridors.
Pets: Accepted. [✓M] [📶] [✕] [🔒] [💻]

REEDLEY

◆◆◆ ▼▼ Edgewater Inn M
(559) 637-7777. **$75-$79.** 1977 W Manning Ave 93654. SR 99 exit 121 (Manning Ave), 11 mi e. Ext corridors. **Pets:** Dogs only. $8 daily fee/pet. Service with restrictions, supervision.
[SAVE] [🍴] [✓M] [📶] [🔒] [💻]

RIDGECREST

◆◆◆ ▼▼▼ Best Western Plus China Lake Inn M
(760) 371-2300. **$90-$140.** 400 S China Lake Blvd 93555. On US 395 business route. Ext corridors. **Pets:** Accepted.
[SAVE] [✓M] [≈] [📶] [🔒] [💻]

▼▼ Budget Inn & Suites M
(760) 375-1351. **$55-$75.** 831 N China Lake Blvd 93555. On US 395 business route; near center. Ext corridors. **Pets:** Small, dogs only. $100 deposit/pet. Designated rooms, service with restrictions, supervision.
[📶] [✕] [🔒]

▼▼ Clarion Inn M
(760) 446-7910. **Call for rates.** 901 N China Lake Blvd 93555. On SR 178 and US 395 business route; center. Ext corridors. **Pets:** Accepted.
[🍴] [✓M] [≈] [✕] [📶] [✕] [🔒] [💻]

▼▼ Econo Lodge Inn & Suites M
(760) 446-2551. **$64-$98.** 201 Inyokern Rd 93555. SR 178 and US 395 business route, just w of China Lake Blvd. Ext corridors. **Pets:** Medium, dogs only. $10 one-time fee/pet. Service with restrictions, supervision.
[≈] [📶] [🔒] [💻]

▼▼ Quality Inn M
(760) 375-9731. **$76-$160.** 507 S China Lake Blvd 93555. On US 395 business route; south end of town. Ext corridors. **Pets:** Accepted.
[≈] [📶] [✕] [🔒] [💻]

◆◆◆ ▼▼ Rodeway Inn & Suites H
(760) 446-6543. **$85-$98.** 1050 N Norma St 93555. On US 395 business route, just w. Int corridors. **Pets:** Other species. $100 deposit/room. Service with restrictions, crate.
[SAVE] [🍴] [✓M] [≈] [📶] [🔒] [💻]

RIO DELL

◆◆◆ ▼▼ Humboldt Gables Motel M
(707) 764-5609. **$75-$200.** 40 W Davis St 95562. US 101 exit 680 (Davis St), 0.5 mi w. Ext corridors. **Pets:** Small, dogs only. $20 daily fee/room. Supervision. [SAVE] [🍴] [✓M] [📶] [✕] [🅰] [🔒] [💻]

RIPON

◆◆◆ ▼▼▼▼ La Quinta Inn & Suites Manteca - Ripon H
(209) 599-8999. **$81-$196.** 1524 Colony Rd 95366. SR 99 exit 237B (Jack Tone Rd), just n, then just e. Int corridors. **Pets:** Accepted.
[SAVE] [✓M] [≈] [✕] [📶] [✕] [🔒] [💻]

RIVERSIDE *(Restaurants p. 600)*

▼▼ Comfort Inn Riverside **M**

(951) 683-6000. **$89-$189.** 1590 University Ave 92507. I-215 and SR 60 exit 32 (University Ave), 0.5 mi w. Ext corridors. **Pets:** Accepted.

🕭 🛌 📶 ✕ 🛢 💻

AAA ▼▼ Hyatt Place Riverside Downtown **H**

(951) 321-3500. **$84-$199.** 3500 Market St 92501. SR 91 exit 64 (University Ave) eastbound; exit 64 (Mission Inn Ave) westbound, 0.5 mi w, then just n; downtown. Int corridors. **Pets:** Accepted.

🆂🅰🆅🅴 🕭 🛌 📶 ✕ 🛢 💻

AAA ▼▼▼ The Mission Inn Hotel & Spa **H**

(951) 784-0300. **$209-$319.** 3649 Mission Inn Ave 92501. SR 91 exit 64 (University Ave) eastbound; exit 64 (Mission Inn Ave) westbound, just w. Ext/int corridors. **Pets:** Accepted.

🆂🅰🆅🅴 🍴 🕭 🛌 ✕ 🔲 ✕ 🛢 💻

ROCKLIN *(Restaurants p. 600)*

▼▼▼ Staybridge Suites **H**

(916) 781-7500. **$120-$201.** 6664 Lonetree Blvd 95765. SR 65 exit 308 (Blue Oaks Blvd), just e, just n to Redwood Dr, then just w; behind Blue Oaks Town Center; directly behind Petco. Int corridors.
Pets: Accepted. 🕭 🛌 📶 ✕ 🛢 💻

ROHNERT PARK

AAA ▼▼▼ Best Western Inn **M**

(707) 584-7435. **$140-$209.** 6500 Redwood Dr 94928. US 101 exit Rohnert Park Expwy, just w. Ext corridors. **Pets:** Accepted.

🆂🅰🆅🅴 🕭 🛌 📶 🛢 💻

▼▼▼ DoubleTree by Hilton Sonoma Wine Country **H**

(707) 584-5466. **$113-$294.** One Doubletree Dr 94928. US 101 exit Golf Course Dr; 3 mi s of Santa Rosa. Int corridors. **Pets:** Accepted.

🅴🅲🅾 🍴 🕭 🛌 🔲 📶 ✕ 🛢 💻

ROSEVILLE

AAA ▼▼▼ Best Western Plus Orchid Hotel & Suites **H**

(916) 784-2222. **$109-$189.** 130 N Sunrise Ave 95661. I-80 exit 103A (E Douglas Blvd) eastbound; exit 103 westbound, just e, then just n. Ext/int corridors. **Pets:** Accepted. 🆂🅰🆅🅴 🕭 🛌 📶 ✕ 🛢 💻

AAA ▼▼▼ Best Western Roseville Inn **M**

(916) 782-4434. **$70-$150.** 220 Harding Blvd 95678. I-80 exit 103 (Douglas Blvd) westbound; exit 103B eastbound, just w, then just n. Ext corridors. **Pets:** Accepted. 🆂🅰🆅🅴 🕭 🛌 📶 🛢 💻

▼▼▼ Homewood Suites by Hilton **H**

(916) 783-7455. **$109-$209.** 401 Creekside Ridge Ct 95678. I-80 exit SR 65, 1 mi w to Galleria Blvd, 0.5 mi s to Antelope Creek Rd, just e, then just n. Int corridors. **Pets:** Accepted. 🕭 🛌 📶 🛢 💻

AAA ▼▼▼ Hyatt Place Sacramento/Roseville **H**

(916) 781-6400. **$69-$209.** 220 Conference Center Dr 95678. I-80 exit 105A (Atlantic St/Eureka Rd), just e on Eureka Rd, 0.4 mi ne on Taylor Rd, 1.1 mi w on E Roseville Pkwy, just n on Gibson Dr, then just e. Int corridors. **Pets:** Accepted. 🆂🅰🆅🅴 🍴 🕭 🛌 📶 ✕ 🛢 💻

AAA ▼▼▼ Larkspur Landing Roseville **H**

(916) 773-1717. **Call for rates.** 1931 Taylor Rd 95661. I-80 exit 105A (Atlantic St/Eureka Rd), just e on Eureka Rd, then 0.4 mi n. Int corridors. **Pets:** Medium. $25 one-time fee/room. Service with restrictions, supervision. 🆂🅰🆅🅴 🅴🅲🅾 🕭 📶 ✕ 🛢 💻

▼▼▼ Residence Inn by Marriott **H**

(916) 772-5500. **$119-$178.** 1930 Taylor Rd 95661. I-80 exit 105A (Atlantic St/Eureka Rd), just n. Int corridors. **Pets:** Other species. $25 daily fee/room. Service with restrictions, supervision.

🕭 🛌 📶 ✕ 🛢 💻

▼▼▼ TownePlace Suites by Marriott Roseville **H**

(916) 782-2232. **$106-$166.** 10569 Fairway Dr 95678. SR 65 exit Blue Oaks Blvd, just e. Int corridors. **Pets:** Accepted.

🕭 🛌 📶 ✕ 🛢 💻

SACRAMENTO *(Restaurants p. 600)*

AAA ▼▼▼ Best Western Plus Sutter House **H**

(916) 441-1314. **$150-$250.** 1100 H St 95814. 4 blks from state capitol; between 11th and 12th sts. Ext/int corridors. **Pets:** Accepted.

🆂🅰🆅🅴 🍴 🕭 🛌 📶 ✕ 🛢 💻

AAA ▼▼▼ Best Western Sandman **H**

(916) 443-6515. **$99-$189.** 236 Jibboom St 95811. I-5 exit 520 (Richards Blvd), just sw. Ext corridors. **Pets:** Accepted.

🆂🅰🆅🅴 🍴 🕭 🛌 📶 🛢 💻

AAA ▼▼▼ The Citizen Hotel, Autograph Collection **H**

(916) 447-2700. **$156-$282.** 926 J St 95814. I-5 exit J St (Old Sacramento), 0.6 mi e; jct 10th St. Int corridors. **Pets:** Accepted.

🆂🅰🆅🅴 🅴🅲🅾 🍴 🕭 🔲 ✕ 🛢 💻

AAA ▼▼▼ Days Inn-Sacramento Downtown **M**

(916) 443-4811. **$55-$90.** 228 Jibboom St 95814. I-5 exit 520 (Richards Blvd), just w, then just s. Int corridors. **Pets:** Medium, dogs only. $50 deposit/pet, $10 daily fee/pet. Designated rooms, service with restrictions, supervision. 🆂🅰🆅🅴 🕭 🛌 📶 🛢 💻

▼▼▼ DoubleTree by Hilton Sacramento **H**

(916) 929-8855. **$99-$269.** 2001 Point West Way 95815. Business Rt I-80 (Capital City Frwy) exit Arden Way, just e. Int corridors.
Pets: Accepted. 🅴🅲🅾 🍴 🕭 🛌 📶 ✕ 🛢 💻

AAA ▼▼▼ Hilton Sacramento Arden West **H**

(916) 922-4700. **$99-$269.** 2200 Harvard St 95815. Business Rt I-80 (Capital City Frwy) exit Arden Way, just w, then just n. Int corridors.
Pets: Accepted. 🆂🅰🆅🅴 🍴 🕭 🛌 🔲 ✕ 💻

▼▼▼ Holiday Inn Express Sacramento Convention Center **H**

(916) 444-4436. **$89-$209, 3 day notice.** 728 16th St 95814. Jct G and 16th sts. Int corridors. **Pets:** Accepted. 🅴🅲🅾 🕭 📶 ✕ 🛢 💻

AAA ▼▼▼▼ Hyatt Regency Sacramento **H**

(916) 443-1234. **$129-$469.** 1209 L St 95814. 1/2 blk from state capitol; jct 12th and L sts. Int corridors. **Pets:** Accepted.

🆂🅰🆅🅴 🅴🅲🅾 📢 🍴 🕭 🛌 🔲 📶 ✕ 🛢 💻

AAA ▼▼▼ Lions Gate Hotel & Conference Center **H**

(916) 643-6222. **$125-$159, 48 day notice.** 3410 Westover St 95652. I-80 exit Watt Ave, 1.3 mi n to Palm St, just w, then just s on Arnold Ave. Ext/int corridors. **Pets:** Small. $25 daily fee/pet. Designated rooms, service with restrictions, crate.

🆂🅰🆅🅴 🍴 🕭 🛌 📶 ✕ 🛢 💻

AAA ▼▼▼ Residence Inn by Marriott-Sacramento Airport Natomas **H**

(916) 649-1300. **$121-$208.** 2410 W El Camino Ave 95833. I-5 exit 521B (W El Camino Ave) northbound, just w, then just s on Gateway Oaks Dr; I-80 exit W El Camino Ave, 1.5 mi e, then just s on Gateway Oaks Dr. Ext corridors. **Pets:** Accepted.

🆂🅰🆅🅴 🕭 🛌 📶 ✕ 🛢 💻

▼▼▼ Residence Inn by Marriott Sacramento Cal Expo **H**

(916) 920-9111. **$120-$198.** 1530 Howe Ave 95825. US 50 exit 9 (Howe Ave), 2.7 mi n. Ext corridors. **Pets:** Accepted.

🅴🅲🅾 🕭 🛌 📶 ✕ 🛢 💻

Residence Inn by Marriott- Sacramento Downtown at Capitol Park H
(916) 443-0500. **$167-$303.** 1121 15th St 95814. Jct 15th and L sts; just e of state capitol. Int corridors. **Pets:** Accepted.

Sheraton Grand Sacramento Hotel H 🐾
(916) 447-1700. **$139-$499.** 1230 J St 95814. I-5 exit J St (Old Sacramento), 1 mi e; between 12th and 13 sts. Int corridors. **Pets:** Medium, dogs only. $100 deposit/room. Designated rooms, service with restrictions, supervision.

Staybridge Suites Sacramento Airport/Natomas H
(916) 575-7907. **Call for rates.** 140 Promenade Cir 95834. I-80 exit 88 (Truxel Rd), just nw, just n on Gateway Park Blvd, just e on N Freeway Blvd, then just s. Int corridors. **Pets:** Medium, dogs only. $75 one-time fee/room. Designated rooms, service with restrictions, supervision.

TownePlace Suites by Marriott Sacramento Cal Expo H
(916) 920-5400. **$109-$168.** 1784 Tribute Rd 95815. Business Rt I-80 exit 9A (Cal Expo) westbound; exit Exposition Blvd eastbound, just sw. Int corridors. **Pets:** Accepted.

The Westin Sacramento H
(916) 443-8400. **$199-$359.** 4800 Riverside Blvd 95822. I-5 exit 515 (Fruitridge/Seamas), just w, then 0.7 mi n. Int corridors. **Pets:** Accepted.

ST. HELENA (Restaurants p. 600)

El Bonita Motel M
(707) 963-3216. **$100-$325, 3 day notice.** 195 Main St 94574. 1 mi s of center on SR 29 at El Bonita Ave. Ext corridors. **Pets:** Medium, other species. $25 daily fee/pet. Service with restrictions, supervision.

Harvest Inn by Charlie Palmer H
(707) 963-9463. **$200-$1000, 7 day notice.** One Main St 94574. 1 mi s of center on SR 29 at Adams St. Ext corridors. **Pets:** Accepted.

SALIDA

La Quinta Inn & Suites Modesto Salida H
(209) 579-8723. **$92-$218.** 4909 Sisk Rd 95368. SR 99 exit 233 (SR 219), just e. Int corridors. **Pets:** Accepted.

SALINAS

Residence Inn by Marriott-Salinas H
(831) 775-0410. **$141-$263.** 17215 El Rancho Way 93907. US 101 exit Laurel Dr, just w. Int corridors. **Pets:** Accepted.

Travelodge M
(831) 424-4801. **$149-$159.** 109 John St 93901. US 101 exit John St, 0.7 mi w. Ext corridors. **Pets:** Accepted.

SAN BERNARDINO

Best Western Hospitality Lane M
(909) 381-1681. **$90-$140.** 294 E Hospitality Ln 92408. I-10 exit 73 (Waterman Ave) westbound; exit 73B eastbound, just n, then just w. Ext corridors. **Pets:** Accepted.

DoubleTree by Hilton San Bernardino H
(909) 889-0133. **$99-$299.** 285 E Hospitality Ln 92408. I-10 exit 73 (Waterman Ave) westbound; exit 73B eastbound, just n, then just w. Int corridors. **Pets:** Medium, dogs only. $75 one-time fee/pet. Service with restrictions, supervision.

Homewood Suites by Hilton San Bernardino H
(909) 799-6500. **$119-$199.** 885 E Hospitality Ln 92408. I-10 exit 74 (Tippecanoe Ave) eastbound; exit 74 (Anderson St/Tippecanoe Ave) westbound, just n, then just w. Int corridors. **Pets:** Small, dogs only. $125 one-time fee/room. Service with restrictions, supervision.

Residence Inn by Marriott San Bernardino H
(909) 382-4564. **$109-$213.** 1040 E Harriman Pl 92408. I-10 exit 74 (Tippecanoe Ave) eastbound; exit 74 (Anderson St/Tippecanoe Ave) westbound, just n, then just w. Int corridors. **Pets:** Accepted.

SAN BRUNO

Staybridge Suites - San Francisco Airport H
(650) 588-0770. **$149-$499.** 1350 Huntington Ave 94066. I-380 exit El Camino Real N, e on Sneath Ln, then just n. Ext corridors. **Pets:** Other species. $15 daily fee/room.

SAN CLEMENTE

Best Western Plus Casablanca Inn H
(949) 361-1644. **$95-$155.** 1601 N El Camino Real 92672. I-5 exit 76 (Avenida Pico), 0.8 mi sw, then just s. Ext/int corridors. **Pets:** Medium. $20 daily fee/room. Designated rooms, service with restrictions, supervision.

Holiday Inn Express H
(949) 498-8800. **Call for rates.** 35 Via Pico Plaza 92672. I-5 exit 76 (Avenida Pico), just w, then just s. Int corridors. **Pets:** Accepted.

SAN DIEGO (Restaurants p. 600)

Andaz San Diego H
(619) 849-1234. **$129-$499, 3 day notice.** 600 F St 92101. I-5 exit 16B (6th Ave/Downtown) northbound, 1 mi n, then just e; exit 17 (Front St/Civic Center) southbound, 0.9 mi s to Broadway, 0.5 mi e to 8th Ave, just s, then just w. Int corridors. **Pets:** Accepted.

Best Western Lamplighter Inn & Suites at SDSU H
(619) 582-3088. **$94-$149.** 6474 El Cajon Blvd 92115. I-8 exit 11 (70th St/Lake Murray Blvd), 0.4 mi s on 70th St, then 0.8 mi w. Ext corridors. **Pets:** Accepted.

Best Western Mission Bay M
(619) 275-5700. **$69-$159.** 2575 Clairemont Dr 92117. I-5 exit 22 (Clairemont Dr/Mission Bay Dr), just e. Ext corridors. **Pets:** Small. $15 daily fee/room. Designated rooms, service with restrictions, crate.

Best Western Plus Hacienda Hotel Old Town H
(619) 298-4707. **$159-$249.** 4041 Harney St 92110. I-5 exit 19 (Old Town Ave), just e, 0.3 mi n on San Diego Ave, then just e. Ext corridors. **Pets:** Medium, dogs only. $50 deposit/pet, $25 daily fee/room. Designated rooms, service with restrictions, supervision.

Best Western San Diego/Miramar Hotel M
(858) 578-6600. **$99-$399.** 9310 Kearny Mesa Rd 92126. I-15 exit 14 (Miramar Rd/Pomerado Rd), just w, then just s. Ext corridors. **Pets:** Accepted.

The Bristol Hotel H
(619) 232-6141. **$139-$399.** 1055 1st Ave 92101. I-5 exit 17 (Front St/Civic Center) southbound, 0.5 mi s, just e on C St, then just s; exit 15B (Pershing Dr/Civic Center) northbound, 1 mi w to 1st Ave, then just s. Int corridors. **Pets:** Accepted.

SAVE ECO 📞 🍴 🔥M 🛜 ✕ 🔒 💻

Candlewood Suites H
(619) 299-3501. **Call for rates.** 1335 Hotel Cir S 92108. I-8 exit 4A (Hotel Cir), just s. Ext/int corridors. **Pets:** Accepted.

🔥M 🛜 ✕ 🔒 💻

Catamaran Resort Hotel & Spa H
(858) 488-1081. **Call for rates.** 3999 Mission Blvd 92109. I-5 exit 23A (Grand Ave/Garnet Ave) northbound, via Mission Bay to Garnet Ave, 2.2 mi w, then 0.5 mi s. Ext/int corridors. **Pets:** Accepted.

SAVE ECO 🍴 🛥 ✕ 🛜 ✕ 🔒 💻

Country Inn & Suites By Carlson San Diego North H ☙
(858) 558-1818. **Call for rates.** 5975 Lusk Blvd 92121. I-805 exit 27 (Mira Mesa Blvd), 1 mi e, then just n. Int corridors. **Pets:** Dogs only. $75 one-time fee/room. Designated rooms, service with restrictions, supervision. 🍴 🔥M 🛥 🛜 ✕ 🔒 💻

Crowne Plaza San Diego H
(619) 297-1101. **$169-$289.** 2270 Hotel Cir N 92108. I-8 exit 3 (Taylor St), just n, then just e. Ext corridors. **Pets:** Accepted.

ECO 🍴 🔥M 🛥 🛜 ✕ 🔒 💻

The Dana On Mission Bay H
(619) 222-6440. **$109-$359.** 1710 W Mission Bay Dr 92109. I-8 exit 1 (Ingraham St/Mission Bay), 0.7 mi n, then just w. Ext corridors. **Pets:** Accepted. SAVE ECO 🍴 🔥M 🛥 ✕ 🛜 ✕ 🔒 💻

DoubleTree by Hilton Hotel San Diego - Del Mar H ☙
(858) 481-5900. **$119-$329.** 11915 El Camino Real 92130. I-5 exit 33 (Carmel Valley Rd), 0.3 mi e, then just n. Int corridors. **Pets:** Small, dogs only. Designated rooms, service with restrictions, supervision.

ECO 🍴 🛥 🛜 🔒 💻

Fairmont Grand Del Mar H ☙
(858) 314-2000. **$445-$1095, 7 day notice.** 5300 Grand Del Mar Ct 92130. I-5 exit 33 (Carmel Valley Rd), 1.5 mi e on SR 56, 0.5 mi s on Carmel Country Rd, 0.5 mi e on Grand Del Mar Way, then just se. Int corridors. **Pets:** Small, dogs only. $150 one-time fee/room. Service with restrictions, supervision.

SAVE ECO 📞 🍴 🔥M 🛥 ✕ 🛜 ✕ 🔒 💻

Hampton Inn San Diego/Del Mar H
(858) 792-5557. **$99-$279.** 11920 El Camino Real 92130. I-5 exit 33 (Carmel Valley Rd), just ne. Int corridors. **Pets:** Accepted.

🔥M 🛥 🛜 ✕ 🔒 💻

Hilton San Diego Airport/Harbor Island H
(619) 291-6700. **$149-$299.** 1960 Harbor Island Dr 92101. I-5 exit 184 (Laurel St) southbound, 1.5 mi w; exit 17 (Hawthorn St) northbound, 0.5 mi w to Harbor Dr, then 1.5 mi nw. Int corridors. **Pets:** Accepted.

SAVE ECO 🍴 🔥M 🛥 ✕ 🔒 💻

Hilton San Diego Bayfront H
(619) 564-3333. **$129-$1399.** One Park Blvd 92101. I-5 exit 17 (Front St/Civic Center) southbound, 1.5 mi s, just w to Harbor Dr, then just s; exit 16B (6th Ave/Downtown) northbound, 1.3 mi s, just w on Market, just s on Front St, just w to Harbor Dr, then just s. Int corridors. **Pets:** Accepted. SAVE ECO 🍴 🔥M 🛥 ✕ 🛜 ✕ 🔒 💻

Hilton San Diego Gaslamp Quarter H
(619) 231-4040. **$169-$489.** 401 K St 92101. I-5 exit 7B (J St/Marina Pkwy) northbound, 0.8 mi w to 4th Ave, then just s; exit 17 (Front St/Civic Center) southbound, 0.5 mi e to 4th Ave, then 1 mi s; in Historic Gaslamp Quarter. Int corridors. **Pets:** Accepted.

🍴 🔥M 🛥 🛜 ✕ 🔒 💻

Hilton San Diego Mission Valley Zoo/ SeaWorld Area H
(619) 543-9000. **$129-$399.** 901 Camino del Rio S 92108. I-8 exit 5 (Mission Center Rd), just s, then just w. Int corridors. **Pets:** Accepted.

SAVE ECO 🍴 🔥M 🛥 🛜 ✕ 🔒 💻

Homewood Suites by Hilton San Diego Mission Valley/Zoo H ☙
(619) 260-0600. **$195-$305.** 445 Camino del Rio S 92108. I-8 exit 5 (Mission Center Rd), just s, then just w. Int corridors. **Pets:** Medium, dogs only. $125 one-time fee/room. Service with restrictions, supervision. 🍴 🔥M 🛜 ✕ 🔒 💻

Hotel Indigo San Diego Gaslamp Quarter H
(619) 727-4000. **Call for rates.** 509 9th Ave 92101. I-5 exit 17 (Front St/Civic Center) southbound, 0.3 mi s, 0.5 mi e on A St, 0.5 mi s on 6th Ave, then just e on Island Ave; exit 16B (6th Ave/Downtown) northbound, 0.5 mi s, then just e on Island Ave. Int corridors. **Pets:** Accepted. ECO 🍴 🔥M 🛜 ✕ 🔒 💻

Hotel Karlan San Diego-A DoubleTree by Hilton H
(858) 672-9100. **$119-$249.** 14455 Penasquitos Dr 92129. I-15 exit 21 (Carmel Mountain Rd), just w. Ext corridors. **Pets:** Accepted.

SAVE ECO 🍴 🔥M 🛥 ✕ 🛜 ✕ 🔒 💻

Hyatt House San Diego/Sorrento Mesa H ☙
(858) 597-0500. **$129-$329.** 10044 Pacific Mesa Blvd 92121. I-805 exit 27 (Mira Mesa Blvd), 1.5 mi e, just n on Pacific Heights, then just w. Int corridors. **Pets:** Medium. $75 one-time fee/room. Service with restrictions. SAVE 🍴 🔥M 🛥 🛜 ✕ 🔒 💻

Hyatt Regency Mission Bay Spa and Marina H ☙
(619) 224-1234. **$129-$459.** 1441 Quivira Rd 92109. I-8 exit 1 (Ingraham St/Mission Bay Dr), 0.7 mi n, just w on Mission Bay Dr, then just sw. Ext/int corridors. **Pets:** Medium. $100 one-time fee/room. Designated rooms, service with restrictions, supervision.

SAVE ECO 🍴 🔥M 🛥 🛜 🔒 💻

The Keating Hotel by Pininfarina H
(619) 814-5700. **Call for rates.** 432 F St 92101. I-5 exit 16B (6th Ave/Downtown) northbound, 1 mi s, then just w; exit 17 (Front St/Civic Center) southbound, 0.9 mi s to Broadway, 0.5 mi e to 8th Ave, just s, then 0.3 mi w. Int corridors. **Pets:** Accepted. 🍴 🔥M 🛜 ✕ 🔒 💻

Kings Inn San Diego H ☙
(619) 297-2231. **$79-$249, 3 day notice.** 1333 Hotel Cir S 92108. I-8 exit 4A (Hotel Cir S), just e. Ext/int corridors. **Pets:** Medium. $15 daily fee/pet. Designated rooms, service with restrictions, supervision.

SAVE 🍴 🔥M 🛥 🛜 ✕ 🔒 💻

Kona Kai Resort & Spa H
(619) 221-8000. **$149-$899.** 1551 Shelter Island Dr 92106. I-5 exit 20 (Rosecrans St) southbound, 3 mi sw, then 1.5 mi sw; exit 17 (Hawthorn St) northbound, 3 mi nw on Harbor Dr to Scott Rd, then 1.5 mi sw. Ext/int corridors. **Pets:** Accepted.

🍴 🔥M 🛥 ✕ 🛜 ✕ 🔒 💻

La Quinta Inn & Suites San Diego SeaWorld Area/Mission Bay H
(858) 483-9800. **$86-$372.** 4610 De Soto St 92109. I-5 exit 23A (Grand Ave/Garnet Ave) northbound, 1 mi w on Mission Bay Dr, then just e on Damon Ave; exit 23B (Balboa Ave/Garnet Ave) southbound, just s, then just e on Damon Ave. Int corridors. **Pets:** Accepted.

📞 🍴 🔥M 🛥 🛜 ✕ 🔒 💻

La Quinta Inn & Suites San Diego SeaWorld/Zoo Area M
(619) 295-6886. **$92-$273.** 641 Camino Del Rio S 92108. I-8 exit 5 (Mission Center Rd), just s, then just w. Ext corridors. **Pets:** Accepted.

🔥M 🛥 🛜 ✕ 🔒 💻

▼▼▼ **La Quinta Inn San Diego Old Town/Airport** Ⓜ
(619) 291-9100. **$108-$466.** 2380 Moore St 92110. I-5 exit 19 (Old Town Ave), just n via Frontage Rd; on east side of freeway. Ext/int corridors. **Pets:** Accepted. 🅴🅲🅾 ⏹ ♨ ⊠ 🛑 🅱 ⊡

🆑 ▼▼▼ **Manchester Grand Hyatt San Diego** Ⓗ
(619) 232-1234. **$109-$459, 7 day notice.** 1 Market Pl 92101. I-5 exit 17 (Front St/Civic Center), 1.3 mi s, then just w. Int corridors. **Pets:** Accepted. 🆂🅰🆅🅴 ⏹ ♨ ⊠ ♨ ⊠ 🅱 ⊡

▼▼ **Marina Inn & Suites** Ⓜ
(619) 232-7551. **Call for rates.** 1943 Pacific Hwy 92101. I-5 exit 17 (Front St/Civic Center) southbound, just s to Cedar St, 0.3 mi w, then just n; exit 17A (Hawthorn St/San Diego Airport) northbound, 0.4 mi w, then just s. Ext corridors. **Pets:** Accepted. ⏹ ♨ ♨ 🅱 ⊡

▼▼ **Marriott Vacation Club Pulse, San Diego** Ⓗ
(619) 696-9800. **$94-$329.** 701 A St 92101. I-5 exit 16 (10th St) southbound, just s to B St, just w, then just n on 7th St; exit 16B (6th Ave/Downtown) northbound, just s, then just e. Int corridors. **Pets:** Accepted. ⏹ ♨ ♨ ♨ ⊠ 🅱 ⊡

▼▼ **Old Town Inn** Ⓜ
(619) 260-8024. **Call for rates.** 4444 Pacific Hwy 92110. I-5 exit 21 (SeaWorld Dr/Tecolote St), just sw, then 1 mi se. Ext corridors. **Pets:** Accepted. ⏹ ♨ ♨ ♨ ⊠ 🅱 ⊡

🆑 ▼▼▼ **Omni San Diego Hotel** Ⓗ
(619) 231-6664. **Call for rates.** 675 L St 92101. I-5 exit 17 (Front St/Civic Center) southbound, 0.3 mi s, 0.3 mi e on A St, 0.6 mi s on 6th Ave, then just e; exit 16B (6th Ave/Downtown) northbound, just s, then just e. Int corridors. **Pets:** Accepted. 🆂🅰🆅🅴 ⏹ ♨ ♨ ⊠ ♨ ⊠ 🅱 ⊡

▼▼ **Pacific Inn Hotel & Suites** Ⓜ
(619) 232-6391. **Call for rates.** 1655 Pacific Hwy 92101. I-5 exit 17 (Front St/Civic Center) southbound, just s to Cedar St, 0.5 mi w, then just n; exit 17A (Hawthorn St/San Diego Airport) northbound, 0.6 mi w, then just s. Ext corridors. **Pets:** Large. $150 deposit/pet, $40 daily fee/pet. Designated rooms, no service, crate. ⏹ ♨ ♨ 🅱 ⊡

🆑 ▼▼ **Pacific Shores Inn** Ⓜ
(858) 483-6300. **$109-$269, 3 day notice.** 4802 Mission Blvd 92109. I-5 exit 23A (Grand Ave/Garnet Ave), via Mission Bay Dr to Garnet Ave, 2.2 mi w, then 0.3 mi n. Ext corridors. **Pets:** Medium. $35 one-time fee/room. Service with restrictions, crate. 🆂🅰🆅🅴 ⏹ ♨ ♨ ⊠ 🅱 ⊡

🆑 ▼▼▼ **Porto Vista Hotel** Ⓗ
(619) 544-0164. **Call for rates.** 1835 Columbia St 92101. I-5 exit 17 (Front St/Civic Center) southbound, just w on Cedar St, then just n on State St; exit 17 (Hawthorn St/San Diego Airport) northbound, just e, then just s. Ext/int corridors. **Pets:** Accepted. 🆂🅰🆅🅴 ⏹ ♨ ♨ ⊠ 🅱 ⊡

▼▼ **Quality Inn I-15 Miramar** Ⓜ
(858) 578-4350. **$79-$225.** 9350 Kearny Mesa Rd 92126. I-15 exit 14 (Miramar Rd/Pomerado), just w, then just s. Int corridors. **Pets:** Small, other species. $10 daily fee/pet. Designated rooms, service with restrictions, crate. ♨ ♨ ♨ 🅱 ⊡

🆑 ▼▼ **Red Roof Inn San Diego - Pacific Beach/SeaWorld Area** Ⓜ
(858) 483-4222. **$59-$349.** 4545 Mission Bay Dr 92109. I-5 exit 23A (Grand Ave/Garnet Ave) northbound, 0.5 mi n; exit 23B (Balboa Ave/Garnet Ave) southbound, 0.3 mi s. Ext corridors. **Pets:** Accepted. 🆂🅰🆅🅴 ♨ ♨ ⊠ 🅱 ⊡

▼▼▼ **Renaissance San Diego Downtown Hotel** Ⓗ
(619) 398-3100. **$162-$304.** 421 W B St 92101. I-5 exit 17 (Front St/Civic Center) southbound, 0.6 mi s, then just w; exit 16B (6th Ave/Downtown) northbound, just s, then just w. Int corridors. **Pets:** Accepted. 🅲 ⏹ ♨ ♨ ♨ ⊠ 🅱 ⊡

▼▼▼ **Residence Inn by Marriott-San Diego Central** Ⓗ
(858) 278-2100. **$142-$279.** 5400 Kearny Mesa Rd 92111. SR 163 exit 8 (Clairemont Mesa Blvd) just w, then just n. Ext corridors. **Pets:** Medium. $100 deposit/room, $10 daily fee/room. Service with restrictions. 🅲 ♨ ♨ ♨ ⊠ 🅱 ⊡

🆑 ▼▼▼ **Residence Inn by Marriott San Diego/Del Mar** Ⓗ
(858) 481-8800. **$130-$236.** 3525 Valley Centre Dr 92130. I-5 exit 33 (Carmel Valley Rd), just ne. Int corridors. **Pets:** Large, other species. $150 one-time fee/room. Service with restrictions, supervision. 🆂🅰🆅🅴 ♨ ♨ ⊠ 🅱 ⊡

▼▼▼ **Residence Inn by Marriott San Diego Downtown** Ⓗ
(619) 338-8200. **$174-$341.** 1747 Pacific Hwy 92101. I-5 exit 17 (Front St/Civic Center) southbound, just s to Cedar St, 0.3 mi w, then just n; exit 17A (Hawthorn St/San Diego Airport) northbound, 0.4 mi w, then just s. Int corridors. **Pets:** Accepted. ⏹ ♨ ♨ ♨ ⊠ 🅱 ⊡

🆑 ▼▼▼ **Residence Inn by Marriott San Diego Downtown Bayfront** Ⓗ
(619) 831-0225. **$183-$321.** 900 Bayfront Ct 92101. I-5 exit 17 (Front St/Civic Center) southbound, 0.5 mi s to Ash St, then 0.5 mi on Pacific Hwy; exit 17A (Hawthorn St/San Diego Airport) northbound, 0.4 mi w to Ash St, then 0.5 mi s on Pacific Hwy. Int corridors. **Pets:** Medium. $100 one-time fee/room. Service with restrictions. 🆂🅰🆅🅴 ⏹ ♨ ♨ ⊠ 🅱 ⊡

▼▼▼ **Residence Inn by Marriott San Diego Downtown Gaslamp Quarter** Ⓗ
(619) 487-1200. **$150-$272.** 356 6th Ave 92101. I-5 exit 17 (Front St/Civic Center) southbound, 0.3 mi s, 0.3 mi e on A St, then 0.6 mi s; exit 16B (6th Ave/Downtown) northbound, 1 mi s. Int corridors. **Pets:** Medium, other species. $100 one-time fee/room. Service with restrictions, crate. ⏹ ♨ ♨ ♨ ⊠ 🅱 ⊡

▼▼▼ **Residence Inn by Marriott San Diego/Mission Valley** Ⓗ
(619) 881-3600. **$163-$262.** 1865 Hotel Cir S 92108. I-8 exit 4A (Hotel Cir S), just s. Int corridors. **Pets:** Accepted. ♨ ♨ ⊠ ♨ ⊠ 🅱 ⊡

🆑 ▼▼▼ **Residence Inn by Marriott San Diego Rancho Bernardo/Carmel Mountain Ranch** Ⓗ
(858) 673-1900. **$134-$252.** 11002 Rancho Carmel Dr 92128. I-15 exit 21 (Carmel Mountain Rd), just e, just s, then just w on Windcrest Ln. Ext/int corridors. **Pets:** Accepted. 🆂🅰🆅🅴 ♨ ♨ ⊠ ♨ ⊠ 🅱 ⊡

▼▼▼ **Residence Inn by Marriott San Diego Rancho Bernardo/Scripps Poway** Ⓗ
(858) 635-5724. **$133-$219.** 12011 Scripps Highlands Dr 92131. I-805 exit 17 (Mercy Rd/Scripps Poway Pkwy), just e, then just n. Int corridors. **Pets:** Accepted. ♨ ♨ ⊠ ♨ ⊠ 🅱 ⊡

🆑 ▼▼▼ **Residence Inn by Marriott San Diego Sorrento Mesa/Sorrento Valley** Ⓗ 🐾
(858) 552-9100. **$122-$257.** 5995 Pacific Mesa Ct 92121. I-805 exit 27 (Mira Mesa Blvd), 1.5 mi e, just n on Pacific Heights, then just se. Int corridors. **Pets:** $100 one-time fee/room. Service with restrictions. 🆂🅰🆅🅴 🅴🅲🅾 ⏹ ♨ ♨ ♨ ⊠ 🅱 ⊡

▼▼▼ **San Diego Marriott Del Mar** Ⓗ
(858) 523-1700. **$117-$240.** 11966 El Camino Real 92130. I-5 exit 33 (Carmel Valley Rd), just ne. Int corridors. **Pets:** Accepted. 🅴🅲🅾 ⏹ ♨ ♨ ♨ ⊠ 🅱 ⊡

AAA ▼▼▼ **Sheraton Mission Valley San Diego Hotel** H ❀

(619) 260-0111. **Call for rates.** 1433 Camino del Rio S 92108. I-8 exit 5 (Mission Center Rd), just s, then just e. Int corridors. **Pets:** Small, dogs only. $100 one-time fee/room. Service with restrictions, supervision. SAVE ⫶ ⅜M ⌦ 🛰 ✕ 🛏 💻

AAA ▼▼▼ **Sheraton San Diego Hotel & Marina** H ❀

(619) 291-2900. **$139-$699.** 1380 Harbor Island Dr 92101. I-5 exit 17 (Hawthorn St) northbound, just e to Harbor Dr, 1.5 mi w, then just s; exit 18A (Kettner Blvd/Hancock St) southbound, just s to Laurel St, just w to Harbor Dr, 1.5 mi w, then just s. Ext/int corridors. **Pets:** Medium, dogs only. $35 daily fee/pet. Designated rooms, supervision.
SAVE ECO ⊂ ⫶ ⅜M ⌦ ✕ 🛰 ✕ 🛏 💻

▼▼▼ **The Sofia Hotel** H

(619) 234-9200. **$139-$369.** 150 W Broadway 92101. I-5 exit 17 (Front St/Civic Center) southbound, 0.5 mi s, just w; exit 15B (Pershing Dr/Civic Center) northbound, 1 mi w to 3rd Ave, just s to Broadway, then just w. Int corridors. **Pets:** Accepted.
⫶ ⅜M ✕ 🛰 ✕ 🛏 💻

▼▼▼ **Sommerset Suites Hotel** H

(619) 692-5200. **Call for rates.** 606 Washington St 92103. SR 163 exit 2B (Washington St), just w. Ext/int corridors. **Pets:** Accepted.
⌦ 🛰 ✕ 🛏 💻

▼▼▼ **Staybridge Suites San Diego-Rancho Bernardo** H

(858) 487-0900. **Call for rates.** 11855 Ave of Industry 92128. I-15 exit 21 (Carmel Mountain Rd), 1 mi ne to second Rancho Carmel Dr, just w to Innovation Dr, just n, then just e. Int corridors. **Pets:** Accepted.
⫶ ⅜M ⌦ 🛰 🛏 💻

▼▼▼ **Staybridge Suites-Sorrento Mesa** H

(858) 453-5343. **Call for rates.** 6639 Mira Mesa Blvd 92121. I-805 exit 27 (Mira Mesa Blvd), 2.3 mi e. Int corridors. **Pets:** Accepted.
⅜M ⌦ 🛰 ✕ 🛏 💻

▼▼▼ **Town & Country Resort Hotel** H

(619) 291-7131. **Call for rates.** 500 Hotel Cir N 92108. I-8 exit 4A (Hotel Cir N), just n. Ext/int corridors. **Pets:** Accepted.
⫶ ⅜M ⌦ ✕ 🛰 ✕ 🛏 💻

AAA ▼▼▼ **The US Grant, A Luxury Collection Hotel, San Diego** H

(619) 232-3121. **$179-$799.** 326 Broadway 92101. I-5 exit 17 (Front St/Civic Center) southbound, 0.9 mi s to Broadway, then just e; exit 16B (6th Ave/Downtown) northbound, 0.6 mi s, then just w. Int corridors. **Pets:** Accepted. SAVE ECO ⫶ ⅜M 🛰 ✕ 🛏 💻

AAA ▼▼▼ **The Westin San Diego** H ❀

(619) 239-4500. **$189-$550.** 400 W Broadway 92101. I-5 exit 17 (Front St/Civic Center) southbound, 0.9 mi s, then just w; exit 16B (6th Ave/Downtown) northbound, 0.6 mi s, then just w. Int corridors.
Pets: Medium. Designated rooms, service with restrictions, crate.
SAVE ⫶ ⅜M ⌦ ✕ 🛰 ✕ 🛏 💻

AAA ▼▼▼ **The Westin San Diego Gaslamp Quarter** H ❀

(619) 239-2200. **$159-$799.** 910 Broadway Cir 92101. I-5 exit 17 (Front St/Civic Center) southbound, 0.9 mi s to Broadway, just e, then just s; exit 16B (6th Ave/Downtown) northbound, 0.6 mi s, just w, then just s. Int corridors. **Pets:** Medium, dogs only. Designated rooms, service with restrictions, supervision. SAVE ⫶ ⅜M ⌦ ✕ 🛰 ✕ 🛏 💻

AAA ▼▼▼ **Wyndham Garden San Diego near SeaWorld** H

(619) 881-6100. **$67-$299.** 3737 Sports Arena Blvd 92110. I-8 exit Sports Arena Blvd, 0.4 mi s. Ext corridors. **Pets:** Accepted.
SAVE ⫶ ⅜M ⌦ 🛰 ✕ 🛏 💻

AAA ▼▼▼ **Wyndham San Diego Bayside** H

(619) 232-3861. **$139-$304.** 1355 N Harbor Dr 92101. I-5 exit 17 (Hawthorn St/San Diego Airport) northbound, 0.4 mi w, then 0.4 mi s; exit 17 (Front St/Civic Center) southbound, 0.5 mi s to Ash St, then just w. Int corridors. **Pets:** Small. $100 deposit/pet. Designated rooms, service with restrictions, supervision. SAVE ECO ⫶ ⅜M ⌦ 🛰 ✕ 🛏 💻

SAN FRANCISCO *(Restaurants p. 601)*

AAA ▼▼▼▼ **The Argonaut** H

(415) 563-0800. **$249-$659, 3 day notice.** 495 Jefferson St 94109. Fisherman's Wharf; adjacent to The Cannery. Int corridors.
Pets: Accepted. SAVE ECO ⫶ ⅜M 🛰 ✕ 🛏 💻

AAA ▼▼▼ **Beresford Hotel** H

(415) 673-9900. **Call for rates.** 635 Sutter St 94102. 1 blk nw of Union Square at Mason St. Int corridors. **Pets:** Accepted.
SAVE ⫶ 🛰 🅰 🛏

AAA ▼▼▼ **Best Western Plus Americania** H

(415) 626-0200. **$149-$289.** 121 7th St 94103. Just s of Market St; between Mission and Howard sts. Ext corridors. **Pets:** Large, dogs only. $20 daily fee/room. Service with restrictions, supervision.
SAVE ⫶ ⅜M ⌦ 🛰 ✕ 🅰 🛏 💻

AAA ▼▼▼ **The Buchanan** H

(415) 921-4000. **$125-$505.** 1800 Sutter St 94115. At Sutter and Buchanan sts; 1 blk from Japan Center. Int corridors. **Pets:** Accepted.
SAVE ⊂ ⫶ ⅜M 🛰 ✕ 🛏 💻

AAA ▼▼▼ **Executive Hotel Vintage Court** H ❀

(415) 392-4666. **Call for rates.** 650 Bush St 94108. Between Powell and Stockton sts; 2 blks n of Union Square. Int corridors. **Pets:** $25 daily fee/pet. Designated rooms, service with restrictions, supervision.
SAVE 🛰 ✕ 🛏 💻

AAA ▼▼▼ **The Fairmont San Francisco** H

(415) 772-5000. **$219-$1449.** 950 Mason St (atop Nob Hill) 94108. Atop Nob Hill at California St. Int corridors. **Pets:** Accepted.
SAVE ECO ⊂ ⫶ ⅜M ✕ 🛰 ✕ 🛏 💻

AAA ▼▼▼ **Four Seasons Hotel San Francisco** H

(415) 633-3000. **Call for rates.** 757 Market St 94103. Between 3rd and 4th sts. Int corridors. **Pets:** Small, other species. $125 one-time fee/room. Designated rooms, service with restrictions, crate.
SAVE ⫶ ⅜M ⌦ ✕ 🛰 ✕ 🛏 💻

AAA ▼▼▼ **Galleria Park Hotel, a Joie de Vivre hotel** H ❀

(415) 781-3060. **$159-$699.** 191 Sutter St 94104. 2 blks ne of Union Square; between Kearny and Trinity sts. Int corridors. **Pets:** Dogs only. Designated rooms, service with restrictions, crate.
SAVE ECO ⫶ ⅜M 🛰 ✕ 🛏 💻

AAA ▼▼▼ **Good Hotel** H

(415) 621-7001. **$109-$349.** 112 7th St 94103. Just s of Market St; at Mission St. Int corridors. **Pets:** Large, dogs only. $20 daily fee/room. Service with restrictions, supervision. SAVE ⅜M 🛰 ✕ 🛏 💻

AAA ▼▼▼ **Grand Hyatt San Francisco** H

(415) 398-1234. **$189-$679.** 345 Stockton St 94108. At Sutter St. Int corridors. **Pets:** Accepted. SAVE ECO ⫶ ⅜M 🛰 ✕ 🛏 💻

AAA ▼▼▼ **The Handlery Union Square Hotel** H ❀

(415) 781-7800. **$189-$799.** 351 Geary St 94102. Between Powell and Mason sts; just sw of Union Square. Int corridors. **Pets:** Medium, dogs only. $250 deposit/room, $25 daily fee/pet. Service with restrictions, supervision. SAVE ECO ⫶ ⅜M 🛰 ✕ 🛏 💻

Harbor Court Hotel H
(415) 882-1300. **Call for rates.** 165 Steuart St 94105. On Embarcadero; between Howard and Mission sts. Int corridors. **Pets:** Accepted.

Hilton Parc 55 San Francisco H
(415) 392-8000. **$159-$499.** 55 Cyril Magnin St 94102. Corner of Cyril Magnin and Eddy sts; just sw of Union Square. Int corridors.
Pets: Accepted.

Hilton San Francisco Financial District H
(415) 433-6600. **$179-$379.** 750 Kearny St 94108. Between Clay and Washington sts. Int corridors. **Pets:** Accepted.

Hilton San Francisco Union Square H
(415) 771-1400. **$159-$499.** 333 O'Farrell St 94102. Just w of Mason and O'Farrell sts. Int corridors. **Pets:** Other species. $50 one-time fee/room. Service with restrictions, supervision.

Holiday Inn Civic Center H
(415) 626-6103. **Call for rates.** 50 8th St 94103. Between Market and Mission sts. Int corridors. **Pets:** Accepted.

Holiday Inn Golden Gateway H
(415) 441-4000. **$159-$399.** 1500 Van Ness Ave 94109. US 101 (Van Ness Ave) at Pine St. Int corridors. **Pets:** Accepted.

Hotel Abri H
(415) 392-8800. **Call for rates.** 127 Ellis St 94102. Just w of Union Square at Mason St. Int corridors. **Pets:** Accepted.

Hotel Adagio, Autograph Collection H
(415) 775-5000. **$159-$406.** 550 Geary St 94102. 2 blks w of Union Square; between Jones and Taylor sts. Int corridors. **Pets:** Accepted.

Hotel Bijou H
(415) 771-1200. **$89-$459.** 111 Mason St 94102. Just n of Market St; between Eddy and Ellis sts. Int corridors. **Pets:** Accepted.

Hotel Carlton, a Joie de Vivre hotel H
(415) 673-0242. **$119-$599, 3 day notice.** 1075 Sutter St 94109. 0.5 mi w of Union Square; between Hyde and Larkin sts. Int corridors.
Pets: Accepted.

Hotel Del Sol, a Joie de Vivre hotel M ☙
(415) 921-5520. **Call for rates.** 3100 Webster St 94123. Just s of Lombard St at Greenwich St. Ext corridors. **Pets:** Medium. Service with restrictions, supervision.

Hotel Diva H
(415) 885-0200. **Call for rates.** 440 Geary St 94102. Between Taylor and Mason sts; on Theater Row. Int corridors. **Pets:** Accepted.

Hotel Kabuki, a Joie de Vivre Hotel H ☙
(415) 922-3200. **$99-$729.** 1625 Post St 94115. Jct Laguna St; in Japan Center. Int corridors. **Pets:** Medium, other species. Designated rooms, service with restrictions, supervision.

Hotel Nikko San Francisco H
(415) 394-1111. **Call for rates.** 222 Mason St 94102. At O'Farrell St. Int corridors. **Pets:** Accepted.

Hotel Rex, a Joie de Vivre hotel H
(415) 433-4434. **Call for rates.** 562 Sutter St 94102. Just nw of Union Square; between Mason and Powell sts. Int corridors. **Pets:** Accepted.

Hotel Triton H ☙
(415) 394-0500. **$139-$599.** 342 Grant Ave 94108. Near Union Square at Bush St. Int corridors. **Pets:** $75 one-time fee/room. Service with restrictions, supervision.

Hotel Union Square H ☙
(415) 397-3000. **Call for rates.** 114 Powell St 94102. At Ellis St; just n of cable car turnaround. Int corridors. **Pets:** Small, dogs only. $50 one-time fee/room. Service with restrictions, supervision.

Hotel Vitale, a Joie de Vivre hotel H
(415) 278-3700. **Call for rates.** 8 Mission St 94105. At The Embarcadero and Mission St. Int corridors. **Pets:** Accepted.

HOTEL ZELOS H ☙
(415) 348-1111. **$220-$599.** 12 4th St 94103. At Market St. Int corridors. **Pets:** Other species. $75 one-time fee/room. Service with restrictions, crate.

Hotel Zephyr H
(415) 617-6565. **Call for rates.** 250 Beach St 94133. At Powell St. Int corridors. **Pets:** Accepted.

Hotel Zeppelin San Francisco H ☙
(415) 563-0303. **$199-$999.** 545 Post St 94102. Just w of Union Square. Int corridors. **Pets:** Other species. $75 one-time fee/room. Service with restrictions.

Hotel Zetta H ☙
(415) 543-8555. **Call for rates.** 55 5th St 94103. Between 4th and 5th sts. Int corridors. **Pets:** Other species. $75 one-time fee/room. Service with restrictions.

Hyatt Centric Fisherman's Wharf H
(415) 563-1234. **$159-$509.** 555 North Point St 94133. Just s of Fisherman's Wharf at Taylor St. Int corridors. **Pets:** Accepted.

Hyatt Regency San Francisco H
(415) 788-1234. **$169-$759.** 5 Embarcadero Center 94111. Foot of California and Market sts; in Financial District. Int corridors. **Pets:** Accepted.

InterContinental Mark Hopkins San Francisco H
(415) 392-3434. **Call for rates.** One Nob Hill 94108. Corner of California and Mason sts. Int corridors. **Pets:** Accepted.

InterContinental San Francisco H ☙
(415) 616-6500. **$199-$999.** 888 Howard St 94103. Between 4th and 5th sts; in SoMa District. Int corridors. **Pets:** Small, dogs only. $50 one-time fee/pet. Service with restrictions, supervision.

JW Marriott San Francisco H
(415) 771-8600. **$207-$431.** 515 Mason St 94102. Just w of Union Square at Mason St. Int corridors. **Pets:** Accepted.

Kensington Park Hotel H
(415) 788-6400. **$189-$599.** 450 Post St 94102. Just w of Union Square. Int corridors. **Pets:** Small. $75 one-time fee/pet. Service with restrictions, supervision.

▼▼ Laurel Inn, a Joie de Vivre hotel 🅷 ☼
(415) 567-8467. **$199-$499.** 444 Presidio Ave 94115. At California St. Int corridors. **Pets:** Large. Designated rooms, service with restrictions, supervision. 🌌Ⓜ 🛜 ✖ 🎟 🔋 💻

▼▼▼ Le Meridien San Francisco 🅷 🐾
(415) 296-2900. **$199-$999.** 333 Battery St 94111. Just s of Clay and Battery sts; in Financial District. Int corridors. **Pets:** Other species. Service with restrictions, supervision. ⒺⒸⓄ 🍴 🌌Ⓜ 🛜 ✖ 🔋 💻

▲▲▲ ▼▼ ▼▼ Loews Regency San Francisco 🅷 ☼
(415) 276-9888. **Call for rates.** 222 Sansome St 94104. Between Pine and California sts; in Financial District. Int corridors. **Pets:** Medium, other species. $100 one-time fee/room. Designated rooms, service with restrictions. 🅢🅐🆅🅔 🍴 🌌Ⓜ 🛜 ✖ 🔋

▼▼ Marina Motel Ⓜ
(415) 921-9406. **Call for rates.** 2576 Lombard St 94123. Between Broderick and Divisadero sts. Ext/int corridors. **Pets:** Accepted.
🛜 ✖ 🎟 🔋 💻

▼▼▼ The Marker San Francisco 🅷
(415) 292-0100. **Call for rates.** 501 Geary St 94102. Just w of Union Square at Taylor St. Int corridors. **Pets:** Accepted.
ⒺⒸⓄ 🍴 🌌Ⓜ ✖ 🛜 ✖ 🔋

▲▲▲ ▼▼ ▼▼ Omni San Francisco Hotel 🅷 ☼
(415) 677-9494. **$225-$2000.** 500 California St 94104. At Montgomery St; in Financial District. Int corridors. **Pets:** Small. $50 one-time fee/room. Service with restrictions, crate.
🅢🅐🆅🅔 🍴 🌌Ⓜ 🕊 ✖ 🔋 💻

▲▲▲ ▼▼ ▼▼ Palace Hotel, A Luxury Collection 🅷
(415) 512-1111. **$239-$1800.** 2 New Montgomery St 94105. Just e of Union Square; at Market St. Int corridors. **Pets:** Accepted.
🅢🅐🆅🅔 🍴 🌌Ⓜ 🐾 🕊 ✖ 🔋 💻

▲▲▲ ▼▼ ▼▼ Park Central Hotel San Francisco 🅷
(415) 974-6400. **$159-$699.** 50 3rd St 94103. Just n of Moscone Convention Center; between Jessie and Stevenson sts. Int corridors.
Pets: Accepted. 🅢🅐🆅🅔 ⒺⒸⓄ 🍴 🌌Ⓜ ✖ 🕊 ✖ 🔋 💻

▲▲▲ ▼▼ ▼▼ The Ritz-Carlton, San Francisco 🅷 ☼
(415) 296-7465. **Call for rates.** 600 Stockton St 94108. Just n of Union Square at California st. Int corridors. **Pets:** Small, dogs only. $125 one-time fee/room. Service with restrictions, supervision.
🅢🅐🆅🅔 ⒺⒸⓄ 🍴 🌌Ⓜ ✖ 🕊 ✖ 🔋 💻

▲▲▲ ▼▼ ▼▼ The St. Regis San Francisco 🅷 ☼
(415) 284-4000. **$425-$995.** 125 3rd St 94103. At Mission St. Int corridors. **Pets:** Small, dogs only. $150 one-time fee/pet. Service with restrictions, supervision. 🅢🅐🆅🅔 🍴 🌌Ⓜ 🐾 ✖ 🛜 ✖ 🔋

▲▲▲ ▼▼▼ San Francisco Marriott Fisherman's Wharf 🅷 ☼
(415) 775-7555. **$189-$380.** 1250 Columbus Ave 94133. Just s of Fisherman's Wharf at Bay St. Int corridors. **Pets:** $100 one-time fee/room. Designated rooms, service with restrictions, supervision.
🅢🅐🆅🅔 🍴 🌌Ⓜ 🕊 🔋 💻

▼▼▼ Serrano Hotel 🅷
(415) 885-2500. **$259-$899, 3 day notice.** 405 Taylor St 94102. Just w of Union Square at O'Farrell St. Int corridors. **Pets:** Accepted.
ⒺⒸⓄ 🍴 🌌Ⓜ ✖ 🕊 ✖ 🔋

▲▲▲ ▼▼▼ Sheraton Fisherman's Wharf 🅷
(415) 362-5500. **$159-$2000.** 2500 Mason St 94133. Just se of Fisherman's Wharf at Beach St. Int corridors. **Pets:** Accepted.
🅢🅐🆅🅔 ⒺⒸⓄ 🍴 🌌Ⓜ 🐾 🕊 ✖ 🔋 💻

▲▲▲ ▼▼ ▼▼ Sir Francis Drake Hotel, a Kimpton Hotel 🅷 ☼
(415) 392-7755. **Call for rates.** 450 Powell St 94102. Just n of Union Square at Sutter St. Int corridors. **Pets:** Other species. Designated rooms, supervision. 🅢🅐🆅🅔 ⒺⒸⓄ 🍴 🌌Ⓜ ✖ 🛜 ✖ 🔋 💻

▲▲▲ ▼▼ ▼▼ Stanford Court Hotel 🅷 ☼
(415) 989-3500. **$199-$1399.** 905 California St 94108. Atop Nob Hill; corner of California and Powell sts. Int corridors. **Pets:** Small, dogs only. $50 one-time fee/room. Supervision.
🅢🅐🆅🅔 ⒺⒸⓄ 🈂 🍴 ✖ 🛜 ✖ 🔋 💻

▼▼ ▼▼ Taj Campton Place 🅷
(415) 781-5555. **Call for rates.** 340 Stockton St 94108. Just n of Union Square; jct Sutter St. Int corridors. **Pets:** Accepted.
ⒺⒸⓄ 🍴 🌌Ⓜ 🛜 ✖ 🔋 💻

▲▲▲ ▼▼ ▼▼ Tilden Hotel 🅷
(415) 673-2332. **$199-$699.** 345 Taylor St 94102. Just w of Union Square. Int corridors. **Pets:** Accepted.
🅢🅐🆅🅔 ⒺⒸⓄ 🍴 🌌Ⓜ 🛜 ✖ 🎟 🔋 💻

▼▼ ▼▼ Travelodge at the Presidio Ⓜ
(415) 931-8581. **$92-$309.** 2755 Lombard St 94123. Between Lyon and Baker sts. Ext corridors. **Pets:** Medium. $20 daily fee/pet. Supervision.
🌌Ⓜ 🛜 ✖ 🔋 💻

▲▲▲ ▼▼ ▼▼ The Tuscan 🅷
(415) 561-1100. **$279-$559.** 425 Northpoint St 94133. Just s of Fisherman's Wharf at Mason St. Int corridors. **Pets:** Accepted.
🅢🅐🆅🅔 ⒺⒸⓄ 🍴 🌌Ⓜ 🛜 ✖ 🔋 💻

▲▲▲ ▼▼ ▼▼ The Westin St. Francis San Francisco on Union Square 🅷 ☼
(415) 397-7000. **$229-$999.** 335 Powell St 94102. Across from Union Square. Int corridors. **Pets:** Medium, dogs only. Service with restrictions, crate. 🅢🅐🆅🅔 🍴 🌌Ⓜ ✖ 🕊 ✖ 🔋 💻

▲▲▲ ▼▼ ▼▼ W San Francisco 🅷
(415) 777-5300. **$225-$575, 3 day notice.** 181 3rd St 94103. At Howard St. Int corridors. **Pets:** Accepted.
🅢🅐🆅🅔 ⒺⒸⓄ 🍴 🌌Ⓜ 🐾 ✖ 🕊 ✖ 🔋 💻

SAN GABRIEL

▲▲▲ ▼▼ ▼▼ Hilton Los Angeles/San Gabriel 🅷
(626) 270-2700. **$179-$359.** 225 W Valley Blvd 91776. I-10 exit 24 (New Ave), 0.6 mi n, then 0.3 mi e. Int corridors. **Pets:** Accepted.
🅢🅐🆅🅔 🍴 🌌Ⓜ 🐾 ✖ 🛜 🔋 💻

SANGER

▼▼ Wonder Valley Ranch Resort & Conference Center 🆁🅐
(559) 787-2551. **$149-$278.** 6450 Elwood Rd 93657. Jct SR 180 and N Piedra Rd, 8 mi ne to Elwood Rd, then 5.5 mi e. Ext corridors.
Pets: Small, dogs only. $25 daily fee/pet. Designated rooms, service with restrictions, crate. 🍴 🌌Ⓜ 🐾 ✖ 🛜 ✖ 🔋 💻

SAN JOSE *(Restaurants p. 601)*

▲▲▲ ▼▼ ▼▼ Aloft San Jose Cupertino 🅷
(408) 864-0300. **Call for rates.** 4241 Moorpark Ave 95129. I-280 exit Saratoga Ave, just s, then just w. Int corridors. **Pets:** Accepted.
🅢🅐🆅🅔 🍴 🌌Ⓜ 🐾 ✖ 🔋 💻

▲▲▲ ▼▼ ▼▼ Aloft Santa Clara 🅷
(408) 263-3900. **Call for rates.** 510 America Center Ct 95002. US 101 exit 396B, 3.3 mi e on SR 237 exit 6 (Great America Pkwy), 0.3 mi n, then just n. Int corridors. **Pets:** Accepted.
🅢🅐🆅🅔 🍴 🛜 ✖ 🔋 💻

AAA ▼▼▼▼ DoubleTree by Hilton Hotel San Jose H
(408) 453-4000. **$135-$499.** 2050 Gateway Pl 95110. 0.3 mi e of Norman Y. Mineta San Jose International Airport via Airport Blvd; w of US 101 exit N 1st St; US 101 exit Brokaw Rd northbound. Int corridors.
Pets: Accepted. 🅢🅐🅥🅔 ECO �️ ⬆M ⊶ 🛜 ✖ 🔋 🖥

AAA ▼▼▼▼ The Fairmont San Jose H
(408) 998-1900. **Call for rates.** 170 S Market St 95113. At Fairmont Plaza. Int corridors. **Pets:** Accepted.
SAVE ECO ⬛ ⏹ ⬆M ⊶ ✖ 🛜 ✖ 🖥

▼▼▼ Hilton San Jose H
(408) 287-2100. **$129-$459.** 300 Almaden Blvd 95110. SR 87 exit Santa Clara St E, 0.4 mi s; at W San Carlos St. Int corridors. **Pets:** Accepted.
⏹ ⬆M ⊶ 🛜 ✖ 🔋 🖥

AAA ▼▼▼ Hotel De Anza H
(408) 286-1000. **$109-$599.** 233 W Santa Clara St 95113. SR 87 exit Santa Clara St, just e. Int corridors. **Pets:** Accepted.
SAVE ⏹ ⬆M 🛜 ✖ 🔋 🖥

AAA ▼▼▼▼ Hyatt House San Jose/Silicon Valley H
(408) 324-1155. **$109-$459.** 75 Headquarters Dr 95134. SR 237 exit N 1st St, just s, then just e. Int corridors. **Pets:** Accepted.
SAVE ⬆M ⊶ 🛜 ✖ 🔋 🖥

AAA ▼▼▼▼ Hyatt Place San Jose/Downtown H
(408) 998-0400. **$129-$499.** 282 Almaden Blvd 95113. I-280 exit Almaden-Vine, 6 blks n. Int corridors. **Pets:** Accepted.
SAVE ⏹ ⬆M 🛜 ✖ 🔋 🖥

AAA ▼▼▼▼ La Quinta Inn & Suites San Jose Airport H
(408) 435-8800. **$104-$383.** 2585 Seaboard Ave 95131. US 101 exit Trimble Rd E; 1 mi ne of Norman Y. Mineta San Jose International Airport. Int corridors. **Pets:** Accepted. ⬆M ⊶ 🛜 ✖ 🔋 🖥

▼▼▼▼ Residence Inn by Marriott San Jose Airport H
(408) 650-0580. **$125-$326.** 10 Skyport Dr 95110. SR 87 exit Skyport Dr, just e. Int corridors. **Pets:** Medium, other species. $75 one-time fee/room. Service with restrictions, crate.
⏹ ⬆M 🛜 ✖ 🔋 🖥

▼▼▼▼ Residence Inn by Marriott San Jose South H
(408) 226-7676. **$119-$261.** 6111 San Ignacio Ave 95119. US 101 exit Bernal Rd, 0.7 w, then just n. Int corridors. **Pets:** Accepted.
⬆M ⊶ 🛜 ✖ 🔋 🖥

AAA ▼▼▼▼ San Jose Marriott H
(408) 280-1300. **$129-$395.** 301 S Market St 95113. SR 87 exit Santa Clara St E, s on Almaden Blvd, then just e on San Carlos St. Int corridors. **Pets:** Accepted. SAVE ECO ⏹ ⬆M ⊶ 🛜 ✖ 🔋 🖥

▼▼▼▼ Staybridge Suites San Jose H
(408) 436-1600. **Call for rates.** 1602 Crane Ct 95112. US 101 exit 1st St/Brokaw Rd, 0.4 mi e to Bering Dr, then 0.5 mi s. Ext/int corridors.
Pets: Accepted. ⬆M ⊶ 🛜 🔋 🖥

▼▼▼▼ TownePlace Suites by Marriott San Jose/Cupertino H
(408) 984-5903. **$143-$316.** 440 Saratoga Ave 95129. I-280 exit Saratoga Ave, just n. Int corridors. **Pets:** Accepted.
⏹ ⬆M ⊶ 🛜 ✖ 🔋 🖥

AAA ▼▼▼▼ The Westin San Jose H
(408) 295-2000. **$149-$459.** 302 S Market St 95113. SR 87 exit Santa Clara St E, s on Almaden Blvd, just e on San Carlos St. Int corridors.
Pets: Accepted. SAVE ECO ⏹ ⬆M 🛜 ✖ 🔋 🖥

SAN JUAN CAPISTRANO
(Restaurants p. 601)

AAA ▼▼ Best Western Capistrano Inn M 🐾
(949) 493-5661. **$100-$180.** 27174 Ortega Hwy 92675. I-5 exit 82 (SR 74/Ortega Hwy), just e. Ext corridors. **Pets:** Medium. $10 daily fee/pet. Service with restrictions. SAVE ⊶ 🛜 ✖ 🔋 🖥

AAA ▼▼▼▼ Residence Inn by Marriott Dana Pointe/San Juan Capistrano H
(949) 443-3600. **$138-$267.** 33711 Camino Capistrano 92675. I-5 exit 81 (Camino Capistrano), 1.3 mi s. Int corridors. **Pets:** Accepted.
SAVE ⏹ ⊶ 🛜 ✖ 🔋 🖥

SAN LUIS OBISPO *(Restaurants p. 601)*

AAA ▼▼▼▼ Best Western Plus Royal Oak Hotel H
(805) 544-4410. **$109-$359, 3 day notice.** 214 Madonna Rd 93405. US 101 exit 201 (Madonna Rd), just s. Ext/int corridors. **Pets:** Large. $20 daily fee/pet. Designated rooms, service with restrictions, supervision.
SAVE ⬆M ⊶ 🛜 ✖ 🔋 🖥

▼▼▼ Garden Street Inn Bed & Breakfast BB
(805) 545-9802. **$179-$299.** 1212 Garden St 93401. US 101 exit 202A (Marsh St), 0.5 mi e; downtown. Int corridors. **Pets:** Dogs only. $20 one-time fee/room. Designated rooms, service with restrictions, crate.
🛜 ✖

▼▼▼ Petit Soleil Bed & Breakfast BB
(805) 549-0321. **$179-$299, 3 day notice.** 1473 Monterey St 93401. US 101 exit 204 (Monterey St), 0.3 mi sw. Ext corridors. **Pets:** Other species. $25 one-time fee/room. Service with restrictions, supervision.
🛜 ✖ 🐾

AAA ▼▼▼ Ramada Inn Olive Tree M
(805) 544-2800. **$59-$269.** 1000 Olive St 93405. US 101 exit 203A (Santa Rosa St) southbound, just ne; exit 203B (SR 1/Morro Bay) northbound, just w on Santa Rosa St, then just s. Ext corridors.
Pets: Small, dogs only. $15 daily fee/pet. Designated rooms, service with restrictions, supervision. SAVE ⊶ 🛜 ✖ 🔋 🖥

AAA ▼▼▼ Rose Garden Inn M
(805) 544-5300. **$69-$319.** 1585 Calle Joaquin 93401. US 101 exit 200 (Los Osos Valley Rd), just w, then just s. Int corridors. **Pets:** Accepted.
SAVE ⬆M 🛜 ✖ 🔋 🖥

AAA ▼▼▼ Sands Inn & Suites M 🐾
(805) 544-0500. **$89-$399.** 1930 Monterey St 93401. US 101 exit 204 (Monterey St), just sw. Ext corridors. **Pets:** Other species. $25 one-time fee/pet. Service with restrictions, supervision. SAVE 🛜 🔋 🖥

▼▼▼ San Luis Creek Lodge H
(805) 541-1122. **Call for rates.** 1941 Monterey St 93401. US 101 exit 204 (Monterey St), just e. Ext/int corridors. **Pets:** Accepted.
⬆M 🛜 ✖ 🔋 🖥

▼▼ Super 8 M
(805) 544-6888. **$79-$299.** 1951 Monterey St 93401. US 101 exit 204 (Monterey St), just e. Ext corridors. **Pets:** Accepted.
⊶ 🛜 ✖ 🔋 🖥

SAN MARCOS
▼▼▼ Residence Inn by Marriott San Diego North/San Marcos H
(760) 591-9828. **$126-$219.** 1245 Los Vallecitos Blvd 92069. SR 78 exit 11B (Las Posas Rd), just ne. Int corridors. **Pets:** Accepted.
ECO ⏹ ⬆M ⊶ 🛜 ✖ 🔋 🖥

SAN MATEO *(Restaurants p. 601)*
▼▼▼ Residence Inn by Marriott H
(650) 574-4700. **$183-$312, 3 day notice.** 2000 Winward Way 94404. US 101 exit 414B (SR 92/E Hayward/Fashion Island), just e to Mariners Island Blvd, exit 14A, just e. Ext corridors. **Pets:** Accepted.
⏹ ⬆M ⊶ 🛜 ✖ 🔋 🖥

SAN RAFAEL

▼▼ **Extended Stay America-San Rafael-Francisco Blvd** E �H

(415) 451-1887. **$140-$230.** 1775 Francisco Blvd E 94901. US 101 exit 451 (I-580/Richmond Br/Oakland) northbound; exit 451B (I-580/Richmond/Oakland) southbound, just e on Bellam Blvd, then 1 mi s. Int corridors. **Pets:** Accepted. 🍴 ⛴ 🛜 🗙 🗄 💻

SAN RAMON

Hyatt House San Ramon �H

(925) 743-1882. **$104-$379.** 2323 San Ramon Valley Blvd 94583. I-680 exit 36 (Crow Canyon Rd), just w, then just n. Int corridors. **Pets:** Medium. $175 one-time fee/room. Designated rooms, service with restrictions, crate. 🆂🅰🆅🅴 ⛴ 🛜 🗙 🗄 💻

▼▼▼ **Residence Inn by Marriott** �H

(925) 277-9292. **$150-$285.** 1071 Market Pl 94583. I-680 exit 34 (Bollinger Canyon Rd), 0.5 mi e. Ext corridors. **Pets:** Large, other species. $100 one-time fee/room. Service with restrictions, crate. 🅴🅲🅾 ⛴ 🛜 🗙 🗄 💻

San Ramon Marriott �H

(925) 867-9200. **$104-$329.** 2600 Bishop Dr 94583. I-680 exit 34 (Bollinger Canyon Rd), just e, n on Sunset Dr, then just w. Int corridors. **Pets:** Accepted. 🆂🅰🆅🅴 🅴🅲🅾 🍴 ⛴ 🗙 🗄 💻

SAN SIMEON

Cavalier Oceanfront Resort �H

(805) 927-4688. **$139-$349, 3 day notice.** 9415 Hearst Dr 93452. Just w of SR 1. Ext corridors. **Pets:** Accepted. 🆂🅰🆅🅴 🍴 ⛴ 🛜 🗙 🗄 💻

▼▼▼ **The Morgan San Simeon** �H

(805) 927-3878. **Call for rates.** 9135 Hearst Dr 93452. Just w of SR 1. Int corridors. **Pets:** Accepted. ⛴ 🛜 🗙 🗄 💻

▼▼ **Sands by the Sea** 🄼 🐾

(805) 927-4668. **$59-$239, 3 day notice.** 9355 Hearst Dr 93452. Just w of SR 1. Ext corridors. **Pets:** Large, dogs only. Service with restrictions, supervision. ⛴ 🛜 🗙 🗄 💻

San Simeon Lodge �H 🐾

(805) 927-4601. **$59-$349, 3 day notice.** 9520 Castillo Dr 93452. Just e of SR 1. Ext corridors. **Pets:** Small, dogs only. $15 daily fee/pet. Designated rooms, service with restrictions, supervision. 🆂🅰🆅🅴 🍴 ⛴ 🛜 🗙 🗄 💻

Silver Surf Motel 🄼

(805) 927-4661. **$69-$289.** 9390 Castillo Dr 93452. Just e of SR 1. Ext corridors. **Pets:** Accepted. 🆂🅰🆅🅴 ⛴ 🛜 🗙 🗄 💻

SANTA ANA *(Restaurants p. 602)*

▼▼▼ **La Quinta Inn & Suites Orange County-Santa Ana** 🄼

(714) 540-1111. **$79-$229.** 2721 Hotel Terrace 92705. SR 55 exit 8 (Dyer Rd) northbound; exit 8B southbound, just w, then just s. Ext corridors. **Pets:** Accepted. ⛴ 🗄 💻

SANTA BARBARA *(Restaurants p. 602)*

Bacara Resort & Spa �H

(805) 968-0100. **$400-$700, 3 day notice.** 8301 Hollister Ave 93117. US 101, exit Winchester Canyon Rd northbound, just w, Calle Rd just w, then 0.5 mi n. Ext/int corridors. **Pets:** Accepted. 🆂🅰🆅🅴 🍴 ⛴ 🗙 🛜 🗙 🗄 💻

Best Western Beachside Inn 🄼

(805) 965-6556. **$200-$450.** 336 W Cabrillo Blvd 93101. US 101 exit 96 (Garden St) northbound, just w; exit 97 (Castillo St) southbound, 0.3 mi w to Cabrillo Blvd, then 0.5 mi n; corner of Cabrillo Blvd and Castillo St. Ext corridors. **Pets:** Accepted. 🆂🅰🆅🅴 ⛴ 🛜 🗙 🗄 💻

▼▼ **Blue Sands Motel** 🄼

(805) 965-1624. **$105-$300, 3 day notice.** 421 S Milpas St 93103. US 101 exit 96A (Milpas St), 0.3 mi s. Ext corridors. **Pets:** Accepted. ⛴ 🛜 🗙 🗄 💻

▼ **Extended Stay America Santa Barbara-Calle Real** �H

(805) 692-1882. **$125-$195.** 4870 Calle Real 93111. US 101 exit Turnpike Rd, just e, then just n. Int corridors. **Pets:** Accepted. ⛴ 🛜 🗄

The Fess Parker, A DoubleTree by Hilton Resort �H

(805) 564-4333. **$169-$539.** 633 E Cabrillo Blvd 93103. US 101 exit 96A (Milpas St), just s, then just w. Ext/int corridors. **Pets:** Accepted. 🆂🅰🆅🅴 🅴🅲🅾 🍴 ⛴ 🗙 🛜 🗙 🗄 💻

▼▼▼ **Holiday Inn Express-Hotel Virginia** �H 🐾

(805) 963-9757. **Call for rates.** 17 W Haley St 93101. US 101 exit 97 (Bath St) northbound; exit 97 (Castillo St) southbound, just n, then just e. Int corridors. **Pets:** Medium. $45 one-time fee/room. Designated rooms, service with restrictions, supervision. ⛴ 🛜 🗙 🗄 💻

Hyatt Centric Santa Barbara �H

(805) 882-1234. **$139-$549, 3 day notice.** 1111 E Cabrillo Blvd 93103. US 101 exit 96A (Milpas St), 0.3 mi s, then just e. Int corridors. **Pets:** Accepted. 🆂🅰🆅🅴 🍴 ⛴ 🗙 🛜 🗙 🗄 💻

▼▼▼ **La Quinta Inn & Suites Santa Barbara** 🄼

(805) 966-0807. **$163-$471.** 1601 State St 93101. US 101 exit 99 (Mission St), 0.4 mi e, then 0.3 mi s. Ext corridors. **Pets:** Accepted. ⛴ 🛜 🗙 🗄 💻

▼▼▼ **Marina Beach Motel** 🄼

(805) 963-9311. **$135-$351.** 21 Bath St 93101. US 101 exit 96B (Garden St), 0.3 mi w to Cabrillo Blvd, 0.4 mi n to Bath St, then just e. Ext corridors. **Pets:** $15 daily fee/pet. Designated rooms, service with restrictions, supervision. 🛜 🗙 🗄 💻

▼▼▼ **Pacifica Suites** �H

(805) 683-6722. **$189-$499.** 5490 Hollister Ave 93111. US 101 exit 104A (Patterson Ave), 0.5 mi w, then 0.5 mi n. Ext/int corridors. **Pets:** Medium, dogs only. $75 one-time fee/room. Designated rooms, service with restrictions, supervision. ⛴ 🛜 🗙 🗄 💻

SANTA CLARA

Avatar Hotel Great America �H 🐾

(408) 235-8900. **$109-$369.** 4200 Great America Pkwy 95054. 0.5 mi e off US 101 exit Great America Pkwy; 0.8 mi s of California's Great America theme park. Ext corridors. **Pets:** Medium, dogs only. $75 one-time fee/room. Designated rooms, service with restrictions, supervision. 🆂🅰🆅🅴 🅴🅲🅾 🍴 ⛴ 🛜 🗙 🗄 💻

Biltmore Hotel & Suites/Silicon Valley �H

(408) 988-8411. **$239-$399.** 2151 Laurelwood Rd 95054. US 101 exit Montague Expwy, just e; 1 mi s of Great America Pkwy. Ext/int corridors. **Pets:** Accepted. 🆂🅰🆅🅴 🍴 ⛴ 🛜 🗙 🗄 💻

▼▼▼ **Candlewood Suites-Silicon Valley/San Jose** �H

(408) 241-9305. **Call for rates.** 481 El Camino Real 95050. I-880 exit The Alameda, 1.5 mi w; enter from Railroad Ave. Int corridors. **Pets:** Accepted. ⛴ 🛜 🗙 🗄 💻

Hilton Santa Clara �H 🐾

(408) 330-0001. **Call for rates.** 4949 Great America Pkwy 95054. US 101 exit Great America Pkwy, 0.5 mi n. Int corridors. **Pets:** Large. $50 one-time fee/room. Service with restrictions, supervision. 🆂🅰🆅🅴 🅴🅲🅾 🍴 ⛴ 🛜 🗄 💻

Hyatt House Santa Clara �H

(408) 486-0800. **$129-$479.** 3915 Rivermark Plaza 95054. US 101 exit Montague Expwy, 1 mi e. Int corridors. **Pets:** Medium. $175 one-time fee/room. Service with restrictions, crate. 🆂🅰🆅🅴 🍴 ⛴ 🛜 🗙 🗄 💻

◭◭◭ ▼▼▼ Hyatt Regency Santa Clara 🄷
(408) 200-1234. **$99-$1500.** 5101 Great America Pkwy 95054. US 101 exit Great America Pkwy, 0.8 mi e. Int corridors. **Pets:** Accepted.
[SAVE] 🍴 🛦ᴹ 🛥 🛜 ⊠ 🛄 🖵

◭◭◭ ▼▼ Quality Inn & Suites Silicon Valley 🄼
(408) 241-3010. **$115-$239.** 2930 El Camino Real 95051. SR 82, 0.5 mi w of San Tomas Expwy; US 101 exit S Bowers Ave. Ext corridors. **Pets:** Small. $20 daily fee/pet. Designated rooms, service with restrictions, crate. [SAVE] 🛦ᴹ 🛥 🛜 ⊠ 🛄 🖵

▼▼▼ TownePlace Suites by Marriott San Jose Santa Clara 🄷
(408) 969-9900. **$132-$320.** 2877 Lakeside Dr 95054. US 101 exit Great America Pkwy, just w. Int corridors. **Pets:** Accepted.
🛦ᴹ 🛜 ⊠ 🛄 🖵

SANTA CLARITA (Restaurants p. 602)

◭◭◭ ▼▼ Best Western Valencia Inn 🄼
(661) 255-0555. **$109-$209.** 27413 Wayne Mills Pl 91355. I-5 exit 170 (Magic Mountain Pkwy), just e. Ext corridors. **Pets:** Accepted.
[SAVE] 🛦ᴹ 🛥 🛜 🛄 🖵

▼▼▼ Fairfield Inn by Marriott 🄷
(661) 290-2828. **$110-$186.** 25340 The Old Rd 91381. I-5 exit 167 (Lyons Ave), just w, then s. Ext/int corridors. **Pets:** Accepted.
🛦ᴹ 🛥 🛜 ⊠ 🛄 🖵

▼▼▼ Residence Inn by Marriott 🄷
(661) 290-2800. **$150-$271.** 25320 The Old Rd 91381. I-5 exit 167 (Lyons Ave), just w. Int corridors. **Pets:** Accepted.
🛦ᴹ 🛥 ⊠ 🛜 ⊠ 🛄 🖵

◭◭◭ ▼▼ Super 8-Santa Clarita 🄼
(661) 252-1722. **$65-$99.** 17901 Sierra Hwy 91351. SR 14 exit 6A (Sierra Hwy/Via Princessa), 1.5 mi n. Int corridors. **Pets:** Medium, dogs only. $25 daily fee/pet. Service with restrictions, supervision.
[SAVE] 🍴 🛦ᴹ 🛥 🛜 🛄 🖵

SANTA CRUZ

◭◭◭ ▼▼▼ Chaminade Resort & Spa 🄷
(831) 475-5600. **$189-$549, 3 day notice.** 1 Chaminade Ln 95065. 1.5 mi e of SR 1 and 17; SR 1 exit Soquel Ave, just w to Paul Sweet Rd, then 0.5 mi n. Int corridors. **Pets:** Accepted.
[SAVE] 🍴 🛦ᴹ 🛥 ⊠ 🛜 ⊠ 🛄 🖵

▼▼ Continental Inn 🄼
(831) 429-1221. **Call for rates.** 414 Ocean St 95060. 5 blks from beach; between Broadway and Soquel aves. Ext corridors.
Pets: Accepted. 🛥 🛜 ⊠ 🛄 🖵

◭◭◭ ▼▼ Edgewater Beach Inn & Suites 🄼 🐾
(831) 423-0440. **$179-$349, 3 day notice.** 525 Second St 95060. Across from beach and boardwalk. Ext corridors. **Pets:** Other species. $30 one-time fee/pet. Designated rooms, service with restrictions.
[SAVE] 🛥 🛜 ⊠ 🗷 🛄 🖵

◭◭◭ ▼▼▼ Hilton Santa Cruz/Scotts Valley 🄷
(831) 440-1000. **$129-$399.** 6001 La Madrona Dr 95060. SR 17 exit Mt Hermon Rd. Int corridors. **Pets:** Accepted.
[SAVE] 🍴 🛦ᴹ 🛥 🛜 ⊠ 🛄 🖵

▼▼ The Inn at Pasatiempo 🄷
(831) 423-5000. **Call for rates.** 555 Hwy 17 95060. 0.8 mi n of jct SR 1 and 17; SR 17 exit Pasatiempo Dr. Ext corridors. **Pets:** Accepted.
🍴 🛦ᴹ 🛥 🛜 ⊠ 🗷 🛄 🖵

▼▼ Ocean Pacific Lodge 🄷
(831) 457-1234. **$89-$599.** 301 Pacific Ave 95060. SR 1 and 17 exit w via Ocean St, 1 mi w to Broadway, turn right, left on Front St to Pacific Ave, then just right. Ext corridors. **Pets:** Accepted.
🍴 🛦ᴹ 🛥 🛜 ⊠ 🛄 🖵

SANTA MARIA (Restaurants p. 602)

◭◭◭ ▼▼▼ Best Western Plus Big America 🄼
(805) 922-5200. **$106-$243.** 1725 N Broadway 93454. US 101 exit 173 (SR 135/S Broadway), 0.5 mi s. Ext corridors. **Pets:** Other species. Service with restrictions, supervision. [SAVE] 🛦ᴹ 🛥 🛜 🛄 🖵

▼▼▼ Candlewood Suites 🄷
(805) 928-4155. **$79-$199.** 2079 N Roemer Ct 93454. US 101 exit 173 (SR 135/S Broadway), 0.8 mi sw, then just s. Int corridors.
Pets: Accepted. 🍴 🛦ᴹ 🛜 🛄 🖵

▼▼▼ Historic Santa Maria Inn 🄷 🐾
(805) 928-7777. **$104-$319.** 801 S Broadway 93454. US 101 exit 171 (Main St), 1 mi w, then 0.5 mi s. Int corridors. **Pets:** $50 deposit/room. Designated rooms, service with restrictions, supervision.
🍴 🛥 ⊠ 🛜 🛄 🖵

▼▼▼ Holiday Inn & Suites Santa Maria 🄷
(805) 928-6000. **Call for rates.** 2100 N Broadway 93454. US 101 exit 173 (SR 135/S Broadway), just s. Int corridors. **Pets:** Accepted.
🍴 🛦ᴹ 🛥 🛜 ⊠ 🛄 🖵

◭◭◭ ▼▼▼ Radisson Hotel Santa Maria 🄷
(805) 928-8000. **$110-$229.** 3455 Skyway Dr 93455. US 101 exit 169 (Betteravia Rd), 2.3 mi w, then 1.8 mi s. Ext/int corridors. **Pets:** Small, dogs only. $50 one-time fee/room. Designated rooms, service with restrictions, supervision. [SAVE] 🍴 🛦ᴹ 🛥 ⊠ 🛜 ⊠ 🛄 🖵

SANTA MONICA

▼▼▼ Channel Road Inn 🄱🄱
(310) 459-1920. **$195-$425.** 219 W Channel Rd 90402. SR 1 (Pacific Coast Hwy), just e. Ext/int corridors. **Pets:** Accepted. 🛜 ⊠

◭◭◭ ▼▼▼ The Fairmont Miramar Hotel & Bungalows 🄷
(310) 576-7777. **Call for rates.** 101 Wilshire Blvd Blvd 90401. I-10 exit 1B (Lincoln Blvd), 0.6 mi n, then 0.6 mi w. Ext/int corridors.
Pets: Accepted. [SAVE] [ECO] 🎝 🍴 🛥 ⊠ 🛜 ⊠ 🖵

▼▼▼ The Georgian Hotel 🄷
(310) 395-9945. **$344-$444.** 1415 Ocean Ave 90401. I-10 exit 1B (Lincoln Blvd), just n, then 0.5 mi w on Broadway. Int corridors.
Pets: Accepted. 🍴 🛜 ⊠ 🛄 🖵

◭◭◭ ▼▼▼ JW Marriott Santa Monica Le Merigot 🄷 🐾
(310) 395-9700. **$408-$470, 7 day notice.** 1740 Ocean Ave 90401. I-10 exit 1B (Lincoln Blvd), 0.3 mi s, 0.6 mi w on Pico Blvd, then just n. Int corridors. **Pets:** Medium, dogs only. $150 one-time fee/pet. Designated rooms, service with restrictions, supervision.
[SAVE] 🍴 🛥 ⊠ 🎝 ⊠ 🖵

◭◭◭ ▼▼▼ Le Méridien Delfina Santa Monica 🄷 🐾
(310) 399-9344. **$599-$819.** 530 Pico Blvd 90405. I-10 exit 1B (Lincoln Blvd), just s. Int corridors. **Pets:** Dogs only. $100 one-time fee/room. Service with restrictions, supervision.
[SAVE] 🍴 🛥 ⊠ 🎝 ⊠ 🛄 🖵

▼▼▼ Loews Santa Monica Beach Hotel 🄷 🐾
(310) 458-6700. **$299-$2000.** 1700 Ocean Ave 90401. I-10 exit 1B (Lincoln Blvd), 0.3 mi s, 0.6 mi w on Pico Blvd, then just n. Int corridors. **Pets:** $100 one-time fee/room. Designated rooms, service with restrictions, supervision. 🎝 🍴 🛥 ⊠ 🛜 ⊠ 🖵

◭◭◭ ▼▼▼ Shore Hotel 🄷
(310) 458-1515. **$329-$799.** 1515 Ocean Ave 90401. I-10 exit 1B (Lincoln Blvd), 0.3 mi s, 0.6 mi w on Pico Blvd, then just n. Int corridors.
Pets: Accepted. [SAVE] 🎝 🍴 🛥 🛜 ⊠ 🛄 🖵

▼▼▼▼ Viceroy Santa Monica 🄷

(310) 260-7500. **$400-$3000.** 1819 Ocean Ave 90401. I-10 exit 1B (Lincoln Blvd), 0.3 mi s, 0.6 mi w on Pico Blvd, then just n. Int corridors. **Pets:** Accepted. 🍴 ⤳ ⊠ 🛜 ✕ 🔌 ▣

▼▼▼▼ Wyndham Santa Monica At The Pier 🄷

(310) 451-0676. **$210-$455.** 120 Colorado Ave 90401. I-10 exit 1B (Lincoln Blvd), just n. Int corridors. **Pets:** Accepted.
🄴🄲🄾 🍴 ⤳ 🛜 ✕ ▣

SANTA NELLA

AAA▷ ▼▼▼ Best Western Andersen's Inn 🄷

(209) 826-5534. **$105-$146.** 12367 Hwy 33 S 95322. I-5 exit 407 (SR 33), just e. Ext corridors. **Pets:** Medium, dogs only. $20 daily fee/room. Designated rooms, service with restrictions, supervision.
🆂🅰🆅🅴 ♿ ⤳ 🛜

▼▼▼ Quality Inn 🄷

(209) 826-8282. **Call for rates.** 28976 Plaza Dr 95322. I-5 exit 407 (SR 33), just e. Ext corridors. **Pets:** Accepted. ♿ ⤳ 🛜 🔌 ▣

SANTA PAULA

▼▼ Glen Tavern Inn 🄷

(805) 933-5550. **$99-$124.** 134 N Mill St 93060. SR 126 exit 12 (10th St) northbound, 0.5 mi w, just s on Santa Barbara St, then just e. Int corridors. **Pets:** Dogs only. $10 daily fee/pet. Designated rooms, service with restrictions, supervision. 🍴 ⤳ 🛜 ✕ 🔌 ▣

SANTA ROSA *(Restaurants p. 602)*

AAA▷ ▼▼▼ Best Western Garden Inn Ⓜ

(707) 546-4031. **$120-$229.** 1500 Santa Rosa Ave 95404. US 101 exit Baker Ave northbound, just n; exit Corby Ave southbound. Ext corridors. **Pets:** Accepted. 🆂🅰🆅🅴 🍴 ♿ ⤳ 🛜 🔌 ▣

AAA▷ ▼▼▼ Best Western Plus Wine Country Inn & Suites 🄷

(707) 545-9000. **$125-$189.** 870 Hopper Ave 95403. US 101 northbound exit Mendocino Ave/Old Redwood Hwy, just s to Mendocino Overcross to Cleveland Ave, just n to Hopper Ave, then just w; southbound exit Hopper Ave, then just w. Ext corridors. **Pets:** Dogs only. $20 one-time fee/room. Designated rooms, service with restrictions, supervision. 🆂🅰🆅🅴 ♿ ⤳ 🛜 🔌 ▣

▼▼▼ Extended Stay America-Santa Rosa-North 🄷

(707) 541-0959. **$100-$165.** 100 Fountain Grove Pkwy 95403. US 101 exit Mendocino Ave/Old Redwood Hwy, just e. Int corridors. **Pets:** Accepted. 🍴 ♿ 🛜 🔌 ▣

▼▼▼ Flamingo Conference Resort and Spa 🄷

(707) 545-8530. **Call for rates.** 2777 4th St 95405. Off SR 12; at Farmers Ln. Int corridors. **Pets:** Accepted.
🄴🄲🄾 🍴 ♿ ⤳ ⊠ 🛜 ✕ 🔌 ▣

▼▼▼▼ Fountaingrove Inn, Hotel & Conference Center 🄷

(707) 578-6101. **Call for rates.** 101 Fountaingrove Pkwy 95403. From US 101 exit Mendocino Ave/Old Redwood Hwy, just e. Int corridors. **Pets:** Accepted. 🍴 ♿ ⤳ 🛜 ✕ 🔌 ▣

AAA▷ ▼▼▼ Hillside Inn Ⓜ

(707) 546-9353. **$86-$103, 3 day notice.** 2901 4th St 95409. US 101, 2.5 mi e on SR 12; at Farmers Ln and 4th St. Ext corridors. **Pets:** Small. Designated rooms, service with restrictions, supervision. 🆂🅰🆅🅴 🍴 ⤳ 🛜 ✕ 🔌 ▣

AAA▷ ▼▼▼ Hilton Sonoma Wine Country 🄷

(707) 523-7555. **$119-$309.** 3555 Round Barn Blvd 95403. US 101 exit Mendocino Ave/Old Redwood Hwy, just e, then just n. Int corridors. **Pets:** Accepted. 🆂🅰🆅🅴 🄴🄲🄾 🍴 ♿ ⤳ 🛜 ✕ 🔌 ▣

▼▼▼▼ Hotel La Rose 🄷

(707) 579-3200. **$139-$269.** 308 Wilson St 95401. 2 blks w off US 101 exit downtown Santa Rosa; on Railroad Square. Ext/int corridors. **Pets:** Accepted. 🍴 ♿ ⤳ ✕ 🔌

▼▼▼ Quality Inn & Suites Santa Rosa 🄷

(707) 521-2100. **$90-$369.** 3000 Santa Rosa Ave 95407. US 101 exit Todd Rd, 1.2 mi n. Int corridors. **Pets:** Other species. $25 daily fee/pet. No service, supervision. ♿ 🛜 ✕ 🔌 ▣

AAA▷ ▼▼▼ Sandman Inn 🄷

(707) 544-8570. **$119-$329.** 3421 Cleveland Ave 95403. US 101 northbound exit Mendocino Ave/Old Redwood Hwy, just s to Mendocino Overcross to Cleveland Ave, then just s; southbound exit Hopper Ave, then just e. Ext corridors. **Pets:** Medium, dogs only. $25 one-time fee/room. Designated rooms, service with restrictions, supervision. 🆂🅰🆅🅴 ♿ ⤳ 🛜 🔌 ▣

SANTEE *(Restaurants p. 602)*

AAA▷ ▼▼ Best Western Santee Lodge Ⓜ

(619) 449-2626. **$79-$199.** 10726 Woodside Ave 92071. SR 52 exit 14 (Mission Gorge Rd), 2 mi e. Ext corridors. **Pets:** Accepted.
🆂🅰🆅🅴 ♿ ⤳ 🛜 ✕ 🔌 ▣

SAN YSIDRO

▼▼ Quality Inn & Suites Near the Border Ⓜ

(619) 690-2633. **$69-$249.** 930 W San Ysidro Blvd 92173. I-5 exit 2 (Dairy Mart Rd), just ne; just n of Tijuana International Border Crossing. Ext corridors. **Pets:** Large. $25 daily fee/pet. Designated rooms, service with restrictions, supervision. ♿ 🛜 ✕ 🔌 ▣

SCOTTS VALLEY

AAA▷ ▼▼▼▼ Best Western Plus Inn Scotts Valley 🄷

(831) 438-6666. **$99-$190.** 6020 Scotts Valley Dr 95066. SR 17 exit Granite Creek, just w. Ext/int corridors. **Pets:** Accepted.
🆂🅰🆅🅴 ♿ ⤳ 🛜 ✕ 🔌 ▣

SEAL BEACH *(Restaurants p. 602)*

AAA▷ ▼▼▼▼ The Pacific Inn 🄷

(562) 493-7501. **$139-$249.** 600 Marina Dr 90740. I-405 exit 22 (Seal Beach Blvd/Los Alamitos Blvd), 2.6 mi s, 0.5 mi w on Pacific Coast Hwy, then just sw. Ext/int corridors. **Pets:** Other species. $50 one-time fee/pet. Designated rooms, service with restrictions, supervision.
🆂🅰🆅🅴 ♿ ⤳ 🛜 ✕ 🔌 ▣

SEASIDE

AAA▷ ▼▼ Sandcastle Inn 🄷

(831) 394-6556. **$59-$700, 3 day notice.** 1011 La Salle Ave 93955. SR 1 exit Sand City/Seaside, just e. Ext corridors. **Pets:** Accepted.
🆂🅰🆅🅴 🛜 ✕ 🔌

SHAVER LAKE

▼▼ Shaver Lake Village Hotel & Cabins Ⓜ

(559) 841-8289. **Call for rates.** 42135 Tollhouse Rd 93664. Center. Ext/int corridors. **Pets:** Medium, dogs only. $25 daily fee/pet. Designated rooms, service with restrictions, supervision.
♿ 🛜 ✕ 🅺 🅩 🔌 ▣

SHERMAN OAKS *(Restaurants p. 602)*

AAA▷ ▼▼▼▼ Best Western Plus Carriage Inn Ⓜ

(818) 787-2300. **$139-$279.** 5525 Sepulveda Blvd 91411. I-405 exit 64 (Burbank Blvd), just e, then just s. Ext/int corridors. **Pets:** Accepted.
🆂🅰🆅🅴 🄴🄲🄾 ♿ ⤳ 🛜 ✕ 🔌 ▣

SIERRA CITY

AAA▷ ▼▼ Herrington's Sierra Pines Resort Ⓜ

(530) 862-1151. **$79-$140, 10 day notice.** 104 Main St 96125. 0.7 mi w of center on SR 49. Ext corridors. **Pets:** Accepted.
🆂🅰🆅🅴 🍴 🛜 ✕ 🅺 🅩 ▣

SIMI VALLEY *(Restaurants p. 602)*

◇◇ **Extended Stay America-Los Angeles-Simi Valley** H
(805) 584-8880. **$105-$125.** 2498 Stearns St 93063. SR 118 exit 28 (Stearns St), just s. Int corridors. **Pets:** Accepted. 📶 🈺 💻

SOLEDAD

AAA ◇◇◇ **Valley Harvest Inn** H
(831) 678-3833. **$99-$149.** 1155 Front St 93960. US 101 exit Soledad, just e. Ext/int corridors. **Pets:** Small, dogs only. $15 daily fee/pet. Designated rooms, service with restrictions, supervision.
SAVE 🍴 🏋 🏊 📶 🈺 💻

SOLVANG *(Restaurants p. 602)*

AAA ◇◇◇ **Hadsten House Inn** M
(805) 688-3210. **Call for rates.** 1450 Mission Dr 93463. On SR 246. Ext corridors. **Pets:** Accepted.
SAVE 🍴 🏋 🏊 📶 🈺 🈺 💻

◇◇◇◇ **The Landsby Inn** H 🐾
(805) 688-3121. **$175-$395, 3 day notice.** 1576 Mission Dr 93463. On SR 246. Int corridors. **Pets:** Small, dogs only. $75 one-time fee/room. Designated rooms, service with restrictions, supervision.
🍴 📶 🈺 🈺

AAA ◇◇◇ **Royal Copenhagen Inn** M
(805) 688-5561. **$89-$275, 3 day notice.** 1579 Mission Dr 93463. On SR 246; center of town. Ext corridors. **Pets:** Other species. $20 daily fee/pet. Designated rooms, service with restrictions, supervision.
SAVE 🏊 📶 🈺 🈺 💻

◇◇ **Solvang Inn & Cottages** M
(805) 688-4702. **$99-$270.** 1518 Mission Dr 93463. On SR 246. Ext corridors. **Pets:** Dogs only. $15 daily fee/pet. Designated rooms, service with restrictions, supervision. 🏊 📶 🈺 🈺 💻

◇◇◇◇ **Wine Valley Inn & Cottages** H
(805) 688-2111. **$104-$494.** 1564 Copenhagen Dr 93463. SR 246, just s on 5th St. Ext/int corridors. **Pets:** Accepted.
🏋 🈺 📶 🈺 🈺 💻

SONOMA *(Restaurants p. 603)*

AAA ◇◇◇◇ **Best Western Sonoma Valley Inn & Krug Event Center** H
(707) 938-9200. **$119-$399, 3 day notice.** 550 2nd St W 95476. 1 blk w of town plaza. Ext corridors. **Pets:** Accepted.
SAVE 🏊 🈺 📶 🈺 🈺 💻

AAA ◇◇◇◇ **The Fairmont Sonoma Mission Inn & Spa** H
(707) 938-9000. **Call for rates.** 100 Boyes Blvd 95476. 2.5 mi n on SR 12. Ext/int corridors. **Pets:** Accepted.
SAVE ECO 🈺 🍴 🏋 🏊 🈺 🈺 🈺 💻

◇◇◇ **Inn at Sonoma** BB
(707) 939-1340. **$225-$425, 7 day notice.** 630 Broadway 95476. On SR 12, just s of Sonoma Plaza. Int corridors. **Pets:** Accepted.
🏋 📶 🈺 🈺 💻

AAA ◇◇◇◇ **The Lodge at Sonoma, A Renaissance Resort & Spa** H
(707) 935-6600. **$201-$486, 5 day notice.** 1325 Broadway 95476. On SR 12, 1 mi s of Sonoma Plaza. Ext/int corridors. **Pets:** Other species. $100 one-time fee/room. Service with restrictions, supervision.
SAVE 🍴 🏋 🏊 🈺 🈺 🈺 💻

◇◇◇ **Sonoma Creek Inn** M
(707) 939-9463. **$99-$245.** 239 Boyes Blvd 95476. SR 12, 0.5 mi w. Ext corridors. **Pets:** Accepted. 🏋 📶 🈺 🈺 💻

SONORA

◇◇◇ **Aladdin Motor Inn** H
(209) 533-4971. **Call for rates.** 14260 Mono Way (Hwy 108) 95370. Jct SR 108 and S Washington St, 2.3 mi e, just s on Hess Ave, then just e. Ext/int corridors. **Pets:** Accepted.
🍴 🏋 🏊 📶 🈺 🈺 💻

◇◇◇◇ **Barretta Gardens Inn** BB
(209) 532-6039. **$159-$254, 14 day notice.** 700 S Barretta St 95370. Just n of jct Mono Way; south end of town. Int corridors. **Pets:** Dogs only. $25 daily fee/pet. Designated rooms, service with restrictions, supervision. 🍴 🏋 📶 🈺 🈺

AAA ◇◇◇◇ **Best Western Plus Sonora Oaks Hotel & Conference Center** H 🐾
(209) 533-4400. **$90-$250.** 19551 Hess Ave 95370. SR 108 westbound exit Phoenix Lake Rd, just e to Hess Ave, then just s; eastbound exit Hess Ave, just s; jct Mono Way. Ext/int corridors. **Pets:** Medium, dogs only. $20 daily fee/room. Designated rooms, service with restrictions, supervision. SAVE 🍴 🏋 🏊 📶 🈺 🈺 💻 🐾

◇◇◇◇ **Bradford Place Inn and Gardens** BB 🐾
(209) 536-6075. **$120-$220, 5 day notice.** 56 W Bradford St 95370. Just w of SR 49 (S Washington St); jct Norlin St; downtown. Ext/int corridors. **Pets:** $15 one-time fee/room. Designated rooms, no service, supervision. 📶 🈺 🈺 🈺 💻

◇◇ **Rodeway Inn** M
(209) 536-4694. **$70-$200.** 128 S Green St 95370. 1 blk w of SR 49 (S Washington St) via W Stockton St. Ext corridors. **Pets:** Medium. $20 daily fee/pet. Designated rooms, service with restrictions, supervision.
🏋 📶 🈺 💻

SOUTH LAKE TAHOE *(Restaurants p. 603)*

◇◇◇ **Alpenrose Inn** M
(530) 544-2985. **$69-$239, 3 day notice.** 4074 Pine Blvd 96150. Just s of casino area to Stateline Ave, 0.3 mi w to Pine Blvd, then just s. Ext corridors. **Pets:** Accepted. 📶 🈺 🈺 💻

◇◇◇ **Basecamp Hotel** H
(530) 208-0180. **$99-$309, 3 day notice.** 4143 Cedar Ave 96150. Just s of casino area to Stateline Ave, just w. Ext/int corridors. **Pets:** Accepted. 🈺 📶 🈺

◇◇◇ **Beach Retreat & Lodge at Tahoe** H
(530) 541-6722. **Call for rates.** 3411 Lake Tahoe Blvd 96150. 1.8 mi s of casino area on US 50. Ext corridors. **Pets:** Accepted.
🍴 🏋 🏊 🈺 📶 🈺 💻

◇◇◇ **Heavenly Valley Lodge** M 🐾
(530) 564-1500. **$159-$340.** 1261 Ski Run Blvd 96150. US 50 exit Ski Run Blvd, 0.5 mi se; jct Pioneer Tr. Ext corridors. **Pets:** Medium, dogs only. $25 daily fee/room. Designated rooms, service with restrictions, crate. 📶 🈺 🈺 🈺 💻

◇◇◇ **Hotel Becket, a Joie de Vivre Hotel** M
(530) 544-6000. **Call for rates.** 4011 Lake Tahoe Blvd 96150. 0.4 mi sw of casino area; at Park Ave and Lake Tahoe Blvd (US 50); across from Heavenly Village. Ext corridors. **Pets:** Accepted.
🏊 📶 🈺 🈺 💻

◇◇ **Howard Johnson Inn** M
(530) 541-4000. **$59-$290.** 3489 Lake Tahoe Blvd 96150. 1.5 mi s of casino area. Ext corridors. **Pets:** Accepted. 🏊 📶 🈺 🈺 💻

◇◇◇ **The Landing Resort & Spa** H
(530) 541-5263. **Call for rates.** 4104 Lakeshore Blvd 96150. 0.5 mi s of casino area to Park Ave, then 0.5 mi w. Ext/int corridors. **Pets:** Accepted. 🈺 🍴 🏋 🈺 📶 🈺 🈺 💻

AAA ◇◇◇ **Tahoe Keys Resort** CO
(530) 544-5397. **$112-$1700.** 599 Tahoe Keys Blvd 96150. 0.5 mi e of jct US 50 and SR 89, 1 mi n. Ext corridors. **Pets:** Dogs only. $100 deposit/pet, $25 one-time fee/pet. Designated rooms, service with restrictions, supervision. SAVE 🏊 🈺 📶 🈺 🈺 💻

♨ ▽▽▽ Tahoe Valley Lodge M
(530) 541-0353. **Call for rates.** 2241 Lake Tahoe Blvd 96150. 0.5 mi e of jct US 50 and SR 89. Ext corridors. **Pets:** Very small, dogs only. $25 daily fee/pet. Designated rooms, service with restrictions, supervision.
SAVE ➔ ⟲ ✕ 🖥 🖵

SOUTH PASADENA
▽▽ Arroyo Vista Inn BB
(323) 478-7300. **$175-$280, 14 day notice.** 335 Monterey Rd 91030. SR 110 exit 64 (Marmion Way) northbound, 0.8 mi e, then just n; exit 31A (Orange Grove Ave) southbound, 0.3 mi e, 0.6 mi s, then just n. Int corridors. **Pets:** Accepted. ⟲ ✕ ☎

SOUTH SAN FRANCISCO
♨ ▽▽▽ Larkspur Landing South San Francisco H
(650) 827-1515. **$202-$232.** 690 Gateway Blvd 94080. US 101 exit 425A (Grand Ave), 0.4 mi e, then 0.4 mi n. Int corridors.
Pets: Accepted. SAVE ECO ᏝM ⟲ ✕ 🖥 🖵

♨ ▽▽▽ Residence Inn by Marriott at Oyster Point H
(650) 837-9000. **$161-$340.** 1350 Veterans Blvd 94080. US 101 exit 425B (Oyster Point Blvd), just ne. Int corridors. **Pets:** Accepted.
SAVE ECO ᏝM ➔ ⟲ ✕ 🖥 🖵

STOCKTON
♨ ▽▽▽ Best Western Plus Heritage Inn H
(209) 474-3301. **$90-$130.** 111 E March Ln 95207. I-5 exit 476 (March Ln), 2.5 mi e; corner of El Dorado St. Int corridors. **Pets:** Accepted.
SAVE ᏝM ➔ ⟲ 🖥 🖵

▽▽▽ Holiday Inn Express Hotel Stockton Southeast H
(209) 946-1234. **$124-$141.** 5045 S Kingsley Rd 95215. SR 99 exit Arch Rd, just se. Int corridors. **Pets:** Medium. $25 daily fee/pet. Service with restrictions, supervision. ᏝM ➔ ⟲ ✕ 🖥 🖵

♨ ▽▽▽ Residence Inn by Marriott H
(209) 472-9800. **$142-$215.** 3240 W March Ln 95219. I-5 exit 476 (March Ln), 0.5 mi w, then just s on Deer Park Dr. Int corridors.
Pets: Accepted. SAVE ᏝM ➔ ⟲ ✕ 🖥 🖵

▽▽▽ University Plaza Waterfront Hotel H
(209) 944-1140. **Call for rates.** 110 W Fremont St 95202. Jct N Madison St; downtown. Int corridors. **Pets:** Accepted.
ECO 🍴 ᏝM ➔ ⟲ ✕ 🖥 🖵

SUISUN CITY
▽▽▽ Hampton Inn & Suites Suisun City Waterfront H
(707) 429-0900. **$149-$259.** 2 Harbor Center Dr 94585. I-80 exit 43 (SR 12 E/Rio Vista/Suisun City), 2.6 mi e; exit 58B (Main St/Suisun City), just s. Int corridors. **Pets:** Medium, dogs only. Designated rooms, no service, supervision. ECO ᏝM ➔ ⟲ ✕ 🖥 🖵

SUN CITY
▽▽ Motel 6 Menifee #4599 M
(951) 679-1133. **$65-$115.** 27955 Encanto Dr 92586. I-215 exit 12 (McCall Blvd), just e, then just s. Ext corridors. **Pets:** Accepted.
🍴 ᏝM ➔ ⟲ 🖥

SUNNYVALE
♨ ▽▽▽ Aloft Sunnyvale H
(408) 736-0300. **Call for rates.** 170 S Sunnyvale Ave 94086. US 101 exit Matilda Ave, 1.7 mi w, just s on W Washington Ave, then just e. Int corridors. **Pets:** Accepted. SAVE 🍴 ᏝM ⟲ ✕ 🖥 🖵

♨ ▽▽▽ Grand Hotel H
(408) 720-8500. **$140-$699.** 865 W El Camino Real 94087. SR 82 (El Camino Real); between S Mary and S Pastoria aves. Ext/int corridors.
Pets: Accepted. SAVE ᏝM ➔ ⟲ ✕ 🖥 🖵

♨ ▽▽▽ Larkspur Landing Sunnyvale H
(408) 733-1212. **$109-$449.** 748 N Mathilda Ave 94085. US 101 exit Mathilda Ave, just s. Int corridors. **Pets:** Accepted.
SAVE ECO ᏝM ⟲ ✕ 🖥 🖵

♨ ▽▽▽ Maple Tree Inn H ✿
(408) 720-9700. **$299.** 711 E El Camino Real 94087. US 101 exit 394 (Lawrence Expwy), 2.9 mi w to El Camino Real exit, then 1.8 mi n. Int corridors. **Pets:** Medium, dogs only. $20 daily fee/pet. Designated rooms, service with restrictions, supervision.
SAVE ᏝM ➔ ⟲ ✕ 🖥 🖵

▽▽▽ Quality Inn Santa Clara Convention Center H
(408) 744-1100. **$99-$649.** 1280 Persian Dr 94089. US 101 exit Lawrence Expwy N, 1 mi n to Persian Dr, then 0.3 mi w. Int corridors.
Pets: Accepted. ᏝM ➔ ⟲ ✕ 🖥 🖵

♨ ▽▽▽ Residence Inn by Marriott Silicon Valley I H
(408) 720-1000. **$123-$351.** 750 Lakeway Dr 94085. US 101 exit Lawrence Expwy S, e on Oakmead Pkwy. Ext corridors. **Pets:** Accepted.
SAVE ᏝM ➔ ⟲ ✕ 🖥 🖵

♨ ▽▽▽ Residence Inn by Marriott Sunnyvale Silicon Valley II H
(408) 720-8893. **$113-$340.** 1080 Stewart Dr 94086. US 101 exit Lawrence Expwy S, w on Duane Ave, just s. Ext corridors. **Pets:** Accepted.
SAVE 🍴 ᏝM ➔ ⟲ ✕ 🖥 🖵

♨ ▽▽▽ Sheraton Sunnyvale H
(408) 745-6000. **$89-$699.** 1100 N Mathilda Ave 94089. SR 237 exit Mathilda Ave, just n. Int corridors. **Pets:** Accepted.
SAVE 🍴 ᏝM ➔ 📶 ✕ 🖥 🖵

♨ ▽▽▽ Staybridge Suites Sunnyvale H
(408) 745-1515. **Call for rates.** 900 Hamlin Ct 94089. SR 237 exit Mathilda Ave S, w on Ross Dr. Ext/int corridors. **Pets:** Accepted.
SAVE 🍴 ᏝM ➔ ⟲ ✕ 🖥 🖵

♨ ▽▽▽ TownePlace Suites by Marriott Sunnyvale/ Mountain View H
(408) 733-4200. **$133-$321.** 606 S Bernardo Ave 94087. SR 85 exit SR 82, 0.5 mi s. Int corridors. **Pets:** Accepted.
SAVE ᏝM ⟲ ✕ 🖥 🖵

▽▽▽ Wild Palms Hotel H
(408) 738-0500. **Call for rates.** 910 E Fremont Ave 94087. US 101 exit Lawrence Expwy S, 1.5 mi s, 0.9 mi n on E El Camino Real, just w on S Wolfe Rd, then just s. Ext/int corridors. **Pets:** Accepted.
ECO ᏝM ➔ ⟲ ✕ 🖥 🖵

SUSANVILLE
♨ ▽▽▽ Best Western Trailside Inn M
(530) 257-4123. **$105-$180.** 2785 Main St 96130. 0.7 mi e on SR 36 from jct SR 139. Ext corridors. **Pets:** Accepted.
SAVE 🍴 ᏝM ➔ ⟲ ✕ 🖥 🖵

♨ ▽▽▽ Diamond Mountain Casino & Hotel H
(530) 252-1100. **$91-$189.** 900 Skyline Dr 96130. 1 mi ne on SR 139 from jct SR 36, then 1 mi w; follow signs to rancheria. Int corridors.
Pets: Medium, other species. $15 daily fee/pet. Designated rooms, supervision. SAVE ECO 🍴 ᏝM ➔ ⟳ ⟲ ✕ 🖥 🖵

♨ ▽▽▽ Red Lion Inn & Suites Susanville H
(530) 257-3450. **$100-$144.** 3015 E Riverside Dr 96130. 1.3 mi e on SR 36 from jct SR 139, then just ne. Int corridors. **Pets:** Dogs only. $15 daily fee/room. Designated rooms, service with restrictions, supervision. SAVE 🎁 ᏝM ➔ ⟲ ✕ 🖥 🖵

▼▼▼▼ The Roseberry House Bed & Breakfast BB
(530) 257-5675. **$125-$150.** 609 North St 96130. 0.7 mi w on SR 36 from jct SR 139 to N Lassen St, then just n. Int corridors. **Pets:** Other species. $10 daily fee/pet. No service, supervision. 🍽 📶 ✕ 🅩

◈◈◈ ▼▼▼ Super 8 M
(530) 257-2782. **$72-$87.** 2975 Johnstonville Rd 96130. 1 mi e on SR 36 from jct 139, then just ne. Ext corridors. **Pets:** Accepted.
SAVE 🍽 ♿ ♒ 📶 ✕ 🛗 🖥

TAHOE CITY *(Restaurants p. 603)*

▼▼◈ Mother Nature's Inn M ❀
(530) 581-4278. **$69-$159, 7 day notice.** 551 N Lake Blvd 96145. SR 28 (N Lake Blvd), 0.5 mi e of jct SR 89; behind Mother Nature's Store. Int corridors. **Pets:** $15 daily fee/pet. Designated rooms, service with restrictions. 📶 ✕ 🛗 🖥

▼▼ River Ranch Lodge M
(530) 583-4264. **$99-$240, 14 day notice.** 2285 River Rd 96145. I-80 exit SR 89, 11 mi s; 3.5 mi n from City Center. Ext/int corridors. **Pets:** Dogs only. $25 daily fee/pet. Designated rooms, service with restrictions, supervision. 🍽 ♿ 📶 ✕ 🐾

TARZANA

◈◈◈ ▼▼▼ St. George Inn & Suites M
(818) 345-6911. **Call for rates.** 19454 Ventura Blvd 91356. US 101 exit 24 (Tampa Ave), just s, then just w. Ext corridors. **Pets:** Accepted.
SAVE ♿ ♒ 📶 ✕ 🛗

TEHACHAPI *(Restaurants p. 603)*

◈◈◈ ▼▼▼ Best Western Mountain Inn M
(661) 822-5591. **$100-$150.** 418 W Tehachapi Blvd 93561. SR 58 exit 148 (SR 202), 1 mi s, then e. Ext corridors. **Pets:** Accepted.
SAVE ♒ 📶 🛗 🖥

▼▼ La Quinta Inn Tehachapi M
(661) 823-8000. **$86-$229.** 500 E Steuber Rd 93561. SR 58 exit 151 (Monolith St/Tehachapi Blvd), just s. Int corridors. **Pets:** Accepted.
♒ 📶 ✕ 🛗 🖥

TEMECULA *(Restaurants p. 603)*

▼▼◈◈ La Quinta Inn & Suites Temecula H
(951) 296-1003. **$79-$323.** 27330 Jefferson Ave 92592. I-15 exit 61 (SR 79 N/Winchester Rd), just w, then just n; east side of Rancho Temecula Plaza. Int corridors. **Pets:** Accepted. ♿ ♒ 📶 ✕ 🛗 🖥

▼▼▼◈ Quality Inn Temecula Wine Country M
(951) 296-3788. **$69-$239.** 27338 Jefferson Ave 92590. I-15 exit 61 (SR 79 N/Winchester Rd), just w, then just n; east side of Rancho Temecula Plaza. Ext corridors. **Pets:** Medium, dogs only. $20 daily fee/room. Designated rooms, service with restrictions, supervision.
♿ ♒ 📶 ✕ 🛗 🖥

▼▼▼▼ Temecula Creek Inn H ❀
(951) 694-1000. **$119-$299, 3 day notice.** 44501 Rainbow Canyon Rd 92592. I-15 exit 58 (SR 79 S), 1 mi e to Pechanga Pkwy, just se, then 0.5 mi s. Ext corridors. **Pets:** Medium, dogs only. $75 one-time fee/room. Service with restrictions, supervision.
🍽 ♒ ✕ 📶 ✕ 🛗 🖥

THOUSAND OAKS *(Restaurants p. 603)*

▼▼◈ Palm Garden Hotel H
(805) 716-4200. **Call for rates.** 495 N Ventu Park Rd 91320. US 101 exit 46 (Ventu Park Rd), just n. Ext corridors. **Pets:** $50 one-time fee/room. Designated rooms, service with restrictions, crate.
🍽 ♿ ♒ 📶 🛗 🖥

▼▼▼▼ TownePlace Suites by Marriott H
(805) 499-3111. **$123-$186.** 1712 Newbury Rd 91320. US 101 exit 46 (Ventu Park Rd), just w, then just n. Int corridors. **Pets:** Accepted.
♿ ♒ 📶 ✕ 🛗 🖥

THREE RIVERS *(Restaurants p. 603)*

◈◈◈ ▼▼◈ Americas Best Value Inn-Lazy J Ranch M
(559) 561-4449. **$165, 3 day notice.** 39625 Sierra Dr 93271. SR 198, 3 mi sw of town center. Ext corridors. **Pets:** Accepted.
SAVE ♒ 📶 ✕ 🛗 🖥

▼▼ Buckeye Tree Lodge M ❀
(559) 561-5900. **$76-$160, 7 day notice.** 46000 Sierra Dr 93271. SR 198, north end of town; 0.5 mi from entrance to Sequoia National Park. Ext corridors. **Pets:** Other species. $10 daily fee/pet. Service with restrictions, crate. ♒ 📶 ✕ 🛗 🖥

▼▼◈ Comfort Inn & Suites M
(559) 561-9000. **$79-$219.** 40820 Sierra Dr 93271. SR 198, 1.5 mi sw of town center. Ext/int corridors. **Pets:** Accepted.
♿ ♒ ✕ 📶 ✕ 🛗 🖥

▼▼ Gateway Lodge M
(559) 561-4133. **$109-$229, 7 day notice.** 45978 Sierra Dr 93271. SR 198, 6 mi ne of town center; 0.5 mi sw of entrance to Sequoia National Park. Ext corridors. **Pets:** Other species. $15 daily fee/pet. Service with restrictions, supervision. 🍽 📶 ✕ 🅩 🛗 🖥

▼▼ Sequoia Village Inn M ❀
(559) 561-3652. **$89-$329, 7 day notice.** 45971 Sierra Dr 93271. SR 198, 6 mi ne of town center; 0.5 mi sw of entrance to Sequoia National Park. Ext corridors. **Pets:** Other species. $10 daily fee/pet. Service with restrictions, crate. ♒ 📶 ✕ 🅩 🛗 🖥

TIBURON

◈◈◈ ▼▼▼ The Lodge at Tiburon H
(415) 435-3133. **$169-$369, 3 day notice.** 1651 Tiburon Blvd 94920. US 101 exit Tiburon-Belvedere, 4 mi e; in village; 1 blk from bay. Ext corridors. **Pets:** Accepted.
SAVE ECO 🍽 ♿ ♒ ✕ 📶 ✕ 🛗 🖥

TORRANCE

◈◈◈ ▼▼▼ Holiday Inn Los Angeles Gateway-Torrance H
(310) 781-9100. **Call for rates.** 19800 S Vermont Ave 90502. I-110 exit 8 (Torrance Blvd/Del Amo Blvd), just n to Del Amo Blvd, just w, then just n. Int corridors. **Pets:** Accepted.
SAVE ECO 🍽 ♒ 📶 ✕ 🛗 🖥

▼▼◈ Ramada Torrance M
(310) 325-0660. **$74-$109.** 2888 Pacific Coast Hwy 90505. I-405 exit 39 (Crenshaw Blvd), 5.2 mi s, then just w. Ext corridors. **Pets:** Medium, other species. $30 daily fee/pet. Service with restrictions, crate.
♒ 📶 ✕ 🛗 🖥

◈◈◈ ▼▼▼ Residence Inn by Marriott Los Angeles Torrance/Redondo Beach H
(310) 543-4566. **$137-$247.** 3701 Torrance Blvd 90503. I-405 exit 42A (Hawthorne Blvd), 3.2 mi s, then just e. Ext corridors. **Pets:** Large, other species. $125 one-time fee/room. Service with restrictions, supervision. SAVE ECO ♒ 📶 ✕ 🛗 🖥

▼▼▼▼ Staybridge Suites Torrance/Redondo Beach H
(310) 371-8525. **Call for rates.** 19901 Prairie Ave 90503. I-405 exit 39 (Crenshaw Blvd), 0.4 mi s to 190th St, 0.9 mi w, then 0.4 mi s. Ext corridors. **Pets:** Accepted. ♒ 📶 🛗 🖥

TRACY

◈◈◈ ▼▼▼ Best Western Luxury Inn H
(209) 832-0271. **$130-$150.** 811 W Clover Rd 95376. I-205 exit 8 (Central Tracy/Tracy Blvd), just s, then just w. Int corridors. **Pets:** Small. $20 daily fee/pet. Designated rooms, service with restrictions, supervision.
SAVE 🍽 ♿ ♒ 📶 ✕ 🛗 🖥

TRINIDAD

▼▼ Emerald Forest of Trinidad CA

(707) 677-3554. **Call for rates.** 753 Patrick's Point Dr 95570. US 101 exit Trinidad, just w on Main St, then 0.7 mi n. Ext corridors.
Pets: Accepted. 🍴 🛎 🖧 ✕ 🐾 📶 📞 💻

▲▲ ▼▼ Trinidad Inn M

(707) 677-3349. **$100-$335, 3 day notice.** 1170 Patrick's Point Dr 95570. US 101 exit Trinidad, just w on Main St, then 1.3 mi n. Ext corridors. **Pets:** Medium, dogs only. $10 daily fee/pet. Designated rooms, supervision. SAVE 🍴 🛎 🖧 ✕ 🐾 📞 💻

TRUCKEE

▲▲ ▼▼▼ Best Western Plus Hotel Truckee Tahoe H

(530) 587-4525. **$179-$329.** 11331 Brockway Rd 96161. I-80 exit 188 (SR 267) westbound; exit 188B eastbound, 1.5 mi se, then just w. Int corridors. **Pets:** Accepted. SAVE 🍴 🛎 🖧 ✕ 📞 💻

▼▼▼ The Cedar House Sport Hotel H ❀

(530) 582-5655. **$180-$400, 3 day notice.** 10918 Brockway Rd 96161. I-80 exit 188 (SR 267) westbound; exit 188B eastbound, 1.5 mi s, then 0.8 mi nw. Int corridors. **Pets:** Large, dogs only. $50 one-time fee/pet. Designated rooms, service with restrictions, supervision.
🖥 🍴 🛎 🖧 ✕ 📞 💻

▲▲ ▼▼▼▼ The Ritz-Carlton, Lake Tahoe H

(530) 562-3000. **$209-$899, 7 day notice.** 13031 Ritz-Carlton Highlands Ct 96161. I-80 exit 188 (SR 267) westbound; exit 188B eastbound, 5.6 mi se, then 2.5 mi sw on Highlands View Rd. Int corridors.
Pets: Accepted.
SAVE ECO 🖥 🍴 🛎 🖧 ✕ 📶 ✕ 📞 💻

TULARE

▲▲ ▼▼▼ Best Western Town & Country Lodge M

(559) 688-7537. **$79-$299.** 1051 N Blackstone St 93274. SR 99 exit 88 (Prosperity Ave/Blackstone St), just w. Int corridors. **Pets:** Medium, dogs only. $25 daily fee/room. Service with restrictions, supervision.
SAVE 🛎 🖧 🖧 ✕ 📞 💻

▼▼ Charter Inn & Suites H 🐾

(559) 685-9500. **$89-$199.** 1016 E Prosperity Ave 93274. SR 99 exit 88 (Prosperity Ave/Blackstone St), just e. Int corridors. **Pets:** Small. $100 deposit/room, $10 daily fee/pet. Service with restrictions, crate.
🛎 🖧 🖧 ✕ 📞 💻

▼▼ La Quinta Inn & Suites Tulare H

(559) 685-8900. **$97-$229.** 1500 Cherry Ct 93274. SR 99 exit 88 (Prosperity Ave/Blackstone St), just w. Int corridors. **Pets:** Accepted.
🖧 🖧 ✕ 📞 💻

▼▼ Quality Inn M

(559) 686-3432. **$81-$175.** 1010 E Prosperity Ave 93274. SR 99 exit 88 (Prosperity Ave/Blackstone St), just e. Int corridors. **Pets:** Small, dogs only. $15 daily fee/pet. Designated rooms, service with restrictions.
ECO 🖥 🛎 🖧 ✕ 🖧 📞 💻

TURLOCK

▲▲ ▼▼▼ Best Western Orchard Inn H

(209) 667-2827. **$95-$110.** 5025 N Golden State Blvd 95382. SR 99 exit 217 (Taylor Rd), just e, then just n. Ext corridors. **Pets:** Accepted.
SAVE 🛎 🖧 🖧 📞 💻

▲▲ ▼▼▼ Candlewood Suites H

(209) 250-1501. **Call for rates.** 1000 Powers Ct 95380. SR 99 exit 215 (Monte Vista Ave), just w, just s on N Tegner Rd, then just e. Int corridors. **Pets:** Accepted. SAVE 🛎 🖧 ✕ 📞 💻

TUSTIN

▲▲▲ ▼▼▼▼ Residence Inn by Marriott Tustin Orange County H ❀

(714) 258-9700. **$126-$216.** 15181 Newport Ave 92780. SR 55 exit 9 (Edinger Ave), just e. Int corridors. **Pets:** Other species. $100 one-time fee/room. Service with restrictions. SAVE 🖧 ✕ 📞 💻

TWENTYNINE PALMS *(Restaurants p. 603)*

▼▼ Americas Best Value Inn Joshua Tree/Twentynine Palms M

(760) 367-0070. **Call for rates.** 71829 Twentynine Palms Hwy 92277. SR 62, 2.3 mi w of Adobe Rd. Ext corridors. **Pets:** Accepted.
🖧 🖧 🖧 ✕ 📞 💻

▼▼▼ Roughley Manor BB

(760) 367-3238. **Call for rates.** 74744 Joe Davis Dr 92277. SR 62, 0.7 mi n on Utah Tr, 0.4 mi e. Ext/int corridors. **Pets:** Accepted.
🖧 🖧 ✕ 📶 📞 💻

UKIAH

▲▲▲ ▼▼▼ Best Western Orchard Inn H

(707) 462-1514. **$99-$399.** 555 S Orchard Ave 95482. US 101 exit Gobbi St, just w, then just n. Int corridors. **Pets:** Medium, dogs only. $20 daily fee/pet. Designated rooms, service with restrictions, supervision. SAVE 🖥 🖧 🖧 🖧 📞 💻

▼▼▼ Comfort Inn & Suites H

(707) 462-3442. **$109-$204.** 1220 Airport Park Blvd 95482. US 101 exit Talmage Rd, just w, then just s. Int corridors. **Pets:** Dogs only. $20 daily fee/pet. Designated rooms, service with restrictions, supervision.
🖧 🖧 🖧 📞 💻

▼▼ Days Inn M

(707) 462-7584. **$59-$159.** 950 N State St 95482. US 101 exit N State St, 0.5 mi s. Ext corridors. **Pets:** Accepted. 🖥 🖧 🖧 📞 💻

▲▲▲ ▼▼▼ Quality Inn M

(707) 462-2906. **$80-$195.** 1050 S State St 95482. US 101 exit Talmage Rd, 0.4 mi w, then just n. Ext corridors. **Pets:** Dogs only. $25 daily fee/pet. Designated rooms, service with restrictions, supervision.
SAVE 🍴 🖧 🖧 📞 💻

▼▼ Super 8 Ukiah M

(707) 468-8181. **$55-$189.** 693 S Orchard Ave 95482. US 101 exit Gobbi St W, just w, then just n. Ext corridors. **Pets:** Accepted.
ECO 🖥 🍴 🖧 🖧 📞 💻

▲▲▲ ▼▼▼ Travelodge Ukiah H

(707) 462-5745. **$80-$190.** 1720 N State St 95482. US 101 exit N State St, then just n. Ext corridors. **Pets:** Dogs only. $25 daily fee/pet. Designated rooms, service with restrictions, supervision.
SAVE 🍴 🖧 🖧 🖧 📞 💻

UNIVERSAL CITY

▲▲▲ ▼▼▼▼ Hilton Los Angeles/Universal City H

(818) 506-2500. **$179-$399.** 555 Universal Hollywood Dr 91608. US 101 exit 12A (Lankershim Blvd), just n, then just e. Int corridors.
Pets: Medium. $50 one-time fee/pet. Designated rooms, service with restrictions, supervision.
SAVE ECO 🖥 🍴 🖧 🖧 🖧 ✕ 📞 💻

▲▲▲ ▼▼▼▼ Sheraton Universal Hotel, at Universal Studios H

(818) 980-1212. **$200-$400.** 333 Universal Hollywood Dr 91608. US 101 exit 12A (Lankershim Blvd), just n, then just e. Int corridors.
Pets: Accepted. SAVE 🍴 🖧 🖧 ✕ 💻

UPPER LAKE *(Restaurants p. 603)*

▲▲▲ ▼▼▼ Super 8 M

(707) 275-0888. **$70-$139, 3 day notice.** 450 E Hwy 20 95485. Jct SR 29, 0.5 mi e. Ext corridors. **Pets:** Accepted. SAVE 🖧 🖧 📞 💻

VACAVILLE

Best Western Heritage Inn M
(707) 448-8453. **$80-$150.** 1420 E Monte Vista Ave 95688. I-80 exit 55 (Monte Vista Ave), westbound, just w; exit eastbound, just n on Allison Dr, then just e. Ext corridors. **Pets:** Medium. $20 daily fee/pet. Designated rooms, service with restrictions, supervision.

Hampton Inn & Suites Vacaville/Napa Valley Area H
(707) 469-6200. **$119-$159.** 800 Mason St 95688. I-80 exit Davis St eastbound, 0.4 mi n, then just e; exit Mason St westbound, just w. Int corridors. **Pets:** Accepted.

Residence Inn by Marriott H
(707) 469-0300. **$104-$179.** 360 Orange Dr 95687. I-80 exit 56 (Orange Dr) eastbound, just ne; exit 57 (Leisure Town Rd) westbound, just s, then 1.5 mi sw on Orange Dr; behind Black Oak Restaurant. Int corridors. **Pets:** Accepted.

VALLEJO

Courtyard by Marriott Vallejo Napa Valley H
(707) 644-1200. **$98-$197.** 1000 Fairgrounds Dr 94589. I-80 exit SR 37 (Marine World Pkwy), just w on SR 37, exit 20 (Discovery Kingdom/ Fairgrounds Dr), then just se; jct Sage St. Int corridors. **Pets:** Medium, dogs only. $100 one-time fee/room. Service with restrictions, supervision.

VENTURA *(Restaurants p. 603)*

Crowne Plaza Ventura Beach Resort H
(805) 648-2100. **Call for rates.** 450 E Harbor Blvd 93001. US 101 exit 70A (California St) northbound, just s; exit 71 (Main St) southbound, 0.5 mi e to California St, then just s. Int corridors. **Pets:** Accepted.

Four Points by Sheraton Ventura Harbor Resort H
(805) 658-1212. **$149-$239.** 1050 Schooner Dr 93001. US 101 exit 68 (Seaward Ave), just w, then 1.5 mi s on Harbor Blvd; at Ventura Harbor. Ext/int corridors. **Pets:** Accepted.

Holiday Inn Express Ventura Harbor H
(805) 856-9533. **$149-$298.** 1080 Navigator Dr 93001. US 101 exit 68 (Seaward Ave), just w, then 1.5 mi s; at Ventura Harbor. Ext/int corridors. **Pets:** Accepted.

Marriott Ventura Beach Hotel H
(805) 643-6000. **$133-$237.** 2055 E Harbor Blvd 93001. US 101 exit 68 (Seaward Ave), just w, then 0.5 mi n. Int corridors. **Pets:** Accepted.

Vagabond Inn Ventura M
(805) 648-5371. **$74-$279.** 756 E Thompson Blvd 93001. US 101 exit 70A (California St) northbound, just n, then just e; exit 70A (Ventura Ave) southbound, 0.6 mi e. Ext corridors. **Pets:** Accepted.

VICTORVILLE

Hawthorn Suites by Wyndham H ❖
(760) 949-4700. **$99-$219.** 11750 Dunia Rd 92392. I-15 exit 147 (Bear Valley Rd), just w, 0.3 mi s on Amargosa Rd, then just w. Int corridors. **Pets:** Medium, other species. $35 daily fee/pet. Designated rooms, service with restrictions, supervision.

VISALIA *(Restaurants p. 603)*

Lamp Liter Inn M
(559) 732-4511. **$79-$199.** 3300 W Mineral King Ave 93291. SR 198 exit 105B (SR 63 S/Mooney Blvd) westbound, 0.5 mi w; exit eastbound, just n, then 0.5 mi w. Ext corridors. **Pets:** Accepted.

La Quinta Inn & Suites Visalia/Sequoia Gateway H
(559) 739-9800. **$97-$378.** 5438 W Cypress Ave 93277. SR 198 exit 104 (Akers St), just s, then just w. Int corridors. **Pets:** Accepted.

Marriott Visalia at the Convention Center H
(559) 636-1111. **$106-$185.** 300 S Court St 93291. SR 198 exit 107A (Central Visalia/SR 63 N), just ne. Int corridors. **Pets:** Other species. $75 one-time fee/room. Designated rooms, service with restrictions, supervision.

Visalia Sequoia Gateway Inn H
(559) 651-3700. **$85-$169.** 9300 W Airport Dr 93277. SR 198 exit 102 (Plaza Dr), just s, then just w. Int corridors. **Pets:** Accepted.

Wyndham Visalia H ❖
(559) 651-5000. **$89-$165.** 9000 W Airport Dr 93277. SR 198 exit 102 (Plaza Dr), just s. Int corridors. **Pets:** Other species. $25 daily fee/pet. Designated rooms, service with restrictions, supervision.

VISTA

Hyatt Place San Diego-Vista/Carlsbad H
(760) 814-8879. **$89-$359.** 2645 S Melrose Dr 92081. SR 78 exit 6 (Vista Village Dr), just s, just w on Hacienda, then 4 mi se. Int corridors. **Pets:** Accepted.

WALNUT

Quality Inn & Suites H
(909) 594-9999. **$90-$300.** 1170 Fairway Dr 91789. SR 60 exit 21 (Fairway Dr), 0.3 mi s. Int corridors. **Pets:** Accepted.

WALNUT CREEK *(Restaurants p. 603)*

Holiday Inn Express Walnut Creek H
(925) 932-3332. **$119-$409.** 2730 N Main St 94597. I-680 exit 47 (N Main St) southbound, just n; exit 48 (Geary Rd/Treat Blvd), just w, then just s. Int corridors. **Pets:** Small, dogs only. $40 daily fee/pet. Designated rooms, service with restrictions, supervision.

WATSONVILLE

Best Western Rose Garden Inn H
(831) 724-3367. **$89-$299.** 740 Freedom Blvd 95076. On SR 152; jct Main St. Ext corridors. **Pets:** Small. $20 daily fee/room. Designated rooms, service with restrictions, crate.

WEAVERVILLE

Weaverville Victorian Inn M
(530) 623-4432. **Call for rates.** 2051 Main St 96093. Jct SR 3 and 299 (Main St), 1.5 mi se. Ext corridors. **Pets:** Accepted.

WEST HOLLYWOOD

Andaz West Hollywood H
(323) 656-1234. **$199-$450, 3 day notice.** 8401 W Sunset Blvd 90069. I-10 exit 7A (La Cienega Blvd), 4.4 mi n, then just e. Int corridors. **Pets:** Accepted.

Chamberlain West Hollywood H ❖
(310) 657-7400. **Call for rates.** 1000 Westmount Dr 90069. I-10 exit 7A (La Cienega Blvd), 4 mi n to Santa Monica Blvd, just w, then just n. Int corridors. **Pets:** Small, dogs only. $110 one-time fee/room. Designated rooms, service with restrictions, crate.

The Grafton on Sunset H
(323) 654-4600. **$279-$429.** 8462 W Sunset Blvd 90069. I-10 exit 7A (La Cienega Blvd), 4.4 mi n, then just e. Int corridors. **Pets:** Accepted.

Le Montrose Suite Hotel H
(310) 855-1115. **Call for rates.** 900 Hammond St 90069. I-10 exit 7A (La Cienega Blvd), 2.6 mi n to San Vicente Blvd, 1.3 mi nw, then just w. Int corridors. **Pets:** Accepted.

Le Parc Suite Hotel H
(310) 855-8888. **$259-$499.** 733 N West Knoll Dr 90069. I-10 exit 7A (La Cienega Blvd), 3.5 mi n, just w on Melrose Ave, then just n. Int corridors. **Pets:** Accepted.

The London West Hollywood at Beverly Hills H
(310) 854-1111. **$399-$899, 3 day notice.** 1020 N San Vicente Blvd 90069. I-10 exit 7A (La Cienega Blvd), 2.6 mi n, then 1.5 mi nw. Int corridors. **Pets:** Accepted.

WESTLAKE VILLAGE *(Restaurants p. 603)*

Four Seasons Hotel Westlake Village H
(818) 575-3000. **Call for rates.** Two Dole Dr 91362. US 101 exit 39 (Lindero Canyon Rd), just e, then just n on Via Colinas. Int corridors. **Pets:** Accepted.

Hyatt Regency Westlake H
(805) 557-1234. **$99-$309.** 880 S Westlake Blvd 91361. US 101 exit 40 (Westlake Blvd), just s. Int corridors. **Pets:** Accepted.

Residence Inn by Marriott Westlake Village H
(818) 707-4411. **$169-$279.** 30950 Russell Ranch Rd 91362. US 101 exit 39 (Lindero Canyon Rd), just e, then just s. Int corridors. **Pets:** Other species. $100 one-time fee/room. Service with restrictions, crate.

Westlake Village Inn H
(818) 889-0230. **Call for rates.** 31943 Agoura Rd 91361. US 101 exit 40 (Westlake Blvd), 1.3 mi se. Ext corridors. **Pets:** Medium, dogs only. $150 one-time fee/room. Service with restrictions, supervision.

WESTLEY

Holiday Inn Express H
(209) 894-8940. **Call for rates.** 4525 Howard Rd 95387. I-5 exit 441 (Westley/Howard Rd), just e, then just s. Int corridors. **Pets:** Accepted.

WESTMORLAND

Americas Best Value Inn M
(760) 351-7100. **$70-$80.** 351 W Main St 92281. On SR 86/78. Int corridors. **Pets:** $20 daily fee/pet. Service with restrictions, supervision.

WEST SACRAMENTO

Rodeway Inn Capitol M
(916) 371-6983. **$70-$150.** 817 W Capitol Ave 95691. Business Rt I-80 (Capital City Frwy) exit Jefferson Blvd, 0.3 mi n, then just e. Ext corridors. **Pets:** Medium, dogs only. $50 deposit/room, $10 daily fee/pet. Designated rooms, service with restrictions, supervision.

WHITTIER

Vagabond Inn M
(562) 698-9701. **Call for rates.** 14125 E Whittier Blvd 90605. I-605 exit 15 (Whittier Blvd), 3.5 mi e. Ext corridors. **Pets:** Accepted.

Whittier Grand Hotel H
(562) 945-8511. **Call for rates.** 7320 Greenleaf Ave 90602. I-605 exit 15 (Whittier Blvd), 2.5 mi e, then 0.6 mi n. Int corridors. **Pets:** Accepted.

WILLIAMS

Granzella's Inn H
(530) 473-3310. **$99-$117.** 391 6th St 95987. I-5 exit 577 (Williams), 0.5 mi w, then just n. Int corridors. **Pets:** Large, other species. $10 daily fee/room. Designated rooms, service with restrictions, supervision.

Ramada H
(530) 473-5120. **$70-$119.** 374 Ruggieri Way 95987. I-5 exit 577 (Williams), just se. Int corridors. **Pets:** Accepted.

Traveler's Inn M
(530) 473-5387. **$55-$90.** 215 N 7th St 95987. I-5 exit 577 (Williams), just w on E St (SR 20 business route), then 0.3 mi n. Ext corridors. **Pets:** Dogs only. $15 daily fee/pet. Designated rooms, service with restrictions, supervision.

WILLITS

Baechtel Creek Inn, an Ascend Hotel Collection Member H
(707) 459-9063. **$119-$240.** 101 Gregory Ln 95490. US 101, just w. Ext corridors. **Pets:** Small, dogs only. $25 daily fee/pet. Designated rooms, service with restrictions, supervision.

WILLOW CREEK

Coho Cottages CA
(530) 629-4000. **Call for rates.** 76 Willow Rd 95573. From SR 299, just n. Ext corridors. **Pets:** Medium, dogs only. $25 one-time fee/pet. Designated rooms, no service, supervision.

WILLOWS

Best Western Willows Inn M
(530) 934-4444. **$98-$169.** 475 N Humboldt Ave 95988. I-5 exit 603 (SR 162/Willows/Oroville), just e, then just n. Ext corridors. **Pets:** Medium. $15 daily fee/pet. Designated rooms, service with restrictions, supervision.

Holiday Inn Express Willows H
(530) 934-8900. **Call for rates.** 545 N Humboldt Ave 95988. I-5 exit 603 (SR 162/Willows/Oroville), just e, then just n. Int corridors. **Pets:** Other species. $20 daily fee/room. Service with restrictions, supervision.

WOODLAND

Days Inn H
(530) 666-3800. **$69-$83.** 1524 E Main St 95776. I-5 exit 537 (Main St) northbound, then just w; exit SR 113 (Davis) southbound, just e; behind McDonalds. Int corridors. **Pets:** Accepted.

Holiday Inn Express Hotel & Suites H
(530) 662-7750. **$109-$249.** 2070 Freeway Dr 95776. I-5 exit 536 (CR 102), just n, just e on E Main St, then just s. Int corridors. **Pets:** Small. $20 daily fee/pet. Designated rooms, service with restrictions, supervision.

WOODLAND HILLS *(Restaurants p. 604)*

Hilton Woodland Hills/Los Angeles H
(818) 595-1000. **$149-$309.** 6360 Canoga Ave 91367. US 101 exit 26B (Canoga Ave), 1 mi n. Int corridors. **Pets:** Accepted.

◆◆◆ ▼▼▼ Warner Center Marriott Hotel H
(818) 887-4800. **$135-$261.** 21850 Oxnard St 91367. US 101 exit 27A (Topanga Canyon Blvd N), 0.6 mi n, then just e. Int corridors.
Pets: Accepted. [SAVE] [YI] [&M] [➜] [⊠] [⌼] [⊗] [∎] [▣]

YERMO (Restaurants p. 604)

▼▼ Oak Tree Inn M
(760) 254-1148. **Call for rates.** 35450 Yermo Rd 92398. I-15 exit 191 (Ghost Town Rd), just se. Int corridors. **Pets:** Accepted.
[YI] [&M] [➜] [⌼] [∎] [▣]

YOSEMITE NATIONAL PARK

▼▼ The Redwoods In Yosemite VH ❀
(209) 375-6666. **Call for rates.** 8038 Chilnualna Falls Rd 95389. 6 mi inside southern entrance via SR 41 and Chilnualna Falls Rd. Ext corridors. **Pets:** Other species. $25 daily fee/pet. Supervision.
[YI] [⌼] [⊗] [∎] [▣]

YOUNTVILLE

▼▼ Lavender BB
(707) 944-1388. **$285-$495, 7 day notice.** 2020 Webber Ave 94599. From SR 29, just e on Madison St, just s on Washington St, then just e. Ext/int corridors. **Pets:** Accepted. [&M] [⌼] [⊗] [∎] [▣]

▼▼▼ Vintage Inn H
(707) 944-1112. **Call for rates.** 6541 Washington St 94599. From SR 29, just e on Madison St, then just s. Ext corridors. **Pets:** Accepted.
[&M] [➜] [⊠] [⌼] [⊗] [∎] [▣]

YREKA

◆◆◆ ▼▼ Best Western Miner's Inn M 🐾
(530) 842-4355. **$95-$179.** 122 E Miner St 96097. I-5 exit 775, just w. Ext corridors. **Pets:** Medium. $15 one-time fee/pet. Service with restrictions, crate. [SAVE] [&M] [➜] [⌼] [∎] [▣]

▼▼ Comfort Inn H
(530) 842-1612. **$80-$120.** 1804-B Fort Jones Rd 96097. I-5 exit 773, just w. Int corridors. **Pets:** Accepted. [&M] [➜] [⌼] [⊗] [∎] [▣]

◆◆◆ ▼ Klamath Motor Lodge M
(530) 842-2751. **$50-$75.** 1111 S Main St 96097. I-5 exit 775, just w to Main St, then 0.9 mi s. Ext corridors. **Pets:** Medium. $7 daily fee/pet. Designated rooms, service with restrictions, supervision.
[SAVE] [YI] [➜] [⌼] [∎] [▣]

◆◆◆ ▼ Rodeway Inn M
(530) 842-4412. **$52-$91.** 1235 S Main St 96097. I-5 exit 775, just w to Main St, then 0.9 mi s. Ext corridors. **Pets:** $30 deposit/room, $7 daily fee/pet. Service with restrictions, supervision.
[SAVE] [&M] [➜] [⌼] [∎] [▣]

◆◆◆ ▼▼ Super 8 M
(530) 842-5781. **$55-$71.** 136 Montague Rd 96097. I-5 exit 776, just w. Ext corridors. **Pets:** Accepted. [SAVE] [&M] [➜] [⌼] [∎] [▣]

YUBA CITY

◆◆◆ ▼▼▼ Best Western Yuba City Inn M
(530) 674-1650. **$89-$299.** 894 W Onstott Rd 95991. Just s of jct SR 99 and 20. Ext corridors. **Pets:** Very small. $20 daily fee/pet. Supervision. [SAVE] [&M] [➜] [⌼] [⊗] [∎] [▣]

◆◆◆ ▼▼ Bonanza Inn-Magnuson Grand Hotel & Convention Center H
(530) 674-8824. **$75-$190.** 1001 Clark Ave 95991. Jct SR 20 and 99, 0.5 mi e, then just n. Ext corridors. **Pets:** Small, dogs only. $10 daily fee/pet. Designated rooms, service with restrictions, supervision.
[SAVE] [&M] [➜] [⌼] [∎] [▣]

YUCCA VALLEY

◆◆◆ ▼▼▼ Best Western Joshua Tree Hotel & Suites H
(760) 365-3555. **$117-$300.** 56525 Twentynine Palms Hwy 92284. On SR 62, 0.6 mi w of jct SR 247. Int corridors. **Pets:** Dogs only. $20 one-time fee/pet. Designated rooms, service with restrictions, supervision.
[SAVE] [&M] [➜] [⌼] [⊗] [∎] [▣]

COLORADO

ALAMOSA

◆◆◆ ▼▼ Best Western Alamosa Inn M ❀
(719) 589-2567. **$73-$200.** 2005 W Main St 81101. On US 160, 1 mi w of center. Ext corridors. **Pets:** Medium, dogs only. $20 daily fee/pet. Designated rooms, service with restrictions, supervision.
[SAVE] [➜] [⌼] [⊗] [∎] [▣]

▼▼▼ Comfort Inn & Suites H ❀
(719) 587-9000. **$99-$219.** 6301 US 160 W 81101. 2.3 mi w of center. Int corridors. **Pets:** Medium, dogs only. $20 daily fee/pet. Designated rooms, service with restrictions, supervision.
[YI] [➜] [⊠] [⌼] [⊗] [∎] [▣]

▼▼▼ Holiday Inn Express & Suites H
(719) 589-4026. **Call for rates.** 3418 Mariposa St 81101. On US 160, 2 mi w of center. Int corridors. **Pets:** Accepted.
[YI] [&M] [➜] [⊠] [⌼] [⊗] [∎] [▣]

◆◆◆ ▼▼ Super 8 of Alamosa M
(719) 589-6447. **$60-$145.** 2505 Main St 81101. On US 160, 1.3 mi w. Int corridors. **Pets:** Accepted. [SAVE] [➜] [⌼] [⊗] [∎] [▣]

ASPEN

◆◆◆ ▼▼▼▼ Aspen Meadows Resort, A Dolce Destination Collection H
(970) 925-4240. **$125-$800, 30 day notice.** 845 Meadows Rd 81611. 0.3 mi n of SR 82 via N 7th Ave, just w. Ext/int corridors.
Pets: Accepted. [SAVE] [YI] [➜] [⊠] [⌼] [⊗] [⅄] [∎] [▣]

▼▼ Aspen Mountain Lodge H
(970) 925-7650. **Call for rates.** 311 W Main St 81611. 0.4 mi w on SR 82; between S 2nd and S 3rd sts. Int corridors. **Pets:** Accepted.
[YI] [➜] [⌼] [⊗] [∎] [▣]

◆◆◆ ▼▼▼▼ Hotel Jerome, An Auberge Resort H
(970) 920-1000. **Call for rates.** 330 E Main St 81611. Jct E Main and N Mill sts; downtown. Int corridors. **Pets:** Accepted.
[SAVE] [⊟] [YI] [➜] [⊠] [⌼] [⊗] [∎] [▣]

◆◆◆ ▼▼▼ The Limelight Hotel H
(970) 925-3025. **Call for rates.** 355 S Monarch St 81611. Just s of SR 82; at S Monarch and E Cooper sts; downtown. Int corridors.
Pets: Accepted. [SAVE] [⊟] [YI] [➜] [⊠] [⌼] [⊗] [∎] [▣]

◆◆◆ ▼▼▼▼ The Little Nell H ❀
(970) 920-4600. **$325-$1475, 30 day notice.** 675 E Durant Ave 81611. Jct E Durant Ave and S Spring St; downtown. Int corridors. **Pets:** Dogs only. $100 one-time fee/pet, $25 daily fee/pet. Service with restrictions, crate. [SAVE] [⊟] [YI] [➜] [⊠] [⌼] [⊗] [∎] [▣]

▼▼▼▼ The Residence Hotel H
(970) 920-6532. **Call for rates.** 305 S Galena St 81611. Jct S Galena St and E Hyman Ave; downtown. Int corridors. **Pets:** Accepted.
🛜 ⊠ ☎ 🛗 🖵

♨ ▼▼▼ ▼▼▼ The St. Regis Aspen Resort H ✿
(970) 920-3300. **$279-$3599, 60 day notice.** 315 E Dean St 81611. Jct S Monarch and E Dean sts; downtown. Int corridors. **Pets:** Other species. $25 one-time fee/room, $25 daily fee/room. Service with restrictions. SAVE 🍴 🏊 ⊠ 🛜 ⊠ 🛗 🖵

AURORA

♨ ▼▼▼▼ Aloft Denver International Airport H
(303) 371-9500. **Call for rates.** 16470 E 40th Cir 80011. I-70 exit 283 (Chambers Rd), just n, 0.7 mi e, then just s. Int corridors.
Pets: Accepted. SAVE 🍴 🏊 🛜 ⊠ 🛗 🖵

♨ ▼▼▼▼ Best Western Plus Gateway Inn & Suites H ✿
(720) 748-4800. **$79-$399.** 800 S Abilene St 80012. I-225 exit 7 (Mississippi Ave), just e, then 0.3 mi n. Int corridors. **Pets:** Medium, other species. $20 daily fee/room. Designated rooms, service with restrictions, crate. SAVE ♿ 🏊 🛜 ⊠ 🛗 🖵

♨ ▼▼▼▼ Hyatt Place Denver Airport H
(303) 371-0700. **$84-$249.** 16250 E 40th Ave 80011. I-70 exit 283 (Chambers Rd), just n, then 0.5 mi e. Int corridors. **Pets:** Accepted.
SAVE 🍴 ♿ 🛜 ⊠ 🛗 🖵

▼▼▼▼ Residence Inn by Marriott H
(303) 459-8000. **$88-$246.** 16490 E 40th Cir 80011. I-70 exit 283 (Chambers Rd), just n, 0.5 mi e, then just s. Int corridors.
Pets: Medium, other species. $100 one-time fee/room. Service with restrictions, supervision. 🏊 🛜 ⊠ 🛗 🖵

▼▼▼ ▼▼▼ Woolley's Classic Suites-Denver Airport H ✿
(720) 599-3750. **$149-$319.** 16450 E 40th Cir 80011. I-70 exit 283 (Chambers Rd), just n, 0.7 mi e, then just s. Int corridors. **Pets:** Dogs only. $100 one-time fee/room. Designated rooms, service with restrictions, supervision. 🍴 ♿ 🛜 ⊠ 🛗 🖵

AVON

♨ ▼▼▼ ▼▼▼ Westin Riverfront Resort & Spa, at Beaver Creek Mountain CO
(970) 790-6000. **$179-$2000, 3 day notice.** 126 Riverfront Ln 81620. I-70 exit 167, 0.6 mi s on Avon Rd, then just w. Int corridors.
Pets: Accepted. SAVE ECO ♿ 🍴 🏊 ⊠ 🛜 ⊠ 🛗 🖵

BASALT

♨ ▼▼▼ Element Basalt- Aspen H ✿
(970) 340-4040. **$99-$290.** 499 Market St 81621. Jct SR 82 and Willits St, just sw to Valley Rd, just se, then just e. Int corridors.
Pets: Medium, other species. $50 one-time fee/room. Designated rooms, service with restrictions, supervision.
SAVE 🍴 ♿ ⊠ 🛜 ⊠ 🛗 🖵

BEAVER CREEK

♨ ▼▼▼ ▼▼▼ Park Hyatt Beaver Creek Resort & Spa H
(970) 949-1234. **$159-$1099, 3 day notice.** 136 E Thomas Pl 81620. I-70 exit 167, 3 mi s on Avon and Village rds, 0.4 mi e on Offerson Rd, then just s. Int corridors. **Pets:** Accepted.
SAVE ECO ♿ 🍴 ♿ 🏊 ⊠ 🛜 ⊠ 🛗 🖵

♨ ▼▼▼ ▼▼▼ The Ritz-Carlton, Bachelor Gulch H ✿
(970) 748-6200. **$159-$1599, 60 day notice.** 0130 Daybreak Ridge 81620. I-70 exit 167, just s past the Beaver Creek Village gatehouse to Prater Rd, then just w; follow signs to Bachelor Gulch Village. Int corridors. **Pets:** Dogs only. $125 one-time fee/room, $25 daily fee/room. Service with restrictions, supervision.
SAVE ♿ 🍴 ♿ 🏊 ⊠ 🛜 ⊠ 🛗 🖵

BLACK FOREST

▼▼▼ Black Forest Bed & Breakfast Lodge BB
(719) 495-4208. **Call for rates.** 11170 Black Forest Rd 80908. Jct Shoup and Black Forest rds, 1.3 mi s, then w at stone columns. Ext/int corridors. **Pets:** Accepted. 🍴 🛜 ⊠ 🛗 🖵

BOULDER *(Restaurants p. 604)*

▼▼▼ Basecamp Boulder, an Ascend Hotel Collecion Member H
(303) 449-7550. **$189-$329.** 2020 Arapahoe Ave 80302. US 36 (28th St), 0.5 mi w. Ext/int corridors. **Pets:** Accepted.
🍴 🏊 ⊠ 🛜 ⊠ 🛗 🖵

♨ ▼▼▼ ▼▼▼ Best Western Plus Boulder Inn H
(303) 449-3800. **$179-$279.** 770 28th St 80303. US 36 (28th St) exit Baseline Rd via Frontage Rd. Int corridors. **Pets:** Medium. $50 deposit/room. Designated rooms, supervision.
SAVE ECO ♿ ♿ 🏊 ⊠ 🛜 ⊠ 🛗 🖵

▼▼▼ Boulder University Inn M
(303) 417-1700. **Call for rates.** 1632 Broadway 80302. US 36 (28th St) exit Baseline Rd, 0.3 mi s, then 3 mi nw. Ext corridors. **Pets:** Large. $100 deposit/room, $15 daily fee/pet. Service with restrictions, supervision. ECO 🏊 🛜 ⊠ 🛗 🖵

▼▼▼ Foot of The Mountain Motel M
(303) 442-5688. **$89-$169.** 200 Arapahoe Ave 80302. 1.8 mi w of US 36 (28th St). Ext corridors. **Pets:** Accepted.
🍴 🛜 ⊠ ⊠ 🛗 🖵

♨ ▼▼▼ Holiday Inn Express H
(303) 442-6600. **Call for rates.** 4777 N Broadway 80304. 3 mi n of Pearl Street Pedestrian Mall. Int corridors. **Pets:** Accepted.
SAVE 🍴 ♿ 🛜 ⊠ 🛗 🖵

▼▼▼ Homewood Suites by Hilton H
(303) 499-9922. **$159-$359.** 4950 Baseline Rd 80303. 1.2 mi e of US 36 (28th St); jct SR 157 (Foothills Pkwy), just w; entry off Baseline Rd. Ext/int corridors. **Pets:** Accepted. 🏊 🛜 ⊠ 🛗 🖵

♨ ▼▼▼ Hotel Boulderado H
(303) 442-4344. **$224-$429.** 2115 13th St 80302. At 13th and Spruce sts, just n of Pearl Street Pedestrian Mall. Int corridors. **Pets:** Accepted.
SAVE 🍴 🛜 ⊠ 🛗 🖵

♨ ▼▼▼ Hyatt Place Boulder/Pearl Street H
(303) 442-0160. **$129-$399.** 2280 Junction Pl 80301. Jct US 36 and Pearl St, just e. Int corridors. **Pets:** Accepted.
SAVE 🍴 ♿ 🛜 ⊠ 🛗 🖵

♨ ▼▼▼ Residence Inn by Marriott H
(303) 449-5545. **$116-$406.** 3030 Center Green Dr 80301. 0.5 mi e of US 36 (28th St), e on Valmont Rd; from Foothills Pkwy, just w on Valmont Rd. Ext corridors. **Pets:** Accepted.
SAVE ECO 🏊 🛜 ⊠ 🛗 🖵

BRECKENRIDGE

♨ ▼▼▼ Beaver Run Resort & Conference Center CO
(970) 453-6000. **$105-$895, 14 day notice.** 620 Village Rd 80424. 0.4 mi sw of SR 9 and Village Rd; at base of Peak 9. Int corridors.
Pets: Accepted. SAVE 🍴 🏊 ⊠ 🛜 ⊠ ⊠ 🛗 🖵

▼▼▼ DoubleTree by Hilton Breckenridge H ✿
(970) 547-5550. **$109-$699.** 550 Village Rd 80424. Jct Main St, just w on S Park Ave, just sw. Int corridors. **Pets:** Large, dogs only. $50 one-time fee/room. Service with restrictions, supervision.
ECO ♿ 🍴 🏊 ⊠ 🛜 ⊠ 🛗 🖵

▼▼▼ The Lodge at Breckenridge 🄷 ❀
(970) 453-9300. **$139-$489, 30 day notice.** 112 Overlook Dr 80424. 0.3 m s of Main St and Ski Hill Rd to Boreas Pass Rd, then 2.2 mi w (uphill) to Overlook Rd. Ext/int corridors. **Pets:** Dogs only. $30 daily fee/room. Designated rooms, service with restrictions.

🍴 🗙 🛜 🗙 🔏 🔒 ▣

BRIGHTON

🔺 ▼▼▼ Best Western Brighton Inn 🄷
(303) 637-7710. **$140-$170.** 15151 Brighton Rd 80601. US 85, 1 mi s of jct SR 7, just w. Int corridors. **Pets:** Medium, dogs only. $25 daily fee/pet. Designated rooms, service with restrictions, supervision.

(SAVE) 🔏 🖙 🛜 🗙 🔒 ▣

BROOMFIELD (Restaurants p. 604)

🔺 ▼▼▼ Aloft Broomfield Denver 🄷
(303) 635-2000. **$99-$399.** 8300 Arista Pl 80021. US 36 (Boulder Tpke) exit US 287/CR 121, 0.6 mi s, then 0.4 mi w on Uptown Ave. Int corridors. **Pets:** Accepted. (SAVE) 🍴 🖙 🛜 🗙 🔒 ▣

🔺 ▼▼▼ Hyatt House Boulder/Broomfield 🄷
(720) 890-4811. **$99-$239.** 13351 W Midway Blvd 80020. US 36 (Boulder Tpke) exit Storagetek Dr/Interlocken Loop, 0.3 mi n, then just e on Via Varra Rd. Int corridors. **Pets:** Accepted.

(SAVE) 🍴 🔏 🖙 🛜 🗙 🔒 ▣

▼▼▼ Omni Interlocken Resort 🄷
(303) 438-6600. **Call for rates.** 500 Interlocken Blvd 80021. US 36 (Boulder Tpke) exit Interlocken Loop, 0.4 mi s, then 0.4 mi e. Int corridors. **Pets:** Accepted. 🍴 🔏 🖙 🗙 🛜 🗙 🔒 ▣

▼▼ TownePlace Suites by Marriott Boulder/Broomfield 🄷
(303) 466-2200. **$71-$248.** 480 Flatiron Blvd 80021. US 36 (Boulder Tpke) exit Interlocken Loop, 0.4 mi s, just w on Interlocken Blvd, then just s. Int corridors. **Pets:** Other species. $25 daily fee/room. Service with restrictions, crate. 🔏 🖙 🛜 🗙 🔒 ▣

BURLINGTON

🔺 ▼▼▼ Best Western Plus Carousel Inn & Suites 🄷
(719) 346-7777. **$110-$170.** 605 S Lincoln St 80807. I-70 exit 437, just s. Int corridors. **Pets:** $20 daily fee/room. Designated rooms, service with restrictions, supervision. (SAVE) 🍴 🔏 🖙 🛜 🗙 🔒 ▣

▼▼ Quality Inn Burlington 🄷
(719) 346-7676. **$109-$159.** 282 S Lincoln St 80807. I-70 exit 437, just n on US 385. Int corridors. **Pets:** $15 daily fee/room. Designated rooms, service with restrictions, supervision. 🖙 🛜 🗙 🔒 ▣

CAÑON CITY

🔺 ▼▼▼ Best Western Cañon City 🄷
(719) 275-2400. **$99-$249.** 110 Latigo Ln 81212. From 9th St, 3 mi e on US 50, just n. Int corridors. **Pets:** Small. $20 daily fee/pet. Designated rooms, service with restrictions, supervision.

(SAVE) 🖙 🗙 🛜 🗙 🔒 ▣

CARBONDALE

▼▼ Comfort Inn & Suites 🄷 ❀
(970) 963-8880. **$109-$229.** 920 Cowen Dr 81623. Jct SR 82 and 133, just sw. Int corridors. **Pets:** Medium. $15 daily fee/pet. Designated rooms, service with restrictions, supervision.

🍴 🖙 🗙 🛜 🗙 🔒 ▣

CASTLE ROCK

🔺 ▼▼▼ Best Western Plus Castle Rock 🄷 ❀
(303) 814-8800. **$100-$210.** 595 Genoa Way 80109. I-25 exit 184 (Meadows Pkwy), just w to Castleton Way, just s, then e. Int corridors. **Pets:** Medium. $20 daily fee/room. Designated rooms, service with restrictions, supervision. (SAVE) 🖙 🛜 🗙 🔒 ▣

CENTENNIAL

▼▼ Drury Inn & Suites-Denver Near the Tech Center 🄷
(303) 694-3400. **$90-$170.** 9445 E Dry Creek Rd 80112. I-25 exit 196 (Dry Creek Rd), just w; on northwest corner. Int corridors.
Pets: Accepted. 🍴 🖙 🛜 🗙 🔒 ▣

▼▼▼ Staybridge Suites Denver Tech Center 🄷
(303) 858-9990. **Call for rates.** 7150 S Clinton St 80112. I-25 exit 197 (Arapahoe Rd), just e to Clinton St, 0.5 mi s, then just e. Int corridors.
Pets: Accepted. 🔏 🖙 🛜 🗙 🔒 ▣

▼▼ TownePlace Suites by Marriott Denver Tech Center 🄷
(720) 875-1113. **$59-$494.** 7877 S Chester St 80112. I-25 exit 196 (Dry Creek Rd), just w to Chester St, then 0.3 mi s. Int corridors.
Pets: Accepted. 🍴 🔏 🖙 🛜 🗙 🔒 ▣

CHIPITA PARK

▼▼▼ Chipita Lodge B & B 🄱🄱 ❀
(719) 684-8454. **$125-$160, 7 day notice.** 9090 Chipita Park Rd 80809. Jct US 24, just s on Fountain Blvd (Pine Peak Hwy), then 1.5 mi w; right at fork. Ext/int corridors. **Pets:** Dogs only. $25 one-time fee/pet. Designated rooms, no service, supervision.

🍴 🛜 🗙 🔏 🔊 🖉

CLIFTON

🔺 ▼▼▼ Best Western Grande River Inn & Suites 🄷 ❀
(970) 434-3400. **$119-$159.** 3228 I-70 Business Loop 81520. I-70 exit 37, 0.8 mi s; east of Grand Junction. Ext corridors. **Pets:** Medium. $10 one-time fee/room, $10 daily fee/pet. Designated rooms, service with restrictions, supervision. (SAVE) 🖙 🛜 🗙 🔒 ▣

COLORADO SPRINGS

🔺 ▼▼▼ The Broadmoor 🄷 ❀
(719) 634-7711. **$325-$8500, 7 day notice.** 1 Lake Ave 80906. I-25 exit 138, 3 mi w on Circle Dr (which becomes Lake Ave). Ext/int corridors. **Pets:** Other species. $50 daily fee/pet. Designated rooms, service with restrictions, crate. (SAVE) 🍴 🔏 🖙 🗙 🛜 🗙 🔒 ▣

🔺 ▼▼▼▼ Cheyenne Mountain Resort 🄷
(719) 538-4000. **Call for rates.** 3225 Broadmoor Valley Rd 80906. I-25 exit 138, 1.4 mi w to SR 115, 0.5 mi s, just w on Cheyenne Mountain Blvd, then just s. Ext/int corridors. **Pets:** Accepted.
(SAVE) (ECO) 🍴 🔏 🖙 🗙 🛜 🗙 🔒 ▣

▼▼▼ DoubleTree by Hilton Colorado Springs 🄷 ❀
(719) 576-8900. **$129-$229.** 1775 E Cheyenne Mountain Blvd 80906. I-25 exit 138, just w. Int corridors. **Pets:** Medium, dogs only. $50 one-time fee/room. Designated rooms, service with restrictions.

🍴 🔏 🖙 🛜 🗙 🔒 ▣

▼▼▼ Drury Inn & Suites Colorado Springs 🄷
(719) 598-2500. **$90-$230.** 1170 InterQuest Pkwy 80921. I-25 exit 153, just e. Int corridors. **Pets:** Accepted. 🍴 🔏 🗙 🔒 ▣

🔺 ▼▼▼ Fairfield Inn & Suites by Marriott Colorado Springs North Air Force Academy 🄷
(719) 488-4644. **$103-$227.** 15275 Struthers Rd 80921. I-25 exit 158, just e on Baptist Rd, then just s. Int corridors. **Pets:** Dogs only. $50 daily fee/pet. Designated rooms, service with restrictions, crate.
(SAVE) 🔌 🔏 🖙 🛜 🗙 🔒 ▣

▼▼▼ Homewood Suites by Hilton Colorado Springs-North 🄷
(719) 265-6600. **$99-$289.** 9130 Explorer Dr 80920. I-25 exit 151 (Briargate Pkwy), 0.8 mi e. Int corridors. **Pets:** Accepted.
🔏 🖙 🛜 🗙 🔒 ▣

Hotel Eleganté Conference & Event Center 🏨 🐾

(719) 576-5900. **$99-$219.** 2886 S Circle Dr 80906. I-25 exit 138, just e. Int corridors. **Pets:** Large. $50 one-time fee/pet. Designated rooms, service with restrictions, crate.

Hyatt House Colorado Springs 🏨

(719) 268-9990. **Call for rates.** 5805 Delmonico Dr 80919. I-25 exit 148 (Rockrimmon Blvd), just nw, then ne; entry around the bank. Int corridors. **Pets:** Accepted.

Hyatt Place Colorado Springs/Garden of the Gods 🏨

(719) 265-9385. **$94-$199.** 503 W Garden of the Gods Rd 80907. I-25 exit 146 (Garden of the Gods Rd), just w. Int corridors. **Pets:** Medium, dogs only. $75 one-time fee/room. Service with restrictions, supervision.

The Mining Exchange, a Wyndham Grand Hotel & Spa 🏨

(719) 323-2000. **$119-$275.** 8 S Nevada Ave 80903. Between Colorado and Pikes Peak aves; downtown. Int corridors. **Pets:** Accepted.

Plaza Inn 🏨

(719) 266-4300. **Call for rates.** 8155 N Academy Blvd 80920. I-25 exit 150, just s, then e. Int corridors. **Pets:** Accepted.

Radisson Hotel Colorado Springs Airport 🏨 🐾

(719) 597-7000. **$119-$239, 7 day notice.** 1645 N Newport Rd 80916. I-25 exit 139, 4.5 mi e on US 24 Bypass. Int corridors. **Pets:** Medium, dogs only. $100 deposit/pet, $25 one-time fee/pet. Designated rooms, service with restrictions, crate.

Residence Inn by Marriott Air Force Academy 🏨

(719) 388-9300. **$98-$261.** 9805 Federal Dr 80921. I-25 exit 153, just e, then s. Int corridors. **Pets:** Accepted.

Residence Inn by Marriott-Colorado Springs South 🏨

(719) 576-0101. **$94-$428.** 2765 Geyser Dr 80906. I-25 exit 138, just w to E Cheyenne Mountain Blvd, then just s. Int corridors. **Pets:** Accepted.

Sonesta ES Suites 🏨

(719) 574-0370. **Call for rates.** 3880 N Academy Blvd 80917. I-25 exit 146 (Garden of the Gods Rd), 4.5 mi e, then 0.3 mi s. Ext corridors. **Pets:** Accepted.

TownePlace Suites by Marriott Colorado Springs/Garden of the Gods 🏨

(719) 594-4447. **$80-$252.** 4760 Centennial Blvd 80919. I-25 exit 146 (Garden of the Gods Rd), 1 mi w, then just n. Int corridors. **Pets:** Accepted.

TownePlace Suites by Marriott Colorado Springs South 🏨

(719) 638-0800. **$79-$261.** 1530 N Newport Rd 80916. I-25 exit 139, 5 mi e on US 24 Bypass, then just n. Int corridors. **Pets:** Accepted.

CORTEZ

Best Western Turquoise Inn & Suites Ⓜ

(970) 565-3778. **$99-$179.** 535 E Main St 81321. 0.6 mi e of center on US 160. Ext corridors. **Pets:** Accepted.

Retro Inn at Mesa Verde Ⓜ

(970) 565-3738. **Call for rates.** 2040 E Main St 81321. 1.3 mi e of center on US 160. Ext corridors. **Pets:** Accepted.

CRAIG

Best Western Plus Deer Park Hotel & Suites 🏨 🐾

(970) 824-9282. **$99-$134.** 262 Commerce St 81625. 0.3 mi s of jct US 40 and SR 13. Int corridors. **Pets:** $50 deposit/room, $10 one-time fee/ room. Designated rooms, service with restrictions, crate.

Candlewood Suites 🏨

(970) 824-8400. **$99-$179.** 92 Commerce St 81625. 0.4 mi s of jct US 40 and SR 13. Int corridors. **Pets:** Large, dogs only. $15 daily fee/room. Service with restrictions, crate.

Hampton Inn & Suites 🏨

(970) 826-9900. **$99-$205.** 377 Cedar Ct 81625. 0.4 mi s of jct US 40 and SR 13, just w. Int corridors. **Pets:** Service with restrictions, supervision.

CRESTED BUTTE *(Restaurants p. 604)*

Elevation Hotel & Spa 🏨

(970) 251-3000. **Call for rates.** 500 Gothic Rd 81225. 5.9 mi n of Elk Ave. Int corridors. **Pets:** Accepted.

Elk Mountain Lodge 🅱🅱

(970) 349-7533. **Call for rates.** 129 Gothic Ave 81224. 0.3 mi w on Elk Ave to 2nd St, just n. Int corridors. **Pets:** Medium, dogs only. $30 daily fee/pet. Designated rooms, supervision.

The Grand Lodge 🏨

(970) 349-8000. **Call for rates.** 6 Emmons Loop 81225. 2.3 mi n of center. Int corridors. **Pets:** Accepted.

Old Town Inn 🏨 🐾

(970) 349-6184. **$99-$149.** 708 Sixth St 81224. On SR 135, just s of Elk Ave. Int corridors. **Pets:** Other species. $10 daily fee/room. Designated rooms, service with restrictions.

WestWall Lodge 🅲🅾

(970) 349-1280. **Call for rates.** 14 Hunter Hill Rd 81225. 2.2 mi n, just e; at Mt. Crested Butte. Int corridors. **Pets:** Accepted.

DENVER *(Restaurants p. 604)*

Aloft Denver Downtown 🏨 🐾

(303) 623-3063. **$99-$499.** 800 15th St 80202. Between Champa and Stout sts. Int corridors. **Pets:** Large, dogs only. Service with restrictions, supervision.

The Art, a hotel 🏨 🐾

(303) 572-8000. **$239-$359.** 1201 Broadway 80203. Northwest corner of 12th Ave and Broadway; Capitol Hill. Int corridors. **Pets:** Large, dogs only. $75 daily fee/room. Service with restrictions, supervision.

The Brown Palace Hotel and Spa, Autograph Collection 🏨 🐾

(303) 297-3111. **$183-$637.** 321 17th St 80202. From Broadway and Tremont Pl, just sw. Int corridors. **Pets:** Large, dogs only. $100 deposit/ room. No service, supervision.

Comfort Inn Denver East 🏨

(303) 375-1500. **$89-$189.** 4380 Peoria St 80239. I-70 exit 281 eastbound; exit 282 westbound, just n. Int corridors. **Pets:** Accepted.

Courtyard by Marriott Denver Stapleton H
(303) 333-3303. **$80-$285.** 7415 E 41st Ave 80216. I-70 exit 278, s on Quebec St exit Smith Rd, then e to Frontage Rd; I-270 exit 4. Int corridors. **Pets:** Accepted.

The Crawford Hotel H
(720) 460-3700. **Call for rates.** 1701 Wynkoop St 80202. Corner of 17th St; in Union Station. Int corridors. **Pets:** Accepted.

Crowne Plaza Denver Airport - Convention Center H
(303) 371-9494. **Call for rates.** 15500 E 40th Ave 80239. I-70 exit 283 (Chambers Rd), just n, then just e. Int corridors. **Pets:** Accepted.

the Curtis - a DoubleTree by Hilton Hotel H
(303) 571-0300. **$149-$299.** 1405 Curtis St 80202. Between 14th and 15th sts. Int corridors. **Pets:** Accepted.

Denver Marriott Tech Center H ✿
(303) 779-1100. **$56-$406.** 4900 S Syracuse St 80237. I-25 exit 199, exit Belleview Ave E to Syracuse St, then just n. Int corridors. **Pets:** Medium, dogs only. $100 one-time fee/pet. Designated rooms, service with restrictions.

DoubleTree by Hilton Hotel Denver H
(303) 321-3333. **Call for rates.** 3203 Quebec St 80207. I-70 exit 278, 0.5 mi s; I-270 exit 4. Int corridors. **Pets:** Accepted.

Drury Inn & Suites Denver Stapleton H
(303) 373-1983. **$100-$180.** 4550 N Central Park Blvd 80238. I-70 exit 279B westbound; exit 279 eastbound, just n. Int corridors. **Pets:** Accepted.

Four Seasons Hotel Denver H
(303) 389-3000. **Call for rates.** 1111 14th St 80202. Between Lawrence and Arapahoe sts. Int corridors. **Pets:** Accepted.

Grand Hyatt Denver H
(303) 295-1234. **$99-$399.** 1750 Welton St 80202. Between 17th and 18th sts. Int corridors. **Pets:** Accepted.

Hampton Inn & Suites Denver Tech Center H
(303) 804-9900. **$99-$299.** 5001 S Ulster St 80237. I-25 exit 199, e to Ulster St, then just n. Int corridors. **Pets:** Accepted.

Holiday Inn Denver East - Stapleton H
(303) 321-3500. **Call for rates.** 3333 Quebec St 80207. I-70 exit 278, 0.3 mi s; I-270 exit 4. Int corridors. **Pets:** Other species. $75 one-time fee/room. Service with restrictions, supervision.

Holiday Inn Express Denver Downtown H
(303) 296-0400. **Call for rates.** 401 17th St 80202. From Broadway and Tremont Pl, just sw. Int corridors. **Pets:** Accepted.

Hotel Monaco Denver H ✿
(303) 296-1717. **Call for rates.** 1717 Champa St 80202. Between 17th and 18th sts. Int corridors. **Pets:** Large, other species. Designated rooms, service with restrictions.

Hotel Teatro H
(303) 228-1100. **$259-$599.** 1100 14th St 80202. Between Lawrence and Arapahoe sts. Int corridors. **Pets:** Accepted.

Hyatt House Denver Airport H
(303) 628-7777. **$89-$249.** 18741 E 71st Ave 80249. I-70 exit 286 (Tower Rd), 4.6 mi n, then just e; from Pena Blvd exit 5 (Tower Rd/SR 32), just s. Int corridors. **Pets:** Accepted.

Hyatt House Denver/Downtown H
(303) 893-3100. **$169-$599.** 440 14th St 80202. Between Glenarm Pl and Tremont Pl. Int corridors. **Pets:** Accepted.

Hyatt Regency Denver Tech Center H
(303) 779-1234. **$89-$289.** 7800 E Tufts Ave 80237. I-225 exit 2 (Tamarac St), just s to Tufts Ave; I-25 exit 199 (Belleview Ave), e to S Ulster St, then 0.5 mi n. Int corridors. **Pets:** Accepted.

JW Marriott Denver Cherry Creek H ✿
(303) 316-2700. **$200-$624.** 150 Clayton Ln 80206. I-25 exit 205 (University Blvd), 2.4 mi n to 1st Ave, just e, then just n. Int corridors. **Pets:** Dogs only. $25 daily fee/room. Designated rooms, service with restrictions, supervision.

La Quinta Inn & Suites Denver Airport DIA H
(303) 371-0888. **$82-$224.** 6801 Tower Rd 80249. I-70 exit 286 (Tower Rd), 4.2 mi n; 0.8 mi s of Pena Blvd. Int corridors. **Pets:** Accepted.

La Quinta Inn & Suites Denver Gateway Park H
(303) 373-2525. **$97-$229.** 4460 Peoria St 80239. I-70 exit 281, just n. Int corridors. **Pets:** Accepted.

Magnolia Hotel-Downtown Denver H
(303) 607-9000. **$159-$419.** 818 17th St 80202. Jct Stout St. Int corridors. **Pets:** Accepted.

The Oxford Hotel H
(303) 628-5400. **Call for rates.** 1600 17th St 80202. Corner of 17th and Wazee sts. Int corridors. **Pets:** Accepted.

Quality Inn & Suites Denver Stapleton H
(303) 388-6161. **$99-$269.** 3737 Quebec St 80207. I-70 exit 278, just s. Int corridors. **Pets:** Accepted.

Renaissance Denver Stapleton Hotel H
(303) 399-7500. **$87-$297.** 3801 Quebec St 80207. I-70 exit 278, just s via Smith Rd exit. Int corridors. **Pets:** Accepted.

Residence Inn by Marriott Denver City Center H
(303) 296-3444. **$109-$362.** 1725 Champa St 80202. Between 17th and 18th sts. Int corridors. **Pets:** Accepted.

Residence Inn by Marriott Denver Downtown H
(303) 458-5318. **$133-$293.** 2777 Zuni St 80211. I-25 exit 212B (Speer Blvd) southbound; exit 212A northbound, just w, then just n. Ext corridors. **Pets:** Accepted.

The Ritz-Carlton, Denver H ✿
(303) 312-3800. **$329-$449.** 1881 Curtis St 80202. Between 18th and 19th sts. Int corridors. **Pets:** Small. $125 one-time fee/room. Service with restrictions.

Sheraton Denver Downtown Hotel H
(303) 893-3333. **$129-$599.** 1550 Court Pl 80202. Between 15th and 16th sts. Int corridors. **Pets:** Accepted.
[SAVE] 📺 🛂 ➡ 📶 ✕ 🛄 💻

Staybridge Suites H
(303) 574-0888. **Call for rates.** 6951 Tower Rd 80249. Just s of jct Pena Blvd. Int corridors. **Pets:** Accepted.
🛂 ➡ 📶 ✕ 🛄 💻

Staybridge Suites Denver Stapleton H
(303) 227-3000. **Call for rates.** 8101 E Northfield Blvd 80238. I-70 exit 278, 0.4 mi nw, then just e. Int corridors. **Pets:** Accepted.
🛂 📶 ✕ 🛄 💻

TownePlace Suites by Marriott-Denver Southeast H
(303) 759-9393. **$62-$225.** 3699 S Monaco Pkwy 80237. I-25 exit 201, just e to Monaco Pkwy, then s. Int corridors. **Pets:** Accepted.
🛂 ➡ 📶 ✕ 🛄 💻

TownePlace Suites by Marriott Downtown Denver H
(303) 722-2322. **$110-$392.** 685 Speer Blvd 80204. I-25 exit 209A (6th Ave), 1.4 mi w, then just n on Acoma St. Int corridors. **Pets:** Accepted.
📺 🛂 📶 ✕ 🛄 💻

TownePlace Suites by Marriott Gateway Park / Denver Airport H
(303) 373-4243. **$69-$253.** 4100 N Kittredge St 80239. I-70 exit 283 (Chambers Rd), just n to 40th Ave, 0.3 mi e, then just n. Int corridors. **Pets:** Accepted. 📺 🛂 ➡ 📶 ✕ 🛄 💻

The Westin Denver Downtown H ❀
(303) 572-9100. **$179-$399.** 1672 Lawrence St 80202. Between 16th and 17th sts. Int corridors. **Pets:** Medium, dogs only. Service with restrictions, supervision. [SAVE] 📺 🛂 ➡ 📶 ✕ 🛄 💻

The Westin Denver International Airport H ❀
(303) 317-1800. **$229-$479.** 8300 Peña Blvd 80249. At Denver International Airport. Int corridors. **Pets:** Medium, dogs only. Service with restrictions, supervision. [SAVE] 📺 🛂 ✕ 📶 ✕ 🛄 💻

DILLON

Best Western Ptarmigan Lodge M
(970) 468-2341. **$99-$250.** 652 Lake Dillon Dr 80435. I-70 exit 205, 1.3 mi s on US 6 to Lake Dillon Dr stop light, then 0.3 mi s. Ext/int corridors. **Pets:** $10 daily fee/pet. Designated rooms, service with restrictions, supervision. [SAVE] ✕ 📶 ✕ ❄ 🛄 💻

DURANGO

Apple Orchard Inn BB
(970) 247-0751. **$90-$250, 21 day notice.** 7758 CR 203 81301. 8.5 mi n on US 550, just w at Trimble Ln, then 1.3 mi n. Ext/int corridors. **Pets:** Dogs only. $20 daily fee/pet. Designated rooms, service with restrictions, supervision. 📺 📶 ✕ ❄ 🛄 💻

Best Western Durango Inn & Suites M
(970) 247-3251. **$89-$209.** 21382 US Hwy 160 W 81303. On US 160, 1 mi w. Ext corridors. **Pets:** Accepted. [SAVE] 📺 ➡ 📶 🛄 💻

Caboose Motel M
(970) 247-1191. **$58-$190.** 3363 Main Ave 81301. 2.5 mi n on US 550. Ext corridors. **Pets:** Accepted. 📶 ✕ ⛄ 🛄 💻

Comfort Inn & Suites H
(970) 259-7900. **$90-$300.** 455 S Camino Del Rio 81303. On US 160 (Frontage Rd), 1.5 mi e of jct US 550. Int corridors. **Pets:** Accepted.
[SAVE] 📺 ➡ 📶 ✕ 🛄 💻

Durango Downtown Inn M
(970) 247-5393. **$89-$189.** 800 Camino Del Rio 81301. On US 550, just n of jct US 160. Ext corridors. **Pets:** Accepted.
[SAVE] 📺 🛂 ➡ 📶 🛄 💻

Hampton Inn H ❀
(970) 247-2600. **$85-$220.** 3777 Main Ave 81301. 2.9 mi n on US 550. Int corridors. **Pets:** Large, other species. $25 one-time fee/room. Designated rooms, service with restrictions, supervision.
🛂 ➡ 📶 ✕ 🛄 💻

Holiday Inn Hotel & Suites Durango Central H
(970) 385-6400. **Call for rates.** 21636 Hwy 160 W 81301. Just w of jct US 550. Int corridors. **Pets:** Accepted. 📺 🛂 📶 ✕ 🛄 💻

Homewood Suites by Hilton H
(970) 259-2996. **$154-$259.** 15 Girard St 81303. On US 160 (Frontage Rd), 2.2 mi e of jct US 550. Int corridors. **Pets:** Accepted.
📺 🛂 📶 ✕ 🛄 💻

Leland House Bed & Breakfast Suites BB ❀
(970) 385-1920. **$139-$449, 14 day notice.** 721 E 2nd Ave 81301. Just e of Main Ave via 7th St, then just n. Ext/int corridors. **Pets:** Medium. $20 daily fee/pet. Designated rooms, service with restrictions, supervision. 📶 ✕ 🛄 💻

The Lodge at Purgatory CO
(970) 385-2100. **Call for rates.** 24 Sheol St 81301. 27 mi n on US 550; at Durango Mountain Resort. Int corridors. **Pets:** Accepted.
📺 ➡ ✕ 📶 ✕ ❄ 🛄 💻

Quality Inn M ❀
(970) 259-5373. **$59-$204.** 2930 N Main Ave 81301. 2 mi n on US 550. Ext corridors. **Pets:** Dogs only. $10 daily fee/room. Designated rooms, service with restrictions, supervision. ➡ 📶 ✕ 🛄 💻

Residence Inn by Marriott H
(970) 259-6200. **$108-$306.** 21691 Hwy 160 W 81301. On US 160, just w. Int corridors. **Pets:** Other species. $75 one-time fee/room. Service with restrictions. 🛂 ➡ 📶 ✕ 🛄 💻

The Rochester Hotel BB ❀
(970) 385-1920. **$139-$449, 14 day notice.** 726 E 2nd Ave 81301. Just e of Main Ave via 7th St, then just n. Ext/int corridors. **Pets:** Medium. $20 daily fee/pet. Designated rooms, service with restrictions, supervision. 🛂 📶 ✕ 🛄 💻

Siesta Motel M
(970) 247-0741. **$68-$255.** 3475 N Main Ave 81301. 2.6 mi n on US 550. Ext corridors. **Pets:** Accepted. 📶 ✕ 🛄 💻

Strater Hotel H ❀
(970) 247-4431. **$124-$289, 3 day notice.** 699 Main St 81301. Corner of 7th St and Main Ave; in historic downtown. Int corridors. **Pets:** Small, dogs only. $50 deposit/pet, $10 daily fee/pet. Designated rooms, service with restrictions, crate. [SAVE] [ECO] 📺 📶 ✕

EAGLE

Best Western Plus Eagle Lodge & Suites H
(970) 328-6316. **$115-$224.** 200 Loren Ln 81631. I-70 exit 147, just s, then just e. Int corridors. **Pets:** Accepted.
[SAVE] ➡ ✕ 📶 ✕ 🛄 💻

ENGLEWOOD

Homewood Suites by Hilton - DTC/Inverness H
(303) 706-0102. **$169-$249.** 199 Inverness Dr W 80112. I-25 exit 195 (County Line Rd), 0.3 mi ne to traffic light, then just n. Int corridors.
Pets: Accepted. 🍴 📺 ➡ 📶 🛄 💻

◆◆◆ **Residence Inn by Marriott Denver South/Park Meadows** H

(720) 895-0200. **$89-$243.** 8322 S Valley Hwy 80112. I-25 exit 195 (County Line Rd), just e to S Valley Hwy, then just w. Int corridors.
Pets: Accepted. ⬛ ▣ ⬛ ⬛ ⬛ ⬛ ⬛

ESTES PARK

◆◆◆ ◆◆ **Castle Mountain Lodge LLC** CA

(970) 586-3664. **$90-$525, 30 day notice.** 1520 Fall River Rd 80517. 1 mi w on US 34. Ext corridors. **Pets:** Dogs only. $15 daily fee/pet. Designated rooms, supervision. SAVE ⬛ ⬛ ⬛ ⬛ ⬛ ⬛ ⬛

◆◆ **Mountain Shadows Resort** CA

(970) 577-0397. **Call for rates.** 871 Riverside Dr 80517. Jct Elkhorn and Moraine aves, 1.4 mi sw to Marys Lake Rd, 0.3 mi s, then just e. Ext corridors. **Pets:** Accepted. ⬛ ⬛ ⬛ ⬛ ⬛ ⬛

◆◆ **Murphy's River Lodge** H 🐾

(970) 480-5081. **$139-$249, 7 day notice.** 481 W Elkhorn Ave 80517. 0.4 mi w of jct Elkhorn and Moraine aves; west end of downtown. Ext corridors. **Pets:** Small. $20 daily fee/pet. Designated rooms, service with restrictions, crate. ⬛ ⬛ ⬛ ⬛ ⬛ ⬛

EVERGREEN

◆◆◆ **Comfort Suites Golden West on Evergreen Parkway** H 🐾

(303) 526-2000. **$124-$264.** 29300 US Hwy 40 80439. I-70 exit 252 (Evergreen Pkwy) westbound; exit 251 eastbound, just s, then just w. Int corridors. **Pets:** Large, dogs only. $10 daily fee/pet. Designated rooms, service with restrictions, supervision.

⬛ ⬛ ⬛ ⬛ ⬛ ⬛ ⬛

FORT COLLINS

◆◆◆ ◆◆ **Best Western Kiva Inn** H

(970) 484-2444. **$89-$250.** 1638 E Mulberry St 80524. I-25 exit 269B, 1.5 mi w on SR 14. Ext/int corridors. **Pets:** Accepted.

SAVE ⬛ ⬛ ⬛ ⬛ ⬛ ⬛

◆◆◆ ◆◆ **Best Western University Inn** M 🐾

(970) 484-2984. **$109-$179.** 914 S College Ave 80524. I-25 exit 268, 4 mi w to College Ave, then just n on US 287. Ext/int corridors. **Pets:** $15 daily fee/pet. Designated rooms, service with restrictions, crate. SAVE ⬛ ⬛ ⬛ ⬛ ⬛

◆◆◆ **Comfort Suites Fort Collins** H

(970) 206-4597. **$94-$277.** 1415 Oakridge Dr 80525. I-25 exit 265 (Harmony Rd), 3.3 mi w to McMurry Ave, just s, then w. Int corridors.
Pets: Accepted. ⬛ ⬛ ⬛ ⬛ ⬛

◆◆◆ **Courtyard by Marriott** H

(970) 282-1700. **$78-$245.** 1200 Oakridge Dr 80525. I-25 exit 265 (Harmony Rd), 3.3 mi w; entry via Lemay Ave. Int corridors.
Pets: Accepted. ⬛ ⬛ ⬛ ⬛ ⬛ ⬛ ⬛ ⬛

◆◆◆ **Fort Collins Marriott** H

(970) 226-5200. **$97-$296.** 350 E Horsetooth Rd 80525. Jct College Ave and Horsetooth Rd, just e, then just n on John F Kennedy Pkwy. Int corridors. **Pets:** Accepted. ⬛ ⬛ ⬛ ⬛ ⬛ ⬛ ⬛ ⬛

◆◆◆ **Hampton Inn** H

(970) 229-5927. **$119-$189.** 1620 Oakridge Dr 80525. I-25 exit 265 (Harmony Rd), 3.3 mi w, just s on McMurry Ave, then just e. Int corridors. **Pets:** Accepted. ⬛ ⬛ ⬛ ⬛ ⬛ ⬛

◆◆◆ ◆◆ **Hilton Ft Collins** H

(970) 482-2626. **Call for rates.** 425 W Prospect Rd 80526. I-25 exit 268, 4.3 mi w. Int corridors. **Pets:** Accepted.

SAVE ⬛ ⬛ ⬛ ⬛ ⬛ ⬛ ⬛

◆◆◆ **Holiday Inn Express & Suites** H

(970) 225-2200. **Call for rates.** 1426 Oakridge Dr 80525. I-25 exit 265 (Harmony Rd), 3 mi w, just s on McMurry Ave, then w. Int corridors. **Pets:** Accepted. ⬛ ⬛ ⬛ ⬛ ⬛ ⬛

◆◆ ◆◆◆ **Homewood Suites by Hilton Fort Collins** H

(970) 225-2400. **$119-$249.** 1521 Oakridge Dr 80525. I-25 exit 265 (Harmony Rd), 3 mi w, just s on McMurry Ave, then just w. Int corridors. **Pets:** Accepted. SAVE ⬛ ⬛ ⬛ ⬛ ⬛ ⬛

◆◆◆ **Quality Inn & Suites** H 🐾

(970) 282-9047. **$89-$168.** 4001 S Mason St 80525. Jct Harmony Rd and College Ave, just w to Mason St, then 0.5 mi n. Int corridors.
Pets: Medium. $15 daily fee/pet. Service with restrictions, supervision. ⬛ ⬛ ⬛ ⬛ ⬛ ⬛

◆◆◆ **Residence Inn by Marriott Fort Collins** H

(970) 223-5700. **$94-$323.** 1127 Oakridge Dr 80525. I-25 exit 265 (Harmony Rd), 3.3 mi w to Lemay Ave, then s to Oakridge Dr. Int corridors.
Pets: Accepted. ⬛ ⬛ ⬛ ⬛ ⬛ ⬛

◆◆ **Super 8** H

(970) 493-7701. **$55-$200.** 409 Centro Way 80524. I-25 exit 269B, just w. Int corridors. **Pets:** Accepted. ⬛ ⬛ ⬛ ⬛ ⬛

FORT MORGAN

◆◆◆ ◆◆ **Central Motel** M

(970) 867-2401. **$64-$70.** 201 W Platte Ave 80701. I-76 exit 80, 0.6 mi s, then w on US 34. Ext corridors. **Pets:** $10 daily fee/pet. Designated rooms, service with restrictions, supervision. SAVE ⬛ ⬛ ⬛

◆◆ **Rodeway Inn** M

(970) 867-9481. **$74-$109.** 1409 Barlow Rd 80701. I-76 exit 82 (Barlow Rd), just n. Ext/int corridors. **Pets:** Accepted. ⬛ ⬛ ⬛ ⬛ ⬛

FRUITA

◆◆ **Comfort Inn** H

(970) 858-1333. **$80-$220.** 400 Jurassic Ave 81521. I-70 exit 19, 0.3 mi s; just e of Dinosaur Journey Museum. Int corridors. **Pets:** Accepted.

⬛ ⬛ ⬛ ⬛ ⬛

GATEWAY

◆◆◆ ◆◆ ◆◆ **Gateway Canyons Resort & Spa** H

(970) 931-2458. **$579-$779, 3 day notice.** 43200 Hwy 141 81522. 43 mi w of US 50; 49 mi n of CR 90. Ext/int corridors. **Pets:** Accepted.

SAVE ⬛ ⬛ ⬛ ⬛ ⬛ ⬛ ⬛

GLENDALE

◆◆◆ ◆◆ ◆◆ **Hyatt Place Denver Cherry Creek** H

(303) 782-9300. **$99-$259.** 4150 E Mississippi Ave 80246. I-25 exit 204, 0.8 mi n on Colorado Blvd, then just e. Int corridors. **Pets:** Accepted.

SAVE ⬛ ⬛ ⬛ ⬛ ⬛ ⬛

◆◆◆ **Residence Inn by Marriott** H

(303) 758-6200. **$93-$361.** 670 S Colorado Blvd 80246. I-25 exit 204, 1.6 mi n. Int corridors. **Pets:** Accepted. ⬛ ⬛ ⬛ ⬛ ⬛

◆◆◆ ◆◆ **Staybridge Suites Denver/Cherry Creek** H

(303) 321-5757. **Call for rates.** 4220 E Virginia Ave 80246. I-25 exit 204, 1.5 mi n on Colorado Blvd to Virginia Ave, then just e. Int corridors. **Pets:** Accepted. SAVE ⬛ ⬛ ⬛ ⬛ ⬛ ⬛

GLENWOOD SPRINGS

◆◆◆ ◆◆ **Best Western Antlers** M

(970) 945-8535. **$99-$169.** 171 W 6th St 81601. I-70 exit 116, just n, then just w. Ext corridors. **Pets:** Accepted.

SAVE ⬛ ⬛ ⬛ ⬛ ⬛

◆◆ **Caravan Inn** M

(970) 945-7451. **$59-$189.** 1826 Grand Ave 81601. I-70 exit 116, 0.9 mi s. Ext corridors. **Pets:** $100 deposit/room, $15 daily fee/pet. Designated rooms, service with restrictions, supervision. ⬛ ⬛ ⬛ ⬛

▼▼ **The Hotel Denver** 🏨
(970) 945-6565. **Call for rates.** 402 7th St 81601. I-70 exit 116; across from historic train station; in town center. Int corridors. **Pets:** Designated rooms, service with restrictions. 🍽 📶 ⊠ 🛢 🖥

▼▼▼ **Residence Inn by Marriott** 🏨
(970) 928-0900. **$89-$249.** 125 Wulfsohn Rd 81601. I-70 exit 114, 2nd exit at roundabout, 1.5 mi e on Midland Ave, then just s. Int corridors. **Pets:** Accepted. ⊟ ⊅ 📶 ⊠ 🛢 🖥

GOLDEN

▼▼▼ **Denver Marriott West** 🏨
(303) 279-9100. **$192-$422.** 1717 Denver West Blvd 80401. I-70 exit 263, just n, then w. Int corridors. **Pets:** Accepted.
🅴🅲🅾 🍽 ♿ ⊅ 📶 ⊠ 🛢 🖥

▼▼▼ **The Golden Hotel, an Ascend Hotel Collection Member** 🏨 🐾
(303) 279-0100. **$189-$379.** 800 11th St 80401. At 11th St and Washington Ave; downtown. Int corridors. **Pets:** Large. $100 deposit/room, $20 daily fee/pet. Designated rooms, service with restrictions, supervision. ⊟ 🍽 ♿ 📶 ⊠ 🛢 🖥

▼▼▼ **Residence Inn by Marriott Denver West/Golden** 🏨
(303) 271-0909. **$88-$418.** 14600 W 6th Ave, Frontage Rd 80401. US 6 exit Indiana Ave, just s to Frontage Rd, then just e. Int corridors. **Pets:** Other species. $100 one-time fee/room. Service with restrictions, crate. 🍽 ♿ ⊅ 📶 ⊠ 🛢 🖥

🅐🅐🅐 ▼▼▼▼ **Table Mountain Inn** 🏨 🐾
(303) 277-9898. **Call for rates.** 1310 Washington Ave 80401. US 6 exit 19th St, 0.5 mi n to Washington Ave, 0.5 mi w; downtown, just s of arch. Int corridors. **Pets:** $15 daily fee/room. Designated rooms, service with restrictions, crate. 🆂🅰🆅🅴 🍽 ♿ 📶 ⊠ 🛢 🖥

GRAND JUNCTION

▼▼ **Americas Best Value Inn** Ⓜ
(970) 245-1410. **Call for rates.** 754 Horizon Dr 81506. I-70 exit 31, just n. Ext corridors. **Pets:** Accepted. ⊅ 📶 🛢 🖥

▼▼ **Candlewood Suites** 🏨 🐾
(970) 255-8093. **$79-$229.** 654 Market St 81505. I-70 exit 28 (24 Rd), 1.3 mi s to F Rd, just e, then just n. Int corridors. **Pets:** Large, other species. $15 daily fee/pet. Service with restrictions, supervision. 📶 ⊠ 🛢 🖥

▼▼ **Clarion Inn** 🏨
(970) 243-6790. **$69-$205.** 755 Horizon Dr 81506. I-70 exit 31, just n. Ext/int corridors. **Pets:** Large, other species. Designated rooms, supervision. 🍽 ⊅ ⊠ 📶 ⊠ 🛢 🖥

▼▼ **Comfort Inn** 🏨
(970) 245-3335. **$89-$174.** 750 3/4 Horizon Dr 81506. I-70 exit 31, just n. Int corridors. **Pets:** Accepted. ⊅ 📶 ⊠ 🛢 🖥

▼▼ **Econo Lodge** 🏨 🐾
(970) 257-1140. **$49-$90.** 751 Horizon Dr 81506. I-70 exit 31, just n. Int corridors. **Pets:** Other species. Designated rooms, service with restrictions, supervision. 📶 ⊠ 🛢 🖥

▼▼▼ **Fairfield Inn & Suites by Marriott Grand Junction Downtown/Historic Main Street** 🏨
(970) 242-2525. **$93-$253.** 225 Main St 81501. At 2nd and Main sts. Int corridors. **Pets:** Accepted. ⊅ 📶 ⊠ 🛢 🖥

▼▼▼ **Hampton Inn Downtown Grand Junction** 🏨
(970) 243-3222. **$129-$219.** 205 Main St 81501. At 2nd and Main sts. Int corridors. **Pets:** Accepted. ⊅ 📶 ⊠ 🛢 🖥

▼▼ **La Quinta Inn & Suites Grand Junction** 🏨
(970) 241-2929. **$79-$251.** 2761 Crossroads Blvd 81506. I-70 exit 31, 0.3 mi n, then 0.3 mi w. Int corridors. **Pets:** Accepted.
⊅ 📶 ⊠ 🛢 🖥

🅐🅐🅐 ▼▼▼ **Quality Inn of Grand Junction** 🏨
(970) 245-7200. **$74-$219.** 733 Horizon Dr 81506. I-70 exit 31, just s. Int corridors. **Pets:** $10 daily fee/room. Designated rooms, service with restrictions, supervision. 🆂🅰🆅🅴 🍽 ⊅ 📶 ⊠ 🛢 🖥

🅐🅐🅐 ▼▼▼ **Residence Inn by Marriott** 🏨
(970) 263-4004. **$80-$289.** 767 Horizon Dr 81506. I-70 exit 31, 0.3 mi n. Int corridors. **Pets:** Accepted. 🆂🅰🆅🅴 ⊅ 📶 ⊠ 🛢 🖥

▼▼▼ **SpringHill Suites by Marriott Grand Junction Downtown/Historic Main Street** 🏨
(970) 424-5777. **$93-$221.** 236 Main St 81501. At 3rd and Main sts. Int corridors. **Pets:** $25 daily fee/room. Designated rooms, service with restrictions, supervision. ⊟ ♿ ⊅ 📶 ⊠ 🛢 🖥

GREELEY

🅐🅐🅐 ▼▼▼ **Comfort Inn-Greeley** 🏨
(970) 330-6380. **$109-$199.** 2467 W 29th St 80631. US 34 Bypass exit 23rd Ave, just sw. Int corridors. **Pets:** Dogs only. $15 daily fee/pet. Designated rooms, service with restrictions, crate.
🆂🅰🆅🅴 ⊅ 📶 ⊠ 🛢 🖥

🅐🅐🅐 ▼▼▼ **Country Inn & Suites By Carlson** 🏨 🐾
(970) 330-3404. **$99-$189.** 2501 W 29th St 80631. US 34 Bypass exit 23rd Ave, just s, then w. Int corridors. **Pets:** $40 one-time fee/room. Service with restrictions, crate. 🆂🅰🆅🅴 ⊅ 📶 ⊠ 🖥

GREENWOOD VILLAGE

🅐🅐🅐 ▼▼▼ **Best Western Plus Denver Tech Center Hotel** 🏨 🐾
(303) 792-9999. **$89-$199.** 9231 E Arapahoe Rd 80112. I-25 exit 197 (Arapahoe Rd), just e. Int corridors. **Pets:** Medium. $20 daily fee/room. Designated rooms, service with restrictions, supervision.
🆂🅰🆅🅴 ♿ ⊅ 📶 ⊠ 🛢 🖥

🅐🅐🅐 ▼▼▼▼ **Hyatt House Denver Tech Center** 🏨
(303) 706-1945. **$89-$259.** 9280 E Costilla Ave 80112. I-25 exit 197 (Arapahoe Rd), e to Clinton St, then just s. Int corridors.
Pets: Accepted. 🆂🅰🆅🅴 ♿ ⊅ 📶 ⊠ 🛢 🖥

🅐🅐🅐 ▼▼▼▼ **Hyatt Place Denver Tech Center** 🏨
(303) 804-0700. **$89-$229.** 8300 E Crescent Pkwy 80111. I-25 exit 199, 0.4 mi e to Crescent Pkwy, then just s. Int corridors. **Pets:** Accepted.
🆂🅰🆅🅴 ⊅ 📶 ⊠ 🛢 🖥

▼▼ **Residence Inn by Marriott-Denver Tech Center** 🏨
(303) 740-7177. **$65-$249.** 6565 S Yosemite St 80111. I-25 exit 197 (Arapahoe Rd), just w, then n. Ext corridors. **Pets:** Accepted.
⊅ 📶 ⊠ 🛢 🖥

🅐🅐🅐 ▼▼▼▼ **Sheraton Denver Tech Center** 🏨
(303) 799-6200. **$99-$189.** 7007 S Clinton St 80112. I-25 exit 197 (Arapahoe Rd), just e, then s. Int corridors. **Pets:** Medium, dogs only. Designated rooms, service with restrictions, supervision.
🆂🅰🆅🅴 🍽 ♿ ⊅ 🔊 ⊠ 🛢 🖥

GUNNISON

▼▼ **Alpine Inn** 🏨
(970) 641-2804. **Call for rates.** 1011 W Rio Grande Rd 81230. 0.5 mi w of center, 0.5 mi s; at US 50 and Rio Grande Ave. Int corridors.
Pets: Accepted. 🍽 ⊅ 📶 ⊠ 🛢 🖥

▼▼ **Econo Lodge Gunnison/Crested Butte** 🏨
(970) 641-3068. **$59-$139.** 411 E Tomichi Ave 81230. On US 50, 0.3 mi e of center. Int corridors. **Pets:** Accepted. 📶 ⊠ 🛢 🖥

▼▼▼ **The Inn at Tomichi Village** **M**
(970) 641-1131. **$89-$199.** 41883 US Hwy 50 E 81230. 2 mi e of center. Ext corridors. **Pets:** Accepted. 🍽️ 🛒 📶 ✖️ 🛗 💻

▼▼ **Rodeway Inn** **M**
(970) 641-0500. **$79-$140.** 37760 W Hwy 50 81230. 0.5 mi w of center, 2 mi sw. Ext corridors. **Pets:** Accepted. 📶 ✖️ 🛗 💻

HIGHLANDS RANCH

𝓐𝓐𝓐 ▼▼▼ **Comfort Suites Highland Ranch Denver Tech Center Area** **H** ✿
(303) 770-5400. **$94-$239.** 7060 E County Line Rd 80126. SR 470 exit Quebec St, just n to County Line Rd, just w, then just s; at Quebec Highlands Center. Int corridors. **Pets:** Medium, dogs only. $15 daily fee/pet. Designated rooms, service with restrictions, supervision. 💲 🛒 📶 ✖️ 🛗 💻

▼▼ **Residence Inn by Marriott Denver Highlands Ranch** **H**
(303) 683-5500. **$79-$267.** 93 W Centennial Blvd 80126. SR 470 exit Broadway, just s, then w. Int corridors. **Pets:** Accepted.
🛒 🛒 📶 ✖️ 🛗 💻

HOT SULPHUR SPRINGS

▼ **Canyon Motel** **M**
(970) 725-3395. **Call for rates.** 221 Byers Ave 80451. On US 40, center. Ext corridors. **Pets:** Accepted. 📶 ✖️ 🔧 🛗 💻

IGNACIO

𝓐𝓐𝓐 ▼▼▼ **Sky Ute Casino Resort** **H**
(970) 563-7777. **$90-$155, 3 day notice.** 14324 Hwy 172 N 81137. Jct US 172 and CR 517. Int corridors. **Pets:** Accepted.
💲 🍽️ 🛒 ✖️ 📶 🛗 💻

KEYSTONE

▼▼▼ **Keystone Lodge & Spa** **H**
(970) 496-3712. **Call for rates.** 22101 Hwy 6 80435. I-70 exit 205, 6 mi e. Int corridors. **Pets:** Accepted.
🍽️ 🛒 🛒 ✖️ 📶 ✖️ 🔧 🛗 💻

KREMMLING

𝓐𝓐𝓐 ▼▼▼ **Allington Inn & Suites** **H**
(970) 724-9800. **Call for rates.** 215 W Central Ave 80459. 0.5 mi w of jct US 40 and SR 9, then just n. Int corridors. **Pets:** Accepted.
💲 🛒 📶 ✖️ 🛗 💻

LA JUNTA

▼▼ **Holiday Inn Express** **H**
(719) 384-2900. **Call for rates.** 27994 US Hwy 50 Frontage Rd 81050. On US 50 Frontage Rd, 0.8 mi w. Int corridors. **Pets:** Accepted.
🛒 📶 ✖️ 🛗 💻

𝓐𝓐𝓐 ▼ **Stagecoach Motel** **M**
(719) 384-5476. **$65-$75.** 905 W 3rd St 81050. Jct US 50 and 350. Ext corridors. **Pets:** Small. $15 daily fee/pet. Designated rooms, service with restrictions, supervision. 💲 🛒 📶 ✖️ 🛗 💻

LAKEWOOD

𝓐𝓐𝓐 ▼▼▼ **Best Western Denver Southwest** **H**
(303) 989-5500. **$90-$220.** 3440 S Vance St 80227. Just ne of jct US 285 (Hampden Ave) and S Wadsworth Blvd, e on Girton Dr, then just s. Int corridors. **Pets:** Large. Designated rooms, service with restrictions, supervision. 💲 🍽️ 🛒 🛒 📶 ✖️ 🛗 💻

𝓐𝓐𝓐 ▼▼▼ **Holiday Inn Denver Lakewood** **H**
(303) 980-9200. **Call for rates.** 7390 W Hampden Ave 80227. US 285 (W Hampden Ave) exit S Wadsworth Blvd, just e on Jefferson Ave, then n on Vance St. Int corridors. **Pets:** Accepted.
💲 🍽️ 🛒 🛒 📶 🛗 💻

▼▼▼ **Home2 Suites by Hilton Denver West/Federal Center** **H**
(303) 985-7100. **$99-$259.** 50 Van Gordon St 80228. US 6 exit Simms St/Union Blvd, 0.6 mi s on Union Blvd to 2nd Pl, just w, then just s. Int corridors. **Pets:** Large, other species. $75 one-time fee/pet. Service with restrictions, crate. 🍽️ 🛒 📶 ✖️ 🛗 💻

▼▼▼ **Residence Inn by Marriott Denver SW/Lakewood** **H**
(303) 985-7676. **$98-$303.** 7050 W Hampden Ave 80227. Just se of jct US 285 (W Hampden Ave) and Wadsworth Blvd, e on Jefferson Ave, then n on frontage road. Int corridors. **Pets:** Accepted.
🍽️ 🛒 🛒 📶 ✖️ 🛗 💻

𝓐𝓐𝓐 ▼▼▼ **Sheraton-Denver West Hotel** **H** ✿
(303) 987-2000. **$109-$299.** 360 Union Blvd 80228. US 6 exit Simms St/Union Blvd, just s. Int corridors. **Pets:** Large, dogs only. $30 one-time fee/room. Designated rooms, service with restrictions, supervision.
💲 🍽️ 🛒 📶 ✖️ 🛗 💻

LAMAR

▼▼▼ **Holiday Inn Express & Suites** **H**
(719) 931-4010. **Call for rates.** 1304 N Main St 81052. 0.8 mi n on US 50 and 287. Int corridors. **Pets:** Accepted.
🛒 🛒 📶 ✖️ 🛗 💻

LEADVILLE

𝓐𝓐𝓐 ▼▼ **Alps Motel** **M**
(719) 486-1223. **$48-$98, 3 day notice.** 207 Elm St 80461. Just s of center on US 24. Ext corridors. **Pets:** Other species. $10 daily fee/pet. Service with restrictions, supervision. 💲 📶 ✖️ 🔧 🛗 💻

LIMON

▼▼▼ **Holiday Inn Express Hotel & Suites** **H**
(719) 775-9033. **Call for rates.** 803 Hwy 24 80828. I-70 exit 359, just s. Int corridors. **Pets:** Accepted. 🛒 🛒 📶 ✖️ 🛗 💻

𝓐𝓐𝓐 ▼ **Safari Inn** **M**
(719) 775-2363. **$58-$140, 3 day notice.** 637 Main St 80828. I-70 exit 361, 0.8 mi w. Ext corridors. **Pets:** Other species. $10 daily fee/pet. Designated rooms, service with restrictions, supervision.
💲 🛒 📶 ✖️ 🛗 💻

LITTLETON *(Restaurants p. 604)*

▼▼▼ **Holiday Inn Express Hotel & Suites Denver SW-Littleton** **H**
(720) 981-1000. **Call for rates.** 12683 W Indore Pl 80127. SR 470 exit Ken Caryl Ave, just e to Shaffer Ave, just n, then w. Int corridors. **Pets:** Medium, dogs only. $150 deposit/room, $30 daily fee/room. Designated rooms, service with restrictions, supervision.
🛒 🛒 📶 ✖️ 🛗 💻

▼▼▼ **Homewood Suites by Hilton-Denver Littleton** **H**
(720) 981-4763. **$129-$399.** 7630 Shaffer Pkwy 80127. SR 470 exit Ken Caryl Ave, just e, then just s. Int corridors. **Pets:** Other species. $100 one-time fee/room. Designated rooms, service with restrictions, crate. 🛒 🛒 📶 🛗 💻

𝓐𝓐𝓐 ▼▼▼ **TownePlace Suites by Marriott-Denver Southwest/Littleton** **H**
(303) 972-0555. **$78-$252.** 10902 W Toller Dr 80127. SR 470 exit Kipling Pkwy, just s, then 0.4 mi w on Ute St. Int corridors. **Pets:** Other species. $20 daily fee/pet. Service with restrictions, crate.
💲 🛒 🛒 📶 ✖️ 🛗 💻

LONE TREE

𝓐𝓐𝓐 ▼▼▼ **Element Denver Park Meadows** **H** ✿
(303) 790-2100. **$169-$229.** 9985 Park Meadows Dr 80124. Jct Yosemite St, 0.4 mi e. Int corridors. **Pets:** Medium. $35 one-time fee/room. Designated rooms, service with restrictions, supervision.
💲 🌿 🛒 📶 ✖️ 🛗 💻

AAA ▼▼▼ Hyatt Place Denver - South/Park Meadows H

(303) 662-8500. **$89-$279.** 9030 E Westview Rd 80124. I-25 exit 195 (County Line Rd), 0.5 mi w to Yosemite St, just s to Parkland Rd, then just w; SR 470 exit Yosemite St, 0.5 mi nw, just n on Parkland Rd, then just w. Int corridors. **Pets:** Medium, dogs only. $75 one-time fee/room. Designated rooms, service with restrictions, supervision.

SAVE 🏊 📶 ❌ 🔌 💻

▼▼▼ Staybridge Suites Denver South-Lone Tree H

(303) 649-1010. **Call for rates.** 7820 Park Meadows Dr 80124. I-25 exit 195 (County Line Rd), w to Acres Green Dr, s to E Park Meadows Dr, then just w; SR 470 exit Quebec St, just s, then just e. Int corridors. **Pets:** Accepted. ♿ 🐾 📶 🔌 💻

LONGMONT

AAA ▼▼▼ Best Western Plus Plaza Hotel H

(303) 776-2000. **$109-$199.** 1900 Ken Pratt Blvd 80501. Jct US 287, 1.3 mi sw on Ken Pratt Blvd (SR 119). Int corridors. **Pets:** Accepted.

SAVE 🍽 🐾 📶 ❌ 🔌 💻

▼▼▼ Holiday Inn Express & Suites H

(303) 684-0404. **$109-$209.** 1355 Dry Creek Dr 80503. Jct Main St and Ken Pratt Blvd (SR 119), 2.2 mi w, just n, then just ne. Int corridors. **Pets:** Other species. $30 one-time fee/room. Service with restrictions, supervision. ♿ 🐾 📶 ❌ 🔌 💻

▼▼▼ Residence Inn by Marriott Boulder/Longmont H

(303) 702-9933. **$87-$347.** 1450 Dry Creek Dr 80503. Jct Main St and Ken Pratt Blvd (SR 119), 2.2 mi w, just n, then just ne; jct Hoover Rd and SR 119. Int corridors. **Pets:** Accepted.

♿ 🐾 📶 ❌ 🔌 💻

LOUISVILLE

AAA ▼▼▼ Best Western Plus Louisville Inn & Suites H

(303) 327-1215. **$99-$249.** 960 W Dillon Rd 80027. US 36 (Boulder Tpke) exit Superior (SR 170), just n on McCaslin Blvd to Dillon Rd, then just e. Int corridors. **Pets:** Accepted.

SAVE 🐾 📶 ❌ 🔌 💻

▼▼▼ Residence Inn by Marriott-Boulder/Louisville H

(303) 665-2661. **$93-$283.** 845 Coal Creek Cir 80027. US 36 (Boulder Tpke) exit Superior (SR 170), n on McCaslin Blvd to Dillon Rd, then 0.6 mi e. Int corridors. **Pets:** Accepted. ♿ 🐾 📶 ❌ 🔌 💻

LOVELAND

AAA ▼▼▼ Best Western Plus Crossroads Inn & Conference Center H 🐾

(970) 667-7810. **$119-$199.** 5542 E US Hwy 34 80537. I-25 exit 257, just w. Ext/int corridors. **Pets:** Medium. $20 daily fee/pet. Designated rooms, service with restrictions, supervision.

SAVE 🍽 ♿ 🏊 📶 ❌ 🔌 💻

▼▼▼ Candlewood Suites H

(970) 667-5444. **Call for rates.** 6046 E Crossroads Blvd 80538. I-25 exit 259, just e. Int corridors. **Pets:** Accepted.

🍽 ♿ 📶 ❌ 🔌 💻

▼▼▼ Embassy Suites by Hilton Loveland H

(970) 593-6200. **$139-$209.** 4705 Clydesdale Pkwy 80538. I-25 exit 259, just e, then just n. Int corridors. **Pets:** Accepted.

🍽 ♿ 🏊 ❌ 🅂📶 ❌ 🔌 💻

MANCOS

▼ Mesa Verde Motel M 🐾

(970) 533-7741. **$60-$113.** 191 W Railroad Ave 81328. On US 160 at SR 184; 7 mi e of Mesa Verde National Park entrance. Ext corridors. **Pets:** Dogs only. $50 deposit/room, $10 daily fee/pet. Designated rooms, service with restrictions, crate. 📶 ❌ 🔌 💻

MONTE VISTA

AAA ▼▼▼ Best Western Movie Manor H

(719) 852-5921. **$89-$159.** 2830 Hwy 160 W 81144. 2 mi w of center. Ext corridors. **Pets:** Accepted. SAVE 🍽 ❌ 📶 ❌ 🔌 💻

MONTROSE

▼▼ Days Inn M

(970) 249-4507. **$55-$105.** 1417 E Main St 81401. 0.8 mi e on US 50. Ext corridors. **Pets:** Accepted. 🐾 📶 🔌 💻

▼▼▼ Hampton Inn H

(970) 252-3300. **$94-$139.** 1980 N Townsend Ave 81401. 1.5 mi n on US 550. Int corridors. **Pets:** Medium. Designated rooms, service with restrictions, supervision. 🍽 ♿ 🐾 📶 ❌ 🔌 💻

▼▼▼ Holiday Inn Express & Suites H

(970) 240-1800. **$99-$139.** 1391 S Townsend Ave 81401. 1 mi s on US 550. Int corridors. **Pets:** Accepted. 🐾 📶 ❌ 🔌 💻

▼▼ Super 8 H

(970) 240-8200. **$55-$119.** 1705 E Main St 81401. 1 mi e on US 50. Int corridors. **Pets:** Medium, dogs only. Designated rooms, service with restrictions, supervision. 📶 🔌 💻

OURAY

▼▼ Comfort Inn M

(970) 325-7203. **$75-$205.** 191 5th Ave 81427. Just w of US 550 (Main St) via 5th Ave. Ext corridors. **Pets:** Accepted. 📶 ❌ 🔌 💻

▼▼ Matterhorn Inn Ouray M

(970) 325-4938. **$75-$250, 3 day notice.** 201 6th Ave 81427. Just w of US 550 (Main St), at 6th Ave and 2nd St. Ext corridors. **Pets:** Accepted. 📶 ❌ 🅼 🔌 💻

AAA ▼▼▼ Ouray Riverside Inn & Cabins M

(970) 325-4061. **Call for rates.** 1804 N Main St 81427. 1 mi n of center on US 550 (Main St). Ext corridors. **Pets:** Dogs only. $5 daily fee/pet. Designated rooms, supervision. SAVE 🍽 📶 ❌ 🔌 💻

▼▼ Ouray Victorian Inn M

(970) 325-7222. **Call for rates.** 50 3rd Ave 81427. Just w of US 550 (Main St) to 3rd Ave. Ext corridors. **Pets:** Accepted. 📶 ❌ 🔌 💻

PAGOSA SPRINGS

▼▼ Fireside Inn Cabins CA

(970) 264-9204. **Call for rates.** 1600 E Hwy 160 81147. 1.3 mi e of downtown. Ext corridors. **Pets:** Accepted. 📶 ❌ 🅼 🔌 💻

▼▼ High Country Lodge & Cabins M

(970) 264-4181. **Call for rates.** 3821 E Hwy 160 81147. 3 mi e of downtown. Ext corridors. **Pets:** Accepted. ❌ 📶 ❌ 🔌 💻

▼▼ Mountain Landing Suites & R.V. Park M 🐾

(970) 731-5345. **Call for rates.** 345 Piedra Rd 81147. 2.5 mi w of downtown to Piedra Rd, 0.5 mi n. Ext corridors. **Pets:** Dogs only. $10 daily fee/pet. Designated rooms, no service, supervision. ❌ 📶 ❌ 🔌 💻

PALISADE

AAA ▼▼▼ Wine Country Inn H

(970) 464-5777. **$99-$429.** 777 Grande River Dr 81526. I-70 exit 42, 0.3 mi w. Int corridors. **Pets:** Medium, dogs only. $40 one-time fee/room. Designated rooms, service with restrictions, supervision.

SAVE 🍽 ♿ 🐾 📶 ❌ 🔌 💻

PARACHUTE

▼▼ ◆ Candlewood Suites 🄷 ❖
(970) 285-9880. **Call for rates.** 233 Grand Valley Way 81635. I-70 exit 75, just se. Int corridors. **Pets:** Large, dogs only. $25 one-time fee/pet. Service with restrictions, crate. 🛜 ⊠ 🖥 📺

▼▼▼▼ Grand Vista Hotel in Parachute 🄷
(970) 285-1122. **$69-$119.** 228 N Railroad Ave 81635. I-70 exit 75, just nw. Int corridors. **Pets:** Accepted. 🛏 🛜 ⊠ 🖥 📺

PARKER

▼▼▼▼ Holiday Inn Denver-Parker 🄷
(303) 248-2147. **Call for rates.** 19308 E Cottonwood Dr 80138. SR 470 (toll road) exit 5 (Parker Rd/SR 83) eastbound, straight at light, follow signs to Cottonwood Dr; exit westbound, just s to Crown Crest Blvd, follow signs to Cottonwood Dr. Int corridors. **Pets:** Accepted.
🍽 🛏 🛜 ⊠ 🖥 📺

PUEBLO

▼▼▼▼ Holiday Inn Express & Suites 🄷
(719) 542-8888. **Call for rates.** 4530 Dillon Dr 81008. I-25 exit 102, just e, then just s. Int corridors. **Pets:** Other species. $25 one-time fee/ room. Supervision. 🍽 🌫M 🛏 🛜 ⊠ 🖥 📺

▼▼ ◆ La Quinta Inn & Suites Pueblo 🄷
(719) 542-3500. **$71-$229.** 4801 N Elizabeth St 81008. I-25 exit 102, just w, then 0.3 mi n. Int corridors. **Pets:** Accepted.
🛏 🛜 ⊠ 🖥 📺

▼▼ ◆ Quality Inn & Suites Pueblo 🄷 ❖
(719) 544-5500. **$79-$200.** 3910 Outlook Blvd 81008. I-25 exit 101 (US 50), 0.9 mi w, just s on Fortino Blvd, e on frontage road, then just s. Int corridors. **Pets:** Medium, dogs only. $15 daily fee/pet. Designated rooms, service with restrictions, supervision. 🛏 🛜 ⊠ 🖥 📺

RIDGWAY

▼▼ ◆ Ridgway Ouray Lodge & Suites 🄷 ❖
(970) 626-5444. **$88-$132.** 373 Palomino Tr 81432. Just e of jct US 550 and SR 62, just s. Int corridors. **Pets:** $25 daily fee/pet. Designated rooms, service with restrictions, supervision.
🛏 ⊠ 🛜 ⊠ 🖥 📺

RIFLE

▼▼▼▼ Comfort Inn & Suites 🄷 ❖
(970) 625-9912. **$79-$199.** 301 S 7th St 81650. I-70 exit 90, just s, then just w. Int corridors. **Pets:** $10 daily fee/pet. Designated rooms, service with restrictions, supervision. 🛏 ⊠ 🛜 ⊠ 🖥 📺

▼▼▼▼ Hampton Inn & Suites 🄷
(970) 625-1500. **$84-$149.** 715 Megan Ave 81650. I-70 exit 90, just s, then just e. Int corridors. **Pets:** Other species. $15 daily fee/room. Service with restrictions, supervision. 🛏 🛜 ⊠ 🖥 📺

▼▼▼▼ La Quinta Inn & Suites Rifle 🄷
(970) 625-2676. **$70-$240.** 600 Wapiti Ct 81650. I-70 exit 90, just s, then just e. Int corridors. **Pets:** Accepted. 🛏 🛜 ⊠ 🖥 📺

SALIDA

▼▼▼▼ Chalets at Tudor Rose 🄲🄰
(719) 539-2002. **$200, 30 day notice.** 6720 CR 104 81201. East end of US 50, just s on CR 104, then 0.5 mi up the hill. Ext corridors.
Pets: Accepted. 🍽 🛜 ⊠ 🖥 📺

▲▲▲ ▼▼▼ Woodland Motel 🄼 ❖
(719) 539-4980. **Call for rates.** 903 W 1st St 81201. 0.5 mi nw on 1st St (SR 291); nw of historic downtown. Ext corridors. **Pets:** Other species. Designated rooms, service with restrictions, crate.
🆂🄰🆅🄴 🛜 ⊠ 🖥 📺

SILT

▼▼▼ Holiday Inn Express & Suites 🄷
(970) 876-5100. **Call for rates.** 1535 River Frontage Rd 81652. I-70 exit 97, just s, then just e. Int corridors. **Pets:** Large, other species. $15 daily fee/pet. Designated rooms, service with restrictions, supervision.
🍽 🌫M 🛏 🛜 ⊠ 🖥 📺

SILVERTON

▲▲▲ ▼▼▼ Inn of the Rockies at the Historic Alma House 🄱🄱
(970) 387-5336. **Call for rates.** 220 E 10th St 81433. Just se of 10th and Main sts. Int corridors. **Pets:** Accepted. 🆂🄰🆅🄴 🛜 ⊠ 🐾 🄲

▼▼ ▼▼ Villa Dallavalle Bed & Breakfast 🄱🄱
(970) 387-5555. **Call for rates.** 1257 Blair St 81433. Corner of 13th and Blair sts. Int corridors. **Pets:** Accepted. 🛜 ⊠ 🐾 🄲

▼▼ ▼▼ The Wyman Hotel & Inn 🄱🄱
(970) 387-5372. **Call for rates.** 1371 Greene St 81433. Corner of 14th and Main sts. Int corridors. **Pets:** Accepted. 🛜 ⊠ 🐾 🖥 📺

SNOWMASS VILLAGE

▼▼▼ ▼▼▼ Viceroy Snowmass 🄲🄾
(970) 923-8000. **Call for rates.** 130 Wood Rd 81615. 6 mi sw of SR 82 via Brush Creek Rd, then 0.3 mi to lower Carriage Way. Int corridors.
Pets: Accepted. 🍽 🛏 ⊠ 🛜 ⊠ 🖥 📺

▲▲▲ ▼▼▼▼ The Westin Snowmass Resort 🄷
(970) 923-8200. **$89-$2999, 30 day notice.** 100 Elbert Ln 81615. 2.4 mi sw of SR 82 via Brush Creek Rd, 2nd exit at roundabout, then 3 mi to Elbert Ln; Lot 8. Int corridors. **Pets:** Accepted.
🆂🄰🆅🄴 🍽 🛏 ⊠ 🛜 ⊠ 🖥 📺

STEAMBOAT SPRINGS

▼▼▼▼ Holiday Inn Steamboat Springs 🄷
(970) 879-2250. **Call for rates.** 3190 S Lincoln Ave 80487. On US 40 (Lincoln Ave), 3 mi s of downtown. Int corridors. **Pets:** Accepted.
🍽 🌫M 🛏 🛜 ⊠ 🖥 📺

▼▼ ◆ La Quinta Inn & Suites Steamboat Springs 🄷
(970) 871-1219. **$67-$185.** 3155 Ingles Ln 80487. On US 40 (Lincoln Ave), 3 mi s of downtown; near Steamboat Ski Resort. Int corridors.
Pets: Accepted. 🛏 🛜 ⊠ 🖥 📺

▼▼ ◆ Nordic Lodge 🄼
(970) 879-0531. **$89-$189, 7 day notice.** 1036 Lincoln Ave 80477. On US 40 (Lincoln Ave), just w of 10th St; downtown. Ext corridors.
Pets: Accepted. 🛏 🛜 🖥 📺

▼▼ ▼▼ Rabbit Ears Motel 🄼
(970) 879-1150. **Call for rates.** 201 Lincoln Ave 80477. On US 40 (Lincoln Ave), just se of 3rd St; downtown. Ext corridors. **Pets:** Accepted.
🛜 🖥 📺

▲▲▲ ▼▼▼▼ Sheraton Steamboat Resort & Villas 🄷
(970) 879-2220. **Call for rates.** 2200 Village Inn Ct 80487. 2.3 mi s from center on US 40 (Lincoln Ave) to Mt. Werner Rd exit, 0.8 mi e, 0.3 mi ne on Mt. Werner Cir, just ne at Ski Time Square, then just s. Int corridors. **Pets:** Accepted.
🆂🄰🆅🄴 🄲🄴 🍽 🛏 ⊠ 🛜 ⊠ 🖥 📺

STERLING

▲▲▲ ▼▼▼ Best Western Sundowner 🄼 ❖
(970) 522-6265. **$119-$219.** 125 Overland Trail St 80751. I-76 exit 125, just w. Ext/int corridors. **Pets:** Other species. $20 daily fee/room. Service with restrictions. 🆂🄰🆅🄴 🍽 🛏 🛜 ⊠ 🖥 📺

TELLURIDE

◈◈◈◈ Fairmont Heritage Place, Franz Klammer Lodge ECO ❀
(970) 728-3318. **$399-$2475, 45 day notice.** 567 Mountain Village Blvd 81435. 2.3 mi e; in Mountain Village. Int corridors. **Pets:** Dogs only. $20 daily fee/room. Designated rooms, service with restrictions, supervision.
ECO 🛬 ⊠ 📶 ⊠ K 🛏 🖥

◈◈◈ Hotel Columbia H
(970) 728-0660. **Call for rates.** 301 W San Juan Ave 81435. At Aspen St and San Juan Ave; opposite gondola. Int corridors. **Pets:** Accepted.
🍴 ⊠ 📶 ⊠ 🛏 🖥

◈◈◈ The Hotel Telluride H
(970) 369-1188. **Call for rates.** 199 N Cornet St 81435. Just s of roundabout, then just e. Int corridors. **Pets:** Accepted.
🍴 ♿ ⊠ 📶 ⊠ 🛏 🖥

AAA ◈◈◈ Lumiere Hotel Telluride H
(970) 369-0400. **Call for rates.** 118 Lost Creek Ln 81435. 1.5 mi e; in Mountain Village. Int corridors. **Pets:** Accepted.
SAVE 🍴 📶 ⊠ K 🛏 🖥

AAA ◈◈◈ Madeline Hotel & Residences H
(970) 369-0880. **$199-$629, 21 day notice.** 568 Mountain Village Blvd 81435. 2.2 mi e; in Mountain Village. Int corridors. **Pets:** Accepted.
SAVE 🍴 🛬 ⊠ 📶 ⊠ 🛏 🖥

◈◈◈ The Peaks Resort & Spa H
(970) 728-6800. **Call for rates.** 136 Country Club Dr 81435. 2.5 mi e; in Mountain Village. Int corridors. **Pets:** Accepted.
🍴 🛬 ⊠ 📶 ⊠ K 🛏 🖥

THORNTON

◈◈◈ Holiday Inn Express Hotel & Suites - Denver North/Thornton H
(303) 452-0800. **$129-$275, 3 day notice.** 12030 Grant St 80241. I-25 exit 223, just e, then just n. Int corridors. **Pets:** Medium, other species. $250 deposit/pet, $20 daily fee/pet. Designated rooms, service with restrictions, supervision. 🍴 ♿ 🛬 📶 ⊠ 🛏 🖥

TRINIDAD

AAA ◈◈◈ Holiday Inn & Suites H
(719) 845-8400. **Call for rates.** 3130 Santa Fe Trail Dr 81082. I-25 exit 11 (Starkville), just e, then just n. Int corridors. **Pets:** Medium, other species. $20 one-time fee/pet. Designated rooms, service with restrictions, supervision. SAVE 🍴 ♿ 🛬 📶 ⊠ 🛏 🖥

◈◈◈ La Quinta Inn & Suites Trinidad H
(719) 845-0102. **$86-$240.** 2833 Toupal Dr 81082. I-25 exit 11 (Starkville), just w, then n. Int corridors. **Pets:** Accepted.
🛬 ⊠ 📶 ⊠ 🛏 🖥

VAIL *(Restaurants p. 604)*

AAA ◈◈◈ The Arrabelle at Vail Square, A RockResort H
(970) 754-7777. **$200-$2000, 30 day notice.** 675 Lionshead Pl 81657. I-70 exit 176, just s to roundabout, 1 mi w on Frontage Rd to W Lionshead Cir, continue just s past No Outlet sign. Int corridors.
Pets: Accepted. SAVE ⊟ 🍴 ♿ 🛬 ⊠ 📶 ⊠ 🛏 🖥

◈◈ Evergreen Lodge at Vail H
(970) 476-7810. **Call for rates.** 250 S Frontage Rd W 81657. I-70 exit 176, just s, then just w. Int corridors. **Pets:** Dogs only. $25 daily fee/pet. Designated rooms, service with restrictions.
🍴 🛬 ⊠ 🛰 ⊠ K 🛏 🖥

AAA ◈◈◈ Four Seasons Resort & Residences Vail H
(970) 477-8600. **Call for rates.** One Vail Rd 81657. I-70 exit 176, just s, then just w of roundabout. Int corridors. **Pets:** Accepted.
SAVE 🍴 🛬 ⊠ 📶 ⊠ 🛏 🖥

◈◈◈ The Lodge at Vail, A RockResort & Spa H ❀
(970) 754-7800. **Call for rates.** 174 E Gore Creek Dr 81657. I-70 exit 176, 0.3 mi s on Vail Rd to Gore Creek Dr. Ext/int corridors.
Pets: Large, dogs only. $75 one-time fee/room. Service with restrictions.
🍴 🛬 ⊠ 📶 ⊠ 🛏 🖥

AAA ◈◈◈ The Sebastian-Vail H
(970) 315-4214. **$295-$6250, 31 day notice.** 16 Vail Rd 81657. I-70 exit 176, just s, take 2nd exit at roundabout, then just s. Int corridors.
Pets: Accepted. SAVE 🍴 ♿ 🛬 ⊠ 📶 ⊠ 🛏 🖥

WALSENBURG

AAA ◈◈ Best Western Rambler M
(719) 738-1121. **$90-$111.** 457 US Hwy 85-87 81089. I-25 exit 52, just w. Ext/int corridors. **Pets:** Large, other species. $10 daily fee/pet. Designated rooms, service with restrictions, supervision.
SAVE 🍴 ♿ 🛬 📶 ⊠ 🛏 🖥

WESTMINSTER

◈◈◈ Drury Inn & Suites H
(303) 460-1220. **$100-$180.** 10393 Reed St 80021. US 36 (Boulder Tpke) exit Church Ranch Blvd W, just s, then just e. Int corridors.
Pets: Accepted. 🍴 ♿ 📶 ⊠ 🛏 🖥

◈◈◈ Residence Inn by Marriott H
(303) 427-9500. **$104-$297.** 5010 W 88th Pl 80031. US 36 (Boulder Tpke) exit Sheridan Blvd, n to 92nd Ave, e to Yates Dr, then s. Int corridors. **Pets:** Accepted. 🛬 📶 ⊠ 🛏 🖥

AAA ◈◈◈ The Westin Westminster H
(303) 410-5000. **$129-$289.** 10600 Westminster Blvd 80020. US 36 (Boulder Tpke) exit 104th Ave, just n. Int corridors. **Pets:** Accepted.
SAVE 🍴 ♿ 🛬 ⊠ 🛰 ⊠ 🛏 🖥

WINTER PARK

AAA ◈◈◈ Best Western Alpenglo Lodge H ❀
(970) 726-8088. **$99-$196.** 78665 US Hwy 40 80482. 0.3 mi n of center. Int corridors. **Pets:** Other species. $10 one-time fee/pet. Designated rooms, service with restrictions. SAVE ♿ 📶 ⊠ 🛏 🖥

WOODLAND PARK

◈◈◈ Bristlecone Lodge CA
(719) 687-9518. **$110-$220.** 510 N Hwy 67 80863. 0.5 mi n. Ext corridors. **Pets:** Accepted. 🍴 📶 ⊠ K ⊠ 🛏 🖥

AAA ◈◈ Woodland Country Lodge H ❀
(719) 687-6277. **Call for rates.** 723 US Hwy 24 W 80863. Just w of jct SR 67. Int corridors. **Pets:** Other species. $10 daily fee/pet. Designated rooms, service with restrictions, supervision.
SAVE 🍴 ♿ 🛬 📶 ⊠ 🛏 🖥

AVON

▼▼◆ Avon Old Farms Hotel 🅷 🐾
(860) 677-1651. **$109-$259.** 279 Avon Mountain Rd 06001. Jct US 44
and SR 10. Ext/int corridors. **Pets:** Medium. $20 daily fee/pet. Desig-
nated rooms, service with restrictions, crate.

🍴 🏊 🛜 ⊠ 🖥 💻

▼▼▼ Residence Inn by Marriott Hartford-Avon 🅷
(860) 678-1666. **$117-$296.** 55 Simsbury Rd (US 202 & SR 10) 06001.
Jct US 44, just n. Int corridors. **Pets:** Accepted.

🍴 ♿M 🏊 🛜 ⊠ 🖥 💻

BERLIN

✈✈ ▼▼▼ Best Western Plus New England Inn &
Suites 🅷
(860) 828-3000. **$105-$119.** 2253 Berlin Tpke 06037. I-91 exit 17 northbound, 4.9 mi n on SR 15 (Berlin Tpke); exit 22N southbound, 2.5 mi n
on SR 9 exit 22, 2.8 mi to US 5 and SR 15 S (Berlin Tpke), follow
signs. Int corridors. **Pets:** Accepted.

SAVE 🍴 ♿M 🏊 🛜 🖥 💻

BETHEL

▼▼ Days Inn Bethel/Danbury 🅼
(203) 743-5990. **$67-$76.** 18 Stony Hill Rd 06801. I-84 exit 8, 1 mi e
on US 6. Ext corridors. **Pets:** Accepted. 🍴 🛜 🖥 💻

▼▼ Microtel Inn & Suites by Wyndham Bethel 🅷
(203) 748-8318. **$74-$87.** 80 Benedict Rd 06801. I-84 exit 8, 1 mi e on
US 6. Int corridors. **Pets:** Accepted. ♿M 🛜 ⊠ 🖥 💻

BRIDGEPORT

▼▼▼ Bridgeport Holiday Inn & Convention Center 🅷
(203) 334-1234. **$119-$189.** 1070 Main St 06604. SR 8 exit 2 northbound, 0.7 mi se; exit southbound, just s, then just e. Int corridors.
Pets: Accepted. 🍴 ♿M 🏊 🛜 ⊠ 🖥 💻

CROMWELL

✈✈ ▼▼▼ Radisson Hotel Cromwell 🅷 🐾
(860) 635-2000. **$109-$189.** 100 Berlin Rd 06416. I-91 exit 21, just e
on SR 372. Int corridors. **Pets:** Other species. $50 one-time fee/pet.
Designated rooms, service with restrictions, crate.

SAVE ECO 🍴 ♿M 🏊 🛜 ⊠ 🖥 💻

DANBURY

▼▼▼ Ethan Allen Hotel 🅷
(203) 744-1776. **Call for rates.** 21 Lake Ave Ext 06811. I-84 exit 4, 0.3
mi w on US 6 and 202. Int corridors. **Pets:** Medium. $50 one-time fee/
pet. Designated rooms, service with restrictions, supervision.

ECO 🍴 ♿M 🏊 🛜 ⊠ 🖥 💻

▼▼▼ Holiday Inn Danbury 🅷
(203) 792-4000. **Call for rates.** 80 Newtown Rd 06810. I-84 exit 8
(Newtown Rd), 0.5 mi s on US 6 W. Int corridors. **Pets:** Accepted.

🍴 ♿M 🏊 🛜 ⊠ 🖥 💻

▼▼▼ Holiday Inn Express & Suites Danbury - I-84 🅷
(203) 205-0800. **Call for rates.** 89 Mill Plain Rd 06811. I-84 exit 2 eastbound; exit 2B westbound, just n, then just e. Int corridors.
Pets: Accepted. ♿M 🏊 🛜 ⊠ 🖥 💻

✈✈ ▼▼▼ La Quinta Inn & Suites 🅷
(203) 798-1200. **$67-$196.** 116 Newtown Rd 06810. I-84 exit 8 (Newtown Rd), just sw. Int corridors. **Pets:** Accepted.

SAVE 🍴 ♿M 🏊 🛜 ⊠ 🖥 💻

✈✈ ▼▼▼ Maron Hotel & Suites 🅷
(203) 791-2200. **$89-$199.** 42 Lake Ave Ext 06811. I-84 exit 4, 0.5 mi
w on US 6 and 202. Int corridors. **Pets:** Accepted.

SAVE 🍴 ♿M 🛜 ⊠ 🖥 💻

✈✈ ▼▼▼ Quality Inn & Suites 🅷
(203) 743-6701. **$90-$120.** 78 Federal Rd 06810. I-84 exit 7 (US 7 N),
0.5 mi n to exit 11 (Federal Rd), 0.8 mi s on White Turkey Rd, then
just w. Int corridors. **Pets:** Small. $25 daily fee/pet. Designated rooms,
service with restrictions, supervision.

SAVE ♿M 🏊 🛜 ⊠ 🖥 💻

✈✈ ▼▼▼ Residence Inn by Marriott Danbury 🅷
(203) 797-1256. **$98-$296.** 22 Segar St 06810. I-84 exit 4 eastbound,
just n; exit westbound, just e on Lake Ave Ext, then just s. Int corridors.
Pets: Accepted. SAVE ECO ♿M 🏊 🛜 ⊠ 🖥 💻

DAYVILLE

▼▼▼ Comfort Inn & Suites 🅷
(860) 779-3200. **$117-$163.** 16 Tracy Rd 06241. I-395 exit 43, just w.
Int corridors. **Pets:** Large. $15 daily fee/pet. Designated rooms, service
with restrictions, crate. ♿M 🏊 🛜 ⊠ 🖥 💻

EAST WINDSOR

▼▼◆ Baymont Inn & Suites East Windsor 🅷
(860) 627-6585. **$79-$149.** 260 Main St 06088. I-91 exit 44, just s. Int
corridors. **Pets:** Accepted. ♿M 🏊 🛜 🖥 💻

ENFIELD

▼▼◆ Holiday Inn Springfield South-Enfield 🅷
(860) 741-2211. **$109-$169.** 1 Bright Meadow Blvd 06082. I-91 exit 49,
just e on service road. Int corridors. **Pets:** Accepted.

🍴 ♿M 🏊 ⊠ 🛜 ⊠ 🖥 💻

FAIRFIELD

✈✈ ▼▼▼ Best Western Plus Black Rock Inn 🅷
(203) 659-2200. **$150-$200.** 100 Kings Hwy Cutoff 06824. I-95 exit 24,
just sw. Int corridors. **Pets:** Accepted. SAVE ♿M 🛜 ⊠ 🖥 💻

▼▼▼ The Fairfield Circle Inn 🅲🅸 🐾
(203) 255-0491. **$99-$399.** 417 Post Rd 06824. I-95 exit 23, 0.7 mi e
Kings Hwy (US 1), then just n on Post Rd. Ext/int corridors.
Pets: Medium. $30 daily fee/pet. Service with restrictions, supervision.

🛜 ⊠ 🖥 💻

▼▼▼ Hotel Hi-Ho 🅷
(475) 888-9100. **$99-$399.** 4180 Black Rock Tpke 06824. Just w on SR
58, just off Merritt Pkwy (SR 15). Ext corridors. **Pets:** Accepted.

🛜 ⊠ 🖥

FARMINGTON

▼▼▼ Extended Stay America Hartford-Farmington 🅷
(860) 676-2790. **$95-$125.** 1 Batterson Park Rd 06032. I-84 exit 37,
just ne. Int corridors. **Pets:** Accepted. ♿M 🛜 🖥

▼▼▼ The Farmington Inn 🅷
(860) 269-3401. **$109-$199.** 827 Farmington Ave 06032. I-84 exit 39,
1.8 mi w on SR 4. Int corridors. **Pets:** Medium. $20 daily fee/pet. Des-
ignated rooms, service with restrictions, crate. 🛜 ⊠ 🖥 💻

▼▼▼ Homewood Suites by Hilton
Hartford-Farmington 🅷
(860) 321-0000. **$104-$259.** 2 Farm Glen Blvd 06032. I-84 exit 39, 0.6
mi e on SR 4. Int corridors. **Pets:** Accepted.

🍴 ♿M 🏊 🛜 ⊠ 🖥 💻

GLASTONBURY
▼▼▼ **Homewood Suites by Hilton Hartford South/Glastonbury** H
(860) 652-8111. **$149-$279.** 65 Glastonbury Blvd 06033. SR 3 exit Main St, just se. Int corridors. **Pets:** Accepted.
(icons)

GREENWICH
▼▼▼ **The Stanton House Inn** BB
(203) 869-2110. **Call for rates.** 76 Maple Ave 06830. Just n of US 1; center. Ext/int corridors. **Pets:** Accepted. (icons)

GRISWOLD
▼▼ **AmericInn Lodge & Suites of Griswold** H
(860) 376-3200. **Call for rates.** 375 Voluntown Rd 06351. I-395 exit 22, w on SR 138. Int corridors. **Pets:** Accepted. (icons)

HARTFORD *(Restaurants p. 604)*
▼▼▼ **The Hilton Hartford Hotel** H
(860) 728-5151. **$139-$339.** 315 Trumbull St 06103. Downtown. Int corridors. **Pets:** Accepted. (icons)

▼▼▼ **Homewood Suites by Hilton Hartford Downtown** H
(860) 524-0223. **$164-$379.** 338 Asylum St 06103. Between Ann and High sts; downtown. Int corridors. **Pets:** Accepted.
(icons)

AAA ▼▼▼ **Residence Inn by Marriott- Downtown Hartford** H
(860) 524-5550. **$218-$480.** 942 Main St 06103. I-91 exit 29A northbound; exit 31 southbound. Int corridors. **Pets:** Accepted.
(icons)

LAKEVILLE
▼▼▼ **Interlaken Inn Resort and Conference Center** H 🐾
(860) 435-9878. **$249, 7 day notice.** 74 Interlaken Rd 06039. On SR 112, 0.5 mi w of jct SR 41. Ext/int corridors. **Pets:** $25 one-time fee/ room. Designated rooms, service with restrictions, supervision.
(icons)

LEDYARD
▼▼ **Almost In Mystic/Mares Inn** BB
(860) 572-7556. **$125-$225, 14 day notice.** 333 Colonel Ledyard Hwy 06339. I-95 exit 89, 1 mi ne to Gold Star Hwy, 0.6 mi w, then 0.7 mi n. Int corridors. **Pets:** Accepted. (icons)

LITCHFIELD
▼▼▼ **Litchfield Inn** H
(860) 567-4503. **Call for rates.** 432 Bantam Rd 06759. 1.5 mi w on US 202. Int corridors. **Pets:** $25 daily fee/pet. Designated rooms, service with restrictions, supervision. (icons)

MANCHESTER *(Restaurants p. 604)*
▼▼ **Extended Stay America Hartford-Manchester** H
(860) 643-5140. **$90-$115.** 340 Tolland Tpke 06040. I-84 exit 63, 0.3 mi se on SR 30, then just sw. Int corridors. **Pets:** Accepted.
(icons)

AAA ▼▼▼ **Residence Inn by Marriott Hartford/Manchester** H 🐾
(860) 432-4242. **$111-$266.** 201 Hale Rd 06042. I-84 exit 63, 0.5 mi nw, then 0.6 mi sw. Int corridors. **Pets:** Other species. $75 one-time fee/room. Service with restrictions, crate.
(icons)

MASHANTUCKET
▼▼▼ **Two Trees Inn at Foxwoods Resort Casino** H
(860) 312-3000. **Call for rates.** 240 Indiantown Rd 06339. Jct SR 214 and 2. Int corridors. **Pets:** Accepted.
(icons)

MERIDEN
▼▼ **Extended Stay America Hartford-Meriden** H
(203) 630-1927. **$85-$105.** 366 Bee St 06451. I-91 exit 17 northbound, just e on E Main St, then 0.7 mi n; exit 19 southbound, 0.5 mi w on Baldwin Ave, then 0.6 mi s. Int corridors. **Pets:** Accepted.
(icons)

AAA ▼▼▼ **Four Points by Sheraton Meriden** H
(203) 238-2380. **$89-$229.** 275 Research Pkwy 06450. I-91 exit 17 southbound; exit 16 northbound, 0.5 mi e, then 0.5 mi s. Int corridors. **Pets:** Accepted. (icons)

▼▼▼ **Hawthorn Suites by Wyndham** H
(203) 379-5048. **$79-$189.** 1151 E Main St 06450. I-91 exit 17 southbound; exit 16 northbound, just n. Int corridors. **Pets:** Accepted.
(icons)

MILFORD
AAA ▼▼▼ **Hyatt Place Milford** H
(203) 877-9800. **$89-$329.** 190 Old Gate Ln 06460. I-95 exit 40, 0.4 mi s. Int corridors. **Pets:** Accepted. (icons)

▼▼ **Motel 6 Milford** H
(203) 877-8588. **Call for rates.** 111 Schoolhouse Rd 06460. I-95 exit 35, just se. Int corridors. **Pets:** Accepted.
(icons)

▼▼▼ **Residence Inn by Marriott Milford** H
(203) 283-2100. **$85-$274.** 62 Rowe Ave 06460. I-95 exit 35, just nw. Int corridors. **Pets:** Accepted. (icons)

MORRIS
AAA ▼▼▼ **Winvian** H 🐾
(860) 567-9600. **$549-$1499, 60 day notice.** 155 Alain White Rd 06763. Jct SR 109, 1 mi n. Ext/int corridors. **Pets:** Dogs only. $80 one-time fee/pet. Designated rooms, service with restrictions, supervision.
(icons)

MYSTIC *(Restaurants p. 604)*
▼▼▼ **Hampton Inn & Suites/Mystic** H
(860) 536-2536. **$89-$269.** 6 Hendel Dr 06355. I-95 exit 90, just s. Int corridors. **Pets:** Other species. Service with restrictions.
(icons)

▼▼ **Howard Johnson Inn** H
(860) 536-2654. **$69-$189.** 253 Greenmanville Ave 06355. I-95 exit 90, just se. Int corridors. **Pets:** Accepted. (icons)

AAA ▼▼▼ **Hyatt Place Mystic** H 🐾
(860) 536-9997. **$89-$299.** 224 Greenmanville Ave 06355. I-95 exit 90, just se. Int corridors. **Pets:** Medium. $75 one-time fee/room. Service with restrictions. (icons)

AAA ▼▼▼ **Residence Inn by Marriott** H
(860) 536-5150. **$87-$367.** 40 Whitehall Ave 06355. I-95 exit 90, just n on SR 27. Int corridors. **Pets:** Accepted.
(icons)

NAUGATUCK
▼▼▼ **Comfort Inn Naugatuck** H
(203) 723-9356. **$85-$165.** 716 New Haven Rd 06770. Jct SR 63 and 8, 0.8 mi s. Int corridors. **Pets:** Accepted. (icons)

NEW HAVEN *(Restaurants p. 604)*

Ⓐ ▼▼▼ **New Haven Village Suites** Ⓗ
(203) 777-5337. **Call for rates.** 3 Long Wharf Dr 06511. I-95 exit 46, 0.6 mi nw. Ext corridors. **Pets:** Accepted.
[SAVE] [ECO] [YI] [🅼] [📶] [✕] [🛢] [🖥]

▼▼▼ **Omni New Haven Hotel at Yale** Ⓗ
(203) 772-6664. **Call for rates.** 155 Temple St 06510. Between Chapel and Crown sts; downtown. Int corridors. **Pets:** Accepted.
[YI] [🅼] [📶] [✕] [🛢] [🖥]

NEW LONDON

Ⓐ ▼ **Red Roof Inn Mystic New London** Ⓜ
(860) 444-0001. **$39-$159.** 707 Colman St 06320. I-95 exit 82A northbound, 0.4 mi e, then just n; exit 83 southbound, 0.6 mi s. Ext corridors. **Pets:** Accepted. [SAVE] [YI] [📶] [✕] [🛢] [🖥]

NORWALK

▼▼ **EVEN Hotels** Ⓗ
(203) 846-9355. **Call for rates.** 426 Main Ave 06851. I-95 exit 15, 3.5 mi n on US 7, just e, then 0.7 mi s. Int corridors. **Pets:** Accepted.
[ECO] [YI] [🅼] [📶] [✕] [🛢] [🖥]

OLD GREENWICH

Ⓐ ▼▼▼▼ **Hyatt Regency Greenwich** Ⓗ
(203) 637-1234. **$89-$399.** 1800 E Putnam Ave 06870. I-95 exit 5, 0.5 mi n on US 1. Int corridors. **Pets:** Small, dogs only. $200 one-time fee/room. Designated rooms, supervision.
[SAVE] [📧] [YI] [🅼] [📶] [s📶] [✕] [🛢] [🖥]

OLD SAYBROOK

▼ **Liberty Inn** Ⓜ
(860) 388-1777. **$69-$139.** 55 Spring Brook Rd 06475. I-95 exit 68 southbound; exit 67 northbound, 0.9 mi n on US 1, then w. Ext corridors. **Pets:** Small, dogs only. $15 daily fee/pet. Designated rooms, service with restrictions, supervision. [YI] [📶] [🛢] [🖥]

Ⓐ ▼▼▼▼ **Saybrook Point Inn, Marina & Spa** Ⓗ
(860) 395-2000. **$319-$799, 3 day notice.** 2 Bridge St 06475. On SR 154, 2.2 mi s of jct US 1; at Saybrook Point. Int corridors. **Pets:** Accepted.
[SAVE] [ECO] [📧] [YI] [🅼] [📶] [✕] [📶] [✕] [🛢] [🖥]

PAWCATUCK

▼▼▼ **La Quinta Inn & Suites** Ⓗ
(860) 599-2400. **$67-$334.** 349 Liberty St 06379. I-95 exit 92, 1 mi s on SR 2. Int corridors. **Pets:** Accepted.
[YI] [🅼] [📶] [📶] [✕] [🛢] [🖥]

ROCKY HILL

▼▼▼ **Residence Inn by Marriott Hartford-Rocky Hill** Ⓗ
(860) 257-7500. **$63-$310.** 680 Cromwell Ave 06067. I-91 exit 23, 0.4 mi w on West St, then just n. Int corridors. **Pets:** Other species. $25 daily fee/room. Service with restrictions. [🅼] [📶] [📶] [✕] [🛢] [🖥]

Ⓐ ▼▼▼ **Sheraton Hartford South** Ⓗ 🐾
(860) 257-6000. **$109-$299.** 100 Capital Blvd 06067. I-91 exit 23, just e. Int corridors. **Pets:** Other species. Designated rooms, service with restrictions, supervision. [SAVE] [ECO] [YI] [🅼] [📶] [📶] [✕] [🛢] [🖥]

SHELTON

▼▼ ▼▼ **Extended Stay America Shelton Connecticut** Ⓗ
(203) 926-6868. **$100-$140.** 945 Bridgeport Ave 06484. SR 8 exit 11, 0.5 mi w. Int corridors. **Pets:** Accepted. [YI] [🅼] [📶] [🛢]

▼▼▼ **Hampton Inn Shelton** Ⓗ
(203) 925-5900. **$99-$169.** 695 Bridgeport Ave 06484. SR 8 exit 12, 0.3 mi w, then just s. Int corridors. **Pets:** Accepted.
[🅼] [📶] [📶] [✕] [🛢] [🖥]

Ⓐ ▼▼▼ **Hyatt House Shelton** Ⓗ 🐾
(203) 225-0700. **$99-$289.** 830 Bridgeport Ave 06484. SR 8 exit 12, 0.7 mi sw. Int corridors. **Pets:** Medium. $75 one-time fee/room. Designated rooms, service with restrictions, crate.
[SAVE] [🅼] [📶] [📶] [✕] [🛢] [🖥]

SIMSBURY

▼▼▼ **The Simsbury Inn** Ⓗ
(860) 651-5700. **Call for rates.** 397 Hopmeadow St 06070. On US 202/SR 10, 0.4 mi n of jct SR 185. Int corridors. **Pets:** Accepted.
[YI] [🅼] [📶] [✕] [📶] [✕] [🛢] [🖥]

SOUTHBURY

▼▼▼ **Cornucopia at Oldfield Bed and Breakfast** ⒷⒷ
(203) 267-6772. **$175-$295, 14 day notice.** 782 Main St N 06488. I-84 exit 15, 1.5 mi n. Int corridors. **Pets:** Accepted.
[ECO] [📶] [📶] [✕] [🅩]

▼▼▼ **Wyndham Southbury** Ⓗ
(203) 598-7600. **Call for rates.** 1284 Strongtown Rd 06488. I-84 exit 16, just n on SR 188. Int corridors. **Pets:** Accepted.
[YI] [🅼] [📶] [📶] [✕] [🖥]

SOUTHINGTON

Ⓐ ▼▼▼ **Residence Inn by Marriott Southington** Ⓗ
(860) 621-4440. **$108-$261.** 778 West St 06489. I-84 exit 31, just s. Int corridors. **Pets:** Accepted. [SAVE] [ECO] [🅼] [📶] [📶] [✕] [🛢] [🖥]

SOUTHPORT

▼▼▼▼ **Delamar Southport** Ⓗ
(203) 259-2800. **Call for rates.** 275 Old Post Rd 06890. I-95 exit 19, just e. Int corridors. **Pets:** Accepted. [YI] [✕] [📶] [✕] [🖥]

STAMFORD *(Restaurants p. 604)*

Ⓐ ▼▼▼ **Hilton Stamford Hotel & Executive Meeting Center** Ⓗ
(203) 967-2222. **$109-$199.** 1 First Stamford Pl 06902. I-95 exit 7 northbound, just s on Greenwich Ave, then just w; exit 6 southbound, just s on West Ave, 0.3 mi w on Baxter Ave, just n on Fairfield Ave, then just e. Int corridors. **Pets:** Accepted.
[SAVE] [YI] [🅼] [📶] [✕] [📶] [✕] [🛢] [🖥]

Ⓐ ▼▼▼ **Sheraton Stamford Hotel** Ⓗ
(203) 358-8400. **$119-$349.** 700 E Main St 06901. I-95 exit 8 southbound, just n on Elm St; exit northbound, n on Atlantic St, 0.3 mi e on Tresser Blvd, then just n on Elm St; downtown. Int corridors.
Pets: Accepted. [SAVE] [YI] [🅼] [📶] [📶] [✕] [🛢] [🖥]

Ⓐ ▼▼▼ **Stamford Marriott Hotel & Spa** Ⓗ
(203) 357-9555. **$102-$370.** 243 Tresser Blvd 06901. I-95 exit 8, just n under viaduct, then n. Int corridors. **Pets:** Accepted.
[SAVE] [YI] [🅼] [📶] [✕] [🛢] [🖥]

STONINGTON *(Restaurants p. 605)*

▼▼▼ **Another Second Penny Inn** ⒷⒷ
(860) 535-1710. **Call for rates.** 870 Pequot Tr 06378. I-95 exit 91, 0.8 mi s on SR 234. Int corridors. **Pets:** $25 one-time fee/pet. Designated rooms, service with restrictions, crate. [YI] [📶] [✕] [🅩] [🛢]

STRATFORD

▼▼▼ **Homewood Suites by Hilton** Ⓗ
(203) 377-3322. **$109-$279.** 6905 Main St 06614. SR 15 exit 53, just n. Int corridors. **Pets:** Accepted. [YI] [🅼] [📶] [📶] [🛢] [🖥]

UNCASVILLE

AAA ▼▼▼▼ **Hyatt Place Mohegan Sun** H
(860) 383-1234. **$119-$429.** 2049 Norwich New London Tpke 06382. I-395 exit 79A, just e on SR 2A, then just s on SR 32. Int corridors. **Pets:** Accepted. SAVE ⫨ ᘒ ⩘ ⧉ ✕ ⊟ ⊡

WALLINGFORD

▼▼▼ **Homewood Suites by Hilton Wallingford/Meriden** H
(203) 284-2600. **$119-$189.** 90 Miles Dr 06492. I-91 exit 15, just nw on SR 68, then just s. Int corridors. **Pets:** Accepted.
ᘒ ᘒ ⩘ ⊟ ⊡

WATERFORD

▼ **Rodeway Inn at Crossroad** M
(860) 442-7227. **$66-$185.** 211 Parkway N 06385. I-95 exit 81 northbound, just nw; exit southbound, 0.6 mi w. Ext corridors.
Pets: Accepted. ⫨ ᘒ ⩘ ⊟

WESTPORT *(Restaurants p. 605)*

▼▼▼▼ **The Westport Inn, an Ascend Hotel Collection Member** H
(203) 557-8124. **$105-$389.** 1595 Post Rd E 06880. I-95 exit 18 northbound, n to US 1, then 1.5 mi e; exit 19 southbound, 1 mi w. Ext/int corridors. **Pets:** Accepted. ⫨ ᘒ ᘒ ⩘ ✕ ⊟ ⊡

WETHERSFIELD

AAA ▼▼ **Comfort Inn** H
(860) 563-2311. **$109-$189.** 1330 Silas Deane Hwy 06109. I-91 exit 24, 0.4 mi n. Int corridors. **Pets:** $20 daily fee/pet. Designated rooms, service with restrictions, crate. SAVE ᘒ ᘒ ⩘ ✕ ⊟ ⊡

WINDSOR

AAA ▼▼▼ **Hyatt House Hartford North/Windsor** H
(860) 298-8000. **$99-$229.** 200 Corporate Dr 06095. I-91 exit 38 northbound; exit 38B southbound. Int corridors. **Pets:** Accepted.
SAVE ᘒ ᘒ ⩘ ✕ ⊟ ⊡

Residence Inn by Marriott Hartford-Windsor

▼▼▼ **Residence Inn by Marriott Hartford-Windsor** H
(860) 688-7474. **$84-$204.** 100 Dunfey Ln 06095. I-91 exit 37, just w on SR 305 to Dunfey Ln, then 0.3 mi n. Ext corridors. **Pets:** Accepted.
ᘒ ᘒ ⩘ ✕ ⊟ ⊡

WINDSOR LOCKS

▼▼▼ **Candlewood Suites** H
(860) 623-2000. **$83-$194.** 149 Ella T Grasso Tpke 06096. I-91 exit 40, 2.5 mi w on SR 20, then 0.6 mi n on SR 75. Int corridors. **Pets:** Medium. $75 one-time fee/pet. Service with restrictions, supervision. ᘒ ᘒ ⩘ ⊟ ⊡

▼▼ **La Quinta Inn Hartford Bradley Airport** H
(860) 623-3336. **$82-$180.** 64 Ella T Grasso Tpke 06096. I-91 exit 40, 2.5 mi w on SR 20, then just n on SR 75. Int corridors.
Pets: Accepted. ᘒ ⩘ ✕ ⊟ ⊡

AAA ▼▼▼▼ **Sheraton Hartford Hotel At Bradley Airport** H ❀
(860) 627-5311. **$129-$309.** 1 Bradley International Airport 06096. Jct SR 75, 0.6 mi w on Schoephoester Rd, 0.5 mi nw on Terminal Rd. Int corridors. **Pets:** Large, other species. $75 one-time fee/room. Designated rooms, service with restrictions, crate.
SAVE ECO ⫨ ᘒ ᘒ ⩘ ✕ ⊟ ⊡

WOODSTOCK *(Restaurants p. 605)*

▼▼▼ **Inn at Woodstock Hill** CI
(860) 928-0528. **Call for rates.** 94 Plaine Hill Rd 06281. 0.8 mi n on SR 169. Int corridors. **Pets:** Other species. $25 one-time fee/pet. Designated rooms. ECO ⫨ ⩘ ✕ ⊟ ⊡

DELAWARE

BEAR

AAA ▼▼▼ **Best Western Plus Newark/Christiana Inn** H
(302) 326-2500. **$100-$130.** 875 Pulaski Hwy 19701. I-95 exit 4, 3.3 mi se on SR 1 exit 160, then just e on US 40. Int corridors.
Pets: Accepted. SAVE ᘒ ᘒ ⩘ ✕ ⊟ ⊡

BETHANY BEACH

▼▼▼ **Bethany Beach Ocean Suites Residence Inn by Marriott** H ❀
(302) 539-3200. **$98-$785, 3 day notice.** 99 Hollywood St 19930. Jct S Atlantic Ave; center. Int corridors. **Pets:** Small. $150 one-time fee/pet, $20 daily fee/pet. Designated rooms, service with restrictions, supervision. ⫨ ᘒ ✕ ⩘ ✕ ⊟ ⊡

DEWEY BEACH

AAA ▼▼▼ **Hyatt Place Dewey Beach** H
(302) 864-9100. **$99-$599.** 1301 Coastal Hwy 19971. On SR 1; center. Int corridors. **Pets:** Medium, dogs only. $75 one-time fee/pet. Designated rooms, service with restrictions, crate.
SAVE ⊟ ⫨ ᘒ ᘒ ⩘ ✕ ⊟ ⊡

DOVER

AAA ▼▼▼ **Best Western Galaxy Inn** M
(302) 735-4700. **$85-$249.** 1700 E Lebanon Rd 19901. SR 1 exit 95, just w on SR 10. Int corridors. **Pets:** Accepted.
SAVE ᘒ ⩘ ⊟ ⊡

▼▼▼ **Hampton Inn-Dover** H
(302) 736-3500. **$99-$379.** 1568 N DuPont Hwy 19901. SR 1 exit 104, 1 mi s. Int corridors. **Pets:** Accepted. ᘒ ᘒ ⩘ ⊟ ⊡

▼▼▼ **Holiday Inn Express Hotel & Suites Dover** H ❀
(302) 678-0600. **Call for rates.** 1780 N DuPont Hwy 19901. SR 1 exit 104, just s on US 13. Int corridors. **Pets:** $20 daily fee/pet. Service with restrictions, crate. ᘒ ᘒ ⩘ ✕ ⊟ ⊡

▼▼▼ **Home2 Suites by Hilton** H
(302) 674-3300. **Call for rates.** 222 S DuPont Hwy 19901. SR 1 exit 98 southbound, 1.2 mi w on SR 8, then just s; exit 95 northbound, 2.1 mi n on US 13. Int corridors. **Pets:** Accepted.
ᘒ ᘒ ⩘ ✕ ⊟ ⊡

▼▼▼ **MainStay Suites Dover** H
(302) 678-8383. **$79-$359.** 201 Stover Blvd 19901. SR 1 exit 95 northbound, just n on Bay Rd; exit 95 southbound, 1.5 mi n on Bay Rd; 0.7 mi s of jct US 13. Int corridors. **Pets:** Accepted.
ECO ⫨ ᘒ ᘒ ⩘ ⊟ ⊡

▼▼▼▼   Residence Inn by Marriott-Dover 🅗 🐾
(302) 677-0777. **$70-$428.** 600 Jefferic Blvd 19901. SR 1 exit 104, 2.7 mi s on US 13. Int corridors. **Pets:** Medium, other species. $100 one-time fee/pet. Service with restrictions, supervision.
🅼 🛏 🛜 ⊗ 🔋 💻

▼▼   Sleep Inn & Suites Dover 🅗 🐾
(302) 735-7770. **$85-$350.** 1784 N DuPont Hwy 19901. SR 1 exit 104, just s on US 13. Int corridors. **Pets:** $10 daily fee/pet. Service with restrictions, crate. 🅼 🛏 🛜 ⊗ 🔋 💻

GEORGETOWN
▼▼   Quality Inn & Suites 🅗
(302) 854-9400. **$89-$365, 3 day notice.** 20530 DuPont Blvd 19947. On US 113, 0.5 mi n of jct SR 404. Int corridors. **Pets:** Accepted.
🍴 🛏 🛜 🔋 💻

HARRINGTON
▼▼   Quality Inn & Suites Harrington 🅗
(302) 398-3900. **$70-$250.** 1259 Corn Crib Rd 19952. On US 13, 0.6 mi s of jct SR 14. Int corridors. **Pets:** Accepted.
🍴 🅼 🛏 🛜 ⊗ 🔋 💻

LEWES *(Restaurants p. 605)*
🆎   ▼▼▼▼   The Inn at Canal Square 🅗
(302) 644-3377. **$105-$330, 7 day notice.** 122 Market St 19958. Just nw of jct Savannah Rd (US 9 business route). Ext/int corridors. **Pets:** Small, dogs only. $200 deposit/room. Designated rooms, service with restrictions, supervision. SAVE 🅼 🛜 ⊗ 🔋 💻

▼▼   Sleep Inn & Suites 🅗
(302) 645-6464. **$85-$394.** 18451 Coastal Hwy 19958. On SR 1, 1.5 mi s. Int corridors. **Pets:** Accepted. 🅼 🛏 🛜 ⊗ 🔋 💻

MIDDLETOWN
▼▼▼▼   Hampton Inn Middletown 🅗
(302) 378-5656. **$169-$249.** 117 Sand Hill Dr 19709. SR 1 exit 136, 2.8 mi w on SR 299, then just n on SR 15. Int corridors. **Pets:** Accepted.
🅼 🛏 🛜 ⊗ 🔋 💻

MILLSBORO
▼▼   Atlantic Inn-Millsboro 🅜
(302) 934-6711. **Call for rates.** 28534 DuPont Blvd 19966. US 113, just s of SR 24. Ext corridors. **Pets:** Accepted. 🛏 🛜 ⊗ 🔋

NEWARK
🆎   ▼▼▼▼   Courtyard by Marriott-Newark at the University of Delaware 🅗
(302) 737-0900. **$132-$271.** 400 David Hollowell Dr 19716. I-95 exit 1B southbound; exit 1 northbound, 3 mi n on SR 896. Int corridors.
Pets: Accepted. SAVE ECO 🍴 🅼 🛏 🛜 ⊗ 🔋 💻

▼▼   Extended Stay America Newark/Christiana 🅗
(302) 283-0800. **$95-$140.** 333 Continental Dr 19713. I-95 exit 4B, 0.3 mi n on SR 7 exit 166, then 0.4 mi w on SR 58 (Churchmans Rd). Int corridors. **Pets:** Accepted. 🅼 🛜 ⊗ 🔋 💻

🆎   ▼▼▼▼   Hilton Wilmington/Christiana 🅗
(302) 454-1500. **$119-$229.** 100 Continental Dr 19713. I-95 exit 4B, 0.3 mi n on SR 7 exit 166, then 0.4 mi w on SR 58 (Churchmans Rd). Int corridors. **Pets:** Other species. $49 one-time fee/room. Designated rooms, service with restrictions. SAVE ECO 🍴 🛏 🛜 🔋 💻

▼▼▼▼   Homewood Suites by Hilton Newark/Wilmington South 🅗 🐾
(302) 453-9700. **$109-$199.** 640 S College Ave 19713. I-95 exit 1B southbound; exit 1 northbound, 0.8 mi n on SR 896. Int corridors. **Pets:** Medium, other species. $25 one-time fee/pet. Service with restrictions, supervision. 🅼 🛏 🛜 🔋 💻

🆎   ▼▼▼▼   Quality Inn Wilmington-Newark/Christiana Mall 🅜
(302) 292-1500. **$79-$179.** 65 Geoffrey Dr 19713. I-95 exit 4B, 0.3 mi n on SR 7 exit 166, then just e on SR 58 (Churchmans Rd). Ext/int corridors. **Pets:** Small. $25 daily fee/room. Designated rooms, service with restrictions, supervision. SAVE 🅼 🛏 🛜 ⊗ 🔋 💻

🆎   ▼▼▼   Ramada Newark/Wilmington 🅗
(302) 738-3400. **$79-$189.** 260 Chapman Rd 19702. I-95 exit 3 southbound; exit 3A northbound, 0.3 mi e on SR 273 E, then just s. Int corridors. **Pets:** Large, other species. $25 daily fee/pet. Service with restrictions, crate. SAVE 🍴 🛏 🛜 ⊗ 🔋 💻

🆎   ▼▼▼   Red Roof PLUS+ Wilmington - Newark 🅜
(302) 292-2870. **$59-$130.** 415 Stanton Christiana Rd 19713. I-95 exit 4B, 0.5 mi n on SR 7. Ext corridors. **Pets:** Accepted.
SAVE 🅼 🛜 ⊗ 🔋 💻

▼▼▼   Residence Inn by Marriott Wilmington/Newark/Christiana 🅗
(302) 453-9200. **$95-$287.** 240 Chapman Rd 19702. I-95 exit 3 southbound; exit 3A northbound, 0.3 mi e on SR 273 E, then 0.5 mi s. Ext corridors. **Pets:** Accepted. 🍴 🛏 🛜 ⊗ 🔋 💻

▼▼▼   Staybridge Suites-Newark/Wilmington 🅗
(302) 366-8097. **Call for rates.** 270 Chapman Rd 19702. I-95 exit 3 southbound; exit 3A northbound, 0.3 mi e on SR 273 E, then just s. Int corridors. **Pets:** Accepted. 🅼 🛏 🛜 ⊗ 🔋 💻

▼▼▼   TownePlace Suites by Marriott-Wilmington/Christiana/Newark 🅗
(302) 369-6212. **$94-$241.** 410 Eagle Run Rd 19702. I-95 exit 3 southbound; exit 3A northbound, just e. Int corridors. **Pets:** Accepted.
🅼 🛏 🛜 ⊗ 🔋 💻

NEW CASTLE
▼▼▼   Clarion Hotel-The Belle 🅗
(302) 428-1000. **$99-$400.** 1612 N DuPont Hwy 19720. Jct I-295, just n on US 13. Int corridors. **Pets:** Accepted.
ECO 🍴 🅼 🛏 🛜 ⊗ 🔋 💻

🆎   ▼▼▼   Sheraton Wilmington South New Castle 🅗
(302) 328-6200. **$109-$399.** 365 Airport Rd 19720. I-95 exit 5A (SR 141 S), just s. Int corridors. **Pets:** Accepted.
SAVE 🍴 🅼 🛏 🛜 ⊗ 🔋 💻

REHOBOTH BEACH *(Restaurants p. 605)*
▼▼   AmericInn Lodge & Suites of Rehoboth Beach 🅗
(302) 226-0700. **Call for rates.** 36012 Airport Rd 19971. Just w of SR 1; just w on Miller Rd, just s. Int corridors. **Pets:** Dogs only. $25 daily fee/room. Designated rooms, service with restrictions.
🅼 🛏 🛜 ⊗ 🔋 💻

WILMINGTON
🆎   ▼▼▼   Best Western Brandywine Valley Inn 🅗
(302) 656-9436. **$139-$159.** 1807 Concord Pike 19803. I-95 exit 8, 1 mi n on US 202. Ext corridors. **Pets:** $15 daily fee/room. Designated rooms, service with restrictions, supervision. SAVE 🛏 🛜 🔋 💻

🆎   ▼▼▼▼   Hotel du Pont 🅗
(302) 594-3100. **$199-$459.** 11th & Market Streets 19801. I-95 exit 7, 0.5 mi se; at 11th St; downtown. Int corridors. **Pets:** Accepted.
SAVE 🍴 🅼 ⊗ 🛜 ⊗ 🔋 💻

🆎   ▼▼▼▼   Inn at Wilmington 🅗
(302) 479-7900. **Call for rates.** 300 Rocky Run Pkwy 19803. I-95 exit 8, 3.8 mi n; just off US 202. Int corridors. **Pets:** Small, dogs only. $25 daily fee/room. Designated rooms, service with restrictions, crate.
SAVE 🅼 🛜 ⊗ 🔋 💻

Westin Wilmington H ❀
(302) 654-2900. **$109-$329.** 818 Shipyard Dr 19801. I-95 exit 6, just w, then 0.5 mi s. Int corridors. **Pets:** Very small, other species. Service with restrictions, supervision. SAVE ❨❬ ⓜ ⓢ ⓧ ⓗ ⓓ

DISTRICT OF COLUMBIA

WASHINGTON, D.C. *(Restaurants p. 605)*

Avenue Suites H
(202) 333-8060. **Call for rates.** 2500 Pennsylvania Ave NW 20037. Jct 25th St NW and Pennsylvania Ave. Int corridors. **Pets:** Accepted.
ⓜ ⓡ ⓧ ⓗ ⓓ

Capitol Hill Hotel H
(202) 543-6000. **Call for rates.** 200 C St SE 20003. At 2nd and C sts SE; 2 blks from Capitol grounds. Int corridors. **Pets:** Accepted.
SAVE ⓡ ⓧ ⓗ ⓓ

The Churchill Hotel H
(202) 797-2000. **Call for rates.** 1914 Connecticut Ave NW 20009. Just n of Dupont Circle. Int corridors. **Pets:** Accepted.
SAVE ❨❬ ⓜ ⓡ ⓧ ⓗ ⓓ

The Dupont Circle Hotel H
(202) 483-6000. **Call for rates.** 1500 New Hampshire Ave NW 20036. At Dupont Circle, Connecticut and Massachusetts aves NW. Int corridors. **Pets:** Accepted. SAVE ❨❬ ⓜ ⓡ ⓧ ⓗ ⓓ

The Embassy Row Hotel H
(202) 265-1600. **Call for rates.** 2015 Massachusetts Ave NW 20036. Just nw of Dupont Circle. Int corridors. **Pets:** Accepted.
SAVE ⊟ ❨❬ ⓜ ⊇ ⓢ ⓧ ⓓ

Fairmont Washington, D.C., Georgetown H ❀
(202) 429-2400. **Call for rates.** 2401 M St NW 20037. 24th and M sts NW. Int corridors. **Pets:** Service with restrictions, supervision.
SAVE ECO ❨❬ ⓜ ⊇ ⓧ ⓢ ⓧ ⓗ ⓓ

Four Seasons Hotel Washington, D.C. H
(202) 342-0444. **$575-$985.** 2800 Pennsylvania Ave NW 20007. Jct M St NW and Pennsylvania Ave NW. Int corridors. **Pets:** Accepted.
SAVE ❨❬ ⓜ ⊇ ⓧ ⓡ ⓗ ⓓ

Glover Park Hotel H
(202) 337-9700. **Call for rates.** 2505 Wisconsin Ave NW 20007. 0.3 mi s of Massachusetts Ave NW; in upper Georgetown area. Int corridors. **Pets:** Accepted. SAVE ⊟ ❨❬ ⓜ ⓢ ⓧ ⓗ

Hamilton Crowne Plaza, Washington DC H
(202) 682-0111. **$99-$700.** 1001 14th St NW 20005. At 14th and K sts NW. Int corridors. **Pets:** Accepted. SAVE ❨❬ ⓜ ⓢ ⓧ ⓗ ⓓ

Hampton Inn & Suites Washington, DC-Navy Yard H ❀
(202) 800-1000. **$109-$409.** 1265 First St SE 20003. I-395 exit Maine Ave SW, 1.1 mi e on M St SW/M St SE; jct N and First sts SE. Int corridors. **Pets:** Medium, dogs only. Designated rooms, service with restrictions. ⓜ ⓡ ⓧ ⓗ ⓓ

The Hay-Adams H
(202) 638-6600. **Call for rates.** 800 16 St NW 20006. 16th and H sts NW; just n of the White House. Int corridors. **Pets:** Accepted.
SAVE ECO ⊟ ❨❬ ⓜ ⓡ ⓧ ⓗ ⓓ

Homewood Suites by Hilton Washington DC Convention Center H
(202) 628-4663. **$159-$269.** 465 New York Ave NW 20001. Between 4th and 5th sts NW. Int corridors. **Pets:** Accepted.
ⓜ ⓡ ⓧ ⓗ ⓓ

Hotel George-a Kimpton Hotel H
(202) 347-4200. **Call for rates.** 15 E St NW 20001. Just n of Capitol grounds. Int corridors. **Pets:** Accepted.
SAVE ECO ⊟ ❨❬ ⓜ ⓢ ⓧ ⓗ ⓓ

Hotel Monaco DC- a Kimpton Hotel H
(202) 628-7177. **$189-$699, 3 day notice.** 700 F St NW 20004. Between 7th and 8th sts NW. Int corridors. **Pets:** Accepted.
SAVE ECO ❨❬ ⓜ ⓧ ⓢ ⓧ ⓗ

Hotel RL by Red Lion Washington, D.C. H
(202) 223-4320. **Call for rates.** 1823 L St NW 20036. Between 18th and 19th sts NW. **Pets:** Accepted.
❨❬ ⓜ ⓡ ⓧ ⓗ

Hotel Rouge-a Kimpton Hotel H
(202) 232-8000. **Call for rates.** 1315 16th St NW 20036. Just n of Scott Circle. Int corridors. **Pets:** Accepted.
SAVE ECO ⊟ ❨❬ ⓜ ⓢ ⓧ ⓗ ⓓ

Hyatt Place Washington DC/Georgetown/West End H
(202) 838-2222. **$116-$449.** 2121 M St NW 20037. Between New Hampsire Ave NW and 22nd St NW. Int corridors. **Pets:** Accepted.
SAVE ⓜ ⓡ ⓧ ⓗ ⓓ

Hyatt Place Washington, D.C./White House H
(202) 830-1900. **$159-$499.** 1522 K St NW 20005. Between 15th and 16th sts NW. Int corridors. **Pets:** Accepted.
SAVE ⓜ ⓡ ⓧ ⓗ ⓓ

Kimpton Hotel Madera H
(202) 296-7600. **Call for rates.** 1310 New Hampshire Ave NW 20036. Between 20th and N sts NW. Int corridors. **Pets:** Accepted.
SAVE ECO ❨❬ ⓜ ⓢ ⓧ ⓗ

Kimpton Hotel Palomar Washington DC H
(202) 448-1800. **Call for rates.** 2121 P St NW 20037. Between 21st and 22nd sts NW; just w of Dupont Circle. Int corridors.
Pets: Accepted. SAVE ECO ⊟ ❨❬ ⓜ ⊇ ⓧ ⓢ ⓧ ⓗ

Kimpton Mason & Rook H
(202) 742-3100. **Call for rates.** 1430 Rhode Island Ave NW 20005. Just e of Scott Circle. Int corridors. **Pets:** Accepted.
SAVE ECO ⊟ ❨❬ ⓜ ⓢ ⓧ ⓗ ⓓ

The Liaison Capitol Hill, a Joie de Vivre Hotel H
(202) 638-1616. **$119-$499.** 415 New Jersey Ave NW 20001. On Capitol Hill, just n of Capitol grounds. Int corridors. **Pets:** Accepted.
SAVE ❨❬ ⓜ ⊇ ⓢ ⓧ ⓗ ⓓ

The Loews Madison H
(202) 862-1600. **$149-$599.** 1177 15th St NW 20005. 15th and M sts NW. Int corridors. **Pets:** Accepted. ❨❬ ⓜ ⓧ ⓡ ⓗ ⓓ

▼▼▼▼ Mandarin Oriental Washington, D.C. 🏨
(202) 554-8588. **Call for rates.** 1330 Maryland Ave SW 20024. Jct Independence Ave SW, just s on 12th St SW. Int corridors. **Pets:** Accepted.

♨ ▼▼▼▼ The Mayflower Hotel, Autograph Collection 🏨
(202) 347-3000. **$161-$397.** 1127 Connecticut Ave NW 20036. Just n of K St NW; in business district. Int corridors. **Pets:** Accepted.

♨ ▼▼▼ The Melrose Georgetown Hotel 🏨
(202) 955-6400. **Call for rates.** 2430 Pennsylvania Ave NW 20037. Between 24th and 25th sts NW. Int corridors. **Pets:** Accepted.

▼▼▼▼ The Normandy Hotel 🏨
(202) 483-1350. **Call for rates.** 2118 Wyoming Ave NW 20008. Just w of Connecticut Ave. Int corridors. **Pets:** Accepted.

▼▼▼▼ Omni Shoreham Hotel 🏨
(202) 234-0700. **$149-$1099.** 2500 Calvert St NW 20008. Just w of Connecticut Ave. Int corridors. **Pets:** Accepted.

▼▼▼ One Washington Circle Hotel 🏨 ☙
(202) 872-1680. **$119-$999.** One Washington Cir NW 20037. Between 23rd St and New Hampshire Ave NW. Int corridors. **Pets:** Other species. Designated rooms, service with restrictions.

♨ ▼▼▼▼ Park Hyatt Washington D.C. 🏨
(202) 789-1234. **$199-$699, 3 day notice.** 1201 24th St NW 20037. 24th and M sts NW. Int corridors. **Pets:** Accepted.

▼▼▼▼ Residence Inn by Marriott DC/Foggy Bottom 🏨
(202) 785-2000. **$120-$307.** 801 New Hampshire Ave NW 20037. Just sw at Washington Circle. Int corridors. **Pets:** Accepted.

▼▼▼▼ Residence Inn by Marriott-Dupont Circle 🏨
(202) 466-6800. **$157-$331.** 2120 P St NW 20037. Between 21st and 22nd sts NW; just w of Dupont Circle. Int corridors. **Pets:** Accepted.

♨ ▼▼▼ Residence Inn by Marriott Washington, DC/Capitol 🏨
(202) 484-8280. **$174-$388.** 333 E St SW 20024. Between 3rd and 4th sts SW. Int corridors. **Pets:** Accepted.

♨ ▼▼▼▼ Residence Inn by Marriott-Washington DC-Downtown 🏨
(202) 898-1100. **$139-$322.** 1199 Vermont Ave NW 20005. Jct 14th St and Vermont Ave NW, at Thomas Circle. Int corridors. **Pets:** Accepted.

♨ ▼▼▼▼ The Ritz-Carlton Georgetown, Washington, D.C. 🏨
(202) 912-4100. **Call for rates.** 3100 South St NW 20007. Just s of jct M St and Wisconsin Ave; in Georgetown. Int corridors. **Pets:** Accepted.

♨ ▼▼▼▼ The Ritz-Carlton, Washington, D.C. 🏨
(202) 835-0500. **Call for rates.** 1150 22nd St NW 20037. At 22nd and M sts NW. Int corridors. **Pets:** Accepted.

▼▼▼ The River Inn 🏨
(202) 337-7600. **Call for rates.** 924 25th St NW 20037. Between K and I sts NW. Int corridors. **Pets:** Accepted.

▼▼▼▼ Rosewood Washington, D.C. 🏨 ☙
(202) 617-2400. **Call for rates.** 1050 31st St NW 20007. Between M and K sts NW; in Georgetown. Int corridors. **Pets:** Dogs only. Service with restrictions, supervision.

♨ ▼▼▼▼ The St. Regis, Washington, D.C. 🏨
(202) 638-2626. **$395-$1195.** 923 16th St NW 20006. 16th and K sts; just n of the White House. Int corridors. **Pets:** Accepted.

♨ ▼▼▼ Topaz Hotel-a Kimpton Hotel 🏨
(202) 393-3000. **Call for rates.** 1733 N St NW 20036. Just e of Connecticut Ave. Int corridors. **Pets:** Accepted.

▼▼▼ The Washington Court Hotel 🏨
(202) 628-2100. **Call for rates.** 525 New Jersey Ave NW 20001. On Capitol Hill, 3 blks n of Capitol grounds. Int corridors. **Pets:** Accepted.

♨ ▼▼▼ Washington Hilton 🏨
(202) 483-3000. **$99-$499.** 1919 Connecticut Ave NW 20009. Just n of Dupont Circle at T St NW. Int corridors. **Pets:** Accepted.

♨ ▼▼▼▼ Washington Marriott Wardman Park 🏨
(202) 328-2000. **$112-$322.** 2660 Woodley Rd NW 20008. Just w of Connecticut Ave. Int corridors. **Pets:** Accepted.

♨ ▼▼▼▼ The Westin Georgetown, Washington, D.C. 🏨
(202) 429-0100. **$139-$599.** 2350 M St NW 20037. At 24th and M sts NW. Int corridors. **Pets:** Accepted.

♨ ▼▼▼▼ The Westin Washington DC City Center Hotel 🏨
(202) 429-1700. **$88-$599.** 1400 M St NW 20005. Just w of Thomas Circle, between 14th and 15th sts NW. Int corridors. **Pets:** Accepted.

♨ ▼▼▼▼ The Willard InterContinental 🏨 ☙
(202) 628-9100. **$259-$699, 5 day notice.** 1401 Pennsylvania Ave NW 20004. Just e of the White House; jct 14th St NW. Int corridors. **Pets:** Medium, dogs only. $200 one-time fee/room. Service with restrictions, crate.

♨ ▼▼▼▼ W Washington, D.C. 🏨
(202) 661-2400. **$199-$499.** 515 15th St NW 20004. At 15th St and Pennsylvania Ave NW; just e of the White House. Int corridors. **Pets:** Accepted.

FLORIDA

ALTAMONTE SPRINGS

Embassy Suites by Hilton Orlando North H

(407) 834-2400. **$149-$189.** 225 Shorecrest Dr 32701. I-4 exit 92 (SR 436), just e to Cranes Roost Blvd, then just n. Int corridors. **Pets:** Accepted.

APALACHICOLA

Coombs Inn & Suites BB

(850) 653-9199. **Call for rates.** 80 Sixth St 32320. US 98 (Market St) and Ave E. Ext/int corridors. **Pets:** Accepted.

Water Street Hotel & Marina CO

(850) 653-3700. **Call for rates.** 329 Water St 32320. Jct Ave I. Ext corridors. **Pets:** Accepted.

ARCADIA

Holiday Inn Express Hotel & Suites H

(863) 494-5900. **Call for rates.** 2709 SE SR 70 34266. On SR 70, 1.9 mi e of US 17; jct SR 31. Int corridors. **Pets:** Accepted.

ATLANTIC BEACH

One Ocean Resort & Spa H ❀

(904) 249-7402. **$169-$900, 3 day notice.** One Ocean Blvd 32233. Jct SR A1A, just e on Atlantic Blvd. Int corridors. **Pets:** Medium. $75 one-time fee/room. Service with restrictions, crate.

AVENTURA

Residence Inn by Marriott Miami Aventura Mall H

(786) 528-1001. **$154-$323.** 19900 W Country Club Dr 33180. I-95 exit 16 (Ives Dairy Rd), 1.1 mi e to US 1 (Biscayne Blvd), 0.5 mi s to 199th St (Aventura Blvd), 0.5 mi e to W Country Club Dr, then just s. Int corridors. **Pets:** Large, other species. $100 one-time fee/room. Service with restrictions, crate.

Turnberry Isle Miami, Autograph Collection H

(305) 932-6200. **$179-$551, 7 day notice.** 19999 W Country Club Dr 33180. I-95 exit 16 (Ives Dairy Rd), 1.1 mi e to US 1 (Biscayne Blvd), just s to 199th St (Aventura Blvd), 0.5 mi e to Country Club Dr, then just s. Ext/int corridors. **Pets:** Accepted.

BAL HARBOUR

The Ritz-Carlton Bal Harbour, Miami H

(305) 455-5400. **$349-$5000, 3 day notice.** 10295 Collins Ave 33154. On SR A1A (Collins Ave); at Haulover Cswy. Int corridors. **Pets:** Accepted.

St. Regis Bal Harbour Resort H

(305) 993-3300. **$429-$1029, 7 day notice.** 9703 Collins Ave 33154. Just n of jct SR A1A (Collins Ave) and 922 (96th St). Int corridors. **Pets:** Accepted.

BOCA RATON *(Restaurants p. 606)*

Boca Raton Resort & Club, A Waldorf Astoria Resort H ❀

(561) 447-3000. **$149-$399.** 501 E Camino Real 33432. I-95 exit 44 (Palmetto Park Rd), 1.9 mi e to US 1 (Federal Hwy), just s to Camino Real, then 0.5 mi e. Ext/int corridors. **Pets:** Medium, dogs only. $150 one-time fee/pet.

Fairfield Inn & Suites by Marriott-Boca Raton H

(561) 417-8585. **$78-$230.** 3400 Airport Rd 33431. I-95 exit 45 (Glades Rd), just e to Airport Rd, then 1.1 mi n. Int corridors. **Pets:** $75 one-time fee/room. Designated rooms, service with restrictions, supervision.

Hilton Boca Raton Suites H

(561) 483-3600. **$109-$309.** 7920 Glades Rd 33434. I-95 exit 45 (Glades Rd), 3.4 mi w; Florida Tpke exit 75 (Glades Rd), just e. Int corridors. **Pets:** Accepted.

Holiday Inn Express Boca Raton-West H

(561) 482-7070. **$99-$189.** 8144 Glades Rd 33434. I-95 exit 45 (Glades Rd), 4.2 mi w; Florida Tpke exit 75 (Glades Rd), just w; in Lakeside Centre Plaza. Int corridors. **Pets:** Medium, other species. $75 one-time fee/pet. Service with restrictions, crate.

Residence Inn by Marriott-Boca Raton H

(561) 994-3222. **$119-$285.** 525 NW 77th St 33487. I-95 exit 50 (Congress Ave), merge onto NW 82nd St, just s on Congress Ave to NW 6th Ave, just e, then n; in Boca Commerce Center. Ext corridors. **Pets:** Large. $100 one-time fee/pet. Service with restrictions, crate.

TownePlace Suites by Marriott Boca Raton H

(561) 994-7232. **$94-$241.** 5110 NW 8th Ave 33487. I-95 exit 48 (Yamato Rd), just w; in Arvida Park of Commerce. Int corridors. **Pets:** Accepted.

Waterstone Resort & Marina, Curio-a Collection by Hilton H

(561) 368-9500. **$149-$369.** 999 E Camino Real 33432. I-95 exit 44 (Palmetto Park Rd), 2.1 mi e to US 1 (Federal Hwy), 0.7 mi s to E Camino Rd, then 0.8 mi e. Int corridors. **Pets:** Accepted.

BONITA SPRINGS

Hyatt Regency Coconut Point Resort & Spa H ❀

(239) 444-1234. **$159-$569, 3 day notice.** 5001 Coconut Rd 34134. I-75 exit 123, 1.9 mi w on Corkscrew Rd, 2.3 mi s on US 41 (Tamiami Tr), then 1.5 mi w. Int corridors. **Pets:** Medium, dogs only. $150 one-time fee/room. Designated rooms, service with restrictions, supervision.

BOYNTON BEACH *(Restaurants p. 606)*

Courtyard by Marriott-Boynton Beach H

(561) 737-4600. **$89-$211.** 1601 N Congress Ave 33426. I-95 exit 59 (Gateway Blvd), 1 mi w to Congress Ave, then just s. Ext/int corridors. **Pets:** Accepted.

TownePlace Suites by Marriott Boynton Beach H

(561) 375-6512. **$166-$271.** 2450 Quantum Blvd 33426. I-95 exit 59 (Gateway Blvd), 1.4 mi w to Congress Ave, just n to Quantum Blvd, then just e. Int corridors. **Pets:** Accepted.

BRADENTON

Best Western Plus Bradenton Hotel & Suites H

(941) 757-5555. **$79-$179.** 648 67th St Cir E 34208. I-75 exit 220 southbound; exit 220B northbound, 0.3 mi w on SR 64, just n on 66th St Ct E. Int corridors. **Pets:** Accepted.

Courtyard by Marriott Bradenton/Sarasota Riverfront H
(941) 747-3727. **$115-$245.** 100 Riverfront Dr W 34205. Just w of US 41 and 301; south side of Hernando Desoto Bridge; just n of jct SR 64 (Manatee Ave W) on 3rd St W. Int corridors. **Pets:** Accepted.

Hampton Inn & Suites Bradenton-Downtown Historic District H
(941) 746-9400. **$119-$249.** 309 10th St W 34205. Just n of jct Manatee Ave W on 9th St W (Business Rt 41); downtown. Int corridors. **Pets:** Accepted.

Quality Inn Bradenton M
(941) 758-7199. **$59-$130.** 6727 14th St W 34207. On US 41, 2 mi s of jct SR 70. Ext corridors. **Pets:** Accepted.

CAPE CANAVERAL

Residence Inn by Marriott Cape Canaveral/Cocoa Beach H
(321) 323-1100. **$145-$234.** 8959 Astronaut Blvd 32920. On SR A1A, 0.3 mi s of jct SR 528. Int corridors. **Pets:** Large, other species. $100 one-time fee/room. Service with restrictions, crate.

CAPE CORAL

Hampton Inn & Suites-Cape Coral/Fort Myers Area H
(239) 540-1050. **$99-$279.** 619 SE 47th Terr 33904. Just w of jct Coronado Pkwy. Int corridors. **Pets:** Accepted.

Holiday Inn Express Cape Coral-Fort Myers Area H
(239) 542-2121. **$89-$325.** 1538 Cape Coral Pkwy E 33904. Jct Del Prado Blvd. Int corridors. **Pets:** Small. $20 daily fee/pet. Designated rooms, service with restrictions, supervision.

The Westin Cape Coral Resort At Marina Village H
(239) 541-5000. **$109-$459.** 5941 Silver King Blvd 33914. 0.9 mi s of jct Cape Coral Pkwy on Pelican Way; 1 mi sw on Rose Garden Rd. Int corridors. **Pets:** Accepted.

CEDAR KEY

Park Place Motel & Condominiums CO
(352) 543-5737. **$65-$115.** 211 2nd St 32625. Just ne of jct SR 24; at A St. Ext corridors. **Pets:** Small. $10 daily fee/pet. Service with restrictions, supervision.

Seahorse Landing Waterfront Condominiums CO
(352) 543-5860. **$160-$175, 3 day notice.** 4050 G St 32625. Just sw of jct SR 24, on 6th St. Ext corridors. **Pets:** Accepted.

CELEBRATION *(Restaurants p. 606)*

Bohemian Hotel Celebration, Autograph Collection H
(407) 566-6000. **$137-$275, 3 day notice.** 700 Bloom St 34747. I-4 exit 64, 0.5 mi e on US 192 (W Irlo Bronson Memorial Hwy); 1.6 mi s on Celebration Ave, then just se on Campus St; downtown. Int corridors. **Pets:** Small, dogs only. $150 deposit/room. Designated rooms, service with restrictions, crate.

CHAMPIONSGATE

Omni-ChampionsGate Resort Hotel LP H
(407) 390-6664. **Call for rates.** 1500 Masters Blvd 33896. I-4 exit 58, 0.5 mi w on ChampionsGate Blvd (CR 532) to Masters Blvd, then just n. Int corridors. **Pets:** Accepted.

CHIEFLAND

Days Inn Chiefland M
(352) 493-9400. **$64-$90.** 809 NW 21st Ave 32626. Just e of Alt US 27/19/98; 1 mi n of jct US 129. Ext corridors. **Pets:** Accepted.

Quality Inn M
(352) 493-0663. **$75-$109.** 1125 N Young Blvd 32626. On Alternate Rt US 27/19/98, just n of jct US 129. Ext corridors. **Pets:** Large, other species. $15 daily fee/pet. Designated rooms, service with restrictions, crate.

CLEARWATER *(Restaurants p. 606)*

Holiday Inn Express Clearwater East-Icot Center H
(727) 536-7275. **Call for rates.** 13625 Icot Blvd 33760. 0.5 mi e of jct US 19; just n of SR 688 (Ulmerton Rd); in Icot Center Business Park. Int corridors. **Pets:** Medium, dogs only. $50 one-time fee/room. Service with restrictions, crate.

Residence Inn by Marriott Clearwater Downtown H
(727) 562-5400. **$122-$238.** 940 Court St 33756. On SR 60, jct S Prospect Ave. Int corridors. **Pets:** Medium, other species. $100 one-time fee/room. Designated rooms, service with restrictions, crate.

Residence Inn by Marriott St. Petersburg/Clearwater H
(727) 573-4444. **$116-$274.** 5050 Ulmerton Rd 33760. I-275 exit 31 southbound, 3.1 mi w on SR 688 (Ulmerton Rd); exit 30 northbound, 1.4 mi w on SR 686, then 1.7 mi w. Ext corridors. **Pets:** Accepted.

TownePlace Suites by Marriott St. Petersburg/Clearwater H
(727) 299-9229. **$115-$191.** 13200 49th St N 33762. I-275 exit 31 southbound, 3.4 mi w on SR 688 (Ulmerton Rd); exit 30 northbound, 1.4 mi w on SR 686, 3 mi w on SR 688 (Ulmerton Rd), then just s; in Turtle Creek. Int corridors. **Pets:** Accepted.

CLERMONT

Fairfield Inn & Suites by Marriott Clermont H
(352) 394-6585. **$93-$188.** 1750 Hunt Trace Blvd 34711. 0.5 mi e of jct US 27 on SR 50, just n on Citrus Tower Blvd. Int corridors. **Pets:** Accepted.

COCOA

Best Western Cocoa Inn H
(321) 632-1065. **$85-$150.** 4225 W King St 32926. I-95 exit 201 (SR 520), just e. Ext corridors. **Pets:** Accepted.

COCOA BEACH

Best Western Cocoa Beach Hotel & Suites H
(321) 783-7621. **$89-$229.** 5600 N Atlantic Ave 32931. SR A1A (Atlantic Ave), 0.8 mi n of jct SR 520. Ext/int corridors. **Pets:** Accepted.

(AAA) ▼▼▼ Comfort Inn & Suites Cocoa Beach-Port Canaveral Area H

(321) 783-2221. **$100-$190.** 3901 N Atlantic Ave 32931. On SR A1A (Atlantic Ave), 0.3 mi s of jct SR 520. Ext corridors. **Pets:** Medium. $10 daily fee/room. Designated rooms, no service, supervision.

SAVE 🍴 ➿ ✕ 🛜 ✕ 🔋 💻

▼▼ Days Inn Cocoa Beach-Port Canaveral M

(321) 784-2550. **$75-$150.** 5500 N Atlantic Ave 32931. SR A1A (Atlantic Ave), 0.8 mi n of SR 520. Ext corridors. **Pets:** Accepted.

➿ 🛜 🔋 💻

(AAA) ▼▼▼ Four Points by Sheraton-Cocoa Beach H

(321) 783-8717. **$85-$379.** 4001 N Atlantic Ave 32931. SR A1A (Atlantic Ave), just s of SR 520. Int corridors. **Pets:** Accepted.

SAVE ECO 🍴 ♿ ➿ ✕ 🛜 ✕ 🔋 💻

(AAA) ▼▼ La Quinta Inn Cocoa Beach-Port Canaveral H

(321) 783-2252. **$71-$268.** 1275 N Atlantic Ave 32931. SR A1A (Atlantic Ave), 1.7 mi s of SR 520. Ext corridors. **Pets:** Accepted.

SAVE 🍴 ♿ ➿ 🛜 ✕ 🔋 💻

COCONUT GROVE *(Restaurants p. 606)*

(AAA) ▼▼▼ Residence Inn by Marriott Miami Coconut Grove H

(305) 285-9303. **$119-$303.** 2835 Tigertail Ave 33133. S Bayshore Dr, w on SW 27th Ave (Cornelia Dr), just s. Ext corridors. **Pets:** Accepted.

SAVE 🍴 ♿ ➿ 🛜 ✕ 🔋 💻

CORAL GABLES *(Restaurants p. 606)*

(AAA) ▼▼▼ ▼▼▼ The Biltmore Hotel Coral Gables H

(305) 445-1926. **$229-$589, 3 day notice.** 1200 Anastasia Ave 33134. US 1, 1.4 mi w on Bird Rd (SW 40th St) to Granada Blvd, 0.5 mi n to Anastasia Ave, then just w. Int corridors. **Pets:** Accepted.

SAVE ECO 🍴 ➿ ✕ 🛜 ✕

CORAL SPRINGS *(Restaurants p. 606)*

▼▼ La Quinta Inn & Suites-Coral Springs University Dr H

(954) 753-9000. **$86-$257.** 3701 N University Dr 33065. SR 869 (Sawgrass Expwy) exit 15 (University Dr/SR 817), 1.9 mi s. Int corridors. **Pets:** Accepted. ♿ ➿ 🛜 🔋 💻

▼▼ La Quinta Inn & Suites-Ft. Lauderdale University Drive South H

(954) 344-2200. **$86-$232.** 3100 N University Dr 33065. SR 869 (Sawgrass Expwy) exit 15 (University Dr/SR 817), 2.4 mi s. Int corridors. **Pets:** Accepted. ♿ ➿ 🛜 🔋 💻

CRESCENT BEACH

(AAA) ▼▼▼ Beacher's Lodge Oceanfront Suites CO 🐾

(904) 471-8849. **Call for rates.** 6970 A1A S 32080. On SR A1A (Atlantic Ave), just s of jct SR 206. Ext corridors. **Pets:** $50 one-time fee/pet. Designated rooms, service with restrictions.

SAVE ➿ 🛜 ✕ 🔋 💻

CRESTVIEW *(Restaurants p. 606)*

▼▼▼ Comfort Inn & Suites - Crestview H

(850) 682-1481. **$89-$259.** 900 Southcrest Dr 32536. I-10 exit 56, just se. Int corridors. **Pets:** Other species. $25 daily fee/pet. Service with restrictions, supervision. 🍴 ➿ 🛜 🔋 💻

▼▼ ▼▼ Quality Inn H

(850) 683-1778. **$94-$209.** 151 Cracker Barrel Dr 32536. I-10 exit 56, just s on SR 85. Int corridors. **Pets:** Small. $20 daily fee/pet. Designated rooms, service with restrictions, supervision.

➿ 🛜 ✕ 🔋 💻

CRYSTAL RIVER

(AAA) ▼▼▼ Best Western Crystal River Resort M

(352) 795-3171. **$150-$170.** 614 NW Hwy 19 34428. On US 19/98, 0.8 mi n of jct SR 44. Ext corridors. **Pets:** Accepted.

SAVE ➿ ✕ 🛜 🔋 💻

DANIA BEACH

(AAA) ▼▼▼ Hyatt House Fort Lauderdale Airport & Cruise Port H

(954) 922-0271. **$109-$359.** 90 SW 18th Ave 33004. I-95 exit 22 (Stirling Rd), just e to SW 18th Ave, then just n. Int corridors. **Pets:** Medium. $75 one-time fee/room. Service with restrictions.

SAVE ➿ 🛜 ✕ 🔋 💻

(AAA) ▼▼▼ Hyatt Place Ft. Lauderdale Airport & Cruise Port H

(954) 922-0436. **$89-$339.** 91 SW 18th Ave 33004. I-95 exit 22 (Stirling Rd), just e to SW 18th Ave, then just n. Int corridors. **Pets:** Accepted.

SAVE ♿ ➿ 🛜 ✕ 🔋 💻

(AAA) ▼▼▼ Residence Inn by Marriott-Fort Lauderdale Airport & Cruise Port H

(954) 989-3636. **$108-$247.** 4801 Anglers Ave 33312. I-95 exit 23 (Griffin Rd), just w. Int corridors. **Pets:** Accepted.

SAVE ♿ 🛜 ✕ 🔋 💻

DAYTONA BEACH

(AAA) ▼▼▼ Hilton Daytona Beach Resort/Ocean Walk Village H

(386) 254-8200. **$99-$399.** 100 N Atlantic Ave 32118. I-95 exit 261A, 6.1 mi e to SR A1A (Atlantic Ave), then 0.5 mi n. Int corridors. **Pets:** Accepted. SAVE ECO 🍴 ➿ ✕ 📶 ✕ 🔋 💻

▼▼▼ Holiday Inn LPGA H ❀

(386) 236-0200. **Call for rates.** 137 Automall Cir 32124. I-95 exit 265, just sw. Int corridors. **Pets:** $30 daily fee/room. Designated rooms, crate. 🍴 ♿ ➿ 🛜 ✕ 🔋 💻

▼▼▼ Homewood Suites by Hilton Daytona Beach Speedway-Airport H

(386) 258-2828. **$104-$299.** 165 Bill France Blvd 32114. I-95 exit 261 (US 92), 2.1 mi e to Bill France Blvd, then just n. Int corridors. **Pets:** Accepted. ♿ ➿ 🛜 ✕ 🔋 💻

(AAA) ▼▼▼ Residence Inn by Marriott-Daytona Beach Speedway/Airport H

(386) 252-3949. **$106-$204.** 1725 Richard Petty Blvd 32114. I-95 exit 261 (US 92), 2.4 mi e to Midway Ave, just s to Richard Petty Blvd, then just e. Int corridors. **Pets:** Accepted.

SAVE ECO 🍴 ♿ ➿ 🛜 ✕ 🔋 💻

DAYTONA BEACH SHORES
(Restaurants p. 606)

(AAA) ▼▼▼ Atlantic Ocean Palm Inn M

(386) 761-8450. **$69-$319, 7 day notice.** 3247 S Atlantic Ave 32118. On SR A1A (Atlantic Ave), 5 mi s of jct US 92 (International Speedway Blvd). Ext corridors. **Pets:** Small, dogs only. $25 daily fee/pet. Designated rooms, service with restrictions, supervision.

SAVE ➿ 🛜 ✕ 🔋 💻

(AAA) ▼▼▼ Hyatt Place Daytona Beach Oceanfront H

(386) 944-2010. **$89-$599.** 3161 S Atlantic Ave 32118. I-95 exit 256 (SR 421), 5 mi e to SR A1A (Atlantic Ave), then 0.8 mi n. Int corridors. **Pets:** Accepted. SAVE ♿ ➿ 🛜 ✕ 🔋 💻

(AAA) ▼▼▼ Residence Inn by Marriott-Daytona Beach Oceanfront H

(386) 944-2000. **$128-$275.** 3209 S Atlantic Ave 32118. I-95 exit 256, 5 mi e to Atlantic Ave, then 0.7 mi n. Int corridors. **Pets:** Accepted.

🍴 ♿ 🛜 ✕ 🔋 💻

The Shores Resort & Spa 🏨 ❀
(386) 767-7350. **$119-$659, 3 day notice.** 2637 S Atlantic Ave 32118. On SR A1A (Atlantic Ave), 3.2 mi s of jct US 92 (International Speedway Blvd). Int corridors. **Pets:** Medium. $200 deposit/room, $25 daily fee/pet. Designated rooms, service with restrictions, crate.

DEERFIELD BEACH (Restaurants p. 607)

Comfort Inn Oceanside 🏨 ❀
(954) 428-0650. **$100-$250, 3 day notice.** 50 S Ocean Dr (SR A1A) 33441. I-95 exit 42 (Hillsboro Blvd), 2.6 mi e; jct Hillsboro Blvd and SR A1A (Ocean Dr). Int corridors. **Pets:** Other species. $35 daily fee/pet. Designated rooms, service with restrictions, supervision.

DoubleTree by Hilton Deerfield Beach-Boca Raton 🏨
(954) 427-7700. **Call for rates.** 100 Fairway Dr 33441. I-95 exit 42A (Hillsboro Blvd), just e to Fairway Dr. Int corridors. **Pets:** Accepted.

Quality Inn & Suites-Deerfield Beach 🏨
(954) 570-8887. **$65-$175.** 1040 E Newport Center Dr 33442. I-95 exit 41 (SW 10th St), just w; in Newport Center Complex. Ext corridors. **Pets:** Accepted.

Wyndham Deerfield Beach Resort 🏨 ❀
(954) 428-2850. **$159-$515.** 2096 NE 2nd St 33441. I-95 exit 42 (Hillsboro Blvd), 2.6 mi e to SR A1A (Ocean Blvd), then just ne. Int corridors. **Pets:** Small. $35 daily fee/room. Designated rooms, service with restrictions, supervision.

DE FUNIAK SPRINGS

Best Western Crossroads Inn 🅼
(850) 892-5111. **$90-$130.** 2343 US Hwy 331 S 32435. I-10 exit 85, just s. Ext/int corridors. **Pets:** Medium. $20 daily fee/room. Service with restrictions.

DELAND

Comfort Inn Deland 🏨
(386) 736-3100. **$85-$225.** 400 E International Speedway Blvd 32724. On US 92 (International Speedway Blvd), 0.5 mi e of US 17-92. Int corridors. **Pets:** Accepted.

DELRAY BEACH (Restaurants p. 607)

Colony Hotel & Cabana Club 🏨 ❀
(561) 276-4123. **$99-$329, 3 day notice.** 525 E Atlantic Ave 33483. I-95 exit 52 (Atlantic Ave), 1.4 mi e. Int corridors. **Pets:** Other species. $25 daily fee/pet.

Delray Beach Marriott 🏨 ❀
(561) 274-3200. **$167-$424.** 10 N Ocean Blvd 33483. I-95 exit 52 (Atlantic Ave), 1.8 mi e, then just n; downtown. Int corridors. **Pets:** Small, dogs only. $75 one-time fee/room. Service with restrictions, supervision.

Hyatt Place Delray Beach 🏨
(561) 330-3530. **$119-$399.** 104 NE 2nd Ave 33444. I-95 exit 52 (Atlantic Ave), 1.2 mi e to NE 2nd Ave, then just n; in Pineapple Grove district of downtown. Int corridors. **Pets:** Accepted.

Residence Inn by Marriott Delray Beach 🏨
(561) 276-7441. **$119-$312, 3 day notice.** 1111 E Atlantic Ave 33483. I-95 exit 52 (Atlantic Ave), 1.7 mi e; downtown. Int corridors. **Pets:** Accepted.

DESTIN (Restaurants p. 607)

Candlewood Suites 🏨
(850) 337-3770. **Call for rates.** 11396 US Hwy 98 W 32550. Jct Geronimo St, just w on US 98. Int corridors. **Pets:** Accepted.

Residence Inn by Marriott Sandestin at Grand Boulevard 🏨
(850) 650-7811. **$100-$276.** 300 Grand Blvd 32550. On US 98; jct Baytowne Ln. Int corridors. **Pets:** Accepted.

SummerPlace Inn 🏨 ❀
(850) 650-8003. **$70-$289.** 14047 Emerald Coast Pkwy 32541. On US 98, 2.5 mi w; jct SR 293. Int corridors. **Pets:** Other species. $50 one-time fee/pet. Designated rooms, service with restrictions, supervision.

DORAL

Aloft Miami Doral 🏨 ❀
(786) 272-7200. **$109-$149.** 3265 NW 107th Ave 33172. Corner of NW 33rd St and 107th Ave; 3.7 mi e of Doral. Int corridors. **Pets:** Medium, dogs only. Service with restrictions, supervision.

Candlewood Suites-Miami Airport West 🏨
(305) 591-9099. **Call for rates.** 8855 NW 27th St 33172. Florida Tpke exit 29 (NW 41st St), 3.2 mi e to NW 87th Ave, 0.7 mi s to NW 27th St, then just w. Int corridors. **Pets:** Accepted.

Element Miami Doral 🏨 ❀
(786) 272-7250. **$119-$199.** 3285 NW 107th Ave 33172. Corner of 32nd St and 107th Ave. Int corridors. **Pets:** Medium, dogs only. Service with restrictions, supervision.

Extended Stay America-Miami-Doral 🏨
(305) 716-9005. **$75-$250.** 7750 NW 25th St 33122. SR 826 (Palmetto Expwy) exit NW 25th St, just w. Int corridors. **Pets:** Accepted.

Hyatt Place Miami Airport-West/Doral 🏨
(305) 718-8292. **$109-$279.** 3655 NW 82nd Ave 33166. Florida Tpke exit 29 (NW 41st St), 3.7 mi e to NW 82nd Ave, then just s; just w of SR 826 (Palmetto Expwy). Int corridors. **Pets:** Accepted.

Staybridge Suites-Miami Doral 🏨
(305) 500-9100. **$109-$209.** 3265 NW 87th Ave 33172. Florida Tpke exit 29 (NW 41st St), 3.2 mi e to NW 87th Ave, then 0.3 mi s. Int corridors. **Pets:** Accepted.

TownePlace Suites by Marriott-Miami Airport West/Doral Area 🏨
(305) 718-4144. **$80-$194.** 10505 NW 36th St 33178. Florida Tpke exit 29 (NW 41st St), 1.2 mi e to 107th Ave, then just s. Int corridors. **Pets:** Accepted.

Trump National Doral® Miami 🏨
(305) 592-2000. **Call for rates.** 4400 NW 87th Ave 33178. Florida Tpke exit 29 (NW 41st St), 3 mi e to NW 87th Ave, then just n. Int corridors. **Pets:** Accepted.

FERNANDINA BEACH

Days Inn & Suites Amelia Island at the Beach 🅼
(904) 277-2300. **$70-$199.** 2707 Sadler Rd 32034. In Fernandina Beach; on east side of island, just w of jct S Fletcher Ave (SR A1A/105). Ext corridors. **Pets:** Accepted.

▼▼ **Hampton Inn Amelia Island at Fernandina Beach** 🅷

(904) 321-1111. **$109-$369.** 2549 Sadler Rd 32034. In Fernandina Beach; just w of jct SR A1A (Atlantic Ave) and Sadler Rd. Int corridors. **Pets:** Medium. $50 one-time fee/pet. Designated rooms, service with restrictions, supervision. 🅼 🛏 📶 ⊠ 🔌 💻

🔷 ▼▼ **The Hoyt House** 🆑

(904) 277-4300. **$235-$369, 14 day notice.** 804 Atlantic Ave 32034. In Fernandina Beach; between S 8th and S 9th sts. Int corridors. **Pets:** Dogs only. $100 one-time fee/room. Designated rooms, crate.

🆂🅰🆅🅴 📞 🛏 ⊠ 📶 ⊠

🔷 ▼▼ ▼▼ **Omni Amelia Island Plantation Resort** 🅷 ✿

(904) 261-6161. **$179-$899, 3 day notice.** 39 Beach Lagoon Rd 32034. In Fernandina Beach; SR A1A (Atlantic Ave), 6.5 mi s of the bridge. Ext corridors. **Pets:** Small. $100 one-time fee/room. Designated rooms, service with restrictions, supervision.

🆂🅰🆅🅴 🅴🅲🅾 🍴 🅼 🛏 ⊠ 📶 ⊠ 🔌 💻

🔷 ▼▼ **Residence Inn by Marriott-Amelia Island** 🅷 ✿

(904) 277-2440. **$110-$181.** 2301 Sadler Rd 32034. In Fernandina Beach; just w of jct S Fletcher Ave (SR A1A/105); on east side of island. Int corridors. **Pets:** Medium, other species. $100 one-time fee/ room. Designated rooms, service with restrictions, crate.

🆂🅰🆅🅴 🅴🅲🅾 🍴 🅼 🛏 ⊠ 📶 ⊠ 🔌 💻

▼▼ **Seaside Amelia Inn** 🅷

(904) 206-5300. **Call for rates.** 2900 Atlantic Ave 32034. In Fernandina Beach; jct SR A1A. Int corridors. **Pets:** Accepted. 📶 ⊠ 🔌 💻

FORT LAUDERDALE *(Restaurants p. 607)*

🔷 ▼▼ ▼▼ **The Atlantic Hotel & Spa** 🅷

(954) 567-8020. **$179-$699, 3 day notice.** 601 N Fort Lauderdale Beach Blvd 33304. I-95 exit 29 (Sunrise Blvd), 4.1 mi e to SR A1A (Fort Lauderdale Beach Blvd), then 0.5 mi s. Int corridors. **Pets:** Accepted. 🆂🅰🆅🅴 🍴 🅼 🛏 ⊠ 📶 ⊠ 🔌 💻

🔷 ▼▼ **Bahia Mar Fort Lauderdale Beach, A DoubleTree by Hilton** 🅷 ✿

(954) 764-2233. **$99-$449.** 801 Seabreeze Blvd 33316. I-95 exit 29 (Sunrise Blvd), 4.1 mi e to SR A1A (Fort Lauderdale Beach Blvd), then 2 mi s. Int corridors. **Pets:** Small. $65 one-time fee/pet. Service with restrictions, supervision. 🆂🅰🆅🅴 🅴🅲🅾 🍴 🛏 ⊠ 📶 ⊠ 🔌 💻

🔷 ▼▼ **Best Western Ft. Lauderdale I-95 Inn** 🅷

(954) 776-6333. **$79-$179.** 4800 Powerline Rd 33309. I-95 exit 32 (Commercial Blvd), just w to Powerline Rd, then just n. Int corridors. **Pets:** Other species. $20 daily fee/room. Designated rooms.

🆂🅰🆅🅴 🅼 🛏 📶 ⊠ 🔌 💻

🔷 ▼▼ **Candlewood Suites Fort Lauderdale Airport/ Cruise Port** 🅷

(954) 522-8822. **$99-$399.** 1120 W State Rd 84 33315. I-95 exit 25 (SR 84), 0.8 mi e. Int corridors. **Pets:** Accepted.

🆂🅰🆅🅴 🅼 📶 ⊠ 🔌 💻

🔷 ▼▼ **Embassy Suites by Hilton Fort Lauderdale-17th Street** 🅷

(954) 527-2700. **$129-$349.** 1100 SE 17th St 33316. I-95 exit 25 (SR 84), 2 mi e to US 1 (SE 6th Ave), 0.5 mi n to SE 17th St, then 0.3 mi e. Int corridors. **Pets:** Accepted.

🆂🅰🆅🅴 🅴🅲🅾 🍴 🛏 ⊠ 🖥 🔌 💻

▼▼▼ **Hampton Inn Ft. Lauderdale Airport North** 🅷

(954) 524-9900. **$119-$309.** 2301 SW 12th Ave 33315. I-95 exit 25 (SR 84), 0.7 mi e to SW 12th Ave, then just n. Int corridors.

Pets: Accepted. 🅴🅲🅾 🅼 🛏 📶 ⊠ 🔌 💻

🔷 ▼▼ ▼▼ **Hilton Fort Lauderdale Marina** 🅷

(954) 463-4000. **$99-$329.** 1881 SE 17th St 33316. I-95 exit 25 (SR 84), 2 mi e to SE 6th Ave (US 1), 0.5 mi n to SE 17th St, then 1 mi e. Ext/int corridors. **Pets:** Accepted.

🆂🅰🆅🅴 🍴 🛏 ⊠ 📶 ⊠ 🔌 💻

▼▼▼ **Holiday Inn Express & Suites Ft. Lauderdale-Executive Airport** 🅷

(954) 772-3032. **Call for rates.** 1500 W Commercial Blvd 33309. I-95 exit 32 (Commercial Blvd), 0.7 mi w. Int corridors. **Pets:** Accepted.

🍴 🛏 📶 ⊠ 🔌 💻

🔷 ▼▼ ▼▼ **Hyatt Place Fort Lauderdale 17th Street Convention Center** 🅷 ✿

(954) 763-7670. **$109-$349.** 1851 SE 10th Ave 33316. US 1 (Federal Hwy), just e on SE 17th St to SE 10th Ave, then just s. Int corridors. **Pets:** Medium, dogs only. $75 one-time fee/pet. Service with restrictions, supervision. 🆂🅰🆅🅴 🅼 🛏 📶 ⊠ 🔌 💻

🔷 ▼▼ ▼▼ **Hyatt Regency Pier Sixty-Six** 🅷

(954) 525-6666. **$119-$379, 3 day notice.** 2301 SE 17th St 33316. I-95 exit 25 (SR 84), 2 mi e to SE 6th Ave (US 1), 0.5 mi n to SE 17th St, then 1.4 mi e. Ext/int corridors. **Pets:** Accepted.

🆂🅰🆅🅴 🅴🅲🅾 📞 🍴 🅼 🛏 ⊠ 📶 ⊠ 🔌 💻

▼▼▼ **La Quinta Inn & Suites-Ft. Lauderdale Cypress Creek/I-95** 🅷

(954) 491-7666. **$82-$268.** 999 W Cypress Creek Rd 33309. I-95 exit 33 (Cypress Creek Rd), 0.7 mi w. Int corridors. **Pets:** Accepted.

🛏 📶 🔌 💻

▼▼▼ **Renaissance Fort Lauderdale Cruise Port Hotel** 🅷

(954) 626-1700. **$119-$252.** 1617 SE 17th St 33316. I-95 exit 25 (SR 84), 2 mi e to US 1 (SE 6th Ave), 0.5 mi n to SE 17th St, then 0.7 mi e. Int corridors. **Pets:** Small, dogs only. $75 one-time fee/pet. Designated rooms, service with restrictions, supervision.

🅴🅲🅾 🍴 🅼 🛏 📶 🔌 💻

🔷 ▼▼ ▼▼ **The Ritz-Carlton, Fort Lauderdale** 🅷

(954) 465-2300. **Call for rates.** 1 N Fort Lauderdale Beach Blvd 33304. I-95 exit 29 (Sunrise Blvd), 4.2 mi e to SR A1A (Fort Lauderdale Beach Blvd), then 1.2 mi s. Int corridors. **Pets:** Accepted.

🆂🅰🆅🅴 🅴🅲🅾 📞 🍴 🅼 🛏 ⊠ 🖥 ⊠ 🔌 💻

🔷 ▼▼ ▼▼ **Riverside Hotel, The International Hotel of Fort Lauderdale** 🅷 ✿

(954) 467-0671. **$129-$799.** 620 E Las Olas Blvd 33301. I-95 exit 27 (Broward Blvd), 2.4 mi e to US 1 (Federal Hwy), just s to Las Olas Blvd, then just e. Int corridors. **Pets:** Large. $75 one-time fee/room. Designated rooms, no service.

🆂🅰🆅🅴 🍴 🅼 🛏 ⊠ 📶 ⊠ 🔌 💻

🔷 ▼▼ ▼▼ **Rodeway Inn & Suites Fort Lauderdale Airport & Cruise Port Hotel** 🅷

(954) 792-8181. **$76-$346.** 2440 W SR 84 33312. I-95 exit 25 (SR 84), just w. Ext/int corridors. **Pets:** Accepted.

🆂🅰🆅🅴 🍴 🛏 🖥 ⊠ 🔌 💻

🔷 ▼▼ ▼▼ **Sheraton Suites Fort Lauderdale at Cypress Creek** 🅷

(954) 772-5400. **Call for rates.** 555 NW 62nd St 33309. I-95 exit 33 (Cypress Creek Rd), just w. Int corridors. **Pets:** Accepted.

🆂🅰🆅🅴 🅴🅲🅾 🍴 🛏 📶 ⊠ 🔌 💻

▼▼▼ **TownePlace Suites by Marriott-Fort Lauderdale West** 🅷

(954) 484-2214. **$88-$222.** 3100 W Prospect Rd 33309. I-95 exit 33 (Cypress Creek Rd), 2.7 mi w to NW 31st Ave, then 0.5 mi s. Int corridors. **Pets:** Accepted. 🍴 🛏 📶 ⊠ 🔌 💻

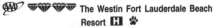

The Westin Fort Lauderdale H
(954) 772-1331. **Call for rates.** 400 Corporate Dr 33334. I-95 exit 33 (Cypress Creek Rd), just e; in Radice Corporate Park. Int corridors. **Pets:** Accepted.

The Westin Fort Lauderdale Beach Resort H
(954) 467-1111. **$150-$550, 3 day notice.** 321 N Fort Lauderdale Beach Blvd 33304. I-95 exit 29 (Sunrise Blvd), 4.2 mi e to SR A1A (Fort Lauderdale Beach Blvd), then 0.8 mi s. Int corridors. **Pets:** Medium, dogs only. Service with restrictions, supervision.

W Fort Lauderdale H
(954) 414-8200. **$299-$899.** 401 N Fort Lauderdale Beach Blvd 33304. I-95 exit 29 (Sunrise Blvd), 4.2 mi e to SR A1A (Fort Lauderdale Beach Blvd), then 0.7 mi s. Int corridors. **Pets:** Small, dogs only. $125 one-time fee/room. Service with restrictions, supervision.

FORT MYERS *(Restaurants p. 607)*

Best Western Airport Inn H
(239) 561-7000. **$109-$299.** 8955 Daniels Pkwy 33912. I-75 exit 131, 0.6 mi w on CR 879 (Daniels Pkwy). Int corridors. **Pets:** Large, other species. $10 daily fee/pet. Designated rooms, service with restrictions, crate.

Candlewood Suites-Fort Myers Sanibel Gateway H
(239) 210-7777. **Call for rates.** 9740 Commerce Center Ct 33908. Just sw of Summerlin Rd on Bass Rd; in Summerlin Park. Int corridors. **Pets:** Accepted.

Homewood Suites by Hilton Fort Myers Airport/FGCU H
(239) 210-7300. **$119-$299.** 16450 Corporate Commerce Way 33913. I-75 exit 128, 0.6 mi e on CR 840 (Alico Rd), just n on Ben Hill Griffin Pkwy, then just w; in Gulfcoast Landings. Int corridors. **Pets:** Accepted.

Hotel Indigo-Fort Myers Downtown River District H
(239) 337-3446. **Call for rates.** 1520 Broadway Ave 33901. Between First and Main sts. Int corridors. **Pets:** Small, dogs only. $125 one-time fee/pet. Designated rooms, service with restrictions, supervision.

Hyatt Place Fort Myers at The Forum H
(239) 418-1844. **$79-$269.** 2600 Champion Ring Rd 33905. I-75 exit 138, just e on SR 82. Int corridors. **Pets:** Accepted.

La Quinta Inn & Suites-Airport H
(239) 466-0012. **$86-$262.** 9521 Marketplace Rd 33912. I-75 exit 131, 0.4 mi w on CR 879 (Daniels Pkwy), then just n on Danport Blvd. Int corridors. **Pets:** Accepted.

Residence Inn by Marriott Fort Myers H
(239) 936-0110. **$103-$258.** 2960 Colonial Blvd 33966. I-75 exit 136, 3.5 mi w on SR 884; jct Metro Pkwy. Int corridors. **Pets:** Accepted.

Residence Inn by Marriott Fort Myers Gulf Coast Center H
(239) 332-7001. **$133-$281.** 10054 Gulf Center Dr 33913. I-75 exit 128, 0.6 mi e on Alico Rd (CR 840), just s on Royal Queen Blvd, then just w. Int corridors. **Pets:** Accepted.

Residence Inn by Marriott-Fort Myers Sanibel H
(239) 415-4150. **$90-$287.** 20371 Summerlin Rd 33908. On CR 869, just ne of jct McGregor Blvd. Int corridors. **Pets:** Accepted.

FORT MYERS BEACH

Best Western Plus Beach Resort H
(239) 463-6000. **$229-$399.** 684 Estero Blvd 33931. 0.4 mi n of Matanzas Pass Bridge (SR 865). Ext corridors. **Pets:** Accepted.

Hampton Inn & Suites Ft. Myers Beach-Sanibel Gateway H
(239) 437-8888. **$119-$399.** 11281 Summerlin Square Rd 33931. Just e of jct Matanzas Pass Bridge (SR 865). Int corridors. **Pets:** Accepted.

FORT PIERCE

Fairfield Inn & Suites by Marriott-Fort Pierce H
(772) 462-2900. **$72-$155.** 6502 Metal Dr 34945. I-95 exit 129 (Okeechobee Rd), 0.6 mi w; Florida Tpke exit 152, 0.3 mi e. Int corridors. **Pets:** Medium, other species. $50 one-time fee/room, $25 daily fee/room. Service with restrictions, crate.

Holiday Inn Express & Suites Fort Pierce West H
(772) 464-5000. **Call for rates.** 7151 Okeechobee Rd 34945. I-95 exit 129 (Okeechobee Rd), 0.7 mi w; Florida Tpke exit 152, just e. Int corridors. **Pets:** Accepted.

Royal Inn Beach Hotel Hutchinson Island H
(772) 672-8888. **$89-$425.** 222 Hernando St 34949. US 1, 2.5 mi e on Seaway Dr (SR A1A) to Hernando St, then just s. Ext corridors. **Pets:** Small, dogs only. $25 daily fee/room. Supervision.

FORT WALTON BEACH

La Quinta Inn & Suites Fort Walton Beach H
(850) 244-1500. **$79-$570.** 3 SW Miracle Strip Pkwy 32548. On US 98; jct SR 189. Int corridors. **Pets:** Accepted.

Ramada Plaza Beach Resort H
(850) 243-9161. **$109-$309, 3 day notice.** 1500 Miracle Strip Pkwy SE 32548. On US 98, 1 mi e. Ext/int corridors. **Pets:** Accepted.

TownePlace Suites by Marriott Fort Walton Beach Eglin AFB H
(850) 315-6000. **$99-$263.** 843 Eglin Pkwy 32547. On SR 85, just e of SR 188. Int corridors. **Pets:** Accepted.

GAINESVILLE

Hilton University of Florida Conference Center Gainesville H
(352) 371-3600. **$99-$529.** 1714 SW 34th St 32607. I-75 exit 384, 0.9 mi e on SR 24 (Archer Rd), then 0.7 mi n on SR 121; on University of Florida campus. Int corridors. **Pets:** Accepted.

Holiday Inn Express H
(352) 376-0004. **$123-$286, 30 day notice.** 3905 SW 43rd St 32608. I-75 exit 384, just w on SR 24 (Archer Rd), then just n. Int corridors. **Pets:** Medium, other species. $25 one-time fee/room, $5 daily fee/room. Designated rooms, service with restrictions, supervision.

Quality Inn H
(352) 378-2405. **$70-$190.** 3455 SW Williston Rd 32608. I-75 exit 382, just sw on SR 121. Int corridors. **Pets:** Accepted.

▼▼▼ **Residence Inn by Marriott Gainesville I-75** H
(352) 264-0000. **$122-$174.** 3275 SW 40th Blvd 32608. I-75 exit 384, just e on SR 24 (Archer Rd), then just n. Int corridors. **Pets:** Other species. $75 one-time fee/room. Service with restrictions.
ECO ➿ 🛜 ✕ 🔒 💻

AAA ▼▼▼▼ **Sweetwater Branch Inn Bed & Breakfast** BB
(352) 373-6760. **Call for rates.** 625 E University Ave 32601. On SR 26/20, just w of jct SE 11th St. Int corridors. **Pets:** Accepted.
SAVE 🛜 ✕ 🔒 💻

AAA ▼▼▼▼ **TownePlace Suites by Marriott Gainesville** H ❀
(352) 415-1111. **$116-$184.** 7451 W Newberry Rd 32605. I-75 exit 387, just w. Int corridors. **Pets:** Other species. $100 one-time fee/room. Service with restrictions, crate. SAVE 🔥M 🛜 ✕ 🔒 💻

HIGHLAND BEACH

AAA ▼▼▼ ▼▼▼ **Delray Sands Resort on Highland Beach** H
(561) 278-6241. **$139-$399.** 2809 S Ocean Blvd 33487. I-95 exit 51 (Linton Blvd), 1.7 mi e to Ocean Blvd (SR A1A), then 1.1 mi s. Ext/int corridors. **Pets:** Accepted.
SAVE ECO 🍽 🔥M ➿ ✕ 🛑 ✕ 🔒 💻

HOLLYWOOD

▼▼ ▼ **La Quinta Inn & Suites-Ft. Lauderdale Airport** H
(954) 922-2295. **$108-$312.** 2620 N 26th Ave 33020. I-95 exit 21 (Sheridan St), just e to 26th Ave, then just n. Int corridors.
Pets: Accepted. 🍽 🔥M ➿ 🛜 🔒 💻

AAA ▼▼▼ ▼▼▼ **Margaritaville Hollywood Beach Resort** H
(954) 874-4444. **Call for rates.** 1111 N Ocean Dr 33019. I-95 exit 21 (Sheridan St), 3.1 mi e to Ocean Dr (SR A1A), then 1.1 mi s. Int corridors. **Pets:** Accepted. SAVE 🍽 🔥M ✕ 🛑 ✕ 🔒 💻

AAA ▼▼▼ **Quality Inn & Suites Hollywood Blvd** M
(954) 981-1800. **$88-$269.** 4900 Hollywood Blvd 33021. I-95 exit 20 (Hollywood Blvd). 1.6 mi w; Florida Tpke exit 49, 1.3 mi e. Ext corridors. **Pets:** Medium, other species. $30 daily fee/pet. Designated rooms, service with restrictions, supervision.
SAVE ➿ 🛜 ✕ 🔒 💻

AAA ▼▼▼ ▼▼▼ **Seminole Hard Rock Hotel & Casino Hollywood** H
(954) 327-7625. **$159-$699.** 1 Seminole Way 33314. I-95 exit 22 (Stirling Rd), 2.9 mi w, then just n on SR 7/US 441; Florida Tpke exit 53, 0.5 mi e, then 0.8 mi s. Int corridors. **Pets:** Accepted.
SAVE ECO 🍽 🔥M ➿ ✕ 🛜 💻

INDIALANTIC

AAA ▼▼▼ **Windemere Inn By The Sea** BB
(321) 728-9334. **$145-$285, 10 day notice.** 815 S Miramar Ave (A1A) 32903. Jct US 192, 0.3 mi s on SR A1A. Ext/int corridors. **Pets:** $25 daily fee/pet. Designated rooms, service with restrictions, crate.
SAVE 🔥 🍽 🛜 ✕ 🎾

ISLAMORADA (Restaurants p. 607)

▼▼ ▼ **Islander Resort, a Guy Harvey Outpost Resort** M
(305) 664-2031. **Call for rates.** 82100 Overseas Hwy 33036. US 1 at MM 82.1. Ext corridors. **Pets:** Accepted.
🍽 ➿ ✕ 🛜 ✕ 🔒 💻

JACKSONVILLE (Restaurants p. 607)

AAA ▼▼▼ **Aloft Jacksonville Tapestry Park** H
(904) 998-4448. **$89-$229.** 4812 Deer Lake Dr W 32246. I-95 exit 340, 4.5 mi n to Southside Blvd, then e. Int corridors. **Pets:** Accepted.
SAVE 🔥 🍽 ➿ 🛜 ✕ 🔒 💻

AAA ▼▼▼ **Crowne Plaza Jacksonville Airport** H
(904) 741-4404. **$89-$299.** 14670 Duval Rd 32218. I-95 exit 363, just w. Int corridors. **Pets:** Accepted. SAVE 🍽 🔥M ➿ 🛜 ✕ 💻

AAA ▼▼▼▼ **Embassy Suites by Hilton Jacksonville Baymeadows** H
(904) 731-3555. **$119-$229.** 9300 Baymeadows Rd 32256. I-95 exit 341 (Baymeadows Rd/SR 152), 0.5 mi e. Int corridors. **Pets:** Accepted.
SAVE ECO 🍽 ➿ 🛜 ✕ 🔒 💻

▼▼▼ **Hampton Inn & Suites by Hilton Jacksonville-St Johns Town Center Area** H
(904) 997-9100. **$109-$219.** 4415 Southside Blvd 32216. I-95 exit 344 (Butler Blvd/SR 202), 2.5 mi e on J Turner Butler Blvd, then 0.9 mi n on SR 115. Int corridors. **Pets:** Accepted. ➿ 🛜 ✕ 🔒 💻

▼▼▼ **Holiday Inn Express Jacksonville East** H
(904) 997-9190. **$89-$199.** 53 Jefferson Rd 32225. I-295 exit 48, just ne. Int corridors. **Pets:** Medium. $40 one-time fee/pet. Service with restrictions, supervision. 🍽 ➿ 🛜 ✕ 🔒 💻

▼▼▼ **Homewood Suites by Hilton Jacksonville Deerwood Park** H
(904) 253-7120. **$115-$163.** 8511 Touchton Rd 32216. I-95 exit 344, 2 mi e on SR 202/J Turner Butler Blvd; 1.8 mi n on SR 115/Southside Blvd, just w. Int corridors. **Pets:** Accepted. 🔥M 🛜 🔒 💻

▼▼▼ **Homewood Suites by Hilton Jacksonville Downtown/Southbank** H
(904) 396-6888. **Call for rates.** 1201 Kings Ave 32207. I-95 exit 350A (Downtown/Prudential St), 0.3 mi e on Prudential St, then just s. Int corridors. **Pets:** Medium. $125 one-time fee/room. Service with restrictions, crate. 🔥M ➿ 🛜 🔒 💻

▼▼▼ **Hotel Indigo Jacksonville Deerwood Park** H
(904) 996-7199. **Call for rates.** 9840 Tapestry Park Cir 32246. I-95 exit 340, 4.5 mi n to Southside Blvd, then e. Int corridors. **Pets:** Accepted.
🍽 ➿ 🛜 ✕ 🔒 💻

AAA ▼▼▼▼ **Hyatt Regency Jacksonville Riverfront** H
(904) 588-1234. **$99-$389, 3 day notice.** 225 E Coast Line Dr 32202. Downtown; just e of The Landing. Int corridors. **Pets:** Accepted.
SAVE ECO 🍽 ➿ ✕ 🛜 ✕ 💻

▼▼▼ **Omni Jacksonville Hotel** H
(904) 355-6664. **$149-$349.** 245 Water St 32202. Corner of Pearl and Water sts; on north side of St. Johns River; downtown; adjacent to The Landing. Int corridors. **Pets:** Accepted.
ECO 🍽 🔥M ➿ 🛑 ✕ 💻

▼▼ **TownePlace Suites by Marriott Jacksonville Butler Boulevard** H
(904) 296-1661. **$89-$130.** 4801 Lenoir Ave 32216. I-95 exit 344 (Butler Blvd/SR 202), just sw, then just nw. Int corridors. **Pets:** Accepted.
🍽 🛜 ✕ 🔒 💻

JACKSONVILLE BEACH (Restaurants p. 607)

AAA ▼▼▼ **Four Points by Sheraton Jacksonville Beachfront** H ❀
(904) 435-3535. **$159-$599.** 11 1st St N 32250. Just n of Beach Blvd (US 90). Int corridors. **Pets:** Medium. $45 daily fee/pet. Designated rooms, service with restrictions, supervision.
SAVE ECO 🔥 🍽 🔥M ➿ ✕ 🔒 💻

AAA ▼▼▼ **Holiday Inn Express Jacksonville Beach** H
(904) 435-3000. **$119-$329, 3 day notice.** 1101 Beach Blvd 32250. 0.7 mi w of 3rd St/SR A1A. Int corridors. **Pets:** Medium, dogs only. $35 daily fee/pet. Designated rooms, service with restrictions, supervision.
SAVE ECO 🔥 🔥 🔥M ➿ ✕ 🛜 ✕ 🔒 💻

JUNO BEACH

◆◆◆ Hampton Inn Jupiter/Juno Beach H
(561) 626-9090. $89-$339. 13801 US Hwy 1 33408. I-95 exit 83 (Donald Ross Rd), 4.5 mi e to US 1, then just s. Int corridors.
Pets: Accepted. ⮔M ⬗ 🛜 ✕ 🖥 ☕

◆◆◆ Holiday Inn Express North Palm
Beach-Oceanview H
(561) 622-4366. Call for rates. 13950 US Hwy 1 33408. I-95 exit 83 (Donald Ross Rd), 4.5 mi e; jct US 1 and Donald Ross Rd. Ext/int corridors. Pets: Accepted. ⬗ 🛜 ✕ 🖥 ☕

JUPITER (Restaurants p. 607)

◆◆◆ Fairfield Inn & Suites by Marriott-Jupiter/West Palm
Beach H
(561) 748-5252. $77-$213. 6748 W Indiantown Rd 33458. I-95 exit 87A (Indiantown Rd), 0.8 mi e. Int corridors. Pets: Accepted.
ECO ⮔M ⬗ 🛜 ✕ 🖥 ☕

◆◆◆◆ Jupiter Beach Resort & Spa H
(561) 746-2511. Call for rates. 5 N A1A 33477. I-95 exit 87A (Indiantown Rd), 4.9 mi e; jct SR 706 (Indiantown Rd) and A1A. Int corridors.
Pets: Accepted. SAVE ECO ⬗ ⮔M ⬗ ✕ 🖾 ✕ 🖥 ☕

◆◆◆ Jupiter Waterfront Inn H
(561) 747-9085. $99-$279. 18903 SE Federal Hwy 33469. On US 1 (Federal Hwy), 2.9 mi n of SR 706 (Indiantown Rd). Ext corridors.
Pets: Accepted. SAVE ⬗ 🛜 ✕ 🖥

KEY BISCAYNE (Restaurants p. 607)

◆◆◆◆◆ The Ritz-Carlton Key Biscayne,
Miami H
(305) 365-4500. Call for rates. 455 Grand Bay Dr 33149. Jct Crandon Blvd, just e. Int corridors. Pets: Accepted.
SAVE ECO ⬗ ⮔M ⬗ ✕ 🛜 ✕ 🖥 ☕

KEY WEST (Restaurants p. 607)

◆◆◆ Amsterdam's Curry Mansion Inn BB
(305) 294-5349. Call for rates. 511 Caroline St 33040. Just e of Duval St; in Old Town. Ext/int corridors. Pets: Small. Designated rooms, supervision. SAVE ⬗ 🛜 ✕ 🖥

◆◆◆ Best Western Key Ambassador Resort
Inn M
(305) 296-3500. $169-$329, 3 day notice. 3755 S Roosevelt Blvd 33040. On SR A1A, 1 mi s of jct US 1. Ext corridors. Pets: Accepted.
SAVE ⬗ 🛜 ✕ 🖥 ☕

◆◆◆ Casa Marina, A Waldorf Astoria
Resort H
(305) 296-3535. $289-$409. 1500 Reynolds St 33040. 4 mi s on Flagler Ave (CR 5A) from jct SR A1A. Ext/int corridors. Pets: Accepted.
SAVE ECO ⬗ ⬗ ✕ 🛜 ✕ 🖥 ☕

◆◆ Courtney's Place Historic Cottages & Inn BB
(305) 294-3480. Call for rates. 720 Whitmarsh Ln 33040. Just e of jct Petronia and Simonton sts; in Old Town. Ext corridors. Pets: Accepted.
⬗ 🛜 ✕ 🖥 ☕

◆◆◆ DoubleTree Resort by Hilton Hotel Grand
Key-Key West H
(305) 293-1818. $209-$499. 3990 S Roosevelt Blvd 33040. From US 1, 0.5 mi s on SR A1A. Int corridors. Pets: Medium. $75 one-time fee/room. Designated rooms, service with restrictions, crate.
SAVE ECO ⬗ ⬗ ✕ 🛜 ✕ 🖥 ☕

◆◆◆ The Gates Hotel Key West H
(305) 320-0930. $149-$699, 3 day notice. 3824 N Roosevelt Blvd 33040. Corner of A1A and N Roosevelt Blvd, just n. Ext corridors.
Pets: Accepted. SAVE ⬗ ⮔M 🛜 ✕ 🖥

◆◆◆ Hyatt Key West Resort & Spa H 🐾
(305) 809-1234. $219-$599, 7 day notice. 601 Front St 33040. Corner of Simonton and Front sts; just n of Mallory Square; in Old Town. Ext corridors. Pets: Medium, dogs only. $150 one-time fee/room. Service with restrictions, supervision.
SAVE ECO ⬗ ⮔M ⬗ ✕ 🛜 ✕ 🖥 ☕

◆◆◆ Margaritaville Key West Resort &
Marina H 🐾
(305) 294-4000. Call for rates. 245 Front St 33040. Corner of Front and Greene sts; in Old Town. Ext/int corridors. Pets: Medium. Service with restrictions, supervision.
SAVE ECO ⬗ ⮔M ⬗ ✕ 🛜 ✕ 🖥 ☕

◆◆◆ Pier House Resort and Spa H
(305) 296-4600. Call for rates. One Duval St 33040. At end of Duval St; in Old Town. Ext/int corridors. Pets: Accepted.
SAVE ⬗ ⬗ ✕ 🛜 ✕ 🖥 ☕

◆◆◆ The Reach, A Waldorf Astoria Resort H
(305) 296-5000. $289-$409. 1435 Simonton St 33040. Just s of jct Truman Ave and Simonton St. Ext corridors. Pets: Accepted.
SAVE ECO ⬗ ⬗ ✕ 🛜 ✕ 🖥 ☕

◆◆◆ Sheraton Suites Key West H 🐾
(305) 292-9800. $199-$799. 2001 S Roosevelt Blvd 33040. Jct US 1 and SR A1A, 3 mi s. Ext/int corridors. Pets: Medium, other species. Designated rooms, service with restrictions, supervision.
SAVE ECO ⬗ ⮔M ⬗ ✕ 🛜 ✕ 🖥 ☕

KISSIMMEE

◆◆◆ Best Western Premier Saratoga Resort
Villas H
(407) 997-3300. $91-$202. 4787 W Irlo Bronson Memorial Hwy 34746. I-4 exit 64, 4.9 mi e on US 192. Ext corridors. Pets: $50 deposit/room, $20 daily fee/pet. Designated rooms, service with restrictions, crate.
SAVE ⬗ ⮔M ⬗ ✕ 🖾 ✕ 🖥

◆◆◆ Quality Suites Royale Parc Suites H 🐾
(407) 396-8040. $79-$309. 5876 W Irlo Bronson Memorial Hwy 34746. I-4 exit 64, 1.9 mi e on US 192. Int corridors. Pets: Medium, dogs only. $125 one-time fee/room. Service with restrictions, supervision.
SAVE ⬗ ⮔M ⬗ ✕ 🛜 ✕ 🖥

LADY LAKE

◆◆◆ Comfort Suites The Villages H
(352) 259-6578. $94-$209. 1202 Avenida Central N 32159. Just w of jct US 441/27. Int corridors. Pets: $35 one-time fee/room. Designated rooms, service with restrictions, crate. SAVE ⬗ 🛜 ✕ 🖥 ☕

◆◆ Microtel Inn & Suites by Wyndham Lady Lake/The
Villages H
(352) 259-0184. $65-$180. 850 S US 27/441 32159. On US 27/441, 2.9 mi s of The Village Center, just s of jct Rolling Acres Rd. Int corridors.
Pets: Accepted. ⬗ 🛜 ✕ 🖥 ☕

◆◆◆ TownePlace Suites by Marriott The
Villages H
(352) 753-8686. $98-$190. 1141 Alonzo Ave 32159. Just w of jct US 27/441 on Main St, just n. Int corridors. Pets: Accepted.
SAVE ⬗ ⮔M ⬗ 🛜 ✕ 🖥 ☕

LAKE BUENA VISTA

◆◆◆ Clarion Inn Lake Buena Vista H 🐾
(407) 996-7300. $60-$150. 8442 Palm Pkwy 32836. I-4 exit 68, 0.6 mi n on SR 535, then 0.5 mi e. Ext corridors. Pets: $15 daily fee/pet. Designated rooms, service with restrictions, supervision.
SAVE ⬗ ⮔M ⬗ 🛜 ✕ 🖥

Four Seasons Resort Orlando at Walt Disney World Resort H
(407) 313-7777. **$479-$1399, 5 day notice.** 10100 Dream Tree Blvd 32836. I-4 exit 67, 1.1 mi nw, 1.5 mi n on Bonnet Creek Pkwy, 0.9 mi n; in Golden Oak. Int corridors. **Pets:** Accepted.

Holiday Inn Resort Orlando-Lake Buena Vista H ✦
(407) 239-4500. **$89-$249.** 13351 State Road 535 32821. I-4 exit 68, 0.3 mi se. Int corridors. **Pets:** Medium. $50 one-time fee/pet. Service with restrictions, crate.

Hyatt Regency Grand Cypress H
(407) 239-1234. **$119-$329, 3 day notice.** 1 Grand Cypress Blvd 32836. I-4 exit 68, 0.8 mi nw on SR 535, just s. Int corridors. **Pets:** Accepted.

Residence Inn by Marriott Orlando Lake Buena Vista H
(407) 465-0075. **$108-$197, 3 day notice.** 11450 Marbella Palms Ct 32836. I-4 exit 68, 0.6 mi n on SR 535, then 1 mi e on Palm Pkwy, just sw. Int corridors. **Pets:** Accepted.

Sheraton Lake Buena Vista Resort H
(407) 239-0444. **$79-$219.** 12205 Apopka-Vineland Rd 32836. I-4 exit 68, 0.6 mi n on SR 535. Ext/int corridors. **Pets:** Accepted.

Westgate Blue Tree Resort at Lake Buena Vista CO
(407) 597-2200. **Call for rates.** 12007 Cypress Run Rd 32836. I-4 exit 68, 1 mi n on SR 535, 0.4 mi e on to Vinings Way Blvd. Ext corridors. **Pets:** Accepted.

Wyndham Grand Orlando Resort Bonnet Creek H
(407) 390-2300. **$229-$489.** 14651 Chelonia Pkwy 32821. I-4 exit 65, 1.3 mi w on W Osceola Pkwy, 1.2 mi n on Victory Way, 0.4 mi ne on Buena Vista Dr, then 0.9 mi s. Int corridors. **Pets:** Accepted.

LAKE CITY

Baymont Inn & Suites Lake City M
(386) 752-3801. **$64-$110.** 3598 W Hwy 90 32055. I-75 exit 427, just w. Ext corridors. **Pets:** Medium. $15 daily fee/pet. Designated rooms, service with restrictions, supervision.

Holiday Inn Hotel & Suites H
(386) 754-1411. **Call for rates.** 213 SW Commerce Dr 32025. I-75 exit 427, just e on US 90, then just s. Int corridors. **Pets:** Accepted.

LAKELAND

Crestwood Suites Lakeland H
(863) 904-2050. **$84-$139.** 4360 Lakeland Park Dr 33809. I-4 exit 33, 0.6 mi se on SR 33, 0.4 mi n on Socrum Loop, then just s. Int corridors. **Pets:** Accepted.

Hyatt Place Lakeland Center H
(863) 413-1122. **$95-$289.** 525 W Orange St 33815. I-4 exit 31, 2.6 mi se on Kathleen Rd, then just w; adjacent to The Lakeland Center. Int corridors. **Pets:** Accepted.

Residence Inn by Marriott Lakeland H ✦
(863) 680-2323. **$119-$250.** 3701 Harden Blvd 33803. SR 570 (Polk Pkwy) exit 5, just n on SR 563. Int corridors. **Pets:** $100 one-time fee/room. Service with restrictions.

LAKE MARY (Restaurants p. 608)

Candlewood Suites Lake Mary H
(407) 585-3000. **Call for rates.** 1130 Greenwood Blvd 32746. I-4 exit 98, just e to Lake Emma Rd, 0.5 mi s to Greenwood Blvd, 0.5 mi w. Int corridors. **Pets:** Accepted.

Extended Stay America-Orlando-Lake Mary-1036 H
(407) 833-0011. **$70-$100.** 1036 Greenwood Blvd 32746. I-4 exit 98, just e to Lake Emma Rd, 0.5 mi s to Greenwood Blvd, then just w. Int corridors. **Pets:** Accepted.

Extended Stay America-Orlando-Lake Mary-1040 H
(407) 829-2332. **$90-$120.** 1040 Greenwood Blvd 32746. I-4 exit 98, just e to Lake Emma Rd, 0.5 mi s to Greenwood Blvd, then just w; in Commerce Park. Int corridors. **Pets:** Accepted.

Hyatt Place Lake Mary/Orlando-North H
(407) 995-5555. **$79-$229.** 1255 S International Pkwy 32746. I-4 exit 98, just w. Int corridors. **Pets:** Accepted.

La Quinta Inn & Suites-Orlando Lake Mary H
(407) 805-9901. **$86-$257.** 1060 Greenwood Blvd 32746. I-4 exit 98, just e to Lake Emma Rd, 0.5 mi s to Greenwood Blvd, then just w. Int corridors. **Pets:** Accepted.

Residence Inn by Marriott-Orlando Lake Mary H
(407) 995-3400. **$115-$186.** 825 Heathrow Park Ln 32746. I-4 exit 101A, 0.5 mi w to International Pkwy, then just s. Int corridors. **Pets:** Small. $100 one-time fee/room. Service with restrictions, supervision.

The Westin Lake Mary, Orlando North H ✦
(407) 531-3555. **$99-$299.** 2974 International Pkwy 32746. I-4 exit 101A, 0.5 mi w. Int corridors. **Pets:** Medium, dogs only. Designated rooms, service with restrictions, crate.

LAKE WORTH (Restaurants p. 608)

Sabal Palm House Bed & Breakfast Inn BB ✦
(561) 582-1090. **$99-$259, 14 day notice.** 109 N Golfview Rd 33460. Just n of SR 802 (Lake Ave); west side of Intracoastal Bridge. Ext/int corridors. **Pets:** Small, dogs only. $25 daily fee/pet. Designated rooms.

LARGO

Holiday Inn Express & Suites Largo Central Park H
(727) 581-3900. **Call for rates.** 210 Seminole Blvd 33770. On Alternate US 19, just s of jct SR 686 (W Bay Dr/E Bay Dr). Int corridors. **Pets:** Accepted.

LECANTO

Holiday Inn Express Hotel & Suites H
(352) 341-3515. **$99-$150.** 903 E Gulf to Lake Hwy 34461. On SR 44, 4.2 mi e. Int corridors. **Pets:** Other species. $25 daily fee/pet. Designated rooms, service with restrictions, supervision.

LEESBURG

Best Western Plus Chain of Lakes Inn & Suites H
(352) 460-0118. **$80-$150.** 1321 N 14th St 34748. Jct US 27 and 441. Int corridors. **Pets:** Small, dogs only. $20 daily fee/pet. Designated rooms, service with restrictions, supervision.

Hampton Inn Leesburg/Tavares H
(352) 315-1053. **$99-$229.** 9630 US Hwy 441 34788. Just s of jct College Dr. Int corridors. **Pets:** Accepted.

LEHIGH ACRES

Microtel Inn & Suites by Wyndham Lehigh H
(239) 369-2121. **$70-$139, 3 day notice.** 1320 Business Way 33936. Just se of jct Lee Blvd (CR 884) on Homestead Rd N, just s on Beth Stacey Blvd, then just n. Int corridors. **Pets:** Accepted.

LIVE OAK

Quality Inn & Suites M
(386) 362-6000. **$95-$170.** 6819 US 129 N 32060. I-10 exit 283, 0.3 mi s. Ext corridors. **Pets:** Accepted.

LUTZ

Residence Inn by Marriott Tampa Suncoast Parkway at NorthPointe Village H
(813) 792-8400. **$137-$207.** 2101 NorthPointe Pkwy 33558. Suncoast Pkwy exit 19, just e on SR 54, then just ne; in Northpointe at Suncoast Crossings. Int corridors. **Pets:** Small, other species. $100 one-time fee/pet. Service with restrictions, crate.

LYNN HAVEN

Wingate by Wyndham Lynn Haven H
(850) 248-8000. **$95-$150.** 2610 Lynn Haven Pkwy 32444. On SR 77, 1.8 mi n of jct SR 368. Int corridors. **Pets:** Medium. $60 deposit/pet. Designated rooms, service with restrictions, crate.

MADISON

Best Western Plus Madison Inn H
(850) 973-2020. **$105-$215.** 167 SE Bandit St 32340. I-10 exit 258, just n on SR 53. Int corridors. **Pets:** Accepted.

MAITLAND (Restaurants p. 608)

Sheraton Orlando North H
(407) 660-9000. **$99-$269.** 600 N Lake Destiny Dr 32751. I-4 exit 90B, just w. Int corridors. **Pets:** Accepted.

MANALAPAN

Eau Palm Beach Resort & Spa H
(561) 533-6000. **$289-$939, 14 day notice.** 100 S Ocean Blvd 33462. I-95 exit 61 (Lantana Rd), 1.1 mi e to US 1 (Dixie Hwy), just s to Ocean Ave, then 0.8 mi e. Int corridors. **Pets:** Accepted.

MARATHON

Hyatt Place Marathon/Florida Keys H
(305) 743-1234. **$134-$459.** 1996 Overseas Hwy 33050. On US A1A; center of town; gulf side. Int corridors. **Pets:** Large. $75 one-time fee/room. Designated rooms, service with restrictions.

Royal Hawaiian Motel/Botel M
(305) 743-7500. **$125-$300, 30 day notice.** 12020 Overseas Hwy 33050. US 1 at MM 53; gulfside. Ext corridors. **Pets:** Medium. $50 one-time fee/pet. Service with restrictions, supervision.

MARIANNA

Microtel Inn & Suites by Wyndham Marianna H
(850) 526-5005. **$80-$109.** 4959 Whitetail Dr 32448. I-10 exit 142, just n on SR 71. Int corridors. **Pets:** Accepted.

MELBOURNE (Restaurants p. 608)

Candlewood Suites Melbourne/Viera H
(321) 821-9009. **Call for rates.** 2930 Pineda Plaza Way 32940. I-95 exit 191 (CR 509/Wickham Rd), 4.5 mi se to Pineda Plaza Way, then just n. Int corridors. **Pets:** Small, other species. $25 daily fee/room. Service with restrictions, crate.

Hilton Melbourne Rialto Place H
(321) 768-0200. **Call for rates.** 200 Rialto Pl 32901. I-95 exit 180 (US 192/New Haven Ave), 4.8 mi e to Airport Blvd, then 0.8 mi n to Rialto Pl. Int corridors. **Pets:** Accepted.

La Quinta Inn & Suites-Melbourne H
(321) 242-9400. **$75-$240.** 7200 George T Edwards Dr 32940. I-95 exit 191 (CR 509/Wickham Rd), just w. Int corridors. **Pets:** Accepted.

Residence Inn by Marriott Melbourne H
(321) 723-5740. **$108-$232.** 1430 S Babcock St 32901. I-95 exit 180 (US 192/New Haven Ave), 5.1 mi e to Babcock St, then 0.5 mi n. Int corridors. **Pets:** Medium, other species. $150 one-time fee/room. Service with restrictions, supervision.

MIAMI (Restaurants p. 608)

Aloft Hotel Miami - Brickell H
(305) 854-6300. **Call for rates.** 1001 SW 2nd Ave 33130. Corner of SW 10th St and SW 2nd Ave; just e of I-95. Int corridors. **Pets:** Accepted.

DoubleTree by Hilton Hotel-Miami Airport Convention Center H
(305) 261-3800. **$119-$289.** 711 NW 72nd Ave 33126. SR 836 (Dolphin Expwy) exit NW 57th Ave/Red Rd/SR 959, 0.6 mi s to NW 7th St, 1.5 mi w to NW 72nd Ave/Milam Dairy Rd, then just n. Int corridors. **Pets:** Accepted.

Element Miami International Airport H
(305) 636-1600. **Call for rates.** 3525 NW 25th St 33142. From LeJeune Rd (NW 42nd Ave), 0.7 mi e. Int corridors. **Pets:** Accepted.

Epic Miami H
(305) 424-5226. **Call for rates.** 270 Biscayne Blvd Way 33131. Just e of US 1 (SE 2nd Ave). Int corridors. **Pets:** Accepted.

Four Seasons Hotel Miami H 🐾
(305) 358-3535. **$259-$699, 3 day notice.** 1435 Brickell Ave 33131. Jct 14th Terr on US 1. Int corridors. **Pets:** Service with restrictions, supervision.

Hilton Miami Downtown H
(305) 374-0000. **Call for rates.** 1601 Biscayne Blvd 33132. On US 1 (Biscayne Blvd), just n of NE 15th St. Int corridors. **Pets:** Accepted.

Hotel Urbano at Brickell H
(305) 854-2070. **Call for rates.** 2500 Brickell Ave 33129. Jct SE 25th Rd and Brickell Ave. Int corridors. **Pets:** Accepted.

Mandarin Oriental, Miami 🄷
(305) 913-8288. **Call for rates.** 500 Brickell Key Dr 33131. US 1 (Brickell Ave), just e on SE 8th St (Brickell Key Dr). Int corridors.
Pets: Accepted.

Pullman Miami Airport Hotel 🄷
(305) 264-4888. **Call for rates.** 5800 Blue Lagoon Dr 33126. SR 836 (Dolphin Expwy) exit NW 57th Ave/Red Rd/SR 959, just s to Blue Lagoon Dr, then just w. Int corridors. **Pets:** Accepted.

MIAMI BEACH (Restaurants p. 608)

1 Hotel South Beach 🄷
(305) 604-1000. **Call for rates.** 2341 Collins Ave 33139. Between 23rd and 24th sts; corner of 23rd St and Collins Ave. Int corridors.
Pets: Accepted.

The Anglers Miami South Beach, A Kimpton Hotel 🄷
(305) 534-9600. **$219-$599, 3 day notice.** 660 Washington Ave 33139. Between 6th and 7th sts. Ext/int corridors. **Pets:** Accepted.

The Betsy-South Beach 🄷
(305) 531-6100. **$220-$1500, 3 day notice.** 1440 Ocean Dr 33139. Between 14th and 15th sts. Int corridors. **Pets:** Accepted.

The Carillon Miami Beach 🄷
(305) 514-7000. **$345-$865, 3 day notice.** 6801 Collins Ave 33141. Between 67th and 68th sts; just s of North Shore Park. Int corridors.
Pets: Accepted.

The Confidante 🄷
(305) 424-1234. **Call for rates.** 4041 Collins Ave 33140. Just e of SR 112/Arthur Godfrey Bridge/41st St; between 41st and 40th sts. Int corridors. **Pets:** Accepted.

Delano South Beach 🄷
(305) 672-2000. **Call for rates.** 1685 Collins Ave 33139. On SR A1A (Collins Ave); at 16th St. Int corridors. **Pets:** Accepted.

Fontainebleau Miami Beach 🄷
(305) 538-2000. **Call for rates.** 4441 Collins Ave 33140. SR A1A (Collins Ave); just n of Arthur Godfrey Rd. Int corridors. **Pets:** Accepted.

Gates Hotel South Beach-a DoubleTree by Hilton 🄷
(305) 860-9444. **$139-$899, 3 day notice.** 2360 Collins Ave 33139. Corner of 23rd St and Collins Ave. Int corridors. **Pets:** Accepted.

Grand Beach Hotel 🄷
(305) 538-8666. **Call for rates.** 4835 Collins Ave 33140. Between 48th and 49th sts. Int corridors. **Pets:** Accepted.

Kimpton Surfcomber 🄷
(305) 532-7715. **Call for rates.** 1717 Collins Ave 33139. Between 17th and 18th sts. Int corridors. **Pets:** Accepted.

Loews Miami Beach Hotel 🄷
(305) 604-1601. **Call for rates.** 1601 Collins Ave 33139. Jct SR A1A (Collins Ave) and 16th Ave. Int corridors. **Pets:** Accepted.

Marriott Stanton South Beach 🄷
(305) 536-7700. **$169-$485, 3 day notice.** 161 Ocean Dr 33139. Just s of SR A1A (Collins Ave); between 1st and 2nd sts. Int corridors.
Pets: Accepted.

The Miami Beach EDITION 🄷
(786) 257-4500. **$254-$1059, 7 day notice.** 2901 Collins Ave 33140. Corner of 29th St and Collins Ave. Int corridors. **Pets:** Accepted.

Mondrian South Beach 🄷
(305) 514-1500. **Call for rates.** 1100 West Ave 33139. Between 10th and 11th sts. Int corridors. **Pets:** Small. $100 one-time fee/room. Service with restrictions, supervision.

The National Hotel 🄷
(305) 532-2311. **$195-$1600, 7 day notice.** 1677 Collins Ave 33139. Jct SR A1A (Collins Ave) and 16th St. Int corridors. **Pets:** Accepted.

Residence Inn by Marriott Miami Beach South Beach 🄷
(305) 604-6070. **$190-$369, 3 day notice.** 1231 17th St 33139. Between West Ave and Alton Ct. Int corridors. **Pets:** Medium, other species. $150 one-time fee/room. Service with restrictions, crate.

The Ritz-Carlton, South Beach 🄷
(786) 276-4000. **Call for rates.** 1 Lincoln Rd 33139. Jct SR A1A (Collins Ave). Int corridors. **Pets:** Accepted.

Royal Palm South Beach Miami, a Tribute Portfolio Resort 🄷
(305) 604-5700. **$199-$1000, 3 day notice.** 1545 Collins Ave 33139. On SR A1A (Collins Ave), just s of 16th Ave. Ext/int corridors.
Pets: Accepted.

The Setai, Miami Beach 🄷
(305) 520-6000. **$489-$1600, 14 day notice.** 2001 Collins Ave 33139. SR A1A (Collins Ave); at 20th St. Int corridors. **Pets:** Accepted.

Shelborne South Beach 🄷
(305) 531-1271. **$249-$419.** 1801 Collins Ave 33139. SR A1A (Collins Ave) at 18th St. Int corridors. **Pets:** Accepted.

W South Beach 🄷
(305) 938-3000. **$299-$1499, 7 day notice.** 2201 Collins Ave 33139. Jct SR A1A (Collins Ave) and 22nd St. Int corridors. **Pets:** Accepted.

MIAMI LAKES

Hotel Indigo Miami Lakes 🄷
(305) 556-0100. **Call for rates.** 7601 Miami Lakes Dr 33014. SR 826 (Palmetto Expwy) exit NW 154th St, just e. Int corridors.
Pets: Accepted.

La Quinta Inn & Suites-Miami Lakes 🄷
(305) 821-8274. **$93-$312.** 7925 NW 154th St 33016. Jct SR 826 (Palmetto Expwy) exit NW 154th St, just w. Int corridors. **Pets:** Accepted.

TownePlace Suites by Marriott Miami Lakes 🄷
(305) 512-9191. **$76-$177.** 8079 NW 154th St 33016. SR 826 (Palmetto Expwy) exit NW 154th St, 0.4 mi w. Int corridors. **Pets:** Accepted.

MIAMI SPRINGS

AAA **▼▼▼** Hyatt Place Miami Airport East Hotel **H**
(305) 667-1003. $119-$399. 3549 NW LeJeune Rd 33142. Just s of SR 112. Int corridors. **Pets:** Accepted. [SAVE] [♦] [⊚] [✕] [🛏] [▭]

MIDWAY

AAA **▼▼▼** Country Inn & Suites By Carlson
    Midway **H**
(850) 514-2222. $90-$100. 85 River Park Dr 32343. I-10 exit 192, just s. Int corridors. **Pets:** Accepted. [SAVE] [♦] [➳] [⊚] [✕] [🛏] [▭]

▼▼ Howard Johnson Express Inn **M**
(850) 574-8888. $65-$199. 81 Commerce Blvd 32343. I-10 exit 192, just n. Ext corridors. **Pets:** Accepted. [♦] [⊚] [🛏] [▭]

MILTON *(Restaurants p. 609)*

AAA **▼▼** Best Western Milton Inn **M**
(850) 623-1511. **Call for rates.** 8936 Hwy 87 S 32583. I-10 exit 31, just s. Int corridors. **Pets:** Small. $20 daily fee/room. Designated rooms, service with restrictions, crate. [SAVE] [&M] [➳] [⊚] [🛏] [▭]

AAA **▼◆** Red Roof Inn & Suites-Pensacola East
    Milton **H**
(850) 995-6100. $70-$104. 2672 Avalon Blvd 32583. I-10 exit 22, just s on SR 281. Int corridors. **Pets:** Accepted.
[SAVE] [&M] [➳] [⊚] [✕] [🛏] [▭]

MIRAMAR

AAA **▼▼▼** Residence Inn by Marriott-Fort Lauderdale
    SW/Miramar **H**
(954) 450-2717. $103-$215. 14700 Hotel Rd 33027. I-75 exit 7A (Miramar Pkwy), just e to SW 148th Ave, just n to Hotel Rd, then just e. Int corridors. **Pets:** Accepted. [SAVE] [ECO] [&M] [➳] [⊚] [✕] [🛏] [▭]

NAPLES *(Restaurants p. 609)*

AAA **▼◆** Gulfcoast Inn **H**
(239) 261-6046. $90-$200. 2555 Tamiami Tr N 34103. On US 41 (Tamiami Tr); jct 26th Ave N. Ext corridors. **Pets:** Accepted.
[SAVE] [♦] [➳] [⊚] [✕] [🛏] [▭]

AAA **▼◆** Hawthorn Suites by
    Wyndham-Naples **H** ❀
(239) 593-1300. $99-$310. 3557 Pine Ridge Rd 34109. I-75 exit 107 (Pine Ridge Rd), 0.8 mi w. Int corridors. **Pets:** Small. $250 one-time fee/room. Designated rooms, service with restrictions.
[SAVE] [ECO] [&M] [➳] [⊚] [✕] [🛏] [▭]

AAA **▼▼▼** Hyatt House Naples/5th Ave **H**
(239) 775-1000. $119-$599. 1345 5th Ave S 34102. I-75 exit 101, just s to Davis Blvd, 6.5 mi w to Tamiami Tr (US 41), then 0.4 mi nw. Int corridors. **Pets:** Accepted. [SAVE] [♦] [&M] [✕] [⊚] [✕] [🛏] [▭]

AAA **▼▼▼** Naples Bay Resort **H** ❀
(239) 530-1199. **Call for rates.** 1500 5th Ave S 34102. On US 41 (Tamiami Tr), just e of jct Goodlette-Frank Rd. Ext/int corridors. **Pets:** Medium. $300 deposit/room, $75 one-time fee/room. Designated rooms, service with restrictions.
[SAVE] [♦] [&M] [➳] [✕] [⊚] [✕] [🛏] [▭]

AAA **▼▼** Red Roof PLUS+ & Suites Naples **H**
(239) 774-3117. $69-$209. 1925 Davis Blvd 34104. Just e of jct US 41 (Tamiami Tr). Ext corridors. **Pets:** Accepted.
[SAVE] [➳] [⊚] [✕] [🛏] [▭]

AAA **▼▼▼** Residence Inn by Marriott
    Naples **H** ❀
(239) 659-1300. $106-$332. 4075 Tamiami Tr N 34103. I-75 exit 107, 3.8 mi w on Pine Ridge Rd (CR 896) to US 41 (Tamiami Tr), then 1 mi s. Int corridors. **Pets:** Medium. $100 one-time fee/pet. Service with restrictions, crate. [SAVE] [&M] [➳] [⊚] [✕] [🛏] [▭]

AAA **▼▼▼** The Ritz-Carlton Golf Resort,
    Naples **H**
(239) 593-2000. $229-$1039, 3 day notice. 2600 Tiburon Dr 34109. I-75 exit 111, 1.8 mi w on Immokalee Rd, 1.3 mi s on CR 31 (Airport-Pulling Rd), then just e. Int corridors. **Pets:** Accepted.
[SAVE] [ECO] [◀] [♦] [&M] [➳] [✕] [⊚] [✕] [▭]

▼▼▼ Staybridge Suites-Naples **H**
(239) 643-8002. **Call for rates.** 4805 Tamiami Tr N 34103. I-75 exit 107, 3.8 mi w on Pine Ridge Rd (CR 896) to US 41 (Tamiami Tr), then 0.9 mi s. Int corridors. **Pets:** Accepted. [&M] [➳] [⊚] [✕] [🛏] [▭]

NEW SMYRNA BEACH *(Restaurants p. 609)*

AAA **▼▼▼** Black Dolphin Inn **BB** ❀
(386) 410-4868. $159-$359, 5 day notice. 916 S Riverside Dr 32168. I-95 exit 249 (SR 44), 4.1 mi e to Riverside Dr, then 0.4 mi s. Ext/int corridors. **Pets:** Large. $50 one-time fee/room. Designated rooms.
[SAVE] [&M] [✕] [⊚] [✕] [🛏]

NORTH FORT MYERS

AAA **▼▼** Best Western Ft. Myers Waterfront **H**
(239) 997-5511. $120-$140. 13021 N Cleveland Ave 33903. On US 41, 0.6 mi s of SR 78A (Pondella Rd), jct N Bay Dr; at base of Caloosahatchee Bridge. Ext corridors. **Pets:** Dogs only. $35 one-time fee/room. Designated rooms, service with restrictions, supervision.
[SAVE] [♦] [&M] [➳] [✕] [⊚] [🛏] [▭]

OCALA

AAA **▼▼▼** Hampton Inn & Suites Ocala **H**
(352) 867-0300. $129-$219. 3601 SW 38th Ave 34474. I-75 exit 350, just w on SR 200 (SW College Rd), then just nw. Int corridors.
Pets: Accepted. [SAVE] [&M] [⊚] [✕] [🛏] [▭]

AAA **▼▼▼** Holiday Inn Express Midtown Medical **H**
(352) 629-7300. **Call for rates.** 1212 S Pine Ave 34474. 0.8 mi s on US 27, 301 and 441; just s of SR 200 (SW College Rd). Int corridors. **Pets:** Small. $25 daily fee/pet. Designated rooms, service with restrictions, supervision. [SAVE] [&M] [➳] [⊚] [✕] [🛏] [▭]

AAA **▼▼** Quality Inn Ocala **H**
(352) 854-3200. $92-$160. 3434 SW College Rd 34474. I-75 exit 350, 0.4 mi e on SR 200 (SW College Rd). Ext corridors. **Pets:** Medium. Designated rooms, service with restrictions, supervision.
[SAVE] [➳] [⊚] [🛏] [▭]

AAA **▼▼▼** Residence Inn by Marriott Ocala **H** ❀
(352) 547-1600. $119-$196. 3610 SW 38th Ave 34474. I-75 exit 350, just w on SR 200 (SW College Rd), then n. Int corridors. **Pets:** Large, other species. $75 one-time fee/room. Designated rooms, service with restrictions. [SAVE] [ECO] [➳] [⊚] [✕] [🛏] [▭]

▼▼ Sleep Inn & Suites **H**
(352) 347-8383. $82-$209. 13600 SW 17th Ct 34473. I-75 exit 341, just e on CR 484. Int corridors. **Pets:** Accepted.
[ECO] [⊚] [✕] [🛏] [▭]

OKEECHOBEE

AAA **▼◆** Best Western Lake Okeechobee **H**
(863) 357-7100. $90-$130. 3975 US Hwy 441 S 34974. US 98/441, 2.5 mi s of jct SR 70; 0.7 mi n of Lake Okeechobee and jct SR 78. Ext corridors. **Pets:** Accepted. [SAVE] [♦] [&M] [➳] [⊚] [🛏] [▭]

OLDSMAR

▼▼▼ Residence Inn by Marriott Tampa/Oldsmar Ⓗ
(813) 818-9400. **$118-$225.** 4012 Tampa Rd 34677. On SR 580, jct St. Petersburg Dr. Int corridors. **Pets:** Accepted.
[ECO] 🅼 ➔ 🛜 ☒ 🔌 🖥

ORLANDO *(Restaurants p. 609)*

◆◆ ▼▼▼ Aloft Orlando Downtown Ⓗ
(407) 380-3500. **$129-$450.** 500 S Orange Ave 32801. On SR 527 (Orange Ave), just s of Anderson St. Int corridors. **Pets:** Accepted.
[SAVE] 🍴 🅼 🛜 ☒ 🔌 🖥

◆◆ ▼▼▼ Best Western Orlando East Inn & Suites Ⓗ 🐾
(407) 282-3900. **$89-$149.** 8750 E Colonial Dr 32817. SR 417 exit 34 (Colonial Dr), just w. Ext corridors. **Pets:** Medium, dogs only. $20 daily fee/pet. Designated rooms, service with restrictions.
[SAVE] ➔ 🛜 🔌 🖥

◆◆ ▼▼▼ Best Western Orlando West Ⓗ
(407) 841-8600. **$95-$166.** 2014 W Colonial Dr 32804. I-4 exit 83A, just n to SR 50 (Colonial Dr), then 1.5 mi w. Int corridors. **Pets:** Small. $10 daily fee/pet. Designated rooms, service with restrictions, supervision.
[SAVE] 🍴 ➔ 🛜 🔌 🖥

◆◆ ▼▼ ▼▼ Castle Hotel Orlando, Autograph Collection Ⓗ
(407) 345-1511. **$79-$261.** 8629 International Dr 32819. I-4 exit 74A (Sand Lake Rd), 0.5 mi e to International Dr, then 0.5 mi s. Int corridors. **Pets:** Accepted. [SAVE] 🍴 🅼 ➔ ☒ 🛜 ☒ 🔌 🖥

◆◆ ▼▼▼ Days Inn Orlando Airport Florida Mall Ⓗ
(407) 855-0308. **$58-$101.** 9301 S Orange Blossom Tr 32837. SR 528 (Beachline Expwy) exit 4, then just s on US 17-92/441. Ext corridors. **Pets:** Medium. $15 daily fee/pet. Service with restrictions, supervision.
[SAVE] 🍴 ➔ 🛜 🔌 🖥

◆◆ ▼▼▼ DoubleTree by Hilton Orlando at SeaWorld Ⓗ
(407) 352-1100. **$89-$199.** 10100 International Dr 32821. I-4 exit 72, 0.5 mi e on SR 528 (Beachline Expwy) exit 1 (International Dr), just e. Ext/int corridors. **Pets:** Accepted.
[SAVE] [ECO] ⊂ 🍴 🅼 ➔ ☒ 🛜 ☒ 🔌 🖥

▼▼▼ Drury Inn & Suites-Orlando Ⓗ
(407) 354-1101. **$99-$209.** 7301 W Sand Lake Rd 32819. I-4 exit 74A (Sand Lake Rd), just w. Int corridors. **Pets:** Accepted.
🅼 ➔ 🛜 ☒ 🔌 🖥

◆◆ ▼▼▼ Floridays Resort Orlando Ⓗ 🐾
(407) 238-7700. **$150-$450, 3 day notice.** 12562 International Dr 32821. I-4 exit 72, 1.3 mi e on SR 528 exit 1, then 3.2 mi s. Ext corridors. **Pets:** Small. $200 one-time fee/room. Designated rooms, service with restrictions, crate.
[SAVE] [ECO] 🍴 🅼 ➔ ☒ 🐾 🔌 🖥

◆◆ ▼▼ ▼▼ The Grand Bohemian Hotel Orlando, Autograph Collection Ⓗ
(407) 313-9000. **$185-$339.** 325 S Orange Ave 32801. I-4 exit 82B, just e on South St to Orange Ave, then just s. Int corridors. **Pets:** Accepted.
[SAVE] [ECO] 🍴 🅼 ➔ ☒ 🛜 ☒ 🖥

◆◆ ▼▼▼▼ Hard Rock Hotel® at Universal Orlando Ⓗ 🐾
(407) 503-2000. **$289-$499, 5 day notice.** 5800 Universal Blvd 32819. I-4 exit 74B; exit 75A eastbound, 1.3 mi n to Vineland Rd, just w to Universal Blvd, then just s. Int corridors. **Pets:** Other species. $50 daily fee/room. Designated rooms, service with restrictions.
[SAVE] [ECO] 🍴 🅼 ➔ ☒ 🛜 ☒ 🔌 🖥

◆◆ ▼▼▼ Holiday Inn & Suites-Across from Universal Orlando Ⓗ
(407) 351-3333. **$89-$169.** 5905 S Kirkman Rd 32819. I-4 exit 75B, 0.9 mi n on SR 435 (Kirkman Rd). Int corridors. **Pets:** Accepted.
[SAVE] 🍴 🅼 ➔ 🛜 🔌 🖥

▼▼▼ Home2 Suites by Hilton Orlando International Drive South Ⓗ
(407) 944-1705. **$89-$229.** 12107 Regency Village Dr 32821. I-4 exit 68, 1.6 mi n on Vineland Ave (SR 535), then 0.4 mi w. Int corridors.
Pets: Accepted. 🅼 🛜 ☒ 🖥

▼▼▼ Homewood Suites by Hilton-Orlando Airport at Gateway Village Ⓗ
(407) 857-5791. **$109-$289.** 5425 Gateway Village Cir 32812. SR 528 exit 11 (Semoran Blvd/SR 436), just n. Int corridors. **Pets:** Accepted.
🅼 🛜 🔌 🖥

◆◆ ▼▼▼ Hyatt Place Orlando Airport Ⓗ
(407) 816-7800. **$79-$269.** 5435 Forbes Pl 32812. SR 528 (Beachline Expwy) exit 11 (Semoran Blvd/SR 436), 1.1 mi n to Frontage Rd, then just w. Int corridors. **Pets:** Accepted.
[SAVE] 🅼 ➔ 🛜 ☒ 🔌 🖥

◆◆ ▼▼▼ Hyatt Place Orlando/Convention Center Ⓗ
(407) 370-4720. **$89-$429.** 8741 International Dr 32819. I-4 exit 74A (Sand Lake Rd), just e to International Dr, then 0.8 mi s. Int corridors.
Pets: Accepted. [SAVE] 🅼 ➔ 🛜 ☒ 🔌 🖥

◆◆ ▼▼▼ Hyatt Place Orlando/Universal Ⓗ
(407) 351-0627. **$99-$259.** 5895 Caravan Ct 32819. I-4 exit 75B, 0.6 mi n to Major Blvd, just e to Caravan Ct, then just s. Int corridors.
Pets: Accepted. [SAVE] 🅼 ➔ 🛜 ☒ 🔌 🖥

◆◆ ▼▼ ▼▼ Hyatt Regency Orlando Ⓗ 🐾
(407) 352-4000. **$119-$549, 3 day notice.** 9801 International Dr 32819. I-4 exit 72 (SR 528), 1.1 mi e to exit 1 (International Dr), then 1 mi nw. Int corridors. **Pets:** Medium, dogs only. $150 one-time fee/room. Service with restrictions, crate.
[SAVE] [ECO] ⊂ 🍴 🅼 ➔ ☒ 🐾 ☒ 🔌 🖥

▼▼ La Quinta Inn & Suites-Orlando Convention Center Ⓗ
(407) 345-1365. **$82-$246.** 8504 Universal Blvd 32819. I-4 exit 74A (Sand Lake Rd), 0.5 mi e to Universal Blvd, then 0.5 mi s. Int corridors.
Pets: Accepted. 🅼 ➔ 🛜 🔌 🖥

◆◆ ▼▼▼ La Quinta Inn-Orlando International Drive North Ⓗ
(407) 351-4100. **$71-$214.** 5825 International Dr 32819. I-4 exit 75A, 0.6 mi s to International Dr, then just w. Int corridors. **Pets:** Accepted.
[SAVE] ➔ 🛜 ☒ 🔌 🖥

◆◆ ▼▼▼ Loews Portofino Bay Hotel at Universal Orlando® Ⓗ
(407) 503-1000. **$314-$519, 5 day notice.** 5601 Universal Blvd 32819. I-4 exit 74B westbound; exit 75A eastbound, 1 mi n. Int corridors.
Pets: Accepted. [SAVE] [ECO] 🍴 🅼 ➔ ☒ 🛜 ☒ 🔌 🖥

◆◆ ▼▼▼ Loews Royal Pacific Resort at Universal Orlando® Ⓗ
(407) 503-3000. **$254-$449, 5 day notice.** 6300 Hollywood Way 32819. I-4 exit 74A, just w to Turkey Lake Rd, 1.3 mi n to Hollywood Way, then just e. Int corridors. **Pets:** Accepted.
[SAVE] [ECO] 🍴 ➔ ☒ 🛜 ☒ 🔌 🖥

◆◆ ▼▼▼ Red Roof Inn Orlando Convention Center Ⓜ
(407) 352-1507. **$50-$130.** 9922 Hawaiian Ct 32819. SR 528 (Beachline Expwy) exit 1 (International Dr), 0.5 mi n to Hawaiian Ct, then just s. Ext corridors. **Pets:** Accepted. [SAVE] 🅼 ➔ 🛜 ☒ 🔌 🖥

Residence Inn by Marriott-Orlando at SeaWorld H
(407) 313-3600. **$97-$218, 7 day notice.** 11000 Westwood Blvd 32821. I-4 exit 71, just e on Central Florida Pkwy, then just s. Int corridors.
Pets: Accepted. [SAVE] [⊤] [&M] [🌊] [✕] [🛰] [✕] [🔌] [🖥]

Residence Inn by Marriott-Orlando Convention Center H
(407) 226-0288. **$99-$230.** 8800 Universal Blvd 32819. I-4 exit 74A (Sand Lake Rd), 0.5 mi e to Universal Blvd, then 0.9 mi s. Int corridors.
Pets: Accepted. [SAVE] [&M] [🌊] [🛰] [✕] [🔌] [🖥]

Residence Inn by Marriott Orlando Downtown H
(407) 482-1500. **$147-$265.** 680 N Orange Ave 32801. I-4 exit 83A, just n to US 92/SR 50, just e to Orange Ave, then just s. Int corridors.
Pets: Large, other species. $100 one-time fee/room. Service with restrictions, crate. [&M] [🛰] [✕]

Residence Inn by Marriott-Orlando East/UCF Area H
(407) 513-9000. **$170-$227.** 11651 University Blvd 32817. SR 417 exit 37A (University Blvd), 1.9 mi e. Int corridors. **Pets:** Accepted.
[🌊] [🛰] [✕] [🔌] [🖥]

Residence Inn by Marriott-Orlando International Airport H
(407) 856-2444. **$98-$190.** 7024 Augusta National Dr 32822. SR 528 (Beachline Expwy) exit 11 (Semoran Blvd/SR 436), 1.2 mi n to Hazeltine Dr, just e to Augusta National Dr, then just s. Int corridors.
Pets: Accepted. [SAVE] [&M] [🌊] [🛰] [✕] [🔌] [🖥]

The Ritz-Carlton Orlando, Grande Lakes H
(407) 206-2400. **Call for rates.** 4012 Central Florida Pkwy 32837. I-4 exit 71, 2.8 mi e. Int corridors. **Pets:** Accepted.
[SAVE] [ECO] [⊂] [⊤] [🌊] [✕] [🛰] [🖥]

Rosen Inn H
(407) 996-4444. **$60-$150.** 6327 International Dr 32819. I-4 exit 74A (Sand Lake Rd), just e to International Dr, then 0.7 mi n. Ext/int corridors. **Pets:** Accepted. [SAVE] [⊤] [&M] [🌊] [🛰] [✕] [🔌] [🖥]

Rosen Inn at Pointe Orlando H ❧
(407) 996-8585. **$69-$159.** 9000 International Dr 32819. I-4 exit 74A (Sand Lake Rd), just e to International Dr, then 1.1 mi s. Ext corridors. **Pets:** Medium. $15 daily fee/pet. Designated rooms, service with restrictions, crate. [SAVE] [⊤] [&M] [🌊] [🛰] [✕] [🖥]

Rosen Inn International H ❧
(407) 996-1600. **$55-$129.** 7600 International Dr 32819. I-4 exit 74A (Sand Lake Rd), just e to International Dr, then just n. Ext corridors. **Pets:** Medium, other species. $15 daily fee/pet. Service with restrictions, supervision. [SAVE] [⊤] [&M] [🌊] [🛰] [✕] [✕] [🔌] [🖥]

Rosen Plaza Hotel H
(407) 996-9700. **Call for rates.** 9700 International Dr 32819. I-4 exit 74A (Sand Lake Rd), just e to International Dr, then 1.5 mi s. Int corridors. **Pets:** Other species. $100 deposit/room, $150 one-time fee/room. Designated rooms, service with restrictions, crate.
[ECO] [⊤] [&M] [🌊] [🛰] [✕] [🔌] [🖥]

Rosen Shingle Creek H
(407) 996-9939. **Call for rates.** 9939 Universal Blvd 32819. I-4 exit 72 (SR 528), 1.7 mi e to exit 2 (Orangewood Blvd), then 0.5 mi n. Int corridors. **Pets:** Accepted.
[SAVE] [ECO] [⊤] [&M] [🌊] [✕] [🛰] [✕] [🔌] [🖥]

Sheraton Suites Orlando Airport H ❧
(407) 240-5555. **Call for rates.** 7550 Augusta National Dr 32822. SR 528 (Beachline Expwy) exit 11 (Semoran Blvd/SR 436), 1 mi n to T.G. Lee Blvd, just e to Augusta National Dr, then just s. Int corridors. **Pets:** Medium, dogs only. Designated rooms, service with restrictions, supervision. [SAVE] [ECO] [⊤] [&M] [🌊] [🛰] [✕] [🖥]

Staybridge Suites Orlando Airport South H
(407) 438-2121. **Call for rates.** 7450 Augusta National Dr 32822. SR 528 (Beachline Expwy) exit 11 (Semoran Blvd), 1 mi n to T.G. Lee Blvd, just e to Augusta National Dr, then just s. Int corridors.
Pets: Accepted. [ECO] [&M] [🌊] [🛰] [✕] [🔌] [🖥]

TownePlace Suites by Marriott-Orlando East/UCF Area H
(407) 243-6100. **$119-$177.** 11801 High Tech Ave 32817. SR 417 exit 37A (University Blvd), 2 mi e to Quadrangle Blvd, just n to High Tech Ave, then just e. Int corridors. **Pets:** Accepted.
[🌊] [🛰] [✕] [🔌] [🖥]

Villas Of Grand Cypress Golf Resort H
(407) 239-4700. **Call for rates.** 1 N Jacaranda St 32836. I-4 exit 68, 0.8 mi n on SR 535, 1.6 mi w on Winter Garden Vineland Rd. Ext corridors. **Pets:** Accepted. [SAVE] [ECO] [⊤] [🌊] [✕] [🛰] [✕] [🔌] [🖥]

Vista Cay Resort by Millenium H
(407) 313-6501. **$129-$249, 3 day notice.** 4874 Cayview Ave 32819. I-4 exit 74A (Sand Lake Rd), 0.5 mi e to Universal Blvd, then 2.3 mi se. Ext/int corridors. **Pets:** Accepted. [SAVE] [✕] [🛰] [✕] [🔌] [🖥]

Westgate Lakes Resort & Spa H
(407) 345-0000. **Call for rates.** 10000 Turkey Lake Rd 32819. I-4 exit 74A (Sand Lake Rd), 1.1 mi s to Sand Lake Rd, just w to Turkey Lake Rd, then 2.1 mi s. Ext/int corridors. **Pets:** Accepted.
[SAVE] [⊂] [⊤] [🌊] [✕] [🛰] [✕] [🔌] [🖥]

Westgate Palace Resort H
(407) 996-6000. **Call for rates.** 6145 Carrier Dr 32819. I-4 exit 74A, 0.3 mi e to International Dr, 0.4 mi n to Carrier Dr, then just e. Int corridors. **Pets:** Accepted. [⊤] [&M] [🌊] [✕] [🛰] [✕] [🔌] [🖥]

Wyndham Orlando Resort International Drive H
(407) 351-2420. **$79-$250, 3 day notice.** 8001 International Dr 32819. I-4 exit 74A (Sand Lake Rd), just e. Ext/int corridors. **Pets:** Accepted.
[SAVE] [⊤] [&M] [🌊] [✕] [🛰] [✕] [🔌] [🖥]

ORMOND BEACH

Hampton Inn Daytona-Ormond Beach H
(386) 677-9999. **$129-$159.** 155 Interchange Blvd 32174. I-95 exit 268 (SR 40/Granada Blvd), just w to Interchange Blvd, then just s. Int corridors. **Pets:** Accepted. [SAVE] [&M] [🌊] [🛰] [✕] [🔌] [🖥]

Howard Johnson Ormond Beach at Destination Daytona H
(386) 944-1500. **$89-$500, 3 day notice.** 1635 N US Hwy 1 32174. I-95 exit 273 (US 1), just nw. Ext/int corridors. **Pets:** Accepted.
[SAVE] [🌊] [🛰] [✕] [🔌] [🖥]

PALM BAY

Holiday Inn Express Hotel & Suites Palm Bay H
(321) 220-2003. **$100-$249.** 1206 SE Malabar Rd 32907. I-95 exit 173 (Malabar Rd), just e; behind Sunoco gas station. Int corridors.
Pets: Small. $20 daily fee/pet. Designated rooms, service with restrictions, crate. [SAVE] [&M] [🌊] [🛰] [✕] [🔌] [🖥]

Quality Inn Palm Bay H
(321) 725-2952. **$79-$149.** 890 Palm Bay Rd NE 32905. I-95 exit 176 (Palm Bay Rd NE), 0.5 mi e. Int corridors. **Pets:** Accepted.
[🌊] [🛰] [🔌] [🖥]

PALM BEACH *(Restaurants p. 609)*

The Brazilian Court H
(561) 655-7740. **Call for rates.** 301 Australian Ave 33480. From Royal Palm Way, just s on Cocoanut Row, then just e; corner of Hibiscus and Australian aves. Int corridors. **Pets:** Accepted.
[SAVE] [⊤] [&M] [🌊] [✕] [🛰] [✕] [🔌]

The Chesterfield Hotel Palm Beach H ❖
(561) 659-5800. **$185-$1235, 7 day notice.** 363 Cocoanut Row 33480. Jct Australian Ave and Cocoanut Row; 2 blks n of Worth Ave. Int corridors. **Pets:** Medium. $90 one-time fee/pet. Supervision.

The Colony Palm Beach H
(561) 655-5430. **Call for rates.** 155 Hammon Ave 33480. 1 blk s of Worth Ave; between S County Rd and SR A1A (Ocean Blvd). Int corridors. **Pets:** Accepted.

Four Seasons Resort Palm Beach H
(561) 582-2800. **$249-$1249, 14 day notice.** 2800 S Ocean Blvd 33480. On SR A1A (Ocean Blvd), 0.5 mi n of SR 802 (Lake Ave). Int corridors. **Pets:** Accepted.

Palm Beach Historic Inn BB ❖
(561) 832-4009. **$119-$499, 8 day notice.** 365 S County Rd 33480. Jct S County Rd and Chilian Ave, just n of Worth Ave. Int corridors. **Pets:** Other species. $75 one-time fee/pet. Designated rooms, service with restrictions.

Tideline Ocean Resort & Spa-Palm Beach, A Kimpton Hotel H
(561) 540-6440. **Call for rates.** 2842 S Ocean Blvd 33480. On SR A1A (Ocean Blvd), 0.4 mi n of SR 802 (Lake Ave). Int corridors. **Pets:** Accepted.

PALM BEACH GARDENS

Homewood Suites by Hilton-Palm Beach Gardens H
(561) 622-7799. **$119-$319.** 4700 Donald Ross Rd 33418. I-95 exit 83 (Donald Ross Rd), 1.1 mi e; in Donald Ross Village. Int corridors. **Pets:** Accepted.

PGA National Resort & Spa H
(561) 627-2000. **$179-$599, 3 day notice.** 400 Ave of the Champions 33418. I-95 exit 79B (PGA Blvd), 2 mi w; Florida Tpke exit 109, just w. Int corridors. **Pets:** Medium. $150 one-time fee/pet. Designated rooms, service with restrictions, crate.

PALM COAST

Days Inn Palm Coast H
(386) 627-7734. **$69-$149.** 120 Garden St N 32137. I-95 exit 289 (Palm Coast Pkwy), just w to Boulder Rock Dr, just n to Plaza Dr, then just e. Int corridors. **Pets:** $25 one-time fee/pet. Designated rooms, service with restrictions.

Econo Lodge M
(386) 446-4457. **$65-$150.** 5 Kingswood Dr 32137. I-95 exit 289 (Palm Coast Pkwy), just e to Kingswood Dr, then just s; in Kingswood Center. Ext corridors. **Pets:** Medium. $10 daily fee/pet. Service with restrictions, supervision.

Fairfield Inn & Suites by Marriott Palm Coast I-95 H
(386) 445-3450. **$82-$115.** 400 Old Kings Rd N 32137. I-95 exit 289 (Palm Coast Pkwy), just e Kingswood Dr, then 0.3 mi s. Int corridors. **Pets:** Other species. $25 one-time fee/pet. Designated rooms, service with restrictions, crate.

Holiday Inn Express Hotel & Suites Palm Coast-Flagler Beach Area H
(386) 439-3939. **Call for rates.** 200 Flagler Plaza Dr 32137. I-95 exit 284 (SR 100), just e. Int corridors. **Pets:** Accepted.

Red Roof Inn-Palm Coast H
(386) 446-8180. **$60-$249.** 10 Kingswood Dr 32137. I-95 exit 289 (Palm Coast Pkwy), just e to Kingswood Dr, then just sw; in Kingswood Center. Int corridors. **Pets:** Accepted.

PANAMA CITY

La Quinta Inn & Suites H
(850) 914-0022. **$67-$251.** 1030 E 23rd St 32405. On SR 368 (23rd St), jct US 231. Int corridors. **Pets:** Accepted.

Red Roof Inn-Panama City H
(850) 215-2727. **$59-$199, 3 day notice.** 217 Hwy 231 32405. On US 231, just ne of jct US 98. Ext/int corridors. **Pets:** Accepted.

Super 8-Panama City M
(850) 784-1988. **$52-$125.** 207 Hwy 231 32405. On US 231, just ne of jct US 98. Ext/int corridors. **Pets:** Small, dogs only. $15 daily fee/pet. Designated rooms, service with restrictions, crate.

TownePlace Suites by Marriott Panama City H
(850) 747-0609. **$104-$197.** 903 E 23rd Pl 32405. Just e of jct SR 77, w of jct US 231 on SR 368 (23rd St), then n on Palo Alto Ave. Int corridors. **Pets:** Accepted.

PANAMA CITY BEACH *(Restaurants p. 609)*

Hawthorn Suites by Wyndham H
(850) 233-7829. **$68-$165.** 7909 Panama City Beach Pkwy 32407. Jct US 98 and SR 30. Int corridors. **Pets:** Accepted.

PENSACOLA *(Restaurants p. 609)*

Hyatt Place Pensacola Airport H
(850) 483-5599. **$109-$239.** 161 Airport Ln 32504. I-110 exit 5, 2.7 mi e on SR 750, just n on 12th Ave, then just e. Int corridors. **Pets:** Accepted.

TownePlace Suites by Marriott Pensacola H
(850) 484-7022. **$101-$177.** 481 Creighton Rd 32504. I-10 exit 13, 0.3 mi s on SR 291, then just w. Int corridors. **Pets:** Accepted.

PLANTATION

Extended Stay America-Fort Lauderdale-Plantation H
(954) 382-8888. **$95-$160.** 7755 SW 6th St 33324. I-595 exit 5 (University Dr), 1.2 mi w to University Dr, 1 mi n to SW 6th St, then just w. Int corridors. **Pets:** Accepted.

La Quinta Inn & Suites Ft. Lauderdale Plantation at SW 6th St H
(954) 473-8257. **$93-$246.** 7901 SW 6th St 33324. I-595 exit 5 (University Dr), 1.2 mi w to University Dr, 1 mi n to SW 6th St, then 0.3 mi w; in Wellesley Corporate Plaza. Int corridors. **Pets:** Accepted.

Residence Inn by Marriott-Fort Lauderdale Plantation H
(954) 723-0300. **$103-$223.** 130 N University Dr 33324. I-95 exit 27 (Broward Blvd), 5.2 mi w to University Dr, then just n. Int corridors. **Pets:** Accepted.

Sheraton Suites Plantation/Ft. Lauderdale West H ❖
(954) 424-3300. **$89-$309.** 311 N University Dr 33324. I-595 exit 5, 1.2 mi w to University Dr, then 1.8 mi n. Int corridors. **Pets:** Medium, dogs only. Designated rooms, service with restrictions, supervision.

▼▼▼ **Staybridge Suites-Ft. Lauderdale/Plantation** H
(954) 577-9696. **Call for rates.** 410 N Pine Island Rd 33324. I-595 exit
4 (Pine Island Rd), 1.7 mi n. Int corridors. **Pets:** Accepted.
🔳M 🛥 🛜 ✕ 🔋 🖥

POMPANO BEACH
▼▼▼ **Residence Inn by Marriott Fort Lauderdale
Pompano Beach/Oceanfront** H
(954) 590-1000. **$161-$365.** 1350 N Ocean Blvd 33062. I-95 exit 36
(Atlantic Blvd), 3.1 mi e to Ocean Blvd (SR A1A), then 1.3 mi n. Ext/int
corridors. **Pets:** Accepted. 🍽 🔳M 🛥 ✕ 🛜 ✕ 🔋 🖥

PORT CHARLOTTE
▼▼▼ **Country Inn & Suites By Carlson** H
(941) 235-1035. **$80-$280.** 24244 Corporate Ct 33954. I-75 exit 170,
just w on CR 769 (Kings Hwy). Int corridors. **Pets:** Accepted.
🔳M 🛥 🛜 🔋 🖥

▼▼ **Days Inn of Port Charlotte** H
(941) 627-8900. **$69-$170.** 1941 Tamiami Tr 33948. On US 41, 2.3 mi
s of jct Toledo Blade Blvd (CR 779). Ext corridors. **Pets:** Small, dogs
only. $10 daily fee/pet. Designated rooms, service with restrictions,
supervision. 🍽 🛥 🛜 ✕ 🔋 🖥

🌐 ▼▼▼ **La Quinta Inn & Suites Port Charlotte** H
(941) 979-4200. **$82-$235.** 812 Kings Hwy 33980. I-75 exit 170, just w
on CR 769 (Kings Hwy), then just s on Veterans Blvd. Int corridors.
Pets: Accepted. SAVE 🔳M 🛥 🛜 ✕ 🔋 🖥

🌐 ▼▼ **Microtel Inn & Suites By Wyndham** H
(941) 624-6339. **$71-$169.** 4056 Tamiami Tr 33952. On US 41; jct
Gardner Dr. Int corridors. **Pets:** Accepted. SAVE 🔳M 🛜 🔋 🖥

PORT ORANGE
▼▼▼ **Country Inn & Suites By Carlson, Port
Orange-Daytona** H
(386) 760-0101. **$99-$599.** 5802 Journey's End Way 32127. I-95 exit
256, just e. Int corridors. **Pets:** Large. $50 one-time fee/room. Service
with restrictions, supervision. 🔳M 🛥 🛜 ✕ 🔋 🖥

▼▼▼ **La Quinta Inn & Suites-Port Orange/Daytona** H
(386) 756-3440. **$75-$455.** 1791 Dunlawton Ave 32129. I-95 exit 256,
just e. Int corridors. **Pets:** Accepted. 🔳M 🛥 🛜 ✕ 🔋 🖥

PORT RICHEY
▼▼▼ **Homewood Suites by Hilton Tampa/Port
Richey** H
(727) 819-1000. **$99-$159.** 11115 US 19 N 34668. 0.9 mi s of SR 52 at
jct Hammock/Ranch Rd. Int corridors. **Pets:** Accepted.
🔳M 🛥 🛜 ✕ 🔋 🖥

PORT ST. LUCIE *(Restaurants p. 610)*
▼▼▼ **Holiday Inn-Port St Lucie** H
(772) 337-2200. **Call for rates.** 10120 S Federal Hwy 34952. On US 1,
0.6 mi n of jct SR 716 (Port St Lucie Blvd). Int corridors.
Pets: Accepted. ECO 🍽 🔳M 🛥 ✕ 🛜 ✕ 🔋 🖥

▼▼▼ **Homewood Suites by Hilton Port St.
Lucie-Tradition** H
(772) 345-5300. **$109-$269.** 10301 SW Innovation Way 34987. I-95 exit
118 (Gatlin Blvd), 0.5 mi w to Village Pkwy, then just s. Int corridors.
Pets: Accepted. 🍽 🔳M 🛥 🛜 🔋 🖥

🌐 ▼▼▼ **Residence Inn by Marriott-Port St.
Lucie** H 🌸
(772) 344-7814. **$86-$201.** 1920 SW Fountainview Blvd 34986. I-95 exit
121 (St. Lucie West Blvd), just e to Paramount Dr, just s to SW Fountainview Blvd, then just sw. Int corridors. **Pets:** Other species. $100
one-time fee/room. Service with restrictions, crate.
SAVE 🔳M 🛥 🛜 ✕ 🔋 🖥

▼▼ **Sleep Inn & MainStay Suites at PGA Village** H
(772) 460-8882. **$81-$100.** 8501 Champions Way 34986. I-95 exit 121
(St. Lucie West Blvd), just w. Int corridors. **Pets:** Accepted.
🔳M 🛥 🛜 ✕ 🔋 🖥

PUNTA GORDA
🌐 ▼▼▼ **Four Points by Sheraton Punta Gorda
Harborside** H
(941) 637-6770. **$100-$300.** 33 Tamiami Tr 33950. On US 41; at Peace
River Bridge. Int corridors. **Pets:** Accepted.
SAVE 🍽 🔳M 🛥 ✕ 🛜 ✕ 🔋 🖥

QUINCY *(Restaurants p. 610)*
▼▼▼ **Allison House Inn** BB
(850) 875-2511. **$85-$250, 14 day notice.** 215 N Madison St 32351.
Just n of town center; in historic district. Int corridors. **Pets:** Small, dogs
only. Designated rooms, service with restrictions, crate.
🍽 🛜 ✕ 🛡

ST. AUGUSTINE *(Restaurants p. 610)*
▼▼▼ **Bayfront Marin House** BB
(904) 824-4301. **Call for rates.** 142 Avenida Menendez 32084. 1 blk s
of Bridge of Lions. Ext corridors. **Pets:** Dogs only. $35 daily fee/pet.
Designated rooms, service with restrictions. 🛜 ✕

🌐 ▼▼▼ **Best Western Bayfront Inn** M
(904) 824-4482. **$119-$399.** 16 Avenida Menendez 32084. I-95 exit 318
(SR 16), 5.5 mi e to San Marco Ave, then 1.7 mi s; in historic district.
Ext corridors. **Pets:** Large, other species. $30 daily fee/pet. Service with
restrictions, supervision. SAVE 🛥 🛜 ✕ 🔋 🖥

🌐 ▼▼▼ **Best Western St. Augustine I-95** M
(904) 829-1999. **$69-$130.** 2445 SR 16 32092. I-95 exit 318 (SR 16),
just w. Ext corridors. **Pets:** Accepted. SAVE 🛥 🛜 ✕ 🖥

🌐 ▼▼▼ **Casa Monica Resort & Spa, Autograph
Collection** H
(904) 827-1888. **$186-$432, 3 day notice.** 95 Cordova St 32084. Downtown; in historic district. Int corridors. **Pets:** Accepted.
SAVE ECO 🍽 🛥 ✕ 🛜 ✕ 🔋 🖥

▼▼▼ **Peace and Plenty Inn** BB
(904) 829-8209. **$149-$249, 7 day notice.** 87 Cedar St 32084. From
King St, just s on Granada St, then just w. Ext/int corridors. **Pets:** Dogs
only. $35 one-time fee/pet. Designated rooms, service with restrictions,
supervision. 🛜 ✕ 🛡 🔋 🖥

ST. AUGUSTINE BEACH
🌐 ▼▼▼ **House of Sea and Sun** BB
(904) 461-1716. **Call for rates.** 2 B St 32080. Jct SR 312 and A1A, 1.9
mi s to B St, then just e. Ext/int corridors. **Pets:** Other species. Service
with restrictions. SAVE 🛜 ✕ 🛡 🔋

ST. CLOUD
🌐 ▼▼ **Budget Inn of St Cloud** M
(407) 892-2858. **$45-$125, 3 day notice.** 602 13th St 34769. On US
192/441, 0.5 mi e of the Water Tower, 2 mi w of jct CR 15. Ext corridors. **Pets:** Very small, dogs only. $10 daily fee/pet.
SAVE 🛜 🔋 🖥

ST. PETE BEACH *(Restaurants p. 610)*
🌐 ▼▼▼ **Bay Palms Waterfront Resort 2** M 🌸
(727) 360-7642. **$79-$249, 7 day notice.** 4237 Gulf Blvd 33706. On SR
699, 0.6 mi n of Pinellas Bayway. Ext corridors. **Pets:** Medium, dogs
only. $50 deposit/pet, $25 daily fee/pet. Designated rooms, no service,
crate. SAVE ECO 🛥 🛜 ✕ 🔋

Bayview Plaza Waterfront Resort 1 M ❖
(727) 367-2791. **$79-$249, 7 day notice.** 4321 Gulf Blvd 33706. On SR 699, 0.6 mi n of Pinellas Bayway. Ext/int corridors. **Pets:** Medium, dogs only. $50 deposit/pet, $25 daily fee/pet. Designated rooms, no service, crate. SAVE ECO 〜 ✕ 🛜 ✕ 📞 ▭

Beach House Suites By Loews Don CeSar H ❖
(727) 363-5050. **$249-$539, 3 day notice.** 3860 Gulf Blvd 33706. On SR 699, 0.4 mi n of jct Pinellas Bayway. Ext corridors. **Pets:** Other species. $45 daily fee/room. Designated rooms, service with restrictions. SAVE 〜 🛜 ✕ 📞 ▭

The Kimpton Hotel Zamora H ❖
(727) 456-8900. **Call for rates.** 3701 Gulf Blvd 33706. On SR 699, jct 37th Ave. Int corridors. **Pets:** Other species. SAVE 〒 🍽 ✕ 🛜 ✕ 📞

Loews Don CeSar Hotel H
(727) 360-1881. **$199-$849, 3 day notice.** 3400 Gulf Blvd 33706. On SR 699, jct Pinellas Bayway. Int corridors. **Pets:** Accepted. SAVE ECO 🍽 ᕦM 〜 ✕ 🛜 ✕ 📞 ▭

TradeWinds Island Grand Beach Resort H ❖
(727) 367-6461. **$255-$684, 3 day notice.** 5500 Gulf Blvd 33706. On SR 699, 1 mi n of Pinellas Bayway. Ext/int corridors. **Pets:** Large, other species. $100 deposit/room, $30 daily fee/room. Designated rooms, service with restrictions.
SAVE ECO 🍽 ᕦM 〜 ✕ 🛜 ✕ 📞 ▭

ST. PETERSBURG *(Restaurants p. 610)*

Staybridge Suites Downtown St Petersburg H
(727) 821-0777. **$129-$499.** 940 5th Ave S 33705. I-275 exit 22, 0.4 mi se on US 175, jct Dr Martin Luther King Jr St. Int corridors.
Pets: Accepted. SAVE 🍽 ᕦM 🛜 ✕ 📞 ▭

SANFORD *(Restaurants p. 610)*

Best Western Plus Sanford Airport/Lake Mary H
(407) 320-0845. **$99-$209.** 3401 S Orlando Dr 32773. I-4 exit 98, 4.5 mi e to US 17-92, then 0.7 mi n. Int corridors. **Pets:** Accepted.
SAVE ᕦM 〜 🛜 ✕ 📞 ▭

SARASOTA *(Restaurants p. 610)*

Aloft Hotel Sarasota H ❖
(941) 870-0900. **$109-$479.** 1401 Ringling Blvd 34236. Jct Palm Ave; downtown. Int corridors. **Pets:** Small, dogs only. Service with restrictions, supervision. SAVE ᕦM ✕ 🛜 ✕ 📞 ▭

Comfort Suites-Sarasota H
(941) 554-4475. **$89-$218.** 5690 Honore Ave 34233. I-75 exit 205, 1.2 mi w on SR 72 (Clark Rd), just n. Int corridors. **Pets:** Accepted.
ᕦM 🛜 ✕ 📞 ▭

Hampton Inn & Suites Sarasota Bradenton Airport H
(941) 355-8140. **$109-$299.** 975 University Pkwy 34234. Just e of jct US 41 (N Tamiami Tr). Int corridors. **Pets:** Accepted.
ᕦM 🛜 ✕ 📞 ▭

Holiday Inn Express & Suites Sarasota East I-75 H
(941) 925-0631. **$89-$349.** 5730 Gantt Rd 34233. I-75 exit 205, 0.3 mi w on SR 72 (Clark Rd), then just n on Hospitality Way. Int corridors. **Pets:** Medium. $25 daily fee/room. Service with restrictions, supervision.
ECO ᕦM 〜 🛜 ✕ 📞 ▭

Holiday Inn Lido Beach H
(941) 388-5555. **$179-$499.** 233 Ben Franklin Dr 34236. On Lido Key at Lido Beach; 0.4 mi s of St. Armands Circle. Int corridors.
Pets: Small, dogs only. $75 one-time fee/pet. Service with restrictions.
SAVE ECO 🍽 〜 🛜 ✕ 📞 ▭

Hotel Indigo Sarasota H
(941) 487-3800. **Call for rates.** 1223 Boulevard of the Arts 34236. Jct US 41 (N Tamiami Tr). Int corridors. **Pets:** Accepted.
🍽 ᕦM ✕ 🛜 ✕ 📞 ▭

Hyatt Place Sarasota/Bradenton Airport H
(941) 554-5800. **$89-$239.** 950 University Pkwy 34234. Just e of US 41 (Tamiami Tr), jct Airport Cir. Int corridors. **Pets:** Accepted.
SAVE ECO 🍽 ᕦM 〜 🛜 ✕ 📞 ▭

Hyatt Regency Sarasota H
(941) 953-1234. **$119-$429, 3 day notice.** 1000 Boulevard of the Arts 34236. Just w of jct US 41 (Tamiami Tr). Int corridors. **Pets:** Accepted.
SAVE ECO 🍽 ᕦM ✕ 🛜 ✕ 📞 ▭

Lido Beach Resort H ❖
(941) 388-2161. **$189-$999.** 700 Ben Franklin Dr 34236. On Lido Key at Lido Beach; 0.8 mi s of St. Armands Circle. Ext/int corridors.
Pets: Medium, dogs only. $75 daily fee/pet. Service with restrictions, supervision. SAVE ECO 🍽 ᕦM 〜 ✕ 🛜 ✕ 📞 ▭

Residence Inn by Marriott Sarasota-Bradenton H ❖
(941) 358-1468. **$120-$307.** 1040 University Pkwy 34234. Just e of jct US 41 (Tamiami Tr). Int corridors. **Pets:** Other species. $75 one-time fee/room. Service with restrictions. ECO ᕦM 〜 🛜 ✕ 📞 ▭

The Ritz-Carlton, Sarasota H
(941) 309-2000. **$249-$759, 5 day notice.** 1111 Ritz-Carlton Dr 34236. On US 41, jct John Ringling Blvd. Int corridors. **Pets:** Accepted.
SAVE ECO 🍽 〜 ✕ 🛜 ✕ 📞 ▭

SEBASTIAN

Best Western Plus Sebastian Hotel & Suites H
(772) 388-9300. **$139-$169, 3 day notice.** 1655 US Hwy 1 32958. I-95 exit 156 (Fellsmere Rd/CR 512), 6.5 mi e to US 1, then 1.2 mi n. Int corridors. **Pets:** Accepted. SAVE ᕦM 〜 🛜 ✕ 📞 ▭

SEBRING

Château Élan Hotel & Conference Center H
(863) 655-7200. **$95-$460.** 150 Midway Dr 33870. Jct US 98, 1.4 mi n on Haywood Taylor Blvd; at entrance to Sebring International Raceway.
Int corridors. **Pets:** Accepted. ECO 🍽 ᕦM 〜 🛜 ✕ 📞 ▭

Holiday Inn Express & Suites Sebring H
(863) 386-1115. **Call for rates.** 4400 US Hwy 27 N 33870. Just n of Sebring Pkwy. Int corridors. **Pets:** Accepted.
ᕦM 〜 🛜 ✕ 📞 ▭

Inn On The Lakes H
(863) 471-9400. **Call for rates.** 3101 Golfview Rd 33875. On US 27/98, just s of jct Sebring Pkwy. Ext/int corridors. **Pets:** Accepted.
🍽 〜 🛜 ✕ 📞 ▭

La Quinta Inn & Suites Sebring H
(863) 386-1000. **$97-$504.** 4115 US Hwy 27 S 33870. On US 27/98, just n of jct Sebring Pkwy. Int corridors. **Pets:** Accepted.
SAVE 🍽 ᕦM 〜 🛜 ✕ 📞 ▭

Residence Inn by Marriott-Sebring H
(863) 314-9100. **$120-$197.** 3221 Tubbs Rd 33870. On US 27/98, 4.5 mi n of jct SR 98. Int corridors. **Pets:** Accepted.
SAVE ᕦM 〜 ✕ 🛜 ✕ 📞 ▭

SEFFNER

▼▼▼ Hampton Inn & Suites Tampa East 🅷
(813) 630-4321. **$109-$189.** 11740 Tampa Gateway Blvd 33584. I-4 exit 10, just n on CR 579, just e. Int corridors. **Pets:** Accepted.

SILVER SPRINGS

▼▼▼ Holiday Inn Express Hotel & Suites 🅷
(352) 304-6111. **$99-$149.** 5360 E Silver Springs Blvd 34488. On SR 40, just e of jct NE 25th St. Int corridors. **Pets:** Medium, other species. $25 daily fee/pet. Designated rooms, service with restrictions, supervision.

SPRING HILL

▼▼ Microtel Inn & Suites by Wyndham, Spring Hill 🅷
(352) 596-3444. **$60-$105.** 4881 Commercial Way 34606. On US 19, 1 mi s of jct Northcliffe Blvd and Frontage Rd. Int corridors. **Pets:** Accepted.

STARKE

AAA ▼▼ Best Western Starke Ⓜ
(904) 964-6744. **$99-$109.** 1290 N Temple Ave 32091. On US 301, 1 mi n from jct SR 100 (Reid St). Ext corridors. **Pets:** Medium. $15 daily fee/pet. Designated rooms, service with restrictions, supervision.

STUART

AAA ▼▼▼ Best Western Downtown Stuart 🅷
(772) 287-6200. **$79-$199.** 1209 SE Federal Hwy 34994. On US 1, 0.5 mi s of jct SR 76. Ext corridors. **Pets:** Accepted.

▼▼▼ Courtyard by Marriott-Stuart 🅷
(772) 781-3344. **$86-$235.** 7615 SW Lost River Rd 34997. I-95 exit 101 (SR 76), 0.7 mi e to SW Lost River Rd, then just nw. Int corridors. **Pets:** Accepted.

SUNNY ISLES BEACH *(Restaurants p. 610)*

AAA ▼▼▼▼ Acqualina Resort & Spa on the Beach 🅷
(305) 918-8000. **Call for rates.** 17875 Collins Ave 33160. I-95 exit 16 (Ives Dairy Rd), 1.2 mi e to US 1 (Biscayne Blvd), 0.6 mi s to William Lehman Cswy, 1.6 mi e to SR A1A (Collins Ave), then 0.8 mi s. Int corridors. **Pets:** Accepted.

AAA ▼▼▼ Newport Beachside Hotel & Resort 🅷 🐾
(305) 949-1300. **Call for rates.** 16701 Collins Ave 33160. I-95 exit 16 (Ives Dairy Rd), 1.1 mi e to US 1 (Biscayne Blvd), 0.6 mi s to William Lehman Cswy, 1.7 mi e to SR A1A (Collins Ave), then 1.6 mi s. Int corridors. **Pets:** Small. $50 one-time fee/pet. Service with restrictions.

SUNRISE

AAA ▼▼▼▼ DoubleTree by Hilton Sunrise-Sawgrass Mills 🅷
(954) 851-1020. **$109-$289.** 13400 W Sunrise Blvd 33323. Sawgrass Expwy (SR 869) exit 1 (Sunrise Blvd), 1 mi e. Int corridors.
Pets: Accepted.

▼▼ La Quinta Inn & Suites-Ft. Lauderdale Sunrise 🅷
(954) 845-9929. **$93-$240.** 13600 NW 2nd St 33325. I-595 exit 1A (SR 84), 0.5 mi w to NW 136th Ave, 0.4 mi n to NW 2nd St, then just w. Int corridors. **Pets:** Accepted.

▼▼▼ La Quinta Inn & Suites-Sunrise Sawgrass Mills Outlet Mall 🅷
(954) 846-1200. **$93-$240.** 13651 NW 2nd St 33325. I-595 exit 1A (SR 84), 0.5 mi w to NW 136th Ave, 0.4 mi n to NW 2nd St, then just w. Int corridors. **Pets:** Accepted.

TALLAHASSEE *(Restaurants p. 610)*

AAA ▼▼▼ Aloft Tallahassee Downtown 🅷 🐾
(850) 513-0313. **$119-$289.** 200 N Monroe St 32301. 0.4 mi n of Capitol. Int corridors. **Pets:** Other species. Designated rooms, service with restrictions, supervision.

AAA ▼▼▼ Best Western Downtown Ⓜ
(850) 656-6312. **$70-$319.** 2016 Apalachee Pkwy 32301. 1 mi se on US 27. Ext corridors. **Pets:** $20 daily fee/pet. Service with restrictions, crate.

▼▼ Extended Stay America Tallahassee-Killearn 🅷
(850) 383-1700. **$70-$105.** 1950 Raymond Diehl Rd 32308. I-10 exit 203, 2.4 mi s, then just n. Int corridors. **Pets:** Accepted.

AAA ▼▼▼ Four Points by Sheraton Tallahassee Downtown 🅷
(850) 422-0071. **$99-$599.** 316 W Tennessee St 32301. Just w of US 27; downtown. Int corridors. **Pets:** Accepted.

▼▼▼ Home2 Suites by Hilton Tallahassee State Capitol 🅷
(850) 402-8900. **Call for rates.** 210 S Magnolia Dr 32301. Jct US 319 and 90, 2.2 mi sw, then 0.5 mi s. Int corridors. **Pets:** Accepted.

▼▼▼ Homewood Suites by Hilton 🅷
(850) 402-9400. **$119-$199.** 2987 Apalachee Pkwy 32301. US 27, 3.5 mi s. Int corridors. **Pets:** Accepted.

▼▼ Quality Inn & Suites Ⓜ
(850) 656-2938. **Call for rates.** 6737 Mahan Dr 32308. I-10 exit 209A, just w on US 90. Ext corridors. **Pets:** Accepted.

AAA ▼▼ Quality Inn & Suites 🅷
(850) 877-4437. **$64-$575.** 2020 Apalachee Pkwy 32301. 2.2 mi s on US 27. Int corridors. **Pets:** Medium. $25 one-time fee/pet. Designated rooms, service with restrictions, supervision.

AAA ▼▼▼ Residence Inn by Marriott Tallahassee North I-10 Capital Circle 🅷
(850) 422-0093. **$121-$210.** 1880 Raymond Diehl Rd 32308. I-10 exit 203, just s. Int corridors. **Pets:** Accepted.

AAA ▼▼▼ Residence Inn by Marriott Tallahassee Universities at the Capitol 🅷
(850) 329-9080. **$115-$250.** 600 W Gaines St 32304. 0.5 mi w of S Monroe St; downtown. Int corridors. **Pets:** Accepted.

▼▼▼ Staybridge Suites Tallahassee 🅷
(850) 219-7000. **Call for rates.** 1600 Summit Lake Dr 32317. I-10 exit 209B, just n. Int corridors. **Pets:** Large, other species. $75 one-time fee/pet. Service with restrictions, supervision.

▼▼ TownePlace Suites by Marriott Tallahassee Northeast/Capital Circle 🅷
(850) 219-0122. **$99-$166.** 1876 Capital Cir NE 32308. I-10 exit 203, just e to US 319, then 2.1 mi s. Int corridors. **Pets:** Other species. $113 one-time fee/room. Service with restrictions, crate.

TAMARAC

La Quinta Inn-Ft. Lauderdale Tamarac East H
(954) 485-7900. **$75-$246.** 3800 W Commercial Blvd 33309. I-95 exit 32 (Commercial Blvd), 3 mi w; Florida Tpke exit 62, 0.7 mi e. Int corridors. **Pets:** Accepted.

TAMPA *(Restaurants p. 610)*

Aloft Tampa Downtown Hotel H
(813) 898-8000. **$99-$509.** 100 W Kennedy Blvd 33602. I-275 exit 44, 0.8 mi s. Int corridors. **Pets:** Accepted.

Clarion Inn Tampa Conference Center M
(813) 621-5555. **$65-$129.** 9331 Adamo Dr 33619. I-75 exit 257, 1.2 mi w on SR 60. **Pets:** Accepted.

Extended Stay America H
(813) 886-5253. **$75-$130.** 4811 Memorial Hwy 33634. SR 589 (Veterans Expwy) exit 3, just sw on CR 576. Int corridors. **Pets:** Accepted.

Grand Hyatt Tampa Bay H
(813) 874-1234. **$99-$399.** 2900 Bayport Dr 33607. On SR 60, at east end of Courtney Campbell Cswy. Ext/int corridors. **Pets:** Accepted.

Hampton Inn Tampa-Veterans Expwy/Airport North H
(813) 901-5900. **$109-$229.** 5628 W Waters Ave 33634. SR 589 (Veterans Expwy) exit 6A, just e on CR 584. Int corridors. **Pets:** Accepted.

Holiday Inn Express Hotel & Suites H
(813) 910-7171. **Call for rates.** 8310 Galbraith Rd 33647. I-75 exit 270, 0.3 mi n on CR 581 (Bruce B Downs Blvd), just w on Highwoods Preserve Pkwy, then just n; in Highwoods Preserve. Int corridors. **Pets:** Small, dogs only. $50 one-time fee/room. Designated rooms, service with restrictions, crate.

Holiday Inn Express Hotel & Suites USF Busch Gardens H
(813) 936-8200. **Call for rates.** 2807 E Busch Blvd 33612. I-275 exit 50, 1.8 mi e on Busch Blvd (SR 580), jct N 30th St. Int corridors. **Pets:** Medium. $50 daily fee/room. Designated rooms, service with restrictions, supervision.

Homewood Suites by Hilton Tampa/Brandon H ❁
(813) 685-7099. **$139-$179.** 10240 Palm River Rd 33619. I-75 exit 257, 0.4 mi w on SR 60, just s on S Falkenburg Rd, then 0.3 mi e. Int corridors. **Pets:** Medium, other species. $100 one-time fee/room. Service with restrictions, crate.

Homewood Suites by Hilton Tampa Westshore H
(813) 282-1950. **$129-$269.** 5325 Avion Park Dr 33607. I-275 exit 40A southbound, 0.7 mi n on Westshore Blvd; exit 39A northbound, 1 mi e on Kennedy Blvd (SR 60), 1.2 mi n on Westshore Blvd, just w on Spruce St, then just s on O'Brien St; in Avion Park Westshore. Int corridors.

La Quinta Inn & Suites Tampa North H
(813) 971-7676. **$67-$273.** 17301 Dona Michelle Dr 33647. I-75 exit 270, just n on CR 581 (Bruce B Downs Blvd); in North Palms. Int corridors. **Pets:** Accepted.

La Quinta Inn Tampa South H
(813) 835-6262. **$86-$207.** 4620 W Gandy Blvd 33611. On US 92, just e of jct S Westshore Blvd. Int corridors. **Pets:** Accepted.

Residence Inn by Marriott Tampa Downtown H
(813) 221-4224. **$126-$241.** 101 E Tyler St 33602. I-275 exit 44, 0.5 mi se on W Ashley Dr/Tampa St; exit 45A southbound, 1.5 mi se on W Ashley Dr. Int corridors. **Pets:** Accepted.

Residence Inn by Marriott Tampa Sabal Park/Brandon H
(813) 627-8855. **$123-$194.** 9719 Princess Palm Ave 33619. I-75 exit 260 southbound; exit 260B northbound, just w on SR 574 (Dr. Martin Luther King Jr Blvd), just s on Falkenburg Rd, then 0.4 mi w; in Sabal Corporate Park. Int corridors. **Pets:** Accepted.

Seminole Hard Rock Hotel & Casino Tampa H
(813) 627-7625. **$189-$1509, 3 day notice.** 5223 N Orient Rd 33610. I-4 exit 6, just w. Int corridors. **Pets:** Accepted.

Sheraton Tampa Riverwalk H
(813) 223-2222. **$99-$369.** 200 N Ashley Dr 33602. I-275 exit 44, 0.8 mi s. Int corridors. **Pets:** Accepted.

SpringHill Suites by Marriott Tampa North/Tampa Palms H
(813) 558-0300. **$98-$177.** 5396 Primrose Lake Cir 33647. I-75 exit 270, just s on CR 581 (Bruce B Downs Blvd), then 0.9 mi ne; in The Pointe. Int corridors. **Pets:** Other species. $50 one-time fee/room. Designated rooms, service with restrictions, supervision.

Staybridge Suites-Tampa East H
(813) 227-4000. **Call for rates.** 3624 N Falkenburg Rd 33619. I-75 exit 260 southbound; exit 260B northbound, just w on SR 574 (Dr. Martin Luther King Jr Blvd), then just s. Int corridors. **Pets:** Accepted.

TownePlace Suites by Marriott Tampa Westshore/Airport H
(813) 282-1081. **$92-$208.** 5302 Avion Park Dr 33607. I-275 exit 40A southbound, 0.7 mi n on Westshore Blvd; exit 39A northbound, 1 mi e on SR 60 (Kennedy Blvd), 1.2 mi n on Westshore Blvd, just w on Spruce St, then just s on O'Brien St; in Avion Park Westshore. Int corridors. **Pets:** Large. $100 one-time fee/room. Supervision.

The Westin Tampa Bay H ❁
(813) 281-0000. **$109-$409.** 7627 Courtney Campbell Cswy 33607. On SR 60, at east end of causeway. Int corridors. **Pets:** Medium, dogs only. Supervision.

The Westin Tampa Harbour Island H
(813) 229-5000. **Call for rates.** 725 S Harbour Island Blvd 33602. I-275 exit 44, 2.4 mi se on W Ashley Dr/Tampa St; exit 45A southbound, 3.9 mi se; on Harbour Island. Int corridors. **Pets:** Accepted.

TAVARES *(Restaurants p. 610)*

Best Western Plus Lake County Inn & Suites H
(352) 253-2378. **$90-$189.** 1380 E Burleigh Blvd 32778. On US 441, 1.5 mi e of SR 19. Int corridors. **Pets:** Accepted.

TEMPLE TERRACE

Residence Inn by Marriott Tampa North I-75 Fletcher H
(813) 972-4400. **$113-$213.** 13420 N Telecom Pkwy 33637. I-75 exit 266, 1.1 mi w on Fletcher Ave (CR 582A), then just s; in Telecom Tampa Park. Int corridors. **Pets:** Accepted.

▼▼ ▼▼ **TownePlace Suites by Marriott Tampa North/I-75 Fletcher** H

(813) 975-9777. **$98-$170.** 6800 Woodstork Rd 33637. I-75 exit 266, 1.1 mi w on Fletcher Ave (CR 582A), then just s on N Telecom Pkwy; in Telecom Tampa Park. Int corridors. **Pets:** Accepted.

⊺⊺ ᴋᴹ 🕿 🛜 ✕ 🚪 🖵

THE VILLAGES

▼▼ ▼▼ **Hampton Inn & Suites - The Villages** H

(352) 259-8246. **$109-$189.** 11727 NE 63rd Dr 32162. 2.6 mi w of jct US 27/441 on CR 466. Int corridors. **Pets:** Accepted.

⊺⊺ 🕿 🛜 ✕ 🚪 🖵

TITUSVILLE

🅰🅰🅰 ▼▼ ▼▼ **Best Western Space Shuttle Inn** H

(321) 269-9100. **$69-$209.** 3455 Cheney Hwy 32780. I-95 exit 215 (SR 50), just e. Ext corridors. **Pets:** Accepted.

ⓈAVE ⊺⊺ ᴋᴹ 🕿 🛜 🚪 🖵

▼▼ ▼▼ **Days Inn Titusville Kennedy Space Center** M

(321) 269-4480. **$85-$161.** 3755 Cheney Hwy 32780. I-95 exit 215 (SR 50), just w. Ext corridors. **Pets:** Accepted. ⊺⊺ 🕿 🛜 🚪 🖵

🅰🅰🅰 ▼▼ ▼▼ **Fairfield Inn & Suites by Marriott-Titusville/ Kennedy Space Center** H

(321) 385-1818. **$92-$174.** 4735 Helen Hauser Blvd 32780. I-95 exit 215 (SR 50), just w. Int corridors. **Pets:** Accepted.

ⓈAVE ᴋᴹ 🕿 🛜 ✕ 🚪 🖵

▼▼ ▼▼ **Hampton Inn Titusville/I-95 Kennedy Space Center** H

(321) 383-9191. **$119-$189.** 4760 Helen Hauser Blvd 32780. I-95 exit 215 (SR 50), just w. Int corridors. **Pets:** Accepted.

🍳 ᴋᴹ 🕿 🛜 ✕ 🚪 🖵

▼▼ ▼▼ **Holiday Inn Titusville-Kennedy Space Center** H

(321) 383-0200. **Call for rates.** 4715 Helen Hauser Blvd 32780. I-95 exit 215 (SR 50), just w to Helen Hauser Blvd, then just n. Int corridors. **Pets:** Other species. $50 daily fee/room. Designated rooms, service with restrictions, crate. ⊺⊺ ᴋᴹ 🕿 🛜 ✕ 🚪 🖵

🅰🅰🅰 ▼▼ ▼▼ **Ramada Inn & Suites-Kennedy Space Center** H

(321) 269-5510. **$79-$120.** 3500 Cheney Hwy 32780. I-95 exit 215 (SR 50), just e. Int corridors. **Pets:** $35 daily fee/room. Designated rooms, service with restrictions, supervision.

ⓈAVE ⊺⊺ 🕿 ✕ 🛜 ✕ 🚪 🖵

TREASURE ISLAND

🅰🅰🅰 ▼▼ ▼▼ **Residence Inn by Marriott St. Petersburg Treasure Island** H

(727) 367-2761. **$169-$385, 3 day notice.** 11908 Gulf Blvd 33706. On SR 699, 0.7 mi n of jct Treasure Island Cswy. Ext/int corridors. **Pets:** Accepted. ⓈAVE ᴋᴹ 🕿 🛜 ✕ 🚪 🖵

🅰🅰🅰 ▼▼ ▼▼ **Treasure Island Beach Resort** H

(727) 322-7022. **$175-$299.** 10800 Gulf Blvd 33706. On SR 699, just n of Treasure Island Cswy. Ext corridors. **Pets:** Small, dogs only. $75 daily fee/room. Designated rooms, service with restrictions, supervision.

ⓈAVE ⊺⊺ ᴋᴹ 🕿 🛜 ✕ 🚪 🖵

TRINITY

▼▼ ▼▼ **Holiday Inn Express & Suites Trinity** H

(727) 835-7820. **Call for rates.** 2125 Corporate Center Dr 34655. Just s of jct SR 54. Int corridors. **Pets:** Accepted. ᴋᴹ 🛜 ✕ 🚪 🖵

VENICE

🅰🅰🅰 ▼▼ ▼▼ **Hotel Venezia A Ramada Hotel** M

(941) 308-7700. **$72-$199.** 425 US 41 Bypass N 34285. 0.4 mi n of jct Venice Ave (CR 772). Ext corridors. **Pets:** Accepted.

ⓈAVE ⊺⊺ 🛜 ✕ 🚪 🖵

VERO BEACH

🅰🅰🅰 ▼▼ ▼▼ **The Caribbean Court Boutique Hotel** H

(772) 231-7211. **Call for rates.** 1601 S Ocean Dr 32963. US 1, 4.3 mi n on Indian River Blvd (CR 603), 1.3 mi e on 17th St (SR 656) to Ocean Dr, then just s; jct Ocean Dr and Jasmine Ln. Ext corridors. **Pets:** $250 deposit/pet. Designated rooms, service with restrictions, crate. ⓈAVE ⊺⊺ 🕿 🛜 ✕ 🚪 🖵

🅰🅰🅰 ▼▼ ▼▼ **Costa d' Este Beach Resort & Spa** H ❀

(772) 562-9919. **Call for rates.** 3244 Ocean Dr 32963. I-95 exit 147 (SR 60), 8.7 mi e to Indian River Blvd, 1 mi n to Merril P Barber Bridge/SR 60, 1.7 mi e to Ocean Dr, then just s. Int corridors. **Pets:** Dogs only. Designated rooms.

ⓈAVE 🍳 ⊺⊺ ᴋᴹ 🕿 ✕ 🛜 ✕ 🚪 🖵

▼▼ ▼▼ **Country Inn & Suites By Carlson, Vero Beach I-95** H

(772) 257-0252. **$89-$169.** 9330 19th Ln 32966. I-95 exit 147 (20th St/SR 60), just w; adjacent to Vero Fashion Outlets Mall. Int corridors. **Pets:** Accepted. ᴋᴹ 🕿 🛜 ✕ 🚪 🖵

🅰🅰🅰 ▼▼ ▼▼ **Holiday Inn Hotel & Suites Vero Beach-Oceanside** H

(772) 231-2300. **Call for rates.** 3384 Ocean Dr 32963. E of SR A1A; at end of SR 60. Ext corridors. **Pets:** Accepted.

ⓈAVE ᴱᶜᴼ ⊺⊺ 🕿 🛜 ✕ 🚪 🖵

🅰🅰🅰 ▼▼ ▼▼ ▼▼ **Vero Beach Hotel & Spa** H

(772) 231-5666. **Call for rates.** 3500 Ocean Dr 32963. On Ocean Dr, just n of SR 60. Ext/int corridors. **Pets:** Accepted.

ⓈAVE ᴱᶜᴼ 🍳 ⊺⊺ ᴋᴹ 🕿 ✕ 🛜 ✕ 🚪 🖵

🅰🅰🅰 ▼▼ ▼▼ **Vero Beach Inn & Suites** H

(772) 567-8321. **$79-$119.** 8797 20th St 32966. I-95 exit 147 (20th St/SR 60), 0.8 mi e. Ext corridors. **Pets:** Accepted.

ⓈAVE ⊺⊺ 🕿 🛜 ✕ 🚪 🖵

WEST MELBOURNE

🅰🅰🅰 ▼▼ ▼▼ **Days Inn Melbourne** M 🐾

(321) 724-2051. **$74-$85.** 4500 W New Haven Ave 32904. I-95 exit 180 (US 192/New Haven Ave), just e. Ext corridors. **Pets:** Other species. $15 daily fee/pet. Designated rooms, service with restrictions, supervision. ⓈAVE 🛜 🚪 🖵

🅰🅰🅰 ▼▼ ▼▼ **Fairfield Inn & Suites by Marriott Melbourne, Palm Bay/Viera** H

(321) 722-2220. **$84-$170.** 4355 W New Haven Ave 32904. I-95 exit 180 (US 192/New Haven Ave), just e. Int corridors. **Pets:** Accepted.

ⓈAVE ᴋᴹ 🕿 🛜 ✕ 🚪 🖵

WESTON

🅰🅰🅰 ▼▼ ▼▼ **Comfort Suites Weston-Sawgrass Mills South** H

(954) 659-1555. **$99-$189.** 2201 N Commerce Pkwy 33326. I-75 exit 15 (Royal Palm Blvd), just w to Weston Rd, n to Commerce Pkwy, then just e. Int corridors. **Pets:** Small, other species. $20 daily fee/pet. Designated rooms, service with restrictions, supervision.

ⓈAVE ᴋᴹ 🕿 🛜 ✕ 🚪 🖵

▼▼ ▼▼ **Residence Inn by Marriott Fort Lauderdale Weston** H

(954) 659-8585. **$118-$248.** 2605 Weston Rd 33331. I-75 exit 15 (Royal Palm Blvd), 0.3 mi w to Weston Rd, then just s. Int corridors. **Pets:** Accepted. ᴋᴹ 🕿 🛜 ✕ 🚪 🖵

▼▼▼ **TownePlace Suites by Marriott Fort Lauderdale Weston** 🅷
(954) 659-2234. **$87-$207.** 1545 Three Village Rd 33326. I-75 exit 15 (Royal Palm Blvd), 1.1 mi e to Bonaventure Blvd, 0.4 mi n to Three Village Rd, then just w. Int corridors. **Pets:** Accepted.
🍴 ♿ 🌊 📶 ✖ 🗄 🖥

WEST PALM BEACH *(Restaurants p. 610)*

🅐🅐🅐 ▼▼▼ **Best Western Palm Beach Lakes Inn** 🅷
(561) 683-8810. **$99-$299.** 1800 Palm Beach Lakes Blvd 33401. I-95 exit 71 (Palm Beach Lakes Blvd), just e. Ext/int corridors.
Pets: Accepted. 🆂🅰🆅🅴 🅴🅲🅾 🌊 📶 🗄 🖥

▼▼▼ **Days Inn-West Palm Beach** Ⓜ
(561) 689-0450. **$66-$145.** 2300 45th St 33407. I-95 exit 74 (45th St), just e. Ext corridors. **Pets:** Accepted. 🍴 🌊 📶 🗄 🖥

🅐🅐🅐 ▼▼▼▼ **Homewood Suites by Hilton West Palm Beach** 🅷
(561) 682-9188. **$104-$309.** 2455 Metrocentre Blvd 33407. I-95 exit 74 (45th St), just w; in Metrocentre Corporate Park. Int corridors. **Pets:** Medium, dogs only. $100 one-time fee/room. Service with restrictions, supervision. 🆂🅰🆅🅴 🍴 ♿ 🌊 📶 🗄 🖥

🅐🅐🅐 ▼▼▼▼ **Hyatt Place West Palm Beach/Downtown** 🅷
(561) 655-1454. **$119-$429.** 295 Lakeview Ave 33401. I-95 exit 70 (Okeechobee Blvd), 1.8 mi e to S Olive Ave, then just n. Int corridors. **Pets:** Accepted. 🆂🅰🆅🅴 ♿ 🌊 📶 ✖ 🗄 🖥

▼▼▼▼ **La Quinta Inn-West Palm Beach City Place** 🅷
(561) 697-3388. **$75-$235.** 5981 Okeechobee Blvd 33417. I-95 exit 70B (Okeechobee Blvd), 3.6 mi w; Florida Tpke exit 99 (Okeechobee Blvd), just e. Ext corridors. **Pets:** Accepted. 🌊 📶 🗄 🖥

▼▼▼▼ **Residence Inn by Marriott-West Palm Beach** 🅷
(561) 687-4747. **$98-$243.** 2461 Metrocentre Blvd E 33407. I-95 exit 74 (45th St), just w to Metrocentre Blvd, then just se; in Metrocentre Corporate Park. Int corridors. **Pets:** Accepted.
♿ 🌊 📶 ✖ 🗄 🖥

🅐🅐🅐 ▼▼▼▼ **Residence Inn by Marriott West Palm Beach Downtown** 🅷 🐾
(561) 653-8100. **$95-$302.** 455 Hibiscus St 33401. I-95 exit 70 (Okeechobee Blvd), 1.2 mi e to Quadrille Blvd, just n to Hibiscus St, then just e; downtown. Int corridors. **Pets:** Large, other species. $100 one-time fee/room. Designated rooms, service with restrictions, supervision. 🆂🅰🆅🅴 ♿ 📶 ✖ 🗄 🖥

🅐🅐🅐 ▼▼▼ **Rodeway Inn** 🅷
(561) 471-8700. **$80-$180.** 1505 Belvedere Rd 33406. I-95 exit 69 (Belvedere Rd), just w. Ext corridors. **Pets:** Accepted.
🆂🅰🆅🅴 ♿ 🌊 📶 🖥

WILDWOOD

▼▼ **Sleep Inn & Suites Wildwood- The Villages** 🅷
(352) 748-0507. **$82-$134.** 1224 S Main St 34785. Florida Tpke exit 304, just n on US 301. Int corridors. **Pets:** Accepted.
🅴🅲🅾 ♿ ♿ 🌊 📶 ✖ 🗄 🖥

WINTER PARK *(Restaurants p. 611)*

🅐🅐🅐 ▼▼▼ ▼▼▼ **The Alfond Inn** 🅷
(407) 998-8090. **$189-$369, 3 day notice.** 300 E New England Ave 32789. I-4 exit 87 (Fairbanks Ave), 2 mi e to Park Ave, just n to New England Ave, then just e. Int corridors. **Pets:** Accepted.
🆂🅰🆅🅴 ♿ 🍴 ♿ 📶 ✖ 🗄 🖥

YULEE

🅐🅐🅐 ▼▼▼▼ **Best Western Plus First Coast Inn & Suites** 🅷
(904) 225-0182. **$79-$129.** 462577 SR 200 32097. I-95 exit 373 (SR 200/A1A), just e. Int corridors. **Pets:** $20 daily fee/room. Designated rooms, service with restrictions, supervision.
🆂🅰🆅🅴 🍴 ♿ 🌊 📶 ✖ 🗄 🖥

▼▼▼ **Comfort Inn** 🅷
(904) 225-2600. **$84-$179.** 76043 Sidney Pl 32097. I-95 exit 373 (SR 200/A1A), just e. Int corridors. **Pets:** Accepted.
🍴 🌊 📶 🗄 🖥

ZEPHYRHILLS

▼▼▼ **Microtel Inn & Suites by Wyndham Zephyrhills** 🅷
(813) 783-2211. **$55-$115.** 7839 Gall Blvd 33541. On US 301, 0.9 mi n of jct Daugherty Rd. Int corridors. **Pets:** Accepted.
♿ 🌊 📶 🗄 🖥

GEORGIA

ACWORTH

🅐🅐🅐 ▼▼▼ **Best Western Acworth Inn** Ⓜ
(770) 974-0116. **$80-$150.** 5155 Cowan Rd 30101. I-75 exit 277, just w. Ext corridors. **Pets:** Medium, other species. $10 daily fee/pet. Designated rooms, service with restrictions, supervision.
🆂🅰🆅🅴 ♿ 🌊 📶 🗄 🖥

🅐🅐🅐 ▼▼▼ **Days Inn Acworth** Ⓜ
(770) 975-9000. **$56-$130, 3 day notice.** 164 N Point Way 30102. I-75 exit 277, just e. Ext corridors. **Pets:** Accepted.
🆂🅰🆅🅴 ♿ 📶 🗄 🖥

🅐🅐🅐 ▼▼▼ **La Quinta Inn Acworth** 🅷
(770) 975-9920. **$67-$150.** 184 N Point Way 30102. I-75 exit 277, just e. Ext/int corridors. **Pets:** Accepted. 🆂🅰🆅🅴 🌊 📶 🗄 🖥

▼▼▼ **Super 8** Ⓜ
(770) 966-9700. **$55-$75.** 4970 Cowan Rd 30101. I-75 exit 277, just w. Ext corridors. **Pets:** Medium, dogs only. $10 daily fee/pet. Service with restrictions, supervision. ♿ 🌊 📶 🗄 🖥

ADAIRSVILLE

▼▼▼ **Knights Inn** Ⓜ
(770) 769-9726. **$60-$85.** 500 Georgia North Cir 30103. I-75 exit 306, 0.3 mi w. Ext corridors. **Pets:** Accepted. ♿ 🌊 📶 🗄 🖥

🅐🅐🅐 ▼▼▼ **Quality Inn** Ⓜ
(770) 773-2886. **$70-$169.** 100 Princeton Blvd 30103. I-75 exit 306, just w. Ext corridors. **Pets:** Medium. $15 daily fee/pet. Designated rooms, service with restrictions, supervision. 🆂🅰🆅🅴 ♿ 🌊 📶 🗄 🖥

ADEL

▼▼▼ **Days Inn** Ⓜ
(229) 896-4574. **$50-$90.** 1204 W 4th St 31620. I-75 exit 39, just sw. Ext corridors. **Pets:** Other species. $10 daily fee/pet. Service with restrictions. 🍴 🌊 📶 🗄 🖥

▼▼▼ **Hampton Inn** 🅷
(229) 896-3099. **$89-$189.** 1500 W 4th St 31620. I-75 exit 39, just nw. Int corridors. **Pets:** Accepted. ♿ 🌊 📶 ✖ 🗄 🖥

ALBANY

▲▲▲◢ ▼▼▼ Baymont Inn & Suites Albany H
(229) 435-3737. **$59-$159.** 2720 Dawson Rd 31707. 0.5 mi se of jct US 82 and SR 520. Ext corridors. **Pets:** Medium. $20 one-time fee/pet. Service with restrictions, supervision. [SAVE] [⊇] [⊜] [❚] [▣]

▼▼ ◆ Quality Inn Albany Mall H
(229) 883-3300. **$70-$134.** 806 N Westover Blvd 31707. 7 mi w on Dawson Rd; 0.5 mi se of jct US 82 and SR 520. Ext corridors. **Pets:** Accepted. [&M] [⊇] [⊜] [❚] [▣]

ALMA

▼▼ Days Inn M
(912) 632-7000. **$63.** 930 S Pierce St 31510. Jct SR 32 and US 1, 0.4 mi s on US 1. Ext/int corridors. **Pets:** Accepted. [⊇] [⊜] [❚] [▣]

ALPHARETTA

▼▼ ◆ Comfort Suites H
(770) 645-6060. **$89-$159.** 3000 Mansell Rd 30022. SR 400 exit 8, 0.7 mi e. Int corridors. **Pets:** Accepted. [&M] [⊇] [⊜] [✗] [❚] [▣]

▲▲▲◢ ▼▼▼ Holiday Inn Express Alpharetta H
(770) 552-0006. **Call for rates.** 2950 Mansell Rd 30022. SR 400 exit 8, 0.7 mi e. Int corridors. **Pets:** Accepted.
[SAVE] [&M] [⊇] [⊜] [✗] [❚] [▣]

▲▲▲◢ ▼▼▼ Hyatt Place Alpharetta/North Point Mall H
(770) 594-8788. **$79-$299.** 7500 North Point Pkwy 30022. SR 400 exit 8, just e to North Point Pkwy, then just n. Int corridors. **Pets:** Accepted.
[SAVE] [❙❙] [&M] [⊇] [⊜] [✗] [❚] [▣]

▲▲▲◢ ▼▼▼ Hyatt Place Atlanta/Alpharetta/Windward Parkway H
(770) 343-9566. **$59-$219.** 5595 Windward Pkwy 30004. SR 400 exit 11, just w. Int corridors. **Pets:** Accepted.
[SAVE] [❙❙] [&M] [⊇] [⊜] [✗] [❚] [▣]

▼▼ ◆ La Quinta Inn & Suites Atlanta Alpharetta H
(770) 754-7800. **$67-$202.** 1350 North Point Dr 30022. SR 400 exit 9, 0.5 mi e. Int corridors. **Pets:** Accepted. [&M] [⊇] [⊜] [❚] [▣]

▲▲▲◢ ▼▼▼ Residence Inn by Marriott Atlanta Alpharetta North Point Mall H
(770) 587-1151. **$79-$250.** 1325 North Point Dr 30022. SR 400 exit 9, just e to North Point Dr, then just s. Int corridors. **Pets:** Accepted.
[SAVE] [&M] [⊇] [⊜] [✗] [❚] [▣]

▲▲▲◢ ▼▼▼ Residence Inn by Marriott Atlanta Alpharetta/Windward H
(770) 664-0664. **$90-$286.** 5465 Windward Pkwy 30004. SR 400 exit 11, 0.4 mi w. Ext/int corridors. **Pets:** Accepted.
[SAVE] [&M] [⊇] [⊜] [✗] [❚] [▣]

▼▼▼ ◆ Staybridge Suites H
(770) 569-7200. **Call for rates.** 3980 North Point Pkwy 30005. SR 400 exit 10, 0.5 mi e. Int corridors. **Pets:** Accepted.
[&M] [⊇] [⊜] [✗] [❚] [▣]

▲▲▲◢ ▼▼ Towneplace Suites by Marriott Alpharetta H
(770) 664-1300. **$76-$212.** 7925 Westside Pkwy 30009. SR 400 exit 9, 0.3 mi w. Int corridors. **Pets:** Accepted.
[SAVE] [&M] [⊇] [⊜] [✗] [❚] [▣]

AMERICUS

▼▼ ◆ Quality Inn H
(229) 924-4431. **$71-$100.** 1205 S Martin Luther King Jr Blvd 31709. Jct US 280 and 19, just n on US 19; west of town. Ext corridors.
Pets: Accepted. [❙❙] [⊇] [⊜] [❚] [▣]

ASHBURN

▲▲▲◢ ▼▼▼ Best Western Ashburn Inn M
(229) 567-0080. **$70-$90.** 820 Shoney's Dr 31714. I-75 exit 82, just sw. Ext corridors. **Pets:** Accepted. [SAVE] [⊇] [⊜] [❚] [▣]

ATHENS (Restaurants p. 611)

▲▲▲◢ ▼▼ Best Western Athens M
(706) 546-7311. **$80-$160.** 170 N Milledge Ave 30601. Jct US 78 business route (Broad St), 0.5 mi w on SR 15. Ext corridors.
Pets: Medium. $25 daily fee/pet. Designated rooms, service with restrictions, supervision. [SAVE] [⊇] [⊜] [❚] [▣]

▼▼ Candlewood Suites H
(706) 548-9663. **Call for rates.** 156 Classic Rd 30606. Jct SR 10 Loop and US 78 business route, 1.1 mi w on US 78 business route to Classic Rd, then just s. Int corridors. **Pets:** Medium. $75 one-time fee/pet. Service with restrictions, crate. [❙❙] [&M] [⊜] [✗] [❚] [▣]

▼▼ ◆ Comfort Inn & Suites H
(706) 227-9700. **$69-$499.** 3980 Atlanta Hwy 30622. SR 10 Loop exit 18 (Atlanta Hwy), 0.7 mi w. Int corridors. **Pets:** Accepted.
[&M] [⊇] [⊜] [✗] [❚] [▣]

▲▲▲◢ ▼▼▼ Graduate Athens M 🐾
(706) 549-7020. **Call for rates.** 295 E Dougherty St 30601. Jct Thomas and Dougherty sts; downtown. Ext/int corridors. **Pets:** Medium, dogs only. $50 one-time fee/room. Designated rooms, service with restrictions, crate. [SAVE] [❙❙] [⊇] [⊜] [❚] [▣]

▼▼▼ Holiday Inn Express Athens H
(706) 546-8122. **Call for rates.** 513 W Broad St 30601. On US 78 business route (Broad St); center. Int corridors. **Pets:** Accepted.
[&M] [⊇] [⊜] [❚] [▣]

▼▼▼ Hotel Indigo Athens Downtown/Univ. Area H 🐾
(706) 546-0430. **Call for rates.** 500 College Ave 30601. Just n of center. Int corridors. **Pets:** Service with restrictions.
[ECO] [⊂▣] [❙❙] [&M] [⊜] [✗] [❚] [▣]

▼▼ ◆ Sleep Inn & Suites H
(706) 850-1261. **$69-$399.** 109 Florence Dr 30622. Jct SR 10 Loop and US 78 business route, 1.2 mi w on US 78 to Florence Dr, then just s. Int corridors. **Pets:** Accepted. [❙❙] [&M] [⊇] [⊜] [❚] [▣]

▲▲▲◢ ▼▼▼ Wingate by Wyndham Athens Near Downtown H
(706) 995-4000. **$80-$240.** 255 North Ave 30601. SR 10 Loop exit 11B (Dougherty St/North Ave); 1 mi n of downtown. Int corridors.
Pets: Medium. $25 daily fee/pet. Designated rooms, service with restrictions, supervision. [SAVE] [❙❙] [&M] [⊇] [⊜] [✗] [❚] [▣]

ATLANTA (Restaurants p. 611)

▲▲▲◢ ▼▼▼ Aloft Hotel Atlanta Downtown H
(678) 515-0300. **$129-$399.** 300 Spring St NW 30308. I-75 exit 249B (Pine St), 0.5 mi sw on Peachtree St NE, then just w. Int corridors.
Pets: Accepted. [SAVE] [⊂▣] [❙❙] [&M] [⊜] [✗] [❚] [▣]

▼▼▼ Artmore Hotel H
(404) 876-6100. **Call for rates.** 1302 W Peachtree St 30309. I-75/85 exit 250 (14th St), just e, then just n on W Peachtree St to 16th St. Int corridors. **Pets:** Accepted. [❙❙] [&M] [⊜] [✗] [❚] [▣]

▲▲▲◢ ▼▼▼ Crowne Plaza Atlanta Midtown H
(404) 877-9000. **Call for rates.** 590 W Peachtree St NW 30308. I-75/85 exit 249D southbound; exit 249C northbound, just e. Int corridors.
Pets: Accepted. [SAVE] [❙❙] [&M] [⊇] [⊜] [✗] [▣]

▼▼▼ DoubleTree by Hilton Hotel Atlanta-Buckhead H
(404) 231-1234. **Call for rates.** 3342 Peachtree Rd NE 30326. Jct Piedmont and Peachtree rds NE, just n. Int corridors. **Pets:** Accepted.
[ECO] [❙❙] [&M] [⊜] [✗] [❚] [▣]

▼▼ ◆◆◆ **Extended Stay America Atlanta-Clairmont** [H]
(404) 679-4333. **$85-$110.** 3115 Clairmont Rd 30329. I-85 exit 91, 0.6 mi w. Int corridors. **Pets:** Accepted. 🅼 📶 ✕ 🛗 🖵

▼▼ ◆◆◆ **Extended Stay America Atlanta-Lenox** [H]
(404) 237-9100. **$90-$115.** 3967 Peachtree Rd NE 30319. I-85 exit 89, 2.8 mi w. Int corridors. **Pets:** Accepted. 🅼 ➔ 📶 🛗 🖵

▼▼ ▼ **Extended Stay America (Atlanta/Marietta/Windy Hill/Int N Pkwy)** [H]
(770) 226-0242. **$70-$90.** 2225 Interstate North Pkwy 30339. I-75 exit 260, just e to Interstate North Pkwy, then just s. Int corridors.
Pets: Accepted. 🅼 ➔ 📶 🛗 🖵

▼▼ ▼ **Extended Stay America Atlanta-Perimeter/Crestline** [H]
(770) 396-5600. **$80-$105.** 905 Crestline Pkwy 30328. SR 400 exit 5A, just e to Peachtree-Dunwoody Rd, then 0.5 mi s. Int corridors.
Pets: Accepted. 🅼 📶 ✕ 🛗 🖵

▼▼ ▼ **Extended Stay America-Atlanta-Perimeter-Hammond Drive** [H]
(770) 522-0025. **$85-$110.** 1050 Hammond Dr 30328. I-285 exit 26 eastbound, 0.5 mi n to Hammond Dr, then 0.5 mi e; exit 28 westbound, just n to Hammond Dr, then just w. Ext corridors. **Pets:** Accepted.
🅼 📶 🛗 🖵

▼▼ ▼ **Extended Stay America Atlanta-Perimeter/Peachtree-Dunwoody** [H]
(770) 379-0111. **$80-$105.** 6330 Peachtree-Dunwoody Rd NE 30328. SR 400 exit 5A, just e to Peachtree-Dunwoody Rd, then 0.5 mi s. Int corridors. **Pets:** Accepted. 🅼 ➔ 📶 🛗 🖵

▼▼ ▼ **Extended Stay America Atlanta-Vinings** [H]
(770) 436-1511. **$95-$115.** 2474 Cumberland Pkwy SE 30339. I-285 exit 18, just e. Int corridors. **Pets:** Accepted. 🅼 ➔ 📶 🛗 🖵

◆◆◆ ▼▼▼▼ **Four Seasons Hotel Atlanta** [H]
(404) 881-9898. **Call for rates.** 75 14th St NE 30309. I-75/85 exit 250 (14th St), 0.3 mi e. Int corridors. **Pets:** Accepted.
[SAVE] ⊞ 🍽 🅼 ➔ ✕ 📶 🛗 🖵

◆◆◆ ▼▼▼▼ **The Georgian Terrace Hotel** [H] ❖
(404) 897-1991. **$139-$849.** 659 Peachtree St NE 30308. I-75/85 exit 249D, 0.3 mi e to Peachtree St, then just n. Int corridors.
Pets: Medium, dogs only. $75 one-time fee/pet. Service with restrictions. [SAVE] 🍽 🅼 ➔ 📶 ✕ 🛗 🖵

◆◆◆ ▼▼▼▼ **Grand Hyatt Atlanta** [H] ❖
(404) 237-1234. **$129-$409.** 3300 Peachtree Rd NE 30305. Corner of Peachtree and Piedmont rds. Int corridors. **Pets:** Medium, dogs only. $100 one-time fee/pet. Service with restrictions, crate.
[SAVE] [ECO] ⊞ 🍽 🅼 ➔ ✕ 📶 🛗 🖵

◆◆◆ ▼▼▼▼ **Hilton Atlanta** [H]
(404) 659-2000. **$99-$259.** 255 Courtland St NE 30303. I-75/85 exit 249A southbound; exit 248C northbound, just w to Piedmont Ave, just n to Baker St, then just w. Int corridors. **Pets:** Accepted.
[SAVE] [ECO] 🍽 🅼 ➔ 📶 ✕ 🖵

▼▼▼▼ **Homewood Suites-Atlanta Buckhead** [H]
(404) 365-0001. **$119-$239.** 3566 Piedmont Rd 30305. SR 400 exit 2, just s to Piedmont Rd, then 1 mi w. Int corridors. **Pets:** Accepted.
🅼 ➔ 📶 🛗 🖵

▼▼▼▼ **Homewood Suites-Cumberland/Galleria** [H]
(770) 988-9449. **$129-$159.** 3200 Cobb Pkwy SE 30339. I-285 exit 19 eastbound; exit 20 westbound, 0.7 mi s. Ext/int corridors.
Pets: Accepted. 🅼 ➔ 📶 🛗 🖵

▼▼▼ **Hotel Indigo Atlanta Midtown** [H]
(404) 874-9200. **$99-$349.** 683 Peachtree St NE 30308. I-75/85 exit 249D, 0.5 mi e to Peachtree St, then just n. Int corridors.
Pets: Accepted. 🍽 🅼 📶 ✕ 🖵

▼▼▼ **Hotel Indigo Atlanta Vinings** [H]
(770) 432-5555. **Call for rates.** 2857 Paces Ferry Rd 30339. I-285 exit 18, 0.6 mi e. Int corridors. **Pets:** Accepted.
🍽 🅼 ➔ 📶 ✕ 🛗 🖵

◆◆◆ ▼▼▼▼ **Hyatt House Atlanta/Cobb Galleria** [H]
(770) 541-2960. **$99-$309.** 3595 Cumberland Blvd SE 30339. I-75 exit 258, just e. Int corridors. **Pets:** Accepted.
[SAVE] 🅼 📶 ✕ 🛗 🖵

◆◆◆ ▼▼▼▼ **HYATT house Atlanta Downtown** [H]
(404) 332-5522. **$89-$399.** 431 Marietta St NW 30313. I-75/85 exit 249D, take Spring St toward Centennial Olympic Park Dr NW, just s onto Ivan Allen Jr Blvd NW, just n. Int corridors. **Pets:** Accepted.
[SAVE] 🍽 🅼 📶 ✕ 🛗 🖵

◆◆◆ ▼▼▼▼ **Hyatt Place Atlanta/Buckhead** [H] ❖
(404) 869-6161. **$109-$299.** 3242 Peachtree Rd NE 30305. Jct Peachtree and Piedmont rds NE, just s. Int corridors. **Pets:** Medium, dogs only. $75 one-time fee/room. Designated rooms, service with restrictions, supervision. [SAVE] 🍽 🅼 ➔ 📶 ✕ 🛗 🖵

◆◆◆ ▼▼▼▼ **Hyatt Place, Atlanta/Downtown** [H]
(404) 577-1980. **$99-$299.** 330 Peachtree St NE 30308. I-75/85 exit 249A to Baker St, 0.3 mi w to Peachtree St, then just n. Int corridors.
Pets: Accepted. [SAVE] 🅼 📶 ✕ 🛗 🖵

◆◆◆ ▼▼▼▼ **Hyatt Place Atlanta/Perimeter Center** [H]
(770) 730-9300. **$79-$289.** 1005 Crestline Pkwy 30328. SR 400 exit 5A (Dunwoody Rd), 0.3 mi e. Int corridors. **Pets:** Accepted.
[SAVE] 🅼 ➔ ✕ 🛗 🖵

▼▼▼ **Inn at the Peachtrees, An Ascend Hotel Collection Member** [M]
(404) 577-6970. **$99-$299.** 330 W Peachtree St 30308. I-75/85 exit 248C northbound, 0.4 mi w to Peachtree St, then 0.3 mi n; exit 249C southbound, just s to Peachtree Pl, then just e. Ext/int corridors.
Pets: Accepted. 🅼 📶 ✕ 🛗 🖵

◆◆◆ ▼▼▼▼▼ **InterContinental Buckhead Atlanta** [H]
(404) 946-9000. **$159-$389.** 3315 Peachtree Rd NE 30326. Jct Piedmont and Peachtree rds NE, just e. Int corridors. **Pets:** Accepted.
[SAVE] ⊞ 🍽 🅼 ➔ ✕ 📶 ✕ 🛗 🖵

▼▼▼ **La Quinta Inn & Suites Atlanta (Paces Ferry/Vinings)** [H]
(770) 801-9002. **$86-$202.** 2415 Paces Ferry Rd SE 30339. I-285 exit 18, just w. Int corridors. **Pets:** Accepted. 🅼 ➔ 📶 ✕ 🛗 🖵

▼▼▼ **La Quinta Inn & Suites Atlanta (Perimeter/Medical Center)** [H]
(770) 350-6177. **$68-$202.** 6260 Peachtree-Dunwoody Rd 30328. I-285 exit 28 westbound, 0.7 mi n; exit 26 eastbound, 0.5 mi n to Hammond Dr, 0.7 mi e, then 0.5 mi n. Int corridors. **Pets:** Accepted.
🅼 ➔ 📶 ✕ 🛗 🖵

◆◆◆ ▼▼▼ ▼▼▼ **Le Méridien Atlanta Perimeter** [H]
(770) 396-6800. **$109-$399.** 111 Perimeter Center W 30346. I-285 exit 29 (Ashford-Dunwoody Rd), 0.5 mi n. Int corridors. **Pets:** Accepted.
[SAVE] 🍽 🅼 ➔ 📶 ✕ 🛗 🖵

◆◆◆ ▼▼▼▼ **Loews Atlanta Hotel** [H]
(404) 745-5000. **Call for rates.** 1075 Peachtree St NE 30309. I-75/85 exit 251 (10th St), 0.5 mi e to Peachtree St NE, then just n. Int corridors. **Pets:** Accepted. [SAVE] 🍽 🅼 ✕ 📶 ✕ 🛗 🖵

▼▼▼ ▼▼▼ **Mandarin Oriental, Atlanta** [H]
(404) 995-7500. **Call for rates.** 3376 Peachtree Rd NE 30326. Jct Peachtree and Lenox rds, just s. Int corridors. **Pets:** Accepted.
⊞ 🍽 🅼 ➔ ✕ 📶 ✕ 🛗 🖵

▼▼▼ ▼▼▼ Omni Hotel at CNN Center 🄷
(404) 659-0000. **Call for rates.** 190 Marrietta St 30303. I-75/85 exit 248C northbound, 0.8 mi w; exit 249C southbound to International Blvd, 0.5 mi w. Int corridors. **Pets:** Small. $50 one-time fee/room. Service with restrictions, crate. 🍴 🛁ᴹ ⛱ ⊠ 📶 ⊠ 🔔 ▣

🄰🄰🄰 ▼▼▼ ▼▼▼ Renaissance Atlanta Midtown 🄷 🌸
(678) 412-2400. **$98-$309.** 866 W Peachtree St NW 30308. I-75/85 exit 249D, just e to W Peachtree St NW, then 0.6 mi n. Int corridors. **Pets:** Medium, other species. $75 one-time fee/room. Designated rooms, service with restrictions, supervision.
🆂🄰🆅🅴 🄴🄲🄾 🍴 🛁ᴹ 📶 ⊠ 🔔 ▣

🄰🄰🄰 ▼▼▼ Residence Inn by Marriott Atlanta Buckhead 🄼
(404) 239-0677. **$127-$263.** 2960 Piedmont Rd NE 30305. Jct Piedmont and Pharr rds, just s. Ext corridors. **Pets:** Accepted.
🆂🄰🆅🅴 🛁ᴹ ⛱ 📶 ⊠ 🔔 ▣

▼▼▼ ▼▼▼ Residence Inn by Marriott Atlanta Buckhead/Lenox Park 🄷
(404) 467-1660. **$89-$217.** 2220 Lake Blvd 30319. I-85 exit 89, 1.6 mi w on N Druid Hills (which becomes E Roxboro Rd), then just n on Lenox Park Blvd. Int corridors. **Pets:** Accepted.
🍴 🛁ᴹ ⛱ 📶 ⊠ 🔔 ▣

▼▼▼ ▼▼▼ Residence Inn by Marriott Atlanta-Downtown 🄷
(404) 522-0950. **$89-$217.** 134 Peachtree St NW 30303. I-75/85 exit 248C northbound, 0.4 mi w, then just s; exit 249A southbound to International Blvd, just w, then just s. Int corridors. **Pets:** Medium. $100 one-time fee/room. Service with restrictions, crate. 📶 ⊠ 🔔 ▣

▼▼▼ ▼▼▼ Residence Inn by Marriott Atlanta-Midtown/Georgia Tech 🄷
(404) 872-8885. **$125-$237.** 1041 W Peachtree St NW 30309. I-75/85 exit 250 (10th St), just e to W Peachtree St, then just n; corner of 11th St. Int corridors. **Pets:** Medium, other species. $100 one-time fee/room. Service with restrictions, supervision. 🛁ᴹ 📶 ⊠ 🔔 ▣

🄰🄰🄰 ▼▼▼ ▼▼▼ Residence Inn by Marriott Atlanta Midtown Peachtree at 17th 🄷
(404) 745-1000. **$118-$227.** 1365 Peachtree St NE 30309. I-75/85 exit 251 northbound; exit 250 (17th St) southbound, 0.5 mi e to Peachtree St. Int corridors. **Pets:** Accepted. 🆂🄰🆅🅴 🛁ᴹ 📶 ⊠ 🔔 ▣

🄰🄰🄰 ▼▼▼ ▼▼▼ Residence Inn by Marriott Atlanta Perimeter Center East 🄷
(770) 455-4446. **$111-$263.** 1901 Savoy Dr 30341. I-285 exit 30, just e. Ext corridors. **Pets:** Accepted. 🆂🄰🆅🅴 🍴 ⛱ 📶 ⊠ 🔔 ▣

🄰🄰🄰 ▼▼▼ ▼▼▼ The Ritz-Carlton, Buckhead 🄷
(404) 237-2700. **Call for rates.** 3434 Peachtree Rd NE 30326. I-85 exit 86, 1.8 mi n on Lenox Rd. Int corridors. **Pets:** Accepted.
🆂🄰🆅🅴 🍴 🛁ᴹ ⛱ ⊠ 📶 ⊠ 🔔 ▣

🄰🄰🄰 ▼▼▼ St. Regis Atlanta Hotel & Residences 🄷 🌸
(404) 563-7900. **Call for rates.** 88 Paces Ferry 30305. Jct Peachtree and W Paces Ferry rds, just w. Int corridors. **Pets:** Medium. $100 one-time fee/room. Supervision. 🆂🄰🆅🅴 ⊟ 🍴 🛁ᴹ ⛱ ⊠ 📶 ⊠

🄰🄰🄰 ▼▼▼ ▼▼▼ Sheraton Atlanta Hotel 🄷 🐾
(404) 659-6500. **$69-$599.** 165 Courtland St NE 30303. I-75/85 exit 249A southbound; exit 248C northbound, just n. Int corridors. **Pets:** Small, dogs only. $65 deposit/pet, $35 one-time fee/pet. Designated rooms, service with restrictions, supervision.
🆂🄰🆅🅴 🍴 🛁ᴹ 📶 ⊠ 🔔 ▣

🄰🄰🄰 ▼▼▼ Sheraton Suites Galleria 🄷
(770) 955-3900. **$139-$269, 5 day notice.** 2844 Cobb Pkwy SE 30339. I-285 exit 20 westbound; exit 19 eastbound, just s. Int corridors.
Pets: Accepted. 🆂🄰🆅🅴 🍴 🛁ᴹ ⛱ 📶 ⊠ 🔔 ▣

🄰🄰🄰 ▼▼▼ Sonesta ES Suites Atlanta 🄷
(404) 250-0110. **Call for rates.** 760 Mt Vernon Hwy NE 30328. I-285 exit 25, 0.8 mi n on Roswell Rd, then 1 mi e. Ext/int corridors.
Pets: Accepted. 🆂🄰🆅🅴 🛁ᴹ ⛱ 📶 ⊠ 🔔 ▣

▼▼▼ Staybridge Suites-Atlanta/Buckhead 🄷
(404) 842-0800. **$109-$250.** 540 Pharr Rd 30305. Jct Pharr and Piedmont rds, just w. Int corridors. **Pets:** Medium. $78 one-time fee/room. Service with restrictions, supervision. 🛁ᴹ ⛱ 📶 ⊠ 🔔 ▣

🄰🄰🄰 ▼▼▼ Staybridge Suites - Atlanta Midtown 🄷
(404) 877-9495. **$119-$499.** 23 Linden Ave NW 30308. I-85 exit 249D southbound; exit 249C northbound, just e. Int corridors. **Pets:** Accepted.
🆂🄰🆅🅴 🍴 🛁ᴹ 📶 ⊠ 🔔 ▣

▼▼▼ Staybridge Suites Atlanta Perimeter 🄷
(678) 320-0111. **Call for rates.** 4601 Ridgeview Rd 30338. I-285 exit 29 (Ashford-Dunwoody Rd), 0.5 mi n, 0.5 mi w on Perimeter Center W to Crowne Pointe Dr, then just n. Int corridors. **Pets:** Accepted.
🛁ᴹ 📶 ⊠ 🔔 ▣

▼▼▼ ▼▼▼ TownePlace Suites by Marriott Atlanta Buckhead 🄷
(404) 949-4820. **$101-$197.** 820 Sidney Marcus Blvd 30324. I-85 exit 86 northbound, 1.9 mi n to Sidney Marcus Blvd, then just w; exit 88 southbound, just w to Sidney Marcus Blvd, then just w. Int corridors.
Pets: Accepted. 🍴 🛁ᴹ 📶 ⊠ 🔔 ▣

🄰🄰🄰 ▼▼▼ TWELVE Atlantic Station, Autograph Collection 🄷
(404) 961-1212. **$149-$409.** 361 17th St NW 30363. I-75 exit 251 northbound; exit 250 southbound, just w; in Atlantic Station. Int corridors. **Pets:** Accepted. 🆂🄰🆅🅴 🍴 🛁ᴹ ⛱ 📶 ⊠ 🔔 ▣

🄰🄰🄰 ▼▼▼ TWELVE Centennial Park, Autograph Collection 🄷
(404) 418-1212. **$170-$409.** 400 W Peachtree St NW 30308. I-75/85 exit 249C, 0.4 mi s; jct W Peachtree St NW. Int corridors. **Pets:** Very small. $100 one-time fee/pet. Service with restrictions, supervision.
🆂🄰🆅🅴 🍴 🛁ᴹ ⛱ 📶 ⊠ 🔔 ▣

▼▼▼ The University Inn at Emory 🄼
(404) 634-7327. **Call for rates.** 1767 N Decatur Rd NE 30307. Adjacent to Emory University. Ext/int corridors. **Pets:** Medium. $30 daily fee/pet. Designated rooms, service with restrictions. ⛱ 📶 ⊠ 🔔 ▣

🄰🄰🄰 ▼▼▼ ▼▼▼ W Atlanta Buckhead 🄷
(678) 500-3100. **Call for rates.** 3377 Peachtree Rd NE 30326. Jct Piedmont and Peachtree rds, 0.3 mi e. Int corridors. **Pets:** Accepted.
🆂🄰🆅🅴 ⊟ 🍴 🛁ᴹ ⛱ 📶 ⊠ 🔔 ▣

🄰🄰🄰 ▼▼▼ ▼▼▼ W Atlanta Downtown 🄷
(404) 582-5800. **$145-$349.** 45 Ivan Allen Jr Blvd 30308. I-75/85 exit 249C, just s. Int corridors. **Pets:** Accepted.
🆂🄰🆅🅴 🍴 🛁ᴹ ⛱ 📶 🔔

🄰🄰🄰 ▼▼▼ ▼▼▼ W Atlanta Midtown Hotel 🄷 🌸
(404) 892-6000. **$159-$359.** 188 14th St NE 30361. I-75/85 exit 250 (14th St), 0.5 mi e. Int corridors. **Pets:** $100 one-time fee/room, $25 daily fee/room. Service with restrictions, supervision.
🆂🄰🆅🅴 🍴 🛁ᴹ ⛱ 📶 ⊠

🄰🄰🄰 ▼▼▼ ▼▼▼ The Westin Atlanta Perimeter North 🄷
(770) 395-3900. **$99-$199.** 7 Concourse Pkwy 30328. I-285 exit 28 westbound; exit 26 eastbound, 0.5 mi n to Hammond Dr, then 0.4 mi e. Int corridors. **Pets:** Accepted.
🆂🄰🆅🅴 ⊟ 🍴 🛁ᴹ ⛱ 📶 ⊠ 🔔 ▣

🄰🄰🄰 ▼▼▼ ▼▼▼ The Westin Buckhead Atlanta 🄷
(404) 365-0065. **$139-$329.** 3391 Peachtree Rd NE 30326. Adjacent to Lenox Square Mall. Int corridors. **Pets:** Accepted.
🆂🄰🆅🅴 ⊟ 🍴 🛁ᴹ ⛱ ⊠ 📶 ⊠ 🔔 ▣

🔺 ▼▼▼ **The Westin Peachtree Plaza** 🅷 ❀
(404) 659-1400. **Call for rates.** 210 Peachtree St NW 30303. I-75/85 exit 248C northbound, 0.4 mi w; exit 249C southbound, 0.5 mi s. Int corridors. **Pets:** Medium, dogs only. Designated rooms, service with restrictions, supervision. 🆂🅰🆅🅴 ECO 🔌 🍴 🆖 ⬚ 🆂 ✕ 🔧 🖵

🔺 ▼▼▼ **Wyndham Atlanta Galleria** 🅷
(770) 955-1700. **$79-$175.** 6345 Powers Ferry Rd NW 30339. I-285 exit 22, just s. Int corridors. **Pets:** Accepted.
🆂🅰🆅🅴 🍴 🆖 ⬚ 🛰 ✕ 🔧 🖵

AUGUSTA *(Restaurants p. 611)*

🔺 ▼▼▼ **Augusta Marriott At The Convention Center** 🅷
(706) 722-8900. **$138-$217.** 2 10th St 30901. I-20 exit 200 (River Watch Pkwy), 5.4 mi se, then just n; downtown. Int corridors. **Pets:** Medium, other species. $50 one-time fee/room. Service with restrictions, supervision.
🆂🅰🆅🅴 🔌 🍴 🆖 ⬚ ✕ 🛰 ✕ 🔧 🖵

▼▼▼ **Candlewood Suites Augusta** 🅷
(706) 733-3300. **Call for rates.** 1080 Claussen Rd 30907. I-20 exit 200 (River Watch Pkwy), just nw, then just sw. Int corridors. **Pets:** Accepted.
🍴 🆖 🛰 🔧 🖵

▼▼▼ **DoubleTree by Hilton Hotel Augusta** 🅷
(706) 855-8100. **$109-$159.** 2651 Perimeter Pkwy 30909. I-520 exit 1C (Wheeler Rd), just w to Perimeter Pkwy, then just n. Int corridors. **Pets:** Accepted. 🍴 🆖 ⬚ 🛰 ✕ 🔧 🖵

▼▼▼ **Home2 Suites by Hilton** 🅷
(706) 733-8787. **$119-$189.** 3606 Exchange Ln 30909. I-520 exit 1C (Wheeler Rd), just ne to Walton Rd Ext, then just nw. Int corridors. **Pets:** Accepted. 🆖 🛰 ✕ 🖵

▼▼▼ **Jameson Suites** 🅷
(706) 733-4656. **Call for rates.** 1062 Clausen Rd 30907. I-20 exit 200 (River Watch Pkwy), just nw, then just sw. Int corridors. **Pets:** Accepted.
🍴 🆖 ⬚ 🛰 ✕ 🔧 🖵

🔺 ▼▼▼ **The Partridge Inn, Curio Collection by Hilton** 🅷
(706) 737-8888. **Call for rates.** 2110 Walton Way 30904. 1.3 mi w off 15th St. Int corridors. **Pets:** Accepted.
🆂🅰🆅🅴 🔌 🍴 ⬚ 🛰 ✕ 🔧 🖵

▼▼▼ **Residence Inn by Marriott** 🅷
(706) 288-1900. **$128-$195.** 1116 Marks Church Rd 30909. I-520 exit 1C (Wheeler Rd), just e. Int corridors. **Pets:** Accepted.
🍴 🆖 🛰 ✕ 🔧 🖵

▼▼▼ **Sheraton Augusta Hotel** 🅷
(706) 396-1000. **$109-$169.** 1069 Stevens Creek Rd 30907. I-20 exit 199 (Washington Rd), just w, then just ne. Int corridors. **Pets:** Accepted.
🔌 🍴 🆖 🛰 ✕ 🔧 🖵

BAINBRIDGE

▼▼ **Quality Inn** 🅷
(229) 243-7000. **$67-$109.** 1403 Tallahassee Hwy 39819. Just s of US 84 Bypass on US 27. Ext corridors. **Pets:** Accepted.
🆖 🛰 🛜 🔧 🖵

BLUE RIDGE

▼▼ **Americas Best Value Inn Blue Ridge** 🅼
(706) 632-2100. **Call for rates.** 4970 Appalachian Hwy 30513. On SR 515 and US 76. Ext corridors. **Pets:** Accepted.
🆖 🛰 🛜 🔧 🖵

🔺 ▼▼▼ **The Blue Ridge Lodge by Comfort Inn & Suites** 🅷 ❀
(706) 946-3333. **$109-$209.** 83 Blue Ridge Overlook 30513. Just off SR 515 and US 76; behind Arby's. Int corridors. **Pets:** $50 one-time fee/room. Service with restrictions, supervision. 🆂🅰🆅🅴 🛜 ✕ 🔧 🖵

BRASELTON

🔺 ▼▼ **Best Western Braselton Inn** 🅼
(706) 654-3081. **$100-$200, 3 day notice.** 303 Zion Church Rd 30517. I-85 exit 129, just e, then 0.3 mi n. Ext corridors. **Pets:** Accepted.
🆂🅰🆅🅴 🍴 🛰 🛜 🔧 🖵

BREMEN

▼▼ **Microtel Inn & Suites by Wyndham-Bremen Georgia** 🅼
(770) 537-8000. **$54-$90.** 104 Price Creek Rd 30110. I-20 exit 11, just n. Int corridors. **Pets:** Small. $10 daily fee/pet. Designated rooms, service with restrictions, supervision. 🍴 🆖 🛰 🛜 🔧 🖵

BRUNSWICK

🔺 ▼▼ **Microtel Inn & Suites by Wyndham Brunswick North** 🅷
(912) 554-1430. **$72-$130.** 146 Gateway Center Blvd 31525. I-95 exit 38 (Golden Isles Pkwy), just se to Glynco Pkwy, then just ne. Int corridors. **Pets:** Accepted. 🆂🅰🆅🅴 🛰 🛜 ✕ 🔧 🖵

🔺 ▼ **Super 8** 🅷
(912) 264-8800. **$50-$124.** 5280 New Jesup Hwy 31523. I-95 exit 36B (New Jesup Hwy/US 25), just nw. Int corridors. **Pets:** $10 daily fee/pet. Designated rooms, service with restrictions, supervision.
🆂🅰🆅🅴 🛜 🔧 🖵

BYRON

🔺 ▼▼ **Best Western Inn & Suites** 🅼 ❀
(478) 956-3056. **$75-$89.** 101 Dunbar Rd 31008. I-75 exit 149 (SR 49), just e. Ext corridors. **Pets:** Medium. $15 daily fee/pet. Service with restrictions, supervision. 🆂🅰🆅🅴 🛰 🛜 🔧 🖵

🔺 ▼▼ **Days Inn Byron** 🅷
(478) 956-5100. **$45-$65.** 246 Hwy 49 N 31008. I-75 exit 149 (SR 49), just sw. Ext corridors. **Pets:** Other species. $10 daily fee/pet. Designated rooms, service with restrictions, supervision.
🆂🅰🆅🅴 🆖 🛰 🛜 🔧 🖵

🔺 ▼▼ **Super 8** 🅷
(478) 956-3311. **$54-$79.** 305 Hwy 49 31008. I-75 exit 149 (SR 49), just e. Ext corridors. **Pets:** Medium, other species. $15 daily fee/pet. Designated rooms, service with restrictions, supervision.
🆂🅰🆅🅴 🛰 🛜 🔧 🖵

CAIRO

🔺 ▼▼ **Best Western Executive Inn** 🅷
(229) 377-8000. **$82-$102.** 2800 Hwy 84 E 39828. 2 mi e. Ext corridors. **Pets:** $10 daily fee/pet. 🆂🅰🆅🅴 🍴 🆖 🛰 🛜 🔧 🖵

CALHOUN

▼▼ **Baymont Inn & Suites** 🅼
(706) 629-8133. **$59-$149.** 189 Jameson 30701. I-75 exit 312, just w. Ext corridors. **Pets:** Accepted. 🆖 🛰 🛜 🔧 🖵

▼▼ **Econo Lodge** 🅼
(706) 629-9501. **$48-$60.** 915 Hwy 53 SE 30701. I-75 exit 312, just e. Ext corridors. **Pets:** Accepted. 🍴 🆖 🛰 🛜 🔧 🖵

▼▼▼ **La Quinta Inn** 🅷
(706) 629-2559. **$68-$152.** 150 Cracker Barrel Dr 30701. I-75 exit 312, just e. Int corridors. **Pets:** Accepted. 🆖 🛰 🛜 ✕ 🔧 🖵

⚜ ▼▼ Quality Inn Calhoun M
(706) 629-9207. **$74-$99.** 1204 Red Bud Rd NE 30701. I-75 exit 315, just w. Ext corridors. **Pets:** Accepted. 🅂🄰🅅🄴 Ⓜ⬈ 🛜 🛗 💻

▼▼ Super 8 Calhoun M
(706) 629-0999. **$59-$150.** 115 Hampton Dr SE 30701. I-75 exit 312, just w. Ext corridors. **Pets:** Accepted. Ⓜ⬈ 🛜 🛗 💻

CARROLLTON
▼▼ Quality Inn M
(770) 834-2600. **$74-$84.** 700 S Park St 30117. On US 27, just s of downtown. Ext corridors. **Pets:** Accepted. Ⓜ⬈ 🛜 🛗 💻

CARTERSVILLE
▼▼ Baymont Inn & Suites Cartersville H
(770) 386-9259. **$70-$95.** 11 Kent Dr 30121. I-75 exit 296, just e. Int corridors. **Pets:** Accepted. Ⓜ⬈ 🛜 🛗 💻

▼▼ Clarion Inn Cartersville H
(770) 386-0830. **$119-$129.** 2336 Hwy 411 30184. I-75 exit 293, just w. Int corridors. **Pets:** Accepted. 🍴Ⓜ⬈ 🛜❌ 🛗 💻

▼▼ Country Inn & Suites By Carlson H
(770) 386-5888. **$99-$289, 3 day notice.** 43 SR 20 Spur 30121. I-75 exit 290, 0.3 mi se. Int corridors. **Pets:** Medium. $15 daily fee/room. Designated rooms, service with restrictions, supervision.
Ⓜ⬈ 🛜❌ 🛗 💻

▼▼ Econo Lodge Cartersville H
(706) 382-8881. **$57-$90.** 41 SR 20 Spur SE 30121. I-75 exit 290, 0.3 mi e. Int corridors. **Pets:** Medium. $10 daily fee/pet. Service with restrictions, supervision. Ⓜ⬈ 🛜 🛗 💻

⚜ ▼▼ Knights Inn M
(770) 386-7263. **$65.** 420 E Church St 30121. I-75 exit 288, 1.5 mi w. Ext corridors. **Pets:** Medium. $10 daily fee/pet. Designated rooms, service with restrictions, supervision. 🅂🄰🅅🄴 ⬈ 🛜

▼▼▼ MainStay Suites, Cartersville-Emerson LakePoint H
(770) 607-3005. **$79-$199.** 146 Old Allatoona Rd SE 30121. I-75 exit 283, just e. Int corridors. **Pets:** Dogs only. $25 daily fee/pet. Service with restrictions, supervision. 🍴Ⓜ 🛜❌ 🛗 💻

▼▼ Microtel Inn & Suites by Wyndham Cartersville H
(678) 605-9331. **$68-$89.** 1348 Joe Frank Harris 30120. I-75 exit 290, 1.8 mi w on SR 20 W, just s on Market Pl Blvd, 1.5 mi w on SR 3 N/US 41 N (Joe Frank Harris Pkwy). Int corridors. **Pets:** Accepted.
Ⓜ 🛜❌ 🛗 💻

▼▼ Motel 6 - #4046 M
(770) 386-1449. **Call for rates.** 5657 Hwy 20 NE 30121. I-75 exit 290, 0.3 mi e. Ext corridors. **Pets:** Accepted. Ⓜ⬈ 🛜 🛗

▼▼▼ Sleep Inn Cartersville-Emerson LakePoint H
(770) 607-3005. **$99-$189.** 146 Old Allatoona Rd SE, Bldg A 30121. I-75 exit 283, just e. Int corridors. **Pets:** Dogs only. $25 daily fee/pet. Service with restrictions, supervision. 🍴Ⓜ 🛜❌ 🛗 💻

CHATSWORTH
▼▼ Super 8 Chatsworth H
(706) 695-0850. **$63-$80.** 613 S 3rd Ave 30705. On US 76/441, 0.5 mi s. Ext corridors. **Pets:** Medium. $10 daily fee/pet. Service with restrictions, supervision. Ⓜ⬈ 🛜 🛗 💻

CLAYTON
▼▼ Americas Best Value Inn M
(706) 782-4702. **Call for rates.** 698 Hwy 441 S 30525. 0.8 mi s. Int corridors. **Pets:** Accepted. Ⓜ 🛜 🛗 💻

▼ Days Inn of Clayton M
(706) 782-4258. **$65-$139.** 54 Hwy 441 N 30525. Center. Ext corridors. **Pets:** Accepted. ⬈ 🛜 🛗 💻

COLLEGE PARK
▼▼▼ Embassy Suites Hotel by Hilton at Atlanta Airport H
(404) 767-1988. **$129-$249.** 4700 Southport Rd 30337. I-85 exit 71, 0.3 mi w on Riverdale Rd. Int corridors. **Pets:** Accepted.
🍴Ⓜ⬈ 🄂❌ 🛗 💻

▼▼▼ Holiday Inn Express-Atlanta Airport H
(404) 761-6500. **Call for rates.** 4601 Best Rd 30337. I-85 exit 71, just w. Int corridors. **Pets:** Accepted. Ⓜ⬈ 🛜❌ 🛗 💻

⚜ ▼▼▼ Hyatt Place Atlanta Airport-South H
(770) 994-2997. **$79-$189.** 1899 Sullivan Rd 30337. I-85 exit 71, just e to Sullivan Rd, then just s; I-285 exit 60 (Riverdale Rd N), 1 mi to Sullivan Rd, then just s. Int corridors. **Pets:** Medium, dogs only. $75 one-time fee/pet. Service with restrictions, crate.
🅂🄰🅅🄴 Ⓜ⬈ 🛜❌ 🛗 💻

▼▼▼ La Quinta Inn & Suites Atlanta Airport H
(770) 996-0000. **$82-$230.** 4820 Massachusetts Blvd 30337. I-85 exit 71, just e to Airport Rd, then just s. Int corridors. **Pets:** Accepted.
⬈ 🛜 🛗 💻

⚜ ▼▼▼ Sheraton Atlanta Airport Hotel H 🐾
(770) 997-1100. **$109-$269.** 1900 Sullivan Rd 30337. I-85 exit 71, just e to Airport Rd, then just s. Int corridors. **Pets:** $50 deposit/room. Designated rooms, service with restrictions, crate.
🅂🄰🅅🄴 🍴Ⓜ⬈ 🄂❌ 🛗 💻

▼▼ Super 8-Atlanta Airport H
(770) 991-8985. **$65-$85.** 2010 Sullivan Rd 30337. I-85 exit 71, just e to Airport Rd, then just sw. Int corridors. **Pets:** Large, dogs only. $100 deposit/pet, $25 daily fee/pet. Designated rooms, service with restrictions, crate. Ⓜ 🛜 🛗 💻

⚜ ▼▼▼▼ The Westin Hotel-Atlanta Airport H 🐾
(404) 762-7676. **$99-$289.** 4736 Best 30337. I-85 exit 71, just w, se on access road to Best Rd, then just s. Int corridors. **Pets:** Medium, dogs only. $100 deposit/room. Service with restrictions, supervision.
🅂🄰🅅🄴 🄴🄲🄾 🍴Ⓜ⬈ ❌ 🛜❌ 🛗 💻

COLUMBUS *(Restaurants p. 611)*
▼▼▼ Clarion Inn H
(706) 324-0231. **Call for rates.** 2800 Manchester Expwy 31904. I-185 exit 7, just w. Int corridors. **Pets:** Accepted.
🍴 🛜❌ 🛗 💻

▼▼▼ Holiday Inn Express & Suites H
(706) 507-7080. **$83-$249.** 3901 Victory Dr 31903. I-185 exit 1B, 1 mi w. Int corridors. **Pets:** Accepted. 🍴Ⓜ⬈ 🛜❌ 🛗 💻

▼▼▼ Home2 Suites by Hilton H
(706) 257-6931. **$104-$159.** 1664 Whittlesey Rd 31904. I-185 exit 10B (US 80/SR 22), 1.3 mi w on US 80 to exit 3A (Bradley Park Rd), just e to Whittlesey Rd, then just n. Int corridors. **Pets:** Other species. $125 deposit/room. Service with restrictions. 🍴Ⓜ 🛜❌ 🛗 💻

⚜ ▼▼▼ Hyatt Place Columbus North H
(706) 507-5000. **$99-$249.** 2974 Northlake Pkwy 31909. US 80/SR 22 exit Veterans Pkwy, 0.4 mi ne, then just se. Int corridors. **Pets:** Accepted. 🅂🄰🅅🄴 🍴Ⓜ⬈ 🛜❌ 🛗 💻

▼▼ La Quinta Inn Columbus Fort Benning M
(706) 568-1740. **$67-$180.** 3201 Macon Rd, Suite 200 31906. I-185 exit 6, just sw. Ext/int corridors. **Pets:** Accepted. ⬈ 🛜 🛗 💻

▼▼ ◆ **La Quinta Inn Columbus State University** H
(706) 323-4344. **$67-$268.** 2919 Warm Springs Rd 31909. I-185 exit 7 southbound; exit 7A northbound, just e. Int corridors. **Pets:** Accepted.
&M 🖾 🛜 🛗 💻

▼▼ **Microtel Inn & Suites by Wyndham Columbus/Near Fort Benning** H
(706) 685-2305. **$70-$105.** 3930 St. Mary's Rd 31907. I-185 exit 3, just e. Int corridors. **Pets:** Medium, dogs only. $25 daily fee/pet. Service with restrictions, supervision. 🍽 🖾 🛜 🛗 💻

▼▼ **Microtel Inn & Suites by Wyndham Columbus North** H
(706) 653-7004. **$65-$80.** 1728 Fountain Ct 31904. I-185 exit 12, just w. Int corridors. **Pets:** Accepted. 🍽 &M 🛜 ✕ 🛗 💻

◍ ▼▼▼ **Residence Inn by Marriott Columbus** H 🐾
(706) 494-0050. **$116-$198.** 2670 Adams Farm Dr 31909. US 80/SR 22 exit Veterans Pkwy, just sw, then just e. Ext corridors. **Pets:** Other species. $100 one-time fee/room. Service with restrictions.
SAVE 🍽 &M 🛜 ✕ 🛗 💻

◍ ▼▼▼ **Staybridge Suites** H
(706) 507-7700. **Call for rates.** 1678 Whittlesey Rd 31904. I-185 exit 10B (US 80/SR 22), 1.3 mi w on US 80 exit 3A (Bradley Park Rd), just e to Whittlesey Rd, then just 0.6 mi n. Int corridors. **Pets:** Accepted.
SAVE 🖾 🛜 🛗 💻

◍ ▼▼▼ **TownePlace Suites by Marriott Columbus** H
(706) 322-3001. **$80-$142.** 4534 Armour Rd 31904. I-185 exit 7 southbound; exit 7A northbound, just w to Armour Rd, then just n. Int corridors. **Pets:** $100 one-time fee/room. Service with restrictions, supervision. SAVE 🍽 &M 🛜 ✕ 🛗 💻

COMMERCE

◍ ▼▼▼ **Best Western Commerce Inn** H
(706) 335-3640. **$75-$225.** 157 Eisenhower Dr 30529. I-85 exit 149, just ne. Int corridors. **Pets:** Accepted.
SAVE &M 🖾 🛜 ✕ 🛗 💻

▼▼▼ **Comfort Suites Commerce** H
(706) 336-0000. **$99-$229.** 30490 Hwy 441 S 30529. I-85 exit 149, just w. Int corridors. **Pets:** Accepted. &M 🖾 🛜 ✕ 🛗 💻

CONYERS

▼▼ **Country Inn & Suites By Carlson** H
(770) 785-2400. **$87-$120, 3 day notice.** 1312 Old Covington Hwy SE 30012. I-20 exit 82, just n. Int corridors. **Pets:** Small. $50 one-time fee/pet. Service with restrictions, supervision.
&M 🖾 🛜 ✕ 🛗 💻

▼▼▼ **Hampton Inn** H
(770) 483-8838. **$99-$159.** 1340 Dogwood Dr SE 30013. I-20 exit 82, just n, then just e. Int corridors. **Pets:** Accepted.
&M 🖾 🛜 ✕ 🛗 💻

▼▼▼ **Hawthorn Suites by Wyndham Conyers** H 🐾
(770) 761-9155. **$89-$205.** 1659 Centennial Olympic Pkwy 30013. I-20 exit 82, 3.7 mi e on SR 138, then 1.7 mi w. Int corridors. **Pets:** Other species. $75 one-time fee/pet. Designated rooms, service with restrictions. 🍽 🖾 ✕ 🛜 ✕ 🛗 💻

▼▼▼ **La Quinta Inn & Suites Atlanta Conyers** H
(770) 918-0092. **$86-$152.** 1184 Dogwood Dr SE 30012. I-20 exit 82, just n to Dogwood Dr, then just w. Int corridors. **Pets:** Accepted.
&M 🖾 🛜 ✕ 🛗 💻

▼▼ **Quality Inn** M
(770) 760-1230. **$66-$100.** 1164 Dogwood Dr SE 30012. I-20 exit 82, just n to Dogwood Dr, then just w. Ext corridors. **Pets:** Accepted.
&M 🖾 🛜 🛗 💻

CORDELE

▼▼ **Baymont Inn & Suites** H
(229) 273-9477. **$70-$79.** 416 S Greer St 31015. I-75 exit 101 (US 280), just w, then just n. Int corridors. **Pets:** $15 daily fee/pet. Designated rooms, service with restrictions, crate.
🍽 🖾 🛜 ✕ 🛗 💻

◍ ▼▼ **Best Western Colonial Inn** H
(229) 273-5420. **$72-$80.** 1706 E 16th Ave (US 280) 31015. I-75 exit 101 (US 280), just w. Ext/int corridors. **Pets:** Accepted.
SAVE 🖾 🛜 ✕ 🛗 💻

▼▼ **Econo Lodge** H
(229) 273-0737. **$64-$85.** 1603 16th Ave E (US 280) 31015. I-75 exit 101 (US 280), just w. Ext corridors. **Pets:** Accepted.
🖾 🛜 🛗 💻

◍ ▼▼ **Quality Inn Cordele** H
(229) 273-2371. **$70-$750.** 1601 E 16th Ave (US 280) 31015. I-75 exit 101 (US 280), just w. Ext corridors. **Pets:** $15 one-time fee/pet, $15 daily fee/room. No service, supervision. SAVE 🖾 🛜 🛗 💻

CORNELIA

▼▼ **Super 8** H
(706) 778-9573. **$50-$111.** 2965 J Warren Rd 30531. Jct SR 365 and US 441 business route, just w. Int corridors. **Pets:** Medium, dogs only. $25 daily fee/pet. Designated rooms, service with restrictions, crate.
&M 🖾 🛜 🛗 💻

COVINGTON

◍ ▼▼ ◆ **Baymont Inn & Suites** M
(770) 787-4900. **$59-$70.** 10111 Alcovy Rd 30014. I-20 exit 92, just n. Ext corridors. **Pets:** Small, dogs only. $15 daily fee/pet. Designated rooms, no service, supervision. SAVE 🍽 &M 🖾 🛜 🛗 💻

DALTON

▼▼▼ ◆ **Hilton Garden Inn Dalton** H
(706) 529-6000. **$149-$399.** 879 College Dr 30720. I-75 exit 333, just w. Int corridors. **Pets:** Accepted. 🍽 &M 🖾 🛜 ✕ 🛗 💻

▼▼ **Howard Johnson Dalton** M
(706) 281-1880. **$69-$100.** 790 College Dr 30720. I-75 exit 333, just w, then 0.3 mi n. Ext corridors. **Pets:** Other species. $15 daily fee/pet. Designated rooms, service with restrictions. &M 🖾 🛜 🛗 💻

▼▼▼ **La Quinta Inn & Suites Dalton** H
(706) 272-9099. **$102-$196.** 715 College Dr 30720. I-75 exit 333, just w to Holiday Inn Dr, then 0.5 mi n. Int corridors. **Pets:** Accepted.
&M 🖾 🛜 ✕ 🛗 💻

◍ ◆ **Quality Inn** M
(706) 278-0500. **$69-$109.** 875 College Dr 30720. I-75 exit 333, just w. Ext corridors. **Pets:** Medium. $10 daily fee/pet. Service with restrictions, supervision. SAVE 🛜 🛗 💻

▼▼ **Super 8 Dalton/Convention Center** H
(706) 529-7800. **$63-$70.** 869 College Dr 30720. I-75 exit 333, just w to Holiday Inn Dr, then just n. Ext corridors. **Pets:** Accepted.
🛜 🛗 💻

DARIEN

◍ ▼▼ **Comfort Inn** H
(912) 437-4200. **$81-$116.** 12924 GA Hwy 251 Rd 31305. I-95 exit 49 (SR 251), just nw. Int corridors. **Pets:** Accepted.
SAVE 🖾 🛜 ✕ 🛗 💻

DAWSONVILLE

▼▼▼ **Quality Inn & Suites** H
(706) 216-1900. **$91-$191.** 127 Beartooth Pkwy 30534. Jct SR 400/53, 0.5 mi s. Int corridors. **Pets:** Accepted. &M 🖾 🛜 ✕ 🛗 💻

DOUGLASVILLE

▼▼ Days Inn M
(770) 949-1499. **$58-$100.** 5489 Westmoreland Plaza 30134. I-20 exit 37, just n. Ext corridors. **Pets:** Accepted. 🍴 🏊 🛜 📶 💻

▼▼ Econo Lodge Inn & Suites H 🐾
(770) 489-4863. **$60-$165.** 8304 Cherokee Blvd 30134. I-20 exit 37, just n to Cherokee Blvd, then just e. Int corridors. **Pets:** Medium. $15 daily fee/pet. Designated rooms, service with restrictions, supervision.
🍴 🛗 🏊 🛜 📶 💻

▼▼▼▼ La Quinta Inn & Suites Atlanta Douglasville H
(770) 577-3838. **$75-$170.** 1000 Linnenkohl Dr 30134. I-20 exit 34, just n. Int corridors. **Pets:** Accepted. 🛗 🏊 🛜 ✖ 📶 💻

DUBLIN

▼▼▼▼ La Quinta Inn & Suites Dublin H
(478) 272-3110. **$86-$196.** 101 Travel Center Blvd 31021. I-16 exit 51 (US 441), just s. Int corridors. **Pets:** Accepted.
🛗 🏊 🛜 ✖ 📶 💻

DULUTH *(Restaurants p. 611)*

▼▼ Candlewood Suites-Atlanta H
(678) 380-0414. **Call for rates.** 3665 Shackleford Rd 30096. I-85 exit 104, just e, then just s. Int corridors. **Pets:** Accepted.
🛗 🛜 📶 💻

▼▼ Extended Stay America-Atlanta-Gwinnett Place H
(770) 623-6800. **$70-$85.** 3390 Venture Pkwy NW 30096. I-85 exit 104, just w to Venture Pkwy, then just n. Int corridors. **Pets:** Accepted.
🛗 🏊 🛜 📶 💻

▼▼ Holiday Inn-Gwinnett Center H
(770) 476-2022. **Call for rates.** 6310 Sugarloaf Pkwy 30097. I-85 exit 108, just w. Int corridors. **Pets:** Accepted.
🍴 🛗 🏊 🛜 ✖ 📶 💻

𝔸𝔸𝔸 ▼▼▼▼ Hyatt Place Atlanta/Duluth/Gwinnett Mall H
(770) 623-9699. **$69-$179.** 3530 Venture Pkwy 30096. I-85 exit 104, just w to Venture Pkwy, then just n. Int corridors. **Pets:** Accepted.
SAVE 🍴 🛗 🏊 🛜 ✖ 📶 💻

▼▼▼▼ Residence Inn by Marriott Atlanta Gwinnett Place H
(770) 921-2202. **$89-$183.** 1760 Pineland Rd 30096. I-85 exit 104, just e to Shackleford Rd, just s to Pineland Rd, then just e. Int corridors.
Pets: Accepted. 🛗 🏊 🛜 ✖ 📶 💻

▼▼▼▼ Residence Inn by Marriott Atlanta NE/Duluth Sugarloaf H 🐾
(770) 814-2929. **$103-$229.** 1940 Satellite Blvd 30097. I-85 exit 108, 0.8 mi e. Int corridors. **Pets:** Other species. $100 one-time fee/room. Service with restrictions, crate. 🍴 🛗 🛜 ✖ 📶 💻

EAST POINT

▼▼▼▼ Crowne Plaza Atlanta Airport H
(404) 768-6660. **$99-$199.** 1325 Virginia Ave 30344. I-85 exit 73 southbound; exit 73B northbound, just w. Int corridors. **Pets:** Accepted.
🍴 🛗 🏊 🛜 ✖ 📶 💻

▼▼▼▼ Drury Inn & Suites-Atlanta Airport H
(404) 761-4900. **$89-$179.** 1270 Virginia Ave 30344. I-85 exit 73 southbound; exit 73A northbound, just e. Int corridors. **Pets:** Accepted.
🛗 🏊 🛜 ✖ 📶 💻

𝔸𝔸𝔸 ▼▼▼▼ Holiday Inn & Suites Atlanta Airport-North H
(404) 305-9990. **Call for rates.** 1380 Virginia Ave 30344. I-85 exit 73 southbound; exit 73B northbound, just w. Int corridors. **Pets:** Accepted.
SAVE 🍴 🏊 🛜 ✖ 📶 💻

𝔸𝔸𝔸 ▼▼▼▼ Hyatt Place Atlanta Airport-North H
(404) 768-8484. **$94-$189.** 3415 Norman Berry Dr 30344. I-85 exit 73B northbound; exit 73 southbound, just e to Bobby Brown Pkwy, then just n. Int corridors. **Pets:** Accepted.
SAVE 🍴 🛗 🏊 🛜 ✖ 📶 💻

FAIRBURN

▼▼▼▼ Country Inn & Suites By Carlson H
(678) 782-4900. **$89-$159.** 7815 Senoia Rd 30213. I-85 exit 61, just e. Int corridors. **Pets:** Accepted. 🛗 🏊 🛜 ✖ 📶 💻

▼▼▼▼ Wingate by Wyndham Atlanta Airport Fairburn H
(770) 892-3006. **$94-$119.** 7882 Senoia Rd 30213. I-85 exit 61, 0.3 mi e. Int corridors. **Pets:** Accepted. 🛗 🏊 ✖ 🛜 ✖ 📶 💻

FITZGERALD

𝔸𝔸𝔸 ▼▼▼ Quality Inn H
(229) 423-5151. **$65-$97.** 263 Ocilla Hwy 31750. US 319/107, just n. Int corridors. **Pets:** Accepted. SAVE 🏊 🛜 📶 💻

▼▼ Western Motel M
(229) 424-9500. **Call for rates.** 111 Bull Run Rd 31750. Jct SR 107 and US 129, just nw on US 129. Ext corridors. **Pets:** Accepted.
🏊 🛜 📶 💻

FOREST PARK

▼▼ Super 8 M
(404) 363-8811. **$45-$100.** 410 Old Dixie Way 30297. I-75 exit 235, just e. Ext corridors. **Pets:** Accepted. 🏊 🛜 📶 💻

▼▼ Travelodge Forest Park Atlanta South M
(404) 361-3600. **$60-$73.** 6025 Old Dixie Rd 30297. I-75 exit 235, just n. Ext corridors. **Pets:** Accepted. 🍴 🛗 🛜 📶 💻

FORSYTH

𝔸𝔸𝔸 ▼▼▼ Comfort Inn Forsyth H
(478) 994-3400. **$79-$89.** 333 Harold G Clark Pkwy 31029. I-75 exit 185 (SR 18), just w. Ext corridors. **Pets:** Accepted.
SAVE 🛗 🏊 🛜 📶 💻

𝔸𝔸𝔸 ▼▼▼ Days Inn Forsyth H
(478) 994-2900. **$45-$80.** 343 N Lee St 31029. I-75 exit 188, 1 mi w. Ext corridors. **Pets:** Small, dogs only. $10 daily fee/pet. Supervision.
SAVE 🛜 📶 💻

▼▼▼▼ Holiday Inn Express H
(478) 994-9697. **$79-$139.** 520 Holiday Cir 31029. I-75 exit 186 (Juliette Rd), just w, then just s on Aaron St. Int corridors.
Pets: Accepted. 🛗 🏊 🛜 ✖ 📶 💻

▼▼▼ Super 8 M
(478) 994-5101. **$57-$62.** 436 Tift College Dr 31029. I-75 exit 186 (Juliette Rd), just w. Ext/int corridors. **Pets:** Accepted.
🏊 🛜 📶 💻

FORT OGLETHORPE

𝔸𝔸𝔸 ▼▼▼ Econo Lodge Inn & Suites M
(706) 866-0222. **$65-$125.** 2120 Lafayette Rd 30742. Jct US 27 (Lafayette Rd) and SR 2, just n. Ext corridors. **Pets:** Accepted.
SAVE 🏊 🛜 📶 💻

GAINESVILLE

𝔸𝔸𝔸 ▼▼▼ The Guest Lodge M
(770) 535-8100. **Call for rates.** 520 Queen City 30501. I-985 exit 20, 1.8 mi nw on SR 60/Queen City Pkwy. Ext corridors. **Pets:** Accepted.
SAVE 🏊 🛜 📶 💻

GREENSBORO

The Ritz-Carlton Reynolds, Lake Oconee H
(706) 467-0600. **$299-$1599, 3 day notice.** 1 Lake Oconee Tr 30642. I-20 exit 130, 7.2 mi sw on SR 44 (Old Eatonton Rd), 1.5 mi e on Linger Longer Rd, then 2 mi ne. Ext/int corridors. **Pets:** Accepted.

HAPEVILLE

Hilton Atlanta Airport H
(404) 767-9000. **$99-$289.** 1031 Virginia Ave 30354. I-85 exit 73 southbound; exit 73A northbound, just e. Int corridors. **Pets:** Accepted.

Residence Inn by Marriott Atlanta Airport North/Virginia Avenue H ❀
(404) 761-0511. **$99-$240.** 3401 International Blvd 30354. I-85 exit 73 southbound; exit 73A northbound, 0.5 mi e to International Blvd, then just n. Ext/int corridors. **Pets:** Medium, other species. $125 deposit/room. Crate.

HARTWELL

Quality Inn M
(706) 376-7298. **$64-$99.** 1091 E Franklin St 30643. Jct SR 366/US 29, 1.2 mi e on US 29 (E Franklin St). Ext corridors. **Pets:** Very small. $20 daily fee/pet. Designated rooms, service with restrictions, supervision.

HELEN *(Restaurants p. 612)*

The Helendorf River Inn & Conference Center M
(706) 878-2271. **Call for rates.** 33 Munich Strasse 30545. SR 17 and 75; center. Ext corridors. **Pets:** Other species. $20 daily fee/pet. Designated rooms, service with restrictions, supervision.

Quality Inn M
(706) 878-2268. **$74-$259.** 15 Yonah St 30545. Just w of Mack St. Ext corridors. **Pets:** Accepted.

HINESVILLE

Baymont Inn & Suites Hinesville Fort Stewart Area H
(912) 408-4444. **$62-$75.** 773 Frank Cochran Dr 31313. Jct SR 119/196, 1 mi sw on SR 196, then just nw. Int corridors. **Pets:** Accepted.

La Quinta Inn & Suites Hinesville/Ft Stewart H
(912) 369-3000. **$86-$180.** 1740 E Oglethorpe Hwy 31313. Jct US 84 and SR 38C, 0.8 mi ne. Int corridors. **Pets:** Accepted.

HIRAM

Country Inn & Suites By Carlson H
(770) 222-0456. **$95-$150.** 70 Enterprise Path 30134. Jct SR 92/6 and US 278, 0.3 mi w. Int corridors. **Pets:** Small. $25 daily fee/pet. Service with restrictions, supervision.

HOGANSVILLE

Woodstream Inn M
(706) 637-9395. **Call for rates.** 1888 E Main St 30230. I-85 exit 28, just w. Ext corridors. **Pets:** Accepted.

JASPER

Microtel Inn & Suites by Wyndham Jasper H
(706) 299-5500. **$60-$100.** 171 H Mullins Ct 30143. Jct SR 515/53, 0.9 mi n. Int corridors. **Pets:** Accepted.

JEKYLL ISLAND *(Restaurants p. 612)*

Hampton Inn & Suites Jekyll Island H
(912) 635-3733. **$129-$279.** 200 S Beachview Dr 31527. Jct Ben Fortson Pkwy (SR 520/Beachview Dr), 2 mi s. Int corridors. **Pets:** Accepted.

Holiday Inn Resort at Jekyll Island M ❀
(912) 635-2211. **$99-$299, 3 day notice.** 701 Beachview 31527. Jct Ben Fortson Pkwy (SR 520)/Beachview Dr, 1.5 mi n. Ext corridors. **Pets:** Other species. $20 daily fee/pet. Service with restrictions.

Villas by the Sea CO
(912) 635-2521. **$119-$399, 3 day notice.** 1175 N Beachview Dr 31527. Jct Ben Fortson Pkwy (SR 520/Beachview Dr), 4 mi n. Ext corridors. **Pets:** Medium, dogs only. $100 one-time fee/room. Designated rooms, service with restrictions, supervision.

The Westin Jekyll Island H
(912) 635-4545. **$229-$349, 3 day notice.** 110 Ocean 31527. Center. Int corridors. **Pets:** Accepted.

JOHNS CREEK

Hyatt Place Atlanta/Duluth/Johns Creek H
(770) 622-5858. **$89-$259.** 11505 Medlock Bridge Rd 30097. Jct SR 141 and 120, 0.7 mi n. Int corridors. **Pets:** Accepted.

KENNESAW *(Restaurants p. 612)*

Days Inn M
(770) 419-1576. **$50-$82.** 760 Cobb Place Blvd 30144. I-75 exit 269, just w. Ext corridors. **Pets:** Accepted.

Extended Stay America Atlanta Kennesaw H
(770) 422-1403. **$75-$100.** 3000 George Busbee Pkwy 30144. I-75 exit 269, just e to George Busbee Pkwy, then 0.8 mi n. Int corridors. **Pets:** Accepted.

Kennesaw Inn M
(770) 424-7666. **$72-$80.** 3375 Busbee Dr 30144. I-75 exit 271, just e. Ext corridors. **Pets:** Accepted.

Quality Inn M
(770) 419-1530. **$60-$159.** 750 Cobb Place Blvd 30144. I-75 exit 269, just w. Ext corridors. **Pets:** Accepted.

Red Roof Inn Atlanta-Kennesaw M
(770) 429-0323. **$57-$100.** 520 Roberts Ct NW 30144. I-75 exit 269, just e. Ext corridors. **Pets:** Accepted.

Residence Inn by Marriott Atlanta Kennesaw/Town Center H ❀
(770) 218-1018. **$102-$237.** 3443 NW Busbee Dr 30144. I-75 exit 271, just e. Int corridors. **Pets:** Small, dogs only. $100 one-time fee/room. Designated rooms, service with restrictions, supervision.

KINGSLAND

Baymont Inn & Suites Kingsland H
(912) 729-9600. **$49-$75.** 105 May Creek Dr 31548. I-95 exit 3 (SR 40), just w. Ext corridors. **Pets:** Other species. $100 one-time fee/pet. Designated rooms, service with restrictions.

Country Inn & Suites By Carlson H
(912) 576-1616. **Call for rates.** 135 The Lakes Blvd 31548. I-95 exit 3 (SR 40), just se. Int corridors. **Pets:** Accepted.

▼▼▼ La Quinta Inn Kingsland Kings Bay H
(912) 882-8010. **$79-$163.** 104 May Creek Dr 31548. I-95 exit 3 (SR 40), just w. Int corridors. **Pets:** Accepted.
ᏋⓂ 🛏 📶 ✖ 🔌 💻

ᏚᏚᏚᐟ ▼▼▼ Microtel Inn & Suites by Wyndham
                    Kingsland H
(912) 729-1555. **$49-$100.** 1325 E King Ave 31548. I-95 exit 3 (SR 40), just ne. Int corridors. **Pets:** $20 daily fee/pet. Designated rooms, service with restrictions, supervision. SAVE 🛏 📶 ✖ 🔌 💻

LA FAYETTE

▼▼ Americas Best Value Inn & Suites M
(706) 639-9362. **Call for rates.** 2209 N Main St 30728. 2.5 mi n on US 27. Ext corridors. **Pets:** Accepted. 🍴 🛏 📶 🔌 💻

▼▼ Key West Inn M
(706) 638-8200. **$52-$89.** 2221 N Main St 30728. 2.5 mi n on US 27. Ext corridors. **Pets:** Accepted. ᏋⓂ 🛏 📶 🔌

LAGRANGE

▼▼ Baymont Inn & Suites H
(706) 885-9002. **$69-$87.** 107 Hoffman Dr 30240. I-85 exit 18 (Lafayette Pkwy), just w. Int corridors. **Pets:** Medium. $10 daily fee/pet. Service with restrictions, crate. ᏋⓂ 🛏 📶 🔌 💻

▼▼▼ Comfort Inn & Suites H
(706) 882-7700. **$84-$139.** 1512 Lafayette Pkwy 30241. I-85 exit 18 (Lafayette Pkwy), just w. Int corridors. **Pets:** Accepted.
ᏋⓂ 🛏 📶 ✖ 🔌 💻

▼▼ Lafayette Garden Inn & Conference Center M
(706) 884-6175. **Call for rates.** 1513 Lafayette Pkwy 30241. I-85 exit 18 (Lafayette Pkwy), just w. Ext corridors. **Pets:** Accepted.
🍴 ᏋⓂ 🛏 📶 🔌 💻

▼▼▼ La Quinta Inn & Suites H
(706) 812-8000. **$84-$169.** 111 Hoffman Dr 30241. I-85 exit 18 (Lafayette Pkwy), just w. Int corridors. **Pets:** Accepted.
🍴 ᏋⓂ 🛏 📶 🔌 💻

▼▼ Quality Inn M
(706) 882-8700. **$69-$84.** 110 Jameson Dr 30240. I-85 exit 18 (Lafayette Pkwy), 0.3 mi w. Ext corridors. **Pets:** Small. $15 daily fee/pet. Service with restrictions, supervision. ᏋⓂ 🛏 📶 🔌 💻

▼▼ Red Roof Inn LaGrange M
(706) 882-9540. **$50-$100.** 1601 Lafayette Pkwy 30241. I-85 exit 18 (Lafayette Pkwy), just e. Ext corridors. **Pets:** Accepted.
ᏋⓂ 🛏 📶 ✖ 🔌 💻

LAKE PARK

▼▼ Days Inn H
(229) 559-0229. **$50-$70.** 4913 Timber Dr 31636. I-75 exit 5, just nw. Ext corridors. **Pets:** Medium, other species. $25 one-time fee/room, $15 daily fee/pet. Service with restrictions, supervision.
🛏 📶 ✖ 🔌 💻

LAVONIA

▼▼▼ Holiday Inn Express & Suites H
(706) 356-2100. **Call for rates.** 110 Owens Dr 30553. I-85 exit 173, just w. Int corridors. **Pets:** Small. $40 one-time fee/room. Designated rooms, service with restrictions, supervision. ᏋⓂ 🛏 📶 ✖ 🔌 💻

▼▼ Super 8 M
(706) 356-8848. **$56-$64.** 14227 Jones St 30553. I-85 exit 173, just w. Ext corridors. **Pets:** Accepted. ᏋⓂ 🛏 📶 ✖ 🔌 💻

LAWRENCEVILLE

ᏚᏚᏚᐟ ▼▼▼ Days Inn M
(770) 995-7782. **$65-$81.** 731 Duluth Hwy 30046. SR 316 exit SR 120, just e. Ext corridors. **Pets:** Other species. $25 daily fee/pet. Service with restrictions, supervision. SAVE 📶 🔌 💻

LITHONIA

ᏚᏚᏚᐟ ▼▼▼▼ Hyatt Place Atlanta-East/Lithonia H
(770) 484-4384. **$69-$209.** 7900 Mall Ring Rd 30038. I-20 exit 75, just s on Turner Hill Rd, then 0.7 mi w. Int corridors. **Pets:** Accepted.
SAVE 🍴 ᏋⓂ 🛏 📶 ✖ 🔌 💻

LOCUST GROVE

ᏚᏚᏚᐟ ▼▼▼ La Quinta Inn & Suites Locust Grove H
(678) 583-8088. **$82-$213.** 4832 Bill Gardner Pkwy 30248. I-75 exit 212, just e. Int corridors. **Pets:** Accepted.
SAVE ᏋⓂ 🛏 📶 ✖ 🔌 💻

ᏚᏚᏚᐟ ▼▼▼ Red Roof Inn-Locust Grove H
(678) 583-0004. **$59-$99.** 4840 Bill Gardner Pkwy 30248. I-75 exit 212, just e. Int corridors. **Pets:** Accepted. SAVE ᏋⓂ 📶 ✖ 🔌 💻

▼▼ Super 8 M
(770) 957-2936. **$54-$96, 3 day notice.** 4605 Bill Gardner Pkwy 30248. I-75 exit 212, just w. Ext corridors. **Pets:** Accepted. 📶 🔌 💻

MACON *(Restaurants p. 612)*

ᏚᏚᏚᐟ ▼▼▼ Best Western Inn & Suites of
                    Macon M 🐾
(478) 781-5300. **$74-$90.** 4681 Chambers Rd 31206. I-475 exit 3 (Eisenhower Pkwy/US 80), just ne, then just se. Ext corridors. **Pets:** Large. $10 daily fee/pet. Designated rooms, service with restrictions. SAVE 🛏 📶 🔌 💻

ᏚᏚᏚᐟ ▼▼▼▼ Best Western Riverside Inn H
(478) 743-6311. **$66-$80.** 2400 Riverside Dr 31204. I-75 exit 167 (Riverside Dr), then 0.4 mi se. Int corridors. **Pets:** Medium. $15 daily fee/pet. Designated rooms, service with restrictions, supervision.
SAVE 🛏 📶 ✖ 🔌 💻

▼▼▼ Candlewood Suites H 🐾
(478) 254-3530. **Call for rates.** 3957 River Place Dr 31210. I-75 exit 169 (Arkwright Rd), just e, then just s. Int corridors. **Pets:** Other species. $75 one-time fee/room. Service with restrictions, crate.
ᏋⓂ 📶 🔌 💻

ᏚᏚᏚᐟ ▼▼▼ Days Inn M
(478) 781-4343. **$50-$65.** 4999 Eisenhower Pkwy 31206. I-475 exit 3 (Eisenhower Pkwy/US 80), just e. Ext corridors. **Pets:** $10 daily fee/pet. Designated rooms, service with restrictions, supervision.
SAVE 🛏 🔌 💻

▼▼▼ La Quinta Inn & Suites Macon H
(478) 475-0206. **$82-$143.** 3944 River Place Dr 31210. I-75 exit 169 (Arkwright Rd), just n, then e. Int corridors. **Pets:** Accepted.
ᏋⓂ 🛏 📶 🔌 💻

▼▼▼ La Quinta Inn & Suites Macon West H
(478) 788-6226. **$86-$220.** 4615 Chambers Rd 31206. I-475 exit 3 (Eisenhower Pkwy/US 80), just e, then 0.5 mi s. Int corridors.
Pets: Accepted. 🍴 🛏 📶 ✖ 🔌 💻

ᏚᏚᏚᐟ ▼▼▼ Microtel Inn & Suites by Wyndham M
(478) 254-3300. **$60-$79.** 2020 Bowman Park 31210. I-75 exit 171 (Riverside Dr), just w on Riverside Park. Int corridors. **Pets:** Accepted.
SAVE ᏋⓂ 📶 🔌 💻

ᏚᏚᏚᐟ ▼▼▼ Ramada Inn H
(478) 788-0120. **$55-$75.** 4755 Chambers Rd 31206. I-475 exit 3 (Eisenhower Pkwy/US 80), just e. Ext corridors. **Pets:** Small. $15 daily fee/pet. Designated rooms, service with restrictions, supervision.
SAVE 🍴 🛏 📶 🔌 💻

Residence Inn by Marriott H ❖
(478) 475-4280. **$116-$187.** 3900 Sheraton Dr 31211. I-75 exit 169 (Ackwright Rd), just n, then just nw. Int corridors. **Pets:** Small, other species. $100 one-time fee/room. Service with restrictions, crate.
SAVE 🍴 ᎤM 🛜 ✕ 🔒 🖵

Super 8 Macon West H
(478) 254-5290. **$49-$60.** 4765 Chambers Rd 31206. I-475 exit 3, just e. Ext corridors. **Pets:** Small. $10 daily fee/pet. Designated rooms, service with restrictions, supervision. SAVE 🍴 🛜 🔒 🖵

MADISON *(Restaurants p. 612)*

Quality Inn M
(706) 342-1839. **$55-$99.** 2001 Eatonton Rd 30650. US 129/441, 0.4 mi w. Ext corridors. **Pets:** Accepted. ᎤM 🛜 🔒 🖵

MARIETTA *(Restaurants p. 612)*

Drury Inn & Suites-Atlanta Northwest H
(770) 612-0900. **$89-$169.** 1170 Powers Ferry Pl 30067. I-75 exit 261, just e. Int corridors. **Pets:** Accepted. ᎤM 🏊 🛜 ✕ 🔒 🖵

Hilton Atlanta/Marietta Hotel & Conference Center H
(770) 427-2500. **$109-$169.** 500 Powder Springs St 30064. I-75 exit 263, 3.5 mi w to Powder Springs St, then just w. Int corridors. **Pets:** Accepted. 🍴 ᎤM 🏊 ✕ 📶 ✕ 🔒 🖵

Hyatt Regency Suites Atlanta NW H
(770) 956-1234. **$109-$289, 3 day notice.** 2999 Windy Hill Rd 30067. I-75 exit 260, 0.5 mi e. Int corridors. **Pets:** Accepted.
SAVE 🍴 ᎤM 🏊 🛜 ✕ 🔒 🖵

Quality Inn Atlanta/Marietta H
(770) 955-0004. **$80-$140.** 1255 Franklin Rd SE 30067. I-75 exit 261, 0.3 mi w to Franklin Rd, then just s. Int corridors. **Pets:** Accepted.
SAVE 🏊 🛜 🔒 🖵

MCDONOUGH

Country Inn & Suites By Carlson H
(770) 957-0082. **$75-$200.** 115 E Greenwood Rd 30253. I-75 exit 216, just w. Int corridors. **Pets:** Accepted. ᎤM 🏊 🔒 🖵

Econo Lodge M
(770) 957-2651. **$46-$55.** 1279 Hwy 20 W 30253. I-75 exit 218, just w. Ext corridors. **Pets:** Small. $10 daily fee/pet. Designated rooms, service with restrictions, supervision. SAVE 🛜 🔒 🖵

Home2 Suites by Hilton Atlanta/South McDonough H
(678) 369-2527. **$109-$169.** 60 Mill Rd 30253. I-75 exit 221, 0.3 mi nw on Jonesboro Rd, then 0.4 mi s. Int corridors. **Pets:** Medium, other species. $75 one-time fee/room. Service with restrictions, crate.
🍴 ᎤM 🛜 ✕ 🔒 🖵

Quality Inn & Suites Conference Center M
(770) 957-5291. **$79-$124.** 930 Hwy 155 S 30253. I-75 exit 216, just w. Ext corridors. **Pets:** Accepted. ᎤM 🏊 🔒 🖵

Sleep Inn H
(770) 898-0804. **$79-$94.** 945 Hwy 155 S 30253. I-75 exit 216, just w. Int corridors. **Pets:** Accepted. SAVE ᎤM 🏊 🛜 ✕ 🔒 🖵

MILLEDGEVILLE

Antebellum Inn BB
(478) 453-3993. **Call for rates.** 200 N Columbia St 31061. Just s of Business Rt US 441 (Columbia St); between SR 22 and 49; downtown. Int corridors. **Pets:** Accepted. 🍴 🏊 🛜 ✕ 🐾 🖵

Heritage Inn M ❖
(478) 453-9491. **Call for rates.** 2474 N Columbia St 31061. US 441, 2.6 mi n of downtown. Int corridors. **Pets:** Medium, cats only. $10 daily fee/pet. Designated rooms, service with restrictions, crate.
🍴 ᎤM 🛜 🔒 🖵

MORROW

Best Western Southlake Inn M
(770) 961-6300. **$69-$89.** 6437 Jonesboro Rd 30260. I-75 exit 233, just e. Ext corridors. **Pets:** Accepted. SAVE 🏊 🛜 🔒 🖵

Drury Inn & Suites-Atlanta South H
(770) 960-0500. **$94-$134.** 6520 S Lee St 30260. I-75 exit 233, just e. Int corridors. **Pets:** Accepted. 🍴 ᎤM 🏊 🛜 ✕ 🔒 🖵

Extended Stay America-Atlanta-Morrow H
(770) 472-0727. **$55-$75.** 2265 Mt. Zion Pkwy 30260. I-75 exit 231, just w, then just s. Int corridors. **Pets:** Accepted. 🛜 🔒 🖵

NEWNAN

Best Western Shenandoah Inn M ❖
(770) 304-9700. **$90-$107.** 620 Hwy 34 E 30265. I-85 exit 47, just w. Ext corridors. **Pets:** Medium. $10 daily fee/pet. Service with restrictions, supervision. SAVE 🏊 🛜 🔒 🖵

NORCROSS

Comfort Inn & Suites H
(770) 263-8883. **$71-$149.** 5200 Peachtree Industrial Blvd 30071. I-285 exit 31B, 5.5 mi n; I-85 exit 99, 4 mi w to Peachtree Industrial Blvd, then 1.5 mi n. Int corridors. **Pets:** Accepted. ᎤM 🏊 🛜 🔒 🖵

Hilton Atlanta Northeast H
(770) 447-4747. **$79-$329.** 5993 Peachtree Industrial Blvd 30092. I-285 exit 31B, 4.5 mi ne. Int corridors. **Pets:** Accepted.
🍴 ᎤM 🏊 📶 ✕ 🔒 🖵

Homewood Suites by Hilton H
(770) 448-4663. **$89-$189.** 450 Technology Pkwy 30092. I-85 exit 99, 4 mi w to Peachtree Industrial Blvd, 0.4 mi n, w on Holcomb Bridge Rd, then 2 blks n on Peachtree Pkwy; I-285 exit 31B, 5 mi n on SR 141. Ext/int corridors. **Pets:** Accepted. ᎤM 🏊 🛜 🔒 🖵

Hyatt Place Atlanta/Norcross/Peachtree Parkway H
(770) 416-7655. **$64-$169.** 5600 Peachtree Pkwy 30092. I-285 exit 31B, 4 mi n on SR 141, then just n. Int corridors. **Pets:** Accepted.
SAVE 🍴 ᎤM 🏊 🛜 ✕ 🔒 🖵

La Quinta Inn Norcross H
(770) 368-9400. **$71-$174.** 5945 Oakbrook Pkwy 30093. I-85 exit 99, 0.3 mi e to Live Oak Pkwy, then 0.8 mi nw. Int corridors.
Pets: Accepted. 🏊 🛜 🔒 🖵

TownePlace Suites by Marriott Atlanta Norcross/Peachtree Corners H
(770) 447-8446. **$74-$126.** 6640 Bay Cir 30071. I-285 exit 31B, 3 mi n on Peachtree Industrial Blvd to Jones Mill Rd. Int corridors.
Pets: Accepted. ECO 🍴 ᎤM 🏊 🛜 ✕ 🔒 🖵

OAKWOOD

Best Western Plus Lake Lanier/Gainesville Hotel & Suites H
(770) 535-8080. **$101-$116.** 4535 Oakwood Rd 30566. I-985 exit 16, just w. Int corridors. **Pets:** Accepted. SAVE 🏊 🛜 ✕ 🔒 🖵

Jameson Inn M
(770) 533-9400. **Call for rates.** 3530 Thurman Tanner Pkwy 30566. I-985 exit 16, 0.4 mi w. Ext corridors. **Pets:** Accepted.
ᎤM 🏊 🛜 🔒 🖵

PEACHTREE CITY

▼▼ Days Inn & Suites Peachtree City M
(770) 632-9700. **$58-$99.** 976 Crosstown Dr 30269. Jct SR 54 and 74, 2.1 mi s on SR 74. Ext corridors. **Pets:** Accepted.
⊘⊘⊘⊘⊘

▼▼▼ Wyndham Peachtree Hotel & Conference Center H
(770) 487-2000. **$99-$199.** 2443 Hwy 54 W 30269. Jct SR 74 and 54, 1 mi e. Int corridors. **Pets:** Accepted.
⊘⊘⊘⊘⊘⊘⊘⊘⊘⊘

PERRY

▼▼ Microtel Inn & Suites by Wyndham Perry H
(478) 987-4004. **$45-$144.** 110 AG Village Blvd 31069. I-75 exit 134, just nw. Int corridors. **Pets:** Accepted.
⊘⊘⊘⊘⊘

PINE MOUNTAIN

▼▼▼ Callaway Gardens - Inn, Cottages & Villas H
(706) 663-2281. **$109-$996, 7 day notice.** 17800 Hwy 27 31822. Jct SR 354, 1.5 mi s on US 27/SR 1; in Callaway Gardens. Ext/int corridors. **Pets:** Accepted.
⊘⊘⊘⊘⊘⊘⊘⊘⊘

▼ White Columns Motel M
(706) 663-2312. **$59-$79.** 524 S Main Ave 31822. Jct SR 354, just n on US 27/SR 1. Ext corridors. **Pets:** Medium. $15 daily fee/pet. Designated rooms, service with restrictions, supervision.
⊘⊘

POOLER

▼▼▼▼ La Quinta Inn & Suites Savannah Airport-Pooler H
(912) 748-3771. **$90-$225.** 414 Gray St 31322. I-95 exit 102 (US 80), just w. Int corridors. **Pets:** Accepted.
⊘⊘⊘⊘⊘⊘

PORT WENTWORTH (Restaurants p. 612)

▼▼▼ Comfort Suites Savannah North H
(912) 965-1445. **$89-$179.** 115 Travelers Way 31407. I-95 exit 109 (SR 21), just n. Int corridors. **Pets:** Accepted.
⊘⊘⊘⊘⊘⊘

▼▼▼ Country Inn & Suites By Carlson Savannah North H
(912) 964-2300. **Call for rates.** 200 Raley Rd 31407. I-95 exit 109 (SR 21), just s. Int corridors. **Pets:** Accepted.
⊘⊘⊘⊘⊘⊘⊘

RICHMOND HILL

▼▼▼▼ Best Western Plus Richmond Hill Inn H
(912) 756-7070. **$69-$159.** 4564 US Hwy 17 31324. I-95 exit 87 (Ocean Hwy/US 17), just w. Int corridors. **Pets:** Accepted.
⊘⊘⊘⊘⊘⊘⊘

▼▼ Econo Lodge-Richmond Hill M
(912) 756-3312. **$56-$130.** 4701 US Hwy 17 31324. I-95 exit 87 (Ocean Hwy/US 17), 0.4 mi sw. Ext corridors. **Pets:** Small. $20 daily fee/pet. Designated rooms, service with restrictions, supervision.
⊘⊘⊘⊘⊘

RINGGOLD

▼▼ Hometown Inn H
(706) 937-7070. **Call for rates.** 22 Gateway Business Park Dr 30736. I-75 exit 350, just e to Smitherman Rd, then just n. Int corridors. **Pets:** Accepted.
⊘⊘⊘⊘⊘⊘⊘

▼ Super 8 Ringgold H
(706) 965-7080. **$60-$70.** 5400 Alabama Hwy 30736. I-75 exit 348, just e. Ext corridors. **Pets:** Accepted.
⊘⊘⊘⊘⊘

ROME

▼▼▼ La Quinta Inn & Suites H
(706) 291-1034. **$67-$174.** 15 Chateau Dr 30161. 2 mi e on US 411. Int corridors. **Pets:** Accepted.
⊘⊘⊘⊘⊘⊘⊘⊘

▼▼ Quality Inn H
(706) 291-7797. **$69-$163.** 40 Grace Dr 30161. 2.2 mi e on US 411. Int corridors. **Pets:** Accepted.
⊘⊘⊘⊘⊘

ST. SIMONS ISLAND (Restaurants p. 612)

▼▼▼▼ The Lodge at Sea Island H
(912) 634-3992. **$325-$850, 7 day notice.** 100 Retreat Ave 31522. FJ Torras Cswy, 1.6 mi se on Kings Way, just s; on Sea Island Club golf course. Int corridors. **Pets:** Accepted.
⊘⊘⊘⊘⊘⊘

SAVANNAH (Restaurants p. 612)

▼▼▼ Andaz Savannah H
(912) 233-2116. **$179-$429.** 14 Barnard St 31401. Jct Barnard and W Bryan sts. Int corridors. **Pets:** Accepted.
⊘⊘⊘⊘⊘⊘⊘

▼▼ Baymont Inn & Suites H
(912) 925-9494. **$69-$275.** 393 Canebrake Rd 31419. I-95 exit 94 (SR 204/Abercorn St), just se. Int corridors. **Pets:** Medium. $20 daily fee/pet. Designated rooms, service with restrictions, supervision.
⊘⊘⊘⊘⊘

▼▼▼ Best Western Plus Savannah Historic District M
(912) 233-1011. **$79-$309.** 412 W Bay St 31401. Jct Montgomery St. Ext corridors. **Pets:** Accepted.
⊘⊘⊘⊘⊘⊘

▼▼▼ Best Western Savannah Gateway M
(912) 925-2420. **$75-$122.** 1 Gateway Blvd E 31419. I-95 exit 94 (SR 204/Abercorn St), just e. Ext corridors. **Pets:** Accepted.
⊘⊘⊘⊘⊘⊘

▼▼▼ The Bohemian Hotel Savannah Riverfront, Autograph Collection H
(912) 721-3800. **$171-$458, 3 day notice.** 102 E Bay St 31401. Between Bull and Whitaker sts. Int corridors. **Pets:** Large, dogs only. $150 one-time fee/room. Service with restrictions, supervision.
⊘⊘⊘⊘⊘

▼▼▼ The Brice H
(912) 238-1200. **Call for rates.** 601 E Bay St 31401. Between Houston and E Broad sts. Int corridors. **Pets:** Accepted.
⊘⊘⊘⊘⊘⊘

▼▼▼ Catherine Ward House Inn BB
(912) 234-8564. **Call for rates.** 118 E Waldburg St 31401. Between Drayton and Abercorn sts. Ext/int corridors. **Pets:** Accepted.
⊘⊘⊘⊘⊘

▼▼ Comfort Inn H
(912) 354-8560. **Call for rates.** 7110 Hodgson Memorial Dr 31406. Jct SR 21 and 204 (Abercorn St), 1.3 mi s, just e on Eisenhower Dr, then just s. Int corridors. **Pets:** Accepted.
⊘⊘⊘⊘⊘

▼▼▼ Comfort Inn & Suites Savannah Airport H
(912) 629-1500. **$79-$199.** 15 Jay R Turner Dr 31408. I-95 exit 104, 0.4 mi e. Int corridors. **Pets:** Small. $25 one-time fee/room. Designated rooms, service with restrictions, supervision.
⊘⊘⊘⊘⊘⊘

▼▼▼ East Bay Inn CI
(912) 238-1225. **$169-$400, 7 day notice.** 225 E Bay St 31401. Between Abercorn and Lincoln sts. Int corridors. **Pets:** Accepted.
⊘⊘⊘

▼▼ Extended Stay America Savannah-Midtown [H]
(912) 692-0076. **$80-$115.** 5511 Abercorn St 31405. Jct SR 21 and 204 (Abercorn St), just s. Int corridors. **Pets:** Accepted. 🛰🗙🖥📺

🔺 ▼▼ Foley House Inn [BB] 🐾
(912) 232-6622. **Call for rates.** 14 W Hull St 31401. Between Bull and Whitaker sts; on Chippewa Square. Ext/int corridors. **Pets:** Other species. $50 one-time fee/pet. Service with restrictions. [SAVE] 🛰🗙

▼▼▼ The Forsyth Park Inn [BB]
(912) 233-6800. **$210-$345, 14 day notice.** 102 W Hall St 31401. Between Whitaker and Howard sts; across from Forsyth Park. Int corridors. **Pets:** Accepted. 🍴🛰🗙🖥

🔺 ▼▼▼ The Gastonian [BB]
(912) 232-2869. **$179-$525, 7 day notice.** 220 E Gaston St 31401. Between Abercorn and Lincoln sts. Ext/int corridors. **Pets:** Accepted. [SAVE]🍴🛰🗙

🔺 ▼▼▼ Hamilton-Turner Inn [BB] 🐾
(912) 233-1833. **Call for rates.** 330 Abercorn St 31401. Between E Charlton and E Harris sts; overlooking Lafayette Square. Ext/int corridors. **Pets:** Small, dogs only. $50 one-time fee/room. Designated rooms, service with restrictions, crate. [SAVE]🍴🛰🗙

🔺 ▼▼ Hotel Indigo Savannah Historic
District [H] 🐾
(912) 236-4440. **Call for rates.** 201 W Bay St 31401. Between Barnard and Jefferson sts; enter at Barnard St and W Bay Ln. Int corridors. **Pets:** Large, other species. $75 one-time fee/room. Service with restrictions. [SAVE]🍴🛗🛰🗙📺

🔺 ▼▼▼ Hyatt Place Savannah Airport [H]
(912) 966-0020. **$79-$299.** 4 Stephen S Green Dr 31408. I-95 exit 104, just se to Crossroads Pkwy, then just sw. Int corridors. **Pets:** Large, dogs only. $75 one-time fee/room. Service with restrictions. [SAVE]🛗🛰🗙📺

▼▼ La Quinta Inn & Suites [H]
(912) 927-7660. **$67-$284.** 8484 Abercorn St 31406. 2.4 mi s of jct SR 21 and 204 (Abercorn St). Int corridors. **Pets:** Accepted. 🏊🛰🖥📺

🔺 ▼▼▼ Mansion on Forsyth Park, Autograph
Collection [H]
(912) 238-5158. **$125-$352.** 700 Drayton St 31401. Between E Hall and E Gwinnett sts; on Forsyth Park. Int corridors. **Pets:** Accepted. [SAVE][ECO]🍴🛰🗙🖥📺

▼▼▼ Olde Harbour Inn [BB]
(912) 234-4100. **$180-$450, 7 day notice.** 508 E Factors Walk 31401. Lincoln St ramp off E Bay St. Ext corridors. **Pets:** Accepted. 🛰🗙🖥📺

🔺 ▼▼▼ Quality Inn Savannah Historic District [M]
(912) 236-6321. **$99-$289.** 300 W Bay St 31401. Between N Montgomery and N Jefferson sts. Ext corridors. **Pets:** Accepted. [SAVE]🛰🗙🖥📺

▼▼▼ Residence Inn by Marriott Downtown/Historic
District [H]
(912) 233-9996. **$137-$248.** 500 W Charlton St 31401. Jct Martin Luther King Jr Blvd. Int corridors. **Pets:** Accepted. 🛗🏊🛰🗙🖥📺

▼▼▼ Residence Inn by Marriott Savannah
Midtown [H]
(912) 356-3266. **$119-$234.** 5710 White Bluff Rd 31405. Jct SR 21, 0.5 mi s. Int corridors. **Pets:** Accepted. 🍴🛗🏊🛰🗙🖥📺

▼▼▼ Staybridge Suites Savannah Historic District [H]
(912) 721-9000. **Call for rates.** 301 E Bay St 31401. Corner of Lincoln St. Int corridors. **Pets:** Accepted. 🛗🛰🗙🖥📺

▼▼▼ TownePlace Suites by Marriott Savannah
Airport [H]
(912) 629-7775. **$106-$171.** 4 Jay R Turner Dr 31408. I-95 exit 104, just e. Int corridors. **Pets:** Accepted. 🛗🛰🗙🖥📺

▼▼▼ TownePlace Suites by Marriott Savannah
Midtown [H]
(912) 920-9080. **$80-$182.** 11309 Abercorn St 31419. Jct SR 21 and 204 (Abercorn St), 4.6 mi s. Int corridors. **Pets:** Accepted. 🛗🏊🛰🗙🖥📺

🔺 ▼▼▼▼ The Westin Savannah Harbor Golf
Resort and Spa [H]
(912) 201-2000. **$179-$479, 3 day notice.** 1 Resort 31421. On Hutchinson Island; 1 mi se of first exit after Eugene Talmadge Memorial Bridge and US 17. Int corridors. **Pets:** Accepted. [SAVE][ECO]🍴🛗🏊🗙🛰🗙🖥📺

▼▼▼ Wingate by Wyndham Savannah Airport [H]
(912) 544-1180. **$69-$279.** 50 Sylvester C Formey Dr 31408. I-95 exit 104, just se to Crossroads Pkwy, sw to Stephen S Green Dr, then just se. Int corridors. **Pets:** Accepted. 🏊🛰🗙🖥📺

SEA ISLAND

🔺 ▼▼▼▼ The Cloister [H]
(912) 638-3611. **Call for rates.** 100 Cloister Dr 31561. Just over Sea Island Bridge Cswy. Ext/int corridors. **Pets:** Accepted. [SAVE]🔌🍴🛗🗙🛰🗙🖥📺

SMYRNA

▼▼ Baymont Inn & Suites [H]
(404) 794-1600. **$69-$121.** 5130 S Cobb Dr 30082. I-285 exit 15, 0.3 mi w. Int corridors. **Pets:** Small. $20 deposit/pet, $20 daily fee/pet. Designated rooms, service with restrictions, supervision. 🛗🏊🛰🖥📺

▼▼ Extended Stay America-Atlanta-Cumberland
Mall [M]
(770) 432-4000. **$75-$100.** 3103 Sports Ave 30080. I-285 exit 20 westbound; exit 19 eastbound, just n to Spring Rd, then 0.3 mi w. Ext corridors. **Pets:** Accepted. 🛗🛰🗙🖥📺

🔺 ▼▼▼ Hyatt Place Atlanta/Cobb Galleria [H] 🐾
(770) 384-0060. **$84-$179.** 2876 Spring Hill Pkwy 30080. I-285 exit 20 westbound; exit 19 eastbound, just n to Spring Rd, then just w. Int corridors. **Pets:** Medium, dogs only. $75 one-time fee/room. Designated rooms, service with restrictions, crate. [SAVE]🍴🛗🏊🛰🗙🖥📺

🔺 ▼▼ Red Roof Inn-Atlanta Smyrna [M]
(770) 952-6966. **$55-$80.** 2200 Corporate Plaza 30080. I-75 exit 260, just w to Corporate Plaza, then just s. Ext corridors. **Pets:** Accepted. [SAVE]🛗🛰🖥📺

▼▼▼ Residence Inn by Marriott-Atlanta
Cumberland [H]
(770) 433-8877. **$79-$206.** 2771 Cumberland Blvd 30080. I-285 exit 20 westbound; exit 19 eastbound, just n to Spring Rd, 0.3 mi w to Cumberland Blvd, then just n. Ext corridors. **Pets:** Accepted. 🛗🏊🛰🗙🖥📺

SNELLVILLE

▼▼▼ La Quinta Inn & Suites Snellville-Stone
Mountain [H]
(770) 736-4723. **$101-$180.** 2971 Main St W 30078. Jct US 78 and SR 124, 0.9 mi w. Int corridors. **Pets:** Accepted. 🛗🏊🛰🗙🖥📺

STOCKBRIDGE

La Quinta Inn & Suites Atlanta Stockbridge H
(770) 506-9991. **$86-$229.** 3581 Cameron Pkwy 30281. I-75 exit 228, just e; I-675 exit 1, just w. Int corridors. **Pets:** Accepted.
[SAVE] [&M] [🏊] [📶] [🛢] [📺]

Quality Inn & Suites M
(770) 507-7911. **$60-$99.** 7325 Davidson Pkwy N 30281. I-675 exit 1, just e, then just n; I-75 exit 228, 1 mi e, then just n. Ext corridors. **Pets:** Accepted. [SAVE] [&M] [🏊] [📶] [🛢] [📺]

Red Roof Inn Atlanta/Southeast H
(678) 782-4100. **$57-$127.** 637 Hwy 138 30281. I-75 exit 228, just e; I-675 exit 1, just w. Int corridors. **Pets:** Accepted. [&M] [📶] [🛢] [📺]

Sleep Inn & Suites H
(770) 474-3870. **$61-$119.** 7423 Davidson Cir W 30281. I-675 exit 1, just e, then just s; I-75 exit 228, 1 mi e, then just s. Int corridors. **Pets:** Accepted. [&M] [🏊] [📶] [✕] [🛢] [📺]

STONE MOUNTAIN

Quality Inn Stone Mountain M
(770) 465-1022. **$65-$149.** 1595 E Park Place Blvd 30087. US 78 exit 9, 0.7 mi n. Ext corridors. **Pets:** Small, dogs only. $25 daily fee/room. Designated rooms, service with restrictions, supervision.
[SAVE] [🏊] [📶] [🛢] [📺]

SUWANEE

Quality Inn M
(770) 945-1608. **$70-$120.** 2945 Lawrenceville Suwanee Rd 30024. I-85 exit 111, just e. Ext corridors. **Pets:** $25 one-time fee/room. Service with restrictions, crate. [SAVE] [🏊] [📶] [🛢] [📺]

SWAINSBORO

Best Western Bradford Inn M
(478) 237-2400. **$70-$99.** 688 S Main St 30401. I-16 exit 90 (US 1), 12.4 mi n. Ext corridors. **Pets:** Medium. $15 daily fee/pet. Service with restrictions, supervision. [SAVE] [🍴] [&M] [🏊] [📶] [🛢] [📺]

THOMASTON

Quality Inn M
(706) 648-2232. **$76-$99.** 1010 Hwy 19 N 30286. Jct SR 74, 2.3 mi n. Ext corridors. **Pets:** Accepted. [&M] [🏊] [📶] [🛢] [📺]

THOMASVILLE *(Restaurants p. 613)*

The Paxton BB ✿
(229) 226-5197. **Call for rates.** 445 Remington Ave 31792. Corner of S Hansell St; just e of downtown. Ext/int corridors. **Pets:** Medium, dogs only. $75 one-time fee/pet. Designated rooms, service with restrictions, crate. [🏊] [📶] [✕] [🛢] [📺]

THOMSON

White Columns Inn M
(706) 595-8000. **$70-$320.** 1890 Washington Rd 30824. I-20 exit 172 (US 78), just s. Ext corridors. **Pets:** Other species. $10 daily fee/pet. Service with restrictions, supervision. [🍴] [🏊] [📶] [🛢] [📺]

TIFTON *(Restaurants p. 613)*

Country Inn & Suites By Carlson H
(229) 382-8100. **Call for rates.** 310 S Virginia Ave 31794. I-75 exit 62, just e on US 82. Int corridors. **Pets:** Accepted.
[🏊] [📶] [✕] [🛢] [📺]

Days Inn & Suites H
(229) 382-8505. **$57-$80.** 1199 Hwy 82 W 31793. I-75 exit 62, just sw. Int corridors. **Pets:** Other species. $10 daily fee/pet. Service with restrictions, supervision. [📶] [🛢] [📺]

Econo Lodge M
(229) 382-0280. **$60-$130.** 1025 W 2nd St 31794. I-75 exit 63A, just e. Ext corridors. **Pets:** Accepted. [🍴] [&M] [📶] [🛢] [📺]

Microtel Inn & Suites by Wyndham Tifton H
(229) 387-0112. **$51-$80.** 196 S Virginia Ave 31794. I-75 exit 62, just e. Int corridors. **Pets:** Accepted. [&M] [📶] [🛢] [📺]

TUCKER

DoubleTree by Hilton Hotel Atlanta-Northlake H
(770) 938-1026. **Call for rates.** 4156 Lavista Rd 30084. I-285 exit 37, just w. Int corridors. **Pets:** Accepted.
[SAVE] [🍴] [&M] [🏊] [📶] [✕] [🛢] [📺]

Quality Inn Atlanta/Northlake M
(770) 491-7444. **$75-$99.** 2155 Ranchwood Dr 30345. I-285 exit 37, 0.4 mi w, then just n. Ext/int corridors. **Pets:** Small. $15 daily fee/pet. Designated rooms, service with restrictions, supervision.
[SAVE] [&M] [🏊] [📶] [🛢] [📺]

TownePlace Suites by Marriott Atlanta Northlake H
(770) 938-0408. **$94-$144.** 3300 Northlake Pkwy 30345. I-285 exit 36 southbound, just w; exit 37 northbound, just w to Parklake Dr, 0.5 mi n, then just w. Int corridors. **Pets:** Accepted.
[ECO] [&M] [🏊] [📶] [✕] [🛢] [📺]

UNION CITY

Magnuson Hotel Atlanta South M
(770) 306-6067. **$50-$125.** 6840 Shannon Pkwy S 30291. I-85 exit 64, 0.3 mi w to Shannon Pkwy, then just s. Ext corridors. **Pets:** Small, dogs only. $11 daily fee/pet. Service with restrictions, crate.
[🏊] [📶] [🛢] [📺]

VALDOSTA *(Restaurants p. 613)*

Best Western Plus Valdosta Hotel & Suites H ✿
(229) 241-9221. **$89-$164.** 4025 Northlake Dr 31602. I-75 exit 22, just e on N Valdosta Rd (US 41). Int corridors. **Pets:** Other species. $20 daily fee/room. Designated rooms, service with restrictions.
[SAVE] [🍴] [&M] [🏊] [📶] [✕] [🛢] [📺]

Country Inn & Suites By Carlson H
(229) 245-1700. **$89-$149.** 1308 N St. Augustine Rd 31601. I-75 exit 18, just se. Int corridors. **Pets:** Medium. $25 daily fee/pet. Designated rooms, service with restrictions, supervision.
[&M] [🏊] [📶] [✕] [🛢] [📺]

Days Inn Valdosta/Near Valdosta Mall H
(229) 244-7600. **$58-$80.** 1383 N St Augustine Rd 31602. I-75 exit 18, just w off SR 94. Ext corridors. **Pets:** Medium, other species. $10 daily fee/room. Service with restrictions, supervision.
[🍴] [&M] [🏊] [📶] [🛢] [📺]

Drury Inn & Suites Valdosta H
(229) 253-0023. **$79-$159.** 1327 N St. Augustine Rd 31601. I-75 exit 18, just e. Int corridors. **Pets:** Accepted. [🍴] [&M] [📶] [✕] [🛢] [📺]

Econo Lodge H
(229) 671-1511. **$57-$100.** 3022 James Rd 31602. I-75 exit 18, just nw. Int corridors. **Pets:** Medium, other species. $10 daily fee/pet. Designated rooms, service with restrictions, crate.
[SAVE] [🍴] [&M] [🏊] [📶] [🛢] [📺]

Sleep Inn & Suites H
(229) 671-1111. **$70-$170.** 3026 James Rd 31602. I-75 exit 18, just nw. Int corridors. **Pets:** Medium, other species. $15 daily fee/pet. Designated rooms, service with restrictions, crate.
[SAVE] [&M] [🏊] [📶] [✕] [🛢] [📺]

▼▼ **Super 8 Valdosta Mall** ⊞

(229) 244-8440. **$58-$80.** 1389 N St. Augustine Rd 31602. I-75 exit 18, just w off SR 94. Ext corridors. **Pets:** Medium, other species. $10 daily fee/room. Service with restrictions, supervision. 🚹M 📶 💻

VILLA RICA

▼▼ **Days Inn** ⊞

(770) 459-8888. **$53-$70.** 195 Hwy 61 Connector 30180. I-20 exit 24, just n. Int corridors. **Pets:** Medium. $10 daily fee/pet. Designated rooms, service with restrictions, supervision. 🚹M 🏊 📶 🛗 💻

▼▼ **Econo Lodge-Villa Rica Inn** Ⓜ

(770) 459-6669. **$65-$131.** 124 Hwy 61 Connector 30180. I-20 exit 24, just n. Ext corridors. **Pets:** Accepted. 🐾 📶 🛗 💻

WARNER ROBINS

▼▼ **Baymont Inn & Suites Warner Robins** ⊞

(478) 953-5522. **$59-$89.** 2731 Watson Blvd 31093. I-75 exit 146 (SR 247C), 4.1 mi e. Ext corridors. **Pets:** Dogs only. $15 daily fee/pet. Service with restrictions, crate. 🐾 📶 🛗 💻

▼▼ **Comfort Inn & Suites** ⊞

(478) 922-7555. **$95-$119.** 95 Georgia Hwy 247 S 31088. Jct SR 247C and US 129/SR 247, 1.6 mi s on US 129/SR 247. Ext/int corridors. **Pets:** Accepted. 🐾 📶 🗙 🛗 💻

🆑 ▼▼ **Days Inn & Suites** ⊞

(478) 953-3800. **$69-$129, 3 day notice.** 2739 Watson Blvd 31093. I-75 exit 146 (SR 247C), 4.1 mi e. Ext corridors. **Pets:** $15 daily fee/pet. Designated rooms, service with restrictions, supervision.
[SAVE] 🐾 📶 🛗 💻

🆑 ▼▼▼ **La Quinta Inn & Suites** ⊞

(478) 333-6920. **$91-$185.** 4080 Watson Blvd 31093. I-75 exit 146 (SR 247C), 2.7 mi e. Int corridors. **Pets:** Accepted.
[SAVE] 🐾 📶 🗙 🛗 💻

WAYCROSS

▼▼ **Baymont Inn & Suites Waycross** Ⓜ

(912) 283-3800. **$59-$79.** 950 S City Blvd 31501. Between US 1 and 82; east of city. Ext corridors. **Pets:** Accepted.
🚹M 🐾 📶 🛗 💻

▼▼▼ **Comfort Suites** ⊞

(912) 548-0555. **$82-$142.** 1922 Memorial Dr 31501. Jct US 1 and 82, just se on US 1 (Memorial Dr). Int corridors. **Pets:** Accepted.
🐾 📶 🗙 🛗 💻

▼▼▼ **Holiday Inn Express & Suites** ⊞

(912) 548-0720. **Call for rates.** 1761 Memorial Dr 31501. Between US 1 and 82. Int corridors. **Pets:** Accepted. 🐾 🗙 📶 🗙 🛗 💻

WAYNESBORO

▼▼ **Quality Inn** Ⓜ

(706) 437-0500. **$89.** 1436 N Liberty St 30830. 0.9 mi n of downtown center on US 25. Ext corridors. **Pets:** $20 daily fee/room. Service with restrictions. 🐾 📶 🛗 💻

WINDER

▼▼ **Quality Inn** ⊞

(770) 868-5303. **$85-$149.** 177 W Athens St 30680. Jct Broad St, 0.8 mi n; downtown. Int corridors. **Pets:** Accepted.
🚹M 🐾 📶 🛗 💻

YOUNG HARRIS

▼▼▼ **Brasstown Valley Resort** ⊞

(706) 379-9900. **Call for rates.** 6321 US Hwy 76 30582. US 76 and US 76/SR 515. Int corridors. **Pets:** Accepted.
[ECO] 🍴 🚹M 🐾 🗙 📶 🗙 🛗 💻

HAWAII

HONOLULU

🆑 ▼▼ **Airport Honolulu Hotel** ⊞

(808) 836-0661. **$129-$209, 3 day notice.** 3401 N Nimitz Hwy 96819. Jct Rodgers Blvd. Int corridors. **Pets:** Accepted.
[SAVE] 🔌 🍴 🚹M 🏊 📶 🗙 🛗 ☕

🆑 ▼▼▼ **Best Western The Plaza Hotel** ⊞

(808) 836-3636. **$169-$239.** 3253 N Nimitz Hwy 96819. Just e of jct Paiea St. Ext/int corridors. **Pets:** Accepted.
[SAVE] [ECO] 🔌 🍴 🚹M 🐾 📶 🗙 🛗 💻

🆑 ▼▼▼ **Courtyard by Marriott Waikiki Beach** ⊞

(808) 954-4000. **$142-$253, 3 day notice.** 400 Royal Hawaiian Ave 96815. Jct Kuhio Ave. Ext/int corridors. **Pets:** Accepted.
[SAVE] 🍴 🚹M 🐾 🗙 📶 🗙 🛗 💻

🆑 ▼▼▼ **Hotel Renew** ⊞

(808) 687-7700. **$169-$289, 3 day notice.** 129 Paoakalani Ave 96815. Between Kalakaua Ave and Lemon Rd. Int corridors. **Pets:** Accepted.
[SAVE] 🚹M 📶 🗙 🛗 💻

🆑 ▼▼▼ **Hyatt Place Waikiki Beach** ⊞

(808) 922-3861. **$169-$479.** 175 Paoakalani Ave 96815. Jct Kuhio Ave. Int corridors. **Pets:** Accepted. [SAVE] 🍴 🚹M 🐾 📶 🗙 🛗 💻

🆑 ▼▼▼ **Hyatt Regency Waikiki Beach Resort & Spa** ⊞ 🐾

(808) 923-1234. **$179-$499, 3 day notice.** 2424 Kalakaua Ave 96815. Between Kaiulani Ave and Uluniu St; entrance on Uluniu St. Int corridors. **Pets:** Medium. $150 one-time fee/room. Service with restrictions, crate. [SAVE] [ECO] 🍴 🚹M 🐾 🗙 📶 🗙 🛗 💻

🆑 ▼▼▼ **The Kahala Hotel & Resort** ⊞ 🐾

(808) 739-8888. **$395-$695, 3 day notice.** 5000 Kahala Ave 96816. E of Diamond Head at end of Kahala Ave. Int corridors. **Pets:** Small, dogs only. $150 one-time fee/room. Service with restrictions.
[SAVE] [ECO] 🍴 🚹M 🐾 🗙 📶 🗙 🛗 💻

▼▼▼ **Lotus Honolulu** ⊞

(808) 922-1700. **$219-$449, 3 day notice.** 2885 Kalakaua Ave 96815. East end of Kapiolani Park. Ext corridors. **Pets:** Accepted.
🚹M 📶 🗙 🛗 💻

🆑 ▼▼▼ **The Modern Honolulu** ⊞ 🐾

(808) 943-5800. **$309-$999, 3 day notice.** 1775 Ala Moana Blvd 96815. Jct Hobron Ln. Int corridors. **Pets:** Small, dogs only. $10 daily fee/pet. Service with restrictions, supervision.
[SAVE] 🍴 🚹M 🐾 📶 🗙 🛗 💻

▼▼▼▼ **Trump International Hotel Waikiki** ⊞

(808) 683-7777. **$489-$775, 3 day notice.** 223 Saratoga Rd 96815. Just sw on Kalakaua Ave via Saratoga Rd. Int corridors.
Pets: Accepted. 🍴 🚹M 🐾 🗙 📶 🗙 🛗 💻

KĀ'ANAPALI

🆑 ▼▼▼▼ **Hyatt Regency Maui Resort & Spa** ⊞

(808) 661-1234. **$229-$599, 3 day notice.** 200 Nohea Kai Dr 96761. SR 30 exit Kaanapali Pkwy, just w, then just s; in Kaanapali Beach resort area. Ext/int corridors. **Pets:** Accepted.
[SAVE] [ECO] 🔌 🍴 🚹M 🐾 📶 🗙 🛗 💻

AAA ◆◆◆ **Sheraton Maui Resort & Spa** H
(808) 661-0031. **$339-$659, 3 day notice.** 2605 Kaanapali Pkwy 96761. SR 30 exit Kaanapali Pkwy, just nw; in Kaanapali Beach resort area. Ext/int corridors. **Pets:** Accepted.

🅢 🝙 ▦ ⟨M⟩ ⧫ ⊠ 🛜 ⊠ ⊟ ▭

KAHUKU

◆◆◆ **Turtle Bay Resort** H
(808) 293-6000. **Call for rates.** 57-091 Kamehameha Hwy 96731. 3 mi nw off SR 83. Ext/int corridors. **Pets:** Small, dogs only. $300 one-time fee/pet. Designated rooms, service with restrictions, crate.

🄴🄲🄾 🝙 ▦ ⟨M⟩ ⧫ ⊠ 🛜 ⊠ ⊟ ▭

KAUPULEHU

AAA ◆◆◆◆ **Four Seasons Resort Hualalai** H
(808) 325-8000. **Call for rates.** 72-100 Ka'upulehu Dr 96740. 6 mi n of Kona International Airport on SR 19, 1.3 mi sw. Ext corridors.
Pets: Accepted. 🅢 🝙 ▦ ⟨M⟩ ⧫ ⊠ 🛜 ⊠ ⊟ ▭

KEAUHOU

AAA ◆◆◆ **Sheraton Kona Resort & Spa at Keauhou Bay** H
(808) 930-4900. **$159-$399, 3 day notice.** 78-128 Ehukai St 96740. SR 11, 1.4 mi sw (toward ocean) on Kamehameha III Rd, 0.7 mi s on Alii Dr, then just w on Kaleiopapa St; watch for Keauhou Bay sign. Ext/int corridors. **Pets:** Accepted. 🅢 🝙 ⟨M⟩ ⊠ 🛜 ⊠ ⊟ ▭

KOHALA COAST

AAA ◆◆◆◆ **The Fairmont Orchid, Hawaii** H 🐾
(808) 885-2000. **$300-$3900, 14 day notice.** One N Kaniku Dr 96743. 19 mi n of Kona International Airport on SR 19, 1 mi w on Mauna Lani Dr, then 1 mi n; in Mauna Lani resort area. Int corridors. **Pets:** Small. $25 daily fee/room. Designated rooms, service with restrictions, crate.

🅢 🄴🄲🄾 🝙 ▦ ⟨M⟩ ⧫ ⊠ 🛜 ⊠ ⊟ ▭

LĀNA'I CITY

AAA ◆◆◆◆ **Four Seasons Resort Lana'i** H
(808) 565-2000. **$800-$25000, 21 day notice.** 1 Manele Bay Rd 96763. From airport, 3 mi e on Kaumalapau Hwy to Lana'i City, 6 mi s on SR 440. Ext corridors. **Pets:** Accepted.

🅢 🝙 ⟨M⟩ ⧫ ⊠ 🛜 ⊠ ⊟ ▭

PO'IPŪ

◆◆◆◆ **Ko'a Kea Hotel & Resort** H 🐾
(808) 742-4200. **$320-$1275, 14 day notice.** 2251 Poipu Rd 96756. 2.3 mi se of Koloa; in Poipu Beach area. Int corridors. **Pets:** Small, dogs only. $150 deposit/pet, $100 daily fee/room. Designated rooms, service with restrictions, supervision. 🝙 ⟨M⟩ ⊠ 🛜 ⊠ ⊟ ▭

AAA ◆◆◆ **Sheraton Kauai Resort** H
(808) 742-1661. **$233-$479, 3 day notice.** 2440 Hoonani Rd 96756. 1.8 mi se of Koloa on Poipu Rd, just se; in Poipu Beach area. Ext corridors. **Pets:** Accepted.

🅢 🄴🄲🄾 🝙 ▦ ⟨M⟩ ⧫ ⊠ 🛜 ⊠ ⊟ ▭

WAILEA

AAA ◆◆◆ ◆◆ **Andaz Maui at Wailea Resort** H
(808) 573-1234. **$399-$1025, 3 day notice.** 3550 Wailea Alanui Dr 96753. From end of SR 31, 0.5 mi n. Ext/int corridors. **Pets:** Accepted.
🅢 🝙 ⟨M⟩ ⊠ 🛜 ⊠ ⊟ ▭

AAA ◆◆◆◆ **Four Seasons Resort Maui at Wailea** H 🐾
(808) 874-8000. **$489-$1879, 21 day notice.** 3900 Wailea Alanui Dr 96753. From end of SR 31, 0.6 mi w on Wailea Ike Dr, then 0.6 mi s. Int corridors. **Pets:** Small, other species. Service with restrictions, supervision. 🅢 🝙 ▦ ⟨M⟩ ⧫ ⊠ 🛜 ⊠ ⊟ ▭

IDAHO

AHSAHKA

AAA ◆◆◆ **High Country Inn Orofino-Ahsahka** BB
(208) 476-7570. **Call for rates.** 70 High Country Ln 83520. 0.5 mi w to Dworshak Visitors Center Rd, 2 mi n, then 1 mi w, follow signs. Ext/int corridors. **Pets:** Accepted. 🅢 🝙 ⊠ ⊠ 🅆 ☎ ⊟ ▭

ATHOL

AAA ◆◆◆ **Log Spirit Bed & Breakfast** BB
(208) 683-4722. **$140-$200, 14 day notice.** 31328 N Tiara Ln 83801. US 95, just e on SR 54 to Howard Rd, 1.8 mi n, then 0.5 mi e. Int corridors. **Pets:** $25 daily fee/pet. Designated rooms, no service, supervision. 🅢 🝙 ⟨M⟩ 🛜 ⊠ 🅇 🅆 ☎ ⊟

BLACKFOOT

AAA ◆◆ **Best Western Blackfoot Inn** H
(208) 785-4144. **$80-$120.** 750 Jensen Grove Dr 83221. I-15 exit 93, 0.3 mi e to Parkway Dr, then 0.4 mi n. Int corridors. **Pets:** Accepted.
🅢 ⧫ 🛜 ⊠ ⊟ ▭

◆◆ **Super 8** H
(208) 785-9333. **$51-$92.** 1279 Parkway Dr 83221. I-15 exit 93, just se, then just w. Int corridors. **Pets:** Accepted. 🝙 🛜 ⊟ ▭

BOISE

AAA ◆◆ **Best Western Airport Inn** M
(208) 384-5000. **$80-$200.** 2660 Airport Way 83705. I-84 exit 53 (Vista Ave), just se. Ext corridors. **Pets:** Medium, dogs only. $10 daily fee/pet. Designated rooms, service with restrictions, supervision.
🅢 ⧫ 🛜 ⊟ ▭

AAA ◆◆◆ **Best Western Northwest Lodge** H
(208) 287-2300. **$89-$139.** 6989 S Federal Way 83716. I-84 exit 57 (Gowen Rd/Idaho City), just e, then just s. Int corridors. **Pets:** Accepted.
🅢 🝙 ⟨M⟩ 🛜 ⊠ ⊟ ▭

AAA ◆◆◆ **Best Western Vista Inn at the Airport** H
(208) 336-8100. **$89-$139.** 2645 Airport Way 83705. I-84 exit 53 (Vista Ave), just s. Ext/int corridors. **Pets:** Small, dogs only. $20 daily fee/room. Designated rooms, service with restrictions, crate.
🅢 ⟨M⟩ ⧫ 🛜 ⊠ ⊟ ▭

◆◆◆ **Candlewood Suites Boise Towne Square** H
(208) 322-4300. **$99-$129.** 700 N Cole Rd 83704. I-84 exit 50A westbound; exit 50B eastbound, 2 mi n on Cole Rd, then just w. Int corridors. **Pets:** Accepted. ▦ ⟨M⟩ 🛜 ⊠ ⊟ ▭

◆◆◆ **Fairfield Inn by Marriott Boise Airport** H
(208) 331-5656. **$85-$156.** 3300 S Shoshone St 83705. I-84 exit 53 (Vista Ave), just n to Elder St, then just w. Int corridors. **Pets:** Accepted.
⟨M⟩ ⧫ 🛜 ⊠ ⊟ ▭

◆◆◆ **Hampton Inn by Hilton Boise Airport** H
(208) 331-5600. **$94-$179.** 3270 S Shoshone St 83705. I-84 exit 53 (Vista Ave), just n to Elder St, then just w. Int corridors. **Pets:** Large, other species. Designated rooms, service with restrictions, supervision.
⟨M⟩ ⧫ 🛜 ⊠ ⊟ ▭

◆◆◆ **Holiday Inn Boise Airport** H
(208) 344-7444. **Call for rates.** 2970 W Elder St 83705. I-84 exit 53 (Vista Ave), just n to Elder St, then just w. Int corridors. **Pets:** Accepted.
🝙 ⟨M⟩ ⧫ 🛜 ⊠ ⊟ ▭

▼▼▼ **Holiday Inn Express Boise-University Area** H
(208) 345-2002. **Call for rates.** 475 W Parkcenter Blvd 83706. I-84 exit 54 (Broadway Ave), 2.3 mi n to Beacon St, then 0.3 mi e. Int corridors. **Pets:** Accepted. 🅂🄼 ⊇ ⊠ 📶 ⊠ 🗲 🖳

🆀 ▼▼▼ **Hyatt Place Boise Towne Square** H
(208) 375-1200. **$79-$199.** 925 N Milwaukee St 83704. I-84 exit 49 (Franklin St), just w, then 0.5 mi n. Int corridors. **Pets:** Accepted.
🅂🄰🅅🄴 🍴 🅂🄼 ⊇ 📶 ⊠ 🗲 🖳

▼▼ **Inn America Boise Airport** H
(208) 389-9800. **$59-$89.** 2275 Airport Way 83705. I-84 exit 53 (Vista Ave), 0.3 mi se. Int corridors. **Pets:** Small, dogs only. $20 daily fee/room. Designated rooms, service with restrictions, supervision.
⊇ 📶 🗲 🖳

▼▼ **La Quinta Inn & Suites Boise Airport** H
(208) 388-0800. **$86-$196.** 2613 S Vista Ave 83705. I-84 exit 53 (Vista Ave), 0.6 mi n. Int corridors. **Pets:** Accepted.
🅂🄼 ⊇ 📶 ⊠ 🗲 🖳

▼▼ **Modern Hotel & Bar** M
(208) 424-8244. **Call for rates.** 1314 W Grove St 83702. At 13th and W Grove sts; downtown. Ext/int corridors. **Pets:** Accepted.
🍴 📶 ⊠ 🗲 🖳

🆀 ▼▼▼ **Oxford Suites Boise Spectrum** H 🐾
(208) 322-8000. **Call for rates.** 1426 S Entertainment Ave 83709. I-84 exit 50A, just s to Spectrum Way, just w, then just n. Int corridors. **Pets:** Medium, $25 one-time fee/pet. Designated rooms, service with restrictions, supervision. 🅂🄰🅅🄴 ⊟ 🅂🄼 ⊇ ⊠ 📶 ⊠ 🗲 🖳

▼▼▼ **Red Lion Hotel Boise Downtowner** H
(208) 344-7691. **Call for rates.** 1800 Fairview Ave 83702. I-184 exit 3 (Fairview Ave), 1 mi n. Int corridors. **Pets:** Accepted.
🍴 🅂🄼 ⊇ ⊠ 📶 ⊠ 🗲 🖳

▼▼▼ **Residence Inn by Marriott Boise West** H
(208) 385-9000. **$91-$178.** 7303 W Denton St 83704. I-84 exit 50A westbound; exit 50B eastbound, 2 mi n on Cole Rd, then just w. Int corridors. **Pets:** Accepted. ⊇ 📶 ⊠ 🗲 🖳

▼▼ **Residence Inn by Marriott Downtown** H
(208) 344-1200. **$122-$184.** 1401 S Lusk Pl 83706. I-84 exit 53 (Vista Ave), 2.4 mi n, just w on Ann Morrison Park Dr, then just s on Lois Ave. Ext corridors. **Pets:** Accepted. ⊇ 📶 ⊠ 🗲 🖳

▼▼▼ **The Riverside Hotel** H
(208) 343-1871. **Call for rates.** 2900 W Chinden Blvd 83714. I-84 exit 49 (Franklin Rd), 2.7 mi ne on I-184 exit 3 (Fairview Ave), just n, then just w. Int corridors. **Pets:** Accepted.
🄴🄲🄾 🍴 🅂🄼 ⊇ ⊠ 📶 🗲 🖳

▼▼ **Safari Inn Downtown** H 🐾
(208) 344-6556. **$89-$129.** 1070 Grove St 83702. At 11th and Grove sts. Int corridors. **Pets:** Other species. $15 one-time fee/room. Designated rooms, service with restrictions, supervision.
⊇ ⊠ 📶 ⊠ 🗲 🖳

▼▼▼ **SpringHill Suites by Marriott Boise-Parkcenter** H
(208) 342-1044. **$100-$178.** 424 E Parkcenter Blvd 83706. I-84 exit 54 (Broadway Ave), 2.3 mi n to Beacon St, 0.3 mi e, then 0.7 mi se. Int corridors. **Pets:** Accepted. 🅂🄼 ⊇ ⊠ 📶 ⊠ 🗲 🖳

▼▼▼ **TownePlace Suites by Marriott Downtown** H
(208) 429-8881. **$94-$167.** 1455 S Capitol Blvd 83706. I-84 exit 53 (Vista Ave), 2.4 mi n. Int corridors. **Pets:** Accepted.
🅂🄼 ⊇ 📶 ⊠ 🗲 🖳

BONNERS FERRY

🆀 ▼▼▼ **Best Western Plus Kootenai River Inn Casino & Spa** H
(208) 267-8511. **$159-$399.** 7169 Plaza St 83805. On US 95; City Center. Int corridors. **Pets:** Medium. $20 daily fee/pet. Service with restrictions, supervision. 🅂🄰🅅🄴 🍴 ⊇ ⊠ 📶 ⊠ 🗲 🖳

BURLEY

🆀 ▼▼▼ **Best Western Plus Burley Inn & Convention Center** H
(208) 678-3501. **$98-$124.** 800 N Overland Ave 83318. I-84 exit 208, just s. Ext/int corridors. **Pets:** $12 daily fee/pet. Designated rooms, service with restrictions, supervision.
🅂🄰🅅🄴 🍴 🅂🄼 ⊇ 📶 ⊠ 🗲 🖳

▼▼ **Super 8 Burley** H
(208) 678-7000. **$75-$95.** 336 S 600 W 83318. I-84 exit 208, just n. Int corridors. **Pets:** Accepted. ⊇ 📶 ⊠ 🗲 🖳

CALDWELL

🆀 ▼▼ **Best Western Plus Caldwell Inn & Suites** H
(208) 454-7225. **$82-$149.** 908 Specht Ave 83605. I-84 exit 29, just s. Int corridors. **Pets:** Accepted. 🅂🄰🅅🄴 🅂🄼 ⊇ 📶 ⊠ 🗲 🖳

▼▼ **La Quinta Inn Caldwell** H
(208) 454-2222. **$67-$235.** 901 Specht Ave 83605. I-84 exit 29, just s. Int corridors. **Pets:** Accepted. 🍴 ⊇ 📶 ⊠ 🗲 🖳

COEUR D'ALENE

▼▼ **Baymont Inn & Suites Coeur d'Alene** H
(208) 667-6777. **$70-$249.** 2209 E Sherman Ave 83814. I-90 exit 15 (Sherman Ave), just s. Int corridors. **Pets:** Accepted.
🍴 🅂🄼 ⊇ 📶 ⊠ 🗲 🖳

🆀 ▼▼▼ **Best Western Plus Coeur d'Alene Inn** H 🐾
(208) 765-3200. **$90-$210.** 506 W Appleway Ave 83814. I-90 exit 12, just nw. Int corridors. **Pets:** Large, other species. $20 daily fee/room. Service with restrictions, supervision.
🅂🄰🅅🄴 🍴 ⊇ ⊠ 🗲 🖳

▼▼ ▼▼ **The Coeur d'Alene Resort** H
(208) 209-5026. **Call for rates.** 115 S 2nd St 83814. I-90 exit 11 (Northwest Blvd), 2 mi s. Ext/int corridors. **Pets:** Accepted.
⊟ 🍴 🅂🄼 ⊇ ⊠ 📶 ⊠ 🗲 🖳

🆀 ▼▼ **Days Inn-Coeur d'Alene** H
(208) 667-8668. **$65-$220.** 2200 Northwest Blvd 83814. I-90 exit 11 (Northwest Blvd), just se. Int corridors. **Pets:** Accepted.
🅂🄰🅅🄴 📶 ⊠ 🗲 🖳

▼▼▼ **Holiday Inn Express Hotel & Suites Coeur d'Alene** H
(208) 667-3100. **$100-$300.** 2300 W Seltice Way 83814. I-90 exit 11 (Northwest Blvd), just s. Ext/int corridors. **Pets:** Accepted.
🅂🄼 ⊇ 📶 ⊠ 🗲 🖳

▼▼ **La Quinta Inn & Suites Coeur d'Alene** H
(208) 665-9000. **$92-$383.** 333 Ironwood Dr 83814. I-90 exit 12, just s. Int corridors. **Pets:** Accepted. 🅂🄼 ⊇ 📶 ⊠ 🗲 🖳

▼▼ **Quality Inn & Suites Coeur d'Alene** H
(208) 765-5500. **$84-$354.** 280 W Appleway Ave 83814. I-90 exit 12, just ne. Int corridors. **Pets:** Medium. Designated rooms, service with restrictions. 🅂🄼 ⊇ ⊠ 📶 ⊠ 🗲 🖳

▼▼ **Ramada Inn Coeur D'Alene** H
(208) 664-1649. **$69-$239.** 2303 N 4th St 83814. I-90 exit 13 (4th St), just n. Int corridors. **Pets:** Accepted. ⊇ 📶 ⊠ 🗲 🖳

Resort City Inn M
(208) 676-1225. **$69-$199, 3 day notice.** 621 Sherman Ave 83814. I-90 exit 11 (Northwest Blvd), 2.5 mi e via Northwest Blvd and Sherman Ave; downtown. Ext corridors. **Pets:** $25 one-time fee/pet. Service with restrictions, supervision.

The Roosevelt Inn and Spa BB
(208) 765-5200. **Call for rates.** 105 E Wallace Ave 83814. I-90 exit 13 (4th St), 2 mi s, then just w; downtown. Int corridors. **Pets:** Accepted.

SpringHill Suites by Marriott Coeur d'Alene
(208) 667-2212. **$99-$231.** 2250 W Seltice Way 83814. I-90 exit 11 (Northwest Blvd), just s. Int corridors. **Pets:** Accepted.

DRIGGS

Teton Valley Cabins CA
(208) 354-8153. **Call for rates.** 1 Mountain Vista Dr 83422. 0.9 mi e of jct SR 33 (Main St) and Little Ave, then just n. Ext corridors.
Pets: Accepted.

GRANGEVILLE

Gateway Inn Grangeville M
(208) 983-2500. **$55-$99.** 700 W Main St 83530. Jct US 95 and SR 13. Ext corridors. **Pets:** Medium. $10 one-time fee/room, $10 daily fee/room. Designated rooms, service with restrictions, supervision.

HAGERMAN

Hagerman Valley Inn M
(208) 837-6196. **$68-$108.** 661 Frog's Landing 83332. South end of town on US 30. Ext corridors. **Pets:** $8 one-time fee/room. Designated rooms, service with restrictions, supervision.

HAILEY

Airport Inn M
(208) 788-2477. **Call for rates.** 820 S 4th Ave 83333. 1 mi s of center to 4th Ave via Main St (SR 75); south end of town. Ext corridors.
Pets: Accepted.

AmericInn Lodge & Suites - Hailey/Sun Valley H
(208) 788-7950. **Call for rates.** 51 Cobblestone Ln 83333. 0.5 mi n of center. Int corridors. **Pets:** Accepted.

Wood River Inn H
(208) 578-0600. **Call for rates.** 601 N Main St 83333. 0.3 mi n of center. Int corridors. **Pets:** Accepted.

HAYDEN

Triple Play Resort Hotel & Suites H
(208) 772-7900. **$90-$399.** 151 W Orchard Ave 83835. I-90 exit 12, 4 mi n. Int corridors. **Pets:** Large, other species. $10 daily fee/pet. Service with restrictions, supervision.

IDAHO FALLS

Best Western Driftwood Inn M
(208) 523-2242. **$79-$179.** 575 River Pkwy 83402. I-15 exit 118 (Broadway), 0.5 mi e, then 0.3 mi n. Ext corridors. **Pets:** Accepted.

Best Western Plus CottonTree Inn H
(208) 523-6000. **$89-$179.** 900 Lindsay Blvd 83402. I-15 exit 119, just e. Int corridors. **Pets:** Medium. $15 daily fee/pet. Designated rooms, service with restrictions, supervision.

Candlewood Suites H
(208) 525-9800. **Call for rates.** 665 Pancheri Dr 83402. I-15 exit 118 (Broadway), 1 mi e (cross bridge), then 0.5 mi s on S Capital Ave. Int corridors. **Pets:** Accepted.

Home2 Suites by Hilton H
(208) 529-0400. **Call for rates.** 1160 Whitewater Dr 83402. I-84 exit 116, 0.7 mi e, then 1.1 mi n. Int corridors. **Pets:** Accepted.

La Quinta Inn & Suites Idaho Falls H
(208) 552-2500. **$93-$299.** 2501 S 25th St E 83406. I-15 exit 118 (Broadway), 1 mi e, 0.5 mi s on Yellowstone Hwy, 3.8 mi e on 17th St to Hitt Rd, then just s. Int corridors. **Pets:** Accepted.

Le Ritz Hotel & Suites H
(208) 528-0880. **$75-$320.** 720 Lindsay Blvd 83402. I-15 exit 118 (Broadway), 0.5 mi e, then 0.4 mi n. Int corridors. **Pets:** Accepted.

Residence Inn by Marriott H
(208) 542-0000. **$112-$212.** 635 W Broadway 83402. I-15 exit 118 (Broadway), 0.4 mi e. Int corridors. **Pets:** Accepted.

Sleep Inn & Suites H 🐾
(208) 821-3647. **$115-$175.** 3200 Outlet Blvd 83405. I-15 exit 116, just w. Int corridors. **Pets:** Other species. $15 one-time fee/pet. Designated rooms, service with restrictions, supervision.

JEROME

Best Western Sawtooth Inn & Suites H 🐾
(208) 324-9200. **$89-$179.** 2653 S Lincoln Ave 83338. I-84 exit 168, just n. Int corridors. **Pets:** Other species. Designated rooms, service with restrictions, supervision.

Comfort Inn & Suites H
(208) 644-1200. **$100-$175.** 379 Crossroads Point Blvd 83338. I-84 exit 173 (US 93), 0.7 mi n. Int corridors. **Pets:** Medium, other species. $15 daily fee/pet. Designated rooms, service with restrictions, supervision.

KAMIAH

Hearthstone Lodge BB
(208) 935-1492. **Call for rates.** 12 at Milepost 64 83536. On SR 12, 2.2 mi w of center; MM 64. Ext corridors. **Pets:** Medium, dogs only. $20 daily fee/pet. Designated rooms, service with restrictions, crate.

KELLOGG

FairBridge Inn & Suites H
(208) 783-1234. **$84-$319.** 601 Bunker Ave 83837. I-90 exit 49, 0.5 mi se. Int corridors. **Pets:** Accepted.

Morning Star Lodge CO
(208) 783-0202. **$101-$720.** 602 Bunker Ave 83837. I-90 exit 49, 0.5 mi se. Int corridors. **Pets:** Accepted.

KETCHUM

Best Western Tyrolean Lodge H
(208) 726-5336. **$110-$180.** 260 Cottonwood St 83340. Just s of center to Rivers St, w to 2nd Ave, s to Cottonwood St, then just w. Int corridors. **Pets:** Accepted.

KOOSKIA

▼▼▼◆ River Dance Lodge 🖼
(208) 926-4300. **Call for rates.** 7743 Hwy 12 83539. On US 12, 16 mi e of Kooskia at MM 89. Ext corridors. **Pets:** Accepted.
🏨 ⊠ 📡 ⊠ 🐾 📶 🚽 🛏 💻

LEWISTON

▲▲▲ ▼▼▼◆ Holiday Inn Express 🖼
(208) 750-1600. **Call for rates.** 2425 Nez Perce Dr 83501. 1.2 mi s on US 12 from jct US 95, 1.2 mi s on 21st St, just e. Int corridors. **Pets:** $100 daily fee/room. Service with restrictions.
SAVE 🔧 ⚘ 🛁 📡 ⊠ 🛏 💻

▼▼▼◆ Inn America 🖼 🐾
(208) 746-4600. **$69-$189.** 702 21st St 83501. 1.2 mi s on US 12 from jct US 95, just s. Int corridors. **Pets:** Dogs only. $10 daily fee/room. Designated rooms, service with restrictions, supervision.
⚘ 🛁 📡 🛏 💻

MCCALL *(Restaurants p. 613)*

▲▲▲ ▼▼▼◆ Best Western Plus McCall Lodge & Suites 🖼
(208) 634-2230. **$189-$244.** 211 S 3rd St 83638. 1 mi s of center on SR 55. Int corridors. **Pets:** Accepted.
SAVE ⚘ 🛁 ⊠ 📡 ⊠ 🛏 💻

▲▲▲ ▼▼▼▼◆ Shore Lodge 🖼 🐾
(208) 634-2244. **$129-$609, 30 day notice.** 501 W Lake St 83638. 1 mi w of center on SR 55. Int corridors. **Pets:** Dogs only. $25 daily fee/pet. Designated rooms, service with restrictions, supervision.
SAVE 🔧 ⚘ 🛁 ⊠ 📡 ⊠ 🛏 💻

MERIDIAN

▲▲▲ ▼▼▼◆ Best Western Plus Rama Inn 🖼
(208) 887-7888. **$89-$170.** 1019 S Progress Ave 83642. I-84 exit 44 (Meridian/Kuna), just ne. Int corridors. **Pets:** Accepted.
SAVE ⚘ 🛁 📡 ⊠ 🛏 💻

▼▼▼◆ Candlewood Suites Boise West-Meridian 🖼
(208) 888-5121. **Call for rates.** 1855 S Silverstone Way 83642. I-84 exit 46 (Eagle Rd), 0.6 mi s, just e on Overland Rd, then just s. Int corridors. **Pets:** Accepted. 🔌 ⚘ ⊠ 📡 ⊠ 🛏 💻

▼▼▼◆ Holiday Inn Express & Suites Boise West-Meridian 🖼 🐾
(208) 288-2060. **$109-$259.** 2610 E Freeway Dr 83642. I-84 exit 46 (Eagle Rd), just n, then 0.3 mi w. Int corridors. **Pets:** Dogs only. $30 daily fee/pet. Designated rooms, service with restrictions, crate.
🔧 ⚘ 🛁 📡 🛏 💻

▼▼▼◆ La Quinta Inn & Suites Boise West-Meridian 🖼
(208) 288-2100. **$81-$257.** 800 S Allen St 83642. I-84 exit 46 (Eagle Rd), just nw. Int corridors. **Pets:** Accepted.
⚘ 🛁 📡 ⊠ 🛏 💻

▲▲▲ ▼▼▼◆ TownePlace Suites by Marriott Boise West-Meridian 🖼 🐾
(208) 884-8550. **$104-$155.** 1415 S Eagle Rd 83642. I-84 exit 46 (Eagle Rd), just sw. Int corridors. **Pets:** Large, other species. $50 one-time fee/room. Service with restrictions, crate.
SAVE ⚘ 🛁 📡 ⊠ 🛏 💻

MONTPELIER

▲▲▲ ▼▼▼ Clover Creek Inn 🅼
(208) 847-1782. **$75-$125.** 243 N 4th St 83254. On US 30, just n of jct US 89. Ext corridors. **Pets:** Dogs only. $10 daily fee/pet. Designated rooms, service with restrictions, supervision.
SAVE 🔧 📡 ⊠ 🛏 💻

MOSCOW

▲▲▲ ▼▼▼▼ Best Western Plus University Inn 🖼
(208) 882-0550. **$130-$260.** 1516 W Pullman Rd 83843. Jct US 95, 1 mi w on SR 8. Int corridors. **Pets:** Accepted.
SAVE 🔧 ⚘ 🛁 ⊠ 📡 ⊠ 🛏 💻

▼▼▼▼ Fairfield Inn & Suites by Marriott Moscow 🖼 🐾
(208) 882-4600. **$94-$161.** 1000 W Pullman Rd 83843. Jct US 95, 0.7 mi w on SR 8. Int corridors. **Pets:** Dogs only. $50 daily fee/room. Designated rooms, service with restrictions, crate. ⚘ 📡 🛏 💻

▼▼▼▼ La Quinta Inn & Suites Moscow 🖼
(208) 882-5365. **$86-$378.** 185 Warbonnet Dr 83843. Jct US 95, 1.6 mi w on SR 8, then just n. Int corridors. **Pets:** Accepted.
⚘ 🛁 📡 ⊠ 🛏 💻

MOUNTAIN HOME

▲▲▲ ▼▼▼ Best Western Foothills Inn 🅼 🐾
(208) 587-8477. **$99-$139.** 1080 Hwy 20 83647. I-84 exit 95, just n. Ext corridors. **Pets:** Large, dogs only. $15 daily fee/room. Designated rooms, service with restrictions, supervision. SAVE ⚘ 🛁 📡 🛏 💻

▼▼▼ Mountain Home Inn 🖼 🐾
(208) 587-9743. **$86-$129.** 1180 Hwy 20 83647. I-84 exit 95, just n. Int corridors. **Pets:** Medium, dogs only. $10 daily fee/pet. Designated rooms, service with restrictions, supervision. 📡 🛏 💻

NAMPA

▼▼▼▼ Holiday Inn Express & Suites Nampa 🖼
(208) 466-4045. **Call for rates.** 4104 E Flamingo Ave 83687. I-84 exit 38, just s, then just w. Int corridors. **Pets:** Dogs only. $25 one-time fee/pet, $10 daily fee/pet. Service with restrictions, supervision.
⚘ 🛁 📡 ⊠ 🛏 💻

▼▼▼ Sleep Inn 🖼
(208) 463-6300. **$74-$199.** 1315 Industrial Rd 83687. I-84 exit 36 (Franklin Blvd), just s. Int corridors. **Pets:** Accepted.
🔧 ⚘ 🛁 📡 ⊠ 🛏 💻

OROFINO

▲▲▲ ▼▼▼ Best Western Plus Lodge at River's Edge 🖼
(208) 476-9999. **$100-$143.** 615 Main St 83544. US 12, 0.3 mi e to Main St, 0.3 mi s. Int corridors. **Pets:** Accepted.
SAVE ⚘ 🛁 ⊠ 📡 ⊠ 🛏 💻

▼▼▼ Helgeson Place Hotel & Suites 🖼
(208) 476-5729. **Call for rates.** 125 Johnson Ave 83544. 0.3 mi e of US 12 at Michigan and Johnson aves; downtown. Int corridors.
Pets: Accepted. ⚘ 📡 ⊠ 🛏 💻

▼▼▼ Konkolville Motel 🅼
(208) 476-5584. **$65-$95.** 2600 Michigan Ave 83544. 3 mi e of downtown. Ext corridors. **Pets:** $15 daily fee/pet. Designated rooms, service with restrictions, supervision. 🔧 ⚘ 🛁 📡 🛏 💻

POCATELLO

▲▲▲ ▼▼▼◆ Best Western Pocatello Inn 🖼 🐾
(208) 237-7650. **$115-$145.** 1415 Bench Rd 83201. I-15 exit 71, just e. Int corridors. **Pets:** Large. $10 daily fee/room. Designated rooms, service with restrictions, supervision. SAVE 🔧 ⚘ 📡 ⊠ 🛏 💻

▲▲▲ ▼▼▼ Comfort Inn 🖼
(208) 237-8155. **$79-$174.** 1333 Bench Rd 83201. I-15 exit 71, just e. Int corridors. **Pets:** Accepted. SAVE ⚘ 🛁 📡 ⊠ 🛏 💻

▼▼▼◆ La Quinta Inn & Suites Pocatello 🖼
(208) 234-7500. **$86-$250.** 1440 Bench Rd 83201. I-15 exit 71, just e. Int corridors. **Pets:** Accepted. ⚘ 🛁 📡 ⊠ 🛏 💻

▼▼ **Super 8** 🅷
(208) 234-0888. **$60-$134.** 1330 Bench Rd 83201. I-15 exit 71, just e. Int corridors. **Pets:** Accepted. 📶 ⊠ 🔋 🖵

▼▼▼ **TownePlace Suites by Marriott** 🅷
(208) 478-7000. **$107-$168.** 2376 Via Caporatti Dr 83201. I-15 exit 69 (Clark St), 0.3 mi e. Int corridors. **Pets:** Accepted.
🍴 🛗 🛬 📶 ⊠ 🔋 🖵

PONDERAY

▼▼ **Days Inn Sandpoint** 🅷
(208) 263-1222. **$60-$83.** 363 Bonner Mall Way 83852. 0.5 mi n on US 95 N from jct SR 200. Int corridors. **Pets:** Accepted.
⊠ 📶 ⊠ 🔋 🖵

▼▼ **FairBridge Inn & Suites Sandpoint** 🅷
(208) 263-2210. **$56-$165, 3 day notice.** 476841 Hwy 95 N 83852. 0.7 mi n on US 95 from jct SR 200. Int corridors. **Pets:** Accepted.
📶 ⊠ 🔋

▼▼▼ **Holiday Inn Express & Suites** 🅷
(208) 255-4500. **Call for rates.** 477326 Hwy 95 N 83852. 0.7 mi n on US 95 from jct SR 200. Int corridors. **Pets:** Small, dogs only. $10 daily fee/room. Designated rooms, service with restrictions, supervision.
🛗 🛬 📶 ⊠ 🔋 🖵

▼▼ **Hotel Ruby Ponderay** 🅷 🐾
(208) 263-5383. **$80-$200.** 477255 Hwy 95 N 83852. 1.2 mi n on US 95 from jct SR 200. Int corridors. **Pets:** Medium, dogs only. $10 daily fee/room. Service with restrictions, supervision. ⊠ 📶 ⊠ 🔋

POST FALLS

▼▼◇ **Red Lion Templin's Hotel on the River - Post Falls** 🅷
(208) 773-1611. **Call for rates.** 414 E 1st Ave 83854. I-90 exit 5 eastbound, just s to 1st Ave; exit 6 westbound, 0.7 mi w on Seltice Way to Spokane St, 0.5 mi s, then just e. Ext/int corridors. **Pets:** Accepted.
🍴 🛗 🛬 ⊠ 📶 ⊠ 🔋 🖵

▼▼ **Sleep Inn** 🅷
(208) 777-9394. **$59-$249.** 157 S Pleasant View Rd 83854. I-90 exit 2, just s. Int corridors. **Pets:** Accepted. 🛗 🛬 📶 ⊠ 🔋 🖵

PRIEST RIVER

▼▼ **Eagle's Nest Motel** Ⓜ
(208) 448-2000. **$70-$149.** 5678 Hwy 2 83856. US 2, 0.5 mi w. Ext corridors. **Pets:** $10 daily fee/pet. Designated rooms, service with restrictions, supervision. 📶 🔋

REXBURG

▼▼ **AmericInn Lodge & Suites of Rexburg** 🅷
(208) 356-5333. **Call for rates.** 1098 Golden Beauty Dr 83440. US 20 exit 332 (S Rexburg). Int corridors. **Pets:** Accepted.
🍴 🛗 🛬 📶 ⊠ 🔋 🖵

◈◈◈ ▼▼ **Quality Inn** 🅷 🐾
(208) 359-1311. **$104-$190.** 885 W Main St 83440. US 20 exit 333 (Salmon), just e. Int corridors. **Pets:** Dogs only. Designated rooms, service with restrictions, supervision. 🆂🅰🆅🅴 🍴 🛬 📶 ⊠ 🔋 🖵

RIGGINS

▼▼ **Pinehurst Resort Cabins & RV** Ⓒ🄰
(208) 628-3323. **Call for rates.** 5604 Hwy 95 83654. 12 mi s of Riggins; MM 182. Ext corridors. **Pets:** $20 daily fee/pet. No service, supervision. 📶 ⊠ 🅿 🔋
🖵

▼▼ **Salmon Rapids Lodge** 🅷
(208) 628-2743. **$110-$135.** 1010 S Main St 83549. 0.3 mi s of center. Int corridors. **Pets:** Accepted. 🛬 ⊠ 📶 ⊠ 🔋 🖵

SAGLE

◈◈◈ ▼▼◇ **The Lodge at Sandpoint** 🅷
(208) 263-2211. **$139-$519, 14 day notice.** 41 Lakeshore Dr 83860. Jct I-95 and Lakeshore Dr, just w; 1 mi s of Sandpoint. Int corridors. **Pets:** Small. $20 daily fee/pet. Designated rooms, service with restrictions, supervision. 🆂🅰🆅🅴 🍴 ⊠ 📶 ⊠ 🔋 🖵

SALMON

▼▼◇ **Stagecoach Inn** 🅷 🐾
(208) 756-2919. **Call for rates.** 201 Riverfront Dr (US 93 N) 83467. Jct US 93 and SR 28, just n. Int corridors. **Pets:** Other species. $10 daily fee/pet. Designated rooms, service with restrictions, supervision.
🛗 🛬 📶 ⊠ 🔋 🖵

SANDPOINT

◈◈◈ ▼▼▼ **Best Western Edgewater Resort** 🅷
(208) 263-3194. **$109-$280.** 56 Bridge St 83864. Just e of US 95; downtown. Int corridors. **Pets:** Medium. $10 daily fee/pet. Service with restrictions, supervision. 🆂🅰🆅🅴 🍴 🛬 ⊠ 📶 ⊠ 🔋 🖵

▼▼◇ **La Quinta Inn Sandpoint** 🅷
(208) 263-9581. **$67-$306.** 415 Cedar St 83864. Jct US 2 and 95; downtown. Ext/int corridors. **Pets:** Accepted.
🍴 🛬 📶 ⊠ 🔋 🖵

▼▼ **Quality Inn Sandpoint** 🅷
(208) 263-2111. **$69-$179.** 807 N 5th Ave 83864. US 2 and 95, just s of jct SR 200. Int corridors. **Pets:** Medium. $10 daily fee/pet. Service with restrictions, supervision. 🍴 🛬 📶 🔋 🖵

TWIN FALLS

◈◈◈ ▼▼◇ **Best Western Plus Twin Falls Hotel** 🅷
(208) 736-8000. **$89-$169.** 1377 Blue Lakes Blvd N 83301. I-84 exit 173, 4 mi s on US 93. Int corridors. **Pets:** Medium, dogs only. $20 daily fee/room. Designated rooms, service with restrictions, supervision.
🆂🅰🆅🅴 🛗 🛬 📶 ⊠ 🔋 🖵

▼▼◇ **La Quinta Inn & Suites** 🅷
(208) 736-9600. **$86-$339.** 539 Pole Line Rd 83301. I-84 exit 173, 3 mi s to Pole Line Rd, then 0.3 mi w. Int corridors. **Pets:** Accepted.
🛗 🛬 📶 ⊠ 🔋 🖵

▼▼◇ **Quality Inn & Suites** 🅷
(208) 734-7494. **$79-$189.** 1910 Fillmore St N 83301. I-84 exit 173, 3.3 mi s. Int corridors. **Pets:** Accepted. 🛬 📶 🔋 🖵

WALLACE *(Restaurants p. 613)*

◈◈◈ ▼▼▼ **The Wallace Inn** 🅷 🐾
(208) 752-1252. **$72-$175.** 100 Front St 83873. I-90 exit 61 (Business Rt 90), just se. Int corridors. **Pets:** Other species. $20 deposit/pet. Service with restrictions, supervision.
🆂🅰🆅🅴 🍴 🛗 🛬 ⊠ 📶 ⊠ 🔋 🖵

WHITE BIRD

▼ **Hells Canyon Jet Boat Trips & Lodging** Ⓜ 🐾
(208) 839-2255. **$85-$105, 7 day notice.** 3252 Waterfront Dr 83554. US 95 exit White Bird, 1.5 mi s of center. Ext corridors. **Pets:** Dogs only. $15 daily fee/pet. Crate. 🍴 📶 ⊠ 🅩 🔋 🖵

WORLEY

◈◈◈ ▼▼▼ **Coeur d'Alene Casino Resort Hotel** 🅷
(208) 769-2600. **$89-$189.** 37914 S Nukwalqw Rd 83876. On US 95, 3 mi n. Int corridors. **Pets:** Small, dogs only. $25 daily fee/room. Designated rooms, service with restrictions, crate.
🆂🅰🆅🅴 🍴 🛗 🛬 ⊠ 📶 🔋 🖵

ILLINOIS

ALTON

Best Western Plus Parkway Hotel H
(618) 433-9900. **$94-$119.** 1900 Homer M Adams Pkwy 62002. On SR 111, 1.8 mi e of jct US 67. Int corridors. **Pets:** Other species. $10 daily fee/pet. Service with restrictions, crate.
SAVE (&M) (~) (🛜) (✕) (🖥) (💻)

Comfort Inn H ❀
(618) 465-9999. **$84-$139.** 11 Crossroads Ct 62002. Jct SR 3, just w on SR 140. Int corridors. **Pets:** Medium. $10 daily fee/room. Service with restrictions, supervision. (&M) (~) (🛜) (✕) (🖥) (💻)

ANNAWAN

Best Western Annawan Inn H
(309) 935-6565. **$90-$110.** 315 N Canal St 61234. I-80 exit 33, just s. Int corridors. **Pets:** Accepted. SAVE (¶) (&M) (~) (🛜) (✕) (🖥) (💻)

ARCOLA

Best Western Plus Green Mill Village Hotel & Suites Convention Center H
(217) 268-5000. **$90-$140.** 917 Green Mill Rd 61910. I-57 exit 203 (SR 133), just e. Int corridors. **Pets:** Medium. $50 deposit/room, $10 daily fee/pet. Designated rooms, no service, supervision.
SAVE (¶) (&M) (🛜) (✕) (🖥) (💻)

Comfort Inn H
(217) 268-4000. **$76-$110.** 610 E Springfield Rd 61910. I-57 exit 203 (SR 133), just w. Int corridors. **Pets:** Accepted. (~) (🛜) (🖥) (💻)

ARLINGTON HEIGHTS

Comfort Inn Arlington Heights/Chicago H
(847) 593-9400. **$84-$289.** 2120 S Arlington Heights Rd 60005. I-90 exit Arlington Heights Rd, 0.6 mi n. Int corridors. **Pets:** Accepted.
(🛜) (✕) (🖥) (💻)

DoubleTree by Hilton Chicago-Arlington Heights H
(847) 364-7600. **$96-$209.** 75 W Algonquin Rd 60005. I-90 exit Arlington Heights Rd, just n to Algonquin Rd, then just w. Int corridors.
Pets: Accepted. (¶) (&M) (~) (🛜) (🖥) (💻)

AURORA

Candlewood Suites Chicago-Aurora H
(630) 907-9977. **$119-$150.** 2625 W Sullivan Rd 60506. I-88 exit Orchard Rd, just sw. Int corridors. **Pets:** Accepted.
(¶) (&M) (🛜) (✕) (🖥) (💻)

Staybridge Suites Aurora/Naperville H
(630) 978-2222. **Call for rates.** 4320 Meridian Pkwy 60504. I-88 exit SR 59, 2 mi s to Meridian Pkwy, then just w. Int corridors.
Pets: Accepted. (&M) (~) (🛜) (🖥) (💻)

BANNOCKBURN

La Quinta Inn & Suites Chicago Bannockburn/Deerfield H
(847) 317-7300. **$68-$218.** 2000 S Lakeside Dr 60015. I-94 exit Half Day Rd (SR 22), just e to Lakeside Dr, then just s. Int corridors.
Pets: Accepted. (¶) (&M) (~) (🛜) (🖥) (💻)

BEDFORD PARK

Extended Stay America Chicago-Midway H
(708) 496-8211. **$105-$150.** 7524 State Rd 60638. Jct SR 50, just w. Int corridors. **Pets:** Accepted. (&M) (🛜) (🖥)

Hyatt Place Chicago Midway Airport H
(708) 594-1400. **$79-$269.** 6550 S Cicero Ave 60638. Jct 65th St. Int corridors. **Pets:** Accepted. SAVE (&M) (🛜) (✕) (🖥) (💻)

Residence Inn by Marriott Chicago Midway Airport H
(708) 458-7790. **$152-$396.** 6638 S Cicero Ave 60638. Jct 65th St. Int corridors. **Pets:** Accepted. (&M) (~) (🛜) (✕) (🖥) (💻)

BLOOMINGDALE

Courtyard by Marriott Chicago Bloomingdale H
(630) 529-9200. **$80-$204.** 275 Knollwood Dr 60108. I-355 exit Army Trail Rd, 4 mi w, then just n. Int corridors. **Pets:** Accepted.
(¶) (&M) (~) (🛜) (✕) (🖥) (💻)

Hilton Chicago Indian Lakes Resort H
(630) 529-0200. **$99-$199.** 250 W Schick Rd 60108. I-355 exit Lake St (US 20), 2.5 mi w, just s on Bloomingdale Rd, then 0.6 mi w. Int corridors. **Pets:** Accepted. (¶) (~) (✕) (🛜) (✕) (🖥) (💻)

Residence Inn by Marriott Chicago Bloomingdale H
(630) 893-9200. **$89-$246.** 295 Knollwood Dr 60108. I-355 exit Army Trail Rd, 4 mi w, then just n. Int corridors. **Pets:** Accepted.
(&M) (~) (🛜) (✕) (🖥) (💻)

BLOOMINGTON

The Chateau Hotel and Conference Center H
(309) 662-2020. **$89-$119.** 1621 Jumer Dr 61704. I-55 exit 167, follow I-55 business route (Veterans Pkwy), just e; 1.3 mi n of jct SR 9; 1 mi s of jct I-55. Int corridors. **Pets:** Small, other species. $25 one-time fee/pet. Designated rooms, supervision.
(¶) (&M) (~) (✕) (🛜) (✕) (🖥) (💻)

Country Inn & Suites By Carlson Bloomington/ Normal West H ❀
(309) 828-7177. **Call for rates.** 923 Maple Hill Rd 61704. I-55/74 exit 160 (SR 9), 0.3 mi w to Wylie Dr, just n, then just e. Int corridors.
Pets: $25 daily fee/room. Designated rooms, service with restrictions, crate. (&M) (~) (🛜) (✕) (🖥) (💻)

Days Inn & Suites H
(309) 828-6000. **$67-$219.** 505 Brock Dr 61701. I-55/74 exit 160 (SR 9), just e. Int corridors. **Pets:** Accepted. (🛜) (🖥) (💻)

DoubleTree by Hilton Bloomington H
(309) 664-6446. **$110-$210.** 10 Brickyard Dr 61701. I-55 business route (Veterans Pkwy), just n of US 150. Int corridors. **Pets:** Accepted.
(¶) (&M) (~) (🔊) (✕) (🖥) (💻)

Eastland Suites Hotel & Conference Center H
(309) 662-0000. **Call for rates.** 1801 Eastland Dr 61704. Jct I-55 business route (Veterans Pkwy) and SR 9, just s to Eastland Dr, then just e. Ext/int corridors. **Pets:** Accepted. (&M) (~) (🛜) (✕) (🖥) (💻)

Holiday Inn Express Bloomington West H
(309) 820-9990. **Call for rates.** 1031 Wylie Dr 61705. I-55/74 exit 160 (SR 9), just w, then just n. Int corridors. **Pets:** Accepted.
(&M) (~) (🛜) (✕) (🖥) (💻)

Holiday Inn Hotel & Suites H
(309) 662-4700. **$99-$219.** 3202 E Empire St 61704. Jct I-55 business route (Veterans Pkwy) and SR 9, 2.3 mi e on SR 9. Int corridors.
Pets: Dogs only. $20 daily fee/pet. Designated rooms, service with restrictions, supervision. (¶) (&M) (~) (✕) (🛜) (✕) (🖥) (💻)

Residence Inn by Marriott Bloomington/Normal H
(309) 661-9822. **$89-$263.** 2160 Ireland Grove Rd 61704. Jct I-55 business route (Veterans Pkwy) and Ireland Grove Rd, 3 mi e. Int corridors. **Pets:** Accepted. (¶) (&M) (~) (✕) (🛜) (🖥) (💻)

BOLINGBROOK

Aloft Bolingbrook H
(630) 410-6367. **$99-$299.** 500 Janes Ave 60440. I-355 exit Boughton Rd, just sw. Int corridors. **Pets:** Accepted.

BUFFALO GROVE

Extended Stay America-Chicago-Buffalo Grove-Deerfield H
(847) 215-0641. **$85-$115.** 1525 Busch Pkwy 60089. I-94 exit W Lake Cook Rd, 2 mi w to Milwaukee Ave (US 45/SR 21), then 1.3 mi n. Int corridors. **Pets:** Accepted.

BURR RIDGE

Extended Stay America Chicago-Burr Ridge H
(630) 323-6630. **$75-$110.** 15 W 122nd S Frontage Rd 60527. I-55 exit 276A (County Line Rd), just sw. Int corridors. **Pets:** Accepted.

CARBONDALE

Best Western Saluki Inn H
(618) 351-6611. **$90-$130.** 801 N Giant City Rd 62902. I-57 exit 54B, 14 mi w on SR 13, just s. Int corridors. **Pets:** Accepted.

Hampton Inn by Hilton H
(618) 549-6900. **$129-$189.** 2175 Reed Station Pkwy 62901. I-57 exit 54B, 11.7 mi w on SR 13. Int corridors. **Pets:** Accepted.

Holiday Inn Hotel and Conference Center H
(618) 549-2600. **Call for rates.** 2300 Reed Station Pkwy 62901. I-57 exit 54B, 12 mi w on SR 13. Int corridors. **Pets:** Accepted.

Super 8 H
(618) 457-8822. **$45-$130.** 1180 E Main St 62901. I-57 exit 54B, 13.9 mi w on SR 13. Int corridors. **Pets:** Accepted.

CHAMPAIGN

Baymont Inn & Suites H
(217) 356-8900. **$69-$189.** 302 W Anthony Dr 61822. I-74 exit 182 (Neil St), just nw. Int corridors. **Pets:** Accepted.

Drury Inn & Suites-Champaign H
(217) 398-0030. **$90-$150.** 905 W Anthony Dr 61821. I-74 exit 181 (Prospect Ave), just n. Int corridors. **Pets:** Accepted.

Hawthorn Suites by Wyndham Champaign H
(217) 398-3400. **$89-$299.** 101 Trade Centre Dr 61820. I-74 exit 182 (Neil St), 2.7 mi s. Int corridors. **Pets:** $25 one-time fee/room. Service with restrictions, supervision.

Home2 Suites by Hilton Champaign/Urbana H
(217) 355-6468. **Call for rates.** 2013 S Neil St 61820. 2.8 mi s. Int corridors. **Pets:** Large. $75 one-time fee/pet. Service with restrictions, crate.

Hyatt Place Champaign Urbana H
(217) 531-2800. **$89-$399.** 217 N Neil St 61820. Jct W Church St. Int corridors. **Pets:** Accepted.

La Quinta Inn Champaign H
(217) 356-4000. **$67-$262.** 1900 Center Dr 61820. I-74 exit 182 (Neil St), just n. Int corridors. **Pets:** Accepted.

Residence Inn by Marriott Champaign H
(217) 398-0000. **$89-$240.** 502 W Marketview Dr 61822. I-74 exit 181, 1 mi ne. Int corridors. **Pets:** Accepted.

Wingate by Wyndham H
(217) 355-5566. **$79-$199.** 516 W Marketview Dr 61822. I-74 exit 181, 1 mi ne. Int corridors. **Pets:** Accepted.

CHESTER

Best Western Chester Hotel H
(618) 826-3034. **$81-$90.** 2150 State St 62233. SR 150, 1 mi e of SR 3. Int corridors. **Pets:** Accepted.

CHICAGO

AC Hotels by Marriott Chicago Downtown H
(312) 981-6600. **$71-$658.** 630 N Rush St 61611. Jct Ontario St, just w of N Michigan Ave. Int corridors. **Pets:** Accepted.

Aloft Chicago City Center H
(312) 661-1000. **Call for rates.** 515 N Clark St 60654. Jct W Grand Ave. Int corridors. **Pets:** Accepted.

Best Western Plus Hawthorne Terrace Hotel H
(773) 244-3434. **$99-$499.** 3434 N Broadway St 60657. Between Belmont Ave and Addison St. Int corridors. **Pets:** Accepted.

Cambria Chicago Magnificent Mile H
(312) 787-6000. **$169-$499.** 166 E Superior St 60611. Just e of Michigan Ave. Int corridors. **Pets:** Accepted.

Carlton Inn Midway M
(773) 582-0900. **$109-$189.** 4944 S Archer Ave 60632. I-55 exit 287 (Pulaski Rd), 1.8 mi s to Archer Ave, then just e. **Pets:** Large, other species. $50 deposit/room, $10 daily fee/room. Designated rooms, service with restrictions, crate.

Crowne Plaza Chicago Metro H
(312) 829-5000. **$99-$409.** 733 W Madison St 60661. I-90/94 exit 51D (Madison St); jct Halsted St. Int corridors. **Pets:** Accepted.

The Drake H
(312) 787-2200. **$105-$510.** 140 E Walton Pl 60611. Jct N Michigan Ave and Lake Shore Dr. Int corridors. **Pets:** Accepted.

Fairmont Chicago, Millennium Park H
(312) 565-8000. **Call for rates.** 200 N Columbus Dr 60601. Jct Michigan Ave and Wacker Dr, just e. Int corridors. **Pets:** Accepted.

Four Seasons Hotel Chicago H ❀
(312) 280-8800. **Call for rates.** 120 E Delaware Pl 60611. Jct Michigan Ave; just nw of John Hancock Building. Int corridors. **Pets:** Small. $40 daily fee/room. Designated rooms, service with restrictions, supervision.

The Gwen, A Luxury Collection Hotel, Chicago H ❀
(312) 645-1500. **$109-$699.** 521 N Rush St 60611. Jct Grand Ave. Int corridors. **Pets:** Small. $75 one-time fee/room. Service with restrictions, supervision.

▼▼▼ Hampton Inn Chicago Downtown/Magnificent Mile H

(312) 706-0888. **$99-$279.** 160 E Huron St 60611. Just e of N Michigan Ave. Int corridors. **Pets:** Small. $100 one-time fee/pet. Designated rooms, service with restrictions, supervision.

⊞ ⌂ 🛜 ✕ 🔋 ▣

◆ ▼▼▼ ▼▼▼ Hilton Chicago H

(312) 922-4400. **$109-$479.** 720 S Michigan Ave 60605. I-290 (Congress Pkwy) exit Michigan Ave, just s. Int corridors. **Pets:** Other species. $50 one-time fee/room. Service with restrictions, crate.

SAVE ECO ⊞ 🄼 ⌂ ✕ 🛜 ✕ ▣

◆ ▼▼▼ Hilton Chicago/Magnificent Mile Suites H

(312) 664-1100. **$99-$499.** 198 E Delaware Pl 60611. Just e of Michigan Ave. Int corridors. **Pets:** Accepted.

SAVE ⊞ 🄼 ⌂ 🛜 ✕ 🔋 ▣

◆ ▼▼▼ Hilton Chicago O'Hare Airport H

(773) 686-8000. **$109-$499.** O'Hare Int'l Airport 60666. Opposite and connected to terminal buildings at Chicago O'Hare International Airport, accessed via I-190. Int corridors. **Pets:** Accepted.

SAVE ⊞ ⌂ ✕ 🛜 ✕ ▣

◆ ▼▼▼ Holiday Inn Chicago O'Hare H

(773) 693-5800. **Call for rates.** 5615 N Cumberland Ave 60631. I-90 exit 79B (N Cumberland Ave), just s. Int corridors. **Pets:** Medium, other species. $50 one-time fee/pet. Service with restrictions.

SAVE ⊞ 🄼 ⌂ 🛜 🔋 ▣

◆ ▼▼▼ Homewood Suites by Hilton Chicago Downtown H

(312) 644-2222. **$129-$229.** 40 E Grand Ave 60611. Jct Wabash Ave, just w of Michigan Ave. Int corridors. **Pets:** Accepted.

SAVE 🄼 ⌂ 🛜 ✕ 🔋 ▣

▼▼▼ Homewood Suites Chicago Downtown/Magnificent Mile H

(312) 585-9333. **Call for rates.** 152 E Huron St 60611. Just e of N Michigan Ave. Int corridors. **Pets:** Small. $100 one-time fee/pet. Designated rooms, service with restrictions, supervision.

⊞ 🛜 ✕ 🔋 ▣

▼▼▼ Hotel Indigo Chicago Downtown Gold Coast H

(312) 787-4980. **$69-$499.** 1244 N Dearborn Pkwy 60610. Just n of Division St. Int corridors. **Pets:** Medium. $75 one-time fee/pet. Service with restrictions, supervision. ⊞ 🛜 ✕ ▣

◆ ▼▼▼ Hotel Monaco Chicago H

(312) 960-8500. **$119-$709, 3 day notice.** 225 N Wabash Ave 60601. Jct Wacker Dr. Int corridors. **Pets:** Accepted.

SAVE ECO ⊞ 🛜 ✕ 🔋

◆ ▼▼▼ ▼▼▼ Hotel Palomar Chicago H ☙

(312) 755-9703. **Call for rates.** 505 N State St 60654. Between Grand and Illinois sts. Int corridors. **Pets:** Other species. Supervision.

SAVE ⊞ 🄼 ⌂ 🛜 ✕ ▣

◆ ▼▼▼ Hyatt Centric The Loop Chicago H

(312) 236-1234. **$99-$899.** 100 W Monroe St 60603. Jct Clark St. Int corridors. **Pets:** Accepted. SAVE ⊞ 🄼 🛜 ✕ 🔋 ▣

◆ ▼▼▼ InterContinental Chicago Magnificent Mile H

(312) 944-4100. **Call for rates.** 505 N Michigan Ave 60611. Just n of Chicago River; between E Grand Ave and E Illinois St. Int corridors. **Pets:** Accepted. SAVE ECO ⊕ ⊞ ⌂ ✕ 🛜 ✕ ▣

▼▼▼ The James Chicago H

(312) 337-1000. **Call for rates.** 55 E Ontario St 60611. Just w of N Michigan Ave. Int corridors. **Pets:** Accepted.

⊞ 🄼 ✕ 🛜 ✕ 🔋 ▣

◆ ▼▼▼ Kimpton Burnham Hotel H

(312) 782-1111. **Call for rates.** 1 W Washington St 60602. Jct State St. Int corridors. **Pets:** Accepted. SAVE ECO ⊞ ✕ 🛜 ✕

◆ ▼▼▼ Kimpton Hotel Allegro H

(312) 236-0123. **Call for rates.** 171 W Randolph St 60601. Jct LaSalle St. Int corridors. **Pets:** Accepted. SAVE ECO ⊞ 🛜 ✕ 🔋

◆ ▼▼▼ Kinzie Hotel H

(312) 395-9000. **Call for rates.** 20 W Kinzie St 60654. Between State and Dearborn sts. Int corridors. **Pets:** Accepted.

SAVE 🄼 🛜 ✕ 🔋 ▣

◆ ▼▼▼ The Langham, Chicago H ☙

(312) 923-9988. **Call for rates.** 330 N Wabash Ave 60611. Jct Kinzie St, just s; at Chicago River. Int corridors. **Pets:** Medium. $100 one-time fee/room. Service with restrictions, crate.

SAVE ⊞ 🄼 🛜 ✕ 🔋 ▣

▼▼▼ La Quinta Inn & Suites Chicago Downtown H

(312) 558-1020. **$99-$317.** 1 S Franklin St 60606. Jct Madison Ave. Int corridors. **Pets:** Accepted. ⊞ 🄼 ⌂ 🛜 ✕ 🔋 ▣

◆ ▼▼▼ ▼▼▼ Loews Chicago Hotel H

(312) 840-6600. **$169-$699.** 455 N Park Dr 60611. Jct N Columbus Dr. Int corridors. **Pets:** Accepted. SAVE ⊕ ⊞ 🄼 🛜 ✕ ▣

◆ ▼▼▼ Omni Chicago Hotel H

(312) 944-6664. **$159-$499.** 676 N Michigan Ave 60611. Jct Huron St. Int corridors. **Pets:** Accepted. SAVE ⊞ 🄼 ✕ 🛜 ✕ ▣

◆ ▼▼▼ Palmer House - A Hilton Hotel H ☙

(312) 726-7500. **$149-$449.** 17 E Monroe St 60603. Between State St and Wabash Ave. Int corridors. **Pets:** Other species. $50 one-time fee/room. Service with restrictions, supervision.

SAVE ECO ⊞ ⌂ ✕ 🛜 ✕ 🔋

◆ ▼▼▼ ▼▼▼ Park Hyatt Chicago H ☙

(312) 335-1234. **$265-$845, 3 day notice.** 800 N Michigan Ave 60611. Jct Chicago Ave at Water Tower Square. Int corridors. **Pets:** Medium. $100 one-time fee/room. Service with restrictions, supervision.

SAVE ECO ⊕ ⊞ 🄼 ⌂ ✕ 🛜 ✕ 🔋 ▣

◆ ▼▼▼ ▼▼▼ The Peninsula Chicago H

(312) 337-2888. **$475-$750.** 108 E Superior St 60611. Jct Michigan Ave. Int corridors. **Pets:** Accepted.

SAVE ECO ⊞ 🄼 ⌂ ✕ 🛜 ✕ ▣

◆ ▼▼▼ Radisson Blu Aqua Hotel H

(312) 565-5258. **$199-$459.** 221 N Columbus Dr 60601. Jct E Water St, just s of the Chicago River. Int corridors. **Pets:** Accepted.

SAVE ⊞ 🄼 ⌂ ✕ 🛜 ✕ ▣

◆ ▼▼▼ Renaissance Blackstone Chicago Hotel H

(312) 447-0955. **$101-$507.** 636 S Michigan Ave 60605. Jct Congress Pkwy, just s. Int corridors. **Pets:** Accepted.

SAVE ⊞ 🄼 🛜 🔋 ▣

◆ ▼▼▼ Residence Inn by Marriott Chicago Downtown/Loop H

(312) 223-8500. **$125-$549.** 11 S LaSalle St 60603. Jct W Madison St. Int corridors. **Pets:** Accepted. SAVE ⊞ 🄼 🛜 ✕ 🔋 ▣

◆ ▼▼▼ Residence Inn by Marriott Chicago Downtown/Magnificent Mile H

(312) 943-9800. **$111-$494.** 201 E Walton Pl 60611. Just e of Michigan Ave at Mies van der Rohe Way. Int corridors. **Pets:** Accepted.

SAVE 🄼 🛜 ✕ 🔋 ▣

AAA ▼▼▼ Residence Inn by Marriott Chicago Downtown River North H
(312) 494-9301. **$94-$492.** 410 N Dearborn St 60654. Between W Kinzie and W Hubbard sts. Int corridors. **Pets:** Accepted.
(SAVE) (&M) 🔲 🛜 ✕ 🔲 🔲

AAA ▼▼▼▼ The Ritz-Carlton Chicago H
(312) 266-1000. **Call for rates.** 160 E Pearson St 60611. Jct N Michigan Ave. Int corridors. **Pets:** Accepted.
(SAVE) (ECO) (¶) (&M) 🔲 ✕ 🛜 ✕ 🔲

AAA ▼▼▼ Sheraton Grand Chicago H
(312) 464-1000. **$89-$249.** 301 E North Water St 60611. Columbus Dr at Chicago River; just e of Michigan Ave. Int corridors. **Pets:** Accepted.
(SAVE) (ECO) (¶) 🔲 ✕ 🛜 ✕ 🔲 🔲

AAA ▼▼▼▼ Sofitel Chicago Magnificent Mile H
(312) 324-4000. **$145-$495.** 20 E Chestnut St 60611. Jct Wabash Ave and Chestnut St, 1/2 blk w of Rush St. Int corridors. **Pets:** Accepted.
(SAVE) (ECO) (¶) (&M) 🛜 ✕ 🔲 🔲

AAA ▼▼▼▼ Swissotel Chicago H
(312) 565-0565. **Call for rates.** 323 E Wacker Dr 60601. Just e of Michigan Ave. Int corridors. **Pets:** Accepted.
(SAVE) (¶) (&M) 🔲 ✕ 🛜 ✕ 🔲 🔲

AAA ▼▼▼ The Talbott Hotel H 🐾
(312) 944-4970. **Call for rates.** 20 E Delaware Pl 60611. Jct Rush St, just w. Int corridors. **Pets:** $75 one-time fee/room. Service with restrictions, crate. (SAVE) (ECO) (¶) 🛜 ✕ 🔲 🔲

▼▼▼▼ Thompson Chicago H
(312) 266-2100. **Call for rates.** 21 E Bellevue Pl 60611. Jct Rush St. Int corridors. **Pets:** Accepted. (¶) (&M) 🛜 ✕ 🔲 🔲

AAA ▼▼▼▼ Trump International Hotel & Tower H
(312) 588-8000. **Call for rates.** 401 N Wabash Ave 60611. Between Hubbard and Kinzie sts; just s of Kinzie St. Int corridors.
Pets: Accepted. (SAVE) (🔌) (¶) (&M) 🔲 ✕ 🛜 ✕ 🔲 🔲

AAA ▼▼▼▼ Waldorf Astoria Chicago H 🐾
(312) 646-1300. **$395-$425.** 11 E Walton St 60611. Between State and Rush sts. Int corridors. **Pets:** Small, dogs only. $45 one-time fee/room. Service with restrictions. (SAVE) (¶) (&M) ✕ 🛜 ✕ 🔲 🔲

AAA ▼▼▼▼ W Chicago-City Center H
(312) 332-1200. **$99-$699.** 172 W Adams St 60603. Between LaSalle and Wells sts. Int corridors. **Pets:** Accepted.
(SAVE) (¶) (&M) 🛜 ✕ 🔲

AAA ▼▼▼ W Chicago Lakeshore H
(312) 943-9200. **$169-$699.** 644 N Lake Shore Dr 60611. Jct Ontario St. Int corridors. **Pets:** Accepted. (SAVE) (¶) 🔲 🛜 ✕

AAA ▼▼▼▼ The Westin Chicago River North H
(312) 744-1900. **$99-$599.** 320 N Dearborn St 60654. Just n of Chicago River; between Dearborn and Clark sts. Int corridors.
Pets: Accepted. (SAVE) (¶) ✕ 🛜 ✕ 🔲 🔲

AAA ▼▼▼▼ The Westin Michigan Avenue Chicago H 🐾
(312) 943-7200. **Call for rates.** 909 N Michigan Ave 60611. Across from John Hancock Center. Int corridors. **Pets:** Dogs only. Service with restrictions, supervision. (SAVE) (ECO) (¶) (&M) 🛜 ✕ 🔲 🔲

▼▼▼ ▼▼▼ Wyndham Grand Chicago Riverfront H
(312) 346-7100. **$99-$525.** 71 E Wacker Dr 60601. Jct N Michigan Ave, just w. Int corridors. **Pets:** Accepted. (¶) (&M) 🛜 ✕ 🔲 🔲

COLLINSVILLE

▼▼▼ Drury Inn Collinsville-St. Louis H
(618) 345-7700. **$90-$155.** 602 N Bluff Rd 62234. I-55/70 exit 11 (SR 157), just n. Int corridors. **Pets:** Accepted.
(&M) 🛜 ✕ 🔲 🔲

▼▼ Super 8-Collinsville H
(618) 345-8008. **$59-$84.** 2 Gateway Dr 62234. I-55/70 exit 11 (SR 157), just n. Int corridors. **Pets:** Other species. $50 one-time fee/room, $15 daily fee/room. Supervision. 🛜 🔲 🔲

COLUMBIA

▼▼▼ Hampton Inn H
(618) 281-9000. **$109-$169.** 165 Admiral Trost Dr 62236. I-255 exit 6 (SR 3), 1.5 mi s, then just e. Int corridors. **Pets:** Accepted.
(¶) (&M) 🔲 🛜 ✕ 🔲 🔲

CRYSTAL LAKE

▼▼▼ Comfort Inn by Choice Hotels H
(815) 444-0040. **$94-$205.** 595 Tracy Tr 60014. Jct US 14 and SR 31, 0.4 mi w, just n on Pingree Rd, then just n. Int corridors.
Pets: Accepted. 🔲 🛜 ✕ 🔲 🔲

▼▼▼ Holiday Inn Chicago-Crystal Lake H
(815) 477-7000. **Call for rates.** 800 S SR 31 60014. At Three Oaks Rd, 0.3 mi s of jct US 14. Int corridors. **Pets:** Accepted.
(¶) 🔲 🛜 🔲 🔲

▼▼ Super 8 H
(815) 788-8888. **$60-$79.** 577 Crystal Point Dr 60014. On US 14, 1 mi w of jct SR 31. Int corridors. **Pets:** Other species. $20 daily fee/pet. Designated rooms, service with restrictions, crate. 🛜 🔲 🔲

DANVILLE

AAA ▼▼▼ Best Western Regency Inn H
(217) 446-2111. **$86-$190.** 360 Eastgate Dr 61834. I-74 exit 220 (Lynch Dr), just n. Ext/int corridors. **Pets:** Medium, other species. $20 daily fee/pet. Designated rooms, service with restrictions, supervision.
(SAVE) 🔲 🛜 🔲 🔲

▼▼ Red Roof Inn & Suites Danville H
(217) 443-3388. **$60-$105.** 389 Lynch Dr 61834. I-74 exit 220 (Lynch Dr), just n. Int corridors. **Pets:** Accepted.
(&M) 🔲 🛜 ✕ 🔲 🔲

AAA ▼▼▼ Sleep Inn & Suites H
(217) 442-6600. **$90-$180.** 361 Lynch Dr 61834. I-74 exit 220 (Lynch Dr), just n. Int corridors. **Pets:** $15 daily fee/pet. Designated rooms, service with restrictions, supervision.
(SAVE) (&M) 🔲 🛜 ✕ 🔲 🔲

▼▼ Super 8 H
(217) 443-4499. **$55-$80.** 377 Lynch Dr 61834. I-74 exit 220 (Lynch Dr), just n. Int corridors. **Pets:** Accepted. 🛜 🔲 🔲

DARIEN

▼▼▼ Extended Stay America Chicago-Darien H
(630) 985-4708. **$70-$105.** 2345 Sokol Ct 60561. I-55 exit 271A, 0.5 mi s to Westgate Rd, then 0.5 mi ne via frontage road. Int corridors.
Pets: Accepted. (¶) 🛜 🔲

DECATUR

▼▼▼ Decatur Conference Center & Hotel H
(217) 422-8800. **Call for rates.** 4191 W Hwy 36 62522. I-72 exit 133A (US 36), 1 mi e. Int corridors. **Pets:** Accepted.
(¶) (&M) ✕ 🛜 🔲 🔲

▼▼▼ Hawthorn Suites by Wyndham H
(217) 864-9311. **$79-$250, 3 day notice.** 2370 S Mount Zion Rd 62521. SR 121, 0.5 mi s of jct US 36. Int corridors. **Pets:** Accepted.
(&M) 🛜 ✕ 🔲 🔲

▼▼▼ **Sleep Inn** 🏨
(217) 872-7700. **$79-$104.** 3920 E Hospitality Ln 62521. I-72 exit 144 (SR 48), just s to Brush College Rd, then just e. Int corridors.
Pets: Accepted. 🍴 📶 🐾 📶 📶 📶

DEERFIELD

◆◆ ▼▼▼ **Chicago Marriott Suites Deerfield** 🏨
(847) 405-9666. **$75-$286.** 2 Parkway North 60015. I-94 exit Deerfield Rd northbound, just w; exit Lake Cook Rd southbound, 0.3 mi e to Saunders Rd, then 0.5 mi n. Int corridors. **Pets:** Accepted.
SAVE 🍴 📶 🏊 📶 ✖ 📶 📶

◆◆ ◇ **Red Roof Inn Chicago -**
   Northbrook/Deerfield 🅼
(847) 205-1755. **$49-$99.** 340 S Waukegan Rd 60015. I-94 exit SR 43 (Waukegan Rd), 0.5 mi ne. Ext corridors. **Pets:** Accepted.
SAVE 📶

▼▼▼ **Residence Inn by Marriott**
   Chicago/Deerfield 🏨 🐾
(847) 940-4644. **$89-$263.** 530 Lake Cook Rd 60015. I-94 exit Lake Cook Rd, 1.8 mi e, then 3 blks n on Corporate 500 Dr access road. Ext corridors. **Pets:** $75 one-time fee/pet. Designated rooms, service with restrictions, supervision. 🏊 📶 ✖ 📶 📶

DEKALB

◆◆ ◇ ▼▼ **Red Roof Inn & Suites DeKalb** 🏨
(815) 758-8661. **$79-$189.** 1212 W Lincoln Hwy 60115. I-88 exit Annie Glidden Rd, 2 mi n to W Lincoln Hwy (SR 38), then just w. Ext/int corridors. **Pets:** Accepted. SAVE 📶 🏊 📶 ✖ 📶 📶

DES PLAINES

◆◆ ▼▼▼ **Comfort Inn O'Hare** 🏨
(847) 635-1300. **$99-$1049.** 2175 E Touhy Ave 60018. I-294 exit Touhy Ave westbound, just w; exit Golf Rd (SR 58) eastbound, 0.3 mi w to River Rd, then 5.5 mi s. Int corridors. **Pets:** Accepted.
SAVE 📶 ✖ 📶 📶

▼▼ **Extended Stay America-Chicago O'Hare** 🏨
(847) 294-9693. **$80-$115.** 1201 E Touhy Ave 60018. SR 72 (Higgins Rd), 0.6 mi w of US 12/45 (Mannheim Rd). Int corridors.
Pets: Accepted. 🍴 📶 📶 ✖ 📶

▼▼ **Extended Stay America – Chicago - Allstate**
   Arena 🏨
(847) 768-0395. **$85-$120.** 1207 E Touhy Ave 60018. SR 72 (Higgins Rd), 0.6 mi w of US 12/45 (Mannheim Rd). Int corridors.
Pets: Accepted. 🍴 📶 📶 ✖ 📶

DIXON

◆◆ ▼▼▼ **Comfort Inn by Choice Hotels** 🏨
(815) 284-0500. **$94-$177.** 136 Plaza Dr 61021. I-88 exit SR 26, just n, then just e. Int corridors. **Pets:** Medium. $15 daily fee/pet. Service with restrictions, supervision. SAVE 🏊 📶 ✖ 📶 📶

DOWNERS GROVE

◇◇ **Holiday Inn Express Chicago Downers**
   Grove 🏨 🐾
(630) 810-9500. **$79-$119.** 3031 Finley Rd 60515. I-355 exit Butterfield Rd (SR 56), just e. Int corridors. **Pets:** Dogs only. $10 daily fee/pet. Designated rooms, service with restrictions, crate. 📶 ✖ 📶 📶

◆◆ ▼ **Red Roof Inn Chicago - Downers Grove** 🅼
(630) 963-4205. **$49-$129.** 1113 Butterfield Rd 60515. I-355 exit Butterfield Rd (SR 56), on frontage road; I-88 exit Highland Ave N, just w. Ext corridors. **Pets:** Accepted. SAVE 📶 ✖ 📶

EAST MOLINE

▼▼▼ **Comfort Inn & Suites** 🏨
(309) 792-4660. **$84-$189.** 2209 John Deere Rd 61244. I-74 exit 4B (John Deere Rd), 5 mi e on SR 5. Int corridors. **Pets:** Accepted.
🏊 📶 ✖ 📶 📶

EAST PEORIA

◆◆ ▼▼▼ **Best Western Plus Peoria** 🏨
(309) 694-4959. **$129-$149.** 300 Eastlight Ct 61611. I-74 exit 95 (Main St), just s to Camp St (SR 8), just w to Altofer Dr, then just ne. Int corridors. **Pets:** Accepted. SAVE 📶 🏊 📶 ✖ 📶 📶

▼▼▼ **Stoney Creek Hotel & Conference Center** 🏨
(309) 694-1300. **Call for rates.** 101 Mariners Way 61611. I-74 exit 95 (Main St) westbound; exit 95A eastbound, just n. Int corridors.
Pets: Accepted. 📶 🏊 ✖ 📶 ✖ 📶 📶

▼▼ **Super 8 Peoria East** 🏨
(309) 698-8889. **$60-$80.** 725 Taylor St 61611. I-74 exit 96, just e. Int corridors. **Pets:** Accepted. 🍴 📶 📶 ✖ 📶 📶

EFFINGHAM

▼▼▼ **Best Western Delta Inn** 🏨
(217) 342-4499. **Call for rates.** 1509 Hampton Dr 62401. I-57/70 exit 160 (SR 32/33), just s. Int corridors. **Pets:** Medium. $15 daily fee/room. Designated rooms, service with restrictions, crate.
📶 🏊 📶 ✖ 📶 📶

▼▼▼ **Fairfield Inn & Suites by Marriott Effingham** 🏨
(217) 540-5454. **$53-$197.** 1111 N Henrietta St 62401. I-57/70 exit 160 (SR 32/33), just se. Int corridors. **Pets:** Accepted.
📶 🏊 📶 ✖ 📶 📶

▼▼▼ **Quality Inn** 🏨
(217) 347-5050. **$85-$139.** 1304 W Evergreen Ave 62401. I-57/70 exit 160 (SR 32/33), just e, then just n. Int corridors. **Pets:** Other species. $25 deposit/pet, $10 daily fee/pet. Designated rooms, service with restrictions, supervision. 📶 🏊 📶 📶 📶

◆◆ ▼▼▼ **Raintree Inn** 🏨
(217) 342-4121. **$65-$89.** 1811 W Fayette Ave 62401. I-57/70 exit 159, just n. Ext/int corridors. **Pets:** Accepted.
SAVE 🍴 📶 🏊 📶 📶 📶

▼▼▼ **Super 8-Effingham** 🅼
(217) 342-6888. **$62-$76.** 1400 Thelma Keller Ave 62401. I-57/70 exit 160 (SR 32/33), 0.5 mi n. Int corridors. **Pets:** Accepted.
📶 ✖ 📶 📶

ELGIN

▼▼▼ **Candlewood Suites** 🏨
(847) 888-0600. **Call for rates.** 1780 Capital St 60124. I-90 exit N Randall Rd, just s to Westfield Dr, then 0.3 mi w. Int corridors.
Pets: Accepted. 🍴 📶 📶 ✖ 📶 📶

▼▼◇ **Quality Inn by Choice Hotels-Elgin** 🏨
(847) 608-7300. **$74-$130.** 500 Tollgate Rd 60123. I-90 exit SR 31 N, just n. Int corridors. **Pets:** Accepted. 🍴 📶 📶 ✖ 📶 📶

ELK GROVE VILLAGE

▼▼▼ **La Quinta Inn Chicago O'Hare Airport** 🏨
(847) 439-6767. **$67-$253.** 1900 E Oakton St 60007. Jct SR 72 (Higgins Rd) and 83 (Busse Rd). Int corridors. **Pets:** Accepted.
🏊 📶 ✖ 📶 📶

◆◆ ▼▼▼ **Sheraton Suites Chicago Elk Grove** 🏨
(847) 290-1600. **$129-$299.** 121 Northwest Point Blvd 60007. I-90 exit Arlington Heights Rd, just s; in Northwest Point Corporate Park. Int corridors. **Pets:** Accepted. SAVE 🍴 📶 🏊 ✖ 📶 📶

ELMHURST

▼▼▼ Clarion Inn Elmhurst-Oakbrook H
(630) 279-0700. **$94-$500.** 933 S Riverside Dr 60126. 2.4 mi s of SR 64 (North Ave), just off SR 83. Int corridors. **Pets:** Accepted.
⊞ ⊇ 🤝 ✕ 🖥 💻

▼▼ Extended Stay America
     Chicago-Elmhurst-O'Hare H
(630) 530-4353. **$80-$110.** 550 W Grand Ave 60126. Jct US 20 (Lake St), 0.4 mi ne; adjacent to I-290 overpass. Int corridors.
Pets: Accepted. ⊞ 🦽M 🤝 🖥

EVANSTON

AAA ▼▼▼▼ Hilton Orrington/Evanston H ❀
(847) 866-8700. **$139-$399.** 1710 Orrington Ave 60201. Jct Church St. Int corridors. **Pets:** Medium. $75 one-time fee/room. Designated rooms, service with restrictions. SAVE ⊞ 🦽M 🤝 ✕ 🖥 💻

FAIRVIEW HEIGHTS

▼▼ Americas Best Value Inn H
(618) 624-3636. **$70-$80.** 305 Salem Pl 62208. I-64 exit 12 (SR 159), just n. Int corridors. **Pets:** Accepted. ⊇ 🤝 🖥 💻

▼▼▼ Comfort Suites H
(618) 394-0202. **$84-$144.** 137 Ludwig Dr 62208. I-64 exit 12 (SR 159), just n, then 0.4 mi w. Int corridors. **Pets:** Accepted.
🦽M ⊇ 🤝 ✕ 🖥 💻

▼▼▼▼ Drury Inn & Suites-Fairview Heights H
(618) 398-8530. **$95-$155.** 12 Ludwig Dr 62208. I-64 exit 12 (SR 159), just n. Int corridors. **Pets:** Accepted. ⊇ 🤝 ✕ 🖥 💻

▼▼ Fairfield Inn by Marriott H
(618) 398-7124. **$89-$152.** 140 Ludwig Dr 62208. I-64 exit 12 (SR 159), just n, then 0.5 mi w. Int corridors. **Pets:** Accepted.
🦽M ⊇ 🤝 ✕ 🖥 💻

▼▼ Super 8 - Fairview Heights, IL H
(618) 398-8338. **$62-$94.** 45 Ludwig Dr 62208. I-64 exit 12 (SR 159), just n. Int corridors. **Pets:** Other species. $15 one-time fee/room. Service with restrictions, supervision. 🤝 🖥 💻

FLORA

AAA ▼▼ Best Western Lorson Inn H
(618) 662-3054. **$82-$102.** 201 Hagen Dr 62839. Jct US 45 and 50. Int corridors. **Pets:** Large, other species. $10 daily fee/room. Designated rooms, supervision. SAVE ⊞ 🦽M 🤝 ✕ 🖥 💻

FORSYTH

▼▼▼ Hampton Inn Decatur-Forsyth H
(217) 877-5577. **$89-$319.** 1429 Hickory Point Dr 62535. I-72 exit 141B (US 51), 0.5 mi n. Int corridors. **Pets:** Accepted.
🦽M ⊇ 🤝 ✕ 🖥 💻

▼▼ Quality Inn Forsyth H
(217) 875-1166. **$74-$94.** 134 Barnett Ave 62535. I-72 exit 141B (US 51), 0.5 mi n. Int corridors. **Pets:** Other species. $10 daily fee/pet. Service with restrictions, crate. 🦽M 🤝 🖥 💻

▼▼▼ Residence Inn by Marriott Decatur Forsyth H
(217) 872-6600. **$84-$260.** 230 Lucile Ave 62535. I-72 exit 141B (US 51), 1 mi n, then just e. Int corridors. **Pets:** Accepted.
🦽M 🤝 ✕ 🖥 💻

FRANKLIN PARK

AAA ▼▼ Best Western Plus O'Hare Intl South H
(847) 233-9292. **$80-$130.** 3001 N Mannheim Rd 60131. Jct US 12/45 (Mannheim Rd) and Grand Ave, just n. Int corridors. **Pets:** Accepted.
SAVE ⊞ ⊇ 🤝 ✕ 🖥 💻

GALESBURG

▼▼▼ Baymont Inn & Suites H ❀
(309) 343-7600. **$70-$130.** 2285 Washington St 61401. I-74 exit 48A (US 150), just w to Michigan Ave, just s to Washington St, then just e. Int corridors. **Pets:** Other species. $25 one-time fee/pet. Designated rooms, service with restrictions. ⊞ 🦽M ⊇ 🤝 ✕ 🖥 💻

AAA ▼▼ Best Western Prairie Inn & Conference
          Center H
(309) 343-7151. **$80-$120.** 300 S Soangetaha Rd 61401. I-74 exit 48 (Main St), just e, then just s. Int corridors. **Pets:** Accepted.
SAVE ⊞ ⊇ 🤝 ✕ 🖥 💻

▼▼▼ Holiday Inn Express & Suites H
(309) 343-7100. **$124-$199.** 2160 E Main St 61401. I-74 exit 48A (US150), just w. Int corridors. **Pets:** Other species. $25 one-time fee/pet. Designated rooms, service with restrictions, supervision.
⊞ 🦽M 🤝 ✕ 🖥 💻

GENESEO

AAA ▼▼ Best Western Geneseo Inn H
(309) 945-9345. **Call for rates.** 1375 S Oakwood Ave 61254. I-80 exit 19 (US 6/SR 82), just n. Int corridors. **Pets:** Accepted.
SAVE 🦽M 🤝 ✕ 🖥 💻

GENEVA

AAA ▼▼▼ The Herrington Inn & Spa CI
(630) 208-7433. **$179-$550, 3 day notice.** 15 S River Ln 60134. Just off SR 38, 0.5 mi w of jct SR 25. Int corridors. **Pets:** Small, dogs only. $100 one-time fee/room, $25 daily fee/pet. Designated rooms, service with restrictions, crate. SAVE ⊞ 🦽M 🤝 🤝 💻

GILMAN

▼▼ Super 8 H
(815) 265-7000. **$58-$65.** 1301 S Crescent St 60938. I-57 exit 283, 0.3 mi e. Int corridors. **Pets:** Accepted. 🤝 ✕ 🖥 💻

GLEN ELLYN

▼▼▼ Crowne Plaza Lombard Glen Ellyn H
(630) 629-6000. **$99-$499.** 1250 Roosevelt Rd 60137. I-355 exit Roosevelt Rd, 0.8 mi e on SR 38. Int corridors. **Pets:** Dogs only. $50 deposit/room. Designated rooms, supervision.
⊞ 🦽M ⊇ 🤝 ✕ 🖥 💻

GLENVIEW

▼▼▼ Staybridge Suites Glenview H
(847) 657-0002. **Call for rates.** 2600 Lehigh Ave 60026. I-294 exit Willow Rd, 2.4 mi e. Int corridors. **Pets:** Accepted.
⊞ 🦽M ⊇ 🤝 ✕ 🖥 💻

GRAYSLAKE

▼▼▼ Comfort Suites by Choice Hotels H
(847) 223-5050. **$94-$249.** 1775 E Belvidere Rd 60030. Just w of jct US 45. Int corridors. **Pets:** Other species. $35 one-time fee/pet. Designated rooms, service with restrictions, supervision.
⊞ 🦽M ⊇ 🤝 ✕ 🖥 💻

GRAYVILLE

▼▼ Super 8 H
(618) 375-7288. **$55-$85.** 2060 CR 2450 N 62844. I-64 exit 130 (SR 1), just n. Int corridors. **Pets:** Medium, other species. $15 one-time fee/room. Service with restrictions, supervision. 🦽M 🤝 ✕ 🖥 💻

GREENVILLE

▼▼ Econo Lodge Inn & Suites M
(618) 664-3030. **$58-$127.** 1731 S SR 127 62246. I-70 exit 45, just n. Ext/int corridors. **Pets:** $12 daily fee/pet. Designated rooms, service with restrictions, supervision. ⊇ 🤝 🖥 💻

▼▼ Super 8-Greenville H

(618) 664-0800. **$50-$76.** 1700 S SR 127 62246. I-70 exit 45, just n. Int corridors. **Pets:** Accepted. 🛜 🔲 💻

GURNEE

▼▼ Comfort Inn by Choice Hotels H

(847) 855-8866. **$90-$165.** 6080 Gurnee Mills Cir E 60031. I-94 exit Grand Ave (SR 132 W), just nw. Int corridors. **Pets:** $30 daily fee/pet. Designated rooms, service with restrictions, supervision.

🛥 🛜 ✕ 🔲 💻

HANOVER PARK

▼▼ Extended Stay America-Chicago-Hanover Park H

(630) 893-4823. **$75-$105.** 1075 Lake St 60133. On US 20; between Gary Ave and Elgin-O'Hare Expwy. Int corridors. **Pets:** Accepted.

🛜 🔲

HILLSIDE

◉ ▼▼ Best Western Plus Chicago Hillside H

(708) 544-9300. **$99-$179.** 4400 Frontage Rd 60162. I-290 exit 14B eastbound; exit 17 westbound to US 12/45 (Mannheim Rd), just nw via frontage road. Int corridors. **Pets:** Large. $20 daily fee/room. Service with restrictions, crate. SAVE 🍴 🛥 🛜 🔲 💻

HOFFMAN ESTATES

▼▼ Hawthorn Suites by Wyndham H

(847) 490-1686. **$79-$159.** 2875 Greenspoint Pkwy 60169. I-90 exit Barrington Rd westbound, just s to SR 72 (Higgins Rd), then just w; exit SR 59 eastbound, 0.5 mi n to SR 72 (Higgins Rd), then 2 mi e. Int corridors. **Pets:** Accepted. 🔥M 🛜 ✕ 🔲 💻

▼▼ Hoffman Inn & Suites H

(847) 882-3312. **$67-$152.** 2280 Barrington Rd 60169. I-90 exit Barrington Rd westbound, 0.3 mi s; exit SR 59 eastbound, 0.5 mi n to SR 72 (Higgins Rd), 2 mi e to Barrington Rd, then just n. Int corridors. **Pets:** Accepted. 🛥 🛜 🔲 💻

◉ ▼▼ Hyatt Place Chicago/Hoffman Estates H

(847) 839-1800. **$75-$199.** 2750 Greenspoint Pkwy 60169. I-90 exit Barrington Rd westbound, 0.3 mi s; exit SR 59 eastbound, 0.5 mi n to SR 72 (Higgins Rd), 2 mi e to Barrington Rd, then just n. Int corridors. **Pets:** Accepted. SAVE 🍴 🔥M 🛥 🛜 ✕ 🔲 💻

HOMEWOOD

▼▼▼ La Banque Hotel H 🐾

(708) 798-6000. **$190-$270.** 2034 Ridge Rd 60430. Jct Harwood and Martin aves; downtown. Int corridors. **Pets:** $50 one-time fee/pet. Service with restrictions. 🔌 🍴 🛜 ✕ 🔲 💻

ITASCA

◉ ▼▼▼▼ Eaglewood Resort & Spa H 🐾

(630) 773-1400. **$109-$899.** 1401 Nordic Rd 60143. I-355 exit US 20 (Lake St), 0.3 mi w to Swift Rd, then just n, follow signs. Int corridors. **Pets:** Small. $10 daily fee/room. Designated rooms, service with restrictions. SAVE ECO 🍴 🔥M 🛥 ✕ 🛜 ✕ 🔲 💻

▼▼ Extended Stay America-Chicago-Itasca H

(630) 250-1111. **$70-$100.** 1181 Rohlwing Rd 60143. I-290 exit Thorndale Ave, 0.5 mi w. Int corridors. **Pets:** Accepted. 🍴 🔥M 🛜 🔲

◉ ▼▼▼ Hyatt Place Chicago/Itasca H

(630) 875-1400. **$84-$399.** 1150 N Arlington Heights Rd 60143. I-290 exit Thorndale Ave, 0.6 mi e, then 0.5 mi n. Int corridors. **Pets:** Accepted. SAVE 🍴 🔥M 🛥 🛜 ✕ 🔲 💻

◉ ▼▼▼ The Westin Chicago Northwest H

(630) 773-4000. **$89-$299.** 400 Park Blvd 60143. I-290 exit Thorndale Ave, just e. Int corridors. **Pets:** Accepted.

SAVE 🍴 🔥M 🛥 ✕ 🛜 ✕ 🔲 💻

JACKSONVILLE

◉ ▼▼▼ Best Western Jacksonville Inn M

(217) 245-4500. **$70-$150.** 1709 W Morton Ave 62650. I-72 exit 64, 2.3 mi n on SR 267 (Main St) to SR 104 (Morton Ave), then 1.5 mi w. Int corridors. **Pets:** $10 daily fee/pet. Service with restrictions, crate.

SAVE 🛥 ✕ 🛜 ✕ 🔲 💻

▼▼ Super 8 H

(217) 479-0303. **$58-$95.** 1003 W Morton Ave 62650. I-72 exit 64, 2.3 mi n on SR 267 (Main St) to SR 104 (Morton Ave), then 0.8 mi w. Int corridors. **Pets:** $10 daily fee/pet. Service with restrictions, crate.

🛜 🔲 💻

JOLIET

▼▼ Comfort Inn by Choice Hotels Joliet North H

(815) 436-5141. **$94-$209.** 3235 Norman Ave 60435. I-55 exit 257, just e. Int corridors. **Pets:** Accepted. 🛥 🛜 ✕ 🔲 💻

▼▼ Fairfield Inn by Marriott Joliet South H

(815) 741-3499. **$78-$219.** 1501 Riverboat Center Dr 60436. I-80 exit 127, just n. Int corridors. **Pets:** Accepted.

🔥M 🛥 🛜 ✕ 🔲 💻

◉ ▼▼▼ TownePlace Suites by Marriott Joliet South H

(815) 741-2400. **$89-$208.** 1515 Riverboat Center Dr 60431. I-80 exit 127, just n. Int corridors. **Pets:** Accepted.

SAVE 🔥M 🛥 🛜 ✕ 🔲 💻

KEWANEE

▼▼ AmericInn Lodge & Suites of Kewanee H

(309) 856-7200. **$120-$200.** 925 Tenney St 61443. On SR 78, 1.9 mi s of jct US 34. Int corridors. **Pets:** Accepted.

🍴 🔥M 🛥 🛜 ✕ 🔲 💻

LAKE FOREST

◉ ▼▼▼▼ Deer Path Inn H

(847) 234-2280. **$269-$329.** 255 E Illinois Rd 60045. Between Green Bay Rd and N Western Ave; downtown. Int corridors. **Pets:** Accepted.

SAVE 🍴 🛜 ✕ 🔲

LAKE ZURICH

▼▼▼ Holiday Inn Express & Suites Lake Zurich-Barrington H

(847) 726-7500. **Call for rates.** 197 S Rand Rd 60047. On US 12, 0.3 mi nw of SR 22. Int corridors. **Pets:** Accepted.

🔥M 🛥 🛜 ✕ 🔲 💻

LANSING

▼▼ Extended Stay America-Chicago-Lansing H

(708) 895-6402. **$85-$110.** 2520 173rd St 60438. I-80/94 exit 161 (Torrence Ave), just n to 173rd St, then just e. Int corridors. **Pets:** Accepted. 🍴 🔥M 🛜 🔲 💻

LEROY

▼▼ Days Inn Le Roy - Bloomington SE M

(309) 962-4700. **$61-$111.** 1 Demma Dr 61752. I-74 exit 149, just sw. Int corridors. **Pets:** Medium. $10 daily fee/pet. Service with restrictions, supervision. 🛜 ✕ 🔲 💻

▼▼ Holiday Inn Express H

(309) 962-4439. **Call for rates.** 705 S Persimmons Ct 61752. I-74 exit 149, just ne. Int corridors. **Pets:** Medium. $25 daily fee/room. Designated rooms, service with restrictions, crate.

🔥M 🛥 🛜 ✕ 🔲 💻

LIBERTYVILLE

Candlewood Suites Chicago-Libertyville H
(847) 247-9900. **Call for rates.** 1100 N US 45 60048. I-94 exit SR 137 (Buckley Rd), 5.6 mi w to US 45, then 1.4 mi s. Int corridors. **Pets:** Accepted.

LINCOLN

Best Western Plus Lincoln Inn H
(217) 732-9641. **$90-$100.** 1750 5th St 62656. I-55 exit 126 (US 121), 1.6 mi e to Lincoln Pkwy, then 0.5 mi s. Int corridors. **Pets:** Accepted.

Holiday Inn Express H
(217) 735-5800. **Call for rates.** 130 Olson Dr 62656. I-55 exit 126 (US 121), just e. Int corridors. **Pets:** Accepted.

LINCOLNSHIRE

Homewood Suites by Hilton Chicago-Lincolnshire H
(847) 945-9300. **Call for rates.** 10 Westminster Way 60069. I-94 exit Half Day Rd, just w. Int corridors. **Pets:** Accepted.

Staybridge Suites Lincolnshire H
(847) 821-0002. **Call for rates.** 100 Barclay Blvd 60069. I-94 exit Half Day Rd, 2.2 mi w to Barclay Blvd, then just s; just w of jct US 45 and SR 21; in Lincolnshire Corporate Center. Int corridors. **Pets:** Accepted.

LISLE

Extended Stay America-Chicago-Lisle H
(630) 434-7710. **$70-$100.** 445 Warrenville Rd 60532. I-355 exit Ogden Ave, just nw. Int corridors. **Pets:** Accepted.

Hyatt Regency Lisle near Naperville H
(630) 852-1234. **$89-$239.** 1400 Corporetum Dr 60532. I-88 exit SR 53 westbound, 0.3 mi s; exit Naperville Rd eastbound to Warrenville Rd, 2 mi e to jct SR 53. Int corridors. **Pets:** Accepted.

Sheraton Lisle Hotel H
(630) 505-1000. **$99-$199.** 3000 Warrenville Rd 60532. I-88 exit Naperville Rd, just n, then 0.3 mi e. Int corridors. **Pets:** Accepted.

LITCHFIELD

Baymont Inn & Suites Litchfield H
(217) 324-4556. **$60-$89.** 1405 W Hudson Dr 62056. I-55 exit 52 (SR 16), just e to Ohren Ln, just s to W Hudson Dr, then just w. Int corridors. **Pets:** Other species. Designated rooms, service with restrictions, supervision.

Hampton Inn Litchfield H
(217) 324-4441. **$71-$157.** 11 Thunderbird Cir 62056. I-55 exit 52 (SR 16), on Corvette Dr, then just e. Int corridors. **Pets:** Medium. $20 daily fee/pet. Service with restrictions, supervision.

Holiday Inn Express & Suites Litchfield West H
(217) 324-4556. **$104-$179.** 4 Thunderbird Cir 62056. I-55 exit 52 (SR 16), on Corvette Dr, then just e. Int corridors. **Pets:** Other species. Designated rooms, service with restrictions, supervision.

Quality Inn Litchfield H
(217) 324-9260. **$65-$99.** 1010 E Columbian Blvd N 62056. I-55 exit 52 (SR 16), just e to Ohren Ln, just s to W Hudson Dr, then just w. Int corridors. **Pets:** Other species. $15 daily fee/pet. Service with restrictions, crate.

LOMBARD

Embassy Suites by Hilton Chicago-Lombard/Oak Brook H
(630) 969-7500. **$109-$229.** 707 E Butterfield Rd 60148. I-88 exit Highland Ave, just n to Butterfield Rd (SR 56), then 0.5 mi e. Int corridors. **Pets:** Accepted.

Hyatt Place Chicago-Lombard/Oak Brook H
(630) 932-6501. **$79-$219.** 2340 S Fountain Square Dr 60148. I-88 exit Highland Ave, just n to Butterfield Rd (SR 56), 0.9 mi e, then just n. Int corridors. **Pets:** Accepted.

Residence Inn by Marriott Chicago-Lombard H 🐾
(630) 629-7800. **$89-$226.** 2001 S Highland Ave 60148. I-88 exit Highland Ave, 0.8 mi n. Ext corridors. **Pets:** Medium. $100 one-time fee/room. Service with restrictions, crate.

TownePlace Suites by Marriott Chicago Lombard H
(630) 932-4400. **$84-$202.** 455 E 22nd St 60148. I-88 exit Highland Ave, 0.8 mi n, then 0.3 mi e. Int corridors. **Pets:** Accepted.

The Westin Lombard Yorktown Center H
(630) 719-8000. **$129-$429.** 70 Yorktown Center 60148. I-88 exit Highland Ave, just n to Butterfield Rd (SR 56), then just e; in The Shops on Butterfield. Int corridors. **Pets:** Accepted.

LOVES PARK

Holiday Inn Express Hotel & Suites Rockford North H
(815) 654-4100. **$100-$150.** 7552 Park Pl 61111. I-39/90 exit E Riverside Blvd, just nw. Int corridors. **Pets:** Other species. $25 daily fee/room. Designated rooms, supervision.

Quality Inn & Suites Rockford/Loves Park H
(815) 282-9300. **$70-$160.** 4313 N Bell School Rd 61111. I-39/90 exit E Riverside Blvd, just nw. Int corridors. **Pets:** Accepted.

MARION

Drury Inn-Marion H
(618) 997-9600. **$85-$150.** 2706 W DeYoung St 62959. I-57 exit 54B (SR 13), 0.5 mi w. Int corridors. **Pets:** Accepted.

Quality Inn & Suites H
(618) 993-6221. **$62-$139.** 2600 W Main St 62959. I-57 exit 53 (Main St), just w. Int corridors. **Pets:** $15 daily fee/pet. Designated rooms, service with restrictions, crate.

Super 8 H
(618) 993-5577. **$61-$100.** 2601 W Vernell Rd 62959. I-57 exit 54B (SR 13), just w. Int corridors. **Pets:** Small, other species. $10 daily fee/pet. Service with restrictions, crate.

MASCOUTAH

Best Western Plus Mascoutah/SAFB H
(618) 808-0280. **$89-$149.** 9730 Hayden Dr 62258. I-64 exit 23, just n. Int corridors. **Pets:** Accepted.

MATTOON

Baymont Inn & Suites H
(217) 234-2420. **$69-$104.** 206 McFall Rd 61938. I-57 exit 190B, just w. Int corridors. **Pets:** Accepted.

▼▼▼ **Holiday Inn Express Hotel & Suites** �H
(217) 235-2060. **Call for rates.** 121 Swords Dr 61938. I-57 exit 190B, just w. Int corridors. **Pets:** Small, dogs only. $25 daily fee/pet. Designated rooms, service with restrictions, supervision.
🅼 ⊇ 🤶 ✕ 🛢 🖵

▼▼▼ **Quality Inn & Suites** �H
(217) 235-0222. **$75-$200.** 4922 Paradise Rd 61938. I-57 exit 184, just w. Int corridors. **Pets:** Accepted. 🤶 ✕ 🛢 🖵

▼▼ **Super 8** 🅼
(217) 235-8888. **$69-$100.** 205 McFall Rd 61938. I-57 exit 190B, just w. Int corridors. **Pets:** Small, other species. $15 one-time fee/room, $15 daily fee/pet. Designated rooms, service with restrictions, supervision.
🤶 🛢 🖵

METROPOLIS

▼▼▼ **Harrah's Metropolis Casino & Hotel** �H
(618) 524-2628. **Call for rates.** 100 E Front St 62960. I-24 exit 37 (US 45), 3.5 mi w, then just s on Ferry St; between Metropolis and Ferry sts. Int corridors. **Pets:** Accepted. 🍴 🅼 🤶 🛢 🖵

METTAWA

▼▼▼ **Residence Inn by Marriott Chicago Lake Forest/Mettawa** �H
(847) 615-2701. **$90-$334.** 26325 N Riverwoods Blvd 60045. I-94 exit SR 60 (Townline Rd), just nw. Int corridors. **Pets:** Accepted.
🅼 ⊇ 🤶 ✕ 🛢 🖵

MOLINE

▼▼ **Comfort Inn by Choice Hotels** �H
(309) 762-7000. **$90-$190.** 2600 52nd Ave 61265. I-280/74 exit 18A eastbound; exit 5B westbound, just s on US 6 and 150, then 0.5 mi nw on 27th St. Int corridors. **Pets:** Dogs only. $10 daily fee/pet. Designated rooms, service with restrictions, supervision.
🅼 ⊇ 🤶 ✕ 🛢 🖵

▼▼▼ **Fairfield Inn by Marriott** �H
(309) 762-9083. **$82-$180.** 2705 48th Ave 61265. I-280/74 exit 5B westbound; exit 18A eastbound, just s on US 6 to traffic light, then 1 mi nw on 27th St. Int corridors. **Pets:** Accepted.
🅼 ⊇ 🤶 ✕ 🛢 🖵

▼▼▼ **Stoney Creek Hotel & Conference Center** �H
(309) 743-0101. **$104-$169.** 101 18th St 61265. Jct 18th St and 2nd Ave. Int corridors. **Pets:** Accepted. 🅼 ⊇ 🗶 🤶 ✕ 🛢 🖵

MONMOUTH

▼▼▼ **AmericInn Lodge & Suites of Monmouth** �H
(309) 734-9958. **$108, 3 day notice.** 1 AmericInn Way 61462. Jct US 34 and N Main St, just s; 18 mi w of jct I-74 and US 34. Int corridors.
Pets: Accepted. 🅼 ⊇ 🤶 ✕ 🛢 🖵

MONTICELLO

AAA ▼▼▼ **Best Western Monticello Gateway Inn** �H
(217) 762-9436. **$80-$185.** 805 Iron Horse Pl 61856. I-72 exit 166, just s. Ext/int corridors. **Pets:** Accepted. 🆂🅰🆅🅴 ⊇ 🤶 ✕ 🛢 🖵

MORRIS

▼▼▼ **Holiday Inn Express & Suites** �H
(815) 941-8700. **Call for rates.** 222 Gore Rd 60450. I-80 exit 112 (SR 47), just nw. Int corridors. **Pets:** Accepted.
🅼 ⊇ 🤶 ✕ 🛢 🖵

▼▼ **Quality Inn by Choice Hotels** �H
(815) 942-6600. **$100-$155.** 200 Gore Rd 60450. I-80 exit 112 (SR 47), 0.3 mi nw. Int corridors. **Pets:** Accepted. 🍴 ⊇ 🤶 🛢 🖵

MORTON

AAA ▼▼▼ **Baymont Inn & Suites** �H
(309) 266-8888. **$75-$90.** 210 E Ashland St 61550. I-74 exit 102, 0.4 mi ne. Int corridors. **Pets:** $15 daily fee/pet. Designated rooms, service with restrictions, supervision. 🆂🅰🆅🅴 ⊇ 🤶 ✕ 🛢 🖵

▼▼▼ **Holiday Inn Express Hotel & Suites Morton-Peoria** �H
(309) 263-4400. **Call for rates.** 140 E Ashland St 61550. I-74 exit 102, 0.3 mi ne. Int corridors. **Pets:** Accepted. 🅼 🤶 ✕ 🛢 🖵

▼▼▼ **Park Inn By Radisson - Morton** �H
(309) 263-5116. **Call for rates.** 201 E Ashland St 61550. I-74 exit 102, 0.3 mi ne. Int corridors. **Pets:** Other species. $10 daily fee/pet. Designated rooms, service with restrictions.
🍴 🅼 ⊇ 🤶 ✕ 🛢 🖵

▼▼ **Quality Inn by Choice Hotels** �H
(309) 266-8310. **$70-$110.** 115 E Ashland Ave 61550. I-74 exit 102B, just w. Ext/int corridors. **Pets:** Accepted. 🅼 🤶 🛢 🖵

MORTON GROVE

AAA ▼▼▼ **Best Western Morton Grove Inn** 🅼
(847) 965-6400. **$69-$299.** 9424 Waukegan Rd 60053. SR 43, just s of Golf Rd (SR 58). Ext corridors. **Pets:** Accepted. 🆂🅰🆅🅴 🤶 🛢 🖵

MOUNT VERNON

▼▼▼ **Comfort Suites** �H
(618) 244-2700. **$95-$170.** 404 S 44th St 62864. I-57/64 exit 95 (SR 15), just e. Int corridors. **Pets:** $25 daily fee/room. Designated rooms, service with restrictions, supervision. 🍴 ⊇ 🤶 ✕ 🛢 🖵

▼▼▼ **Drury Inn & Suites Mt.Vernon** �H
(618) 246-5201. **$105-$170.** 145 N 44th St 62864. I-57/64 exit 95 (SR 15), just e, then just n; entry through restaurant parking lot. Int corridors. **Pets:** Accepted. ⊇ 🤶 ✕ 🛢 🖵

▼▼▼ **Holiday Inn** �H
(618) 244-7100. **Call for rates.** 222 Potomac Blvd 62864. I-57/64 exit 95 (SR 15), just w to Potomac Blvd, then just n. Int corridors.
Pets: Accepted. 🍴 🅼 ⊇ 🤶 🛢 🖵

MUNDELEIN

▼▼▼ **DoubleTree by Hilton Libertyville - Mundelein** �H
(847) 949-5100. **$99-$199.** 510 E Illinois (Rt 83) 60060. Jct US 45. Int corridors. **Pets:** Large. $50 one-time fee/room. Designated rooms, service with restrictions, crate. 🍴 🅼 ⊇ 🤶 ✕ 🛢 🖵

AAA ▼ **Super 8 Motel Mundelein** �H
(847) 949-8842. **Call for rates.** 1950 S Lake St 60060. Jct US 45, SR 60 and 83. Int corridors. **Pets:** Accepted. 🆂🅰🆅🅴 🤶 ✕ 🛢 🖵

NAPERVILLE

AAA ▼▼▼ **Best Western Naperville Inn** �H
(630) 505-0200. **$75-$119.** 1617 N Naperville Wheaton Rd 60563. I-88 exit Naperville Rd, just e on Diehl Rd to Naperville Rd, then just s. Ext/int corridors. **Pets:** Medium, other species. $10 daily fee/pet. Designated rooms, service with restrictions, supervision. 🆂🅰🆅🅴 🤶 🛢 🖵

AAA ▼▼▼ **Country Inn & Suites By Carlson** �H 🐾
(630) 505-3353. **$79-$219.** 1837 Centre Point Cir 60563. I-88 exit Naperville Rd, 0.3 mi s to Diehl Rd, 0.7 mi w, then just n. Int corridors. **Pets:** Other species. $100 one-time fee/room. Service with restrictions, crate. 🆂🅰🆅🅴 🄴🄲🄾 ⊇ 🤶 ✕ 🛢 🖵

▼▼ **Extended Stay America Chicago-Naperville-East** �H
(630) 577-0200. **$70-$100.** 1827 Centre Point Cir 60563. I-88 exit Naperville Rd, just s to Diehl Rd, 0.8 mi w, then just n. Int corridors. **Pets:** Accepted. 🍴 🅼 🤶 🛢

◇◇◇ ▽▽▽▽ Hotel Arista at CityGate Centre H ❀

(630) 579-4100. **Call for rates.** 2139 CityGate Ln 60563. I-88 exit SR 59, just n. Int corridors. **Pets:** Small, dogs only. $250 deposit/room, $50 daily fee/room. Designated rooms, service with restrictions, crate.

[SAVE] [ECO] [⫟] [&M] [📶] [✕] [🛢] [🖥]

◇◇◇ ▽ Red Roof PLUS+ Chicago - Naperville M

(630) 369-2500. **$59-$90.** 1698 W Diehl Rd 60563. I-88 exit SR 59, just s. Ext corridors. **Pets:** Accepted. [SAVE] [📶] [✕] [🛢]

▽▽▽▽ TownePlace Suites by Marriott Naperville H

(630) 548-0881. **$85-$261.** 1843 W Diehl Rd 60563. I-88 exit SR 59, just s to Diehl Rd, then just w. Int corridors. **Pets:** Accepted.

[&M] [🛏] [📶] [✕] [🛢] [🖥]

NASHVILLE

◇◇◇ ▽▽▽ Best Western U. S. Inn H

(618) 478-5341. **$98-$110.** 11640 SR 127 62263. I-64 exit 50 (SR 127), 0.3 mi s. Int corridors. **Pets:** Medium. $10 daily fee/pet. Designated rooms, service with restrictions, supervision.

[SAVE] [&M] [🛏] [📶] [✕] [🛢] [🖥]

NORMAL

▽▽ Comfort Suites by Choice Hotels Bloomington/Normal H

(309) 452-8588. **$84-$179.** 310B Greenbriar Dr 61761. I-55 exit 167, follow I-55 business route (Veterans Pkwy), 1.3 mi s; jct Fort Jesse Rd. Int corridors. **Pets:** Medium, other species. $20 one-time fee/room. Designated rooms, service with restrictions, crate.

[&M] [🛏] [📶] [✕] [🛢] [🖥]

◇◇◇ ▽▽▽ Hyatt Place Bloomington Normal H

(309) 454-9288. **$84-$229.** 200 Broadway Ave 61761. Jct Beaufort St; downtown. Int corridors. **Pets:** Accepted.

[SAVE] [⫟] [&M] [📶] [✕] [🛢] [🖥]

NORTHBROOK

◇◇◇ ▽▽▽▽ Hilton Chicago/Northbrook H

(847) 480-7500. **$99-$199.** 2855 N Milwaukee Ave 60062. On SR 21, s of jct US 45 and Willow Rd. Int corridors. **Pets:** Accepted.

[SAVE] [⫟] [&M] [🛏] [✕] [📶] [✕] [🛢] [🖥]

◇◇◇ ▽▽▽▽ Renaissance Chicago North Shore H

(847) 498-6500. **$79-$231.** 933 Skokie Blvd 60062. I-94 exit Dundee Rd W northbound; exit SR 43 (Waukegan Rd) southbound, 0.5 mi s to SR 68, then 1.5 mi e. Int corridors. **Pets:** Accepted.

[SAVE] [⫟] [&M] [🛏] [📶] [✕] [🛢] [🖥]

◇◇◇ ▽▽▽▽ Sheraton Chicago Northbrook Hotel H

(847) 480-1900. **$99-$259.** 1110 Willow Rd 60062. 2 mi w of jct I-94; 3.2 mi e of jct I-294. Int corridors. **Pets:** Accepted.

[SAVE] [⫟] [&M] [🛏] [📶] [✕] [🛢] [🖥]

OAK BROOK

◇◇◇ ▽▽▽▽ Hilton Chicago/Oak Brook Hills Resort & Conference Center H

(630) 850-5555. **$109-$199.** 3500 Midwest Rd 60523. I-88 exit SR 83 westbound, 0.5 mi s to 31st St, 1 mi w to Midwest Rd, then 0.6 mi s; exit Midwest Rd eastbound, 1.3 mi s. Int corridors. **Pets:** Small, dogs only. $50 one-time fee/room. Service with restrictions, supervision.

[SAVE] [⫟] [&M] [🛏] [✕] [📶] [✕] [🛢] [🖥]

◇◇◇ ▽▽▽▽ Le Meridien Chicago - Oak brook Center H

(630) 368-9900. **$119-$329.** 2100 Spring Rd 60523. Just e of SR 83, just n of 22nd St (Cermak Rd). Int corridors. **Pets:** Accepted.

[SAVE] [⫟] [&M] [🛏] [📶] [✕] [🛢] [🖥]

▽▽▽ Residence Inn by Marriott Chicago/Oak Brook H

(630) 571-1200. **$99-$250.** 790 Jorie Blvd 60523. I-88 exit Midwest Rd eastbound, just n to 22nd St (Cermak Rd), 1.7 mi e to Jorie Blvd, then just sw; exit 22nd St (Cermak Rd) westbound, 0.4 mi e to Jorie Blvd. Int corridors. **Pets:** Accepted. [⫟] [&M] [🛏] [📶] [✕] [🛢] [🖥]

OAKBROOK TERRACE

◇◇◇ ▽▽▽▽ Holiday Inn Chicago-Oak Brook H

(630) 833-3600. **Call for rates.** 17 W 350 22nd St 60181. I-88 exit Midwest Rd eastbound, 0.4 mi n to 22nd St (Cermak Rd), then just e; exit 22nd St (Cermak Rd) westbound, then 0.9 mi w. Int corridors. **Pets:** Medium. $50 deposit/pet. Service with restrictions.

[SAVE] [⫟] [&M] [🛏] [📶] [✕] [🛢] [🖥]

◇◇◇ ▽▽▽▽ Staybridge Suites Chicago-Oakbrook Terrace H

(630) 953-9393. **Call for rates.** 200 Royce Blvd 60181. I-88 exit Midwest Rd eastbound to 22nd St (Cermak Rd), 0.4 mi w to Butterfield Rd (SR 56), just n, then just n on Renaissance Blvd; exit 22nd St (Cermak Rd) westbound, 2.5 mi w on 22nd St to SR 56, just n, then just n on Renaissance Blvd. Int corridors. **Pets:** Large. $75 one-time fee/room. Designated rooms, service with restrictions, crate.

[SAVE] [&M] [📶] [✕] [🛢] [🖥]

O'FALLON

▽▽ Candlewood Suites H

(618) 622-9555. **Call for rates.** 1332 Park Plaza Dr 62269. I-64 exit 14 (US 50), just s on Lincoln Hwy, 0.5 mi e on Hartman Ln, then just n on 2nd entrance to Park Plaza Dr. Int corridors. **Pets:** Accepted.

[&M] [📶] [🛢] [🖥]

▽▽▽ Drury Inn & Suites-O'Fallon H

(618) 624-2211. **$100-$165.** 1118 Central Park Dr 62269. I-64 exit 16, just s. Int corridors. **Pets:** Accepted. [&M] [🛏] [📶] [✕] [🛢] [🖥]

▽▽▽ Extended Stay America-St. Louis-O'Fallon H

(618) 624-1757. **$70-$90.** 154 Regency Park Dr 62269. I-64 exit 14 (US 50), just w to Regency Park Dr, then 0.4 mi s. Int corridors. **Pets:** Accepted. [⫟] [&M] [📶] [🛢] [🖥]

◇◇◇ ▽▽▽ Super 8 O'Fallon/ Scott Air Force Base H

(618) 624-6060. **$55-$110.** 1100 Eastgate Dr 62269. I-64 exit 19B (SR 158), 0.5 mi n, then just sw. Int corridors. **Pets:** Accepted.

[SAVE] [&M] [🛏] [📶] [✕] [🛢] [🖥]

OGLESBY

◇◇◇ ▽▽▽ Best Western Oglesby Inn H

(815) 883-3535. **$89-$129.** 900 Holiday St 61348. I-39 exit 54, just e. Int corridors. **Pets:** Other species. $20 one-time fee/room. Service with restrictions, supervision. [SAVE] [&M] [🛏] [📶] [🛢] [🖥]

▽▽▽ Days Inn Oglesby/Starved Rock H

(815) 883-9600. **$100-$150.** 120 N Lewis Ave 61348. I-39 exit 54, just e. Int corridors. **Pets:** Other species. $15 one-time fee/pet. Service with restrictions, supervision. [🛏] [📶] [✕] [🛢] [🖥]

OLNEY

▽ Super 8 Motel M

(618) 392-7888. **$60-$70.** 425 S West St 62450. Jct US 50 and SR 130 S, 5.9 mi s. Int corridors. **Pets:** Accepted.

[⫟] [&M] [📶] [✕] [🛢] [🖥]

ORLAND PARK

▽▽▽▽ Homewood Suites by Hilton and Elements Conference Center H

(708) 364-9411. **$139-$329.** 16245 S La Grange Rd 60467. I-80 exit 145 (US 45/La Grange Rd), 2.8 mi n. Int corridors. **Pets:** Accepted.

[&M] [🛏] [📶] [✕] [🛢] [🖥]

OTTAWA

▼▼▼ Fairfield Inn & Suites by Marriott Ottawa/Starved Rock Area ℍ
(815) 431-8955. **$99-$185.** 3000 Fairfield Ln 61350. I-80 exit 90 (SR 23), just s to Etna Rd, then just e. Int corridors. **Pets:** Other species. $25 one-time fee/pet. Service with restrictions, supervision.
🛏️ 🆓 🐾 🛜 ⊗ 🅿️ 💻

▼▼▼ Hampton Inn-Starved Rock Area ℍ
(815) 434-6040. **$119-$159.** 4115 Holiday Ln 61350. I-80 exit 90 (SR 23), just n. Int corridors. **Pets:** Accepted. 🆓 🐾 🛜 🅿️ 💻

▼▼▼ Comfort Inn ℍ
(815) 433-0029. **$150-$180.** 120 W Stevenson Rd 61350. I-80 exit 90 (SR 23), just n. Int corridors. **Pets:** Accepted.
🆓 🐾 🛜 ⊗ 🅿️ 💻

PALATINE

▼▼▼ Holiday Inn Express Palatine/Arlington Heights ℍ
(847) 934-4900. **Call for rates.** 1550 E Dundee Rd 60074. SR 53 exit Dundee Rd (SR 68), just w. Int corridors. **Pets:** Accepted.
🆓 🐾 ⊗ 🛜 ⊗ 🅿️ 💻

PEORIA

▼▼ Candlewood Suites Peoria at Grand Prairie ℍ
(309) 691-1690. **$119-$145, 30 day notice.** 5300 W Landens Way 61615. SR 6 exit 2 (US 150/War Memorial Dr), follow US 150 NW to Summershade Cir, then just w. Int corridors. **Pets:** $150 one-time fee/room. Service with restrictions, crate. 🆓 🛜 ⊗ 🅿️ 💻

▼▼ Comfort Suites by Choice Hotels ℍ
(309) 688-3800. **$74-$154.** 1812 W War Memorial Dr 61614. I-74 exit 89 (US 150/War Memorial Dr), just e, then just s. Int corridors. **Pets:** Small, other species. $25 one-time fee/room. Service with restrictions, crate. 🐾 🛜 ⊗ 🅿️ 💻

▼▼▼ Country Inn & Suites By Carlson Peoria-North ℍ
(309) 589-0044. **Call for rates.** 5309 W Landens Way 61615. SR 6 exit 2 (US 150/War Memorial Dr), just n. Int corridors. **Pets:** Accepted.
🆓 🐾 🛜 ⊗ 🅿️ 💻

▼▼▼ Hampton Inn & Suites Peoria at Grand Prairie ℍ
(309) 589-0001. **$144-$189.** 7806 N Rt 91 61615. SR 6 exit 2 (US 150/War Memorial Dr), just w, then 0.3 mi n. Int corridors. **Pets:** Accepted.
🆓 🐾 🛜 ⊗ 🅿️ 💻

🆑 ▼▼▼ Quality Inn & Suites ℍ
(309) 685-2556. **$74-$179.** 4112 N Brandywine Dr 61614. I-74 exit 89 (US 150/War Memorial Dr), just e. Int corridors. **Pets:** Accepted.
🆂 🆓 🐾 🛜 🅿️ 💻

▼▼▼ Residence Inn by Marriott ℍ
(309) 681-9000. **$114-$253.** 2000 W War Memorial Dr 61614. I-74 exit 89 (US 150/War Memorial Dr), just w; entrance through Northwoods Mall. Int corridors. **Pets:** Accepted. 🍴 🆓 🛏️ 🛜 ⊗ 🅿️ 💻

▼▼▼ Staybridge Suites Peoria Downtown ℍ
(309) 673-7829. **Call for rates.** 300 W Romeo B Garrett Ave 61605. I-74 exit 92, 0.5 mi w on Glendale Ave (which becomes William Kumpf St), then just w on Fourth Ave. Int corridors. **Pets:** Accepted.
🆓 🐾 🛜 ⊗ 🅿️ 💻

▼▼ Super 8 ℍ
(309) 688-8074. **$59-$96.** 1816 W War Memorial Dr 61614. I-74 exit 89 (US 150/War Memorial Dr), just e. Int corridors. **Pets:** Accepted.
🛜 🅿️ 💻

▼▼▼ Wingate by Wyndham Peoria ℍ 🌸
(309) 589-0033. **$139-$179.** 7708 N Rt 91 61615. SR 6 exit 2 (US 150/War Memorial Dr), just w, then 0.3 mi n. Int corridors. **Pets:** Other species. $75 one-time fee/room. Service with restrictions.
🆓 🐾 🛜 ⊗ 🅿️ 💻

PERU

▼▼▼ Holiday Inn Express & Suites Peru ℍ
(815) 224-2500. **$96-$138.** 5253 Trompeter Rd 61354. I-80 exit 75 (SR 251), just n. Int corridors. **Pets:** Accepted. 🆓 🛜 ⊗ 🅿️ 💻

▼▼ La Quinta Inn & Suites Peru ℍ
(815) 224-9000. **$67-$165.** 4389 Venture Dr 61354. I-80 exit 75 (SR 251), 0.4 mi s to 38th St, just w to Venture Dr, then 0.4 mi nw. Int corridors. **Pets:** Accepted. 🐾 🛜 🅿️ 💻

PONTIAC

🆑 ▼▼▼ Best Western Pontiac Inn ℍ
(815) 842-2777. **$110-$120.** 1821 W Reynolds St 61764. I-55 exit 197 (SR 116), just e. Int corridors. **Pets:** Small. $10 daily fee/pet. Service with restrictions, supervision. 🆂 🍴 🐾 🛜 ⊗ 🅿️ 💻

▼▼ Quality Inn ℍ
(815) 844-4444. **$100-$130.** 1823 W Reynolds St 61764. I-55 exit 197 (SR 116), just e. Int corridors. **Pets:** Small. $10 daily fee/pet. Service with restrictions, supervision. 🍴 🛜 🅿️ 💻

PONTOON BEACH

▼▼ Super 8 ℍ
(618) 931-8808. **$50-$78.** 4141 Timber Lake Dr 62040. I-270 exit 6A (SR 11), just s. Int corridors. **Pets:** Accepted. 🛜 🅿️ 💻

PROSPECT HEIGHTS

▼▼▼ Country Inn & Suites By Carlson, Prospect Heights ℍ
(847) 419-3600. **Call for rates.** 600 N Milwaukee Ave 60070. Jct SR 21 and US 45. Int corridors. **Pets:** Accepted. 🍴 🛜 🅿️ 💻

QUINCY

▼▼ Quincy Inn & Suites ℍ
(217) 228-8808. **$69.** 224 N 36th St 62301. I-172 exit 14 (SR 104), 1.8 mi w, then just s. Int corridors. **Pets:** Accepted. 🛜 🅿️ 💻

▼▼ Stoney Creek Hotel & Conference Center ℍ
(217) 223-2255. **$81-$100.** 3809 E Broadway St 62305. I-172 exit 14 (SR 104), 1 mi w. Int corridors. **Pets:** Accepted.
🍴 🐾 ⊗ 🛜 ⊗ 🅿️ 💻

RANTOUL

🆑 ▼▼▼ First Heritage Inn 🅼
(217) 892-9292. **$65-$70.** 420 S Murray Rd 61866. I-57 exit 250 (US 136), 0.5 mi e, then just s. Ext corridors. **Pets:** Medium. $10 daily fee/pet. Service with restrictions, supervision. 🆂 🐾 🛜 🅿️ 💻

▼▼ Super 8 ℍ
(217) 893-8888. **$60-$110.** 207 S Murray Rd 61866. I-57 exit 250 (US 136), just e. Int corridors. **Pets:** Accepted. 🛜 🅿️ 💻

RICHMOND

▼▼ Super 8 Richmond/Geneva Lakes ℍ
(815) 678-4711. **$65-$106.** 11200 N US Hwy 12 60071. 0.5 mi n of jct SR 173. Int corridors. **Pets:** Accepted. 🍴 🛜 🅿️ 💻

ROBINSON

🆑 ▼▼▼ Best Western Robinson Inn ℍ
(618) 544-8448. **$82-$100.** 1500 W Main St 62454. 1.2 mi w on SR 33. Int corridors. **Pets:** Accepted. 🆂 🛜 🅿️ 💻

ROCHELLE

Comfort Inn & Suites by Choice Hotels ♿ ❀
(815) 562-5551. $93-$205. 1133 N 7th St 61068. I-39 exit 99 (SR 38), 2.5 mi w; jct SR 38 and 251; downtown. Int corridors. Pets: Other species. $15 one-time fee/room. Service with restrictions.

Holiday Inn Express ♿
(815) 562-9994. $139-$159. 1240 Dement Rd 61068. I-39 exit 99 (SR 38), just nw. Int corridors. Pets: Accepted.

ROCKFORD

Baymont Inn & Suites Rockford ♿
(815) 229-8200. $74-$165. 662 N Lyford Rd 61107. I-90 exit US 20 business route, just e, then just n. Int corridors. Pets: Other species. $10 daily fee/pet. Designated rooms, service with restrictions, supervision.

Candlewood Suites ♿
(815) 229-9300. $99-$139. 7555 Walton St 61108. I-90 exit US 20 business route, 0.3 mi e to Bell School Rd, just s to Walton St, then just e. Int corridors. Pets: Large, other species. $75 one-time fee/pet. Designated rooms, service with restrictions, crate.

Extended Stay America - Rockford East ♿
(815) 397-8316. $70-$100. 747 N Bell School Rd 61107. I-90 exit US 20 business route, just w to Bell School Rd, then 0.3 mi n. Int corridors. Pets: Accepted.

Holiday Inn ♿
(815) 398-2200. $110-$249. 7550 E State St 61108. I-90 exit US 20 business route, 0.3 mi w to Bell School Rd. Int corridors. Pets: Accepted.

Red Roof Inn Rockford Ⓜ
(815) 398-9750. $49-$129. 7434 E State St 61108. I-90 exit US 20 business route, just w. Ext corridors. Pets: Accepted.

Residence Inn by Marriott ♿
(815) 227-0013. $90-$209. 7542 Colosseum Dr 61107. I-90 exit US 20 business route, 0.3 mi w to Bell School Rd, then just n. Int corridors. Pets: Accepted.

Sleep Inn-Rockford ♿
(815) 398-8900. $65-$120. 725 Clark Dr 61107. I-90 exit US 20 business route, just w to Bell School Rd, just n to Clark Dr, then 0.4 mi ne. Int corridors. Pets: Accepted.

Staybridge Suites ♿
(815) 397-0200. Call for rates. 633 N Bell School Rd 61107. I-90 exit US 20 business route, 0.3 mi w to Bell School Rd, then just n. Int corridors. Pets: Accepted.

ROMEOVILLE

Country Inn & Suites By Carlson, Romeoville (Chicago) ♿
(630) 378-1052. $95-$139. 1265 Lakeview Dr 60446. I-55 exit 263, just n. Int corridors. Pets: Accepted.

Extended Stay America Chicago-Romeoville ♿
(630) 226-8966. $70-$105. 1225 Lakeview Dr 60446. I-55 exit 263, just n. Int corridors. Pets: Accepted.

ROSEMONT

Aloft Chicago O'Hare ♿
(847) 671-4444. $129-$209. 9700 Balmoral Ave 60018. I-190 exit 1B, just s. Int corridors. Pets: Accepted.

Crowne Plaza Chicago O'Hare Hotel & Conference Center ♿
(847) 671-6350. Call for rates. 5440 N River Rd 60018. I-190 exit 1B (River Rd), just s. Int corridors. Pets: Accepted.

DoubleTree by Hilton Chicago O'Hare Airport-Rosemont ♿
(847) 292-9100. $109-$299. 5460 N River Rd 60018. I-190 exit 1B (River Rd), just s. Int corridors. Pets: Small. $75 deposit/room, $100 one-time fee/room. Service with restrictions, crate.

Embassy Suites by Hilton Hotel O'Hare Rosemont ♿
(847) 678-4000. $119-$309. 5500 N River Rd 60018. I-190 exit 1B (River Rd), just s. Int corridors. Pets: Accepted.

Hilton Rosemont Chicago O'Hare ♿
(847) 678-4488. $99-$399. 5550 N River Rd 60018. I-190 exit 1B (River Rd), just s. Int corridors. Pets: Accepted.

Hyatt Place Chicago O'Hare Airport ♿
(224) 563-1800. $99-$319. 6810 Mannheim Rd 60018. On US 12 and 45, 0.3 mi n of SR 72 (Higgins Rd). Int corridors. Pets: Accepted.

Loews Chicago O'Hare Hotel ♿ ❀
(847) 544-5300. $149-$329, 3 day notice. 5300 N River Rd 60018. I-190 exit 1B (River Rd), 0.4 mi s. Int corridors. Pets: Dogs only. $120 one-time fee/room. Service with restrictions, supervision.

Residence Inn by Marriott Chicago-O'Hare ♿
(847) 375-9000. $101-$305. 7101 Chestnut St 60018. Jct US 12, 45 and Touhy Ave. Int corridors. Pets: Accepted.

Sheraton Chicago O'Hare ♿
(847) 699-6300. $99-$369. 6501 N Mannheim Rd 60018. On US 12 and 45, at SR 72 (Higgins Rd). Int corridors. Pets: Accepted.

The Westin O'Hare ♿
(847) 698-6000. Call for rates. 6100 N River Rd 60018. I-190 exit 1B (River Rd), just n. Int corridors. Pets: Accepted.

ST. CHARLES

Geneva Motel Inn ♿
(630) 513-6500. Call for rates. 100 S Tyler Rd 60174. Jct SR 64, just s. Int corridors. Pets: Medium, dogs only. $10 daily fee/pet. Designated rooms, service with restrictions, crate.

Pheasant Run Resort ♿ ❀
(630) 584-6300. Call for rates. 4051 E Main St 60174. On SR 64, 2.4 mi w of SR 59. Int corridors. Pets: Dogs only. $50 one-time fee/room. Designated rooms, no service.

Quality Inn & Suites Saint Charles ♿
(630) 584-5300. $80-$150. 1600 E Main St 60174. On SR 64, 0.5 mi e of SR 25. Int corridors. Pets: Accepted.

SALEM

Super 8 ♿
(618) 548-5882. $64-$79. 118 Woods Ln 62881. I-57 exit 116 (US 50), just w. Ext/int corridors. Pets: Other species. Supervision.

SAVOY

Best Western Paradise Inn H
(217) 356-1824. **$95-$110.** 709 N Dunlap Ave 61874. I-57 exit 229, 2.5 mi e to US 45, then 2.5 mi n. Ext corridors. **Pets:** Small. $10 daily fee/ pet. Designated rooms, service with restrictions, crate.

SCHAUMBURG

Extended Stay America Chicago-Schaumburg Convention Center H
(847) 882-6900. **$70-$100.** 51 E State Pkwy 60173. I-90 exit Roselle Rd, 0.8 mi s, then just e. Int corridors. **Pets:** Accepted.

Extended Stay America Chicago-Schaumburg I-90 H
(847) 882-7011. **$70-$100.** 2000 N Roselle Rd 60195. I-90 exit Roselle Rd, just sw. Int corridors. **Pets:** Accepted.

Extended Stay America-Chicago-Woodfield H
(847) 517-7255. **$75-$110.** 1200 American Ln 60173. I-290 exit SR 72 (Higgins Rd), 0.5 mi w to Meacham Rd, 0.5 mi n to American Ln, then just w. Int corridors. **Pets:** Accepted.

Hawthorn Suites by Wyndham Chicago-Schaumburg H
(847) 517-7644. **$79-$159.** 1200 E Bank Dr 60173. I-290 exit SR 72 (Higgins Rd), 0.8 mi w to National Pkwy, then just n. Int corridors. **Pets:** Large, other species. $15 daily fee/pet. Designated rooms, service with restrictions, crate.

Homewood Suites by Hilton-Schaumburg H
(847) 605-0400. **$99-$209.** 815 E American Ln 60173. I-290 exit SR 72 (Higgins Rd), 1.5 mi w, then 0.4 mi n on Plum Grove Rd. Ext/int corridors. **Pets:** Medium, other species. $100 one-time fee/room. Designated rooms, service with restrictions, crate.

Hyatt House Chicago/Schaumburg H
(847) 706-9007. **$79-$209.** 1251 E American Ln 60173. I-290 exit SR 72 (Higgins Rd), 0.5 mi w to Meacham Rd, 0.5 mi n to American Ln, then just w. Int corridors. **Pets:** Medium. $75 one-time fee/room. Service with restrictions, supervision.

Hyatt Place Chicago/Schaumburg H
(847) 330-1060. **$69-$239.** 1851 McConnor Pkwy 60173. I-290 exit 1A (Woodfield Rd/Golf Rd) northbound, just n to Golf Rd, just w to McConnor Pkwy, then just n; exit 1B (Woodfield Rd/Golf Rd) southbound. Int corridors. **Pets:** Accepted.

Residence Inn by Marriott-Chicago/Schaumburg H 🐾
(847) 517-9200. **$66-$286.** 1610 McConnor Pkwy 60173. I-290 exit 1A (Woodfield Rd/Golf Rd) northbound, follow signs n to Golf Rd, just w to McConnor Pkwy, then 0.8 mi n; exit 1B (Woodfield Rd/Golf Rd) southbound. Int corridors. **Pets:** Other species. $100 one-time fee/room. Service with restrictions, crate.

Sonesta ES Suites Chicago/Schaumburg H
(847) 619-6677. **Call for rates.** 901 E Woodfield Office Ct 60173. I-290 exit SR 72 (Higgins Rd), 1.5 mi w, then 0.3 mi n on Plum Grove Rd. Ext/int corridors. **Pets:** Accepted.

SCHILLER PARK

Comfort Suites O'Hare Airport H
(847) 233-9000. **$89-$219.** 4200 N River Rd 60176. Jct SR 19 (Irving Park Rd) and Des Plaines St/River Rd, just n. Int corridors. **Pets:** Accepted.

Four Points by Sheraton Chicago O'Hare H
(847) 671-6000. **$92-$160.** 10249 W Irving Park Rd 60176. Jct US 12, 45 and SR 19 (Irving Park Rd). Int corridors. **Pets:** Accepted.

SKOKIE

Extended Stay America-Chicago-Skokie H
(847) 663-9031. **$95-$120.** 5211 Old Orchard Rd 60077. I-94 exit 35 (Old Orchard Rd), just s. Int corridors. **Pets:** Accepted.

Holiday Inn Chicago North Shore H
(847) 679-8900. **Call for rates.** 5300 W Touhy Ave 60077. I-94 exit 39A, 0.5 mi w. Int corridors. **Pets:** Medium. $50 deposit/pet. Service with restrictions.

SOUTH BELOIT

Best Western Legacy Inn & Suites Beloit/ South Beloit H
(815) 389-4211. **$99-$159.** 5910 Technology Dr 61080. I-90/39 exit 1, just sw. Int corridors. **Pets:** Accepted.

SOUTH JACKSONVILLE

Holiday Inn Express & Suites Jacksonville H
(217) 245-6500. **Call for rates.** 2501 Holliday Ln 62650. I-72 exit 64, just n. Int corridors. **Pets:** Accepted.

SPRINGFIELD

Baymont Inn & Suites Springfield H
(217) 529-6655. **$69-$210.** 5871 S 6th St 62703. I-55 exit 90 (Toronto Rd), just e to 6th St, then just n. Int corridors. **Pets:** Medium. $200 deposit/room, $10 daily fee/pet. Designated rooms, service with restrictions, supervision.

Best Western Clearlake Plaza H
(217) 525-7420. **$100-$189.** 3440 E Clear Lake Ave 62702. I-55 exit 98B, just w. Int corridors. **Pets:** Small. $20 daily fee/pet. Service with restrictions, supervision.

Candlewood Suites H
(217) 522-5100. **Call for rates.** 2501 Sunrise Dr 62703. I-55 exit 94 (Stevenson Dr), just w to Dirksen Pkwy, then 0.4 mi n. Int corridors. **Pets:** Other species. $75 one-time fee/room. Service with restrictions, crate.

Crowne Plaza Hotel H
(217) 529-7777. **Call for rates.** 3000 S Dirksen Pkwy 62703. I-55 exit 94 (Stevenson Dr), just w to Dirksen Pkwy, then 0.4 mi n. Int corridors. **Pets:** Accepted.

Drury Inn & Suites-Springfield H
(217) 529-3900. **$90-$140.** 3180 S Dirksen Pkwy 62703. I-55 exit 94 (Stevenson Dr), just w to Dirksen Pkwy, then just n. Int corridors. **Pets:** Accepted.

Holiday Inn Express Hotel & Suites H
(217) 529-7771. **Call for rates.** 3050 S Dirksen Pkwy 62703. I-55 exit 94 (Stevenson Dr), just w to S Dirksen Pkwy, then 0.4 mi n. Int corridors. **Pets:** Accepted.

Microtel Inn & Suites by Wyndham Springfield H
(217) 753-2636. **$74-$105.** 2636 Sunrise Dr 62703. I-55 exit 94 (Stevenson Dr), just w to Dirksen Pkwy, then 0.4 mi n. Int corridors. **Pets:** Accepted.

Quality Inn & Suites Springfield H
(217) 787-2250. **$79-$209.** 3442 Freedom Dr 62704. I-72 exit 93 (Veterans Pkwy), 0.7 mi n to Lindbergh Blvd, just w to Freedom Dr, then just s. Int corridors. **Pets:** Accepted.

▼▼▼ Residence Inn by Marriott Springfield South 🅷
(217) 527-1100. **$123-$277.** 2915 Stanford Ave 62703. I-55 exit 94
(Stevenson Dr), just w to Dirksen Pkwy, then 0.4 mi n. Int corridors.
Pets: Accepted. 🔌ᴹ 🛰 ✖ 🔒 💻

▼▼ Sleep Inn by Choice Hotels 🅷
(217) 787-6200. **$59-$209.** 3470 Freedom Dr 62704. I-72 exit 93 (Veterans Pkwy), 0.7 mi n to Lindbergh Blvd, just w to Freedom Dr, then
just s. Int corridors. **Pets:** Medium. $25 one-time fee/room. Service with
restrictions, crate. 🔌ᴹ 🛰 🔒 💻

▼▼▼ Staybridge Suites Springfield South 🅷
(217) 793-6700. **Call for rates.** 4231 Schooner Dr 62711. I-72 exit 93
(Veterans Pkwy), 0.4 mi se. Int corridors. **Pets:** Medium. $75 one-time
fee/room. Service with restrictions, crate.
🔌ᴹ 🏊 🛰 ✖ 🔒 💻

AAA ▼▼▼ Wyndham Springfield City Centre 🅷
(217) 789-1530. **$70-$175.** 700 E Adams St 62701. Jct 7th St, just e of
Old State Capitol; downtown. Int corridors. **Pets:** Accepted.
SAVE 🍴 🔌ᴹ 🏊 🛰 ✖ 🔒 💻

STAUNTON
▼▼ Super 8 Staunton 🅷
(618) 635-5353. **$50-$65.** 1527 Herman Rd 62088. I-55 exit 41, 0.6 mi
w. Int corridors. **Pets:** Accepted. 🛰 🔒 💻

STOCKTON
▼▼ Country Inn & Suites By Carlson 🅷
(815) 947-6060. **$110-$165.** 200 Dillon Ave 61085. On US 20, just e of
SR 78. Int corridors. **Pets:** Accepted. 🔌ᴹ 🏊 🛰 ✖ 🔒 💻

TINLEY PARK
▼▼ La Quinta Inn & Suites Chicago-Tinley Park 🅷
(708) 633-1200. **$82-$240.** 7255 W 183rd St 60477. I-80 exit 148B, 0.5
mi n to 183rd St, then just w to North Creek Business Center. Int corridors. **Pets:** Accepted. 🔌ᴹ 🏊 🛰 ✖ 🔒 💻

▼▼ Sleep Inn by Choice Hotels 🅷
(708) 342-1700. **$79-$219.** 18420 Spring Creek Dr 60477. I-80 exit
148B, 0.5 mi n to 183rd St, just w to North Creek Business Center,
then just s. Int corridors. **Pets:** Accepted. 🔌ᴹ 🛰 🔒 💻

TUSCOLA
▼▼ Baymont Inn & Suites 🅷
(217) 253-3500. **$69-$120.** 1006 Southline Rd 61953. I-57 exit 212 (US
36), 0.3 mi w. Int corridors. **Pets:** Small, dogs only. $10 daily fee/pet.
Service with restrictions, supervision. 🔌ᴹ 🏊 🛰 ✖ 🔒 💻

▼▼▼ Holiday Inn Express 🅷
(217) 253-6363. **$98-$130, 3 day notice.** 1201 Tuscola Blvd 61953.
I-57 exit 212 (US 36), 0.3 mi w to Progress Blvd, just s to Tuscola
Blvd, then 0.4 mi se. Int corridors. **Pets:** Small. Service with restrictions,
crate. 🔌ᴹ 🏊 🛰 ✖ 🔒 💻

URBANA
**▼▼▼ Comfort Suites by Choice Hotels
Urbana/Champaign** 🅷 ❀
(217) 328-3500. **$100-$330.** 2001 N Lincoln Ave 61801. I-74 exit 183
(Lincoln Ave), 0.5 mi s. Int corridors. **Pets:** Medium, other species. $20
daily fee/pet. Designated rooms, service with restrictions, crate.
🔌ᴹ 🏊 🛰 ✖ 🔒 💻

AAA ▼▼▼ Ramada-Urbana/Champaign 🅷
(217) 328-4400. **$79-$201.** 902 W Killarney St 61801. I-74 exit 183
(Lincoln Ave), just s to Killarney St, then just w. Int corridors.
Pets: Small. $10 daily fee/pet. Designated rooms, service with restric-
tions, crate. SAVE 🏊 🛰 ✖ 🔒 💻

UTICA
▼▼▼ Brightwood Inn 🅲🅸
(815) 667-4600. **Call for rates.** 2407 N SR 178 61348. I-80 exit 81 (SR
178), 6.2 mi s. Int corridors. **Pets:** Accepted. 🍴 🛰 ✖ 🔒 💻

VANDALIA
▼▼▼ Holiday Inn Express Hotel & Suites 🅷
(618) 283-0010. **Call for rates.** 21 Mattes Ave 62471. I-70 exit 61, just
s. Int corridors. **Pets:** Accepted. 🔌ᴹ 🏊 🛰 ✖ 🔒 💻

AAA ▼ Jay's Inn 🅼
(618) 283-1200. **$56-$65.** 720 Gochenour St 62471. I-70 exit 63 (US
51), just s. Ext corridors. **Pets:** Other species. Service with restrictions,
crate. SAVE 🛰 🔒 💻

▼▼ Ramada Inn Vandalia 🅷
(618) 283-1400. **$59-$63.** 2707 Veterans Ave 62471. I-70 exit 61, just
s. Int corridors. **Pets:** Large, other species. $10 daily fee/pet. Supervi-
sion. 🏊 🛰 🔒 💻

VERNON HILLS
**▼▼ Extended Stay America-Chicago-Vernon Hills-Lake
Forest** 🅷
(847) 821-7101. **$85-$115.** 215 N Milwaukee Ave 60061. I-94 exit SR
60 (Townline Rd), 2.1 mi w to SR 21 (Milwaukee Ave), then 0.3 mi s.
Int corridors. **Pets:** Accepted. 🔌ᴹ 🛰 ✖ 🔒

**▼▼ Extended Stay America Chicago/Vernon
Hills-Lincolnshire** 🅷
(847) 955-1111. **$85-$115.** 675 Woodlands Pkwy 60061. I-94 exit SR 60
(Townline Rd), 2.1 mi w to SR 21 (Milwaukee Ave), 1.9 mi s to Woodlands Pkwy, then just w. Int corridors. **Pets:** Accepted.
🍴 🛰 ✖ 🔒

▼▼ Holiday Inn Express/Vernon Hills 🅷
(847) 367-8031. **Call for rates.** 975 Lakeview Pkwy 60061. Jct SR 21
(Milwaukee Ave), 0.7 mi w on SR 60 (Townline Rd) to Lakeview Pkwy,
then just n. Int corridors. **Pets:** Accepted.
🔌ᴹ 🏊 🛰 ✖ 🔒 💻

▼▼▼ Hotel Indigo Chicago/Vernon Hills 🅷
(847) 918-1400. **Call for rates.** 450 N Milwaukee Ave 60061. I-94 exit
SR 60 (Townline Rd), 2.1 mi w to SR 21 (Milwaukee Ave), then 0.3 mi
s. Int corridors. **Pets:** Other species. $75 one-time fee/room. Designated
rooms, service with restrictions, supervision.
🍴 🔌ᴹ 🏊 🛰 ✖ 🔒 💻

WARRENVILLE
**AAA ▼▼▼ Hyatt House
Chicago/Naperville/Warrenville** 🅷
(630) 836-2960. **$89-$239.** 27554 Maecliff Dr 60555. I-88 exit Winfield
Rd, just n to Ferry Rd, then just e. Int corridors. **Pets:** Medium. Service
with restrictions. SAVE 🍴 🔌ᴹ 🏊 🛰 ✖ 🔒 💻

**▼▼▼ Residence Inn by Marriott Chicago
Naperville/Warrenville** 🅷
(630) 393-3444. **$85-$242.** 28500 Bella Vista Pkwy 60555. I-88 exit
Winfield Rd, just n to Ferry Rd, then just e. Int corridors.
Pets: Accepted. 🍴 🔌ᴹ 🏊 🛰 ✖ 🔒 💻

WASHINGTON
▼▼ Super 8 🅷
(309) 444-8881. **$49-$85.** 1884 Washington Rd 61571. On Business Rt
US 24, 1.5 mi w. Int corridors. **Pets:** Accepted. 🛰 🔒 💻

WATSEKA
▼▼ Super 8 🅷
(815) 432-6000. **$58-$94.** 710 W Walnut St 60970. On US 24; center of
downtown. Int corridors. **Pets:** Accepted. 🛰 ✖ 🔒 💻

WAUKEGAN

▼▼ Candlewood Suites Chicago/Waukegan H
(847) 578-5250. Call for rates. 1151 S Waukegan Rd 60085. I-94 exit
SR 137 (Buckley Rd), 0.5 mi e to SR 43 (Waukegan Rd), then 1.9 mi
n. Int corridors. Pets: Accepted. 🍴 📶 ⊠ 🔌 💻

▼▼ Residence Inn by Marriott
    Chicago-Waukegan/Gurnee H
(847) 689-9240. $89-$329. 1440 S White Oak Dr 60085. I-94 exit SR
137 (Buckley Rd), 0.5 mi e to SR 43 (Waukegan Rd), 1.5 mi n to Lakeside Dr, then just e. Int corridors. Pets: Accepted.
🌱 🍴 ♿ ➰ 📶 ⊠ 🔌 💻

WENONA

▼ ▼ Americas Best Value Inn M
(815) 853-4371. $60-$80. 5 Cavalry Dr 61377. I-39 exit 35, just e. Int
corridors. Pets: Medium. $10 deposit/pet. Designated rooms, service
with restrictions, supervision. 📶 🔌 💻

WEST DUNDEE

▼▼ TownePlace Suites by Marriott Chicago West
    Dundee/Elgin H 🐾
(847) 608-6320. $58-$186. 2185 Marriott Dr 60118. I-90 exit SR 31, 0.4
mi n to Marriott Dr, then just e. Int corridors. Pets: Medium, other species. $150 one-time fee/room. Service with restrictions, supervision.
🌱 ♿ ➰ 📶 ⊠ 🔌 💻

WESTMONT

▼▼ Extended Stay America - Chicago - Westmont - Oak
    Brook H
(630) 323-9292. $75-$110. 855 Pasquinelli Dr 60559. SR 83 exit US 34
(Ogden Ave), just w to Pasquinelli Dr, then 0.5 mi n. Int corridors.
Pets: Accepted. ♿ 📶 🔌

WHEELING

▼▼ Hawthorn Suites by Wyndham -
    Northbrook/Wheeling H
(847) 520-1684. $79-$169. 8000 Capitol Dr 60090. Jct S Wolf and E
Palatine rds. Int corridors. Pets: Accepted.
🍴 ♿ 📶 ⊠ 🔌 💻

◈ ▼▼ Ramada Plaza Chicago North Shore H
(847) 215-9900. Call for rates. 1090 S Milwaukee Ave 60090. I-294
exit Willow Rd, 0.6 mi w to Milwaukee Ave, then 0.3 mi n. Int corridors.
Pets: Medium. $25 deposit/room. Service with restrictions.
💾 🍴 📶 ⊠ 🔌 💻

◈ ▼▼▼ The Westin Chicago North Shore H
(847) 777-6500. $89-$299. 601 N Milwaukee Ave 60090. Jct Lake Cook
Rd, just s. Int corridors. Pets: Accepted.
💾 🌱 🍴 ♿ ➰ ⊠ 📶 ⊠ 🔌 💻

WILLOWBROOK

▼▼ La Quinta Inn Chicago-Willowbrook H
(630) 654-0077. $71-$225. 855 79th St 60527. I-55 exit 274, just n. Int
corridors. Pets: Accepted. 📶 🔌 💻

◈ ▼ Red Roof PLUS+ Chicago - Willowbrook M
(630) 323-8811. $59-$130. 7535 Kingery Hwy Rt 83 60527. I-55 exit
274, 0.5 mi n on SR 83. Ext corridors. Pets: Accepted.
💾 📶 ⊠ 🔌 💻

WILMETTE

▼▼▼ Residence Inn by Marriott Chicago Wilmette H
(847) 251-6600. $99-$216. 3205 Old Glenview Rd 60091. I-94 exit 35
(Old Orchard Rd), just w to Lockwood Rd, then just n. Int corridors.
Pets: $100 one-time fee/room. Designated rooms, service with restric-
tions, crate. 🍴 ♿ 📶 ⊠ 🔌 💻

WOODSTOCK

◈ ▼▼ Best Western Woodstock Inn H
(815) 337-0065. $80-$116. 990 Lake Ave 60098. On SR 47, 0.5 mi n of
jct US 14. Int corridors. Pets: Accepted. 💾 ➰ 📶 ⊠ 🔌 💻

▼ Super 8 H
(815) 337-8808. $65-$85. 1220 Davis Rd 60098. On SR 47, s of jct US
14. Int corridors. Pets: Accepted. 🍴 📶 🔌 💻

INDIANA

ANDERSON

◈ ▼▼▼ Best Western Plus Anderson H
(765) 649-2500. $79-$149. 2114 E 59th St 46013. I-69 exit 226, just
nw. Int corridors. Pets: Accepted. 💾 ♿ ➰ 📶 ⊠ 🔌 💻

▼▼ Motel 6 Indianapolis Anderson #4898 H
(765) 644-4422. Call for rates. 2205 E 59th St 46013. I-69 exit 226,
just nw. Int corridors. Pets: Accepted. ➰ 📶 ⊠ 🔌

ANGOLA

▼▼ Ramada Angola/Fremont Area H
(260) 665-9471. $85-$114. 3855 N SR 127 46703. I-69 exit 354, just e,
then 0.4 mi s. Int corridors. Pets: Other species. $25 daily fee/room.
Service with restrictions, crate. 🍴 ➰ ⊠ 📶 ⊠ 💻

AUBURN

▼▼▼ Holiday Inn Express Auburn H
(260) 925-1900. $99-$134. 404 Touring Dr 46706. I-69 exit 329 (SR 8),
just e, then just s. Int corridors. Pets: Accepted.
♿ ➰ 📶 ⊠ 🔌 💻

▼▼ La Quinta Inn & Conference Center H
(260) 920-1900. $67-$273. 306 Touring Dr 46706. I-69 exit 329 (SR 8),
0.5 mi e. Int corridors. Pets: Accepted. ♿ ➰ 📶 ⊠ 🔌 💻

BATESVILLE

▼▼▼ Hampton Inn by Hilton Batesville H
(812) 934-6262. $101-$140. 1030 SR 229 N 47006. I-74 exit 149, just
n. Int corridors. Pets: Medium. Designated rooms, service with restrictions, supervision. ♿ ➰ 📶 ⊠ 🔌 💻

BEDFORD

◈ ▼▼▼ Holiday Inn Express & Suites H
(812) 279-1206. Call for rates. 2800 Express Ln 47421. On US 50/SR
37, 1.4 mi s of jct SR 450. Int corridors. Pets: Small, dogs only. $15
deposit/pet. Designated rooms, service with restrictions, supervision.
💾 🍴 ➰ 📶 ⊠ 🔌 💻

▼▼ Super 8 Bedford H
(812) 275-8881. $89-$145. 501 Bell Back Rd 47421. Jct US 50, just n
on SR 37. Int corridors. Pets: Accepted.
🍴 ➰ ⊠ 📶 ⊠ 🔌 💻

BERNE

▼▼ Clock Tower Inn H
(260) 589-8955. Call for rates. 1335 US 27 N 46711. On US 27, 1 mi
n. Int corridors. Pets: Accepted. ♿ ➰ 📶 ⊠ 🔌 💻

BLOOMINGTON

▼▼▼ Comfort Inn Bloomington 🅗 ❀

(812) 650-0010. **$99-$269.** 1700 N Kinser Pike 47404. On SR 45 and 45 Bypass, 1 mi e of jct SR 37. Int corridors. **Pets:** Other species. $25 one-time fee/room. Designated rooms, service with restrictions.

🏊 🛰 ✕ 🛅 🖥

▼▼▼ Fairfield Inn & Suites by Marriott Bloomington 🅗 ❀

(812) 331-1122. **$72-$290.** 120 Fairfield Dr 47404. Just e from SR 37 at 3rd St. Int corridors. **Pets:** Medium, other species. $75 one-time fee/room. Designated rooms, service with restrictions, supervision.

🅱 🏊 🛰 ✕ 🛅 🖥

▼▼▼ Hampton Inn Bloomington 🅗

(812) 334-2100. **$99-$179.** 2100 N Walnut St 47404. 1 mi e of jct SR 37 on SR 45 and 46 Bypass, then just s on College Ave/Walnut St. Int corridors. **Pets:** Large, other species. $75 one-time fee/pet. Service with restrictions. 🏊 🛰 ✕ 🛅 🖥

▼▼▼ Holiday Inn Bloomington 🅗

(812) 334-3252. **Call for rates.** 1710 N Kinser Pike 47404. On SR 45 and 46 Bypass, 1 mi e of jct SR 37. Int corridors. **Pets:** Medium. $25 one-time fee/room. Service with restrictions.

🍽 🅱 🏊 🛰 ✕ 🛅 🖥

ⓐ ▼▼▼ Hyatt Place Bloomington 🅗

(812) 339-5950. **$109-$709.** 217 W Kirkwood Ave 47404. Jct S Gentry St. Int corridors. **Pets:** Accepted. 🆂 🍽 🅱 🛰 ✕ 🛅 🖥

▼▼▼ TownePlace Suites by Marriott 🅗 ❀

(812) 334-1234. **$50-$317.** 105 S Franklin Rd 47404. Just e from SR 37 at 3rd St, then 0.3 mi n. Int corridors. **Pets:** Other species. $75 one-time fee/room. Service with restrictions, crate. 🏊 🛰 ✕ 🛅 🖥

BLUFFTON

▼▼▼ Americas Best Value Inn & Suites Bluffton 🅗

(260) 824-5553. **Call for rates.** 100 Charles Deam Ct 46714. Jct SR 1 and 124 (E Division Rd), just n. Int corridors. **Pets:** Accepted.

🛰 ✕ 🛅 🖥

BREMEN

▼▼▼ Scottish Bed and Breakfast 🅱🅱

(574) 220-6672. **$130-$205, 14 day notice.** 2180 Miami Tr 46506. Jct SR 331, 2 mi w on SR 106, just s. Int corridors. **Pets:** Small, dogs only. $25 one-time fee/pet. Designated rooms, service with restrictions, supervision. 🍽 🏊 🛰 ✕ 🈺 🛅

BROWNSBURG

▼▼ Quality Inn & Suites Brownsburg 🅗

(317) 852-5353. **$69-$254.** 31 Maplehurst Dr 46112. I-74 exit 66, just n on SR 267. Int corridors. **Pets:** Accepted.

🅱 🏊 🛰 ✕ 🛅 🖥

CARMEL *(Restaurants p. 613)*

▼▼▼ Residence Inn by Marriott Indianapolis/Carmel 🅗

(317) 846-2000. **$141-$310.** 11895 N Meridian St 46032. I-465 exit 31, 2 mi n on US 31, just e on 116th St, then just n on N Pennsylvania St. Int corridors. **Pets:** Accepted. 🅱 🏊 🛰 ✕ 🛅 🖥

▼▼▼ Staybridge Suites Indianapolis-Carmel 🅗

(317) 582-1500. **Call for rates.** 10675 N Pennsylvania St 46280. I-465 exit 31, 0.7 mi n to 106th St, just e, then just n. Int corridors. **Pets:** Accepted. 🍽 🅱 🏊 ✕ 🛅 🖥

CLARKSVILLE

ⓐⓐⓐ ▼▼▼ Best Western Green Tree Inn 🅼

(812) 288-9281. **$87-$120.** 1425 Broadway St 47129. I-65 exit 4, just w. Ext corridors. **Pets:** Medium, dogs only. $15 daily fee/pet. Designated rooms, service with restrictions, supervision.

🆂 🏊 🛰 ✕ 🛅 🖥

ⓐⓐⓐ ▼▼▼ Candlewood Suites Louisville North 🅗

(812) 284-6113. **$139-$189.** 1419 Bales Ln 47129. I-65 exit 4, just w, then just n on Broadway St. Int corridors. **Pets:** Accepted.

🆂 🅱 🏊 🛰 ✕ 🛅 🖥

CLOVERDALE

▼▼ Days Inn Cloverdale Greencastle 🅗

(765) 795-6400. **$50-$200.** 1031 N Main St 46120. I-70 exit 41, just s on US 231. Ext corridors. **Pets:** Accepted. 🛰 ✕ 🛅 🖥

▼▼ Super 8 Cloverdale/Greencastle 🅗

(765) 795-7373. **$57-$172.** 1020 N Main St 46120. I-70 exit 41, just s on US 231. Int corridors. **Pets:** Small, dogs only. $10 daily fee/pet. Service with restrictions, supervision. 🏊 🛰 ✕ 🛅 🖥

COLUMBUS

▼▼▼ Hotel Indigo 🅗

(812) 375-9100. **$130-$200.** 400 Brown St 47201. Jct 4th St. Int corridors. **Pets:** Accepted. 🍽 🅱 🏊 🛰 ✕ 🛅 🖥

▼▼▼ La Quinta Inn & Suites 🅗

(812) 379-4657. **$86-$202.** 101 Carrie Ln 47201. I-65 exit 68, just w on SR 46. Int corridors. **Pets:** Accepted. 🅱 🏊 🛰 ✕ 🛅 🖥

▼▼▼ Residence Inn by Marriott 🅗

(812) 342-2400. **$89-$207.** 4525 W SR 46 47201. I-65 exit 68, 0.8 mi w on SR 46. Int corridors. **Pets:** $75 one-time fee/room. Service with restrictions, crate. 🍽 🅱 🏊 🛰 ✕ 🛅 🖥

CORYDON

▼▼ Comfort Inn Corydon 🅗

(812) 738-3900. **$77-$169.** 115 Skypark Dr 47112. I-64 exit 105, just n. Int corridors. **Pets:** Accepted. 🏊 🛰 ✕ 🛅 🖥

CRAWFORDSVILLE

▼▼ Comfort Inn 🅗

(765) 361-0665. **$89-$169.** 2991 Gandhi Dr 47933. I-74 exit 34, just s on US 231. Int corridors. **Pets:** Accepted.

🍽 🏊 🛰 ✕ 🛅 🖥

▼▼▼ Hampton Inn & Suites 🅗

(765) 362-8884. **$99-$199.** 2895 Gandhi Dr 47933. I-74 exit 34, just s on US 231. Int corridors. **Pets:** Accepted.

🍽 🅱 🏊 🛰 ✕ 🛅 🖥

▼▼▼ Holiday Inn Express Hotel & Suites 🅗

(765) 323-4575. **Call for rates.** 2506 N Lafayette Rd 47933. I-74 exit 34, 0.3 mi s on US 231. Int corridors. **Pets:** Accepted.

🅱 🏊 🛰 ✕ 🛅 🖥

EDINBURGH

ⓐⓐⓐ ▼▼▼ Best Western Edinburgh/Columbus 🅗

(812) 526-9883. **$90-$130.** 11780 N US 31 46124. I-65 exit 76B, just n. Int corridors. **Pets:** Accepted. 🆂 🏊 🛰 ✕ 🛅 🖥

ELKHART

▼▼▼ Baymont Inn & Suites Elkhart 🅗

(574) 264-7222. **$49-$219.** 3010 Brittany Ct 46514. I-80/90 exit 92, 0.3 mi s on SR 19. Int corridors. **Pets:** Medium. $20 deposit/pet. Designated rooms, service with restrictions, supervision.

🏊 🛰 ✕ 🛅 🖥

▼▼▼ **Candlewood Suites** ⊞

(574) 262-8600. **$90-$299.** 300 Northpointe Blvd 46514. I-80/90 exit 92, just n on SR 19, then just w. Int corridors. **Pets:** Accepted.

⌘ ⌘ ⌘ ⌘ ⌘ ⌘

⊕ ▼▼▼ **Staybridge Suites Elkhart North** ⊞

(574) 970-8488. **Call for rates.** 3252 Cassopolis St 46514. I-80/90 exit 92, just n on SR 19, then just e. Int corridors. **Pets:** Accepted.

SAVE ⌘ ⌘ ⌘ ⌘ ⌘

EVANSVILLE

▼▼ **Baymont Inn & Suites Evansville East** ⊞

(812) 477-2677. **$74-$130.** 8005 E Division St 47715. I-69 exit 7B (SR 66/Lloyd Expwy), 0.5 mi w to Cross Pointe Blvd, just n to Division St, then 0.5 mi e. Int corridors. **Pets:** Accepted.

⌘ ⌘ ⌘ ⌘ ⌘ ⌘ ⌘

▼▼ **Comfort Inn East** ⊞

(812) 476-3600. **$81-$184.** 8331 E Walnut St 47715. I-69 exit 7B (SR 66/Lloyd Expwy), 0.5 mi w to Eagle Crest Blvd, 0.3 mi se to Fuquay St, just s to Walnut St, then 0.4 mi e. Int corridors. **Pets:** Medium, other species. $150 deposit/pet, $20 daily fee/pet. Designated rooms, service with restrictions, crate. ⌘ ⌘ ⌘ ⌘ ⌘ ⌘

▼▼ **Comfort Inn Evansville North** ⊞

(812) 867-1600. **$90-$300.** 19622 Elpers Rd 47725. I-64 exit 25A (US 41), 0.5 mi s, then just w. Int corridors. **Pets:** Accepted.

⌘ ⌘ ⌘ ⌘ ⌘ ⌘ ⌘

▼▼▼ **Drury Inn & Suites-Evansville East** ⊞

(812) 471-3400. **$95-$155.** 100 Cross Pointe Blvd 47715. I-69 exit 7B (SR 66/Lloyd Expwy), 0.5 mi w. Int corridors. **Pets:** Accepted.

⌘ ⌘ ⌘ ⌘ ⌘ ⌘

▼▼ **Holiday Inn Express - Evansville West** ⊞

(812) 421-9773. **Call for rates.** 5737 Pearl Dr 47712. Jct US 41 and SR 62 (Lloyd Expwy), 5.7 mi w on SR 62 (Lloyd Expwy), then just s on Boehne Camp Rd. Int corridors. **Pets:** Accepted.

⌘ ⌘ ⌘ ⌘ ⌘ ⌘

▼▼ **Howard Johnson Evansville East** ⊞

(812) 476-9626. **$59-$79.** 1101 N Green River Rd 47715. I-69 exit 9 (SR 62 E/Morgan Ave), 1.5 mi w on SR 62, then just s. Int corridors. **Pets:** Accepted. ⌘ ⌘ ⌘ ⌘ ⌘ ⌘

▼▼▼ **La Quinta Inn & Suites Evansville** ⊞

(812) 471-3414. **$73-$185.** 8015 E Division St 47715. I-69 exit 7B (SR 66/Lloyd Expwy), 0.5 mi w to Cross Pointe Blvd, just n, then 0.5 mi e. Int corridors. **Pets:** Accepted. ⌘ ⌘ ⌘ ⌘ ⌘

▼▼▼ **Residence Inn by Marriott Evansville East** ⊞

(812) 471-7191. **$84-$259.** 8283 E Walnut St 47715. I-69 exit 7B (SR 66/Lloyd Expwy), 0.5 mi w to Eagle Crest Blvd, 0.3 mi se to Fuquay St, then 0.3 mi e. Int corridors. **Pets:** Accepted.

⌘ ⌘ ⌘ ⌘ ⌘ ⌘

⊕ ▼▼▼ **Tropicana Evansville** ⊞

(812) 433-4000. **$89-$299.** 421 NW Riverside Dr 47708. SR 62 (Lloyd Expwy), just s on Fulton St. Int corridors. **Pets:** Medium. $100 deposit/room. Designated rooms, service with restrictions, crate.

SAVE ⌘ ⌘ ⌘ ⌘ ⌘

FISHERS

▼▼▼ **AmericInn Hotel & Suites Indianapolis - Northeast** ⊞

(317) 578-9000. **Call for rates.** 9780 North by Northeast Blvd 46037. I-69 exit 203, just ne. Int corridors. **Pets:** Accepted.

⌘ ⌘ ⌘ ⌘ ⌘

⊕ ▼▼▼ **Baymont Inn and Suites Fishers / Indianapolis Area** ⊞

(317) 578-2000. **$60-$229.** 9790 North by Northeast Blvd 46038. I-69 exit 203, just ne. Int corridors. **Pets:** $25 one-time fee/pet. Designated rooms, no service. SAVE ⌘ ⌘ ⌘ ⌘ ⌘ ⌘

▼▼▼ **Comfort Suites** ⊞

(317) 578-1200. **$94-$229.** 9760 Crosspoint Blvd 46256. I-69 exit 203, just w on 96th St, then just n. Int corridors. **Pets:** Accepted.

⌘ ⌘ ⌘ ⌘ ⌘

▼▼▼ **Residence Inn by Marriott Indianapolis/Fishers** ⊞

(317) 842-1111. **$104-$259.** 9765 Crosspoint Blvd 46256. I-69 exit 203, just nw. Int corridors. **Pets:** Accepted. ⌘ ⌘ ⌘ ⌘ ⌘ ⌘

▼▼▼ **Staybridge Suites Indianapolis-Fishers** ⊞

(317) 577-9500. **Call for rates.** 9780 Crosspoint Blvd 46256. I-69 exit 203, just nw. Int corridors. **Pets:** Accepted.

⌘ ⌘ ⌘ ⌘ ⌘ ⌘

FLORENCE

▼▼▼ **Belterra Casino Resort** ⊞

(812) 427-7777. **Call for rates.** 777 Belterra Dr 47020. Jct SR 101, 1.2 mi e on SR 56. Int corridors. **Pets:** Accepted.

⌘ ⌘ ⌘ ⌘ ⌘ ⌘

FORT WAYNE

⊕ ▼▼▼ **Best Western Luxbury Inn Fort Wayne** ⊞ ✿

(260) 436-0242. **$99-$139.** 5501 Coventry Ln 46804. I-69 exit 302, just w. Int corridors. **Pets:** Medium. $20 daily fee/room. Designated rooms, service with restrictions, supervision. SAVE ⌘ ⌘ ⌘ ⌘ ⌘

▼▼ **Candlewood Suites** ⊞

(260) 484-1400. **$89-$99.** 5250 Distribution Dr 46825. I-69 exit 311A, just e. Int corridors. **Pets:** Accepted.

⌘ ⌘ ⌘ ⌘ ⌘ ⌘ ⌘

⊕ ▼▼▼ **Comfort Suites Southwest** ⊞

(260) 436-4300. **$104-$209.** 5775 Coventry Ln 46804. I-69 exit 302, just w. Int corridors. **Pets:** Accepted. SAVE ⌘ ⌘ ⌘ ⌘ ⌘ ⌘

▼▼ **Don Hall's Guesthouse** ⊞

(260) 489-2524. **$89-$109.** 1313 W Washington Center Rd 46825. I-69 exit 311B, just n on SR 3, then 0.3 mi e. Ext/int corridors. **Pets:** Dogs only. $20 one-time fee/room. Designated rooms, service with restrictions, crate. ⌘ ⌘ ⌘ ⌘ ⌘ ⌘ ⌘

▼▼ **Extended Stay America-Fort Wayne-South** ⊞

(260) 432-1916. **$70-$85.** 8309 W Jefferson Blvd 46804. I-69 exit 302, 0.4 mi e on US 24, then 0.6 mi s. Int corridors. **Pets:** Accepted.

⌘ ⌘ ⌘ ⌘ ⌘

▼▼ **Hawthorn Suites by Wyndham Fort Wayne** ⊞

(260) 484-4700. **$79-$179.** 4919 Lima Rd 46808. I-69 exit 311A, 0.4 mi s on US 27. Ext corridors. **Pets:** Medium, dogs only. $50 one-time fee/room. Service with restrictions, crate.

⌘ ⌘ ⌘ ⌘ ⌘ ⌘ ⌘

⊕ ▼▼▼ **Hilton Fort Wayne at the Grand Wayne Convention Center** ⊞ ✿

(260) 420-1100. **$119-$299.** 1020 S Calhoun St 46802. Jct Jefferson Blvd; center. Int corridors. **Pets:** Dogs only. $50 one-time fee/room. Designated rooms, service with restrictions, crate.

SAVE ⌘ ⌘ ⌘ ⌘ ⌘ ⌘ ⌘

▼▼▼ **Homewood Suites by Hilton Fort Wayne** ⊞

(260) 432-5100. **$109-$189.** 8621 US 24 W 46804. I-69 exit 302, just w. Int corridors. **Pets:** Other species. $50 one-time fee/room. Service with restrictions, crate. ⌘ ⌘ ⌘ ⌘ ⌘

⊕ ▼▼▼ **Hotel Fort Wayne** ⊞ ✿

(260) 484-0411. **$89-$169.** 305 E Washington Center Rd 46825. I-69 exit 312A, just s. Int corridors. **Pets:** $50 one-time fee/room. Designated rooms, service with restrictions. SAVE ⌘ ⌘ ⌘ ⌘ ⌘ ⌘

Hyatt Place Fort Wayne H
(260) 471-8522. **$94-$199.** 111 W Washington Center Rd 46825. I-69 exit 312A, just s on Coldwater Rd, then just w. Int corridors.
Pets: Accepted. SAVE

Quality Inn H
(260) 489-5554. **$79-$185.** 1734 W Washington Center Rd 46818. I-69 exit 311B, just n on SR 3. Int corridors. **Pets:** $15 daily fee/pet. Designated rooms, service with restrictions, supervision.
SAVE

Residence Inn by Marriott Southwest H
(260) 432-8000. **$87-$219.** 7811 W Jefferson Blvd 46804. I-69 exit 302, 0.5 mi e. Int corridors. **Pets:** Accepted.

Staybridge Suites - Fort Wayne H
(260) 432-2427. **Call for rates.** 5925 Ellison Rd 46804. I-69 exit 302, just w. Int corridors. **Pets:** Accepted.

TownePlace Suites by Marriott Fort Wayne North H
(260) 483-1160. **$78-$183.** 3949 Ice Way 46805. I-69 exit 311A, 1.2 mi se on Lima Rd. Int corridors. **Pets:** Other species. $100 one-time fee/room. Service with restrictions, crate.

FRANKFORT

Super 8 Frankfort M
(765) 670-6068. **$60-$90.** 1875 W SR 28 46041. I-65 exit 158, 6.4 mi e; jct US 421/SR 38/39, 1.6 mi w. Int corridors. **Pets:** Accepted.

FREMONT

Holiday Inn Express Fremont (Angola Area) H
(260) 833-6464. **Call for rates.** 6245 N Old 27, Suite 400 46737. I-80/90 exit 144, just s; I-69 exit 357, just w, then 1 mi s. Int corridors.
Pets: Accepted.

FRENCH LICK

Comfort Suites H
(812) 936-5300. **$108-$178.** 9530 W SR 56 47432. Jct SR 145, 1.2 mi sw. Int corridors. **Pets:** Accepted.

French Lick Springs Hotel H
(812) 936-9300. **Call for rates.** 8670 W SR 56 47432. Jct SR 145. Int corridors. **Pets:** Accepted.
SAVE

GAS CITY

Best Western Plus Gas City H
(765) 998-2331. **$80-$120.** 4936 Kaybee Dr 46933. I-69 exit 259, just e. Int corridors. **Pets:** Medium, other species. $20 one-time fee/pet. Designated rooms, service with restrictions, supervision.
SAVE

GOSHEN

Best Western Inn M
(574) 533-0408. **$99-$129.** 900 Lincolnway E 46526. 1 mi se on US 33. Ext corridors. **Pets:** Accepted. SAVE

GREENFIELD

Comfort Inn-Greenfield H
(317) 467-9999. **$82-$180.** 178 E Martindale Dr 46140. I-70 exit 104, 0.4 mi s on State St. Int corridors. **Pets:** Accepted.
SAVE

Holiday Inn Express & Suites H
(317) 318-9859. **Call for rates.** 321 Barrett Dr 46140. I-70 exit 104, 0.4 mi s on State St. Int corridors. **Pets:** Accepted.

Quality Inn & Suites Greenfield H
(317) 462-7112. **$59-$210.** 2270 N State St 46140. I-70 exit 104, just s. Int corridors. **Pets:** Accepted.

GREENSBURG

Hampton Inn & Suites by Hilton H
(812) 663-5000. **$99-$139.** 2075 N Michigan Ave 47240. I-74 exit 132, 0.9 mi s on US 421. Int corridors. **Pets:** Accepted.

Holiday Inn Express H
(812) 663-5500. **$89-$129.** 915 Ann Blvd 47240. I-74 exit 134A, 1.4 mi s on SR 3. Int corridors. **Pets:** Accepted.

GREENWOOD

Candlewood Suites Indy-South H
(317) 882-4300. **Call for rates.** 1190 N Graham Rd 46143. I-65 exit 101, just e. Int corridors. **Pets:** Accepted.

HAMMOND

Best Western Northwest Indiana Inn H
(219) 844-2140. **$110-$150.** 3830 179th St 46323. I-80/94 exit 5, 0.6 mi s on Cline Ave (SR 912), then 0.6 mi n on frontage road (179th St). Int corridors. **Pets:** Very small. $50 deposit/pet, $20 daily fee/pet. Designated rooms, service with restrictions, supervision.
SAVE

Residence Inn by Marriott Chicago Southeast H
(219) 844-8440. **$102-$257.** 7740 Corinne Dr 46323. I-80/94 exit 3 (Kennedy Ave S), just s. Int corridors. **Pets:** Accepted.

HOWE

Holiday Inn Express-Howe/Sturgis H
(260) 562-3660. **$140-$150.** 45 W 750 N 46746. I-80/90 exit 121 (US 66), just s. Int corridors. **Pets:** Accepted.

HUNTINGTON

Super 8 H
(260) 358-8888. **$65-$90.** 2801 Guilford St 46750. US 24, just n. Int corridors. **Pets:** Accepted.

INDIANAPOLIS *(Restaurants p. 613)*

The Alexander - A Dolce Hotel H
(317) 624-8200. **$189-$365, 3 day notice.** 333 S Delaware St 46204. Jct Delaware and South sts. Int corridors. **Pets:** Accepted.

Baymont Inn & Suites H
(317) 322-2000. **$89-$149, 3 day notice.** 1540 Brookville Crossing Way 46239. I-465 exit 47, 0.3 mi e. Int corridors. **Pets:** Accepted.
SAVE

Baymont Inn & Suites Indianapolis South H
(317) 784-7006. **$59-$300.** 4402 E Creekview Dr 46237. I-65 exit 103, just w. Int corridors. **Pets:** Other species. $20 daily fee/pet. Service with restrictions.

Baymont Inn & Suites Indianapolis West H
(317) 299-6165. **$85-$300.** 3850 Eagle View Dr 46254. I-465 exit 17, just w on 38th St, then just n. Int corridors. **Pets:** Accepted.

Best Western Airport Suites H
(317) 246-1505. **$80-$220.** 55 S High School Rd 46241. I-465 exit 13B, just w. Int corridors. **Pets:** Accepted. SAVE

Best Western Country Suites H
(317) 879-1700. **$72-$159.** 3871 W 92nd St 46268. I-465 exit 27, just s on Michigan Rd. Int corridors. **Pets:** Accepted.

Candlewood Suites Indianapolis NE H
(317) 595-9292. **Call for rates.** 8111 Bash St 46250. I-69 exit 201, just w. Int corridors. **Pets:** Other species. $25 one-time fee/room. Service with restrictions.

Candlewood Suites Indianapolis NW H
(317) 298-8000. **Call for rates.** 7455 Woodland Dr 46278. I-465 exit 21 (73rd St), just n. Int corridors. **Pets:** Large, other species. $25 one-time fee/pet. Service with restrictions.

Comfort Stay Inn H
(317) 353-6966. **Call for rates.** 7610 Old Trails Rd 46219. I-465 exit 46, just sw. Int corridors. **Pets:** Medium, other species. $25 daily fee/pet. Service with restrictions, supervision.

Conrad Indianapolis H
(317) 713-5000. **$179-$409.** 50 W Washington St 46204. Jct Illinois St. Int corridors. **Pets:** Other species. $150 one-time fee/room. Service with restrictions, crate.

Drury Inn & Suites Indianapolis Northeast H
(317) 849-8900. **$110-$210.** 8180 N Shadeland Ave 46250. I-69 exit 201, just e. Int corridors. **Pets:** Accepted.

Drury Inn-Indianapolis Northwest H
(317) 876-9777. **$95-$180.** 9320 N Michigan Rd 46268. I-465 exit 27, just s. Int corridors. **Pets:** Accepted.

Drury Plaza Hotel Indianapolis Carmel H
(317) 587-2701. **$110-$240.** 9625 N Meridian St 46290. I-465 exit 31, just n. Int corridors. **Pets:** Accepted.

Extended Stay America - 86th Street/Northwest H
(317) 334-7829. **$70-$90.** 8520 Northwest Blvd 46278. I-465 exit 23, just e. Int corridors. **Pets:** Accepted.

Extended Stay America Indianapolis - North - Carmel H
(317) 843-1181. **$75-$100.** 9750 Lakeshore Dr E 46280. I-465 exit 33, 0.4 mi n on Keystone Ave, 0.6 mi e on 96th St, then just n on Bauer Dr. Int corridors. **Pets:** Accepted.

Hilton Indianapolis Hotel & Suites H
(317) 972-0600. **$119-$269.** 120 W Market St 46204. Jct Illinois St. Int corridors. **Pets:** Medium, other species. $50 one-time fee/room. Supervision.

Holiday Inn Express South H
(317) 783-5151. **$89-$189.** 5151 S East St 46227. I-465 exit 2B, 0.3 mi s. Int corridors. **Pets:** Medium. $50 one-time fee/pet. Designated rooms, service with restrictions, crate.

Hyatt Place Indianapolis Airport H
(317) 227-0950. **$94-$249.** 5500 W Bradbury Ave 46241. I-465 exit 11A, 0.3 mi e on Sam Jones Expwy to Executive Dr exit. Int corridors. **Pets:** Accepted.

Hyatt Place Indianapolis/Keystone H
(317) 843-0064. **$89-$389.** 9104 Keystone Crossing 46240. I-465 exit 33, 0.5 mi s on SR 431, just e on 86th St, then 0.5 mi n. Int corridors. **Pets:** Accepted.

Indianapolis Conference Center Hotel H
(317) 359-1021. **Call for rates.** 7304 E 21st St 46219. I-70 exit 89, just s, then just e; 0.5 mi w of jct I-465. Int corridors. **Pets:** Accepted.

Indy Speedway Inn M
(317) 297-1848. **$80-$195, 3 day notice.** 3851 Shore Dr 46254. I-465 exit 17, just w on 38th St, then just n. Ext corridors. **Pets:** Other species. $15 daily fee/pet. Service with restrictions, crate.

La Quinta Inn Indianapolis Airport Executive Drive H
(317) 244-8100. **$67-$170.** 2650 Executive Dr 46241. I-465 exit 11 southbound; exit 11B northbound, 0.3 mi e. Int corridors. **Pets:** Accepted.

La Quinta Inn Indianapolis Airport Lynhurst H
(317) 247-4281. **$67-$148.** 5316 W Southern Ave 46241. I-465 exit 11A, 0.5 mi e on Sam Jones Expwy to Lynhurst Dr. Int corridors. **Pets:** Accepted.

Le Meridien Indianapolis H
(317) 737-1600. **Call for rates.** 123 S Illinois St 46225. Between Georgia and Maryland sts. Int corridors. **Pets:** Accepted.

Omni Severin Hotel H
(317) 634-6664. **Call for rates.** 40 W Jackson Pl 46225. Corner of Illinois and Georgia sts. Int corridors. **Pets:** Small. $50 one-time fee/room. Service with restrictions, supervision.

Quality Inn Indy Castleton H
(317) 849-8555. **$75-$200.** 8380 Kelly Ln 46250. I-465 exit 35 (Allisonville Rd), just s. Int corridors. **Pets:** Medium. $15 daily fee/pet. Service with restrictions, crate.

Red Roof Inn Indianapolis North-College Park H
(317) 872-3030. **$45-$99.** 9520 Valparaiso Ct 46268. I-465 exit 27, just n. Ext corridors. **Pets:** Accepted.

Residence Inn by Marriott Indianapolis Airport H
(317) 244-1500. **$71-$296.** 5224 W Southern Ave 46241. I-465 exit 11A, 0.5 mi e on Sam Jones Expwy to Lynhurst Dr. Int corridors. **Pets:** Medium. $100 one-time fee/room. Service with restrictions, crate.

Residence Inn by Marriott Indianapolis Downtown on the Canal H
(317) 822-0840. **$99-$399.** 350 W New York St 46202. Jct Senate Ave. Int corridors. **Pets:** Accepted.

Residence Inn by Marriott Northwest-Indianapolis H
(317) 275-6000. **$87-$271.** 6220 Digital Way 46278. I-465 exit 21, just w. Int corridors. **Pets:** Medium, other species. $100 one-time fee/room. Designated rooms, service with restrictions, crate.

Sheraton Indianapolis at Keystone Crossing H
(317) 846-2700. **Call for rates.** 8787 Keystone Crossing 46240. I-465 exit 33, 0.5 mi s on SR 431, just e on 86th St, then just n. Int corridors. **Pets:** Accepted.

Staybridge Suites City Centre H
(317) 536-7500. **Call for rates.** 535 S West St 46225. Just s of South St. Int corridors. **Pets:** Accepted.

Suburban Extended Stay Hotel H
(317) 598-1914. **$49-$119.** 8055 Bash St 46250. I-69 exit 201, just w. Int corridors. **Pets:** Accepted.

▼▼▼ **TownePlace Suites by Marriott Keystone** 🄷
(317) 255-3700. **$210-$461.** 8468 Union Chapel Rd 46240. I-465 exit 33, 0.5 mi s on SR 431, just e on 86th St, then just s. Int corridors. **Pets:** Accepted. 🅑🄼 🍽 🛜 ✖ 🛏 🖳

▼▼▼ **TownePlace Suites by Marriott Park 100** 🄷
(317) 290-8900. **$69-$166.** 5802 W 71st St 46278. I-465 exit 21, 0.3 mi e. Int corridors. **Pets:** Accepted. 🍽 🛜 ✖ 🛏 🖳

🄬 ▼▼▼▼ **The Westin Indianapolis** 🄷
(317) 262-8100. **$189-$529.** 50 S Capitol Ave 46204. Jct Washington and Maryland sts. Int corridors. **Pets:** Accepted.
[SAVE] 🍴 🅑🄼 🍽 ✖ 🛜 ✖ 🛏 🖳

▼▼▼ **Wingate By Wyndham Indianapolis Airport-Rockville Rd** 🄷
(317) 243-8310. **$99-$250.** 5797 Rockville Rd 46224. I-465 exit 13A, just e. Int corridors. **Pets:** Accepted. 🅑🄼 🍽 🛜 ✖ 🛏 🖳

▼▼▼ **Wingate by Wyndham Indianapolis Northwest** 🄷
(317) 275-7000. **$75-$150.** 6240 Intech Commons Dr 46278. I-465 exit 21, just w. Int corridors. **Pets:** Accepted. 🛜 ✖ 🛏 🖳

▼▼▼ **Wyndham Indianapolis West** 🄷
(317) 248-2481. **$99-$209.** 2544 Executive Dr 46241. I-465 exit 11A southbound; exit 11B northbound, just e on Sam Jones Expwy to Executive Dr. Int corridors. **Pets:** Accepted.
🍴 🅑🄼 🍽 🛜 ✖ 🛏 🖳

JEFFERSONVILLE
▼▼ **Hawthorn Suites by Wyndham Louisville North** 🄷
(812) 280-8200. **$99-$450.** 703 N Shore Dr 47130. I-65 exit 0, just w. Int corridors. **Pets:** Accepted. 🅑🄼 🍽 🛜 ✖ 🛏 🖳

🄬 ▼▼▼ **Sheraton Louisville Riverside Hotel** 🄷
(812) 284-6711. **$91-$399.** 700 W Riverside Dr 47130. I-65 exit 0, just w. Int corridors. **Pets:** Accepted. [SAVE] 🍴 🍽 🛜 ✖ 🛏 🖳

KENDALLVILLE
🄬 ▼▼▼ **Best Western Kendallville Inn** 🄷 🐾
(260) 347-5263. **$99-$139.** 621 Professional Way 46755. 1 mi e on US 6. Int corridors. **Pets:** Medium. $15 daily fee/room. Designated rooms, service with restrictions, supervision.
[SAVE] 🅑🄼 🍽 🛜 ✖ 🛏 🖳

▼▼▼ **Holiday Inn Express Kendallville** 🄷
(260) 343-0000. **Call for rates.** 1917 Dowling St 46755. I-69 exit 334, 9.3 mi e on US 6. Int corridors. **Pets:** Accepted.
🍴 🅑🄼 🍽 🛜 ✖ 🛏 🖳

KOKOMO
▼▼ **Comfort Inn by Choice Hotels** 🄷
(765) 452-5050. **$59-$169.** 522 Essex Dr 46901. Jct US 35, 0.3 mi n on US 31. Int corridors. **Pets:** Accepted. 🍽 🛜 ✖ 🛏 🖳

▼▼▼ **Hampton Inn & Suites** 🄷
(765) 455-2900. **$109-$209.** 2920 S Reed Rd (US Hwy 31) 46902. US 31, 2 mi s of jct US 35. Int corridors. **Pets:** Dogs only. Designated rooms, service with restrictions, crate. 🅑🄼 🍽 🛜 ✖ 🛏 🖳

LAFAYETTE
▼▼ **Baymont Inn & Suites** 🄷
(765) 449-4808. **$69-$199.** 201 Frontage Rd 47905. I-65 exit 172, just e on SR 26, then just n. Int corridors. **Pets:** Accepted.
🛜 ✖ 🛏 🖳

▼▼▼ **Candlewood Suites** 🄷
(765) 807-5735. **Call for rates.** 240 Meijer Dr 47905. I-65 exit 172, just e on SR 26. Int corridors. **Pets:** Accepted.
🅑🄼 🍽 🛜 ✖ 🛏 🖳

▼▼▼ **Comfort Inn** 🄷
(765) 447-3434. **$89-$229.** 4701 Meijer Ct 47905. I-65 exit 172, just e on SR 26. Int corridors. **Pets:** Small. $15 daily fee/pet. Designated rooms, service with restrictions, supervision. 🍽 🛜 ✖ 🛏 🖳

▼▼ **Days Inn & Suites** 🄷
(765) 446-8558. **$60-$250.** 151 Frontage Rd 47905. I-65 exit 172, just e. Int corridors. **Pets:** Accepted. 🛜 ✖ 🛏 🖳

▼▼▼ **Homewood Suites by Hilton** 🄷
(765) 448-9700. **$139-$199.** 3939 South St 47905. I-65 exit 172, 0.8 mi w. Ext/int corridors. **Pets:** Medium, other species. $250 deposit/room, $10 daily fee/pet. 🍽 🛜 ✖ 🛏 🖳

▼▼▼ **Lafayette Comfort Suites** 🄷
(765) 447-0016. **$95-$220.** 31 Frontage Rd 47905. I-65 exit 172, just e. Int corridors. **Pets:** Accepted. 🅑🄼 🍽 🛜 ✖ 🛏 🖳

▼ **Motel 6 #4291** 🄼
(765) 447-7566. **Call for rates.** 139 Frontage Rd 47905. I-65 exit 172, just e on SR 26, then just n. Ext corridors. **Pets:** Accepted.
🛜 ✖ 🛏

🄬 ▼▼▼ **TownePlace Suites by Marriott** 🄷 🐾
(765) 446-8668. **$128-$282.** 163 Frontage Rd 47905. I-65 exit 172, just e. Int corridors. **Pets:** Other species. $75 one-time fee/room. Service with restrictions. [SAVE] 🍽 🛜 ✖ 🛏 🖳

LA PORTE
🄬 ▼▼▼ **Best Western Plus La Porte Hotel & Conference Center** 🄷
(219) 362-4585. **$120-$210.** 444 Pine Lake Ave 46350. 1.5 mi n on US 35. Int corridors. **Pets:** $20 deposit/room. Designated rooms, service with restrictions, crate. [SAVE] 🍴 🍽 ✖ 🛜 ✖ 🛏 🖳

LAWRENCEBURG
▼▼▼ **Comfort Inn & Suites** 🄷
(812) 539-3600. **$90-$280.** 1610 Flossie Dr 47025. I-275 exit 16, 0.3 mi e. Int corridors. **Pets:** Accepted. 🅑🄼 🍽 🛜 ✖ 🛏 🖳

LEBANON
▼▼▼ **Holiday Inn Express** 🄷
(765) 483-4100. **Call for rates.** 335 N Mt Zion Rd 46052. I-65 exit 140, just w. Int corridors. **Pets:** Accepted.
🍴 🅑🄼 🍽 🛜 ✖ 🛏 🖳

MARION
▼▼▼ **Comfort Suites Marion** 🄷
(765) 651-1006. **$105-$190.** 1345 N Baldwin Ave 46952. On SR 9, 1.5 mi n of SR 18. Int corridors. **Pets:** Accepted.
🅑🄼 🍽 🛜 ✖ 🛏 🖳

MARTINSVILLE
🄬 ▼▼▼ **Best Western Martinsville Inn** 🄷
(765) 342-1842. **$70-$290.** 50 Bill's Blvd 46151. SR 37 to Ohio St, just w. Int corridors. **Pets:** Small, other species. $15 daily fee/pet. Service with restrictions, supervision. [SAVE] 🅑🄼 🍽 🛜 ✖ 🛏 🖳

🄬 ▼▼▼ **Holiday Inn Express & Suites Martinsville-Bloomington Area** 🄷 🐾
(765) 813-3999. **$99-$299.** 2233 Burton Ln 46151. SR 37 to Burton Ln, just e. Int corridors. **Pets:** Other species. $15 daily fee/room. Service with restrictions, supervision. [SAVE] 🅑🄼 🍽 🛜 ✖ 🛏 🖳

MERRILLVILLE

▼▼ **Candlewood Suites** H ❀

(219) 791-9100. **Call for rates.** 8339 Ohio St 46410. I-65 exit 253, 0.3 mi e, just s on Mississippi St, 0.4 mi w on 83rd Ave, then just s. Int corridors. **Pets:** Medium. $75 one-time fee/room. Service with restrictions, supervision. 🛜 ✖ 📧 💻

▲▲▲ ▼▼▼ **Country Inn & Suites By Carlson** H

(219) 736-1300. **Call for rates.** 8311 Ohio St 46410. I-65 exit 253, 0.3 mi e, just s on Mississippi St, 0.4 mi w on 83rd Ave, then just s. Int corridors. **Pets:** Accepted. SAVE �ᴹ 🛜 ✖ 📧 💻

▼▼ **Extended Stay America-Merrillville-US Rte 30** H

(219) 769-4740. **$75-$105.** 1355 E 83rd Ave 46410. I-65 exit 253, 0.3 mi e on US 30, just s on Mississippi St, then 0.4 mi w. Int corridors. **Pets:** Accepted. 🛜 ✖ 📧 💻

▲▲▲ ▼▼ **Red Roof Inn Merrillville** H

(219) 738-2430. **$55-$110.** 8290 Georgia St 46410. I-65 exit 253B (US 30), 0.3 mi sw. Ext corridors. **Pets:** Accepted. SAVE 🛜 ✖ 📧 💻

▼▼▼ **Residence Inn by Marriott Merrillville** H

(219) 791-9000. **$133-$293.** 8018 Delaware Pl 46410. I-65 exit 253, just nw. Int corridors. **Pets:** Accepted. ⓜ ⓜ 🛜 ✖ 📧 💻

▼▼▼ **Staybridge Suites - Merrillville** H

(219) 472-8400. **Call for rates.** 8415 Louisiana St 46410. I-65 exit 253, 0.3 mi e on US 30, just s on Mississippi St, then just w. Int corridors. **Pets:** Accepted. ⓜ 🛜 ✖ 📧 💻

MISHAWAKA

▲▲▲ ▼▼▼ **Best Western Plus Mishawaka Inn** H

(574) 273-2309. **$80-$108.** 445 W University Dr 46545. I-80/90 exit 83, just n on SR 331 to SR 23, 1.6 mi sw to Main St, just s to University Dr, then just w. Int corridors. **Pets:** Large. Designated rooms, service with restrictions. SAVE ⓜ ⓜ 🛜 ✖ 📧 💻

▼▼▼ **Country Inn & Suites By Carlson** H

(574) 271-1700. **Call for rates.** 120 W University Dr 46545. I-80/90 exit 83, just n on SR 331 to SR 23, 0.6 mi sw on SR 23, then just s on Main St. Int corridors. **Pets:** Accepted. ⓜ ⓜ 🛜 ✖ 📧 💻

▼▼▼ **Holiday Inn Express Mishawaka** H

(574) 277-2520. **Call for rates.** 420 W University Dr 46545. I-80/90 exit 83, just n on SR 331 to 23, 1.6 mi sw to Main St, just s to University Dr, then just w. Int corridors. **Pets:** Accepted.

ⓜ ⓜ 🛜 ✖ 📧 💻

▲▲▲ ▼▼▼ **Hyatt Place South Bend/Mishawaka** H

(574) 258-7777. **$79-$529.** 215 W Day Rd 46545. I-80/90 exit 83, just n on SR 331 to SR 23, 1.6 mi sw, then 1.3 mi s on Main St. Int corridors. **Pets:** Accepted. SAVE 🍴 ⓜ ⓜ 🛜 ✖ 📧 💻

▼▼▼ **Residence Inn by Marriott South Bend/Mishawaka** H

(574) 271-9283. **$148-$326.** 231 Park Pl 46545. I-80/90 exit 83, just n on SR 331 to SR 23, 1.6 mi sw, then 1.3 mi s on Main St. Int corridors. **Pets:** Accepted. ⓜ ⓜ 🛜 ✖ 📧 💻

MOUNT VERNON

▼▼ **Four Seasons Motel** M

(812) 838-4821. **$82-$122.** 70 Hwy 62 W 47620. 1.8 mi w. Ext corridors. **Pets:** Accepted. ⓜ 🛜 ✖ 📧 💻

MUNCIE

▼▼ **Super 8** H

(765) 286-4333. **$50-$105, 3 day notice.** 3601 W Fox Ridge Ln 47304. I-69 exit 241, 6.3 mi e on SR 332. Int corridors. **Pets:** Small, dogs only. $10 daily fee/pet. Designated rooms, service with restrictions, supervision. 🛜 ✖ 📧 💻

NEW HARMONY

▲▲▲ ▼▼▼ **The New Harmony Inn Resort and Conference Center** H

(812) 682-4431. **$125-$140, 3 day notice.** 504 North St 47631. Jct Brewery St. Int corridors. **Pets:** Small. $25 daily fee/pet. Designated rooms, no service, supervision.

SAVE 🍴 ⓜ ⓜ ✖ 🛜 ✖ 📧 💻

NOBLESVILLE

▼▼ **Baymont Inn & Suites** H

(317) 770-6772. **$71-$190.** 16025 Prosperity Dr 46060. I-69 exit 205, 4 mi n on SR 37. Int corridors. **Pets:** Accepted.

ⓜ ⓜ 🛜 ✖ 📧 💻

▼▼ **Quality Inn** H

(317) 776-7088. **$59-$139.** 17070 Dragonfly Dr 46060. Jct SR 37 and 38, 0.5 mi s on SR 37. Int corridors. **Pets:** Accepted.

ⓜ 🛜 ✖ 📧 💻

NORTH VERNON

▼▼ **Comfort Inn** H

(812) 352-9999. **$85-$135.** 150 FDR Dr 47265. Jct US 50, 0.6 mi n on SR 7. Int corridors. **Pets:** Medium, dogs only. $25 daily fee/pet. Designated rooms, service with restrictions, crate.

ⓜ ⓜ 🛜 ✖ 📧 💻

PERU

▲▲▲ ▼▼▼ **Best Western Circus City Inn** H ❀

(765) 473-8800. **$105-$115.** 2642 Business Rt US 31 S 46970. Just e of jct US 31. Int corridors. **Pets:** Large, other species. $20 deposit/pet. Designated rooms, supervision. SAVE ⓜ 🛜 ✖ 📧 💻

PLAINFIELD

▼▼▼ **Holiday Inn Express-Indianapolis Airport** H

(317) 839-9000. **Call for rates.** 6296 Cambridge Way 46168. I-70 exit 66, 0.4 mi n on SR 267, just e on Hadley Rd, then just s. Int corridors. **Pets:** Accepted. ⓜ ⓜ 🛜 ✖ 📧 💻

▼▼▼ **La Quinta Inn & Suites Indianapolis Airport-Plainfield** H

(317) 279-2650. **$92-$246.** 2251 Manchester Dr 46168. I-70 exit 66, 0.4 mi n on SR 267, just e on Perry Rd. Int corridors. **Pets:** Accepted.

ⓜ ⓜ 🛜 ✖ 📧 💻

▼▼▼ **Staybridge Suites Indianapolis Airport** H

(317) 839-2700. **Call for rates.** 6295 Cambridge Way 46168. I-70 exit 66, 0.4 mi n on SR 267, just e on Hadley Rd, then just s. Int corridors. **Pets:** Accepted. ⓜ ⓜ 🛜 ✖ 📧 💻

PORTAGE

▼▼ **Comfort Inn** H

(219) 763-7177. **$70-$190.** 2300 Willowcreek Rd 46368. I-80/90 exit 23; I-94 exit 19, 1.5 mi s on CR 249. Int corridors. **Pets:** Accepted.

🍴 🛜 ✖ 📧 💻

▼▼ **Holiday Inn Express-Portage** H

(219) 762-7777. **Call for rates.** 2323 Willowcreek Rd 46368. I-80/90 exit 23; I-94 exit 19, 1.5 mi s. Int corridors. **Pets:** Accepted.

ⓜ ⓜ 🛜 ✖ 📧 💻

PRINCETON

▼▼▼ **Fairfield Inn by Marriott** H

(812) 385-4300. **$75-$165.** 2828 Dixon St 47670. Jct US 41 and SR 64, 0.3 mi w. Int corridors. **Pets:** Accepted.

🍴 ⓜ ⓜ 🛜 ✖ 📧 💻

REMINGTON

▼▼ **Super 8-Remington** H

(219) 261-2883. **$73-$150.** 4278 W US 24 47977. I-65 exit 201, 0.5 mi w. Int corridors. **Pets:** Accepted. 🛜 ✖ 📧 💻

RICHMOND

AAA ▼▼▼ **Best Western Classic Inn** H
(765) 939-9500. **$92-$119.** 533 W Eaton Pike 47374. I-70 exit 156A, just s. Int corridors. **Pets:** Other species. $10 daily fee/pet. Designated rooms, service with restrictions, supervision.
SAVE ▢ ▢ ▢ ▢ ▢ ▢

RUSHVILLE

▼▼ **Quality Inn & Suites** H
(765) 932-2999. **$86-$99.** 320 Conrad Harcourt Way 46173. Just e of SR 3. Int corridors. **Pets:** Small, dogs only. $40 daily fee/pet. Designated rooms, service with restrictions, supervision.
▢ ▢ ▢ ▢ ▢

SCHERERVILLE

▼▼▼ **Staybridge Suites - Schererville** H
(219) 227-5125. **Call for rates.** 1758 Fountain Park Dr 46375. I-65 exit 253, 7.3 mi w on US 30. Int corridors. **Pets:** Accepted.
▢ ▢ ▢ ▢ ▢

SCOTTSBURG

▼▼▼ **Hampton Inn & Suites by Hilton** H
(812) 752-1999. **$99-$314.** 1535 W McClain Ave 47170. I-65 exit 29, just w. Int corridors. **Pets:** Accepted. ▢ ▢ ▢ ▢ ▢ ▢

SELLERSBURG

▼▼ **Ramada Sellersburg** H
(812) 246-3131. **$70-$189.** 360 Triangle Dr 47172. I-65 exit 9, just e. Int corridors. **Pets:** Accepted. ▢ ▢ ▢ ▢ ▢ ▢

SHELBYVILLE

▼▼ **Comfort Inn** H
(317) 398-8044. **$79-$109.** 36 W Rampart Dr 46176. I-74 exit 113, just s. Int corridors. **Pets:** Accepted. ▢ ▢ ▢ ▢ ▢

SOUTH BEND

AAA ▼▼▼ **Comfort Suites University Area** H 🐾
(574) 272-1500. **$104-$459.** 52939 US 933 N 46637. I-80/90 exit 77, just e to Business Rt US 31/SR 933, then 1 mi n. Int corridors. **Pets:** Medium, dogs only. $25 daily fee/pet. Designated rooms, service with restrictions, supervision. SAVE ▢ ▢ ▢ ▢ ▢

AAA ▼▼▼ **Morris Inn** H 🐾
(574) 631-2000. **$109-$499.** 1399 N Notre Dame Ave 46556. On campus of University of Notre Dame. Int corridors. **Pets:** Other species. $50 one-time fee/room. Designated rooms.
SAVE ▢ ▢ ▢ ▢ ▢ ▢

▼▼▼ **The Oliver Inn Bed & Breakfast** BB
(574) 232-4545. **$140-$339, 14 day notice.** 630 W Washington St 46601. 0.3 mi w of SR 933 and Business Rt US 31. Int corridors.
Pets: Accepted. ▢ ▢ ▢ ▢

AAA ▼▼ **Sleep Inn** H
(574) 232-3200. **$80-$380.** 4134 Lincolnway W 46628. I-80/90 exit 72, 1.5 mi s on US 31 to South Bend Regional Airport exit, then 2 mi e. Int corridors. **Pets:** Medium. $20 daily fee/pet. Designated rooms, service with restrictions, supervision. SAVE ▢ ▢ ▢ ▢ ▢ ▢

▼▼ **Staybridge Suites South Bend-University Area** H
(574) 968-7440. **Call for rates.** 52860 SR 933 N 46637. I-80/90 exit 77, 1 mi n. Int corridors. **Pets:** Accepted.
▢ ▢ ▢ ▢ ▢ ▢

▼▼ **Suburban Extended Stay Hotel** H
(574) 968-4737. **$49-$299.** 52825 SR 933 N 46637. I-80/90 exit 77, 1 mi n. Int corridors. **Pets:** Accepted. ▢ ▢ ▢ ▢ ▢ ▢

AAA ▼▼▼ **Super 8 - South Bend** H
(574) 243-0200. **$70-$300, 3 day notice.** 4124 Ameritech Dr 46628. I-80/90 exit 72, 0.7 mi n on US 31, just e on Cleveland Rd, then just s. Int corridors. **Pets:** Medium. $25 daily fee/pet. Service with restrictions, supervision. SAVE ▢ ▢ ▢ ▢ ▢ ▢

▼▼▼ **Waterford Estates Lodge** H
(574) 272-5220. **$109-$119.** 52890 SR 933 N 46637. I-80/90 exit 77, 1 mi n. Int corridors. **Pets:** Other species. $30 one-time fee/pet. Designated rooms, service with restrictions, crate.
▢ ▢ ▢ ▢ ▢ ▢ ▢

SYRACUSE

▼▼▼ **Oakwood Resort** H
(574) 457-7100. **$109-$309.** 702 E Lake View Rd 46567. Int corridors. **Pets:** Medium, dogs only. $25 daily fee/room. Designated rooms, service with restrictions, supervision. ▢ ▢ ▢ ▢ ▢ ▢

TAYLORSVILLE

▼▼ **Red Roof Inn Columbus/Taylorsville** M
(812) 526-9747. **$69-$100.** 10330 US 31 47280. I-65 exit 76A, just s. Ext corridors. **Pets:** Accepted. ▢ ▢ ▢ ▢ ▢

TELL CITY

▼▼▼ **Holiday Inn Express** H
(812) 547-0800. **$76-$199.** 310 Orchard Hill Dr 47586. Just off SR 66, 1.7 mi se of jct SR 37. Int corridors. **Pets:** Accepted.
▢ ▢ ▢ ▢ ▢ ▢

▼▼ **Ramada Limited** H
(812) 547-3234. **$79-$109.** 235 Orchard Hill Dr 47586. Just off SR 66, 1.7 mi se of jct SR 37. Int corridors. **Pets:** Accepted.
▢ ▢ ▢ ▢ ▢

TERRE HAUTE

▼▼▼ **Candlewood Suites** H 🐾
(812) 234-3400. **Call for rates.** 721 Wabash Ave 47807. I-70 exit 7 (US 41/150), 2.2 mi n, 0.4 mi e, then just s. Int corridors. **Pets:** Other species. $75 one-time fee/room. Service with restrictions, supervision.
▢ ▢ ▢ ▢ ▢

▼▼▼ **Drury Inn-Terre Haute** H
(812) 238-1206. **$80-$165.** 3040 Hwy 41 S 47802. I-70 exit 7 (US 41/150), just n. Int corridors. **Pets:** Accepted.
▢ ▢ ▢ ▢ ▢ ▢

▼▼▼ **Holiday Inn Express & Suites** H
(812) 234-3200. **Call for rates.** 2645 S Joe Fox St 47803. I-70 exit 11, just n. Int corridors. **Pets:** Large, other species. $25 one-time fee/room. Service with restrictions, crate. ▢ ▢ ▢ ▢ ▢ ▢

▼▼ **Pear Tree Inn by Drury-Terre Haute** H
(812) 234-4268. **$55-$100.** 3050 Hwy 41 S 47802. I-70 exit 7 (US 41/150), just n. Int corridors. **Pets:** Accepted. ▢ ▢ ▢ ▢ ▢ ▢

VALPARAISO *(Restaurants p. 613)*

▼▼▼ **The Inn at Aberdeen** BB
(219) 465-3753. **$108-$205.** 3158 S SR 2 46385. Jct US 30 and SR 2, 2.7 mi s. Int corridors. **Pets:** Other species. $25 daily fee/pet. Designated rooms, service with restrictions, supervision. ▢ ▢ ▢ ▢

VINCENNES

AAA ▼▼ **Red Roof Inn Vincennes** M
(812) 882-2100. **$90-$100.** 1800 S Old Decker Rd 47591. Jct US 41 Bypass and Willow St, just nw. Ext corridors. **Pets:** Accepted.
SAVE ▢ ▢ ▢ ▢ ▢ ▢

▼▼▼ **TownePlace Suites by Marriott Vincennes** 🄷
(812) 255-1500. **$72-$166.** 1320 Willow St 47591. Jct US 41 Bypass and Willow St, 1.2 mi nw. Int corridors. **Pets:** Accepted.
🅼 🛌 📶 ✖ 🛗 🖥️

WARREN
▼▼▼ **Comfort Inn** 🄷
(260) 375-4800. **Call for rates.** 7275 S 75 E 46792. I-69 exit 78, just n on SR 5. Int corridors. **Pets:** Accepted. 🅼 🛌 📶 ✖ 🛗 🖥️

WARSAW
🟡 ▼▼▼ **Comfort Inn & Suites** 🄷
(574) 269-6655. **$94-$239.** 3328 E Center St 46580. 3.2 mi e of SR 15 on US 30. Int corridors. **Pets:** Small, dogs only. $25 daily fee/pet. Designated rooms, service with restrictions, supervision.
🆂🅰🆅🅴 🅼 🛌 📶 ✖ 🛗 🖥️

▼▼▼ **Holiday Inn Express Hotel & Suites-Warsaw** 🄷
(574) 268-1600. **Call for rates.** 3825 Lake City Hwy 46580. Jct US 30 and SR 15, 4 mi e on US 30. Int corridors. **Pets:** Accepted.
🅼 🛌 📶 ✖ 🛗 🖥️

▼▼▼ **Wyndham Garden of Warsaw** 🄷
(574) 269-2323. **$119-$169.** 2519 E Center St 46580. 2.8 mi e of SR 15 on US 30, just s. Int corridors. **Pets:** Accepted.
🔌 🍴 🅼 🛌 ✖ 📶 ✖ 🛗 🖥️

WASHINGTON
▼▼ **Baymont Inn & Suites Washington** 🄷
(812) 254-7000. **$75-$99.** 7 Cumberland Dr 47501. Just ne of jct US 50 and SR 57. Int corridors. **Pets:** Accepted.
🛌 ✖ 📶 ✖ 🛗 🖥️

▼▼ **Holiday Inn Express** 🄷
(812) 254-6666. **Call for rates.** 1808 E National Hwy 47501. On US 50 business route, 0.4 mi e of SR 257. Int corridors. **Pets:** Accepted.
🍴 🛌 📶 ✖ 🛗 🖥️

WEST BADEN SPRINGS
🟡 ▼▼▼ ▼▼▼ **West Baden Springs Hotel** 🄷
(812) 936-5501. **Call for rates.** 8538 W Baden Ave 47469. On SR 56. Int corridors. **Pets:** Accepted.
🆂🅰🆅🅴 🔌 🍴 🅼 🛌 ✖ 📶 ✖ 🛗 🖥️

WEST LAFAYETTE
🟡 ▼▼▼ **Four Points by Sheraton West Lafayette** 🄷
(765) 463-5511. **$89-$499.** 1600 Cumberland Ave 47906. I-65 exit 175, 1.5 mi sw on Schuyler Ave, then 3.8 mi nw on US 52. Int corridors. **Pets:** Small, dogs only. $75 one-time fee/room. Designated rooms, no service, crate. 🆂🅰🆅🅴 🍴 🅼 🛌 📶 ✖ 🛗 🖥️

IOWA

ALGONA
▼▼▼ **AmericInn Lodge & Suites of Algona** 🄷
(515) 295-3333. **Call for rates.** 600 Hwy 18 W 50511. Just w of jct US 169/18. Int corridors. **Pets:** Accepted.
🍴 🅼 🛌 📶 ✖ 🛗 🖥️

ALTOONA
▼▼ **Comfort Inn Altoona** 🄷
(515) 967-7888. **$90-$210.** 2101 Adventureland Dr 50009. I-80 exit 142, just se. Int corridors. **Pets:** Accepted. 🛌 📶 ✖ 🛗 🖥️

AMES
▼▼ **AmericInn of Ames** 🄷
(515) 233-1005. **$89-$189.** 2507 SE 16th St 50010. US 30 exit 150, just ne. Int corridors. **Pets:** Medium, other species. $30 one-time fee/room. Designated rooms, service with restrictions, supervision.
🅼 🛌 📶 ✖ 🛗 🖥️

🟡 ▼▼▼ **Best Western Plus University Park Inn & Suites** 🄷
(515) 296-2500. **$110-$229.** 2500 University Blvd 50010. US 30 exit 146, just s. Int corridors. **Pets:** Accepted.
🆂🅰🆅🅴 🛌 📶 ✖ 🛗 🖥️

▼▼ **Country Inn & Suites By Carlson** 🄷
(515) 233-3935. **$119-$249.** 2605 SE 16th St 50010. US 30 exit 150, just ne. Int corridors. **Pets:** Accepted. 🅼 🛌 📶 ✖ 🛗 🖥️

▼▼ **Econo Lodge** 🄷
(515) 233-6060. **$60-$250.** 2600 SE 16th St 50010. US 30 exit 150, just ne. Int corridors. **Pets:** Accepted. 🛌 📶 🛗 🖥️

▼▼▼ **Gateway Hotel & Conference Center** 🄷
(515) 292-8600. **Call for rates.** 2100 Green Hills Dr 50014. US 30 exit 146, just sw. Int corridors. **Pets:** Accepted.
🍴 🅼 🛌 ✖ 📶 ✖ 🛗 🖥️

▼▼▼ **GrandStay Hotel & Suites** 🄷
(515) 232-8363. **$125-$250.** 1606 S Kellogg Ave 50010. US 30 exit 148, just n. Int corridors. **Pets:** Other species. $15 daily fee/pet. Service with restrictions, crate. 🅼 🛌 📶 ✖ 🛗 🖥️

▼▼ **Quality Inn & Suites Starlite Village Conference Center** 🄷
(515) 232-9260. **$99-$369, 3 day notice.** 2601 E 13th St 50010. I-35 exit 113 (13th St), 0.5 mi w. Int corridors. **Pets:** Accepted.
🍴 🅼 🛌 📶 ✖ 🛗 🖥️

▼▼ **Red Roof Inn** 🄷
(515) 239-9999. **Call for rates.** 1400 S Dayton Pl 50010. US 30 exit 150, just ne. Int corridors. **Pets:** Accepted.
🍴 🅼 🛌 📶 ✖ 🛗 🖥️

ANAMOSA
▼▼ **AmericInn Lodge & Suites** 🄷
(319) 462-4119. **Call for rates.** 101 Harley Ave 52205. US 151, exit 54, 1 mi n. Int corridors. **Pets:** Accepted.
🍴 🅼 🛌 📶 ✖ 🛗 🖥️

ANKENY
🟡 ▼▼▼ **Comfort Inn** 🄷
(515) 963-1100. **$105-$225.** 2602 SE Creekview Dr 50021. I-35 exit 90, just ne. Int corridors. **Pets:** Very small. $35 daily fee/pet. Designated rooms, no service, supervision. 🆂🅰🆅🅴 🛌 📶 ✖ 🛗 🖥️

▼▼▼ **Homewood Suites** 🄷
(515) 963-0006. **Call for rates.** 2455 SE Creekview Dr 50021. I-35 exit 90, just e. Int corridors. **Pets:** Medium. $75 one-time fee/room. Designated rooms, service with restrictions. 🍴 🅼 📶 ✖ 🛗 🖥️

ARNOLDS PARK
▼▼ **Fillenwarth Beach** 🅼
(712) 332-5646. **$88-$1922, 60 day notice.** 87 Lake Shore Dr 51331. Just w of US 71. Ext corridors. **Pets:** Other species. Service with restrictions, crate. 🛌 ✖ 📶 ✖ 🛗 🖥️

ATLANTIC

▽▽ Americas Best Value Inn & Suites 🔲
(712) 243-4723. **$80-$90.** 1902 E 7th St 50022. I-80 exit 60 (US 71), 6 mi s, then 2 mi w; east side of town. Int corridors. **Pets:** Accepted.

CARTER LAKE

▽▽ Super 8 🔲
(712) 347-5588. **$66-$200.** 3000 Airport Dr 51510. I-480 W exit 4 to 10th St, 2.3 mi n, follow Eppley Airfield signs. Int corridors.
Pets: Accepted.

CEDAR FALLS

▽▽ AmericInn Lodge & Suites of Cedar Falls 🔲
(319) 277-6166. **$105-$300.** 5818 Nordic Dr 50613. US 20 exit 225, 1.4 mi n on SR 58. Int corridors. **Pets:** Accepted.

▽▽▽ Comfort Suites 🔲
(319) 273-9999. **$94-$190.** 7402 Nordic Dr 50613. US 20 exit 225, just nw. Int corridors. **Pets:** Other species. $10 daily fee/pet. Designated rooms, crate.

▽▽ Suburban Extended Stay Hotel 🔲
(319) 268-2222. **$60-$170.** 300 Viking Rd 50613. US 20 exit 225, 1.4 mi n on SR 58, then just w. Int corridors. **Pets:** Accepted.

CEDAR RAPIDS

▽▽ AmericInn Lodge & Suites of Cedar Rapids 🔲
(319) 632-1800. **$100-$196.** 8910 6th St SW 52404. I-380 exit 13, just nw. Int corridors. **Pets:** Accepted.

▽▽ Baymont Inn & Suites 🔲
(319) 362-6002. **$56-$85, 3 day notice.** 720 33rd Ave SW 52404. I-380 exit 17 (33rd Ave SW), 0.4 mi w. Int corridors. **Pets:** Accepted.

◬ ▽▽▽ Best Western Plus Longbranch Hotel & Convention Center 🔲
(319) 377-6386. **$110-$150.** 90 Twixt Town Rd NE 52402. I-380 exit 24A (SR 100/Collins Rd), 2.5 mi e, then just n. Int corridors.
Pets: Medium. $10 daily fee/pet. Designated rooms, service with restrictions, supervision.

▽▽ Clarion Hotel & Convention Center 🔲 🐾
(319) 366-8671. **Call for rates.** 525 33rd Ave SW 52404. I-380 exit 17 (33rd Ave SW), just w. Int corridors. **Pets:** Small, dogs only. $25 one-time fee/room. Designated rooms, service with restrictions, supervision.

▽▽ Comfort Inn & Suites 🔲
(319) 378-8888. **$95-$195.** 2025 Werner Ave NE 52402. I-380 exit 24A (SR 100/Collins Rd), just se. Int corridors. **Pets:** Accepted.

▽▽▽ Hometown Inn & Suites 🔲
(319) 362-9012. **Call for rates.** 3315 Southgate Ct SW 52404. I-380 exit 17 (33rd Ave SW), just sw. Int corridors. **Pets:** Accepted.

▽▽▽ Homewood Suites 🔲
(319) 378-1140. **$119-$169.** 1140 Park Pl NE 52402. I-380 exit 24A (SR 100/Collins Rd) to Collins Rd, n on Council St, then just e. Int corridors. **Pets:** Small. $75 one-time fee/room. Designated rooms, service with restrictions, supervision.

▽▽▽▽ La Quinta Inn & Suites 🔲
(319) 378-8000. **$75-$163.** 1220 Park Pl NE 52402. I-380 exit 24A (SR 100/Collins Rd), 0.9 mi e, then just n. Int corridors. **Pets:** Accepted.

▽▽ MainStay Suites 🔲
(319) 363-7829. **$70-$185.** 5145 Rockwell Dr NE 52402. I-380 exit 24A (SR 100/Collins Rd), 1 mi e, then just n. Int corridors. **Pets:** Accepted.

▽▽ Quality Inn at Collins Road 🔲
(319) 393-8247. **$75-$110.** 5055 Rockwell Dr NE 52402. I-380 exit 24A (SR 100/Collins Rd), 1 mi e. Int corridors. **Pets:** Accepted.

▽▽ Quality Inn South by Choice Hotels 🔲
(319) 363-7934. **$70-$100.** 390 33rd Ave SW 52404. I-380 exit 17 (33rd Ave SW), just w. Int corridors. **Pets:** Accepted.

▽▽▽ Residence Inn by Marriott 🔲
(319) 395-0111. **$94-$307.** 1900 Dodge Rd NE 52402. I-380 exit 24A (SR 100/Collins Rd), just e. Int corridors. **Pets:** Accepted.

▽▽▽ Residence Inn by Marriott Cedar Rapids South 🔲
(319) 450-7647. **$94-$208.** 730 33rd Ave SW 52404. I-380 exit 17 (33rd Ave SW), 0.6 mi w. Int corridors. **Pets:** Accepted.

CHARLES CITY

▽▽▽ Sleep Inn & Suites 🔲
(641) 257-6700. **$100-$195.** 1416 S Grand Ave 50616. US 218/18 exit 218, 0.7 mi n on US 218 business route; south side of town. Int corridors. **Pets:** Accepted.

▽▽ Super 8-Charles City 🔲
(641) 228-2888. **$62-$90.** 1411 S Grand Ave 50616. US 218/18 exit 218, 0.8 mi n on US 218 business route; south side of town. Int corridors. **Pets:** Small, dogs only. $15 daily fee/pet. Designated rooms, service with restrictions, supervision.

CHEROKEE

◬ ▽▽ Best Western La Grande Hacienda 🔲
(712) 225-5701. **$80-$120.** 1401 N 2nd St 51012. Just s of jct SR 3 and US 59 (N 2nd St). Int corridors. **Pets:** $5 daily fee/room. Designated rooms, service with restrictions, supervision.

CLARINDA

▽▽ Clarinda Super 8 🔲
(712) 542-6333. **$66-$99.** 1203 S 12th St 51632. Jct US 71 and SR 2, just e. Int corridors. **Pets:** Small. $10 daily fee/pet. Designated rooms, service with restrictions, supervision.

CLEAR LAKE

▽▽ AmericInn Lodge & Suites of Clear Lake 🔲
(641) 357-8954. **$103-$125.** 1406 N 25th St 50428. I-35 exit 194 (US 18), just nw. Int corridors. **Pets:** Dogs only. $15 one-time fee/room. Designated rooms, service with restrictions, supervision.

◬ ▽▽▽ Best Western Holiday Lodge 🔲
(641) 357-5253. **$109-$169.** 2023 7th Ave N 50428. I-35 exit 194 (US 18), 0.3 mi w. Ext/int corridors. **Pets:** Accepted.

▽▽ Microtel Inn by Wyndham Clear Lake 🔲
(641) 357-0966. **$70-$125.** 1305 N 25th St 50428. I-35 exit 194 (US 18), just nw. Int corridors. **Pets:** Accepted.

CLINTON

▽▽ Country Inn & Suites By Carlson 🔲
(563) 244-9922. **Call for rates.** 2224 Lincoln Way 52732. On US 30, just e of jct US 30 and 67. Int corridors. **Pets:** Accepted.

Oak Tree Inn H
(563) 243-1000. **Call for rates.** 2300 Valley W Ct 52732. Just n of jct US 30 and 67; west side of town. Int corridors. **Pets:** Accepted.

CLIVE

Best Western Plus Des Moines West Inn & Suites H
(515) 221-2345. **$90-$199.** 1450 NW 118th St 50325. I-80/35 exit 124 (University Ave), just nw. Int corridors. **Pets:** Dogs only. $20 daily fee/pet. Supervision. SAVE

Country Inn & Suites By Carlson, Des Moines West H
(515) 223-9254. **$99-$200.** 1350 NW 118th St 50325. I-80/35 exit 124 (University Ave), just nw. Int corridors. **Pets:** Medium, dogs only. $25 one-time fee/room. Designated rooms, service with restrictions, supervision. SAVE

Wildwood Lodge H
(515) 222-9876. **$89-$179.** 11431 Forest Ave 50325. I-80/35 exit 124 (University Ave), just e. Int corridors. **Pets:** Accepted.

COLFAX

Microtel Inn & Suites by Wyndham Colfax/Newton H
(515) 674-0600. **$60-$120.** 11000 Federal Ave 50054. I-80 exit 155 (SR 117), just nw. Int corridors. **Pets:** Accepted.
SAVE

CORALVILLE

Best Western Cantebury Inn & Suites H
(319) 351-0400. **$76-$200.** 704 1st Ave 52241. I-80 exit 242, just s. Int corridors. **Pets:** Small. $20 daily fee/pet. Designated rooms, service with restrictions, supervision. SAVE

Country Inn & Suites By Carlson H
(319) 545-8464. **Call for rates.** 2571 Heartland Pl 52241. I-80 exit 240, just n. Int corridors. **Pets:** Accepted.

Quality Inn H
(319) 351-8144. **$75-$219.** 209 W 9th St 52241. I-80 exit 242, just s. Int corridors. **Pets:** Accepted.

Residence Inn by Marriott H
(319) 338-6000. **$98-$316.** 2681 James St 52241. I-80 exit 240, just s. Int corridors. **Pets:** Accepted.

Super 8 H
(319) 337-8388. **$70-$169.** 611 1sr Ave 52241. I-80 exit 242, 0.4 mi s. Int corridors. **Pets:** Medium, other species. $10 daily fee/pet. Designated rooms, service with restrictions, supervision.

COUNCIL BLUFFS

Best Western Crossroads of the Bluffs H
(712) 322-3150. **Call for rates.** 2216 27th Ave 51501. I-29/80 exit 1B (24th St), just ne. Int corridors. **Pets:** Accepted.
SAVE

Days Inn H
(712) 323-2200. **$55-$140.** 3619 9th Ave 51501. I-29 exit 53A (9th Ave), just s. Int corridors. **Pets:** Accepted.

Harrah's Casino & Hotel H
(712) 329-6000. **Call for rates.** 1 Harrah's Blvd 51501. I-29 exit 53A (9th Ave), just w. Int corridors. **Pets:** Accepted.

Microtel Inn & Suites by Wyndham Council Bluffs H
(712) 256-2900. **$75-$145.** 2141 S 35th St 51501. I-29/80 exit 1B (24th St), 0.4 mi n, then 0.8 mi w on 23rd Ave. Int corridors. **Pets:** $25 one-time fee/room. No service, crate. SAVE

Super 8 H
(712) 322-2888. **$66-$146.** 2712 S 24th St 51501. I-29/80 exit 1B (24th St), just nw. Int corridors. **Pets:** Other species. $10 daily fee/pet. Service with restrictions, supervision.

CRESCO

Cresco Motel M
(563) 547-2240. **$53-$81.** 620 2nd Ave SE (Hwy 9) 52136. East side of town. Ext corridors. **Pets:** Dogs only. Designated rooms, service with restrictions, supervision. SAVE

CRESTON

Super 8-Creston H
(641) 782-6541. **$65-$80.** 804 W Taylor St 50801. Jct US 34 and SR 25, on US 34. Int corridors. **Pets:** Accepted.

DAVENPORT

Best Western Plus SteepleGate Inn H
(563) 386-6900. **$130-$210.** 100 W 76th St 52806. I-80 exit 295A (US 61), 0.5 mi s to 65th St and west frontage road entrance, then just nw. Int corridors. **Pets:** Medium, other species. $10 daily fee/pet. Service with restrictions, supervision. SAVE

Country Inn & Suites By Carlson H
(563) 388-6444. **Call for rates.** 140 E 55th St 52806. I-80 exit 295A (US 61), 1.4 mi s. Int corridors. **Pets:** Other species. $25 one-time fee/room. Service with restrictions.

Fairfield Inn by Marriott H
(563) 355-2264. **$59-$167.** 3206 E Kimberly Rd 52807. I-74 exit 2, just w. Int corridors. **Pets:** Other species. $35 one-time fee/room.

Holiday Inn Express & Suites H
(563) 386-2300. **$120-$150.** 401 Veterans Memorial Pkwy 52807. I-80 exit 295A, just s, then just e. Int corridors. **Pets:** Large, dogs only. $50 one-time fee/room. Service with restrictions, supervision.

Homewood Suites by Hilton H
(563) 344-4750. **Call for rates.** 4750 Progress Dr 52807. I-74 exit 1 (53rd St), 0.5 mi e, then 0.5 mi s on CR 216 (Utica Ridge Rd). Int corridors. **Pets:** Accepted.

Hotel Blackhawk, Autograph Collection H
(563) 322-5000. **$103-$292.** 200 E 3rd St 52801. Between Brady St (US 61 N) and Pershing Ave; downtown. Int corridors. **Pets:** Accepted.
SAVE

Residence Inn by Marriott H
(563) 391-8877. **$96-$227.** 120 E 55th St 52806. I-80 exit 295A (US 61), 1.4 mi s. Int corridors. **Pets:** Accepted.

Staybridge Suites H
(563) 359-7829. **$110-$300.** 4729 Progress Dr 52807. I-74 exit 1 (53rd St), 0.5 mi e, then 0.4 mi s on CR 216 (Utica Ridge Rd). Int corridors. **Pets:** Large, other species. $13 daily fee/room. Service with restrictions.

DECORAH

Hotel Winneshiek H
(563) 382-4164. **Call for rates.** 104 E Water St 52101. Downtown. Int corridors. **Pets:** Accepted.

◇◇ **Quality Inn & Suites** H
(563) 382-2269. **$95-$254.** 705 Commerce Dr 52101. Jct US 52, 1.5 mi e on SR 9. Int corridors. **Pets:** Accepted.
[icons]

DES MOINES

AAA ◇◇ **Econo Lodge Inn & Suites** H
(515) 278-8858. **Call for rates.** 4755 Merle Hay Rd 50322. I-80/35 exit 131 (Merle Hay Rd), just s. Int corridors. **Pets:** Accepted.
[icons]

◇◇◇ **Holiday Inn Airport & Conference Center** H
(515) 287-2400. **$135-$265.** 6111 Fleur Dr 50321. SR 5 exit 97, 1 mi n; opposite the airport. Int corridors. **Pets:** Dogs only. $25 daily fee/room. Designated rooms, service with restrictions, crate.
[icons]

AAA ◇◇◇ **Holiday Inn Express & Suites Des Moines Downtown** H
(515) 657-8181. **$129-$199.** 333 SW 11th St 50309. Jct W Martin Luther King Jr Pkwy, just s. Int corridors. **Pets:** Accepted.
[icons]

AAA ◇◇◇ **Hyatt Place-Des Moines** H
(515) 282-5555. **$79-$799.** 418 6th Ave 50309. Downtown. Int corridors. **Pets:** Medium, dogs only. $75 one-time fee/room. Service with restrictions, supervision.
[icons]

◇◇ **Quality Inn & Suites** H
(515) 287-3434. **$95-$200.** 5231 Fleur Dr 50321. Opposite the airport. Int corridors. **Pets:** Accepted.
[icons]

◇◇◇ **Residence Inn by Marriott Des Moines Downtown** H
(515) 288-4500. **$67-$365.** 100 SW Water St 50309. Jct Court Ave, just s; downtown. Int corridors. **Pets:** Large, other species. $100 one-time fee/room. Service with restrictions, crate.
[icons]

DE WITT

◇◇ **De Witt Super 8** H
(563) 659-8888. **$55-$85.** 918 Westwood Dr 52742. On US 30, just e of jct US 30 and 61. Int corridors. **Pets:** Medium. $5 daily fee/pet. Service with restrictions, supervision.
[icons]

DUBUQUE

AAA ◇◇◇ **Best Western Plus Dubuque Hotel & Conference Center** H 🐾
(563) 557-8000. **$101-$191.** 3100 Dodge St 52003. US 20, 2.3 mi w of jct US 52/61/151 and Mississippi Bridge. Int corridors. **Pets:** Large, other species. $15 daily fee/pet. Designated rooms, service with restrictions, supervision.
[icons]

AAA ◇◇◇ **Days Inn** H
(563) 583-3297. **$60-$85.** 1111 Dodge St 52003. US 20, 0.8 mi w of jct US 52/61/151 and Mississippi Bridge exit Hill St/Bryant St. Ext corridors. **Pets:** Medium. $15 one-time fee/pet. Designated rooms, service with restrictions, crate.
[icons]

◇◇◇ **Holiday Inn Dubuque/Galena** H
(563) 556-2000. **$99-$179, 3 day notice.** 450 Main St 52001. At Main and 4th sts; downtown. Int corridors. **Pets:** Accepted.
[icons]

◇◇ **Holiday Inn Express & Suites** H
(563) 556-4600. **$89-$189.** 2080 Holiday Dr 52002. Jct US 20 and SR 32, 1.5 mi n. Int corridors. **Pets:** Accepted.
[icons]

◇◇ **MainStay Suites** H
(563) 557-7829. **$62-$149.** 1275 Associates Dr 52002. Just n of jct US 20 and NW Arterial Rd; west side of town. Int corridors. **Pets:** Accepted.
[icons]

DYERSVILLE

◇◇ **Comfort Inn** H
(563) 875-7700. **$86-$199.** 527 16th Ave SE 52040. US 20 exit 294 (SR 136), just nw. Int corridors. **Pets:** Small. $20 daily fee/room. Designated rooms, service with restrictions, supervision.
[icons]

EMMETSBURG

◇◇ **Super 8** H
(712) 852-2667. **$60-$110.** 3501 Main St 50536. Jct US 18 and SR 4, 0.8 mi w. Int corridors. **Pets:** $10 daily fee/pet. Designated rooms, service with restrictions, supervision.
[icons]

ESTHERVILLE

◇◇ **Super 8** H
(712) 362-2400. **$56-$90.** 1919 Central Ave 51334. Jct SR 4 and 9, 1 mi e. Int corridors. **Pets:** Accepted.
[icons]

EVANSDALE

◇◇ **Days Inn** H
(319) 235-1111. **$79-$105.** 450 Evansdale Dr 50707. I-380/US 20 exit 68, just n. Int corridors. **Pets:** Accepted.
[icons]

FAIRFIELD

AAA ◇◇ **Best Western Fairfield Inn** H
(641) 472-2200. **$100-$110.** 2200 W Burlington Ave 52556. On US 34, 1 mi w of jct SR 1. Int corridors. **Pets:** Small. $10 daily fee/room. Designated rooms, service with restrictions, supervision.
[icons]

AAA ◇◇ **Super 8** H
(641) 469-2000. **$65-$85.** 3001 W Burlington Ave 52556. On US 34, 1.5 mi w of jct SR 1. Int corridors. **Pets:** Medium, dogs only. $100 deposit/room, $25 daily fee/pet. Designated rooms, service with restrictions, supervision.
[icons]

FORT DODGE

◇◇ **AmericInn Lodge & Suites of Fort Dodge** H
(515) 576-2100. **Call for rates.** 100 Kenyon Rd 50501. 3 mi n of jct US 20 and 169. Int corridors. **Pets:** Accepted.
[icons]

AAA ◇◇ **Best Western Starlite Village** H
(515) 573-7177. **$88-$199.** 1518 3rd Ave NW 50501. Jct US 169 and SR 7. Ext/int corridors. **Pets:** Accepted.
[icons]

◇◇ **Comfort Inn** H
(515) 573-5000. **$85-$170.** 2938 5th Ave S 50501. US 20 exit 124 (Coalville), 3.5 mi n on CR P59, then 1.4 mi w on 5th Ave and Business Rt US 20. Int corridors. **Pets:** Accepted.
[icons]

◇◇◇ **Holiday Inn Express & Suites** H
(515) 576-3313. **$125-$250.** 300 S 31st St 50501. US 20 exit 124 (Coalville), 3.5 mi n on CR P59, then 1.2 mi w on 5th Ave and Business Rt US 20. Int corridors. **Pets:** Accepted.
[icons]

GRINNELL

AAA ◇◇◇ **Best Western Pioneer Inn & Suites** H
(641) 236-6116. **$120-$180.** 2210 West St S 50112. I-80 exit 182, just n. Int corridors. **Pets:** Medium. $20 daily fee/pet. Designated rooms, service with restrictions, supervision.
[icons]

◇◇◇ **Comfort Inn & Suites** H
(641) 236-5236. **$95-$220.** 1630 West St S 50112. I-80 exit 182, 0.7 mi n. Int corridors. **Pets:** Accepted.
[icons]

◆◆ **Country Inn & Suites By Carlson** H
(641) 236-9600. **$85-$195.** 1710 West St S 50112. I-80 exit 182, 0.7 mi n. Int corridors. **Pets:** Small. $15 daily fee/room. Designated rooms, service with restrictions, supervision. 🍴 🏊 📶 ✕ 🛗 💻

GRUNDY CENTER
◆◆ **AmericInn Motel & Suites of Grundy Center** H
(319) 824-5272. **$85-$112.** 2101 Commerce Dr 50638. Jct SR 175 and 14, 1.2 mi w; west side of town. Int corridors. **Pets:** $25 one-time fee/room. Designated rooms, service with restrictions, supervision. 🏊 📶 ✕ 🛗 💻

HAMPTON
◆◆ **AmericInn Lodge & Suites of Hampton** H
(641) 456-5559. **Call for rates.** 702 Central Ave W 50441. On SR 3 (Central Ave W), 0.7 mi w of jct US 65 and SR 3. Int corridors. **Pets:** $15 daily fee/pet. Designated rooms, service with restrictions, supervision. ♿ 🏊 📶 🛗 💻

IDA GROVE
◆◆ **Super 8** H
(712) 364-3988. **$66-$100.** 90 E Hwy 175 51445. Just n of SR 175/US 59. Int corridors. **Pets:** Accepted. ♿ 🏊 📶 ✕ 🛗 💻

INDEPENDENCE
◆◆ **Super 8** H
(319) 334-7041. **$70-$90.** 2000 1st St W 50644. US 20 exit 252, 1.4 mi n. Int corridors. **Pets:** Small. $25 daily fee/pet. Service with restrictions. ♿ 📶 🛗 💻

IOWA CITY
◆◆◆ ◆◆◆ **hotelVetro conference center** H
(319) 337-4961. **$139-$499.** 201 S Linn St 52240. I-80 exit 244, s on Dubuque St, e on Washington St, then just s. Int corridors.
Pets: Accepted. [SAVE] ♿ 🏊 📶 ✕ 🛗 💻

◆◆◆ ◆◆◆ **Sheraton Iowa City Hotel** H
(319) 337-4058. **$79-$399.** 210 S Dubuque St 52240. Jct Dubuque and Burlington sts (SR 1); downtown. Int corridors. **Pets:** Accepted.
[SAVE] 🍴 ♿ 🏊 📶 ✕ 🛗 💻

IOWA FALLS
◆◆ **Iowa Falls Super 8** H
(641) 648-4618. **$64-$70.** 839 S Oak St 50126. Jct US 65 and Washington Ave, 1 mi s; US 20 exit 168, 3.8 mi n. Int corridors. **Pets:** Other species. $15 one-time fee/pet. Service with restrictions, crate.
🏊 📶 🛗 💻

LE CLAIRE
◆◆ **Comfort Inn & Suites-Riverview** H 🐾
(563) 289-4747. **$114-$269.** 902 Mississippi View Ct 52753. I-80 exit 306 (US 67), 0.5 mi n to Eagle Ridge Rd, then just sw. Int corridors. **Pets:** Medium. $10 daily fee/pet. Service with restrictions, crate.
♿ 🏊 📶 ✕ 🛗 💻

◆◆◆ **Holiday Inn Express** H
(563) 289-9978. **$140-$280.** 1201 Canal Shore Dr SW 52753. I-80 exit 306 (US 67), just n. Int corridors. **Pets:** Medium. $35 one-time fee/room. Service with restrictions, supervision.
♿ 🏊 📶 ✕ 🛗 💻

◆◆ **Super 8 of Le Claire** H
(563) 289-5888. **$73-$116.** 1552 Welcome Center Dr 52753. I-80 exit 306 (US 67), 0.5 mi n to Eagle Ridge Rd, then just sw to Mississippi View Ct. Int corridors. **Pets:** Medium. $10 daily fee/pet. Service with restrictions. ♿ 📶 ✕ 🛗 💻

MARION
◆◆ **Microtel Inn & Suites by Wyndham** H
(319) 373-7400. **$61-$86.** 5500 Dyer Ave 52302. Jct US 151 and SR 13. Int corridors. **Pets:** Accepted. ♿ 📶 ✕ 🛗 💻

MARQUETTE
◆◆ **Cobblestone Inn & Suites** H
(563) 873-8900. **Call for rates.** 100 North St 52158. Jct US 18 and SR 76, just n. Int corridors. **Pets:** Accepted. ♿ 📶 ✕ 🛗 💻

◆ **The Frontier Motel** M
(563) 873-3497. **Call for rates.** 101 S 1st St 52158. Just s of jct US 18 and SR 76; between Mississippi River Bridge and casino. Ext corridors. **Pets:** Accepted. 🍴 🏊 📶 🛗 💻

MARSHALLTOWN
◆◆ **Comfort Inn** H
(641) 752-6000. **$105-$135.** 2613 S Center St 50158. 0.5 mi n of jct US 30 and SR 14. Int corridors. **Pets:** Accepted.
🏊 📶 ✕ 🛗 💻

MASON CITY
◆◆ **Mason City Super 8** H
(641) 423-8855. **$70-$101.** 3010 4th St SW 50401. I-35 exit 194 (SR 122), 5.3 mi e. Int corridors. **Pets:** Accepted. ♿ 🏊 📶 🛗 💻

◆◆ **Quality Inn & Suites** H
(641) 423-4444. **$105-$170.** 410 5th St SW 50401. Jct US 65 and SR 122, 0.3 mi w. Int corridors. **Pets:** $25 daily fee/pet. Service with restrictions, crate. 🏊 📶 ✕ 🛗 💻

MISSOURI VALLEY
◆◆ **Oak Tree Inn** H
(712) 642-3000. **Call for rates.** 128 S Willow Rd 51555. I-29 exit 75, 0.4 mi ne. Int corridors. **Pets:** Medium. $10 daily fee/pet. Service with restrictions, supervision. ♿ 📶 ✕ 🛗 💻

MOUNT PLEASANT
◆◆◆ ◆◆ **Best Western Mt. Pleasant Inn** H
(319) 385-2102. **$70-$100.** 810 N Grand Ave 52641. US 218 exit 45, 0.6 mi s. Int corridors. **Pets:** Accepted.
[SAVE] 🏊 ✕ 📶 ✕ 🛗 💻

◆◆ **Super 8** H
(319) 385-8888. **$57-$74.** 1000 N Grand Ave 52641. US 218 exit 45, 0.6 mi s. Int corridors. **Pets:** Accepted. ♿ 📶 ✕ 🛗 💻

MOUNT VERNON
◆◆ **Sleep Inn & Suites** H
(319) 895-0055. **$85-$155.** 310 Virgil Ave 52314. Jct US 30 and SR 1, just se. Int corridors. **Pets:** Large, dogs only. $25 daily fee/pet. Designated rooms, service with restrictions, supervision.
♿ 🏊 📶 ✕ 🛗 💻

MUSCATINE
◆◆ **AmericInn Lodge & Suites of Muscatine** H
(563) 263-0880. **Call for rates.** 3115 Hwy 61 N 52761. Jct US 61 and SR 38, just n. Int corridors. **Pets:** Accepted.
♿ 🏊 📶 ✕ 🛗 💻

◆◆◆ ◆◆ **Best Western Pearl City Inn** H
(563) 264-5566. **$110-$155.** 305 Cleveland St 52761. Jct US 61 and SR 38. Int corridors. **Pets:** Accepted.
[SAVE] ♿ 🏊 📶 ✕ 🛗 💻

NEW HAMPTON

▼▼ Super 8-New Hampton 🄷

(641) 394-3838. **$65-$110.** 825 S Linn Ave 50659. US 63 exit 201, 1.5 mi ne on US 63 business route. Int corridors. **Pets:** Accepted.

🍴 ᴄᴍ 🏊 🛜 ✖ 🔌 🖥️

NEWTON

▼▼▼ AmericInn Lodge & Suites of Newton 🄷

(641) 791-1160. **Call for rates.** 4401 S 22nd Ave E 50208. I-80 exit 168, just sw. Int corridors. **Pets:** Accepted.

🍴 ᴄᴍ 🏊 🛜 ✖ 🔌 🖥️

⍟ ▼▼▼ Best Western Holiday Manor 🄷

(641) 792-3333. **$89-$139.** 208 W 4th St N 50208. Downtown. Int corridors. **Pets:** Accepted. 🆂🅰🆅🅴 ᴄᴍ 🏊 🛜 ✖ 🔌 🖥️

NORTH LIBERTY

▼▼ Sleep Inn & Suites 🄷

(319) 665-2700. **$90-$200.** 485 Madison Ave N 52317. I-380 exit 4, just se. Int corridors. **Pets:** Medium, other species. $13 daily fee/room. Service with restrictions, supervision. 🍴 ᴄᴍ 🏊 🛜 ✖ 🔌 🖥️

NORTHWOOD

▼▼▼▼ Country Inn & Suites By Carlson 🄷

(641) 323-7000. **$109-$299, 14 day notice.** 711 Diamond Jo Ln 50459. I-35 exit 214, just nw. Int corridors. **Pets:** Medium, other species. $25 one-time fee/room. Service with restrictions, supervision.

ᴄᴍ 🏊 🛜 ✖ 🔌 🖥️

▼▼▼ Holiday Inn Express & Suites 🄷

(641) 323-7500. **$109-$239.** 4712 Wheelerwood Rd 50459. I-35 exit 214, just nw. Int corridors. **Pets:** Other species. $25 one-time fee/room. Service with restrictions, supervision. ᴄᴍ 🏊 🛜 ✖ 🔌 🖥️

OELWEIN

▼▼ Super 8-Oelwein 🄼

(319) 283-2888. **$70-$90.** 210 10th St SE 50662. Jct SR 3 and 150, 1 mi s on SR 150; south end of downtown. Int corridors. **Pets:** Accepted.

🍴 ᴄᴍ 🛜 🔌 🖥️

OKOBOJI

▼▼ AmericInn Lodge & Suites of Okoboji 🄷

(712) 332-9000. **$99-$319, 7 day notice.** 1005 Brooks Park Dr 51355. Jct US 71 and SR 9, 2.5 mi s. Int corridors. **Pets:** Medium, dogs only. $200 deposit/room, $40 one-time fee/pet. Service with restrictions, supervision. ᴄᴍ 🏊 🛜 ✖ 🔌 🖥️

▼▼ The Inn at Okoboji Resort & Conference Center 🄷

(712) 332-2113. **Call for rates.** 3301 Lakeshore Dr 51355. Jct US 71 and Sanborn Ave, 1 mi w. Ext corridors. **Pets:** Other species. $25 one-time fee/pet. Designated rooms, service with restrictions, crate.

🍴 🏊 ✖ 🛜 ✖ 🔌 🖥️

OSCEOLA

⍟ ▼▼▼ Americas Best Value Inn 🄼

(641) 342-2123. **$68-$96.** 1520 Jeffreys Dr 50213. I-35 exit 33 (Osceola/US 34), just e. Int corridors. **Pets:** Very small, dogs only. Designated rooms, service with restrictions, supervision.

🆂🅰🆅🅴 🛜 🔌 🖥️

▼▼ AmericInn Lodge & Suites of Osceola 🄷

(641) 342-9400. **Call for rates.** 111 Ariel Cir 50213. I-35 exit 33 (Osceola/US 34), just w. Int corridors. **Pets:** Accepted.

🏊 🛜 ✖ 🔌 🖥️

OSKALOOSA

▼▼ Comfort Inn Oskaloosa 🄷

(641) 676-6000. **Call for rates.** 2401 A Ave W 52577. SR 163 exit 57 (SR 92), just e. Int corridors. **Pets:** Accepted.

🍴 🏊 🛜 ✖ 🔌 🖥️

OTTUMWA

▼▼ AmericInn of Ottumwa 🄷

(641) 684-8222. **Call for rates.** 222 W 2nd St 52501. Just se of US 63 and 4th St W; downtown. Int corridors. **Pets:** Medium, dogs only. $20 one-time fee/room. Designated rooms, service with restrictions, supervision. ᴄᴍ 🏊 ✖ 🔌 🖥️

▼▼ Quality Inn & Suites 🄷

(641) 682-8526. **$74-$214.** 125 W Joseph Ave 52501. Jct US 34, 2 mi n on US 63. Int corridors. **Pets:** Medium, other species. $15 daily fee/pet. Designated rooms, service with restrictions, supervision.

🏊 🛜 ✖ 🔌 🖥️

PELLA

⍟ ▼▼ Super 8 🄷

(641) 628-8181. **$70-$128.** 105 E Oskaloosa St 50219. SR 163 exit 42, 1 mi n, then 0.5 mi e. Int corridors. **Pets:** Accepted.

🆂🅰🆅🅴 ᴄᴍ 🛜 ✖ 🔌 🖥️

PERCIVAL

⍟ ▼▼▼ Super 8-Percival/Nebraska City 🄷

(712) 382-2828. **$62-$70.** 2103 249th St 51648. I-29 exit 10 (SR 2), just w. Int corridors. **Pets:** Dogs only. $10 one-time fee/room. Service with restrictions, supervision. 🆂🅰🆅🅴 🍴 🛜 ✖ 🔌 🖥️

PERRY

▼▼▼▼ Hotel Pattee 🄷

(515) 465-3511. **$139-$159.** 1112 Willis Ave 50220. I-80/35 exit 127 (SR 141), nw to Perry, right at First St, then just n. Int corridors. **Pets:** Very small, dogs only. $35 one-time fee/room. Designated rooms, service with restrictions, crate. 🍴 ᴄᴍ ✖ 🛜 ✖ 🔌 🖥️

PLEASANT HILL

▼▼ Sleep Inn & Suites 🄷 🐾

(515) 299-9922. **$109-$250.** 5850 Morning Star Ct 50327. US 65 exit 79 (SR 163/E University Ave), just e. Int corridors. **Pets:** Other species. $15 daily fee/pet. Supervision. 🍴 ᴄᴍ 🏊 🛜 ✖ 🔌 🖥️

RIVERSIDE

▼▼▼ Riverside Casino & Golf Resort 🄷

(319) 648-1234. **$80-$250.** 3184 Hwy 22 52327. I-218 exit 80, 1.5 mi ne. Int corridors. **Pets:** Accepted. 🍴 ᴄᴍ 🏊 ✖ 🛜 🔌 🖥️

SHELDON

▼▼▼▼ Holiday Inn Express & Suites Sheldon 🄷

(712) 324-3000. **Call for rates.** 201 34th Ave 51201. SR 60 exit 34, just sw. Int corridors. **Pets:** Accepted. ᴄᴍ 🏊 🛜 ✖ 🔌 🖥️

▼▼ Super 8 🄼

(712) 324-8400. **$82-$120.** 210 N 2nd Ave 51201. SR 60 exit 34, 2 mi w on US 18, then just n on Business Rt SR 60. Int corridors. **Pets:** Large. $10 daily fee/pet. Designated rooms, service with restrictions, supervision. ᴄᴍ 🏊 🔌 🖥️

SIGOURNEY

▼▼ Belva Deer Inn 🄷

(641) 622-3200. **Call for rates.** 21638 Hwy 92 52591. Jct SR 149 and 92, 1.1 mi e. Int corridors. **Pets:** Accepted. ᴄᴍ 🛜 ✖ 🔌 🖥️

SIOUX CENTER

▼▼ Econo Lodge Ⓜ

(712) 722-4000. **$85-$131.** 86 9th St Cir NE 51250. On US 75, 1 mi n of jct SR 840; north side of town. Ext/int corridors. **Pets:** Accepted.
🔥 📶 ✖ 📦 💻

SIOUX CITY

▼▼ AmericInn Lodge & Suites of Sioux City Ⓗ

(712) 255-1800. **$119.** 4230 S Lewis Blvd 51106. I-29 exit 143, just e. Int corridors. **Pets:** Accepted. 🏊 📶 ✖ 📦 💻

▼▼ Fairfield Inn by Marriott Ⓗ

(712) 276-5600. **$91-$162.** 4716 Southern Hills Dr 51106. I-29 exit 144A, 1 mi e on US 20, then just s. Int corridors. **Pets:** Accepted.
🔥 🏊 📶 ✖ 📦 💻

▼▼ Hilton Garden Inn-Sioux City Riverfront Ⓗ

(712) 255-4200. **$119-$179.** 1132 Larsen Park Rd 51103. I-29 exit 149, just sw. Int corridors. **Pets:** $30 one-time fee/room. Designated rooms, service with restrictions, supervision.
🍴 🔥 🏊 ✖ 📶 ✖ 📦 💻

▼▼ Stoney Creek Hotel & Conference Center Ⓗ

(712) 234-1100. **Call for rates.** 300 3rd St 51101. I-29 exit 147B (Tyson Event Center), 0.3 mi w on US 20 (Gordon Dr), then just n. Int corridors. **Pets:** Accepted. 🔥 🏊 📶 ✖ 📦 💻

▼▼ Super 8 Singing Hills Ⓜ

(712) 255-8888. **$75-$90.** 2530 Singing Hills Blvd 51111. I-29 exit 143, just w. Int corridors. **Pets:** Accepted. 🔥 📶 📦 💻

SPENCER

▼▼ AmericInn Hotel & Suites of Spencer Ⓗ

(712) 262-7525. **Call for rates.** 1005 13th St SW 51301. On US 71, 1 mi w of southern jct US 18 and 71. Int corridors. **Pets:** Accepted.
🍴 🔥 🏊 📶 ✖ 📦 💻

▼▼ Days Inn Spencer Ⓗ

(712) 580-4077. **$75-$93.** 10 11th St SE 51301. Jct US 71 and 11th St SW, then just 1 mi e. Int corridors. **Pets:** Other species. $10 daily fee/pet. Designated rooms, service with restrictions, supervision.
🍴 🔥 📶 ✖ 📦 💻

SPIRIT LAKE

▼▼ Spirit Lake Super 8 Ⓗ

(712) 336-4901. **$80-$165.** 2203 Circle Dr W 51360. Jct US 71 and SR 9. Int corridors. **Pets:** Accepted. 🔥 📶 📦 💻

STORM LAKE

▼▼▼ King's Pointe Waterpark Resort Ⓗ

(712) 213-4500. **Call for rates.** 1520 E Lakeshore Dr 50588. Jct Business Rt US 71 and SR 7, just n. Int corridors. **Pets:** Accepted.
🍴 🔥 🏊 ✖ 📶 ✖ 📦 💻

STORY CITY

▼▼ Comfort Inn Ⓗ

(515) 733-6363. **$100-$250.** 425 Timberland Dr 50248. I-35 exit 124, just sw. Int corridors. **Pets:** Accepted. 🔥 🏊 📶 📦 💻

STUART

▼▼ Americas Best Value Inn & Suites Ⓗ

(515) 523-2888. **Call for rates.** 203 SE 7th St 50250. I-80 exit 93, just ne. Int corridors. **Pets:** Accepted. 🍴 🔥 🏊 📶 📦 💻

URBANDALE

▼▼▼ Holiday Inn Hotel & Suites Northwest Ⓗ

(515) 278-4755. **Call for rates.** 4800 Merle Hay Rd 50322. I-35/80 exit 131 (Merle Hay Rd), just s. Int corridors. **Pets:** Accepted.
🍴 🔥 🏊 📶 ✖ 📦 💻

▼▼ Microtel Inn & Suites by Wyndham Urbandale/Des Moines Ⓗ

(515) 727-5424. **$59-$90.** 8711 Plum Dr 50322. I-35/80 exit 129 (86th St), just sw. Int corridors. **Pets:** $10 daily fee/pet. Designated rooms, service with restrictions, crate. 📶 ✖ 📦 💻

▼▼▼ Ramada Tropics Resort/Conference Center Des Moines Ⓗ

(515) 278-0271. **$101-$250.** 5000 Merle Hay Rd 50322. I-35/80 exit 131 (Merle Hay Rd), just s. Int corridors. **Pets:** Other species. $10 daily fee/pet. Designated rooms, service with restrictions, crate.
🍴 🏊 ✖ 📶 ✖ 📦 💻

▼▼ Sleep Inn Ⓗ

(515) 270-2424. **$100-$190.** 11211 Hickman Rd 50322. I-35/80 exit 125 (Hickman Rd), just ne. Int corridors. **Pets:** Accepted.
🔥 🏊 📶 📦 💻

▼▼▼ TownePlace Suites by Marriott Des Moines/Urbandale Ⓗ

(515) 727-4066. **$95-$208.** 8800 Northpark Dr 50131. I-35/80 exit 129 (86th St), just nw. Int corridors. **Pets:** Large, dogs only. $100 one-time fee/room. Service with restrictions, supervision.
🏊 📶 ✖ 📦 💻

VINTON

▼▼ Cobblestone Inn & Suites Ⓗ

(319) 472-2220. **Call for rates.** 1202 W 11th St 52349. Jct US 218, just sw. Int corridors. **Pets:** Accepted. 🔥 📶 ✖ 📦 💻

WALCOTT

▼▼ Davenport/Walcott Comfort Inn Ⓗ

(563) 284-9000. **$104-$250.** 501 W Walker St 52773. I-80 exit 284, just nw. Int corridors. **Pets:** Accepted. 🔥 🏊 📶 💻

WALNUT

▼▼ Super 8 Ⓗ

(712) 784-2221. **$70-$130.** 2109 Antique City Dr 51577. I-80 exit 46, just n. Int corridors. **Pets:** Accepted. 🔥 🏊 📶 📦 💻

WATERLOO

▼▼ Baymont Inn & Suites Waterloo Ⓗ

(319) 234-7411. **$65-$84.** 1945 LaPorte Rd 50702. I-380 exit 72 (E San Marnan Dr), just sw. Int corridors. **Pets:** Other species. $15 one-time fee/room. Designated rooms, supervision. 🏊 📶 📦 💻

▼▼ Days Inn & Suites Ⓗ

(319) 235-4461. **$79-$115.** 1809 LaPorte Rd 50702. I-380 exit 72 (E San Marnan Dr), just nw. Int corridors. **Pets:** Accepted.
🏊 📶 ✖ 📦 💻

▼▼ Howard Johnson Ⓗ

(319) 232-7467. **$79-$109.** 3052 Marnie Ave 50701. 1 mi n of jct US 20 and 63 exit 227. Int corridors. **Pets:** Accepted.
🏊 📶 ✖ 📦 💻

WAUKON

▼▼ Stoney Creek Inn Ⓗ

(563) 568-2220. **Call for rates.** 407 Rossville Rd 52172. Jct SR 9 and 76, 1.7 mi n. Int corridors. **Pets:** Accepted. 📶 📦 💻

WAVERLY

▼▼ Comfort Inn Ⓗ

(319) 352-0399. **$86-$210.** 404 29th Ave SW 50677. US 218 exit 198, 0.7 mi n. Int corridors. **Pets:** Accepted.
🔥 🏊 ✖ 📶 ✖ 📦 💻

▼▼ Super 8 Waverly Ⓗ

(319) 352-0888. **$66-$110.** 301 13th Ave SW 50677. US 218 exit 198, 1.4 mi n. Int corridors. **Pets:** Accepted. 🔥 📶 📦 💻

WEBSTER CITY

AmericInn Motel & Suites of Webster City H
(515) 832-3999. **Call for rates.** 411 Closz Dr 50595. Just s of jct US 20 and SR 17. Int corridors. **Pets:** Accepted.

WEST DES MOINES

Candlewood Suites-West Des Moines H
(515) 221-0001. **Call for rates.** 7625 Office Plaza Dr N 50266. I-80 exit 121 (Jordan Creek Pkwy), just sw. Int corridors. **Pets:** Accepted.

Drury Inn & Suites H
(515) 457-9500. **$110-$180.** 5505 Mills Civic Pkwy 50266. I-35 exit 70 (Mills Civic Pkwy), just w. Int corridors. **Pets:** Accepted.

Homewood Suites by Hilton West Des Moines/ SW-Mall Area H
(515) 218-7500. **Call for rates.** 6220 Stagecoach Dr 50266. I-35 exit 70 (Mills Civic Pkwy), just w. Int corridors. **Pets:** Accepted.

Residence Inn by Marriott-Des Moines West H
(515) 267-0338. **$94-$229.** 160 S Jordan Creek Pkwy 50266. I-35 exit 70 (Mills Civic Pkwy), 1.2 mi w to 68th St, then just nw. Int corridors. **Pets:** Accepted.

Staybridge Suites H
(515) 223-0000. **$129-$229.** 6905 Lake Dr 50266. I-80 exit 121 (Jordan Creek Pkwy), just ne. Int corridors. **Pets:** Medium, other species. $35 one-time fee/room. Service with restrictions, supervision.

TownePlace Suites Des Moines West/Jordan Creek H ❀
(515) 223-8015. **$82-$240.** 125 S 68th St 50266. I-35 exit 70 (Mills Civic Pkwy), 1.2 mi w to 68th St, then just nw. Int corridors. **Pets:** Medium. $50 one-time fee/pet. Service with restrictions, crate.

West Des Moines Marriott H
(515) 267-1500. **$82-$250.** 1250 Jordan Creek Pkwy 50266. I-80 exit 121 (Jordan Creek Pkwy), just sw. Int corridors. **Pets:** Accepted.

WILLIAMS

Super 8 Williams M
(515) 854-2281. **$79-$99.** 3086 220th St 50271. I-35 exit 144, just e. Int corridors. **Pets:** Accepted.

WILLIAMSBURG

Crest Country Inn M
(319) 668-1522. **$70-$90.** 340 W Evans St 52361. I-80 exit 220, just nw. Ext corridors. **Pets:** Dogs only. $15 daily fee/pet. Designated rooms, service with restrictions, supervision.

Ramada Williamsburg and Wasserbahn Waterpark H ❀
(319) 668-1175. **$81-$135.** 2211 U Ave 52361. I-80 exit 225 (US 151), just sw. Int corridors. **Pets:** Medium. $20 daily fee/room. Designated rooms, service with restrictions.

KANSAS

ABILENE

Holiday Inn Express Hotel & Suites H
(785) 263-4049. **Call for rates.** 110 E Lafayette Ave 67410. I-70 exit 275, just n. Int corridors. **Pets:** Accepted.

ANDOVER

Days Inn Andover M
(316) 733-8881. **$65-$70.** 222 W US Hwy 54 67002. 2.2 mi e of jct SR 96. Ext corridors. **Pets:** Medium. $10 daily fee/pet. Service with restrictions, crate.

Holiday Inn Express & Suites H
(316) 733-8833. **$79-$109.** 600 S Allen St 67002. 2.2 mi e of jct SR 96 and US 54. Int corridors. **Pets:** Other species. $10 daily fee/room. Service with restrictions, crate.

ARKANSAS CITY

Best Western Plus Patterson Park Inn H ❀
(620) 307-6767. **$99-$199.** 6100 Patterson Pkwy 67005. Just w of jct US 77. Int corridors. **Pets:** Medium. $50 deposit/room, $10 daily fee/pet. Designated rooms, supervision.

BURLINGTON

Country Haven Inn H
(620) 364-8260. **$69-$75.** 207 Cross St 66839. Just e of US 75; 1 mi n of center. Int corridors. **Pets:** Very small, dogs only. $50 deposit/pet. Designated rooms, service with restrictions, supervision.

CLAY CENTER

Cedar Court Motel M
(785) 632-2148. **$60-$85.** 905 Crawford St 67432. On US 24, just e of jct SR 15. Ext corridors. **Pets:** Medium, dogs only. $10 daily fee/pet. Designated rooms, service with restrictions, supervision.

COFFEYVILLE

Best Western Bricktown Lodge H
(620) 251-3700. **$98-$128.** 605 Northeast St 67337. 1 mi e of center. Int corridors. **Pets:** $20 daily fee/pet. Service with restrictions, crate.

Sleep Inn & Suites H
(620) 688-6400. **$100-$145.** 202 W 11th St 67337. Center. Int corridors. **Pets:** Accepted.

COLBY

Comfort Inn H
(785) 462-3833. **$100-$160.** 2225 S Range Ave 67701. I-70 exit 53 (SR 25), just s. Int corridors. **Pets:** Accepted.

Days Inn H
(785) 462-8691. **$77-$82.** 1925 S Range Ave 67701. I-70 exit 53 (SR 25), 0.3 mi n. Int corridors. **Pets:** Accepted.

Holiday Inn Express Hotel & Suites H ❀
(785) 462-8787. **Call for rates.** 645 W Willow St 67701. I-70 exit 53 (SR 25), just ne. Int corridors. **Pets:** Other species. $25 daily fee/room. Designated rooms, service with restrictions, supervision.

▼▼▼▼ **Sleep Inn & Suites** 🅷

(785) 460-0310. **$110-$140.** 2075 Sewell Ave 67701. I-70 exit 53 (SR 25), just ne. Int corridors. **Pets:** Accepted.
🍽 🏃ᴹ 🔜 🛜 ✖ 🔋 💻

▼▼ **Super 8** 🅷

(785) 462-8248. **$65-$70.** 1040 Zelfer Ave 67701. I-70 exit 53 (SR 25), 0.3 mi n, then just w. Int corridors. **Pets:** Medium. $15 daily fee/pet. Designated rooms, service with restrictions, supervision. 🛜 🔋 💻

COTTONWOOD FALLS *(Restaurants p. 613)*

▼▼▼▼ **Grand Central Hotel** 🆑 ❀

(620) 273-6763. **$160-$190.** 215 Broadway 66845. US 177, just w on Main St, then just s; center of downtown. Int corridors. **Pets:** Designated rooms, no service, supervision. [SAVE] 🍽 🛜 ✖ 💻

DERBY

▼▼▼▼ **Hampton Inn Derby** 🅷

(316) 425-7900. **$109-$139.** 1701 Cambridge St 67037. Just sw of jct Rock Rd. Int corridors. **Pets:** Small, dogs only. $10 daily fee/room. Service with restrictions, supervision. 🏃ᴹ 🔜 🛜 ✖ 🔋 💻

DODGE CITY

▨▨ ▼▼▼▼ **Best Western North Edge Inn** 🅷

(620) 371-6441. **$94-$159.** 404 W Frontview 67801. Jct US 50 and Central Ave, just n, just w. Int corridors. **Pets:** Accepted.
[SAVE] 🍽 🏃ᴹ 🛜 ✖ 🔋 💻

▨▨ ▼▼▼▼ **Best Western Plus Country Inn & Suites** 🅷

(620) 225-7378. **$99-$189.** 506 N 14th Ave 67801. Just n of jct US 50 business route. Ext/int corridors. **Pets:** Accepted.
[SAVE] 🏃ᴹ 🔜 🛜 ✖ 🔋 💻

▼▼ **Super 8** 🅷

(620) 225-3924. **$75-$76.** 1708 W Wyatt Earp Blvd 67801. 1.2 mi w on US 50 business route. Int corridors. **Pets:** Dogs only. $25 one-time fee/room. Designated rooms, service with restrictions, supervision.
🔜 🛜 🔋 💻

▼▼▼▼ **TownePlace Suites by Marriott Dodge City** 🅷

(620) 371-7171. **$76-$105.** 2800 W Wyatt Earp Blvd 67801. 1.7 mi w on US 50 business route. Int corridors. **Pets:** Accepted.
🍽 🛜 ✖ 🔋 💻

EL DORADO

▨▨ ▼▼▼▼ **Red Coach Inn** 🅷

(316) 321-6900. **$79-$82.** 2525 W Central Ave 67042. I-35 exit 71, 0.5 mi e. Ext corridors. **Pets:** Very small, dogs only. $15 daily fee/pet. Designated rooms, service with restrictions, supervision.
[SAVE] 🔜 🛜 🔋 💻

▼▼▼ **Super 8-El Dorado** Ⓜ

(316) 321-4888. **$68-$69.** 2530 W Central Ave 67042. I-35 exit 71, 0.5 mi e. Int corridors. **Pets:** Accepted. 🛜 🔋 💻

ELLIS

▼▼▼▼ **Days Inn** 🅷

(785) 726-2511. **$75-$85.** 205 N Washington St 67637. I-70 exit 145, just s. Int corridors. **Pets:** Accepted. 🔜 🛜 ✖ 🔋 💻

EMPORIA

▨▨ ▼▼▼▼ **Best Western Hospitality House** 🅷

(620) 342-7587. **$97-$140.** 3021 W US Hwy 50 66801. I-35 exit 127A, just s to US 50, follow roundabout directions, then 0.5 mi e. Ext/int corridors. **Pets:** Accepted. [SAVE] 🍽 🔜 🛜 ✖ 🔋 💻

▼▼ **Candlewood Suites** 🅷

(620) 343-7756. **Call for rates.** 2602 Candlewood Dr 66801. I-35 exit 128 (Industrial St), just n, then just e. Int corridors. **Pets:** Accepted.
🏃ᴹ 🛜 ✖ 🔋 💻

▼▼ **Super 8** 🅷

(620) 342-7567. **$62-$105.** 2913 W US Hwy 50 66801. I-35 exit 127A, just s to US 50, follow roundabout directions, then 0.7 mi e. Int corridors. **Pets:** Small. $10 daily fee/pet. Designated rooms, service with restrictions, supervision. 🛜 ✖ 🔋 💻

FORT SCOTT

▼▼▼▼ **Lyons' Twin Mansions B & B Hotel** 🆑

(620) 223-3644. **$109-$225, 14 day notice.** 742 S National Ave 66701. Jct US 69 and 54 E, 0.3 mi w on Wall St, 0.6 mi s. Ext/int corridors. **Pets:** Accepted. 🍽 🛜 ✖ ⓩ 🔋 💻

GARDEN CITY

▨▨ ▼▼▼ **AmericInn Lodge & Suites of Garden City** 🅷

(620) 272-9860. **Call for rates.** 3020 E Kansas Ave 67846. Jct US 50, 83 and SR 156. Int corridors. **Pets:** Accepted.
[SAVE] 🏃ᴹ 🔜 🛜 ✖ 🔋 💻

▨▨ ▼▼▼ **Clarion Inn & Conference Center** 🅷

(620) 275-7471. **$100-$200.** 1911 E Kansas Ave 67846. 0.5 mi w of US 50 and 83 Bypass, on SR 156. Int corridors. **Pets:** Accepted.
[SAVE] 🍽 🔜 🛜 ✖ 🔋 💻

▼▼▼ **Comfort Inn** 🅷

(620) 275-5800. **$80-$120.** 2608 E Kansas Ave 67846. Jct US 50, 83 and SR 156. Int corridors. **Pets:** Accepted.
🍽 🏃ᴹ 🔜 ✖ 🛜 ✖ 🔋 💻

▼▼▼▼ **Holiday Inn Express Hotel & Suites** 🅷

(620) 275-5900. **Call for rates.** 2502 E Kansas Ave 67846. Jct US 50, 83 and SR 156. Int corridors. **Pets:** Accepted.
🍽 🏃ᴹ 🔜 🛜 ✖ 🔋 💻

▼▼▼▼ **TownePlace Suites by Marriott Garden City** 🅷

(620) 805-6717. **$79-$117.** 3510 E Kansas Ave 67846. Jct US 50, 83 and SR 156, 0.8 mi ne. Int corridors. **Pets:** Medium, other species. $50 one-time fee/room. Service with restrictions.
🍽 🏃ᴹ 🛜 ✖ 🔋 💻

GOODLAND

▨▨ ▼▼▼ **Holiday Inn Express Hotel & Suites** 🅷

(785) 890-9060. **Call for rates.** 2631 Enterprise Rd 67735. I-70 exit 17 (SR 27), just s. Int corridors. **Pets:** Accepted.
[SAVE] 🎟 🍽 🏃ᴹ 🔜 🛜 ✖ 🔋 💻

GREAT BEND

▨▨ ▼▼▼ **Best Western Angus Inn** 🅷 ❀

(620) 792-3541. **$85-$95.** 2920 10th St 67530. 0.8 mi w on US 56 and SR 96/156. Ext/int corridors. **Pets:** Other species. $10 daily fee/pet. Designated rooms, service with restrictions, crate.
[SAVE] 🍽 🏃ᴹ 🔜 ✖ 🛜 ✖ 🔋 💻

▼▼▼▼ **Holiday Inn Express & Suites** 🅷

(620) 603-6565. **Call for rates.** 3821 10th St 67530. 1.1 mi w on US 56 and SR 96/156. Int corridors. **Pets:** Other species. $25 one-time fee/room. Designated rooms, service with restrictions, crate.
🍽 🏃ᴹ 🛜 ✖ 🔋 💻

GREENSBURG

▨▨ ▼▼▼ **Best Western Plus Night Watchman Inn & Suites** 🅷

(620) 723-2244. **$109-$112.** 515 W Kansas Ave 67054. Just e of jct US 54 and 183. Int corridors. **Pets:** Other species. $25 deposit/pet. Service with restrictions, supervision. [SAVE] 🔜 🛜 ✖ 🔋 💻

HAYS

▼▼ Comfort Inn & Suites [H]
(785) 625-9322. $109-$154. 1001 E 41st St 67601. I-70 exit 159 (US 183), just n. Int corridors. Pets: Medium, dogs only. $15 daily fee/pet. Designated rooms, service with restrictions, supervision.

🏊 🛰 ⊠ 🛢 💻

HAYSVILLE

▼▼▼ Sleep Inn & Suites [H]
(316) 425-6077. $90-$180. 651 E 71 St S 67060. I-35 exit 39, just w. Int corridors. Pets: $10 daily fee/pet. Service with restrictions, crate.

🍴 🛰 ⊠ 🛢 💻

HERINGTON

▼▼ Herington Inn & Suites [H]
(785) 258-3300. $75-$92. 565 Hwy 77 67449. US 77, just w. Int corridors. Pets: Accepted. &M 🛰 ⊠ 🛢 💻

HESSTON

▼▼ AmericInn Lodge & Suites of Hesston [H]
(620) 327-2053. Call for rates. 2 Leonard Ct 67062. I-135 exit 40, just e. Int corridors. Pets: Accepted. 🏊 🛰 ⊠ 🛢 💻

HIAWATHA

AAA⁀ ▼▼▼ Best Western Plus Hiawatha Hotel [H]
(785) 740-7000. $95-$106. 119 E Lodge Rd 66434. Jct US 73 and 36, just ne. Int corridors. Pets: Dogs only. $100 deposit/room, $20 daily fee/room. Service with restrictions, crate.

SAVE 🍴 &M 🛰 ⊠ 🛢 💻

HILLSBORO

▼▼ Country Haven Inn [H]
(620) 947-2929. $71-$73. 804 Western Heights Cir 67063. On US 56; center. Int corridors. Pets: Accepted. 🍴 &M 🛰 ⊠ 🛢 💻

HUTCHINSON

▼▼▼ Comfort Inn & Suites [H]
(620) 669-5200. $90-$190. 1601 Super Plaza 67501. Just w of jct SR 61 and N 17th Ave. Int corridors. Pets: Small, other species. $25 daily fee/pet. Designated rooms, service with restrictions, supervision.

&M 🏊 🛰 ⊠ 🛢 💻

▼▼▼ Holiday Inn Express Hutchison [H]
(620) 259-8656. Call for rates. 911 Porter St 67501. Just se of jct SR 61. Int corridors. Pets: Accepted. 🍴 &M 🛰 ⊠ 🛢 💻

IOLA

▼▼ Super 8 Iola [H]
(620) 365-3030. $68-$80. 200 Bills Way 66749. Jct US 54 and 169. Int corridors. Pets: Accepted. 🍴 &M 🏊 🛰 ⊠ 🛢 💻

JUNCTION CITY

AAA⁀ ▼▼ Best Western J C Inn [H]
(785) 210-1212. $89-$169. 604 E Chestnut St 66441. I-70 exit 298, just w. Int corridors. Pets: Accepted. SAVE 🏊 🛰 🛢 💻

▼▼ Candlewood Suites Junction City [H]
(785) 238-1454. $89-$149. 100 S Hammons Dr 66441. I-70 exit 298, just w. Int corridors. Pets: Accepted. &M 🛰 ⊠ 🛢 💻

▼▼▼ Courtyard by Marriott Junction City [H]
(785) 210-1500. $85-$114. 310 Hammons Dr 66441. I-70 exit 298, just w. Int corridors. Pets: Accepted. 🍴 &M 🏊 🛰 ⊠ 🛢 💻

▼▼ Holiday Inn Express [H]
(785) 762-4200. Call for rates. 120 N East St 66441. I-70 exit 298, just nw. Int corridors. Pets: Accepted. 🏊 🛰 ⊠ 🛢 💻

KANSAS CITY

▼▼ Candlewood Suites [H]
(913) 788-9929. Call for rates. 10920 Parallel Pkwy 66109. I-435 exit 14B, just w. Int corridors. Pets: Accepted. 🛰 ⊠ 🛢 💻

▼▼ Comfort Suites Speedway [H]
(913) 299-4466. $95-$300. 3000 N 103rd Terr 66109. I-435 exit 15A, just e. Int corridors. Pets: Small. $40 one-time fee/pet. Designated rooms, service with restrictions, supervision. 🍴 🛰 ⊠ 🛢 💻

▼▼▼ Residence Inn Kansas City at The Legends [H]
(913) 788-5650. $118-$169. 1875 Village West Pkwy 66111. I-435 exit 13B (State Ave), just sw. Int corridors. Pets: Other species. $100 one-time fee/room. Service with restrictions. &M 🛰 ⊠ 🛢 💻

LANSING

▼ Econo Lodge Lansing/Leavenworth [H]
(913) 727-2777. $58-$125. 504 N Main 66043. I-70 exit 224 (Leavenworth), 10 mi n on US 73 and SR 7. Int corridors. Pets: Accepted.

🛰 🛢 💻

LAWRENCE

AAA⁀ ▼▼▼ Best Western Lawrence [H]
(785) 843-9100. $79-$149. 2309 Iowa St 66046. On US 59; jct SR 10. Ext/int corridors. Pets: Accepted. SAVE 🏊 🛰 🛢 💻

▼▼▼ DoubleTree by Hilton Lawrence [H]
(785) 841-7077. $89-$209. 200 McDonald Dr 66044. I-70 exit 202, 0.5 mi s on US 59. Int corridors. Pets: $50 one-time fee/room. Service with restrictions, crate. 🍴 &M 🏊 🛰 ⊠ 🛢 💻

▼▼▼ TownePlace Suites by Marriott Lawrence Downtown [H]
(785) 842-8800. $122-$194. 900 New Hampshire St 66044. I-70 exit 204, just w, then 1.4 mi e on 9th St. Int corridors. Pets: Accepted.

🍴 &M 🛰 ⊠ 🛢 💻

LEAWOOD

AAA⁀ ▼▼▼ Aloft Leawood-Overland Park [H]
(913) 345-9430. $99-$199. 11620 Ash St 66211. I-435 exit 77B (Nall Ave), 1.1 mi s, then just e. Int corridors. Pets: Accepted.

SAVE &M 🏊 🛰 ⊠ 🛢 💻

LENEXA

AAA⁀ ▼▼▼ Hyatt Place Kansas City/Lenexa City Center [H]
(913) 742-7777. $94-$249. 8741 Ryckert St 66219. I-435 exit 3, just w, then just s. Int corridors. Pets: Accepted.

SAVE &M 🛰 ⊠ 🛢 💻

LIBERAL

AAA⁀ ▼ Americas Best Value Inn [M]
(620) 624-6203. $62-$72. 564 E Pancake Blvd 67901. 0.8 mi w of jct US 54 and 83. Ext corridors. Pets: Medium. $15 daily fee/pet. Designated rooms, service with restrictions, supervision. SAVE 🛰 🛢 💻

LYONS

▼▼ Celebration Centre Inn & Suites [H]
(620) 680-6022. Call for rates. 1108 E Hwy 56 67554. 2 mi e of jct SR 14 and US 56. Int corridors. Pets: $20 one-time fee/room. Designated rooms, supervision. &M 🛰 🛢 💻

MANHATTAN

AAA⁀ ▼▼ Best Western Manhattan Inn [H]
(785) 537-8300. $90-$260. 601 E Poyntz Ave 66502. SR 177, 0.5 mi e on US 24 (Frontage Rd). Int corridors. Pets: Accepted.

SAVE 🍴 🏊 🛰 ⊠ 🛢 💻

▼▼▼ Candlewood Suites H
(785) 320-7995. **Call for rates.** 210 Blue Earth Pl 66502. Just w of jct SR 177 and 18 (Ft. Riley Blvd). Int corridors. **Pets:** Accepted.
🍴 ᴹ 🛏 📶 ✕ 🎁 💻

▼▼▼ Holiday Inn at the Campus H
(785) 539-7531. **Call for rates.** 1641 Anderson Ave Ave 66502. 1 mi n of SR 18 (Ft. Riley Blvd). Int corridors. **Pets:** Accepted.
🍴 ᴹ 🛏 📶 ✕ 🎁 💻

▼▼▼ Holiday Inn Express & Suites H
(785) 320-7454. **$80-$299.** 115 Blue Earth Pl 66502. Just w of jct SR 177 and 18 (Fort Riley Blvd). Int corridors. **Pets:** Other species. $25 one-time fee/room. Service with restrictions, supervision.
ᴹ 📶 ✕ 🎁 💻

🔺 ▼▼▼ Parkwood Inn & Suites H 🐾
(785) 320-5440. **$100-$230.** 505 S 17th St 66502. 1.5 mi w of jct SR 177 and 18 (Ft. Riley Blvd), just n. Int corridors. **Pets:** Other species. $10 daily fee/pet. Service with restrictions, crate.
SAVE 📶 ✕ 🎁 💻

MARYSVILLE
▼▼ Heritage Inn Express H
(785) 562-5588. **Call for rates.** 1155 Pony Express Hwy 66508. 2 mi e on US 36 (Pony Express Hwy). Int corridors. **Pets:** Accepted.
🍴 📶 ✕ 🎁 💻

🔺 ▼▼ Oak Tree Inn H
(785) 562-1234. **Call for rates.** 1127 Pony Express Hwy 66508. 1.6 mi e on US 36 (Pony Express Hwy). Ext/int corridors. **Pets:** Other species. $10 daily fee/pet. Service with restrictions, crate.
SAVE 📶 ✕ 💻

MCPHERSON
🔺 ▼▼▼ Best Western Holiday Manor H
(620) 241-5343. **$75-$119.** 2211 E Kansas Ave 67460. I-135 exit 60, just w. Ext/int corridors. **Pets:** Accepted. SAVE 🍴 🛏 📶 🎁 💻

MERRIAM
▼▼ Drury Inn-Merriam/Shawnee Mission H
(913) 236-9200. **$95-$150.** 9009 Shawnee Mission Pkwy 66202. I-35 exit 228B (Shawnee Mission Pkwy), just se. Int corridors.
Pets: Accepted. ᴹ 🛏 📶 ✕ 🎁 💻

MULVANE
▼▼▼ Hampton Inn & Suites H
(316) 524-3777. **$109-$189.** 785 Kansas Star Dr 67110. I-35 exit 33, just w. Int corridors. **Pets:** Medium. $50 one-time fee/room. Service with restrictions, supervision. 🍴 ᴹ 📶 🎁 💻

NEWTON
▼▼ Comfort Inn & Suites H
(316) 804-4866. **$90-$150.** 1205 E 1st St 67114. I-135 exit 31, just w; exit southbound, just w at 2nd roundabout. Int corridors.
Pets: Accepted. ᴹ 🛏 📶 ✕ 🎁 💻

OLATHE
🔺 ▼▼▼ Best Western Plus Olathe Hotel H
(913) 440-9762. **$107-$169.** 1580 S Hamilton Cir 66061. I-35 exit 215 (151st St), just nw. Int corridors. **Pets:** Other species. $10 daily fee/pet. Designated rooms, service with restrictions, supervision.
SAVE 🍴 ᴹ 🛏 📶 ✕ 🎁 💻

▼▼ Candlewood Suites Olathe H
(913) 768-8888. **Call for rates.** 15490 S Rogers Rd 66062. I-35 exit 215 (151st St), just sw. Int corridors. **Pets:** Accepted.
🍴 ᴹ 📶 ✕ 🎁 💻

▼▼▼ Residence Inn by Marriott H
(913) 829-6700. **$125-$207.** 12215 S Strang Line Rd 66062. I-35 exit 220 (119th St), just e to Strang Line Rd, then 0.8 mi s. Int corridors.
Pets: Accepted. ᴹ 🛏 📶 ✕ 🎁 💻

OTTAWA
🔺 ▼▼▼ Best Western Ottawa Inn H
(785) 242-2224. **$81-$95.** 212 E 23rd St 66067. I-35 exit 183 (US 59), just w. Ext/int corridors. **Pets:** Accepted. SAVE 🛏 📶 🎁 💻

OVERLAND PARK
▼▼ Candlewood Suites H
(913) 469-5557. **Call for rates.** 11001 Oakmont St 66210. I-435 exit 82 (Quivira Rd), 0.5 mi s, 0.3 mi w on College Blvd, then just n. Int corridors. **Pets:** Accepted. ᴹ 📶 ✕ 🎁 💻

▼▼▼ DoubleTree by Hilton Kansas City-Overland Park H
(913) 451-6100. **$90-$199.** 10100 College Blvd 66210. I-435 exit 81 (US 69), 0.5 mi s, then just e. Int corridors. **Pets:** Accepted.
🍴 ᴹ 🛏 ✕ 📶 ✕ 🎁 💻

▼▼▼ Drury Inn & Suites-Overland Park H
(913) 345-1500. **$100-$180.** 10963 Metcalf Ave 66210. I-435 exit 79 (Metcalf Ave/US 169), just se. Int corridors. **Pets:** Accepted.
ᴹ 🛏 📶 ✕ 🎁 💻

🔺 ▼▼▼ Hyatt Place Kansas City/Overland Park/ Convention Center H
(913) 491-9002. **$79-$189.** 5001 W 110th St 66211. I-435 exit 77B (Nall Ave), just se. Int corridors. **Pets:** Accepted.
SAVE 🍴 ᴹ 🛏 📶 ✕ 🎁 💻

🔺 ▼▼▼ Hyatt Place Kansas City/Overland Park/Metcalf H
(913) 451-2553. **$69-$189.** 6801 W 112th St 66211. I-435 exit 79 (Metcalf Ave/US 169), 0.6 mi s. Int corridors. **Pets:** Accepted.
SAVE 🍴 ᴹ 🛏 📶 ✕ 🎁 💻

▼▼▼ Residence Inn by Marriott H
(913) 491-4444. **$119-$208.** 12010 Blue Valley Pkwy 66213. I-435 exit 79 (Metcalf Ave/US 169), 1.3 mi s. Int corridors. **Pets:** Accepted.
ᴹ 🛏 📶 ✕ 🎁 💻

🔺 ▼▼▼ Sheraton Overland Park Hotel at the Convention Center H
(913) 234-2100. **$99-$499.** 6100 College Blvd 66211. I-435 exit 79 (Metcalf Ave/US 169), just s to College Blvd, then 0.6 mi e. Int corridors. **Pets:** Accepted. SAVE ECO 🍴 ᴹ 🛏 📶 ✕ 💻

PARK CITY
🔺 ▼▼ Best Western Wichita North Hotel & Suites H 🐾
(316) 832-9387. **$100-$150.** 915 E 53rd St N 67219. I-135 exit 13, just w. Ext/int corridors. **Pets:** Small, dogs only. $10 daily fee/pet. Service with restrictions, crate. SAVE 🍴 🛏 📶 🎁 💻

🔺 ▼▼ Quality Inn & Suites H
(316) 927-3900. **$73-$115.** 792 Beaumont St 67219. I-135 exit 14, just sw. Int corridors. **Pets:** Accepted. SAVE 🍴 🛏 📶 🎁 💻

▼ Super 8-Wichita North/Park City M
(316) 744-2071. **$60-$70.** 6075 N Air Cap Dr 67219. I-135 exit 14, just sw. Int corridors. **Pets:** Accepted. 📶 🎁 💻

PARSONS
🔺 ▼▼ Best Western Parsons Inn H
(620) 423-0303. **$90-$120.** 101 E Main St 67357. 1.5 mi e; center. Int corridors. **Pets:** Very small. $20 daily fee/pet. Service with restrictions, supervision. SAVE 🍴 🛏 📶 ✕ 🎁 💻

AAA ▼▼▼ **Rodeway Inn & Suites** H
(620) 421-6129. **$90-$110.** 1807 Harding Dr 67357. Just sw of jct US 59 and 400. Int corridors. **Pets:** Small. $25 one-time fee/room. Service with restrictions, supervision. [SAVE] [▲] [&M] [≋] [≋] [✕] [🔧] [💻]

PHILLIPSBURG
▼▼ **Cottonwood Inn** M
(785) 543-2125. **$72-$105.** 1200 State St 67661. 1 mi e on US 36/183. Ext corridors. **Pets:** Other species. Service with restrictions, supervision.
[≋] [≋] [✕] [🔧] [💻]

PITTSBURG
▼▼ **Lamplighter Inn & Suites** H
(620) 231-8700. **$79-$109.** 4020 Parkview Dr 66762. 2.3 mi n on US 69 from jct SR 126. Ext/int corridors. **Pets:** Small, dogs only. $10 daily fee/pet. Designated rooms, service with restrictions, crate.
[▲] [≋] [≋] [🔧] [💻]

PRATT
AAA ▼▼ **Best Western Plus Pratt** H
(620) 508-6466. **$89-$119.** 112 NE SR Hwy 61 67124. Just n of jct US 54 and SR 61. Int corridors. **Pets:** Accepted.
[SAVE] [▲] [&M] [≋] [✕] [🔧] [💻]

AAA ▼▼ **Comfort Suites** H
(620) 672-9999. **$80-$150.** 704 Allison Ln 67124. Just n of jct US 54 and SR 61. Int corridors. **Pets:** Accepted.
[SAVE] [▲] [&M] [≋] [≋] [✕] [🔧] [💻]

▼ **Evergreen Inn & RV Park** M
(620) 672-6431. **$59-$100.** 20001 W US Hwy 54 67124. 3 mi w. Ext corridors. **Pets:** Accepted. [≋] [≋] [🔧]

▼▼▼ **Hampton Inn Pratt** H
(620) 508-6499. **$79-$119.** 1705 Maple St 67124. Jct US 54 and SR 61, just n. Int corridors. **Pets:** Other species. Service with restrictions.
[▲] [&M] [≋] [✕] [🔧] [💻]

▼▼▼ **Holiday Inn Express** H
(620) 508-6350. **$99-$109.** 1903 Pauline Pl 67124. Jct US 54 and SR 61, just n. Int corridors. **Pets:** Accepted.
[▲] [&M] [≋] [≋] [✕] [🔧] [💻]

SALINA
AAA ▼▼▼ **Best Western Plus Midwest Inn & Suites** H
(785) 493-9800. **$90-$129.** 745 W Schilling Rd 67401. I-135 exit 89 (Schilling Rd), just w. Int corridors. **Pets:** Accepted.
[SAVE] [▲] [&M] [≋] [≋] [✕] [🔧] [💻]

▼▼ **Candlewood Suites** H
(785) 823-6939. **$69-$120.** 2650 Planet Ave 67401. I-135 exit 89 (Schilling Rd), just e to S 9th St, 0.5 mi n to Belmont Blvd, then just w. Int corridors. **Pets:** Accepted. [&M] [≋] [✕] [🔧] [💻]

▼▼▼ **La Quinta Inn & Suites** H
(785) 827-9000. **$92-$218.** 201 E Diamond Dr 67401. I-70 exit 252, just ne. Int corridors. **Pets:** Accepted. [&M] [▲] [≋] [✕] [🔧] [💻]

AAA ▼▼ **Super 8 I-70** H
(785) 823-8808. **$68-$72.** 120 E Diamond Dr 67401. I-70 exit 252, just ne. Int corridors. **Pets:** Medium. $15 one-time fee/room. Service with restrictions, crate. [SAVE] [▲] [≋] [✕] [🔧] [💻]

TOPEKA
AAA ▼▼▼ **Best Western Topeka Inn & Suites** H
(785) 228-2223. **$89-$129.** 700 SW Fairlawn Rd 66606. I-70 exit 357A, just ne. Int corridors. **Pets:** Accepted.
[SAVE] [▲] [≋] [≋] [✕] [🔧] [💻]

▼▼ **ClubHouse Inn & Suites** H
(785) 273-8888. **$98-$148.** 924 SW Henderson Rd 66615. I-70 exit 356 (Wanamaker Rd), just sw. Int corridors. **Pets:** Small. $10 daily fee/pet. Service with restrictions, crate. [▲] [≋] [✕] [🔧] [💻]

▼▼▼ **Comfort Suites** H
(785) 246-6777. **$85-$198.** 6213 SW 10th Ave 66615. I-70 exit 356 (Wanamaker Rd), just s. Int corridors. **Pets:** Other species. $40 one-time fee/room. Service with restrictions, supervision.
[▲] [&M] [≋] [✕] [🔧] [💻]

AAA ▼▼▼ **Hyatt Place Topeka** H
(785) 273-0066. **$69-$189.** 6021 SW 6th Ave 66615. I-70 exit 356 (Wanamaker Rd), just n. Int corridors. **Pets:** Accepted.
[SAVE] [▲] [&M] [▲] [≋] [✕] [🔧] [💻]

▼▼ **Sleep Inn & Suites** H
(785) 228-2500. **$95-$140.** 1024 SW Wanamaker Rd 66604. I-70 exit 356 (Wanamaker Rd), just s. Int corridors. **Pets:** Medium, other species. $10 daily fee/pet. Designated rooms, service with restrictions, supervision. [▲] [&M] [▲] [≋] [✕] [🔧] [💻]

▼▼▼ **Super 8 at Forbes Landing** H
(785) 862-2222. **$73-$92.** 5922 SW Topeka Blvd 66619. I-470 exit 6, 2.2 mi s. Int corridors. **Pets:** Accepted. [▲] [≋] [🔧] [💻]

ULYSSES
▼▼ **Single Tree Inn** H
(620) 356-1500. **$73-$77.** 2033 W Oklahoma Ave 67880. 1.5 mi w on US 160. Int corridors. **Pets:** Dogs only. $20 daily fee/pet. Designated rooms, service with restrictions, supervision. [≋] [✕] [🔧] [💻]

WAKEENEY
AAA ▼▼ **Best Western Plus Wakeeney Inn & Suites** H 🐾
(785) 743-2700. **$89-$99.** 525 S 1st St 67672. I-70 exit 127, just n. Int corridors. **Pets:** Large, other species. $10 daily fee/pet. Designated rooms, service with restrictions, supervision.
[SAVE] [&M] [▲] [≋] [✕] [🔧] [💻]

▼▼ **Super 8** H
(785) 743-6442. **$68-$90.** 709 S 13th St 67672. I-70 exit 128, just n. Int corridors. **Pets:** Accepted. [▲] [≋] [✕] [🔧] [💻]

WELLINGTON
▼▼ **Oak Tree Inn Wellington** H
(620) 326-8191. **Call for rates.** 1130 E 16th St 67152. I-35 exit 19, 2 mi w on US 160. Ext/int corridors. **Pets:** Accepted. [≋] [✕] [🔧] [💻]

WICHITA
AAA ▼▼▼ **Airport Inn & Conference Center** H
(316) 942-5600. **$89-$114.** 6815 W Kellogg St 67209. I-235 exit 7, 0.6 mi w on US 54 (S Frontage Rd). Int corridors. **Pets:** Accepted.
[SAVE] [▲] [▲] [✕] [≋] [✕] [🔧] [💻]

AAA ▼▼▼ **Ambassador Hotel Wichita, Autograph Collection** H
(316) 239-7100. **$142-$246.** 104 S Broadway 67202. Jct Douglass Ave; downtown. Int corridors. **Pets:** Accepted.
[SAVE] [▲] [&M] [≋] [✕] [🔧] [💻]

AAA ▼▼▼ **Best Western Governors Inn & Suites** H
(316) 522-0775. **$79-$149.** 4742 S Emporia St 67216. I-135 exit 1A/B (47th St S), just sw. Int corridors. **Pets:** Accepted.
[SAVE] [&M] [▲] [≋] [✕] [🔧] [💻]

▼▼ **Candlewood Suites** H
(316) 942-0400. **Call for rates.** 570 S Julia St 67209. I-235 exit 7, 0.3 mi w to Dugan St, just n to Taft St, just e, then just s. Int corridors. **Pets:** Accepted. [≋] [🔧] [💻]

▼▼ ▼▼ **Candlewood Suites-Wichita Northeast** H
(316) 634-6070. **Call for rates.** 3141 N Webb Rd 67226. SR 96 exit Webb Rd, just nw. Int corridors. **Pets:** Accepted. ⬇ 🛜 📶 🖥

▼▼ **Comfort Inn by Choice Hotels** H
(316) 686-2844. **$75-$139.** 9525 E Corporate Hills Dr 67207. I-35 exit 50, just ne. Int corridors. **Pets:** Accepted. 🍴 🛜 ✕ 📶 🖥

▲▲▲ ▼▼ **Country Inn & Suites By Carlson Wichita Northeast** H
(316) 634-3900. **Call for rates.** 7824 E 32nd St N 67226. SR 96 E exit Rock Rd, just sw. Int corridors. **Pets:** Accepted.
SAVE 🍴 🛜 ✕ 📶 🖥

▼▼▼ **Drury Plaza Hotel Broadview-Wichita** H
(316) 262-5000. **$110-$220.** 400 W Douglas Ave 67202. Jct Waco St; downtown. Int corridors. **Pets:** Accepted. 🍴 ⬇ 🛜 ✕ 📶 🖥

▼▼ ▼▼ **Fairfield Inn & Suites by Marriott Wichita East** H
(316) 685-3777. **$67-$113.** 333 S Webb Rd 67207. I-35 exit 50, just ne. Int corridors. **Pets:** Other species. $25 one-time fee/pet. Designated rooms, service with restrictions, crate. 🛜 ⬇ 🛜 ✕ 📶 🖥

▼▼▼ **Hampton Inn by Hilton** H
(316) 686-3576. **$124-$149.** 9449 E Corporate Hills Dr 67207. I-35 exit 50, just ne. Int corridors. **Pets:** Accepted. 🛜 ⬇ 🛜 📶 🖥

▼▼▼ **Homewood Suites by Hilton at The Waterfront** H
(316) 260-8844. **$129-$199.** 1550 N Waterfront Pkwy 67206. Just e of jct 13th St and Webb Rd, then just n. Int corridors. **Pets:** Accepted.
🛜 ⬇ 🛜 ✕ 📶 🖥

▼▼ ▼▼ **La Quinta Inn & Suites Wichita Airport** H
(316) 943-2181. **$67-$207.** 5500 W Kellogg Dr 67209. I-235 exit 7, just nw. Int corridors. **Pets:** Accepted. 🍴 ⬇ 🛜 ✕ 📶 🖥

▼▼▼ **Residence Inn by Marriott at Plazzio** H
(316) 682-7300. **$99-$167.** 1212 N Greenwich Rd 67206. SR 96 exit 13th St, 0.5 mi sw. Int corridors. **Pets:** Accepted.
🛜 ⬇ 🛜 ✕ 📶 🖥

▼▼▼ **Staybridge Suites** H
(316) 927-3888. **Call for rates.** 2250 N Greenwich Rd 67226. Just e of jct 21st St and Greenwich Rd. Int corridors. **Pets:** Medium. $75 one-time fee/room. Service with restrictions, supervision.
🍴 🛜 ⬇ 🛜 📶 🖥

▼▼▼ **TownePlace Suites by Marriott** H
(316) 631-3773. **$71-$122.** 9444 E 29th St N 67226. SR 96 exit Webb Rd, just sw. Int corridors. **Pets:** Medium, other species. $75 one-time fee/room. Service with restrictions, crate. 🛜 🛜 ✕ 📶 🖥

▼▼ **Wesley Inn** H
(316) 858-3343. **Call for rates.** 3343 E Central Ave 67208. Just e of jct Hillside St. Int corridors. **Pets:** Accepted. 🛜 ✕ 📶 🖥

WINFIELD
▼▼ **Quality Inn & Suites** H
(620) 221-7529. **$89-$190.** 3800 S Pike Rd 67156. On US 77, 1 mi s. Ext/int corridors. **Pets:** Accepted. ⬇ 🛜 📶 🖥

KENTUCKY

ASHLAND
▲▲▲ ▼▼▼ **Best Western River Cities** H
(606) 326-0357. **$106-$118.** 31 Russell Plaza Dr 41101. I-64 exit 185, 6 mi nw on US 60, then 3 mi n on US 23. Int corridors. **Pets:** Accepted.
SAVE ⬇ 🛜 ✕ 📶 🖥

▼▼ **Quality Inn** H
(606) 325-8989. **$70-$129.** 4708 Winchester Ave 41101. I-64 exit 191, 4.8 mi n on US 23. Ext corridors. **Pets:** Medium. $15 daily fee/pet. Designated rooms, no service, supervision. 🍴 ⬇ 🛜 📶 🖥

BARDSTOWN
▲▲▲ ▼▼ **General Nelson Inn** M
(502) 348-3977. **$69-$89.** 411 W Stephen Foster Ave 40004. 0.5 mi w on US 62. Ext corridors. **Pets:** Medium. $25 daily fee/pet. Designated rooms, service with restrictions, supervision.
SAVE ⬇ 🛜 ✕ 📶 🖥

▼▼▼ **Hampton Inn by Hilton** H
(502) 349-0100. **$119-$249.** 985 Chambers Blvd 40004. Jct US 150, 0.5 mi n on SR 245. Int corridors. **Pets:** Accepted.
🛜 ⬇ 🛜 ✕ 📶 🖥

BENTON
▼▼ **Quality Inn & Suites Benton – Draffenville** H
(270) 527-5300. **$96-$136.** 173 Carroll Rd 42025. Purchase Pkwy (SR 9003) exit 47, just e. Int corridors. **Pets:** Accepted.
🍴 ⬇ 🛜 📶 🖥

BEREA
▲▲▲ ▼▼▼ **Boone Tavern Hotel & Restaurant of Berea College** H
(859) 985-3700. **Call for rates.** 100 Main St 40404. I-75 exit 76, 1.5 mi ne on SR 21. Int corridors. **Pets:** Small, dogs only. $50 one-time fee/room. Service with restrictions, crate.
SAVE ECO 🍴 🛜 🛜 ✕ 📶 🖥

▼▼▼ **Holiday Inn Express** H
(859) 985-5500. **$89-$185.** 219 Paint Lick Rd 40403. I-75 exit 76, just w. Int corridors. **Pets:** Medium. $25 daily fee/pet. Service with restrictions, supervision. 🛜 ⬇ 🛜 ✕ 📶 🖥

BOWLING GREEN *(Restaurants p. 613)*
▲▲▲ ▼▼▼ **Best Western Bowling Green** H
(270) 782-6933. **$99-$159.** 1940 Mel Browning St 42104. I-65 exit 22 (Scottsville Rd), just se. Ext/int corridors. **Pets:** Accepted.
SAVE 🛜 ⬇ 🛜 ✕ 📶 🖥

▲▲▲ ▼▼▼ **Candlewood Suites** H
(270) 843-5505. **$99-$189, 3 day notice.** 540 Wall St 42103. I-65 exit 22 (Scottsville Rd), just nw. Int corridors. **Pets:** Large, other species. $50 one-time fee/room. Service with restrictions, crate.
SAVE 🛜 ⬇ 📶 🖥

▼▼▼ **Drury Inn-Bowling Green** H
(270) 842-7100. **$100-$170.** 3250 Scottsville Rd 42104. I-65 exit 22 (Scottsville Rd), just w. Int corridors. **Pets:** Accepted.
🛜 ⬇ 🛜 ✕ 📶 🖥

▼▼ ▼▼ **Econo Lodge Bowling Green** M
(270) 781-3460. **Call for rates.** 3160 Scottsville Rd 42104. I-65 exit 22 (Scottsville Rd), just w. Ext corridors. **Pets:** Accepted.
🛜 🛜 📶 🖥

▼▼▼ Hampton Inn H
(270) 842-4100. $99-$199. 233 Three Springs Rd 42104. I-65 exit 22 (Scottsville Rd), 0.3 mi w. Int corridors. Pets: Accepted.
&M ⇔ 📶 ✕ 🛢 💻

▼▼▼ Holiday Inn Express H
(270) 843-3200. $119-$189. 165 Three Springs Rd 42104. I-65 exit 22 (Scottsville Rd), 0.3 mi w. Int corridors. Pets: Accepted.
&M ⇔ 📶 ✕ 🛢 💻

▼▼▼ Holiday Inn University Plaza H
(270) 745-0088. Call for rates. 1021 Wilkinson Trace 42103. I-65 exit 22 (Scottsville Rd), 2.5 mi w, then just n. Int corridors. Pets: Accepted.
🍴 &M ⇔ 📶 ✕ 🛢 💻

▲▲▲ ▼▼▼ Hyatt Place Bowling Green H
(270) 467-0001. $99-$289. 1347 Center St 42101. Center. Int corridors. Pets: Accepted. SAVE 🍴 📶 ✕ 🛢 💻

▼▼▼ La Quinta Inn & Suites H
(270) 783-0083. $93-$204. 1953 Mel Browning St 42104. I-65 exit 22 (Scottsville Rd), just e. Int corridors. Pets: Accepted.
&M ⇔ 📶 ✕ 🛢 💻

▲▲▲ ▼▼▼ Ramada Bowling Green H
(270) 781-3000. $74-$90. 4767 Scottsville Rd 42104. I-65 exit 22 (Scottsville Rd), 0.3 mi e. Int corridors. Pets: Medium. $10 daily fee/pet. Designated rooms, service with restrictions, supervision.
SAVE 🍴 ⇔ 📶 🛢 💻

▼▼▼ Red Roof Inn Bowling Green M
(270) 781-6550. $50-$150. 3140 Scottsville Rd 42104. I-65 exit 22 (Scottsville Rd), 0.3 mi w. Ext corridors. Pets: Accepted. 📶 🛢 💻

▼▼▼ Staybridge Suites Bowling Green H
(270) 904-0480. Call for rates. 680 Campbell Ln 42101. I-65 exit 20B (Natcher Pkwy), 3.7 mi w to exit 6 (SR 31 W), then 1.7 mi n. Int corridors. Pets: Accepted. &M 📶 ✕ 🛢 💻

▼▼▼ TownePlace Suites by Marriott H
(270) 782-4714. $87-$219. 1818 Cave Mill Rd 42104. I-65 exit 22, 0.7 mi nw, then 0.5 mi w. Int corridors. Pets: Accepted.
🍴 &M 📶 ✕ 🛢 💻

CALVERT CITY
▼▼ Super 8 Calvert City/KY Lake Area H
(270) 395-5566. $54-$75. 86 Campbell Dr 42029. I-24/69 exit 27, 0.3 mi w on US 62. Int corridors. Pets: Accepted.
🍴 &M ⇔ 📶 🛢 💻

CARROLLTON
▼▼ Red Roof Inn Carrollton H
(502) 732-7027. $76-$100. 10 Slumber Ln 41008. I-71 exit 44, just nw. Int corridors. Pets: Accepted. &M ⇔ 📶 🛢 💻

▼▼ Super 8 Carrollton H
(502) 732-0252. $60-$200. 130 Slumber Ln 41008. I-71 exit 44, just nw. Int corridors. Pets: Accepted. 📶 🛢 💻

CATLETTSBURG
▼▼▼ Ramada Limited Hotel H
(606) 739-5700. $89-$105. 6000 Crider Dr 41129. I-64 exit 191, 0.5 mi n on US 23. Int corridors. Pets: Medium. $20 daily fee/pet. Designated rooms, service with restrictions, supervision. 🍴 ⇔ 📶 🛢 💻

CAVE CITY (Restaurants p. 614)
▼▼ Super 8 H
(270) 773-3161. $60-$110. 1009 Doyle Ave 42127. I-65 exit 53, just e. Ext corridors. Pets: Accepted. ⇔ 📶 🛢 💻

CENTRAL CITY
▼▼ Days Inn H
(270) 754-1222. $84-$99. 640 S 2nd St 42330. Western Kentucky Pkwy exit 58, just n. Int corridors. Pets: Accepted. 🍴 ⇔ 📶 🛢 💻

COLUMBIA
▲▲▲ ▼▼▼ Best Western Columbia M
(270) 384-9744. $90-$140. 710 Bomar Heights 42728. Cumberland Pkwy exit 49, just n on SR 55, then just w. Ext corridors.
Pets: Accepted. SAVE 🍴 ⇔ 📶 🛢 💻

CORBIN
▲▲▲ ▼▼▼ Best Western Corbin Inn M
(606) 528-2100. $95-$159. 2630 Cumberland Falls Hwy 40701. I-75 exit 25, just w. Ext corridors. Pets: Accepted. SAVE ⇔ 📶 🛢 💻

DANVILLE
▲▲▲ ▼▼▼ Comfort Suites H
(859) 936-9300. $99-$259. 864 Ben Ali Dr 40422. Jct US 127 Bypass, just w on US 150 (Perryville Rd). Int corridors. Pets: Small, dogs only. $35 daily fee/pet. Designated rooms, service with restrictions, supervision. SAVE &M ⇔ 📶 ✕ 🛢 💻

DRY RIDGE
▼▼▼ Comfort Inn H
(859) 824-7121. $80-$180. 1050 Fashion Ridge Rd 41035. I-75 exit 159, just nw. Int corridors. Pets: Medium. $15 daily fee/pet. Designated rooms, service with restrictions, supervision. &M 📶 ✕ 💻

EDDYVILLE
▼▼▼ Eddy Creek Marina Resort M
(270) 388-2271. $82-$195, 45 day notice. 7612 SR 93 S 42038. I-24 exit 45, just w to SR 93, then 4 mi s. Ext corridors. Pets: Accepted.
🍴 ⇔ ✕ 📶 ✕ 🎿 🛢 💻

ELIZABETHTOWN
▼▼▼ Holiday Inn Express H
(270) 769-1334. Call for rates. 107 Buffalo Creek Dr 42701. I-65 exit 94, just w. Int corridors. Pets: Accepted. &M ⇔ 📶 ✕ 🛢 💻

▼▼▼ La Quinta Inn & Suites Elizabethtown H
(270) 765-4747. $90-$229. 210 Commerce Dr 42701. I-65 exit 94, just sw. Int corridors. Pets: Accepted. &M ⇔ 📶 ✕ 🛢 💻

▲▲▲ ▼▼▼ Wingfield Inn & Suites H
(270) 769-3030. $90-$121. 1043 Executive Dr 42701. I-65 exit 94, just nw. Int corridors. Pets: Accepted. SAVE ⇔ 📶 🛢 💻

ERLANGER
▼▼▼ Residence Inn by Marriott, Cincinnati Airport H
(859) 282-7400. $64-$221. 2811 Circleport Dr 41018. I-275 exit 2, just s. Int corridors. Pets: Accepted. 🍴 &M ⇔ 📶 ✕ 🛢 💻

FLORENCE
▼▼▼ Ashley Quarters Hotel H
(859) 525-9997. Call for rates. 4880 Houston Rd 41042. I-71/75 exit 182, 0.6 mi w on Turfway and Houston rds. Int corridors.
Pets: Accepted. &M ⇔ 📶 ✕ 🛢 💻

▲▲▲ ▼▼▼ Best Western Inn Florence H
(859) 525-0090. $109-$150. 7821 Commerce Dr 41042. I-71/75 exit 181, just ne. Int corridors. Pets: Medium. $20 deposit/pet. Designated rooms, service with restrictions, crate.
SAVE 🍴 &M ⇔ 📶 ✕ 🛢 💻

▼▼ Comfort Inn Greater Cincinnati Airport on Turfway Rd H
(859) 647-2700. **$95-$179.** 7454 Turfway Rd 41042. I-71/75 exit 182, 0.8 mi sw. Int corridors. **Pets:** Accepted. 🄼 📶 🛄 💻

ΔΔΔ ▼▼▼ Hyatt Place Cincinnati Airport/Florence H
(859) 647-1170. **$79-$219.** 300 Meijer Dr 41042. I-71/75 exit 182, 0.4 mi sw. Int corridors. **Pets:** Medium, dogs only. $75 one-time fee/room. Designated rooms, service with restrictions, supervision.
SAVE 🍴 🄼 ➰ 📶 ✕ 🛄 💻

▼▼▼ La Quinta Inn & Suites Cincinnati Airport Florence H
(859) 282-8212. **$97-$356.** 350 Meijer Dr 41042. I-71/75 exit 182, 0.4 mi sw. Int corridors. **Pets:** Accepted. 🄼 ➰ 📶 ✕ 🛄 💻

FRANKLIN
▼▼▼ Holiday Inn Express & Suites-Franklin H
(270) 586-7626. **Call for rates.** 85 Neha Dr 42134. I-65 exit 2, just w. Int corridors. **Pets:** Accepted. 🄼 ➰ 📶 ✕ 🛄 💻

GEORGETOWN
ΔΔΔ ▼▼▼ Best Western Plus Georgetown Corporate Center Hotel H
(502) 868-0055. **$100-$150.** 132 Darby Dr 40324. I-75 exit 126, just nw. Int corridors. **Pets:** Accepted. SAVE 🄼 ➰ ✕ 📶 ✕ 🛄 💻

ΔΔΔ ▼▼▼ Comfort Suites H
(502) 868-9500. **$75-$365.** 121 Darby Dr 40324. I-75 exit 126, just w. Int corridors. **Pets:** Medium, other species. $20 daily fee/pet. Designated rooms, service with restrictions, supervision.
SAVE 🄼 ➰ 📶 ✕ 🛄 💻

▼▼▼ Country Inn & Suites By Carlson H
(502) 868-6800. **Call for rates.** 131 Darby Dr 40324. I-75 exit 126, just nw. Int corridors. **Pets:** Accepted. 🄼 ➰ 📶 ✕ 🛄 💻

ΔΔΔ ▼▼▼ Fairfield Inn & Suites by Marriott Lexington Georgetown/College Inn H
(502) 868-9955. **$63-$233.** 200 Tiger Way St 40324. I-75 exit 126, just nw. Int corridors. **Pets:** Accepted. SAVE 🄼 ➰ 📶 ✕ 🛄 💻

▼▼▼ Holiday Inn Express Lexington North-Georgetown H
(502) 570-0220. **Call for rates.** 140 Osbourne Way 40324. I-75 exit 126, 0.3 mi e on Cherry Blossom Way, then just n. Int corridors. **Pets:** Accepted. 🄼 ➰ 📶 ✕ 🛄 💻

GLASGOW
▼▼ Comfort Inn M
(270) 651-9099. **$85-$134.** 210 Cavalry Dr 42141. Cumberland Pkwy exit 11, just n, just w. Ext corridors. **Pets:** $25 daily fee/pet. Service with restrictions, supervision. ➰ 📶 🛄 💻

GRAND RIVERS *(Restaurants p. 614)*
ΔΔΔ ▼▼▼ Green Turtle Bay Resort CO
(270) 362-8364. **Call for rates.** 263 Green Turtle Bay Dr 42045. I-24 exit 31 (SR 453), 3 mi s to W Commerce Ave, just e to JH O'Bryan Ave, just n to Barkley Dr, then 0.7 mi e. Ext corridors. **Pets:** $95 one-time fee/pet. Designated rooms, no service.
SAVE 🍴 ➰ ✕ 📶 ✕ 🛄 💻

▼▼▼ Patti's Inn and Suites H
(270) 928-2740. **Call for rates.** 1017 Dover Rd 42045. I-24 exit 31 (SR 453), just n. Int corridors. **Pets:** Accepted.
🍴 🄼 ➰ 📶 ✕ 🛄 💻

GRAYSON
▼▼▼ Super 8 H
(606) 474-8811. **$50-$75.** 125 Super 8 Ln 41143. I-64 exit 172, just s. Int corridors. **Pets:** Accepted. 🄼 📶 🛄 💻

HARLAN
▼▼ Comfort Inn H
(606) 573-3385. **$114-$189.** 2608 S Hwy 421 40831. On US 421, 2.8 mi s. Int corridors. **Pets:** Accepted. ➰ 📶 🛄 💻

HARRODSBURG
▼▼▼ Shaker Village of Pleasant Hill CI
(859) 734-5411. **$110-$375.** 3501 Lexington Rd 40330. On US 68, 7 mi ne; jct SR 33. Ext/int corridors. **Pets:** $20 daily fee/pet. Designated rooms, service with restrictions, crate. 🄲 🍴 📶 ✕ 🛄 💻

HEBRON
ΔΔΔ ▼▼▼ DoubleTree by Hilton Hotel Cincinnati Airport H
(859) 371-6166. **$120-$300.** 2826 Terminal Dr 41048. I-275 exit 4B, 1.2 mi w. Int corridors. **Pets:** Accepted.
SAVE 🍴 🄼 ➰ 📶 ✕ 💻

HOPKINSVILLE
ΔΔΔ ▼▼▼ Best Western Hopkinsville H
(270) 886-9000. **$89-$90.** 4101 Ft Campbell Blvd 42240. I-24 exit 81 (Pennyrile Pkwy) to exit 7, then just s. Int corridors. **Pets:** Accepted.
SAVE 🄼 ➰ 📶 ✕ 🛄 💻

▼▼▼ Hampton Inn & Suites H
(270) 886-8800. **Call for rates.** 210 Richard Mills Dr 42240. Pennyrile Pkwy exit 7, just s. Int corridors. **Pets:** Accepted.
🄼 ➰ 📶 🛄 💻

ΔΔΔ ▼▼▼ Holiday Inn H
(270) 886-4413. **$104-$169.** 2910 Ft Campbell Blvd 42240. I-24 exit 81 (Pennyrile Pkwy) to exit 7, then 0.6 mi n on US 41A. Int corridors. **Pets:** Other species. $25 one-time fee/pet, $13 daily fee/pet. Service with restrictions, crate. SAVE 🍴 🄼 ➰ ✕ 📶 🛄 💻

▼▼▼ La Quinta Inn & Suites Hopkinsville H
(270) 886-5151. **Call for rates.** 345 Griffin Bell Dr 42240. Pennyrile Pkwy exit 7, just s. Int corridors. **Pets:** Accepted.
🄼 ➰ 📶 ✕ 🛄 💻

HURSTBOURNE
▼▼▼ Drury Inn & Suites-Louisville H
(502) 326-4170. **$100-$230.** 9501 Blairwood Rd 40222. I-64 exit 15, just n. Int corridors. **Pets:** Accepted. 🄼 ➰ 📶 ✕ 🛄 💻

ΔΔΔ ▼▼ Red Roof Inn Louisville East - Hurstbourne M
(502) 426-7621. **$49-$250.** 9330 Blairwood Rd 40222. I-64 exit 15, 0.3 mi nw of Hurstbourne Pkwy. Ext corridors. **Pets:** Accepted.
SAVE 🄼 📶 ✕ 🛄 💻

JEFFERSONTOWN
▼▼▼ Hawthorn Suites by Wyndham Louisville/Jeffersontown H
(502) 261-0085. **$89-$359.** 11762 Commonwealth Dr 40299. I-64 exit 17, 0.5 mi s on Blankenbaker Pkwy. Int corridors. **Pets:** Accepted.
🄼 📶 ✕ 🛄 💻

ΔΔΔ ▼▼▼ Hyatt Place Louisville-East H
(502) 426-0119. **$79-$229.** 701 S Hurstbourne Pkwy 40222. I-64 exit 15, 0.8 mi n. Int corridors. **Pets:** Accepted.
SAVE 🍴 🄼 ➰ 📶 ✕ 🛄 💻

▼▼▼▼ **La Quinta Inn & Suites Louisville** 🅷
(502) 267-8889. **$86-$515.** 1501 Alliant Ave 40299. I-64 exit 17, just s. Int corridors. **Pets:** Accepted. 🛇🖐 🛍 📶 ✖ 🔋 💻

▼ **Microtel Inn by Wyndham Louisville East** 🅷
(502) 266-6590. **$53-$200.** 1221 Kentucky Mills Dr 40299. I-64 exit 17, just s. Int corridors. **Pets:** Small, dogs only. $30 one-time fee/pet. Designated rooms, service with restrictions, supervision. 🖐 📶 ✖

KUTTAWA
▼▼ **Days Inn** 🅼
(270) 388-5420. **$65-$110.** 139 Days Inn Dr 42055. I-24 exit 40 (US 62), just s. Ext corridors. **Pets:** Other species. $20 one-time fee/room. Service with restrictions. 🛍 📶 🔋 💻

▼▼ **Relax Inn & Suites** 🅼
(270) 388-2285. **$50-$100.** 224 New Circle Dr 42055. I-24 exit 40 (US 62), just e. Ext corridors. **Pets:** Accepted. 🍽 📶 🔋 💻

LA GRANGE
🅰🅰🅰 ▼▼ **Best Western Ashbury Inn** 🅷
(502) 222-5500. **$90-$100.** 1005 New Moody Ln 40031. I-71 exit 22, just se. Int corridors. **Pets:** Dogs only. $20 daily fee/pet. Service with restrictions, supervision. 🆂🅰🆅🅴 🛍 📶 ✖ 🔋 💻

▼▼ **Comfort Inn & Suites La Grange** 🅷
(502) 222-5678. **$92-$210.** 1001 Paige Pl 40031. I-71 exit 22, just se. Int corridors. **Pets:** Accepted. 🖐 🛍 📶 ✖ 🔋 💻

LAWRENCEBURG
🅰🅰🅰 ▼▼ **Best Western Lawrenceburg Inn** 🅷
(502) 839-3444. **$100-$150.** 200 Plaza Dr 40342. Blue Grass Pkwy exit 59 (US 127), 4 mi n. Int corridors. **Pets:** Medium, other species. $50 deposit/room, $20 daily fee/room. Designated rooms, service with restrictions, supervision. 🆂🅰🆅🅴 🍽 🖐 🛍 📶 ✖ 🔋 💻

LEBANON
▼▼▼▼ **Hampton Inn Lebanon** 🅷
(270) 699-4000. **$102-$130.** 1125 Loretto Rd 40033. Jct SR 49/52 (Loretto Rd) and 2154 (Veterans Memorial Hwy). Int corridors. **Pets:** Accepted. 🍽 🖐 🛍 📶 🔋 💻

LEXINGTON
▼▼▼▼ ▼▼▼▼ **21c Museum Hotel** 🅷 ❀
(859) 899-6800. **Call for rates.** 167 W Main St 40507. Jct Upper St. Int corridors. **Pets:** Medium. $150 one-time fee/room. Designated rooms, service with restrictions, crate. 🍽 📶 ✖ 💻

▼▼ **Candlewood Suites** 🅷
(859) 967-1940. **Call for rates.** 603 Adcolor Dr 40511. Jct SR 4 (New Circle Rd) exit 9A, and Newtown Pike, just s. Int corridors. **Pets:** Accepted. 🍽 🖐 🛍 📶 🔋 💻

▼▼ **Clarion Hotel Lexington Conference Center South** 🅷
(859) 263-5241. **$90-$999.** 5532 Athens-Boonesboro Rd 40509. I-75 exit 104, just e. Int corridors. **Pets:** Accepted. 🛍 📶 ✖ 🔋 💻

▼▼▼▼ **Comfort Suites by Choice Hotels** 🅷
(859) 296-4446. **$85-$195.** 3060 Fieldstone Way 40513. Jct SR 4 (New Circle Rd) and US 68 (Harrodsburg Rd), just sw. Int corridors. **Pets:** Accepted. 🖐 🛍 📶 ✖ 🔋 💻

▼▼ **Days Inn-South** 🅼
(859) 263-3100. **$58-$150.** 5575 Athens-Boonesboro Rd 40509. I-75 exit 104, just e. Ext corridors. **Pets:** Accepted. 📶 🔋 💻

▼▼▼ **DoubleTree Suites by Hilton Hotel Lexington** 🅷 ❀
(859) 268-0060. **Call for rates.** 2601 Richmond Rd 40509. SR 4 (New Circle Rd) exit 15, just s; in French Quarter Square. Int corridors. **Pets:** Large. $75 one-time fee/room. Service with restrictions, crate. 🍽 🖐 🛍 📶 ✖ 🔋 💻

▼▼▼ **Fairfield Inn & Suites by Marriott-Lexington North** 🅷
(859) 977-5870. **$54-$208.** 2100 Hackney Pl 40511. I-75/64 exit 115, just n, then 0.3 mi e; on Stanton Way. Int corridors. **Pets:** Accepted. 🖐 🛍 📶 ✖ 🔋 💻

🅰🅰🅰 ▼▼▼▼ **Four Points by Sheraton Hotel** 🅷
(859) 259-1311. **$96-$299.** 1938 Stanton Way 40511. I-75/64 exit 115, just n on SR 922, then just e. Int corridors. **Pets:** Other species. $25 daily fee/room. Service with restrictions, supervision. 🆂🅰🆅🅴 🍽 🖐 🛍 📶 ✖ 🔋 💻

🅰🅰🅰 ▼▼▼▼ **Hampton Inn by Hilton I-75** 🅷
(859) 299-2613. **$89-$229.** 2251 Elkhorn Rd 40505. I-75 exit 110, just nw. Int corridors. **Pets:** Large, other species. Designated rooms, service with restrictions, supervision. 🆂🅰🆅🅴 🖐 🛍 📶 ✖ 🔋 💻

🅰🅰🅰 ▼▼▼▼ **Hilton Suites of Lexington Green** 🅷
(859) 271-4000. **Call for rates.** 245 Lexington Green Cir 40503. SR 4 (New Circle Rd) exit 19, just s on US 27 (Nicholasville Rd), then just w. Int corridors. **Pets:** Accepted. 🆂🅰🆅🅴 🍽 🖐 🛍 📶 ✖ 🔋 💻

🅰🅰🅰 ▼▼▼▼ **Hyatt Place Lexington** 🅷
(859) 296-0091. **$109-$249.** 2001 Bryant Rd 40509. I-75 exit 108, 0.3 mi w on Man O' War Blvd, just s on Pleasant Ridge Dr, 0.3 mi e on Justice Dr, then just s. Int corridors. **Pets:** Medium. $75 one-time fee/room. Service with restrictions, crate. 🆂🅰🆅🅴 🍽 🖐 🛍 📶 ✖ 🔋 💻

▼▼▼▼ **La Quinta Inn & Suites Lexington South/Hamburg** 🅷
(859) 543-1877. **$81-$218.** 100 Canebrake Dr 40509. I-75 exit 104, just e. Int corridors. **Pets:** Accepted. 🖐 🛍 📶 ✖ 🔋 💻

▼▼▼▼ **Marriott Griffin Gate Resort & Spa** 🅷
(859) 231-5100. **$76-$400.** 1800 Newtown Pike 40511. I-75/64 exit 115, 0.5 mi s on SR 922. Int corridors. **Pets:** Accepted. 🍽 🛍 ✖ 🛁 ✖ 🔋 💻

🅰🅰🅰 ▼▼ **Red Roof Inn Lexington South** 🅷
(859) 277-9400. **$55-$99.** 2651 Wilhite Dr 40503. SR 4 (New Circle Rd) exit 19, just n on US 27. Ext corridors. **Pets:** Accepted. 🆂🅰🆅🅴 🖐 📶 ✖ 🔋 💻

▼▼▼▼ **Residence Inn by Marriott Lexington Keeneland/Airport** 🅷
(859) 296-0460. **$85-$240.** 3110 Wall St 40513. Jct SR 4 (New Circle Rd) and US 68 (Harrodsburg Rd), just sw. Int corridors. **Pets:** Accepted. 🖐 🛍 ✖ 🔋 💻

▼▼▼▼ **Residence Inn by Marriott Lexington North** 🅷
(859) 231-6191. **$48-$239.** 1080 Newtown Pike 40511. I-75/64 exit 115, 1 mi s on SR 922. Ext corridors. **Pets:** Other species. $75 one-time fee/room. Service with restrictions, crate. 🖐 🛍 📶 ✖ 🔋 💻

▼▼▼▼ **Residence Inn by Marriott Lexington South/Hamburg Place** 🅷
(859) 263-9979. **$94-$263.** 2688 Pink Pigeon Pkwy 40509. I-75 exit 108, 0.6 mi w, then 0.3 mi n. Int corridors. **Pets:** Large, other species. $100 one-time fee/room. Service with restrictions, supervision. 🍽 🖐 🛍 📶 ✖ 🔋 💻

▼▼▼▼ **TownePlace Suites by Marriott Lexington South/Hamburg Place** 🅷
(859) 263-0018. **$80-$211.** 1790 Vendor Way 40509. I-75 exit 108, 0.6 mi w on Man O'War Blvd, then 0.3 mi n on Pink Pigeon Pkwy. Int corridors. **Pets:** Accepted. 🍽 🖐 📶 ✖ 🔋 💻

LONDON

▼▼▼▼ Country Inn & Suites By Carlson H
(606) 878-9900. Call for rates. 2035 W Hwy 192 40741. I-75 exit 38,
just e. Int corridors. Pets: Accepted. ⓜ ⌨ ☎ 🖥 ✕ 🖨 🖵

▼▼ Red Roof Inn London I-75 H
(606) 862-8844. $59-$120. 110 Melcon Ln 40741. I-75 exit 41, southwest corner. Int corridors. Pets: Accepted.
ⓜ ⌨ ☎ ✕ 🖨 🖵

LOUISA

▼▼ Super 8-Louisa H
(606) 638-7888. $63-$77. 191 Falls Creek Dr 41230. Jct US 23 and SR
3. Int corridors. Pets: Accepted. ⓜ ☎ 🖨 🖵

LOUISVILLE

▼▼▼▼ 21c Museum Hotel H
(502) 217-6300. Call for rates. 700 W Main St 40202. Jct 7th and
Main sts. Int corridors. Pets: Accepted. ⓣ ⓜ ✕ ☎ ✕ 🖵

AAA ▼▼▼ Aloft Louisville Downtown H ✿
(502) 583-1888. $129-$1400. 102 W Main St 40202. Jct First St. Int
corridors. Pets: Medium, dogs only. Supervision.
SAVE ⓣ ☎ ✕ 🖨 🖵

▼▼ Candlewood Suites Louisville Airport H
(502) 357-3577. Call for rates. 1367 Gardiner Ln 40213. I-264 exit 14,
just s on Poplar Level Rd, then 0.4 mi e. Int corridors. Pets: Medium,
other species. $25 one-time fee/room. Service with restrictions, crate.
ⓣ ☎ ✕ 🖨 🖵

AAA ▼▼▼ Crowne Plaza Louisville H
(502) 367-2251. Call for rates. 830 Phillips Ln 40209. I-264 exit 11
(Fairgrounds/Expo Center Main Gate). Int corridors. Pets: Accepted.
SAVE ⓣ ⓜ ⌨ ☎ ✕ 🖨 🖵

▼▼▼ Drury Inn & Suites Louisville North H
(502) 425-5500. $95-$220. 9597 Brownsboro Rd 40241. I-265 exit 34,
just w. Int corridors. Pets: Accepted. ⓜ ☎ ✕ 🖨 🖵

AAA ▼▼ La Quinta Inn & Suites Louisville Airport
Expo H
(502) 368-0007. $90-$669. 4125 Preston Hwy 40213. I-65 exit 130, 1
mi n. Int corridors. Pets: Accepted. SAVE ⓜ ⌨ ☎ ✕ 🖨 🖵

AAA ▼▼▼ Red Roof Inn Louisville Fair And Expo H
(502) 456-2993. $55-$250. 3322 Red Roof Inn Pl 40218. I-264 exit 15
eastbound; exit 15B westbound, 0.3 mi s. Ext corridors. Pets: Accepted.
SAVE ☎ ✕ 🖨 🖵

▼▼▼ Residence Inn by Marriott-Louisville Airport H
(502) 363-8800. $98-$323. 700 Phillips Ln 40209. I-264 exit 11
(Fairgrounds/Expo Center Main Gate), 0.4 mi w. Int corridors.
Pets: Accepted. ⓜ ⌨ ☎ ✕ 🖨 🖵

▼▼▼ Residence Inn by Marriott Louisville
Downtown H
(502) 589-8998. $101-$347. 333 E Market St 40202. Jct Preston St. Int
corridors. Pets: Accepted. ⓜ ⌨ ☎ ✕ 🖨 🖵

▼▼▼ Residence Inn by Marriott Louisville East H
(502) 425-1821. $98-$282. 120 N Hurstbourne Pkwy 40222. I-64 exit
15, 1.8 mi n. Ext corridors. Pets: $100 one-time fee/room. Service with
restrictions, crate. ⌨ ☎ ✕ 🖨 🖵

▼▼▼ Residence Inn by Marriott-Louisville NE H
(502) 412-1311. $93-$284. 3500 Springhurst Commons Dr 40241. I-265
exit 32, 0.7 mi w on Westport Rd, then just n. Int corridors.
Pets: Accepted. ⓣ ⓜ ⌨ ☎ ✕ 🖨 🖵

AAA ▼▼▼▼ The Seelbach Hilton Louisville H
(502) 585-3200. $179-$299. 500 4th 40202. I-65 exit 136C (Muhammad
Ali Blvd). Int corridors. Pets: Accepted.
SAVE ⓣ ⓜ ☎ ✕ 🖨 🖵

▼▼▼ Staybridge Suites Louisville East H
(502) 244-9511. Call for rates. 11711 Gateworth Way 40299. I-64 exit
17, just n. Int corridors. Pets: Accepted. ⓜ ⌨ ☎ 🖨 🖵

MADISONVILLE

▼▼ Baymont Inn & Suites Madisonville Inn H
(270) 821-2121. $90-$118. 1891 Lantaff Blvd 42431. I-69 exit 116, just
w. Int corridors. Pets: Small, dogs only. $20 daily fee/pet. Service with
restrictions, supervision. ⓜ ⌨ ☎ ✕ 🖨 🖵

MAYSVILLE

▼▼ French Quarter Inn H
(606) 564-8000. $89-$199. 25 E McDonald Pkwy 41056. Corner of
Limestone St and McDonald Pkwy; near Ohio River Bridge; downtown.
Int corridors. Pets: Small. Designated rooms, service with restrictions,
supervision. ⓣ ⓜ ⌨ ☎ 🖨 🖵

MOREHEAD

AAA ▼▼▼ Best Western Eagles Inn H
(606) 784-5796. $99-$110. 110 Toms Dr 40351. I-64 exit 137 (SR 32),
just sw. Int corridors. Pets: $20 daily fee/room. Service with restrictions,
supervision. SAVE ⓜ ⌨ ☎ ✕ 🖨 🖵

AAA ▼▼▼ Comfort Inn & Suites H
(606) 780-7378. $89-$209. 2650 Kentucky 801 N 40351. I-64 exit 133,
just s. Int corridors. Pets: Small. $10 daily fee/room. Supervision.
SAVE ⓣ ⓜ ⌨ ☎ 🖨 🖵

MOUNT VERNON

▼▼▼ Days Inn-Renfro Valley/Mt. Vernon M
(606) 256-3300. $55-$120. 1630 Richmond St 40456. I-75 exit 62, just
w. Ext corridors. Pets: Small. $20 one-time fee/pet. Service with restric-
tions, supervision. ☎ 🖨 🖵

MURRAY

AAA ▼▼▼ Best Western University Inn M
(270) 753-5353. $93-$130. 1503 N 12th St 42071. 1.9 mi n on US 641.
Ext corridors. Pets: Accepted. SAVE ⌨ ☎ 🖨 🖵

OAK GROVE

▼▼▼▼ Candlewood Suites Fort Campbell - Oak
Grove H
(270) 605-9300. Call for rates. 12885 Fort Campbell Blvd 42262. I-24
exit 84, just s. Int corridors. Pets: Accepted. ⓣ ⓜ ☎ 🖨 🖵

▼▼▼ Quality Inn @ Ft. Campbell H
(270) 439-3311. $75-$119. 201 Auburn St 42262. I-24 exit 86, just s.
Ext corridors. Pets: Medium. $20 daily fee/pet. Service with restrictions.
⌨ ☎ 🖨 🖵

▼▼▼ Sleep Inn & Suites H
(270) 640-7170. $64-$178. 220 Auburn St 42262. I-24 exit 86, just e.
Int corridors. Pets: Accepted. ⓣ ⓜ ☎ ✕ 🖨 🖵

PADUCAH (Restaurants p. 614)

▼▼▼ Candlewood Suites H
(270) 442-3969. $89-$129. 3940 Coleman Crossing Cir 42001. I-24 exit
4, just nw. Int corridors. Pets: Accepted. ⓣ ⓜ ☎ 🖨 🖵

AAA ▼▼▼ Courtyard by Marriott H
(270) 442-3600. $82-$198. 3835 Technology Dr 42001. I-24 exit 4, just
ne. Int corridors. Pets: Accepted.
SAVE ⓣ ⓜ ⌨ ☎ ✕ 🖨 🖵

▼▼▼ **Drury Inn** H
(270) 443-3313. **$90-$155.** 3975 Hinkleville Rd 42001. I-24 exit 4, just e. Int corridors. **Pets:** Accepted. 🔇M 🛏 📶 ✕ 🛎 🖥

▼▼▼ **Drury Suites** H
(270) 441-0024. **$105-$170.** 2930 James Sanders Blvd 42001. I-24 exit 4, just s. Int corridors. **Pets:** Accepted. 🔇M 🛏 📶 ✕ 🛎 🖥

▼▼▼ **La Quinta Inn & Suites Paducah** H
(270) 443-4800. **Call for rates.** 3960 Coleman Crossing Cir 42001. I-24 exit 4, just nw. Int corridors. **Pets:** Accepted.
🍴 🔇M 📶 ✕ 🛎 🖥

▼▼ **Pear Tree Inn by Drury** H
(270) 444-7200. **$71-$105.** 5006 Hinkleville 42001. I-24 exit 4, just w. Int corridors. **Pets:** Accepted. 🛏 📶 🛎 🖥

▼▼▼ **Residence Inn by Marriott** H
(270) 444-3966. **$81-$240.** 3900 Coleman Crossing Cir 42001. I-24 exit 4, just nw. Int corridors. **Pets:** $50 one-time fee/room. Service with restrictions. 🍴 🔇M 🛏 📶 ✕ 🛎 🖥

RICHMOND
▼▼▼ **Holiday Inn Express Hotel & Suites** H
(859) 624-4055. **Call for rates.** 1990 Colby Taylor Dr 40475. I-75 exit 87, just w. Int corridors. **Pets:** Medium. $25 daily fee/pet. Designated rooms, service with restrictions, supervision.
🔇M 🛏 📶 ✕ 🛎 🖥

SHELBYVILLE
AAA ▼▼▼ **Best Western Shelbyville Lodge** H
(502) 633-4400. **$70-$150.** 115 Isaac Shelby Dr 40065. I-64 exit 32, 0.5 mi n on SR 55. Int corridors. **Pets:** Accepted.
SAVE 🔇M 🛏 📶 🛎 🖥

▼▼ **Econo Lodge** H
(502) 633-5771. **Call for rates.** 100 Howard Dr 40065. I-64 exit 32, 0.5 mi n on SR 55. Int corridors. **Pets:** Accepted. 🔇M 📶 ✕ 🛎 🖥

▼▼ **Ramada** H
(502) 633-9933. **$84-$169, 3 day notice.** 251 Breighton Cir 40065. I-64 exit 32, just s. Int corridors. **Pets:** Accepted.
🔇M 🛏 📶 ✕ 🛎 🖥

SHEPHERDSVILLE
AAA ▼▼ **Best Western Shepherdsville** H
(502) 543-7097. **$89-$160.** 211 S Lakeview Dr 40165. I-65 exit 117 (SR 44 W), just se. Int corridors. **Pets:** Designated rooms, service with restrictions, crate. SAVE 🛏 📶 ✕ 🛎 🖥

▼▼ **Comfort Inn Louisville South** H
(502) 955-5566. **$109-$189.** 191 Brenton Way 40165. I-65 exit 121, just ne. Int corridors. **Pets:** Medium. $25 one-time fee/pet. Service with restrictions, supervision. 🛏 📶 ✕ 🛎 🖥

▼▼ **Sleep Inn & Suites-Louisville South** H
(502) 921-1001. **$64-$199.** 130 Spring Pointe Dr 40165. I-65 exit 117 (SR 44 W), just e. Int corridors. **Pets:** Other species. $25 one-time fee/room. Service with restrictions, crate. 🔇M 🛏 📶 ✕ 🛎 🖥

SMITHS GROVE
▼ **Bryce Inn** M
(270) 563-5141. **Call for rates.** 592 S Main St 42171. I-65 exit 38, 0.3 mi n. Ext corridors. **Pets:** Accepted. 🛏 📶 🛎 🖥

SOMERSET
▼▼ **Quality Inn & Suites** H
(606) 678-2023. **$69-$129.** 240 N Hwy 27 42503. Jct SR 80, just n; at traffic light 2. Int corridors. **Pets:** Accepted.
🍴 🔇M 🛏 📶 🛎 🖥

WEST LIBERTY
▼▼ **Days Inn** H
(606) 743-4206. **$70-$105.** 1613 W Main St 41472. Jct SR 519 and 460, just w. Int corridors. **Pets:** Other species. $10 daily fee/room. Service with restrictions. 🔇M 📶 🛎 🖥

WILLIAMSBURG
▼▼ **Cumberland Inn** H
(606) 539-4100. **Call for rates.** 649 S 10th St 40769. I-75 exit 11, just e on SR 92, then just n on SR 2386. Int corridors. **Pets:** Accepted.
🍴 🔇M 🛏 📶 ✕ 🛎 🖥

WINCHESTER
AAA ▼▼▼ **Best Western Winchester Hotel** M
(859) 744-7210. **$79-$299.** 1307 W Lexington Ave 40391. I-64 exit 94 (US 60), 0.9 mi se. Ext corridors. **Pets:** Accepted.
SAVE 🛏 📶 ✕ 🛎 🖥

LOUISIANA

ALEXANDRIA
AAA ▼▼▼ **Best Western of Alexandria Inn & Suites & Conf. Ctr.** H
(318) 445-5530. **$89-$129.** 2720 N MacArthur Dr 71303. I-49 exit 86 (MacArthur Dr), 1.3 mi sw. Ext/int corridors. **Pets:** Accepted.
SAVE 🔇M 🛏 📶 🛎 🖥

▼▼ **Candlewood Suites** H
(318) 427-9020. **Call for rates.** 2344 N MacArthur Dr 71303. I-49 exit 86 (MacArthur Dr), just s. Int corridors. **Pets:** Accepted.
🔇M 📶 🛎 🖥

▼▼▼ **Hampton Inn & Suites by Hilton** H
(318) 445-4449. **$109-$199.** 6124 Calhoun 71303. I-49 exit 90 (Air Base Rd), just w. Int corridors. **Pets:** Accepted.
🔇M 🛏 📶 ✕ 🛎 🖥

▼▼▼ **La Quinta Inn & Suites Alexandria Airport** H
(318) 442-3700. **$79-$204.** 6116 W Calhoun Dr 71303. I-49 exit 90 (Air Base Rd), just w. Int corridors. **Pets:** Accepted.
🔇M 🛏 📶 🛎 🖥

AVONDALE
▼▼ **Candlewood Suites Avondale/New Orleans** H
(504) 875-3500. **Call for rates.** 3079 Hwy 90 W 70094. 2.6 mi w off Clearview Pkwy. Int corridors. **Pets:** Large, other species. $75 one-time fee/pet. Service with restrictions, crate. 🔇M 📶 🛎 🖥

BATON ROUGE *(Restaurants p. 614)*

Best Western Chateau Louisianne Suite Hotel 🅷
(225) 927-6700. **$79-$100.** 710 N Lobdell Blvd 70806. 4.6 mi e on Florida Blvd, 0.3 mi n. Int corridors. **Pets:** Accepted.

Best Western Plus Richmond Inn & Suites-Baton Rouge 🅷
(225) 924-6500. **$109-$159.** 2683 Energy Dr 70808. I-10 exit 158 (College Dr), just n, just e on Corporate Dr, then just s. Int corridors. **Pets:** Accepted.

Chase Suites by Woodfin 🅷
(225) 927-5630. **$109-$269.** 5522 Corporate Blvd 70808. I-10 exit 158 (College Dr), just n, then just e. Ext corridors. **Pets:** Accepted.

Drury Inn & Suites Baton Rouge 🅷
(225) 766-2022. **$94-$159.** 7939 Essen Park Ave 70809. I-10 exit 160 (Essen Ln), just s. Int corridors. **Pets:** Accepted.

Hilton Baton Rouge Capitol Center 🅷
(225) 344-5866. **$139-$219.** 201 Lafayette St 70801. I-110 exit 1C (Florida Blvd), 0.5 mi w to Lafayette St, then just s. Int corridors. **Pets:** Accepted.

Hotel Indigo Baton Rouge Downtown Riverfront 🅷
(225) 343-1515. **$129-$269.** 200 Convention St 70801. Corner of Lafayette St; downtown. Int corridors. **Pets:** Accepted.

Hyatt Place Baton Rouge/I-10 🅷
(225) 769-4400. **$89-$289.** 6080 Bluebonnet Blvd 70809. I-10 exit 162 (Bluebonnet Blvd), just s. Int corridors. **Pets:** Medium, dogs only. $75 one-time fee/room. Service with restrictions, supervision.

Microtel Inn & Suites by Wyndham Baton Rouge Airport 🅷
(225) 356-9191. **$60-$116.** 3444 Harding Blvd 70807. I-110 exit 6, just e. Int corridors. **Pets:** Accepted.

Quality Suites 🅷
(225) 615-8890. **$67-$169.** 1755 O'Neal Ln 70816. I-12 exit 7, just n. Int corridors. **Pets:** Accepted.

Radisson Hotel Baton Rouge 🅷
(225) 236-4000. **Call for rates.** 2445 S Acadian Thruway 70808. I-10 exit 157B, just n. Int corridors. **Pets:** Accepted.

Red Roof Inn Baton Rouge 🅷
(225) 275-6600. **$50-$90.** 11314 Boardwalk Dr 70816. I-12 exit 4, just n. Ext corridors. **Pets:** Accepted.

Residence Inn by Marriott-Baton Rouge-Siegen Lane 🅷
(225) 293-8700. **$97-$193.** 10333 N Mall Dr 70809. I-10 exit 163 (Siegen Ln), just s; in Siegen Marketplace. Int corridors. **Pets:** Accepted.

TownePlace Suites by Marriott Baton Rouge South 🅷
(225) 819-2112. **$84-$136.** 8735 Summa Ave 70809. I-10 exit 162 (Bluebonnet Blvd), just s to Picardy Ave, just w to Summa Ave, then 0.5 mi nw. Int corridors. **Pets:** Medium. $75 one-time fee/pet. Service with restrictions, crate.

BELLE CHASSE

Microtel Inn & Suites by Wyndham, Belle Chasse 🅷
(504) 684-8540. **$80-$190.** 14740 Hwy 23 70037. Jct SR 428 and 23, 14.4 mi s. Int corridors. **Pets:** Accepted.

BOSSIER CITY

Holiday Inn Express & Suites 🅷
(318) 841-9800. **Call for rates.** 7970 E Texas St 71111. I-20 exit 26 (I-220 W), exit 17A, just n. Int corridors. **Pets:** Accepted.

Homewood Suites Shreveport/Bossier City 🅷
(318) 759-1940. **$109-$179.** 2015 Old Minden Rd 71111. I-20 exit 21 (Old Minden Rd), just e. Int corridors. **Pets:** $20 daily fee/pet. Service with restrictions, crate.

Microtel Inn & Suites by Wyndham Bossier City 🅷
(318) 742-7882. **$60-$80.** 2713 Village Ln 71112. I-20 exit 22 (Airline Dr), just s, then just w. Int corridors. **Pets:** Accepted.

TownePlace Suites by Marriott 🅷 🐾
(318) 741-9090. **$94-$131.** 1009 Gould Dr 71111. I-20 exit 21 (Old Minden Rd), just e, then 0.5 mi n. Int corridors. **Pets:** Medium, other species. $50 one-time fee/room. Service with restrictions, supervision.

BREAUX BRIDGE

Holiday Inn Express of Breaux Bridge 🅷
(337) 667-8913. **Call for rates.** 2942 H Grand Point Hwy 70517. I-10 exit 115, just n. Int corridors. **Pets:** Other species. $25 one-time fee/room. Service with restrictions.

Microtel Inn & Suites by Wyndham Breaux Bridge 🅷
(337) 332-0432. **$65-$95.** 2280 Rees St Ext 70517. I-10 exit 109 (Breaux Bridge), just e. Int corridors. **Pets:** Small. $25 one-time fee/room. Designated rooms, supervision.

BROUSSARD

La Quinta Inn & Suites Broussard - Lafayette Area 🅷
(337) 330-8081. **$90-$207.** 104 Sweetland Ave 70518. US 90, just w on Albertson Pkwy, just n. Int corridors. **Pets:** Accepted.

COVINGTON *(Restaurants p. 614)*

Best Western Northpark Inn 🅷 🐾
(985) 892-2681. **$80-$170.** 625 N Hwy 190 70433. I-12 exit 63B, just n. Ext/int corridors. **Pets:** Medium, dogs only. $20 daily fee/pet. Designated rooms, service with restrictions, crate.

Residence Inn by Marriott New Orleans Covington/North Shore 🅷
(985) 246-7222. **$102-$169.** 101 Park Pl Blvd 70433. I-12 exit 63B, 0.5 mi n, then just w. Int corridors. **Pets:** Other species. $100 one-time fee/room. Service with restrictions.

Staybridge Suites Covington-Northpark 🅷
(985) 892-0003. **$109-$299.** 140 Holiday Blvd 70433. I-12 exit 63B, just n, then just w. Int corridors. **Pets:** Large, other species. $15 daily fee/room. Service with restrictions, crate.

DELHI

Best Western Delhi Inn 🅼
(318) 878-5126. **$85-$95.** 135 Snider Rd 71232. I-20 exit 153, just s. Ext corridors. **Pets:** Accepted.

GONZALES

▼▼ TownePlace Suites by Marriott Baton Rouge Gonzales 🅷
(225) 450-3400. **$101-$179.** 2823 S Outfitters Dr 70737. I-10 exit 177, just w, then just s. Int corridors. **Pets:** Accepted.
🅖🅜 📶 ✕ 🔒 💻

GRETNA

▼▼ La Quinta Inn New Orleans West Bank/Gretna 🅷
(504) 368-5600. **$79-$581.** 50 Terry Pkwy 70056. US 90 business route exit 9A (Terry Pkwy) southbound; US 90 (Westbank Expwy) exit 9 (Terry Pkwy/General DeGaulle) northbound. Ext corridors.
Pets: Accepted. 🔜 📶 🔒 💻

HAMMOND *(Restaurants p. 614)*

◈◈ ▼▼▼ Historic Michabelle Inn 🅲🅸
(985) 419-0550. **Call for rates.** 1106 S Holly St 70403. I-12 exit 40 (US 51), 0.8 mi n, just e on Old Covington Hwy, then n, follow signs. Ext/int corridors. **Pets:** Accepted. 🆂🅰🆅🅴 🍴 🔜 📶 ✕ 🏊 🔒 💻

▼▼ Lexington Inn 🅷
(985) 345-0003. **Call for rates.** 46053 N Puma Dr 70401. I-55 exit 32 (Wardline/University), just e. Ext corridors. **Pets:** Accepted.
🍴 🔜 📶 🔒 💻

HARAHAN

▼▼▼ TownePlace Suites by Marriott New Orleans Metairie 🅷
(504) 818-2400. **$98-$169.** 5424 Citrus Blvd 70123. I-10 exit 226 (Clearview Pkwy S), 3 mi s, then just w. Int corridors. **Pets:** Accepted.
🅖🅜 📶 ✕ 🔒 💻

HOUMA

▼▼ Microtel Inn & Suites by Wyndham Houma 🅷
(985) 223-9910. **$68-$89.** 1801 Martin Luther King Blvd 70360. US 90 exit 202, 3.4 mi s on Main St to Martin Luther King Blvd, then just w. Int corridors. **Pets:** Accepted. 🍴 🅖🅜 🔜 📶 🔒 💻

IOWA

▼▼▼ La Quinta Inn & Suites Iowa 🅷
(337) 582-2261. **$92-$253.** 204 W Frontage Rd 70647. I-10 exit 43, just n. Int corridors. **Pets:** Accepted. 🍴 🔜 📶 ✕ 🔒 💻

KENNER

▼▼ La Quinta Inn New Orleans (Airport) 🅷
(504) 466-1401. **$82-$570.** 2610 Williams Blvd 70062. I-10 exit 223A (Williams Blvd), 0.3 mi s. Int corridors. **Pets:** Accepted.
🍴 🅖🅜 🔜 📶 🔒 💻

KINDER

◈◈ ▼▼ Best Western Inn At Coushatta 🅷
(337) 738-4800. **$99-$169.** 12102 US Hwy 165 70648. 5 mi n of jct US 190/165. Int corridors. **Pets:** $10 deposit/pet. Service with restrictions, supervision. 🆂🅰🆅🅴 🅖🅜 🔜 📶 🔒 💻

▼▼▼ Seven Clans Hotel 🅷
(337) 738-3008. **$99-$339.** 797 Coushatta Dr 70648. 5 mi n of jct US 190/165. Int corridors. **Pets:** Accepted. 🍴 🅖🅜 ✕ 📶 ✕ 💻

LAFAYETTE *(Restaurants p. 614)*

▼▼ Baymont Inn & Suites Lafayette Airport 🅷
(337) 291-2916. **$69-$86.** 2200 NE Evangeline Thruway 70501. I-10 exit 103A, just s. Int corridors. **Pets:** Accepted. 🔜 📶 🔒 💻

◈◈ ▼▼ Best Western Lafayette Inn 🅷 🐾
(337) 769-2900. **$72-$90.** 2207 NW Evangeline Thruway 70501. I-10 exit 103A, just s. Int corridors. **Pets:** Medium, dogs only. $20 daily fee/pet. Designated rooms, service with restrictions, supervision.
🆂🅰🆅🅴 🔜 📶 ✕ 🔒 💻

▼▼▼ Drury Inn & Suites-Lafayette 🅷
(337) 262-0202. **$89-$139.** 120 Alcide Dominique 70506. I-10 exit 101, just s on University Ave, then just w. Int corridors. **Pets:** Accepted.
🅖🅜 🔜 📶 ✕ 🔒 💻

▼▼▼ Homewood Suites by Hilton Lafayette Airport 🅷
(337) 264-6044. **$109-$189.** 201 Kaliste Saloom Rd 70508. I-10 exit 103A, 3.9 mi s on US 90/Evangeline Thruway to Kaliste Saloom Rd, then 1 mi w. Int corridors. **Pets:** Accepted. 🅖🅜 🔜 📶 🔒 💻

▼▼ Pear Tree Inn By Drury 🅷
(337) 289-9907. **$59-$109.** 126 Alcide Dominique 70506. I-10 exit 101, just s on University Ave, then just w. Int corridors. **Pets:** Accepted.
🅖🅜 🔜 📶 🔒 💻

▼▼▼ Residence Inn by Marriott, Lafayette Airport 🅷
(337) 232-3341. **$104-$186.** 128 James Comeaux Rd 70508. I-10 exit 103A, 3.9 mi s on US 90/Evangeline Thruway to Kaliste Saloom Rd, then 1 mi w. Int corridors. **Pets:** Large, other species. $100 one-time fee/room. Service with restrictions, supervision.
🍴 🅖🅜 🔜 ✕ 📶 ✕ 🔒 💻

▼▼▼ Staybridge Suites Lafayette Airport 🅷 🐾
(337) 267-4666. **$99-$229.** 129 E Kaliste Saloom Rd 70508. I-10 exit 103A, 3.9 mi s on US 90/Evangeline Thruway to Kaliste Saloom Rd, then 0.7 mi w. Int corridors. **Pets:** Medium. $15 daily fee/room. Designated rooms, service with restrictions, supervision.
🅖🅜 🔜 ✕ 📶 ✕ 🔒 💻

LAKE CHARLES *(Restaurants p. 614)*

◈◈ ▼▼▼ La Quinta Inn & Suites-Prien Lake 🅷
(337) 478-9889. **$97-$309.** 1201 W Prien Lake Rd 70601. I-210 exit 4 (Nelson Rd), just n, then 0.5 mi e. Int corridors. **Pets:** Accepted.
🆂🅰🆅🅴 🔜 📶 ✕ 🔒 💻

▼▼▼ Wingate by Wyndham Lake Charles Casino Area 🅷
(337) 502-5112. **$79-$250.** 1731 W Prien Lake Rd 70601. I-210 exit 4 (Nelson Rd), just n, then 0.3 mi e. Int corridors. **Pets:** Other species. $35 daily fee/pet. Service with restrictions, crate.
🅖🅜 📶 ✕ 🔒 💻

LA PLACE

◈◈ ▼▼ Best Western La Place Inn 🅼
(985) 651-4000. **$90-$130, 3 day notice.** 4289 Main St 70068. I-10 exit 209, just s. Ext corridors. **Pets:** Accepted. 🆂🅰🆅🅴 🔜 📶 🔒 💻

METAIRIE

▼▼ La Quinta Inn New Orleans Causeway 🅼
(504) 835-8511. **$71-$581.** 3100 S I-10 Service Rd E 70001. I-10 exit 228 (Causeway Blvd), just s. Ext corridors. **Pets:** Accepted.
🅖🅜 🔜 📶 🔒 💻

◈◈ ▼▼▼ Residence Inn by Marriott New Orleans Metairie 🅷
(504) 832-0888. **$136-$220, 3 day notice.** 3 Galleria Blvd 70001. I-10 exit 228 (Causeway Blvd), just se to 36th St, then just e. Int corridors.
Pets: Accepted. 🆂🅰🆅🅴 🅖🅜 🔜 📶 ✕ 🔒 💻

◈◈ ▼▼▼ Sheraton Metairie New Orleans 🅷
(504) 837-6707. **Call for rates.** 4 Galleria Blvd 70001. I-10 exit 228 (Causeway Blvd), just s to 36th St, just e, then just n. Int corridors.
Pets: Accepted. 🆂🅰🆅🅴 🍴 🅖🅜 🔜 📶 ✕ 🔒 💻

MINDEN

AAA ▼▼▼ **Best Western Minden Inn** 🅷
(318) 377-1001. **$96-$105.** 1411 Sibley Rd 71055. I-20 exit 47, just n. Ext corridors. **Pets:** Medium. $15 daily fee/pet. Service with restrictions, supervision. 🆂🅰🆅🅴 &ᴹ ⌦ 🛜 🅱 🖵

MONROE

▼▼▼▼ **Residence Inn by Marriott** 🅷
(318) 387-0210. **$116-$199.** 4960 Millhaven Rd 71203. I-20 exit 120, just n of Pecanland Mall. Int corridors. **Pets:** Accepted.
&ᴹ ⌦ 🛜 ✕ 🅱 🖵

AAA ▼▼▼▼ **TownePlace Suites by Marriott** 🅷
(318) 387-7277. **$112-$158.** 4919 Pecanland Mall Dr 71203. I-20 exit 120, just w of Pecanland Mall. Int corridors. **Pets:** Accepted.
🆂🅰🆅🅴 &ᴹ ⌦ 🛜 ✕ 🅱 🖵

MORGAN CITY

AAA ▼▼ **Best Western Morgan City Inn & Suites** 🅷
(985) 385-9175. **$70-$90.** 1011 Brashear Ave 70380. US 90 exit Morgan City/SR 70 eastbound; exit Brashear Ave westbound, just n of jct US 90 and SR 70. Ext corridors. **Pets:** Other species. $25 one-time fee/pet. Designated rooms, service with restrictions, crate.
🆂🅰🆅🅴 &ᴹ ⌦ 🛜 🅱 🖵

▼▼ **Clarion Inn** 🅷
(985) 385-2200. **Call for rates.** 520 Roderick St 70380. 1.5 mi s of jct US 90 and SR 70. Ext corridors. **Pets:** Accepted.
🍽 &ᴹ ⌦ 🛜 🅱 🖵

▼▼ **La Quinta Inn & Suites Morgan City** 🅷
(985) 300-0200. **$76-$218.** 2018 Allison St 70380. US 90 exit Dr Martin Luther King Jr Blvd, just s. Int corridors. **Pets:** Accepted.
&ᴹ ⌦ 🛜 ✕ 🅱 🖵

NEW IBERIA

AAA ▼▼▼▼ **La Quinta Inn & Suites** 🅷
(337) 321-6000. **$86-$174.** 611A Queen City Dr 70560. US 90 exit SR 14, just e. Int corridors. **Pets:** Accepted. 🆂🅰🆅🅴 ⌦ 🛜 ✕ 🅱 🖵

NEW ORLEANS *(Restaurants p. 614)*

▼▼▼ **ACE Hotel New Orleans** 🅷
(504) 900-1180. **Call for rates.** 600 Carondelet St 70130. Jct Lafayette St. Int corridors. **Pets:** Accepted. 🍽 &ᴹ 🛜 ✕ 🅱

AAA ▼▼▼ **Aloft New Orleans Downtown** 🅷
(504) 581-9225. **$89-$409.** 225 Baronne St 70112. Corner of Baronne and Gravier sts. Int corridors. **Pets:** Accepted.
🆂🅰🆅🅴 &ᴹ 🛜 ✕ 🅱 🖵

AAA ▼▼▼ **Best Western Plus St. Charles Inn** 🅷 ❀
(504) 899-8888. **$139-$310.** 3636 St. Charles Ave 70115. US 90 business route exit St. Charles Ave, 1.8 mi s. Int corridors. **Pets:** Other species. $20 daily fee/room. Service with restrictions.
🆂🅰🆅🅴 🛜 ✕ 🅱 🖵

AAA ▼▼▼ **Best Western Plus St. Christopher Hotel** 🅷
(504) 648-0444. **$79-$309, 3 day notice.** 114 Magazine St 70130. Between Canal and Common sts. Int corridors. **Pets:** Accepted.
🆂🅰🆅🅴 &ᴹ ⌦ ✕ 🅱 🖵

AAA ▼▼▼ **The Bienville House Hotel** 🅷
(504) 529-2345. **$99-$369, 3 day notice.** 320 Decatur St 70130. Between Conti and Bienville sts. Ext/int corridors. **Pets:** Accepted.
🆂🅰🆅🅴 🍽 &ᴹ ⌦ 🛜 ✕ 🅱 🖵

▼▼▼ **Drury Inn & Suites-New Orleans** 🅷
(504) 529-7800. **$99-$259.** 820 Poydras St 70112. Between Baronne and Carondelet sts. Int corridors. **Pets:** Accepted.
&ᴹ ⌦ 🛜 ✕ 🅱 🖵

AAA ▼▼▼▼ **Embassy Suites by Hilton New Orleans Convention Center** 🅷
(504) 525-1993. **$109-$189.** 315 Julia St 70130. Corner of Julia and S Peters sts. Int corridors. **Pets:** Accepted.
🆂🅰🆅🅴 🍽 &ᴹ ⌦ 🛜 ✕ 🅱 🖵

AAA ▼▼▼▼ **Hotel Indigo New Orleans Garden District** 🅷
(504) 522-3650. **$149-$409.** 2203 St. Charles Ave 70130. 1 mi w of US 90; corner of Jackson Ave. Int corridors. **Pets:** Accepted.
🆂🅰🆅🅴 🍽 &ᴹ 🛜 ✕ 🅱 🖵

AAA ▼▼▼▼ **Hotel Monteleone** 🅷
(504) 523-3341. **$159-$479, 3 day notice.** 214 Royal St 70130. Between Iberville and Bienville sts. Int corridors. **Pets:** Accepted.
🆂🅰🆅🅴 🅴🅲🅾 🍽 &ᴹ ⌦ 🛜 ✕ 🅱 🖵

AAA ▼▼▼▼ **Hyatt Place New Orleans Convention Center** 🅷 ❀
(504) 524-1881. **$129-$499.** 881 Convention Center Blvd 70130. Between N Diamond and St. Joseph sts. Int corridors. **Pets:** Medium. $75 one-time fee/room. Service with restrictions, crate.
🆂🅰🆅🅴 🍽 🛜 ✕ 🅱 🖵

AAA ▼▼▼▼ **InterContinental New Orleans** 🅷
(504) 525-5566. **Call for rates.** 444 St. Charles Ave 70130. Between Perdido and Poydras sts. Int corridors. **Pets:** Accepted.
🆂🅰🆅🅴 🍽 &ᴹ ⌦ 🛜 ✕ 🅱 🖵

▼▼▼ **La Quinta Inn & Suites New Orleans French Quarter** 🅷
(504) 598-9977. **$86-$600.** 301 Camp St 70130. Corner of Gravier and Camp sts. Int corridors. **Pets:** Accepted. &ᴹ ⌦ 🛜 ✕ 🅱 🖵

AAA ▼▼▼▼ **Le Méridien New Orleans** 🅷
(504) 525-9444. **$129-$359.** 333 Poydras St 70130. Jct Poydras and S Peters sts; close to Riverfront area/convention center. Int corridors.
Pets: Accepted. 🆂🅰🆅🅴 🍽 &ᴹ ⌦ 🛜 ✕ 🅱

AAA ▼▼▼▼ **Loews New Orleans Hotel** 🅷 ❀
(504) 595-3300. **Call for rates.** 300 Poydras St 70130. Corner of S Peters St. Int corridors. **Pets:** Other species. $100 one-time fee/room, $25 daily fee/room. Designated rooms, supervision.
🆂🅰🆅🅴 🍽 ⌦ ✕ 🛜 ✕

AAA ▼▼▼ **Maison St. Charles Hotel & Suites** 🅷
(504) 522-0187. **$94-$399.** 1319 St. Charles Ave 70130. Just s of US 90 business route (Pontchartrain Expwy); between Erato and Thalia sts. Ext/int corridors. **Pets:** Accepted. 🆂🅰🆅🅴 ⌦ 🛜 ✕ 🅱 🖵

AAA ▼▼▼▼ **Omni Riverfront Hotel** 🅷 ❀
(504) 524-8200. **$109-$429, 3 day notice.** 701 Convention Center Blvd 70130. Just s of Poydras St; center. Int corridors. **Pets:** Small. $50 one-time fee/room. Designated rooms, service with restrictions, supervision. 🆂🅰🆅🅴 🍽 🛜 ✕ 🅱 🖵

AAA ▼▼▼ **Omni Royal Crescent Hotel** 🅷
(504) 527-0006. **Call for rates.** 535 Gravier St 70130. 0.3 mi w of Canal St. Int corridors. **Pets:** Accepted.
🆂🅰🆅🅴 🍽 &ᴹ ✕ 🛜 ✕ 🅱 🖵

AAA ▼▼▼▼ **Omni Royal Orleans Hotel** 🅷
(504) 529-5333. **Call for rates.** 621 St. Louis St 70140. At Royal and St. Louis sts. Int corridors. **Pets:** Accepted.
🆂🅰🆅🅴 🍽 ⌦ 🛜 ✕ 🅱 🖵

△△△△ ▼▼▼▼ The Pontchartrain Hotel 🄷
(504) 941-9000. **Call for rates.** 2031 St. Charles Ave 70130. 1 mi w of US 90. Int corridors. **Pets:** Accepted. 🆂🅰🆅🅴 ⑪ ♿ 🛜 ⊠ 🛄 ▣

△△△ ▼▼▼▼ Q & C Hotel/Bar 🄷
(504) 587-9700. **$139-$359, 3 day notice.** 344 Camp St 70130. Jct Natchez St. Int corridors. **Pets:** Accepted.
🆂🅰🆅🅴 ⑪ ♿ 🛜 ⊠ 🛄 ▣

△△△ ▼▼▼▼ Residence Inn by Marriott Downtown New Orleans 🄷
(504) 522-1300. **$121-$308.** 345 St. Joseph St 70130. At Tchoupitoulas St. Int corridors. **Pets:** Accepted. 🆂🅰🆅🅴 ♿ ⇆ 🛜 ⊠ 🛄 ▣

△△△ ▼▼▼ ▼▼▼ The Ritz-Carlton, New Orleans 🄷
(504) 524-1331. **$199-$699, 3 day notice.** 921 Canal St 70112. Between Burgundy and Dauphine sts. Int corridors. **Pets:** Accepted.
🆂🅰🆅🅴 ⑪ ♿ ⊠ 🛟 ⊠ 🛄 ▣

△△△ ▼▼▼ ▼▼▼ The Roosevelt New Orleans, A Waldorf Astoria Hotel 🄷
(504) 648-1200. **$239-$399.** 130 Roosevelt Way 70112. Just s of Canal St. Int corridors. **Pets:** Accepted.
🆂🅰🆅🅴 ⑪ ♿ ⇆ ⊠ 🛟 ⊠ 🛄

△△△ ▼▼▼ ▼▼▼ Royal Sonesta Hotel New Orleans 🄷
(504) 586-0300. **Call for rates.** 300 Bourbon St 70130. Garage entrance on Conti or Bienville sts. Int corridors. **Pets:** Accepted.
🆂🅰🆅🅴 ⑪ ♿ ⇆ 🛜 ⊠ 🛄 ▣

△△△ ▼▼▼ ▼▼▼ Sheraton New Orleans Hotel 🄷 ❁
(504) 525-2500. **$109-$289.** 500 Canal St 70130. Between Camp and Magazine sts. Int corridors. **Pets:** Medium, dogs only. Service with restrictions, supervision. 🆂🅰🆅🅴 ⑪ ♿ ⇆ 🛟 ⊠ 🛄 ▣

△△△ ▼▼▼ Staybridge Suites Hotel 🄷
(504) 571-1818. **Call for rates.** 501 Tchoupitoulas St 70130. Corner of Poydras St. Int corridors. **Pets:** Accepted.
🆂🅰🆅🅴 ♿ ⇆ 🛜 ⊠ 🛄 ▣

△△△ ▼▼▼ ▼▼▼ The Westin New Orleans Canal Place 🄷
(504) 566-7006. **$179-$399, 3 day notice.** 100 Iberville St 70130. At Canal Place, near Mississippi River. Int corridors. **Pets:** Accepted.
🆂🅰🆅🅴 ⑪ ⇆ 🛜 ⊠ 🛄 ▣

△△△ ▼▼▼ ▼▼▼ W French Quarter 🄷
(504) 581-1200. **$160-$275.** 316 Chartres St 70130. Between Conti and Bienville sts. Int corridors. **Pets:** Accepted.
🆂🅰🆅🅴 ⑪ ♿ ⇆ 🛟 ⊠ 🛄 ▣

△△△ ▼▼▼ ▼▼▼ Windsor Court Hotel 🄷
(504) 523-6000. **$195-$600, 3 day notice.** 300 Gravier St 70130. Between Magazine and Tchoupitoulas sts. Int corridors. **Pets:** Accepted.
🆂🅰🆅🅴 ⑪ ♿ ⇆ ⊠ 🛜 ⊠ ▣

OPELOUSAS

▼▼▼ Comfort Inn Opelousas 🄷
(337) 942-4900. **$95-$169.** 5454 I-49 N Frontage Rd 70570. I-49 exit 18, just s. Int corridors. **Pets:** Accepted.
⑪ ♿ ⇆ 🛜 ⊠ 🛄 ▣

▼▼▼ Evangeline Downs Hotel, an Ascend Collection Hotel Member 🄷
(337) 407-2121. **$96-$399.** 2235 Creswell Ln, Lot B 70570. I-49 exit 18, 0.6 mi e on SR 31, then 0.7 mi n on entry driveway. Int corridors.
Pets: Accepted. ⑪ ♿ ⇆ 🛜 🛄 ▣

▼▼▼ Holiday Inn & Suites Opelousas 🄷
(337) 948-3300. **$109-$139.** 5696 N I-49 Service Rd 70570. I-49 exit 18, just s. Int corridors. **Pets:** $150 deposit/room, $35 daily fee/room. Service with restrictions, supervision. ⑪ ♿ 🛜 ⊠ 🛄 ▣

PONCHATOULA

▼▼▼ Microtel Inn & Suites by Wyndham 🄷
(985) 386-8866. **$40-$89.** 727 W Pine St 70454. I-55 exit 26, 0.5 mi e on SR 22. Int corridors. **Pets:** Other species. $10 daily fee/room. Designated rooms, service with restrictions, supervision.
♿ ⇆ 🛜 ⊠ 🛄 ▣

RUSTON

△△△ ▼▼▼ ▼ Country Inn & Suites By Carlson-Ruston 🄷
(318) 513-9777. **$104-$159.** 1825 Roberta Ave 71270. I-20 exit 86, just se. Int corridors. **Pets:** Medium. Designated rooms, service with restrictions. 🆂🅰🆅🅴 ♿ ⇆ 🛜 ⊠ 🛄 ▣

ST. FRANCISVILLE

▼▼▼ Lake Rosemound Inn Bed & Breakfast 🄱🄱
(225) 635-3176. **Call for rates.** 10473 Lindsey Ln 70775. 13 mi n on SR 61, then 3 mi w using Rosemound Loop, Sligo Rd, Lake Rosemound Rd and Lindsey Ln, follow signs. Ext/int corridors.
Pets: Accepted. ⊠ 🛜 ⊠ 🗷

ST. ROSE

▼▼▼ ▼▼▼ Holiday Inn Express & Suites New Orleans Airport South 🄷
(504) 466-1355. **Call for rates.** 110 James Dr E 70087. I-310 exit 2, 1.5 mi e on SR 61. Int corridors. **Pets:** Accepted.
⑪ ♿ ⇆ 🛜 ⊠ 🛄 ▣

SHREVEPORT

△△△ ▼▼▼ ▼▼▼ Eldorado Resort Casino Shreveport 🄷
(318) 220-0711. **$86-$279.** 451 Clyde Fant Pkwy 71101. I-20 exit 19A (Spring St), 0.8 mi n to Crockett St, just e, then just n. Int corridors. **Pets:** Large, dogs only. $100 deposit/room. Designated rooms, service with restrictions, supervision. 🆂🅰🆅🅴 ⑪ 🛜 🛄 ▣

▼▼▼ ▼▼▼ Homewood Suites - Shreveport 🄷
(318) 549-2000. **Call for rates.** 5485 Financial Plaza 71129. I-20 exit 10 (Pines Rd), just s, then 1.2 mi e. Int corridors. **Pets:** Accepted.
⑪ ♿ ⇆ 🛜 🛄 ▣

△△△ ▼▼▼ Residence Inn by Marriott Shreveport - Airport 🄷
(318) 635-8000. **$97-$169.** 4910 W Monkhouse Dr 71109. I-20 exit 13, just nw. Int corridors. **Pets:** Accepted.
🆂🅰🆅🅴 ♿ ⇆ 🛜 ⊠ 🛄 ▣

SLIDELL

▼▼▼ ▼▼ Candlewood Suites-Slidell/Northshore 🄷
(985) 326-0120. **Call for rates.** 100 Holiday Blvd 70460. I-12 exit 80, just sw. Int corridors. **Pets:** Accepted. ⑪ ♿ 🛜 ⊠ 🛄 ▣

▼▼▼ Holiday Inn Hotel & Suites Slidell 🄷
(985) 639-0890. **$109-$149.** 372 Voter's Rd 70461. I-10 exit 263, just ne. Int corridors. **Pets:** Small, other species. $150 deposit/room, $20 daily fee/room. Service with restrictions, supervision.
⑪ ♿ ⇆ 🛜 ⊠ 🛄 ▣

VILLE PLATTE

△△△ ▼▼▼ Best Western Ville Platte 🄷
(337) 360-9961. **$98-$159.** 1919 E Main St (Hwy 167) 70586. I-49 exit 23, 14 mi nw. Int corridors. **Pets:** Accepted. 🆂🅰🆅🅴 ⇆ 🛜 🛄 ▣

VINTON

△△△ ▼▼▼ Best Western Casino Inn 🄷
(337) 551-6350. **$90-$150.** 2466 Toomey Rd 70668. I-10 exit 4, just s. Int corridors. **Pets:** Accepted. 🆂🅰🆅🅴 🔌 ⑪ ♿ 🛜 ⊠ 🛄 ▣

WALKER

▼▼▼ **La Quinta Inn & Suites Walker** 🄷
(225) 667-1966. **$79-$207.** 13450 Vera McGowan 70785. I-12 exit 15, just n. Int corridors. **Pets:** Accepted. 🍽 ➿ 🛜 ✕ 🎒 💻

WESTLAKE

▼▼▼ **Isle of Capri Casino & Hotel** 🄷
(337) 430-2400. **Call for rates.** 100 Westlake Ave 70669. I-10 exit 27, just s. Int corridors. **Pets:** Accepted.
🍽 ♿ ➿ ✕ 🛜 🎒 💻

WEST MONROE

▼▼ **Quality Inn & Suites-West Monroe** 🄷
(318) 387-2711. **$94-$179.** 503 Constitution Dr 71292. I-20 exit 114 (Thomas Rd), just s to Constitution Dr, then 0.6 mi w. Int corridors. **Pets:** Small. $20 one-time fee/pet. Designated rooms, service with restrictions, supervision. ♿ ➿ 🛜 🎒 💻

ZACHARY

🅐🅐🅐 ▼▼◆ **Best Western Zachary Inn** 🄷
(225) 658-2550. **$96-$100.** 4030 Hwy 19 70791. Just s of jct SR 64. Int corridors. **Pets:** Accepted. 🆂🅰🆅🅴 ➿ 🛜 🎒 💻

MAINE

AUBURN

🅐🅐🅐 ▼▼▼▼ **Residence Inn by Marriott Auburn** 🄷
(207) 777-3400. **$99-$345.** 670 Turner St 04210. I-95 exit 80 southbound; exit 75 northbound; from SR 100, just w. Int corridors. **Pets:** Accepted. 🆂🅰🆅🅴 ♿ ➿ 🛜 ✕ 🎒 💻

AUGUSTA

🅐🅐🅐 ▼▼▼ **Best Western Plus Civic Center Inn** 🄷
(207) 622-4751. **$89-$209.** 110 Community Dr 04330. I-95 exit 112A northbound; exit 112 southbound, just s on SR 8, 11 and 27. Int corridors. **Pets:** Other species. $10 daily fee/room. Service with restrictions, supervision. 🆂🅰🆅🅴 🍽 ♿ ➿ 🛜 🎒 💻

▼▼▼ **Homewood Suites by Hilton Augusta** 🄷
(207) 480-2050. **Call for rates.** 377 Western Ave 04330. I-95 exit 109 northbound; exit 109B southbound, just w on US 202. Int corridors. **Pets:** Accepted. 🍽 ♿ 🛜 ✕ 🎒 💻

🅐🅐🅐 ▼▼▼ **Senator Inn & Spa** 🄷
(207) 622-5804. **$80-$229.** 284 Western Ave 04330. I-95 exit 109 northbound; exit 109A southbound, on US 202, SR 11 and 100. Ext/int corridors. **Pets:** Other species. $12 daily fee/pet. Designated rooms, service with restrictions, supervision.
🆂🅰🆅🅴 🄴🄲🄾 🍽 ➿ ✕ 🛜 ✕ 🎒 💻

BANGOR

🅐🅐🅐 ▼▼◆ **Best Western White House Inn** 🄷
(207) 862-3737. **$130-$300.** 155 Littlefield Ave 04401. I-95 exit 180 (Coldbrook Rd), 5.5 mi s of downtown. Int corridors. **Pets:** Large, other species. $10 daily fee/pet. Designated rooms, service with restrictions, supervision. 🆂🅰🆅🅴 ➿ 🛜 ✕ 🎒 💻

🅐🅐🅐 ▼▼◆ **Fairfield Inn by Marriott Bangor** 🄷
(207) 990-0001. **$80-$307.** 300 Odlin Rd 04401. I-95 exit 182B, just e on US 2 and SR 100. Int corridors. **Pets:** Medium, other species. $50 one-time fee/room. Service with restrictions, crate.
🆂🅰🆅🅴 🄴🄲🄾 ♿ ➿ ✕ 🛜 ✕ 🎒 💻

▼▼◆ **Fireside Inn & Suites** 🄷 🐾
(207) 942-1234. **$100-$350, 3 day notice.** 570 Main St 04401. I-395 exit 3B, just n on US Rt 1A. Int corridors. **Pets:** Other species. $10 daily fee/pet. Designated rooms, service with restrictions, supervision.
🄴🄲🄾 🍽 🛜 ✕ 🎒 💻

🅐🅐🅐 ▼▼◆ **Four Points by Sheraton Bangor Airport**
(207) 947-6721. **$145-$250.** 308 Godfrey Blvd 04401. At Bangor International Airport. Int corridors. **Pets:** Accepted.
🆂🅰🆅🅴 🍽 ♿ ➿ 🛜 ✕ 🎒 💻

▼▼▼ **Holiday Inn-Bangor** 🄷
(207) 947-0101. **Call for rates.** 404 Odlin Rd 04401. I-95 exit 182B, jct Odlin Rd and I-395. Int corridors. **Pets:** Accepted.
🍽 ♿ 🛜 ✕ 🎒 💻

▼▼ **Howard Johnson Inn** 🄷
(207) 942-5251. **$59-$180.** 336 Odlin Rd 04401. I-95 exit 182B; jct Odlin Rd and I-395. Int corridors. **Pets:** Accepted.
🍽 ➿ 🛜 ✕ 🎒 💻

▼▼ **Quality Inn Bangor** 🄷 🐾
(207) 942-7899. **$90-$190.** 750 Hogan Rd 04401. I-95 exit 187 (Hogan Rd), 0.5 mi nw. Int corridors. **Pets:** Service with restrictions, supervision. 🛜 ✕ 🎒 💻

▼▼ **Ramada** 🄷
(207) 947-6961. **$89-$179.** 357 Odlin Rd 04401. I-95 exit 182B; jct Odlin Rd and I-395. Int corridors. **Pets:** Accepted.
🍽 ➿ 🛜 🎒 💻

🅐🅐🅐 ▼▼◆ **Residence Inn by Marriott Bangor** 🄷
(207) 433-0800. **$76-$299.** 22 Bass Park Blvd 04401. I-395 exit 3B, just n. Int corridors. **Pets:** Accepted. 🆂🅰🆅🅴 🍽 ♿ 🛜 ✕ 🎒 💻

◆ **Rodeway Inn** 🄼
(207) 945-0111. **$70-$189.** 327 Odlin Rd 04401. I-95 exit 182B, just e on US 2 and SR 100. Int corridors. **Pets:** Accepted.
♿ ➿ 🛜 ✕ 🎒 💻

▼▼◆ **TownePlace Suites by Marriott Bangor** 🄷
(207) 262-4000. **$93-$303.** 240 Sylvan Rd 04401. I-95 exit 187 (Hogan Rd), just se, then 0.5 mi sw; in Sylvan Business Park. Int corridors. **Pets:** Accepted. ♿ 🛜 ✕ 🎒 💻

BAR HARBOR *(Restaurants p. 614)*

🅐🅐🅐 ▼▼▼ **Atlantic Eyrie Lodge** 🄷
(207) 288-9786. **Call for rates.** 6 Norman Rd 04609. 1 mi w on SR 3 to Highbrook Rd. Ext corridors. **Pets:** Accepted.
🆂🅰🆅🅴 ♿ ➿ 🛜 ✕ 🎒 💻

▼▼ **A Wonder View Inn** 🄷
(207) 288-3358. **$99-$299, 3 day notice.** 50 Eden St 04609. 0.5 mi w on SR 3. Ext corridors. **Pets:** Accepted. 🍽 ➿ 🛜 ✕ 🎒 💻

🅐🅐🅐 ▼▼◆▼◆ **Balance Rock Inn 1903** 🄱🄱 🐾
(207) 288-2610. **$195-$995, 14 day notice.** 21 Albert Meadow 04609. Just s of Main St; center. Ext/int corridors. **Pets:** Dogs only. $40 daily fee/pet. Designated rooms, service with restrictions.
🆂🅰🆅🅴 🍽 ➿ 🛜 ✕ 🎒 💻

🅐🅐🅐 ▼▼◆ **Bar Harbor Regency Holiday Inn** 🄷
(207) 288-9723. **Call for rates.** 123 Eden St 04609. 1 mi w on SR 3. Int corridors. **Pets:** Accepted. 🆂🅰🆅🅴 🍽 ➿ ✕ 🛜 ✕ 🎒 💻

▼▼ **Hutchins Mountain View Cottages** 🄲🄰
(207) 288-4833. **$88-$140, 14 day notice.** 286 State Hwy 3 04609. On SR 3, 4 mi w. Ext corridors. **Pets:** Other species. Service with restrictions. 🄴🄻🄾 ➿ 🛜 ✕ 🅇 🔟 🎒 💻

▼▼ **Primrose Place** M ❀

(207) 288-3771. **Call for rates.** 51 Holland Ave 04609. Jct Holland Ave and Mt Desert St (SR 3). Ext corridors. **Pets:** Dogs only. $30 one-time fee/room. Designated rooms, service with restrictions, crate.

🛜 ⊠ 🗷 🖥

◈◈ ▼▼▼▼ **West Street Hotel** H

(207) 288-0825. **Call for rates.** 50 West St 04609. Jct Main St. Ext/int corridors. **Pets:** Accepted. ⟨SAVE⟩ ⟨¶⟩ ⟨&M⟩ ⟨⇆⟩ ⟨🛜⟩ ⊠ 🖥

BATH

◈◈ ▼▼▼▼ **Residence Inn by Marriott - Bath Brunswick Area** H

(207) 443-9741. **$93-$380.** 139 Richardson St 04530. 0.3 mi s on US 1; at State Rd. Int corridors. **Pets:** Accepted.

⟨SAVE⟩ ⟨ECO⟩ ⟨¶⟩ ⟨&M⟩ ⟨⇆⟩ 🛜 ⊠ 🖥 🖳

BELFAST

▼▼ **Fireside Inn & Suites, Ocean's Edge** H

(207) 338-2090. **Call for rates.** 159 Searsport Ave 04915. On US 1, 2.6 mi n from jct SR 3. Int corridors. **Pets:** Accepted.

⟨ECO⟩ ⟨¶⟩ ⟨&M⟩ ⟨⇆⟩ ⊠ 🛜 ⊠ 🖥 🖳

▼▼ **Yankee Clipper Motel** M

(207) 338-2353. **$79-$149, 3 day notice.** 50 Searsport Ave 04915. On US 1, 1.6 mi n from jct SR 3. Ext corridors. **Pets:** Dogs only. $20 daily fee/pet. Designated rooms, service with restrictions, supervision.

🛜 ⊠ 🖥 🖳

BETHEL

▼▼ **The Inn At the Rostay** M

(207) 824-3111. **$89-$160, 3 day notice.** 186 Mayville Rd (US 2) 04217. On US 2, 2 mi e. Ext corridors. **Pets:** Dogs only. $20 daily fee/room. Designated rooms, service with restrictions, supervision.

⟨⇆⟩ 🛜 ⊠ 🖥

BOOTHBAY HARBOR

▼▼ **Beach Cove Waterfront Inn** M

(207) 633-0353. **Call for rates.** 48 Lakeview Rd 04538. Off SR 27. Ext/int corridors. **Pets:** Accepted. ⟨⇆⟩ 🛜 ⊠ 🖥 🖳

▼▼ **Boothbay Harbor Inn** H

(207) 633-6302. **Call for rates.** 31 Atlantic Ave 04538. 0.3 mi e of SR 27; on east side of Boothbay Harbor. Ext/int corridors. **Pets:** Accepted.

⟨¶⟩ 🛜 ⊠ 🖥 🖳

▼▼ **Cap'n Fish's Waterfront Inn** H

(207) 633-6605. **$90-$175, 7 day notice.** 63 Atlantic Ave 04538. 0.3 mi se of SR 27; on east side of Boothbay Harbor. Ext corridors.
Pets: Accepted. 🛜 ⊠ 🖥 🖳

◈◈ ▼▼▼▼ **Flagship Inn & Suites** M ❀

(207) 633-5094. **$99-$154, 3 day notice.** 200 Townsend Ave 04538. On SR 27, just n of jct SR 96. Ext corridors. **Pets:** $10 one-time fee/room. Designated rooms, service with restrictions, crate.

⟨SAVE⟩ ⟨ECO⟩ ⟨⇆⟩ 🛜 ⊠ 🖥 🖳

▼▼ **Tugboat Inn** H ❀

(207) 633-4434. **$109-$279, 3 day notice.** 80 Commercial St 04538. Center. Ext corridors. **Pets:** $20 daily fee/pet. Designated rooms, service with restrictions, supervision. ⟨¶⟩ 🛜 ⊠ 🖥 🖳

BRUNSWICK

◈◈ ▼▼▼ **Best Western Plus Brunswick Bath** H

(207) 725-5251. **$99-$269.** 71 Gurnet Rd 04011. On SR 24, 1 mi s of US 1. Int corridors. **Pets:** Accepted.

⟨SAVE⟩ ⟨¶⟩ ⟨&M⟩ ⟨⇆⟩ 🛜 ⊠ 🖥 🖳

◈◈ ▼▼▼▼ **The Brunswick Hotel & Tavern** H

(207) 837-6565. **$129-$399.** 4 Noble St 04011. Center. Int corridors.
Pets: Accepted. ⟨SAVE⟩ ⟨¶⟩ ⟨&M⟩ 🛜 ⊠ 🖥 🖳

BRYANT POND

▼▼ **Mollyockett Motel & Swim Spa** M

(207) 674-2345. **Call for rates.** 1132 S Main St 04219. 1.3 mi n on SR 26 from jct SR 219. Ext/int corridors. **Pets:** Dogs only. $10 one-time fee/pet. Service with restrictions, supervision.

⟨¶⟩ ⟨⇆⟩ ⊠ 🛜 ⊠ 🗷 🖥 🖳

BUCKSPORT

▼▼ **Bucksport Motor Inn** M

(207) 469-3111. **$69-$119.** 70 US Route 1 04416. Just e of downtown. Ext corridors. **Pets:** Dogs only. $25 one-time fee/room. Designated rooms, supervision. 🛜 ⊠ 🖥 🖳

CAMDEN

◈◈ ▼▼▼▼ **16 Bay View** H ❀

(207) 706-7990. **$159-$699, 3 day notice.** 16 Bay View St 04843. Just e of Main St; center. Int corridors. **Pets:** Dogs only. $35 daily fee/pet. Designated rooms, service with restrictions, supervision.

⟨SAVE⟩ 🛜 ⊠ 🖥 🖳

◈◈ ▼▼▼◈ **Grand Harbor Inn** H ❀

(207) 230-7177. **$169-$699, 3 day notice.** 14 Bay View Landing 04843. Just e of Main St; center. Int corridors. **Pets:** Dogs only. $35 daily fee/pet. Designated rooms, service with restrictions, supervision.

⟨SAVE⟩ ⟨¶⟩ 🛜 ⊠ 🖥 🖳

▼▼▼ **Hartstone Inn & Hideaway** CI

(207) 236-4259. **Call for rates.** 41 Elm St 04843. On US 1, just s of Washington St; center. Ext/int corridors. **Pets:** Accepted.

⟨¶⟩ 🛜 ⊠ 🗷 🖥 🖳

◈◈ ▼▼▼▼ **Lord Camden Inn** H ❀

(207) 236-4325. **$99-$399.** 24 Main St 04843. Just n of Washington St; center. Int corridors. **Pets:** Dogs only. $35 daily fee/pet. Designated rooms, service with restrictions, supervision.

⟨SAVE⟩ ⟨ECO⟩ 🛜 ⊠ 🖥 🖳

CAPE ELIZABETH *(Restaurants p. 614)*

◈◈ ▼▼▼▼ **Inn by the Sea** H

(207) 799-3134. **$219-$2499, 30 day notice.** 40 Bowery Beach Rd 04107. On SR 77, 7 mi s. Ext/int corridors. **Pets:** Accepted.

⟨SAVE⟩ ⟨ECO⟩ ⟨¶⟩ ⟨&M⟩ ⟨⇆⟩ ⊠ 🛜 ⊠ 🖥 🖳

CASTINE

▼▼ **The Castine Inn** BB

(207) 326-4365. **Call for rates.** 33 Main St 04421. Center. Int corridors.
Pets: Accepted. 🛜 ⊠ 🗷

▼▼▼ **Pentagoet Inn** CI

(207) 326-8616. **Call for rates.** 26 Main St 04421. Center. Int corridors.
Pets: Accepted. ⟨¶⟩ 🛜 ⊠ 🗶 🗷

EAGLE LAKE

▼ **Overlook Motel & Lakeside Cottages** M

(207) 444-4535. **$82.** 3232 Aroostook Rd 04739. On SR 11; center. Ext corridors. **Pets:** Accepted. ⟨¶⟩ ⊠ 🛜 ⊠ 🖥 🖳

ELLSWORTH

▼▼ **Comfort Inn Ellsworth-Bar Harbor** H

(207) 667-1345. **$105-$229.** 130 High St 04605. On US 1 and SR 3; center. Int corridors. **Pets:** Accepted. ⟨&M⟩ 🛜 ⊠ 🖥 🖳

▼ **The Eagle's Lodge** M ❀

(207) 667-3311. **$89-$139.** 278 High St 04605. Jct US 1 and 1A, 1.3 mi se on SR 3. Ext/int corridors. **Pets:** Dogs only. $10 daily fee/room. Designated rooms, service with restrictions, supervision.

⟨¶⟩ ⟨⇆⟩ 🛜 🖥

◇◇◇ Ellsworth Ramada 🄷

(207) 667-9341. **$139-$219.** 215 High St 04605. Jct US 1, 1A and SR 3. Int corridors. **Pets:** Accepted.

[SAVE] 🛆ᴹ 🍽 ⊠ 📶 ⊠ 📠 🖥

◇ Sunset Motel 🄲🄰

(207) 667-8390. **Call for rates.** 210 Twin Hill Rd 04605. 6 mi s on US 1 and SR 3. Ext corridors. **Pets:** Accepted. 📶 ⊠ ⊠ 📠 🖥

FREEPORT

◇◇◇ Candlebay Inn 🄱🄱 ❀

(207) 865-1868. **$109-$249, 7 day notice.** 8 Maple Ave 04032. Just w of US 1 and n of SR 125. Int corridors. **Pets:** Dogs only. $25 one-time fee/room. Crate. 📶 ⊠ ⊠

GREENVILLE

◇◇ Chalet Moosehead Lakefront Motel 🄼

(207) 695-2950. **$125-$170, 7 day notice.** 12 N Birch St 04442. 1.5 mi w on SR 15. Ext corridors. **Pets:** Accepted. 📶 ⊠ 📠 🖥

◇◇ Kineo View Motor Lodge 🄼

(207) 695-4470. **Call for rates.** 50 Overlook Dr 04441. 2.5 mi s on SR 15; gravel access road from highway. Ext corridors. **Pets:** Accepted.

🍽 📶 ⊠ 📠 🖥

◇◇ ◇◇ The Lodge at Moosehead Lake 🄲🄸

(207) 695-4400. **Call for rates.** 368 Lily Bay Rd 04441. 2.5 mi n. Int corridors. **Pets:** Accepted. [SAVE] 🍽 📶 ⊠ ⊠ 📠 🖥

JACKMAN

◇◇ Bishop's Country Inn Motel 🄼

(207) 668-3231. **$65-$100.** 461 Main St 04945. On US 201; center. Ext corridors. **Pets:** $10 deposit/pet. Service with restrictions.

🛆ᴹ 📶 ⊠ 📠 🖥

KENNEBUNK

◇◇ Port Inn Kennebunk, an Ascend Hotel Collection Member 🄼

(207) 985-6100. **$134-$339.** 55 York St 04043. Jct SR 35 (US 1), 0.7 mi s. Ext corridors. **Pets:** Accepted. 🍴 🍽 📶 ⊠ 📠 🖥

KENNEBUNKPORT

◇◇◇ The Captain Jefferds Inn 🄱🄱 ❀

(207) 967-2311. **$179-$439, 7 day notice.** 5 Pearl St 04046. From Dock Square, 0.3 mi s on Ocean Ave, just ne; corner of Pearl and Pleasant sts. Int/int corridors. **Pets:** Other species. $30 daily fee/pet. Designated rooms, supervision. 🍴 📶 ⊠ 📠

◇◇◇ The Colony Hotel 🄷

(207) 967-3331. **Call for rates.** 140 Ocean Ave 04046. From Dock Square, 1 mi s. Int corridors. **Pets:** Accepted.

🄴🄲🄾 🍽 🍽 📶 ⊠ 📠

◇◇ Lodge At Turbat's Creek 🄼

(207) 967-8700. **$89-$179, 14 day notice.** 7 Turbats Creek Rd 04046. From Dock Square, 0.5 mi se on Maine St, 0.6 mi ne on Wildes District Rd, then just se. Ext corridors. **Pets:** Accepted.

🍽 🛆ᴹ 🍽 📶 ⊠ 📠

◇◇◇ The Yachtsman Lodge & Marina 🄼 ❀

(207) 967-2511. **$109-$369, 14 day notice.** 57 Ocean Ave 04046. From Dock Square, just s. Ext corridors. **Pets:** Other species. $35 daily fee/ pet. Designated rooms, service with restrictions, crate.

🍴 ⊠ 📶 ⊠ 📠 🖥

KITTERY

◇◇ ◇◇◇ The Coachman Inn 🄼 ❀

(207) 439-4434. **$69-$329.** 380 US 1 03904. I-95 exit 2, 1.5 mi n. Ext/ int corridors. **Pets:** $10 daily fee/pet. Designated rooms, service with restrictions, supervision. [SAVE] 🍽 🛆ᴹ 🍽 📶 ⊠ 📠

LEWISTON

◇◇ ◇◇◇ Hampton Inn by Hilton Lewiston-Auburn 🄷

(207) 344-1000. **Call for rates.** 15 Lincoln St 04243. On SR 196, just s of SR 11 and 202. Int corridors. **Pets:** Accepted.

[SAVE] 🛆ᴹ 📶 ⊠ 📠 🖥

◇◇ Ramada Conference Center 🄷

(207) 784-2331. **$90-$180.** 490 Pleasant St 04240. I-95 exit 80, right turn on Foch St, follow signs. Int corridors. **Pets:** Accepted.

🍽 🛆ᴹ 🍽 ⊠ 📶 ⊠ 📠

LINCOLNVILLE

◇◇◇ Victorian By The Sea 🄱🄱

(207) 236-3785. **Call for rates.** 33 Sea View Dr 04849. On US 1, 1.2 mi s of jct SR 173. Int corridors. **Pets:** Accepted.

📶 ⊠ ⊠ ⊠ ⊠

◇◇◇ Youngtown Inn & Restaurant 🄲🄸

(207) 763-4290. **$199-$275, 14 day notice.** 581 Youngtown Rd 04849. Jct SR 52 and 173, 1.5 mi s. Int corridors. **Pets:** Accepted.

🍽 📶 ⊠

LUBEC

◇◇ The Eastland Motel 🄼

(207) 733-5501. **Call for rates.** 385 County Rd 04652. Jct US 1 and SR 189, 8.4 mi e on SR 189. Ext/int corridors. **Pets:** Accepted.

🍽 🛆ᴹ 📶 ⊠ 📠 🖥

MACHIAS

◇◇ ◇◇ Machias River Inn 🄼

(207) 255-4861. **$91-$139.** 103 Main St 04654. 0.5 mi e on US 1. Ext/ int corridors. **Pets:** Dogs only. $10 daily fee/pet. Designated rooms, service with restrictions, supervision. [SAVE] 📶 📠 🖥

MILFORD

◇◇ ◇ Milford Motel On The River 🄼

(207) 827-3200. **Call for rates.** 174 Main Rd 04461. 0.5 mi n on US 2. Ext corridors. **Pets:** Small, dogs only. Service with restrictions, supervision. [SAVE] 📶 📠 🖥

MILLINOCKET

◇◇◇ 5 Lakes Lodge 🄱🄱

(207) 723-5045. **Call for rates.** 46 Marina Dr 04462. On SR 11, 7 mi s of center. Int corridors. **Pets:** Accepted. 🍽 ⊠ 📶 ⊠ ⊠ 📠

NAPLES

◇◇◇ Augustus Bove House 🄱🄱

(207) 693-6365. **Call for rates.** 11 Sebago Rd 04055. Corner of US 302 and SR 114. Int corridors. **Pets:** Accepted.

🍽 📶 ⊠ ⊠ 📠 🖥

NEWCASTLE

◇◇◇ Newcastle Inn 🄱🄱

(207) 563-5685. **$150-$295, 14 day notice.** 60 River Rd 04553. Jct US 1, 0.5 mi ne via Snead Spur. Ext/int corridors. **Pets:** Accepted.

🍴 🍽 📶 ⊠ ⊠

NORTHEAST HARBOR

◇◇ Asticou Inn 🄷

(207) 276-3344. **$155-$350, 14 day notice.** 15 Peabody Dr 04662. Jct SR 3 and Peabody Dr; center. Int corridors. **Pets:** Dogs only. Designated rooms, service with restrictions, supervision.

🍽 📶 ⊠ 📠 🖥

NORTHPORT

AAA **WWW** Point Lookout Resort & Conference Center **CA**

(207) 789-2000. **Call for rates.** 67 Atlantic Hwy 04849. 4 mi s on US 1; at Lincolnville town line. Ext corridors. **Pets:** Medium, dogs only. $50 one-time fee/room. Designated rooms, service with restrictions, supervision. [SAVE] [ECO] [icons]

OGUNQUIT

WW Studio East Motor Inn **M**

(207) 646-7297. **$69-$249, 8 day notice.** 267 Main St 03907. On US 1, just n. Ext corridors. **Pets:** Dogs only. $15 daily fee/room. Designated rooms, service with restrictions, supervision. [icons]

ORONO

WW Black Bear Inn Conference Center **H** ❀

(207) 866-7120. **$69-$229.** 4 Godfrey Dr 04473. I-95 exit 193 (Stillwater Ave), just se. Int corridors. **Pets:** $10 daily fee/room. Designated rooms, service with restrictions, supervision. [icons]

WW University Inn Academic Suites **H**

(207) 866-4921. **$92-$229, 3 day notice.** 5 College Ave (US 2) 04473. I-95 exit 191, 1 mi e on Kelley, then 1.5 mi n on US 2; 8 mi n of Bangor. Ext/int corridors. **Pets:** Dogs only. $10 daily fee/room. Designated rooms, service with restrictions, supervision. [icons]

POLAND

WWW Wolf Cove Inn **BB**

(207) 998-4976. **Call for rates.** 5 Jordan Shore Dr 04274. Just w of SR 11. Ext corridors. **Pets:** Accepted. [icons]

PORTLAND

WWW Clarion Hotel Portland **H**

(207) 774-5611. **$99-$999.** 1230 Congress St 04102. I-295 exit 5, w on SR 22. Int corridors. **Pets:** Accepted.
[icons]

WWWW Embassy Suites by Hilton Hotel **H**

(207) 775-2200. **$109-$600.** 1050 Westbrook St 04102. At Portland International Jetport. Int corridors. **Pets:** Accepted.
[icons]

WW Fireside Inn & Suites **H** ❀

(207) 774-5601. **$100-$220.** 81 Riverside St 04103. I-95 exit 48, just s. Int corridors. **Pets:** Medium. $20 daily fee/pet. Designated rooms, service with restrictions, supervision.
[icons]

AAA **WWWW** Hilton Garden Inn Portland Airport **H**

(207) 828-1117. **$109-$399.** 145 Jetport Blvd 04102. At Portland International Jetport. Int corridors. **Pets:** Accepted.
[SAVE] [icons]

WWWW Hilton Garden Inn Portland Downtown Waterfront **H**

(207) 780-0780. **$179-$469.** 65 Commercial St 04101. In the Old Port; across from Casco Bay ferry terminal. Int corridors. **Pets:** Dogs only. $50 one-time fee/room. Designated rooms, service with restrictions.
[icons]

AAA **WWWW** Hyatt Place Portland Old Port **H**

(207) 775-1000. **$149-$599.** 433 Fore St 04101. At Union St; in Old Port. Int corridors. **Pets:** Accepted. [SAVE] [icons]

AAA **WWWW** Portland Harbor Hotel **H** ❀

(207) 775-9090. **$169-$650.** 468 Fore St 04101. In the Old Port; at Union St. Int corridors. **Pets:** Medium, other species. $25 daily fee/pet. Designated rooms, supervision. [SAVE] [icons]

AAA **WWW** Portland Regency Hotel & Spa **H**

(207) 774-4200. **$149-$359.** 20 Milk St 04101. In the Old Port; between Market and Silver sts; downtown. Int corridors. **Pets:** Small. $75 one-time fee/pet. Designated rooms, service with restrictions, supervision.
[SAVE] [ECO] [icons]

WWW Ramada Plaza Portland **H** ❀

(207) 774-5861. **$72-$215.** 155 Riverside St 04103. I-95 exit 48; jct SR 25. Int corridors. **Pets:** $50 deposit/room. Service with restrictions.
[icons]

WWW Residence Inn by Marriott Portland Downtown/Waterfront **H**

(207) 761-1660. **$104-$603.** 145 Fore St 04101. In the Old Port; across from Casco Bay ferry terminal. Int corridors. **Pets:** Accepted.
[icons]

AAA **WWWW** The Westin Portland Harborview **H**

(207) 775-5411. **Call for rates.** 157 High St 04101. At Congress St. Int corridors. **Pets:** Accepted. [SAVE] [icons]

RANGELEY

WW Rangeley Saddleback Inn **H** ❀

(207) 864-3434. **Call for rates.** 2303 Main St 04970. On SR 4, just s of village. Ext corridors. **Pets:** Other species. $10 daily fee/room. Designated rooms, service with restrictions.
[icons]

ROCKLAND

WW Trade Winds Inn **H**

(207) 596-6661. **$99-$165.** 2 Park Dr 04841. On US 1; center. Int corridors. **Pets:** Accepted. [icons]

ROCKPORT

AAA **WWWW** The Country Inn At Camden/Rockport **H** ❀

(207) 236-2725. **$119-$249.** 8 Country Inn Way 04856. Jct SR 90, 0.9 mi n on US 1. Ext/int corridors. **Pets:** Other species. $15 daily fee/pet. Designated rooms, service with restrictions, supervision.
[SAVE] [icons]

AAA **WWWW** Samoset Resort On The Ocean **H** ❀

(207) 594-2511. **$109-$429, 7 day notice.** 220 Warrenton St 04856. Jct SR 90, 4.8 mi s on US 1, 0.5 mi e. Ext/int corridors. **Pets:** Small, other species. $75 one-time fee/room. Designated rooms, service with restrictions, supervision. [SAVE] [ECO] [icons]

WW Schooner Bay Motor Inn **M**

(207) 236-2205. **$119-$199, 3 day notice.** 337 Commercial St 04856. Jct SR 90, 0.5 mi s on US 1. Ext corridors. **Pets:** Accepted.
[icons]

SACO

AAA **WWWW** Hampton Inn by Hilton **H** ❀

(207) 282-7222. **$99-$279.** 48 Industrial Park Rd 04072. I-95 exit 36 (I-195) to exit 1 (Industrial Park Rd), just ne. Int corridors. **Pets:** Other species. $200 deposit/room. Service with restrictions, supervision.
[SAVE] [icons]

AAA **WWW** Ramada Saco Old Orchard Beach Area **H**

(207) 286-9600. **$75-$260.** 352 North St 04072. I-95 exit 36, 0.6 mi sw to SR 112, then 0.4 mi nw. Int corridors. **Pets:** Accepted.
[SAVE] [icons]

WW Wagon Wheel Motel I & II **M**

(207) 283-3258. **Call for rates.** 726 Portland Rd 04072. I-95 exit 36, 1.5 mi se to US 1, then 0.7 mi ne. Ext corridors. **Pets:** Accepted.
[icons]

SCARBOROUGH

AAA **WWW** Homewood Suites by Hilton Portland **H**

(207) 775-2700. **$139-$339.** 200 Southborough Dr 04074. I-95 exit 45, just s. Int corridors. **Pets:** Other species. $75 one-time fee/room. Designated rooms, service with restrictions, supervision.

SAVE &M 🏊 📶 🔋 📺

WWW Residence Inn by Marriott Portland/Scarborough **H**

(207) 883-0400. **$80-$266.** 800 Roundwood Dr 04074. I-95 exit 42, 1.5 mi n on Payne Rd. Int corridors. **Pets:** Accepted.

📶 &M 🏊 📶 ✕ 🔋 📺

SKOWHEGAN

WW Belmont Motel **M**

(207) 474-8315. **Call for rates.** 273 Madison Ave 04976. 1 mi n on US 201. Ext corridors. **Pets:** Accepted. &M 🏊 📶 ✕ 🔋 📺

AAA **WWW** Breezy Acres Motel **M**

(207) 474-2703. **Call for rates.** 315 Waterville Rd 04976. 1.5 mi s on US 201. Ext corridors. **Pets:** Accepted. SAVE 🏊 📶 ✕ 🔋 📺

SOUTHPORT

AAA **WWW** Ocean Gate Resort **H**

(207) 633-3321. **$119-$384, 7 day notice.** 70 Ocean Gate Rd 04576. SR 27, 2.5 mi s of Boothbay Harbor, 0.5 mi s of bridge to Southport Island. Ext corridors. **Pets:** $25 one-time fee/room. Designated rooms, service with restrictions. SAVE 🍴 🏊 ✕ 📶 ✕ 🔋 📺

SOUTH PORTLAND

AAA **WW** Best Western Merry Manor Inn **H** 🐾

(207) 774-6151. **$129-$279.** 700 Main St 04106. I-95 exit 45, 1.3 mi e to US 1. Ext/int corridors. **Pets:** Other species. $10 daily fee/pet. Designated rooms, service with restrictions, supervision.

SAVE 🍴 &M 🏊 📶 ✕ 🔋 📺

WW Comfort Inn Airport **H** 🐾

(207) 775-0409. **$104-$259.** 90 Maine Mall Rd 04106. I-95 exit 45, 1 mi n. Int corridors. **Pets:** Other species. Designated rooms, service with restrictions, supervision. ECO 🍴 &M 📶 ✕ 🔋 📺

WW Days Inn Airport/Maine Mall **H**

(207) 772-3450. **$53-$200.** 461 Maine Mall Rd 04106. I-95 exit 45, just n. Int corridors. **Pets:** Medium. $10 daily fee/pet. Designated rooms, service with restrictions, supervision. &M 🏊 📶 ✕ 🔋 📺

AAA **WWW** DoubleTree by Hilton **H**

(207) 775-6161. **Call for rates.** 363 Maine Mall Rd 04106. I-95 exit 45, just se. Int corridors. **Pets:** Accepted.

SAVE 🍴 &M 🏊 📶 ✕ 🔋 📺

WWW Hampton by Hilton Portland Airport **H**

(207) 773-4400. **$89-$349.** 171 Philbrook Ave 04106. I-95 exit 45, just ne. Int corridors. **Pets:** Accepted. &M 🏊 📶 ✕ 🔋 📺

AAA **WWWW** Holiday Inn Express & Suites **H**

(207) 775-3900. **Call for rates.** 303 Sable Oaks Dr 04106. I-95 exit 45, just n on Maine Mall Rd, then just w on Running Hill Rd. Int corridors. **Pets:** Accepted. SAVE ECO 🍴 &M 🏊 📶 ✕ 🔋 📺

AAA **WWWW** Portland Marriott at Sable Oaks **H**

(207) 871-8000. **$98-$325.** 200 Sable Oaks Dr 04106. I-95 exit 45, just n on Maine Mall Rd, then just w on Running Hill Rd. Int corridors. **Pets:** Accepted. SAVE ECO 🍴 &M 🏊 ✕ 📶 ✕ 🔋 📺

SPRUCE HEAD

WWW The Craignair Inn & Restaurant **CI**

(207) 594-7644. **$95-$225, 14 day notice.** 5 Third St 04859. 2.5 mi w on SR 73, 1.5 mi s on Clark Island Rd; 10 mi s of Rockland. Ext/int corridors. **Pets:** Accepted. ECO 🍴 📶 ✕ 🌀

STANDISH

WWW Sebago Lake Lodge and Cottages **BB**

(207) 892-2698. **Call for rates.** 661 White's Bridge Rd 04084. 1 mi w on US 302. Ext/int corridors. **Pets:** Large. $20 daily fee/pet. Designated rooms, service with restrictions, supervision.

🍴 ✕ 📶 ✕ 🅧 🌀 🔋 📺

WATERVILLE *(Restaurants p. 614)*

AAA **WWWW** Best Western Plus Waterville Grand Hotel **H**

(207) 873-0111. **$99-$199.** 375 Main St 04901. I-95 exit 130 (Main St), on SR 104. Int corridors. **Pets:** Other species. Designated rooms, service with restrictions, crate. SAVE ECO 🍴 🏊 📶 🔋 📺

WWW Fireside Inn & Suites **H** 🐾

(207) 873-3335. **Call for rates.** 376 Main St 04901. I-95 exit 130 (Main St). Int corridors. **Pets:** $20 one-time fee/room. Designated rooms, service with restrictions, supervision.

ECO 🍴 &M 🏊 📶 ✕ 🔋 📺

WELLS

WW Wells-Moody Motel **M**

(207) 646-5601. **Call for rates.** 119 Post Rd 04054. I-95 exit 19, jct SR 109 and US 1, 3.4 mi s. Ext corridors. **Pets:** Accepted.

&M 🏊 📶 ✕ 🔋 📺

WESTBROOK

AAA **WWW** Super 8 **H**

(207) 854-1881. **$99-$130.** 208 Larrabee Rd 04092. I-95 exit 48, jut w. Int corridors. **Pets:** Accepted. SAVE 🍴 &M 🏊 📶 🔋 📺

WEST FORKS

WWW Inn by the River **CI**

(207) 663-2181. **Call for rates.** 2777 US Rt 201 04985. Center. Int corridors. **Pets:** Dogs only. $20 daily fee/pet. Designated rooms, service with restrictions, supervision. 🍴 📶 ✕ 🅧 🌀 📺

WESTPORT

WWW Squire Tarbox Inn & Restaurant **CI**

(207) 882-7693. **Call for rates.** 1181 Main Rd 04578. Jct US 1, 8.5 mi s on SR 144, follow signs. Ext/int corridors. **Pets:** Accepted.

🍴 📶 ✕ 🅧 🌀

WILTON

WWW Farmington/Wilton Comfort Inn & Suites **H**

(207) 645-5155. **$109-$209.** 1026 US Rt 2 E 04294. On US 2, just w of jct SR 133. Int corridors. **Pets:** Accepted.

🍴 &M 🏊 📶 ✕ 🔋 📺

YORK HARBOR

WWWW York Harbor Inn **CI**

(207) 363-5119. **$99-$479, 14 day notice.** 480 York St 03911. On US 1A; center. Ext/int corridors. **Pets:** Accepted.

ECO 🍴 &M 📶 ✕ 🔋

MARYLAND

ABERDEEN

▼▼▼ Home2 Suites by Hilton Baltimore - Aberdeen H ❀
(410) 272-0203. **$109-$199.** 20 Newton Rd 21001. I-95 exit 85, 2 mi e on SR 22, then 2 mi w on US 40; jct US 40 and SR 715. Int corridors. **Pets:** $75 deposit/pet. 〔icons〕

▼▼ Red Roof Inn Aberdeen M
(410) 273-7800. **$60-$99.** 988 Hospitality Way 21001. I-95 exit 85, just e on SR 22. Ext corridors. **Pets:** Accepted. 〔icons〕

▼▼▼ Residence Inn by Marriott Aberdeen at Ripken Stadium H ❀
(410) 272-0444. **$110-$235.** 830 Long Dr 21001. I-95 exit 85, 0.5 mi w on SR 22, then 0.5 mi n. Int corridors. **Pets:** Medium, other species. $100 one-time fee/room. Supervision.
〔icons〕

ANNAPOLIS (Restaurants p. 614)

𝔸𝔸𝔸 ▼▼▼ Annapolis Waterfront Hotel, Autograph Collection H
(410) 268-7555. **$173-$349.** 80 Compromise St 21401. At the city dock. Int corridors. **Pets:** Accepted. 〔icons〕

𝔸𝔸𝔸 ▼▼▼ Best Western Annapolis M
(410) 224-2800. **$69-$139.** 2520 Riva Rd 21401. 2.3 mi sw on US 50 and 301 exit 22, just e; in Parole area. Ext/int corridors. **Pets:** $20 daily fee/room. Designated rooms, service with restrictions, supervision.
〔icons〕

▼▼ Country Inn & Suites By Carlson H
(410) 571-6700. **Call for rates.** 2600 Housley Rd 21401. US 50 and 301 exit 23 eastbound; exit 23B westbound, 1 mi w on SR 450; in Parole area. Int corridors. **Pets:** Accepted.
〔icons〕

𝔸𝔸𝔸 ▼▼▼ DoubleTree by Hilton Hotel Annapolis H
(410) 224-3150. **$104-$274.** 210 Holiday Ct 21401. 2.3 mi sw on US 50 and 301 exit 22 to Riva Rd, 0.3 mi n; in Parole area. Int corridors. **Pets:** $50 one-time fee/pet. Designated rooms, service with restrictions.
〔icons〕

▼▼ Extended Stay America-Annapolis-Admiral Cochrane Dr H
(410) 571-6600. **$90-$130.** 120 Admiral Cochrane Dr 21401. 2.3 mi sw on US 50 and 301 exit 22, just s, then just e; in Parole area. Int corridors. **Pets:** Accepted. 〔icons〕

▼▼▼ Hampton Inn & Suites by Hilton-Annapolis H
(410) 571-0200. **$99-$299.** 124 Womack Dr 21401. 2.3 mi sw on US 50 and 301 exit 22, just s, then just e on Admiral Cochrane Dr; n on Spruill Rd, then just w; in Parole area. Int corridors. **Pets:** Accepted.
〔icons〕

▼▼▼ Loews Annapolis Hotel H
(410) 263-7777. **$119-$309.** 126 West St 21401. US 50 and 301 exit 24 eastbound; exit 24A westbound, 1.4 mi s on SR 70, just sw on Calvert St, then just w. Int corridors. **Pets:** Accepted.
〔icons〕

𝔸𝔸𝔸 ▼▼▼ Residence Inn by Marriott Annapolis H
(410) 573-0300. **$110-$256.** 170 Admiral Cochrane Dr 21401. 2.3 mi sw on US 50 and 301 exit 22 to Riva Rd, just s, then just e; in Parole area. Ext corridors. **Pets:** Accepted.
〔icons〕

𝔸𝔸𝔸 ▼▼▼ The Westin Annapolis H ❀
(410) 972-4300. **$159-$599.** 100 Westgate Cir 21401. US 50 and 301 exit 24 eastbound; exit 24A westbound, 0.7 mi s on SR 70, then 0.8 mi e on SR 435; 0.5 mi n of Church Circle. Int corridors. **Pets:** Medium, dogs only. $50 one-time fee/room. Designated rooms, service with restrictions, supervision. 〔icons〕

BALTIMORE (Restaurants p. 615)

▼▼▼ Brookshire Suites H
(410) 625-1300. **Call for rates.** 120 E Lombard St 21202. Corner of Calvert and Lombard sts. Int corridors. **Pets:** Accepted.
〔icons〕

𝔸𝔸𝔸 ▼▼▼ Days Inn Inner Harbor Baltimore H
(410) 576-1000. **$139-$209.** 100 Hopkins Pl 21201. Between W Pratt and W Lombard sts. Int corridors. **Pets:** Small, dogs only. $100 deposit/ room. Service with restrictions, supervision.
〔icons〕

𝔸𝔸𝔸 ▼▼▼ Embassy Suites by Hilton Baltimore-Inner Harbor H
(410) 727-2222. **$129-$309.** 222 St. Paul Pl 21202. At St. Paul Pl and Saratoga St. Int corridors. **Pets:** Large, other species. $150 deposit/ room. Service with restrictions. 〔icons〕

▼▼▼ Four Seasons Hotel Baltimore H
(410) 576-5800. **Call for rates.** 200 International Dr 21202. In Harbor East. Int corridors. **Pets:** Accepted.
〔icons〕

𝔸𝔸𝔸 ▼▼▼ Hilton Baltimore H
(443) 573-8700. **$149-$359.** 401 W Pratt St 21201. Between Eutaw and S Paca sts. Int corridors. **Pets:** Accepted.
〔icons〕

𝔸𝔸𝔸 ▼▼▼ Holiday Inn Express Baltimore/Downtown H
(410) 400-8045. **$99-$199.** 221 N Gay St 21202. Jct N Gay St and Fallsway. Int corridors. **Pets:** Accepted. 〔icons〕

𝔸𝔸𝔸 ▼▼▼ Holiday Inn-Inner Harbor H
(410) 685-3500. **$89-$409.** 301 W Lombard St 21201. Between S Howard and Eutaw sts. Int corridors. **Pets:** Accepted.
〔icons〕

▼▼▼ Home2 Suites by Hilton-Downtown Baltimore H
(410) 576-1200. **$90-$180.** 8 E Pleasant St 21202. Just e of Charles St. Int corridors. **Pets:** Accepted. 〔icons〕

▼▼▼ Homewood Suites by Hilton Baltimore Inner Harbor H
(410) 234-0999. **$159-$189.** 625 S President St 21202. In Harbor East; at President St traffic circle. Int corridors. **Pets:** Accepted.
〔icons〕

▼▼ Hotel Brexton H
(443) 478-2100. **Call for rates.** 868 Park Ave 21201. Between Tyson and Brexton sts; 1 blk e of Martin Luther King Jr Blvd. Int corridors. **Pets:** Accepted. 〔icons〕

𝔸𝔸𝔸 ▼▼▼ Hyatt Place Baltimore/Inner Harbor H
(410) 558-1840. **$129-$349.** 511 S Central Ave 21202. Jct Central Ave and Fleet St; in East Harbor area. Int corridors. **Pets:** Accepted.
〔icons〕

𝔸𝔸𝔸 ▼▼▼ Hyatt Regency Baltimore Inner Harbor H
(410) 528-1234. **$99-$459.** 300 Light St 21202. Facing the Inner Harbor. Int corridors. **Pets:** Accepted.
〔icons〕

▼▼▼ Inn at The Colonnade Baltimore - A DoubleTree by Hilton Hotel H
(410) 235-5400. **$149-$369.** 4 W University Pkwy 21218. I-83 exit 9A, 0.5 mi e on Cold Springs Ln to Roland Ave/University Pkwy, then 1 mi s. Int corridors. **Pets:** Accepted.

♦♦♦ ▼▼▼ Kimpton Hotel Monaco Baltimore H ✿
(443) 692-6170. **Call for rates.** 2 N Charles St 21201. Jct Baltimore and N Charles sts. Int corridors. **Pets:** Designated rooms, service with restrictions, supervision.

♦♦♦ ▼▼▼ Pier 5, an Ascend Hotel Collection Member H
(410) 539-2000. **$179-$759.** 711 Eastern Ave 21202. On the Inner Harbor, at Pier 5. Int corridors. **Pets:** Accepted.

▼▼▼ Radisson Hotel at Cross Keys H
(410) 532-6900. **Call for rates.** 5100 Falls Rd 21210. I-83 exit 10A (Northern Pkwy), just e, then 0.4 mi s on Falls Rd; in Village of Cross Keys. Int corridors. **Pets:** Accepted.

▼▼▼ Residence Inn by Marriott-Baltimore Downtown/ Inner Harbor H
(410) 962-1220. **$113-$261.** 17 Light St 21202. Jct Redwood and Light sts. Int corridors. **Pets:** Accepted.

♦♦♦ ▼▼▼ Sheraton Inner Harbor Hotel H ✿
(410) 962-8300. **Call for rates.** 300 S Charles St 21201. At Conway St; 1 blk from the Inner Harbor. Int corridors. **Pets:** Medium, dogs only. Designated rooms, service with restrictions, supervision.

♦♦♦ ▼▼▼ Sleep Inn & Suites Downtown Inner Harbor H
(410) 779-6166. **$89-$339.** 301 Fallsway 21202. Between E Lexington and Gay sts. Int corridors. **Pets:** Large, other species. $30 daily fee/room. Designated rooms, service with restrictions, crate.

BELCAMP

▼▼ Candlewood Suites Aberdeen H
(410) 914-3060. **Call for rates.** 4216 Philadelphia Rd 21015. I-95 exit 80 (SR 543), just s to SR 7 (Philadelphia Rd N), then just w. Int corridors. **Pets:** Accepted.

▼▼ Extended Stay America-Baltimore-Bel Air-Aberdeen H
(410) 273-0194. **$95-$145.** 1361 James Way 21015. I-95 exit 80 (SR 543), just ne. Int corridors. **Pets:** Accepted.

▼▼▼ Homewood Suites by Hilton Aberdeen/Bel Air H
(410) 297-8585. **$109-$289.** 4170 Philadelphia Rd 21015. I-95 exit 80 (SR 543), just s to SR 7 (Philadelphia Rd N), then just w. Int corridors. **Pets:** Accepted.

BELTSVILLE

♦♦♦ ▼▼▼ Sheraton College Park North Hotel H
(301) 937-4422. **$99-$359.** 4095 Powder Mill Rd 20705. I-95 exit 29B, just w on SR 212; 2 mi n of I-495. Int corridors. **Pets:** Medium, dogs only. Designated rooms, service with restrictions, supervision.

BETHESDA *(Restaurants p. 615)*

♦♦♦ ▼▼▼ Residence Inn by Marriott-Bethesda Downtown H
(301) 718-0200. **$137-$288.** 7335 Wisconsin Ave 20814. I-495 exit 34, 2.5 mi s on SR 355; entrance on Waverly St. Int corridors. **Pets:** Accepted.

BOWIE *(Restaurants p. 615)*

♦♦♦ ▼▼▼ Comfort Inn Conference Center-Bowie H
(301) 464-0089. **$100-$165.** 4500 NW Crain Hwy 20716. US 50 exit 13A; jct US 50/301 and SR 3. Int corridors. **Pets:** Accepted.

CALIFORNIA

▼▼▼ La Quinta Inn & Suites Lexington Park - Patuxent H
(301) 862-4100. **$67-$230.** 22769 Three Notch Rd 20619. On SR 235, 1.4 mi s of jct SR 4. Int corridors. **Pets:** Accepted.

CAMBRIDGE

▼▼▼ Comfort Inn & Suites Cambridge H
(410) 901-0926. **$100-$280.** 2936 Ocean Gateway 21613. On US 50, 0.8 mi e of jct SR 16. Int corridors. **Pets:** Accepted.

♦♦♦ ▼▼▼▼ Hyatt Regency Chesapeake Bay Golf Resort, Spa and Marina H ✿
(410) 901-1234. **$159-$469, 3 day notice.** 100 Heron Blvd 21613. US 50, 1.2 mi e of Frederick C Malkus Jr Bridge. Int corridors. **Pets:** Medium, dogs only. $150 one-time fee/room. Designated rooms, supervision.

CAMP SPRINGS

▼▼▼ Country Inn & Suites By Carlson Andrews Air Force Base/DC Area H
(240) 492-1070. **Call for rates.** 4950 Mercedes Blvd 20746. I-95/495 exit 7B, just e to Auth Rd, then just n. Int corridors. **Pets:** Accepted.

CHESTERTOWN

▼▼▼ Holiday Inn Express Hotel & Suites Chestertown H
(410) 778-0778. **$110-$319.** 150 Scheeler Rd 21620. 0.4 mi ne of jct SR 213 and 291. Int corridors. **Pets:** Accepted.

CLINTON

♦♦♦ ▼▼▼ Comfort Inn at Joint Base Andrews H
(301) 856-5200. **$79-$199.** 7979 Malcolm Rd 20735. I-95/495 exit 7A, 3.2 mi s on SR 5. Int corridors. **Pets:** Accepted.

♦♦♦ ▼▼▼ TownePlace Suites by Marriott at Joint Base Andrews H ✿
(301) 856-2266. **$110-$188.** 7800 Ferry Ave 20735. I-95/495 exit 7A, 2.9 mi s on SR 5 exit Coventry Way E, follow signs to Andrews AFB, then 0.5 mi ne on Old Alexandria Ferry Rd. Int corridors. **Pets:** Small. $100 one-time fee/room. Designated rooms, service with restrictions, supervision.

COLUMBIA *(Restaurants p. 615)*

▼▼▼ Homewood Suites by Hilton Columbia H
(410) 872-9200. **$109-$299.** 8320 Benson Dr 21045. I-95 exit 41B, 0.5 mi w on SR 175 (Little Patuxent Pkwy), just nw on SR 108, then just w on Lark Brown Rd. Int corridors. **Pets:** Accepted.

AAA ▼▼▼ Sheraton Columbia Town Center
Hotel 🅷 ❀

(410) 730-3900. **$99-$499.** 10207 Wincopin Cir 21044. 1.2 mi w on SR 175 (Little Patuxent Pkwy) from jct US 29, then just s; center. Int corridors. **Pets:** Large, dogs only. Service with restrictions, supervision.

[SAVE] [ECO] [❤] [⑤M] [🛒] [📶] [✕] [🔌] [🖥]

AAA ▼▼▼ Sonesta ES Suites Columbia 🅷

(410) 964-9494. **Call for rates.** 8844 Columbia 100 Pkwy 21045. I-95 exit 43B, 4 mi w on SR 100 exit 1B, then just e. Int corridors.
Pets: Accepted. [SAVE] [⑤M] [🛒] [📶] [✕] [🔌] [🖥]

CUMBERLAND

▼▼▼ Ramada Cumberland Downtown 🅷

(301) 724-8800. **$81-$150.** 100 S George St 21502. I-68 exit 43C, just n; downtown. Int corridors. **Pets:** Medium. $25 daily fee/pet. Designated rooms, service with restrictions, supervision.

[❤] [🛒] [📶] [✕] [🔌] [🖥]

EASTON

▼▼ Quality Inn Easton 🅼

(410) 820-8333. **$90-$229.** 8523 Ocean Gateway 21601. US 50, 0.7 mi n of jct SR 331. Ext corridors. **Pets:** Medium, dogs only. $25 daily fee/pet. Designated rooms, service with restrictions, supervision.

[🛒] [📶] [🔌] [🖥]

▼▼ Tidewater Inn 🅷

(410) 822-1300. **Call for rates.** 101 E Dover St 21601. On SR 231, 0.8 mi w of US 50; center. Int corridors. **Pets:** Accepted.

[❤] [📶] [✕] [🔌] [🖥]

EDGEWOOD

▼▼ La Quinta Inn & Suites 🅷

(410) 676-6969. **$93-$213.** 2112B Emmorton Park Rd 21040. I-95 exit 77A, just e on SR 24. Int corridors. **Pets:** Accepted.

[⑤M] [📶] [✕] [🔌] [🖥]

▼▼ Ramada Edgewood Hotel and Conference
Center 🅷

(410) 679-0770. **$74-$129.** 1700 Van Bibber Rd 21040. I-95 exit 77A, just e on SR 24. Ext corridors. **Pets:** Accepted. [🛒] [📶] [🔌] [🖥]

ELKTON

▼▼▼ Elk Forge Bed & Breakfast Inn, Spa and
Events 🅱🅱

(410) 392-9007. **Call for rates.** 807 Elk Mills Rd 21921. I-95 exit 109B, 1 mi w on SR 279 to Fletchwood Rd (SR 277), then 2 mi s. Ext/int corridors. **Pets:** Accepted. [❤] [⑤M] [✕] [📶] [✕] [🔌] [🖥]

ELLICOTT CITY

▼▼▼ Residence Inn by Marriott Columbia 🅷

(410) 997-7200. **$113-$227.** 4950 Beaver Run Way 21043. I-95 exit 43B, 4 mi w on SR 100 exit 1B. Int corridors. **Pets:** Accepted.

[ECO] [⑤M] [🛒] [📶] [✕] [🔌] [🖥]

▼▼▼ Turf Valley Resort 🅷

(410) 465-1500. **Call for rates.** 2700 Turf Valley Rd 21042. I-70 exit 82 eastbound, 1.5 mi e on US 40; exit 83 westbound, 0.6 mi s on Marriottsville Rd, then 0.8 mi e on US 40. Int corridors. **Pets:** Accepted.

[ECO] [❤] [⑤M] [✕] [📶] [✕] [🔌] [🖥]

EMMITSBURG

▼▼ Sleep Inn & Suites in Emmitsburg 🅷

(301) 447-0044. **$94-$274.** 501 Silo Hill Pkwy 21727. US 15 exit SR 140, just w, then just n. Int corridors. **Pets:** Accepted.

[❤] [⑤M] [🛒] [📶] [✕] [🔌] [🖥]

FREDERICK *(Restaurants p. 615)*

AAA ▼▼▼ Clarion Inn 🅷

(301) 694-7500. **Call for rates.** 5400 Holiday Dr 21703. I-270 exit 31A, just se of SR 85. Int corridors. **Pets:** Accepted.

[SAVE] [❤] [🛒] [✕] [📶] [✕] [🔌] [🖥]

AAA ▼▼▼ Country Inn & Suites By Carlson, Frederick,
MD 🅷

(301) 695-2881. **$89-$179.** 5579 Spectrum Dr 21703. I-270 exit 31A, just e on SR 85. Int corridors. **Pets:** Small. $20 daily fee/room. Designated rooms, service with restrictions, supervision.

[SAVE] [⑤M] [📶] [✕] [🔌] [🖥]

AAA ▼▼▼ Days Inn 🅼

(301) 694-6600. **$79-$99.** 5646 Buckeystown Pike 21704. I-270 exit 31A, 0.5 mi e on SR 85; I-70 exit 54, 0.5 mi w. Ext corridors.
Pets: $20 daily fee/pet. Designated rooms, service with restrictions, crate. [SAVE] [🛒] [📶] [🔌] [🖥]

▼▼ Extended Stay America-Frederick-Westview Dr 🅼

(301) 668-0808. **$90-$115.** 5240 Westview Dr 21703. I-270 exit 31B, 0.5 mi sw on SR 85, then 0.4 mi n. Int corridors. **Pets:** Accepted.

[⑤M] [📶] [🔌]

▼▼▼ Hampton Inn by Hilton Frederick 🅷 ❀

(301) 698-2500. **$99-$219.** 5311 Buckeystown Pike 21704. I-270 exit 31B, 0.6 mi w. Int corridors. **Pets:** Medium, dogs only. $75 one-time fee/room. Service with restrictions, crate.

[❤] [⑤M] [🛒] [📶] [✕] [🔌] [🖥]

AAA ▼▼▼ MainStay Suites Frederick 🅷

(301) 668-4600. **$65-$109.** 7310 Executive Way 21704. I-270 exit 31B, 0.7 mi sw on SR 85. Int corridors. **Pets:** Small. $10 daily fee/pet. Designated rooms, service with restrictions, supervision.

[SAVE] [🛒] [📶] [🔌] [🖥]

▼▼▼ Residence Inn by Marriott Frederick 🅷

(301) 360-0010. **$140-$237.** 5230 Westview Dr 21703. I-270 exit 31B, 0.5 mi sw on SR 85, then 0.3 mi n on Crestwood Blvd. Int corridors.
Pets: Accepted. [⑤M] [🛒] [📶] [✕] [🔌] [🖥]

▼▼▼ TownePlace Suites by Marriott Frederick 🅷

(301) 624-0050. **$127-$210.** 5050 Westview Dr 21703. I-270 exit 31B, 0.9 mi sw on SR 85. Int corridors. **Pets:** Accepted.

[📇] [⑤M] [🛒] [📶] [✕] [🔌] [🖥]

FROSTBURG

AAA ▼▼▼ Quality Inn & Suites 🅼

(301) 689-2050. **$80-$135.** 11100 New Georges Creek Rd 21532. I-68 exit 34, 1 mi n on SR 36. Int corridors. **Pets:** Medium. $25 daily fee/pet. Designated rooms, service with restrictions, crate.

[SAVE] [❤] [✕] [📶] [🔌] [🖥]

GAITHERSBURG

▼▼▼ Comfort Inn Shady Grove 🅷 ❀

(301) 330-0023. **$99-$159.** 16216 Frederick Rd 20877. I-270 exit 8, 1 mi e on Shady Grove Rd at SR 355. Int corridors. **Pets:** Large, other species. $15 daily fee/pet. Service with restrictions, crate.

[📇] [🛒] [📶] [✕] [🔌] [🖥]

AAA ▼▼▼ Hilton Washington DC
North/Gaithersburg 🅷

(301) 977-8900. **$99-$219.** 620 Perry Pkwy 20877. I-270 exit 11, then e. Int corridors. **Pets:** Accepted. [SAVE] [❤] [🛒] [📶] [✕] [🔌] [🖥]

▼▼▼ Homewood Suites by Hilton Washington DC North
Gaithersburg 🅷

(301) 670-0008. **$119-$229.** 805 Russell Ave 20879. I-270 exit 11, 0.5 mi e. Int corridors. **Pets:** Accepted. [❤] [⑤M] [🛒] [📶] [✕] [🔌] [🖥]

Hyatt House Gaithersburg H
(301) 527-6000. **$84-$249.** 200 Skidmore Blvd 20877. I-370 exit SR 355, just n to Westland Rd. Ext corridors. **Pets:** Accepted.
[SAVE] [&M] [≈] [≈] [X] [♿] [▣]

Residence Inn by Marriott-Gaithersburg H
(301) 590-3003. **$90-$174.** 9721 Washingtonian Blvd 20878. I-270 exit 9B (I-370/Sam Eig Hwy), just w to Fields Rd, 0.8 mi se, then just ne. Int corridors. **Pets:** Accepted. [¶] [&M] [≈] [≈] [X] [♿] [▣]

TownePlace Suites by Marriott-Gaithersburg H
(301) 590-2300. **$95-$150.** 212 Perry Pkwy 20877. I-270 exit 10 northbound, just ne; exit 11 southbound, just e on SR 124 to SR 355, 0.3 mi s, then 0.5 mi sw. Int corridors. **Pets:** Medium. $100 one-time fee/pet. Designated rooms, service with restrictions, supervision.
[¶] [&M] [≈] [X] [♿] [▣]

GLEN BURNIE *(Restaurants p. 615)*

Extended Stay America Baltimore-Glen Burnie H
(410) 761-2708. **$95-$125.** 104 Chesapeake Centre Ct 21061. I-695 exit 3B eastbound; exit 2 westbound, 0.9 mi s on SR 2, just e on E Ordnance Rd, then just s. Int corridors. **Pets:** Accepted. [&M] [≈] [♿]

La Quinta Inn & Suites Baltimore South Glen Burnie H
(410) 636-4300. **$79-$174.** 6323 Ritchie Hwy 21061. I-695 exit 3A eastbound; exit 2 westbound, jct SR 2. Int corridors. **Pets:** Accepted.
[SAVE] [¶] [&M] [≈] [≈] [♿] [▣]

GRANTSVILLE

Comfort Inn H
(301) 895-5993. **$89-$144.** 2541 Chestnut Ridge Rd 21536. I-68 exit 22, just s on US 219. Int corridors. **Pets:** Accepted.
[SAVE] [¶] [≈] [≈] [X] [♿] [▣]

GREENBELT

Residence Inn by Marriott-Greenbelt H
(301) 982-1600. **$111-$228.** 6320 Golden Triangle Dr 20770. I-95/495 exit 23, 0.5 mi sw of jct SR 201, off SR 193 (Greenbelt Rd), then just n on Walker Dr. Int corridors. **Pets:** Accepted.
[SAVE] [&M] [≈] [≈] [X] [♿] [▣]

HAGERSTOWN

Comfort Suites H
(301) 791-8100. **$79-$149.** 1801 Dual Hwy 21740. I-70 exit 32B, 0.8 mi w on US 40. Int corridors. **Pets:** Medium, dogs only. $30 daily fee/room. Designated rooms, service with restrictions, supervision.
[SAVE] [≈] [≈] [X] [♿] [▣]

Days Inn Hagerstown M
(301) 733-2700. **$60-$120.** 1101 Dual Hwy 21740. I-70 exit 32B, 2.2 mi w on US 40. Int corridors. **Pets:** Accepted. [≈] [♿] [▣]

Grand Venice Hotel Wedding & Conference Center H
(301) 733-0830. **$65-$120.** 431 Dual Hwy 21740. I-70 exit 32B, 2.7 mi s on US 40. Int corridors. **Pets:** Accepted.
[SAVE] [ECO] [¶] [≈] [≈] [X] [♿] [▣]

Halfway Hagerstown Super 8 M
(301) 582-1992. **$63-$73.** 16805 Blake Rd 21740. I-81 exit 5B, just w. Int corridors. **Pets:** Other species. $15 daily fee/pet. Designated rooms, service with restrictions, supervision. [¶] [≈] [♿] [▣]

Holiday Inn Express Hotel & Suites H
(301) 745-5644. **Call for rates.** 241 Railway Ln 21740. I-81 exit 5A, just e. Int corridors. **Pets:** Accepted.
[SAVE] [&M] [≈] [X] [≈] [♿] [▣]

Homewood Suites by Hilton H
(301) 665-3816. **$119-$159.** 1650 Pullman Ln 21740. I-81 exit 5, 0.3 mi e; 0.5 mi n of jct I-70 and 81. Int corridors. **Pets:** Accepted.
[SAVE] [≈] [≈] [♿] [▣]

Sleep Inn & Suites H
(301) 766-9449. **$99-$159.** 18216 Col Henry K Douglas Dr 21740. I-70 exit 29, just s. Int corridors. **Pets:** Accepted. [≈] [≈] [♿] [▣]

HANOVER *(Restaurants p. 616)*

Aloft Arundel Mills H
(443) 577-0077. **$89-$225.** 7520 Teague Rd 21076. I-95 exit 43A, 3.6 mi e on SR 100 exit 10A (Arundel Mills Blvd), then 0.4 mi s to SR 713. Int corridors. **Pets:** Accepted. [SAVE] [ECO] [&M] [≈] [≈] [X] [♿] [▣]

Candlewood Suites H
(410) 691-0550. **Call for rates.** 1525 Dorsey Rd 21076. SR 100 exit 10B, 0.3 mi n on SR 713, then 0.7 mi w on SR 176. Int corridors. **Pets:** Accepted. [¶] [&M] [≈] [♿] [▣]

Element Arundel Mills H
(443) 577-0050. **$89-$249.** 7522 Teague Rd 21076. I-95 exit 43A, 3.6 mi e on SR 100 exit 10A (Arundel Mills Blvd), then 0.4 mi s to SR 713. Int corridors. **Pets:** Accepted.
[SAVE] [ECO] [⊖] [¶] [&M] [≈] [≈] [X] [♿] [▣]

Home2 Suites by Hilton Arundel Mills BWI Airport H
(410) 684-2003. **$99-$199.** 7545 Teague Rd 21076. I-95 exit 43A, 3.6 mi e on SR 100 exit 10A (Arundel Mills Blvd), 0.4 mi s to SR 713. Int corridors. **Pets:** $100 one-time fee/pet. No service.
[¶] [&M] [≈] [X] [♿] [▣]

Red Roof PLUS+ Baltimore- Washington DC/BW Parkway M
(410) 712-4070. **$60-$130.** 7306 Parkway Dr S 21076. I-95 exit 43A, 2 mi e on SR 100 exit 8 (Coca Cola Dr), then 0.5 mi se. Ext corridors.
Pets: Accepted. [SAVE] [&M] [X] [♿] [▣]

Residence Inn by Marriott-Arundel Mills/BWI H
(410) 799-7332. **$125-$191.** 7035 Arundel Mills Cir 21076. I-95 exit 43A, 3.6 mi e on SR 100 exit 10A (Arundel Mills Blvd). Int corridors.
Pets: Accepted. [&M] [≈] [≈] [X] [♿] [▣]

TownePlace Suites by Marriott Arundel Mills/BWI H
(410) 379-9000. **$98-$166.** 7021 Arundel Mills Cir 21076. I-95 exit 43A, 3.6 mi e on SR 100 exit 10A (Arundel Mills Blvd). Int corridors.
Pets: Accepted. [&M] [≈] [≈] [X] [♿] [▣]

HUNT VALLEY

Hunt Valley Inn, A Wyndham Grand Hotel H
(410) 785-7000. **$88-$199.** 245 Shawan Rd 21031. I-83 exit 20A (Shawan Rd), just e. Int corridors. **Pets:** Accepted.
[¶] [&M] [≈] [≈] [X] [♿] [▣]

Residence Inn by Marriott Baltimore Hunt Valley H
(410) 527-2333. **$126-$204.** 45 Schilling Rd 21031. I-83 exit 20A (Shawan Rd), just e, just s on McCormick Rd, then just e. Int corridors.
Pets: Other species. $75 one-time fee/room. Designated rooms, service with restrictions, supervision. [¶] [&M] [≈] [≈] [X] [♿] [▣]

JESSUP

Extended Stay America-Columbia-Laurel-Ft. Meade H
(301) 725-3877. **$95-$130.** 8550 Washington Blvd 20794. I-95 exit 38A, 1.4 mi e on SR 32, then 0.5 mi n on US 1. Int corridors.
Pets: Accepted. [&M] [≈] [♿]

◆◆ **La Quinta Inn & Suites Columbia Jessup** H
(410) 799-1500. **$68-$229.** 7300 Crestmount Rd 20794. I-95 exit 41A, just e on SR 175, then just s on US 1. Int corridors. **Pets:** Accepted.
⬛ 📶 ▣

◆◆ ◆◆ **Red Roof Inn Washington DC- Columbia/Fort Meade** M
(410) 796-0380. **$60-$130.** 8000 Washington Blvd 20794. I-95 exit 41A, 0.3 mi s of jct US 1 and SR 175. Ext corridors. **Pets:** Accepted.
SAVE ⬛ 📶 ✕ ▣ ▣

LARGO

◆◆ ◆◆ **DoubleTree by Hilton Hotel Largo-Washington, DC** H
(301) 773-0700. **$119-$219.** 9100 Basil Ct 20774. I-95/495 exit 17A (SR 202), just se; in business park. Int corridors. **Pets:** Accepted.
SAVE ⅋ ⬛ ➔ 📶 ✕ ▣

◆◆◆◆ **Residence Inn by Marriott Largo Capital Beltway** H
(301) 925-7806. **$125-$279.** 1330 Caraway Ct 20774. I-95/495 exit 16, 0.4 mi e on Arena Dr, 0.3 mi n on Lottsford Rd, then just w on McCormick Dr. Int corridors. **Pets:** Accepted. ⅋ ⬛ 📶 ✕ ▣ ▣

LAUREL

◆◆◆◆ **DoubleTree by Hilton Laurel** H
(301) 776-5300. **$99-$189.** 15101 Sweitzer Ln 20707. I-95 exit 33B, just w on SR 198. Ext/int corridors. **Pets:** Accepted.
⅋ ⬛ ➔ 📶 ✕ ▣ ▣

LA VALE

◆◆◆ ◆◆◆◆ **Best Western Braddock Motor Inn** H
(301) 729-3300. **$76-$120.** 1268 National Hwy 21502. On US 40, jct SR 53. Int corridors. **Pets:** Accepted.
SAVE ⅋ ➔ ✕ 📶 ▣ ▣

◆◆ **Super 8 LaVale** M
(301) 729-6265. **$41-$100.** 1301 National Hwy 21502. I-68 exit 40 eastbound, 0.5 mi s; exit 39 westbound, 0.4 mi n. Int corridors.
Pets: Accepted. 📶 ▣ ▣

LEXINGTON PARK (Restaurants p. 616)

◆◆◆◆ **Hampton Inn by Hilton Lexington Park** H
(301) 863-3200. **$109-$169.** 22211 Three Notch Rd 20653. On SR 235, 0.9 mi n of jct SR 246. Int corridors. **Pets:** Accepted.
⬛ ➔ 📶 ✕ ▣ ▣

◆◆◆◆ **Home2 Suites by Hilton Lexington Park/Pax River NAS** H 🐾
(301) 866-1416. **$109-$149.** 22175 Franklin Delano Roosevelt Blvd 20653. On SR 235, 0.9 mi n of jct SR 246. Int corridors. **Pets:** $75 one-time fee/pet. Service with restrictions.
ECO ⬛ ➔ 📶 ✕ ▣ ▣

◆◆◆◆ **TownePlace Suites by Marriott Patuxent River Naval Air Station** H
(301) 863-1111. **$84-$230.** 22520 Three Notch Rd 20653. On SR 235, 1 mi n of Gate 1 at Naval Air Station Patuxent River. Int corridors.
Pets: Accepted. ⅋ ⬛ ➔ 📶 ✕ ▣ ▣

LINTHICUM HEIGHTS (Restaurants p. 616)

◆◆◆ ◆◆◆◆ **Aloft Baltimore Washington Intl Airport** H
(410) 691-6969. **Call for rates.** 1741 W Nursery Rd 21090. I-695 exit 7A, 1 mi s on SR 295, then 1.2 mi e. Int corridors. **Pets:** Accepted.
SAVE ⅋ ⬛ ➔ 📶 ✕ ▣ ▣

◆◆ ◆◆ **Candlewood Suites-BWI** H
(410) 850-9214. **$80-$120.** 1247 Winterson Rd 21090. I-695 exit 7A, 1 mi s on SR 295, 1.3 mi e on W Nursery Rd, then 0.3 mi w. Int corridors. **Pets:** Accepted. ⅋ ⬛ 📶 ✕ ▣ ▣

◆◆◆◆ **Hampton Inn BWI Airport** H
(410) 850-0600. **$119-$139.** 829 Elkridge Landing Rd 21090. I-695 exit 7A, 1 mi s on SR 295, 1.3 mi e on W Nursery Rd, then just w. Int corridors. **Pets:** Accepted. ⅋ ⬛ 📶 ✕ ▣ ▣

◆◆◆ ◆◆◆◆ **Holiday Inn BWI** H
(410) 691-1000. **Call for rates.** 815 Elkridge Landing Rd 21090. I-695 exit 7A, 1 mi s on SR 295, then 1.3 mi e on W Nursery Rd. Int corridors. **Pets:** Other species. $30 daily fee/pet. Designated rooms, service with restrictions, crate. SAVE ⅋ ⬛ 📶 ✕ ▣ ▣

◆◆◆ ◆◆◆◆ **Hyatt Place Baltimore/BWI Airport** H
(410) 859-3366. **$89-$229.** 940 International Dr 21090. I-695 exit 7A, 1 mi s on SR 295, then just e on W Nursery Rd. Int corridors.
Pets: Accepted. SAVE ⅋ ➔ 📶 ✕ ▣ ▣

◆◆ ◆◆ **La Quinta Inn & Suites BWI Airport** H
(410) 859-2333. **$75-$183.** 1734 W Nursery Rd 21090. I-695 exit 7A, 1 mi s on SR 295, then 1.3 mi e. Int corridors. **Pets:** Accepted.
➔ 📶 ✕ ▣ ▣

◆◆◆ ◆◆ ◆◆ **Red Roof PLUS+ Baltimore-Washington DC/BWI Airport** M
(410) 850-7600. **$60-$130.** 827 Elkridge Landing Rd 21090. I-695 exit 7A, 1 mi s on SR 295, 1.3 mi e on W Nursery Rd, then just w. Ext corridors. **Pets:** Accepted. SAVE 📶 ✕ ▣ ▣

◆◆◆ ◆◆◆◆ **Residence Inn by Marriott-BWI Airport** H
(410) 691-0255. **$98-$207.** 1160 Winterson Rd 21090. I-695 exit 7A, 1 mi s on SR 295, 0.7 mi e on W Nursery Rd, then just n. Int corridors.
Pets: Accepted. SAVE ECO ⅋ ⬛ ➔ 📶 ✕ ▣ ▣

◆◆◆ ◆◆◆◆ **Sheraton Baltimore Washington Airport Hotel** H
(443) 577-2100. **$99-$299.** 1100 Old Elkridge Landing Rd 21090. I-695 exit 7A, 1 mi s on SR 295, 1.3 mi e on W Nursery Rd, then 0.4 mi w on Winterson Rd. Int corridors. **Pets:** Accepted.
SAVE ⅋ ⬛ ➔ 📶 ✕ ▣ ▣

◆◆◆◆ **Staybridge Suites BWI** H
(410) 850-5666. **Call for rates.** 1301 Winterson Rd 21090. I-695 exit 7A, 1 mi s on SR 295, 1.3 mi e on Nursery Rd, then 0.4 mi w. Int corridors. **Pets:** Accepted. ⅋ ⬛ ➔ 📶 ▣ ▣

◆◆◆ ◆◆◆◆ **TownePlace Suites by Marriott Baltimore/ BWI Airport** H
(410) 694-0060. **$79-$154.** 1171 Winterson Rd 21090. I-695 exit 7A, 1 mi s on SR 295, 0.7 mi e on W Nursery Rd, then just n. Int corridors. **Pets:** Other species. $100 one-time fee/room. Service with restrictions, crate. SAVE ECO ⅋ ⬛ ➔ 📶 ✕ ▣ ▣

◆◆◆ ◆◆◆◆ **The Westin Baltimore Washington Airport** H 🐾
(443) 577-2300. **Call for rates.** 1110 Old Elkridge Landing Rd 21090. I-695 exit 7A, 1 mi s on SR 295, 1.3 mi e on W Nursery Rd, then 0.4 mi w on Winterson Rd. Int corridors. **Pets:** Dogs only. Designated rooms, service with restrictions, supervision.
SAVE ⅋ ⬛ ➔ 📶 📶 ✕ ▣ ▣

MCHENRY

◆◆◆◆ **Wisp Resort Hotel & Conference Center** H
(301) 387-5581. **Call for rates.** 290 Marsh Hill Rd 21541. 1 mi s on US 219 from jct SR 42, just w on Sang Run Rd, then 0.3 mi s. Int corridors. **Pets:** Accepted. ⅋ ➔ ✕ 📶 ✕ ▣ ▣

NATIONAL HARBOR

Residence Inn by Marriott National Harbor H

(301) 749-4755. **$129-$329.** 192 Waterfront St 20745. I-95/495 exit 2A, 0.5 mi e. Int corridors. **Pets:** Accepted.

The Westin Washington National Harbor H

(301) 567-3999. **$179-$454.** 171 Waterfront St 20745. I-95/495 exit 2A, 0.5 mi e. Int corridors. **Pets:** Accepted.

NORTH EAST *(Restaurants p. 616)*

Best Western North East Inn H

(410) 287-5450. **$100-$189.** 39 Elwoods Rd 21901. I-95 exit 100 southbound; exit 100B northbound, 0.5 mi n on SR 272, then just w on Joseph Biggs Hwy to Old Bayview Rd. Int corridors. **Pets:** Large. $10 daily fee/pet. Designated rooms, service with restrictions, supervision.

Comfort Inn & Suites North East H

(410) 287-7100. **$89-$219.** 1 Center Dr 21901. I-95 exit 100 southbound; exit 100A northbound, just s on SR 272. Int corridors. **Pets:** Small. $15 daily fee/pet. Designated rooms, service with restrictions, crate.

OCEAN CITY *(Restaurants p. 616)*

Clarion Resort Fontainebleau Hotel H

(410) 524-3535. **$69-$419, 3 day notice.** 10100 Coastal Hwy 21842. At 101st St. Int corridors. **Pets:** Other species. $37 daily fee/pet. Designated rooms, service with restrictions.

Comfort Suites Ocean City H

(410) 213-7171. **$60-$350.** 12718 Ocean Gateway 21842. US 50; 0.7 mi w of Ocean City Bridge. Int corridors. **Pets:** Accepted.

Fenwick Inn H

(410) 250-1100. **Call for rates.** 13801 Coastal Hwy 21842. 138th St and Coastal Hwy. Int corridors. **Pets:** Accepted.

La Quinta Inn & Suites H

(410) 289-5762. **$67-$564.** 106 32nd St 21842. Jct Philadelphia Ave. Int corridors. **Pets:** Accepted.

Paradise Plaza Inn H

(410) 289-6381. **Call for rates.** 3 9th St 21842. 9th St and The Boardwalk. Int corridors. **Pets:** Accepted.

OWINGS MILLS

Hyatt Place Baltimore/Owings Mills H

(410) 998-3630. **$89-$209.** 4730 Painters Mill Rd 21117. I-795 exit 4 (Owings Mills Blvd), 0.5 mi s, then 0.7 mi e on Red Run Blvd. Int corridors. **Pets:** Accepted.

PERRYVILLE

Days Inn Perryville M

(410) 642-2866. **$69-$94.** 61 Heather Ln 21903. I-95 exit 93, just e. Ext corridors. **Pets:** Accepted.

ROCK HALL

Mariners Motel M

(410) 639-2291. **Call for rates.** 5681 S Hawthorne Ave 21661. 0.3 mi e of SR 20. Ext corridors. **Pets:** Accepted.

ROCKVILLE *(Restaurants p. 616)*

Best Western Plus Rockville Hotel & Suites H

(301) 424-4940. **$89-$139.** 1251 W Montgomery Ave 20850. I-270 exit 6B, just w on SR 28. Int corridors. **Pets:** Accepted.

Cambria Suites Rockville H

(301) 294-2200. **$79-$314.** 1 Helen Heneghan Way 20850. I-270 exit 5 (Falls Rd), 1 mi e on Falls Rd/Maryland Ave; just w of SR 355 at Middle Rd. Int corridors. **Pets:** Accepted.

EVEN Hotels-Rockville/Washington, DC Area H 🐾

(301) 881-3836. **$79-$499.** 1775 Rockville Pike 20852. SR 355, 2 mi s of jct SR 28. Int corridors. **Pets:** Large, dogs only. $50 deposit/pet. Designated rooms, service with restrictions, supervision.

Extended Stay America-Washington DC-Rockville H

(301) 987-9100. **$100-$140.** 2621 Research Blvd 20850. I-270 exit 8 (Shady Grove Rd), just w, then just n. Int corridors. **Pets:** Accepted.

Red Roof PLUS+ Washington DC-Rockville M

(301) 987-0965. **$79-$150.** 16001 Shady Grove Rd 20850. I-270 exit 8 (Shady Grove Rd), 0.5 mi e. Ext corridors. **Pets:** Accepted.

Sheraton Rockville H

(240) 912-8200. **Call for rates.** 920 King Farm Blvd 20850. I-270 exit 8 (Shady Grove Rd), 0.3 mi e to Choke Cherry Rd, just s to Piccard Dr, then just sw; 1 mi w of SR 355 via Redland Blvd. Int corridors. **Pets:** Accepted.

ROSEDALE

La Quinta Inn & Suites Baltimore North H

(410) 574-8100. **$79-$181.** 4 Philadelphia Ct 21237. I-695 exit 34, just n. Int corridors. **Pets:** Accepted.

ST. MICHAELS

St. Michaels Harbour Inn, Marina & Spa H

(410) 745-9001. **Call for rates.** 101 N Harbor Rd 21663. 0.3 mi e on SR 33, just n on Seymour Ave, just w. Int corridors. **Pets:** Accepted.

St. Michaels Inn M

(410) 745-3333. **$79-$300.** 1228 S Talbot St 21663. 1 mi e on SR 33. Ext/int corridors. **Pets:** Other species. $20 daily fee/pet. Designated rooms, supervision.

SALISBURY

Best Western Salisbury Plaza M

(410) 546-1300. **$69-$229.** 1735 N Salisbury Blvd 21801. US 13 business route, 0.5 mi s of US 50 Bypass. Ext corridors. **Pets:** Medium, other species. $10 daily fee/pet. Designated rooms, service with restrictions, crate.

Hampton Inn-Salisbury H

(410) 334-3080. **$99-$249.** 121 E Naylor Mill Rd 21804. US 13, 0.5 mi n of jct US 50 Bypass. Int corridors. **Pets:** Accepted.

La Quinta Inn & Suites H

(410) 546-4400. **$79-$646.** 300 S Salisbury Blvd 21801. US 13 business route, 0.4 mi s of jct US 50 business route; downtown. Int corridors. **Pets:** Accepted.

▼▼▼▼ **Residence Inn by Marriott Salisbury** 🅗
(410) 543-0033. **$105-$219.** 140 Centre Rd 21801. Just off US 13 business route at US 50. Int corridors. **Pets:** Accepted.
🔳🅜 ⇌ 📶 ✕ 🔋 🖵

SILVER SPRING

🅐🅐🅐 ▼▼▼▼ **Residence Inn by Marriott Silver**
Spring 🅗
(301) 572-2322. **$118-$229.** 12000 Plum Orchard Dr 20904. I-95 exit 29B, 1.2 mi w on SR 212, then 1 mi n on Cherry Hill Rd. Int corridors. **Pets:** Accepted. 🔳 🔳 🅜 ⇌ 📶 ✕ 🔋 🖵

🅐🅐🅐 ▼▼▼▼ **Sheraton Silver Spring** 🅗
(301) 589-0800. **$109-$299.** 8777 Georgia Ave 20910. I-495 exit 31B, 1 mi s. Int corridors. **Pets:** Accepted. 🔳 🍽 🅜 ⇌ 📶 ✕ 🖵

SNOW HILL

▼▼▼ **River House Inn** 🅱🅱
(410) 632-2722. **$175-$500, 7 day notice.** 201 E Market St 21863. 1 mi w on SR 394 from jct SR 113. Ext/int corridors. **Pets:** Dogs only. $15 daily fee/pet. Designated rooms, service with restrictions.
⇌ 📶 ✕ 🛡 🔋 🖵

SYKESVILLE *(Restaurants p. 616)*

▼▼▼▼ **Inn at Norwood** 🅱🅱
(410) 549-7868. **$135-$225, 7 day notice.** 7514 Norwood Ave 21784. I-70 exit 80 (SR 32), 3.6 mi n, 0.6 mi w on W Friendship Rd (which becomes Main St), then just s on Church St. Ext/int corridors. **Pets:** Dogs only. $20 daily fee/pet. Designated rooms, service with restrictions. 📶 ✕ 🛡 🔋 🖵

TILGHMAN ISLAND

▼▼ **Knapp's Narrows Marina & Inn** 🅜
(410) 886-2720. **$90-$260, 7 day notice.** 6176 Tilghman Island Rd 21671. On SR 33, east side of the bridge. Ext corridors. **Pets:** Other species. $25 daily fee/room. Designated rooms, supervision.
⇌ 📶 ✕ 🔋 🖵

TIMONIUM

🅐🅐🅐 ▼▼▼ **Red Roof PLUS+ Baltimore North-**
Timonium 🅜
(410) 666-0380. **$69-$129.** 111 W Timonium Rd 21093. I-83 exit 16A northbound; exit 16 southbound, just e. Ext corridors. **Pets:** Accepted.
🔳 🅜 📶 ✕ 🔋 🖵

TOWSON

🅐🅐🅐 ▼▼▼▼ **Sheraton Baltimore North Hotel** 🅗
(410) 321-7400. **Call for rates.** 903 Dulaney Valley Rd 21204. I-695 exit 27A (Dulaney Valley Rd), 0.3 mi s. Int corridors. **Pets:** Accepted.
🔳 🍽 ⇌ 📶 ✕ 🔋 🖵

UPPER MARLBORO

🅐🅐🅐 ▼▼ 🔷🔷 **Executive Inn & Suites** 🅜
(301) 627-3969. **$95-$145.** 2901 Crain Hwy 20774. On US 301, 2.5 mi n of jct SR 4; 7 mi s of jct US 50. Ext corridors. **Pets:** Medium. $20 daily fee/pet. Service with restrictions, supervision.
🔳 🍽 🅜 📶 🔋 🖵

WALDORF

▼▼▼▼ **Holiday Inn Express Waldorf** 🅗
(301) 932-9200. **Call for rates.** 11370 Days Ct 20603. 0.5 mi s on US 301 from jct SR 228. Int corridors. **Pets:** Accepted.
🅜 📶 ✕ 🔋 🖵

▼▼▼▼ **Residence Inn by Marriott Waldorf** 🅗
(301) 632-2111. **$114-$177.** 3020 Technology Pl 20601. SR 228, just w of jct US 301. Int corridors. **Pets:** Medium. $150 one-time fee/room. Designated rooms, service with restrictions, supervision.
🅜 ⇌ 📶 ✕ 🔋 🖵

WESTMINSTER

🅐🅐🅐 ▼▼▼ **Best Western Westminster Catering &**
Conference Center 🅗 🐾
(410) 857-1900. **$104-$200.** 451 WMC Dr 21158. 1.7 mi w on SR 140 from jct SR 27. Int corridors. **Pets:** Dogs only. $15 daily fee/pet. Service with restrictions, crate. 🔳 ⇌ 📶 ✕ 🔋 🖵

▼▼ **The Boston Inn** 🅜
(410) 848-9095. **Call for rates.** 533 Baltimore Blvd 21157. 0.9 mi se on SR 140 and 97 from jct SR 27. Ext corridors. **Pets:** Accepted.
⇌ 📶 🔋 🖵

WHITE MARSH *(Restaurants p. 616)*

▼▼▼▼ **Home2 Suites by Hilton Baltimore White**
Marsh 🅗
(410) 933-1010. **$129-$219.** 10465 Philadelphia Rd 21162. I-95 exit 67, 0.5 mi e on SR 43, then just s on CR 7. Int corridors. **Pets:** Accepted.
🍽 🅜 ⇌ 📶 ✕ 🔋 🖵

▼▼▼▼ **Residence Inn by Marriott Baltimore/White**
Marsh 🅗
(410) 933-9554. **$132-$178.** 4980 Mercantile Rd 21236. I-95 exit 67, 0.5 mi w on SR 43 (White Marsh Blvd), just s on Honeygo Blvd, then just e. Int corridors. **Pets:** Other species. $75 one-time fee/room. Service with restrictions, crate. 🅜 ⇌ 📶 ✕ 🔋 🖵

WILLIAMSPORT

🅐🅐🅐 ▼▼ **Red Roof Inn- Hagerstown-Williamsport** 🅜
(301) 582-3500. **$60-$175.** 310 E Potomac St 21795. I-81 exit 2, 0.3 mi sw on US 11. Ext corridors. **Pets:** Accepted. 🔳 📶 🔋

MASSACHUSETTS

ANDOVER

▼▼▼▼ **Homewood Suites by Hilton Boston/Andover** 🅗
(978) 475-6000. **Call for rates.** 4 Riverside Dr 01810. I-93 exit 45, 0.5 mi e. Int corridors. **Pets:** Medium. $75 one-time fee/pet. Service with restrictions. 🍽 🅜 ⇌ 📶 ✕ 🔋 🖵

▼▼▼▼ **Residence Inn by Marriott Boston-Andover** 🅗
(978) 683-0382. **$101-$318.** 500 Minuteman Rd 01810. I-93 exit 45, 0.3 mi w, then 0.5 mi n. Int corridors. **Pets:** Other species. $100 one-time fee/pet. Service with restrictions. 🍽 🅜 ⇌ 📶 ✕ 🔋 🖵

🅐🅐🅐 ▼▼▼▼ **Sonesta ES Suites** 🅗
(978) 686-2000. **Call for rates.** 4 Tech Dr 01810. I-93 exit 45, just sw to Shattuck Rd. Int corridors. **Pets:** Accepted.
🔳 🍽 🅜 ⇌ 📶 ✕ 🔋 🖵

AUBURN

▼▼ **La Quinta Inn Auburn Worcester** 🅗
(508) 832-7000. **$82-$214.** 446 Southbridge St 01501. I-90 exit 10, 1.2 mi n on SR 12. Int corridors. **Pets:** Accepted. 📶 ✕ 🔋 🖵

BARRE

▼▼▼▼ **Jenkins Inn** 🅲🅸
(978) 355-6444. **$185-$265, 30 day notice.** 7 West St 01005. On SR 122 and 32. Int corridors. **Pets:** Dogs only. $10 daily fee/pet. Service with restrictions, supervision. 🍽 📶 ✕ 🔋 🖵

BEDFORD

▼▼▼ Homewood Suites by Hilton ⊞

(978) 670-7111. **$109-$409.** 35 Middlesex Tpke 01730. I-95 exit 32B, 2.5 mi n. Int corridors. **Pets:** Accepted. 🔲🛏️🛜⊠🍴📺

BOSTON *(Restaurants p. 616)*

▼▼▼ Aloft Boston Seaport ⊞

(617) 530-1600. **$149-$489.** 401-403 D St 02210. Just sw of Summer St. Int corridors. **Pets:** Accepted. SAVE 🍴🛏️🛜⊠🍴📺

▼▼▼ Ames Boston Hotel, Curio Collection by Hilton ⊞

(617) 979-8100. **$179-$599.** 1 Court St 02108. At Washington St; across from Old State House. Int corridors. **Pets:** Accepted. 🍴🛏️⊠🛜⊠📺

▼▼▼ Battery Wharf Hotel, Boston Waterfront ⊞

(617) 994-9000. **Call for rates.** 3 Battery Wharf 02109. At Battery Wharf; east of North End. Int corridors. **Pets:** Accepted. SAVE ECO 🍴🛏️⊠🛜⊠📺

▼▼▼ Best Western Plus Roundhouse Suites ⊞

(617) 989-1000. **$129-$299.** 891 Massachusetts Ave 02118. I-93 exit 18, just sw; just n of Newmarket Square; in South Boston. Int corridors. **Pets:** Accepted. SAVE 🛏️🛜⊠🍴📺

▼▼▼ Boston Harbor Hotel ⊞

(617) 439-7000. **Call for rates.** 70 Rowes Wharf 02110. At Atlantic Ave. Int corridors. **Pets:** Accepted. SAVE 🍴🛏️🛏️⊠🍴📺

▼▼▼ Boston Park Plaza ⊞ ❀

(617) 426-2000. **$139-$599.** 50 Park Plaza 02116. At Park Plaza and Arlington St, just s of Boston Common and Public Garden. Int corridors. **Pets:** Medium, dogs only. $75 one-time fee/room. Designated rooms, service with restrictions, supervision. SAVE 🍴🛏️⊠🛜📺

▼▼▼ The Boxer ⊞

(617) 624-0202. **$119-$699.** 107 Merrimac St 02114. At Merrimac and Causeway sts. Int corridors. **Pets:** Accepted. SAVE 🍴🛏️🛜⊠🍴📺

▼▼ Chandler Inn Hotel ⊞

(617) 482-3450. **Call for rates.** 26 Chandler St 02116. At Berkeley St; in South End. Int corridors. **Pets:** Accepted. 🍴🛜⊠

▼▼▼ The Colonnade Hotel Boston ⊞

(617) 424-7000. **Call for rates.** 120 Huntington Ave 02116. Just s of Copley Square. Int corridors. **Pets:** Accepted. SAVE 🍴🛏️🛏️🛜⊠🍴📺

▼▼▼ Copley Square Hotel ⊞

(617) 536-9000. **$149-$699.** 47 Huntington Ave 02116. I-90 exit 22, just n. Int corridors. **Pets:** Accepted. SAVE 🍴🛏️🛜⊠

▼▼▼ Element Boston Seaport ⊞

(617) 530-1700. **Call for rates.** 391-395 D St 02210. Just sw of Summer St. Int corridors. **Pets:** Accepted. SAVE 🛏️🛜⊠🍴📺

▼▼▼ The Eliot Hotel ⊞

(617) 267-1607. **$285-$595.** 370 Commonwealth Ave 02215. Corner of Massachusetts Ave; in historic Back Bay. Int corridors. **Pets:** Accepted. SAVE 🍴🛏️🛜⊠📺

▼▼ enVision Hotel Boston, an Ascend Hotel Collection Member ⊞

(617) 383-5229. **$159-$489.** 81 S Huntington Ave 02130. Jct Huntington Ave (SR 9). Int corridors. **Pets:** Accepted. 🛏️🛜⊠🍴📺

▼▼▼ The Envoy Hotel, Autograph Collection ⊞ ❀

(617) 338-3030. **$159-$751.** 70 Sleeper St 02210. At Northern Ave. Int corridors. **Pets:** $100 one-time fee/pet. Designated rooms, service with restrictions. SAVE 🍴🛏️🛜⊠🍴

▼▼▼ The Fairmont Copley Plaza Boston ⊞

(617) 267-5300. **Call for rates.** 138 St. James Ave 02116. At Copley Square. Int corridors. **Pets:** Accepted.
SAVE ECO 🍴🛏️🛜⊠📺

▼▼▼ Four Seasons Hotel Boston ⊞

(617) 338-4400. **$565-$1000.** 200 Boylston St 02116. Between Arlington and Charles sts. Int corridors. **Pets:** Accepted. SAVE 🍴🛏️⊠🛜⊠

▼▼▼ Hilton Boston Downtown/Faneuil Hall ⊞ ❀

(617) 556-0006. **$159-$499.** 89 Broad St 02110. Corner of Broad and Franklin sts. Int corridors. **Pets:** Dogs only. $75 one-time fee/room. Service with restrictions, supervision. SAVE 🍴🛏️🛜⊠🍴📺

▼▼▼ Hilton Boston Logan Airport ⊞ ❀

(617) 568-6700. **$139-$499.** 1 Hotel Dr 02128. At Boston Logan International Airport. Int corridors. **Pets:** Medium, other species. Designated rooms, service with restrictions, supervision. SAVE 🍴🛏️🛏️🛜⊠

▼▼▼ Hotel Commonwealth ⊞ ❀

(617) 933-5000. **$199-$599.** 500 Commonwealth Ave 02215. On SR 2; at Beacon St and Brookline Ave. Int corridors. **Pets:** Dogs only. $125 one-time fee/room. Service with restrictions, supervision. SAVE 🍴🛏️🛜⊠🍴

▼▼▼ Hyatt Regency Boston ⊞

(617) 912-1234. **$159-$599.** One Avenue de Lafayette 02111. Just e of Boston Common. Int corridors. **Pets:** Accepted. SAVE ECO 🍴🛏️🛏️⊠🛜⊠🍴📺

▼▼▼ Hyatt Regency Boston Harbor ⊞ ❀

(617) 568-1234. **$129-$649.** 101 Harborside Dr 02128. I-90 exit 20, follow Hotel Dr to Harborside Dr. Int corridors. **Pets:** Medium. $100 one-time fee/room. Service with restrictions, supervision. SAVE ECO 🛏️🛏️⊠🛜⊠

▼▼▼ InterContinental Boston ⊞

(617) 747-1000. **$219-$699.** 510 Atlantic Ave 02210. I-93 exit 23 southbound; exit 20 northbound; at Pearl St. Int corridors. **Pets:** Accepted. SAVE 🍴🛏️⊠🛏️🛜⊠📺

▼▼▼ The Lenox Hotel ⊞

(617) 536-5300. **Call for rates.** 61 Exeter St 02116. I-90 exit 22, just n at Boylston St. Int corridors. **Pets:** Accepted. SAVE ECO 🍴🛏️🛜⊠🍴

▼▼▼ The Liberty, a Starwood Luxury Collection Hotel, Boston ⊞ ❀

(617) 224-4000. **$200-$6000.** 215 Charles St 02114. I-93 exit 26, just n. Int corridors. **Pets:** Medium, dogs only. $100 one-time fee/pet. Designated rooms, service with restrictions. SAVE 🍴🛏️⊠🛜⊠📺

▼▼▼ Loews Boston Hotel ⊞

(617) 266-7200. **$169-$649.** 154 Berkeley St 02116. At Stuart St. Int corridors. **Pets:** Other species. $50 one-time fee/pet. Designated rooms, service with restrictions, crate. SAVE 🍴🛏️🛜⊠🍴📺

▼▼▼ Mandarin Oriental Boston ⊞

(617) 535-8888. **Call for rates.** 776 Boylston St 02199. At Prudential Center. Int corridors. **Pets:** Accepted. SAVE 🍴🛏️⊠🛏️🛜⊠📺

The Midtown Hotel H ❀
(617) 262-1000. **$89-$409.** 220 Huntington Ave 02115. 3 blks sw of Copley Pl; just n of Symphony Hall and Massachusetts Ave. Int corridors. **Pets:** Other species. $30 one-time fee/room. Service with restrictions, crate.

Nine Zero Hotel H ❀
(617) 772-5800. **$159-$2000, 24 day notice.** 90 Tremont St 02108. Just ne of Boston Common; motor entrance on Bosworth St. Int corridors. **Pets:** Other species.

Onyx Hotel H
(617) 557-9955. **Call for rates.** 155 Portland St 02114. Corner of Merrimac and Traverse sts, just n; 3 blks s of TD Garden. Int corridors. **Pets:** Accepted.

Residence Inn by Marriott Boston Back Bay - Fenway H
(617) 236-8787. **$175-$730.** 125 Brookline Ave 02215. Just sw of Kenmore Square; at Burlington Ave. Int corridors. **Pets:** Large. $100 one-time fee/room. Service with restrictions, supervision.

Residence Inn by Marriott Boston Downtown/Seaport Hotel H
(617) 478-0840. **$177-$700.** 370 Congress St 02210. At Congress and Stillings sts; in Seaport District. Int corridors. **Pets:** Medium, other species. $100 one-time fee/room. Designated rooms, service with restrictions, crate.

Residence Inn by Marriott Boston Harbor on Tudor Wharf H
(617) 242-9000. **$143-$578.** 34-44 Charles River Ave 02129. Just se of SR 99 at Charlestown Bridge. Int corridors. **Pets:** Accepted.

Revere Hotel Boston Common H
(617) 482-1800. **Call for rates.** 200 Stuart St 02116. At Park Square and Charles St; in Back Bay. Int corridors. **Pets:** Accepted.

The Ritz-Carlton, Boston H
(617) 574-7100. **$475-$895.** 10 Avery St 02111. At Washington and Avery sts; 1 blk e of Boston Common. Int corridors. **Pets:** Accepted.

Seaport Hotel & Seaport World Trade Center H
(617) 385-4000. **$159-$779.** 1 Seaport Ln 02210. At Seaport World Trade Center. Int corridors. **Pets:** Accepted.

Sheraton Boston H
(617) 236-2000. **$179-$799.** 39 Dalton St 02199. I-90 exit 22, at Belvidere St. Int corridors. **Pets:** Accepted.

Taj Boston H
(617) 536-5700. **$249-$499.** 15 Arlington St 02117. At Arlington and Newbury sts; overlooks Public Garden. Int corridors. **Pets:** Accepted.

The Verb Hotel M
(617) 566-4500. **$99-$599.** 1271 Boylston St 02215. Between Ipswich St and Yawkey Way. Int corridors. **Pets:** Accepted.

W Boston Hotel & Residences H
(617) 261-8700. **Call for rates.** 100 Stuart St 02116. At Tremont St; in Theater District. Int corridors. **Pets:** Accepted.

Westin Boston Waterfront H
(617) 532-4600. **$139-$799.** 425 Summer St 02210. I-93 exit 23, 1 mi se on Purchase St to Summer St. Int corridors. **Pets:** Accepted.

The Westin Copley Place Boston H
(617) 262-9600. **Call for rates.** 10 Huntington Ave 02116. I-90 exit 22, at Copley Place Mall. Int corridors. **Pets:** Accepted.

Wyndham Boston Beacon Hill H
(617) 742-7630. **$129-$549.** 5 Blossom St 02114. At Cambridge and Blossom sts; center. Int corridors. **Pets:** Large, dogs only. $100 deposit/room. Designated rooms, service with restrictions, supervision.

XV Beacon H ❀
(617) 670-1500. **Call for rates.** 15 Beacon St 02108. Between Bowdoin and Somerset sts. Int corridors. **Pets:** Dogs only. Designated rooms, service with restrictions, supervision.

BRAINTREE

Candlewood Suites Boston - Braintree H
(781) 849-7450. **Call for rates.** 235 Wood Rd 02184. I-93 exit 6, just n on SR 37, then 0.5 mi w. Int corridors. **Pets:** Accepted.

Hampton Inn Braintree H ❀
(781) 380-3300. **$139-$249.** 215 Wood Rd 02184. I-93 exit 6, just n on SR 37, then 0.5 mi w. Int corridors. **Pets:** Service with restrictions, crate.

Hyatt Place Boston Braintree H
(781) 848-0600. **$89-$299.** 50 Forbes Rd 02184. I-93 exit 6, just se. Int corridors. **Pets:** Accepted.

BROCKTON

Residence Inn by Marriott Boston Brockton H
(508) 583-3600. **$125-$266.** 124 Liberty St 02301. SR 24 exit 17B, just w, just s on Pearl St, then 0.3 mi se to Mill St connector. Int corridors. **Pets:** Accepted.

BROOKLINE

Holiday Inn Boston Brookline H
(617) 277-1200. **Call for rates.** 1200 Beacon St 02446. On SR 2; 1 mi sw of Kenmore Square. Int corridors. **Pets:** Accepted.

BURLINGTON

Candlewood Suites Boston-Burlington H
(781) 229-4300. **$89-$139.** 130 Middlesex Tpke 01803. I-95 exit 32B, just n. Int corridors. **Pets:** Other species. $15 daily fee/room. Service with restrictions, crate.

Hyatt House Boston/Burlington H
(781) 270-0800. **$89-$309.** 2 Van de Graaff Dr 01803. I-95 exit 33A, just s on US 3, then 0.5 mi w on Wayside Rd. Int corridors. **Pets:** Accepted.

Sonesta ES Suites H
(781) 221-2233. **Call for rates.** 11 Old Concord Rd 01803. I-95 exit 32B, just s on Middlesex Tpke. Int corridors. **Pets:** Accepted.

BUZZARDS BAY

Bay Motor Inn M
(508) 759-3989. **Call for rates.** 223 Main St 02532. SR 25 exit 3, 0.5 mi w of Bourne rotary. Ext corridors. **Pets:** Accepted.

CAMBRIDGE *(Restaurants p. 616)*

△△△▽ ▽▽▽▽ **The Charles Hotel, Harvard Square** H

(617) 864-1200. **$199-$599.** 1 Bennett St 02138. Just s of Harvard Square; at Eliot St. Int corridors. **Pets:** Accepted.
[SAVE] [⊞] [🍴] [ḷM] [⇌] [✕] [🛜] [✕]

△△△ ▽▽▽▽ **Freepoint Hotel - West Cambridge** H

(617) 491-8000. **$139-$329.** 220 Alewife Brook Pkwy 02138. Jct SR 2, 16 and US 3; I-90 exit Cambridge/Allston to SR 2 W (Fresh Pond Pkwy). Int corridors. **Pets:** Accepted. [SAVE] [ḷM] [🛜] [✕] [🔌] [💻]

△△△ ▽▽▽▽ **Hotel Marlowe** H

(617) 868-8000. **Call for rates.** 25 Edwin H Land Blvd 02141. Just sw of jct SR 28. Int corridors. **Pets:** Accepted.
[SAVE] [ECO] [🍴] [ḷM] [✕] [🛜] [✕]

△△△ ▽▽▽▽ **Hyatt Regency Cambridge** H

(617) 492-1234. **$129-$459.** 575 Memorial Dr 02139. On US 3 and SR 2, at Amesbury St. Int corridors. **Pets:** Accepted.
[SAVE] [🍴] [ḷM] [⇌] [✕] [🛜] [✕] [🔌] [💻]

△△△ ▽▽▽▽ **Le Meridien Cambridge** H

(617) 577-0200. **$119-$899.** 20 Sidney St 02139. On SR 2A, 1 mi n of river. Int corridors. **Pets:** Accepted. [SAVE] [🍴] [ḷM] [🛜] [✕] [🔌] [💻]

▽▽▽▽ **Residence Inn by Marriott Boston Cambridge** H

(617) 349-0700. **$143-$642.** 120 Broadway 02142. Corner of Ames St; Kendall Sq. Int corridors. **Pets:** Other species. $150 one-time fee/room.
[ḷM] [⇌] [✕] [🔌] [💻]

△△△ ▽▽▽▽ **Royal Sonesta Boston** H

(617) 806-4200. **$199-$799.** 40 Edwin H Land Blvd 02142. Just sw of SR 28. Int corridors. **Pets:** Accepted.
[SAVE] [🍴] [ḷM] [⇌] [✕] [🛜] [✕] [🔌] [💻]

△△△ ▽▽▽▽ **Sheraton Commander Hotel** H

(617) 547-4800. **$189-$549.** 16 Garden St 02138. Just n of Harvard Square. Int corridors. **Pets:** Accepted. [SAVE] [🍴] [ḷM] [🛜] [✕] [💻]

CHATHAM

△△△ ▽▽▽▽ **Chatham Bars Inn Resort & Spa** H 🐾

(508) 945-0096. **Call for rates.** 297 Shore Rd 02633. 0.8 mi e of rotary on Main St, 0.8 mi n. Ext/int corridors. **Pets:** Large, dogs only. $100 one-time fee/pet, $40 daily fee/pet. Designated rooms, service with restrictions, crate. [SAVE] [🍴] [⇌] [✕] [🛜] [✕] [🔌] [💻]

CHELSEA

▽▽▽▽ **Residence Inn by Marriott Boston Logan Airport/Chelsea** H

(617) 889-9990. **$98-$438.** 200 Maple St 02150. 0.3 mi se of SR 16. Int corridors. **Pets:** Accepted. [🍴] [ḷM] [⇌] [🛜] [✕] [🔌] [💻]

▽▽▽▽ **TownePlace Suites by Marriott Boston Logan Airport/Chelsea** H

(617) 887-0290. **$88-$386.** 30 Eastern Ave 02150. 0.4 mi w of SR 1A, via Curtis St and Chelsea St Bridge. Int corridors. **Pets:** Accepted.
[🍴] [ḷM] [🛜] [✕] [🔌] [💻]

CHICOPEE

▽▽▽▽ **Residence Inn by Marriott-Springfield/Chicopee** H

(413) 331-4440. **$103-$319.** 500 Memorial Dr 01020. I-90 exit 5, just s. Int corridors. **Pets:** Medium, dogs only. $100 one-time fee/room. Designated rooms, service with restrictions, crate.
[⊞] [ḷM] [🛜] [✕] [🔌] [💻]

CONCORD

△△△ ▽▽▽ **Best Western at Historic Concord** H

(978) 369-6100. **$134-$199.** 740 Elm St 01742. 1.8 mi w, just off SR 2 and 2A. Int corridors. **Pets:** $15 daily fee/room. Designated rooms, service with restrictions, supervision. [SAVE] [ḷM] [⇌] [🛜] [✕] [🔌] [💻]

▽▽▽▽ **Residence Inn by Marriott Boston Concord** H

(978) 341-0003. **$128-$254.** 320 Baker Ave 01742. Just s of SR 2. Int corridors. **Pets:** Accepted. [🍴] [ḷM] [🛜] [✕] [🔌] [💻]

DANVERS

△△△ ▽▽▽▽ **DoubleTree by Hilton Boston North Shore** H

(978) 777-2500. **$145-$190.** 50 Ferncroft Rd 01923. I-95 exit 50, follow signs for US 1 S to Ferncroft Village. Int corridors. **Pets:** Medium, other species. $250 deposit/room. Service with restrictions, crate.
[SAVE] [🍴] [ḷM] [⇌] [✕] [🛜] [✕] [🔌] [💻]

▽▽▽▽ **Residence Inn by Marriott Boston-North Shore/Danvers** H

(978) 777-7171. **$89-$344.** 51 Newbury St 01923. US 1 N, just s of jct SR 114. Ext corridors. **Pets:** Accepted. [ḷM] [⇌] [🛜] [✕] [🔌] [💻]

△△△ ▽▽▽▽ **TownePlace Suites by Marriott Boston-North Shore** H

(978) 777-6222. **$80-$229.** 238 Andover St 01923. SR 114 eastbound, enter just w of US 1 (no westbound entrance); US 1 southbound, enter through shopping center; southwest corner of jct US 1 and SR 114. Int corridors. **Pets:** Accepted.
[SAVE] [ECO] [🍴] [ḷM] [⇌] [🛜] [✕] [🔌] [💻]

DEDHAM

▽▽▽▽ **Residence Inn by Marriott Dedham** H

(781) 407-0999. **$107-$340.** 259 Elm St 02026. I-95 exit 15A, just n, then 0.4 mi e. Int corridors. **Pets:** Accepted. [⇌] [🛜] [✕] [🔌] [💻]

EAST FALMOUTH

▽▽▽ **Capewind Waterfront Motel** M

(508) 548-3400. **Call for rates.** 34 Maravista Ext 02536. 2.2 mi e to SR 28, just s, follow signs. Ext corridors. **Pets:** Accepted.
[⇌] [🛜] [✕] [🔌] [💻]

EASTHAM

▽ **Ocean Park Inn** M 🐾

(508) 255-1132. **Call for rates.** 3900 State Hwy 02642. On US 6; 1 mi n of National Seashore Visitor's Center. Ext corridors. **Pets:** Other species. $25 daily fee/pet. Service with restrictions, supervision.
[⇌] [🛜] [✕]

EAST WAREHAM

△△△ ▽ **Atlantic Motel** M

(508) 295-0210. **$90-$300, 10 day notice.** 7 Depot St 02538. Jct SR 25 exit 1; between eastbound and westbound lanes of US 6/SR 28. Ext corridors. **Pets:** Medium, dogs only. $25 daily fee/pet. Designated rooms, service with restrictions, supervision.
[SAVE] [🍴] [⇌] [🛜] [🔌] [💻]

EDGARTOWN

△△△ ▽▽▽▽ **Harbor View Hotel** H

(508) 627-7000. **$99-$595, 21 day notice.** 131 N Water St 02539. 0.3 mi n; center. Ext/int corridors. **Pets:** Accepted.
[SAVE] [⊞] [🍴] [ḷM] [⇌] [✕] [🛜] [✕] [🔌] [💻]

△△△ ▽▽▽▽ **Kelley House** H

(508) 627-7900. **Call for rates.** 23 Kelley St 02539. At N Water St; center. Ext/int corridors. **Pets:** Accepted.
[SAVE] [🍴] [⇌] [🛜] [✕] [🔌] [💻]

▼▼▼ **Vineyard Square Hotel & Suites** CI
(508) 627-4711. **Call for rates.** 38 N Water St 02539. Just n from Main St. Int corridors. **Pets:** Accepted. 🍴 ⊠ 🛜 ⊠ 🛢 🖵

FAIRHAVEN
▼▼ **Seaport Inn Conference Center & Marina** H
(508) 997-1281. **Call for rates.** 110 Middle St 02719. I-195 exit 15, 1 mi s, then just off US 6. Int corridors. **Pets:** Accepted.
🍴 🕭 ⊠ 🛜 ⊠ 🛢 🖵

FALMOUTH
◈◈◈ ▼▼ **Seaside Inn** M
(508) 540-4120. **$69-$355, 14 day notice.** 263 Grand Ave 02540. Jct SR 28, 1.3 mi s from Falmouth Heights Rd. Ext/int corridors.
Pets: Medium. $15 daily fee/pet. Designated rooms, service with restrictions, supervision. SAVE 🍴 🛜 ⊠ 🛢 🖵

FOXBORO
▼▼▼ **Residence Inn by Marriott Foxborough** H
(508) 698-2800. **$93-$454.** 250 Foxborough Blvd 02035. I-95 exit 7A, 0.6 mi s on SR 140, 0.7 mi e, then just n. Int corridors.
Pets: Accepted. 🕭 🛋 🛜 ⊠ 🛢 🖵

FRAMINGHAM
▼▼▼ **Residence Inn by Marriott Boston/Framingham** H
(508) 370-0001. **$91-$351.** 400 Staples Dr 01702. SR 9 W to Crossing Blvd, then s. Int corridors. **Pets:** Accepted.
🕭 🛋 🛜 ⊠ 🛢 🖵

◈◈◈ ▼▼▼ **Sheraton Framingham Hotel & Conference Center** H
(508) 879-7200. **$129-$599.** 1657 Worcester Rd 01701. I-90 exit 12, follow signs to SR 9 W. Int corridors. **Pets:** Accepted.
SAVE 🍴 🕭 🛋 🛜 ⊠ 🖵

FRANKLIN
▼▼ **Hawthorn Suites by Wyndham Franklin Milford** H
(508) 553-3500. **$79-$259.** 835 Upper Union St 02038. I-495 exit 16, just s, then 0.3 mi e. Int corridors. **Pets:** Accepted.
🍴 🕭 🛋 🛜 ⊠ 🛢 🖵

▼▼▼ **Residence Inn by Marriott-Boston/Franklin** H
(508) 541-8188. **$96-$385.** 4 Forge Pkwy 02038. I-495 exit 17, 0.7 mi nw off SR 140 N. Int corridors. **Pets:** Accepted.
🍴 🕭 🛋 🛜 ⊠ 🛢 🖵

GARDNER
▼▼▼ **Colonial Hotel** H
(978) 630-2500. **Call for rates.** 625 Betty Spring Rd 01440. SR 2 exit 24 eastbound; exit 24B westbound, 0.9 mi n on SR 140, then 0.5 mi w. Int corridors. **Pets:** Accepted. 🍴 🛋 ⊠ 🛜 ⊠ 🛢 🖵

HAVERHILL
◈◈◈ ▼▼ **Best Western Merrimack Valley** H
(978) 373-1511. **$89-$199.** 401 Lowell Ave 01832. I-495 exit 49, just e. Int corridors. **Pets:** Accepted. SAVE 🕭 🛋 🛜 ⊠ 🖵

▼▼▼ **Hampton Inn** H
(978) 374-7755. **$109-$199.** 106 Bank Rd 01832. I-495 exit 49 (SR 110), 0.5 mi s. Int corridors. **Pets:** Accepted.
🍴 🕭 🛜 ⊠ 🛢 🖵

HOLYOKE
▼▼▼ **Homewood Suites by Hilton Holyoke-Springfield North** H
(413) 532-3100. **$129-$159.** 375 Whitney Ave 01040. I-91 exit 15, just w on Lower Westfield Rd, then 0.4 mi s. Int corridors. **Pets:** Accepted.
🍴 🕭 🛋 🛜 🛢 🖵

HYANNIS *(Restaurants p. 616)*
▼ **Cape Cod Harbor House Inn** M
(508) 771-1880. **Call for rates.** 119 Ocean St 02601. Opposite ferry docks. Ext corridors. **Pets:** Small, dogs only. $27 daily fee/pet. Designated rooms, service with restrictions, supervision. 🛜 ⊠ 🛢 🖵

▼▼ **Heritage House Hotel** H
(508) 775-7000. **$59-$229, 7 day notice.** 259 Main St 02601. Center. Int corridors. **Pets:** Dogs only. $35 daily fee/pet. Designated rooms, service with restrictions, supervision. 🍴 🛋 🛜 ⊠ 🛢 🖵

LAWRENCE
▼▼ **Holiday Inn Express** H
(978) 975-4050. **Call for rates.** 224 Winthrop Ave 01843. I-495 exit 42A, just s on SR 114. Int corridors. **Pets:** Accepted.
🕭 🛜 ⊠ 🖵

LENOX
▼▼▼▼ **Wheatleigh** CI
(413) 637-0610. **$495-$2500, 30 day notice.** 11 Hawthorne Rd 01240. 1.8 mi s on SR 183, 1 mi e. Int corridors. **Pets:** Accepted.
🍴 🕭 🛋 ⊠ 🛜 ⊠

LEXINGTON
◈◈◈ ▼▼▼ **Aloft Lexington** H
(781) 761-1700. **Call for rates.** 727 Marrett Rd - A 02421. I-95 exit 30B, just w. Int corridors. **Pets:** Accepted.
SAVE ⊟ 🍴 🕭 🛋 🛜 ⊠ 🛢 🖵

◈◈◈ ▼▼▼ **Element Lexington** H
(781) 761-1750. **Call for rates.** 727 Marrett Rd - B 02421. I-95 exit 30B, just w. Int corridors. **Pets:** Accepted.
SAVE ECO ⊟ 🍴 🕭 🛋 🛜 ⊠ 🛢 🖵

MANSFIELD
◈◈◈ ▼▼ **Red Roof Inn Boston-Mansfield/Foxboro** H
(508) 339-2323. **$70-$199.** 60 Forbes Blvd 02048. I-95 exit 7A, 1.3 mi n; I-495 exit 12, just off SR 140. Int corridors. **Pets:** Accepted.
SAVE 🛋 🛜 ⊠ 🛢 🖵

MARLBOROUGH
◈◈◈ ▼▼ **Best Western Royal Plaza Hotel & Trade Center** H
(508) 460-0700. **$159-$439.** 181 Boston Post Rd W 01752. I-495 exit 24B, 1 mi w on US 20. Int corridors. **Pets:** Accepted.
SAVE 🍴 🛋 🛜 ⊠ 🛢 🖵

▼▼▼ **Courtyard by Marriott Boston Marlborough** H
(508) 480-0015. **$84-$268.** 75 Felton St 01752. I-495 exit 24B, just w; just off US 20. Int corridors. **Pets:** Accepted.
🍴 🕭 🛋 🛜 ⊠ 🛢 🖵

◈◈◈ ▼▼▼ **Embassy Suites by Hilton Hotel-Boston Marlborough** H
(508) 485-5900. **$130-$280.** 123 Boston Post Rd W 01752. I-495 exit 24B, 0.5 mi w; just off US 20. Int corridors. **Pets:** Accepted.
SAVE 🍴 🕭 🛋 ⊠ 🛜 🛢 🖵

▼▼▼ Residence Inn by Marriott Boston
Marlborough H

(508) 481-1500. $92-$312. 112 Donald Lynch Blvd 01752. I-290 exit
25B, 3 mi ne. Int corridors. Pets: Accepted.

MEDFORD

◆◆◆ ▼▼▼ Hyatt Place Boston/Medford H

(781) 395-8500. $109-$369. 116 Riverside Ave 02155. I-93 exit 32, just
sw to SR 60 and River St. Int corridors. Pets: Accepted.

MILFORD

▼▼▼ Holiday Inn Express H

(508) 634-1054. Call for rates. 50 Fortune Blvd 01757. I-495 exit 20,
just sw on SR 85, then just se. Int corridors. Pets: Accepted.

NATICK

◆◆◆ ▼▼▼ The Verve Crowne Plaza H

(508) 653-8800. $109-$249. 1360 Worcester St 01760. I-90 exit 12, 5
mi e; SR 9, 4 mi e of Framingham Center. Int corridors.
Pets: Accepted.

NEEDHAM

▼▼▼▼ Residence Inn by Marriott Boston Needham H

(781) 444-5750. $96-$336. 80 B St 02494. I-95 exit 19A, just se. Int
corridors. Pets: Accepted.

◆◆◆ ▼▼▼ Sheraton Needham Hotel H

(781) 444-1110. Call for rates. 100 Cabot St 02494. I-95 exit 19A, just
e. Int corridors. Pets: Large. Service with restrictions, crate.

NEWBURYPORT

▼▼▼ Garrison Inn H

(978) 499-8500. $210-$440, 7 day notice. 11 Brown Square 01950.
I-95 exit 57, 2.6 mi e on SR 1A, just n on Green St, just w on Pleasant
St, then just s. Int corridors. Pets: Dogs only. $30 daily fee/pet. Service
with restrictions, supervision.

NEWTON

◆◆◆ ▼▼▼ Crowne Plaza Boston Newton H

(617) 969-3010. $99-$600. 320 Washington St 02458. I-90 exit 17, just
e. Int corridors. Pets: Accepted.

◆◆◆ ▼▼▼ Hotel Indigo Boston-Newton
Riverside H

(617) 969-5300. $129-$359. 399 Grove St 02462. I-95 exit 22, just e.
Int corridors. Pets: Accepted.

NORTH DARTMOUTH

◆◆◆ ▼▼▼ Residence Inn by Marriott New
Bedford/Dartmouth H

(508) 984-5858. $101-$351. 181 Faunce Corner Rd 02747. I-195 exit
12A westbound; exit 12 eastbound, just s. Int corridors. Pets: Other
species. $100 one-time fee/room. Service with restrictions, crate.

NORTH FALMOUTH

◆◆◆ ▼▼▼ Sea Crest Beach Hotel H

(508) 540-9400. Call for rates. 350 Quaker Rd 02556-2943. 2.8 mi sw
of jct SR 28 and 151 via SR 28A, Shore Rd/Curley Blvd. Ext/int corridors. Pets: Accepted.

NORWOOD

▼▼▼ Hampton Inn Boston-Norwood H

(781) 769-7000. $99-$349. 434 Providence Hwy 02062. I-95 exit 9
northbound, 5.9 mi ne on US 1; exit 11B southbound, 1.3 mi nw on
Neponset St, then 0.4 mi n on US 1. Int corridors. Pets: Accepted.

▼▼▼ Residence Inn by Marriott
Boston-Norwood-Canton H

(781) 278-9595. $92-$439. 275 Norwood Park S 02062. I-95 exit 9
northbound, 3.7 mi n on US 1; exit 11B southbound, 0.5 mi nw on Neponset St, 0.6 mi w on Dean St, then 0.8 mi s on US 1. Int corridors.
Pets: Accepted.

ORLEANS

▼▼ Orleans Inn CI

(508) 255-2222. $250-$450. 3 Old County Rd 02653. On SR 28 and 6A
exit rotary, just w. Int corridors. Pets: Accepted.

◆◆◆ ▼◆▼ Skaket Beach Motel M

(508) 255-1020. $69-$180, 10 day notice. 203 Cranberry Hwy (Rt 6A)
02653. US 6 exit 12, just e. Ext corridors. Pets: Dogs only. $20 daily
fee/pet. Designated rooms, service with restrictions, supervision.

PEABODY

▼▼▼ Homewood Suites by Hilton Boston-Peabody H

(978) 536-5050. $129-$299. 57 Newbury St 01960. On US 1 northbound. Int corridors. Pets: Accepted.

PLYMOUTH

▼▼▼ Hampton Inn & Suites-Plymouth Kingston H

(508) 747-5000. $119-$309. 10 Plaza Way 02360. SR 3 exit 7. Int corridors. Pets: Other species. $35 one-time fee/pet. Designated rooms,
service with restrictions, supervision.

PROVINCETOWN

▼▼ Bayshore & Chandler CO ❀

(508) 487-9133. Call for rates. 493 Commercial St 02657. 0.8 mi e of
Town Hall. Ext corridors. Pets: Other species. $25 daily fee/room. Ser-
vice with restrictions.

◆◆◆ ▼◆▼◆▼ Crowne Pointe Historic Inn & Spa CI

(508) 487-6767. $109-$659, 21 day notice. 82 Bradford St 02657. On
SR 6A, just w of Town Hall. Ext/int corridors. Pets: Accepted.

REHOBOTH

▼▼▼ Five Bridge Inn Bed & Breakfast BB ❀

(508) 252-3190. Call for rates. 152 Pine St 02769. 1.6 mi n of US 44;
3.3 mi w of jct SR 118; US 44, n on Blanding Rd, e on Broad St, n on
Salisbury St, then w. Int corridors. Pets: Large, other species. $100
deposit/room.

REVERE

▼▼▼ Comfort Inn & Suites Boston Logan International
Airport H

(781) 485-3600. $139-$339. 85 American Legion Hwy 02151. Jct SR 1A
and 60; 3 mi n of Boston Logan International Airport. Int corridors.
Pets: Accepted.

▼▼▼ Hampton Inn Boston Logan Airport H

(781) 286-5665. $119-$299. 230 Lee Burbank Hwy 02151. On SR 1A,
0.6 mi s of terminus SR 60; 1.9 mi n of Boston Logan International
Airport. Int corridors. Pets: Accepted.

RICHMOND

▼▼▼ The Inn at Richmond & Berkshire Equestrian
Center BB
(413) 698-2100. Call for rates. 802 State Rd 01254. 2.5 mi s of jct US
20. Ext/int corridors. Pets: Accepted. 🗙 🛜 🗙 🗷 🔔 🖵

ROCKPORT

▼▼▼ Rockport Inn & Suites M
(978) 546-3300. Call for rates. 183 Main St 01966. On SR 127. Ext
corridors. Pets: Accepted. 🍴 👤M 🛌 🗙 🛜 🗙 🔔 🖵

SALEM

▼▼▼ Hawthorne Hotel H ❖
(978) 744-4080. Call for rates. 18 Washington Square W 01970. On
SR 1A. Int corridors. Pets: Large, other species. $25 daily fee/room.
Designated rooms, service with restrictions, supervision. 🍴 🛜 🔔

▼▼▼ The Salem Inn BB
(978) 741-0680. $139-$420, 7 day notice. 7 Summer St 01970. On SR
114 at Essex St; SR 128 exit 25A, 3 mi e. Int corridors. Pets: $20 daily
fee/pet. Designated rooms, service with restrictions.
🛜 🗙 🔔 🖵

SAUGUS

AAA ▼▼▼ Red Roof PLUS+ Boston Logan H
(781) 941-1400. $89-$229. 920 Broadway 01906. I-95 exit 44 northbound, 3.2 mi s on US 1 exit Main St/Saugus; exit southbound to
U-turn. Int corridors. Pets: Accepted. 🆂🅰🆅🅴 👤M 🛜 🗙 🔔 🖵

SEEKONK

▼▼▼▼ Clarion Providence-Seekonk H
(508) 336-7300. $109-$419. 940 Fall River Ave 02771. I-195 exit 1, just
s. Int corridors. Pets: Accepted. 🍴 👤M 🛌 🛜 🗙 🔔 🖵

AAA ▼▼▼ Comfort Inn Providence/Seekonk H
(508) 336-7900. $94-$239. 341 Highland Ave 02771. I-195 exit 1, just s
on US 6. Int corridors. Pets: Accepted. 🆂🅰🆅🅴 🛌 🛜 🗙 🔔 🖵

SOMERVILLE

▼▼▼ La Quinta Inn & Suites Boston Somerville H
(617) 625-5300. $97-$482. 23 Cummings St 02143. I-93 exit 29 northbound, just ne on SR 28, then just s on Middlesex Ave; exit 31 southbound, 1 mi e on SR 16, then 0.5 mi s on SR 28 to Middlesex Ave. Int
corridors. Pets: Accepted. 👤M 🛜 🗙 🔔 🖵

SOUTH YARMOUTH

AAA ▼▼▼ Red Jacket Blue Rock Resort M ❖
(508) 398-6962. Call for rates. 39 Todd Rd 02664. SR 28, 1 mi ne via
N Main St and High Bank Rd, then 0.5 mi nw on Country Club Dr, follow signs. Ext corridors. Pets: Medium, dogs only. $35 daily fee/pet.
Designated rooms, service with restrictions, supervision.
🆂🅰🆅🅴 🍴 🛌 🛜 🗙 🔔 🖵

AAA ▼▼▼ Red Jacket Blue Water Resort on the
Ocean H ❖
(508) 398-2288. $99-$379, 10 day notice. 291 S Shore Dr 02664. 1 mi
s off SR 28. Ext/int corridors. Pets: Medium, dogs only. $35 daily fee/
pet. Designated rooms, service with restrictions, supervision.
🆂🅰🆅🅴 🍴 🛌 🗙 🛜 🗙 🔔 🖵

SPRINGFIELD

▼▼▼ La Quinta Inn & Suites H
(413) 781-0900. $97-$207. 100 Congress St 01104. I-291 exit 2A, just s
of Chestnut St. Int corridors. Pets: Accepted. 🍴 🛜 🗙 🔔 🖵

AAA ▼▼▼ Sheraton Springfield Monarch Place
Hotel H
(413) 781-1010. $139-$229. One Monarch Pl 01144. I-91 exit 6 northbound; exit 7 southbound, just n; downtown. Int corridors.
Pets: Accepted. 🆂🅰🆅🅴 🍴 👤M 🛌 🗙 🛜 🗙 🔔 🖵

STOCKBRIDGE

▼▼▼ The Inn at Stockbridge BB
(413) 298-3337. $150-$400, 14 day notice. 30 East St 01262. Jct US
102; 1.5 mi n. Ext/int corridors. Pets: Accepted.
🔌 🛌 🛜 🗙 🗷 🔔 🖵

STURBRIDGE

▼▼▼ Publick House Historic Inn & Country Lodge CI
(508) 347-3313. Call for rates. 277 Main St 01566. I-84 exit 3B, 0.5 mi
s of jct US 20. Ext/int corridors. Pets: Accepted.
🍴 👤M 🛌 🛜 🗙 🔔

AAA ▼▼▼ Sturbridge Host Hotel & Conference Center
on Cedar Lake H
(508) 347-7393. $115-$199. 366 Main St 01566. I-90 exit 9, just w on
US 20; I-84 exit 3B. Int corridors. Pets: Other species. $25 one-time
fee/room. Designated rooms, service with restrictions, supervision.
🆂🅰🆅🅴 🍴 👤M 🛌 🗙 🛜 🔔 🖵

▼▼▼ Super 8 Sturbridge M
(508) 347-9000. $69-$209. 358 Main St 01566. I-84 exit 3B; on US 20.
Ext corridors. Pets: Accepted. 🛌 🛜 🗙 🔔 🖵

TAUNTON

▼▼▼ Holiday Inn Taunton/Foxboro H ❖
(508) 823-0430. $119-$229. 700 Myles Standish Blvd 02780. I-495 exit
9, just sw. Int corridors. Pets: Small. $26 daily fee/room. Designated
rooms, service with restrictions, supervision.
🍴 👤M 🛌 🗙 🛜 🔔 🖵

TEWKSBURY

AAA ▼▼▼ Holiday Inn Tewksbury-Andover H
(978) 640-9000. Call for rates. 4 Highwood Dr 01876. I-495 exit 39,
just w on SR 133. Int corridors. Pets: Medium. $50 one-time fee/pet.
Designated rooms, service with restrictions, supervision.
🆂🅰🆅🅴 🍴 👤M 🛌 🛜 🗙 🔔 🖵

▼▼▼ Residence Inn by Marriott
Boston-Tewksbury-Andover H
(978) 640-1003. $83-$195. 1775 Andover St 01876. I-495 exit 39, 0.3
mi w on SR 133. Ext/int corridors. Pets: Other species. $100 one-time
fee/room. Designated rooms, service with restrictions, crate.
👤M 🛌 🛜 🗙 🔔 🖵

▼▼▼ TownePlace Suites by Marriott Boston
Tewksbury H
(978) 863-9800. $71-$198. 20 International Pl 01876. I-495 exit 39, 0.3
mi nw. Int corridors. Pets: Accepted.
🆔 👤M 🛌 🛜 🗙 🔔 🖵

VINEYARD HAVEN

▼▼▼ Mansion House Inn, Health Club & Spa H ❖
(508) 693-2200. $99-$509, 14 day notice. 9 Main St 02568. West of
ferry dock; corner of Beach Rd. Int corridors. Pets: Other species. $75
one-time fee/pet. Designated rooms, service with restrictions, supervision. 🍴 🛌 🗙 🛜 🗙 🔔 🖵

WAKEFIELD

AAA ▼▼▼ Four Points by Sheraton Wakefield Boston
Hotel & Conference Center H
(781) 245-9300. $79-$319. 1 Audubon Rd 01880. I-95 exit 42, just n.
Int corridors. Pets: Accepted. 🆂🅰🆅🅴 🍴 👤M 🛌 🛜 🗙 🖵

WALTHAM

▼▼▼ Courtyard by Marriott Boston-Waltham �H
(781) 419-0900. **$84-$494.** 387 Winter St 02451. I-95 exit 27B northbound; exit 27A southbound, just ne. Int corridors. **Pets:** Accepted.
🍴 ♿ 🛏 📶 ✕ 🔔 💻

▼▼▼ Holiday Inn Express Boston-Waltham �H
(781) 890-2800. **$89-$369.** 385 Winter St 02451. I-95 exit 27B northbound; exit 27A southbound, just ne. Int corridors. **Pets:** Accepted.
♿ 📶 ✕ 🔔 💻

🅰🅰 ▼▼▼ ▼▼▼ The Westin Waltham-Boston �H 🐾
(781) 290-5600. **$119-$399.** 70 3rd Ave 02451. I-95 exit 27A, just se. Int corridors. **Pets:** Medium, other species. Designated rooms, service with restrictions, supervision. SAVE ECO 🍴 ♿ 🛏 📶 ✕ 💻

WATERTOWN

▼▼▼ Residence Inn by Marriott Boston/Watertown �H
(617) 926-4500. **$115-$476.** 570 Arsenal St 02472. Between Elm and Arlington sts. Int corridors. **Pets:** Accepted.
🍴 ♿ 📶 ✕ 🔔 💻

WESTBOROUGH

▼▼ Extended Stay America-Boston-Westborough �H
(508) 616-9213. **$100-$130.** 180 E Main St 01581. I-495 exit 23B, 1.4 mi w, then just sw on SR 30. Int corridors. **Pets:** Accepted.
🍴 ♿ 📶 ✕ 🔔

🅰🅰 ▼▼▼ Residence Inn by Marriott Boston Westborough �H
(508) 366-7700. **$101-$342.** 25 Connector Rd 01581. I-495 exit 23B, just w on SR 9 exit Computer and Research drs, then 0.3 mi s. Ext/int corridors. **Pets:** Accepted.
SAVE ECO 🍴 ♿ 🛏 📶 ✕ 🔔 💻

WEST DENNIS

▼▼ Inn at Swan River Ⓜ
(508) 394-5415. **Call for rates.** 829 Main St 02670. On SR 28, just w of SR 134. Ext corridors. **Pets:** Accepted. 🛏 📶 ✕ 🔔 💻

WESTFORD

▼▼▼ Residence Inn by Marriott Boston Westford �H
(978) 392-1407. **$101-$340.** 7 Lan Dr 01886. I-495 exit 32, just s, then 0.5 w on SR 110. Int corridors. **Pets:** Other species. $25 one-time fee/room. ♿ 🛏 📶 ✕ 🔔 💻

WESTPORT

▼▼▼ Hampton Inn-Fall River-Westport �H
(508) 675-8500. **$109-$199.** 53 Old Bedford Rd 02790. I-195 exit 9 eastbound; exit 10 westbound, just s to US 6, then 1.3 mi w. Int corridors. **Pets:** Medium. $35 daily fee/pet. Designated rooms, service with restrictions, supervision. 🛏 ✕ 📶 🔔 💻

WEST SPRINGFIELD

▼▼ Candlewood Suites �H
(413) 739-1122. **Call for rates.** 572 Riverdale St 01089. I-91 exit 13B, 1.3 mi s. Int corridors. **Pets:** Accepted.
🍴 ♿ 🛏 📶 ✕ 🔔 💻

▼▼▼ Hampton Inn by Hilton West Springfield �H
(413) 732-1300. **$129-$169.** 1011 Riverdale St 01089. I-91 exit 13B, 0.3 mi s. Int corridors. **Pets:** Accepted. ♿ 🛏 📶 ✕ 🔔 💻

▼▼▼ Residence Inn by Marriott West Springfield �H
(413) 732-9543. **$103-$300.** 64 Border Way 01089. I-91 exit 13A, on US 5. Int corridors. **Pets:** Accepted.
🍴 ♿ 🛏 📶 ✕ 🔔 💻

WILLIAMSTOWN

▼▼ The 1896 House Country Inn Ⓜ 🐾
(413) 458-1896. **Call for rates.** 910 Cold Spring Rd 01267. 1.8 mi s on US 7 and SR 2. Ext/int corridors. **Pets:** Other species. $20 daily fee/pet. Designated rooms, service with restrictions, crate.
🍴 ♿ 🛏 ✕ 📶 ✕ 🔔 💻

▼▼ Berkshire Hills Country Inn Ⓜ
(413) 458-3950. **Call for rates.** 1146 Cold Spring Rd 01267. 2.3 mi s on US 7 and SR 2. Ext/int corridors. **Pets:** Accepted.
🛏 📶 ✕ 🔔 💻

▼▼ Maple Terrace Motel Ⓜ 🐾
(413) 458-9677. **$59-$178, 10 day notice.** 555 Main St 01267. On SR 2, 1 mi e of jct US 7. Ext corridors. **Pets:** Dogs only. $20 one-time fee/pet. Designated rooms, service with restrictions, crate.
🛏 📶 ✕ 🔔 💻

WOBURN

🅰🅰 ▼▼▼ Best Western Plus New Englander �H
(781) 935-8160. **$99-$300.** 1 Rainin Rd 01801. I-93 exit 36, just e. Int corridors. **Pets:** Accepted. SAVE 🍴 ♿ 🛏 📶 ✕ 🔔 💻

▼▼▼ Hilton Boston/Woburn �H
(781) 932-0999. **$109-$179.** 2 Forbes Rd 01801. I-95 exit 36, 0.5 mi s via Washington St, then just e at Lukoil; jct Cedar St. Int corridors. **Pets:** Accepted. 🍴 ♿ 🛏 📶 ✕ 🔔 💻

🅰🅰 ▼▼▼ Residence Inn by Marriott-Boston-Woburn �H
(781) 376-4000. **$91-$417.** 300 Presidential Way 01801. I-93 exit 37C, just nw. Int corridors. **Pets:** Accepted.
SAVE 🍴 ♿ 🛏 📶 ✕ 🔔 💻

WORCESTER

🅰🅰 ▼▼▼▼ Beechwood Hotel �H
(508) 754-5789. **$189-$259.** 363 Plantation St 01605. I-290 exit 22 westbound, 0.5 mi w on Lincoln St, then 1.5 mi s; exit 21 eastbound, 1.3 mi s. Int corridors. **Pets:** Medium, dogs only. $80 daily fee/room. Designated rooms, service with restrictions, crate.
SAVE 🍴 ♿ 📶 ✕ 🔔 💻

▼▼▼ Residence Inn by Marriott Worcester �H
(508) 753-6300. **$109-$265.** 503 Plantation St 01605. I-290 exit 21, 0.5 mi sw. Int corridors. **Pets:** Accepted.
🍴 ♿ 🛏 📶 ✕ 🔔 💻

MICHIGAN

ACME

▼▼ Sleep Inn & Suites �H
(231) 938-7000. **$70-$330.** 5520 US 31 N 49610. Jct US 31 and SR 72, 0.5 mi sw. Int corridors. **Pets:** Accepted.
♿ 🛏 📶 ✕ 🔔 💻

ADRIAN

▼▼▼ Holiday Inn Express Adrian �H
(517) 265-5700. **Call for rates.** 1077 W US 223 49221. Jct SR 52, just w. Int corridors. **Pets:** Accepted. 🛏 📶 ✕ 🔔 💻

▼▼ Super 8 Adrian H
(517) 265-8888. **$76-$130.** 1091 W US 223 49221. Jct SR 52, just w.
Int corridors. **Pets:** $25 one-time fee/room. Service with restrictions,
supervision. 🛰 ✕ 🛏 ☕

ALLEN PARK
◢◣ ▼▼▼ Best Western Greenfield Inn H
(313) 271-1600. **$89-$149.** 3000 Enterprise Dr 48101. I-94 exit 206
(Oakwood Blvd), just s, then just w. Int corridors. **Pets:** Accepted.
SAVE 🍴 🏊 ✕ 🛰 ✕ 🛏 ☕

ALMA
◢◣ ▼▼ Triangle Motel M
(989) 463-2296. **$70-$85.** 131 W Lincoln Rd 48801. US 127 exit 123
(Lincoln Rd) northbound; exit 124 (State Rd) southbound, just w on US
127 business route. Ext corridors. **Pets:** Dogs only. Designated rooms,
service with restrictions, supervision. SAVE 🛰 ✕ 🛏

ALPENA
◢◣ ▼▼ Best Western of Alpena H
(989) 356-9087. **$79-$100.** 1285 Hwy M-32 W 49707. 2.3 mi w of jct
US 23. Ext/int corridors. **Pets:** Dogs only. $15 daily fee/pet. Service
with restrictions, supervision. SAVE 🏊 ✕ 🛰 ✕ 🛏 ☕

▼▼ Days Inn H
(989) 356-6118. **$80-$125.** 1496 Hwy M-32 W 49707. 2.5 mi w of jct
US 23. Int corridors. **Pets:** Accepted. 🏊 ✕ 🛰 ✕ 🛏 ☕

▼▼ Ramada Alpena H
(989) 356-2151. **Call for rates.** 1000 Hwy 23 N 49707. On US 23, 1 mi
n. Int corridors. **Pets:** Large, dogs only. $25 daily fee/room. Designated
rooms, service with restrictions, supervision.
🍴 🏊 ✕ 🛰 ✕ 🛏 ☕

ANN ARBOR (Restaurants p. 616)
▼▼▼ Candlewood Suites Detroit-Ann Arbor H
(734) 663-2818. **Call for rates.** 701 Waymarket Dr 48103. I-94 exit 175
(Ann Arbor/Saline Rd), just n, just e on Eisenhower Rd, then just s. Int
corridors. **Pets:** Accepted. 🔼M 🛰 ✕ 🛏 ☕

▼▼▼ Extended Stay America University South H
(734) 997-7623. **$95-$120.** 3265 Boardwalk Dr 48108. I-94 exit 177
(State St), just n, just e on Victors Way, then just n. Int corridors.
Pets: Accepted. 🛰 ✕ 🛏 ☕

▼▼▼ Graduate Ann Arbor H
(734) 769-2200. **Call for rates.** 615 E Huron St 48104. Jct State St. Int
corridors. **Pets:** Accepted. 🍴 🛰 ✕ 🛏 ☕

▼▼▼ Holiday Inn Near the University of Michigan H
(734) 769-9800. **Call for rates.** 3600 Plymouth Rd 48105. US 23 exit
41 (Plymouth Rd), just sw. Int corridors. **Pets:** Accepted.
🍴 🏊 ✕ 🛰 ✕ 🛏 ☕

◢◣ ▼▼▼ Red Roof PLUS+ Ann Arbor-University of
Michigan North M
(734) 996-5800. **$60-$190.** 3621 Plymouth Rd 48105. US 23 exit 41
(Plymouth Rd), just nw. Ext corridors. **Pets:** Accepted.
SAVE 🔼M 🛰 ✕ 🛏 ☕

◢◣ ▼▼▼ Residence Inn by Marriott Ann Arbor H
(734) 996-5666. **$110-$439.** 800 Victors Way 48108. I-94 exit 177
(State St), just n, then just e. Ext/int corridors. **Pets:** Accepted.
SAVE 🔼M 🏊 🛰 ✕ 🛏 ☕

▼▼▼ Residence Inn by Marriott Ann Arbor
Downtown H
(734) 662-9999. **$149-$439.** 120 W Huron St 48104. Jct Ashley St;
downtown. Int corridors. **Pets:** Accepted. 🔼M 🛰 ✕ 🛏 ☕

▼▼▼ Residence Inn by Marriott Ann Arbor North H
(734) 327-0011. **$107-$444.** 3535 Green Ct 48105. US 23 exit 41
(Plymouth Rd), just sw. Int corridors. **Pets:** Accepted.
🔼M 🏊 🛰 ✕ 🛏 ☕

◢◣ ▼▼▼ Sheraton Ann Arbor Hotel H
(734) 996-0600. **$129-$599.** 3200 Boardwalk Dr 48108. I-94 exit 177
(State St), just n, just e on Victors Way, then just n. Int corridors.
Pets: Accepted. SAVE ☕ 🍴 🔼M 🏊 🛰 ✕ 🛏 ☕

▼▼▼ TownePlace Suites by Marriott Ann Arbor H
(734) 327-5900. **$94-$384.** 1301 Briarwood Cir 48108. I-94 exit 177
(State St), just n, then 0.6 mi w. Int corridors. **Pets:** Accepted.
🔼M 🏊 🛰 ✕ 🛏 ☕

AUBURN HILLS
▼▼ Extended Stay America Detroit-Auburn
Hills-Featherstone Road H
(248) 335-5200. **$90-$110.** 2100 Featherstone Rd 48326. I-75 exit 79,
0.5 mi w on University Dr, then 0.8 mi s on Opdyke Rd. Int corridors.
Pets: Accepted. 🍴 🔼M 🏊 🛰 ✕ 🛏 ☕

▼▼ Extended Stay America Detroit-Auburn
Hills-University Drive H
(248) 340-8888. **$90-$110.** 3315 University Dr 48326. I-75 exit 79, 0.9
mi e. Int corridors. **Pets:** Accepted. 🔼M 🛰 ✕ 🛏

▼▼ Hawthorn Suites by Wyndham Detroit Auburn
Hills H
(248) 373-3342. **$89-$219.** 1650 N Opdyke Rd 48326. I-75 exit 79, just
w on University Dr, then 0.4 mi n. Int corridors. **Pets:** $15 one-time
fee/room, $10 daily fee/room. Designated rooms, service with restric-
tions, supervision. 🛰 ✕ 🛏 ☕

◢◣ ▼▼▼ Hilton Auburn Hills Suites H
(248) 334-2222. **$109-$199.** 2300 Featherstone Rd 48326. I-75 exit 79,
just w on University Dr, 0.5 mi s on Opdyke Rd, then just e. Int corridors. **Pets:** Accepted. SAVE 🍴 🏊 🛰 ✕ 🛏 ☕

◢◣ ▼▼▼ Hyatt Place Detroit/Auburn Hills H
(248) 475-9393. **$84-$199.** 1545 N Opdyke Rd 48326. I-75 exit 79, 0.5
mi w on University Dr, then just n. Int corridors. **Pets:** Accepted.
SAVE 🍴 🔼M 🏊 🛰 ✕ 🛏 ☕

◢◣ ▼▼▼ Sonesta ES Suites Auburn Hills H
(248) 322-4600. **Call for rates.** 2050 Featherstone Rd 48326. I-75 exit
79, just w on University Dr, 0.5 mi s on Opdyke Rd, then just e. Int
corridors. **Pets:** Accepted. SAVE 🔼M 🏊 🛰 ✕ 🛏 ☕

▼▼▼ TownePlace Suites by Marriott Detroit Auburn
Hills H 🐾
(248) 454-0650. **$98-$261.** 3900 Baldwin Rd 48326. I-75 exit 84B, just
s. Int corridors. **Pets:** $100 one-time fee/pet. Service with restrictions.
🍴 🔼M 🛰 ✕ 🛏 ☕

BATTLE CREEK
▼▼ Baymont Inn & Suites Battle Creek/I-94 H
(269) 979-5400. **$99-$119.** 4725 Beckley Rd 49015. I-94 exit 97 (Capital Ave), just sw. Int corridors. **Pets:** Accepted.
🏊 🛰 ✕ 🛏 ☕

BAY CITY (Restaurants p. 616)
▼▼ AmericInn Bay City H
(989) 671-0071. **$89-$159, 7 day notice.** 3915 Three Mile Rd 48706.
I-75 exit 164 (Wilder Rd), just nw. Int corridors. **Pets:** Medium, dogs
only. $25 daily fee/pet. Designated rooms, service with restrictions,
supervision. 🏊 🛰 ✕ 🛏 ☕

▼▼ Fairfield Inn by Marriott Bay City H
(989) 667-7050. **$83-$157.** 4105 E Wilder Rd 48706. 1 mi e of SR 13.
Int corridors. **Pets:** Large, other species. $50 one-time fee/room. Ser-
vice with restrictions, supervision. 🔼M 🏊 🛰 ✕ 🛏 ☕

▼▼▼ Holiday Inn Express & Suites Bay City **H**
(989) 667-3800. **Call for rates.** 3959 Traxler Ct 48706. I-75 exit 164 (Wilder Rd), 0.3 mi e. Int corridors. **Pets:** Accepted.

🚗 🍳 📶 ✖ 🔌 💻

BELLAIRE

▼▼▼ Shanty Creek Resorts Lakeview Hotel **H**
(231) 533-8621. **Call for rates.** 5780 Shanty Creek Rd 49615. Jct SR 88/US 131, 4 mi nw to Shanty Creek Rd, then 1.5 mi e; in Summit Village. Int corridors. **Pets:** Accepted.

🍴 🚗 🍳 ✖ 📶 ✖ 🔌 💻

BELLEVILLE

▼▼▼ Holiday Inn Express & Suites-Belleville (Airport Area) **H**
(734) 857-6200. **$99-$199.** 46194 N I-94 Service Dr 48111. I-94 exit 190 (Belleville Rd), just n, then just w. Int corridors. **Pets:** Dogs only. $50 one-time fee/pet. Service with restrictions.

🚗 🍳 ✖ 📶 ✖ 🔌 💻

BENTON HARBOR

▼▼▼ Holiday Inn Express & Suites Benton Harbor **H**
(269) 927-4599. **Call for rates.** 2276 Pipestone Rd 49022. I-94 exit 29 (Pipestone Rd), just se. Int corridors. **Pets:** Accepted.

🚗 📶 ✖ 🔌 💻

BEULAH

🆁🆁🆁 ▼▼▼ Best Western Scenic Hill Resort **H**
(231) 882-7754. **$105-$205.** 1400 US Hwy 31 49617. On US 31, 0.8 mi e. Int corridors. **Pets:** Accepted.

SAVE 🚗 🍳 ✖ 📶 ✖ 🔌 💻

BIG RAPIDS

▼▼ Country Inn & Suites By Carlson, Big Rapids **H** 🐾
(231) 527-9000. **Call for rates.** 15344 Waldron Way 49307. US 131 exit 139, just ne. Int corridors. **Pets:** $10 one-time fee/pet. Service with restrictions. 🚗 🍳 📶 ✖ 🔌 💻

BIRCH RUN

▼▼ Americas Best Value Inn & Suites **H**
(989) 624-4440. **$50-$175.** 9235 E Birch Run Rd 48415. I-75 exit 136 (Birch Run Rd), just e. Int corridors. **Pets:** Other species. Service with restrictions, crate. 📶 ✖ 🔌 💻

▼▼▼ Holiday Inn Express Birch Run (Frankenmuth Area) **H**
(989) 624-9300. **$80-$250.** 12150 Dixie Hwy 48415. I-75 exit 136 (Birch Run Rd), just e. Int corridors. **Pets:** Accepted.

🚗 ✖ 📶 ✖ 🔌 💻

BIRMINGHAM

🆁🆁🆁 ▼▼▼▼ The Townsend Hotel **H** 🐾
(248) 642-7900. **$348-$565.** 100 Townsend St 48009. Center. Int corridors. **Pets:** Dogs only. $150 one-time fee/room, $5 daily fee/pet. Service with restrictions, crate.

SAVE ECO 🔌 🍴 🚗 📶 ✖ 🔌 💻

BRIDGEPORT

▼▼ Baymont Inn & Suites-Frankenmuth/Bridgeport **H**
(989) 777-3000. **$55-$260.** 6460 Dixie Hwy 48722. I-75 exit 144, just w. Int corridors. **Pets:** Other species. Designated rooms, service with restrictions, supervision. 🚗 🍳 📶 ✖ 🔌 💻

BRIGHTON

🆁🆁🆁 ▼▼▼ Courtyard by Marriott Detroit Brighton **H**
(810) 225-9200. **$87-$228.** 7799 Conference Center Dr 48114. I-96 exit 145 (Grand River Ave), just n, then 0.4 mi w. Int corridors. **Pets:** Small, dogs only. $75 one-time fee/room. Service with restrictions, supervision.

SAVE 🍴 🚗 🍳 📶 ✖ 🔌 💻

BROOKLYN

▼▼ Super 8-Brooklyn **H**
(517) 592-0888. **$76-$89.** 419 S Main/M-50 49230. Jct SR 50 (Main St) and 124; downtown. Int corridors. **Pets:** Accepted.

🚗 📶 ✖ 🔌 💻

BYRON CENTER

▼▼▼ Comfort Suites-Grand Rapids South **H**
(616) 301-2255. **$100-$220.** 7644 Caterpillar Ct SW 49548. US 131 exit 75, just se. Int corridors. **Pets:** Accepted.

🚗 🍳 📶 ✖ 🔌 💻

CADILLAC

▼▼ Evergreen Resort **H** 🐾
(231) 775-9947. **$89-$214.** 7880 Mackinaw Tr 49601. US 131 exit 177, 0.7 mi n, then 0.5 mi w. Ext/int corridors. **Pets:** $25 daily fee/room. Designated rooms, service with restrictions, supervision.

🍴 🚗 🍳 📶 ✖ 🔌 💻

CALUMET

▼▼ AmericInn Lodge & Suites of Calumet **H**
(906) 337-6463. **$107-$147.** 56925 S 6th St 49913. On US 41; just w of Visitors Center. Int corridors. **Pets:** Medium, dogs only. $10 daily fee/room. Designated rooms, service with restrictions, supervision.

🚗 🍳 📶 ✖ 🔌 💻

CANTON

▼▼ La Quinta Inn Detroit Canton **H**
(734) 981-1808. **$67-$141.** 41211 Ford Rd 48187. I-275 exit 25 (Ford Rd), just w on SR 153. Int corridors. **Pets:** Accepted.

📶 ✖ 🔌 💻

CASCADE

▼▼▼ Crowne Plaza Grand Rapids **H**
(616) 957-1770. **$99-$199.** 5700 28th St SE 49546. I-96 exit 43B, 0.3 mi e on SR 11. Int corridors. **Pets:** Small, other species. $20 one-time fee/pet. Designated rooms, service with restrictions, crate.

🍴 🚗 🍳 📶 ✖ 🔌 💻

▼▼▼ Drury Inn & Suites Grand Rapids **H**
(616) 942-8511. **$100-$210.** 5175 28th St SE 49512. I-96 exit 43A, just w. Int corridors. **Pets:** Accepted. 🚗 📶 ✖ 🔌 💻

▼▼▼ Holiday Inn Express & Suites Grand Rapids Airport **H**
(616) 940-8100. **Call for rates.** 5401 28th St SE 49546. I-96 exit 43B, just e on SR 11. Int corridors. **Pets:** Accepted.

🍴 🚗 🍳 📶 ✖ 🔌 💻

CHARLEVOIX

▼▼ AmericInn Lodge & Suites of Charlevoix **H**
(231) 237-0988. **Call for rates.** 11800 US 31 N 49720. On US 31, 2.4 mi n. Int corridors. **Pets:** Accepted. 🚗 🍳 📶 ✖ 🔌 💻

🆁🆁🆁 ▼▼▼ Charlevoix Inn & Suites **H**
(231) 547-0300. **$69-$259.** 800 Petoskey Ave 49720. 1 mi n on US 31. Int corridors. **Pets:** Other species. $10 daily fee/pet. Designated rooms, service with restrictions, crate. SAVE 🚗 📶 ✖ 🔌 💻

CHEBOYGAN

Best Western River Terrace H
(231) 627-5688. **$90-$230.** 847 S Main St 49721. 1 mi s on SR 27.
Ext/int corridors. **Pets:** Accepted. [icons]

Birch Haus Motel M
(231) 627-5862. **$40-$85.** 1301 Mackinaw Ave 49721. On US 23, 0.8
mi nw. Ext corridors. **Pets:** Small, dogs only. $10 daily fee/pet. Designated rooms, service with restrictions, supervision. [icons]

Continental Inn M
(231) 627-7164. **$45-$130, 3 day notice.** 613 N Main St 49721. Jct US
23 and SR 27. Ext corridors. **Pets:** Small, dogs only. $10 daily fee/pet.
Designated rooms, service with restrictions, supervision.
[icons]

CHELSEA

Baymont Inn & Suites Chelsea H
(734) 433-1600. **$70-$270.** 1540 Commerce Park Dr 48118. I-94 exit
159 (SR 52/Main St), just n, then just w. Int corridors. **Pets:** Large. $40
one-time fee/pet. Service with restrictions, supervision.
[icons]

**Chelsea Comfort Inn & Village Conference
Center** H
(734) 433-8000. **$104-$299.** 1645 Commerce Park Dr 48118. I-94 exit
159 (SR 52/Main St), just n. Int corridors. **Pets:** Accepted.
[icons]

CLARE

Days Inn of Clare H
(989) 386-1111. **$80-$150.** 10318 S Clare Ave 48617. On Business Rt
US 10 and 127; just w of jct US 127 and Old US 27. Int corridors.
Pets: Accepted. [icons]

COLDWATER

Best Western Plus Coldwater Hotel H
(517) 279-0900. **$99-$149.** 630 E Chicago St 49036. I-69 exit 13 (US
12), just sw. Int corridors. **Pets:** Accepted.
[icons]

COMMERCE

**TownePlace Suites by Marriott Detroit
Commerce** H [icon]
(248) 669-3200. **$86-$246.** 199 Loop Rd 48390. Jct SR 5 and 14 Mile
Rd. Int corridors. **Pets:** Large, other species. $100 one-time fee/room.
[icons]

COPPER HARBOR

Lake Fanny Hooe Resort M
(906) 289-4451. **$105-$135, 7 day notice.** 505 2nd St 49918. Just s on
Manganese Rd. Ext corridors. **Pets:** Other species. $10 daily fee/pet.
Service with restrictions, crate. [icons]

DAVISON

Best Western Davison Inn H
(810) 658-2700. **$104-$129.** 10082 Lapeer Rd 48423. I-69 exit 145 (SR
15), just n, then e. Int corridors. **Pets:** Accepted.
[icons]

DEARBORN

Extended Stay America Detroit Dearborn H
(313) 336-0021. **$105-$125.** 260 Towne Center Dr 48126. SR 39
(Southfield Frwy); between Ford Rd and Michigan Ave exits; just w of
jct Service and Hubbard drs. Int corridors. **Pets:** Accepted.
[icons]

The Henry, Autograph Collection H
(313) 441-2000. **$125-$395.** 300 Town Center Dr 48126. SR 39 (Southfield Frwy); between Ford Rd and Michigan Ave exits, on Service Dr. Int
corridors. **Pets:** Accepted.
[icons]

**Red Roof Inn Detroit - Dearborn/Greenfield
Village** M
(313) 278-9732. **$61-$169.** 24130 Michigan Ave 48124. Jct US 24
(Telegraph Rd) and 12 (Michigan Ave). Ext corridors. **Pets:** Accepted.
[icons]

Staybridge Suites Dearborn H
(313) 565-1500. **Call for rates.** 24105 Michigan Ave 48124. Jct US 24
(Telegraph Rd) and 12 (Michigan Ave). Int corridors. **Pets:** Accepted.
[icons]

**TownePlace Suites by Marriott-Detroit
Dearborn** H
(313) 271-0200. **$97-$323.** 6141 Mercury Dr 48126. SR 39 (Southfield
Frwy) exit 7 (Ford Rd), just e, then 0.8 mi n. Int corridors.
Pets: Accepted. [icons]

DETROIT

Aloft Detroit at The David Whitney H
(313) 237-1700. **Call for rates.** 1 Park Ave 48226. Jct Woodward Ave.
Int corridors. **Pets:** Accepted. [icons]

**DoubleTree Suites by Hilton Detroit Downtown-Fort
Shelby** H
(313) 963-5600. **$149-$249.** 525 W Lafayette Blvd 48226. Jct First Ave.
Int corridors. **Pets:** Accepted. [icons]

Holiday Inn Express & Suites-Detroit H
(313) 887-7000. **Call for rates.** 1020 Washington Blvd 48226. Corner of
Washington Blvd and Michigan Ave. Int corridors. **Pets:** Medium. $25
one-time fee/pet. Designated rooms, service with restrictions, supervision. [icons]

MotorCity Casino Hotel H
(313) 237-7711. **$129-$599, 3 day notice.** 2901 Grand River Ave
48201. I-75 exit 50 (Grand River Ave), just n. Int corridors.
Pets: Accepted. [icons]

**Trumbull and Porter, an Ascend Hotel Collection
Member** H
(313) 496-1400. **Call for rates.** 1331 Trumbull St 48126. Jct Porter St;
in Corktown. Int corridors. **Pets:** Accepted. [icons]

**The Westin Book Cadillac
Detroit** H [icon]
(313) 442-1600. **$129-$599.** 1114 Washington Blvd 48226. Corner of
Washington Blvd and Michigan Ave. Int corridors. **Pets:** Medium, dogs
only. Service with restrictions, supervision.
[icons]

DEWITT

Sleep Inn H
(517) 669-8823. **$80-$160.** 1101 Commerce Park Dr 48820. I-69 exit 87
(Old US 27), 0.7 mi n. Int corridors. **Pets:** Small, dogs only. $25 daily
fee/pet. Service with restrictions, supervision.
[icons]

EAST LANSING

Hampton Inn East Lansing H
(517) 324-2072. **$119-$189.** 2500 Coolidge Rd 48823. US 127 exit 79
(Lake Lansing Rd), just e. Int corridors. **Pets:** Accepted.
[icons]

◆◆◆◆ **Residence Inn by Marriott-East Lansing** 🅷
(517) 657-2875. **$81-$274.** 2841 Hannah Blvd 48823. I-496 exit 9
(Trowbridge Rd), 0.6 mi e, just s on Harrison Rd, then 2 mi e. Int corridors. **Pets:** Accepted. 🔌 🐾 🛜 ✖ 🛏 🖵

EAST TAWAS
◆◆ **Tawas Bay Beach Resort** 🅷
(989) 362-8600. **Call for rates.** 300 E Bay St 48730. On US 23; jct
Main St. Int corridors. **Pets:** Accepted.
🍴 🐾 ✖ 🛜 ✖ 🛏 🖵

ESCANABA
⒜⒜⒜ ◆ **Econo Lodge** Ⓜ
(906) 789-1066. **$64-$120.** 921 N Lincoln Rd 49829. 0.5 mi n on US
2/41 and SR 35. Int corridors. **Pets:** Small. $10 daily fee/pet. Service
with restrictions, supervision. [SAVE] 🛜 ✖ 🛏 🖵

FARMINGTON HILLS
◆◆ **Extended Stay America Detroit-Farmington**
Hills 🅷
(248) 473-4000. **$65-$85.** 27775 Stansbury Blvd 48334. I-696 exit 5
(Orchard Lake Rd), just n, just e on 12 Mile Rd, then just s. Int corridors. **Pets:** Accepted. 🐾 🛜 ✖ 🛏 🖵

◆◆ **Hawthorn Suites by Wyndham Detroit Farmington**
Hills 🅷
(248) 324-0540. **$89-$219.** 37555 Hills Tech Dr 48331. I-696 exit I-96
E/I-275 S/SR 5, just s to SR 5 N, 2 mi n to 12 Mile Rd, 1.3 mi e, then
0.3 mi s on Halsted Rd. Int corridors. **Pets:** Accepted.
🐾 🛜 ✖ 🛏 🖵

◆◆ **Radisson Hotel Detroit-Farmington Hills** 🅷
(248) 553-0000. **Call for rates.** 31525 12 Mile Rd 48334. I-696 exit 5
(Orchard Lake Rd), just nw. Int corridors. **Pets:** Accepted.
🐾 🛜 ✖ 🛏 🖵

FENTON
◆◆◆ **Comfort Inn & Suites** 🅷
(810) 714-7171. **$89-$179.** 17800 Silver Pkwy 48430. US 23 exit 78
(Owen Rd), just w, then 0.4 mi n. Int corridors. **Pets:** Accepted.
🐾 🐾 🛜 ✖ 🛏 🖵

FLINT
◆◆ **Baymont Inn & Suites-Flint/Flushing** 🅷
(810) 732-2300. **$59-$99.** 4160 Pier North Blvd 48504. I-75 exit 122
(Pierson Rd), just w. Int corridors. **Pets:** Medium, other species. $25
one-time fee/pet. Designated rooms, service with restrictions, supervision. 🐾 🛜 ✖ 🛏 🖵

◆◆ **Courtyard by Marriott Flint Grand Blanc** 🅷
(810) 232-3500. **$71-$246.** 5205 Gateway Center 48507. US 23 exit 90
(Hill Rd), just e to Gateway Center, then just n. Int corridors.
Pets: Accepted. 🍴 🐾 🐾 🛜 ✖ 🛏 🖵

◆◆ **Holiday Inn Express Flint Campus Area** 🅷
(810) 238-7744. **Call for rates.** 1150 Robert T Longway Blvd 48503.
I-475 exit 8A (Robert T Longway Blvd), just w. Int corridors.
Pets: Medium, dogs only. $25 daily fee/pet. Designated rooms, service
with restrictions, supervision. 🐾 🛜 ✖ 🛏 🖵

◆◆◆ **Holiday Inn Flint/Grand Blanc Area** 🅷
(810) 232-5300. **$104-$259.** 5353 Gateway Centre Dr 48507. US 23,
exit 90 (Hill Rd), just e to Gateway Center. Int corridors.
Pets: Accepted. 🍴 🐾 ✖ 🛜 ✖ 🛏 🖵

◆◆◆◆ **Residence Inn by Marriott Flint Grand Blanc** 🅷
(810) 424-7000. **$107-$219.** 2202 W Hill Rd 48507. US 23 exit 90 (Hill
Rd), just e. Int corridors. **Pets:** Accepted.
🐾 🐾 🛜 ✖ 🛏 🖵

FRANKENMUTH
◆◆◆ **Drury Inn & Suites Frankenmuth** 🅷
(989) 652-2800. **$85-$155.** 260 S Main St 48734. On SR 83; downtown. Int corridors. **Pets:** Accepted. 🐾 🐾 🛜 ✖ 🛏 🖵

◆ **Frankenmuth Motel** Ⓜ
(989) 652-6171. **$49-$125.** 1218 Weiss St 48734. Just e of SR 83. Ext
corridors. **Pets:** Other species. $10 daily fee/pet. Designated rooms,
service with restrictions. 🛜 ✖ 🛏

GLEN ARBOR
◆◆ **The Homestead** 🅷
(231) 334-5000. **$84-$272, 28 day notice.** 4800 Wood Ridge Rd 49636.
In Homestead Resort. Ext/int corridors. **Pets:** Other species. $10 daily
fee/pet. Designated rooms, service with restrictions, supervision.
🍴 🐾 🐾 ✖ 🛜 ✖ 🛏 🖵

GRAND BLANC
◆◆ **Comfort Inn** 🅷
(810) 694-0000. **$84-$179.** 9040 Holly Rd 48439. I-75 exit 108 (Holly
Rd), just e. Int corridors. **Pets:** Accepted.
🐾 🐾 🛜 ✖ 🛏 🖵

GRAND RAPIDS *(Restaurants p. 617)*
⒜⒜⒜ ◆◆◆ **Holiday Inn Grand Rapids Downtown** 🅷
(616) 235-7611. **$174-$254.** 310 Pearl St NW 49504. US 131 exit 85B
(Pearl St), just se. Int corridors. **Pets:** Other species. $25 daily fee/
room. Service with restrictions, crate.
[SAVE] [ECO] 🍴 🐾 🐾 🛜 ✖ 🛏 🖵

◆◆◆ **Homewood Suites by Hilton Grand Rapids** 🅷
(616) 285-7100. **$129-$209.** 3920 Stahl Dr SE 49546. I-96 exit 43A
(28th St/SR 11), 1.6 mi w, just n on E Paris Ave, then just w. Int corridors. **Pets:** Accepted. 🍴 🐾 🐾 🛜 ✖ 🛏 🖵

GRANDVILLE
◆◆◆ **Residence Inn by Marriott Grand Rapids**
West 🅷
(616) 538-1100. **$83-$271.** 3451 Rivertown Point Ct SW 49418. I-196
exit 67, 1.5 mi e. Int corridors. **Pets:** Accepted.
[ECO] 🐾 🐾 🛜 ✖ 🛏 🖵

GRAYLING
◆◆ **Ramada Hotel & Conference Center** 🅷
(989) 348-7611. **$80-$189.** 2650 S I-75 Business Loop 49738. I-75 exit
254 northbound, 1 mi nw; exit 256 southbound, 4 mi sw. Int corridors.
Pets: Dogs only. $25 daily fee/pet. Designated rooms, service with
restrictions, supervision. 🐾 ✖ 🛜 ✖ 🛏 🖵

◆◆ **Super 8 Grayling** 🅷 ✿
(989) 348-8888. **$62-$80.** 5828 Nelson A Miles Pkwy 49738. I-75 exit
251, just w. Int corridors. **Pets:** Other species. $75 one-time fee/pet.
Designated rooms, service with restrictions.
🍴 🐾 🛜 ✖ 🛏 🖵

GREENVILLE
◆◆ **AmericInn Lodge & Suites Greenville** 🅷
(616) 754-4500. **$107-$112.** 2525 W Washington St 48838. Jct SR 91,
1.9 mi w on SR 57. Int corridors. **Pets:** Medium, dogs only. $20 daily
fee/pet. Designated rooms, service with restrictions, supervision.
🐾 🐾 🛜 ✖ 🛏 🖵

HARRISON
◆ **Lakeside Waterfront Lodging** Ⓜ
(989) 539-0706. **$63-$99.** 515 E Park St, US 127 Business Rt 48625.
US 127 exit US 127 business route/SR 61, 2.2 mi w exit 170. Ext corridors. **Pets:** Other species. $50 deposit/room. Service with restrictions,
crate. 🛜 ✖ 🛏 🖵

HARTLAND

AAA **WWW** Best Western of Hartland **M**

(810) 632-7177. **$90-$140.** 10087 M-59 48353. US 23 exit 67 (SR 59), just w. Ext corridors. **Pets:** Medium. $20 one-time fee/pet. Designated rooms, service with restrictions. [icons]

HASTINGS

WWW Holiday Inn Express Hastings **H**

(269) 945-0000. **Call for rates.** 1099 W SR 43 Hwy 49058. 1.3 mi w on SR 43. Int corridors. **Pets:** Medium, dogs only. $25 daily fee/pet. Designated rooms, service with restrictions, supervision. [icons]

HOLLAND

AAA **WWW** Best Western Plus Holland Inn & Suites **H**

(616) 994-0400. **$89-$269.** 2888 W Shore Dr 49424. US 31 exit Felch St E, just ne. Ext/int corridors. **Pets:** Accepted. [icons]

WWW Residence Inn by Marriott Holland **H**

(616) 393-6900. **$98-$329.** 631 Southpoint Ridge Rd 49423. I-196 exit 49, 0.7 mi n on SR 40. Int corridors. **Pets:** Accepted. [icons]

HOUGHTON

WWW Holiday Inn Express Houghton **H**

(906) 482-1066. **Call for rates.** 1110 Century Way 49931. 1 mi w on SR 26. Int corridors. **Pets:** Accepted. [icons]

HOUGHTON LAKE

WW Super 8 Houghton Lake **H**

(989) 422-3119. **$65-$110.** 9580 W Lake City Rd 48629. Jct US 127 and SR 55. Int corridors. **Pets:** Accepted. [icons]

HOWELL

WW Baymont Inn & Suites-Howell **H**

(517) 546-0712. **$69-$108.** 4120 Lambert Dr 48855. I-96 exit 133 (US 59/Grand River Ave), just n, then 0.5 mi e. Int corridors. **Pets:** Accepted. [icons]

WW Magnuson Hotel Howell/Brighton **M**

(517) 548-2900. **Call for rates.** 1500 Pinckney Rd 48843. I-96 exit 137 (Pinckney Rd), just s on CR D19 (Michigan Ave). Ext corridors. **Pets:** Small, dogs only. $25 daily fee/pet. Designated rooms, service with restrictions, supervision. [icons]

IMLAY CITY

WW Super 8-Imlay City **H**

(810) 724-8700. **$60-$85.** 6951 Newark Rd 48444. I-69 exit 168 (SR 53/Van Dyke Rd), just n, then just e. Int corridors. **Pets:** Accepted. [icons]

IRON MOUNTAIN

AAA **WW** Comfort Inn **H**

(906) 774-5505. **$89-$144.** 1565 N Stephenson Ave 49801. On US 2/41, 1.3 mi nw. Int corridors. **Pets:** Medium, dogs only. $15 daily fee/pet. Designated rooms, service with restrictions, supervision. [icons]

WW Country Inn & Suites By Carlson **H**

(906) 774-1900. **Call for rates.** 2005 S Stephenson Ave 49801. On US 2, 0.8 mi e of jct SR 141. Int corridors. **Pets:** Dogs only. $20 daily fee/room. Designated rooms, service with restrictions, supervision. [icons]

IRONWOOD

W Americas Best Value Inn **H**

(906) 932-3395. **$75-$119.** 160 E Cloverland Dr 49938. On US 2. Int corridors. **Pets:** Dogs only. $15 daily fee/pet. Designated rooms, service with restrictions, supervision. [icons]

WW AmericInn of Ironwood **H**

(906) 932-7200. **Call for rates.** 1117 E Cloverland Dr 49938. On US 2. Int corridors. **Pets:** Other species. $25 daily fee/pet. Service with restrictions, supervision. [icons]

JACKSON

WW Baymont Inn & Suites Jackson **H** ❀

(517) 789-6000. **$69-$189.** 2035 Bondsteel Dr 49202. I-94 exit 138 (US 127), just n to Springport Rd, then just w. Int corridors. **Pets:** $10 daily fee/pet. Service with restrictions, crate. [icons]

WWW Hampton Inn Jackson **H**

(517) 789-5151. **$129-$199.** 2225 Shirley Dr 49202. I-94 exit 138 (US 127), just n to Springport Rd, then just e. Int corridors. **Pets:** Accepted. [icons]

KALAMAZOO

WW Baymont Inn & Suites Kalamazoo **H**

(269) 372-7999. **$69-$129.** 2203 S 11th St 49009. US 131 exit 36 (Stadium Dr), just nw. Int corridors. **Pets:** Medium, other species. $20 daily fee/pet. Designated rooms, no service, crate. [icons]

WWW Candlewood Suites Kalamazoo **H** ❀

(269) 270-3203. **$129-$189.** 3443 Retail Place Dr 49048. I-94 exit 80 (Sprinkle Rd), just s. Int corridors. **Pets:** Large, dogs only. $25 daily fee/room. Designated rooms, service with restrictions, supervision. [icons]

AAA **WWW** Clarion Inn Kalamazoo **H**

(269) 381-1900. **$70-$170.** 3640 E Cork St 49001. I-94 exit 80 (Sprinkle Rd), just nw. Int corridors. **Pets:** Accepted. [icons]

AAA **WWWW** Four Points by Sheraton Kalamazoo **H**

(269) 385-3922. **$109-$329.** 3600 E Cork Street Ct 49001. I-94 exit 80 (Sprinkle Rd), just nw. Int corridors. **Pets:** Accepted. [icons]

AAA **WWWW** Henderson Castle Inn, Restaurant, Winery, Tours and Weddings **CI**

(269) 344-1827. **$99-$299, 8 day notice.** 100 Monroe St 49006. US 131 exit 38A, 2.9 mi e. Int corridors. **Pets:** Dogs only. $25 daily fee/pet. Service with restrictions, supervision. [icons]

AAA **WWW** Holiday Inn Kalamazoo West **H** ❀

(269) 375-6000. **$119-$189.** 2747 S 11th St 49009. US 131 exit 36 (Stadium Dr), just sw. Int corridors. **Pets:** Medium, dogs only. $15 daily fee/pet. Designated rooms, service with restrictions, crate. [icons]

AAA **WWW** Quality Inn **H**

(269) 381-7000. **$70-$150.** 3820 S Sprinkle Rd 49001. I-94 exit 80 (Sprinkle Rd), 0.3 mi s. Int corridors. **Pets:** Medium. $15 one-time fee/pet. Service with restrictions, supervision. [icons]

AAA **WW** Red Roof Inn Kalamazoo West-Western Michigan Univ. **H**

(269) 375-7400. **$49-$90.** 5425 W Michigan Ave 49009. US 131 exit 36 (Stadium Dr), just nw. Ext corridors. **Pets:** Accepted. [icons]

▼▼▼ **Residence Inn by Marriott Kalamazoo East** **H**
(269) 349-0855. **$85-$166.** 1500 E Kilgore Rd 49001. I-94 exit 78 (Portage Rd), just n, then just w. Ext/int corridors. **Pets:** Other species. $75 one-time fee/room. Service with restrictions.
ECO 🅜 ➤ 🛜 ✕ 🔒 💻

▼▼▼ **Staybridge Suites Kalamazoo** **H**
(269) 372-8000. **Call for rates.** 2001 Seneca Ln 49008. US 131 exit 36 (Stadium Dr), 0.3 mi e. Int corridors. **Pets:** Accepted.
🅜 ➤ 🛜 ✕ 🔒 💻

▼▼▼ **TownePlace Suites by Marriott Kalamazoo** **H**
(269) 353-1500. **$79-$152.** 5683 S 9th St 49009. I-94 exit 72 (9th St), just s. Int corridors. **Pets:** Accepted. 🅜 ➤ 🛜 ✕ 🔒 💻

KALKASKA

▼▼ ▼ **All Seasons Hotel & Resort** **H** 🐾
(231) 258-0000. **$89-$299, 3 day notice.** 760 S Cedar St 49646. On US 131 and SR 72, 0.8 mi n. Int corridors. **Pets:** Other species. $15 daily fee/room. Designated rooms, service with restrictions, supervision.
🅜 ➤ ✕ 🛜 ✕ 🔒 💻

KENTWOOD

▼▼▼ **Residence Inn by Marriott Grand Rapids Airport** **H**
(616) 285-1280. **$123-$271.** 4443 28th St 49512. I-96 exit 43A, 1 mi w on SR 11. Int corridors. **Pets:** Accepted. 🅜 🛜 ✕ 🔒 💻

▼▼▼ **Staybridge Suites-Grand Rapids** **H**
(616) 464-3200. **Call for rates.** 3000 Lake Eastbrook Blvd SE 49512. I-96 exit 43A, 2 mi w on SR 11, then just s. Int corridors.
Pets: Accepted. 🅜 ➤ 🛜 ✕ 🔒 💻

LANSING

ⒶⒶⒶ ▼▼ **Candlewood Suites East Lansing** **H** 🐾
(517) 351-8181. **$98-$143.** 3545 Forest Rd 48910. I-496 exit 11 (Jolly Rd), 0.3 mi e to Collins Rd, 0.7 mi n, then just w. Int corridors. **Pets:** Other species. $75 one-time fee/pet. Designated rooms.
SAVE 🅜 🛜 ✕ 🔒 💻

▼▼▼ **Comfort Inn** **H** 🐾
(517) 627-8381. **$90-$145.** 525 N Canal Rd 48917. I-96 exit 93B (SR 43/Saginaw Hwy), just e. Int corridors. **Pets:** Medium, other species. $50 deposit/room. Designated rooms, service with restrictions, supervision. ➤ 🛜 ✕ 🔒 💻

ⒶⒶⒶ ▼▼▼ **Courtyard by Marriott Lansing** **H**
(517) 482-0500. **$93-$248.** 2710 Lake Lansing Rd 48912. US 127 exit 79 (Lake Lansing Rd), just w. Int corridors. **Pets:** Accepted.
SAVE 🍽 ➤ 🛜 ✕ 🔒 💻

ⒶⒶⒶ ▼▼▼ **Crowne Plaza Lansing West** **H**
(517) 323-7100. **Call for rates.** 925 S Creyts Rd 48917. I-496 exit 1 (Creyts Rd), just n. Int corridors. **Pets:** Accepted.
SAVE 🍽 🅜 🛜 ✕ 🔒 💻

ⒶⒶⒶ ▼▼▼ **Hyatt Place Lansing/Eastwood Towne Center** **H**
(517) 679-7600. **$89-$299.** 2401 Showtime Dr 48912. US 127 exit 79 (Lake Lansing Rd), just nw. Int corridors. **Pets:** Accepted.
SAVE 🍽 🅜 🛜 ✕ 🔒 💻

ⒶⒶⒶ ▼▼▼ **Quality Suites** **H**
(517) 886-0600. **$109-$249.** 901 Delta Commerce Dr 48917. I-96 exit 93B (SR 43/Saginaw Hwy), just e, then just n. Int corridors.
Pets: Accepted. **SAVE** **ECO** 🅜 🛜 ✕ 🔒 💻

▼▼▼ **Residence Inn by Marriott Lansing West** **H**
(517) 886-5030. **$85-$257.** 922 Delta Commerce Dr 48917. I-96 exit 93B (SR 43/Saginaw Hwy), just e, then just n. Int corridors.
Pets: Accepted. 🅜 ➤ 🛜 ✕ 🔒 💻

LIVONIA

▼▼▼ **Comfort Inn Livonia** **H**
(734) 458-7111. **$89-$140.** 29235 Buckingham Dr 48154. I-96 exit 176 (Middlebelt Rd), just n. Int corridors. **Pets:** Dogs only. Designated rooms, service with restrictions, crate. 🛜 ✕ 🔒 💻

▼▼▼ **Detroit Marriott Livonia** **H**
(734) 462-3100. **$79-$189.** 17100 Laurel Park Dr N 48152. I-96/275 exit 170 (6 Mile Rd), just e, then just n. Int corridors. **Pets:** Accepted.
ECO 🍽 ➤ 🛰 ✕ 🔒 💻

▼▼▼ **Embassy Suites Hotel by Hilton Detroit-Livonia/Novi** **H**
(734) 462-6000. **$119-$219.** 19525 Victor Pkwy 48152. I-96/275 exit 169B (7 Mile Rd), just e, then 0.5 mi n. Int corridors. **Pets:** Accepted.
🍽 ➤ 🛰 ✕ 🔒 💻

ⒶⒶⒶ ▼▼▼ **Hyatt Place Detroit/Livonia** **H**
(734) 953-9224. **$89-$199.** 19300 Haggerty Rd 48152. I-96/275 exit 169A (7 Mile Rd), just w, then just n. Int corridors. **Pets:** Accepted.
SAVE 🍽 🅜 ➤ 🛜 ✕ 🔒 💻

▼▼▼ **Residence Inn by Marriott Detroit-Livonia** **H**
(734) 462-4201. **$85-$282.** 17250 Fox Dr 48152. I-96/275 exit 170 (6 Mile Rd), just w, then just n. Int corridors. **Pets:** Accepted.
🅜 ➤ 🛜 ✕ 🔒 💻

ⒶⒶⒶ ▼▼▼ **TownePlace Suites by Marriott Detroit Livonia** **H** 🐾
(734) 542-7400. **$80-$219.** 17450 Fox Dr 48152. I-96/275 exit 170 (6 Mile Rd), just w, then just n. Int corridors. **Pets:** Other species. $100 one-time fee/room. Designated rooms.
SAVE 🅜 ➤ 🛜 ✕ 🔒 💻

LUDINGTON

ⒶⒶⒶ ▼▼▼ **Best Western Lakewinds** **H**
(231) 843-2140. **$90-$220.** 5005 W US 10 49431. US 31 exit 170B, 0.9 mi w. Int corridors. **Pets:** Accepted.
SAVE 🅜 ✕ 🛜 ✕ 🔒 💻

▼▼▼ **Comfort Inn** **H** 🐾
(231) 845-7004. **Call for rates.** 5323 W US 10 49431. US 31 exit 170B, 1.3 mi w. Int corridors. **Pets:** Medium, dogs only. $10 daily fee/pet. Designated rooms, service with restrictions, supervision.
ECO 🅜 ➤ ✕ 🛜 ✕ 🔒 💻

MACKINAW CITY

▼▼ ▼ **Baymont Inn & Suites Mackinaw City** **H**
(231) 436-7737. **$59-$269.** 109 S Nicolet St 49701. I-75 exit 337, just e. Int corridors. **Pets:** Accepted. 🅜 ➤ 🛜 ✕ 🔒 💻

▼▼ **The Beach House** **CA**
(231) 436-5353. **Call for rates.** 11490 W US 23 49701. 1.3 mi s. Ext corridors. **Pets:** Medium. $20 one-time fee/pet. Service with restrictions.
➤ 🛜 ✕ 🔒

ⒶⒶⒶ ▼▼▼ **Days Inn & Suites Bridgeview Lodge** **M**
(231) 436-8961. **$75-$300.** 206 N Nicolet St 49701. I-75 exit 339; at bridge. Ext/int corridors. **Pets:** Medium, dogs only. Designated rooms, service with restrictions, supervision. **SAVE** ➤ ✕ 🔒 💻

ⒶⒶⒶ ▼▼ **Days Inn Lakeview** **M**
(231) 436-5557. **$39-$299, 3 day notice.** 825 S Huron Ave 49701. I-75 exit 337 northbound, 0.5 mi n to US 23, then 0.3 mi e; exit 338 southbound, 0.8 mi se on US 23. Ext/int corridors. **Pets:** Accepted.
SAVE ➤ ✕ 🛜 ✕ 🔒 💻

ⒶⒶⒶ ▼▼ **Econo Lodge Bayview** **M**
(231) 436-5777. **$49-$399, 3 day notice.** 712 S Huron Ave 49701. I-75 exit 337 northbound, 0.5 mi n to US 23, 0.3 mi e, then just n; exit 338 southbound, 0.8 mi se on US 23, then just n. Ext corridors.
Pets: Accepted. **SAVE** ➤ ✕ 🛜 ✕ 🔒 💻

Fairview Beachfront Inn M
(231) 436-8831. **$49-$198, 3 day notice.** 907 S Huron Ave 49701. 0.8 mi se on US 23. Ext corridors. **Pets:** Accepted.
SAVE ⊇ 🛜 ✕ 🛏 💻

Lamplighter Motel M
(231) 436-5350. **$35-$130.** 303 Jamet St 49701. I-75 exit 339, just n of town. Ext corridors. **Pets:** $10 daily fee/pet. Designated rooms, service with restrictions, supervision. 🛜 ✕ 🛏 💻

Mackinaw Waterfront Inn M
(231) 436-5527. **$38-$288, 3 day notice.** 1009 S Huron Ave 49701. 1.2 mi se on US 23. Ext corridors. **Pets:** Accepted. ⊇ 🛜 ✕ 🛏

Quality Inn & Suites Lakefront M
(231) 436-5051. **$49-$399, 3 day notice.** 917 S Huron Ave 49701. 1 mi se on US 23. Ext corridors. **Pets:** Accepted.
SAVE ⊇ 🛜 ✕ 🛏 💻

Super 8 Beachfront M
(231) 436-7111. **$39-$399, 3 day notice.** 519 S Huron Ave 49701. I-75 exit 337 northbound, 0.5 mi n to US 23, 0.3 mi e, then just n; exit 338 southbound, 0.8 mi se on US 23, then just n. Ext corridors.
Pets: Accepted. SAVE ⊇ 🛜 ✕ 🛏 💻

Super 8 Bridgeview H
(231) 436-5252. **$39-$399, 3 day notice.** 601 N Huron Ave 49701. I-75 exit 339 northbound, just n, then just e. Ext/int corridors.
Pets: Accepted. SAVE ⊇ 🛜 ✕ 🛏 💻

Thunderbird Inn Mackinaw City M
(231) 436-5433. **$49-$300.** 146 Old US 31 49701. I-75 exit 337 northbound, just ne; exit 338 southbound, 0.7 mi se. Ext corridors.
Pets: Accepted. SAVE ⊇ 🛜 ✕ 🛏 💻

MADISON HEIGHTS
Residence Inn by Marriott-Detroit Troy/Madison Heights H
(248) 583-4322. **$83-$237.** 32650 Stephenson Hwy 48071. I-75 exit 65B, just w on W 14 Mile Rd, then just s. Ext corridors.
Pets: Accepted. 🅼 ⊇ 🛜 ✕ 🛏 💻

MANISTIQUE
Comfort Inn H
(906) 341-6981. **$100-$170.** 617 E Lakeshore Dr 49854. 0.5 mi e on US 2. Int corridors. **Pets:** Other species. $25 one-time fee/room. Service with restrictions, supervision. 🛜 ✕ 🛏 💻

Quality Inn & Suites Manistique H
(906) 341-3777. **$100-$150.** 955 E Lakeshore Dr 49854. 1.4 mi e on US 2. Int corridors. **Pets:** Accepted. 🛜 ✕ 🛏 💻

MARQUETTE
Cedar Motor Inn M ❖
(906) 228-2280. **$49-$125.** 2523 US Hwy 41 W 49855. 2.8 mi w on SR 28. Ext/int corridors. **Pets:** Dogs only. $10 daily fee/pet. Designated rooms, service with restrictions. SAVE ⊇ 🛜 ✕ 🛏 💻

Days Inn H
(906) 225-1393. **$89-$116, 3 day notice.** 2403 US 41 W 49855. 2.3 mi w on SR 28. Int corridors. **Pets:** Accepted.
🅼 ⊇ ✕ 🛜 ✕ 🛏 💻

Holiday Inn H
(906) 225-1351. **$129-$300.** 1951 US 41 W 49855. 1.8 mi w on SR 28. Int corridors. **Pets:** Accepted. 🍴 🅼 ⊇ ✕ 🛜 ✕ 🛏 💻

Ramada Marquette H
(906) 228-6000. **$99-$260.** 412 W Washington St 49855. 0.4 mi w on US 42 business route. Int corridors. **Pets:** Dogs only. $30 one-time fee/pet. Service with restrictions, supervision.
🍴 ⊇ ✕ 🛜 ✕ 🛏 💻

MARSHALL
Comfort Inn H
(269) 789-7890. **$89-$189.** 204 Winston Dr 49068. I-69 exit 36 (Michigan Ave), just se. Int corridors. **Pets:** Accepted.
🅼 ⊇ ✕ 🛜 ✕ 🛏 💻

Hampton Inn Marshall H
(269) 789-0131. **$109-$169.** 325 Sam Hill Dr 49068. I-94 exit 110 (SR 227), just s. Int corridors. **Pets:** Accepted.
🅼 ⊇ 🛜 ✕ 🛏 💻

Holiday Inn Express Marshall H
(269) 789-9301. **$111-$119, 7 day notice.** 329 Sam Hill Dr 49068. I-94 exit 110 (SR 227), just s. Int corridors. **Pets:** Accepted.
🅼 ⊇ 🛜 ✕ 🛏 💻

MENOMINEE
AmericInn Menominee on the Bay H
(906) 863-8699. **Call for rates.** 2330 10th St 49858. 0.8 mi n on US 41. Int corridors. **Pets:** Medium, dogs only. $30 deposit/pet. Designated rooms, service with restrictions, supervision. ⊇ 🛜 ✕ 🛏 💻

Econo Lodge On The Bay H
(906) 863-4431. **$79-$139.** 2516 10th St 49858. 1 mi n on US 41. Int corridors. **Pets:** Accepted. 🛜 ✕ 🛏 💻

MIDLAND
Baymont Inn & Suites Midland H
(989) 631-0070. **$68-$150.** 2200 W Wackerly St 48640. US 10 exit 122 (Eastman Ave), just s, then just w. Int corridors. **Pets:** Accepted.
⊇ ✕ 🛜 ✕ 🛏 💻

Residence Inn by Marriott Midland H
(989) 837-9990. **$116-$325.** 850 Joe Mann Blvd 48642. US 10 exit 122 (Eastman Ave), 1 mi e. Int corridors. **Pets:** Accepted.
🅼 ⊇ ✕ 🛏 💻

Sleep Inn Midland H
(989) 837-1010. **$77-$169.** 2100 W Wackerly St 48640. US 10 exit 122 (Eastman Ave), just s, then just w. Int corridors. **Pets:** Accepted.
⊇ 🛜 ✕ 🛏 💻

MOUNT PLEASANT
Comfort Inn & Suites Hotel and Conference Center H
(989) 772-4000. **$119-$369.** 2424 S Mission St 48858. 2 mi s on US 127 business route. Int corridors. **Pets:** Accepted.
🍴 🅼 ⊇ 🛜 ✕ 🛏 💻

Fairfield Inn & Suites by Marriott Mt. Pleasant H
(989) 775-5000. **$98-$216.** 2525 S University Park Dr 48858. 2.5 mi s on US 127 business route. Int corridors. **Pets:** Accepted.
⊟ 🅼 ⊇ 🛜 ✕ 🛏 💻

MUNISING
Alger Falls Motel M
(906) 387-3536. **Call for rates.** E9427 Hwy M-28 49862. 2 mi e on SR 28 and 94. Ext corridors. **Pets:** Accepted. 🛜 ✕ 🛏 💻

Holiday Inn Express Munising-Lakeview H
(906) 387-4800. **$109-$350.** E8890 M-28 49862. On SR 28, 2 mi w of town. Int corridors. **Pets:** Other species. $15 daily fee/room. Designated rooms, crate. 🍴 🅼 ⊇ ✕ 🛜 ✕ 🛏 💻

Terrace Motel M
(906) 387-2735. **$45-$100.** 420 Prospect St 49862. 0.5 mi e, just off SR 28. Ext corridors. **Pets:** Medium, dogs only. $10 daily fee/room. Designated rooms, service with restrictions, crate.
SAVE 🍴 ✕ 🛜 ✕ 🐾 📞

NEW BUFFALO

Baymont Inn & Suites New Buffalo H
(269) 469-4193. **$90-$295.** 18800 Harbor Country Dr 49117. I-94 exit 1 (Harbor Country Dr), just w. Int corridors. **Pets:** $25 daily fee/pet. Designated rooms, service with restrictions, supervision.

NILES

Quality Inn & Suites Niles H
(269) 684-3900. **$85-$350.** 1265 S 11th St 49120. Jct US 12, 0.8 mi n on SR 51. Int corridors. **Pets:** Other species. $25 daily fee/pet. Service with restrictions, supervision.

NOVI

Extended Stay America-Detroit-Novi H
(248) 305-9955. **$80-$105.** 21555 Haggerty Rd 48375. I-96/275 exit 167 (8 Mile Rd), just w, then 0.5 mi n. Int corridors. **Pets:** Accepted.

Residence Inn by Marriott-Detroit/Novi H
(248) 735-7400. **$93-$287.** 27477 Cabaret Dr 48377. I-96 exit 162 (Novi Rd), just n, just w on 12 Mile Rd, then just s. Int corridors. **Pets:** Accepted.

Sheraton Detroit Novi H
(248) 349-4000. **$109-$499.** 21111 Haggerty Rd 48375. I-96/275 exit 167 (8 Mile Rd), just w, then just n. Int corridors. **Pets:** Accepted.

Staybridge Suites Detroit-Novi H 🐾
(248) 349-4600. **$99-$399.** 27000 Providence Pkwy 48374. I-96 exit 160 (Beck Rd), just s, 0.6 mi w on Grand River Ave, then just s. Int corridors. **Pets:** Medium, dogs only. $75 one-time fee/pet. Designated rooms, service with restrictions, crate.

TownePlace Suites by Marriott Detroit Novi H
(248) 305-5533. **$89-$263.** 42600 W 11 Mile Rd 48375. I-96 exit 162 (Novi Rd), 0.4 mi s, just e on Grand River Ave, just n on Town Center Dr, then just e. Int corridors. **Pets:** $100 one-time fee/room. Service with restrictions.

OKEMOS

Comfort Inn Okemos-East Lansing H
(517) 347-6690. **$97-$240.** 2187 University Park Dr 48864. I-96 exit 110 (Okemos Rd), just n, then just e. Int corridors. **Pets:** Accepted.

Holiday Inn Express & Suites Lansing-Okemos (MSU Area) H
(517) 349-8700. **Call for rates.** 2209 University Park Dr 48864. I-96 exit 110 (Okemos Rd), just n, then just e. Int corridors. **Pets:** Accepted.

Staybridge Suites-Lansing/Okemos H
(517) 347-3044. **Call for rates.** 3553 Meridian Crossing Dr 48864. I-96 exit 110 (Okemos Rd), just n. Int corridors. **Pets:** Accepted.

PAW PAW

Comfort Inn & Suites H
(269) 655-0303. **$75-$185.** 153 Ampey Rd 49079. I-94 exit 60 (SR 40), just nw. Int corridors. **Pets:** Accepted.

PETOSKEY *(Restaurants p. 617)*

Apple Tree Inn H
(231) 348-2900. **$69-$399, 3 day notice.** 915 Spring St 49770. 1.1 mi s on US 131. Int corridors. **Pets:** Accepted.

@ Michigan Inn & Lodge M
(231) 348-3900. **$65-$189.** 1420 S US 131 Hwy 49770. US 131, 1.3 mi s. Ext corridors. **Pets:** Accepted.

PLAINWELL

Comfort Inn H
(269) 685-9891. **$104-$174.** 622 Allegan St 49080. US 131 exit 49A, just e. Int corridors. **Pets:** $15 daily fee/pet. Designated rooms, service with restrictions, supervision.

PLYMOUTH *(Restaurants p. 617)*

Red Roof Inn Detroit-Plymouth/Canton M
(734) 459-3300. **$45-$110.** 39700 Ann Arbor Rd 48170. I-275 exit 28 (Ann Arbor Rd), just e, then just n. Ext corridors. **Pets:** Accepted.

PONTIAC

Residence Inn by Marriott Detroit Pontiac/Auburn Hills H
(248) 858-8664. **$88-$235.** 3333 Centerpoint Pkwy 48341. I-75 exit 75, 1 mi w on Square Lake Rd, then just n on Opdyke Rd. Int corridors. **Pets:** Accepted.

PORTAGE

Homewood Suites by Hilton Kalamazoo/Portage H
(269) 382-5817. **Call for rates.** 500 Trade Centre Way 49002. I-94 exit 76 (Westnedge Ave), just nw. Int corridors. **Pets:** Accepted.

PORT HURON

Best Western Port Huron/Hospitality Inn H 🐾
(810) 987-1600. **$80-$140.** 2282 Water St 48060. I-94 exit 274B (Water St), just n. Int corridors. **Pets:** Large, other species. $20 daily fee/room. Designated rooms, service with restrictions, supervision.

Comfort Inn H
(810) 982-5500. **$90-$200.** 1700 Yeager St 48060. I-94 exit 274B (Water St), just s, then just n. Int corridors. **Pets:** Medium, other species. $30 daily fee/pet. Designated rooms, service with restrictions, supervision.

ROMULUS

Extended Stay America-Detroit-Metropolitan Airport H
(734) 722-7780. **$70-$85.** 30325 Flynn Dr 48174. I-94 exit 198 (Merriman Rd), just n, then 0.4 mi e. Int corridors. **Pets:** Accepted.

La Quinta Inn & Suites-Detroit Metro Airport H
(734) 721-1100. **$79-$185.** 30847 Flynn Dr 48174. I-94 exit 198 (Merriman Rd), just n, then just e. Int corridors. **Pets:** Accepted.

Sheraton Detroit Metro Airport H 🐾
(734) 729-2600. **$89-$209.** 8000 Merriman Rd 48174. I-94 exit 198 (Merriman Rd), 0.4 mi n. Int corridors. **Pets:** Medium, dogs only. Service with restrictions, supervision.

The Westin Detroit Metropolitan Airport H
(734) 942-6500. **$119-$679.** 2501 Worldgateway Pl 48242. I-94 exit 198 (Merriman Rd), 2 mi s. Int corridors. **Pets:** Accepted.

ROSEVILLE

▼▼▼ Days Inn and Suites Roseville **M**
(586) 294-0400. **$54-$80.** 31327 Gratiot Ave 48066. I-94 exit 232 (Little Mack Ave), just s, 0.5 mi e on 13 Mile Rd, then just n on SR 3. Ext corridors. **Pets:** Accepted. 🍽 🏊 📶 ✕ 🛄 💻

AAA ▼▼▼ Red Roof Inn Detroit-St Clair Shores **M**
(586) 296-0310. **$49-$109.** 31800 Little Mack Ave 48066. I-94 exit 232 (Little Mack Ave), just n. Ext corridors. **Pets:** Accepted.
SAVE ⎗M 📶 ✕ 🛄 💻

SAGINAW

▼▼▼▼ Comfort Suites Saginaw **H**
(989) 797-8000. **$90-$160.** 5180 Fashion Square Blvd 48604. I-675 exit 6, 0.6 mi w on Tittabawassee Rd. Int corridors. **Pets:** Accepted.
🏊 📶 ✕ 🛄 💻

▼▼▼▼ Country Inn & Suites By Carlson Saginaw **H**
(989) 792-7666. **$75-$170.** 2222 Tittabawassee Rd 48604. I-675 exit 6, just w. Int corridors. **Pets:** Dogs only. $25 daily fee/pet. Designated rooms, service with restrictions, supervision. 🏊 📶 ✕ 🛄 💻

▼▼▼▼ Residence Inn by Marriott Saginaw **H**
(989) 799-9000. **$84-$167.** 5230 Fashion Square Blvd 48604. I-675 exit 6, 0.8 mi w, then just n. Int corridors. **Pets:** Accepted.
🏊 📶 ✕ 🛄 💻

▼▼▼▼ TownePlace Suites by Marriott Saginaw **H**
(989) 792-2200. **$71-$140.** 5368 Fashion Square Blvd 48604. I-675 exit 6, 0.8 mi w, then just n. Int corridors. **Pets:** Accepted.
⎗M 📶 ✕ 🛄 💻

ST. IGNACE

AAA ▼▼▼ Budget Host Inn & Suites **H**
(906) 643-9666. **$83-$271.** 700 N State St 49781. 1.8 mi n of bridge tollgate on I-75 business route. Ext/int corridors. **Pets:** Other species. $10 daily fee/pet. Service with restrictions, supervision.
SAVE 🏊 ✕ 📶 ✕ 🛄 💻

ST. JOSEPH

▼▼▼▼ Holiday Inn Express & Suites St. Joseph **H**
(269) 982-0004. **Call for rates.** 3019 Lake Shore Dr 49085. I-94 exit 23, 3.5 mi n on Business Rt I-94. Int corridors. **Pets:** Accepted.
⎗M 🏊 📶 ✕ 🛄 💻

▼▼▼ Silver Beach Hotel **H**
(269) 983-7341. **$94-$350.** 100 Main St 49085. I-94 exit 23, 6 mi nw on Business Rt I-94. Int corridors. **Pets:** $45 one-time fee/pet, $15 daily fee/pet. Designated rooms, service with restrictions, supervision.
🏊 ✕ 📶 ✕ 🛄 💻

SAULT STE. MARIE

▼▼▼ Americas Best Value Inn **H**
(906) 632-8882. **Call for rates.** 3826 I-75 Business Loop 49783. I-75 exit 392, 0.5 mi ne. Int corridors. **Pets:** Accepted. 📶 ✕ 🛄 💻

▼▼▼ Budget Host Crestview Inn **M**
(906) 635-5213. **$69-$129.** 1200 Ashmun St 49783. I-75 exit 392, 2.8 mi ne on I-75 business loop. Ext corridors. **Pets:** Other species. $10 one-time fee/pet. Designated rooms, service with restrictions, supervision. 📶 ✕ 🛄

AAA ▼▼▼ Days Inn **H** ✿
(906) 635-5200. **$72-$170.** 3651 I-75 Business Spur 49783. I-75 exit 392, 0.8 mi ne on I-75 business loop. Int corridors. **Pets:** Dogs only. $15 daily fee/pet. Designated rooms, service with restrictions, supervision. SAVE 🏊 ✕ 📶 ✕ 🛄 💻

▼▼▼ Super 8 Sault Ste. Marie **H**
(906) 632-6000. **$69-$109.** 3525 I-75 Business Spur 49783. I-75 exit 392, 0.8 mi ne. Int corridors. **Pets:** Accepted.
⎗M 🏊 ✕ 📶 ✕ 🛄 💻

SILVER CITY

▼▼▼ AmericInn Lodge & Suites **H**
(906) 885-5311. **Call for rates.** 120 Lincoln Ave 49953. On SR 107, 0.3 mi w of SR 64. Int corridors. **Pets:** Accepted.
🍽 ⎗M 📶 ✕ 📶 ✕ 🛄 💻

SOUTHFIELD

AAA ▼▼▼ The Westin Southfield Detroit **H**
(248) 827-4000. **$109-$369.** 1500 Town Center Dr 48075. SR 10 (Northwestern Hwy) exit 10 (10 Mile Rd/Evergreen Rd), 0.3 mi n. Int corridors. **Pets:** Accepted.
SAVE 🍽 ⎗M 🏊 ✕ 📶 ✕ 🛄 💻

SOUTHGATE

▼▼▼ La Quinta Inn-Detroit Southgate **H**
(734) 374-3000. **$68-$141.** 12888 Reeck Rd 48195. I-75 exit 37 (Northline Rd), just w. Int corridors. **Pets:** Accepted. 📶 ✕ 🛄 💻

SOUTH HAVEN

AAA ▼▼▼ Baymont Inn & Suites Conference Center South Haven **M**
(269) 639-9900. **$60-$250.** 1555 Phoenix Rd 49090. I-196 exit 20, just e. Int corridors. **Pets:** Dogs only. $15 daily fee/pet. Designated rooms, service with restrictions, supervision.
SAVE ⎗M 🏊 📶 ✕ 🛄 💻

▼▼▼ Comfort Suites **H**
(269) 639-2014. **$95-$270.** 1755 Phoenix St 49090. I-196 exit 20, 0.5 mi e. Int corridors. **Pets:** Accepted. SAVE ⎗M 🏊 📶 ✕ 🛄 💻

SPRING LAKE

▼▼▼▼ Grand Haven/Spring Lake Waterfront Holiday Inn **H**
(616) 846-1000. **$89-$299, 3 day notice.** 940 W Savidge St 49456. On SR 104, just e of US 31. Int corridors. **Pets:** Accepted.
🍽 🏊 ✕ 📶 ✕ 🛄 💻

STERLING HEIGHTS

AAA ▼▼▼ TownePlace Suites by Marriott Detroit Sterling Heights **H**
(586) 566-0900. **$83-$193.** 14800 Lakeside Cir 48313. 1 mi e of jct SR 53 (Van Dyke Ave) on SR 59 (Hall Rd), then just s. Int corridors. **Pets:** Accepted. SAVE ⎗M 🏊 📶 ✕ 🛄 💻

SUTTONS BAY *(Restaurants p. 617)*

▼▼▼ Red Lion Motor Lodge **M**
(231) 271-6694. **$79-$249.** 4290 S West Bayshore Dr 49682. 5 mi s on SR 22. Ext corridors. **Pets:** $10 daily fee/pet. Designated rooms, no service, supervision. 🍽 📶 ✕ 🐾 🛄 💻

TAWAS CITY

AAA ▼▼▼ Bay Inn Tawas **H**
(989) 362-0088. **$75-$150, 3 day notice.** 1020 W Lake St 48763. 1.5 mi s on US 23. Int corridors. **Pets:** Medium. $15 one-time fee/pet. Service with restrictions, supervision.
SAVE ⎗M 🏊 ✕ 📶 ✕ 🛄 💻

TAYLOR

AAA ▼▼▼ Red Roof Inn Detroit Southwest-Taylor **M**
(734) 374-1150. **$50-$90.** 21230 Eureka Rd 48180. I-75 exit 36 (Eureka Rd), just w. Ext corridors. **Pets:** Accepted. SAVE 📶 ✕ 🛄 💻

THOMPSONVILLE

Crystal Mountain H

(231) 378-2000. **Call for rates.** 12500 Crystal Mountain Dr 49683. On SR 115, 2 mi w. Ext/int corridors. **Pets:** $50 one-time fee/room. Designated rooms, service with restrictions, crate.

TRAVERSE CITY

Best Western Four Seasons H

(231) 946-8424. **$89-$349.** 305 Munson Ave 49686. 2 mi e on US 31/SR72. Int corridors. **Pets:** Accepted.

Country Inn & Suites by Carlson-Traverse City H

(231) 941-0208. **$100-$286.** 420 Munson Ave 49686. 2 mi e on US 31. Ext/int corridors. **Pets:** Accepted.

Park Place Hotel H

(231) 946-5000. **Call for rates.** 300 E State St 49684. Corner of E State and Park sts; downtown. Int corridors. **Pets:** Accepted.

Quality Inn By the Bay H

(231) 929-4423. **$79-$330.** 1492 US 31 N 49686. On US 31, 3.3 mi e. Ext/int corridors. **Pets:** Medium, dogs only. $20 daily fee/room. Designated rooms, service with restrictions, supervision.

West Bay Beach, a Holiday Inn Resort Traverse City H

(231) 947-3700. **Call for rates.** 615 E Front St 49686. 0.5 mi e on US 31. Int corridors. **Pets:** Accepted.

TROY

Drury Inn & Suites Detroit Troy H

(248) 528-3330. **$80-$180.** 575 W Big Beaver Rd 48084. I-75 exit 69A, just e. Int corridors. **Pets:** Accepted.

Hawthorn Suites by Wyndham Troy H

(248) 689-6856. **$99-$199.** 2600 Livernois Rd 48083. I-75 exit 69A, 0.5 mi e on E Big Beaver Rd, then 0.5 mi s. Ext corridors. **Pets:** Medium. $20 daily fee/pet. Designated rooms, service with restrictions, supervision.

Red Roof Inn Detroit - Troy M

(248) 689-4391. **$54-$99.** 2350 Rochester Ct 48083. I-75 exit 67 (Stephenson Hwy), 0.3 mi sw. Ext corridors. **Pets:** Accepted.

TownePlace Suites by Marriott Detroit Troy H

(248) 585-7000. **$125-$191.** 325 Stephenson Hwy 48083. I-75 exit 65B (14 Mile Rd), just w. Int corridors. **Pets:** Accepted.

UTICA

Comfort Inn Utica H

(586) 739-7111. **$66-$210.** 11401 Hall Rd 48317. Van Dyke Ave (SR 53) exit 17, just w on Hall Rd (SR 59). Int corridors. **Pets:** Accepted.

Hyatt Place Detroit/Utica H

(586) 803-0100. **$99-$199.** 45400 Park Ave 48315. Van Dyke Ave (SR 53) exit 17A, just e on Hall Rd (SR 59), then just n. Int corridors. **Pets:** Medium, dogs only. $75 one-time fee/pet. Designated rooms, service with restrictions, supervision.

La Quinta Inn & Suites Detroit Utica H

(586) 731-4700. **$79-$154.** 45311 Park Ave 48315. Van Dyke Ave (SR 53) exit 17A, just n on Hall Rd (SR 59), then just n. Int corridors. **Pets:** Accepted.

Staybridge Suites-Utica H

(586) 323-0101. **Call for rates.** 46155 Utica Park Blvd 48315. Van Dyke Ave (SR 53) exit 17A, just e on Hall Rd (SR 59), then just n. Int corridors. **Pets:** Large. $75 one-time fee/room. Designated rooms, service with restrictions, crate.

WALKER

SpringHill Suites by Marriott Grand Rapids North H

(616) 785-1600. **$91-$303.** 450 Center Dr 49544. I-96 exit 30, just n on Alpine Rd, then 0.3 mi e. Int corridors. **Pets:** Accepted.

WARREN

Candlewood Suites-Detroit Warren H

(586) 978-1261. **$89-$99.** 7010 Convention Blvd 48092. I-696 exit 23, 2.8 mi on Van Dyke Ave (SR 53), just w. Int corridors. **Pets:** Medium. $15 daily fee/room. Service with restrictions, crate.

Extended Stay America Detroit-Warren H

(586) 558-5554. **$75-$100.** 30125 N Civic Center Blvd 48093. I-696 exit 23, 1.5 mi n on Van Dyke Ave (SR 53), then just e. Int corridors. **Pets:** Accepted.

Hawthorn Suites by Wyndham Warren H

(586) 558-7870. **$99-$189, 3 day notice.** 30180 N Civic Center Blvd 48093. I-696 exit 23, 1.5 mi n on Van Dyke Ave (SR 53), then just e. Ext/int corridors. **Pets:** Accepted.

Red Roof Inn Detroit - Warren M

(586) 573-4300. **$56-$89.** 26300 Dequindre Rd 48091. I-696 exit 20, just ne. Ext corridors. **Pets:** Accepted.

TownePlace Suites by Marriott Detroit Warren H

(586) 264-8800. **$93-$219.** 7601 Chicago Rd 48092. I-696 exit 23, 2.4 mi n on Van Dyke Ave (SR 53), then just w. Int corridors. **Pets:** Accepted.

WETMORE

AmericInn Lodge & Suites of Munising H

(906) 387-2000. **Call for rates.** E9926 Hwy M-28 49895. On SR 28, 2.7 mi e. Int corridors. **Pets:** Accepted.

WHITEHALL

Comfort Inn H

(231) 893-4833. **$89-$600.** 2822 N Durham Rd 49461. US 31 exit 128, just ne. Int corridors. **Pets:** Small. $35 one-time fee/pet. Designated rooms, service with restrictions, supervision.

WHITMORE LAKE

Best Western of Whitmore Lake M

(734) 449-2058. **$90-$120.** 9897 Main St 48189. US 23 exit 53, just e. Ext corridors. **Pets:** Other species. $20 daily fee/pet. Designated rooms, service with restrictions, crate.

WOODHAVEN

Best Western Woodhaven Inn H

(734) 676-8000. **$93-$146.** 21700 West Rd 48183. I-75 exit 32B (West Rd), just w. Int corridors. **Pets:** Accepted.

WYOMING

Hyatt Place Grand Rapids-South H

(616) 724-1234. **$129-$249.** 2150 Metro Ln 49519. SR 6 exit 5 (Byron Center Ave), just ne. Int corridors. **Pets:** Accepted.

MINNESOTA

ALBERT LEA

▼▼ ◆◆ AmericInn Lodge & Suites of Albert Lea H
(507) 373-4324. **$100.** 811 E Plaza St 56007. I-90 exit 157 (CR 22), just se. Int corridors. **Pets:** $25 daily fee/pet. Designated rooms, service with restrictions, supervision. ⊞ 🕭M ⊇ 🛜 ✕ 🖥 ▣

◆◆◆ ▼▼◆▼ Best Western Plus Albert Lea I-90/I-35 Hotel H ❀
(507) 373-4000. **$89-$149.** 821 E Plaza St 56007. I-90 exit 157 (CR 22), just se. Int corridors. **Pets:** Medium. $20 daily fee/room. Designated rooms, service with restrictions, supervision.
⟨SAVE⟩ 🕭M ⊇ 🛜 ✕ 🖥 ▣

▼▼ ◆▼ Comfort Inn H
(507) 377-1100. **$94-$196.** 810 Happy Trails Ln 56007. I-35 exit 11, just se. Int corridors. **Pets:** Accepted. 🕭M ⊇ 🛜 ✕ 🖥 ▣

▼◆▼◆▼ Country Inn & Suites By Carlson H
(507) 373-5513. **Call for rates.** 2214 E Main St 56007. I-35 exit 12 southbound; exit 11 northbound, 1 mi w. Int corridors. **Pets:** Accepted.
🕭M ⊇ 🛜 ✕ 🖥 ▣

▼◆▼◆▼ Holiday Inn Express & Suites H ❀
(507) 473-2300. **$79-$159.** 77820 Main St E 56007. I-35 exit 11, just e. Ext corridors. **Pets:** Other species. $25 one-time fee/room. Service with restrictions, supervision. 🍽 🕭M 🛜 ✕ 🖥 ▣

ALEXANDRIA

▼▼ ◆▼ AmericInn Lodge & Suites H
(320) 763-6808. **Call for rates.** 4520 Hwy 29 S 56308. I-94 exit 103, 0.3 mi n. Int corridors. **Pets:** Accepted. 🕭M ⊇ 🛜 ✕ 🖥 ▣

◆◆◆ ▼▼ ◆▼ Best Western Alexandria Inn H
(320) 762-5161. **$90-$140.** 508 Twin Blvd 56308. I-94 exit 103, just n, then just e on 50th St. Int corridors. **Pets:** Medium. $10 deposit/pet. Designated rooms, service with restrictions, supervision.
⟨SAVE⟩ 🕭M ⊇ 🛜 ✕ 🖥 ▣

▼▼ ◆▼ Holiday Inn Alexandria H
(320) 763-6577. **Call for rates.** 5637 Hwy 29 S 56308. I-94 exit 103, just s. Int corridors. **Pets:** Accepted.
🍽 🕭M ⊇ ✕ 🛜 ✕ 🖥 ▣

AUSTIN

▼▼ ◆▼ AmericInn Lodge & Suites of Austin H
(507) 437-7337. **$110-$177.** 1700 8th St NW 55912. I-90 exit 178A (4th St NW), just nw. Int corridors. **Pets:** Small, dogs only. $25 one-time fee/room. Designated rooms, service with restrictions, supervision.
🕭M ⊇ 🛜 ✕ 🖥 ▣

▼▼ ◆▼ Days Inn H
(507) 433-8600. **$59-$90.** 700 16th Ave NW 55912. I-90 exit 178A (4th St NW), just nw. Int corridors. **Pets:** Accepted. 🛜 ✕ 🖥 ▣

▼◆▼◆▼ Holiday Inn & Austin Conference Center H
(507) 433-1000. **Call for rates.** 1701 4th St NW 55912. I-90 exit 178A (4th St NW), just nw. Int corridors. **Pets:** Accepted.
🍽 🕭M ⊇ 🛜 ✕ 🖥 ▣

BAUDETTE

▼▼ ◆▼ AmericInn Lodge & Suites of Baudette H
(218) 634-3200. **Call for rates.** 1179 Main St W 56623. 0.5 mi w on SR 11. Int corridors. **Pets:** Medium, dogs only. $25 one-time fee/pet. Designated rooms, service with restrictions, supervision.
🕭M ⊇ ✕ 🛜 ✕ 🖥 ▣

BAXTER

▼▼ ◆▼ Baymont Inn & Suites H
(218) 822-1133. **$58-$224.** 7208 Fairview Rd 56425. On SR 210, just w of jct SR 371. Int corridors. **Pets:** Accepted.
🍽 🕭M ⊇ ✕ 🛜 ✕ 🖥 ▣

◆▼ ◆▼ Country Inn & Suites By Carlson H
(218) 828-2161. **$99-$179.** 15058 Dellwood Dr N 56425. On SR 371, 1.2 mi n of jct SR 210. Int corridors. **Pets:** Accepted.
🕭M ⊇ 🛜 ✕ 🖥 ▣

▼◆▼◆▼ Holiday Inn Express, Three Bear Waterpark H
(218) 824-3232. **Call for rates.** 15739 Audubon Way 56425. On SR 371, 0.4 mi s of jct CR 77/49. Int corridors. **Pets:** Accepted.
🍽 🕭M ✕ 🛜 ✕ 🖥 ▣

◆◆◆ ▼▼ ◆▼ Super 8 H
(218) 828-4288. **$75-$350.** 14341 Edgewood Dr 56425. On SR 371, 0.5 mi n of jct SR 210. Int corridors. **Pets:** Accepted.
⟨SAVE⟩ 🛜 ✕ 🖥 ▣

BAY LAKE

▼▼ ◆▼ Ruttger's Bay Lake Lodge CO
(218) 678-2885. **$95-$875, 60 day notice.** 25039 Tame Fish Lake Rd 56444. On CR 14 at jct SR 6. Ext/int corridors. **Pets:** Large, dogs only. $25 daily fee/pet. Designated rooms, service with restrictions, supervision. 🍽 ⊇ ✕ 🛜 ✕ 🖥 ▣

BEMIDJI

▼▼ ◆▼ AmericInn Lodge & Suites of Bemidji H
(218) 751-3000. **Call for rates.** 1200 Paul Bunyan Dr NW 56601. On SR 197, 0.5 mi e of northwest jct US 2 and 71. Int corridors.
Pets: Accepted. 🕭M ⊇ 🛜 ✕ 🖥 ▣

◆◆◆ ▼▼ ◆▼ Best Western Bemidji Inn H
(218) 751-0390. **$105-$125.** 2420 Paul Bunyan Dr 56601. Jct US 71 N and SR 197. Int corridors. **Pets:** Other species. $15 daily fee/room. Designated rooms, service with restrictions, crate.
⟨SAVE⟩ ⊇ 🛜 ✕ 🖥 ▣

▼◆▼◆▼ Candlewood Suites Bemidji-Paul Bunyan H
(218) 497-3000. **$99-$119.** 401 Paul Bunyan Dr SE 56601. 1.6 mi n on SR 197 from jct US 2 and 71. Int corridors. **Pets:** Accepted.
🍽 🕭M 🛜 ✕ 🖥 ▣

▼◆▼◆▼ Country Inn & Suites By Carlson H ❀
(218) 441-4800. **$119-$209.** 927 Lake Shore Dr NE 56601. Jct SR 197 and CR 12 (1st St SE), just ne. Int corridors. **Pets:** Medium, dogs only. $50 one-time fee/room. Designated rooms, service with restrictions, crate. 🍽 🕭M ✕ 🖥 ▣

◆◆◆ ▼▼ ◆▼ Holiday Inn Express H
(218) 751-2487. **Call for rates.** 2422 Ridgeway Ave NW 56601. Just n of SR 197, 0.5 mi e of northwest jct US 2 and 71. Int corridors.
Pets: Other species. $20 daily fee/room. Designated rooms, service with restrictions, supervision. ⟨SAVE⟩ 🕭M ⊇ ✕ 🛜 ✕ 🖥 ▣

BLAINE

◆◆◆ ▼▼◆▼ Best Western Plus Blaine At The National Sports Center H ❀
(763) 792-0750. **$109-$169.** 10580 Baltimore St NE 55449. US 10 exit SR 65, 2 mi n on Central Ave, just e on 107th Ave NE, then just s. Int corridors. **Pets:** Large, other species. $20 daily fee/room. Designated rooms, service with restrictions, crate.
⟨SAVE⟩ 🕭M ✕ 🛜 ✕ 🖥 ▣

▼▼ ◆▼ Super 8 H
(763) 786-8888. **$80-$250.** 9410 Baltimore St NE 55449. Jct SR 65 and 93rd St NE, just ne. Int corridors. **Pets:** Accepted.
🕭M ⊇ 🛜 ✕ 🖥 ▣

BLOOMINGTON

▼▼▼ DoubleTree by Hilton Bloomington-Minneapolis South H

(952) 835-7800. **$99-$189.** 7800 Normandale Blvd 55439. SR 100 exit Industrial Blvd, just sw. Int corridors. **Pets:** Accepted.

▼▼▼ Hilton Minneapolis/Bloomington H ❀

(952) 893-9500. **$129-$429.** 3900 American Blvd W 55437. I-494 exit 6B (France Ave), just sw. Int corridors. **Pets:** $75 deposit/room. Designated rooms, service with restrictions, crate.

▼▼▼ Hilton Minneapolis/St. Paul Airport - Mall of America H

(952) 854-2100. **$109-$249.** 3800 American Blvd E 55425. I-494 exit 1B (34th Ave), just se. Int corridors. **Pets:** Very small. $75 one-time fee/pet. Service with restrictions, supervision.

▲▲▲ ▼▼▼ Hyatt Place Minneapolis Airport-South H ❀

(952) 854-0700. **$99-$299.** 7800 International Dr 55425. I-494 exit 1B (34th Ave), just sw. Int corridors. **Pets:** Medium, other species. $75 one-time fee/room. Service with restrictions, crate.

▼▼ La Quinta Inn & Suites Minneapolis Bloomington West H

(952) 830-1300. **$82-$209.** 5151 American Blvd W 55437. I-494 exit 6B (France Ave), 1 mi w on s frontage road. Int corridors. **Pets:** Accepted.

▲▲▲ ▼▼▼ Radisson Blu Mall of America H

(952) 881-5258. **Call for rates.** 2100 Killebrew Dr 55425. SR 77, 0.3 mi e. Int corridors. **Pets:** Accepted.

▼▼▼ Residence Inn Bloomington by Mall of America H

(952) 876-0900. **$79-$323.** 7850 Bloomington Ave S 55425. I-494 exit 3 (Portland Ave/12th Ave), just se. Int corridors. **Pets:** Accepted.

▲▲▲ ▼▼▼ Sheraton Bloomington Hotel H

(952) 835-1900. **$99-$349.** 5601 W 78th St 55439. SR 100 exit Industrial Blvd, just sw. Int corridors. **Pets:** Accepted.

▼▼▼ Staybridge Suites H ❀

(952) 831-7900. **Call for rates.** 5150 American Blvd W 55437. I-494 exit 6B (France Ave), 1 mi w on s frontage road. Int corridors. **Pets:** Medium. $75 one-time fee/room. Service with restrictions, supervision.

▼▼▼ TownePlace Suites by Marriott Minneapolis Mall of America H ❀

(952) 540-4000. **$93-$365.** 2500 Lindau Ln 55425. I-494 exit 2A (24th Ave S), 0.4 mi s. Int corridors. **Pets:** Medium, other species. $100 one-time fee/room. Service with restrictions.

BROOKLYN CENTER

▲▲▲ ▼▼▼ Best Western Plus Minneapolis-Northwest H

(763) 566-7500. **$90-$160.** 2050 Freeway Blvd 55430. I-94/694 exit 34 (Shingle Creek Pkwy), just nw. Int corridors. **Pets:** Accepted.

BURNSVILLE

▲▲▲ ▼▼▼ Best Western Premier Nicollet Inn H

(952) 435-2100. **$140-$200.** 14201 Nicollet Ave 55337. Jct I-35W and CR 42, just ne. Int corridors. **Pets:** Accepted.

CANBY

▲▲▲ ▼▼▼ Canby Inn & Suites M

(507) 223-6868. **$90-$175.** 127 1st St W 56220. Just w of US 75; center. Int corridors. **Pets:** Accepted.

CHANHASSEN

▼▼ AmericInn of Chanhassen H

(952) 934-3888. **Call for rates.** 570 Pond Promenade 55317. Just se of jct SR 5 and 101 S. Int corridors. **Pets:** Accepted.

COOK

▼▼▼ Ludlow's Island Resort CA ❀

(218) 666-5407. **$195-$875, 90 day notice.** 8166 Ludlow Dr 55723. US 53, 3.5 mi ne on CR 24, 5.1 mi e on CR 78 and 540. Ext corridors. **Pets:** Other species. $20 daily fee/pet.

COON RAPIDS

▼▼ Fairfield Inn by Marriott H

(763) 785-8922. **$79-$213.** 8965 Springbrook Dr 55433. SR 47 exit Coon Rapids Blvd NW, just sw. Int corridors. **Pets:** Accepted.

CROSSLAKE

▼▼ Pine Peaks Lodge and Suites H

(218) 692-7829. **Call for rates.** 14047 Swann Dr 56442. On CR 66. Int corridors. **Pets:** Accepted.

DEERWOOD

▼▼ Country Inn of Deerwood H

(218) 534-3101. **$85-$165.** 23884 Front St 56444. On SR 6 and 210, just e of jct CR 12. Int corridors. **Pets:** Accepted.

DELANO

▼▼▼ GrandStay Hotel & Suites H

(763) 972-4303. **Call for rates.** 395 13th St S 55328. Just e on US 12. Int corridors. **Pets:** $70 daily fee/room. Designated rooms, service with restrictions, crate.

DETROIT LAKES

▼▼ AmericInn Lodge & Suites of Detroit Lakes H

(218) 847-8795. **$85-$250.** 777 Hwy 10 E 56501. 1.4 mi se. Int corridors. **Pets:** Other species. $15 daily fee/room. Service with restrictions.

▲▲▲ ▼▼▼ Best Western Plus Holland House H

(218) 847-4483. **$109-$269.** 615 Hwy 10 E 56501. 1.3 mi se. Ext/int corridors. **Pets:** Large, other species. $15 daily fee/pet. Designated rooms, service with restrictions, supervision.

▼▼▼ Holiday Inn on the Lake H

(218) 847-2121. **Call for rates.** 1155 US 10 E 56501. 2 mi se. Int corridors. **Pets:** Accepted.

DULUTH

▲▲▲ ▼▼▼ AmericInn Hotel & Suites of Duluth South H

(218) 624-1026. **$85-$300.** 185 US 2 55810. 0.8 mi w of jct I-35. Int corridors. **Pets:** $25 one-time fee/room. Designated rooms, service with restrictions, supervision.

▼▼▼ Country Inn & Suites By Carlson Duluth North H ❀

(218) 740-4500. **$139-$249.** 4257 Haines Rd 55811. On CR 91, just n of jct US 53. Int corridors. **Pets:** Other species. $30 one-time fee/room. Service with restrictions, crate.

◆◆◆ ▼◆▼ Days Inn Duluth by the Mall H
(218) 727-3110. **$85-$170.** 909 Cottonwood Ave 55811. Jct US 53 and SR 194, just nw. Int corridors. **Pets:** Accepted. ☟ ⊠ 🖥 🖵

◆◆◆ ▼◆▼ Days Inn Lakewalk H
(218) 728-5141. **$77-$175.** 2211 London Rd 55812. I-35 exit 258 (21st Ave E), just nw. Int corridors. **Pets:** Accepted.
SAVE ☟ ⊠ 🖥 🖵

◆◆◆ ▼◆▼ Fairfield Inn by Marriott H
(218) 723-8607. **$64-$225.** 901 Joshua Ave 55811. Jct US 53 and SR 194. Int corridors. **Pets:** Accepted.
SAVE ECO &M ➔ ☟ ⊠ 🖥 🖵

◆◆◆ ▼◆▼ Fitger's Inn H
(218) 722-8826. **$150-$395.** 600 E Superior St 55802. I-35 exit 256B (Lake Ave), just ne. Int corridors. **Pets:** Other species. Designated rooms, service with restrictions, supervision.
SAVE ¶ ☟ ⊠ 🖥 🖵

▼◆▼ Pier B Resort H
(218) 481-8888. **Call for rates.** 800 W Railroad St 55802. I-35 exit 256B, just se. Int corridors. **Pets:** Accepted.
¶ &M ⊠ ☟ ⊠ 🖥 🖵

▼◆▼ Residence Inn by Marriott H
(218) 279-2885. **$107-$351.** 517 W Central Entrance 55811. Just e on SR 194 from jct US 53. Int corridors. **Pets:** Accepted.
¶ &M ➔ ☟ ⊠ 🖥 🖵

◆◆◆ ▼◆▼ Sheraton Duluth Hotel H ❀
(218) 733-5660. **Call for rates.** 301 E Superior St 55802. I-35W exit 256B (Lake Ave), just nw. Int corridors. **Pets:** Dogs only. Designated rooms, service with restrictions, supervision.
SAVE ¶ &M ➔ ☟ ⊠ 🖥 🖵

EAGAN

◆◆◆ ▼◆▼ Best Western Plus Dakota Ridge H
(651) 452-0100. **$109-$199.** 3450 Washington Dr 55122. I-35E exit 97B (Yankee Doodle Rd), just sw. Int corridors. **Pets:** Accepted.
SAVE ☟ ⊠ 🖥 🖵

▼◆▼ Holiday Inn Express & Suites Eagan-Minneapolis Area H
(651) 452-3400. **Call for rates.** 3434 Washington Dr 55122. I-35E exit 97B (Yankee Doodle Rd), just sw. Int corridors. **Pets:** Accepted.
&M ☟ ⊠ 🖥 🖵

◆◆◆ ▼◆▼ Sonesta ES Suites Minneapolis-St. Paul Airport H
(651) 688-0363. **Call for rates.** 3040 Eagandale Pl 55121. I-35E exit 98 (Lone Oak Rd), just sw. Ext corridors. **Pets:** Accepted.
SAVE ➔ ☟ ⊠ 🖥 🖵

▼◆▼ Staybridge Suites H
(651) 994-7810. **Call for rates.** 4675 Rahncliff Rd 55122. I-35E exit 93 (Cliff Rd), just sw. Int corridors. **Pets:** Accepted.
➔ ☟ ⊠ 🖥 🖵

◆◆◆ ▼◆▼ TownePlace Suites by Marriott Minneapolis St. Paul Airport/Eagan H
(651) 994-4600. **$82-$230.** 3615 Crestridge Dr 55122. I-35E exit 97A (Pilot Knob Rd), just se. Int corridors. **Pets:** Accepted.
SAVE &M ➔ ☟ ⊠ 🖥 🖵

EDEN PRAIRIE

◆◆◆ ▼◆▼ Best Western Eden Prairie Inn H
(952) 829-0888. **$121-$299.** 11500 W 78th St 55344. I-494 exit 11A (Prairie Center Dr), just sw. Int corridors. **Pets:** Dogs only. $20 daily fee/pet. Service with restrictions, crate. SAVE ➔ ☟ ⊠ 🖥 🖵

◆◆◆ ▼◆▼ Hyatt Place Minneapolis/Eden Prairie H
(952) 944-9700. **$99-$299.** 11369 Viking Dr 55344. I-494 exit 11A (Prairie Center Dr), just w. Int corridors. **Pets:** Accepted.
SAVE &M ➔ ☟ ⊠ 🖥 🖵

EDINA

◆◆◆ ▼◆▼ Residence Inn by Marriott Minneapolis-Edina H
(952) 893-9300. **$79-$304.** 3400 Edinborough Way 55435. I-494 exit 6B (France Ave), just n to Minnesota Dr, then 0.4 mi e. Int corridors.
Pets: Accepted. SAVE ☟ ⊠ 🖥 🖵

◆◆◆ ▼◆▼ The Westin Edina Galleria H
(952) 567-5000. **Call for rates.** 3201 Galleria 55435. I-494 exit 6B (France Ave), 1.5 mi n, then just e; at the Galleria. Int corridors.
Pets: Accepted. SAVE ¶ &M ➔ ☟ ⊠ 🖥 🖵

ELY

◆◆◆ ◆ Motel Ely-Budget Host M
(218) 365-3237. **Call for rates.** 1047 E Sheridan St 55731. On SR 1 and 169. Ext corridors. **Pets:** Accepted. SAVE ☟ ⊠ 🖥 🖵

EVELETH

◆◆ Super 8 H
(218) 744-1661. **$80-$110.** 1080 Industrial Park Dr 55734. On US 53, 0.5 mi n of jct SR 37. Int corridors. **Pets:** Accepted.
¶ &M ➔ ⊠ ☟ 🖥 🖵

FAIRMONT

◆◆◆ ▼◆▼ Hampton Inn Fairmont H
(507) 235-2626. **$139-$199.** 100 Hampton Dr 56031. I-90 exit 102 (SR 15), just sw. Int corridors. **Pets:** Accepted.
SAVE &M ➔ ☟ ⊠ 🖥 🖵

▼◆▼ Holiday Inn H
(507) 238-4771. **$134-$219.** 1201 Torgerson Dr 56031. I-90 exit 102 (SR 15), just s. Int corridors. **Pets:** Accepted.
¶ &M ➔ ⊠ ☟ ⊠ 🖥 🖵

▼◆▼ Quality Inn H
(507) 238-5444. **$110-$160.** 2225 N State St 56031. I-90 exit 102 (SR 15), just s. Int corridors. **Pets:** Accepted. ➔ ☟ ⊠ 🖥 🖵

▼◆▼ Super 8 H
(507) 238-9444. **$75-$95.** 1200 Torgerson Dr 56031. I-90 exit 102 (SR 15), just s. Int corridors. **Pets:** Accepted. ☟ 🖥 🖵

FARIBAULT

▼◆▼ Boarders Inn & Suites H
(507) 334-9464. **Call for rates.** 1801 Lavender Dr 55021. I-35 exit 59 (SR 21), just se. Int corridors. **Pets:** Accepted.
&M ➔ ⊠ ☟ ⊠ 🖥 🖵

FERGUS FALLS

▼◆▼ AmericInn Lodge & Suites of Fergus Falls H
(218) 739-3900. **Call for rates.** 526 Western Ave N 56537. I-94 exit 54 (SR 210), just se. Int corridors. **Pets:** Other species. $10 one-time fee/room. Designated rooms, service with restrictions, crate.
&M ➔ ⊠ ☟ ⊠ 🖥 🖵

FOREST LAKE

▼◆▼ Country Inn & Suites By Carlson H
(651) 982-9799. **$89-$120.** 1954 Broadway Ave W 55025. I-35 exit 131 (CR 2), just sw. Int corridors. **Pets:** Accepted.
&M ➔ ☟ ⊠ 🖥 🖵

FOSSTON

▼▼▼ **LePier Lodge** ☐

(218) 435-1088. **Call for rates.** 108 S Amber Ave 56542. US 2, 0.5 mi e. Int corridors. **Pets:** Dogs only. $100 deposit/room, $5 daily fee/pet. Service with restrictions, supervision. 📶 ☒ ⬜ 💻

GLENWOOD

▼▼▼ **Oak Tree Inn Glenwood** ☐

(320) 634-1944. **Call for rates.** 100 15th St SE 56334. On SR 28 at jct SR 55. Int corridors. **Pets:** Accepted. 🍴 ⬜ 📶 ☒ ⬜ 💻

GRAND MARAIS

▲▲▲ ▼▼▼ **Best Western Plus Superior Inn** ☐

(218) 387-2240. **$129-$349.** 104 1st Ave E 55604. SR 61, just ne of center. Int corridors. **Pets:** Large, other species. $15 daily fee/pet. Designated rooms, service with restrictions, supervision.

[SAVE] 📶 ☒ ⬜ 💻

▼▼ **Gunflint Lodge** 🄥🄷 ✿

(218) 388-2294. **$99-$449, 30 day notice.** 143 S Gunflint Lake 55604. 43 mi nw on CR 12 (Gunflint Tr) from jct SR 61; 0.8 mi e on CR 50. Ext corridors. **Pets:** Dogs only. $20 daily fee/pet. Service with restrictions. 🍴 ⬜ ☒ 📶 ☒ 🅺 ☒ ⬜ 💻

▼▼ **Nor'Wester Lodge and Outfitter** 🄲🄰 ✿

(218) 388-2252. **$119-$289, 60 day notice.** 7778 Gunflint Tr 55604. 30 mi nw on CR 12 from jct SR 61. Ext corridors. **Pets:** Dogs only. $15 daily fee/pet. No service, supervision.

🍴 ☒ 📶 ☒ 🅺 🅦 ☒ ⬜ 💻

▼ **Outpost Motel** 🄼

(218) 387-1833. **$59-$104.** 2935 SR 61 E 55604. 9 mi ne. Ext corridors. **Pets:** Other species. $10 daily fee/pet. Service with restrictions, supervision. 🍴 📶 ☒ 🅺 ⬜ 💻

GRAND RAPIDS

▼▼ **AmericInn of Grand Rapids** ☐ ✿

(218) 326-8999. **Call for rates.** 1812 S Pokegama Ave 55744. On US 169, 1.6 mi s of jct US 2. Int corridors. **Pets:** Dogs only. $25 one-time fee/pet. Designated rooms, service with restrictions, supervision.

🍴 ⬜ 📶 ☒ ⬜ 💻

▲▲▲ ▼▼ **Country Inn By Carlson** ☐ ✿

(218) 327-4960. **$99-$150.** 2601 Pokegama Ave S 55744. On US 169, 1.8 mi s of jct US 2. Int corridors. **Pets:** Medium, dogs only. Supervision. [SAVE] ⬜ ☒ 📶 ☒ ⬜ 💻

▲▲▲ ▼▼ **Super 8** ☐

(218) 327-1108. **$90-$102.** 1702 S Pokegama Ave 55744. On US 169, 1.5 mi s of jct US 2. Int corridors. **Pets:** Other species. $100 deposit/pet. Service with restrictions, supervision.

[SAVE] ⬜ 📶 ☒ ⬜ 💻

HOYT LAKES

▼▼ **Country Inn of Hoyt Lakes** ☐

(218) 225-3555. **Call for rates.** 99 Kennedy Memorial Dr 55750. On SR 110. Int corridors. **Pets:** Large, other species. $25 one-time fee/room. Service with restrictions, supervision.

🍴 ☒ ☒ 📶 ☒ ⬜ 💻

HUTCHINSON

▼▼ **AmericInn of Hutchinson** ☐

(320) 587-5515. **Call for rates.** 1115 Hwy 7 E 55350. On SR 7, 1 mi e of jct SR 15. Int corridors. **Pets:** Accepted.

🍴 ⬜ ☒ ☒ 📶 ☒ ⬜ 💻

INVER GROVE HEIGHTS

▲▲▲ ▼▼▼ **Microtel Inn & Suites by Wyndham Inver Grove Heights/Minneapolis** ☐

(651) 552-0555. **$65-$140.** 5681 Bishop Ave 55076. US 52 exit Upper 55th St E, just ne. Int corridors. **Pets:** Small, dogs only. $25 daily fee/pet. Designated rooms, service with restrictions, supervision.

[SAVE] ⬜ 📶 ☒ ⬜ 💻

JACKSON

▲▲▲ ▼▼ **AmericInn Lodge & Suites of Jackson** ☐

(507) 847-2444. **$129-$229, 7 day notice.** 110 Belmont Ln 56143. I-90 exit 73 (US 71), just sw. Int corridors. **Pets:** Small, dogs only. $50 deposit/room, $25 daily fee/pet. Designated rooms, service with restrictions, supervision. [SAVE] ⬜ ☒ 📶 ☒ ⬜ 💻

LAKEVILLE

▼▼▼ **Holiday Inn & Suites** ☐

(952) 469-1134. **Call for rates.** 20800 Kenrick Ave 55044. I-35 exit 81 (CR 70), just ne. Int corridors. **Pets:** Accepted.

🍴 ⬜ ☒ ☒ 📶 ☒ ⬜ 💻

LITTLE FALLS

▼▼ **AmericInn Lodge & Suites of Little Falls** ☐

(320) 632-1964. **Call for rates.** 306 Lemieur St SE 56345. Just se of jct US 10 and SR 27. Int corridors. **Pets:** Accepted.

⬜ ☒ 📶 ☒ ⬜ 💻

LUVERNE

▲▲▲ ▼▼▼ **GrandStay Hotel & Suites of Luverne** ☐

(507) 449-4949. **Call for rates.** 908 S Kniss Ave 56156. I-90 exit 12 (US 75), just n. Int corridors. **Pets:** Accepted.

[SAVE] ⬜ ☒ 📶 ☒ ⬜ 💻

MAHNOMEN

▲▲▲ ▼▼▼ **Shooting Star Casino Hotel & Events Center** ☐

(218) 935-2701. **Call for rates.** 777 Casino Rd 56557. 1 mi s on SR 59. Int corridors. **Pets:** Accepted.

[SAVE] 🍴 ⬜ ☒ ☒ 📶 ⬜ 💻

MANKATO

▲▲▲ ▼▼▼▼ **Best Western Hotel & Restaurant** ☐

(507) 625-9333. **$102-$160.** 1111 Range St 56003. 0.6 mi s of jct US 169 and 14. Int corridors. **Pets:** Large. $10 daily fee/pet. Designated rooms, service with restrictions, supervision.

[SAVE] 🍴 ☒ ☒ 📶 ☒ ⬜ 💻

▼▼▼ **Holiday Inn Express & Suites** ☐

(507) 388-1880. **Call for rates.** 2051 Adams St 56001. Jct US 14 and SR 22, 0.4 mi s, then just e. Int corridors. **Pets:** Accepted.

⬜ ☒ ☒ 📶 ☒ ⬜ 💻

▼▼ **Mankato City Center Hotel** ☐

(507) 345-1234. **Call for rates.** 101 E Main St 56001. Main St at Riverfront Dr; downtown. Int corridors. **Pets:** Accepted.

🍴 ⬜ ☒ ☒ 📶 ☒ ⬜ 💻

▼▼ **Microtel Inn & Suites by Wyndham Mankato** ☐ ✿

(507) 388-2818. **$66-$114.** 200 St. Andrews Dr 56001. US 14 exit CR 3, 0.4 mi n. Int corridors. **Pets:** Other species. $15 one-time fee/room. Service with restrictions, supervision. ⬜ 📶 ⬜ 💻

MAPLE GROVE

▼▼▼ **Staybridge Suites Minneapolis-Maple Grove** ☐

(763) 494-8856. **Call for rates.** 7821 Elm Creek Blvd N 55369. Just ne of jct I-94/494/694. Int corridors. **Pets:** Accepted.

⬜ ☒ 📶 ☒ ⬜ 💻

MARSHALL

▼▼ AmericInn Lodge & Suites of Marshall H
(507) 537-9424. **Call for rates.** 1406 E Lyon St 56258. Just se on US 59 from jct SR 23. Int corridors. **Pets:** Accepted.

▼▼ Quality Inn H
(507) 532-3070. **$90-$210.** 1511 E College Dr 56258. SR 19, just w of jct SR 23. Int corridors. **Pets:** $10 daily fee/pet. Service with restrictions, crate.

▼▼ Super 8 M
(507) 537-1461. **$68-$96.** 1106 E Main St 56258. 0.3 mi se on US 59 from jct SR 23. Int corridors. **Pets:** Accepted.

MINNEAPOLIS (Restaurants p. 617)

▼▼▼ Aloft Minneapolis H ❖
(612) 455-8400. **Call for rates.** 900 Washington Ave S 55415. At 9th Ave. Int corridors. **Pets:** Medium, dogs only.

▼▼▼ Best Western Plus The Normandy Inn & Suites H
(612) 370-1400. **$99-$269.** 405 S 8th St 55404. Corner of S 8th St and S 4th Ave. Int corridors. **Pets:** Dogs only. $10 daily fee/pet. Designated rooms, service with restrictions, supervision.

▼▼▼ The Commons Hotel H
(612) 379-8888. **$139-$559.** 615 Washington Ave SE 55414. I-35W exit 18, 0.8 mi e to Oak St, just s to Washington Ave, then just w. Int corridors. **Pets:** Accepted.

▼▼▼ Courtyard by Marriott H
(612) 333-4646. **$93-$345.** 1500 Washington Ave S 55454. At S 15th Ave. Int corridors. **Pets:** Accepted.

▼▼ Days Hotel on University H
(612) 623-3999. **$75-$459.** 2407 University Ave SE 55414. I-35W exit University Ave, 1 mi se. Int corridors. **Pets:** $20 one-time fee/room. Designated rooms, service with restrictions, supervision.

▼▼▼ The Grand Hotel Minneapolis-A Kimpton Hotel H
(612) 288-8888. **$199-$699.** 615 2nd Ave S 55402. Between S 6th and 7th sts. Int corridors. **Pets:** Accepted.

▼▼▼ Hampton Inn and Suites Minneapolis University Area H
(612) 259-8797. **Call for rates.** 2812 University Ave SE 55414. On CR 36, 0.8 mi w of jct SR 280. Int corridors. **Pets:** Accepted.

▼▼▼ Hilton Minneapolis H
(612) 376-1000. **$89-$359.** 1001 Marquette Ave S 55403. Between S 10th and S 11th sts. Int corridors. **Pets:** Accepted.

▼▼▼ Hotel Ivy, A Luxury Collection Hotel, Minneapolis H ❖
(612) 746-4600. **$209-$699.** 201 S 11th St 55403. Jct 2nd Ave. Int corridors. **Pets:** Medium. $50 one-time fee/room. Service with restrictions, supervision.

▼▼▼ The Hotel Minneapolis, Autograph Collection H
(612) 340-2000. **$76-$463.** 215 4th St S 55401. On 2nd Ave. Int corridors. **Pets:** Accepted.

▼▼▼ Hyatt Regency Minneapolis H
(612) 370-1234. **$89-$399.** 1300 Nicollet Mall 55403. Jct Grant St. Int corridors. **Pets:** Accepted.

▼▼▼ Loews Minneapolis Hotel H ❖
(612) 677-1100. **$164-$289.** 601 1st Ave N 55403. Between S 6th and 7th sts. Int corridors. **Pets:** Other species. $100 one-time fee/room. Service with restrictions, crate.

▼▼▼ The Marquette Hotel H
(612) 333-4545. **$129-$499.** 710 Marquette Ave 55402. At S 7th St. Int corridors. **Pets:** Accepted.

▼▼▼ Minneapolis Marriott City Center H
(612) 349-4000. **$84-$472.** 30 S 7th St 55402. Between Hennepin and Nicollet aves; in City Center Shopping Complex. Int corridors. **Pets:** Accepted.

▼▼▼ Radisson Blu Minneapolis Downtown H ❖
(612) 339-4900. **Call for rates.** 35 S 7th St 55402. Between Nicollet and Hennepin aves. Int corridors. **Pets:** Medium, dogs only. $100 one-time fee/room. Service with restrictions, crate.

▼▼▼ Ramada Plaza Minneapolis H
(612) 331-1900. **$109-$219.** 1330 Industrial Blvd NE 55413. I-35W exit 22 (Industrial Blvd), 3 mi n of downtown. Int corridors. **Pets:** Accepted.

▼▼▼ The Renaissance Minneapolis Hotel at the Depot H
(612) 375-1700. **$69-$395.** 225 3rd Ave S 55401. At Washington Ave. Int corridors. **Pets:** Accepted.

▼▼▼ The Residence Inn Minneapolis Downtown at The Depot H
(612) 340-1300. **$77-$428.** 425 S 2nd St 55401. At 5th Ave S. Int corridors. **Pets:** Accepted.

▼▼ TownePlace Suites by Marriott Minneapolis Downtown/North Loop H
(612) 340-1000. **$74-$333.** 525 N 2nd St 55401. At N 5th Ave. Int corridors. **Pets:** Accepted.

▼▼▼ The Westin Minneapolis H
(612) 333-4006. **$99-$599.** 88 S 6th St 55402. At Marquette Ave. Int corridors. **Pets:** Accepted.

▼▼▼ W Minneapolis-The Foshay H
(612) 215-3700. **$159-$799.** 821 Marquette Ave 55402. Between 9th and 8th sts. Int corridors. **Pets:** Accepted.

MINNETONKA

▼▼ La Quinta Inn & Suites H
(952) 541-1094. **$79-$199.** 10420 Wayzata Blvd 55305. I-394 exit 2 (Hopkins Crossroad/CR 73), 0.4 mi e on north frontage road. Int corridors. **Pets:** Accepted.

▼▼▼ Minneapolis Marriott-Southwest H
(952) 935-5500. **$63-$296.** 5801 Opus Pkwy 55343. US 169 exit Bren Rd, just w. Int corridors. **Pets:** Medium. $75 one-time fee/pet. Service with restrictions, crate.

▼▼▼ Sheraton Minneapolis West Hotel H
(952) 593-0000. **$99-$399.** 12201 Ridgedale Dr 55305. I-394 exit 1D (Ridgedale Dr), 0.3 mi s. Int corridors. **Pets:** Accepted.

MONTEVIDEO

▼▼▼ Crossings by GrandStay Inn & Suites **H**

(320) 269-8000. **$105-$197.** 1805 E SR 7 56265. On SR 7; east of downtown. Int corridors. **Pets:** $200 deposit/room, $20 daily fee/pet. Designated rooms, service with restrictions, supervision.

MONTICELLO

A ▼▼▼ Best Western Chelsea Inn & Suites **H**

(763) 271-8880. **$110-$150.** 89 Chelsea Rd 55362. I-94 exit 193 (SR 25), 0.3 mi se. Int corridors. **Pets:** Accepted.

MOORHEAD

▼▼ Travelodge & Suites **H**

(218) 233-5333. **$50-$150.** 3027 S Frontage Rd 56560. Just s of US 10 E; east of downtown. Int corridors. **Pets:** Accepted.

MOUNTAIN IRON

▼▼ AmericInn Lodge & Suites of Virginia **H**

(218) 741-7839. **Call for rates.** 5480 Mountain Iron Dr 55792. On US 53, just s of jct US 169. Int corridors. **Pets:** Accepted.

▼▼▼ Holiday Inn Express & Suites **H**

(218) 741-7411. **$129-$189.** 8570 Rock Ridge Dr 55768. On US 169, just w of jct US 53. Int corridors. **Pets:** Large, other species. $25 daily fee/room. Service with restrictions, supervision.

NEW BRIGHTON

▼▼▼ Homewood Suites New Brighton **H**

(651) 631-8002. **$109-$209.** 1815 Old Hwy 8 NW 55112. I-35W exit 28A (CR 96), just w. Int corridors. **Pets:** $150 one-time fee/room, $75 daily fee/room. Service with restrictions, crate.

NEW ULM

A ▼▼▼ Best Western Plus New Ulm **H**

(507) 359-2941. **$139-$164.** 2101 S Broadway 56073. 1.8 mi se on SR 15. Int corridors. **Pets:** Accepted.

NORTH BRANCH

▼▼ AmericInn Lodge & Suites of North Branch **H**

(651) 674-8627. **$108.** 38675 14th Ave 55056. I-35 exit 147 (SR 95), just se. Int corridors. **Pets:** $30 one-time fee/room. Service with restrictions, supervision.

NORTHFIELD

▼▼ AmericInn Lodge & Suites of Northfield **H**

(507) 645-7761. **Call for rates.** 1320 Bollenbacher Dr 55057. On SR 3, 1 mi s of jct SR 19. Int corridors. **Pets:** Accepted.

OAK PARK HEIGHTS

▼▼ AmericInn Lodge & Suites of Oak Park Heights **H**

(651) 275-0980. **Call for rates.** 13025 60th St N 55082. SR 36 at Stillwater Blvd (CR 5), just se. Int corridors. **Pets:** Accepted.

ORR

▼ North Country Inn **M**

(218) 757-3778. **Call for rates.** 4483 Hwy 53 55771. 0.3 mi s on US 53. Int corridors. **Pets:** Accepted.

OTTERTAIL

▼▼▼ Thumper Pond Resort **H**

(218) 367-2000. **Call for rates.** 300 Thumper Lodge Rd 56571. Jct SR 108 and 78. Int corridors. **Pets:** Accepted.

OWATONNA

▼▼ AmericInn of Owatonna **H**

(507) 455-1142. **Call for rates.** 245 Florence Ave 55060. I-35 exit 41 (Bridge St), 0.3 mi ne. Int corridors. **Pets:** Accepted.

▼▼▼ Comfort Inn **H**

(507) 444-0818. **$102-$189.** 2345 43rd St NW 55060. I-35 exit 45 (Clinton Falls), just sw. Int corridors. **Pets:** Accepted.

PARKERS PRAIRIE

A ▼▼▼ Crossings by GrandStay Inn & Suites of Parkers Prairie **H** 🐾

(218) 338-3380. **$62-$135.** 211 W Main St 56361. On SR 235 and CR 38, just w of jct SR 29. Int corridors. **Pets:** Large. $25 daily fee/room. Designated rooms, service with restrictions, crate.

PARK RAPIDS

▼▼ C'mon Inn **H**

(218) 732-1471. **Call for rates.** 1009 1st St E 56470. On SR 34, 0.8 mi e of jct US 71. Int corridors. **Pets:** Accepted.

PAYNESVILLE

▼▼ Paynesville Inn & Suites **H**

(320) 243-4146. **$90-$99.** 700 Diekmann Dr 56362. On SR 23 business route, 0.3 mi s of jct SR 55. Int corridors. **Pets:** Accepted.

PEQUOT LAKES

▼▼ AmericInn Lodge & Suites of Pequot Lakes **H**

(218) 568-8400. **Call for rates.** 32912 Paul Bunyan Trail Dr 56472. On SR 371, 2 mi n of downtown. Int corridors. **Pets:** Accepted.

PERHAM

▼ Super 8-Perham **H**

(218) 346-7888. **$60-$110.** 106 Jake St SE 56573. SR 78, just nw of jct US 10. Int corridors. **Pets:** Accepted.

PIPESTONE

▼▼ Crossings by GrandStay Inn & Suites **H**

(507) 562-1100. **$85-$110.** 915 7th St SE 56164. Just w of jct SR 30 and US 75 S. Int corridors. **Pets:** Other species. $25 one-time fee/room. Designated rooms, service with restrictions.

PLYMOUTH

▼▼ Comfort Inn **H**

(763) 559-1222. **$110-$190.** 3000 Harbor Ln 55447. I-494 exit 22 (SR 55), 0.3 mi nw. Int corridors. **Pets:** Accepted.

▼▼▼ Crowne Plaza Minneapolis West **H**

(763) 559-6600. **$99-$299.** 3131 Campus Dr 55441. I-494 exit 22 (SR 55), just e to CR 61 (Northwest Blvd), then 0.8 mi nw. Int corridors. **Pets:** Accepted.

▼▼▼ Residence Inn by Marriott 🅷
(763) 577-1600. **$80-$285.** 2750 Annapolis Cir 55441. I-494 exit 22 (SR 55), just e to CR 61, then just nw. Int corridors. **Pets:** Accepted.
🐾 🛜 ✕ 🔌 ▥

RICHFIELD
▼▼▼ Candlewood Suites 🅷
(612) 869-7704. **Call for rates.** 351 W 77th St 55423. I-494 exit 4B (Lyndale Ave), just ne. Int corridors. **Pets:** $15 one-time fee/room, $10 daily fee/room. Service with restrictions, supervision.
🍴 🅼 🛜 ✕ 🔌 ▥

◢◣ ▼▼▼ Four Points by Sheraton Mall of America Minneapolis Airport 🅷
(612) 861-1000. **Call for rates.** 7745 Lyndale Ave S 55423. I-494 exit 4B (Lyndale Ave), just ne. Int corridors. **Pets:** Accepted.
SAVE 🍴 🐾 🛜 ✕ 🔌 ▥

ROCHESTER
▼▼ Aspen Select 🅷
(507) 288-2671. **Call for rates.** 1215 2nd St SW 55902. Just e of US 52, 14 and 63. Int corridors. **Pets:** Accepted. 🅼 🛜 ✕ 🔌 ▥

▼▼▼ Aspen Suites 🅷
(507) 289-6600. **$125-$230.** 1211 2nd St SW 55902. 0.5 mi e of US 52, 14 and 63. Int corridors. **Pets:** Accepted.
🅼 🐾 🗙 🛜 ✕ 🔌 ▥

▼▼▼ Holiday Inn Express & Suites 🅷
(507) 226-8700. **Call for rates.** 155 16th Ave SW 55902. US 52 exit 55B (2nd St SW), just ne. Int corridors. **Pets:** Accepted.
🅼 🛜 ✕ 🔌 ▥

▼▼▼ La Quinta Inn & Suites 🅷
(507) 289-4200. **$97-$229.** 4353 Canal Pl SE 55904. US 63 (Broadway) exit 40th St S, just se. Int corridors. **Pets:** Accepted.
🅼 🛜 ✕ 🔌 ▥

▼▼▼ Marriott Hotel 🅷
(507) 280-6000. **$109-$356.** 101 1st Ave SW 55902. Just e of Mayo Clinic; downtown. Int corridors. **Pets:** Accepted.
🍴 🐾 🛜 ✕ 🔌 ▥

▼▼ Microtel Inn & Suites by Wyndham Rochester South 🅷
(507) 289-4900. **$66-$79.** 4165 Main Ave SE 55904. US 63 (Broadway) exit 40th St, just e. Int corridors. **Pets:** Designated rooms, service with restrictions. 🍴 🅼 🛜 ✕ 🔌 ▥

▼▼▼ Residence Inn by Marriott 🅷
(507) 292-1400. **$98-$282.** 441 W Center St 55902. Just n of Mayo Clinic; downtown. Int corridors. **Pets:** Accepted.
🅼 🛜 ✕ 🔌 ▥

▼▼▼ Staybridge Suites Rochester 🅷
(507) 280-9000. **Call for rates.** 2350 Commerce Dr NW 55901. 0.7 mi n on CR 22 (W Circle Dr NW) from jct US 14, just e on 22nd St NW. Int corridors. **Pets:** Accepted. 🅼 🛜 ✕ 🔌 ▥

▼▼ TownePlace Suites by Marriott 🅷
(507) 281-1200. **$84-$197.** 2829 NW 43rd St 55901. US 52 exit 58 (41st St NW) just nw. Int corridors. **Pets:** $100 one-time fee/room. Service with restrictions, supervision. 🅼 🐾 🛜 ✕ 🔌 ▥

ROGERS
▼▼ AmericInn Lodge & Suites of Rogers 🅷
(763) 428-4346. **Call for rates.** 21800 Industrial Blvd 55374. I-94 exit 207A (SR 101), just nw. Int corridors. **Pets:** Accepted.
🅼 🐾 🛜 ✕ 🔌 ▥

◢◣ ▼▼▼ Hampton Inn & Suites 🅷
(763) 425-0044. **$109-$159.** 13550 Commerce Blvd 55374. I-94 exit 207A (SR 101), 0.4 mi se. Int corridors. **Pets:** Accepted.
SAVE 🍴 🅼 🐾 🛜 ✕ 🔌 ▥

ROSEAU
◢◣ ▼▼▼ AmericInn Lodge & Suites of Roseau 🅷
(218) 463-1045. **$90-$140.** 1110 3rd St NW 56751. 1 mi w on SR 11. Int corridors. **Pets:** Other species. $25 one-time fee/room. Service with restrictions. SAVE 🍴 🅼 🐾 🗙 🛜 ✕ 🔌 ▥

ROSEVILLE
▼▼▼ Home2 Suites by Hilton Roseville Minneapolis 🅷
(651) 925-8600. **$119-$219.** 2020 Iona Ln W 55113. I-35W exit 24 (CR C), just ne. Int corridors. **Pets:** Accepted.
🍴 🅼 🛜 ✕ 🔌 ▥

▼▼▼ Residence Inn by Marriott 🅷
(651) 636-0680. **$82-$333.** 2985 Centre Pointe Dr 55113. I-35W exit 25A (CR D), just se. Int corridors. **Pets:** Accepted.
🍴 🅼 🛜 ✕ 🔌 ▥

ST. CLOUD
▼▼▼ AmericInn Lodge & Suites of St. Cloud 🅷
(320) 253-6337. **Call for rates.** 4385 Clearwater Rd 56301. I-94 exit 171 (CR 75), just ne. Int corridors. **Pets:** Accepted.
🐾 🛜 ✕ 🔌 ▥

◢◣ ▼▼▼ Best Western Plus Kelly Inn 🅷
(320) 253-0606. **$110-$150.** 100 4th Ave S 56301. On SR 23; center. Int corridors. **Pets:** Service with restrictions, supervision.
SAVE 🍴 🅼 🐾 🛜 ✕ 🔌 ▥

▼▼▼ GrandStay Residential Suites Hotel 🅷
(320) 251-5400. **$89-$200.** 213 6th Ave S 56301. On SR 23; center. Int corridors. **Pets:** Dogs only. $200 deposit/room, $20 daily fee/pet. Service with restrictions, crate. 🅼 🐾 🛜 ✕ 🔌 ▥

◢◣ ▼▼▼ Holiday Inn Express & Suites 🅷 🐾
(320) 240-8000. **$90-$180.** 4322 Clearwater Rd 56301. I-94 exit 171 (CR 75), just ne. Int corridors. **Pets:** Dogs only. $20 daily fee/room. Designated rooms, service with restrictions, supervision.
SAVE 🐾 🛜 ✕ 🔌 ▥

ST. JAMES
▼▼ Super 8 St. James 🅷
(507) 375-4708. **$73-$94.** 1210 Heckman Ct 56081. SR 60 exit 30/730th Ave, just n, then just e. Int corridors. **Pets:** Accepted.
🅼 🛜 🔌 ▥

ST. LOUIS PARK
◢◣ ▼▼▼ DoubleTree by Hilton Hotel Minneapolis-Park Place 🅷
(952) 542-8600. **$109-$319.** 1500 Park Place Blvd 55416. I-394 exit 5A (Park Place Blvd), just sw. Int corridors. **Pets:** Medium. $50 one-time fee/room. Service with restrictions. SAVE 🍴 🐾 🛜 ✕ 🔌 ▥

▼▼▼ Homewood Suites St. Louis Park/Minneapolis West 🅷
(952) 544-0495. **$99-$259.** 5305 Wayzata Blvd 55416. I-394 exit 5 (Park Place Blvd), just se. Int corridors. **Pets:** Accepted.
🅼 🐾 🛜 ✕ 🔌 ▥

◢◣ ▼▼▼ TownePlace Suites by Marriott Minneapolis West St. Louis Park 🅷
(952) 847-6900. **$66-$284.** 1400 Zarthan Ave S 55416. I-394 exit 5 (Park Place Blvd), just sw. Int corridors. **Pets:** Accepted.
SAVE 🐾 🛜 ✕ 🔌 ▥

ST. PAUL

Best Western Plus Bandana Square H
(651) 647-1637. **$129-$229.** 1010 Bandana Blvd W 55108. I-94 exit
239B (Lexington Pkwy), 1.3 mi n, then 0.3 mi w. Int corridors.
Pets: Large, other species. $10 daily fee/room. Service with restrictions,
supervision. SAVE 🏊 🐾 🚫 🛜 ✕ 🛏 💻

Hyatt Place St. Paul Downtown H
(651) 647-5000. **Call for rates.** 180 Kellogg Blvd E 55101. Between
Sibley and Jackson sts; downtown. Int corridors. **Pets:** Accepted.
SAVE 🍴 🐾 🛜 ✕ 🛏 💻

SAUK CENTRE

**AmericInn Lodge & Suites of Sauk
Centre** H 🐾
(320) 352-2800. **$94-$149.** 1230 Timberlane Dr 56378. I-94 exit 127
(US 71), just ne. Int corridors. **Pets:** Medium, dogs only. $15 daily fee/
pet. Designated rooms, service with restrictions, crate.
🍴 🐾 🚫 🛜 ✕ 🛏 💻

SHAKOPEE

AmericInn Lodge & Suites H
(952) 445-6775. **Call for rates.** 4100 12th Ave E 55379. US 169 exit
CR 83 (Canterbury Rd), just ne. Int corridors. **Pets:** Accepted.
SAVE 🐾 🛜 ✕ 🛏 💻

Best Western Shakopee Inn H
(952) 445-9779. **$100-$180.** 511 S Marschall Rd 55379. On CR 17, just
s of jct CR 17. Int corridors. **Pets:** Accepted.
SAVE ECO 🐾 🚫 🛜 ✕ 🛏 💻

SHOREVIEW

Country Inn & Suites By Carlson H
(651) 784-6000. **Call for rates.** 5995 Rice Creek Pkwy 55126. I-35W
exit 85th Ave (CR J), just se. Int corridors. **Pets:** Accepted.
🐾 🐾 🛜 ✕ 🛏 💻

SILVER BAY

AmericInn Lodge & Suites of Silver Bay H
(218) 226-4300. **$120-$200.** 150 Mensing Dr 55614. On SR 61, 0.5 mi
ne of jct Outer Dr. Int corridors. **Pets:** Dogs only. $20 daily fee/pet.
Designated rooms, service with restrictions, supervision.
🍴 🐾 🚫 🛜 ✕ 🛏 💻

STILLWATER

GrandStay Hotel & Suites Stillwater H
(651) 430-2699. **Call for rates.** 2200 W Frontage Rd 55082. SR 36 at
Washington Ave, just nw. Int corridors. **Pets:** Accepted.
🐾 🐾 🛜 ✕ 🛏 💻

THIEF RIVER FALLS

C'mon Inn Hotel & Suites H
(218) 681-3000. **Call for rates.** 1586 US 59 S 56701. 1 mi se. Int corridors. **Pets:** Accepted. 🐾 🛜 ✕ 🛏 💻

TOFTE

AmericInn Lodge & Suites of Tofte H
(218) 663-7899. **$80-$180.** 7231 W SR 61 55615. On SR 61. Int corridors. **Pets:** $20 daily fee/room. Designated rooms, service with restric-
tions, crate. SAVE 🐾 🚫 🛜 ✕ 🛏 💻

Bluefin Bay on Lake Superior CO
(218) 663-7296. **Call for rates.** 7192 W Hwy 61 55615. On SR 61. Ext
corridors. **Pets:** Accepted. 🍴 🐾 🚫 🛜 ✕ 🛏 💻

Surfside on Lake Superior CO
(218) 663-6870. **Call for rates.** 10 Surfside Dr 55615. On SR 61. Ext
corridors. **Pets:** Accepted. 🍴 🐾 🚫 🛜 ✕ 🛏 💻

TWO HARBORS

AmericInn Lodge & Suites of Two Harbors H
(218) 834-3000. **Call for rates.** 1088 SR 61 N 55616. Jct CR 11. Int
corridors. **Pets:** Medium, dogs only. $15 daily fee/room. Designated
rooms, service with restrictions, supervision.
🍴 🐾 🐾 🚫 🛜 ✕ 🛏 💻

Country Inn of Two Harbors M 🐾
(218) 834-5557. **$94-$204.** 1204 7th Ave 55616. On SR 61, 0.5 mi s of
center. Int corridors. **Pets:** Medium, dogs only. $15 daily fee/pet. Desig-
nated rooms, service with restrictions, supervision.
SAVE 🐾 🐾 🚫 🛜 ✕ 🛏 💻

Superior Shores Resort & Conference Center CO
(218) 834-5671. **$79-$849, 14 day notice.** 1521 Superior Shores Dr
55616. On SR 61, 1.5 mi n of center. Ext/int corridors. **Pets:** Accepted.
🍴 🐾 🚫 🛜 ✕ 🛏 💻

VIRGINIA

Pine View Inn M
(218) 741-8918. **$70-$85.** 903 N 17th St 55792. 0.5 mi n on US 53
from jct US 169, 0.7 mi e on 9th St N, then 0.5 mi n. Ext corridors.
Pets: Dogs only. $10 daily fee/room. Designated rooms, supervision.
SAVE 🍴 🛜 🛏 💻

WABASHA

AmericInn Lodge & Suites of Wabasha H
(651) 565-5366. **$96-$150.** 150 Commerce Dr 55981. Jct US 61 and
SR 60. Int corridors. **Pets:** Accepted.
🍴 🐾 🐾 🚫 🛜 ✕ 🛏 💻

WACONIA

AmericInn Lodge & Suites of Waconia H
(952) 442-8787. **Call for rates.** 550 Cherry Dr 55387. Just n of SR 5;
center. Int corridors. **Pets:** Accepted. 🐾 🛜 ✕ 🛏 💻

WADENA

AmericInn Lodge & Suites of Wadena H
(218) 631-1580. **Call for rates.** 695 Jefferson St N 56482. On US 71,
0.5 mi n of jct US 10. Int corridors. **Pets:** Accepted.
🍴 🐾 🐾 🚫 🛜 ✕ 🛏 💻

WALKER

Country Inn Walker H
(218) 547-1400. **$99-$219.** 442 Walker Bay Blvd 56484. 1 mi s on SR
371. Int corridors. **Pets:** Accepted. 🐾 🐾 🛜 ✕ 🛏 💻

WHITE BEAR LAKE

AmericInn Lodge & Suites of White Bear Lake H
(651) 429-7131. **Call for rates.** 4675 White Bear Pkwy 55110. I-35E
exit 117 (SR 96), just ne. Int corridors. **Pets:** Medium, dogs only. $10
daily fee/pet. Designated rooms, service with restrictions, supervision.
🍴 🐾 🐾 🛜 ✕ 🛏 💻

**Best Western Plus White Bear Country
Inn** H
(651) 429-5393. **$90-$150.** 4940 N Hwy 61 55110. 0.8 mi n of jct SR
96. Int corridors. **Pets:** Accepted.
SAVE 🍴 🐾 🐾 🚫 🛜 ✕ 🛏 💻

WILLMAR

Best Western Plus Willmar H
(320) 235-6060. **$119-$169.** 2100 US 12 E 56201. 1.8 mi e. Int corridors. **Pets:** Accepted. SAVE 🍴 🐾 🐾 🛜 ✕ 🛏 💻

Days Inn Willmar H
(320) 231-1275. **$70-$100.** 225 28th St SE 56201. On US 12 at jct US
71/SR 23 bypass. Int corridors. **Pets:** Accepted.
🍴 🛜 ✕ 🛏 💻

WINONA

▼▼▼▼ **Holiday Inn Express & Suites** ⊞
(507) 474-1700. **Call for rates.** 1128 Homer Rd 55987. Jct SR 43, just sw. Int corridors. **Pets:** Accepted. 🅼 🛏 ⊠ 📶 ⊠ 📱 💻

WOODBURY

▼▼▼ **Residence Inn by Marriott St. Paul Woodbury** ⊞
(651) 731-9010. **$125-$209.** 205 Radio Dr 55125. I-94 exit 250 (Radio Drive/CR13), just se. Int corridors. **Pets:** Accepted.
🅼 📶 ⊠ 📱 💻

WORTHINGTON

▼▼▼ **AmericInn Lodge & Suites of Worthington** ⊞
(507) 376-4500. **Call for rates.** 1475 Darling Dr 56187. I-90 exit 43 (US 59), just se. Int corridors. **Pets:** Accepted. 🛏 📶 ⊠ 📱 💻

AAA ▼▼▼ **Sheraton St. Paul Woodbury Hotel** ⊞
(651) 209-3280. **$109-$329.** 676 Bielenberg Dr 55125. I-494 exit 58C (Tamarack Rd), just ne. Int corridors. **Pets:** Accepted.
SAVE 🛏 🅼 🛏 📶 ⊠ 📱 💻

MISSISSIPPI

BILOXI

AAA ▼▼▼▼ **Hard Rock Hotel & Casino Biloxi** ⊞
(228) 374-7625. **$89-$899.** 777 Beach Blvd 39530. I-110 exit 1A (US 90), just e. Int corridors. **Pets:** Accepted.
SAVE 🛏 🅼 🛏 ⊠ 📶 📱 💻

▼▼▼ **La Quinta Inn & Suites** ⊞
(228) 392-5978. **$82-$306.** 957 Cedar Lake Rd 39532. I-10 exit 44, just s. Int corridors. **Pets:** Accepted. 🅼 🛏 📶 ⊠ 📱 💻

CANTON

AAA ▼▼▼ **Best Western Canton Inn** ⊞
(601) 859-8600. **$70-$85.** 137 Soldier Colony Rd 39046. I-55 exit 119, just se. Int corridors. **Pets:** Accepted. SAVE 🛏 📶 📱 💻

CLARKSDALE

▼▼▼ **Comfort Inn of Clarksdale** ⊞
(662) 627-5122. **$79-$125.** 818 S State St 38614. 1.2 mi s of jct US 49 and SR 161. Int corridors. **Pets:** Other species. $25 daily fee/room. Service with restrictions, crate. 🛏 🛏 📶 📱 💻

CLINTON

AAA ▼▼ **Best Western Ridgeland Inn** ⊞
(601) 926-4323. **$75-$89.** 102 Clinton Loop Dr 39056. I-20 exit 36, just s, then just w on Clinton Center Dr. Int corridors. **Pets:** Accepted.
SAVE 🛏 📶 📱 💻

COLUMBUS (Restaurants p. 617)

▼▼ **Quality Inn** ⊞
(662) 329-2422. **$78-$110.** 1210 US 45 N 39705. Jct US 82 Bypass and US 45 N. Ext corridors. **Pets:** Accepted. 📶 📱 💻

D'IBERVILLE

▼▼▼ **Home2 Suites by Hilton Biloxi North/D'Iberville** ⊞
(228) 392-6265. **$109-$209.** 3810 Promenade Pkwy 39540. I-10 exit 46B, just nw; in The Promenade. Int corridors. **Pets:** Accepted.
🅼 📶 📱 💻

▼▼ **Suburban Extended Stay Hotel** ⊞
(228) 396-5780. **$43-$170.** 10221 Rodriguez St 39540. I-110 exit 2, just sw. Ext corridors. **Pets:** Accepted. 🅼 📶 📱 💻

▼▼▼ **Wingate by Wyndham** ⊞
(228) 396-0036. **$84-$159.** 12009 Indian River Rd 39540. I-10 exit 46B, just ne. Int corridors. **Pets:** Accepted. 🅼 🛏 📶 ⊠ 📱 💻

GRENADA

▼▼▼▼ **Comfort Inn & Suites** ⊞
(662) 227-8444. **$89-$155.** 255 SW Frontage Rd 38901. I-55 exit 206, just sw. Int corridors. **Pets:** Accepted. 🛏 🛏 📶 ⊠ 📱 💻

GULFPORT

AAA ▼▼▼ **Best Western Seaway Inn** ⊞
(228) 864-0050. **$70-$159.** 9475 Hwy 49 39503. I-10 exit 34A, just sw. Ext corridors. **Pets:** Accepted. SAVE 🅼 🛏 📶 📱 💻

AAA ▼▼▼ **Clarion Inn Gulfport/Airport** ⊞
(228) 868-3300. **$65-$199.** 9445 Hwy 49 39503. I-10 exit 34A, just sw. Ext corridors. **Pets:** Accepted. SAVE 🅼 🛏 📶 📱 💻

▼▼▼ **Home2 Suites by Hilton Gulfport I-10** ⊞
(228) 357-9684. **$89-$129.** 15600 Daniel Blvd 39503. I-10 exit 34B, just n on US 49, just w on Landon Rd, then just s. Int corridors.
Pets: Accepted. 🅼 📶 ⊠ 📱 💻

▼▼▼ **Residence Inn by Marriott Gulfport-Biloxi Airport** ⊞
(228) 867-1722. **$87-$163.** 14100 Airport Rd 39503. I-10 exit 34A, 0.8 mi s on US 49, then 1.2 mi e. Int corridors. **Pets:** Accepted.
🅼 🛏 📶 ⊠ 📱 💻

HATTIESBURG (Restaurants p. 617)

▼▼▼ **Candlewood Suites** ⊞
(601) 264-9666. **Call for rates.** 9 Gateway Dr 39402. I-59 exit 67B, just nw to Classic Dr, then just sw. Int corridors. **Pets:** Accepted.
🅼 📶 📱 💻

▼▼▼ **La Quinta Inn & Suites** ⊞
(769) 223-6000. **$103-$202.** 109 Lundy Ln 39402. I-59 exit 65 (N 40th Ave), just w, then just s. Int corridors. **Pets:** Accepted.
🅼 📶 ⊠ 📱 💻

▼▼▼ **Red Lion Inn & Suites** ⊞ 🐾
(601) 264-8080. **$79-$109.** 4301 Hardy St 39402. I-59 exit 65, just nw. Ext/int corridors. **Pets:** Dogs only. $35 one-time fee/room. Designated rooms, service with restrictions, supervision. 🛏 📶 📱 💻

AAA ▼▼▼▼ **Residence Inn by Marriott Hattiesburg** ⊞
(601) 264-9202. **$123-$193.** 116 Grand Dr 39401. I-59 exit 65 (N 40th Ave), just w. Int corridors. **Pets:** Accepted.
SAVE 🅼 🛏 📶 ⊠ 📱 💻

▼▼▼ **TownePlace Suites by Marriott Hattiesburg** ⊞
(601) 582-2030. **$102-$177.** 235 Thornhill Dr 39402. I-59 exit 65, just e on SR 198, then 0.5 mi n on frontage road. Int corridors. **Pets:** Other species. $100 one-time fee/room. Service with restrictions, crate.
🛏 🅼 📶 ⊠ 📱 💻

HOLLY SPRINGS

AAA ▼▼▼ **Quality Inn** ⊞
(662) 252-5444. **$80-$130.** 100 Brooks Rd 38635. US 78 exit 30, just sw. Int corridors. **Pets:** Accepted. SAVE 🛏 📶 📱 💻

HORN LAKE

◆◆◆ Comfort Inn H
(662) 349-3493. **$89-$109.** 801 Desoto Cove 38637. I-55 exit 289, just w, then just n. Int corridors. **Pets:** Accepted. 🅼 🏊 🛜 🖥 📺

◆◆◆ Drury Inn & Suites-Memphis South H
(662) 349-6622. **$89-$179.** 735 Goodman Rd W 38637. I-55 exit 289, just w, then just s. Int corridors. **Pets:** Accepted.
🅼 🏊 🛜 ✕ 🖥 📺

◆◆◆ La Quinta Inn & Suites Horn Lake Southaven H
(662) 510-6500. **$90-$208.** 721 Southwest Dr 38637. I-55 exit 289, just sw. Int corridors. **Pets:** Accepted. 🍴 🅼 🏊 🛜 ✕ 🖥 📺

JACKSON

◆◆◆ Cabot Lodge Millsaps H
(601) 948-8650. **Call for rates.** 2375 N State St 39202. I-55 exit 98A northbound, 1 mi w on Woodrow Wilson Ave, then just s. Int corridors. **Pets:** Accepted. 🍴 🅼 🏊 🛜 🖥 📺

◆◆◆ Comfort Inn H
(601) 956-3611. **$75-$110.** 465 Briarwood Dr 39206. I-55 exit 102, just w. Int corridors. **Pets:** Large, other species. $25 daily fee/pet. Designated rooms, service with restrictions. 🅼 🏊 🛜 ✕ 🖥 📺

AAA ◆◆◆◆ Fairview Inn BB ✿
(601) 948-3429. **$199-$339, 3 day notice.** 734 Fairview St 39202. I-55 exit 98A (Woodrow Wilson Ave), 0.8 mi w to State St, 0.4 mi s, then just e. Int corridors. **Pets:** Small, dogs only. $35 daily fee/pet. Designated rooms, service with restrictions, supervision.
SAVE 🍴 🅼 🛜 ✕ 📺

AAA ◆◆◆◆ Hilton Jackson H
(601) 957-2800. **$129-$189.** 1001 E County Line Rd 39211. I-55 exit 103 (County Line Rd), just e. Int corridors. **Pets:** Large. $75 one-time fee/room. Service with restrictions, supervision.
SAVE 🍴 🅼 🏊 🛜 🖥 📺

◆◆◆◆ Holiday Inn Express & Suites-Jackson Downtown-Coliseum H
(601) 948-4466. **Call for rates.** 310 Greymont Ave 39202. I-55 exit 96B (High St), just sw. Int corridors. **Pets:** Medium, other species. $50 one-time fee/pet. Service with restrictions, supervision. 🛜 ✕ 🖥 📺

◆◆ Quality Inn & Suites Southwest H
(601) 922-5600. **$73-$100.** 2800 Greenway Dr 39204. I-20 exit 40 eastbound; exit 40A westbound, just se. Ext corridors. **Pets:** Medium, dogs only. $25 daily fee/pet. Designated rooms, service with restrictions, supervision. 🅼 🏊 🛜 🖥 📺

LUCEDALE

◆◆◆◆ Holiday Inn Express & Suites H
(601) 947-2099. **Call for rates.** 1287 Beaver Dam Rd 39452. Jct US 98 and SR 63, 1.5 mi se. Int corridors. **Pets:** Accepted.
🍴 🏊 🛜 ✕ 🖥 📺

MERIDIAN

AAA ◆◆◆ Baymont Inn & Suites Meridian M
(601) 483-3315. **$59-$80.** 524 Bonita Lakes Dr 39301. I-20/59 exit 154 southbound; exit 154A northbound, just s. Ext corridors. **Pets:** Accepted.
SAVE 🅼 🏊 🛜 🖥 📺

◆◆◆ Drury Inn & Suites H
(601) 483-5570. **$94-$159.** 112 Hwy 11 & 80 N 39301. I-20/59 exit 154, jct US 11/80 N. Int corridors. **Pets:** Accepted.
🅼 🏊 🛜 ✕ 🖥 📺

◆◆ La Quinta Inn & Suites-Meridian H
(601) 693-2300. **$71-$159.** 1400 Roebuck Dr 39301. I-20/59 exit 153, just s. Int corridors. **Pets:** Accepted. 🅼 🏊 🛜 🖥 📺

AAA ◆◆◆ Super 8 M
(601) 482-8088. **$67-$75.** 124 Hwy 11 & 80 E 39301. I-20/59 exit 154 westbound; exit 154B eastbound, on northeast frontage road. Ext corridors. **Pets:** Medium, dogs only. $15 one-time fee/room. Service with restrictions, supervision. SAVE 🛜 🖥 📺

MOSS POINT

AAA ◆◆◆ Best Western Flagship Inn H
(228) 475-5000. **$69-$99.** 4830 Amoco Dr 39563. I-10 exit 69, just s. Ext corridors. **Pets:** Accepted. SAVE 🏊 🛜 🖥 📺

NATCHEZ

AAA ◆◆◆ Hampton Inn & Suites H
(601) 446-6770. **$129-$250.** 627 S Canal St 39120. US 84/65 exit just before Mississippi River. Int corridors. **Pets:** Accepted.
SAVE 🍴 🅼 🏊 🛜 ✕ 🖥 📺

◆◆◆ Holiday Inn Express & Suites Natchez-South H
(601) 442-4462. **$99-$169.** 639 S Canal St 39120. US 84/65 exit just before Mississippi River. Ext corridors. **Pets:** Other species. $50 one-time fee/room. Service with restrictions, crate.
🍴 🅼 🛜 ✕ 🖥 📺

OLIVE BRANCH

◆◆ Candlewood Suites H
(662) 890-7491. **Call for rates.** 7448 Craft Goodman Rd 38654. US 78 exit 1 westbound, 0.5 mi se; exit 2 (SR 302) eastbound, 1.4 mi ne. Int corridors. **Pets:** Accepted. 🍴 🅼 🛜 🖥 📺

◆◆ Magnolia Inn & Suites H
(662) 895-4545. **Call for rates.** 6935 W Hamilton Cir 38654. US 78 exit 2 (SR 302), 0.5 mi w. Int corridors. **Pets:** Accepted.
🍴 🅼 🏊 🛜 🖥 📺

◆◆ Whispering Woods Hotel and Conference Center H
(662) 895-2941. **$79-$119, 3 day notice.** 11200 E Goodman Rd 38654. US 78 exit 2 (SR 302), 3.6 mi e. Int corridors. **Pets:** Accepted.
🍴 🏊 🛜 ✕ 🖥 📺

PEARL

◆◆◆ Candlewood Suites H
(601) 936-3442. **$89-$99.** 632 S Pearson Rd 39208. I-20 exit 48, just s. Int corridors. **Pets:** Large. $25 one-time fee/room. Service with restrictions, crate. 🅼 🛜 🖥 📺

◆◆◆ La Quinta Inn & Suites Jackson Airport H
(601) 664-0065. **$90-$169.** 501 S Pearson Rd 39208. I-20 exit 48, just s. Int corridors. **Pets:** Accepted. 🅼 🏊 🛜 ✕ 🖥 📺

PHILADELPHIA

◆◆◆ Dancing Rabbit Inn H
(601) 389-6600. **Call for rates.** 13240 Hwy 16 W 39350. Jct SR 15, 2 mi w. Int corridors. **Pets:** Accepted.
🍴 🅼 🏊 🛜 ✕ 🖥 📺

RIDGELAND

◆◆◆ Cabot Lodge Jackson North H
(601) 957-0757. **Call for rates.** 120 Dyess Rd 39157. I-55 exit 103 (County Line Rd), just ne. Int corridors. **Pets:** Accepted.
🅼 🏊 🖥 📺

◆◆◆ Drury Inn & Suites Ridgeland-Jackson H
(601) 956-6100. **$99-$179.** 610 E County Line Rd 39157. I-55 exit 103 (County Line Rd), just w. Int corridors. **Pets:** Accepted.
🅼 🏊 🛜 ✕ 🖥 📺

▼▼▼ **Home2 Suites by Hilton Jackson/Ridgeland** H
(601) 898-2222. **Call for rates.** 526 Evergreen St 39157. I-55 exit 105B, just e, just n on Sunnybrook Rd, then just w. Int corridors. **Pets:** Accepted. 🍽 &M 🛜 ✕ 🛗 💻

▼▼▼ **Homewood Suites by Hilton** H
(601) 899-8611. **$119-$179.** 853 Centre St 39157. I-55 exit 103 (County Line Rd), just e to Ridgewood Rd, 0.4 mi ne, then just e. Int corridors. **Pets:** Accepted. &M 🏊 🛜 🛗 💻

⨀ ▼▼▼ **Hyatt Place Jackson/Ridgeland** H
(601) 898-8815. **$99-$259.** 1016 Highland Colony Pkwy 39157. I-55 exit 105, just w. Int corridors. **Pets:** Small, dogs only. $75 daily fee/room. Service with restrictions, crate. SAVE &M 🏊 🛜 ✕ 🛗 💻

▼▼▼ **Residence Inn by Marriott Jackson Ridgeland** H
(601) 206-7755. **$107-$172.** 855 Centre St 39157. I-55 exit 103 (County Line Rd), just e to Ridgewood Rd, then just e. Int corridors. **Pets:** Accepted. &M 🏊 🛜 ✕ 🛗 💻

⨀ ▼▼▼ **TownePlace Suites by Marriott Jackson Ridgeland/The Township at Colony Park** H
(601) 898-9880. **$104-$166.** 310 Southlake Ave 39157. I-55 exit 105C (Old Agency Rd), just w, 0.8 mi n on Highland Colony Pkwy, just w on Steed Rd, then just n. Int corridors. **Pets:** Small. $100 one-time fee/pet. Service with restrictions, supervision. SAVE &M 🛜 ✕ 🛗 💻

RIPLEY

⨀ ▼▼ **Econo Lodge** M
(662) 837-0002. **$76-$100.** 922 City Ave S 38663. Jct US 4 and 15, 0.5 mi s. Ext corridors. **Pets:** Medium, dogs only. $15 daily fee/pet. Service with restrictions, supervision. SAVE 🏊 🛜 🛗 💻

SOUTHAVEN

▼▼ **Magnolia Inn & Suites** H
(662) 280-5555. **Call for rates.** 5069 Pepper Chase Dr 38671. I-55 exit 287, just w. Int corridors. **Pets:** Accepted. 🛜 🛗

▼▼▼ **Residence Inn by Marriott Memphis Southaven** H
(662) 996-1500. **$107-$157.** 7165 Sleepy Hollow Dr 38671. I-55 exit 289, just e, just n on Southcrest Pkwy, then w on Market Plaza. Int corridors. **Pets:** Accepted. &M 🏊 🛜 ✕ 🛗 💻

STARKVILLE

▼▼▼ **Comfort Suites Starkville** H
(662) 324-9595. **$99-$289.** 801 Russell St 39759. 0.5 mi s of jct US 82 and SR 12. Int corridors. **Pets:** Accepted. &M 🏊 🛜 ✕ 🛗 💻

▼▼▼ **Hampton Inn** H
(662) 324-1333. **$119-$129.** 700 Hwy 12 E 39759. 1.1 mi sw of jct SR 182. Int corridors. **Pets:** Accepted. &M 🏊 🛜 ✕ 🛗 💻

▼▼▼ **Holiday Inn Express & Suites** H
(662) 324-0076. **$109-$250.** 110-B Hwy 12 W 39759. Jct Jackson St and SR 12. Int corridors. **Pets:** Other species. $50 one-time fee/room. Designated rooms, service with restrictions, supervision. &M 🛜 ✕ 🛗 💻

TUNICA RESORTS

▼ **Key West Inn Tunica** M
(662) 363-0021. **$45-$199.** 11635 Hwy 61 N 38664. US 61, 0.3 mi n of SR 304. Ext corridors. **Pets:** Small. $10 daily fee/pet. Service with restrictions, supervision. 🍽 🛜 ✕ 🛗 💻

TUPELO *(Restaurants p. 617)*

▼▼▼ **Candlewood Suites Tupelo North** H
(662) 553-4649. **Call for rates.** 979 N Gloster St 38804. US 45 exit McCullough Blvd, just w, then just s. Int corridors. **Pets:** Accepted. &M 🛜 🛗 💻

▼▼▼ **La Quinta Inn & Suites** H
(662) 847-8000. **$90-$198.** 1013 N Gloster St 38804. On SR 145, just n of McCullough Blvd. Int corridors. **Pets:** Accepted. &M 🏊 🛜 ✕ 🛗 💻

▼▼ **Quality Inn Tupelo** M
(662) 842-5100. **$66-$72.** 1190 N Gloster St 38804. Jct McCullough Blvd and SR 145, 1.3 mi s to McCullough Blvd, w to N Gloster St, then 0.3 mi n. Ext corridors. **Pets:** Accepted. 🛜 🛗 💻

VICKSBURG

▼▼▼ **Anchuca** CI
(601) 661-0111. **$135-$210, 3 day notice.** 1010 1st East St 39183. I-20 exit 4B, 2.2 mi w on Clay St, then 0.4 mi n on Cherry St; in historic downtown. Ext/int corridors. **Pets:** Accepted. 🍽 🏊 🛜 ✕ 🈴 🛗 💻

⨀ ▼▼▼ **Best Western Vicksburg** H
(601) 636-5800. **$85-$119.** 2445 N Frontage Rd 39180. I-20 exit 3, just w on NW Frontage Rd. Ext corridors. **Pets:** Medium. $15 daily fee/pet. Designated rooms, service with restrictions, supervision. SAVE &M 🏊 🛜 🛗 💻

▼▼▼ **Candlewood Suites** H
(601) 638-6900. **Call for rates.** 1296 S Frontage Rd 39180. I-20 exit 1C, just s, then just e. Int corridors. **Pets:** Medium. $75 one-time fee/room. Service with restrictions, supervision. 🍽 &M 🛜 ✕ 🛗 💻

⨀ ▼▼▼ **Cedar Grove Mansion Inn & Restaurant** CI
(601) 636-1000. **$100-$215, 3 day notice.** 2200 Oak St 39180. I-20 exit 1A, 2.3 mi n on Washington St, then w on Klein St to gated entrance. Ext/int corridors. **Pets:** Accepted. SAVE 🍽 🏊 🛜 ✕ 🛗 💻

▼▼▼ **Corners Mansion Inn, a Bed & Breakfast** BB
(601) 636-7421. **$125-$210, 3 day notice.** 601 Klein St 39180. I-20 exit 1A, 2.3 mi n on Washington St, then just w. Ext/int corridors. **Pets:** Accepted. 🛜 ✕ 🛗 💻

▼▼▼ **La Quinta Inn & Suites** H
(601) 802-0525. **$86-$174.** 4160 S Frontage Rd 39180. I-20 exit 4A eastbound; exit 5B westbound, just s. Int corridors. **Pets:** Accepted. &M 🏊 🛜 ✕ 🛗 💻

▼▼ **Quality Inn** H
(601) 619-7799. **Call for rates.** 3975 S Frontage Rd 39180. I-20 exit 4A, on southeast frontage road. Ext corridors. **Pets:** Accepted. 🏊 🛜 🛗 💻

▼▼ **Travel Inn** M
(601) 630-0100. **Call for rates.** 1675 N Frontage Rd 39180. I-20 exit 1C, just ne. Ext corridors. **Pets:** Dogs only. $20 daily fee/pet. Designated rooms, service with restrictions, supervision. 🛜 🛗

WIGGINS

▼▼▼ **Hampton Inn & Suites** H
(601) 528-5255. **$104-$169.** 1121 E Frontage Rd 39577. Jct US 49 and SR 26, 1.2 mi s. Int corridors. **Pets:** Accepted. &M 🏊 🛜 ✕ 🛗 💻

WINONA

Holiday Inn Express Inn & Suites Winona North Mississippi 🄷

(662) 283-9992. **$109-$129.** 413 SE Frontage Rd 38967. I-55 exit 185, just e, then just s. Int corridors. **Pets:** Accepted.

MISSOURI

ARNOLD

Drury Inn & Suites Arnold 🄷

(636) 287-3111. **$100-$190.** 3800 SR 141 63010. I-55 exit 191 (SR 141), just e. Int corridors. **Pets:** Accepted.

Pear Tree Inn Arnold 🄷

(636) 296-9600. **$65-$110.** 1201 Drury Ln 63010. I-55 exit 191 (SR 141), just e. Int corridors. **Pets:** Accepted.

AVA

Ava Super 8 🄷

(417) 683-1343. **$75.** 1711 S Jefferson St 65608. 1.8 mi s of jct SR 5, 14 and 76. Int corridors. **Pets:** Accepted.

BETHANY

Bethany Super 8 🄼

(660) 425-8881. **$53-$71.** 811 S 38th St 64424. I-35 exit 92, just w. Int corridors. **Pets:** Other species. $10 daily fee/pet. Designated rooms, service with restrictions, crate.

BLUE SPRINGS

Hampton Inn by Hilton Blue Springs 🄷

(816) 220-3844. **$99-$159.** 900 NW South Outer Rd 64015. I-70 exit 20, just s on SR 7, then just w. Int corridors. **Pets:** Other species. Service with restrictions, supervision.

BOONVILLE

Boonville Comfort Inn 🄷

(660) 882-5317. **$80-$170.** 2427 Mid America Industrial Dr 65233. I-70 exit 101, just sw. Int corridors. **Pets:** Small. $15 daily fee/pet. Designated rooms, service with restrictions, supervision.

BRANSON

Baymont Inn & Suites 🄷 🐾

(417) 334-1985. **$59-$120.** 1000 W Main St 65616. Just sw of jct US 65 and SR 76 (Country Blvd). Int corridors. **Pets:** Dogs only. $40 one-time fee/pet. Designated rooms, service with restrictions, crate.

Best Western Plus Landing View Inn & Suites 🄷

(417) 334-6464. **$79-$134.** 403 W Main (Hwy 76) 65616. 0.3 mi e of jct SR 76 (Country Blvd) and US 65. Ext corridors. **Pets:** Medium. $10 daily fee/pet. Designated rooms, service with restrictions.

Calm Waters Resort 🄲🄰

(417) 338-8963. **Call for rates.** 1043 Jakes Creek Tr 65616. Jct SR 76 (Country Blvd) and 265, 0.6 mi w, 1 mi s on Indian Point Rd, then 1 mi e. Ext corridors. **Pets:** Accepted.

Chateau on the Lake Resort & Spa 🄷

(417) 334-1161. **$129-$349, 3 day notice.** 415 N State Hwy 265 65616. Just n of jct SR 165. Int corridors. **Pets:** Small, dogs only. $50 one-time fee/room. Designated rooms, service with restrictions, crate.

Econo Lodge 🄼

(417) 336-4849. **$55-$100.** 230 S Wildwood Dr 65616. Just s of jct SR 76 (Country Blvd). Ext corridors. **Pets:** Other species. $10 daily fee/pet. Designated rooms, service with restrictions.

Fall Creek Inn & Suites 🄷

(417) 348-1683. **Call for rates.** 995 Hwy 165 65616. Jct SR 76 (Country Blvd), 1.5 mi s on SR 165. Ext corridors. **Pets:** Accepted.

Hilton Branson Convention Center Hotel 🄷 🐾

(417) 336-5400. **$109-$249.** 200 E Main St 65616. Center. Int corridors. **Pets:** Medium. $50 one-time fee/room. Service with restrictions, supervision.

Hilton Promenade at Branson Landing 🄷 🐾

(417) 336-5500. **$119-$259.** 3 Branson Landing 65616. Jct Main St, just e; in Branson Landing Shopping District. Int corridors. **Pets:** Medium. $50 one-time fee/room. Service with restrictions, supervision.

Hotel Grand Victorian 🄷

(417) 336-2935. **$80-$239.** 2325 W Hwy 76 (Country Blvd) 65616. 2.3 mi w of jct US 65. Int corridors. **Pets:** Dogs only. Designated rooms, service with restrictions, supervision.

Lazy Valley Resort 🄼

(417) 334-2397. **Call for rates.** 285 River Ln 65616. Jct SR 76 (Country Blvd), 2.5 mi s on Fall Creek Rd to River Valley Rd. Ext corridors. **Pets:** Small, dogs only. $10 daily fee/pet. Crate.

Ozark Regal Hotel 🄷

(417) 336-2200. **$80-$85, 3 day notice.** 3010 Green Mountain Dr 65616. From jct US 65, 2 mi w on SR 76 (Country Blvd), just s. Int corridors. **Pets:** Accepted.

Ozark Valley Inn 🄼

(417) 336-4666. **$50-$149.** 2693 Shepherd of the Hills Expwy 65616. Jct SR 76 (Country Music Blvd), 0.9 mi e. Ext corridors. **Pets:** Accepted.

Residence Inn by Marriott 🄷

(417) 336-4077. **$83-$153.** 280 Wildwood Dr S 65616. Just s of jct Green Mountain Dr. Int corridors. **Pets:** Other species. $100 one-time fee/room. Service with restrictions, crate.

Thousand Hills Golf Resort 🄲🄾

(417) 336-5873. **Call for rates.** 245 S Wildwood Dr 65616. 0.5 mi s of jct SR 76 (Country Blvd). Ext corridors. **Pets:** Accepted.

AAA ▼▼▼ The Village At Indian Point CO
(417) 338-8800. **$140-$330, 31 day notice.** 24 Village Tr 65616. 2.5 mi s of jct SR 76 (Country Blvd) on Indian Point Rd. Ext corridors. **Pets:** Medium, dogs only. $15 daily fee/pet. Designated rooms, no service, supervision. SAVE ⏹ ➔ ⊠ 🖥 ⊠ 🛄 💻

BRANSON WEST

AAA ▼▼ Best Western Branson Inn & Conference Center H
(417) 338-2141. **$90-$130.** 8514 State Hwy 76 65737. 0.9 mi w of jct SR 265. Int corridors. **Pets:** Small, dogs only. $20 daily fee/pet. Designated rooms, service with restrictions, crate.
SAVE ⏹ ➔ 🖥 ⊠ 🛄 💻

BRENTWOOD

▼▼▼ Drury Inn & Suites Brentwood H
(314) 968-3704. **Call for rates.** 8700 Eager Rd 63144. I-64/US 40 exit 31B (Brentwood/Hanley Rd), 1 mi w. Int corridors. **Pets:** Accepted.
🛗 🖥 ⊠ 🛄 💻

BROOKFIELD

AAA ▼▼ Best Western Brookfield H
(660) 258-4900. **$105-$115.** 28622 Hwy 11 64628. US 36 exit Business Rt 36, just se. Int corridors. **Pets:** Accepted.
SAVE ⏹ 🛗 ➔ 🖥 🛄 💻

CANTON

▼▼ Oak Hill Inn & Suites H
(573) 288-8800. **Call for rates.** 1701 Oak St 63435. US 61 exit US 61 business route/CR P, just e. Int corridors. **Pets:** Accepted.
⏹ ➔ 🖥 🛄 💻

CAPE GIRARDEAU

▼▼ Auburn Place Hotel & Suites H
(573) 651-4486. **Call for rates.** 3265 William St 63701. I-55 exit 96 (William St), just e. Ext/int corridors. **Pets:** Accepted.
🛗 ➔ ⊠ 🖥 ⊠ 🛄 💻

▼▼▼ Candlewood Suites H
(573) 334-6868. **Call for rates.** 485 S Mount Auburn Rd 63703. I-55 exit 95 (Shawnee Pkwy), 0.5 mi e. Int corridors. **Pets:** Accepted.
⏹ 🛗 🖥 ⊠ 🛄 💻

▼▼▼ Drury Suites-Cape Girardeau H
(573) 339-9500. **$120-$195.** 3303 Campster Dr 63701. I-55 exit 96 (William St), just w. Int corridors. **Pets:** Accepted.
🛗 ➔ 🖥 ⊠ 🛄 💻

▼▼ Pear Tree Inn by Drury Cape Girardeau West H
(573) 651-3000. **$70-$125.** 103 Cape W Pkwy 63701. I-55 exit 96 (William St), 0.3 mi sw. Int corridors. **Pets:** Accepted.
⏹ 🛗 🖥 ⊠ 🛄 💻

▼▼ Pear Tree Inn Cape Girardeau Medical Center H
(573) 334-3000. **$70-$125.** 3248 William St 63701. I-55 exit 96 (William St), just e. Int corridors. **Pets:** $25 daily fee/room. Service with restrictions, supervision. 🛗 ➔ 🖥 ⊠ 🛄 💻

CARTHAGE

▼▼ Econo Lodge H
(417) 358-3900. **$65-$250.** 1441 W Central Ave 64836. I-49 exit 53, just ne. Ext/int corridors. **Pets:** Accepted. ➔ 🖥 🛄 💻

▼▼ Quality Inn & Suites H
(417) 359-5900. **$75-$95.** 2701 Hazel St 64836. I-49 exit 50, just ne. Int corridors. **Pets:** Medium, dogs only. $10 daily fee/pet. Designated rooms, service with restrictions, crate. ➔ 🖥 ⊠ 🛄 💻

CHESTERFIELD

▼▼▼ Drury Plaza Hotel-Chesterfield H
(636) 532-3300. **$120-$210.** 355 Chesterfield Center E 63017. I-64/US 40 exit 19B (Clarkson Rd/Olive Blvd), just s on Clarkson Rd, then just w. Int corridors. **Pets:** Accepted. 🛗 ➔ 🖥 ⊠ 🛄 💻

▼▼▼ Hampton Inn-Chesterfield H
(636) 537-2500. **$109-$189.** 16201 Swingley Ridge Rd 63017. I-64/US 40 exit 19B (Clarkson Rd/Olive Blvd), just n on Olive Blvd, then just w. Int corridors. **Pets:** Accepted. ⏹ 🛗 🖥 ⊠ 🛄 💻

▼▼▼ Homewood Suites by Hilton H
(636) 530-0305. **$99-$209.** 840 Chesterfield Pkwy W 63017. I-64/US 40 exit 19B (Clarkson Rd/Olive Blvd), 0.5 mi n on Olive Blvd, then just w. Int corridors. **Pets:** Accepted. 🛗 ➔ 🖥 🛄 💻

AAA ▼▼▼ Hyatt Place St. Louis/Chesterfield H 🐾
(636) 536-6262. **$79-$259.** 333 Chesterfield Center E 63017. I-64/US 40 exit 19B (Clarkson Rd/Olive Blvd), just s on Clarkson Rd, then just w. Int corridors. **Pets:** $75 one-time fee/room. Service with restrictions.
SAVE ⏹ 🛗 🖥 ⊠ 🛄 💻

CLAYTON

▼▼▼ Clayton Plaza Hotel H
(314) 726-5400. **Call for rates.** 7750 Carondelet Ave 63105. I-64/US 40 exit 31B (Brentwood/Hanley Rd), 1.3 mi n on Hanley Rd, then just w. Int corridors. **Pets:** Medium, dogs only. $25 deposit/pet. Designated rooms, service with restrictions, crate.
⏹ 🛗 ➔ ⊠ 🖥 ⊠ 🛄 💻

AAA ▼▼▼ The Ritz-Carlton, St. Louis H
(314) 863-6300. **Call for rates.** 100 Carondelet Plaza 63105. I-64/US 40 exit 31B (Brentwood/Hanley Rd), 1.2 mi n on Hanley Rd, then just e. Int corridors. **Pets:** Small, dogs only. $125 one-time fee/room. Service with restrictions, supervision.
SAVE ⏹ 🛗 ➔ ⊠ 📻 ⊠ 💻

AAA ▼▼▼ Sheraton Clayton Plaza Hotel H
(314) 863-0400. **$99-$379.** 7730 Bonhomme Ave 63105. I-64/US 40 exit 31B (Brentwood/Hanley Rd), 1.2 mi n on Hanley Rd, then just w. Int corridors. **Pets:** Accepted. SAVE ⏹ 🛗 ➔ 📻 ⊠ 🛄 💻

COLUMBIA

▼▼▼ Candlewood Suites Hwy 63 & I-70 H 🐾
(573) 256-0200. **Call for rates.** 1400 Creekwood Pkwy 65202. I-70 exit 128A (US 63), just ne. Int corridors. **Pets:** Other species. $150 one-time fee/room. Designated rooms, service with restrictions, crate.
🛗 🖥 ⊠ 🛄 💻

▼▼▼ Drury Inn Columbia Stadium Boulevard H
(573) 445-1800. **$100-$170.** 1000 Knipp St 65203. I-70 exit 124 (Stadium Blvd), just s. Int corridors. **Pets:** Accepted.
⏹ ➔ 🖥 ⊠ 🛄 💻

▼▼▼ Holiday Inn Executive Center H
(573) 445-8531. **Call for rates.** 2200 I-70 Dr SW 65203. I-70 exit 124 (Stadium Blvd), just w. Int corridors. **Pets:** Accepted.
⏹ 🛗 ➔ 🖥 ⊠ 🛄 💻

▼▼ Ramada H
(573) 443-4141. **$59-$199.** 901 Conley Rd 65201. I-70 exit 128A (US 63), just sw. Int corridors. **Pets:** Accepted. ➔ 🖥 ⊠ 🛄 💻

AAA ▼▼▼ Residence Inn by Marriott H
(573) 442-5601. **$122-$187.** 1100 Woodland Springs Ct 65202. I-70 exit 128A (US 63), just n, then 0.4 mi e. Int corridors. **Pets:** Other species. $75 one-time fee/room. Service with restrictions, crate.
SAVE ➔ 🖥 ⊠ 🛄 💻

▼▼▼▼ Stoney Creek Hotel & Conference
Center 🅗 ❖

(573) 442-6400. **$109-$175.** 2601 S Providence Rd 65203. I-70 exit 126 (Providence Rd), 3 mi s; on west outer road. Int corridors. **Pets:** Large. $25 daily fee/pet. Service with restrictions, supervision.

🍴 🛗 🏊 📶 ✕ 🔌 💻

▼ Super 8 Columbia Clark Lane Ⓜ

(573) 474-8488. **$63-$150.** 3216 Clark Ln 65202. I-70 exit 128A (US 63); northeast corner. Int corridors. **Pets:** Accepted. 📶 🔌 💻

CREVE COEUR
▼▼▼▼ Drury Inn & Suites-Creve Coeur 🅗

(314) 989-1100. **$100-$185.** 11980 Olive Blvd 63141. I-270 exit 14 (Olive Blvd), just e. Int corridors. **Pets:** Accepted.

🛗 🏊 📶 ✕ 🔌 💻

CUBA
▼▼ Super 8 🅗

(573) 885-2087. **$67-$77.** 28 Hwy P 65453. I-44 exit 208 (SR 19), just n, then just w. Ext/int corridors. **Pets:** $15 one-time fee/pet. Designated rooms, service with restrictions, supervision. 📶 🔌 💻

EARTH CITY
▼▼▼ Candlewood Suites St. Louis 🅗

(314) 770-2744. **Call for rates.** 3250 Rider Tr S 63045. I-70 exit 231B (Earth City Expwy N), just n, then just e. Int corridors. **Pets:** Accepted.

🛗 📶 🔌 💻

▼▼▼▼ Residence Inn by Marriott St. Louis Airport/Earth
City 🅗

(314) 209-0995. **$119-$174.** 3290 Rider Tr S 63045. I-70 exit 231B (Earth City Expwy N), just n, then just e. Int corridors. **Pets:** Accepted.

🛗 🏊 📶 ✕ 🔌 💻

EDMUNDSON
▼▼▼▼ Drury Inn-St. Louis Airport 🅗

(314) 423-7700. **$80-$180.** 10490 Natural Bridge Rd 63134. I-70 exit 236 (Lambert Airport), just s, then just e. Int corridors. **Pets:** Accepted.

🛗 🏊 📶 ✕ 🔌 💻

🅐🅐🅐 ▼▼▼▼ Marriott-St. Louis Airport 🅗

(314) 423-9700. **$89-$228.** 10700 Pear Tree Ln 63134. I-70 exit 236 (Lambert Airport), just s. Int corridors. **Pets:** Accepted.

[SAVE] 🍴 🛗 🏊 🍽 ✕ 🔌 💻

EUREKA
▼▼▼▼ Holiday Inn at Six Flags 🅗

(636) 938-6661. **Call for rates.** 4901 Six Flags Rd 63025. I-44 exit 261 (Allenton Rd), just e. Ext/int corridors. **Pets:** Accepted.

🍴 🏊 ✕ 📶 ✕ 🔌 💻

EXCELSIOR SPRINGS
▼▼▼▼ The Elms Hotel & Spa 🅗

(816) 630-5500. **Call for rates.** 401 Regent 64024. Off SR 10; at Elms Blvd. Int corridors. **Pets:** Accepted. 🍴 ✕ 📶 ✕ 🔌 💻

FENTON
▼▼▼▼ Drury Inn & Suites-Fenton 🅗

(636) 343-7822. **$80-$180.** 1088 S Highway Dr 63026. I-44 exit 274A eastbound, just e; exit 274 westbound, just s on Bowles Ave, then just e. Int corridors. **Pets:** Accepted. 🏊 📶 ✕ 🔌 💻

▼▼ Pear Tree Inn by Drury-Fenton 🅗

(636) 343-8820. **$65-$110.** 1100 S Highway Dr 63026. I-44 exit 274A eastbound, just e; exit 274 westbound, just s on Bowles Ave, then just e. Int corridors. **Pets:** Accepted. 🏊 📶 ✕ 🔌 💻

▼▼▼ TownePlace Suites by Marriott 🅗

(636) 305-7000. **$85-$144.** 1662 Fenton Business Park Ct 63026. I-44 exit 275 westbound, 0.5 mi ne on Soccer Park Rd, 0.7 mi nw on Rudder Rd, then just s; exit 274B eastbound, 1 mi e on S Highway Dr, just sw on Rudder Rd, then just s. Int corridors. **Pets:** Accepted.

🍴 🛗 🏊 📶 ✕ 🔌 💻

FULTON
▼▼▼ Loganberry Inn Bed & Breakfast 🅑🅑

(573) 642-9229. **$129-$199, 14 day notice.** 310 W 7th St 65251. Jct US 54 exit CR F, 1 mi e, just n to Westminster Ave, then just e. Int corridors. **Pets:** Medium, dogs only. $15 one-time fee/room. Designated rooms, service with restrictions. 🍴 📶 ✕ 🈂 🔌 💻

HANNIBAL
🅐🅐🅐 ▼▼▼▼ Quality Inn & Suites 🅗

(573) 221-4001. **$99-$329.** 120 Lindsey Dr 63401. 2 mi w on US 36 exit Shinn Ln to south service road, then 0.6 mi e. Int corridors. **Pets:** Medium. $20 daily fee/pet. Designated rooms, service with restrictions, supervision. [SAVE] 🍴 🏊 📶 🔌 💻

HAYTI
▼▼ Drury Inn & Suites Hayti/Caruthersville 🅗

(573) 359-2702. **$70-$110.** 1317 Hwy 84 63851. I-55 exit 19 (US 412/SR 84), just w. Int corridors. **Pets:** Accepted.

🏊 📶 ✕ 🔌 💻

HERMANN
▼▼▼▼ Hermann Hill Vineyard Inn and Spa 🅑🅑 ❖

(573) 486-4455. **$242-$625, 10 day notice.** 711 Wein St 65041. SR 19 (Market St), just w on W 6th St, just s on Washington St, then 0.3 mi w on W 10th St. Ext/int corridors. **Pets:** Dogs only. $50 one-time fee/ room. Designated rooms, service with restrictions, supervision.

🍴 📶 ✕ 🔌 💻

HOLLISTER
🅐🅐🅐 ▼▼▼ La Quinta Inn & Suites 🅗

(417) 239-0066. **$87-$214.** 291 Financial Dr 65672. Just e of jct US 65. Int corridors. **Pets:** Accepted. [SAVE] 🍴 🛗 📶 ✕ 🔌 💻

🅐🅐🅐 ▼▼▼ Westgate Branson Lakes at Emerald
Pointe 🅒🅞

(417) 334-4944. **Call for rates.** 750 Emerald Pointe Dr 65672. Jct US 65 and SR 265, 1 mi w to Hill Haven Rd, then 2 mi s. Ext corridors. **Pets:** Accepted. [SAVE] 🍴 🛗 🏊 ✕ 📶 ✕ 🔌 💻

INDEPENDENCE
🅐🅐🅐 ▼▼▼ Best Western Truman Inn 🅗

(816) 254-0100. **$90-$150.** 4048 S Lynn Court Dr 64055. I-70 exit 12, just n on Noland Rd, then just w. Ext corridors. **Pets:** Medium. $10 daily fee/pet. Designated rooms, service with restrictions, supervision. [SAVE] 🏊 📶 🔌 💻

▼▼▼ Comfort Suites-Independence 🅗

(816) 373-9880. **$100-$220.** 19751 E Valley View Pkwy 64057. I-70 exit 17 (Little Blue Pkwy), just s, then just w. Int corridors. **Pets:** Accepted.

🛗 🏊 📶 ✕ 🔌 💻

▼▼▼ Drury Inn & Suites Kansas
City-Independence 🅗

(816) 795-9393. **$105-$160.** 20300 E 42nd St S 64015. I-70 exit 17 (Little Blue Pkwy), just s. Int corridors. **Pets:** Accepted.

🛗 🏊 📶 ✕ 🔌 💻

🅐🅐🅐 ▼▼▼ Holiday Inn Express & Suites-Independence/
Kansas City 🅗

(816) 795-8889. **$89-$209.** 19901 E Valley View Pkwy 64057. I-70 exit 17 (Little Blue Pkwy), just s, then just w. Int corridors. **Pets:** $25 daily fee/room. Designated rooms, service with restrictions, crate.

[SAVE] 🛗 🏊 📶 ✕ 🔌 💻

▼▼▼ **Stoney Creek Hotel & Conference Center** H
(816) 908-9600. **Call for rates.** 18011 Bass Pro Dr 64055. I-470 exit
16A (US 40), 0.7 mi nw. Int corridors. **Pets:** Accepted.
🍴 🕹M 🛜 ❌ 🛏 💻

JACKSON
▼▼▼ **Drury Inn & Suites-Jackson, MO** H
(573) 243-9200. **$85-$125.** 225 Drury Ln 63755. I-55 exit 105 (SR 61),
just w. Int corridors. **Pets:** Accepted.
🍴 🕹M 🛟 🛜 ❌ 🛏 💻

JANE
▼ ▼ **Booneslick Lodge** H
(417) 226-1888. **$56-$70.** 21140 US Hwy 71 64856. Just s on US 71.
Int corridors. **Pets:** Accepted. 🍴 🛟 🛜 🛏 💻

JEFFERSON CITY
▼ ▼ **Capitol Plaza Hotel & Convention Center** H
(573) 634-8716. **$83-$169.** 415 W McCarty St 65101. On US 50 and
63 S, just e of jct US 54. Int corridors. **Pets:** Accepted.
🍴 🛟 🛜 ❌ 🛏 💻

▼ ▼ **Oak Tree Inn Jefferson City** H
(573) 636-5456. **Call for rates.** 1710 Jefferson St 65110. US 54 exit
Ellis Blvd, 0.3 mi nw on frontage road. Int corridors. **Pets:** $10 deposit/
pet, $10 one-time fee/pet. Designated rooms, service with restrictions,
crate. 🛜 ❌ 🛏 💻

JOPLIN
AAA ▼▼▼ **Best Western Oasis Inn & Suites** H 🐾
(417) 781-6776. **$85-$110.** 3508 S Range Line Rd 64804. I-44 exit 8,
just nw. Ext corridors. **Pets:** Medium, dogs only. $10 daily fee/pet. Des-
ignated rooms, service with restrictions, supervision.
SAVE 🛟 🛜 🛏 💻

▼▼▼ **Candlewood Suites** H
(417) 623-9595. **$89-$139.** 3512 S Range Line Rd 64804. I-44 exit 8,
just nw. Int corridors. **Pets:** Accepted. 🍴 🕹M 🛜 🛏 💻

▼▼▼ **Drury Inn & Suites-Joplin** H
(417) 781-8000. **$100-$150.** 3601 S Range Line Rd 64804. I-44 exit 8,
just ne. Int corridors. **Pets:** Accepted. 🛟 🛜 ❌ 🛏 💻

▼▼▼ **Homewood Suites by Hilton** H
(417) 623-1900. **$119-$169.** 2642 E 32nd St 64804. I-44 exit 8B, just w
of US 71 business route (Range Line Rd). Int corridors. **Pets:** $75 one-
time fee/room. Service with restrictions, supervision.
🕹M 🛜 ❌ 🛏 💻

▼▼▼ **La Quinta Inn & Suites Joplin** H
(417) 781-0500. **$81-$295.** 3320 S Range Line Rd 64804. I-44 exit 8B,
just n. Int corridors. **Pets:** Accepted. 🍴 🛟 🛜 ❌ 🛏 💻

▼▼▼ **Residence Inn by Marriott-Joplin** H
(417) 782-0908. **$98-$152.** 3128 E Hammons Blvd 64804. I-44 exit 8,
just ne. Int corridors. **Pets:** Accepted. 🕹M 🛟 🛜 ❌ 🛏 💻

▼ ▼ **Sleep Inn** H
(417) 782-1212. **$84-$169.** 4100 Hwy 43 S 64803. I-44 exit 4, just s.
Int corridors. **Pets:** Accepted. 🛜 ❌ 🛏 💻

AAA ▼▼▼ **TownePlace Suites by Marriott**
Joplin H 🐾
(417) 659-8111. **$85-$122.** 4026 Arizona Ave 64804. I-44 exit 8, just sw.
Int corridors. **Pets:** Other species. $100 one-time fee/room. Service with
restrictions, crate. SAVE 🕹M 🛟 🛜 ❌ 🛏 💻

KANSAS CITY (Restaurants p. 617)
AAA ▼▼▼ ▼▼▼ **The Ambassador Kansas City,**
Autograph Collection H
(816) 298-7700. **$194-$303.** 1111 Grand Blvd 64106. Jct 11th St, south-
east corner. Int corridors. **Pets:** Accepted.
SAVE 🍴 🕹M 🛜 ❌ 🛏 💻

AAA ▼▼▼ **Best Western Country Inn North** M
(816) 459-7222. **$69-$179.** 2633 NE 43rd St 64117. I-35 exit 8C (Antioch Rd), just s on SR 1, then just e. Ext corridors. **Pets:** Medium, other
species. $15 daily fee/pet. Designated rooms, service with restrictions,
supervision. SAVE 🛟 🛜 🛏 💻

AAA ▼▼▼ **Best Western Plus Seville Plaza Hotel** H
(816) 561-9600. **$99-$159.** 4309 Main St 64111. Jct 43rd St, just s. Int
corridors. **Pets:** Accepted. SAVE 🕹M 🛜 ❌ 🛏 💻

▼▼▼ **Candlewood Suites Kansas City Airport** H ❀
(816) 886-9700. **$79-$159.** 11110 NW Ambassador Dr 64153. I-29 exit
12, just se. Int corridors. **Pets:** Medium. $20 daily fee/pet. Service with
restrictions, crate. 🍴 🕹M 🛜 🛏 💻

▼▼▼ **Candlewood Suites Kansas City Northeast** H
(816) 886-9311. **Call for rates.** 4450 N Randolph Rd 64117. I-435 exit
54, just s. Int corridors. **Pets:** Accepted. 🕹M 🛟 🛜 🛏 💻

▼▼▼ **Chase Suite Hotel** H
(816) 891-9009. **Call for rates.** 9900 NW Prairie View Rd 64153. I-29
exit 10, just w, then just n. Ext corridors. **Pets:** Accepted.
🍴 🛟 🛜 ❌ 🛏 💻

▼▼▼ **Comfort Inn & Suites near Worlds of Fun** H
(816) 454-3500. **$85-$199.** 7300 NE Parvin Rd 64117. I-435 exit 54,
just w. Int corridors. **Pets:** Other species. $25 daily fee/pet. Service with
restrictions. 🕹M 🛟 🛜 ❌ 🛏 💻

▼▼ **Drury Inn & Suites-Kansas City Airport** H
(816) 880-9700. **$90-$170.** 7900 NW Tiffany Springs Pkwy 64153. I-29
exit 10, just w. Int corridors. **Pets:** Accepted.
🕹M 🛟 🛜 ❌ 🛏 💻

▼▼▼ **Drury Inn & Suites-Kansas City Stadium** H
(816) 923-3000. **$85-$165.** 3830 Blue Ridge Cutoff 64133. I-70 exit
Blue Ridge Cutoff/Sports Complex, just nw. Int corridors.
Pets: Accepted. 🕹M 🛟 🛜 ❌ 🛏 💻

▼▼▼ **Embassy Suites Kansas City-International**
Airport H
(816) 891-7788. **$109-$259.** 7640 NW Tiffany Springs Pkwy 64153. I-29
exit 10, just e. Int corridors. **Pets:** Accepted.
🍴 🕹M 🛟 🔊 🛏 💻

AAA ▼▼▼ **Holiday Inn Country Club Plaza** H
(816) 753-7400. **$99-$209.** 1 E 45th St 64111. Jct Main St; in Country
Club Plaza. Int corridors. **Pets:** Accepted.
SAVE 🍴 🕹M 🛟 🛜 ❌ 🛏 💻

AAA ▼▼▼ **Holiday Inn Kansas City Northeast** H
(816) 455-1060. **$89-$120.** 7333 NE Parvin Rd 64117. I-435 exit 54,
just w. Int corridors. **Pets:** Accepted.
SAVE 🍴 🕹M 🛟 ❌ 🛜 ❌ 🛏 💻

AAA ▼▼▼ **Holiday Inn KCI Airport & KCI Expo**
Center H
(816) 801-8400. **Call for rates.** 11728 NW Ambassador Dr 64153. I-29
exit 13, just e on CR D, then just s. Int corridors. **Pets:** Accepted.
SAVE 🍴 🕹M 🛟 🛜 ❌ 🛏 💻

▼▼▼ **Homewood Suites by Hilton Kansas City**
Airport H
(816) 880-9880. **$109-$259.** 7312 NW Polo Dr 64153. I-29 exit 10, just
e. Int corridors. **Pets:** Accepted. 🍴 🛟 🛜 🛏 💻

Hotel Phillips Kansas City, Curio Collection by Hilton H
(816) 221-7000. **Call for rates.** 106 W 12th St 64105. Jct Wyandotte St, just e. Int corridors. **Pets:** Accepted. [SAVE] ⓎⓊ 🛜 ✕

Hyatt Place Kansas City/Airport H
(816) 891-0871. **$74-$199.** 7600 NW 97th Terr 64153. I-29 exit 10, just sw. Int corridors. **Pets:** Accepted. [SAVE] ⓊⓎ 🛜 ✕ 🔋 🖥

The InterContinental Kansas City at the Plaza H
(816) 756-1500. **Call for rates.** 401 Ward Pkwy 64112. Jct Wornall Rd; in Country Club Plaza. Int corridors. **Pets:** Accepted.
[SAVE] ⓎⓊ 🏊 ✕ 🛜 ✕ 🔋 🖥

Residence Inn by Marriott Downtown/Union Hill H
(816) 561-3000. **$133-$229.** 2975 Main St 64108. Jct 31st St, just n. Ext corridors. **Pets:** Accepted.
[ECO] ⓎⓊ Ⓜ 🏊 🛜 ✕ 🔋 🖥

Residence Inn by Marriott, Kansas City Airport H
(816) 741-2300. **$104-$205.** 10300 N Ambassador Dr 64153. I-29 exit 10, 1.5 mi ne. Int corridors. **Pets:** Accepted.
ⓎⓊ Ⓜ 🏊 🛜 ✕ 🔋 🖥

Residence Inn by Marriott Kansas City Country Club Plaza H
(816) 753-0033. **$132-$234.** 4601 Broadway Blvd 64112. Jct J.C. Nichols Pkwy, just w on 46th Terr; in Country Club Plaza. Ext/int corridors. **Pets:** Accepted. 🏊 🛜 ✕ 🔋 🖥

Residence Inn by Marriott Kansas City Downtown/ Convention Center H
(816) 221-1400. **$160-$319.** 1535 Baltimore Ave 64108. Jct 15th St and Baltimore Ave. Int corridors. **Pets:** Small, dogs only. $150 one-time fee/ room, $15 daily fee/pet. Designated rooms, service with restrictions, supervision. ⓎⓊ Ⓜ 🛜 ✕ 🔋 🖥

The Sheraton Kansas City Hotel at Crown Center H
(816) 841-1000. **$119-$329.** 2345 McGee St 64108. In Crown Center area. Int corridors. **Pets:** Accepted.
[SAVE] [ECO] ⓎⓊ Ⓜ 🏊 🛜 ✕ 🔋 🖥

Sheraton Suites Country Club Plaza H
(816) 931-4400. **$169-$399.** 770 W 47th St 64112. Jct Summit St; in Country Club Plaza. Int corridors. **Pets:** Accepted.
[SAVE] ⓎⓊ Ⓜ 🏊 🛜 ✕ 🔋 🖥

The Westin Kansas City at Crown Center H
(816) 474-4400. **$119-$329.** 1 E Pershing Rd 64108. 0.5 mi s. Int corridors. **Pets:** Accepted. [SAVE] ⓎⓊ Ⓜ 🏊 ✕ 🛜 ✕ 🔋 🖥

KEARNEY
Kearney Super 8 H
(816) 628-6800. **$63-$80.** 210 Platte Clay Way 64060. I-35 exit 26, just e on SR 92, then just n. Int corridors. **Pets:** Accepted.
ⓎⓊ 🏊 🛜 🔋 🖥

KIRKWOOD
Best Western Kirkwood Inn H 🐾
(314) 821-3950. **$109-$139.** 1200 S Kirkwood Rd 63122. I-44 exit 277B (Lindbergh Blvd), just n. Int corridors. **Pets:** Large, other species. $10 daily fee/pet. Designated rooms, service with restrictions, crate.
[SAVE] ⓎⓊ Ⓜ 🏊 🛜 ✕ 🔋 🖥

LAMAR
Super 8-Lamar H
(417) 682-6888. **$60-$95.** 45 SE 1st Ln 64759. I-49 exit 77, just ne. Ext/int corridors. **Pets:** Accepted. 🏊 🛜 🔋 🖥

LEBANON
Super 8 H
(417) 588-2574. **$70-$75.** 1831 W Elm St 65536. I-44 exit 127, just n. Int corridors. **Pets:** Accepted. ⓎⓊ 🏊 🛜 🔋 🖥

LICKING
Scenic Rivers Inn M
(573) 674-4809. **$65-$75.** 209 S Hwy 63 65542. On US 63. Ext corridors. **Pets:** Dogs only. $10 daily fee/pet. Designated rooms, service with restrictions, supervision. ⓎⓊ 🏊 🛜 🔋 🖥

MACON
Super 8 H
(660) 385-5788. **$65-$73.** 203 E Briggs Dr 63552. Jct US 36 and 63. Int corridors. **Pets:** Accepted. ⓎⓊ 🛜 ✕ 🔋 🖥

MARYLAND HEIGHTS
Comfort Inn St. Louis - Westport H 🐾
(314) 878-1400. **$85-$210.** 12031 Lackland Rd 63146. I-270 exit 16A (Page Ave), just e to Lackland Rd, then just w. Int corridors. **Pets:** Medium, dogs only. $10 daily fee/pet. Designated rooms, service with restrictions, supervision.
[SAVE] 🍴 ⓎⓊ Ⓜ 🏊 🛜 ✕ 🔋 🖥

Drury Inn & Suites-St. Louis-Westport H
(314) 576-9966. **$90-$150.** 12220 Dorsett Rd 63043. I-270 exit 17 (Dorsett Rd), just e. Int corridors. **Pets:** Accepted.
Ⓜ 🏊 🛜 ✕ 🔋 🖥

Hawthorn Suites by Wyndham St. Louis Westport Plaza H
(314) 469-0060. **$89-$149.** 1881 Craigshire Rd 63146. I-270 exit 16A (Page Ave), just e, just s on Concourse Dr, just s on Craig Rd, then just w. Ext corridors. **Pets:** Accepted. Ⓜ 🏊 🛜 🔋 🖥

Sheraton Westport Lakeside Chalet H
(314) 878-1500. **$99-$299.** 191 Westport Plaza 63146. I-270 exit 16A (Page Ave), just e, just s on Concourse Dr, just w on Lackland Rd, then 0.4 mi n. Int corridors. **Pets:** Accepted.
[SAVE] ⓎⓊ Ⓜ 🏊 🛜 ✕ 🔋 🖥

Sheraton Westport Plaza Tower H
(314) 878-1500. **$99-$209.** 900 Westport Plaza 63146. I-270 exit 16A (Page Ave), just e, just s on Concourse Dr, just w on Lackland Rd, then 0.4 mi n. Int corridors. **Pets:** Accepted.
[SAVE] ⓎⓊ Ⓜ 🏊 🛜 ✕ 🔋 🖥

Sonesta ES Suites St. Louis H
(314) 878-1555. **$109-$199.** 1855 Craigshire Rd 63146. I-270 exit 16A (Page Ave), just e, just s on Concourse Dr, just s on Craig Rd, then just w. Ext/int corridors. **Pets:** Accepted.
[SAVE] Ⓜ 🏊 🛜 ✕ 🔋 🖥

MARYVILLE
Americas Best Value Inn H
(660) 582-8088. **Call for rates.** 222 E Summit Dr 64468. On Business Rt US 71; just n of US 71 Bypass. Int corridors. **Pets:** Accepted.
🛜 ✕ 🔋 🖥

MEHLVILLE
Best Western St. Louis Inn H
(314) 416-7639. **$74-$134.** 6224 Heimos Industrial Park Dr 63129. I-55 exit 193, just e on Meramec Bottom Rd, then just n. Int corridors. **Pets:** Medium. $10 daily fee/pet. Designated rooms, service with restrictions, crate. [SAVE] 🏊 🛜 ✕ 🔋 🖥

MINER

Best Western Plus Sikeston 🅷
(573) 481-9500. **$79-$119.** 120 S Interstate Dr 63801. I-55 exit 67, just e, 0.4 mi s on Interstate Dr (frontage road). Int corridors. **Pets:** Large, other species. $15 daily fee/pet. Designated rooms, service with restrictions, crate.

Drury Inn & Suites-Sikeston 🅷
(573) 472-2299. **$110-$155.** 2608 E Malone Ave 63801. I-55 exit 67, just nw. Int corridors. **Pets:** Accepted.

Pear Tree Inn by Drury 🅷
(573) 471-4100. **$75-$115.** 2602 E Malone Ave 63801. I-55 exit 67, just nw. Int corridors. **Pets:** Accepted.

MOBERLY

Comfort Inn 🅷
(660) 269-9700. **$94-$159.** 1801 W Outer Rd 65270. Jct US 36 and 24, 0.4 mi e. Int corridors. **Pets:** Small. $20 one-time fee/pet. Designated rooms, service with restrictions, supervision.

NEOSHO

Best Western Big Spring Lodge 🅷 🐾
(417) 455-2300. **$83-$150.** 1810 Southern View Dr 64850. I-49 exit 24, 0.9 mi e. Int corridors. **Pets:** Large. $20 daily fee/room. Designated rooms, service with restrictions, supervision.

NEVADA

Holiday Inn Express & Suites Nevada 🅷
(417) 283-6177. **Call for rates.** 311 S Johnson Dr 64772. US 71 exit Camp Clark, just w. Int corridors. **Pets:** Accepted.

O'FALLON

Staybridge Suites O'Fallon 🅷
(636) 300-0999. **Call for rates.** 1155 Technology Dr 63368. US 40/61 exit 9 (CR K), just nw. Int corridors. **Pets:** Accepted.

OSAGE BEACH

Scottish Inns 🅼
(573) 348-3123. **$55-$95, 3 day notice.** 5404 Osage Beach Pkwy 65065. US 54 exit Case Rd, just s. Ext/int corridors. **Pets:** Small. $10 daily fee/pet. Service with restrictions, crate.

POPLAR BLUFF

Comfort Inn 🅷
(573) 686-5200. **$89-$140.** 2582 N Westwood Blvd 63901. 1.3 mi se of jct US 60 and 67. Int corridors. **Pets:** Medium. $25 one-time fee/room. Designated rooms, service with restrictions, supervision.

Drury Inn-Poplar Bluff 🅷
(573) 686-2451. **$95-$140.** 2220 N Westwood Blvd 63901. 1.4 mi se of jct US 60 and 67. Int corridors. **Pets:** Accepted.

REPUBLIC

AmericInn Lodge & Suites of Republic 🅷
(417) 732-5335. **$85-$145.** 950 N Austin Ln 65738. I-44 exit 67, 4.4 mi s to SR 174, then 0.7 mi e. Int corridors. **Pets:** Accepted.

RICHMOND HEIGHTS

Residence Inn by Marriott-St. Louis Galleria 🅷
(314) 862-1900. **$123-$211.** 8011 Galleria Pkwy 63117. I-64/US 40 exit 31B (Brentwood/Hanley Rd), 0.4 mi n on Brentwood Blvd, then 0.5 mi e. Ext corridors. **Pets:** Accepted.

ROLLA

Best Western Coachlight 🅼
(573) 341-2511. **$89-$99.** 1403 Martin Springs Dr 65401. Jct I-44 and Business Rt 44 S exit 184. Ext corridors. **Pets:** Accepted.

Pear Tree Inn by Drury-Rolla 🅷
(573) 364-4000. **$70-$120.** 2006 N Bishop Ave 65401. I-44 exit 186 (US 63), just ne. Int corridors. **Pets:** Accepted.

ST. ANN

Pear Tree Inn by Drury-St. Louis Airport 🅷
(314) 427-3400. **$80-$120.** 10810 Pear Tree Ln 63074. I-70 exit 236 (Airport Dr), just s, then just w. Int corridors. **Pets:** Accepted.

ST. CHARLES

Best Western Plus The Charles Hotel 🅷 🐾
(636) 946-6936. **$119-$179.** 1425 S 5th St 63301. I-70 exit 229B (5th St N), just n, then w. Int corridors. **Pets:** Dogs only. $10 one-time fee/pet. Service with restrictions, supervision.

Comfort Suites-St. Charles 🅷
(636) 949-0694. **$94-$250.** 1400 S 5th St 63301. I-70 exit 229 and 229B, just n on 5th St, just e on Ameristar Blvd, then just s. Int corridors. **Pets:** Medium, other species. $15 daily fee/pet. Designated rooms, service with restrictions, supervision.

TownePlace Suites by Marriott 🅷
(636) 949-6800. **$86-$128.** 1800 Zumbehl Rd 63303. I-70 exit 227 (Zumbehl Rd), 0.6 mi s, then just se. Int corridors. **Pets:** Accepted.

ST. CLAIR

Budget Lodging 🅼 🐾
(636) 629-1000. **$89-$99.** 866 S Outer Rd 63077. I-44 exit 240, just w. Ext corridors. **Pets:** Dogs only. $10 daily fee/room. Designated rooms, service with restrictions, supervision.

ST. JOSEPH

Candlewood Suites 🅷
(816) 232-2600. **Call for rates.** 3505 N Village Dr 64506. I-29 exit 50, just sw, then 0.3 mi n. Int corridors. **Pets:** Accepted.

Drury Inn & Suites-St. Joseph 🅷
(816) 364-4700. **$100-$140.** 4213 Frederick Blvd 64506. I-29 exit 47, just e. Int corridors. **Pets:** Accepted.

Radisson Hotel St. Joseph 🅷
(816) 279-8000. **$79-$109.** 102 S Third St 64501. I-229 exit Edmond St northbound; exit Felix St southbound; downtown. Int corridors. **Pets:** Accepted.

Stoney Creek Hotel & Conference Center 🅷
(816) 901-9600. **Call for rates.** 1201 N Woodbine Rd 64506. I-29 exit 47, just w. Int corridors. **Pets:** Accepted.

ST. LOUIS (Restaurants p. 617)

▲▲▲ ▼▼▼ **The Cheshire** H ❖
(314) 647-7300. **$149-$499.** 6300 Clayton Rd 63117. I-64/US 40 exit 33C (McCausland Ave/Skinker Blvd), just n on Skinker Blvd, then just w. Int corridors. **Pets:** Large, other species. $30 one-time fee/pet. Service with restrictions, supervision.
SAVE 〔Ⅱ〕 〔♿M〕 〔⛱〕 〔📶〕 〔✕〕 〔🛅〕 〔💻〕

▼▼▼▼ **Drury Inn & Suites Near Forest Park** H
(314) 646-0770. **$120-$210.** 2111 Sulphur Ave 63139. I-44 exit 286, just s. Int corridors. **Pets:** Accepted. 〔Ⅱ〕 〔♿M〕 〔⛱〕 〔📶〕 〔✕〕 〔🛅〕 〔💻〕

▼▼▼▼ **Drury Inn & Suites-St. Louis-Convention Center** H
(314) 231-8100. **$100-$200.** 711 N Broadway 63102. Between Convention Plaza and Lucas Ave. Int corridors. **Pets:** Accepted.
〔Ⅱ〕 〔♿M〕 〔⛱〕 〔📶〕 〔✕〕 〔🛅〕 〔💻〕

▼▼▼▼ **Drury Inn-St. Louis/Union Station** H
(314) 231-3900. **$100-$200.** 201 S 20th St 63103. I-64/US 40 exit 39 westbound (Market St at 21st St), just n, just e on Market St, then just s; exit 38A eastbound, just n on Jefferson Ave, 0.5 mi e on Market St, then just s. Int corridors. **Pets:** Accepted.
〔Ⅱ〕 〔♿M〕 〔📶〕 〔✕〕 〔🛅〕 〔💻〕

▼▼▼▼ **Drury Plaza Hotel-St. Louis at the Arch** H
(314) 231-3003. **$110-$210.** 2 S 4th St 63102. Between Walnut and Market sts. Int corridors. **Pets:** Accepted.
〔Ⅱ〕 〔♿M〕 〔⛱〕 〔📶〕 〔✕〕 〔🛅〕 〔💻〕

▲▲▲ ▼▼▼ **Four Seasons Hotel St. Louis** H ❖
(314) 881-5800. **Call for rates.** 999 N 2nd St 63102. Jct Washington Ave, just n on 4th St, just e on Cole St, just e on Carr St, then just s. Int corridors. **Pets:** Other species. $35 one-time fee/pet. Service with restrictions, supervision. SAVE 〔Ⅱ〕 〔♿M〕 〔⛱〕 〔✕〕 〔📶〕 〔💻〕

▲▲▲ ▼▼▼ **Hilton St. Louis at the Ballpark** H
(314) 421-1776. **$109-$374.** 1 S Broadway 63102. Between Walnut and Market sts. Int corridors. **Pets:** Accepted.
SAVE 〔⊟〕 〔Ⅱ〕 〔♿M〕 〔⛱〕 〔✕〕 〔📡〕 〔✕〕 〔🛅〕 〔💻〕

▲▲▲ ▼▼▼ **Hilton-St. Louis Downtown at the Arch** H
(314) 436-0002. **$129-$259.** 400 Olive St 63102. Jct 4th St. Int corridors. **Pets:** Accepted. SAVE 〔Ⅱ〕 〔♿M〕 〔📡〕 〔✕〕 〔🛅〕 〔💻〕

▲▲▲ ▼▼▼ **Holiday Inn Forest Park** H
(314) 645-0700. **$99-$229.** 5915 Wilson Ave 63110. I-44 exit 286, just s on Hampton Ave. Int corridors. **Pets:** Medium, other species. $75 deposit/pet, $25 one-time fee/pet. Designated rooms, service with restrictions, supervision. SAVE 〔Ⅱ〕 〔♿M〕 〔⛱〕 〔📶〕 〔✕〕 〔🛅〕 〔💻〕

▼▼▼▼ **Home2 Suites by Hilton St. Louis/Forest Park** H ❖
(314) 531-4446. **$119-$209.** 920 S Taylor Ave 63110. I-64 exit 36B, just s on A Boyle Ave, 0.4 mi w on Chouteau Ave, then just n. Int corridors. **Pets:** Other species. $75 one-time fee/room. Service with restrictions.
〔Ⅱ〕 〔♿M〕 〔📶〕 〔✕〕 〔🛅〕 〔💻〕

▲▲▲ ▼▼▼▼ **Hotel Ignacio** H
(314) 977-4411. **$120-$270.** 3411 Olive St 63103. I-64/US 40 exit 38A westbound, just w on Forest Park Ave, just n on Grand Blvd, then just e on Lindell Blvd; exit 37B eastbound, 0.4 mi n on Grand Blvd, then just e on Lindell Blvd. Int corridors. **Pets:** Medium, dogs only. $75 one-time fee/room. Service with restrictions, supervision.
SAVE 〔Ⅱ〕 〔♿M〕 〔📶〕 〔✕〕 〔🛅〕 〔💻〕

▲▲▲ ▼▼▼▼ **Hyatt Regency St. Louis at The Arch** H ❖
(314) 655-1234. **$79-$399.** 315 Chestnut St 63102. Jct 4th St; across from Gateway Arch. Int corridors. **Pets:** Medium, dogs only. $100 one-time fee/room. Designated rooms, service with restrictions, supervision.
SAVE 〔Ⅱ〕 〔♿M〕 〔📶〕 〔🛅〕 〔💻〕

▲▲▲ ▼▼▼ ▼▼▼ **Magnolia St. Louis** H
(314) 436-9000. **Call for rates.** 421 N 8th St 63101. Just s of convention center. Int corridors. **Pets:** Accepted.
SAVE 〔⊟〕 〔Ⅱ〕 〔♿M〕 〔⛱〕 〔📶〕 〔✕〕 〔🛅〕 〔💻〕

▲▲▲ ▼▼▼ ▼▼▼ **Moonrise Hotel** H ❖
(314) 721-1111. **Call for rates.** 6177 Delmar Blvd 63112. I-64/US 40 exit 33C (McCausland Ave/Skinker Blvd), 1.7 mi n on Skinker Blvd, then just e; in The Loop. Int corridors. **Pets:** $40 one-time fee/pet. Designated rooms, service with restrictions.
SAVE 〔⊟〕 〔Ⅱ〕 〔♿M〕 〔📶〕 〔✕〕 〔🛅〕 〔💻〕

▼▼▼▼ **Pear Tree Inn Union Station** H
(314) 241-3200. **$90-$175.** 2211 Market St 63103. I-64/US 40 exit 39 westbound (Market St at 21st St), just n, then just w; exit 38A eastbound just n on Jefferson Ave, then just e. Int corridors.
Pets: Accepted. 〔Ⅱ〕 〔♿M〕 〔⛱〕 〔📶〕 〔✕〕 〔🛅〕 〔💻〕

▲▲▲ ▼▼▼ **Red Roof PLUS+ St. Louis-Forest Park/ Hampton Ave.** H
(314) 645-0101. **$69-$139.** 5823 Wilson Ave 63110. I-44 exit 286, 0.3 mi se. Ext corridors. **Pets:** Accepted. SAVE 〔📶〕 〔✕〕 〔🛅〕 〔💻〕

▼▼▼▼ **Residence Inn by Marriott St. Louis Downtown** H
(314) 289-7500. **$133-$246.** 525 S Jefferson Ave 63103. I-64/US 40 exit 38A eastbound, just s; exit 39 westbound, just n, just w on Market St, then just s. Int corridors. **Pets:** $100 one-time fee/pet. Designated rooms, service with restrictions, crate.
〔Ⅱ〕 〔♿M〕 〔⛱〕 〔📶〕 〔✕〕 〔🛅〕 〔💻〕

▲▲▲ ▼▼▼ ▼▼▼ **St. Louis Union Station Hotel** H
(314) 231-1234. **$129-$899.** 1820 Market St 63103. I-64/US 40 exit 39 westbound (Market St at 21st St), just n, then just e; exit 38A eastbound, just n on Jefferson Ave, then 0.5 mi e. Int corridors.
Pets: Accepted. 〔Ⅱ〕 〔♿M〕 〔⛱〕 〔📶〕 〔✕〕 〔🛅〕 〔💻〕

▲▲▲ ▼▼▼ ▼▼▼ **The Westin St. Louis** H ❖
(314) 621-2000. **$119-$429.** 811 Spruce St 63102. I-64/US 40 exit 39C eastbound, just n on 11th St, then just e; exit 40A westbound, just n, just e on Clark Ave, just s on 8th St, then just w. Int corridors. **Pets:** Medium, dogs only. Service with restrictions, supervision.
SAVE 〔Ⅱ〕 〔♿M〕 〔✕〕 〔📡〕 〔✕〕 〔🛅〕 〔💻〕

ST. PETERS

▼▼▼▼ **Drury Inn St. Peters** H
(636) 397-9700. **$100-$160.** 170 Mid Rivers Mall Cir 63376. I-70 exit 222 (Mid Rivers Mall Dr), just s, then just e. Int corridors.
Pets: Accepted. 〔♿M〕 〔⛱〕 〔📶〕 〔✕〕 〔🛅〕 〔💻〕

ST. ROBERT

▲▲▲ ▼▼ ▼▼ **Best Western Montis Inn** H
(573) 336-4299. **$70-$75.** 14086 Hwy Z 65584. I-44 exit 163, just s. Ext corridors. **Pets:** Dogs only. $10 daily fee/pet. Designated rooms, service with restrictions, supervision. SAVE 〔⛱〕 〔📶〕 〔🛅〕 〔💻〕

▼▼▼▼ **MainStay Suites** H
(573) 451-2700. **$69-$183.** 227 St. Robert Blvd 65584. I-44 exit 159, 0.8 mi nw. Ext/int corridors. **Pets:** Other species. $15 daily fee/room. Service with restrictions, crate. ECO 〔♿M〕 〔⛱〕 〔📶〕 〔✕〕 〔🛅〕 〔💻〕

STE. GENEVIEVE

▲▲▲ ▼▼ ▼▼ **Microtel Inn & Suites by Wyndham Sainte Genevieve** H
(573) 883-8884. **$80-$89.** 21958 Hwy 32 63670. I-55 exit 150 (SR 32), 3.9 mi e. Int corridors. **Pets:** Other species. $10 daily fee/pet. Designated rooms, service with restrictions, supervision.
SAVE 〔♿M〕 〔📶〕 〔✕〕 〔🛅〕 〔💻〕

SEDALIA

◬ ▽▽◈ Best Western State Fair Inn H
(660) 826-6100. $94-$132. 3120 S Limit Ave 65301. Jct US 50, 1.5 mi s on US 65. Ext/int corridors. Pets: Large, other species. Designated rooms, service with restrictions, supervision.

SAVE 🍴 🏊 🛜 🔌 🖵

SEYMOUR

▽▽ Americas Best Value Inn H
(417) 935-9888. $68-$73. 1000 E Clinton Rd 65746. Just s of jct US 60. Int corridors. Pets: Medium. $15 daily fee/pet. Designated rooms, no service, supervision. 🍴 🛜 🔌 🖵

SIKESTON

◬ ▽▽▽ Comfort Inn & Suites H
(573) 472-0197. $105-$180. 109 Matthews Ln 63801. I-55 exit 67, just sw. Int corridors. Pets: $15 daily fee/pet. Designated rooms, service with restrictions, supervision. SAVE 🏊 🛜 🗙 🔌 🖵

SPRINGFIELD

▽▽ Baymont Inn & Suites H
(417) 887-2323. $70-$119. 3343 E Battlefield Rd 65804. US 65 exit Battlefield St, just w. Int corridors. Pets: Accepted.

🛆 🏊 🛜 🗙 🔌 🖵

◬ ▽▽▽ Best Western Plus Coach House H
(417) 862-0701. $85-$115. 2535 N Glenstone Ave 65803. I-44 exit 80, just s. Ext corridors. Pets: Accepted. SAVE 🔌 🏊 🛜 🔌 🖵

◬ ▽▽ Best Western Plus Springfield Airport Inn H ♣
(417) 799-2200. $99-$115. 4445 W Chestnut Expwy 65802. I-44 exit 72, 0.8 mi s. Int corridors. Pets: Large, other species. $15 daily fee/pet. Designated rooms, service with restrictions, supervision.

SAVE 🔌 🍴 🏊 🛜 🔌 🖵

◬ ▽▽ Best Western Route 66 Rail Haven M
(417) 866-1963. $99-$105. 203 S Glenstone Ave 65802. I-44 exit 80, 3 mi s. Ext corridors. Pets: Accepted.

SAVE 🍴 🏊 🛜 🗙 🔌 🖵

▽▽▽ Candlewood Suites South H
(417) 881-8500. $94-$149. 1035 E Republic Rd 65807. US 60 (James River Frwy) exit National Ave, just s. Int corridors. Pets: Accepted.

🏊 🛜 🗙 🔌 🖵

▽▽▽ Candlewood Suites Springfield I-44 H ♣
(417) 866-4242. Call for rates. 1920 E Kerr St 65803. I-44 exit 80, just e to Evergreen St. Int corridors. Pets: $75 one-time fee/pet. Service with restrictions, crate. 🏊 🛜 🔌 🖵

▽▽▽ Courtyard by Marriott Airport H
(417) 869-6700. $89-$154. 3527 W Kearney St 65803. I-44 exit 75 (US 160 W Bypass), just se to SR 744, then just w. Int corridors. Pets: Accepted. 🍴 🏊 🛜 🗙 🔌 🖵

◬ ▽▽▽ DoubleTree by Hilton Springfield H ♣
(417) 831-3131. $119-$189. 2431 N Glenstone Ave 65803. I-44 exit 80, just s. Int corridors. Pets: Other species. $50 one-time fee/room. Designated rooms. SAVE 🔌 🍴 🏊 🛜 🗙 🔌 🖵

▽▽▽ Drury Inn & Suites-Springfield H
(417) 863-8400. $100-$145. 2715 N Glenstone Ave 65803. I-44 exit 80, just s. Int corridors. Pets: Accepted. 🏊 🛜 🗙 🔌 🖵

◬ ▽▽▽ Greenstay Hotel & Suites H
(417) 863-1440. $69-$109. 222 N Ingram Mill Rd 65802. US 65 exit Chestnut Expwy, just sw. Ext/int corridors. Pets: Accepted.

SAVE 🔌 🍴 🏊 🛜 🗙 🔌 🖵

◬ ▽▽▽ Hilton Garden Inn Springfield H
(417) 875-8800. $109-$179. 4155 S Nature Center Way 65804. US 60 (James River Frwy) exit Glenstone Ave (US 65 business route), just s. Int corridors. Pets: Small. $75 one-time fee/room. Designated rooms, service with restrictions, crate.

SAVE 🍴 🏊 🛜 🗙 🔌 🖵

◬ ▽▽▽ Hotel Vandivort H ♣
(417) 832-1515. $149-$599. 305 E Walnut St 65806. Jct E Walnut St and S Robinson Ave; downtown. Int corridors. Pets: Other species. $50 one-time fee/room. Service with restrictions.

SAVE 🍴 🏊 🛜 🗙 🔌 🖵

▽▽▽ La Quinta Inn & Suites Springfield Airport Plaza H
(417) 447-4466. $93-$218. 2445 N Airport Plaza Ave 65803. I-44 exit 75 (US 160 W Bypass), just se. Int corridors. Pets: Accepted.

🍴 🏊 🛜 🗙 🔌 🖵

▽▽▽ La Quinta Inn & Suites Springfield South H
(417) 890-6060. $86-$172. 2535 S Campbell Ave 65807. Jct Battlefield Rd and Campbell Ave, 0.5 mi n. Int corridors. Pets: Accepted.

SAVE 🏊 🛜 🗙 🔌 🖵

◬ ▽▽▽ TownePlace Suites by Marriott Springfield H ♣
(417) 881-8118. $106-$161. 2009 N National Ave 65804. US 60 (James River Expwy) exit National Ave, 2.5 mi n. Int corridors. Pets: $45 one-time fee/room. Service with restrictions.

SAVE 🔌 🍴 🏊 🛜 🗙 🔌 🖵

◬ ▽▽▽ University Plaza Hotel and Convention Center H
(417) 864-7333. $99-$189. 333 John Q Hammons Pkwy 65806. 0.5 mi e on St. Louis St. Int corridors. Pets: $25 daily fee/room. Designated rooms, service with restrictions, crate.

SAVE 🍴 🏊 🏊 🗙 🛜 🗙 🔌 🖵

SULLIVAN

▽▽ Baymont Inn & Suites H
(573) 860-3333. $79-$95. 275 N Service Rd W 63080. I-44 exit 225, just e, then 0.4 mi n. Int corridors. Pets: Other species. $10 daily fee/pet. Designated rooms, service with restrictions, crate.

🏊 🏊 🛜 🔌 🖵

◬ ▽▽▽ Comfort Inn H
(573) 468-7800. $99-$134. 736 S Service Rd W 63080. I-44 exit 225, just sw. Int corridors. Pets: Medium. $15 daily fee/pet. Designated rooms, service with restrictions, supervision.

SAVE 🍴 🏊 🛜 🗙 🔌 🖵

SUNSET HILLS

◬ ▽▽▽ Holiday Inn St. Louis SW-Route 66 H
(314) 821-6600. Call for rates. 10709 Watson Rd 63127. I-44 exit 277B (Lindbergh Blvd), just s on US 61/67. Int corridors. Pets: Small. $35 one-time fee/room. Service with restrictions, crate.

SAVE 🍴 🏊 🏊 🛜 🔌 🖵

UNION

▽▽ Super 8 H
(636) 583-8808. $80-$95. 1015 E Main St 63084. I-44 exit 247 (US 50), 4.7 mi w; just w of jct SR 47. Int corridors. Pets: Medium, dogs only. $10 daily fee/pet. Designated rooms, service with restrictions, supervision. 🍴 🏊 🏊 🛜 🔌 🖵

VALLEY PARK

▽▽▽ Drury Inn & Suites-St. Louis Southwest H
(636) 861-8300. $80-$180. 5 Lambert Drury Dr 63088. I-44 exit 272 (SR 141), just sw. Int corridors. Pets: Accepted.

🏊 🏊 🛜 🗙 🔌 🖵

WASHINGTON

Best Western Plus Washington Hotel H
(636) 390-8877. **$109-$159.** 2621 E 5th St 63090. I-44 exit 251, 8.5 mi w on SR 100. Int corridors. **Pets:** Accepted.
[SAVE] [TI] [≈] [⊚] [✕] [🔒] [▯]

Super 8 Washington H
(636) 390-0088. **$80-$95.** 2081 Eckelkamp Ct 63090. I-44 exit 251, 10 mi w on SR 100; just s of SR 100 and 47. Int corridors. **Pets:** Medium, dogs only. $10 daily fee/pet. Designated rooms, service with restrictions, supervision. [TI] [⊚] [🔒] [▯]

WEST PLAINS

Quality Inn West Plains H
(417) 257-2711. **$90-$130.** 220 Jan Howard Expwy 65775. 0.5 mi nw of jct US 63 and 160. Int corridors. **Pets:** Accepted.
[&M] [≈] [⊚] [✕] [🔒] [▯]

WILLOW SPRINGS

Comfort Inn of Willow Springs H
(417) 469-0410. **$90-$170.** 1204 E Main St 65793. Just n of US 60/63. Int corridors. **Pets:** Accepted. [&M] [⊚] [✕] [🔒] [▯]

WOODSON TERRACE

Hilton St. Louis Airport H
(314) 426-5500. **$99-$309.** 10330 Natural Bridge Rd 63134. I-70 exit 236 (Lambert Airport), 0.5 mi se. Int corridors. **Pets:** Accepted.
[SAVE] [TI] [&M] [≈] [s⊚] [✕] [🔒] [▯]

MONTANA

BELGRADE

Holiday Inn Express & Suites Belgrade H
(406) 388-7100. **$94-$235.** 309 W Madison Ave 59714. I-90 exit 298, just n on SR 85. Int corridors. **Pets:** Accepted.
[SAVE] [&M] [⊚] [✕] [🔒] [▯]

La Quinta Inn & Suites Belgrade/Bozeman H
(406) 388-2222. **$67-$262.** 6445 Jackrabbit Ln 59714. I-90 exit 298, just s on SR 85. Int corridors. **Pets:** Accepted.
[&M] [≈] [✕] [⊚] [✕] [🔒] [▯]

Quality Inn H
(406) 388-0800. **$59-$199.** 6261 Jackrabbit Ln 59714. I-90 exit 298, just s on SR 85. Int corridors. **Pets:** Accepted.
[SAVE] [&M] [⊚] [✕] [🔒] [▯]

Super 8-Belgrade/Bozeman Airport H
(406) 388-1493. **$70-$120.** 6450 Jackrabbit Ln 59714. I-90 exit 298, just s on SR 85. Int corridors. **Pets:** Accepted. [≈] [⊚] [🔒] [▯]

BIGFORK

Mountain Lake Lodge H 🐾
(406) 837-3800. **$149-$285, 7 day notice.** 14735 Sylvan Dr 59911. On SR 35, 5 mi s. Ext corridors. **Pets:** Dogs only. $15 daily fee/pet. Designated rooms, service with restrictions, supervision.
[SAVE] [TI] [&M] [≈] [⊚] [✕] [🔒] [▯]

Timbers Motel M
(406) 837-6200. **Call for rates.** 8540 Hwy 35 59911. Just n on SR 35 from jct SR 209. Ext corridors. **Pets:** Accepted.
[≈] [⊚] [✕] [🔒] [▯]

BIG SKY

Rainbow Ranch Lodge H
(406) 995-4132. **$135-$285, 14 day notice.** 42950 Gallatin Rd 59730. 5 mi s on US 191. Ext corridors. **Pets:** $41 one-time fee/room. Designated rooms, service with restrictions, supervision.
[TI] [✕] [⊚] [✕] [🔑] [🔒] [▯]

BIG TIMBER

Big Timber Super 8 H
(406) 932-8888. **$84-$103.** 20A Big Timber Loop Rd 59011. I-90 exit 367, just s. Int corridors. **Pets:** Accepted. [⊚] [🔒] [▯]

River Valley Inn H
(406) 932-4943. **Call for rates.** 600 W 2nd St 59011. I-90 exit 367, just n, then 0.6 mi e. Int corridors. **Pets:** Small. $20 one-time fee/pet. Designated rooms, service with restrictions, supervision. [&M] [⊚] [🔒]

BILLINGS

Best Western Plus Clocktower Inn H 🌼
(406) 259-5511. **$119-$149.** 2511 1st Ave N 59101. On I-90 business loop; downtown. Ext/int corridors. **Pets:** Other species. $20 daily fee/pet. Designated rooms, service with restrictions.
[SAVE] [TI] [≈] [⊚] [✕] [🔒] [▯]

Best Western Plus Kelly Inn & Suites H 🐾
(406) 256-9400. **$150-$190.** 4915 Southgate Dr 59101. I-90 exit 447, just w. Ext/int corridors. **Pets:** Large. Designated rooms, service with restrictions, supervision. [SAVE] [&M] [≈] [⊚] [✕] [🔒] [▯]

Billings Super 8 H
(406) 248-8842. **$79-$109.** 5400 Southgate Dr 59101. I-90 exit 447, just n on S Billings Blvd, 0.8 mi w on King Ave, then just s on Parkway Ln. Int corridors. **Pets:** Accepted. [&M] [⊚] [🔒] [▯]

Days Inn H
(406) 252-4007. **$73-$169.** 843 Parkway Ln 59101. I-90 exit 447, just n on S Billings Blvd, 0.8 mi w on King Ave, then just s. Int corridors. **Pets:** Accepted. [⊚] [✕] [🔒] [▯]

Extended Stay America-Billings-West End H
(406) 245-3980. **$80-$140.** 4950 Southgate Dr 59101. I-90 exit 447, just w. Int corridors. **Pets:** Accepted. [&M] [⊚] [✕] [🔒] [▯]

Hilltop Inn by Riversage H
(406) 245-5000. **$95-$105.** 1116 N 28th St 59101. I-90 exit 450, 2 mi n on 27th St, just w on 11th Ave, then just n. Int corridors. **Pets:** Large, other species. $8 daily fee/pet. Service with restrictions.
[&M] [⊚] [✕] [🔒] [▯]

Kelly Inn H 🌼
(406) 248-9800. **Call for rates.** 5610 S Frontage Rd 59101. I-90 exit 446, just s. Ext/int corridors. **Pets:** Other species. Service with restrictions, supervision. [&M] [≈] [⊚] [✕] [🔒] [▯]

La Quinta Inn and Suites H
(406) 252-1188. **$103-$262.** 5720 S Frontage Rd 59101. I-90 exit 446, just s. Int corridors. **Pets:** Accepted. [&M] [⊚] [✕] [🔒] [▯]

My Place Hotel H 🐾
(406) 259-9970. **$85-$143.** 4770 King Ave E 59101. I-90 exit 447, just e. Int corridors. **Pets:** Other species. $10 daily fee/room. Service with restrictions, crate. [⊚] [✕] [🔒] [▯]

▼▼ **Quality Inn Homestead** H
(406) 652-1320. **$94-$199.** 2036 Overland Ave 59102. I-90 exit 446, 0.5 mi n, then just s. Int corridors. **Pets:** Accepted.
⊛ ☒ 🛇 🛏 💻

▼▼▼ **Residence Inn by Marriott** H ❀
(406) 656-3900. **$123-$213.** 956 S 25th St W 59102. I-90 exit 446, 1.5 mi w, just s on S 24th St, then just s. Int corridors. **Pets:** Large, other species. $75 one-time fee/room. Service with restrictions, supervision.
♿ ⊛ 📶 ☒ 🛏 💻

▼▼ **Riversage Billings Inn** H
(406) 252-6800. **Call for rates.** 880 N 29th St 59101. I-90 exit 450, 2 mi n on 27th St, then just w on 9th Ave. Int corridors. **Pets:** Large, other species. $100 deposit/room, $8 daily fee/pet. Designated rooms, service with restrictions, crate. 📶 ☒ 🛏 💻

𝔸𝔸𝔸 ▼▼▼ **TownePlace Suites by Marriott Billings** H
(406) 652-7106. **Call for rates.** 2480 Grant Rd 59102. Jct King Ave and S 24th St W, 0.4 mi s, then just w. Int corridors. **Pets:** Accepted.
SAVE ♿ 📶 ☒ 🛏 💻

𝔸𝔸𝔸 ▼▼ **Western Executive Inn** H
(406) 294-8888. **$90-$210.** 3121 King Ave W 59102. I-90 exit 446, 2.5 mi w. Int corridors. **Pets:** Medium. $20 daily fee/pet. Service with restrictions, crate. SAVE ♿ 📶 🛏 💻

BOZEMAN (Restaurants p. 617)

𝔸𝔸𝔸 ▼▼▼▼ **Best Western Plus GranTree Inn** H ❀
(406) 587-5261. **$129-$269.** 1325 N 7th Ave 59715. I-90 exit 306, just s. Int corridors. **Pets:** $10 daily fee/pet. Service with restrictions, supervision. SAVE 🍽 ⊛ 📶 ☒ 🛏 💻

▼▼ **Bozeman Days Inn & Suites** H
(406) 587-5251. **$65-$150.** 1321 N 7th Ave 59715. I-90 exit 306, just s. Int corridors. **Pets:** Accepted. ⊛ 📶 ☒ 🛏 💻

▼▼ **Bozeman's Western Heritage Inn** H ❀
(406) 586-8534. **Call for rates.** 1200 E Main St 59715. I-90 exit 309 (Main St), 0.5 mi w. Int corridors. **Pets:** Other species. $10 daily fee/pet. Designated rooms, service with restrictions, supervision.
📶 ☒ 🛏 💻

▼▼▼ **Comfort Inn of Bozeman** H
(406) 587-2322. **$74-$209.** 1370 N 7th Ave 59715. I-90 exit 306, just s. Int corridors. **Pets:** Accepted. ⊛ 📶 ☒ 🛏 💻

▼▼▼ **Holiday Inn Bozeman** H
(406) 587-4561. **$79-$219.** 5 E Baxter Ln 59715. I-90 exit 306, just s. Int corridors. **Pets:** Other species. Designated rooms, service with restrictions, supervision. 🍽 ⊛ 📶 ☒ 🛏 💻

▼▼▼ **Holiday Inn Express & Suites** H
(406) 582-4995. **Call for rates.** 2305 Catron St 59718. I-90 exit 305, just s on CR 41 (19th St), then just w on E Valley Center Rd. Int corridors. **Pets:** Accepted. ECO ♿ ⊛ 📶 ☒ 🛏 💻

▼▼ **La Quinta Inn & Suites** H
(406) 585-9300. **$86-$284.** 620 Nikles Dr 59715. I-90 exit 306, just ne. Int corridors. **Pets:** Accepted. ♿ ⊛ 📶 ☒ 🛏 💻

▼▼ **Motel 6 Bozeman #4818** H
(406) 585-7888. **Call for rates.** 817 Wheat Dr 59718. I-90 exit 306, just n. Int corridors. **Pets:** Accepted. ♿ ⊛ 📶 ☒ 🛏 💻

▼▼ **MountainView Lodge & Suites** H
(406) 522-8686. **$89-$179.** 1121 Reeves Rd W 59718. I-90 exit 305, just n. Int corridors. **Pets:** Dogs only. $10 daily fee/pet. Designated rooms, service with restrictions, supervision.
♿ ⊛ ☒ 📶 🛏 💻

▼▼ **My Place Hotel** H
(406) 586-8228. **Call for rates.** 5889 E Valley Center Rd 59718. I-90 exit 305, just s on CR 41 (19th St), then just w. Int corridors. **Pets:** Accepted. ♿ 📶 ☒ 🛏 💻

▼▼ **Ramada** H
(406) 585-2626. **$60-$140, 3 day notice.** 2020 Wheat Dr 59715. I-90 exit 306, just n, then just w. Ext/int corridors. **Pets:** Accepted.
♿ ⊛ 📶 ☒ 🛏 💻

▼▼ **Super 8** H
(406) 586-1521. **$59-$159.** 800 Wheat Dr 59715. I-90 exit 306, just n, then just w. Int corridors. **Pets:** Accepted. 📶 ☒ 🛏 💻

BROWNING

𝔸𝔸𝔸 ◇ **Going to the Sun Inn & Suites** M
(406) 338-7572. **Call for rates.** 121 Central Ave E 59417. On US 2; center. Ext corridors. **Pets:** Small, other species. $15 daily fee/pet. Service with restrictions, supervision. SAVE 🍽 📶 ☒ 🛏

BUTTE

▼▼ **Americas Best Value Inn** M
(406) 723-5464. **Call for rates.** 122001 W Brown's Gulch Rd 59701. I-90/15 exit 122 (Rocker Rd), just n. Int corridors. **Pets:** Accepted.
📶

𝔸𝔸𝔸 ▼▼▼ **Best Western Plus Butte Plaza Inn** H
(406) 494-3500. **$112-$165.** 2900 Harrison Ave 59701. I-90/15 exit 127 (Harrison Ave), just s. Int corridors. **Pets:** Accepted.
SAVE ⎚ 🍽 ⊛ ☒ 📶 ☒ 🛏 💻

𝔸𝔸𝔸 ▼▼▼ **Comfort Inn of Butte** H ❀
(406) 494-8850. **$115-$195.** 2777 Harrison Ave 59701. I-90/15 exit 127 (Harrison Ave), just s. Int corridors. **Pets:** Large, other species. $20 daily fee/room. Designated rooms, service with restrictions, supervision.
SAVE ECO ♿ ⊛ ☒ 📶 ☒ 🛏 💻

▼▼ **Finlen Hotel** H
(406) 723-5461. **$76-$110.** 100 E Broadway 59701. Jct Wyoming St; in Historic Uptown. Ext/int corridors. **Pets:** Accepted. 📶 ☒ 🛏

▼▼▼ **La Quinta Inn & Suites** H
(406) 494-6999. **$86-$224.** 1 Holiday Park Dr 59701. I-90/15 exit 127 (Harrison Ave), just n to Cornell St, then just e, follow signs. Int corridors. **Pets:** Accepted. ♿ 📶 ☒ 🛏 💻

𝔸𝔸𝔸 ▼▼▼ **Super 8 of Butte** H
(406) 494-6000. **$72-$100.** 2929 Harrison Ave 59701. I-90/15 exit 127 (Harrison Ave), just s. Int corridors. **Pets:** Medium. $15 one-time fee/pet. Designated rooms, service with restrictions, supervision.
SAVE ♿ 📶 ☒ 🛏 💻

COLUMBIA FALLS

▼▼▼ **Bad Rock Bed & Breakfast** BB
(406) 892-2829. **$135-$250, 30 day notice.** 480 Bad Rock Dr 59912. Jct US 2 and SR 206, 2.4 mi s on SR 206, 0.9 mi w. Int corridors. **Pets:** Accepted. ♿ 📶 ☒ 🛏 💻

COLUMBUS

▼▼ **Super 8 of Columbus** H
(406) 322-4101. **$73-$99.** 602 8th Ave N 59019. I-90 exit 408, just s on SR 78. Int corridors. **Pets:** Accepted. 📶 ☒ 🛏 💻

CONRAD

▼▼ **Super 8** H ❀
(406) 278-7676. **$86-$96.** 215 N Main St 59425. I-15 exit 339, just w. Int corridors. **Pets:** Other species. $15 daily fee/pet. Service with restrictions, crate. 📶 ☒ 🛏 💻

DEER LODGE

◆ Travelodge M
(406) 846-2370. **$80-$90.** 1150 N Main St 59722. I-90 exit 184, 0.3 mi s. Int corridors. **Pets:** Accepted. 📶 ✕ 🛢 🖥

◆ Western Big Sky Inn M
(406) 846-2590. **Call for rates.** 210 N Main St 59722. I-90 exit 184, 1 mi w. Ext corridors. **Pets:** Accepted. 📶 ✕ 🛢 🖥

DILLON

◆◆ Best Western Paradise Inn H
(406) 683-4214. **$89-$160.** 650 N Montana St 59725. I-15 exit 63, 0.3 mi s on SR 41. Ext corridors. **Pets:** Accepted.
🅢 ⇌ 📶 ✕ 🛢 🖥

◆◆ Comfort Inn of Dillon H
(406) 683-6831. **$99-$175.** 450 N Interchange 59725. I-15 exit 63, just e. Int corridors. **Pets:** $15 daily fee/pet. Designated rooms, service with restrictions, supervision. 🅢 ⇌ 📶 ✕ 🛢 🖥

◆◆ FairBridge Inn Express H
(406) 683-3636. **Call for rates.** 580 Sinclair St 59725. I-15 exit 63, just e. Int corridors. **Pets:** Accepted. 🍴 ⇌ 📶 ✕ 🛢 🖥

EAST GLACIER PARK

◆◆ Dancing Bears Inn & Suites M
(406) 226-4402. **Call for rates.** 40 Montana Ave 59434. Just off US 2, follow signs; center. Ext/int corridors. **Pets:** Accepted.
🅢 📶 ✕ 🛢 🖥

ENNIS

◆◆ Fan Mountain Inn M
(406) 682-5200. **$75-$100, 14 day notice.** 204 N Main St 59729. US 287, just nw of City Center. Ext corridors. **Pets:** Accepted.
🅢 📶 ✕ 🛢

FORSYTH

◆◆ Rails Inn Motel H
(406) 346-2242. **$69-$99, 3 day notice.** 290 Front St 59327. I-94 exit 93, just n, then 0.5 mi e. Int corridors. **Pets:** Other species. $6 daily fee/pet. Designated rooms, service with restrictions, supervision.
🅢 🍴 📶 ✕ 🛢 🖥

◆◆ Restwel Motel M
(406) 346-2771. **$80-$100.** 810 Front St 59327. I-94 exit 95, 0.8 mi nw. Ext corridors. **Pets:** Accepted. 🅢 📶 🛢

◆◆ Sundowner Inn M
(406) 346-2115. **$100-$140.** 1018 Front St 59327. I-94 exit 95, 0.5 mi nw. Ext corridors. **Pets:** Dogs only. $15 daily fee/pet. Service with restrictions, supervision. 🅢 📶 ✕ 🛢 🖥

◆◆ Westwind Motor Inn M
(406) 346-2038. **$69-$99, 3 day notice.** 225 Westwind Ln 59327. I-94 exit 93, 0.3 mi n. Int corridors. **Pets:** Other species. $6 daily fee/pet. Designated rooms, service with restrictions, supervision.
🅢 🍴 📶 ✕ 🛢 🖥

GARDINER

◆◆ Best Western By Mammoth Hot Springs M
(406) 848-7311. **$109-$260.** 905 Scott St W 59030. 0.5 mi n. Ext/int corridors. **Pets:** Accepted. 🅢 🍴 ⇌ 📶 ✕ 🛢 🖥

◆◆ Yellowstone River Motel M
(406) 848-7303. **$70-$195.** 14 E Park St 59030. Just e of US 89. Ext corridors. **Pets:** Accepted. 🅢 📶 ✕ 🛢 🖥

◆◆ Yellowstone Super 8-Gardiner H
(406) 848-7401. **$50-$222.** 702 Scott St W 59030. 0.4 mi n. Int corridors. **Pets:** $10 daily fee/pet. Designated rooms, supervision.
🍴 ⇌ 📶 ✕ 🛢 🖥

GLASGOW

◆◆ Cottonwood Inn H
(406) 228-8213. **$97-$117.** 45 1st Ave NE 59230. 0.5 mi e on US 2. Int corridors. **Pets:** $5 daily fee/room. Designated rooms, service with restrictions, supervision. 🍴 ⇌ 📶 🛢 🖥

GLENDIVE

◆◆ Astoria Hotel & Suites H
(406) 377-6000. **Call for rates.** 201 California St 59330. I-94 exit 215, just n. Int corridors. **Pets:** Accepted. 🅓 ⇌ 📶 ✕ 🛢 🖥

GREAT FALLS

◆◆ Best Western Plus Heritage Inn H
(406) 761-1900. **$104-$149.** 1700 Fox Farm Rd 59404. I-15 exit 278, 0.8 mi e on 10th Ave S, US 87/89 and SR 3/200. Int corridors.
Pets: Accepted. 🅢 🍴 ⇌ ✕ 📶 ✕ 🛢 🖥

◆◆ Comfort Inn & Suites H
(406) 455-1000. **$89-$229.** 1801 Market Place Dr 59404. I-15 exit 278, just sw. Int corridors. **Pets:** Accepted. 🅓 📶 ✕ 🛢 🖥

◆◆ Comfort Inn by Choice Hotels H
(406) 454-2727. **$94-$200.** 1120 9th St S 59405. I-15 exit 278, 3 mi e on 10th Ave S, US 87/89 and SR 3/200, then just s. Int corridors. **Pets:** Other species. $20 daily fee/pet. Designated rooms, no service, crate. 🅢 🅓 ⇌ 📶 🛢 🖥

◆◆ Crystal Inn Hotel & Suites Great Falls H
(406) 727-7788. **Call for rates.** 3701 31st St SW 59404. I-15 exit 277, just e. Int corridors. **Pets:** Accepted. ⇌ 📶 🛢 🖥

◆◆ Days Inn of Great Falls H
(406) 727-6565. **$78-$121.** 101 14th Ave NW 59404. I-15 exit 280 (Central Ave), 1.3 mi e on Central Ave/Business Rt I-15, 0.8 mi n on 3rd St NW, then just w. Int corridors. **Pets:** Dogs only. $10 daily fee/room. Designated rooms, service with restrictions, supervision.
📶 ✕ 🛢 🖥

◆◆ Extended Stay America-Great Falls-Missouri River H
(406) 761-7524. **$75-$125.** 800 River Dr S 59405. I-15 exit 278, 1.7 mi e on 10th Ave S, then 0.7 mi n. Int corridors. **Pets:** Accepted.
🅓 📶 ✕ 🛢 🖥

◆◆ The Great Falls Inn by Riversage H
(406) 453-6000. **Call for rates.** 1400 28th St S 59405. I-15 exit 278, 5.3 mi e on 10th Ave S, 0.3 mi s on 26th St S, then just e on 15th Ave S. Int corridors. **Pets:** Medium. $7 daily fee/pet. Designated rooms, service with restrictions, supervision. 🅓 📶 ✕ 🛢 🖥

◆◆ Holiday Inn H
(406) 727-7200. **Call for rates.** 1100 5th St S 59405. I-15 exit 278, 2 mi e on 10th Ave S, then just s. Int corridors. **Pets:** Accepted.
🅢 🍴 🅓 ⇌ ✕ 📶 ✕ 🛢 🖥

◆◆ La Quinta Inn & Suites Riverside H
(406) 761-2600. **$86-$301.** 600 River Dr S 59405. I-15 exit 278, 1.7 mi e on 10th Ave S, then 0.8 mi n. Int corridors. **Pets:** Accepted.
🅓 ⇌ ✕ 📶 ✕ 🛢 🖥

◆◆ Motel 6 #4238 M
(406) 453-1602. **$67-$95.** 2 Treasure State Dr 59404. I-15 exit 278, 0.8 mi e on 10th Ave S and US 87/89 and SR 3/200. Int corridors.
Pets: Accepted. 🅢 📶 ✕ 🛢

▼▼ O'Haire Motor Inn 🅜

(406) 454-2141. **Call for rates.** 17 7th St S 59401. Center of downtown. Ext/int corridors. **Pets:** Accepted. 🍽 ➰ 📶 🚪 🖥

▼▼▼ Staybridge Suites 🅗

(406) 761-4903. **Call for rates.** 201 3rd St NW (US 87) 59404. I-15 exit 280 (Central Ave), 1 mi w, then just n. Int corridors. **Pets:** Accepted.
🅜 ➰ 📶 ✕ 🚪 🖥

HAMILTON

▼▼ Bitterroot River Inn & Conference Center 🅗

(406) 375-2525. **$79-$159.** 139 Bitterroot Plaza Dr 59840. US 93, 1 mi n, then just w. Int corridors. **Pets:** Designated rooms, service with restrictions, supervision. 🅜 ➰ ✕ 📶 ✕ 🚪 🖥

ⒶⒶⒶ ▼▼ Town House Inns 🅗

(406) 363-6600. **Call for rates.** 1113 N 1st St 59840. On US 93, n of City Center. Int corridors. **Pets:** Accepted. (SAVE) 📶 🚪 🖥

HARLOWTON

▼ Countryside Inn 🅜

(406) 632-4119. **$60-$66.** 309 3rd St NE 59036. US 12 E. Ext corridors. **Pets:** Accepted. 🍽 🎦 🚪

HAVRE

ⒶⒶⒶ ▼▼ TownHouse Inn of Havre 🅗 🐾

(406) 265-6711. **$80-$130.** 601 1st St W 59501. Just w of town center on US 2. Int corridors. **Pets:** Other species. $10 daily fee/pet. Service with restrictions, crate. (SAVE) ➰ 📶 ✕ 🚪 🖥

HELENA

▼▼▼ Barrister Bed & Breakfast 🅱🅱

(406) 443-7330. **$110-$124, 3 day notice.** 416 N Ewing St 59601. I-15 exit 192 (Prospect Ave), 1.5 mi sw via Prospect and Montana aves to 9th Ave, 0.8 mi w, then just s. Int corridors. **Pets:** Dogs only.
📶 ✕ 🚳

ⒶⒶⒶ ▼▼▼ Best Western Premier Helena Great Northern Hotel 🅗

(406) 457-5500. **$147-$197.** 835 Great Northern Blvd 59601. I-15 exit 193 (Cedar St), 2 mi w, just w on Lyndale Ave, then just s on Getchell St; downtown. Int corridors. **Pets:** Accepted.
(SAVE) 🍽 🅜 ➰ 📶 ✕ 🚪 🖥

ⒶⒶⒶ ▼▼▼ Comfort Suites 🅗

(406) 495-0505. **$109-$189.** 3180 N Washington St 59602. I-15 exit 194 (Custer Ave), just e. Int corridors. **Pets:** Accepted.
(SAVE) 🅜 ➰ 📶 ✕ 🚪 🖥

▼▼ Days Inn Helena 🅗

(406) 442-3280. **$80-$110.** 2001 Prospect Ave 59601. I-15 exit 192 (Prospect Ave), just w. Int corridors. **Pets:** Accepted.
🅜 📶 🚪 🖥

▼▼ Jorgenson's Inn & Suites 🅗 🐾

(406) 442-1770. **$69-$149.** 1714 11th Ave 59601. I-15 exit 192 (Prospect Ave), just w of I-15 and US 287/12. Ext/int corridors. **Pets:** Other species. $20 one-time fee/room. Service with restrictions, crate.
🍽 🅜 ➰ 📶 ✕ 🚪 🖥

▼▼ La Quinta Inn & Suites Helena 🅗

(406) 449-4000. **$79-$192.** 701 Washington St 59601. I-15 exit 192 (Prospect Ave), just w. Int corridors. **Pets:** Accepted.
🅜 📶 ✕ 🚪 🖥

▼▼▼ Radisson Colonial Hotel Helena 🅗

(406) 443-2100. **$119-$189.** 2301 Colonial Dr 59601. I-15 exit 192 (Prospect Ave) southbound; exit 192B northbound. Int corridors.
Pets: Accepted. 🍽 🅜 ➰ 📶 ✕ 🚪 🖥

▼▼▼ Residence Inn by Marriott 🅗

(406) 443-8010. **$126-$187.** 2500 E Custer Ave 59602. I-15 exit 194 (Custer Ave), just e. Int corridors. **Pets:** Accepted.
🍽 🅜 ➰ ✕ 🚪 🖥

▼▼▼ Wingate by Wyndham 🅗

(406) 449-3000. **$126-$199.** 2007 N Oakes St 59601. I-15 exit 193 (Cedar St), just sw. Int corridors. **Pets:** Accepted.
🅜 ➰ 📶 ✕ 🚪 🖥

KALISPELL

▼▼ Americas Best Value Inn 🅗

(406) 756-3222. **$70-$150.** 1550 Hwy 93 N 59901. 1.3 mi n on US 93 from jct US 2. Int corridors. **Pets:** Accepted. 📶 ✕ 🚪 🖥

ⒶⒶⒶ ▼▼▼ Best Western Plus Flathead Lake Inn & Suites 🅗 🐾

(406) 857-2400. **$89-$269.** 4824 Hwy 93 S 59901. 7 mi s; jct SR 82. Int corridors. **Pets:** Dogs only. Designated rooms, service with restrictions, supervision. (SAVE) 🍽 🅜 ➰ 📶 ✕ 🚪 🖥

▼▼▼ Holiday Inn Express & Suites 🅗

(406) 755-7405. **Call for rates.** 275 Treeline Rd 59901. 3 mi n on US 93 from jct US 2, just w. Ext/int corridors. **Pets:** Accepted.
🅜 ➰ 📶 ✕ 🚪 🖥

▼▼▼ Homewood Suites by Hilton 🅗

(406) 755-8080. **$114-$309.** 195 Hutton Ranch Rd 59901. US 93 N, just e. Int corridors. **Pets:** Other species. $35 one-time fee/room. Supervision. 🅜 📶 ✕ 🚪 🖥

▼▼▼ La Quinta Inn & Suites Kalispell 🅗

(406) 257-5255. **$75-$361.** 255 Montclair Dr 59901. Jct US 93 and 2, 1 mi e. Int corridors. **Pets:** Accepted. 🅜 ➰ 📶 ✕ 🚪 🖥

▼▼ Quality Inn 🅗

(406) 755-6700. **$79-$279.** 1330 Hwy 2 W 59901. 1 mi w on US 2 from jct US 93. Int corridors. **Pets:** Accepted.
🍽 ➰ 📶 ✕ 🚪 🖥

▼▼▼ Red Lion Hotel Kalispell 🅗

(406) 751-5050. **Call for rates.** 20 N Main St 59901. Just s on US 93 from jct US 2; connected to Kalispell Center Mall. Int corridors.
Pets: Accepted. 🍴 🅜 ➰ ✕ 📶 ✕ 🚪 🖥

▼▼ Super 8-Kalispell/Glacier National Park 🅗

(406) 755-1888. **$53-$123.** 1341 1st Ave E 59901. 1.2 mi s on US 93 from jct US 2. Int corridors. **Pets:** Accepted. 🅜 📶 ✕ 🚪 🖥

LAUREL

ⒶⒶⒶ ▼▼▼ Best Western Yellowstone Crossing 🅗 🐾

(406) 628-6888. **$80-$86.** 205 SE 4th St 59044. I-90 exit 434, just n, then just e. Int corridors. **Pets:** Other species. $15 daily fee/pet. Designated rooms, service with restrictions.
(SAVE) 🅜 ➰ 📶 ✕ 🚪 🖥

LEWISTOWN

▼ B & B Motel 🅜

(406) 535-5496. **Call for rates.** 520 E Main St 59457. Downtown. Ext corridors. **Pets:** Accepted. 📶 ✕ 🚪 🖥

▼▼ Lewistown Super 8 🅗

(406) 538-2581. **$65-$150.** 102 Wendell Ave 59457. On US 87, west side of town; near airport. Int corridors. **Pets:** Accepted.
📶 ✕ 🚪 🖥

LIBBY

▼ Sandman Motel M ❖
(406) 293-8831. **Call for rates.** 31901 US 2 59923. Just w on US 2 from jct SR 37. Ext corridors. **Pets:** Medium. $20 deposit/pet, $10 daily fee/pet. Designated rooms, service with restrictions, supervision.
🛜 ✕ 🗹 🔒

▼▼ Venture Inn H
(406) 293-7711. **$108-$125.** 1015 W 9th St (US 2) 59923. Just w on US 2 from jct SR 37. Int corridors. **Pets:** Large, dogs only. $10 daily fee/pet. Designated rooms, service with restrictions, supervision.
🍽 ➴ 🛜 ✕ 🔒 🖥

LIVINGSTON

▼▼ Livingston Rodeway Inn M
(406) 222-6320. **$60-$180.** 102 Rogers Ln 59047. I-90 exit 333, just n on US 89, then just w. Ext/int corridors. **Pets:** Accepted.
🍽 ⅙M ➴ 🛜 🔒 🖥

▼▼ Super 8 Livingston M
(406) 222-7711. **$70-$140.** 105 Centennial Dr 59047. I-90 exit 333, just s on US 89. Int corridors. **Pets:** Accepted. 🛜 ✕ 🔒 🖥

ⒶⒶⒶ ◆◆ Yellowstone Pioneer Lodge H ❖
(406) 222-6110. **Call for rates.** 1515 W Park St 59047. I-90 exit 333, just n. Int corridors. **Pets:** $10 daily fee/pet. Service with restrictions, supervision. SAVE 🍽 ⅙M ➴ 🛜 🔒 🖥

ⒶⒶⒶ ◆◆ Yellowstone Valley Lodge, an Ascend Hotel Collection Member CA
(406) 333-4787. **$169-$599.** 3840 US Hwy 89 S 59047. I-90 exit 333, 15 mi s on US 89 S; between MM 38 and 39. Ext corridors. **Pets:** $25 one-time fee/pet. Designated rooms, service with restrictions, supervision. SAVE 🍽 ⅙M 🛜 ✕ 🗹 🔒 🖥

MALTA

ⒶⒶⒶ ▼ Maltana Motel M
(406) 654-2610. **Call for rates.** 138 S 1st Ave W 59538. Just s of US 2 via US 191, just w; downtown. Ext corridors. **Pets:** Accepted.
SAVE 🛜 ✕ 🔒 🖥

MILES CITY

ⒶⒶⒶ ▼▼ Best Western War Bonnet Inn M
(406) 234-4560. **$118-$131.** 1015 S Haynes Ave 59301. I-94 exit 138 (Broadus), 0.3 mi n. Ext corridors. **Pets:** Accepted.
SAVE ➴ ✕ 🛜 ✕ 🔒 🖥

▼▼ Comfort Inn Miles City H
(406) 234-3141. **$100-$130.** 1615 S Haynes Ave 59301. I-94 exit 138 (Broadus), just s. Int corridors. **Pets:** Dogs only. $15 daily fee/pet. Designated rooms, supervision. ⅙M ➴ 🛜 ✕ 🔒 🖥

ⒶⒶⒶ ◆◆◆ Sleep Inn & Suites Miles City H
(406) 232-3000. **$104-$174.** 1006 S Haynes Ave 59301. I-94 exit 138 (S Haynes Ave), 0.3 mi n. Int corridors. **Pets:** Accepted.
SAVE ⅙M 🛜 ✕ 🔒 🖥

MISSOULA

ⒶⒶⒶ ◆◆◆ Best Western Plus Grant Creek Inn H
(406) 543-0700. **$109-$204.** 5280 Grant Creek Rd 59808. I-90 exit 101 (Reserve St), just n. Int corridors. **Pets:** Accepted.
SAVE ⊞ ⅙M ➴ ✕ 🛜 ✕ 🔒 🖥

▼▼ Broadway Inn Conference Center H
(406) 532-3300. **$70-$200.** 1609 W Broadway 59808. I-90 exit 104 (Orange St), 0.5 mi s, then 1 mi w. Int corridors. **Pets:** Accepted.
🍽 ⅙M ➴ 🛜 🔒 🖥

▼▼ Comfort Inn - University H
(406) 549-7600. **$95-$350.** 1021 E Broadway 59802. I-90 exit 105 (Van Buren St), just s, then just e. Int corridors. **Pets:** Accepted.
⅙M 🛜 ✕ 🔒 🖥

▼▼ Days Inn/Missoula Airport H
(406) 721-9776. **$64-$74.** 8600 Truck Stop Rd 59808. I-90 exit 96, just n. Int corridors. **Pets:** Accepted. 🛜 🔒 🖥

ⒶⒶⒶ ◆◆◆ DoubleTree by Hilton Hotel Missoula - Edgewater H
(406) 728-3100. **$109-$219.** 100 Madison St 59802. I-90 exit 105 (Van Buren St), just s, then just w on Front St. Int corridors. **Pets:** Accepted.
SAVE 🍽 ⅙M ➴ 🛜 ✕ 🔒 🖥

▼▼ Econo Lodge H
(406) 542-7550. **$65-$109.** 4953 N Reserve St 59808. I-90 exit 101 (Reserve St), just s. Int corridors. **Pets:** Accepted.
⅙M 🛜 ✕ 🔒 🖥

ⒶⒶⒶ ◆◆◆ Hampton Inn by Hilton H ❖
(406) 549-1800. **$99-$189.** 4805 N Reserve St 59808. I-90 exit 101 (Reserve St), just s. Int corridors. **Pets:** Other species. $10 one-time fee/room. Designated rooms, service with restrictions, supervision.
SAVE ⅙M ➴ 🛜 ✕ 🔒 🖥

ⒶⒶⒶ ◆◆◆ Holiday Inn Missoula-Downtown H
(406) 721-8550. **$100-$399.** 200 S Pattee St 59802. I-90 exit 104 (Orange St), 0.5 mi s to Broadway, just e to Pattee St, then just s. Int corridors. **Pets:** Accepted.
SAVE 🍽 ⅙M ➴ ✕ 🛜 ✕ 🔒 🖥

▼▼ La Quinta Inn Missoula H
(406) 549-9000. **$81-$295.** 5059 N Reserve St 59808. I-90 exit 101 (Reserve St), just s. Int corridors. **Pets:** Accepted.
⅙M ➴ 🛜 ✕ 🔒 🖥

▼▼ My Place Hotel H
(406) 926-1001. **$60-$160.** 2952 Expo Pkwy 59808. I-90 exit 101 (Reserve St), just n. Int corridors. **Pets:** Accepted.
⅙M 🛜 ✕ 🔒 🖥

▼▼ Quality Inn & Suites-Missoula H
(406) 542-0888. **$75-$180.** 4545 N Reserve St 59808. I-90 exit 101 (Reserve St), 0.7 mi s. Int corridors. **Pets:** Small, dogs only. $20 daily fee/pet. Designated rooms, service with restrictions, supervision.
⅙M ➴ 🛜 ✕ 🔒 🖥

▼▼ Red Lion Inn M
(406) 728-3300. **$89-$199.** 700 W Broadway 59802. I-90 exit 104 (Orange St), just s, then just w. Ext corridors. **Pets:** Other species. $15 one-time fee/room. Designated rooms, service with restrictions, crate.
➴ 🛜 🔒 🖥

ⒶⒶⒶ ◆◆◆ Ruby's Inn & Convention Center H
(406) 721-0990. **Call for rates.** 4825 N Reserve St 59808. I-90 exit 101 (Reserve St), just s. Ext/int corridors. **Pets:** Accepted.
SAVE ⅙M ➴ ✕ 🛜 🔒 🖥

◆◆◆ Staybridge Suites H
(406) 830-3900. **Call for rates.** 120 Expressway Blvd 59808. I-90 exit 101 (Reserve St), just s. Int corridors. **Pets:** Accepted.
⅙M 🛜 ✕ 🔒 🖥

▼▼ Super 8-Brooks St H
(406) 251-2255. **$78-$89.** 3901 Brooks St 59804. I-90 exit 101 (Reserve St), 5 mi s to Brooks St, then just w. Int corridors.
Pets: Accepted. 🛜 ✕ 🔒 🖥

◆◆◆ TownePlace Suites by Marriott Missoula H
(406) 721-6000. **$92-$169.** 3055 Stockyard Rd 59808. I-90 exit 101, 0.3 mi s on N Reserve St, then 0.3 mi e. Int corridors. **Pets:** Accepted.
⅙M 🛜 ✕ 🔒 🖥

Wingate by Wyndham H
(406) 541-8000. **$89-$199.** 5252 Airway Blvd 59808. I-90 exit 99 (Airway Blvd), just s to E Harrier Dr. Int corridors. **Pets:** Dogs only. $20 one-time fee/room. Designated rooms, service with restrictions, supervision.

MONTANA CITY

Elkhorn Mountain Inn H
(406) 442-6625. **$70-$90.** 1 Jackson Creek Rd 59634. I-15 exit 187 (Montana City), just w. Int corridors. **Pets:** Other species. $10 daily fee/room. Designated rooms, supervision.

POLSON (Restaurants p. 617)

KwaTaqNuk Resort and Casino H
(406) 883-3636. **Call for rates.** 49708 US Hwy 93 E 59860. Just s of downtown. Int corridors. **Pets:** Accepted.

Red Lion Inn & Suites H
(406) 872-2200. **Call for rates.** 209 Ridgewater Dr 59860. US 93 exit Ridgewater Dr, then just n. Int corridors. **Pets:** Accepted.

RED LODGE

Comfort Inn of Red Lodge H
(406) 446-4469. **$114-$220.** 612 N Broadway Ave 59068. Jct US 212 and SR 78, north entrance. Int corridors. **Pets:** Other species. $15 daily fee/room. Designated rooms, service with restrictions, supervision.

Rock Creek Resort H
(406) 446-1111. **$130-$390, 15 day notice.** 6380 US Hwy 212 S 59068. 5.8 mi s. Ext/int corridors. **Pets:** Accepted.

Yodeler Motel M
(406) 446-1435. **$65-$165.** 601 S Broadway Ave 59068. Just s on US 212. Ext corridors. **Pets:** Accepted.

RONAN

Starlite Motel M
(406) 676-7000. **Call for rates.** 18 Main St SW 59864. Just w of jct US 93 and Main St. Ext corridors. **Pets:** Accepted.

ST. REGIS

Little River Motel M
(406) 649-2713. **$50-$85.** 424 Little River Ln 59866. I-90 exit 33, just n to flashing light, just w, then just sw. Ext corridors. **Pets:** Medium. $10 daily fee/pet. Service with restrictions, supervision.

Super 8-St. Regis H
(406) 649-2422. **$65-$149.** 9 Old Hwy 10 E 59866. I-90 exit 33, just n. Ext/int corridors. **Pets:** Accepted.

SHELBY

Best Western Shelby Inn & Suites H
(406) 424-4560. **$89-$149.** 1948 Roosevelt Hwy 59474. I-15 exit 363, just w. Int corridors. **Pets:** Other species. $15 one-time fee/room. Designated rooms, service with restrictions, supervision.

Comfort Inn of Shelby H 🐾
(406) 434-2212. **$99-$209.** 455 McKinley Ave 59474. I-15 exit 363, just e, then just s. Int corridors. **Pets:** Other species. $15 one-time fee/pet. Service with restrictions, supervision.

SIDNEY

Best Western Golden Prairie Inn & Suites H
(406) 433-4560. **$85-$125.** 820 S Central Ave 59270. 1.8 mi n of jct SR 16 and 200. Int corridors. **Pets:** Accepted.

Candlewood Suites Sidney H
(406) 482-9692. **$109-$129.** 201 6th St NW 59270. Just n of jct SR 16 and 200. Int corridors. **Pets:** Dogs only. $20 daily fee/room. Service with restrictions, crate.

Microtel Inn & Suites by Wyndham Sidney H
(406) 482-9011. **$116-$149.** 1500 S Central Ave 59270. 1.3 mi n of jct SR 16 and 200. Int corridors. **Pets:** Accepted.

Richland Inn & Suites M
(406) 433-6400. **Call for rates.** 1200 S Central Ave 59270. 1.5 mi n of jct SR 16 and 200. Int corridors. **Pets:** Accepted.

STEVENSVILLE

Bitterroot River Bed and Breakfast BB
(406) 777-5205. **$95-$155, 14 day notice.** 501 South Ave 59870. 1 mi s on Main St (SR 269), just w. Int corridors. **Pets:** Accepted.

THREE FORKS

Broken Spur Motel M
(406) 285-3237. **$75-$130.** 124 W Elm (Hwy 2) 59752. I-90 exit 278 westbound, 1.3 mi sw; exit 274 eastbound, 1 mi s on SR 287 to jct SR 2, then 3 mi se. Ext corridors. **Pets:** Medium. $15 daily fee/pet. Designated rooms, service with restrictions, supervision.

Fort Three Forks Motel & RV Park M
(406) 285-3233. **Call for rates.** 10776 Hwy 287 59752. I-90 exit 274, just n. Ext corridors. **Pets:** Accepted.

WEST YELLOWSTONE

Best Western Desert Inn H
(406) 646-7376. **$90-$310.** 133 N Canyon St 59758. Jct US 191 (N Canyon St) and Firehole Ave; 0.3 mi n of park entrance. Int corridors. **Pets:** Accepted.

Best Western Weston Inn M
(406) 646-7373. **$179-$349, 3 day notice.** 103 Gibbon Ave 59758. Jct US 191 (N Canyon St) and Gibbon Ave; 0.5 mi n of park entrance. Ext/int corridors. **Pets:** Accepted.

Brandin' Iron Inn M
(406) 646-9411. **$79-$229, 3 day notice.** 201 Canyon St 59758. Jct US 20 (Firehole Ave) and 191 (Canyon St); 0.3 mi n of park entrance. Ext corridors. **Pets:** Other species. $15 one-time fee/room. Designated rooms, service with restrictions, supervision.

City Center Motel M
(406) 646-7337. **$69-$169, 3 day notice.** 214 Madison Ave 59758. Jct Madison Ave and Dunraven St; 0.4 mi nw of park entrance. Ext corridors. **Pets:** Other species. $15 one-time fee/room. Service with restrictions, supervision.

ClubHouse Inn H
(406) 646-4892. **$129-$339.** 105 S Electric St 59758. Just sw of jct US 20/191/287; 0.4 mi sw of park entrance. Int corridors. **Pets:** Accepted.

Cross Winds Inn M 🐾
(406) 646-9557. **$85-$299.** 201 Firehole Ave 59758. At US 20 (Firehole Ave) and Dunraven St; 0.5 mi n of park entrance. Ext corridors. **Pets:** Dogs only. $20 one-time fee/room. Designated rooms, service with restrictions, supervision.

Explorer Cabins at Yellowstone CA
(406) 646-7075. **$149-$499, 3 day notice.** 201 Grizzly Ave 59758. 0.5 mi sw of park entrance. Ext corridors. **Pets:** Accepted.

Gray Wolf Inn and Suites H
(406) 646-0000. **$89-$309, 3 day notice.** 250 S Canyon St 59758. Just w of park entrance, then just s. Int corridors. **Pets:** Accepted.

Holiday Inn West Yellowstone Conference Hotel H
(406) 646-7365. **Call for rates.** 315 Yellowstone Ave 59758. 0.4 mi w of park entrance. Int corridors. **Pets:** Accepted.

Stage Coach Inn H
(406) 646-7381. **$69-$359, 3 day notice.** 209 Madison Ave 59758. At Dunraven St and Madison Ave; 0.4 mi nw of park entrance. Int corridors. **Pets:** Accepted.

Three Bear Lodge H
(406) 646-7353. **$99-$259.** 217 Yellowstone Ave 59758. Just w of park entrance. Ext/int corridors. **Pets:** $25 daily fee/pet. Designated rooms, service with restrictions, crate.

Yellowstone Lodge H
(406) 646-0020. **$89-$309.** 251 S Electric St 59758. Just s of Yellowstone Ave and Electric St; 0.6 mi sw of park entrance. Int corridors. **Pets:** Dogs only. Designated rooms, service with restrictions, crate.

Yellowstone West Gate Hotel H
(406) 646-4212. **Call for rates.** 638 Madison Ave 59758. At Iris St and Madison Ave; 1 mi nw of park entrance. Int corridors. **Pets:** Accepted.

WHITEFISH

Best Western Rocky Mountain Lodge H ❀
(406) 862-2569. **$99-$350.** 6510 Hwy 93 S 59937. 1.3 mi s on US 93 from jct SR 487. Ext/int corridors. **Pets:** Medium. $20 daily fee/room. Designated rooms, service with restrictions.

Grouse Mountain Lodge H
(406) 862-3000. **Call for rates.** 2 Fairway Dr 59937. 1 mi w on US 93 from jct SR 487. Int corridors. **Pets:** Accepted.

North Forty Resort CA ❀
(406) 862-7740. **$119-$309, 14 day notice.** 3765 Hwy 40 W 59912. 2.5 mi e on SR 40 from jct US 93. Ext corridors. **Pets:** Medium. $10 daily fee/pet. Designated rooms, service with restrictions, crate.

Pine Lodge H ❀
(406) 862-7600. **$89-$229.** 920 Spokane Ave 59937. 1 mi s on US 93 from jct SR 487. Int corridors. **Pets:** Medium. $20 daily fee/room. Designated rooms, service with restrictions, supervision.

NEBRASKA

BELLEVUE

Hampton Inn by Hilton H
(402) 292-1607. **$109-$239.** 3404 Samson Way 68123. US 75, 1 mi n on SR 370, just w on Golden Blvd, 0.3 mi n. Int corridors. **Pets:** Accepted.

Microtel Inn & Suites by Wyndham Bellevue H
(402) 292-0191. **$65-$160.** 3008 Samson Way 68123. Jct US 75, 1 mi w on SR 370, just n on Golden Blvd, then just w. Int corridors. **Pets:** Accepted.

SureStay PLUS Hotel, Omaha South H
(402) 293-1600. **$59-$219.** 305 Fort Crook Rd N 68005. US 75, 1.8 mi n of jct SR 370 and Fort Crook Rd N. Int corridors. **Pets:** Accepted.

CHADRON

Best Western West Hills Inn H ❀
(308) 432-3305. **$99-$119.** 1100 W 10th St 69337. Just s of jct US 385 and 20. Ext/int corridors. **Pets:** Large, other species. $13 daily fee/pet. Designated rooms, service with restrictions, supervision.

COLUMBUS

Sleep Inn & Suites Hotel H
(402) 562-5200. **$79-$154.** 303 23rd St 68601. On US 30, 2 mi e of jct US 30 and 81; east side of town. Int corridors. **Pets:** Accepted.

FREMONT

Oak Tree Inn H
(402) 721-3700. **Call for rates.** 2700 N Diers Pkwy 68025. US 30, just n. Int corridors. **Pets:** Accepted.

GERING

Monument Inn & Suites H
(308) 436-1950. **$75-$190.** 1130 M St 69341. 1 mi e of SR 71, just w of M (SR 92) and 10th sts. Int corridors. **Pets:** Medium, dogs only. $15 one-time fee/room. Designated rooms, service with restrictions, crate.

GRAND ISLAND

Days Inn-Grand Island I-80 H
(308) 384-5006. **$69-$150.** 7800 S US Hwy 281 68803. I-80 exit 312 (US 281), just s. Int corridors. **Pets:** Large, other species. $15 daily fee/room. Service with restrictions.

Quality Inn and Conference Center H
(308) 384-7770. **$87-$200.** 7838 S US Hwy 281 68803. I-80 exit 312 (US 281), just s. Int corridors. **Pets:** Large, other species. $15 daily fee/room. Service with restrictions.

Rodeway Inn H
(308) 384-1333. **$61-$106.** 3205 S Locust St 68801. I-80 exit 314, 4 mi n. Int corridors. **Pets:** Accepted.

Super 8 H
(308) 384-4380. **$77-$102.** 2603 S Locust St 68801. I-80 exit 314, 4.7 mi n. Int corridors. **Pets:** Accepted.

KEARNEY

AmericInn Lodge & Suites of Kearney H
(308) 234-7800. **Call for rates.** 215 W Talmadge Rd 68845. I-80 exit 272 (SR 44), just n. Int corridors. **Pets:** Accepted.

▼▼▼ **Candlewood Suites-Kearney** H
(308) 234-1100. **Call for rates.** 210 4th Ave 68845. I-80 exit 272 (SR 44), just n, then just w. Int corridors. **Pets:** Accepted.
🚹M 🛜 ✖ 🔋 💻

▼▼▼ **La Quinta Inn & Suites Kearney** H
(308) 237-4400. **$97-$368.** 108 3rd Ave 68845. I-80 exit 272 (SR 44), just n, then just w. Int corridors. **Pets:** Accepted.
🚹M 🛏 🛜 ✖ 🔋 💻

✦✦✦ ▼▼ **Microtel Inn & Suites by Wyndham Kearney** H 🐾
(308) 698-3003. **$64-$100.** 104 Talmadge Rd 68847. I-80 exit 272 (SR 44), just se. Int corridors. **Pets:** Other species. $10 daily fee/room. Designated rooms, service with restrictions, supervision.
SAVE 🚹M 🛜 ✖ 🔋 💻

LEXINGTON

▼▼▼▼ **Holiday Inn Express & Suites** H
(308) 324-9900. **$120-$200.** 2605 Plum Creek Pkwy 68850. I-80 exit 237 (US 283), 0.5 mi n. Int corridors. **Pets:** Accepted.
🍴 🚹M 🛏 🛜 ✖ 🔋 💻

▼▼ **Lexington Comfort Inn** H
(308) 324-3747. **$109-$130.** 2810 Plum Creek Pkwy 68850. I-80 exit 237 (US 283), 0.3 mi n. Ext/int corridors. **Pets:** Other species. $15 one-time fee/pet. Service with restrictions.
🍴 🚹M 🛏 🛜 ✖ 🔋 💻

LINCOLN

✦✦✦ ▼▼ **AmericInn Lodge & Suites of Lincoln North** H
(402) 435-1600. **Call for rates.** 6555 N 27th St 68521. I-80 exit 403 (27th St), 0.3 mi s, just w on Whitehead Dr, then just s. Int corridors. **Pets:** Accepted. SAVE 🚹M 🛏 🛜 ✖ 🔋 💻

▼▼ **AmericInn Lodge & Suites of Lincoln South** H
(402) 420-0027. **Call for rates.** 8701 Amber Hill Ct 68526. 5.8 mi se on SR 2 (Nebraska Hwy), just w at 87th St. Int corridors. **Pets:** Accepted.
🚹M 🛏 🛜 ✖ 🔋 💻

▼▼▼ **Comfort Suites** H
(402) 476-8080. **$99-$270, 3 day notice.** 4231 Industrial Ave 68504. I-80 exit 403 (27th St), 2.3 mi s. Int corridors. **Pets:** Other species. $10 one-time fee/room. Designated rooms, service with restrictions.
🚹M 🛏 🛜 ✖ 🔋 💻

▼▼▼ **Comfort Suites East** H
(402) 325-8800. **$99-$189.** 331 N Cotner Blvd 68505. I-180 exit 9th St, 3.3 mi e on US 34 (O St), then 0.3 mi n. Int corridors. **Pets:** Medium. $20 one-time fee/pet. Service with restrictions, supervision.
🚹M 🛏 🛜 ✖ 🔋 💻

▼▼▼▼ **Country Inn & Suites By Carlson, Lincoln North Hotel & Conference Center** H
(402) 476-5353. **$89-$299.** 5353 N 27th St 68521. I-80 exit 403 (27th St), 1.5 mi s. Int corridors. **Pets:** Other species. $40 one-time fee/room. Designated rooms, service with restrictions, crate.
🍴 🚹M 🛏 🛜 ✖ 🔋

▼▼▼ **Holiday Inn Express & Suites Lincoln Airport** H
(402) 464-0588. **Call for rates.** 1101 W Commerce Way 68521. I-80 exit 399, just n, then just e. Int corridors. **Pets:** Accepted.
🚹M 🛏 🛜 ✖ 🔋 💻

✦✦✦ ▼▼▼ **Hyatt Place Lincoln/Downtown-Haymarket** H
(402) 742-6007. **$99-$399.** 600 Q St 68508. Jct Q and 6th sts; in Historic Haymarket District. Int corridors. **Pets:** Accepted.
SAVE 🚹M 🛜 ✖ 🔋 💻

✦✦✦ ▼▼▼ **La Quinta Inn Lincoln** H
(402) 476-2222. **$67-$196.** 4433 N 27th St 68521. I-80 exit 403 (27th St), 2.3 mi s. Int corridors. **Pets:** Accepted.
SAVE 🚹M 🛏 🛜 ✖ 🔋 💻

✦✦✦ ▼▼▼▼ **The Lincoln Marriott Cornhusker Hotel** H
(402) 474-7474. **$84-$307.** 333 S 13th St 68508. Downtown. Int corridors. **Pets:** Accepted. SAVE 🍴 🚹M 🛏 🛜 ✖ 🔋 💻

▼▼ **New Victorian Suites** H
(402) 464-4400. **$64-$189.** 225 N 50th St 68504. 2.5 mi e on US 6 and 34; just ne of jct O St; entrance off 48th St. Int corridors.
Pets: Medium, dogs only. $15 daily fee/pet. Designated rooms, service with restrictions, supervision. 🚹M 🛏 🛜 ✖ 🔋 💻

▼▼▼ **Residence Inn by Marriott-Lincoln South** H
(402) 423-1555. **$71-$241.** 5865 Boboli Ln 68516. 1 mi s of SR 2 (Nebraska Hwy) via 56th St, just e on Pine Lake Rd. Int corridors.
Pets: Accepted. 🍴 🚹M 🛏 🛜 ✖ 🔋 💻

▼▼▼ **Staybridge Suites Lincoln-I-80** H
(402) 438-7829. **$99-$326.** 2701 Fletcher Ave 68504. I-80 exit 403 (27th St), 0.4 mi s, then just e. Int corridors. **Pets:** Other species. $25 one-time fee/room. Service with restrictions. 🚹M 🛜 🔋 💻

▼▼ **Super 8-Lincoln/West 'O' Street** H
(402) 476-8887. **$53-$68.** 2635 West O St 68528. I-80 exit 396 eastbound, 0.5 mi e; exit 397 westbound, 0.5 mi w. Int corridors.
Pets: Accepted. 🍴 🚹M 🛜 🔋 💻

▼▼▼ **TownePlace Suites by Marriott Lincoln North** H
(402) 323-2000. **$80-$229.** 7353 Husker Cir 68504. I-80 exit 403 (27th St), just s to Wildcat Dr, just e, then just n. Int corridors. **Pets:** Dogs only. $25 daily fee/room. Designated rooms, service with restrictions, crate. 🚹M 🛜 ✖ 🔋 💻

MORRILL

▼▼ **Oak Tree Inn** M
(308) 247-2111. **Call for rates.** 707 E Webster St 69358. 0.4 mi e of center on US 26. Ext/int corridors. **Pets:** Accepted.
🍴 🛜 ✖ 🔋 💻

NORTH PLATTE

✦✦✦ ▼ **Americas Best Value Travelers Inn** M
(308) 534-4020. **$45-$70.** 602 E 4th St 69101. I-80 exit 177 (US 83), 1.5 mi n, then 0.3 mi e. Ext corridors. **Pets:** Small, other species. Service with restrictions, supervision. SAVE 🍴 🛏 🛜 ✖ 🔋 💻

✦✦✦ ▼▼▼ **Best Western Plus North Platte Inn & Suites** H
(308) 534-3120. **$100-$195.** 3201 S Jeffers St 69101. I-80 exit 177 (US 83), 0.3 mi s. Int corridors. **Pets:** Accepted.
SAVE 🍴 🛏 🛜 ✖ 🔋 💻

▼▼ **Holiday Inn Express Hotel & Suites** H
(308) 532-9500. **$125-$300.** 300 Holiday Frontage Rd 69101. I-80 exit 177 (US 83), just s. Int corridors. **Pets:** Accepted.
🛏 🛜 ✖ 🔋 💻

✦✦✦ ▼▼▼ **La Quinta Inn & Suites North Platte** H
(308) 534-0700. **$104-$214.** 2600 Eagles Wings Pl 69101. I-80 exit 179, just n, then just w. Int corridors. **Pets:** Accepted.
SAVE 🚹M 🛏 🛜 ✖ 🔋 💻

OGALLALA

✦✦✦ ▼▼▼ **Days Inn** M
(308) 284-6365. **$80-$99.** 601 Stagecoach Tr 69153. I-80 exit 126 (US 26/SR 61), just n, then e on frontage road. Int corridors.
Pets: Accepted. SAVE 🛜 ✖ 🔋 💻

▼▼ **Quality Inn & Ogallala Conference Center** H
(308) 284-3623. **Call for rates.** 201 Chuckwagon Rd 69153. I-80 exit 126, just nw. Ext/int corridors. **Pets:** Accepted.
⛔ 🍴 🛏 📶 ✕ 🛢 💻

OMAHA *(Restaurants p. 617)*

▲▲ ▼▼ **Best Western Old Mill Inn** H
(402) 431-1246. **$79-$180.** 650 N 109th Ct 68154. I-680 exit 3 (W Dodge Rd), 0.7 mi w to 108th St and Old Mill Rd, then just w on Mill Valley Rd. Int corridors. **Pets:** Small, dogs only. $15 daily fee/pet. Designated rooms, supervision. SAVE &M 🛏 📶 ✕ 🛢 💻

▲▲ ▼▼ **Best Western Plus Kelly Inn** H ❀
(402) 339-7400. **$99-$209.** 4706 S 108th St 68137. I-80 exit 445 (L St E), 0.3 mi e, then just s. Int corridors. **Pets:** Other species. Designated rooms, service with restrictions, crate.
SAVE &M 🛏 📶 ✕ 🛢 💻

▼▼ **Comfort Inn at the Zoo** H
(402) 342-8000. **$75-$267.** 2920 S 13th Ct 68108. I-80 exit 454 (13th St) westbound; exit 454 (13th St N) eastbound, just w. Int corridors. **Pets:** Other species. $20 one-time fee/room. No service, crate.
&M 🛏 📶 ✕ 🛢 💻

▲▲ ▼▼ **DoubleTree by Hilton Hotel Omaha Downtown** H ❀
(402) 346-7600. **Call for rates.** 1616 Dodge St 68102. Jct 16th and Dodge sts; downtown. Int corridors. **Pets:** Medium, other species. $50 one-time fee/pet. Designated rooms, service with restrictions, crate.
SAVE 🍴 &M 🛏 📶 ✕ 🛢 💻

▲▲ ▼▼ **Element Omaha Midtown Crossing** H
(402) 614-8080. **Call for rates.** 3253 Dodge St 68131. I-480 exit 2B westbound; exit 2A northbound, just w; in Midtown Crossing. Int corridors. **Pets:** Accepted. SAVE 🔌 📶 ✕ 🛢 💻

▼▼ **Hawthorn Suites by Wyndham Omaha** H
(402) 758-2848. **$79-$259.** 360 S 108th Ave 68154. I-680 exit 3 (W Dodge Rd), 0.7 mi to 108th Ave, then 0.8 mi s. Int corridors. **Pets:** $50 one-time fee/pet. Designated rooms, service with restrictions, crate.
🍴 &M 📶 🛢 💻

▲▲ ▼▼▼ **Hilton Omaha** H
(402) 998-3400. **$99-$249.** 1001 Cass St 68102. Jct Cass and 10th sts; downtown. Int corridors. **Pets:** Large, dogs only. $50 one-time fee/room. Service with restrictions, crate.
SAVE 🍴 &M 🛏 ✕ 🛰 ✕ 🛢 💻

▼▼▼ **Holiday Inn Express Hotel & Suites-Omaha West** H
(402) 333-5566. **Call for rates.** 17677 Wright St 68130. I-80 exit 445 (L St W), 5.5 mi w, then just s. Int corridors. **Pets:** Accepted.
&M 🛏 📶 ✕ 🛢 💻

▼▼▼ **Home2 Suites by Hilton Omaha West** H
(402) 289-9886. **Call for rates.** 17889 Chicago St 68118. I-680 exit 6 (W Dodge Rd), 6 mi w on US 6 (180th St), just s, then e. Int corridors. **Pets:** Accepted. 🍴 &M 📶 ✕ 🛢 💻

▲▲ ▼▼ ▼▼ **Hotel Deco XV** H
(402) 991-4981. **$99-$549.** 1504 Harney St 68102. Jct Harney and 15th sts; downtown. Int corridors. **Pets:** Accepted.
SAVE 🍴 📶 ✕ 🛢 💻

▲▲ ▼▼▼ **Magnolia Hotel Omaha** H
(402) 341-2500. **$129-$339.** 1615 Howard St 68102. Jct 16th St. Int corridors. **Pets:** Medium. Service with restrictions, crate.
SAVE 🍴 &M 📶 ✕ 🛢 💻

▼▼▼ **Residence Inn by Marriott Aksarben Village** H
(402) 551-8000. **$55-$305.** 1717 S 67th St 68106. I-80 exit 449 (72nd St), 1.4 mi n, then 0.4 mi e on Pine St. Int corridors. **Pets:** Accepted.
&M 📶 ✕ 🛢 💻

▼▼▼ **Residence Inn by Marriott, Omaha Downtown/Old Market Area** H
(402) 342-4770. **$80-$340.** 106 S 15th St 68102. Jct 15th and Dodge sts; downtown. Int corridors. **Pets:** Accepted. 📶 ✕ 🛢 💻

▲▲ ▼▼▼ **Sheraton Omaha Hotel** H
(402) 496-0850. **$99-$179.** 655 N 108th Ave 68154. I-680 exit 3 (W Dodge Rd), 0.7 mi to 108th St to 108th Ave and N Old Mill Rd exits, then just n. Int corridors. **Pets:** Accepted.
SAVE 🍴 &M 🛏 📶 ✕ 🛢 💻

▲▲ ▼▼▼ **Sonesta ES Suites Omaha** H ❀
(402) 553-8898. **Call for rates.** 6990 Dodge St 68132. I-680 exit 3 (Dodge St E), 3 mi e. Ext corridors. **Pets:** $75 one-time fee/room. Service with restrictions, crate. SAVE &M 🛏 📶 ✕ 🛢 💻

▼▼▼ **Staybridge Suites Omaha West** H
(402) 502-0202. **Call for rates.** 2720 Oak Dr 68130. I-681 exit 1 (W Center St), 4.8 mi w. Int corridors. **Pets:** Accepted.
🍴 &M 📶 ✕ 🛢 💻

▼▼▼ **TownePlace Suites by Marriott Omaha West** H
(402) 590-2800. **$84-$252.** 10865 W Dodge Rd 68154. I-680 exit 3 (W Dodge Rd), 0.7 mi to 108th St to 108th Ave and N Old Mill Rd exits, then just s. Int corridors. **Pets:** Accepted.
&M 🛏 📶 ✕ 🛢 💻

SCOTTSBLUFF

▼▼ **Scottsbluff Super 8** H
(308) 635-1600. **$59-$82.** 2202 Delta Dr 69361. 1.8 mi e on US 26. Int corridors. **Pets:** Accepted. 🛏 📶 🛢 💻

SIDNEY

▲▲ ▼▼▼ **Best Western Plus Sidney Lodge** H
(308) 254-0100. **$130-$200.** 645 Cabela Dr 69162. I-80 exit 59, just nw. Int corridors. **Pets:** Accepted. SAVE &M 🛏 📶 ✕ 🛢 💻

▼▼▼ **Country Inn & Suites By Carlson** H
(308) 254-2000. **Call for rates.** 664 Chase Blvd 69162. I-80 exit 59, just s. Int corridors. **Pets:** Accepted. &M 🛏 📶 ✕ 🛢 💻

SOUTH SIOUX CITY

▼▼▼ **Marina Inn Conference Center** H
(402) 494-4000. **Call for rates.** 385 E 4th St 68776. I-29 exit 149 southbound; exit 148 northbound, e at traffic light by Nebraska side of bridge; on banks of Missouri River. Ext/int corridors. **Pets:** Accepted.
🍴 &M 🛏 📶 ✕ 🛢 💻

VALENTINE

▼▼ **Econo Lodge Inn & Suites** M ❀
(402) 376-3131. **$89-$179.** 340 E Hwys 20 & 83 69201. Jct US 20/83, 0.3 mi e. Ext corridors. **Pets:** Other species. $10 daily fee/pet. Designated rooms, service with restrictions, supervision. 📶 ✕ 🛢 💻

▼▼ **Niobrara Lodge** H
(402) 376-3000. **Call for rates.** 803 E Hwy 20 69201. Jct US 20/83, 0.5 mi se. Int corridors. **Pets:** Accepted. &M 🛏 📶 ✕ 🛢 💻

▼▼ **Trade Winds Motel** M
(402) 376-1600. **$75-$115.** 1009 E Hwy 20 69201. Jct US 20/83, 1 mi se. Ext corridors. **Pets:** $10 daily fee/pet. Designated rooms, service with restrictions, supervision. 📶 🛢 💻

YORK

▲▲ ▼▼▼ **Americas Best Value Inn-Palmer Inn** M
(402) 362-5585. **$45-$95.** 2426 S Lincoln Ave 68467. I-80 exit 353 (US 81), 1 mi n. Ext corridors. **Pets:** Accepted.
SAVE 🍴 &M 🛏 📶 🛢 💻

Best Western Plus York Hotel & Conference Center H
(402) 362-6661. **$89-$134.** 4619 S Lincoln Ave 68467. I-80 exit 353 (US 81), just s. Int corridors. **Pets:** Accepted.

NEVADA

BEATTY *(Restaurants p. 617)*

Stagecoach Hotel Casino H
(775) 553-2419. **$68-$78.** 900 E Hwy 95 N 89003. North end of town; west side of US 95. Ext/int corridors. **Pets:** Other species. $5 one-time fee/pet. Designated rooms, service with restrictions.

CARSON CITY

Holiday Inn Express & Suites H
(775) 283-4055. **Call for rates.** 4055 N Carson St 89701. US 395 exit 43, 0.7 mi se. Int corridors. **Pets:** Accepted.

ELKO

Americas Best Value Gold Country Inn & Casino M
(775) 738-8421. **$79-$169, 14 day notice.** 2050 Idaho St 89801. I-80 exit 303, just s. Ext corridors. **Pets:** Other species. $15 one-time fee/room. Designated rooms, crate.

Best Western Elko Inn H
(775) 738-8787. **$100-$190.** 1930 Idaho St 89801. I-80 exit 303, 0.3 mi sw. Int corridors. **Pets:** Accepted.

Oak Tree Inn H
(775) 777-2222. **Call for rates.** 95 Spruce Rd 89801. I-80 exit 301, just n. Int corridors. **Pets:** Accepted.

Red Lion Hotel & Casino H
(775) 738-2111. **$79-$209.** 2065 Idaho St 89801. I-80 exit 303, just s. Int corridors. **Pets:** Accepted.

Rodeway Inn M
(775) 738-7152. **$60-$120.** 736 Idaho St 89801. I-80 exit 303, just sw of 8th and Idaho sts. Ext corridors. **Pets:** Medium, dogs only. $25 daily fee/pet. Designated rooms, supervision.

TownePlace Suites by Marriott H
(775) 738-9900. **$104-$182.** 2625 E Jennings Way 89801. I-80 exit 303, 0.3 mi nw. Int corridors. **Pets:** Other species. $100 one-time fee/room.

ELY

Four Sevens Motel M
(775) 289-4747. **Call for rates.** 500 High St 89301. Just n of 5th St; downtown. Ext corridors. **Pets:** Accepted.

Historic Hotel Nevada & Gambling Hall H
(775) 289-6665. **Call for rates.** 501 Aultman St 89301. 1.1 mi w of jct US 50 and 93. Int corridors. **Pets:** Accepted.

La Quinta Inn & Suites-Ely H
(775) 289-8833. **$97-$246.** 1591 Great Basin Blvd 89301. 0.4 mi s of jct US 6, 50 and 93. Int corridors. **Pets:** Accepted.

Magnuson Hotel Park Vue M
(775) 289-4497. **Call for rates.** 930 Aultman St 89301. 0.8 mi w of jct US 50 and 93. Ext corridors. **Pets:** Accepted.

Prospector Hotel Gambling Hall H
(775) 289-8900. **Call for rates.** 1501 E Aultman St 89301. 0.8 mi e of jct US 50 and 93. Int corridors. **Pets:** Other species. $10 one-time fee/pet. Designated rooms.

EUREKA

Eureka Gold Country Inn H
(775) 237-5247. **Call for rates.** 251 N Main St 89316. On east side of Main St; center. Int corridors. **Pets:** Other species. $15 daily fee/pet. Designated rooms.

FALLON

Best Western Fallon Inn & Suites H
(775) 423-6005. **$93-$190.** 1035 W Williams Ave 89406. 0.4 mi w of jct US 50 and 95. Ext corridors. **Pets:** Accepted.

Econo Lodge Fallon Naval Air Station M
(775) 423-2194. **$70-$110.** 70 E Williams Ave 89406. Just e of jct US 50 and 95. Ext corridors. **Pets:** Medium, dogs only. $10 daily fee/pet. Service with restrictions, supervision.

Holiday Inn Express H
(775) 428-2588. **$119-$139.** 55 Commercial Way 89406. At Williams Ave, 0.8 mi w of US 95. Int corridors. **Pets:** Large. $30 one-time fee/room. Service with restrictions, crate.

Motel 6 #4140 M
(775) 423-2277. **$55-$99.** 1705 S Taylor St 89406. 0.8 mi s of jct US 50. Ext corridors. **Pets:** Accepted.

Rodeway Inn & Suites M
(775) 428-0300. **$60-$120.** 1051 W Williams Ave 89406. Just w of US 95. Int corridors. **Pets:** Accepted.

Super 8 Motel H
(775) 423-6031. **$65-$80.** 855 W Williams Ave 89406. 0.4 mi w of jct US 50 and 95. Ext/int corridors. **Pets:** Accepted.

FERNLEY

Best Western Fernley Inn M
(775) 575-6776. **$73-$105.** 1405 E Newlands Dr 89408. I-80 exit 48 (Craig Rd), just s. Ext corridors. **Pets:** Accepted.

GARDNERVILLE

Best Western Topaz Lake Inn H
(775) 266-4661. **$90-$225.** 3410 Sandy Bowers Ave 89410. US 395 S at Topaz Lake, 20 mi s. Ext/int corridors. **Pets:** Accepted.

Westerner Motel M
(775) 782-3602. **$50-$90.** 1353 US Hwy 395 S 89410. US 395, south end of town. Ext corridors. **Pets:** Dogs only. $5 daily fee/pet. Designated rooms, service with restrictions, supervision.

GOLD HILL
▼ **Gold Hill Hotel** H
(775) 847-0111. **Call for rates.** 1540 S Main St 89440. 1 mi s on SR 342. Ext/int corridors. **Pets:** Accepted. 🍴 📶 🗙 🛢 💻

HAWTHORNE
▼◆ **America's Best Inn & Suites** M
(775) 945-2660. **$100-$120.** 1402 E 5th St 89415. US 95, 0.5 mi e. Ext corridors. **Pets:** Other species. $10 daily fee/pet. Designated rooms, service with restrictions, supervision. 🔁 📶 🛢 💻

HENDERSON *(Restaurants p. 617)*
🌀 ▼◆◆ **Best Western Plus Henderson Hotel** H
(702) 564-9200. **$70-$239.** 1553 N Boulder Hwy 89011. Jct Sunset Rd, 0.5 mi s. Int corridors. **Pets:** Accepted.
SAVE 👨‍🦽 🔁 📶 🗙 🛢 💻

🌀 ▼◆◆ **Best Western Plus St. Rose Pkwy/Las Vegas South Hotel** H
(702) 568-0027. **$89-$189.** 3041 St. Rose Pkwy 89052. I-215 exit 6 (St. Rose Pkwy), 2 mi s. Int corridors. **Pets:** Accepted.
SAVE 👨‍🦽 🔁 📶 🗙 🛢 💻

🌀 ▼◆◆ **Fiesta-Henderson** H
(702) 558-7000. **Call for rates.** 777 W Lake Mead Pkwy 89015. I-515 exit 61A southbound; exit 61 (Lake Mead Pkwy) northbound, just e. Int corridors. **Pets:** Small, dogs only. $25 one-time fee/pet. Designated rooms, service with restrictions, supervision.
SAVE 🍴 👨‍🦽 🔁 📶 🛢 💻

▼◆◆ **Hampton Inn & Suites** H
(702) 385-2200. **$99-$189.** 3245 St. Rose Pkwy 89052. I-215 exit 6 (St. Rose Pkwy), 2.1 mi s. Int corridors. **Pets:** Accepted.
👨‍🦽 🔁 📶 🗙 🛢 💻

▼◆◆ **Hampton Inn & Suites** H
(702) 992-9292. **$89-$189.** 421 Astaire Dr 89014. I-215 exit 3A (Stephanie St) eastbound; exit 3 westbound, 1.8 mi n, just e on Warm Springs Rd, then just n. Int corridors. **Pets:** Medium, dogs only. Designated rooms, service with restrictions, supervision.
👨‍🦽 🔁 📶 🗙 🛢 💻

▼◆◆ **Hawthorn Suites by Wyndham** H
(702) 568-7800. **$66-$255.** 910 S Boulder Hwy 89015. Jct Lake Mead Pkwy, 1.4 mi s. Int corridors. **Pets:** Accepted. 🔁 📶 🗙 🛢 💻

🌀 ▼◆◆◆ **Hilton Lake Las Vegas Resort & Spa** H 🐾
(702) 567-4700. **$119-$189.** 1610 Lake Las Vegas Pkwy 89011. I-515 exit 61A southbound; exit 61 northbound (Lake Mead Pkwy), 6.3 mi ne, then 2.8 mi n, follow signs. Int corridors. **Pets:** Large, other species. $100 deposit/room, $50 one-time fee/room. Designated rooms, service with restrictions, supervision.
SAVE 🍴 👨‍🦽 🔁 📶 🗙 🛢 💻

▼◆◆◆ **Holiday Inn Express & Suites** H
(702) 990-2323. **Call for rates.** 441 Astaire Dr 89014. I-215 exit Stephanie St N, 1.8 mi n, just e on Warm Springs Rd, then just n. Ext/int corridors. **Pets:** Accepted. 👨‍🦽 🔁 📶 🗙 🛢 💻

🌀 ▼◆◆◆ **Residence Inn by Marriott Las Vegas/Henderson/Green Valley** H 🐾
(702) 434-2700. **$105-$187.** 2190 Olympic Ave 89014. I-215 exit 5 (Green Valley Pkwy), 3 mi n at Sunset Rd. Int corridors. **Pets:** Medium. $100 deposit/room. Designated rooms, service with restrictions, supervision. SAVE ECO 👨‍🦽 🔁 📶 🗙 🛢 💻

🌀 ▼◆◆ **TownePlace Suites by Marriott Las Vegas Henderson** H
(702) 896-2900. **$98-$143.** 1471 Paseo Verde Pkwy 89012. I-215 exit 3A (Stephanie St) eastbound; exit 3 westbound, just s. Int corridors. **Pets:** Small, other species. $100 one-time fee/pet. Designated rooms, service with restrictions. SAVE 👨‍🦽 🔁 📶 🗙 🛢 💻

🌀 ▼◆◆◆ **The Westin Lake Las Vegas Resort & Spa** H
(702) 567-6000. **$99-$399, 3 day notice.** 101 Montelago Blvd 89011. I-515 exit 61A southbound; exit 61 northbound (Lake Mead Pkwy), 6.3 mi ne, then 4 mi n, follow signs. Int corridors. **Pets:** Medium, dogs only. $35 one-time fee/room. Service with restrictions, crate.
SAVE 🍴 👨‍🦽 🔁 🗙 🔊 🗙 🛢 💻

INCLINE VILLAGE
🌀 ▼◆◆◆ **Hyatt Regency Lake Tahoe Resort, Spa and Casino** H
(775) 832-1234. **$119-$529, 3 day notice.** 111 Country Club Dr 89450. 0.4 mi w of SR 28, toward lake via Country Club Dr; 2 mi s of Mt. Rose Hwy. Int corridors. **Pets:** Accepted.
SAVE ECO 🍴 👨‍🦽 🔁 🗙 🔊 🗙 🛢 💻

JACKPOT
▼◆▼ **Horseshu Hotel & Casino** H
(775) 755-2321. **$59-$109.** 1385 Hwy 93 89825. Center. Int corridors. **Pets:** Accepted. 🍴 🔁 📶 💻

LAS VEGAS *(Restaurants p. 618)*
▼◆▼ **Alexis Park All Suite Resort** H
(702) 796-3300. **Call for rates.** 375 E Harmon Ave 89169. Jct Las Vegas Blvd, just e. Ext corridors. **Pets:** Accepted.
🍴 👨‍🦽 🔁 🗙 📶 🗙 🛢 💻

🌀 ▼◆◆◆ **Bellagio** H 🐾
(702) 693-7111. **$159-$799, 3 day notice.** 3600 Las Vegas Blvd S 89109. I-15 exit 38 (Flamingo Rd), just e. Int corridors. **Pets:** Very small, dogs only. $125 daily fee/room. Service with restrictions, crate.
SAVE ECO 🍴 👨‍🦽 🔁 🗙 🔊 🛢 💻

🌀 ▼◆◆ **Best Western Plus Las Vegas West** H
(702) 256-3766. **$115-$175.** 8669 W Sahara Ave 89117. Jct Durango Dr. Int corridors. **Pets:** Accepted. SAVE 🔁 📶 🗙 🛢 💻

▼◆▼ **Candlewood Suites** H
(702) 836-3660. **Call for rates.** 4034 S Paradise Rd 89169. I-15 exit 38 (Flamingo Rd) to Paradise Rd, just ne. Int corridors. **Pets:** Accepted.
👨‍🦽 🔁 📶 🗙 🛢 💻

🌀 ▼◆◆◆ **The Cosmopolitan of Las Vegas** H
(702) 698-7000. **$152-$437, 3 day notice.** 3708 Las Vegas Blvd S 89109. Between Flamingo Rd and Tropicana Ave; on the Strip. Int corridors. **Pets:** Accepted. SAVE 🍴 👨‍🦽 🔁 🗙 🔊 🗙 🛢

🌀 ▼◆◆ **Delano Las Vegas** H
(702) 632-7777. **Call for rates.** 3940 Las Vegas Blvd S 89119. I-15 exit 36 (Russell Rd), e to the Strip, then just n. Int corridors.
Pets: Accepted. SAVE 🍴 👨‍🦽 🔁 🗙 🔊 🗙 🛢 💻

🌀 ▼◆◆ **Element by Westin Las Vegas Summerlin** H
(702) 589-2000. **$109-$329, 14 day notice.** 10555 Discovery Dr 89135. I-215 exit 23 (Town Center), just n. Int corridors. **Pets:** Medium, dogs only. $50 one-time fee/room. Designated rooms, service with restrictions, supervision. SAVE 👨‍🦽 🔁 📶 🗙 🛢 💻

▼◆▼ **Extended Stay America-Las Vegas/Midtown** H
(702) 369-1414. **$70-$85.** 3045 S Maryland Pkwy 89109. I-15 exit 40 (Sahara Ave), 1.7 mi e, then 0.6 mi s. Int corridors. **Pets:** Accepted.
👨‍🦽 📶 🗙 🛢

▼◆▼ **Flamingo Las Vegas** H
(702) 733-3111. **Call for rates.** 3555 Las Vegas Blvd S 89109. I-15 exit 38 (Flamingo Rd), just n on the Strip. Int corridors. **Pets:** Accepted.
🍴 👨‍🦽 🔁 🗙 🔊 🛢 💻

Four Seasons Hotel Las Vegas H ❀

(702) 632-5000. **Call for rates.** 3960 Las Vegas Blvd S 89119. I-15 exit 37 (Tropicana Ave), just s on the Strip. Int corridors. **Pets:** Small. $100 daily fee/pet. Designated rooms, service with restrictions, supervision.

Holiday Inn Express-Nellis H

(702) 644-5700. **$109-$169.** 4035 N Nellis Blvd 89115. I-15 exit 48 (Craig Rd), 2.3 mi e, then just s. Int corridors. **Pets:** Accepted.

Hyatt Place Las Vegas H

(702) 369-3366. **$99-$309.** 4520 Paradise Rd 89169. Jct Harmon Ave, just s. Int corridors. **Pets:** Accepted.

La Quinta Inn & Suites Airport South H

(702) 492-8900. **$81-$273.** 6560 Surrey St 89119. Jct Eastern Ave and Sunset Rd, just w, just s. Int corridors. **Pets:** Accepted.

La Quinta Inn & Suites Las Vegas Redrock/Summerlin H

(702) 243-0356. **$92-$251.** 9570 W Sahara Ave 89117. Jct Fort Apache Rd, just w. Int corridors. **Pets:** Accepted.

La Quinta Inn & Suites Tropicana H

(702) 798-7736. **$86-$262.** 4975 S Valley View Blvd 89118. I-15 exit 37 (Tropicana Ave), 0.6 mi w. Int corridors. **Pets:** Accepted.

La Quinta Inn Las Vegas Nellis H

(702) 632-0229. **$92-$235.** 4288 N Nellis Blvd 89115. Jct Las Vegas Blvd, just n. Int corridors. **Pets:** Accepted.

The Mirage H

(702) 791-7111. **Call for rates.** 3400 Las Vegas Blvd S 89109. I-15 exit 39 (Spring Mountain Rd E), e to the Strip, then just s. Int corridors. **Pets:** Accepted.

Palace Station Hotel & Casino H

(702) 367-2411. **Call for rates.** 2411 W Sahara Ave 89102. I-15 exit 40 (Sahara Ave); southwest corner of Sahara Ave and Rancho Dr. Int corridors. **Pets:** Accepted.

Platinum Hotel & Spa H

(702) 365-5000. **Call for rates.** 211 E Flamingo Rd 89169. I-15 exit 38 (Flamingo Rd), 1.2 mi e. Int corridors. **Pets:** Accepted.

Residence Inn by Marriott-Hughes Center H

(702) 650-0040. **$109-$226.** 370 Hughes Center Dr 89169. Jct Flamingo and Paradise rds, just n. Int corridors. **Pets:** Accepted.

Residence Inn by Marriott Las Vegas Convention Center H

(702) 796-9300. **$120-$273.** 3225 Paradise Rd 89109. Opposite Las Vegas Convention Center. Ext corridors. **Pets:** Accepted.

Residence Inn by Marriott Las Vegas South H

(702) 795-7378. **$127-$217.** 5875 Dean Martin Rd 89118. I-15 exit 36 (Russell Rd), just sw. Int corridors. **Pets:** Medium, other species. $100 one-time fee/room. Service with restrictions, crate.

Trump International Hotel Las Vegas H

(702) 982-0000. **Call for rates.** 2000 Fashion Show Dr 89109. Jct Las Vegas Blvd, just w. Int corridors. **Pets:** Accepted.

Vdara Hotel & Spa H

(702) 590-2767. **$109-$999, 3 day notice.** 2600 W Harmon Ave 89158. Between Flamingo Rd and Tropicana Ave; on the Strip. Int corridors. **Pets:** Accepted.

MESQUITE

Best Western Mesquite Inn M

(702) 346-7444. **$80-$150.** 390 N Sandhill Blvd 89027. I-15 exit 122, just e. Ext corridors. **Pets:** Medium. $20 daily fee/room. Designated rooms, service with restrictions, supervision.

Holiday Inn Express & Suites H

(702) 346-2200. **Call for rates.** 1030 W Pioneer Blvd 89027. I-15 exit 120, just w. Int corridors. **Pets:** Accepted.

Virgin River Hotel Casino Bingo M

(702) 346-7777. **Call for rates.** 100 E Pioneer Blvd 89027. I-15 exit 122, just w. Ext corridors. **Pets:** Accepted.

MINDEN

Holiday Inn Express & Suites Minden H

(775) 782-7500. **$109-$259.** 1659 SR 88 89423. Jct US 395 N. Int corridors. **Pets:** Other species. $20 one-time fee/pet. Designated rooms, service with restrictions, supervision.

NORTH LAS VEGAS

Aliante Casino + Hotel + Spa H

(702) 692-7777. **Call for rates.** 7300 Aliante Pkwy 89084. I-215 exit 43 (Aliante Pkwy), just n. Int corridors. **Pets:** Accepted.

Best Western Plus North Las Vegas Inn & Suites H

(702) 649-3000. **$99-$169.** 4540 Donovan Way 89081. I-15 exit 48 (Craig Rd), just w. Int corridors. **Pets:** Accepted.

Hampton Inn Las Vegas North Speedway H

(702) 655-0111. **$109-$299.** 2852 E Craig Rd 89030. I-15 exit 48 (Craig Rd), just w. Int corridors. **Pets:** Accepted.

OVERTON

North Shore Inn at Lake Mead H

(702) 397-6000. **$81-$125, 3 day notice.** 520 N Moapa Valley Blvd 89040. I-15 exit 93, 10 mi ne on SR 169. Int corridors. **Pets:** Accepted.

PAHRUMP

Best Western Pahrump Oasis M

(775) 727-5100. **$109-$150.** 1101 S Hwy 160 89048. Downtown. Ext/int corridors. **Pets:** Accepted.

Holiday Inn Express & Suites H

(775) 727-9100. **Call for rates.** 861 S Hwy 160 89048. Center. Int corridors. **Pets:** Dogs only. $20 daily fee/pet. Designated rooms, service with restrictions, supervision.

RENO (Restaurants p. 618)

Best Western Airport Plaza Hotel H ❀
(775) 348-6370. **$90-$140.** 1981 Terminal Way 89502. I-580/US 395 exit 65A southbound (E Plumb Ln/Villanova Dr), just e on Villanova Dr; exit 65 northbound, just e on E Plumb Ln. Int corridors. **Pets:** Medium, dogs only. $20 daily fee/room. Designated rooms, service with restrictions, supervision. [SAVE] [Y1] [&M] [icons]

Extended Stay America-Reno-South Meadows H
(775) 852-5611. **$80-$105.** 9795 Gateway Dr 89521. I-580/US 395 exit 60 (S Meadows Pkwy), just e, then n. Int corridors. **Pets:** Accepted. [icons]

Holiday Inn Express & Suites Reno Airport H
(775) 229-7070. **Call for rates.** 2375 Market St 89502. I-580/US 395 exit 66, just n. Int corridors. **Pets:** Medium. $30 daily fee/pet. Designated rooms, service with restrictions, supervision. [icons]

Homewood Suites by Hilton Reno H
(775) 853-7100. **$99-$269.** 5450 Kietzke Ln 89511. I-580/US 395 exit 62 (Neil Rd), just sw. Int corridors. **Pets:** Accepted. [SAVE] [icons]

Hyatt Place Reno-Tahoe Airport H ❀
(775) 826-2500. **$79-$219.** 1790 E Plumb Ln 89502. I-580/US 395 exit 65A southbound (E Plumb Ln/Villanova Dr); exit 65 northbound, just se. Int corridors. **Pets:** Medium, dogs only. $75 one-time fee/pet. Service with restrictions, supervision. [SAVE] [icons]

La Quinta Inn Reno M
(775) 348-6100. **$67-$130.** 4001 Market St 89502. I-580/US 395 exit 65A southbound (E Plumb Ln/Villanova Dr), just w on Villanova Dr; exit 65 northbound, just n, then just w on Villanova Dr. Ext corridors.
Pets: Accepted. [icons]

Renaissance Reno Downtown Hotel H ❀
(775) 682-3900. **$129-$429.** 1 S Lake St 89501. I-80 exit 13 (Virginia St), 0.8 mi s; at Mill St. Int corridors. **Pets:** Medium, dogs only. $50 one-time fee/pet. Designated rooms, service with restrictions, supervision. [SAVE] [icons]

Residence Inn by Marriott Reno H
(775) 853-8800. **$130-$214.** 9845 Gateway Dr 89521. I-580/US 395 exit 60 (S Meadows Pkwy), just e. Int corridors. **Pets:** Accepted. [SAVE] [ECO] [icons]

Sands Regency Casino Hotel H
(775) 348-2200. **Call for rates.** 345 N Arlington Ave 89501. At 3rd St. Int corridors. **Pets:** Accepted. [SAVE] [icons]

Staybridge Suites Reno H
(775) 657-8999. **$89-$399.** 10559 Professional Cir 89511. I-580/US 395 exit 59 (Damonte Ranch Pkwy), just e, just n on Double R Blvd, then just w. Int corridors. **Pets:** Accepted. [icons]

Whitney Peak Hotel H
(775) 398-5400. **Call for rates.** 255 N Virginia St 89501. I-80 exit 13 (Virginia St), 0.6 mi s; jct W Commercial Row; downtown. Int corridors. **Pets:** Accepted. [icons]

SPARKS

Holiday Inn-Reno/Sparks H ❀
(775) 358-6900. **$119-$209.** 55 E Nugget Ave 89431. I-80 exit 19 (McCarran Blvd), just se. Int corridors. **Pets:** Medium. $25 daily fee/pet. Designated rooms, service with restrictions, supervision. [SAVE] [icons]

Super 8-Sparks/Reno H
(775) 358-8884. **$72-$126.** 1900 E Greg St 89431. I-80 exit 20, 0.6 mi s, then just e. Int corridors. **Pets:** $10 daily fee/pet. Designated rooms, service with restrictions, supervision. [icons]

TONOPAH

Best Western Hi-Desert Inn H ❀
(775) 482-3511. **$109-$169.** 320 Main St 89049. On US 6 and 95. Int corridors. **Pets:** Dogs only. Designated rooms, service with restrictions, supervision. [SAVE] [icons]

Mizpah Hotel H ❀
(775) 482-3030. **Call for rates.** 100 N Main St 89049. Center. Int corridors. **Pets:** Large, dogs only. $10 daily fee/pet. Designated rooms, service with restrictions, supervision. [icons]

Tonopah Station H
(775) 482-9777. **Call for rates.** 1137 S Main St 89049. On US 6 and 95. Int corridors. **Pets:** Other species. $10 one-time fee/room, $10 daily fee/room. Service with restrictions, supervision. [SAVE] [icons]

WINNEMUCCA

Best Western Plus Gold Country Inn H
(775) 623-6999. **$135-$181.** 921 W Winnemucca Blvd 89445. 0.6 mi sw of center. Int corridors. **Pets:** Accepted. [SAVE] [icons]

Candlewood Suites H
(775) 623-2700. **Call for rates.** 460 E Winnemucca Blvd 89445. I-80 exit 178, just s. Int corridors. **Pets:** Accepted. [icons]

Holiday Inn Express H
(775) 625-3100. **Call for rates.** 1987 W Winnemucca Blvd 89445. I-80 exit 176, just s. Int corridors. **Pets:** Accepted. [icons]

Town House Motel M
(775) 623-3620. **$85-$95.** 375 Monroe St 89445. 0.4 mi sw of center to Monroe St, just se. Ext corridors. **Pets:** Medium, dogs only. $10 daily fee/pet. Designated rooms, supervision. [SAVE] [icons]

Winnemucca Holiday Motel M
(775) 623-3684. **Call for rates.** 670 W Winnemucca Blvd 89445. 0.4 mi sw of center. Ext corridors. **Pets:** Other species. $75 deposit/room, $10 daily fee/pet. Designated rooms, service with restrictions, supervision. [SAVE] [icons]

The Winnemucca Inn & Casino H
(775) 623-2565. **Call for rates.** 741 W Winnemucca Blvd 89445. I-80 exit 176, 1.1 mi nw. Ext/int corridors. **Pets:** Accepted. [icons]

ZEPHYR COVE

Zephyr Cove Resort CA
(775) 589-4980. **Call for rates.** 760 Hwy 50 89448. 4 mi n of Stateline, NV. Ext/int corridors. **Pets:** Medium, dogs only. $15 daily fee/pet. Designated rooms, service with restrictions, supervision. [SAVE] [icons]

ASHLAND

▼▼ Comfort Inn H

(603) 968-7668. **$85-$250.** 53 West St 03217. I-93 exit 24 (SR 25 and US 3), just e. Int corridors. **Pets:** Accepted. ⛔ 🛏 🛜 📶 🖥

BARTLETT

▼▼ The Bartlett Inn BB 🐾

(603) 374-2353. **$99-$249, 14 day notice.** 1477 US Rt 302 03812. On US 302, 7 mi w of jct SR 16. Ext/int corridors. **Pets:** Dogs only. $25 one-time fee/pet. Designated rooms, service with restrictions, supervision. ⛔ 🛏 ✖ 🛜 ✖ 📶 🖥

BEDFORD

◆ Country Inn & Suites By Carlson, Manchester Airport H

(603) 666-4600. **Call for rates.** 250 S River Rd 03110. I-293 exit US 3 (Kilton Rd/S River Rd), 0.7 mi s. Int corridors. **Pets:** Accepted.

⛔ 🛏 ✖ 🛜 ✖ 📶 🖥

BRETTON WOODS

▼▼▼ Omni Bretton Arms Inn CI

(603) 278-3000. **$199-$509, 7 day notice.** 173 Mount Washington Hotel Rd 03575. Center. Int corridors. **Pets:** Accepted.

⛔ ✖ 🛜 ✖ 📶

CHESTERFIELD

▼▼▼ Chesterfield Inn CI

(603) 256-3211. **Call for rates.** 20 Cross Rd 03466. I-91 exit 3, 2 mi e on SR 9. Ext/int corridors. **Pets:** Large, other species. Designated rooms, service with restrictions, supervision.

ECO ⛔ ⛔ ✖ 🛜 ✖ 📶 🖥

COLEBROOK

◆ ▼▼ Northern Comfort Motel M

(603) 237-4440. **$79-$99, 3 day notice.** 1 Trooper Scott Phillips Hwy 03576. 1.5 mi s on US 3. Ext corridors. **Pets:** Accepted.

SAVE ⛔ 🛏 🛜 ✖ 📶

CONCORD

◆ ▼▼ Best Western Concord Inn & Suites H

(603) 228-4300. **$99-$299.** 97 Hall St 03301. I-93 exit 13, just n on Main St, then 0.5 mi w. Int corridors. **Pets:** Dogs only. $15 daily fee/pet. Designated rooms, service with restrictions, supervision.

SAVE ⛔ ⛔ 🛏 🛜 ✖ 📶 🖥

▼▼ Concord Comfort Inn H

(603) 226-4100. **$94-$269.** 71 Hall St 03301. I-93 exit 13, just n on Main St, then 0.5 mi w. Int corridors. **Pets:** Small, dogs only. $15 daily fee/room. Designated rooms, service with restrictions, supervision.

⛔ ⛔ 🛏 ✖ 🛜 ✖ 📶 🖥

▼▼▼ Residence Inn by Marriott Concord H

(603) 226-0012. **$107-$306.** 91 Hall St 03301. I-93 exit 13, just n on Main St, then 0.5 mi w. Int corridors. **Pets:** Accepted.

⛔ ⛔ ⛔ 🛏 🛜 ✖ 📶 🖥

DOVER

▼▼▼▼ Comfort Inn & Suites H

(603) 750-7507. **$99-$249.** 10 Hotel Dr 03820. SR 16 exit 9, 0.4 mi ne. Int corridors. **Pets:** Accepted. ⛔ 🛏 🛜 ✖ 📶 🖥

▼▼▼▼ Homewood Suites by Hilton Dover H

(603) 516-0929. **$129-$289.** 21 Members Way 03820. SR 16 exit 9, 0.4 mi w. Int corridors. **Pets:** Accepted. ⛔ 🛏 🛜 📶 🖥

DURHAM

▼▼ Holiday Inn Express Durham-UNH H

(603) 868-1234. **Call for rates.** 2 Main St 03824. On SR 108; center. Int corridors. **Pets:** Accepted. ⛔ 🛜 ✖ 📶 🖥

▼▼▼ Three Chimneys Inn CI

(603) 868-7800. **Call for rates.** 17 Newmarket Rd 03824. On SR 108; center. Ext/int corridors. **Pets:** Accepted. ⛔ ⛔ 🛜 ✖ 📶 🖥

EXETER

▼▼▼ Hampton Inn & Suites by Hilton H

(603) 658-5555. **$89-$299.** 59 Portsmouth Ave 03833. I-101 exit 11. Int corridors. **Pets:** Accepted. ⛔ ⛔ 🛏 🛜 ✖ 📶 🖥

FRANCONIA

◆ ▼▼ Best Western White Mountain Inn H

(603) 823-7422. **$89-$230.** 87 Wallace Hill Rd 03580. I-93 exit 38, just e. Int corridors. **Pets:** Accepted. SAVE ⛔ 🛏 🛜 ✖ 📶 🖥

▼ Gale River Motel M 🐾

(603) 823-5655. **$55-$220, 7 day notice.** 1 Main St 03580. I-93 exit 38, 0.8 mi n on SR 18. Ext corridors. **Pets:** Dogs only. $10 daily fee/pet. Designated rooms, service with restrictions, supervision.

ECO ⛔ ⛔ 🛏 🛜 ✖ 🖥

▼▼▼ Lovetts Inn by Lafayette Brook CI

(603) 823-7761. **Call for rates.** 1474 Profile Rd 03580. I-93 exit 38, just w on Wallace Hill Rd, then 2.1 mi s on SR 18. Ext/int corridors.

Pets: Accepted. ⛔ 🛏 🛜 ✖ ✖ 📶 🖥

GILFORD

▼▼ Fireside Inn & Suites H 🐾

(603) 293-7526. **Call for rates.** 17 Harris Shore Rd 03249. Jct SR 11 and 11B, 2.5 mi e of jct US 3 N. Int corridors. **Pets:** Medium. $25 deposit/pet. Designated rooms, no service, supervision.

🛏 ✖ 🛜 ✖ 📶 🖥

▼▼▼ TownePlace Suites by Marriott Gilford H

(603) 524-5533. **$90-$549.** 14 Sawmill Rd 03249. Just e of jct SR 3 and 11A. Int corridors. **Pets:** Accepted.

⛔ ⛔ 🛏 🛜 ✖ 📶 🖥

AAA PetBook® Photo Contest Entries

The winning entry in AAA's PetBook Photo Contest, sponsored by Best Western® appears on the cover of *Traveling With Your Pet: The AAA PetBook®* and also received other great prizes. You have already met the contest winners, but here are more great entries that we just had to make room for!

Piper enjoying the view in Chicago, Ill.
Owner: Madison Roberts from New York, N.Y.

Benji posing in the Moab Valley, Moab, Utah
Owner: Josephine Quesenberry from Grafton, W.Va.

Ninda & Kobe at Rock Run Gristmill, Havre de Grace, Md. Owner: Solimar Castro from Aberdeen Proving Ground, Md.

Pocono playing at Leland Park, Woburn, Mass.
Owner: Colleen Lynch from Haverhill, Mass.

Sophie Grace in Cuyahoga Valley National
Park, Ohio
Owner: Beth Niermann from Stow, Ohio

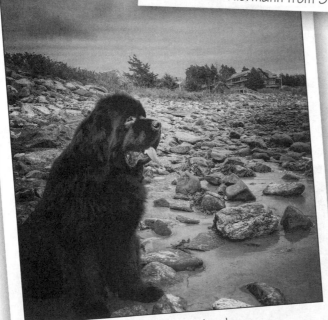

Judge vacationing in Rhode Island
Owner: Beth Boring from Maryville, Tenn.

Joey at Comb Ridge in southeastern Utah
Owners: Joyce Tanihara & Art Trevena from
Cedaredge, Colo.

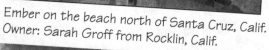

Ember on the beach north of Santa Cruz, Calif.
Owner: Sarah Groff from Rocklin, Calif.

Chloe relaxing in Fredericksburg, Texas
Owner: Leoria Moore from Johnson City, Texas

Bella & McKenzie posing in Dayton, Ore.
Owner: Cassandra Anderson from Dayton, Ore.

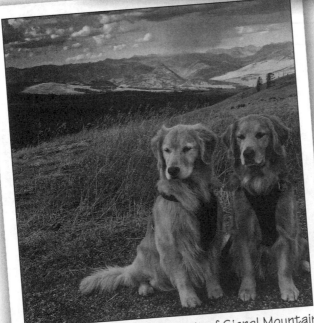

Maddi & Wyatt at the summit of Signal Mountain
Road in Grand Teton National Park, Wyo.
Owner: Mar Sension from Altoona, Pa.

Rusty at Salisbury Beach, Salisbury, Mass. Owners: Kathy & Lou Diamontopoulos from Haverhill, Mass.

Raven boating on Bobs Lake, Ont. Owner: Melissa Clewell from Allentown, Pa.

Yoshi & Sachi playing in Mammoth Lakes, Calif. Owners: Bill & Jean Mumbleau from Alta Loma, Calif.

Burton posing on the Schoodic Peninsula, Maine
Owner: Diane Nightingale from Hagaman, N.Y.

BG & Peetie visiting Sedona, Ariz.
Owner: Kevin Tong from Orange, Calif.

Riley "parking" near Telluride, Colo.
Owner: Doreen Myles from Phoenix, Ariz.

Boogieman playing at Trestle Park, Adrian, Mich.
Owner: Kay Darrow from Brooklyn, Mich.

Denali in Monterey, Calif.
Owner: Irene Zeppelin from White Bear Lake, Minn.

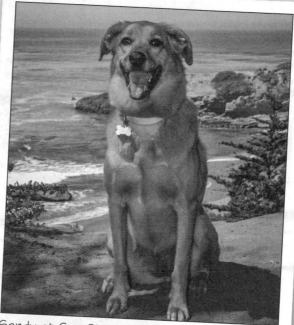

Sandy at San Simeon Cove, San Simeon, Calif.
Owner: Ellen Zuckerman from Chatsworth, Calif.

Finnley on the beach in Myrtle Beach, S.C.
Owner: Nicole Baim from Lynchburg, Va.

Stormy & Rosie sightseeing at Crater Lake, Ore.
Owner: Candy Lidstrom from Camarillo, Calif.

Hooper in Angeles National Forest, Calif.
Owner: Katherine Dumalski from Long Beach, Calif.

Sidney enjoying Balboa Park, San Diego, Calif.
Owner: Geri Sterling from Vista, Calif.

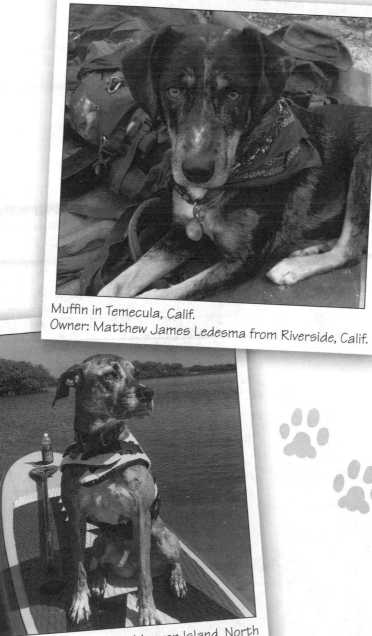

Muffin in Temecula, Calif.
Owner: Matthew James Ledesma from Riverside, Calif.

Morgan on the water at Munyon Island, North Palm Beach, Fla.
Owner: Sonia Walker from Miami, Fla.

Lovely in Teton Pass, Mont.
Owner: Sarah Bechtel from Vacaville, Calif.

Ace at Gooseberry Falls State Park, Minn.
Owner: Teresa Stiefel from Big Lake, Minn.

Henry hiking in Corona del Mar, Calif.
Owner: Caroline McAndrews from Laguna Niguel, Calif.

Oreo in Duluth, Minn.
Owner: Tabitha Chonka-Michaud from Black River Falls, Wis.

Kolby at Mount Defiance, Ticonderoga, N.Y.
Owner: Lorrie Lynn Koch from Weissport, Pa.

Kato at Shaver Lake, Calif.
Owner: Sophia Ota from Fullerton, Calif.

Ego in Zumbrota, Minn.
Owner: Sydney Ryan from Minneapolis, Minn.

Paulo at Sequoia National Forest, Calif.
Owner: Ryan Moorehouse from Phoenix, Ariz.

Roxy sightseeing in San Pedro, Calif.
Owner: Monica Almeida from Laguna Hills, Calif.

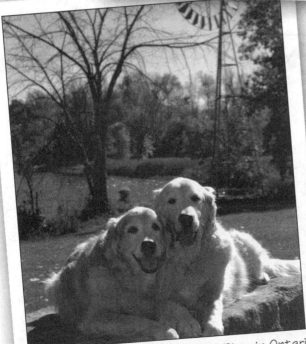

Brie & Bentley by the Mississippi River in Ontario
Owner: Sandra Lindsay from Ottawa, Ont.

A few more tail-wagging travelers

1) Murphy in Cape San Blas, Fla., Owner: Marie Roop from Carrollton, Ga. 2) Gus at the top of Boreas Pass, Colo., Owner: Pamela Zimmerman from Aurora, Colo. 3) Simon Snorkel & Mackenzie Hut exploring the Rockfish Valley Trail, Nellysford, Va., Owner: Kim Holzer from Adams, Mass. 4) Buster in Malibu, Calif., Owner: Carleen Domenico from Westlake Village, Calif. 5) Oscar visiting Wild Goose Island, Glacier National Park, Mont., Owners: Joe & Brenna Loretta from Jacksonville Beach, Fla. 6) Enzo on the shore in La Jolla, Calif., Owner: Rosemary McRobbie from Fallbrook, Calif. 7) Maddie Faye & Sophie Ann at the beach in Gulf Shores, Ala., Owner: Melanie Smith from Hoover, Ala.

GORHAM

▼ Moose Brook Motel Ⓜ
(603) 466-5400. **$89-$109, 7 day notice.** 65 Lancaster Rd 03581. Jct SR 16, 0.5 mi w on US 2. Ext corridors. **Pets:** $10 one-time fee/pet. Service with restrictions, crate. 🛍 🤶 ☒ 🛎 🚹 💻

▼▼ Royalty Inn Ⓗ
(603) 466-3312. **$84-$169.** 130 Main St 03581. On US 2 and SR 16; center. Ext/int corridors. **Pets:** Accepted.
ⒺⒸⓄ 👤 🛍 ☒ 🤶 🚹 💻

▼▼ Top Notch Inn Ⓜ
(603) 466-5496. **Call for rates.** 265 Main St 03581. On US 2 and SR 16; center. Ext/int corridors. **Pets:** Accepted.
🔲 🛍 🤶 ☒ 🚹 💻

▼▼ Town & Country Inn & Resort Ⓗ
(603) 466-3315. **Call for rates.** 20 SR 2 03581. 0.5 mi e of jct SR 16. Ext/int corridors. **Pets:** Accepted. 👤 🛍 ☒ 🤶 🚹 💻

HAMPTON

⟨AAA⟩ ▼▼▼ Lamie's Inn Ⓒ
(603) 926-0330. **$109-$229, 3 day notice.** 490 Lafayette Rd 03842. Jct SR 27 on US 1. Int corridors. **Pets:** Accepted.
ⓈⒶⓥⒺ 👤 👤 🤶 ☒ 🚹

HANCOCK

▼▼▼▼ The Hancock Inn & Fox Tavern Ⓒ
(603) 525-3318. **$169-$405, 7 day notice.** 33 Main St 03449. Jct SR 123 and 137; center. Int corridors. **Pets:** Accepted.
🔲 👤 👤 🤶 ☒

HANOVER

⟨AAA⟩ ▼▼▼ ▼▼▼ The Hanover Inn Dartmouth Ⓗ
(603) 643-4300. **$199-$579, 3 day notice.** 2 E Wheelock St 03755. Center. Int corridors. **Pets:** Accepted. ⓈⒶⓥⒺ 👤 🤶 ☒ 🚹 💻

▼▼▼ Six South Street Hotel Hanover Ⓗ
(603) 643-0600. **$119-$799.** 6 South St 03755. I-89 exit 18, n on SR 120 to Lebanon St, left on Sanborn Rd (which becomes South St). Int corridors. **Pets:** Accepted. 👤 🤶 ☒ 🚹 💻

HARTS LOCATION

▼▼▼ Notchland Inn Ⓒ
(603) 374-6131. **$199-$295, 14 day notice.** 2 Morey Rd 03812. On US 302, 6.4 mi w of town. Ext/int corridors. **Pets:** $20 daily fee/pet. Designated rooms, service with restrictions.
ⒺⒸⓄ 🔲 👤 🤶 ☒ Ⓦ 🚹 💻

HEBRON

▼▼▼▼ Coppertoppe Inn & Retreat Center ⒷⒷ 🐾
(603) 744-3636. **$189-$295, 14 day notice.** 8 Range Rd 03241. I-93 exit 23, 6 mi w on SR 104, 8.7 mi n on SR 3A, then 0.6 mi w on N Shore Rd. Int corridors. **Pets:** Other species. $15 daily fee/pet.
ⒺⒸⓄ 👤 ☒ 🤶 ☒ 🅩 🚹 💻

HENNIKER

▼▼▼▼ Colby Hill Inn Ⓒ
(603) 428-3281. **Call for rates.** 33 The Oaks St 03242. 0.5 mi s of US 202 and SR 9, via SR 114, 0.5 mi w on Western Ave. Int corridors. **Pets:** Accepted. 🔲 👤 👤 🛍 🤶 ☒ 🚹 💻

INTERVALE

▼▼ The New England Inn & Lodge Ⓒ
(603) 356-5541. **Call for rates.** 336 SR 16A 03845. Jct US 302/SR 16, follow SR 16A Intervale Resort Loop. Ext/int corridors. **Pets:** Accepted.
👤 🛍 🤶 ☒ 🚹 💻

JACKSON

▼▼ Nordic Village Resort ⒸⓄ
(603) 383-9101. **Call for rates.** Rt 16 03846. 1 mi n of jct US 302. Ext/int corridors. **Pets:** Dogs only. $25 daily fee/pet. Designated rooms, no service, supervision. 👤 🛍 ☒ 🤶 ☒ 🚹 💻

▼▼▼ The Snowflake Inn ⒷⒷ
(603) 383-8259. **$179-$375, 14 day notice.** 95 Main St (SR 16A) 03846. On SR 16A; center. Int corridors. **Pets:** Accepted.
🛍 ☒ 🤶 ☒

JEFFERSON

▼▼ Jefferson Inn ⒷⒷ
(603) 586-7998. **Call for rates.** 6 Renaissance Ln 03583. US 2, just e of SR 116. Int corridors. **Pets:** Accepted.
👤 ☒ 🤶 ☒ 🅩 🚹

KEENE

⟨AAA⟩ ▼▼ Best Western Plus Keene Hotel Ⓗ
(603) 357-3038. **$99-$289.** 401 Winchester St 03431. SR 10, just s of jct SR 12 and 101. Int corridors. **Pets:** Large, dogs only. $20 daily fee/room. Designated rooms, service with restrictions, supervision.
ⓈⒶⓥⒺ 👤 👤 🛍 🤶 🚹 💻

▼▼ Courtyard by Marriott Keene Downtown Ⓗ
(603) 354-7900. **$93-$421.** 75 Railroad St 03431. Just off Main St; downtown. Int corridors. **Pets:** Large, dogs only. $25 daily fee/pet. Designated rooms, service with restrictions, supervision.
ⒺⒸⓄ 👤 👤 🛍 🤶 🚹 💻

⟨AAA⟩ ▼▼ Holiday Inn Express Ⓗ
(603) 352-7616. **$123-$199.** 175 Key Rd 03431. SR 101, just n, via Winchester St, then 0.3 mi w. Int corridors. **Pets:** Dogs only. $25 daily fee/room. Designated rooms, service with restrictions, supervision.
ⓈⒶⓥⒺ 👤 🛍 🤶 ☒ 🚹 💻

LANCASTER

⟨AAA⟩ ▼▼ Coos Motor Inn Ⓗ
(603) 788-3079. **Call for rates.** 209 Main St 03584. On US 2 and 3; center. Int corridors. **Pets:** Accepted.
ⓈⒶⓥⒺ 👤 👤 🤶 ☒ 🚹 💻

LEBANON

⟨AAA⟩ ▼▼▼ Element by Westin Hanover-Lebanon Ⓗ
(603) 448-5000. **$159-$599.** 25 Foothill St 03766. I-89 exit 18, 1.8 mi n on SR 120, e on Altaria Park, then just n. Int corridors. **Pets:** Accepted.
ⓈⒶⓥⒺ 👤 🤶 ☒ 🚹 💻

LINCOLN

⟨AAA⟩ ▼▼ Econo Lodge Inn & Suites Ⓜ 🐾
(603) 745-3661. **$77-$205.** 381 US Rt 3 03251. I-93 exit 33 (US 3), 0.3 mi ne. Ext/int corridors. **Pets:** $25 daily fee/pet. Designated rooms, service with restrictions, crate. ⓈⒶⓥⒺ 🛍 ☒ 🤶 ☒ 🚹

LITTLETON

▼▼ Eastgate Inn Ⓜ
(603) 444-3971. **Call for rates.** 335 Cottage St 03561. I-93 exit 41, just e. Ext corridors. **Pets:** Accepted. 👤 🤶 🚹 💻

MANCHESTER *(Restaurants p. 618)*

⟨AAA⟩ ▼▼▼ Best Western Plus Executive Court Inn & Conference Center Ⓗ
(603) 627-2525. **$130-$135.** 13500 S Willow St 03103. I-293 exit 1, 0.5 mi s on SR 28, then 1 mi e. Int corridors. **Pets:** Accepted.
ⓈⒶⓥⒺ 👤 👤 🛍 ☒ 🤶 ☒ 🚹 💻

▼▼▼▼ Holiday Inn Express Hotel & Suites-Manchester
Airport H
(603) 669-6800. Call for rates. 1298 S Porter St 03103. I-293 exit 1,
just n. Int corridors. Pets: Accepted.
🍴 ⓜ 🛏 🛜 ✕ 🛗 💻

▼▼▼▼ Homewood Suites by Hilton H
(603) 668-2200. Call for rates. 1000 Perimeter Rd 03103. I-293 exit 2,
follow signs to Manchester-Boston Regional Airport. Int corridors.
Pets: Accepted. 🍴 ⓜ 🛏 🛜 ✕ 🛗 💻

▼▼▼▼ La Quinta Inn & Suites Manchester H
(603) 669-5400. $82-$273. 21 Front St 03102. I-293 exit 6, just se. Int
corridors. Pets: Accepted. 🍴 ⓜ 🛏 🛜 ✕ 🛗 💻

▼▼▼▼ Quality Inn Manchester H
(603) 668-6110. $99-$279. 55 John E Devine Dr 03103. I-293 exit 1,
just nw on SR 28. Int corridors. Pets: Accepted.
🍴 ⓜ 🛏 🛜 ✕ 🛗 💻

ⒶⒶⒶ ▼▼▼▼ Radisson Hotel Manchester
Downtown H
(603) 625-1000. $119-$219. 700 Elm St 03101. Jct Granite St; downtown. Int corridors. Pets: $25 one-time fee/room. Designated rooms,
service with restrictions, supervision.
SAVE ECO 🍴 ⓜ 🛏 ✕ 🛜 ✕ 🛗 💻

▼▼▼ TownePlace Suites by Marriott Manchester-Boston
Regional Airport H
(603) 641-2288. $78-$219. 686 Huse Rd 03103. I-293 exit 1, 0.5 mi se
on SR 28. Int corridors. Pets: Accepted. ⓜ 🛏 🛜 ✕ 🛗 💻

MEREDITH
▼▼▼ Church Landing at Mill Falls H ❀
(603) 279-7006. $279-$650, 7 day notice. 281 Daniel Webster Hwy
03253. Jct US 3 and SR 104, 0.6 mi n. Ext/int corridors. Pets: Other
species. $350 deposit/room, $25 daily fee/pet. Designated rooms, service with restrictions. ⊟ 🍴 ⓜ 🛏 ✕ 🛜 ✕ 🛗 💻

NASHUA
▼▼▼▼ Crowne Plaza Hotel Nashua H
(603) 886-1200. $109-$399. 2 Somerset Pkwy 03063. US 3 (Everett
Tpke) exit 8, just w. Int corridors. Pets: Large. $25 daily fee/room. Ser-
vice with restrictions, supervision.
🍴 ⓜ 🛏 ✕ 🛜 ✕ 🛗 💻

▼▼▼▼ Hampton Inn by Hilton Nashua H
(603) 883-5333. $108-$179. 407 Amherst St 03063. US 3 (Everett
Tpke) exit 8; just w. Int corridors. Pets: Accepted.
ECO ⓜ 🛏 🛜 ✕ 🛗 💻

ⒶⒶⒶ ▼▼▼▼ Holiday Inn & Suites Nashua H
(603) 888-1551. Call for rates. 9 Northeastern Blvd 03062. US 3 exit
4, just w, then 0.3 mi n. Int corridors. Pets: Accepted.
SAVE 🍴 🛏 🛜 ✕ 🛗 💻

▼▼▼▼ Radisson Hotel Nashua H
(603) 888-9970. $109-$209. 11 Tara Blvd 03062. US 3/Everett Tpke exit
1, just w. Int corridors. Pets: Accepted.
ECO 🍴 ⓜ 🛏 ✕ 🛜 ✕ 🛗 💻

▼▼▼▼ Residence Inn by Marriott Nashua H ❀
(603) 882-8300. $98-$286. 25 Trafalgar Sq 03063. US 3 (Everett Tpke)
exit 8, just w. Int corridors. Pets: Small, cats only. $25 daily fee/pet.
Designated rooms, service with restrictions, supervision.
ⓜ 🛜 ✕ 🛗 💻

NEWBURY
▼▼ Sunapee Lake Lodge H
(603) 763-2010. Call for rates. 1403 SR 103 03255. Jct SR 103B, just
e. Int corridors. Pets: Accepted. ⓜ 🛏 🛜 ✕ 🛗 💻

NEW CASTLE
ⒶⒶⒶ ▼▼▼▼ Wentworth By The Sea, A Marriott Hotel
& Spa H
(603) 422-7322. $134-$683, 3 day notice. 588 Wentworth Rd 03854.
On SR 1B, 2 mi e of SR 1A. Ext/int corridors. Pets: Accepted.
SAVE 🍴 ⓜ 🛏 ✕ 🛜 ✕ 🛗 💻

NEW LONDON
▼▼▼ New London Inn CI
(603) 526-2791. Call for rates. 353 Main St 03257. Center. Int corridors. Pets: Other species. $25 one-time fee/room. Designated rooms,
service with restrictions, crate. 🍴 ⓜ 🛜 ✕

NORTH CONWAY
ⒶⒶⒶ ▼▼▼ Green Granite Inn and Conference
Center H ❀
(603) 356-6901. $99-$300. 1515 White Mountain Hwy (Rt 16) 03860.
2.3 mi s on US 302/SR 16; village center. Ext/int corridors. Pets: Dogs
only. $25 one-time fee/pet. Designated rooms, service with restrictions.
SAVE 🛏 ✕ 🛜 ✕ 🛗 💻

▼▼▼ Hampton Inn & Suites North Conway H ❀
(603) 356-7736. $99-$319. 1788 White Mountain Hwy 03860. Jct US
302/SR 16, 1 mi n. Int corridors. Pets: Designated rooms, service with
restrictions, supervision. ECO ✕ 🛜 ✕ 🛗 💻

▼▼▼ Merrill Farm Inn M
(603) 447-3866. $69-$169, 5 day notice. 428 White Mountain Hwy
03860. Jct US 302/SR 16, 1.5 mi s on SR 16; 0.5 mi n of village center. Ext/int corridors. Pets: Designated rooms, service with restrictions,
supervision. 🛏 ✕ 🛜 ✕ 🛗 💻

ⒶⒶⒶ ▼▼▼ North Conway Mountain Inn M
(603) 356-2803. $79-$229. 2114 White Mountain Hwy 03860. 1 mi s on
US 302/SR 16. Ext corridors. Pets: $20 daily fee/pet. Designated
rooms, service with restrictions, crate. SAVE 🛜 ✕ 🛗 💻

ⒶⒶⒶ ▼▼▼ Red Jacket Mountain View Resort and
Indoor Water Park H
(603) 356-5411. Call for rates. 2251 White Mountain Hwy 03860. 1 mi
s on US 302/SR 16. Ext/int corridors. Pets: Accepted.
SAVE ECO ⊟ 🍴 ⓜ 🛏 ✕ 🛜 ✕ 🛗 💻

▼▼▼ Residence Inn by Marriott, North Conway H
(603) 356-3024. $90-$388. 1801 White Mountain Hwy 03860. Jct US
302/SR 16, 1 mi n. Int corridors. Pets: Accepted.
ⓜ 🛏 🛜 ✕ 🛗 💻

ⒶⒶⒶ ▼▼▼ White Mountain Hotel & Resort H ❀
(603) 356-7100. Call for rates. 2560 West Side Rd 03860. Jct SR
16/113/153 at Conway traffic light, turn onto Washington St to West
Side Rd (do not cross covered bridge), then 5 mi on left. Ext/int corridors. Pets: Small, dogs only. $75 one-time fee/pet. Designated rooms,
service with restrictions, supervision.
SAVE ECO 🍴 ⓜ 🛏 ✕ 🛜 ✕ 🛗 💻

NORTH WOODSTOCK
ⒶⒶⒶ ▼▼▼ Woodstock Inn, Station &
Brewery CI ❀
(603) 745-3951. $117-$257, 7 day notice. 135 Main St 03262. I-93 exit
32, 0.5 mi w on SR 112, then just n on US 3. Int corridors. Pets: Designated rooms. SAVE ⊟ 🍴 ⓜ 🛜 ✕ 🛗 💻

PLYMOUTH
▼ Red Carpet Inn & Suites M
(603) 536-2155. Call for rates. 166 Highland St 03264. 1 mi w of center. Ext corridors. Pets: Accepted. 🍴 🛜 ✕ 🛗 💻

PORTSMOUTH

▼▼▼ **Hampton Inn Portsmouth Central** H

(603) 431-6111. **$109-$289.** 99 Durgin Ln 03801. I-95 exit 7, 1 mi w via Market St and Woodbury Ave to Durgin Ln, then 0.3 mi s. Int corridors. **Pets:** Accepted. 🍴 🕭 ⚑ 📶 ✕ 🛢 💻

▼▼▼ **Homewood Suites by Hilton** H

(603) 427-5400. **$119-$299.** 100 Portsmouth Blvd 03801. I-95 exit 7, 0.5 mi w, then 0.3 mi n. Int corridors. **Pets:** Accepted.
🍴 🕭 ⚑ 📶 ✕ 🛢 💻

▼▼▼ **Port Inn Portsmouth, An Ascend Collection Member** M

(603) 436-4378. **$119-$699.** 505 US Hwy 1 Bypass 03801. I-95 exit 5, jct US 1 Bypass and Portsmouth Traffic Circle. Ext corridors. **Pets:** Accepted. 🔌 🍴 ⚑ 📶 ✕ 🛢 💻

🆎 ▼▼▼ **Residence Inn by Marriott** H

(603) 436-8880. **$103-$386.** 1 International Dr 03801. Spaulding Tpke (US 4) exit 1, just .5 mi w. Int corridors. **Pets:** Accepted.
🆂🅰🆅🅴 🅴🅲🅾 🍴 🕭 ⚑ 📶 ✕ 🛢 💻

▼▼▼ **Residence Inn by Marriott Downtown/Waterfront** H

(603) 422-9200. **$117-$416.** 100 Deer St 03801. Downtown; at Portwalk Place. Int corridors. **Pets:** Accepted. 🕭 ⚑ 📶 ✕ 🛢 💻

🆎 ▼▼▼ **Sheraton Portsmouth Harborside Hotel** H

(603) 431-2300. **$109-$429.** 250 Market St 03801. At Russell St; downtown. Int corridors. **Pets:** Accepted.
🆂🅰🆅🅴 🅴🅲🅾 🍴 🕭 ⚑ 📶 ✕ 🛢 💻

ROCHESTER

▼▼▼ **Holiday Inn Express Hotel & Suites Rochester** H

(603) 994-1175. **$89-$209.** 77 Farmington Rd 03867. SR 16 (Spaulding Tpke), exit 15 then 1 mi w on SR 11. Int corridors. **Pets:** Medium, dogs only. $50 one-time fee/room, $25 daily fee/room. Designated rooms, service with restrictions, supervision. 🕭 ⚑ 📶 ✕ 🛢 💻

SUGAR HILL

▼▼ **The Hilltop Inn** BB 🐾

(603) 823-5695. **$120-$195.** 9 Norton Ln 03586. I-93 exit 38, 0.5 mi n on SR 18, then 2.8 mi w on SR 117. Int corridors. **Pets:** Dogs only. $10 daily fee/room. 🍴 📶 ✕ 🎿 📺 🎞 🛢

THORNTON

▼ **Shamrock Motel** M

(603) 726-3534. **$60-$95, 7 day notice.** 2913 US 3 03285. I-93 exit 29, 2.3 mi n. Ext corridors. **Pets:** Other species. $5 daily fee/room. Designated rooms, no service, supervision.

🅴🅲🅾 🍴 ⚑ 📶 ✕ 🎞 🛢 💻

TILTON

▼▼▼ **Super 8 of Tilton** M

(603) 286-8882. **$59-$209.** 7 Tilton Rd 03276. I-93 exit 20; behind McDonald's. Int corridors. **Pets:** Accepted. 🕭 📶 🛢 💻

TROY

▼▼▼ **The Inn at East Hill Farm** CI 🐾

(603) 242-6495. **$270-$314, 21 day notice.** 460 Monadnock St 03465. Jct SR 12 and Monadnock St, 2 mi e. Ext/int corridors. **Pets:** Other species. $20 daily fee/pet. Designated rooms, service with restrictions, supervision. 🅴🅲🅾 🍴 🕭 ⚑ 📶 📶 ✕ 🛢

WEST LEBANON

▼▼ **Baymont Inn & Suites** M

(603) 298-8888. **$79-$239.** 45 Airport Rd 03784. I-89 exit 20 (SR 12A), just s, then just e. Int corridors. **Pets:** Accepted. ⚑ 📶 🛢 💻

▼▼ **Fireside Inn and Suites** H

(603) 298-5900. **Call for rates.** 25 Airport Rd 03784. I-89 exit 20 (SR 12A), just s. Int corridors. **Pets:** Accepted.
🍴 ⚑ 📶 ✕ 🛢 💻

WOLFEBORO

▼▼▼ **Wolfeboro Inn** H

(603) 569-3016. **Call for rates.** 90 N Main St 03894. On SR 109, 0.5 mi n of jct SR 28; center. Int corridors. **Pets:** Dogs only. $50 one-time fee/room. Designated rooms, service with restrictions, crate.
🍴 ✕ 📶 ✕ 🛢

WOODSVILLE

🆎 ▼ **All Seasons Motel** M

(603) 747-2157. **Call for rates.** 36 Smith St 03785. I-91 exit 17, 4.1 mi e on US 302, then just s. Ext corridors. **Pets:** $10 daily fee/pet. Designated rooms, service with restrictions, crate.
🆂🅰🆅🅴 ⚑ 📶 ✕ 🛢 💻

🆎 ▼▼▼ **Nootka Lodge** M

(603) 747-2418. **Call for rates.** 4982 Dartmouth College Hwy 03785. I-91 exit 17, 4.5 mi e on US 302. Ext/int corridors. **Pets:** $15 daily fee/pet. Designated rooms, service with restrictions, crate.
🆂🅰🆅🅴 ⚑ ✕ 📶 ✕ 🛢 💻

NEW JERSEY

ASBURY PARK

▼▼▼ **Hotel Tides** H

(732) 897-7744. **Call for rates.** 408 Seventh Ave 07712. Jct Main St, just e. Int corridors. **Pets:** Accepted. 🍴 ⚑ 📶 ✕ 🛢

ATLANTIC CITY

▼▼▼ **Harrah's Resort Atlantic City** H

(609) 441-5000. **Call for rates.** 777 Harrah's Blvd 08401. 0.9 mi n of US 30 on Brigantine Blvd. Int corridors. **Pets:** Accepted.
🍴 🕭 ⚑ ✕ 🎰 🛢 💻

🆎 ▼▼▼ **Sheraton Atlantic City Convention Center Hotel** H

(609) 344-3535. **$79-$499, 3 day notice.** 2 Convention Blvd 08401. Garden State Pkwy exit 38 to Atlantic City Expwy to Arctic Ave, just e to Michigan Ave, then just n. Int corridors. **Pets:** Accepted.
🆂🅰🆅🅴 🍴 🕭 ⚑ 🎰 ✕ 🛢 💻

BASKING RIDGE

▼▼▼ ▼▼ **Dolce Basking Ridge** H

(908) 953-3000. **$119-$349.** 300 N Maple Ave 07920. I-287 exit 30A, 0.3 mi e. Int corridors. **Pets:** Other species. $100 deposit/room. No service, supervision. 🍴 🕭 ⚑ 🎰 📶 ✕ 🛢 💻

▼▼▼ **Hotel Indigo Basking Ridge** H

(908) 580-1300. **Call for rates.** 80 Allen Rd 07920. I-78 exit 33, 0.3 mi n on CR 525, then 0.3 mi w. Int corridors. **Pets:** Accepted.
🍴 🕭 📶 ✕ 🛢 💻

BAY HEAD

▼▼ **The Grenville Hotel** H

(732) 892-3100. **Call for rates.** 345 Main Ave (SR 35) 08742. SR 35 S; at Bridge Ave. Int corridors. **Pets:** Accepted. 🍴 📶 ✕ 🎞 🛢

BORDENTOWN

AAA ▼▼▼ **Best Western Bordentown Inn** M ❀
(609) 298-8000. **$80-$140.** 1068 US Hwy 206 S 08505. New Jersey Tpke exit 7, 0.8 mi n. Ext corridors. **Pets:** Medium. $100 daily fee/room. Designated rooms, service with restrictions, supervision.
SAVE 🛆M ➡ ✕ 📶 🛅 🖵

AAA ▼▼▼ **Days Inn-Bordentown** M
(609) 298-6100. **$70-$149.** 1073 US Hwy 206 N 08505. New Jersey Tpke exit 7, 0.8 mi n. Ext corridors. **Pets:** Accepted.
SAVE ➡ 📶 🛅 🖵

BRANCHBURG

AAA ▼▼▼▼ **Hyatt House Branchburg** H
(908) 704-2191. **$89-$329.** 3141 Rt 22 E 08876. I-287 exit 14B northbound, 6.7 mi w; exit 17 southbound, 3.7 mi w. Int corridors.
Pets: Accepted. SAVE 🛆M ➡ ✕ 📶 ✕ 🛅 🖵

BRIDGEPORT

▼▼▼ **Hampton Inn-Bridgeport** H ❀
(856) 467-6200. **$109-$199.** 2 Pureland Dr 08085. I-295 exit 10, just se. Int corridors. **Pets:** $75 deposit/room. Designated rooms, service with restrictions, supervision. 🛆M ➡ 📶 ✕ 🛅 🖵

BRIDGEWATER

AAA ▼▼▼ **Hyatt House Bridgewater** H
(908) 725-0800. **$109-$319.** 530 US 22 E 08807. I-287 exit 14B northbound, 4.7 mi w; exit 17 southbound, 1.8 mi w. Ext corridors.
Pets: Accepted. SAVE 🛆M ➡ ✕ 📶 ✕ 🛅 🖵

CAPE MAY

▼▼▼ **Madison Avenue Beach Club Motel** M
(609) 884-8266. **Call for rates.** 605 Madison Ave 08204. Jct Columbia Ave. Ext corridors. **Pets:** Accepted. 🍽 ➡ 📶 ✕ 🛅 🖵

AAA ▼▼▼ **Marquis de Lafayette Hotel** H
(609) 884-3500. **Call for rates.** 501 Beach Ave 08204. Between Decatur and Ocean sts. Ext/int corridors. **Pets:** Other species. $100 deposit/room, $25 daily fee/pet. Designated rooms, service with restrictions.
SAVE 🍽 🛆M ➡ 📶 ✕ 🛅 🖵

▼▼▼ **Victorian Lace Inn** BB
(609) 884-1772. **Call for rates.** 901 Stockton Ave 08204. At Jefferson St; just w of Beach Ave. Ext/int corridors. **Pets:** Accepted.
🍽 📶 ✕ 🎬 🛅 🖵

CAPE MAY COURT HOUSE

▼▼▼ **The Doctors Inn** BB
(609) 463-9330. **$99-$250, 14 day notice.** 2 N Main St 08210. At Main (US 9) and Mechanic sts; just s of Garden State Pkwy. Int corridors.
Pets: Small. $25 daily fee/pet. Designated rooms, service with restrictions, supervision. 🍽 📶 ✕ 🎬 🛅

CARNEYS POINT

▼▼▼ **Comfort Inn & Suites** H
(856) 299-8282. **$70-$159.** 634 Sodders Rd 08069. I-295 exit 2B, just e on Pennsville-Auburn Rd, then 0.3 mi s. Int corridors. **Pets:** Medium. $20 daily fee/pet. Designated rooms, service with restrictions, crate.
🛆M 📶 ✕ 🛅 🖵

AAA ▼▼▼ **Holiday Inn Express Hotel & Suites** H
(856) 351-9222. **$125-$165.** 506 S Pennsville-Auburn Rd 08069. I-295 exit 2B, just e. Int corridors. **Pets:** Accepted.
SAVE 🛆M 📶 ✕ 🛅 🖵

CHERRY HILL

▼▼▼ **Extended Stay America-Philadelphia/Cherry Hill** H
(856) 616-1200. **$95-$125.** 1653 E SR 70 (Marlton Pike) 08034. I-295 exit 34A, just e. Int corridors. **Pets:** Accepted. 🍽 📶 🛅 🖵

▼▼▼ **Holiday Inn Philadelphia-Cherry Hill** H
(856) 663-5300. **Call for rates.** 2175 W Marlton Pike 08002. I-295 exit 34B, 2.5 mi w. Int corridors. **Pets:** Accepted.
🍽 🛆M ➡ 📶 ✕ 🛅 🖵

CLINTON

▼▼▼ **Hampton Inn Clinton** H
(908) 713-4800. **$129-$145.** 16 Frontage Dr 08809. I-78 exit 15, 0.3 mi s on CR 513, then left at next light. Int corridors. **Pets:** Large, other species. $35 one-time fee/pet. Designated rooms, service with restrictions, supervision. 🛆M ➡ 📶 🛅 🖵

▼▼▼ **Holiday Inn-Clinton** H
(908) 735-5111. **Call for rates.** 111 Rt 173 08809. I-78 exit 15, just nw. Int corridors. **Pets:** Accepted. 🍽 🛆M ➡ 📶 ✕ 🛅 🖵

COOKSTOWN

▼▼ **Quality Inn McGuire AFB** H
(609) 723-6500. **$95-$175.** 21 Wrightstown/Cookstown Rd 08511. 0.3 mi n of main entrance to McGuire Air Force Base. Int corridors.
Pets: Other species. $100 deposit/room, $35 one-time fee/room. Designated rooms, no service. 🛆M ➡ 📶 🛅 🖵

CRANBURY

AAA ▼▼▼ **Courtyard by Marriott Cranbury/South Brunswick** H
(609) 655-9950. **$66-$217.** 420 Forsgate Dr 08512. New Jersey Tpke exit 8A to SR 32 W toward town, just s. Int corridors. **Pets:** Accepted.
SAVE 🍽 🛆M ➡ 📶 ✕ 🛅 🖵

AAA ▼▼▼ **Residence Inn by Marriott/Cranbury-South Brunswick** H
(609) 395-9447. **$95-$363.** 2662 US 130 08512. New Jersey Tpke exit 8A to SR 32 W toward town, 2 mi s on River Rd. Int corridors.
Pets: Accepted. SAVE 🛆M ➡ ✕ 📶 ✕ 🛅 🖵

▼▼▼ **Staybridge Suites/Cranbury** H
(609) 409-7181. **Call for rates.** 1272 S River Rd 08512. New Jersey Tpke exit 8A to SR 32 W toward town, 2 mi s. Int corridors.
Pets: Accepted. 🛆M ➡ 📶 ✕ 🛅 🖵

DEPTFORD

▼▼▼ **Residence Inn by Marriott Deptford** H
(856) 686-9188. **$99-$383.** 1154 Hurffville Rd 08096. SR 42 exit Deptford, Runnemede, Woodbury to CR 544, just e to SR 41 S. Int corridors. **Pets:** Accepted. 🛆M ➡ 📶 ✕ 🛅 🖵

DOVER

▼▼▼ **Homewood Suites by Hilton Dover-Rockaway** H
(973) 989-8899. **$109-$169.** 2 Commerce Center Dr 07801. 1.2 mi n on Mt Hope Ave, just w on Mt Pleasant Ave. Int corridors. **Pets:** Accepted.
🍽 🛆M ➡ 📶 🛅 🖵

EAST BRUNSWICK

AAA ▼▼▼ **Best Western East Brunswick Inn** H
(732) 238-4900. **$89-$159.** 764 SR 18 N 08816. Between Rue Ln and Racetrack Rd; New Jersey Tpke exit 9 (SR 18 N), 4 mi s. Ext/int corridors. **Pets:** Accepted. SAVE 🛆M 📶 ✕ 🛅 🖵

EAST RUTHERFORD

▼▼▼ **Residence Inn by Marriott East Rutherford Meadowlands** H

(201) 939-0020. **$135-$286.** 10 Murray Hill Pkwy 07073. New Jersey Tpke exit 16W (from western spur) to SR 3 W to SR 17 N, 1.5 mi n to Paterson Plank Rd (SR 120), then just e. Int corridors. **Pets:** Accepted.

⧉ 🛏 ㋹ ➿ ⊠ 🛜 ⊠ 🔋 🖳

EAST WINDSOR

▼▼ **Days Inn East Windsor** H

(609) 448-3200. **$69-$169.** 460 Rt 33 E 08520. New Jersey Tpke exit 8, just e. Int corridors. **Pets:** Medium. $50 one-time fee/room. Service with restrictions, crate. 🛏 ㋹ ➿ 🛜 ⊠ 🔋 🖳

EATONTOWN

ⒶⒶⒶ ▼▼▼ **Homewood Suites by Hilton Eatontown** H

(732) 380-9300. **$129-$299.** 4 Industrial Way E 07724. Garden State Pkwy exit 105, 0.7 mi e on SR 36, then 1 mi s on SR 35. Int corridors. **Pets:** $100 one-time fee/room. Designated rooms, service with restrictions, crate. ⧉ 🛏 ㋹ ➿ ⊠ 🛜 🔋 🖳

EDISON

▼ **Red Roof Inn Edison** M

(732) 248-9300. **$65-$99.** 860 New Durham Rd 08817. I-287 exit 2A northbound, 0.3 mi w via Bridge St, then left; exit 3 southbound, just w. Ext corridors. **Pets:** Accepted. ㋹ 🛜 🔋 🖳

ⒶⒶⒶ ▼▼▼ **Sheraton Edison Hotel Raritan Center** H

(732) 225-8300. **Call for rates.** 125 Raritan Center Pkwy 08837. New Jersey Tpke exit 10, 0.5 mi se on CR 514, keep right after tolls. Int corridors. **Pets:** Accepted.

⧉ 🛏 ㋹ ➿ ⊠ 🛜 ⊠ 🔋 🖳

ELIZABETH

ⒶⒶⒶ ▼▼▼ **Residence Inn by Marriott Newark Elizabeth/ Liberty International Airport** H

(908) 352-4300. **$127-$312.** 83 International Blvd 07201. New Jersey Tpke exit 13A, 1 mi se on Jersey Garden Blvd, just n on Kapkowski Rd, then just w. Int corridors. **Pets:** Medium. $100 one-time fee/room. Designated rooms, service with restrictions, crate.

⧉ ㋹ ➿ 🛜 ⊠ 🔋 🖳

EWING

ⒶⒶⒶ ▼▼▼ **Element by Westin Ewing Princeton** H

(609) 671-0050. **Call for rates.** 1000 Sam Weinroth Rd E 08628. I-95 exit 3A, just e. Int corridors. **Pets:** Accepted.

⧉ 🔋 🛏 ㋹ ➿ ⊠ 🛜 ⊠ 🔋 🖳

FAIRFIELD

▼▼ **La Quinta Inn & Suites Fairfield** H

(973) 575-1742. **$82-$229.** 38 Two Bridges Rd 07004. I-80 exit 52 westbound; exit 47B (Caldwells) eastbound, 7 mi e on US 46 exit Passaic Ave. Int corridors. **Pets:** Accepted. ㋹ ➿ 🛜 ⊠ 🔋 🖳

FAIR LAWN

ⒶⒶⒶ ▼▼▼ **Hyatt Place Fair Lawn/Paramus** H

(201) 475-3888. **$74-$209.** 41-01 Broadway (Rt 4 W) 07410. Garden State Pkwy exit 161 northbound, 0.7 mi w; entrance from SR 4 W. Int corridors. **Pets:** Accepted.

⧉ ㋹ ➿ 🛜 ⊠ 🔋 🖳

FLORHAM PARK

ⒶⒶⒶ ▼▼▼ **Wyndham Hamilton Park Hotel & Conference Center** H

(973) 377-2424. **$119-$349.** 175 Park Ave 07932. SR 24 exit 2A, 0.4 mi w on CR 510, then 1 mi s on CR 623. Int corridors. **Pets:** $75 one-time fee/pet. Service with restrictions, supervision.

⧉ 🛏 ㋹ ➿ ⊠ 🛜 ⊠ 🔋 🖳

FORT LEE

ⒶⒶⒶ ▼▼▼ **Best Western Fort Lee** M

(201) 461-7000. **$115-$149.** 2300 Rt 4 W 07024. 0.5 mi w of George Washington Bridge (SR 4 W). Int corridors. **Pets:** Accepted.

⧉ 🛏 ㋹ 🛜 🔋 🖳

GALLOWAY

ⒶⒶⒶ ▼▼▼ **Stockton Seaview Hotel & Golf Club** H

(609) 652-1800. **$124-$349.** 401 S New York Rd 08205. US 9, 2.5 mi ne of White Horse Pike (US 30). Int corridors. **Pets:** Accepted.

⧉ 🛏 ㋹ ➿ ⊠ 🛜 ⊠ 🔋 🖳

HADDONFIELD

▼▼▼ **Haddonfield Inn** BB ❖

(856) 428-2195. **Call for rates.** 44 W End Ave 08033. I-295 exit 28, 0.7 mi n on SR 168, 2.6 mi e on Kings Hwy, then just n. Int corridors. **Pets:** Dogs only. $25 daily fee/pet. Designated rooms, service with restrictions, supervision. ㋹ 🛜 ⊠ 🔋

HAMILTON (MERCER COUNTY)

▼▼▼ **Homewood Suites** H

(609) 689-1260. **$129-$239.** 960 US Hwy 130 08690. I-195 exit 5B, just n; jct US 130 and Kuser Rd. Int corridors. **Pets:** Accepted.

⧉ 🛏 ㋹ 🛜 ⊠ 🔋 🖳

▼▼▼ **Residence Inn by Marriott Hamilton** H

(609) 585-2111. **$120-$251.** 559 Route 130 N 08620. I-195 exit 5A, 0.5 mi w. Int corridors. **Pets:** Accepted. 🛏 ㋹ 🛜 ⊠ 🔋 🖳

HARRISON

ⒶⒶⒶ ▼▼▼ **Element Harrison-Newark** H ❖

(973) 484-1500. **Call for rates.** 399 Somerset St 07029. I-95 exit 15W; I-280 exit 16 (Essex St), just s on Frank E Rodgers Blvd S. Int corridors. **Pets:** Small. Service with restrictions, crate.

⧉ 🛏 ㋹ 🛜 ⊠ 🔋 🖳

HAZLET

▼▼▼ **Holiday Inn/Hazlet** H

(732) 888-2000. **$79-$999.** 2870 SR 35 07730. Garden State Pkwy exit 117A to SR 35 S, 2.5 mi s. Int corridors. **Pets:** Accepted.

⧉ 🛏 ㋹ ➿ 🛜 ⊠ 🔋 🖳

HOBOKEN (Restaurants p. 618)

ⒶⒶⒶ ▼▼▼ **W Hoboken** H

(201) 253-2400. **$189-$619.** 225 River St 07030. Between 1st and 2nd sts. Int corridors. **Pets:** Accepted.

⧉ 🛏 ㋹ ⊠ ㋡ ⊠ 🔋 🖳

JERSEY CITY

ⒶⒶⒶ ▼▼▼ ▼▼ **The Westin Jersey City Newport** H ❖

(201) 626-2900. **$189-$529.** 479 Washington Blvd 07310. At The Waterfront, just n of 6th St. Int corridors. **Pets:** Small, dogs only. Designated rooms, service with restrictions, crate.

⧉ 🛏 ㋹ ➿ ⊠ ㋡ ⊠ 🔋 🖳

LAWRENCEVILLE

▼ **Red Roof Inn Princeton-Ewing** M

(609) 896-3388. **$60-$179.** 3203 Brunswick Pike (US 1) 08648. I-295 exit 67A, just n. Ext corridors. **Pets:** Accepted. 🛜 ⊠ 🔋 🖳

LONG BRANCH

ⒶⒶⒶ ▼▼▼ **Ocean Place Resort & Spa** H

(732) 571-4000. **Call for rates.** 1 Ocean Blvd 07740. Jct SR 71, 3 mi e on SR 36, 0.5 mi s. Int corridors. **Pets:** Accepted.

⧉ 🛏 ㋹ ➿ ⊠ 🛜 ⊠ 🔋 🖳

MAHWAH

▼▼▼ Homewood Suites by Hilton H
(201) 760-9994. **$129-$209.** 375 Corporate Dr 07430. I-287 exit 66, 1.7 mi on SR 17 S to MacArthur Blvd, then 0.4 mi w. Int corridors.
Pets: Accepted. [icons]

◈◈◈ ▼▼▼ Sheraton Mahwah Hotel H
(201) 529-1660. **$169-$339.** 1 International Blvd (Rt 17) 07495. I-287 exit 66, at SR 17 N. Int corridors. **Pets:** Accepted.
[icons]

▼▼ Super 8 Mahwah H
(201) 512-0800. **$80.** 160 Rt 17 S 07430. I-287 exit 66, 0.7 mi s. Int corridors. **Pets:** Accepted. [icons]

MANCHESTER

▼▼ Comfort Inn Manchester H
(732) 657-7100. **$89-$229.** 2016 Rt 37 W 08759. Garden State Pkwy exit 82A, 5 mi w. Int corridors. **Pets:** Small, dogs only. $25 daily fee/pet. Service with restrictions, supervision. [icons]

MIDDLETOWN

◈◈◈ ▼▼▼ Comfort Inn Middletown-Red Bank H
(732) 671-3400. **$98-$400.** 750 State Rt 35 S 07748. Garden State Pkwy exit 114, 2 mi e on Red Hill Rd, 1 mi s on Kings Hwy to SR 35, then 0.3 mi s. Int corridors. **Pets:** Large. $30 daily fee/room. Service with restrictions, supervision. [icons]

MONMOUTH JUNCTION

◈◈◈ ▼▼▼ Sonesta ES Suites South Brunswick-Princeton H
(732) 329-9600. **$80-$350.** 4225 US 1 S 08543. 0.5 mi s of Raymond Rd. Int corridors. **Pets:** Accepted.
[icons]

MORRIS PLAINS

▼▼▼ Candlewood Suites Parsippany-Morris Plains H
(973) 984-9960. **Call for rates.** 100 Candlewood Dr 07950. I-287 exit 39 northbound; exit 39B southbound, 2 mi w on SR 10. Int corridors.
Pets: Accepted. [icons]

MORRISTOWN

◈◈◈ ▼▼▼ Hyatt House Morristown H ☙
(973) 971-0008. **$99-$359.** 194 Park Ave 07960. SR 24 exit 2A (Morristown), just w. Int corridors. **Pets:** Medium. $75 one-time fee/room. Service with restrictions. [icons]

◈◈◈ ▼▼▼ The Westin Governor Morris H ☙
(973) 539-7300. **$169-$549.** 2 Whippany Rd 07960. I-287 exit 36 southbound, left lane to light, left to stop sign, then 1 mi e; exit 36A northbound to Morris Ave, 0.8 mi e, follow signs. Int corridors.
Pets: Medium, dogs only. $50 one-time fee/pet. Service with restrictions, supervision. [icons]

MOUNT LAUREL

▼▼ Candlewood Suites Mt. Laurel H
(856) 642-7567. **Call for rates.** 4000 Crawford Pl 08054. New Jersey Tpke exit 4, 1 mi s on SR 73 S. Int corridors. **Pets:** Accepted.
[icons]

▼▼ Extended Stay America Pacilli Place Philadelphia/Mt. Laurel H
(856) 608-9820. **$85-$110.** 500 Diemer Dr 08054. New Jersey Tpke exit 4, 1 mi se on SR 73, just n on Crawford Pl, then just e. Int corridors.
Pets: Accepted. [icons]

◈◈◈ ▼▼▼ Hyatt House Mt. Laurel H
(856) 222-1313. **$99-$399.** 3000 Crawford Pl 08054. I-295 exit 36A, 1.5 mi s on SR 73. Ext corridors. **Pets:** Accepted.
[icons]

◈◈◈ ▼▼▼ Hyatt Place Mt. Laurel H
(856) 840-0770. **$99-$199.** 8000 Crawford Pl 08054. I-295 exit 36A, 1.5 mi s on SR 73. Int corridors. **Pets:** Accepted.
[icons]

◈◈◈ ▼▼▼ La Quinta Mt. Laurel-Philadelphia H
(856) 235-7500. **$75-$306.** 5000 Clover Rd 08054. New Jersey Tpke exit 4, just se; I-295 exit 36A, 0.8 mi se. Int corridors. **Pets:** Accepted.
[icons]

▼▼▼ Philadelphia/Mount Laurel Homewood Suites by Hilton H
(856) 222-9001. **Call for rates.** 1422 Nixon Dr 08054. I-295 exit 36B, follow ramp to end, then just n. Int corridors. **Pets:** Medium, other species. $100 one-time fee/room. Service with restrictions, crate.
[icons]

▼▼▼ Residence Inn by Marriott Mount Laurel at Bishop's Gate H
(856) 234-1025. **$99-$214.** 1000 Bishops Gate Blvd 08054. I-295 exit 40A, just e. Int corridors. **Pets:** Accepted.
[icons]

◈◈◈ ▼▼▼ Staybridge Suites H
(856) 722-1900. **Call for rates.** 4115 Church Rd 08054. New Jersey Tpke exit 4, 0.5 mi s on SR 73, then 0.5 mi w. Int corridors.
Pets: Accepted. [icons]

◈◈◈ ▼▼▼ The Westin Mount Laurel H
(856) 778-7300. **$109-$309.** 555 Fellowship Rd 08054. I-295 exit 36A, just se on SR 73 to Fellowship Rd, then just n. Int corridors.
Pets: Accepted. [icons]

MOUNT OLIVE

▼▼▼ Residence Inn by Marriott Mt. Olive at The International Trade Center H
(973) 691-1720. **$65-$327.** 271 Continental Dr 07828. I-80 exit 25, just n, follow signs for International Trade Center. Int corridors.
Pets: Accepted. [icons]

NEPTUNE

▼▼▼ Residence Inn by Marriott Neptune at Gateway Centre H
(732) 643-9350. **$101-$542.** 230 Jumping Brook Rd 07753. Garden State Pkwy exit 100B, 0.5 mi e on SR 33, then 0.5 mi n. Int corridors.
Pets: Accepted. [icons]

NEWARK

◈◈◈ ▼▼▼ DoubleTree by Hilton Newark Airport H
(973) 690-5500. **$89-$299.** 128 Frontage Rd 07114. I-95 (New Jersey Tpke) exit 14, 2nd right after toll booth, then just w. Int corridors.
Pets: Accepted. [icons]

◈◈◈ ▼▼▼ Hotel Indigo Newark Downtown H
(973) 242-0065. **Call for rates.** 810 Broad St 07102. Between Edison Pl and Lafayette St. Int corridors. **Pets:** Accepted.
[icons]

NORTH BERGEN (Restaurants p. 618)

◈◈◈ ▼▼▼ Meadowlands View Hotel H
(201) 348-3600. **Call for rates.** 2750 Tonnelle Ave 07047. Jct SR 3, 0.4 mi s. Int corridors. **Pets:** Other species. $100 deposit/pet. Designated rooms, service with restrictions, crate. [icons]

PARSIPPANY

◈◈◈ ▼▼▼ Embassy Suites by Hilton Parsippany H
(973) 334-1440. **$89-$219.** 909 Parsippany Blvd 07054. I-80 exit 42 to US 202 N; just ne of jct US 202 and 46 W. Int corridors.
Pets: Accepted. [icons]

AAA ▼▼▼ Hyatt House Parsippany-East H
(973) 428-8875. **$99-$299.** 299 Smith Rd 07054. I-287 exit 41A northbound; exit 42 southbound to US 46 E, 0.5 mi s. Int corridors.
Pets: Accepted. SAVE ▦ ⛧ ➔ 🛜 ✕ 🖥 🖵

AAA ▼▼▼ Red Roof Inn Parsippany M
(973) 334-3737. **$55-$99.** 855 US Hwy 46 E 07054. I-80 exit 47 westbound; exit 45 eastbound, 0.5 mi e. Ext corridors. **Pets:** Accepted.
SAVE ⛧ 🛜 🖥 🖵

AAA ▼▼▼ Residence Inn by Marriott Parsippany H
(973) 984-3313. **$175-$384.** 3 Gatehall Dr 07054. I-287 exit 39 northbound; exit 39B southbound, 2 mi w on SR 10. Ext/int corridors.
Pets: Accepted. SAVE ▦ ⛧ ➔ ⊠ ✕ 🖥 🖵

AAA ▼▼▼ Sheraton Parsippany Hotel H
(973) 515-2000. **$109-$499.** 199 Smith Rd 07054. I-287 exit 41A northbound; exit 42 to US 46 E, 0.4 mi s. Int corridors. **Pets:** Accepted.
SAVE ECO ▦ ⛧ ➔ ⊠ 🔊 ✕ 🖵

AAA ▼▼▼ Sonesta ES Suites Parsippany H
(973) 334-2907. **$99-$499.** 61 Interpace Pkwy 07054. I-80 exit 42, 0.3 mi s on Cherry Hill Rd, then just w. Int corridors. **Pets:** Accepted.
SAVE ▦ ⛧ ➔ 🛜 ✕ 🖥 🖵

PISCATAWAY (Restaurants p. 618)

▼▼▼ Embassy Suites by Hilton Hotel Piscataway-Somerset H
(732) 980-0500. **$119-$239.** 121 Centennial Ave 08854. I-287 exit 9 (Highland Park), just s to Centennial Ave. Int corridors. **Pets:** Accepted.
▦ ⛧ ➔ 🛜 ✕ 🖥 🖵

▼▼ Extended Stay America Piscataway-Rutgers University H
(732) 235-1000. **$105-$145.** 410 S Randolphville Rd 08854. I-287 exit 7, 0.4 mi s. Int corridors. **Pets:** Accepted. ⛧ ➔ 🛜 🖥

PRINCETON

AAA ▼▼▼ Chauncey Hotel and Conference Center H
(609) 921-3600. **$119-$379.** 1 Chauncey Rd 08541. 0.5 mi w on Stockton Rd, 0.5 mi n on Elm Rd, 1.8 mi w. Int corridors.
SAVE ▦ ⛧ ➔ 🛜 ✕ 🖥 🖵

AAA ▼▼ Clarion Hotel Palmer Inn H
(609) 452-2500. **$79-$159.** 3499 US 1 S 08540. 2 mi s of jct CR 526 and 571. Ext/int corridors. **Pets:** Accepted.
SAVE ▦ ⛧ ➔ 🛜 🖥 🖵

AAA ▼▼▼ Hampton Inn Princeton H
(609) 951-0066. **$109-$199.** 4385 US 1 S 08540. Just past Ridge Rd.
Int corridors. **Pets:** Accepted. SAVE ⛧ ➔ 🛜 ✕ 🖥 🖵

▼▼▼ Holiday Inn Princeton H
(609) 520-1200. **Call for rates.** 100 Independence Way 08540. I-295 exit 67A (SR 1) northbound; exit 67 (SR 1) southbound, 7 mi n. Int corridors. **Pets:** Accepted. ▦ ⛧ ➔ 🛜 ✕ 🖵

AAA ▼▼▼ Hyatt Place Princeton H
(609) 720-0200. **$119-$409.** 3565 US 1 S 08540. 1.5 mi s of jct CR 526 and 571. Int corridors. **Pets:** Accepted.
SAVE ⛧ ➔ 🛜 ✕ 🖥 🖵

AAA ▼▼▼ Nassau Inn H
(609) 921-7500. **Call for rates.** 10 Palmer Square E 08542. Center. Int corridors. **Pets:** Accepted. SAVE ▦ ⛧ 🔊 ✕ 🖥 🖵

▼▼▼ Residence Inn by Marriott-Princeton at Carnegie Center H
(609) 799-0550. **$116-$240.** 3563 US 1 S 08540. 1.5 mi s of jct CR 527 and 571. Int corridors. **Pets:** Accepted.
⛧ ➔ 🛜 ✕ 🖥 🖵

AAA ▼▼▼ Sonesta ES Suites Princeton H
(609) 951-0009. **Call for rates.** 4375 US 1 S 08543. Just past Ridge Rd. Ext corridors. **Pets:** Accepted. SAVE ⛧ ➔ 🛜 ✕ 🖥 🖵

AAA ▼▼▼ Westin Princeton at Forrestal Village H
(609) 452-7900. **Call for rates.** 201 Village Blvd 08540. On US 1 southbound, 1.5 mi n of CR 571. Int corridors. **Pets:** Accepted.
SAVE ▦ ⛧ ➔ ⊠ 🛜 ✕ 🖥 🖵

RAHWAY

▼▼▼ Home2 Suites by Hilton H
(732) 388-5500. **$119-$149.** 667 E Milton Ave 07065. Jct Paterson St and US 1/9. Int corridors. **Pets:** Accepted. ⛧ 🛜 ✕ 🖥 🖵

RAMSEY

AAA ▼▼▼ Best Western The Inn at Ramsey H
(201) 327-6700. **$130-$180.** 1315 Rt 17 S 07446. Jct I-287 and SR 17 S, 3 mi s. Int corridors. **Pets:** Accepted.
SAVE ▦ ⛧ 🛜 ✕ 🖥 🖵

RUNNEMEDE

▼▼▼ La Quinta Inn & Suites Runnemede H
(856) 312-8521. **$86-$251.** 109 E 9th Ave 08078. New Jersey Tpke exit 3, 0.3 mi se, then just e; I-295 exit 28, 1.2 mi se. Int corridors.
Pets: Accepted. ▦ ➔ 🛜 ✕ 🖥 🖵

RUTHERFORD

▼▼ Extended Stay America-Meadowlands-Rutherford H
(201) 635-0266. **$105-$145.** 750 Edwin L Ward Sr Memorial Hwy 07070. I-95 exit 16W, 1.5 mi w on SR 3 to SR 17 N service road exit, then 0.5 mi e. Int corridors. **Pets:** Accepted.
▦ ⛧ 🛜 ✕ 🖥 🖵

SECAUCUS

AAA ▼▼▼ Holiday Inn Secaucus Meadowlands H
(201) 348-2000. **$139-$349.** 300 Plaza Dr 07094. New Jersey Tpke exits 16E, 17 or 16W via SR 3 to Harmon Meadow Blvd. Int corridors.
Pets: Accepted. SAVE ▦ ⛧ 🛜 ✕ 🖥 🖵

AAA ▼▼▼ Hyatt Place Secaucus/Meadowlands H
(201) 422-9480. **$109-$349.** 575 Park Plaza Dr 07094. New Jersey Tpke exits 16E, 17 or 16W via SR 3 to Harmon Meadow Blvd, then just w. Int corridors. **Pets:** Accepted. SAVE ⛧ 🛜 ✕ 🖥 🖵

AAA ▼▼▼ La Quinta Inn & Suites Secaucus Meadowlands H
(201) 863-8700. **$67-$170.** 350 Lighting Way 07094. Between eastern and western spurs of New Jersey Tpke exits 16E, 17 or 16W via SR 3 W and Harmon Meadow Blvd; in Mill Creek Mall. Int corridors.
Pets: Accepted. SAVE ⛧ ➔ 🛜 ✕ 🖥 🖵

AAA ▼▼ Red Roof PLUS+ Secaucus-Meadowlands H
(201) 319-1000. **$94-$169.** 15 Meadowlands Pkwy 07094. Between eastern and western spurs of New Jersey Tpke exits 16E, 17 or 16W to SR 3 exit Meadowlands Pkwy. Ext corridors. **Pets:** Accepted.
SAVE 🛜 ✕ 🖥 🖵

▼▼▼ Residence Inn by Marriott Secaucus Meadowlands H
(201) 223-9901. **$149-$331.** 800 Plaza Dr 07094. Off SR 3; in Harmon Meadows complex. Int corridors. **Pets:** Accepted.
⛧ ➔ 🛜 ✕ 🖥 🖵

SOMERSET

▼▼ ▼▼ **Candlewood Suites** Ⓗ
(732) 748-1400. **Call for rates.** 41 Worlds Fair Dr 08873. I-287 exit 10 (CR 527), left on ramp (CR 527 S/Easton Ave), 0.3 mi, then 0.5 mi w. Int corridors. **Pets:** Accepted. 🍴 ㊋ 🛏 🛜 🔌 💺 📺

▼▼▼ **Clarion Hotel Somerset** Ⓗ
(732) 560-9880. **$75-$159.** 60 Cottontail Ln 08873. I-287 exit 12, just sw via Weston Canal Rd. Int corridors. **Pets:** Accepted.
🍴 ㊋ 🛏 🛜 🔌 💺 📺

▼▼▼▼ **Homewood Suites by Hilton-Somerset** Ⓗ
(732) 868-9155. **$109-$199.** 101 Pierce St 08873. I-287 exit 10 (CR 527), left on ramp (CR 527 S/Easton Ave), 0.3 mi, 0.7 mi w on Worlds Fair Dr, then just s. Int corridors. **Pets:** Accepted.
🍴 ㊋ 🛏 🔌 🛜 🔌 💺 📺

▲▲▲ ▼▼▼ **Residence Inn by Marriott-Somerset** Ⓗ
(732) 627-0881. **$89-$282.** 37 Worlds Fair Dr 08873. I-287 exit 10 (CR 527), 0.3 mi left on ramp (CR 527 S/Easton Ave), then 0.5 mi w. Int corridors. **Pets:** Accepted.
🆂🅰🆅🅴 🍴 ㊋ 🛏 🔌 🛜 🔌 💺 📺

▲▲▲ ▼▼▼ **Sonesta ES Suites Somerset** Ⓗ 🌿
(732) 356-8000. **Call for rates.** 260 Davidson Ave 08873. I-287 exit 10 (CR 527), just n toward Bound Brook to Davidson Ave, then 0.8 mi sw. Ext/int corridors. **Pets:** Small, other species. $75 one-time fee/pet. Service with restrictions, supervision. 🆂🅰🆅🅴 ㊋ 🛏 🛜 🔌 💺 📺

SOMERS POINT

▲▲▲ ▼▼▼ **Sonesta ES Suites Somers Point** Ⓗ
(609) 927-6400. **Call for rates.** 900 Mays Landing Rd 08244. Garden State Pkwy exit 30 southbound; exit 29 northbound, 1 mi e. Ext corridors. **Pets:** Accepted. 🆂🅰🆅🅴 ㊋ 🛏 🛜 🔌 💺 📺

SOUTH PLAINFIELD

▲▲▲ ▼▼ ▼▼ **Best Western The Garden Executive Hotel** Ⓗ
(908) 561-4488. **$90-$129.** 101 New World Way 07080. I-287 exit 5, just s. Int corridors. **Pets:** $50 deposit/room, $10 daily fee/room. Designated rooms, service with restrictions, crate.
🆂🅰🆅🅴 🍴 ㊋ 🛜 🔌 💺 📺

STOCKTON

▼▼▼ **Woolverton Inn** 🅱🅱
(609) 397-0802. **Call for rates.** 6 Woolverton Rd 08559. Jct CR 523 N and SR 29 N, just n to Woolverton Rd, then just w. Int corridors. **Pets:** Accepted. 🍴 🛜 🔌 📺 💺 📺

SWEDESBORO

▼▼▼ **Holiday Inn** Ⓗ
(856) 467-3322. **Call for rates.** 1 Pureland Dr 08085. I-295 exit 10, 0.4 mi e. Int corridors. **Pets:** Accepted. 🍴 ㊋ 🛏 🛜 🔌 💺 📺

THOROFARE

▲▲▲ ▼▼▼ **Best Western West Deptford Inn** Ⓗ
(856) 848-4111. **$99-$159.** 98 Friars Blvd 08086. I-295 exit 20, just e on Mid Atlantic Pkwy, then 0.4 mi n. Int corridors. **Pets:** Accepted.
🆂🅰🆅🅴 🍴 🛏 🛜 🔌 💺 📺

TINTON FALLS

▼ **Red Roof Inn Tinton Falls Jersey Shore** Ⓜ
(732) 389-4646. **$69-$169.** 11 Centre Plaza 07724. Garden State Pkwy exit 105, just right at 1st light after toll. Ext corridors. **Pets:** Accepted.
🛜 🔌 💺 📺

▼▼▼ **Residence Inn by Marriott Tinton Falls** Ⓗ
(732) 389-8100. **$98-$323.** 90 Park Rd 07724. Garden State Pkwy exit 105, 1st jughandle after toll, then just n. Ext corridors. **Pets:** Accepted.
🍴 🛏 🛜 🔌 💺 📺

TOMS RIVER

▲▲▲ ▼▼▼ **Howard Johnson Hotel-Toms River** Ⓗ
(732) 244-1000. **$99-$229.** 955 Hooper Ave 08753. Garden State Pkwy exit 82, 1 mi e on SR 37. Int corridors. **Pets:** Other species. $50 daily fee/pet. Designated rooms, service with restrictions, supervision.
🆂🅰🆅🅴 🍴 ㊋ 🛏 🛜 🔌 💺 📺

VERNON

▲▲▲ ▼▼▼ **Appalachian Motel** Ⓜ
(973) 764-6070. **Call for rates.** 367 Rt 94 N 07462. 1 mi n. Ext corridors. **Pets:** Accepted. 🆂🅰🆅🅴 🍴 🛜 🔌 💺 📺

VINELAND

▼▼▼ **Quality Inn Vineland - Millville** Ⓗ
(856) 692-8070. **$72-$199.** 29 W Landis Ave 08360. SR 55 exit 32A, 2 mi e. Int corridors. **Pets:** Accepted. 🛜 🔌 💺 📺

VOORHEES

▲▲▲ ▼▼▼ **Wingate by Wyndham Voorhees Mt. Laurel** Ⓗ
(856) 627-1000. **$85-$158.** 1000 Laurel Oak Rd 08043. I-295 exit 32, 3 mi e, then just s. Int corridors. **Pets:** Accepted.
🆂🅰🆅🅴 ㊋ 🛏 🛜 🔌 💺 📺

WANTAGE

▼ **High Point Country Inn** Ⓜ
(973) 702-1860. **$79-$89.** 1328 SR 23 N 07461. 1 mi n of Colesville Village Center. Ext corridors. **Pets:** Other species. $10 one-time fee/pet, $10 daily fee/pet. Service with restrictions.
🍴 🛜 🔌 🅿 💺 📺

WAYNE

▼▼▼ **La Quinta Inn & Suites Wayne** Ⓗ
(973) 696-8050. **$67-$185.** 1850 SR 23 07470. I-80 exit 53 (Butler-Verona) westbound to SR 23 N, 3 mi to Ratzer Rd (service road), then just n; exit 54 eastbound to Minnisink Rd, U-turn for US 80 W exit 53. Int corridors. **Pets:** Accepted. 🍴 ㊋ 🛏 🛜 🔌 💺 📺

▼▼▼ **Ramada Wayne Fairfield Area** Ⓗ
(973) 256-7000. **$90-$129.** 334 Rt 46 E/Service Rd 07470. I-80 exit 53 (Butler-Verona) westbound to SR 23 S, service road off US 46 eastbound Caldwells; exit 47B eastbound, 7 mi e on US 46 to service road. Ext corridors. **Pets:** $25 one-time fee/room. Service with restrictions, crate. 🍴 🛏 🛜 🔌 💺 📺

▼▼▼ **Residence Inn by Marriott Wayne** Ⓗ
(973) 872-7100. **$113-$333.** 30 Nevins Rd 07470. Jct CR 640 (Riverview Dr) and 681 (Valley Rd), 3.5 mi n, just w on Barbour Pond Dr, then just n. Int corridors. **Pets:** Accepted.
🍴 ㊋ 🛏 🔌 🛜 🔌 💺 📺

WEEHAWKEN

▲▲▲ ▼▼▼ **Sheraton Lincoln Harbor Hotel** Ⓗ
(201) 617-5600. **$189-$399.** 500 Harbor Blvd 07086. Just se of Lincoln Tunnel entrance, at 19th St. Int corridors. **Pets:** Accepted.
🆂🅰🆅🅴 🍴 ㊋ 🛏 🛜 🔌 📺

WESTAMPTON

▲▲▲ ▼▼▼ **Best Western Burlington Inn** Ⓗ
(609) 261-3800. **$79-$129.** 2020 Burlington Mt Holly Rd 08060. New Jersey Tpke exit 5, just n. Int corridors. **Pets:** Accepted.
🆂🅰🆅🅴 🛏 🛜 🔌 💺 📺

▼▼▼▼ **Holiday Inn Express Hotel & Suites** Ⓗ
(609) 702-5800. **Call for rates.** 18 Western Dr 08060. New Jersey Tpke exit 5, 0.3 mi n. Int corridors. **Pets:** Accepted.
㊋ 🛏 🛜 🔌 💺 📺

WEST LONG BRANCH

▼▼ **La Quinta Inn West Long Branch** 🄷
(732) 403-8700. **$68-$284.** 109 Rt 36 07764. 1.9 mi w of jct SR 35. Int corridors. **Pets:** Accepted. 🄼 🛜 ✕ 🔋 💻

WEST ORANGE

▼▼▼ **Residence Inn by Marriott-West Orange** 🄷
(973) 669-4700. **$161-$285.** 107 Prospect Ave 07052. I-280 exit 8B, 1 mi n on CR 577 (Prospect Ave). Int corridors. **Pets:** Accepted.
🍴 🄼 ⇆ 🛜 ✕ 🔋 💻

🄰🄰🄰 ▼▼▼ **The Wilshire Grand Hotel** 🄷 ✿
(973) 731-7007. **$199-$449.** 350 Pleasant Valley Way 07052. I-280 exit 8B, just n to Eagle Rock Ave, 0.9 mi n, then just n. Int corridors. **Pets:** Medium, other species. $35 one-time fee/pet. Designated rooms, supervision. 🆂🅰🆅🅴 🍴 🄼 ✕ ⇆ 🛜 ✕ 🔋 💻

WHIPPANY

🄰🄰🄰 ▼▼▼▼ **Hyatt House Parsippany/Whippany** 🄷
(973) 605-1001. **$99-$299.** 1 Ridgedale Ave N 07981. I-287 exit 39, just nw. Int corridors. **Pets:** Accepted.
🆂🅰🆅🅴 🍴 🄼 ⇆ 🛜 ✕ 🔋 💻

WILLIAMSTOWN

🄰🄰🄰 ▼▼▼ **Best Western Monroe Inn & Suites** 🄷
(856) 340-7900. **$89-$149.** 1151 N Black Horse Pike 08094. New Jersey Tpke exit 3, 3.2 mi s on SR 168, then 9 mi s on SR 42; 2 mi s of jct CR 689. Int corridors. **Pets:** Accepted.
🆂🅰🆅🅴 🍴 🄼 ⇆ 🛜 ✕ 🔋 💻

WOODBRIDGE

▼▼ **Extended Stay America Woodbridge-Newark** 🄷
(732) 442-8333. **$105-$130.** 1 Hoover Way 07095. I-95 (New Jersey Tpke) exit 11, 1.4 mi to US 9 N, then just w on King Georges Post Rd. Int corridors. **Pets:** Accepted. 🍴 🄼 ⇆ 🛜 ✕ 🔋 💻

▼▼▼ **Residence Inn by Marriott-Woodbridge Edison/Raritan Center** 🄷
(732) 510-7100. **$104-$292.** 2 Regency Pl 07095. I-95 (New Jersey Tpke) exit 11, just e on SR 184 (Pond Rd), then 1.2 mi n on US 9. Int corridors. **Pets:** Accepted. 🍴 🄼 ⇆ 🛜 ✕ 🔋 💻

NEW MEXICO

ALBUQUERQUE *(Restaurants p. 618)*

🄰🄰🄰 ▼▼▼▼ **Albuquerque Sheraton Uptown Hotel** 🄷
(505) 881-0000. **$89-$299.** 2600 Louisiana Blvd NE 87110. I-40 exit 162, 0.8 mi n; in Northeast Heights. Int corridors. **Pets:** Accepted.
🆂🅰🆅🅴 ♿ 🍴 🄼 ⇆ 🛜 ✕ 🔋 💻

🄰🄰🄰 ▼▼▼ **Best Western Airport Albuquerque InnSuites Hotel & Suites** 🄷 ✿
(505) 242-7022. **$69-$149.** 2400 Yale Blvd SE 87106. I-25 exit 222 (Gibson Blvd) northbound; exit 222A southbound, 1 mi e, then just s. Int corridors. **Pets:** Large, other species. $20 one-time fee/pet. Designated rooms, service with restrictions, supervision. 🆂🅰🆅🅴 ⇆ 🛜 💻

🄰🄰🄰 ▼▼▼ **Best Western Plus Rio Grande Inn** 🄷
(505) 843-9500. **$99-$149.** 1015 Rio Grande Blvd NW 87104. I-40 exit 157A (Rio Grande Blvd), just s. Int corridors. **Pets:** Medium, dogs only. $20 daily fee/room. Designated rooms, supervision.
🆂🅰🆅🅴 🍴 ⇆ 🛜 ✕ 🔋 💻

▼▼▼ **Candlewood Suites** 🄷
(505) 888-3424. **Call for rates.** 3025 Menaul Blvd NE 87107. I-40 exit 160, just n to Menaul Blvd, then 0.5 mi w. Int corridors. **Pets:** Accepted.
🄼 🛜 🔋 💻

▼▼▼ **ClubHouse Inn & Suites** 🄷
(505) 345-0010. **Call for rates.** 1315 Menaul Blvd NE 87107. I-25 exit 227A southbound, 1.5 mi s to Menaul Blvd, then just w; exit 225 northbound, 1.8 mi n, then just w. Int corridors. **Pets:** Other species. $15 daily fee/pet. Service with restrictions, crate.
🍴 ⇆ 🛜 ✕ 🔋 💻

🄰🄰🄰 ▼▼▼ **Comfort Inn Airport** 🄷
(505) 242-0036. **$72-$150.** 1801 Yale Blvd SE 87106. I-25 exit 222 (Gibson Blvd) northbound; exit 222A southbound, 1 mi e on Gibson Blvd, then just n. Int corridors. **Pets:** Other species. $15 one-time fee/pet. Designated rooms, service with restrictions, supervision.
🆂🅰🆅🅴 🄼 ⇆ 🛜 💻

▼▼▼ **Comfort Inn & Suites by Choice Hotels** 🄷
(505) 822-1090. **$77-$219.** 5811 Signal Ave NE 87113. I-25 exit 233 (Alameda Blvd), just e. Int corridors. **Pets:** Accepted.
🄼 ⇆ 🛜 ✕ 🔋 💻

🄰🄰🄰 ▼▼▼ **Comfort Suites** 🄷
(505) 797-0850. **$89-$220.** 5251 San Antonio Dr NE 87109. I-25 exit 231 (San Antonio Dr), just e. Int corridors. **Pets:** Accepted.
🆂🅰🆅🅴 🄼 ⇆ 🛜 ✕ 🔋 💻

🄰🄰🄰 ▼▼▼ **Courtyard by Marriott Journal Center** 🄷
(505) 823-1919. **$86-$129.** 5151 Journal Center Blvd NE 87109. I-25 exit 232, just s on Pan American Frwy NE. Int corridors.
Pets: Accepted. 🆂🅰🆅🅴 🍴 🄼 ⇆ 🛜 🔋 💻

🄰🄰🄰 ▼▼▼ **Crowne Plaza Albuquerque** 🄷
(505) 884-2500. **Call for rates.** 1901 University Blvd NE 87102. I-40 exit 160, just n to Menaul Blvd, then 1.1 mi w. Int corridors.
Pets: Accepted. 🆂🅰🆅🅴 🍴 🄼 ⇆ 🛜 ✕ 🔋 💻

▼▼ **Days Inn Albuquerque Downtown** 🄼
(505) 247-8897. **$60-$125.** 615 Central Ave NE 87102. I-25 exit 224A northbound; exit 224B southbound, just w. Ext corridors.
Pets: Accepted. 🛜 ✕ 🔋 💻

▼▼▼ **Drury Inn & Suites-Albuquerque** 🄷
(505) 341-3600. **$89-$154.** 4310 The 25 Way NE 87109. I-25 exit 229 (Jefferson St); northwest quadrant of exchange. Int corridors.
Pets: Accepted. 🄼 ⇆ 🛜 ✕ 🔋 💻

▼▼ **Econo Lodge Midtown** 🄷
(505) 880-0080. **$50-$120.** 2412 Carlisle Blvd NE 87110. I-40 exit 160, just n. Ext corridors. **Pets:** Accepted. 🛜 ✕ 🔋 💻

▼▼ **Econo Lodge Old Town Albuquerque** 🄷
(505) 243-8475. **$55-$130.** 2321 Central Ave NW 87104. I-40 exit 157A, 0.6 mi s on Rio Grande Blvd, then 0.4 mi w. Ext corridors.
Pets: Accepted. ⇆ 🛜 🔋 💻

🄰🄰🄰 ▼▼▼ **Fairfield Inn by Marriott Albuquerque-University Area** 🄷
(505) 889-4000. **$76-$100.** 1760 Menaul Blvd NE 87102. I-40 exit 160, just n to Menaul Blvd, then 1 mi w. Int corridors. **Pets:** Small, other species. $50 one-time fee/room. Designated rooms, service with restrictions, supervision. 🆂🅰🆅🅴 🄼 ⇆ ✕ 🛜 ✕ 🔋 💻

▼▼▼ **Home2 Suites by Hilton** 🄷
(505) 242-0002. **$84-$154.** 1660 University Blvd NE 87102. SE of jct I-25 and I-40. Int corridors. **Pets:** Accepted. 🄼 🛜 ✕ 🔋 💻

Hotel Andaluz H ✿
(505) 242-9090. **Call for rates.** 125 2nd St NW 87102. I-25 exit 224A northbound; exit 224B southbound, jct Copper Ave and 2nd St. Int corridors. **Pets:** $75 one-time fee/room. Designated rooms, service with restrictions.

Hotel Parq Central H
(505) 242-0040. **$139-$249.** 806 Central Ave SE 87102. I-25 exit 224A northbound; exit 224B southbound, just w. Int corridors. **Pets:** Accepted.

Hyatt Place Albuquerque Airport H
(505) 242-9300. **$79-$259.** 1400 Sunport Pl SE 87106. I-25 exit 221, 0.3 mi e to University Blvd exit, then just n to Woodward Rd. Int corridors. **Pets:** Accepted.

Hyatt Place Albuquerque Uptown H
(505) 872-9000. **$99-$249.** 6901 Arvada Ave NE 87110. I-40 exit 162, 0.7 mi n. Int corridors. **Pets:** Medium, dogs only. $75 one-time fee/pet. Designated rooms, service with restrictions, supervision.

Hyatt Regency Albuquerque H
(505) 842-1234. **$99-$299.** 330 Tijeras Ave NW 87102. I-25 exit 224B (Central Ave), 0.5 mi w. Int corridors. **Pets:** Accepted.

La Quinta Inn Albuquerque Airport H
(505) 243-5500. **$67-$235.** 2116 Yale Blvd SE 87106. I-25 exit 222 (Gibson Blvd) northbound; exit 222A southbound, 1 mi e. Ext corridors. **Pets:** Accepted.

La Quinta Inn & Suites Albuquerque Midtown H
(505) 761-5600. **$97-$240.** 2011 Menaul Blvd 87107. Jct University and Menaul blvds, just e. Int corridors. **Pets:** Accepted.

La Quinta Inn & Suites Albuquerque West H
(505) 839-1744. **$67-$246.** 6101 Iliff Rd NW 87121. I-40 exit 155, just sw. Int corridors. **Pets:** Accepted.

Mauger Bed & Breakfast Inn BB ✿
(505) 242-8755. **$99-$204, 10 day notice.** 701 Roma Ave NW 87102. I-25 exit 225, 1 mi w, then just s on 7th Ave. Int corridors. **Pets:** Dogs only. $20 one-time fee/room. Designated rooms, service with restrictions.

Residence Inn by Marriott Albuquerque Airport H
(505) 242-2844. **$101-$177.** 2301 International Dr SE 87106. I-25 exit 222 (Gibson Blvd) northbound; exit 222A southbound, 1 mi e, just n of jct Yale Blvd. Int corridors. **Pets:** Accepted.

Residence Inn by Marriott North H
(505) 761-0200. **$107-$156.** 4331 The Lane at 25 NE 87109. I-25 exit 229 (Jefferson St), just w, just n to The Lane at 25 NE, then just e. Int corridors. **Pets:** $100 one-time fee/room. Service with restrictions.

Sheraton Albuquerque Airport Hotel H
(505) 843-7000. **$99-$248.** 2910 Yale Blvd SE 87106. I-25 exit 222 (Gibson Blvd) northbound; exit 222A southbound, 1 mi e, then 0.5 mi s. Int corridors. **Pets:** Accepted.

Staybridge Suites Albuquerque Airport H ✿
(505) 338-3900. **Call for rates.** 1350 Sunport Pl SE 87106. I-25 exit 221, 0.3 mi e to University Blvd exit, then just n to Woodward Rd. Int corridors. **Pets:** Large. $75 one-time fee/room. Designated rooms, service with restrictions, supervision.

Staybridge Suites Albuquerque North H ✿
(505) 266-7829. **$90-$250.** 5817 Signal Ave NE 87113. I-25 exit 233 (Alameda Blvd), just e; jct Alameda Blvd and Signal Ave. Int corridors. **Pets:** Medium. $75 one-time fee/pet. Designated rooms, service with restrictions, crate.

TownePlace Suites by Marriott H
(505) 232-5800. **$84-$120.** 2400 Centre Ave SE 87106. I-25 exit 222 (Gibson Blvd) northbound; exit 222A southbound, 1 mi e to Yale Blvd, at northeast jct of Gibson and Yale blvds, then just e. Int corridors. **Pets:** Medium. $100 one-time fee/pet. Service with restrictions, supervision.

TownePlace Suites by Marriott Albuquerque North H
(505) 345-3131. **$108-$151.** 5511 Office Blvd NE 87109. I-25 exit 229 (Jefferson St), just s. Int corridors. **Pets:** Accepted.

ALGODONES

Hacienda Vargas Bed and Breakfast Inn BB
(505) 867-9115. **Call for rates.** 1431 SR 313 (El Camino Real) 87001. I-25 exit 248, 0.3 mi w, then 0.3 mi s. Int corridors. **Pets:** Accepted.

ARROYO SECO

Adobe and Stars B & B BB
(575) 776-2776. **Call for rates.** 584 State Hwy 150 87571. 1.1 mi ne of Arroyo Seco village, at Valdez Rd. Ext/int corridors. **Pets:** Accepted.

ARTESIA

Artesia Inn M
(575) 746-9801. **Call for rates.** 1820 S 1st St 88210. 1.5 mi s on US 285. Ext corridors. **Pets:** Accepted.

Best Western Pecos Inn H
(575) 748-3324. **$129-$179.** 2209 W Main St 88210. 1.5 mi w on US 82. Int corridors. **Pets:** Accepted.

Hotel Artesia H
(575) 746-2066. **Call for rates.** 203 N 2nd St 88210. Jct US 285 and Main St, just n. Int corridors. **Pets:** Accepted.

La Quinta Inn & Suites Artesia H
(575) 736-2400. **$93-$240.** 2207 W Main St 88210. 1.5 mi w on US 82. Int corridors. **Pets:** Accepted.

AZTEC

Microtel Inn & Suites by Wyndham H ✿
(505) 334-4014. **$53-$100.** 623 Phoenix Ct 87410. Jct SR 516 and US 550, 3 mi s. Int corridors. **Pets:** Other species. $25 daily fee/pet. Service with restrictions, supervision.

BERNALILLO

Days Inn Bernalillo H
(505) 771-7000. **$65-$140.** 107 N Camino del Pueblo 87004. I-25 exit 242, just w. Int corridors. **Pets:** Accepted.

Hyatt Regency Tamaya Resort and Spa H ✿
(505) 867-1234. **$119-$309, 3 day notice.** 1300 Tuyuna Tr 87004. I-25 exit 242, 1 mi w on US 550 to Tamaya Blvd, then 1 mi n, follow signs. Int corridors. **Pets:** Medium, dogs only. $150 one-time fee/pet. Service with restrictions.

BLOOMFIELD

▼▼ Super 8 M
(505) 632-8886. **$70-$79, 3 day notice.** 525 W Broadway Blvd 87413. Jct of US 64 and 550. Int corridors. **Pets:** Other species. $15 daily fee/room. Service with restrictions, supervision. 🛜 📶 💻

CARLSBAD

▼▼▼▼ Candlewood Suites Carlsbad South H
(575) 941-3711. **$189-$499.** 3711 San Jose Blvd 88220. 1 mi s on US 62, 180 and 285. Int corridors. **Pets:** Accepted.
♿M 🛜 ✖ 📶 💻

�️🔍 ▼▼▼▼ La Quinta Inn & Suites H
(575) 236-1010. **$141-$400.** 4020 National Parks Highway 88220. 1.5 mi s on US 62, 180 and 285. Int corridors. **Pets:** Accepted.
SAVE ♿M 🛜 ✖ 📶 💻

▼▼▼▼ TownePlace Suites by Marriott H ♣
(575) 689-8850. **$152-$306.** 311 Pompa St 88220. 0.5 mi s on US 62, 180 and 285. Int corridors. **Pets:** Other species. $100 one-time fee/room. Designated rooms, service with restrictions, crate.
♿M 🛜 ✖ 📶 💻

CHIMAYÓ *(Restaurants p. 618)*

▼▼▼▼ Casa Escondida Bed & Breakfast BB
(505) 351-4805. **$116-$208, 14 day notice.** 64 CR 100 87522. Jct SR 76 and 98, just w on SR 76, then 0.5 mi ne, follow signs; 7.5 mi e of Espanola on SR 76. Ext/int corridors. **Pets:** Accepted.
🛜 ✖ 🅿 🎦 📶 💻

CIMARRON

▼ Cimarron Inn & RV Park M
(575) 376-2268. **Call for rates.** 212 10th St 87714. On US 64. Ext corridors. **Pets:** Accepted. 🛜 ✖ 📶 💻

CLAYTON

🔍🔍 ▼▼▼▼ Best Western Kokopelli Lodge H
(575) 374-2589. **$115-$135.** 702 S 1st St 88415. US 87, 0.5 mi se of jct US 56 and 64. Ext corridors. **Pets:** Accepted.
SAVE 🍴 ➿ 🛜 ✖ 📶 💻

▼▼ Days Inn & Suites H
(575) 374-0133. **$105-$122.** 1120 S 1st St 88415. US 87, 1 mi s of jct US 56 and 64. Int corridors. **Pets:** Accepted. ➿ 🛜 ✖ 📶 💻

CLOVIS

▼▼▼▼ Comfort Inn & Suites H
(575) 762-4536. **$89-$209.** 201 Schepps Blvd 88101. Jct US 60/70/84, 1.6 mi e on Mabry Dr, then just n. Int corridors. **Pets:** Accepted.
➿ 🛜 ✖ 📶 💻

▼▼▼▼ La Quinta Inn & Suites Clovis H
(575) 763-8777. **$104-$185.** 4521 N Prince St 88101. Jct US 60/84, 3.1 mi n. Int corridors. **Pets:** Accepted. 🍴 ➿ 🛜 ✖ 📶 💻

▼▼ Super 8 Clovis H
(575) 762-5600. **$68-$81.** 2912 Mabry Dr 88101. Jct US 60/70/84, 1.7 mi e. Ext corridors. **Pets:** Accepted. ➿ 🛜 📶 💻

DEMING

🔍🔍 ▼▼▼ Best Western Deming Southwest Inn H
(575) 546-4544. **$85-$125.** 1500 W Pine St 88030. I-10 exit 81, just e. Ext corridors. **Pets:** Accepted. SAVE ➿ 🛜 📶 💻

🔍🔍 ▼▼▼ Days Inn M
(575) 546-8813. **$57-$75.** 1601 E Pine St 88030. I-10 exit 85, 2 mi w on business loop; exit 81 eastbound, 1 mi e on business loop. Ext corridors. **Pets:** Medium, other species. $7 daily fee/pet. Service with restrictions, crate. SAVE ➿ 🛜 📶 💻

▼▼▼▼ Hampton Inn H
(575) 546-2022. **$89-$109.** 3751 E Cedar St 88030. I-10 exit 85, just s to Cedar St, then just w. Int corridors. **Pets:** Accepted.
♿M ➿ 🛜 ✖ 📶 💻

▼▼▼▼ Holiday Inn Express & Suites H
(575) 545-6500. **Call for rates.** 3801 E Cedar St 88030. I-10 exit 85, just s to Cedar St, then just w. Int corridors. **Pets:** Other species. Designated rooms, service with restrictions, supervision.
♿M 🛜 ✖ 📶 💻

ELEPHANT BUTTE

🔍🔍 ▼▼▼ Elephant Butte Inn H ♣
(575) 744-5431. **$85-$140.** 401 Hwy 195 87935. I-25 exit 83, 4 mi e. Ext corridors. **Pets:** $20 one-time fee/pet. Designated rooms, service with restrictions, supervision. SAVE 🍴 ♿M ➿ 🛜 ✖ 📶 💻

ESPAÑOLA *(Restaurants p. 618)*

▼▼▼▼ Inn at the Delta BB
(505) 753-9466. **Call for rates.** 243 Paseo de Onate 87532. US 84 and 285, 1 mi n of jct SR 68; 0.3 mi n of jct SR 30. Ext corridors.
Pets: Accepted. 🛜 ✖ 📶 💻

▼▼▼▼ Santa Claran Hotel Casino H
(505) 367-4900. **Call for rates.** 464 N Riverside Dr 87532. SR 68; center. Int corridors. **Pets:** Accepted. 🍴 ♿M ✖ 🛜 📶 💻

FARMINGTON

🔍🔍 ▼▼▼ Best Western Plus The Four Corners Inn H
(505) 564-8100. **$99-$149.** 4751 Cortez Way 87402. On US 550 at Cortez Way. Int corridors. **Pets:** Accepted.
SAVE ➿ 🛜 ✖ 📶 💻

🔍🔍 ▼▼▼ Comfort Inn H
(505) 325-2626. **$75-$114.** 555 Scott Ave 87401. 1 mi e on SR 516 (Main St), just s. Int corridors. **Pets:** Medium. $35 one-time fee/pet. Designated rooms, service with restrictions, supervision.
SAVE ➿ 🛜 ✖ 📶 💻

▼▼▼▼ Holiday Inn Express & Suites H ♣
(505) 325-2545. **Call for rates.** 2110 Bloomfield Blvd 87401. 1.6 mi e on US 64 (Bloomfield Blvd), just past jct Broadway; on Frontage Rd. Int corridors. **Pets:** Medium, other species. $25 one-time fee/room. Service with restrictions, crate. ➿ 🛜 ✖ 📶 💻

▼▼▼▼ Home2 Suites by Hilton H
(505) 325-1500. **$89-$139.** 777 S Browning Pkwy 87401. Jct US 64, just n. Int corridors. **Pets:** Accepted. 🍴 ♿M 🛜 ✖ 📶 💻

▼▼▼▼ TownePlace Suites by Marriott H
(505) 327-2442. **$85-$142.** 4200 Sierra Vista Dr 87402. 5 mi e on SR 516 (E Main St), just s. Int corridors. **Pets:** Medium, other species. $100 one-time fee/room. Designated rooms, service with restrictions, crate. 🔌 🛜 ✖ 📶 💻

GALLUP

🔍🔍 ▼▼▼ Comfort Suites H
(505) 863-3445. **$95-$150.** 3940 E Hwy 66 87301. I-40 exit 26, just e. Int corridors. **Pets:** Accepted. SAVE ➿ 🛜 ✖ 📶 💻

▼▼▼▼ Holiday Inn Express & Suites H
(505) 722-7500. **Call for rates.** 3850 E Hwy 66 87301. I-40 exit 26, just e. Int corridors. **Pets:** Accepted. ♿M 🛜 ✖ 📶 💻

▼▼▼▼ La Quinta Inn & Suites Gallup H
(505) 722-2233. **$67-$210.** 3880 E Hwy 66 87301. I-40 exit 26, just e. Int corridors. **Pets:** Accepted. ➿ ♿ 🛜 ✖ 📶 💻

Red Roof Inn-Gallup M
(505) 722-7765. **$40-$110.** 3304 W Hwy 66 87301. I-40 exit 16, just se. Ext corridors. **Pets:** Accepted. 〔SAVE〕〔¶¶〕〔≈〕〔🛜〕〔✕〕〔🔌〕〔💻〕

GRANTS
Days Inn H
(505) 287-8883. **$70-$90.** 1504 E Santa Fe Ave 87020. I-40 exit 85, 0.3 mi n. Ext corridors. **Pets:** Accepted. 〔¶¶〕〔&M〕〔🛜〕〔✕〕〔🔌〕〔💻〕

Quality Inn & Suites H
(505) 285-4676. **$84-$109.** 1496 E Santa Fe Ave 87020. I-40 exit 85, 0.3 mi n. Int corridors. **Pets:** Small. Designated rooms, service with restrictions, supervision. 〔≈〕〔🛜〕〔✕〕〔🔌〕〔💻〕

HOBBS
Best Western Executive Inn H
(575) 397-7171. **$80-$100.** 309 N Marland Blvd 88240. US 62, 180 and Snyder St. Ext corridors. **Pets:** Medium, dogs only. $10 daily fee/pet. Designated rooms, service with restrictions, crate.
〔SAVE〕〔≈〕〔🛜〕〔🔌〕〔💻〕

La Quinta Inn & Suites Hobbs H
(575) 397-8777. **$104-$185.** 3312 N Lovington Hwy 88240. SR 18 N (N Lovington Hwy), just s of jct Joe Harvey Blvd. Int corridors.
Pets: Accepted. 〔&M〕〔≈〕〔🛜〕〔✕〕〔🔌〕〔💻〕

Sleep Inn & Suites H
(575) 393-3355. **$79-$139.** 4630 N Lovington Hwy 88240. Jct SR 18 N (N Lovington Hwy) and W Millen Dr, 0.8 mi s. Int corridors.
Pets: Accepted. 〔¶¶〕〔&M〕〔≈〕〔🛜〕〔✕〕〔🔌〕〔💻〕

LAS CRUCES *(Restaurants p. 618)*
Best Western Mission Inn H
(575) 524-8591. **$85-$130.** 1765 S Main St 88005. I-10 exit 142 (University Ave), 1 mi n. Ext corridors. **Pets:** Medium. $15 daily fee/pet. Designated rooms, service with restrictions, supervision.
〔SAVE〕〔≈〕〔🛜〕〔🔌〕〔💻〕

Comfort Inn & Suites de Mesilla H
(575) 527-1050. **$90-$140.** 1300 Avenida de Mesilla 88005. I-10 exit 140, just s. Int corridors. **Pets:** Accepted. 〔&M〕〔≈〕〔🛜〕〔🔌〕〔💻〕

Comfort Suites H
(575) 521-1030. **$99-$179.** 236 N Telshor Blvd 88011. I-25 exit 3, just e, then just n. Int corridors. **Pets:** Medium. $10 daily fee/pet. Designated rooms, service with restrictions, supervision.
〔&M〕〔✕〕〔🛜〕〔✕〕〔🔌〕〔💻〕

Comfort Suites by Choice Hotels H
(575) 522-1300. **$69-$124.** 2101 S Triviz Dr 88001. I-25 exit 1 (University Ave), just w, then just n. Int corridors. **Pets:** Accepted.
〔&M〕〔≈〕〔✕〕〔🔌〕〔💻〕

Days Inn Las Cruces H
(575) 526-8311. **$46-$99.** 755 Avenida de Mesilla 88005. I-10 exit 140, just e. Ext corridors. **Pets:** Accepted. 〔SAVE〕〔≈〕〔🛜〕〔🔌〕〔💻〕

Drury Inn & Suites Las Cruces H
(575) 523-4100. **$84-$159.** 1631 Hickory Loop 88005. I-10 exit 140, just e. Int corridors. **Pets:** Accepted. 〔&M〕〔≈〕〔🛜〕〔✕〕〔🔌〕〔💻〕

Holiday Inn Express & Suites North H
(575) 522-0700. **$124-$169.** 2142 Telshor Ct 88011. I-25 exit 6 (US 70), just s. Int corridors. **Pets:** Accepted. 〔&M〕〔≈〕〔🛜〕〔✕〕〔🔌〕〔💻〕

Hotel Encanto de Las Cruces H
(575) 522-4300. **$129-$179.** 705 S Telshor Blvd 88011. I-25 exit 3 (Lohman Ave), just e, then just s. Int corridors. **Pets:** Accepted.
〔SAVE〕〔¶¶〕〔≈〕〔🛜〕〔✕〕〔🔌〕〔💻〕

La Quinta Inn & Suites Las Cruces Organ Mountain H
(575) 523-0100. **$67-$158.** 1500 Hickory Dr 88005. I-10 exit 140, just se of jct I-25 and Avenida de Mesilla. Int corridors. **Pets:** Accepted.
〔&M〕〔≈〕〔🛜〕〔🔌〕〔💻〕

Lundeen's Inn of the Arts BB
(575) 526-3326. **$79-$125, 3 day notice.** 618 S Alameda Blvd 88005. Jct Lohman Ave, just s; center. Int corridors. **Pets:** Medium, dogs only. $15 one-time fee/room. Service with restrictions, supervision.
〔¶¶〕〔🛜〕〔✕〕〔🔌〕〔💻〕

Ramada Palms de Las Cruces H
(575) 526-4411. **$79-$109.** 201 E University Ave 88005. I-10 exit 142 (University Ave), just n. Int corridors. **Pets:** Accepted.
〔¶¶〕〔&M〕〔≈〕〔🛜〕〔✕〕〔🔌〕〔💻〕

Staybridge Suites H
(575) 521-7999. **Call for rates.** 2651 Northrise Dr 88011. I-25 exit 6 (US 70), just e. Int corridors. **Pets:** Accepted.
〔&M〕〔≈〕〔🛜〕〔✕〕〔🔌〕〔💻〕

Super 8 East White Sands Area H
(575) 382-1490. **$55-$73.** 3405 Bataan Memorial W 88012. US 70, exit Rinconda, just w. Int corridors. **Pets:** Other species. $10 daily fee/pet. Designated rooms, service with restrictions. 〔SAVE〕〔🛜〕〔🔌〕〔💻〕

TownePlace Suites by Marriott Las Cruces H 🐾
(575) 532-6500. **$98-$157.** 2143 Telshor Ct 88011. I-25 exit 6 (US 70), just s. Int corridors. **Pets:** Other species. $15 daily fee/pet. Service with restrictions, crate. 〔&M〕〔≈〕〔🛜〕〔✕〕〔🔌〕〔💻〕

LAS VEGAS
Best Western Plus Montezuma Inn & Suites H
(505) 426-8000. **$90-$150.** 2020 N Grand Ave 87701. I-25 exit 347, just sw. Int corridors. **Pets:** Accepted.
〔SAVE〕〔&M〕〔≈〕〔✕〕〔🛜〕〔✕〕〔🔌〕〔💻〕

Holiday Inn Express Hotel & Suites H
(505) 426-8182. **$109-$140.** 816 S Grand Ave 87701. I-25 exit 343, just n. Int corridors. **Pets:** Accepted. 〔&M〕〔≈〕〔🛜〕〔✕〕〔🔌〕〔💻〕

LORDSBURG
Comfort Inn & Suites H
(575) 542-3355. **$89-$114.** 400 W Wabash St 88045. I-10 exit 22, just n, then w. Int corridors. **Pets:** Accepted.
〔SAVE〕〔&M〕〔≈〕〔✕〕〔🛜〕〔✕〕〔🔌〕〔💻〕

Hampton Inn H 🐾
(575) 542-8900. **$94-$119.** 412 W Wabash St 88045. I-10 exit 22, just w. Int corridors. **Pets:** Medium, other species. Designated rooms, service with restrictions. 〔&M〕〔≈〕〔🛜〕〔✕〕〔🔌〕〔💻〕

Motel-6 Lordsburg M
(575) 542-8807. **Call for rates.** 1303 S Main St 88045. I-10 exit 22, just s. Ext corridors. **Pets:** Accepted. 〔SAVE〕〔≈〕〔🛜〕〔🔌〕

LOS ALAMOS *(Restaurants p. 618)*
Holiday Inn Express & Suites H
(505) 661-2646. **Call for rates.** 60 Entrada Dr 87544. Jct Airport Basin Dr and SR 502. Int corridors. **Pets:** Accepted.
〔¶¶〕〔&M〕〔≈〕〔🛜〕〔✕〕〔🔌〕〔💻〕

LOS LUNAS
Western Skies Inn & Suites H
(505) 865-0001. **$65-$95, 3 day notice.** 2258 Sun Ranch Village Loop 87031. I-25 exit 203, just w. Int corridors. **Pets:** Other species. $10 daily fee/pet. Service with restrictions, supervision.
〔SAVE〕〔&M〕〔≈〕〔🛜〕〔🔌〕〔💻〕

MORIARTY

Americas Best Value Inn H
(505) 832-4457. **$52-$85.** 1316 Route 66 W 87035. I-40 exit 194, 0.5 mi se on US 66 and I-40 business loop. Int corridors. **Pets:** Medium, other species. $10 daily fee/pet. Designated rooms, service with restrictions, supervision. (SAVE)

Best Western Moriarty Heritage Inn H
(505) 832-5000. **$99-$100.** 111 Anaya Blvd 87035. I-40 exit 194, 0.4 mi e. Int corridors. **Pets:** Other species. $15 one-time fee/room. Designated rooms, service with restrictions, supervision.
(SAVE)

Quality Inn H
(505) 832-6666. **$80-$120.** 119 Route 66 E 87035. I-40 exit 196, just s, then just e. Int corridors. **Pets:** $20 one-time fee/room. Service with restrictions.

Super 8 H
(505) 832-6730. **$62-$81.** 1611 W Old Route 66 87035. I-40 exit 194, 0.5 mi e on Central Ave. Int corridors. **Pets:** Medium, other species. $10 daily fee/pet. Designated rooms, service with restrictions, supervision. (SAVE)

PINOS ALTOS

Bear Creek Motel & Cabins CA
(575) 388-4501. **$99-$269.** 88 Main St 88053. 1 mi n of town on SR 15. Ext corridors. **Pets:** Accepted.

PORTALES

Super 8 Portales H
(575) 356-8518. **$50-$120.** 1805 W 2nd St 88130. 1 mi s. Int corridors. **Pets:** Accepted.

RATON

Best Western Plus Raton Hotel H
(575) 445-8501. **$129-$179.** 473 Clayton Rd 87740. I-25 exit 451, just w. Ext/int corridors. **Pets:** Dogs only. $20 daily fee/room. Designated rooms, service with restrictions, supervision.
(SAVE)

Holiday Inn Express Hotel & Suites H
(575) 445-1500. **$139-$199.** 101 Card Ave 87740. I-25 exit 450, just w. Int corridors. **Pets:** Accepted.

RED RIVER

Best Western Rivers Edge H
(575) 754-1766. **$99-$229.** 301 W River St 87558. 1 blk s of W Main St (SR 38); center. Ext corridors. **Pets:** Accepted.
(SAVE)

RIO RANCHO

Extended Stay America Albuquerque-Rio Rancho M
(505) 792-1338. **$45-$100.** 2608 The American Rd NW 87124. Corner of SR 528 and Cottonwood Dr, just n, just w. Int corridors.
Pets: Accepted.

ROSWELL

Best Western El Rancho Palacio H
(575) 622-2721. **$75-$119.** 2205 N Main St 88201. Jct US 70 and 285, 1.8 mi n. Ext corridors. **Pets:** Accepted. (SAVE)

Candlewood Suites Roswell H
(575) 623-4300. **$109-$159.** 4 Military Heights Dr 88201. Jct US 70 and 285, just n of US 385. Int corridors. **Pets:** Other species. $15 daily fee/room. Service with restrictions, crate.

Days Inn H
(575) 623-4021. **$70-$90.** 1310 N Main St 88201. Jct US 70 and 285, 0.8 mi n. Ext corridors. **Pets:** Accepted. (SAVE)

Holiday Inn H
(575) 623-3216. **$109-$179.** 3620 N Main St 88201. Jct US 70 and 285 N, 1 mi s. Int corridors. **Pets:** Accepted.

Holiday Inn Express & Suites H
(575) 627-9900. **Call for rates.** 2300 N Main St 88201. Jct US 70 and 285, 1.8 mi n. Int corridors. **Pets:** Accepted.

Sally Port Inn & Suites H
(575) 622-6430. **$109-$149.** 2000 N Main St 88201. Jct US 70 and 285, 1.5 mi n. Int corridors. **Pets:** Accepted.

TownePlace Suites by Marriott H
(575) 622-5460. **$98-$184.** 180 E 19th St 88201. Jct Main St, just e. Int corridors. **Pets:** Other species. $300 one-time fee/room. Designated rooms, service with restrictions, crate.

RUIDOSO *(Restaurants p. 618)*

MCM Eleganté Lodge & Resort H
(575) 258-5500. **$129-$239.** 107 Sierra Blanca Dr 88345. Jct Sudderth Dr. Int corridors. **Pets:** Small. $50 one-time fee/room. Service with restrictions, crate.

Ruidoso Mountain Inn H
(575) 257-3736. **Call for rates.** 400 W Hwy 70 88345. US 70, just w of jct Sudderth Dr. Int corridors. **Pets:** Accepted.

Whispering Pine Cabins CA
(575) 257-4311. **$99-$350, 14 day notice.** 422 Main Rd 88345. 0.9 mi w of jct SR 48 and Sudderth Dr. Ext corridors. **Pets:** Accepted.

RUIDOSO DOWNS

Best Western Pine Springs Inn H
(575) 378-8100. **$80-$250.** 111 Pine Springs Dr 88346. Just e of jct US 70 and SR 48. Ext corridors. **Pets:** Accepted.
(SAVE)

SANTA FE *(Restaurants p. 619)*

Baymont Inn & Suites H
(505) 474-4442. **$65-$139.** 4150 Cerrillos Rd 87505. I-25 exit 278, 2 mi n. Int corridors. **Pets:** Medium. $25 daily fee/pet. Designated rooms, service with restrictions, supervision.

Best Western Plus Inn of Santa Fe H
(505) 438-3822. **$100-$200.** 3650 Cerrillos Rd 87507. I-25 exit 278, 2.8 mi n. Int corridors. **Pets:** Service with restrictions, supervision.
(SAVE)

The Drury Plaza Hotel in Santa Fe H
(505) 424-2175. **$129-$339.** 828 E Paseo de Peralta 87501. At Palace Ave. Int corridors. **Pets:** Accepted.
(SAVE)

Eldorado Hotel & Spa H
(505) 988-4455. **Call for rates.** 309 W San Francisco St 87501. Just w of The Plaza; at Sandoval St. Int corridors. **Pets:** Accepted.
(SAVE)

El Paradero Bed & Breakfast BB
(505) 988-1177. **$100-$200, 14 day notice.** 220 W Manhattan Ave 87501. 0.3 mi s on Cerrillos Rd, 1/2 blk e. Ext/int corridors.
Pets: Accepted. (SAVE)

El Rey Inn H
(505) 982-1931. Call for rates. 1862 Cerrillos Rd 87505. I-25 exit 278, 6 mi nw. Ext corridors. Pets: Medium, dogs only. $50 one-time fee/pet, $25 daily fee/pet. Designated rooms, no service, supervision.

Four Seasons Resort Rancho Encantado Santa Fe H
(505) 946-5700. $309-$1999, 3 day notice. 198 State Road 592 87506. US 285/84 N exit 172 (CR 73/Tesuque), 0.5 mi se to SR 592, then 2 mi ne. Ext corridors. Pets: Accepted.

Hampton Inn Santa Fe H
(505) 474-3900. $99-$149. 3625 Cerrillos Rd 87505. I-25 exit 278, 2.5 mi n. Int corridors. Pets: Accepted.

Hilton Santa Fe Buffalo Thunder H
(505) 455-5555. Call for rates. 20 Buffalo Thunder Tr 87506. N on US 285 exit Buffalo Thunder Rd, just e. Int corridors. Pets: Accepted.

Hilton Santa Fe Historic Plaza H
(505) 988-2811. $129-$259. 100 Sandoval St 87501. Just sw of The Plaza; between San Francisco and W Alameda sts. Ext/int corridors. Pets: Accepted.

Holiday Inn Express-Santa Fe H
(505) 474-7570. Call for rates. 3450 Cerrillos Rd 87507. I-25 exit 278, 3 mi n. Int corridors. Pets: Accepted.

Homewood Suites By Hilton-Santa Fe North H
(505) 455-9100. $99-$199. 10 Buffalo Thunder Tr 87506. US 84/285 exit 177, just e. Ext/int corridors. Pets: Accepted.

Hotel Chimayó de Santa Fe H
(505) 988-4900. $96-$189, 3 day notice. 125 Washington Ave 87501. Just ne of The Plaza; center. Ext/int corridors. Pets: Accepted.

Hotel Santa Fe, The Hacienda & Spa H
(505) 982-1200. $109-$349, 3 day notice. 1501 Paseo de Peralta 87501. At Cerrillos Rd, 0.6 mi s of The Plaza. Int corridors. Pets: Accepted.

Hyatt Place Santa Fe H
(505) 474-7777. $79-$249. 4320 Cerrillos Rd 87507. I-25 exit 278, 2 mi e. Int corridors. Pets: Accepted.

The Inn & Spa at Loretto H
(505) 988-5531. Call for rates. 211 Old Santa Fe Tr 87501. Just s of The Plaza. Int corridors. Pets: Accepted.

Inn at Santa Fe H
(505) 474-9500. $79-$249. 8376 Cerrillos Rd 87507. I-25 exit 278, 0.3 mi n. Pets: Other species. $25 one-time fee/room. Designated rooms, service with restrictions, supervision.

The Inn of The Five Graces CI
(505) 992-0957. $425-$2500, 7 day notice. 150 E DeVargas St 87501. Jct Old Pecos Trail. Ext/int corridors. Pets: Accepted.

Inn On The Alameda H
(505) 984-2121. Call for rates. 303 E Alameda St 87501. Just e of The Plaza; jct Paseo de Peralta. Ext/int corridors. Pets: $50 daily fee/room. Designated rooms, service with restrictions.

Inn on the Paseo BB
(505) 984-8200. Call for rates. 282 Paseo de Peralta 87501. I-25 exit 282, 2 mi e; jct St. Francis Dr. Ext/int corridors. Pets: Accepted.

La Fonda On the Plaza H
(505) 982-5511. $159-$419. 100 E San Francisco St 87501. On The Plaza. Int corridors. Pets: Medium, dogs only. $50 daily fee/pet. Service with restrictions, supervision.

La Posada de Santa Fe, a Tribute Portfolio Resort & Spa H
(505) 986-0000. Call for rates. 330 E Palace Ave 87501. Jct Paseo de Peralta and E Palace Ave. Ext corridors. Pets: Accepted.

La Quinta Inn Santa Fe H
(505) 471-1142. $67-$218. 4298 Cerrillos Rd 87507. I-25 exit 278, 1.8 mi n. Ext/int corridors. Pets: Accepted.

Las Palomas H
(505) 982-5560. Call for rates. 460 W San Francisco St 87501. Just w of jct Guadalupe St. Ext corridors. Pets: Dogs only. $20 daily fee/pet. Service with restrictions, supervision.

The Lodge at Santa Fe H
(505) 992-5800. Call for rates. 750 N St. Francis Dr 87501. Jct of Cerrillos Rd and St. Francis Dr (US 84/285), 1.1 mi nw to Alamo Dr, just w, then just n. Ext/int corridors. Pets: Accepted.

Motel 6-150 M
(505) 473-1380. $45-$105. 3007 Cerrillos Rd 87507. I-25 exit 278, 3.8 mi n. Ext corridors. Pets: Accepted.

The Old Santa Fe Inn M
(505) 995-0800. $99-$390, 3 day notice. 320 Galisteo St 87501. Just sw of The Plaza; center. Ext/int corridors. Pets: Medium. $30 daily fee/pet. Designated rooms, service with restrictions, supervision.

Pecos Trail Inn M
(505) 982-1943. Call for rates. 2239 Old Pecos Tr 87505. I-25 exit 284, 0.8 mi n on CR 466 (Old Pecos Tr). Ext corridors. Pets: Accepted.

Rosewood Inn of the Anasazi H
(505) 988-3030. Call for rates. 113 Washington Ave 87501. Just ne of The Plaza. Int corridors. Pets: Accepted.

Santa Fe Motel & Inn M
(505) 982-1039. $129-$249, 3 day notice. 510 Cerrillos Rd 87501. 4 blks sw of The Plaza. Ext corridors. Pets: Dogs only. $25 daily fee/pet. Designated rooms, service with restrictions, crate.

Santa Fe Sage Inn & Suites H
(505) 982-5952. $89-$169, 3 day notice. 725 Cerrillos Rd 87505. 0.4 mi ne of St. Francis Dr (US 84). Ext corridors. Pets: Medium, other species. $15 daily fee/pet. Designated rooms, service with restrictions, crate.

SANTA ROSA

Best Western Santa Rosa Inn M
(575) 472-5877. $90-$160. 2491 Historic Route 66 88435. I-40 exit 277, 0.5 mi w. Ext corridors. Pets: Small. $10 daily fee/pet. Designated rooms, service with restrictions, supervision.

⚜ ▼▼▼ Days Inn & Suites ℍ
(575) 472-3446. **$70-$85.** 2255 Historic Route 66 88435. I-40 exit 275, just w. Ext corridors. **Pets:** $10 one-time fee/room. Service with restrictions, supervision. ⬛ ⬛ ⬛ ⬛ ⬛ ⬛

▼▼▼ La Quinta Inn Santa Rosa ℍ
(575) 472-4800. **$99-$185.** 2277 Historic Route 66 88435. I-40 exit 275, just e. Int corridors. **Pets:** Accepted. ⬛ ⬛ ⬛ ⬛

▼▼ Quality Inn ℍ
(575) 472-5570. **$75-$119.** 2533 E Historic Route 66 88435. I-40 exit 277, 0.3 mi w. Ext corridors. **Pets:** Accepted. ⬛ ⬛ ⬛ ⬛ ⬛

▼▼ Super 8-Santa Rosa Ⓜ
(575) 472-5388. **$53-$76.** 2075 Historic Route 66 88435. I-40 exit 275, just w. Int corridors. **Pets:** Accepted. ⬛ ⬛ ⬛

SANTA TERESA

▼▼ Oak Tree Inn Santa Teresa ℍ
(575) 589-0552. **Call for rates.** 2680 Airport Rd 88008. I-10 exit 8, 12 mi w. Int corridors. **Pets:** Accepted. ⬛ ⬛ ⬛ ⬛ ⬛

SILVER CITY

▼▼ Comfort Inn ℍ
(575) 534-1883. **$90-$170.** 1060 E Hwy 180 88061. Just e of jct SR 15. Int corridors. **Pets:** Accepted. ⬛ ⬛ ⬛ ⬛ ⬛

▼▼ Econo Lodge Silver City ℍ
(575) 534-1111. **$74-$180.** 1120 Hwy 180 E 88061. 1.5 mi ne on US 180 and SR 90. Int corridors. **Pets:** Large, other species. $7 daily fee/pet. Designated rooms, service with restrictions, supervision. ⬛ ⬛ ⬛ ⬛ ⬛

▼▼▼ Holiday Inn Express ℍ
(575) 538-2525. **$130-$154.** 1103 Superior St 88061. 3 mi ne on US 180 and SR 90. Int corridors. **Pets:** Other species. Designated rooms, service with restrictions, supervision. ⬛ ⬛ ⬛ ⬛

SOCORRO

⚜ ▼▼▼ Best Western Socorro Hotel & Suites ℍ
(575) 838-0556. **$95-$105.** 1100 California Ave NE 87801. I-25 exit 150, just s. Ext/int corridors. **Pets:** Medium. $10 daily fee/pet. Designated rooms, service with restrictions, crate.
⬛ ⬛ ⬛ ⬛ ⬛ ⬛ ⬛ ⬛ ⬛

▼▼▼ Comfort Inn & Suites ℍ
(575) 838-4400. **$89-$114.** 1259 Frontage Rd NW 87801. I-25 exit 150, just nw. Int corridors. **Pets:** Accepted. ⬛ ⬛ ⬛ ⬛ ⬛ ⬛

⚜ ▼▼▼ Econo Lodge Ⓜ
(575) 835-1500. **$60-$124.** 713 California St NW 87801. I-25 exit 150, 1 mi s. Ext corridors. **Pets:** Medium. $10 daily fee/pet. Service with restrictions, supervision. ⬛ ⬛ ⬛ ⬛ ⬛ ⬛

TAOS *(Restaurants p. 619)*

⚜ ▼▼▼▼ El Monte Sagrado ℍ
(575) 758-3502. **Call for rates.** 317 Kit Carson Rd 87571. 0.5 mi e of jct US 64 and SR 68. Ext/int corridors. **Pets:** Accepted.
⬛ ⬛ ⬛ ⬛ ⬛ ⬛ ⬛

⚜ ▼▼▼▼ La Posada de Taos 𝔹𝔹
(575) 758-8164. **$149-$250, 14 day notice.** 309 Juanita Ln 87571. From Taos Plaza, just w on Don Fernando St, just s on Manzanares St, then just w. Ext/int corridors. **Pets:** Accepted. ⬛ ⬛ ⬛ ⬛ ⬛

TRUTH OR CONSEQUENCES
(Restaurants p. 619)

▼▼▼ Holiday Inn Express & Suites ℍ
(575) 894-3900. **Call for rates.** 2201 FG Amin St 87901. I-25 exit 79, just e. Int corridors. **Pets:** Accepted. ⬛ ⬛ ⬛ ⬛ ⬛ ⬛

▼▼▼▼ Sierra Grande Lodge & Spa ℍ
(575) 894-6976. **$155-$520, 7 day notice.** 501 McAdoo St 87901. Just w of Foch St; center. Ext/int corridors. **Pets:** Small, dogs only. $25 daily fee/pet. Designated rooms, service with restrictions, supervision.
⬛ ⬛ ⬛ ⬛ ⬛ ⬛

TUCUMCARI

⚜ ▼▼▼▼ Best Western Discovery Inn ℍ
(575) 461-4884. **$79-$139.** 200 E Estrella Ave 88401. I-40 exit 332, just n. Ext corridors. **Pets:** Accepted. ⬛ ⬛ ⬛ ⬛ ⬛ ⬛

▼▼ Days Inn ℍ
(575) 461-3158. **$60-$100.** 2623 S 1st St 88401. I-40 exit 332, just n. Ext/int corridors. **Pets:** Accepted. ⬛ ⬛ ⬛

NEW YORK

ALBANY *(Restaurants p. 619)*

⚜ ▼▼ Best Western Sovereign Hotel-Albany ℍ ❀
(518) 489-2981. **$79-$159.** 1228 Western Ave 12203. I-90 exit 1S, 1 mi e on US 20 (Western Ave). Int corridors. **Pets:** Medium. $21 daily fee/room. Designated rooms, service with restrictions, crate.
⬛ ⬛ ⬛ ⬛ ⬛ ⬛ ⬛ ⬛

▼▼▼ CrestHill Suites ℍ
(518) 454-0007. **$99-$159.** 1415 Washington Ave 12206. I-90 exit 2 westbound, just s on Fuller Rd, then just e; exit eastbound, just e. Int corridors. **Pets:** Medium. $15 daily fee/room. Designated rooms, service with restrictions, supervision. ⬛ ⬛ ⬛ ⬛ ⬛ ⬛

▼▼▼ Days Inn-Albany/SUNY ℍ
(518) 489-4423. **$79-$99.** 1230 Western Ave 12203. I-90 exit 1S, 0.7 mi e on US 20 (Western Ave). Int corridors. **Pets:** Accepted.
⬛ ⬛ ⬛ ⬛

▼▼ Extended Stay America Albany - SUNY ℍ
(518) 446-0680. **$100-$125.** 1395 Washington Ave 12206. I-90 exit 2 westbound, just s on Fuller Rd, then 0.5 mi e; exit eastbound, just e. Int corridors. **Pets:** Accepted. ⬛ ⬛ ⬛ ⬛

⚜ ▼▼▼▼ TownePlace Suites by Marriott Albany Downtown/Medical Center ℍ
(518) 860-1500. **$84-$230.** 22 Holland Ave 12209. I-90 exit 5 (Everett Rd), 2.6 mi on SR 5, then just e. Int corridors. **Pets:** Medium, other species. $150 one-time fee/room, $20 daily fee/pet. Designated rooms, service with restrictions, supervision.
⬛ ⬛ ⬛ ⬛ ⬛ ⬛

⚜ ▼▼▼▼ TownePlace Suites by Marriott Albany University Area ℍ
(518) 435-1900. **$98-$189.** 1379 Washington Ave 12206. I-90 exit 2 westbound, just s on Fuller Rd, then 0.6 mi e; exit eastbound, just e. Int corridors. **Pets:** Accepted. ⬛ ⬛ ⬛ ⬛ ⬛ ⬛ ⬛

ALLEGANY

The New Lantern Motel M ❀
(716) 373-1672. **Call for rates.** 4004 NYS Rt 417 14706. I-86 exit 24, 0.4 mi w on SR 417 (State St). Ext corridors. **Pets:** Large, dogs only. $20 one-time fee/room. Service with restrictions, supervision.
SAVE 🛜 ✕ 📶

AMHERST

Candlewood Suites H
(716) 688-2100. **$129-$199.** 20 Flint Rd 14226. I-290 exit 5B, just n on SR 263 (Millersport Hwy), then just w. Int corridors. **Pets:** $25 one-time fee/pet. Service with restrictions. 🍴M 🛜 ✕ 📶 💻

Comfort Inn University H
(716) 688-0811. **$76-$225.** 1 Flint Rd 14226. I-290 exit 5B, just n on SR 263 (Millersport Hwy), then just w. Int corridors. **Pets:** Large. $20 daily fee/pet. Designated rooms, service with restrictions, crate.
🏊 🛜 ✕ 📶 💻

DoubleTree by Hilton Buffalo-Amherst H
(716) 689-4414. **$129-$199.** 10 Flint Rd 14226. I-290 exit 5B, just n on SR 263 (Millersport Hwy), then just w. Int corridors. **Pets:** Accepted.
🍴 🍴M 🏊 🛜 ✕ 📶 💻

Homewood Suites Buffalo/Amherst H
(716) 833-2277. **$129-$219.** 1138 Millersport Hwy 14226. I-290 exit 5A, just s on SR 263. Int corridors. **Pets:** Accepted.
🍴 🍴M 🏊 🛜 📶 💻

Hyatt Place Buffalo/Amherst H
(716) 839-4040. **$89-$399.** 5020 Main St 14226. I-290 exit 7A (Main St/SR 5 W), just sw. Int corridors. **Pets:** Accepted.
SAVE 🍴M 🛜 ✕ 📶 💻

Red Roof PLUS+ University at Buffalo-Amherst M
(716) 689-7474. **$44-$179.** 42 Flint Rd 14226. I-290 exit 5B, just n on SR 263 (Millersport Hwy), then just w. Ext corridors. **Pets:** Accepted.
SAVE 🍴M 🛜 ✕ 📶 💻

Staybridge Suites-Buffalo/Amherst H
(716) 276-8750. **Call for rates.** 1290 Sweet Home Rd 14228. I-290 exit 5B, just n on SR 263 (Millersport Hwy) exit Maple Rd, 0.7 mi w, then just n. Int corridors. **Pets:** Accepted. 🍴 🍴M 🛜 📶 💻

ARMONK

La Quinta Inn & Suites Armonk H
(914) 273-9090. **$101-$196.** 94 Business Park Dr 10504. I-684 exit 3S northbound; exit 3 southbound, 0.3 mi s on SR 22. Int corridors.
Pets: Accepted. 🍴M 🛜 📶 💻

AUBURN

Days Inn Auburn/Finger Lakes Region H
(315) 252-7567. **$60-$100.** 37 William St 13021. Just s on SR 34, just w. Ext/int corridors. **Pets:** Accepted. 🛜 📶 💻

Inn at the Finger Lakes H
(315) 253-5000. **$69-$169.** 12 Seminary Ave 13021. Jct SR 34/38, just e on US 20/SR 5; center. Int corridors. **Pets:** Medium. $25 one-time fee/pet. Designated rooms, service with restrictions, supervision.
🍴M 🛜 ✕ 📶 💻

BALDWINSVILLE

Microtel Inn & Suites by Wyndham Baldwinsville/Syracuse H
(315) 635-9556. **$70-$129.** 131 Downer St 13027. SR 690 exit SR 31 W, 0.4 mi e. Int corridors. **Pets:** Accepted. 🍴M 🛜 ✕ 📶 💻

The Red Mill Inn H
(315) 635-4871. **Call for rates.** 4 Syracuse St 13027. Just w of jct SR 31 on SR 48; center. Int corridors. **Pets:** Accepted. 🛜 ✕ 📶 💻

BATAVIA

Budget Inn M
(585) 343-7921. **Call for rates.** 301 Oak St 14020. I-90 exit 48, just n on SR 98. Int corridors. **Pets:** Medium. $10 daily fee/pet. Designated rooms, no service, supervision. 🛜 📶

La Quinta Inn & Suites Batavia H
(585) 344-7000. **$67-$306.** 8200 Park Rd 14020. I-90 exit 48, just w. Int corridors. **Pets:** Accepted. SAVE 🍴M 🏊 🛜 ✕ 📶 💻

Quality Inn & Suites Palm Island Indoor Water Park H
(585) 344-2100. **$89-$1009.** 8250 Park Rd 14020. I-90 exit 48, just w. Int corridors. **Pets:** Accepted. SAVE 🍴 🍴M 🛜 📶 💻

Super 8 H
(585) 345-0800. **$55-$146.** 202 Oak St 14020. I-90 exit 48, just s. Int corridors. **Pets:** Medium. $10 daily fee/pet. Service with restrictions, supervision. ECO 🍴M 🛜 📶 💻

BATH

Bath Super 8 H
(607) 776-2187. **$50-$115, 3 day notice.** 333 W Morris St 14810. I-86 exit 38, just n. Int corridors. **Pets:** Accepted. 🛜 📶 💻

Microtel Inn & Suites by Wyndham Bath H
(607) 776-5333. **$70-$130.** 370 W Morris St 14810. I-86 exit 38, just n. Int corridors. **Pets:** Accepted. 🍴M 🛜 ✕ 📶 💻

BINGHAMTON

Comfort Inn of Binghamton H
(607) 724-3297. **$110-$184.** 1000 Upper Front St 13905. I-81 exit 6 southbound, 2 mi s on US 11 (Front St); exit 5 northbound, 1 mi n on US 11 (Front St). Int corridors. **Pets:** Medium, other species. $10 daily fee/pet. Designated rooms, service with restrictions, supervision.
🍴M 🏊 🛜 ✕ 📶 💻

DoubleTree by Hilton-Binghamton H ❀
(607) 722-7575. **$129-$209.** 225 Water St 13901. SR 17 exit 72 to US 11 (Front St), 1 mi s, just e on E Clinton St, then just s; downtown. Int corridors. **Pets:** Medium. $35 one-time fee/room. Designated rooms, service with restrictions, supervision.
📶 🍴 🍴M 🏊 ⊠ 🛜 ✕ 📶 💻

Holiday Inn Binghamton H ❀
(607) 722-1212. **$109-$189.** 2-8 Hawley St 13901. Downtown. Int corridors. **Pets:** Other species. $40 one-time fee/room. Service with restrictions, supervision. SAVE 🍴M 🛜 ✕ 📶 💻

Microtel Inn & Suites by Wyndham Binghamton H
(607) 677-0321. **Call for rates.** 400 Prospect St 13905. I-86 exit 71 (Airport Road), just s. Int corridors. **Pets:** Accepted.
SAVE 🍴 🍴M 🛜 ✕ 📶 💻

BLASDELL

Econo Lodge South M
(716) 825-7530. **$58-$158.** 4344 Milestrip Rd 14219. I-90 exit 56, just e on SR 179. Ext corridors. **Pets:** Accepted. 🛜 💻

BOHEMIA

La Quinta Inn & Suites Islip Macarthur Airport H
(631) 881-7700. **$86-$269.** 10 Aero Rd 11716. I-495 exit 57, 5.1 mi se on SR 454, just s on Johnson Ave, then just e. Int corridors.
Pets: Accepted. 🍴 🍴M 🛜 📶 💻

BOWMANSVILLE

▲▲▲ **▼▼▼** **Red Roof Inn Buffalo Niagara Airport** **M**
(716) 633-1100. **$44-$170.** 146 Maple Dr 14026. Just e of SR 78; just
n of entrance to I-90 (New York State Thruway) exit 49. Ext corridors.
Pets: Accepted. [SAVE] [&M] [wifi] [X] [📞] [🖥]

BREWERTON

▼▼▼ **Days Inn Brewerton/Syracuse** **H**
(315) 676-3222. **$61-$129.** 5552 Bartell Rd 13029. I-81 exit 31 (Bartell
Rd), just w. Int corridors. **Pets:** Accepted.
[🍴] [&M] [wifi] [X] [📞] [🖥]

BRIDGEHAMPTON

▼▼▼ **▼▼▼** **Topping Rose House** **H**
(631) 537-0870. **Call for rates.** 1 Bridgehampton-Sag Harbor Tpke
11932. Jct SR 27 (Montauk Hwy); northeast corner. Ext/int corridors.
Pets: Accepted. [🍴] [X] [wifi] [X] [📞] [🖥]

BROCKPORT

▲▲▲ **▼▼▼** **Dollinger's Inn and Suites** **H**
(585) 395-1000. **$75-$150.** 4908 Lake Rd S 14420. On SR 19 S, just s
of jct SR 31. Int corridors. **Pets:** Other species. $25 one-time fee/room.
Designated rooms, service with restrictions, crate. [SAVE] [wifi] [📞] [🖥]

BROOKLYN *(Restaurants p. 619)*

▲▲▲ **▼▼▼▼** **Aloft New York Brooklyn** **H** ❀
(718) 256-3833. **Call for rates.** 216 Duffield St 11201. Between Willoughby St and Fulton Mall. Int corridors. **Pets:** Medium. $100 deposit/
room. Designated rooms, service with restrictions, supervision.
[SAVE] [🍴] [&M] [🏊] [wifi] [X] [📞] [🖥]

▲▲▲ **▼▼▼▼** **The Dazzler Brooklyn Hotel** **H**
(718) 329-9537. **$109-$349.** 85 Flatbush Ave Ext 11201. Corner of Flatbush Ave and Tillary St. Int corridors. **Pets:** Accepted.
[SAVE] [🍴] [&M] [wifi] [X] [📞] [🖥]

▲▲▲ **▼▼▼▼** **Even Hotel Brooklyn** **H**
(718) 552-3800. **Call for rates.** 46 Nevins St 11217. Nevins and
Schermerhorn sts; downtown. Int corridors. **Pets:** Accepted.
[SAVE] [🍴] [&M] [wifi] [X] [📞] [🖥]

▼▼▼ **Fairfield Inn & Suites by Marriott New
York-Brooklyn** **H**
(718) 522-4000. **$97-$417.** 181 3rd Ave 11217. Jct Butler St; in Park
Slope. Int corridors. **Pets:** Accepted. [&M] [wifi] [X] [📞] [🖥]

▲▲▲ **▼▼▼▼** **Holiday Inn Brooklyn Downtown** **H**
(718) 624-2211. **$129-$499.** 300 Schermerhorn St 11217. Between Nevins and Bond sts; downtown. Int corridors. **Pets:** Accepted.
[SAVE] [🍴] [&M] [X] [wifi] [X] [📞] [🖥]

▼▼▼ **Holiday Inn Express Brooklyn** **H**
(718) 797-1133. **Call for rates.** 625 Union St 11215. Between 3rd and
4th aves. Int corridors. **Pets:** Accepted. [&M] [wifi] [X] [📞] [🖥]

▲▲▲ **▼▼▼▼** **Hotel Indigo Brooklyn** **H**
(718) 254-7800. **$199-$1590.** 229 Duffield St 11201. Between Willoughby St and Fulton Mall. Int corridors. **Pets:** Medium. $75 one-time
fee/pet. Service with restrictions, crate.
[SAVE] [🍴] [&M] [wifi] [X] [📞] [🖥]

▼▼▼ **McCarren Hotel & Pool** **H**
(718) 218-7500. **Call for rates.** 160 N 12th St 11249. In Williamsburg;
between Bedford Ave and Berry St. Int corridors. **Pets:** Accepted.
[🍴] [&M] [🏊] [X] [wifi] [X] [📞] [🖥]

▲▲▲ **▼▼▼▼** **NU Hotel Brooklyn** **H**
(718) 852-8585. **Call for rates.** 85 Smith St 11201. Between Atlantic
Ave and State St. Int corridors. **Pets:** Accepted.
[SAVE] [&M] [X] [wifi] [X] [📞] [🖥]

▼▼▼ **Red Lion Inn & Suites Brooklyn** **H**
(718) 855-9600. **Call for rates.** 279 Butler St 11217. In Park Slope;
between 3rd Ave and Nevins St. Int corridors. **Pets:** Accepted.
[&M] [wifi] [X] [📞] [🖥]

▲▲▲ **▼▼▼▼** **Sheraton Brooklyn New York Hotel** **H**
(718) 855-1900. **$199-$1999.** 228 Duffield St 11201. Between Willoughby St and Fulton Mall. Int corridors. **Pets:** Accepted.
[SAVE] [🍴] [&M] [🏊] [📶] [X] [🖥]

▲▲▲ **▼▼▼** **Super 8 Brooklyn** **H**
(718) 534-0451. **$117-$350.** 267 3rd Ave 11215. Between Union and
President sts; downtown. Int corridors. **Pets:** Accepted.
[SAVE] [🍴] [&M] [wifi] [X] [📞] [🖥]

▲▲▲ **▼▼▼** **Wyndham Garden Brooklyn Sunset
Park** **H** ❀
(718) 972-0900. **$85-$339.** 457 39th St 11232. Between 4th and 5th
aves. Int corridors. **Pets:** Small. $50 daily fee/pet. Designated rooms,
service with restrictions, supervision.
[SAVE] [🍴] [&M] [wifi] [X] [📞] [🖥]

BUFFALO

▲▲▲ **▼▼▼▼** **Hyatt Regency Buffalo Hotel and
Conference Center** **H** ❀
(716) 856-1234. **$89-$319.** 2 Fountain Plaza 14202. I-190 exit 8, just se
on Niagara St, just ne on Carolina St, 0.4 mi e on W Huron St, then
just s on Pearl St. Int corridors. **Pets:** Medium, dogs only. $100 deposit/
pet. Service with restrictions. [SAVE] [🍴] [🏊] [wifi] [X] [📞] [🖥]

CALCIUM

▼▼▼ **Microtel Inn by Wyndham Calcium/Near Fort
Drum** **H**
(315) 629-5000. **$55-$70.** 8000 Virginia Smith Dr 13616. Jct SR 342
and US 11, just s. Int corridors. **Pets:** Accepted.
[&M] [wifi] [X] [📞] [🖥]

CANANDAIGUA

▲▲▲ **▼▼▼▼** **The Inn On The Lake** **H**
(585) 394-7800. **$117-$196.** 770 S Main St 14424. I-90 exit 44 (SR
332), just s of jct US 20 and SR 5. Int corridors. **Pets:** Dogs only. $20
daily fee/pet. Designated rooms, service with restrictions, crate.
[SAVE] [🍴] [&M] [🏊] [X] [wifi] [X] [📞] [🖥]

▼▼▼▼ **Morgan-Samuels Inn/BB & Spa** **BB**
(585) 394-9232. **Call for rates.** 2920 Smith Rd 14424. I-90 exit 43, 4.1
mi s on SR 21, just e on SR 488 to East Ave/Smith Rd, then 2 mi s.
Ext/int corridors. **Pets:** Accepted. [🍴] [wifi] [X] [🖥] [📞]

▼▼▼ **Super 8** **H**
(585) 396-7224. **$60-$114.** 4450 Eastern Blvd 14424. Jct SR 332, 5
and US 20, 0.5 mi e. Int corridors. **Pets:** Other species. $10 daily fee/
room. Service with restrictions. [&M] [wifi] [📞] [🖥]

CARLE PLACE *(Restaurants p. 619)*

▼▼▼ **Homewood Suites by Hilton Carle Place-Garden
City** **H**
(516) 747-0230. **$189-$399.** 40 Westbury Ave 11514. Jct SR 25, 0.5 mi
s on Glen Cove Rd, just w. Int corridors. **Pets:** Accepted.
[&M] [wifi] [X] [📞] [🖥]

CARTHAGE

▲▲▲ **▼▼▼** **Pleasant Night Inn** **H**
(315) 493-2500. **$75-$115.** 30 N Broad St 13619. Just se on SR 126.
Int corridors. **Pets:** Accepted. [SAVE] [🍴] [&M] [wifi] [X] [📞] [🖥]

CAZENOVIA

▼▼▼▼ **Brae Loch Inn** **CI**
(315) 655-3431. **Call for rates.** 5 Albany St 13035. On US 20. Int corridors. **Pets:** Accepted. ⊤⊤ 🛜 ✕ 🖥

CHEEKTOWAGA

ΔΔΔ⁄ ▼▼▼▼ **Aloft Buffalo Airport** **H** 🐾
(716) 626-1800. **Call for rates.** 4219 Genesee St 14225. I-90 exit 51E, 1.5 mi e on SR 33, then just s on Burgess Blvd. Int corridors. **Pets:** Designated rooms, service with restrictions, supervision.
SAVE 🕹M 🛜 ✕ 🖥 🖳

ΔΔΔ⁄ ▼▼▼▼ **Comfort Inn-Cheektowaga** **H**
(716) 896-2800. **$90-$400.** 475 Dingens St 14206. I-190 exit 1, just n, then just e. Int corridors. **Pets:** Accepted.
SAVE 🛏 🛜 ✕ 🖥 🖳

▼▼▼ **Comfort Suites-Buffalo Airport** **H**
(716) 633-6000. **$71-$230.** 901 Dick Rd 14225. I-90 exit 51E, 1.2 mi e on SR 33 exit Dick Rd, just s. Int corridors. **Pets:** Accepted.
🕹M 🛏 🛜 ✕ 🖥 🖳

▼▼▼ **Holiday Inn-Buffalo Airport** **H**
(716) 634-6969. **$79-$209.** 4600 Genesee St 14225. I-90 exit 51E, 2.3 mi e on SR 33. Int corridors. **Pets:** Medium. $50 one-time fee/room. Service with restrictions, supervision.
⊤⊤ 🕹M 🛏 ✕ 🛜 ✕ 🖥 🖳

▼▼▼ **Holiday Inn Express Hotel & Suites-Buffalo Airport** **H**
(716) 631-8700. **$159-$189.** 131 Buell Ave 14225. I-90 exit 51E, 1.4 mi e on SR 33, then just s. Int corridors. **Pets:** Other species. $50 one-time fee/pet. Service with restrictions, crate.
🕹M 🛏 🛜 ✕ 🖥 🖳

▼▼▼ **Home2 Suites-Buffalo Airport/Galleria Mall** **H** 🐾
(716) 249-2700. **Call for rates.** 1999 Walden Ave 14225. I-290 exit 52E, just e, just s on Duke Rd, then just w. Int corridors. **Pets:** Medium, other species. $75 one-time fee/room. Service with restrictions, crate. 🕹M 🛜 🖥 🖳

▼▼▼ **Homewood Suites by Hilton** **H**
(716) 685-0700. **$129-$219.** 760 Dick Rd 14225. I-90 exit 51E, 1.2 mi e on SR 33 exit Dick Rd, just s. Int corridors. **Pets:** Accepted.
⊤⊤ 🕹M 🛏 🛜 🖥 🖳

▼▼▼ **Oak Tree Inn** **H**
(716) 681-2600. **Call for rates.** 3475 Union Rd 14225. I-90 exit 52E, just e on Walden Ave, then just n on SR 277 (Union Rd). Int corridors. **Pets:** Accepted. 🕹M 🛜 ✕ 🖥 🖳

▼▼▼ **Residence Inn by Marriott Buffalo-Cheektowaga** **H**
(716) 892-5410. **$116-$255.** 107 Anderson Rd 14225. I-90 exit 52W, just w on Walden Ave, then just s. Int corridors. **Pets:** Other species. $100 one-time fee/room. Service with restrictions, crate.
🕹M 🛏 🛜 ✕ 🖥 🖳

▼▼▼ **TownePlace Suites by Marriott-Buffalo Airport** **H** 🐾
(716) 839-1880. **$84-$208.** 4265 Genesee St 14225. I-90 exit 51E, 1.8 mi e on SR 33. Int corridors. **Pets:** Large, other species. $75 one-time fee/room. Service with restrictions. 🔌 ⊤⊤ 🕹M 🛜 ✕ 🖥 🖳

CHESTER

ΔΔΔ⁄ ▼▼▼▼ **Holiday Inn Express Hotel & Suites Chester/Monroe/Goshen** **H**
(845) 469-3000. **Call for rates.** 2 Bryle Pl 10918. SR 17 exit 126, just n on SR 94, then just w on SR 17M (Brookside Ave). Int corridors.
Pets: Accepted. SAVE 🕹M 🛏 🛜 ✕ 🖥 🖳

CICERO

ΔΔΔ⁄ ◆◆ **Budget Inn** **M**
(315) 458-3510. **$55-$275, 7 day notice.** 901 South Bay Rd 13039. I-481 exit 10, just n. Ext corridors. **Pets:** Small, dogs only. $10 daily fee/pet. Designated rooms, service with restrictions, supervision.
SAVE 🛜 🖥 🖳

ΔΔΔ⁄ ▼▼▼▼ **Comfort Suites Cicero Syracuse North** **H**
(315) 752-0150. **$99-$239.** 5875 Carmenica Dr 13039. I-80 exit 31, just e. Int corridors. **Pets:** Small. $25 one-time fee/room. Service with restrictions, supervision. SAVE 🕹M 🛏 🛜 ✕ 🖥 🖳

CLARENCE

ΔΔΔ⁄ ▼▼▼▼ **Asa Ransom House** **CI**
(716) 759-2315. **$139-$198, 7 day notice.** 10529 Main St 14031. Jct SR 78 (Transit Rd), 5.3 mi e on SR 5 (Main St). Int corridors.
Pets: Medium, dogs only. $50 deposit/room. Designated rooms, service with restrictions. SAVE ECO ⊤⊤ 🕹M 🛜 ✕ 🖥

ΔΔΔ⁄ ▼▼▼▼ **Staybridge Suites-Buffalo Airport** **H**
(716) 810-7829. **$139-$229, 3 day notice.** 8005 Sheridan Dr 14221. I-90 exit 49, 3 mi n on SR 78 (Transit Rd); jct SR 324; next to Eastern Hills Mall. Int corridors. **Pets:** Accepted. SAVE 🕹M 🛏 🛜 🖥 🖳

CLAY

▼▼▼▼ **Hampton Inn by Hilton - Syracuse/Clay** **H** 🐾
(315) 622-3443. **$99-$189.** 3948 SR 31 13090. SR 481 exit 12, just w. Int corridors. **Pets:** Medium, dogs only. $100 deposit/pet. Service with restrictions, supervision. 🕹M 🛏 🛜 🖥 🖳

CLAYTON

▼▼▼ **Fair Wind Lodge** **M**
(315) 686-5251. **Call for rates.** 38201 NYS Rt 12E 13624. 2.3 mi sw. Ext corridors. **Pets:** Accepted. 🛏 🛜 ✕ 🔏 🖥 🖳

CLINTON

▼▼▼▼ **Amidst the Hedges** **BB**
(315) 723-2035. **Call for rates.** 180 Sanford Ave 13323. SR 412 (College St), 0.3 mi n on Elm St. Int corridors. **Pets:** Accepted.
✕ 🛜 ✕ 🖥 🖳

COBLESKILL

ΔΔΔ⁄ ▼▼▼ **Rodeway Inn & Suites** **H**
(518) 234-4321. **Call for rates.** 121 Burgin Dr 12043. I-88 exit 21 eastbound on SR 7, 0.8 mi e of jct SR 10; exit 22 westbound, 2.9 mi w on SR 7. Int corridors. **Pets:** Other species. $25 daily fee/room. Designated rooms, supervision. SAVE ⊤⊤ 🛏 🛜 ✕ 🖥 🖳

▼▼▼ **Super 8** **H**
(518) 234-4888. **$85-$140.** 955 E Main St 12043. I-88 exit 22 westbound, 2.4 mi w on SR 7; exit 21 eastbound, 3.1 mi e on SR 7. Int corridors. **Pets:** Dogs only. $10 daily fee/pet. Service with restrictions, supervision. 🕹M 🛜 🖥 🖳

COLONIE

ΔΔΔ⁄ ▼▼▼▼ **Best Western Albany Airport Inn** **H**
(518) 458-1000. **$79-$149.** 200 Wolf Rd 12205. I-87 exit 4, just se to Wolf Rd, then just sw. Int corridors. **Pets:** $20 daily fee/room. Service with restrictions, supervision. SAVE ⊤⊤ 🛏 🛜 ✕ 🖥 🖳

ΔΔΔ⁄ ▼▼▼ **Cocca's Inn & Suites, Wolf Rd** **M**
(518) 459-2240. **$59-$149.** 2 Wolf Rd 12205. I-87 exit 2E, just e. Ext/int corridors. **Pets:** Very small, other species. $10 daily fee/pet. Service with restrictions, supervision. SAVE 🕹M 🛜 🖥 🖳

▼▼▼▼ **Radisson Hotel Albany** **H**
(518) 458-7250. **$99-$199.** 205 Wolf Rd 12205. I-87 exit 4, 0.3 mi se. Int corridors. **Pets:** Accepted. ⊤⊤ 🕹M 🛏 ✕ 🛜 ✕ 🖥 🖳

◇◇◇ ▼▼▼ Travelodge Inn & Suites, Albany Airport H

(518) 459-5670. $60-$80. 42 Wolf Rd 12205. I-87 exit 2E, just e, then just n. Int corridors. **Pets:** Very small, other species. $10 daily fee/pet. Service with restrictions, supervision. [SAVE] [M] 🛰 ☒ 🖥 💻

CORNING

▼▼▼ Staybridge Suites H

(607) 936-7800. **Call for rates.** 201 Townley Ave 14830. I-86/SR 17 exit 46, just s. Int corridors. **Pets:** Large, other species. $150 one-time fee/room. Designated rooms, service with restrictions, crate.

[M] 🛰 ☒ 🖥 💻

CORNWALL

▼▼▼▼ Cromwell Manor Inn BB

(845) 534-7136. **Call for rates.** 174 Angola Rd 12518. Jct US 9W and SR 94, 5.5 mi s on US 9W, 0.5 mi w. Ext/int corridors. **Pets:** Accepted.

[||] [M] 🛰 ☒ ☎

DUNKIRK

◇◇◇ ▼▼▼ Best Western Dunkirk & Fredonia Inn H

(716) 366-7100. $90-$239. 3912 Vineyard Dr 14048. I-90 exit 59, continue straight. Int corridors. **Pets:** $10 daily fee/pet. Service with restrictions, supervision. [SAVE] [M] 🛰 ☒ 🖥 💻

◇◇◇ ▼▼▼ Comfort Inn H

(716) 672-4450. $125-$240. 3925 Vineyard Dr 14048. I-90 exit 59, continue straight. Int corridors. **Pets:** $10 daily fee/pet. Service with restrictions, supervision. [SAVE] [M] 🛰 ☒ 🖥 💻

EAST GREENBUSH

▼▼▼▼ Residence Inn by Marriott Albany East Greenbush/Tech Valley H

(518) 720-3600. $105-$296. 3 Tech Valley Dr 12061. I-90 exit 9, just e. Int corridors. **Pets:** Other species. $75 one-time fee/room. Service with restrictions, crate. [||] [M] 🛰 ☒ 🖥 💻

EAST HAMPTON *(Restaurants p. 619)*

▼▼▼▼ c/o The Maidstone H

(631) 324-5006. **Call for rates.** 207 Main St 11937. Jct SR 114, just s on SR 27. Ext/int corridors. **Pets:** Accepted. [||] 🛰 ☒ 🖥 💻

EAST SYRACUSE

▼▼ Candlewood Suites, East Syracuse-Carrier Circle H

(315) 432-1684. **Call for rates.** 6550 Baptist Way 13057. I-90 exit 35 (Carrier Cir) to SR 298 E to Old Collamer Rd, just n. Int corridors. **Pets:** Accepted. [M] 🛰 🖥 💻

◇◇◇ ▼▼▼ CrestHill Suites H

(315) 432-5595. $109-$249. 6410 New Venture Gear Dr 13057. I-90 exit 35 (Carrier Cir) to SR 298 E, 0.7 mi s, then just e. Int corridors. **Pets:** Medium. $15 daily fee/room. Designated rooms, service with restrictions, crate. [SAVE] [||] 🛰 🛰 ☒ 🖥 💻

◇◇◇ ▼▼▼ Homewood Suites by Hilton Syracuse-Carrier Circle H

(315) 433-1009. **Call for rates.** 6006 Fair Lakes Rd 13057. I-90 exit 35 (Carrier Cir) to SR 298 E, 0.7 mi to New Venture Gear Dr, then just e. Int corridors. **Pets:** $75 one-time fee/room. Designated rooms, service with restrictions, crate. [SAVE] [||] [M] 🛰 ☒ 🖥 💻

◇◇◇ ▼▼▼ Ramada Carrier Circle H

(315) 437-2761. $71-$399. 6555 Old Collamer Rd S 13057. I-90 exit 35 (Carrier Cir) to SR 298 E, just n. Int corridors. **Pets:** Medium. $20 daily fee/pet. Designated rooms, service with restrictions, supervision.

[SAVE] [||] 🛰 🛰 ☒ 🖥 💻

◇◇◇ ▼▼▼ Residence Inn by Marriott Syracuse H

(315) 432-4488. $99-$306. 6420 Yorktown Cir 13057. I-90 exit 35 (Carrier Cir) to SR 298 E, just n. Ext/int corridors. **Pets:** Accepted.

[SAVE] [M] 🛰 🛰 ☒ 🖥 💻

ELLICOTTVILLE

▼▼▼ The Jefferson Inn of Ellicottville BB ❀

(716) 699-5869. $99-$289, 30 day notice. 3 Jefferson St 14731. Just n of jct US 219 and SR 242. Ext/int corridors. **Pets:** Other species. $15 daily fee/pet. Designated rooms, service with restrictions.

🛰 ☒ 🖥 💻

ELMIRA

▼▼ Coachman Motor Lodge M

(607) 733-5526. $90-$120. 908 Pennsylvania Ave 14904. I-86/SR 17 exit 56, 0.7 mi w on SR 352 (Church St), 0.5 mi s on Madison Ave (which becomes Pennsylvania Ave), then 1.4 mi s. Ext corridors. **Pets:** Small. $20 daily fee/pet. Designated rooms, service with restrictions, supervision. 🛰 🖥 💻

▼▼▼ Holiday Inn-Elmira Riverview H

(607) 734-4211. $99-$300. 760 E Water St 14901. I-86/SR 17 exit 56, 0.5 mi s. Int corridors. **Pets:** $25 one-time fee/room. Designated rooms, service with restrictions, supervision. [||] 🛰 🛰 ☒ 🖥 💻

EVANS MILLS

▼▼▼ Candlewood Suites Watertown/Fort Drum H

(315) 629-6990. $89-$160. 26513 Herrick Dr 13637. Jct US 11, just n. Int corridors. **Pets:** Large, other species. $150 one-time fee/pet. Service with restrictions, crate. [M] 🛰 ☒ 🖥 💻

FARMINGTON

◇◇◇ ▼ Budget Inn M

(585) 924-5020. $54-$149, 3 day notice. 6001 Rt 96 14425. I-90 exit 44, 1 mi s on SR 332, then just e. Ext corridors. **Pets:** Small, dogs only. $15 daily fee/pet. Designated rooms, service with restrictions, supervision. [SAVE] 🛰 🖥 💻

FAYETTEVILLE

▼▼ Craftsman Inn and Conference Center H

(315) 637-8000. **Call for rates.** 7300 E Genesee St (SR 5) 13066. Across from Fayetteville Towne Center. Int corridors. **Pets:** Accepted.

[||] [M] 🛰 ☒ 🖥 💻

FISHKILL

▼▼ Extended Stay America Fishkill Route 9 H

(845) 897-2800. $105-$150. 25 Merritt Blvd 12524. I-84 exit 13, just n. Int corridors. **Pets:** Accepted. [M] 🛰 ☒ 🖥 💻

▼▼ Extended Stay America-Fishkill-Westage H

(845) 896-0592. $95-$140. 55 W Merritt Blvd 12524. I-84 exit 13, just n. Int corridors. **Pets:** Accepted. [M] 🛰 ☒ 🖥 💻

◇◇◇ ▼▼▼ Hyatt House Fishkill/Poughkeepsie H

(845) 897-5757. $99-$289. 100 Westage Business Center Dr 12524. I-84 exit 13, just n on US 9, just w on Merritt Blvd, then just s. Int corridors. **Pets:** Small, dogs only. $75 one-time fee/room. Designated rooms, service with restrictions, crate.

[SAVE] [M] 🛰 🛰 ☒ 🖥 💻

FLUSHING

▼▼ Extended Stay America-NY City-LaGuardia Airport H

(718) 357-3661. $135-$230. 18-30 Whitestone Expwy 11357. In Whitestone; I-678 (Van Wyck Expwy) exit 15, just w. Int corridors. **Pets:** Accepted. [||] [M] 🛰 ☒ 🖥 💻

▼▼▼ **The Parc Hotel** 🅗 ❄️
(718) 358-8897. **$129-$999, 3 day notice.** 39-16 College Point Blvd 11354. In Flushing; Whitestone Expwy exit 14, just s on Linden Pl, just w on 28th ave. Int corridors. **Pets:** Medium. $150 one-time fee/room. Service with restrictions. 🚹 🛜 ✕ 📶 💻

🅐🅐🅐 ▼▼▼ **Sheraton LaGuardia East Hotel** 🅗
(718) 460-6666. **$189-$459, 3 day notice.** 135-20 39th Ave 11354. In Flushing; Grand Central Pkwy to Northern Blvd, 1 mi e to Main St, 0.3 mi s to 39th Ave, then just w. Int corridors. **Pets:** Accepted.
SAVE 🍴 🛜 ✕ 📶 💻

GARDEN CITY

🅐🅐🅐 ▼▼▼▼ **The Garden City Hotel** 🅗 ❄️
(516) 747-3000. **$209-$699.** 45 7th St 11530. 0.3 mi w of jct Franklin and Stewart aves to Hilton Ave, then just s. Int corridors. **Pets:** Medium. $75 daily fee/pet. Designated rooms, service with restrictions, crate. SAVE 🍴 🚹 🏊 ✕ 🛜 ✕ 📶 💻

▼▼ **La Quinta Inn & Suites Garden City** 🅗
(516) 705-9000. **$126-$471.** 821 Stewart Ave 11530. Meadowbrook Pkwy exit 3, 0.5 mi w. Int corridors. **Pets:** Accepted.
🍴 🚹 🛜 📶 💻

GATES

▼▼▼ **Lexington Hotel Rochester Airport** 🅗
(585) 328-6000. **$69-$129.** 911 Brooks Ave 14624. I-390 exit 18A (SR 204), just e. Int corridors. **Pets:** Accepted.
🍴 🏊 ✕ 🛜 📶 💻

▼▼ **Quality Inn-Rochester Airport** 🅗
(585) 464-8800. **$64-$159.** 1273 Chili Ave 14624. I-390 exit 19, just w on SR 33. Int corridors. **Pets:** Medium. $25 daily fee/pet. Designated rooms, no service, supervision. 🍴 🏊 🛜 ✕ 📶 💻

GENESEO

▼▼ **Quality Inn Geneseo** 🅗
(585) 243-0500. **$106-$210.** 4242 Lakeville Rd 14454. I-390 exit 8, 3.4 mi w on US 20A. Int corridors. **Pets:** Accepted.
🚹 🏊 🛜 ✕ 📶 💻

GENEVA

🅐🅐🅐 ▼▼▼▼ **Cobtree Vacation Rentals Resort** 🆅🅷
(315) 789-1144. **$140-$680, 90 day notice.** 440-458 Armstrong Rd 14456. 3 mi n on SR 14. Ext corridors. **Pets:** Accepted.
SAVE 🍴 🛜 ✕ 📶 💻

▼▼ **Microtel Inn & Suites by Wyndham Geneva** 🅗
(315) 789-7890. **$59-$155.** 550 Hamilton St 14456. Jct SR 14, 2 mi w on US 20/SR 5. Int corridors. **Pets:** Accepted.
🚹 🛜 ✕ 📶 💻

▼▼▼▼ **Ramada Geneva Lakefront** 🅗
(315) 789-0400. **$89-$359.** 41 Lakefront Dr 14456. Just e of US 20, SR 14 and 5; downtown. Int corridors. **Pets:** Accepted.
🍴 🚹 🏊 🛜 ✕ 📶 💻

GLENS FALLS

🅐🅐🅐 ▼▼▼ **Queensbury Hotel** 🅗
(518) 792-1121. **$89-$309.** 88 Ridge St 12801. Corner of Maple St. Int corridors. **Pets:** Dogs only. $50 daily fee/pet. Designated rooms.
SAVE 🍴 🏊 ✕ 🛜 ✕ 📶 💻

GREAT NECK

▼▼▼ **The Andrew Hotel** 🅗 ❄️
(516) 482-2900. **$179-$289.** 75 N Station Plaza 11021. Jct SR 25A, 0.8 mi n on Middle Neck Rd, just e. Int corridors. **Pets:** Medium. $150 one-time fee/pet. Service with restrictions, crate.
🍴 🚹 🛜 ✕ 📶 💻

GREECE

▼▼ **Comfort Inn Greece** 🅗
(585) 621-5700. **$95-$194.** 1501 W Ridge Rd 14615. Jct I-390 and SR 104 (Ridge Rd), 0.5 mi e. Int corridors. **Pets:** Other species. $15 daily fee/pet. Service with restrictions, crate. 🛜 ✕ 📶 💻

▼▼▼ **Hampton Inn by Hilton Rochester-Greece** 🅗
(585) 663-6070. **$109-$179.** 500 Center Place Dr 14615. I-390 exit 24A, just e on SR 104 (Ridge Rd), then just n on Buckman Rd. Int corridors. **Pets:** Accepted. 🚹 🏊 🛜 ✕ 📶 💻

▼▼▼ **Residence Inn by Marriott Rochester West/Greece** 🅗
(585) 865-2090. **$104-$303.** 500 Paddy Creek Cir 14615. I-390 exit 24A, just e on SR 104 (Ridge Rd), just s on Hoover Dr, then just w. Int corridors. **Pets:** Accepted. 🚹 🏊 🛜 ✕ 📶 💻

HAMBURG

▼▼ **Comfort Inn & Suites** 🅗
(716) 648-2922. **$70-$209.** 3615 Commerce Pl 14075. I-90 exit 57, just s on SR 75, then just w. Int corridors. **Pets:** Accepted.
🚹 🏊 🛜 ✕ 📶 💻

🅐🅐🅐 ▼▼▼ **Red Roof Inn Buffalo Hamburg** 🅜
(716) 648-7222. **$49-$179.** 5370 Camp Rd 14075. I-90 exit 57, just s on SR 75, then just w. Ext corridors. **Pets:** Accepted.
SAVE 🛜 ✕ 📶 💻

HANCOCK

▼ **Smith's Colonial Motel** 🅜
(607) 637-2989. **Call for rates.** 23085 State Hwy 97 13783. SR 17 exit 87, 2.7 mi s. Ext corridors. **Pets:** Accepted. 🍴 🛜 ✕ 📶 💻

HAUPPAUGE

🅐🅐🅐 ▼▼▼ **Residence Inn by Marriott Long Island-Hauppauge/Islandia** 🅗
(631) 724-4188. **$118-$329.** 850 Veterans Memorial Hwy 11788. I-495 exit 57, 1.2 mi nw. Int corridors. **Pets:** Accepted.
SAVE 🍴 🚹 🏊 🛜 ✕ 📶 💻

HENRIETTA

▼▼▼ **Homewood Suites by Hilton-Rochester** 🅗
(585) 334-9150. **$104-$214.** 2095 Hylan Dr 14623. I-390 exit 13, just e. Int corridors. **Pets:** Accepted. 🚹 🏊 🛜 📶 💻

▼ **Microtel Inn by Wyndham Henrietta/Rochester** 🅗
(585) 334-3400. **$60-$130.** 905 Lehigh Station Rd 14467. I-390 exit 12 northbound; exit 12A southbound, just w on SR 253. Int corridors. **Pets:** Medium. $25 daily fee/pet. Crate. 🛜 📶

▼▼▼ **Radisson Rochester Airport** 🅗 ❄️
(585) 475-1910. **$109-$159.** 175 Jefferson Rd 14623. I-390 exit 14A southbound; exit 14 northbound, 3 mi w on SR 252 (Jefferson Rd). Int corridors. **Pets:** Medium. $25 one-time fee/pet. Designated rooms, service with restrictions, supervision. 🍴 🚹 🏊 🛜 ✕ 📶 💻

🅐🅐🅐 ▼▼▼ **Red Roof Inn Rochester Henrietta** 🅜
(585) 359-1100. **$44-$139.** 4820 W Henrietta Rd 14467. I-390 exit 12 northbound; exit 12A southbound, 0.5 mi w on SR 253, then just s on SR 15 (Henrietta Rd). Ext corridors. **Pets:** Accepted.
SAVE 🚹 🛜 ✕ 📶 💻

▼▼▼ **Residence Inn by Marriott Rochester** 🅗
(585) 272-8850. **$95-$274.** 1300 Jefferson Rd 14623. I-390 exit 14A southbound, 0.5 mi e on SR 252 (Jefferson Rd); exit 14 northbound, just n on SR 15A, then 0.5 mi e on SR 252 (Jefferson Rd). Ext/int corridors. **Pets:** Accepted. 🚹 🏊 🛜 ✕ 📶 💻

▼▼▼▼ R I T Inn & Conference Center H
(585) 359-1800. **$94-$129.** 5257 W Henrietta Rd 14467. I-390 exit 12 northbound; exit 12A southbound, 0.5 mi w on SR 253, then 0.7 mi s. Int corridors. **Pets:** Other species. $50 one-time fee/room. Service with restrictions, supervision. ECO ▯▮ ⊇ ⊠ 🛜 ⊠ ▮ ▯

HERKIMER
AAA▷ ▼▼▼▼ Red Roof Inn & Suites-Herkimer M
(315) 866-0490. **$78-$150.** 100 Marginal Rd 13350. I-90 exit 30, just n on SR 28. Ext/int corridors. **Pets:** Accepted.
SAVE ⊇ 🛜 ⊠ ▮ ▯

HIGHLAND
▼▼▼ Super 8 M
(845) 691-6888. **$47-$180.** 3423 Rt 9W 12528. Just s of jct SR 299 and US 9W. Int corridors. **Pets:** Accepted. ▯▮ ᕒM 🛜 ▮ ▯

HOGANSBURG
▼▼▼▼ Comfort Inn & Suites Hogansburg H
(518) 358-1000. **$125-$299.** 865 State Route 37 13655. Jct SR 95, 0.3 mi w. Int corridors. **Pets:** Medium, other species. $10 daily fee/pet. Designated rooms, service with restrictions, supervision.
ᕒM ⊇ 🛜 ⊠ ▮ ▯

HORSEHEADS
▼▼▼ Candlewood Suites H
(607) 873-7676. **$79-$299.** 198 Colonial Dr 14845. I-86/SR 17 exit 51B westbound; exit 51A eastbound, just e. Int corridors. **Pets:** Accepted.
🛜 ⊠ ▮ ▯

HUNTINGTON
AAA▷ ▼▼▼ ▼▼▼ Oheka Castle Hotel & Estate CI
(631) 659-1400. **$395-$1095, 3 day notice.** 135 West Gate Dr 11743. Jct SR 25, 0.5 mi ne. Int corridors. **Pets:** Accepted.
SAVE ▯▮ ⊠ 🛜 ⊠ ▮

INLET
AAA▷ ▼ Marina Motel M
(315) 357-3883. **Call for rates.** 6 S Shore Rd 13360. Center. Ext corridors. **Pets:** $15 daily fee/pet. Designated rooms, service with restrictions, crate. SAVE ⊠ 🛜 ⊠ ▮

IRONDEQUOIT
▼▼▼▼ Holiday Inn Express H 🐾
(585) 342-0430. **$99-$209.** 2200 Goodman St N 14609. SR 104 exit Goodman St, just n. Int corridors. **Pets:** Other species. $75 deposit/room. Designated rooms, service with restrictions, crate.
ᕒM ⊇ 🛜 ⊠ ▮ ▯

ITHACA *(Restaurants p. 619)*
AAA▷ ▼▼▼ Best Western University Inn M
(607) 272-6100. **$149-$249.** 1020 Ellis Hollow Rd 14850. SR 79 E, 1 mi ne on Pine Tree Rd, just n; in East Hill Plaza. **Pets:** Medium. $20 daily fee/pet. Designated rooms, service with restrictions, supervision. SAVE ⊇ 🛜 ⊠ ▮ ▯

▼▼▼▼ Country Inn & Suites By Carlson H 🐾
(607) 256-1100. **Call for rates.** 1100 Danby Rd (SR 96B) 14850. 0.5 mi past entrance to Ithaca College and jct SR 96B. Int corridors. **Pets:** Medium, other species. $25 daily fee/pet. Designated rooms, service with restrictions, supervision. ᕒM ⊇ 🛜 ⊠ ▮ ▯

AAA▷ ▼▼▼▼ Hampton Inn by Hilton H
(607) 277-5500. **$129-$229.** 337 Elmira Rd 14850. On SR 13. Int corridors. **Pets:** Accepted. SAVE ᕒM ⊇ 🛜 ⊠ ▮ ▯

AAA▷ ▼▼▼▼ La Tourelle Hotel & Bistro Spa CI
(607) 273-2734. **Call for rates.** 1150 Danby Rd 14850. 2.7 mi s on SR 96B. Int corridors. **Pets:** Designated rooms, service with restrictions.
SAVE ECO ▯▮ ⊠ 🛜 ⊠ ▮ ▯

JAMAICA
▼▼▼▼ Radisson Hotel JFK Airport H
(718) 322-2300. **Call for rates.** 135-30 140th St 11436. In Jamaica; I-678 (Van Wyck Expwy) exit 2 (Rockaway Blvd), just e to 140th St, then s. Int corridors. **Pets:** Accepted. ▯▮ ᕒM 🛜 ⊠ ▮ ▯

AAA▷ ▼▼▼▼ Sheraton JFK Airport Hotel H
(718) 322-7190. **$159-$289.** 132-26 S Conduit Ave 11430. In Jamaica; between S Conduit and 149th aves; off Nassau Expwy. Int corridors.
Pets: Accepted. SAVE ▯▮ 🛜 ⊠ ▯

JAMESTOWN
AAA▷ ▼▼▼ Comfort Inn H 🐾
(716) 664-5920. **$100-$220.** 2800 N Main St 14701. I-86/SR 17 exit 12, just s on SR 60 (Main St). Int corridors. **Pets:** Small, dogs only. $25 one-time fee/pet. Designated rooms, service with restrictions, supervision. SAVE ᕒM 🛜 ⊠ ▮ ▯

JOHNSON CITY
AAA▷ ▼▼▼▼ Best Western Plus of Johnson City H
(607) 729-9194. **$89-$220.** 569 Harry L Dr 13790. SR 17 exit 70N, 0.3 mi n. Int corridors. **Pets:** Accepted. SAVE 🛜 ▮ ▯

AAA▷ ▼▼▼ La Quinta Inn Binghamton-Johnson City H
(607) 770-9333. **$93-$235.** 581 Harry L Dr 13790. SR 17 exit 70N, 0.3 mi n. Int corridors. **Pets:** Accepted. SAVE 🛜 ▮ ▯

AAA▷ ▼▼▼ Red Roof Inn Binghamton-Johnson City M
(607) 729-8940. **$49-$120.** 590 Fairview St 13790. SR 17 exit 70N, 0.3 mi n, then just n on Reynolds Rd. Ext corridors. **Pets:** Accepted.
SAVE 🛜 ⊠ ▮ ▯

JOHNSTOWN
▼▼▼ Holiday Inn H 🐾
(518) 762-4686. **$100-$175.** 308 N Comrie Ave 12095. Jct SR 30A and 29 E, 1.3 mi n. Int corridors. **Pets:** Medium. Designated rooms, service with restrictions, supervision. ⊟ ▯▮ ᕒM ⊇ 🛜 ⊠ ▮ ▯

▼▼▼ Microtel Inn & Suites by Wyndham Johnstown H
(518) 762-5425. **$76-$109.** 136 N Comrie Ave 12095. I-90 exit 28 (SR 30A), 4 mi n. Int corridors. **Pets:** Dogs only. $10 daily fee/pet. Designated rooms, service with restrictions, supervision.
ᕒM 🛜 ⊠ ▮ ▯

▼▼▼ Super 8 H
(518) 736-1800. **$70-$150.** 301 N Comrie Ave 12095. Jct SR 30A and 29 E, 1.2 mi n. Int corridors. **Pets:** Accepted. 🛜 ▮ ▯

KENMORE
▼ Super 8-Buffalo/Niagara Falls M 🐾
(716) 876-4020. **$48-$115.** 1288 Sheridan Dr 14217. I-190 exit 15, 1.5 mi e on SR 324 (Sheridan Dr); I-290 exit 1A 1 mi s on SR 384 (Delaware Ave), then 0.7 mi w. Int corridors. **Pets:** $100 deposit/pet. Service with restrictions, supervision. 🛜 ▮ ▯

KINGSTON
AAA▷ ▼▼▼▼ Best Western Plus Kingston Hotel & Conference Center H
(845) 338-0400. **$129-$269.** 503 Washington Ave 12401. I-87 exit 19, just e of traffic circle. Int corridors. **Pets:** Accepted.
SAVE ▯▮ ⊇ 🛜 ⊠ ▮ ▯

LAKE GEORGE

◇◇ Green Haven Resort M
(518) 668-2489. **Call for rates.** 3136 Lake Shore Dr 12845. I-87 exit 22, 0.8 mi n on SR 9N. Ext corridors. **Pets:** Accepted.
◻◻◻◻◻◻◻

◇◇ Lake George Inn M
(518) 668-2673. **Call for rates.** 444 Canada St 12845. I-87 exit 22, 0.3 mi s on US 9. Ext corridors. **Pets:** Accepted. ◻◻◻◻◻

◇◇ Lake Haven Motel M
(518) 668-2260. **$49-$135, 10 day notice.** 442 Canada St 12845. I-87 exit 22, 0.4 mi s on US 9. Ext corridors. **Pets:** Small, dogs only. $15 daily fee/pet. Designated rooms, service with restrictions.
◻◻◻◻

◇◇ Roaring Brook Ranch & Tennis Resort H
(518) 668-5767. **Call for rates.** 2206 State Rt 9N S 12845. I-87 exit 21, 1 mi s. Ext/int corridors. **Pets:** Accepted. ◻◻◻◻◻

◇◇ Travelodge Lake George M
(518) 668-5421. **$69-$168.** 2011 US 9 12845. I-87 exit 21, just s. Ext/int corridors. **Pets:** Accepted. ◻◻◻◻◻

LAKE LUZERNE

◇◇ Luzerne Court M
(518) 696-2734. **Call for rates.** 508 Lake Ave 12846. I-87 exit 21, 8.7 mi s on SR 9N. Ext corridors. **Pets:** Accepted.
◻◻◻◻◻

LAKE PLACID

AAA ◇◇ Art Devlin's Olympic Motor Inn, Inc. M
(518) 523-3700. **$78-$498, 14 day notice.** 2764 Main St 12946. 0.5 mi e on SR 86. Ext corridors. **Pets:** Dogs only. $8 daily fee/pet. Service with restrictions, crate. ◻◻◻◻◻◻

AAA ◇◇ Courtyard by Marriott Lake Placid H
(518) 523-2900. **$97-$365, 3 day notice.** 5920 Cascade Rd (SR 73) 12946. 1 mi s of jct SR 86. Int corridors. **Pets:** Accepted.
◻◻◻◻◻◻◻

AAA ◇◇ Crowne Plaza & Golf Club Lake Placid H
(518) 523-2556. **$119-$359, 7 day notice.** 101 Olympic Dr 12946. Downtown. Ext/int corridors. **Pets:** Accepted.
◻◻◻◻◻◻◻◻

◇◇ Golden Arrow Lakeside Resort H
(518) 523-3353. **Call for rates.** 2559 Main St 12946. On SR 86; center. Int corridors. **Pets:** Accepted. ◻◻◻◻◻◻◻◻

◇◇ High Peaks Resort H 🐾
(518) 523-4411. **$129-$349, 7 day notice.** 2384 Saranac Ave 12946. 0.3 mi w on SR 86. Int corridors. **Pets:** Dogs only. $25 daily fee/pet. Designated rooms, service with restrictions, supervision.
◻◻◻◻◻◻◻

◇◇ The Lake House at High Peaks Resort H
(518) 523-4422. **Call for rates.** 1 Mirror Lake Dr 12946. 0.3 mi w on SR 86. Int corridors. **Pets:** Accepted. ◻◻◻◻◻

AAA ◇◇ Lake Placid Summit Hotel H
(518) 523-2587. **$79-$399, 3 day notice.** 2375 Saranac Ave 12946. 0.3 mi w on SR 86. Int corridors. **Pets:** Dogs only. $25 daily fee/pet. Designated rooms, service with restrictions, supervision.
◻◻◻◻◻◻◻

LANSING

◇◇ Courtyard by Marriott Ithaca H
(607) 330-1000. **$116-$312.** 29 Thornwood Dr 14850. Jct SR 13 N and Warren Rd, just w to Brown Rd, just e. Int corridors. **Pets:** Accepted.
◻◻◻◻◻◻◻

◇◇ Homewood Suites by Hilton H
(607) 266-0000. **$149-$279.** 36 Cinema Dr 14850. SR 13 exit Triphammer Rd, just e, then just n on Sheraton Dr (which becomes Cinema Dr). Int corridors. **Pets:** Accepted. ◻◻◻◻◻◻◻

LATHAM

AAA ◇◇ The Century House, an Ascend Hotel Collection Member H 🐾
(518) 785-0931. **$99-$449.** 997 New Loudon Rd 12110. I-87 exit 7 (SR 7), just e, then 0.5 mi n on US 9. Int corridors. **Pets:** Dogs only. $25 daily fee/pet. Designated rooms, service with restrictions, crate.
◻◻◻◻◻◻◻◻

◇◇ Days Inn Airport & Conference Center H
(518) 783-1364. **$75-$150.** 20 Airport Park Blvd 12110. I-87 exit 4, 2.2 mi nw on Albany Shaker Rd. Int corridors. **Pets:** Accepted.
◻◻◻◻

◇◇ Hotel Indigo H
(518) 869-9100. **Call for rates.** 254 Old Wolf Rd 12110. I-87 exit 4, just w on Albany Shaker Rd. Int corridors. **Pets:** Accepted.
◻◻◻◻◻◻

AAA ◇◇ La Quinta Inn & Suites Latham Albany Airport H
(518) 640-2200. **$86-$252.** 833 New Loudon Rd 12110. I-87 exit 7 (SR 7), just s on US 9 to Latham Cir, then just n on US 9. Int corridors. **Pets:** Accepted. ◻◻◻◻◻◻◻

AAA ◇◇ Microtel Inn by Wyndham Albany Airport H
(518) 782-9161. **$65-$130.** 7 Rensselaer Ave 12110. I-87 exit 6, just w. Int corridors. **Pets:** Medium. $20 daily fee/pet. Designated rooms, service with restrictions, supervision. ◻◻◻◻◻

◇◇ Residence Inn by Marriott Albany Airport H 🐾
(518) 783-0600. **$98-$246.** 1 Residence Inn Dr 12110. I-87 exit 6, 2 mi w on SR 7. Ext corridors. **Pets:** Other species. $100 one-time fee/room. Service with restrictions. ◻◻◻◻◻◻

◇◇ TownePlace Suites by Marriott Latham Albany Airport H
(518) 362-8990. **$109-$190.** 5 Forts Ferry Rd 12110. I-87 exit 6, 0.4 mi e. Int corridors. **Pets:** Accepted. ◻◻◻◻◻◻◻

LITTLE FALLS

AAA ◇◇ Travelodge Inn & Suites Little Falls H
(315) 823-4954. **$70-$154, 3 day notice.** 20 Albany St 13365. On SR 5 and 167. Int corridors. **Pets:** Other species. $10 one-time fee/pet. Designated rooms, service with restrictions, crate.
◻◻◻◻◻◻

LIVERPOOL

AAA ◇◇ Best Western Plus Inn Suites - Syracuse H
(315) 701-4400. **$99-$209.** 136 Transistor Pkwy 13088. I-90 exit 37 (Electronics Pkwy), just n. Int corridors. **Pets:** Small. $25 one-time fee/pet. Service with restrictions, supervision.
◻◻◻◻◻◻◻

◇◇ Homewood Suites by Hilton H
(315) 451-3800. **$109-$209.** 275 Elwood Davis Rd 13088. I-81 exit 25 (7th North St), 1 mi w; I-90 exit 36. Int corridors. **Pets:** Accepted.
◻◻◻◻

AAA ◇◇ Knights Inn M
(315) 453-6330. **$59-$169.** 430 Electronics Pkwy 13088. I-90 exit 37 (Electronics Pkwy), just w; I-81 exit 25 (7th North St), 1.3 mi nw, then just w. Ext corridors. **Pets:** Medium, dogs only. $25 daily fee/pet. Designated rooms, service with restrictions, supervision. ◻◻◻

AAA ▼▼ Super 8 Route 57 H
(315) 451-8550. **$69-$159, 3 day notice.** 7360 Oswego Rd 13090. I-90 exit 38, 1 mi n on CR 57. Int corridors. **Pets:** Medium. $25 daily fee/pet. Designated rooms, service with restrictions, supervision.
[SAVE] [&M] [📶] [✕] [🛏] [💻]

LOCKPORT
AAA ▼▼ Quality Inn Lockport H
(716) 434-4411. **$80-$190.** 551 S Transit St 14094. 1 mi s on SR 78. Int corridors. **Pets:** Medium. $20 daily fee/pet. Designated rooms, service with restrictions, supervision. [SAVE] [&M] [📶] [✕] [🛏] [💻]

LONG ISLAND CITY
AAA ▼▼▼ Courtyard by Marriott Long Island City/New York Manhattan View H ❖
(718) 786-0003. **$119-$323.** 29-15 Queens Plaza N 11101. In Long Island City; at Queens Plaza North. Int corridors. **Pets:** Small, other species. $100 one-time fee/pet. Service with restrictions, supervision.
[SAVE] [🍴] [&M] [✕] [🛏] [💻]

▼▼▼ Wyndham Garden Long Island City Manhattan View H
(718) 906-1900. **$179-$619.** 44-29 9th St 11101. In Long Island City; at 44th Dr and Vernon Blvd. Int corridors. **Pets:** Accepted.
[&M] [📶] [✕] [🛏] [💻]

MALONE
AAA ▼▼ Four Seasons Motel M
(518) 483-3490. **$59-$99.** 206 W Main St 12953. 1 mi w on US 11. Ext corridors. **Pets:** Accepted. [SAVE] [🏊] [📶] [🛏]

▼▼ Red Roof PLUS+ & Suites Malone H
(518) 483-8123. **$80-$150.** 42 Finney Blvd 12953. On SR 30, just s of jct US 11. Int corridors. **Pets:** Accepted. [🍴] [&M] [📶] [✕] [🛏] [💻]

MALTA
AAA ▼▼▼ Hyatt Place Saratoga/Malta H
(518) 885-1109. **$109-$399.** 20 State Farm Pl 12020. I-87 exit 12, just w. Int corridors. **Pets:** Accepted.
[SAVE] [ECO] [&M] [🏊] [📶] [✕] [🛏] [💻]

MARGARETVILLE
▼▼ Hanah Mountain Resort and Country Club H
(845) 586-4849. **Call for rates.** 576 W Hubbell Hill Rd 12455. 2.5 mi n on SR 30. Ext corridors. **Pets:** Accepted.
[🍴] [🏊] [✕] [📶] [✕] [🛏] [💻]

MASSENA
▼▼ Econo Lodge-Meadow View Motel H
(315) 764-0246. **$65-$140.** 15054 State Hwy 37 13662. On SR 37, 2.7 mi sw. Int corridors. **Pets:** Accepted. [🍴] [📶] [🛏] [💻]

MELVILLE
▼▼▼ Extended Stay America-Long Island-Melville H
(631) 777-3999. **$115-$155.** 100 Spagnoli Rd 11747. I-495 exit 49S eastbound, 0.5 mi e on south service road, then 1.1 mi s on SR 110; exit westbound, 1.5 mi s on SR 110. Int corridors. **Pets:** Accepted.
[🍴] [&M] [📶] [✕]

▼▼▼ Hilton Long Island/Huntington H
(631) 845-1000. **$135-$295.** 598 Broad Hollow Rd (SR 110) 11747. I-495 exit 49, 1 mi s on SR 110. Int corridors. **Pets:** Medium, dogs only. $50 one-time fee/pet. Supervision.
[🍴] [&M] [🏊] [✕] [📶] [✕] [🛏] [💻]

MIDDLETOWN *(Restaurants p. 619)*
▼▼▼ Hampton Inn Middletown H
(845) 344-3400. **$129-$189.** 20 Crystal Run Crossing 10941. SR 17 exit 122, just ne. Int corridors. **Pets:** Accepted.
[&M] [🏊] [📶] [✕] [🛏] [💻]

▼▼ Microtel Inn & Suites by Wyndham Middletown H
(845) 692-0098. **$99-$159.** 19 Crystal Run Crossing 10941. SR 17 exit 122, just nw. Int corridors. **Pets:** Other species. $20 daily fee/pet. Designated rooms, service with restrictions, supervision.
[&M] [📶] [✕] [🛏] [💻]

MOUNT MORRIS
▼▼ Country Inn & Suites By Carlson H ❖
(585) 658-4080. **$120-$340.** 130 N Main St 14510. On SR 36; center. Int corridors. **Pets:** $25 daily fee/room. Designated rooms, service with restrictions, crate. [&M] [🏊] [📶] [✕] [🛏] [💻]

NANUET
▼▼ Candlewood Suites H
(845) 371-4445. **$110-$120.** 20 Overlook Blvd 10954. I-287/87 (New York State Thruway) exit 14 (SR 59 W) to New Clarkstown Rd. Int corridors. **Pets:** Accepted. [&M] [📶] [✕] [🛏] [💻]

▼▼▼ DoubleTree by Hilton Hotel Nanuet H
(845) 623-6000. **$109-$169.** 425 E Rt 59 10954. Palisades Interstate Pkwy exit 8W, just w. Int corridors. **Pets:** $50 one-time fee/room. Designated rooms, service with restrictions, crate.
[🍴] [&M] [🏊] [📶] [✕] [🛏] [💻]

NEWFANE
▼▼ Lake Ontario Motel M
(716) 778-5004. **$71-$107, 5 day notice.** 3330 Lockport-Olcott Rd 14108. 2.5 mi n of jct SR 104 on SR 78. Int corridors. **Pets:** Other species. $5 daily fee/pet. Service with restrictions, supervision.
[📶] [✕] [🛏]

NEW HARTFORD
▼▼▼ Holiday Inn Utica H ❖
(315) 797-2131. **$129-$209.** 1777 Burrstone Rd 13413. I-90 (New York State Thruway) exit 31, 4.5 mi w on SR 5 W and 12 S exit Burrstone Rd, then 1 mi nw. Int corridors. **Pets:** Medium, dogs only. $35 one-time fee/pet. Designated rooms, service with restrictions, supervision.
[ECO] [🍴] [&M] [🏊] [📶] [✕] [🛏] [💻]

NEW ROCHELLE
AAA ▼▼▼ Radisson Hotel New Rochelle H
(914) 576-3700. **$129-$299.** 1 Radisson Plaza 10801. I-95 exit 16, via Cedar St. Int corridors. **Pets:** Accepted.
[SAVE] [🍴] [&M] [🏊] [📶] [✕] [🛏] [💻]

NEW YORK *(Restaurants p. 619)*
AAA ▼▼▼▼ Algonquin Hotel, Autograph Collection H ❖
(212) 840-6800. **$161-$756, 3 day notice.** 59 W 44th St 10036. Between 5th and 6th (Ave of the Americas) aves. Int corridors. **Pets:** Other species. Service with restrictions, crate.
[SAVE] [ECO] [🍴] [&M] [📶] [✕]

AAA ▼▼▼ Aloft Harlem Hotel H ❖
(212) 749-4000. **$139-$459.** 2296 Frederick Douglass Blvd 10027. At W 124th St. Int corridors. **Pets:** Small. Service with restrictions.
[SAVE] [&M] [📶] [✕] [🛏] [💻]

AAA ▼▼▼ Aloft Hotel Manhattan Downtown Financial District H
(212) 513-0003. **$179-$500.** 49-53 Ann St 10038. Between Nassau and William sts. Int corridors. **Pets:** Accepted.
[SAVE] [🍴] [&M] [📶] [✕] [💻]

◈ ✦✦✦ Andaz 5th Avenue H
(212) 601-1234. **$295-$925.** 485 5th Ave 10017. At 41st St. Int corridors. **Pets:** Accepted. [SAVE] [❢] [&M] [☎] [✕] [❂] [▣]

◈ ✦✦✦ Andaz Wall Street H
(212) 590-1234. **$175-$615.** 75 Wall St 10005. Between Pearl and Water sts. Int corridors. **Pets:** Accepted.
[SAVE] [⊟] [❢] [&M] [✕] [☎] [✕] [❂] [▣]

◈ ✦✦✦ Archer Hotel New York H ✿
(212) 719-4100. **Call for rates.** 45 W 38th St 10018. Between 5th and 6th (Ave of the Americas) aves. Int corridors. **Pets:** Small. $250 one-time fee/room. Supervision. [SAVE] [❢] [&M] [☎] [✕] [❂] [▣]

◈ ✦✦✦ The Benjamin Hotel H ✿
(212) 715-2500. **Call for rates.** 125 E 50th St 10022. Between Lexington and 3rd aves. Int corridors. **Pets:** Other species. $60 one-time fee/pet. Designated rooms, service with restrictions, supervision.
[SAVE] [❢] [&M] [✕] [☎] [✕] [❂] [▣]

✦✦✦ Bentley Hotel H
(212) 644-6000. **Call for rates.** 500 E 62nd St 10021. At York Ave. Int corridors. **Pets:** Accepted. [❢] [&M] [☎] [✕] [❂] [▣]

✦✦✦ The Bowery Hotel H
(212) 505-9100. **Call for rates.** 335 Bowery 10003. Between E 2nd and 3rd sts. Int corridors. **Pets:** Accepted. [❢] [&M] [☎] [❂] [▣]

◈ ✦✦ Candlewood Suites Times Square H
(212) 967-2254. **$119-$799, 3 day notice.** 339 W 39th St 10018. Between 8th and 9th aves. Int corridors. **Pets:** Accepted.
[SAVE] [❢] [&M] [☎] [✕] [❂] [▣]

✦✦✦ The Carlton Hotel, Autograph Collection H
(212) 532-4100. **$110-$732.** 88 Madison Ave 10016. Between 28th and 29th sts. Int corridors. **Pets:** Accepted. [❢] [&M] [☎] [✕] [❂] [▣]

✦✦✦ The Carlyle, A Rosewood Hotel H
(212) 744-1600. **Call for rates.** 35 E 76th St 10021. At Madison Ave. Int corridors. **Pets:** Accepted. [⊟] [❢] [&M] [✕] [☎] [✕] [❂] [▣]

✦✦✦ Chambers Hotel H
(212) 974-5656. **Call for rates.** 15 W 56th St 10019. Between 5th and 6th (Ave of the Americas) aves. Int corridors. **Pets:** Accepted.
[❢] [&M] [☎] [✕] [❂] [▣]

◈ ✦✦✦ The Chatwal, A Luxury Collection Hotel H ✿
(212) 764-6200. **Call for rates.** 130 W 44th St 10036. Between 6th (Ave of the Americas) and 7th aves. Int corridors. **Pets:** Small, dogs only. $100 one-time fee/pet. Supervision.
[SAVE] [❢] [&M] [⊇] [✕] [☎] [✕] [❂] [▣]

✦✦ Comfort Inn Manhattan Bridge H
(212) 925-1212. **$139-$409.** 61-63 Chrystie St 10002. At Hester and Canal sts. Int corridors. **Pets:** Small. $50 one-time fee/pet. Designated rooms, service with restrictions, crate. [☎] [✕] [▣]

✦✦✦ Conrad New York H
(212) 945-0100. **$259-$659.** 102 North End Ave 10282. In Battery Park City; between Vesey and Murray sts. Int corridors. **Pets:** Accepted.
[❢] [&M] [☎] [✕] [❂] [▣]

◈ ✦✦✦ Courtyard by Marriott Central Park H
(212) 324-3773. **$104-$714.** 1717 Broadway 10019. Between 54th and 55th sts; entrance on 54th St. Int corridors. **Pets:** Other species. $100 one-time fee/room. Service with restrictions, crate.
[SAVE] [&M] [☎] [✕] [❂] [▣]

◈ ✦✦✦ Courtyard by Marriott/Manhattan-Times Square H
(212) 391-0088. **$102-$688.** 114 W 40th St 10018. Between Broadway and 6th Ave (Ave of the Americas). Int corridors. **Pets:** Accepted.
[SAVE] [❢] [&M] [☎] [✕] [❂] [▣]

◈ ✦✦✦ DoubleTree by Hilton Metropolitan Hotel-New York City H
(212) 752-7000. **$109-$799.** 569 Lexington Ave 10022. At E 51st St. Int corridors. **Pets:** Accepted. [SAVE] [❢] [&M] [☎] [✕] [❂]

◈ ✦✦✦ DoubleTree by Hilton New York City-Chelsea H
(212) 564-0994. **$149-$1299.** 128 W 29th St 10001. Between 6th (Ave of the Americas) and 7th aves. Int corridors. **Pets:** Medium, other species. $520 one-time fee/room. Service with restrictions, crate.
[SAVE] [❢] [&M] [☎] [✕] [▣]

◈ ✦✦✦ DoubleTree by Hilton Times Square South H
(212) 542-8990. **$129-$499.** 341 W 36th St 10018. Between 8th and 9th aves. Int corridors. **Pets:** Small, other species. $50 one-time fee/pet. Designated rooms, no service, supervision.
[SAVE] [❢] [&M] [☎] [✕] [❂] [▣]

◈ ✦✦✦ DoubleTree Suites by Hilton New York City - Times Square H
(212) 719-1600. **$199-$399.** 1568 Broadway 10036. Jct 47th St and 7th Ave. Int corridors. **Pets:** Large, dogs only. $50 one-time fee/room. Service with restrictions, crate. [SAVE] [❢] [&M] [☎] [✕] [❂] [▣]

◈ ✦✦✦ Dream Downtown H
(212) 229-2559. **Call for rates.** 355 W 16th St 10011. Between 8th and 9th aves. Int corridors. **Pets:** Accepted.
[SAVE] [❢] [&M] [⊇] [☎] [✕] [❂] [▣]

◈ ✦✦✦ Duane Street Hotel H
(212) 964-4600. **Call for rates.** 130 Duane St 10013. Between Church St and W Broadway. Int corridors. **Pets:** Accepted.
[SAVE] [❢] [&M] [☎] [✕] [❂] [▣]

✦✦✦ Dumont NYC, an Affinia hotel H
(212) 481-7600. **Call for rates.** 150 E 34th St 10016. Between Lexington and 3rd aves. Int corridors. **Pets:** Accepted.
[❢] [&M] [☎] [✕] [❂] [▣]

◈ ✦✦✦ Element by Westin Times Square West H
(212) 643-0770. **Call for rates.** 311 W 39th St 10018. Between 8th and 9th aves. Int corridors. **Pets:** Accepted. [SAVE] [&M] [☎] [✕] [❂] [▣]

✦✦✦ Even Hotels New York - Times Square South H
(212) 356-0034. **Call for rates.** 321 W 35th St 10001. Between 8th and 9th aves. Int corridors. **Pets:** Accepted.
[❢] [&M] [✕] [☎] [✕] [❂] [▣]

✦✦✦ Executive Hotel Le Soleil H ✿
(212) 695-0003. **Call for rates.** 38 W 36th St 10018. Between 5th and 6th aves. Int corridors. **Pets:** Medium, dogs only. $150 one-time fee/room. Service with restrictions, crate. [❢] [&M] [☎] [✕] [❂] [▣]

◈ ✦✦✦ Fifty NYC, an Affinia hotel H
(212) 751-5710. **Call for rates.** 155 E 50th St 10022. Between 3rd and Lexington aves. Int corridors. **Pets:** Accepted.
[SAVE] [&M] [☎] [✕] [❂] [▣]

◈ ✦✦✦ Four Points by Sheraton Midtown Times Square H
(212) 967-8585. **$159-$1999.** 326 W 40th St 10018. Between 8th and 9th aves. Int corridors. **Pets:** Accepted.
[SAVE] [❢] [&M] [☎] [✕] [❂] [▣]

Four Seasons Hotel New York H
(212) 758-5700. **Call for rates.** 57 E 57th St 10022. Between Park and Madison aves. Int corridors. **Pets:** Accepted.

The Franklin Hotel H
(212) 369-1000. **Call for rates.** 164 E 87th St 10128. Between 3rd and Lexington aves. Int corridors. **Pets:** Accepted.

Gansevoort Meatpacking NYC H
(212) 660-6700. **Call for rates.** 18 9th Ave 10014. At 13th St. Int corridors. **Pets:** Accepted.

Gansevoort Park Avenue NYC H
(212) 317-2900. **Call for rates.** 420 Park Ave S 10016. Between 28th and 29th sts. Int corridors. **Pets:** Accepted.

Gardens NYC, an Affinia hotel H 🐾
(212) 355-1230. **$189-$829.** 215 E 64th St 10065. Between 2nd and 3rd aves. Int corridors. **Pets:** Other species. $50 one-time fee/pet. Service with restrictions, supervision.

Gild Hall A Thompson Hotel H
(212) 232-7700. **Call for rates.** 15 Gold St 10038. At Platt St. Int corridors. **Pets:** Accepted.

Hampton Inn Empire State Building H
(212) 564-3688. **$189-$699.** 59 W 35th St 10001. Between 5th and 6th (Ave of the Americas) aves. Int corridors. **Pets:** Accepted.

Hampton Inn-Manhattan/Chelsea H
(212) 414-1000. **$109-$999.** 108 W 24th St 10011. Between 6th (Ave of the Americas) and 7th aves. Int corridors. **Pets:** Small, other species. Service with restrictions, supervision.

Hampton Inn Manhattan/Downtown-Financial District H
(212) 480-3500. **$99-$999.** 32 Pearl St 10004. Between Broad and Whitehall sts. Int corridors. **Pets:** Accepted.

Hampton Inn Manhattan/Madison Square Garden Area H
(212) 947-9700. **$99-$999.** 116 W 31st St 10001. Between 6th (Ave of the Americas) and 7th aves. Int corridors. **Pets:** Accepted.

Hampton Inn-Manhattan/Seaport/Financial District H
(212) 571-4400. **$99-$999.** 320 Pearl St 10038. Between Peck Slip and Dover St. Int corridors. **Pets:** Accepted.

Hampton Inn Manhattan/Times Square South H
(212) 967-2344. **$99-$999.** 337 W 39th St 10018. Between 8th and 9th aves. Int corridors. **Pets:** Accepted.

Hilton Garden Inn New York/Central Park South-Midtown West H
(212) 253-6000. **Call for rates.** 237 W 54th St 10019. Between Broadway and 8th Ave. Int corridors. **Pets:** Accepted.

Hilton Times Square H
(212) 840-8222. **$159-$699.** 234 W 42nd St 10036. Between 7th and 8th aves. Int corridors. **Pets:** Large, other species. $75 one-time fee/room. Service with restrictions, crate.

Holiday Inn Express Fifth Ave H
(212) 302-9088. **$159-$599.** 15 W 45th St 10036. Between 5th and 6th (Ave of the Americas) aves. Int corridors. **Pets:** Accepted.

Holiday Inn Express Manhattan Times Square South H
(212) 897-3388. **Call for rates.** 60 W 36th St 10018. Between 5th and 6th (Ave of the Americas) aves. Int corridors. **Pets:** Accepted.

Holiday Inn Express New York City-Chelsea H
(212) 695-7200. **Call for rates.** 232 W 29th St 10001. Between 7th and 8th aves. Int corridors. **Pets:** Accepted.

Holiday Inn Manhattan 6th Ave Chelsea H
(212) 430-8500. **$159-$999.** 125 W 26th St 10001. Between 6th (Ave of the Americas) and 7th aves. Int corridors. **Pets:** Accepted.

Homewood Suites by Hilton Midtown Manhattan H
(212) 244-0644. **Call for rates.** 312 W 37th St 10018. Between 8th and 9th aves. Int corridors. **Pets:** Accepted.

Hotel 48LEX New York H
(212) 888-3500. **Call for rates.** 517 Lexington Ave 10017. At 48th St. Int corridors. **Pets:** Accepted.

Hotel Hayden H
(212) 973-9000. **Call for rates.** 127 W 28th St 10001. Between 6th (Ave of the Americas) and 7th aves. Int corridors. **Pets:** Accepted.

Hotel Hugo H
(212) 608-4848. **$200-$700.** 525 Greenwich St 10013. Downtown. Int corridors. **Pets:** Accepted.

Hotel Mela H
(212) 710-7000. **Call for rates.** 120 W 44th St 10036. Between Broadway and 6th Ave (Ave of the Americas). Int corridors. **Pets:** Accepted.

Hotel Plaza Athénée H
(212) 734-9100. **Call for rates.** 37 E 64th St 10065. Between Madison and Park aves. Int corridors. **Pets:** Accepted.

Hotel Wales H
(212) 876-6000. **Call for rates.** 1295 Madison Ave 10128. Between 92nd and 93rd sts E. Int corridors. **Pets:** $50 daily fee/pet. Service with restrictions, crate.

Hyatt Herald Square H
(212) 330-1234. **$199-$1399.** 30-32 W 31st St 10001. Between 5th Ave and Broadway. Int corridors. **Pets:** Accepted.

Hyatt Place Midtown South H
(212) 239-9100. **$149-$1299.** 52 W 36th St 10018. Between 5th and 6th (Ave of the Americas) aves. Int corridors. **Pets:** Accepted.

Hyatt Union Square New York H
(212) 253-1234. **$239-$639.** 134 Fourth Ave 10003. At 13th St. Int corridors. **Pets:** Accepted.

IBEROSTAR 70 Park Avenue H
(212) 973-2400. **Call for rates.** 70 Park Ave 10016. At 38th St. Int corridors. **Pets:** Accepted.

INNSIDE New York NoMad H ❋
(212) 951-1000. **$199-$899.** 132 W 27th St 10001. Between 6th and 7th aves. Int corridors. **Pets:** Small, dogs only. $100 one-time fee/room. Service with restrictions, supervision. ⊞ 🛠M 📶 ✕ 🅿 💻

InterContinental New York Barclay H
(212) 755-5900. **Call for rates.** 111 E 48th St 10017. Between Park and Lexington aves. Int corridors. **Pets:** Accepted.
⊞ 🛠M 📶 ✕ 🅿 💻

InterContinental New York Times Square H
(212) 803-4500. **Call for rates.** 300 W 44th St 10036. Between 8th and 9th aves. Int corridors. **Pets:** Accepted.
SAVE ⊞ 🛠M 📶 ✕ 🅿 💻

The James Hotel New York Soho H
(212) 465-2000. **Call for rates.** 27 Grand St 10013. Between 6th Ave (Ave of the Americas) and Thompson St. Int corridors. **Pets:** Accepted.
⊞ 🛠M 🏊 ✕ 📶 ✕ 🅿 💻

JW Marriott Essex House New York H
(212) 247-0300. **$221-$1401.** 160 Central Park S 10019. Between 6th (Ave of the Americas) and 7th aves. Int corridors. **Pets:** Accepted.
⊞ 🛠M ✕ 📶 ✕ 🅿 💻

Kimpton Hotel Eventi H ❋
(212) 564-4567. **$199-$1200.** 851 Ave of the Americas 10001. Between 29th and 30th sts. Int corridors. **Pets:** Other species. Designated rooms, service with restrictions.
SAVE ⊞ 🛠M ✕ 📶 ✕ 🅿 💻

Kimpton, Ink 48 New York City H
(212) 757-0088. **Call for rates.** 653 11th Ave 10036. Between 47th and 48th sts. Int corridors. **Pets:** Accepted.
SAVE ⊞ 🛠M ✕ 📶 ✕ 🅿 💻

The Kimpton Muse Hotel H
(212) 485-2400. **Call for rates.** 130 W 46th St 10036. Between 6th (Ave of the Americas) and 7th aves. Int corridors. **Pets:** Accepted.
SAVE ECO ⊞ 🛠M 📶 ✕ 🅿 💻

Langham Place, New York, Fifth Avenue H
(212) 695-4005. **Call for rates.** 400 Fifth Ave 10018. Between 36th and 37th sts. Int corridors. **Pets:** Accepted.
⊞ 🛠M ✕ 📶 ✕ 🅿 💻

Le Parker Meridien New York H ❋
(212) 245-5000. **$890-$6367.** 119 W 56th St 10019. Between 6th (Ave of the Americas) and 7th aves. Int corridors. **Pets:** Other species. $50 daily fee/pet. Service with restrictions, crate.
SAVE ⊞ 🛠M 🏊 ✕ 📶 ✕ 🅿 💻

The Lexington New York City, Autograph Collection H
(212) 755-4400. **$115-$795.** 511 Lexington Ave 10017. At E 48th St. Int corridors. **Pets:** Accepted. SAVE ⊞ 🛠M 📶 ✕ 🅿 💻

Loews Regency Hotel H
(212) 759-4100. **$299-$799, 3 day notice.** 540 Park Ave 10065. At 61st St. Int corridors. **Pets:** Accepted. ⊞ 🛠M ✕ 📶 ✕ 🅿 💻

The London NYC H
(212) 307-5000. **Call for rates.** 151 W 54th St 10019. Between 6th (Ave of the Americas) and 7th aves. Int corridors. **Pets:** Accepted.
⊞ 🛠M 📶 ✕ 🅿 💻

Lotte New York Palace H
(212) 888-7000. **$229-$799.** 455 Madison Ave 10022. Between 50th and 51st sts. Int corridors. **Pets:** Accepted.
SAVE ⊞ 🛠M ✕ 📶 ✕ 🅿 💻

The Lowell Hotel H ❋
(212) 838-1400. **Call for rates.** 28 E 63rd St 10021. Between Park and Madison aves. Int corridors. **Pets:** Other species. $200 one-time fee/room. Service with restrictions. ⊞ 🛠M 📶 ✕ 🅿 💻

Mandarin Oriental, New York H
(212) 805-8800. **$695-$1795.** 80 Columbus Cir at 60th St 10023. Entrance on 60th St. Int corridors. **Pets:** Accepted.
SAVE ⊞ 🛠M 🏊 ✕ 📶 ✕ 🅿 💻

The Mansfield Hotel H
(212) 277-8700. **Call for rates.** 12 W 44th St 10036. Between 5th and 6th (Ave of the Americas) aves. Int corridors. **Pets:** Accepted.
⊞ 📶 ✕

The Maritime Hotel H
(212) 242-4300. **Call for rates.** 363 W 16th St 10011. Between 8th and 9th aves. Int corridors. **Pets:** Accepted. ⊞ 🛠M 📶 ✕ 🅿 💻

The Michelangelo H
(212) 765-1900. **Call for rates.** 152 W 51st St 10019. At 7th Ave. Int corridors. **Pets:** Small, dogs only. $75 one-time fee/pet. Service with restrictions, supervision. SAVE ⊞ 🛠M 📶 ✕ 🅿 💻

Millennium Broadway Hotel-Times Square-New York H
(212) 768-4400. **Call for rates.** 145 W 44th St 10036. Between 6th Ave (Ave of the Americas) and Broadway; in Times Square. Int corridors.
Pets: Accepted. ⊞ 🛠M 📶 ✕ 🅿 💻

The New York Hilton Midtown H
(212) 586-7000. **$159-$609.** 1335 Ave of the Americas 10019. Between 53rd and 54th sts. Int corridors. **Pets:** Accepted.
SAVE ⊞ 🛠M 📶 ✕ 🅿

The New York Renaissance Home and Guesthouse BB
(212) 470-3696. **Call for rates.** 464 W 141 St 10031. Between Amsterdam and Convent aves. Int corridors. **Pets:** Accepted.
⊞ 📶 🚭 🅿 💻

The NoMad Hotel H
(212) 796-1500. **Call for rates.** 1170 Broadway 10001. At 28th St. Int corridors. **Pets:** Accepted. ⊞ 🛠M 📶 ✕ 🅿

NOMO SOHO H
(646) 218-6400. **Call for rates.** 9 Crosby St 10013. Just s of Grand St. Int corridors. **Pets:** Accepted. ⊞ 🛠M 📶 ✕ 🅿

Novotel New York Times Square H
(212) 315-0100. **$129-$899.** 226 W 52nd St 10019. At Broadway. Int corridors. **Pets:** Accepted. ⊞ 🛠M 📶 ✕ 🅿 💻

NYLO New York City H
(212) 362-1100. **Call for rates.** 2178 Broadway 10024. At 77th St. Int corridors. **Pets:** Accepted. SAVE ⊞ 🛠M 📶 ✕ 🅿 💻

Omni Berkshire Place H
(212) 753-5800. **Call for rates.** 21 E 52nd St 10022. Between Madison and 5th aves. Int corridors. **Pets:** Accepted.
SAVE ⊞ 🛠M 📶 ✕ 🅿 💻

The Paramount Hotel New York H
(212) 764-5500. **Call for rates.** 235 W 46th St 10036. Between Broadway and 8th Ave. Int corridors. **Pets:** Accepted.
⊞ 🛠M 📶 ✕ 🅿

Park Hyatt New York H
(646) 774-1234. **$525-$1475.** 153 W 57th St 10019. Between 6th (Ave of the Americas) and 7th aves. Int corridors. **Pets:** Accepted.
SAVE ⊞ 🛠M ✕ 📶 ✕ 🅿 💻

Park Lane Hotel New York H
(212) 371-4000. **$149-$999.** 36 Central Park S 10019. Between 5th and 6th (Ave of the Americas) aves. Int corridors. **Pets:** Accepted.

The Peninsula New York H
(212) 956-2888. **$695-$1195.** 700 5th Ave 10019. At 55th St. Int corridors. **Pets:** Accepted.

The Pierre New York-A Taj Hotel H
(212) 838-8000. **Call for rates.** 2 E 61st St 10065. At 5th Ave and E 61st St. Int corridors. **Pets:** Accepted.

The Plaza Hotel H ❀
(212) 759-3000. **Call for rates.** 5th Ave at Central Park S 10019. Corner of 5th Ave and Central Park S. Int corridors. **Pets:** $75 one-time fee/room. Service with restrictions, supervision.

The Quin H
(212) 245-7846. **Call for rates.** 101 W 57th St 10019. At 6th Ave (Ave of the Americas). Int corridors. **Pets:** Accepted.

Radisson Martinique on Broadway H
(212) 736-3800. **$275-$525.** 49 W 32nd St 10001. Between Broadway and 5th Ave. Int corridors. **Pets:** Accepted.

Refinery Hotel New York H ❀
(646) 664-0310. **Call for rates.** 63 W 38th St 10018. Between 5th and 6th (Ave of the Americas) aves. Int corridors. **Pets:** Small, dogs only. $500 deposit/pet. Service with restrictions, crate.

Renaissance New York Hotel 57 H
(212) 753-8841. **$108-$718.** 130 E 57th St 10022. At Lexington Ave. Int corridors. **Pets:** Accepted.

Renaissance New York Hotel Times Square H
(212) 765-7676. **$181-$831.** 2 Times Square, 7th Ave at W 48th St 10036. At Broadway and 7th Ave; motor access from 7th Ave, s of W 48th St. Int corridors. **Pets:** Accepted.

Residence Inn by Marriott Central Park H
(212) 324-3774. **$137-$787.** 1717 Broadway 10019. Between 54th and 55th sts; entrance on 54th St, between 8 Ave and Broadway. Int corridors. **Pets:** Other species. $100 one-time fee/room. Service with restrictions, crate.

Residence Inn by Marriott Manhattan/Midtown East H
(212) 980-1003. **$127-$804.** 148 E 48th St 10017. Between 3rd and Lexington aves. Int corridors. **Pets:** Small. $250 one-time fee/pet. Designated rooms, service with restrictions, supervision.

Residence Inn by Marriott New York Manhattan/World Trade Center Area H
(212) 600-8900. **$113-$598.** 170 Broadway 10038. At Maiden Lane; downtown. Int corridors. **Pets:** Small. $100 one-time fee/room. Service with restrictions, crate.

Residence Inn by Marriott Times Square H
(212) 768-0007. **$115-$805.** 1033 Ave of the Americas 10018. Between 38th and 39th sts. Int corridors. **Pets:** Accepted.

The Ritz-Carlton New York, Battery Park H ❀
(212) 344-0800. **$295-$895.** Two West St 10004. Jct Battery Pl. Int corridors. **Pets:** Medium. $125 one-time fee/room. Service with restrictions.

The Ritz-Carlton New York, Central Park H
(212) 308-9100. **Call for rates.** 50 Central Park S 10019. Jct 59th St (Central Park S) and 6th Ave (Ave of the Americas). Int corridors. **Pets:** Accepted.

Royalton Hotel H
(212) 869-4400. **Call for rates.** 44 W 44th St 10036. Between 5th and 6th (Ave of the Americas) aves. Int corridors. **Pets:** Accepted.

St Giles The Court-A Premier Hotel H
(212) 685-1100. **Call for rates.** 130 E 39th St 10016. Between Park and Lexington aves. Int corridors. **Pets:** Accepted.

Seaport Inn Downtown H
(212) 766-6600. **Call for rates.** 33 Peck Slip on Front St 10038. North end of South St Seaport. Int corridors. **Pets:** Accepted.

Shelburne NYC, an Affinia hotel H
(212) 689-5200. **Call for rates.** 303 Lexington Ave 10016. Between 37th and 38th sts. Int corridors. **Pets:** Accepted.

Sheraton New York Times Square Hotel H
(212) 581-1000. **$199-$699.** 811 7th Ave 10019. At 52nd St. Int corridors. **Pets:** Accepted.

Sheraton Tribeca New York Hotel H
(212) 966-3400. **Call for rates.** 370 Canal St 10013. Just e of W Broadway. Int corridors. **Pets:** Accepted.

The Sherry-Netherland H ❀
(212) 355-2800. **Call for rates.** 781 5th Ave 10022. Between 59th and 60th sts. Int corridors. **Pets:** Service with restrictions.

The Shoreham Hotel H
(212) 247-6700. **Call for rates.** 33 W 55th St 10019. Between 5th and 6th (Ave of the Americas) aves. Int corridors. **Pets:** Accepted.

Skyline Hotel H
(212) 586-3400. **Call for rates.** 725 10th Ave 10019. At 49th and 50th sts. Int corridors. **Pets:** Accepted.

Smyth, a Thompson Hotel H
(212) 587-7000. **Call for rates.** 85 W Broadway 10007. Between Chambers and Warren sts. Int corridors. **Pets:** Accepted.

Sofitel New York H
(212) 354-8844. **$180-$1500.** 45 W 44th St 10036. Between 5th and 6th (Ave of the Americas) aves. Int corridors. **Pets:** Accepted.

Staybridge Suites Times Square H
(212) 757-9000. **Call for rates.** 340 W 40th St 10018. Between 8th and 9th aves. Int corridors. **Pets:** Accepted.

Stewart Hotel H
(212) 563-1800. **Call for rates.** 371 7th Ave 10001. At 31st St. Int corridors. **Pets:** Accepted.

The Surrey H ❀
(212) 288-3700. **$495-$895.** 20 E 76th St 10021. Jct E 76th St and Madison Ave. Int corridors. **Pets:** $150 one-time fee/room. Service with restrictions.

Trump International Hotel & Tower H ❀
(212) 299-1000. **$475-$995.** 1 Central Park W 10023. Jct Central Park W; at Columbus Cir. Int corridors. **Pets:** Medium, dogs only. $250 one-time fee/room. Service with restrictions.

Trump SoHo® New York H ❀
(212) 842-5500. **Call for rates.** 246 Spring St 10013. Between Varick St and 6th Ave (Ave of the Americas). Int corridors. **Pets:** Small, dogs only. $250 one-time fee/room. Service with restrictions.

TRYP Times Square South H
(212) 600-2440. **$179-$525.** 345 W 35th St 10001. Between 8th and 9th aves. Int corridors. **Pets:** Accepted.

Viceroy New York H
(212) 830-8000. **Call for rates.** 120 W 57th St 10019. Between 6th (Ave of the Americas) and 7th aves. Int corridors. **Pets:** Accepted.

Waldorf Astoria New York H
(212) 355-3000. **Call for rates.** 301 Park Ave 10022. Between E 49th and 50th sts. Int corridors. **Pets:** Accepted.

Warwick New York Hotel H
(212) 247-2700. **Call for rates.** 65 W 54th St 10019. At 6th Ave (Ave of the Americas). Int corridors. **Pets:** Accepted.

WestHouse Hotel New York H
(212) 707-4888. **Call for rates.** 201 W 55th St 10019. Between 7th Ave and Broadway. Int corridors. **Pets:** Accepted.

The Westin New York at Times Square H
(212) 201-2700. **$199-$699.** 270 W 43rd St 10036. Corner of 8th Ave. Int corridors. **Pets:** Accepted.

The Westin New York Grand Central H
(212) 490-8900. **Call for rates.** 212 E 42nd St 10017. Between 2nd and 3rd aves. Int corridors. **Pets:** Accepted.

W New York H
(212) 755-1200. **$109-$899.** 541 Lexington Ave 10022. At 49th St. Int corridors. **Pets:** Accepted.

W New York-Downtown H ❀
(646) 826-8600. **$159-$799.** 8 Albany St 10006. At Albany St. Int corridors. **Pets:** Medium. $25 daily fee/pet. Designated rooms, service with restrictions, crate.

W New York Times Square H
(212) 930-7400. **Call for rates.** 1567 Broadway at 47th St 10036. Corner of 47th St. Int corridors. **Pets:** Accepted.

W New York-Union Square H ❀
(212) 253-9119. **Call for rates.** 201 Park Ave S 10003. At 17th St. Int corridors. **Pets:** Medium. $100 one-time fee/room, $30 daily fee/room. Service with restrictions.

Wyndham Garden Chinatown H ❀
(646) 329-3400. **$129-$459.** 93 Bowery 10002. At Hester St. Int corridors. **Pets:** Other species. $50 daily fee/room. Service with restrictions.

Wyndham New Yorker H
(212) 971-0101. **$135-$375.** 481 8th Ave 10001. Between 33rd and 34th sts. Int corridors. **Pets:** Accepted.

NIAGARA FALLS

Four Points by Sheraton Niagara Falls H
(716) 299-0344. **$79-$219.** 7001 Buffalo Ave 14304. I-190 exit 21 (Robert Moses Pkwy), just e. Int corridors. **Pets:** Small, dogs only. $40 daily fee/pet. Service with restrictions, supervision.

Motel 6 M
(716) 297-9902. **Call for rates.** 9100 Niagara Falls Blvd 14304. I-190 exit 22, 1.8 mi e. Int corridors. **Pets:** Accepted.

Sheraton At The Falls H ❀
(716) 285-3361. **$79-$599.** 300 3rd St 14303. I-190 exit 21 (Robert Moses Pkwy) to City Traffic exit, just w on Rainbow Blvd, just n. Int corridors. **Pets:** Medium, dogs only. Designated rooms, service with restrictions.

NORTH SYRACUSE

Best Western Syracuse Airport Inn H
(315) 455-7362. **$110-$160.** 900 Col. Eileen Collins Blvd 13212. I-81 exit 27 (Syracuse Hancock International Airport). Int corridors. **Pets:** Accepted.

Candlewood Suites Syracuse Airport H
(315) 454-8999. **$89-$249.** 5414 South Bay Rd 13212. I-90 exit 36; I-81 exit 26 (Mattydale Rd), follow South Bay Rd signs, just n. Int corridors. **Pets:** Accepted.

NORWICH

Super 8 of Norwich H
(607) 336-8880. **$55-$85.** 6067 State Hwy 12 13815. On SR 12, 0.9 mi n. Int corridors. **Pets:** Accepted.

OGDENSBURG

Quality Inn Gran-View M
(315) 393-4550. **$100-$365.** 6765 SR 37 13669. On SR 37, 3 mi sw. Ext/int corridors. **Pets:** Accepted.

Windjammer Lodge M
(315) 393-6300. **Call for rates.** 5843 SR 37 13669. On SR 37, 5 mi sw. Ext corridors. **Pets:** Other species. $15 daily fee/pet. Service with restrictions, crate.

OLD FORGE

Adirondack Lodge Old Forge M
(315) 369-6836. **Call for rates.** 2752 SR 28 13420. 0.3 mi s. Ext/int corridors. **Pets:** Accepted.

OLEAN

▼▼ Microtel Inn & Suites by Wyndham Olean/Allegany **H**

(716) 373-5333. **$79-$165.** 3234 NYS Rt 417 14760. I-86 exit 24, 2.1 mi e on SR 417 (State St). Int corridors. **Pets:** Other species. $20 daily fee/pet. Service with restrictions, supervision. ⓜ 🛜 ✕ 🔌 💻

ONEIDA

▼▼ Super 8-Oneida **H**

(315) 363-5168. **$60-$170.** 215 Genesee St 13421. I-90 exit 33, 4 mi s on SR 365 to SR 5, then 0.5 mi w. Int corridors. **Pets:** Accepted. 🛜 🔌 💻

ONEONTA

▼▼▼ Holiday Inn Oneonta/Cooperstown Area **H**

(607) 433-2250. **Call for rates.** 5206 State Hwy 23 13820. I-88 exit 15 (SR 23 and 28), 1.5 mi e. Int corridors. **Pets:** $25 one-time fee/room. Designated rooms, service with restrictions, supervision.

🍴 ⓜ 🛜 ✕ 🔌 💻

PAINTED POST

AAA ◆ Americas Best Value Inn Lodge on the Green **M** 🐾

(607) 962-2456. **$76-$160.** 196 S Hamilton St 14870. I-86/SR 17 exit 44B, 0.5 mi sw on SR 417 W; US 15 exit 3, 0.8 mi ne on SR 417 E, then just w on Canada Rd. Ext corridors. **Pets:** Other species. $10 one-time fee/room. Service with restrictions, supervision.

🆊 🍴 ⓜ 🛜 🔌 💻

PEMBROKE

▼▼ Darien Lakes Econo Lodge **H**

(585) 599-4681. **$70-$160.** 8493 Alleghany Rd 14036. I-90 exit 48A, just s. Int corridors. **Pets:** Accepted. ⓜ 🛜 🔌 💻

PENN YAN

AAA ▼▼▼ Best Western Plus Vineyard Inn & Suites **H** 🐾

(315) 536-8473. **$109-$259.** 142 Lake St 14527. I-90 exit 43, just e on SR 54, then just s; corner of SR 54 and 14A. Int corridors. **Pets:** Dogs only. $20 daily fee/pet. Designated rooms, service with restrictions, crate. 🆊 ⓜ 🛜 ✕ 🔌 💻

PINE VALLEY

▼▼ Rodeway Inn Marshall Manor **M**

(607) 739-3891. **$80-$186.** 3527 Watkins Rd 14845. I-86 exit 52B, 5 mi n on SR 14. Ext corridors. **Pets:** Accepted. 🗺 🛜 🔌 💻

PLAINVIEW

AAA ▼▼▼ Four Points by Sheraton-Plainview Long Island **H**

(516) 694-6500. **$159-$299.** 333 S Service Rd 11803. I-495 exit 48, just se. Int corridors. **Pets:** Small, dogs only. $50 daily fee/pet. Designated rooms, service with restrictions, supervision.

🆊 🍴 ⓜ 🗺 🛜 ✕ 🔌 💻

▼▼ Homewood Suites Long Island/Melville **H**

(516) 293-4663. **$149-$259.** 1585 Round Swamp Rd 11803. I-495 exit 48, just s. Int corridors. **Pets:** Accepted. ⓜ 🗺 🛜 ✕ 🔌 💻

▼▼ Residence Inn by Marriott Plainview Long Island **H**

(516) 433-6200. **$204-$230.** 9 Gerhard Rd 11803. I-495 exit 44, 1.6 mi s on SR 135 exit 10, then just e on Old Country Rd. Int corridors. **Pets:** Accepted. 🍴 ⓜ 🗺 ✕ 🛜 ✕ 🔌 💻

PLATTSBURGH

AAA ▼▼▼ Best Western Plus The Inn at Smithfield **H**

(518) 561-7750. **$124-$179.** 446 Rt 3 12901. I-87 exit 37, just e. Int corridors. **Pets:** Other species. $10 daily fee/room. Designated rooms, service with restrictions, crate.

🆊 🍴 ⓜ 🗺 🛜 ✕ 🔌 💻

▼▼▼ Comfort Inn & Suites Plattsburgh New York **H** 🐾

(518) 562-2730. **$119-$249.** 411 Rt 3 12901. I-87 exit 37, 0.5 mi e. Int corridors. **Pets:** Large, other species. Designated rooms, service with restrictions, supervision. 🍴 ⓜ 🗺 ✕ 🛜 🔌 💻

▼▼▼ La Quinta Inn & Suites Plattsburgh **H**

(518) 562-4000. **$71-$328.** 16 Plaza Blvd 12901. I-87 exit 37, just w. Int corridors. **Pets:** Accepted. ⓜ 🗺 🛜 🔌 💻

▼▼ Microtel Inn & Suites by Wyndham Plattsburgh **H**

(518) 324-3800. **$69-$174.** 554 SR 3 12901. I-87 exit 37, just w. Int corridors. **Pets:** Medium, dogs only. $10 daily fee/room. Supervision.

ⓜ 🛜 ✕ 🔌 💻

POUGHKEEPSIE

AAA ▼▼▼ Best Western Plus The Inn & Suites at the Falls **H**

(845) 462-5770. **$99-$399.** 50 Red Oaks Mill Rd (CR 44) 12603. Jct SR 376 and CR 113, just se. Int corridors. **Pets:** Accepted.

🆊 🍴 ⓜ 🛜 ✕ 🔌 💻

AAA ▼▼ Days Inn **M**

(845) 454-1010. **$100-$215.** 536 Haight Ave 12603. 2 mi e of Mid-Hudson Bridge on US 44 and SR 55. Ext/int corridors. **Pets:** Accepted. 🆊 🗺 🛜 🔌 💻

▼▼▼ Poughkeepsie Hampton Inn & Suites **H**

(845) 463-7500. **$119-$289.** 2361 South Rd (US Rt 9) 12601. 3.2 mi s of Mid-Hudson Bridge. Int corridors. **Pets:** Accepted. ⓜ 🗺 🛜 ✕ 🔌 💻

AAA ▼▼▼ Residence Inn by Marriott **H**

(845) 463-4343. **$125-$406.** 2525 South Rd 12601. 3.1 mi s of Mid-Hudson Bridge. Int corridors. **Pets:** Accepted. 🆊 ⓜ 🛜 ✕ 🔌 💻

QUEENSBURY

▼▼ Quality Inn of Glens Falls **H**

(518) 793-3800. **$85-$239.** 547 Aviation Rd 12804. I-87 exit 19, just e. Int corridors. **Pets:** Medium, dogs only. $30 daily fee/pet. Service with restrictions, supervision. ⓜ 🗺 🛜 ✕ 🔌 💻

▼ Super 8 Queensbury/Glens Falls **H**

(518) 761-9780. **$85-$129.** 191 Corinth Rd 12804. I-87 exit 18, just w. Int corridors. **Pets:** $20 one-time fee/room. Designated rooms, service with restrictions, supervision. 🍴 ✕ ✕ 🔌 💻

RHINEBECK

▼▼▼ Beekman Arms & Delamater Inn and Conference Center **CI**

(845) 876-7077. **Call for rates.** 6387 Mill St (Rt 9) 12572. Jct US 9 and SR 308; center of village. Ext/int corridors. **Pets:** Accepted.

🍴 🛜 🔌 💻

RIVERHEAD

▼▼▼ Holiday Inn Express East End **H**

(631) 548-1000. **Call for rates.** 1707 Old Country Rd (SR 58) 11901. I-495 exit 73, 0.5 mi e. Int corridors. **Pets:** Medium, dogs only. $50 one-time fee/room. Service with restrictions.

ⓜ 🗺 🛜 ✕ 🔌 💻

▼▼▼▼ Hotel Indigo East End H
(631) 369-2200. **Call for rates.** 1830 RT 25 11901. I-495 exit 72 (SR 25 E), just e. Int corridors. **Pets:** Accepted.
⊞ 🐾 📶 ✕ 🔌 💻

AAA ▼▼▼▼ Hyatt Place Long Island/East End H 🐾
(631) 208-0002. **$119-$419.** 451 E Main St 11901. On SR 25. Int corridors. **Pets:** Medium, dogs only. $75 one-time fee/room.
SAVE ⊞ 🐾 📶 ✕ 🔌 💻

ROCHESTER

AAA ▼▼▼▼ Holiday Inn Rochester Downtown H
(585) 546-3450. **$99-$269.** 70 State St 14614. Jct Main St; downtown. Int corridors. **Pets:** Large. $50 one-time fee/room. Service with restrictions, supervision. SAVE ⊞ 🐾 📶 ✕ 🔌 💻

AAA ▼▼▼▼ Hyatt Regency Rochester H
(585) 546-1234. **$89-$319.** 125 E Main St 14604. Jct South Ave; downtown. Int corridors. **Pets:** Accepted.
SAVE ⊞ 🐾 📶 ✕ 🔌 💻

▼▼ Microtel Inn & Suites by Wyndham Rochester/Chili H
(585) 889-5690. **$51-$165.** 3258 Chili Ave 14624. I-490 exit 5, 1.5 mi sw on SR 33A and 386. Int corridors. **Pets:** Accepted.
⊞ 🐾 📶 ✕ 🔌 💻

▼▼▼ Radiance Inn & Suites H
(585) 254-1000. **Call for rates.** 1956 Lyell Ave 14606. I-390 exit 21 (SR 31), just e. Int corridors. **Pets:** Accepted. ⊞ 📶 🔌 💻

AAA ▼▼▼▼ Radisson Hotel Rochester Riverside H
(585) 546-6400. **Call for rates.** 120 E Main St 14604. Downtown. Int corridors. **Pets:** Medium. $50 daily fee/room. Designated rooms, service with restrictions, crate. SAVE ⊞ 🐾 📶 ✕ 🔌 💻

ROCK HILL

▼▼▼▼ Ramada Inn at The Sullivan Event Center H
(845) 796-3100. **$99-$250.** 283 Rock Hill Dr 12775. SR 17 exit 109, just e. Int corridors. **Pets:** Dogs only. $50 daily fee/pet. Designated rooms, service with restrictions, supervision.
🐾 🛏 ✕ 📶 ✕ 🔌 💻

ROME

AAA ▼▼▼▼ Inn at the Beeches M
(315) 336-1775. **$95-$295.** 7900 Turin Rd 13440. Jct SR 46, 2 mi n on SR 26 (Turin Rd). Ext corridors. **Pets:** Medium. $10 daily fee/pet. Designated rooms, service with restrictions. SAVE ⊞ 🐾 📶 🔌 💻

RYE BROOK

AAA ▼▼▼▼ Hilton Westchester H
(914) 939-6300. **$119-$219.** 699 Westchester Ave 10573. I-287 (Cross Westchester Expwy) exit 10 eastbound, 0.6 mi ne on SR 120A; exit westbound, 0.3 mi n on Webb Ave, then 0.4 mi ne on SR 120A. Int corridors. **Pets:** Accepted.
SAVE ⊞ 🛏 🐾 ✕ 📶 ✕ 🔌 💻

SACKETS HARBOR

▼▼ Ontario Place Hotel H
(315) 646-8000. **Call for rates.** 103 General Smith Dr 13685. Corner of W Main St; center. Int corridors. **Pets:** Accepted. 📶 ✕ 🔌 💻

SAG HARBOR

AAA ▼▼▼▼ Baron's Cove M
(631) 725-2101. **$169-$1799, 21 day notice.** 31 W Water St 11963. W on Long Island Ave to W Water St. Ext corridors. **Pets:** Accepted.
SAVE 🔌 ⊞ ✕ 📶 ✕ 🔌

SALAMANCA

AAA ▼▼▼▼ Holiday Inn Express & Suites H
(716) 945-7600. **$140-$190.** 779 Broad St 14779. I-86 exit 20, just n. Int corridors. **Pets:** $50 deposit/room, $25 one-time fee/room. Designated rooms, service with restrictions, supervision.
SAVE 🛏 🐾 📶 ✕ 🔌 💻

SARANAC LAKE

▼▼▼ Adirondack Motel M
(518) 891-2116. **Call for rates.** 248 Lake Flower Ave 12983. 0.5 mi e on SR 86. Ext corridors. **Pets:** Accepted. ⊞ 📶 ✕ 🔌 💻

AAA ▼▼▼ Best Western Mountain Lake Inn H
(518) 891-1970. **$99-$279.** 487 Lake Flower Ave 12983. 1.1 mi e on SR 86. Int corridors. **Pets:** Other species. $15 daily fee/room. Designated rooms, service with restrictions, supervision.
SAVE ⊞ 🐾 📶 ✕ 🔌 💻

▼▼▼ Lake Flower Inn M
(518) 891-2310. **Call for rates.** 234 Lake Flower Ave 12983. 0.5 mi e on SR 86. Ext corridors. **Pets:** Accepted. ⊞ 🐾 📶 ✕ 🔌

SARATOGA SPRINGS

AAA ▼▼▼▼ Best Western Plus Park Inn H
(518) 584-2350. **$110-$378.** 3291 S Broadway 12866. I-87 exit 13N, 1.1 mi n on US 9. Int corridors. **Pets:** Large. $20 daily fee/pet. Designated rooms, service with restrictions.
SAVE ⊞ 🛏 🐾 📶 ✕ 🔌 💻

AAA ▼▼▼▼ Comfort Inn & Suites H
(518) 587-6244. **$130-$480.** 17 Old Gick Rd 12866. I-87 exit 15, just e, then just n. Int corridors. **Pets:** Accepted.
SAVE 🛏 🐾 📶 ✕ 🔌 💻

AAA ▼▼▼▼ Holiday Inn H
(518) 584-4550. **$139-$499, 3 day notice.** 232 Broadway 12866. Jct SR 50, on US 9. Int corridors. **Pets:** Accepted.
SAVE ⊞ 🛏 🐾 📶 ✕ 🔌 💻

▼▼▼▼ Residence Inn by Marriott-Saratoga Springs H
(518) 584-9600. **$108-$582.** 295 Excelsior Ave 12866. I-87 exit 15, just n, just s, then just e. Int corridors. **Pets:** Other species. $75 one-time fee/pet. Service with restrictions, crate.
⊞ 🛏 🐾 📶 ✕ 🔌 💻

▼▼▼ Saratoga Downtowner Motel M
(518) 584-6160. **$79-$309.** 413 Broadway 12866. On US 9; corner of Division St. Ext/int corridors. **Pets:** Medium, dogs only. $13 daily fee/pet. Designated rooms, service with restrictions, crate.
SAVE 🐾 📶 ✕ 🔌

▼▼▼▼ Union Gables Inn and Suites BB 🐾
(518) 584-1558. **Call for rates.** 55 Union Ave 12866. I-87 exit 14, 1.5 mi w. Int corridors. **Pets:** $50 one-time fee/pet. Designated rooms, service with restrictions. 📶 ✕ 📷 🔌 💻

SENECA FALLS

AAA ▼▼▼ Microtel Inn & Suites by Wyndham Seneca Falls H
(315) 539-8438. **$60-$100.** 1966 Rt 5 & 20 13148. I-90 (New York State Thruway) exit 41, 4 mi s on SR 414, then just e. Int corridors. **Pets:** Other species. $15 daily fee/room. Supervision.
SAVE 🛏 📶 ✕ 🔌 💻

SKANEATELES

▼▼▼ Finger Lakes Lodging M
(315) 217-0222. **Call for rates.** 834 W Genesee St 13152. On US 20, just w. Ext/int corridors. **Pets:** Accepted. 🛏 📶 ✕ 🔌

WWWW Skaneateles Suites M
(315) 685-7568. **$100-$200.** 4114 E Genesee St 13021. On US 20, 2 mi w. Ext corridors. **Pets:** Other species. $35 one-time fee/pet. Service with restrictions, crate. 🍴 🛜 ⊗ 🛏 🖥

SOUTHAMPTON
AAA WWWW Southampton Inn H ❀
(631) 283-6500. **$134-$583.** 91 Hill St 11968. 0.3 mi n from corner of Main St and Jobs Ln. Ext/int corridors. **Pets:** Other species. $49 daily fee/pet. Designated rooms, service with restrictions.
SAVE 🍴 ♿ 🏊 ⊗ 🛜 ⊗ 🛏

SPRINGVILLE
WWW Microtel Inn & Suites by Wyndham Springville H
(716) 592-3141. **$70-$121.** 270 S Cascade Dr 14141. US 219 exit SR 39 just e, then just s. Int corridors. **Pets:** Medium. $20 daily fee/pet. Service with restrictions, supervision. ♿ 🛜 ⊗ 🛏 🖥

STONY BROOK
WWW Holiday Inn Express Stony Brook H
(631) 471-8000. **Call for rates.** 3131 Nesconset Hwy 11720. I-495 exit 62 (CR 97/Nicolls Rd N), 8 mi n, then 0.6 mi e on SR 347. Int corridors. **Pets:** Accepted. 🍴 ♿ 🏊 🛜 ⊗ 🛏 🖥

SUFFERN
AAA WWWW Crowne Plaza Suffern-Mahwah Hotel and Conference Center H
(845) 357-4800. **$109-$229.** 3 Executive Blvd 10901. I-87 (New York State Thruway) exit 14B, just n. Int corridors. **Pets:** Accepted.
SAVE ♿ 🍴 ♿ 🛜 ⊗ 🛏 🖥

SYLVAN BEACH
WW Cinderella's Restaurant, Bar & Suites M
(315) 762-4280. **$59-$299, 15 day notice.** 1208 Main St 13157. On SR 13; center. Ext corridors. **Pets:** Other species. Service with restrictions, crate. 🍴 🛜 ⊗ 🛏 🖥

SYRACUSE *(Restaurants p. 619)*
WW Clarion Inn & Suites H
(315) 457-8700. **$75-$310.** 100 Farrell Rd 13209. I-690 exit 3 (Farrell Rd) westbound; exit 4 (John Glenn Blvd) eastbound, just n to Farrell Rd. Int corridors. **Pets:** Accepted. 🍴 🏊 🛜 ⊗ 🛏 🖥

WW Comfort Inn & Suites/Syracuse Airport H
(315) 457-4000. **$95-$359.** 6701 Buckley Rd 13088. I-81 exit 25 (7th North St), just w. Int corridors. **Pets:** Accepted.
🍴 ♿ 🏊 🛜 ⊗ 🛏 🖥

AAA WWW Comfort Inn - Carrier Circle H
(315) 437-0222. **$77-$219.** 6491 Thompson Rd S 13206. I-90 exit 35 (Carrier Cir), just s. Ext/int corridors. **Pets:** Accepted.
SAVE 🍴 ♿ 🛜 ⊗ 🛏 🖥

WWW Crowne Plaza Syracuse-Hotel & Conference Center H
(315) 479-7000. **$119-$299.** 701 E Genesee St 13210. Jct Almond St; downtown. Int corridors. **Pets:** Other species. $50 one-time fee/pet. Designated rooms, service with restrictions.
🍴 ♿ ⊗ 🛏 🖥

WWW Genesee Grande Hotel H
(315) 476-4212. **Call for rates.** 1060 E Genesee St 13210. I-81 exit 18, 0.7 mi e on SR 92 (Genesee St). Int corridors. **Pets:** Accepted.
🍴 🛜 ⊗ 🛏 🖥

AAA WWW Red Roof Inn Syracuse M
(315) 437-3309. **$54-$180.** 6614 N Thompson Rd 13206. I-90 exit 35 (Carrier Cir), just n. Ext corridors. **Pets:** Accepted.
SAVE ♿ 🛜 ⊗ 🛏 🖥

AAA WWWW Sheraton Syracuse University Hotel & Conference Center H ❀
(315) 475-3000. **$129-$499.** 801 University Ave 13210. I-81 exit 18, just e. Int corridors. **Pets:** Medium, dogs only. Service with restrictions, supervision. SAVE ECO 🍴 ♿ 🏊 🛜 ⊗ 🛏 🖥

TARRYTOWN
AAA WWW Sheraton Tarrytown Hotel H
(914) 332-7900. **Call for rates.** 600 White Plains Rd 10591. I-87 exit 9 northbound, 0.8 mi e on SR 119; exit southbound, just n on US 9, then 1 mi e on SR 119. Int corridors. **Pets:** Accepted.
SAVE 🍴 ♿ 🏊 🔊 ⊗ 🖥

AAA WWWW Westchester Marriott Hotel H
(914) 631-2200. **$94-$362.** 670 White Plains Rd 10591. I-87 (New York State Thruway) exit 9 northbound, 0.8 mi e on SR 119; exit southbound, just n on US 9, then 1 mi e on SR 119. Int corridors.
Pets: Accepted. SAVE ECO 🍴 ♿ 🏊 ⊗ 🛜 ⊗ 🛏 🖥

THE BRONX
WWW Residence Inn New York The Bronx at Metro Center Atrium
(718) 239-3939. **$163-$351.** 1776 Eastchester Rd 10461. Between Marconi St and Bassett Ave; on Calvary Hospital access road. Int corridors.
Pets: Accepted. 🍴 ♿ 🛜 ⊗ 🛏 🖥

TICONDEROGA
AAA WWW Best Western Plus Ticonderoga Inn & Suites H
(518) 585-2378. **$105-$165.** 260 Burgoyne Rd 12883. Jct SR 9N and 74/22, just se on SR 22, just s. Int corridors. **Pets:** Accepted.
SAVE 🍴 ♿ 🏊 🛜 ⊗ 🛏 🖥

WWW Super 8 Ticonderoga H
(518) 585-2617. **$70-$105.** 1144 Wicker St 12883. Jct SR 9N and 74/22. Int corridors. **Pets:** Accepted. 🛜 ⊗ 🛏 🖥

TROY
AAA WWW Best Western Plus Franklin Square Inn Troy/Albany H ❀
(518) 274-8800. **$100-$300.** One 4th St 12180. I-787 exit 8, just e on 23rd to Federal St, just e to 4th St, then just s; downtown. Int corridors. **Pets:** Other species. $25 one-time fee/room. Service with restrictions.
SAVE ♿ 🛜 ⊗ 🛏 🖥

TULLY
AAA WWW Best Western Tully Inn H
(315) 696-6061. **$88-$220.** 5779 SR 80 13159. I-81 exit 14, just e. Int corridors. **Pets:** Medium. $10 daily fee/pet. Designated rooms, no service, supervision. SAVE 🍴 ♿ 🛜 ⊗ 🛏 🖥

UTICA
AAA WWW Best Western Gateway Adirondack Inn H
(315) 732-4121. **$96-$176.** 175 N Genesee St 13502. I-90 (New York State Thruway) exit 31, 0.5 mi s. Int corridors. **Pets:** Medium, dogs only. $20 daily fee/pet. Designated rooms, service with restrictions, supervision. SAVE 🛜 ⊗ 🛏 🖥

WWW Hotel Utica H
(315) 724-7829. **Call for rates.** 102 Lafayette St 13502. I-90 (New York State Thruway) exit 31, 1.1 mi s on Genesee St; center. Int corridors.
Pets: Accepted. 🍴 🛜 ⊗ 🛏 🖥

AAA WWW Red Roof Inn Utica M
(315) 724-7128. **$49-$190.** 20 Weaver St 13502. I-90 (New York State Thruway) exit 31. Ext corridors. **Pets:** Accepted.
SAVE 🛜 ⊗ 🛏 🖥

WWW Rosemont Inn Bed & Breakfast BB
(315) 797-9033. **Call for rates.** 1423 Genesee St 13501. I-90 (New York State Thruway) exit 31, 2.5 mi s. Int corridors. **Pets:** Accepted.

VERONA
WWW Microtel Inn & Suites by Wyndham Verona H
(315) 363-1850. **$81-$159.** 5118 NY S Rt 365 13478. I-90 (New York State Thruway) exit 33, 0.5 mi s. Int corridors. **Pets:** Accepted.

VICTOR
AAA WWWW Best Western Plus Victor Inn & Suites H
(585) 924-3933. **$90-$160.** 7449 SR 96 14564. I-90 (New York State Thruway) exit 45, 0.5 mi s. Int corridors. **Pets:** Small, dogs only. $35 daily fee/room. Service with restrictions, supervision.

WWWW Hampton Inn & Suites-Rochester/Victor H
(585) 924-4400. **$122-$229.** 7637 Pittsford-Victor Rd/SR 96 14564. I-90 (New York State Thruway) exit 45, just n. Int corridors. **Pets:** Very small. $75 one-time fee/room. Designated rooms, service with restrictions, supervision.

WWWW Homewood Suites by Hilton H
(585) 869-7500. **$99-$219.** 575 Fishers Station Dr 14564. I-90 (New York State Thruway) exit 45, just s on SR 96, then just w. Int corridors. **Pets:** Accepted.

WWW Microtel Inn by Wyndham Victor/Rochester H
(585) 924-9240. **$55-$150.** 7498 Main St Fishers 14564. I-90 (New York State Thruway) exit 45, just s on SR 96, then just e. Int corridors. **Pets:** Accepted.

WARNERS
WWWW Holiday Inn Express Syracuse/Fairgrounds H
(315) 701-5000. **$102-$164, 3 day notice.** 6946 Winchell Rd 13164. I-690 exit 5 eastbound, just n on State Fair Blvd; exit westbound, just s on State Fair Blvd, 1 mi w on Walters Rd, then just n. Int corridors. **Pets:** Accepted.

WARRENSBURG
WWW Super 8 Lake George - Warrensburg M ☙
(518) 623-2811. **$85-$95.** 3619 SR 9 12845. I-87 exit 23, just w. Int corridors. **Pets:** Other species. $15 one-time fee/room. Designated rooms, service with restrictions, crate.

WATERLOO
WWWW Holiday Inn Waterloo-Seneca Falls H ☙
(315) 539-5011. **Call for rates.** 2468 SR 414 13165. I-90 (New York State Thruway) exit 41, 4 mi s; just n of jct SR 414/5 and US 20. Int corridors. **Pets:** Medium. $15 daily fee/room. Service with restrictions, supervision.

WATERTOWN
AAA WWWW Best Western Watertown Fort Drum H
(315) 782-8000. **$90-$159.** 300 Washington St 13601. Center. Int corridors. **Pets:** Accepted.

WWWW Comfort Inn & Suites H
(315) 782-2700. **$89-$139.** 110 Commerce Park Dr 13601. I-81 exit 45, 0.4 mi e on Arsenal St, then just n. Int corridors. **Pets:** Accepted.

WWW Ramada H
(315) 788-0700. **$89-$94.** 21000 NYS Rt 3 13601. I-81 exit 45, just sw. Int corridors. **Pets:** $30 one-time fee/room. Designated rooms, service with restrictions, supervision.

WATKINS GLEN
AAA WWW Anchor Inn and Marina M
(607) 535-4159. **Call for rates.** 3425 Salt Point Rd 14891. Just n on SR 14, 0.8 mi n. Ext corridors. **Pets:** Medium, dogs only. $25 deposit/pet. Service with restrictions, supervision.

WEEDSPORT
WWW Rodeway Inn & Suites M
(315) 834-6623. **$55-$150.** 2709 Erie Dr 13166. I-90 exit 40, just s to jct SR 34 and 31, then 0.3 mi w on SR 31. Ext corridors. **Pets:** Accepted.

WELLSVILLE
WWW Microtel Inn & Suites by Wyndham Wellsville H
(585) 593-3449. **$70-$115.** 30 W Dyke St 14895. Just n off SR 19 and 417. Int corridors. **Pets:** Accepted.

WESTBURY
WWW Viana Hotel & Spa H
(516) 338-7777. **Call for rates.** 3998 Brush Hollow Rd 11590. Northern Pkwy exit 34, just ne. Int corridors. **Pets:** Accepted.

WEST COXSACKIE
AAA WWW Best Western New Baltimore Inn H
(518) 731-8100. **$99-$169.** 12600 Rt 9W 12192. I-87 (New York State Thruway) exit 21B, 0.5 mi s. Int corridors. **Pets:** Accepted.

WEST SENECA
WWW Staybridge Suites Buffalo-South H
(716) 939-3100. **Call for rates.** 164 Slade Ave 14224. I-90 exit 55 (Ridge Rd E), northbound, just n; exit 55 southbound, just e on Ridge Rd, then just n. Int corridors. **Pets:** Accepted.

WHITE PLAINS
AAA WWW Hyatt House White Plains H
(914) 251-9700. **$129-$359.** 101 Corporate Park Dr 10604. I-287 (Cross Westchester Expwy) exit 9A eastbound, 0.6 mi e on Westchester Ave, then 0.3 mi n; exit 9N-S westbound, 0.9 mi w on Westchester Ave. Int corridors. **Pets:** Medium, dogs only. $150 one-time fee/pet. Designated rooms, service with restrictions, crate.

WWW Residence Inn by Marriott White Plains H
(914) 761-7700. **$125-$328.** 5 Barker Ave 10601. I-287 exit 6 westbound, w on service road to SR 22 (Broadway), 0.8 mi s to Barker Ave, then 0.5 mi w; exit eastbound, s on Broadway. Int corridors. **Pets:** Accepted.

WILLIAMSVILLE
WWW La Quinta Inn Buffalo Airport H
(716) 633-1011. **$75-$328.** 6619 Transit Rd 14221. I-90 exit 49, just n. Int corridors. **Pets:** Accepted.

AAA WWW Residence Inn by Marriott Buffalo/Amherst H
(716) 632-6622. **$101-$246.** 100 Maple Rd 14221. I-290 exit 5B, just n on Millersport Hwy exit Maple Rd, then just e. Ext corridors. **Pets:** Large, other species. $100 one-time fee/room. Service with restrictions.

WILMINGTON
WWW Hungry Trout Resort M
(518) 946-2217. **Call for rates.** 5239 Rt 86 12997. On SR 86, 2 mi w. Ext corridors. **Pets:** Accepted.

Willkommen Hof Bed & Breakfast BB
(518) 946-7669. **Call for rates.** 5367 SR 86 12997. On SR 86, 1.5 mi sw of jct CR 431. Int corridors. **Pets:** Other species. $50 deposit/room, $10 daily fee/pet. Designated rooms, service with restrictions, crate.

WOODBURY

Best Western Woodbury Inn M
(516) 921-6900. **$99-$109.** 7940 Jericho Tpke (SR 25) 11797. Jct SR 25 and 135, 0.9 mi e. Ext/int corridors. **Pets:** Accepted.

The Inn at Fox Hollow H ✿
(516) 224-8100. **Call for rates.** 7755 Jericho Tpke 11797. Jct SR 25 and 135, 0.4 mi e. Int corridors. **Pets:** Small, dogs only. $150 one-time fee/room, $15 daily fee/pet. Designated rooms, service with restrictions.

YONKERS

Hampton Inn & Suites H
(914) 377-1144. **$169-$299.** 160 Corporate Blvd 10701. Sawmill Pkwy exit 9, 0.8 mi w. Int corridors. **Pets:** Accepted.

Hyatt Place New York/Yonkers H
(914) 377-1400. **$109-$399.** 7000 Mall Walk 10704. I-87 exit 4, just ne; in Cross County Mall Plaza. Int corridors. **Pets:** Accepted.

NORTH CAROLINA

ABERDEEN

Hampton Inn & Suites H
(910) 693-4330. **$109-$169.** 200 Columbus Dr 28315. Jct US 1, just n on US 15/501, then just s. Int corridors. **Pets:** Accepted.

ALBEMARLE

Quality Inn M
(704) 983-6990. **$80-$85.** 735 NC 24/27 Bypass E 28001. Jct US 52 S, 1.4 mi e. Ext corridors. **Pets:** Accepted.

APEX

Candlewood Suites-Apex/Raleigh H
(919) 387-8595. **Call for rates.** 1005 Marco Dr 27502. US 1 exit 95, just w on SR 55. Int corridors. **Pets:** Accepted.

ARCHDALE

Comfort Inn Near High Point University H
(336) 434-4797. **$80-$220.** 10123 N Main St 27263. I-85 exit 111, just n on US 311 business route. Int corridors. **Pets:** Accepted.

Hampton Inn-High Point H
(336) 434-5200. **$109-$159.** 10066 N Main St 27263. I-85 exit 111, just n on US 311 business route. Int corridors. **Pets:** Accepted.

Holiday Inn Express Hotel & Suites H
(336) 861-3310. **$89-$149.** 10050 N Main St 27263. I-85 exit 111, just n on US 311 business route. Int corridors. **Pets:** Accepted.

ASHEBORO

Holiday Inn Express Hotel & Suites H
(336) 636-5222. **Call for rates.** 1113 E Dixie Dr 27203. Jct SR 42, 0.5 mi w on US 64. Int corridors. **Pets:** Accepted.

Quality Inn H ✿
(336) 626-3680. **$75-$110.** 242 Lakecrest Rd 27203. US 64, just nw on SR 42. Ext corridors. **Pets:** Medium, other species. $20 daily fee/pet. Service with restrictions, crate.

ASHEVILLE *(Restaurants p. 619)*

1889 WhiteGate Inn & Cottage BB ✿
(828) 253-2553. **$169-$379, 14 day notice.** 173 E Chestnut St 28801. I-240 exit 5B (Charlotte St), just n, then just w; in historic district. Ext/int corridors. **Pets:** Dogs only. $50 one-time fee/room. Designated rooms, service with restrictions, supervision.

1900 Inn on Montford BB ✿
(828) 254-9569. **$155-$625, 14 day notice.** 296 Montford Ave 28801. I-240 exit 4C (Montford Ave/Haywood St), 0.7 mi n; in historic district. Ext/int corridors. **Pets:** Other species. Designated rooms, no service, supervision.

Abbington Green Bed & Breakfast Inn BB ✿
(828) 251-2454. **$219-$399, 30 day notice.** 46 Cumberland Cir 28801. I-240 exit 4C (Montford Ave/Haywood St), just n on Montford Ave, just e on W Chestnut St, just n on Cumberland Ave, just n on Montford Historic District. Ext/int corridors. **Pets:** Dogs only. $30 daily fee/pet. Designated rooms, crate.

Aloft Asheville Downtown H ✿
(828) 232-2838. **$149-$599.** 51 Biltmore Ave 28801. On US 25. Int corridors. **Pets:** Other species. Service with restrictions, supervision.

The Applewood Manor BB
(828) 254-2244. **$170-$265, 5 day notice.** 62 Cumberland Cir 28801. I-240 exit 4C (Montford Ave/Haywood St), just n on Montford Ave, just e on W Chestnut St, just n on Cumberland Ave, then just ne. Ext/int corridors. **Pets:** Medium, dogs only. $35 daily fee/room. Designated rooms.

Best Western of Asheville Biltmore East M
(828) 298-5562. **$89-$169.** 501 Tunnel Rd 28805. I-240 exit 7, 0.5 mi e on US 70 (Tunnel Rd). Ext corridors. **Pets:** Dogs only. $10 daily fee/pet. Service with restrictions, supervision.

Cedar Crest Inn BB
(828) 252-1389. **Call for rates.** 674 Biltmore Ave 28803. I-40 exit 50, 1.1 mi n. Ext/int corridors. **Pets:** $50 one-time fee/room. Designated rooms, service with restrictions.

Comfort Inn-West H
(828) 665-6500. **$90-$350.** 15 Crowell Rd 28806. I-40 exit 44, just n on US 19 and 23, just w on Old Haywood Rd, then just s. Int corridors. **Pets:** Medium. $24 daily fee/pet. Designated rooms, no service, supervision.

Comfort Suites Outlet Center H ❧
(828) 665-4000. **$105-$330.** 890 Brevard Rd 28806. I-26 exit 33, 0.3 mi w. Int corridors. **Pets:** Other species. $25 daily fee/room. Designated rooms, service with restrictions, crate.

Country Inn & Suites by Carlson Asheville - Westgate H ❧
(828) 772-3188. **$109-$399.** 22 Westgate Pkwy 28806. I-240 exit 3B (Westgate Resort Dr), 0.5 mi w. Int corridors. **Pets:** Dogs only. $50 one-time fee/pet. Designated rooms, service with restrictions.

Crowne Plaza Tennis & Golf Resort H
(828) 254-3211. **$99-$369, 3 day notice.** One Resort Dr 28806. I-240 exit 3B (Resort Dr), just w. Int corridors. **Pets:** Accepted.

Days Inn-Biltmore East H
(828) 298-4000. **$65-$200.** 1435 Tunnel Rd 28805. I-40 exit 55, just n. Int corridors. **Pets:** Dogs only. $10 daily fee/pet. Designated rooms, no service, supervision.

DoubleTree by Hilton Hotel Asheville-Biltmore H
(828) 274-1800. **$119-$299.** 115 Hendersonville Rd 28803. I-40 exit 50 eastbound; exit 50B westbound, just n on US 25. Int corridors. **Pets:** Accepted.

Extended Stay America Asheville-Tunnel Rd H
(828) 253-3483. **$85-$115.** 6 Kenilworth Knoll 28805. I-240 exit 6, 0.7 mi e on US 70 (Tunnel Rd), then just n. Int corridors. **Pets:** Accepted.

Four Points by Sheraton Asheville Downtown H
(828) 253-1851. **$99-$399.** 22 Woodfin St 28801. I-240 exit 5A (Merrimon Ave), just s, then just w. Int corridors. **Pets:** $50 one-time fee/room. Designated rooms, service with restrictions, supervision.

Grand Bohemian Hotel Asheville, Autograph Collection H ❧
(828) 505-2949. **$161-$438, 3 day notice.** 11 Boston Way 28803. I-40 exit 50/50B, just se of US 25; at Biltmore Village. Int corridors. **Pets:** Dogs only. $150 one-time fee/room. Designated rooms, service with restrictions, supervision.

Haywood Park Hotel & Atrium H ❧
(828) 252-2522. **Call for rates.** One Battery Park Ave 28801. I-240 exit 4C (Montford Ave/Haywood St), 0.6 mi se on Haywood St, then just w. Int corridors. **Pets:** Large, dogs only. $50 one-time fee/pet. Designated rooms, service with restrictions.

Hill House BB
(828) 232-0345. **$111-$300, 14 day notice.** 120 Hillside St 28801. I-240 exit 5A (Merrimon Ave), just n, then just w. Ext/int corridors. **Pets:** Dogs only. $12 daily fee/room. Designated rooms, service with restrictions.

Hilton Asheville Biltmore Park H ❧
(828) 209-2700. **$149-$309.** 43 Town Square Blvd 28803. I-26 exit 37, just e on Long Shoals Rd, then w; in Biltmore Park Town Square. Int corridors. **Pets:** Large. $50 one-time fee/room. Designated rooms, service with restrictions.

Holiday Inn-Biltmore East at the Blue Ridge Parkway H ❧
(828) 298-5611. **Call for rates.** 1450 Tunnel Rd 28805. I-40 exit 55, just n. Int corridors. **Pets:** Other species. $35 daily fee/room. Designated rooms, service with restrictions, crate.

Hotel Indigo H ❧
(828) 239-0239. **$169-$539, 7 day notice.** 151 Haywood St 28801. I-240 exit 4C (Montford Ave/Haywood St), just s, then just w. Int corridors. **Pets:** Large, other species. $75 one-time fee/room. Designated rooms, service with restrictions, crate.

The Omni Grove Park Inn H
(828) 252-2711. **Call for rates.** 290 Macon Ave 28804. I-240 exit 5B (Charlotte St), 2 mi n on Macon Ave via Charlotte St, follow signs. Int corridors. **Pets:** Accepted.

Quality Inn & Suites M
(828) 298-5519. **$80-$190.** 1430 Tunnel Rd 28805. I-40 exit 55, just n. Ext corridors. **Pets:** Designated rooms, service with restrictions, supervision.

Ramada H ❧
(828) 298-9141. **$79-$200, 3 day notice.** 148 River Ford Pkwy 28803. I-240 exit 8; just nw of jct I-40 and US 74. Int corridors. **Pets:** Other species. $15 one-time fee/pet, $10 daily fee/pet. Designated rooms, service with restrictions, supervision.

Red Roof Inn-Asheville West M
(828) 667-9803. **$50-$159.** 16 Crowell Rd 28806. I-40 exit 44, just n on US 19 and 23, just w on Old Haywood Rd, then just s. Ext corridors. **Pets:** Accepted.

Renaissance Asheville Hotel H
(828) 252-8211. **$133-$321.** 31 Woodfin St 28801. I-240 exit 5A (Merrimon Ave), Jct US 25 (Broadway St), just e. Int corridors. **Pets:** Small, dogs only. $75 one-time fee/pet. Designated rooms, service with restrictions, supervision.

Residence Inn by Marriott Biltmore H
(828) 281-3361. **$156-$295.** 701 Biltmore Ave 28803. I-40 exit 50, 1 mi n. Int corridors. **Pets:** Accepted.

Rodeway Inn & Suites at Asheville Outlet Mall H
(828) 670-8800. **$65-$159.** 9 Wedgefield Dr 28806. I-26 exit 33, just nw. Int corridors. **Pets:** Medium. $15 daily fee/pet. Service with restrictions, supervision.

The Windsor Boutique Hotel H
(828) 225-1995. **Call for rates.** 36 Broadway St 28801. Jct Walnut St. Int corridors. **Pets:** Accepted.

ATLANTIC BEACH

DoubleTree by Hilton Hotel Atlantic Beach Oceanfront H
(252) 240-1155. **Call for rates.** 2717 W Ft Macon Rd 28512. 2.3 mi n on SR 58 N, at MP 4.5. Int corridors. **Pets:** Accepted.

BANNER ELK

Best Western Mountain Lodge at Banner Elk H ❧
(828) 898-4571. **$80-$170.** 1615 Tynecastle Hwy 28604. Jct SR 194, 1.3 mi s on SR 184. Ext corridors. **Pets:** Large. $10 daily fee/room. Designated rooms, service with restrictions, supervision.

BATTLEBORO

AAA ▼▼▼ Baymont Inn & Suites I-95/Rocky Mount **M** ❀

(252) 985-1450. **$75-$99.** 7095 NC 4 27809. I-95 exit 145, just e. Ext corridors. **Pets:** Medium, other species. $22 daily fee/pet.

SAVE &M 🛏 🛜 🖫 💻

BEAUFORT

▼▼▼ Pecan Tree Inn **BB**

(252) 728-6733. **$135-$200, 7 day notice.** 116 Queen St 28516. Jct US 70, just s. Ext/int corridors. **Pets:** Accepted. 🍴 🛜 ✕ 💤

BLACK MOUNTAIN

AAA ▼▼▼ Quality Inn Black Mountain **M**

(828) 669-9950. **$90-$210.** 585 NC Hwy 9 28711. I-40 exit 64, just s. Ext corridors. **Pets:** Dogs only. $20 daily fee/pet. Designated rooms, service with restrictions, supervision.

SAVE &M 🛏 🛜 ✕ 🖫 💻

BLOWING ROCK *(Restaurants p. 620)*

▼▼▼ Alpine Village Inn **M**

(828) 295-7206. **$69-$199, 7 day notice.** 297 Sunset Dr 28605. Jct US 321, just w. Ext corridors. **Pets:** $15 daily fee/pet. Designated rooms, service with restrictions, supervision. 🛜 ✕ 🖫 💻

▼▼▼ Hillwinds Inn **M**

(828) 295-7660. **$89-$350, 3 day notice.** 315 Sunset Dr 28605. Jct US 321 bypass, just w. Ext/int corridors. **Pets:** Dogs only. $25 daily fee/room. Designated rooms, service with restrictions, crate.

🛜 ✕ 🖫 💻

▼▼▼ Homestead Inn **M**

(828) 295-9559. **$59-$129, 4 day notice.** 153 Morris St 28605. Jct US 321 business route (Main St), just e. Ext corridors. **Pets:** Accepted.

&M 🛜 ✕ 🖫 💻

BOLIVIA

▼▼▼ Holiday Inn & Suites Southport-Oak Island **H**

(910) 253-9100. **Call for rates.** 3400 Southport Supply Rd 28422. On SR 211 just e of jct Midway Rd SE. Int corridors. **Pets:** Accepted.

&M 🛜 ✕ 🖫 💻

BOONE

▼▼ Baymont Inn & Suites Boone South **H**

(828) 264-0077. **$70-$149.** 1075 Hwy 105 28607. Jct US 321, just sw. Int corridors. **Pets:** Medium. $50 one-time fee/room. Designated rooms, service with restrictions. 🛏 🛜 ✕ 🖫 💻

▼▼▼ La Quinta Inn & Suites Boone **H**

(828) 262-1234. **$71-$317.** 165 Hwy 105 N Ext 28607. Jct US 421, just s. Int corridors. **Pets:** Accepted. &M 🛏 🛜 ✕ 🖫 💻

BREVARD

▼▼▼ Hampton Inn-Brevard **H**

(828) 883-4800. **$109-$199.** 275 Forest Gate Dr 28768. Jct US 64, just e on SR 280, then just n. Int corridors. **Pets:** Accepted.

&M 🛏 🛜 ✕ 🖫 💻

▼▼▼ Holiday Inn Express & Suites Brevard **H**

(828) 862-8900. **Call for rates.** 2228 Asheville Hwy 28712. Jct SR 280, just w on US 64. Int corridors. **Pets:** Accepted.

&M 🛏 🛜 ✕ 🖫 💻

AAA ▼▼▼ The Inn at Brevard **BB**

(828) 884-2105. **Call for rates.** 315 E Main St 28712. Jct US 64 (Broad St), just e; center. Ext/int corridors. **Pets:** Accepted.

SAVE 🛜 ✕ 💤 💻

BURLINGTON

▼▼▼▼ Drury Inn & Suites Burlington **H**

(336) 584-2004. **$85-$170.** 1767 Glidewell Dr 27215. I-40/85 exit 140, just n on University Dr, then just e on Boone Station Dr. Int corridors. **Pets:** Accepted. 🍴 &M 🛜 ✕ 🖫 💻

BUXTON

▼▼ Lighthouse View Oceanfront Lodging **H**

(252) 995-5680. **$74-$179, 7 day notice.** 46677 NC Hwy 12 27920. 0.5 mi n of Cape Hatteras Lighthouse. Ext corridors. **Pets:** $10 daily fee/pet. Designated rooms, no service. 🛏 🛜 🖫 💻

CANTON

▼▼ Americas Best Value Inn Canton **M**

(828) 648-0300. **Call for rates.** 1963 Champion Dr 28716. I-40 exit 31, just n. Ext corridors. **Pets:** Accepted. 🛏 🛜 🖫 💻

CARY

AAA ▼▼▼ Best Western Plus Cary Inn - NC State **H**

(919) 481-1200. **$89-$119.** 1722 Walnut St 27511. I-40 exit 293A, just s on US 1 exit 101A, just e on Walnut St, then just s on Ledsome Ln. Ext/int corridors. **Pets:** Accepted. SAVE 🛏 🛜 ✕ 🖫 💻

▼▼▼ Comfort Suites Regency Park **H**

(919) 852-4318. **$84-$149.** 350 Ashville Ave 27518. US 1 exit 98A, 0.8 mi e on Tryon Rd, then just n. Int corridors. **Pets:** Other species. $50 one-time fee/room. Designated rooms. &M 🛏 🛜 ✕ 🖫 💻

▼▼▼ Hampton Inn & Suites **H**

(919) 233-1798. **$99-$199.** 111 Hampton Woods Ln 27607. I-40 exit 290, just w on SR 54, then just s. Int corridors. **Pets:** Accepted.

🍴 &M 🛏 🛜 ✕ 🖫 💻

▼▼▼ Hawthorn Suites by Wyndham Raleigh **H**

(919) 468-4222. **$79-$159.** 1020 Buck Jones Rd 27606. I-40 exit 293A, just s on US 1 exit 101B, 0.5 mi nw; in Buck Jones Village. Int corridors. **Pets:** $15 daily fee/room. Service with restrictions, crate.

&M 🛜 ✕ 🖫 💻

▼▼▼ La Quinta Inn & Suites Raleigh (Cary) **H**

(919) 851-2850. **$82-$163.** 191 Crescent Commons Dr 27518. US 1 exit 98A, 0.5 mi e on Tryon Rd, then just n. Int corridors. **Pets:** Accepted. &M 🛏 🛜 🖫 💻

▼▼▼ Residence Inn by Marriott Raleigh Cary **H**

(919) 467-4080. **$79-$229.** 2900 Regency Pkwy 27518. US 1 exit 98A, 0.5 mi e on Tryon Rd, then just s. Int corridors. **Pets:** Accepted.

ECO &M 🛏 🛜 ✕ 🖫 💻

▼▼▼ TownePlace Suites by Marriott-Raleigh/Cary/Weston Parkway **H**

(919) 678-0005. **$89-$177.** 120 Sage Commons Way 27513. I-40 exit 287, 0.5 mi s on Harrison Ave, 2.3 mi w on Weston Pkwy, then just n. Int corridors. **Pets:** Accepted. 🍴 &M 🛏 🛜 ✕ 🖫 💻

AAA ▼▼▼▼▼ The Umstead Hotel & Spa **H** ❀

(919) 447-4000. **$279-$639.** 100 Woodland Pond Dr 27513. I-40 exit 287, just s on Harrison Ave, then just n on SAS Campus Dr, then just n. Int corridors. **Pets:** Other species. $200 one-time fee/room.

SAVE 🍴 🍴 &M 🛏 ✕ 🛜 ✕ 💻

CASHIERS *(Restaurants p. 620)*

AAA ▼▼▼▼ High Hampton Inn & Country Club **H**

(828) 743-2411. **Call for rates.** 1525 Hwy 107 28717. Jct US 64, 1.5 mi s. Ext/int corridors. **Pets:** Accepted.

SAVE 🍴 ✕ 🛜 ✕ ⛳ 🎾 💤 🖫

CHAPEL HILL

⬜⬛ ◈◈◈◈ Aloft - Chapel Hill ⊞
(919) 932-7772. **$69-$369.** 1001 S Hamilton Rd 27517. I-40 exit 273/ 273A, 2.6 mi w on SR 54, then just s. Int corridors. **Pets:** Accepted.

SAVE 🅼 🛌 🛜 ✕ 🖥 🖵

◈◈ Chapel Hill University Inn Ⓜ
(919) 929-2171. **Call for rates.** 1301 Fordham Blvd 27514. I-40 exit 270, 2 mi s on US 15/501. Ext corridors. **Pets:** Accepted.

🍽 🛌 🛜 🖥 🖵

◈◈ Quality Inn ⊞
(919) 968-3000. **$61-$99.** 1740 Fordham Blvd 27514. I-40 exit 270, 1 mi s on US 15/501, just e on Europa Dr, then just s on service road. Ext corridors. **Pets:** Accepted. 🅼 🛌 🛜 🖥 🖵

◈◈◈◈ Residence Inn by Marriott-Chapel Hill ⊞
(919) 933-4848. **$125-$177.** 101 Erwin Rd 27514. I-40 exit 270, 1.2 mi s on US 15/501, then just w. Int corridors. **Pets:** Accepted.

🅼 🛌 🛜 ✕ 🖥 🖵

◈◈◈◈ Sheraton Chapel Hill ⊞
(919) 968-4900. **$109-$359.** 1 Europa Dr 27517. I-40 exit 270, 1 mi s, then just e. Int corridors. **Pets:** Accepted.

SAVE 🍽 🛌 🛜 ✕ 🖥 🖵

◈◈◈◈ The Siena Hotel, Autograph Collection ⊞
(919) 929-4000. **$130-$208.** 1505 E Franklin St 27514. I-40 exit 270, 2 mi s on US 15/501, then 0.5 mi w. Int corridors. **Pets:** Accepted.

SAVE 🍽 🅼 🛜 ✕ 🖥 🖵

CHARLOTTE *(Restaurants p. 620)*

◈◈◈◈ Aloft Charlotte-Ballantyne ⊞ 🐾
(704) 247-2222. **Call for rates.** 13139 Ballantyne Corporate Pl 28277. I-485 exit 61 or 61B, 0.5 mi s on US 521 (Johnston Rd), just e on Ballantyne Commons Pkwy, then just n. Int corridors. **Pets:** Small, dogs only. Designated rooms, service with restrictions, supervision.

SAVE ECO 🅼 🛌 🛜 ✕ 🖥 🖵

◈◈◈◈ Aloft Charlotte Uptown @ the EpiCentre ⊞
(704) 333-1999. **Call for rates.** 210 E Trade St 28202. I-77 exit 10 or 10B, 0.6 mi e on Trade St, just s on Mint St, just e on 3rd St, then just n on College St. Int corridors. **Pets:** Accepted.

SAVE 🅼 🛌 🛜 🖥 🖵

◈◈◈◈ Candlewood Suites-Charlotte University ⊞
(704) 598-9863. **$80-$200.** 8812 University East Dr 28213. I-85 exit 45A (W.T. Harris Blvd), 2.5 mi e on SR 24, then just s; in University East Business Park. Int corridors. **Pets:** Accepted.

🅼 🛜 ✕ 🖥 🖵

◈◈◈◈ Comfort Suites-Airport ⊞
(704) 971-4400. **$109-$174.** 3425 Mulberry Church Rd 28208. I-85 exit 33, just s, then just e. Int corridors. **Pets:** Accepted.

SAVE 🍽 🅼 🛌 🛜 ✕ 🖥 🖵

◈◈◈◈ DoubleTree Suites by Hilton Hotel Charlotte-SouthPark ⊞
(704) 364-2400. **$199-$309.** 6300 Morrison Blvd 28211. I-77 exit 5 (Tyvola Rd), 3.3 mi e on Tyvola/Fairview rds, just n on Barclay Downs, then just e. Int corridors. **Pets:** Accepted.

SAVE 🍽 🛌 🛜 ✕ 🖥 🖵

◈◈◈◈ Drury Inn & Suites-Charlotte Northlake ⊞
(704) 599-8882. **$99-$179.** 6920 Northlake Mall Dr 28216. I-77 exit 18 (W.T. Harris Blvd), just w on SR 24. Int corridors. **Pets:** Accepted.

🅼 🛌 🛜 ✕ 🖥 🖵

◈◈◈◈ Drury Inn & Suites-Charlotte University Place ⊞
(704) 593-0700. **$89-$169.** 415 W W.T. Harris Blvd 28262. I-85 exit 45A (W.T. Harris Blvd), just e on SR 24. Int corridors. **Pets:** Accepted.

🅼 🛌 🛜 ✕ 🖥 🖵

◈◈ Extended Stay America-Charlotte-Pineville-Park Rd ⊞
(704) 341-0929. **$100-$115.** 10930 Park Rd 28226. I-485 exit 64A, just n on SR 51, then just e; behind Terraces at Park Place Shopping Center. Int corridors. **Pets:** Accepted. 🅼 🛜 🖥 🖵

◈◈ Extended Stay America-Charlotte-Pineville-Pineville Matthews Rd ⊞
(704) 542-9521. **$120-$140.** 8405 Pineville-Matthews Rd 28226. I-485 exit 64A, 0.7 mi n on SR 51. Int corridors. **Pets:** Accepted.

🛌 🛜 ✕ 🖥

◈◈ Extended Stay America-Charlotte-Tyvola Rd-Executive Park ⊞
(704) 527-1960. **$95-$110.** 5830 Westpark Dr 28217. I-77 exit 5 (Tyvola Rd), just e, then 0.4 mi s. Int corridors. **Pets:** Accepted.

🛌 🛜 ✕ 🖥 🖵

◈◈◈◈ Four Points by Sheraton-Charlotte ⊞
(704) 522-0852. **Call for rates.** 315 E Woodlawn Rd 28217. I-77 exit 6A, 0.5 mi e. Int corridors. **Pets:** Small. $150 one-time fee/room. Designated rooms, no service, supervision.

SAVE 🍽 🛌 🛜 ✕ 🖥 🖵

◈◈◈ Hawthorn Suites by Wyndham Charlotte Executive Park ⊞ 🐾
(704) 529-7500. **$89-$189.** 5840 Westpark Dr 28217. I-77 exit 5 (Tyvola Rd), just e, then 0.5 mi s. Int corridors. **Pets:** Medium, other species. $15 daily fee/pet. Service with restrictions, supervision.

🅼 🛜 ✕ 🖥 🖵

◈◈◈ Home2 Suites by Hilton Charlotte/I-77 South ⊞
(704) 405-4000. **$109-$189.** 6025 Tyvola Glen Cir 28217. I-77 exit 5 (Tyvola Rd), just w, then just n. Int corridors. **Pets:** Small, other species. $50 one-time fee/room. Service with restrictions, supervision.

🅼 🛜 🖥 🖵

◈◈◈ Homewood Suites by Hilton Airport ⊞
(704) 357-0500. **$109-$279.** 2770 Yorkmont Rd 28208. I-77 exit 6B, 2 mi nw on Billy Graham Pkwy exit Coliseum/Tyvola Rd, just se on Tyvola Rd, then just w. Int corridors. **Pets:** Accepted.

🍽 🅼 🛌 🛜 ✕ 🖥 🖵

◈◈◈ Homewood Suites by Hilton-University Research Park ⊞
(704) 549-8800. **$109-$179.** 8340 N Tryon St 28262. I-85 exit 45A (W.T. Harris Blvd), 0.5 mi e on SR 24, then just s on US 29 (N Tryon St). Ext/int corridors. **Pets:** Accepted. 🅼 🛌 🛜 🖥 🖵

◈◈◈◈ Hyatt House Charlotte Airport ⊞
(704) 525-2600. **$99-$289.** 4920 S Tryon St 28217. I-77 exit 6B northbound, just w, then just s; exit southbound, just s. Int corridors. **Pets:** Accepted. SAVE 🅼 🛌 🛜 ✕ 🖥 🖵

◈◈◈◈ Hyatt Place Charlotte/Airport/Lake Pointe ⊞ 🐾
(704) 357-8555. **$89-$229.** 4119 South Stream Blvd 28217. I-77 exit 6B, 2 mi nw on Billy Graham Pkwy exit Coliseum/Tyvola Rd, then 0.8 mi se on Tyvola Rd, then just s. Int corridors. **Pets:** Small, dogs only. $75 one-time fee/pet. Service with restrictions, supervision.

SAVE 🛌 🛜 ✕ 🖥 🖵

◈◈◈◈ Hyatt Place Charlotte Airport/Tyvola Road-Yorkmont ⊞
(704) 423-9931. **$89-$229.** 2950 Oak Lake Blvd 28208. I-77 exit 6B, 2 mi nw on Billy Graham Pkwy exit Coliseum/Tyvola Rd, just se on Tyvola Rd, just w on Yorkmont Rd, then just n. Int corridors. **Pets:** Accepted. SAVE 🛌 🛜 ✕ 🖥 🖵

Hyatt Place Charlotte/Arrowood H
(704) 522-8400. **$89-$269.** 7900 Forest Point Blvd 28273. I-77 exit 3 southbound; exit 2 northbound, just e. Int corridors. **Pets:** Accepted.
SAVE ⌖M 🏊 🛜 ✕ 🛗 🖵

La Quinta Inn & Suites Charlotte Airport North H
(704) 392-1600. **$79-$247.** 3127 Sloan Dr 28208. I-85 exit 33, just n on Mulberry Church Rd, then just w. Int corridors. **Pets:** Accepted.
⌖M 🛜 🛗 🖵

La Quinta Inn & Suites Charlotte Airport South H
(704) 523-5599. **$71-$257.** 4900 S Tryon St 28217. I-77 exit 6B northbound, just w, then just s; exit southbound, just s. Int corridors.
Pets: Accepted. ⌖M 🏊 🛜 ✕ 🛗 🖵

MainStay Suites H
(704) 521-3232. **$62-$145.** 7926 Forest Pine Dr 28273. I-77 exit 3 southbound; exit 2 northbound, just e, then just s. Int corridors.
Pets: Accepted. ⌖M 🏊 🛜 ✕ 🛗 🖵

Microtel Inn & Suites by Wyndham Charlotte/Northlake H
(704) 227-3377. **$59-$500.** 6309 Banner Elk Dr 28216. I-77 exit 16B, just w on Sunset Rd, then just s. Int corridors. **Pets:** Small. $20 daily fee/pet. Service with restrictions, supervision.
SAVE ⌖M 🏊 🛜 🛗 🖵

Morehead Inn BB
(704) 376-3357. **$149-$289.** 1122 E Morehead St 28204. I-277 exit 2A, 0.4 mi s on Kenilworth Ave, then just w. Ext/int corridors.
Pets: Accepted. 🛜 ✕ 🖵

Omni Charlotte Hotel H 🐾
(704) 377-0400. **$169-$599.** 132 E Trade St 28202. I-77 exit 10 or 10B, 0.8 mi e. Int corridors. **Pets:** Small. $50 one-time fee/room. Service with restrictions. SAVE 🍴 ⌖M 🏊 💦 ✕ 🖵

Residence Inn by Marriott Charlotte South at I-77/Tyvola Rd H
(704) 527-8110. **$85-$194.** 5816 Westpark Dr 28217. I-77 exit 5 (Tyvola Rd), just e, then 0.4 mi s. Ext/int corridors. **Pets:** Accepted.
SAVE ⌖M 🏊 🛜 ✕ 🛗 🖵

Residence Inn by Marriott Charlotte SouthPark H
(704) 554-7001. **$116-$237.** 6030 Piedmont Row Dr S 28210. I-77 exit 5 (Tyvola Rd), 3.2 mi e on Tyvola/Fairview rds, then just s. Int corridors.
Pets: Accepted. ⌖M 🏊 🛜 ✕ 🛗 🖵

Residence Inn by Marriott-Charlotte University Research Park H
(704) 547-1122. **$98-$194.** 8503 N Tryon St 28262. I-85 exit 45A (W.T. Harris Blvd), 0.5 mi e on SR 24, then just s on US 29 (N Tryon St).
Ext corridors. **Pets:** Accepted. ⌖M 🏊 🛜 ✕ 🛗 🖵

Residence Inn by Marriott-Charlotte Uptown H
(704) 340-4000. **$119-$263.** 404 S Mint St 28202. I-77 exit 10 or 10B, 0.6 mi e on Trade St, then just s. Int corridors. **Pets:** Accepted.
SAVE ECO 🍴 ⌖M 🛜 ✕ 🛗 🖵

Residence Inn by Marriott-Piper Glen H
(704) 319-3900. **$89-$229.** 5115 Piper Station Dr 28277. I-485 exit 59, just s on Rea Rd, then just e. Int corridors. **Pets:** Accepted.
⌖M 🏊 🛜 🛗 🖵

Sheraton Charlotte Airport Hotel H
(704) 392-1200. **$100-$400.** 3315 Scott Futrell Dr 28208. I-85 exit 33, just s on Mulberry Church Rd, then just w. Int corridors.
Pets: Accepted. SAVE 🍴 🏊 🛜 ✕ 🛗 🖵

Sleep Inn-Airport/Billy Graham Parkway H
(704) 525-5005. **$81-$159.** 701 Yorkmont Rd 28217. I-77 exit 6B northbound, just w, just s on S Tryon St, then just w; exit southbound, just s on S Tryon St, then just w. Int corridors. **Pets:** Accepted.
⌖M 🏊 🛜 ✕ 🛗 🖵

Sleep Inn Northlake H
(704) 399-7778. **$79-$199.** 6300 Banner Elk Dr 28216. I-77 exit 16B, just w on Sunset Rd, then just s. Int corridors. **Pets:** Accepted.
SAVE 🏊 🛜 ✕ 🛗 🖵

Sleep Inn University Place H
(704) 549-4544. **$84-$139.** 8525 N Tryon St 28262. I-85 exit 45A (W.T. Harris Blvd), 0.5 mi e on SR 24, just s on US 29 (N Tryon St). Int corridors. **Pets:** Accepted. ⌖M 🏊 🛜 🛗 🖵

Sonesta ES Suites Charlotte H
(704) 527-6767. **Call for rates.** 7925 Forest Pine Dr 28273. I-77 exit 3 southbound; exit 2 northbound, just e, then just s. Int corridors.
Pets: Accepted. SAVE ⌖M 🏊 🛜 ✕ 🛗 🖵

Staybridge Suites Charlotte-Ballantyne H
(704) 248-5000. **Call for rates.** 15735 Brixham Hill Ave 28277. I-485 exit 61 or 61B, just s on US 521 (Johnston Rd), then just w. Int corridors. **Pets:** Accepted. ⌖M 🏊 🛜 ✕ 🛗 🖵

TownePlace Suites by Marriott Charlotte Arrowood H
(704) 227-2000. **$99-$171.** 7805 Forest Point Blvd 28217. I-77 exit 3 southbound; exit 2 northbound, just e. Int corridors. **Pets:** Accepted.
SAVE ⌖M 🏊 🛜 ✕ 🛗 🖵

TownePlace Suites by Marriott-University H
(704) 548-0388. **$79-$144.** 8710 Research Dr 28262. I-85 exit 45B (W.T. Harris Blvd), just w on SR 24, then just n. Int corridors.
Pets: Accepted. SAVE ⌖M 🏊 🛜 ✕ 🛗 🖵

The Westin Charlotte H
(704) 375-2600. **$119-$449.** 601 S College St 28202. I-277 exit 1E (College St), 0.5 mi n; jct E Stonewall St. Int corridors. **Pets:** Accepted.
SAVE 🍴 ⌖M 🏊 ✕ 💦 ✕ 🛗 🖵

Wyndham Garden Charlotte Executive Park H
(704) 525-0747. **$89-$189.** 440 Griffith Rd 28217. I-77 exit 5 (Tyvola Rd), just e, just s on Westpark Dr, then just e. Int corridors.
Pets: Accepted. SAVE 🏊 🛜 ✕ 🛗 🖵

CHEROKEE

Microtel Inn & Suites by Wyndham Cherokee H
(828) 497-7800. **$65-$179.** 674 Casino Tr 28719. Jct US 441, just n on US 441 business route. Int corridors. **Pets:** Accepted.
⌖M 🏊 🛜 ✕ 🛗 🖵

CHOCOWINITY

Baymont Inn & Suites Chocowinity/Washington M
(252) 946-8001. **$69-$90.** 3635 US Hwy 17 S 27817. On US 17 business route. Ext corridors. **Pets:** Small. $10 daily fee/pet. Designated rooms, service with restrictions, supervision.
🍴 ⌖M 🏊 🛜 🛗 🖵

CLEMMONS

Super 8 Clemmons H
(336) 778-0931. **$59-$119.** 6204 Ramada Dr 27012. I-40 exit 184, just s, then just e. Int corridors. **Pets:** Small. $15 daily fee/pet. Supervision.
🛜 🛗 🖵

COLUMBUS

🏅 ◆◆◆ Days Inn Ⓜ
(828) 894-3303. **$95-$145.** 626 W Mills St 28722. I-26 exit 67, just w on SR 108. Ext corridors. **Pets:** Accepted.
🅂🅰🅅🅴 🍽 🌊 🛜 🔒 💻

CONCORD

◆ Americas Best Value Inn Ⓜ
(704) 788-8550. **$60-$145, 7 day notice.** 2451 Kannapolis Hwy 28025. I-85 exit 58, just s on US 29, then just w. Ext corridors.
Pets: Accepted. 🛜 🔒 💻

🏅 ◆◆◆ Comfort Suites-Concord Mills Ⓗ
(704) 979-3800. **$99-$249.** 7800 Gateway Ln NW 28027. I-85 exit 49, just e, just n on Weddington Rd, then just w. Int corridors.
Pets: Accepted. 🅂🅰🅅🅴 🌊 🛜 ✖ 🔒 💻

◆◆◆ Embassy Suites by Hilton Charlotte-Concord Golf Resort & Spa Ⓗ 🐾
(704) 455-8200. **$139-$289.** 5400 John Q Hammons Dr 28027. I-85 exit 49, 1 mi e on Bruton Smith Blvd, then just n. Int corridors. **Pets:** Large. $75 one-time fee/room. Designated rooms, service with restrictions.
🍽 🔥 🌊 ✖ 📶 ✖ 🔒 💻

◆◆◆ Residence Inn by Marriott Charlotte Concord Ⓗ
(704) 454-7862. **$79-$183.** 7601 Scott Padgett Pkwy 28027. I-85 exit 49, 1 mi e, then just n. Int corridors. **Pets:** Accepted.
🌊 🛜 ✖ 🔒 💻

🏅 ◆◆◆ Sleep Inn-Concord Ⓗ
(704) 788-2150. **$72-$149.** 1120 Copperfield Blvd 28025. I-85 exit 60, just e. Int corridors. **Pets:** Dogs only. $25 deposit/pet, $5 daily fee/pet. Supervision. 🅂🅰🅅🅴 🌊 🛜 ✖ 🔒 💻

CONOVER

◆◆◆ La Quinta Inn & Suites Hickory/Conover Ⓗ
(828) 465-1100. **$101-$284.** 1607 Fairgrove Church Rd 28613. I-40 exit 128, just s. Int corridors. **Pets:** Accepted.
🔥 🌊 🛜 ✖ 🔒 💻

CORNELIUS

🏅 ◆◆◆ Clarion Inn-Lake Norman Ⓗ
(704) 896-0660. **$70-$1129.** 19608 Liverpool Pkwy 28031. I-77 exit 28, just w, then s. Int corridors. **Pets:** Accepted.
🅂🅰🅅🅴 🌊 🛜 ✖ 🔒 💻

◆◆◆ Comfort Inn & Suites Ⓗ
(704) 896-7622. **$94-$219.** 19521 Liverpool Pkwy 28031. I-77 exit 28, just w, then just s. Int corridors. **Pets:** Accepted.
🔥 🌊 🛜 ✖ 🔒 💻

◆◆◆ Hampton Inn Lake Norman Ⓗ
(704) 892-9900. **$99-$179.** 19501 Statesville Rd 28031. I-77 exit 28, just e, then just s. Int corridors. **Pets:** Accepted.
🔥 🌊 🛜 ✖ 🔒 💻

DUNN

◆◆ Baymont Inn & Suites Dunn Ⓜ
(910) 891-5758. **$49-$85.** 901 Jackson Rd 28334. I-95 exit 73, just w, then just s. Ext corridors. **Pets:** Accepted. 🔥 🌊 🛜 🔒 💻

DURHAM *(Restaurants p. 620)*

◆◆◆◆ 21c Museum Hotel Durham Ⓗ
(919) 956-6700. **Call for rates.** 111 N Corcoran St 27701. SR 147 (Durham Frwy) exit 13, 0.5 mi e on Chapel Hill St, then just s. Int corridors. **Pets:** Accepted. 🍽 ✖ 🛜 ✖ 💻

◆◆ Candlewood Suites Ⓗ
(919) 484-9922. **Call for rates.** 1818 E NC Hwy 54 27713. I-40 exit 278, just s, then just w. Int corridors. **Pets:** Accepted.
🔥 🛜 ✖ 🔒 💻

◆◆◆ Extended Stay America-Research Triangle Park Ⓗ
(919) 998-0400. **$85-$100.** 4919 S Miami Blvd 27703. I-40 exit 281, just s. Int corridors. **Pets:** Accepted. 🔥 🌊 🛜 ✖ 🔒 💻

🏅 ◆◆◆ Hilton Durham near Duke University Ⓗ
(919) 564-2900. **$177-$186.** 3800 Hillsborough Rd 27705. I-85 exit 173, just e on Cole Mill Rd, then 0.5 mi w on US 70 business route. Int corridors. **Pets:** Accepted. 🅂🅰🅅🅴 🍽 🌊 🛜 ✖ 🔒 💻

◆◆◆ Holiday Inn Express Ⓗ
(919) 313-3244. **$114-$299.** 2516 Guess Rd 27705. I-85 exit 175, just e. Int corridors. **Pets:** Medium, other species. $50 one-time fee/room. Designated rooms, service with restrictions, crate.
🔥 🌊 🛜 ✖ 🔒 💻

◆◆◆ Holiday Inn Express Hotel & Suites-RTP Ⓗ
(919) 474-9800. **$79-$169.** 4912 S Miami Blvd 27703. I-40 exit 281, just s. Int corridors. **Pets:** Accepted. 🔥 🌊 🛜 ✖ 🔒 💻

◆◆◆ Hotel Indigo RDU at RTP Ⓗ
(919) 474-3000. **Call for rates.** 151 Tatum Dr 27703. I-40 exit 281, just s on Miami Blvd, then just e. Int corridors. **Pets:** Accepted.
🍽 🔥 🌊 🛜 ✖ 🔒 💻

🏅 ◆◆◆ Hyatt Place Durham Southpoint Ⓗ
(919) 688-7800. **$109-$259.** 7840 NC Hwy 751 27713. I-40 exit 274, just s on SR 751, then just w. Int corridors. **Pets:** Accepted.
🅂🅰🅅🅴 🍽 🔥 🛜 ✖ 🔒 💻

◆◆◆ La Quinta Inn & Suites Raleigh (Durham-Chapel Hill) Ⓗ
(919) 401-9660. **$71-$317.** 4414 Durham Chapel Hill Blvd 27707. I-40 exit 270, 1.7 mi n on US 15/501. Int corridors. **Pets:** Accepted.
🔥 🌊 🛜 ✖ 🔒 💻

◆◆◆ La Quinta Inn & Suites Raleigh (Research Triangle Park) Ⓗ
(919) 484-1422. **$68-$262.** 1910 W Westpark Dr 27713. I-40 exit 278, just n on SR 55, then just e. Int corridors. **Pets:** Accepted.
🔥 🌊 🛜 🔒 💻

🏅 ◆◆◆ Quality Inn & Suites Ⓗ
(919) 382-3388. **$69-$149.** 3710 Hillsborough Rd 27705. I-85 exit 173, just e on Cole Mill Rd, then just w on US 70 business route. Ext/int corridors. **Pets:** Accepted. 🅂🅰🅅🅴 🌊 🛜 ✖ 🔒 💻

🏅 ◆◆ Red Roof Inn Chapel Hill-UNC Ⓜ
(919) 489-9421. **$45-$85.** 5623 Durham-Chapel Hill Blvd 27707. I-40 exit 270, just s on US 15/501, then just ne on E Lakeview Dr. Ext corridors. **Pets:** Accepted. 🅂🅰🅅🅴 🍽 🛜 ✖ 🔒 💻

◆◆◆ Residence Inn by Marriott Durham/McPherson Duke University Medical Center Area Ⓗ
(919) 680-4440. **$130-$203.** 1108 W Main St 27701. SR 147 (Durham Frwy) exit 12C (Duke St), just n, just w on Main St, then just n on Watts St. Int corridors. **Pets:** Medium, other species. $100 one-time fee/room. Service with restrictions, crate. 🔥 🛜 ✖ 🔒 💻

🏅 ◆◆◆ Residence Inn by Marriott Durham/Research Triangle Park Ⓗ
(919) 361-1266. **$88-$212.** 201 Residence Inn Blvd 27713. I-40 exit 278, just s on SR 55, then just w. Ext/int corridors. **Pets:** Accepted.
🅂🅰🅅🅴 🔥 🌊 🛜 ✖ 🔒 💻

◆◆◆ Staybridge Suites of Durham Ⓗ
(919) 401-9800. **Call for rates.** 3704 Mt. Moriah Rd 27707. I-40 exit 270, just n on US 15/501, then just e. Int corridors. **Pets:** Accepted.
🔥 🌊 🛜 🔒 💻

◬ ▽▽ ▽▽ Washington Duke Inn & Golf Club H
(919) 490-0999. **$209-$389.** 3001 Cameron Blvd 27705. US 15/501 Bypass exit 107, 0.8 mi s on SR 751. Int corridors. **Pets:** Dogs only. $250 one-time fee/pet. Designated rooms, service with restrictions, supervision. [SAVE] [⊺] [&M] [⊇] [⊠] [◌] [⊠] [◫] [⊡]

EDEN

▽▽ Baymont Inn & Suites Eden M
(336) 627-0472. **$49-$79.** 716 Linden Dr 27288. Jct SR 700/770, 1.4 mi s on SR 87/14, just e. Ext corridors. **Pets:** Accepted.
[&M] [⊇] [◌] [◫] [⊡]

◬ ▽▽ Econo Lodge M
(336) 627-5131. **$60-$200.** 110 E Arbor Ln 27288. Jct SR 700/770, 1.4 mi s on SR 87/14, just e. Ext corridors. **Pets:** Medium. $10 daily fee/pet. Service with restrictions, supervision. [SAVE] [◌] [◫]

FAYETTEVILLE

▽▽ Ambassador Inn M
(910) 485-8135. **$63-$70.** 2035 Eastern Blvd 28306. Jct SR 87, 1.2 mi s on I-95 business route/US 301; jct Owen Dr. Ext corridors. **Pets:** $10 daily fee/room. Service with restrictions. [⊇] [◌] [◫]

▽▽ Baymont Inn & Suites Fayetteville Fort Bragg Area H
(910) 323-0112. **$75-$114.** 1707-B Owen Dr 28304. Jct I-95 business route/US 301 S, 2.3 mi w. Int corridors. **Pets:** Accepted.
[⊺] [◌] [⊠] [◫] [⊡]

▽▽▽ Candlewood Suites-Fayetteville/Ft. Bragg H
(910) 868-0873. **Call for rates.** 4108 Legend Ave 28303. US 401 Bypass, just e on McPherson Church Rd, just n on Sycamore Dairy Rd, then just w. Int corridors. **Pets:** Accepted. [&M] [◌] [◫] [⊡]

▽▽▽ Comfort Inn near Fort Bragg H
(910) 867-1777. **$80-$140.** 1922 Skibo Rd 28314. All American Frwy exit US 401 Bypass, 0.8 mi s. Int corridors. **Pets:** Accepted.
[&M] [⊇] [◌] [◫] [⊡]

▽▽ Days Inn & Suites - Cross Creek M
(910) 867-7659. **$50-$70.** 1720 Skibo Rd 28303. All American Frwy exit US 401 Bypass, just s; enter through Cross Creek Plaza entrance. Ext/int corridors. **Pets:** Accepted. [⊇] [◌] [◫] [⊡]

◬ ▽▽ Econo Lodge I-95 M
(910) 433-2100. **$57-$85.** 1952 Cedar Creek Rd 28312. I-95 exit 49, just w. Ext corridors. **Pets:** Medium. $15 daily fee/pet. Designated rooms, service with restrictions, supervision. [SAVE] [⊇] [◌] [◫]

▽▽ Extended Stay America Fayetteville-Cross Creek Mall H
(910) 868-5662. **$110-$125.** 4105 Sycamore Dairy Rd 28303. All American Frwy exit Morganton Rd, just e, then just n. Int corridors. **Pets:** Accepted. [◌] [⊠] [◫] [⊡]

▽▽ Extended Stay America Fayetteville-Owen Dr. M
(910) 485-2747. **$75-$85.** 408 Owen Dr 28304. Jct All American Frwy. Ext corridors. **Pets:** Accepted. [◌] [⊠] [◫] [⊡]

◬ ▽▽▽ Home2 Suites by Hilton H
(910) 223-1170. **Call for rates.** 4035 Sycamore Dairy Rd 28303. US 401 Bypass, just e on McPherson Church Rd, then just s. Int corridors. **Pets:** Accepted. [SAVE] [&M] [⊇] [◌] [◫] [⊡]

▽▽▽ Ramada Plaza Fayetteville Fort Bragg Area H
(910) 323-0111. **$109-$124.** 1707-A Owen Dr 28304. Jct I-95 business route/US 301 S, 2.3 mi w. Ext/int corridors. **Pets:** Accepted.
[⊺] [◌] [◌] [⊠] [◫] [⊡]

◬ ▽▽▽ Red Roof Inn Fayetteville M
(910) 438-0748. **$60-$90.** 1902 Cedar Creek Rd 28312. I-95 exit 49, just w. Ext corridors. **Pets:** Accepted. [SAVE] [⊇] [◌] [⊠] [◫] [⊡]

▽▽▽ Residence Inn by Marriott Fayetteville Cross Creek H
(910) 868-9005. **$90-$183.** 1468 Skibo Rd 28303. Jct SR 24/87, just s on US 401 Bypass. Int corridors. **Pets:** Accepted.
[&M] [◌] [⊠] [◫] [⊡]

◬ ▽▽ Sleep Inn H
(910) 433-9090. **$84-$119.** 1915 Cedar Creek Rd 28312. I-95 exit 49, just w. Int corridors. **Pets:** Small, other species. $20 daily fee/room. Designated rooms, service with restrictions. [SAVE] [◌] [⊠] [◫] [⊡]

◬ ▽▽▽ TownePlace Suites by Marriott Fayetteville Cross Creek H
(910) 764-1100. **$103-$183.** 1464 Skibo Rd 28303. Jct SR 24/87, just s on US 401 Bypass. Int corridors. **Pets:** Accepted.
[SAVE] [⊇] [◌] [⊠] [◫] [⊡]

FEARRINGTON VILLAGE

◬ ▽▽▽▽ The Fearrington House Inn CI
(919) 542-2121. **$350-$725, 3 day notice.** 2000 Fearrington Village Center 27312. US 64 exit 383, 6 mi n on US 15/501. Ext/int corridors. **Pets:** Accepted. [SAVE] [⊺] [&M] [⊇] [⊠] [◌] [⊠]

FLAT ROCK

▽▽▽ Highland Lake Inn H
(828) 693-6812. **Call for rates.** 86 Lily Pad Ln 28731. I-26 exit 53, 1.1 mi w on Upward Rd, 0.5 mi w on N Highland Lake Rd, then just s on Highland Lake Dr. Ext/int corridors. **Pets:** Small, dogs only. $35 one-time fee/pet. Designated rooms, service with restrictions, supervision.
[⊺] [⊇] [⊠] [◌] [⊠] [◫] [⊡]

FLETCHER *(Restaurants p. 620)*

▽▽ Comfort Inn Asheville Airport H
(828) 687-9199. **$83-$226.** 15 Rockwood Rd 28732. I-26 exit 40, just e on SR 280, then just s. Int corridors. **Pets:** Medium. $20 daily fee/room. Service with restrictions, supervision. [&M] [⊇] [◌] [⊠] [◫] [⊡]

FOREST CITY

▽▽ Baymont Inn & Suites Forest City M
(828) 287-8788. **$59-$119.** 164 Jameson Inn Dr 28043. US 74 Bypass exit 181, 1.8 mi nw on US 74A. Ext corridors. **Pets:** Medium. $15 daily fee/room. Service with restrictions, supervision.
[&M] [⊇] [◌] [◫] [⊡]

FORT BRAGG

◬ ▽▽ The Landmark Inn - Ft. Bragg H 🐾
(910) 495-1215. **$68-$77.** 1208 Glider St 28307. Jct SR 24/87, just w on Randolph St, just n on Souter Pl, then just e; All-American Frwy gate exit Gruber Rd, 0.5 mi e, 1.6 mi n on Knox St, 0.5 mi e on Randolph St, just n on Souter Pl, then just e. Int corridors. **Pets:** Other species. $50 one-time fee/room. Designated rooms, service with restrictions, crate. [SAVE] [&M] [⊠] [◫] [⊡]

FUQUAY-VARINA

▽▽ Comfort Inn H
(919) 557-9000. **$89-$184.** 7616 Purfoy Rd 27526. Jct SR 55, 1 mi n on US 401/SR 55, then just e. Int corridors. **Pets:** Accepted.
[&M] [⊇] [◌] [◫] [⊡]

GASTONIA

◬ ▽▽▽ Best Western Gastonia H
(704) 868-2000. **$90-$230.** 360 Best Western Ct 28054. I-85 exit 20, just nw on SR 279, then just e. Ext/int corridors. **Pets:** Other species. $25 daily fee/pet. Service with restrictions.
[SAVE] [⊇] [◌] [⊠] [◫] [⊡]

◬ ▽▽ Days Inn M
(704) 864-0081. **$50-$63.** 1700 N Chester St 28052. I-85 exit 17, just s on US 321. Ext/int corridors. **Pets:** Accepted.
[SAVE] [⊺] [⊇] [◌] [◫] [⊡]

◆◆◆ **Hampton Inn** H

(704) 866-9090. **$79-$219.** 1859 Remount Rd 28054. I-85 exit 20, just nw on SR 279, then just e. Int corridors. **Pets:** Accepted.

🅑🅜 🏊 🛜 ✕ 🔋 🖥

GOLDSBORO

♨ ◆◆◆ **Best Western Plus Goldsboro** H

(919) 751-1999. **$90-$150.** 909 N Spence Ave 27534. US 70 E Bypass exit Spence Ave, just s. Int corridors. **Pets:** Medium, other species. $20 daily fee/room. Service with restrictions, supervision.

SAVE 🅑🅜 🏊 🛜 ✕ 🔋 🖥

◆◆◆ **Hampton Inn** H

(919) 778-1800. **$99-$169.** 905 N Spence Ave 27534. US 70 E Bypass exit Spence Ave, just s. Int corridors. **Pets:** Accepted.

🅑🅜 🏊 🛜 ✕ 🔋 🖥

◆◆◆ **TownePlace Suites by Marriott** H

(919) 429-4530. **$99-$133.** 2603 North Park Dr 27534. US 70 E Bypass, exit Spence Ave, just n, then just e. Int corridors. **Pets:** Small. $100 one-time fee/room. Service with restrictions, crate.

🅑🅜 🛜 ✕ 🔋 🖥

GRAHAM

◆◆◆ **Comfort Suites Graham** H

(336) 221-9199. **$94-$185.** 769 Woody Dr 27253. I-85/40 exit 148, just s, then just w. Int corridors. **Pets:** Accepted.

🅑🅜 🏊 🛜 ✕ 🔋 🖥

GREENSBORO *(Restaurants p. 620)*

♨ ◆◆ **Best Western Plus Greensboro Airport Hotel** H

(336) 454-0333. **$79-$126.** 7800 National Service Rd 27409. I-40 exit 210 (SR 68), just s, just w on Thorndike Rd, then just n. Int corridors. **Pets:** Accepted. SAVE 🅑🅜 🏊 🛜 ✕ 🔋 🖥

♨ ◆◆◆ **Best Western Plus Windsor Suites** H

(336) 294-9100. **$95-$170.** 2006 Veasley St 27407. I-40 exit 217, just s on Gate City Blvd, then just w. Int corridors. **Pets:** Accepted.

SAVE 🅑🅜 🏊 🛜 ✕ 🔋 🖥

◆◆◆ **Comfort Inn Greensboro** H

(336) 297-1055. **$75-$280.** 1103 Lanada Rd 27407. I-40 exit 214 or 214A, just sw on Wendover Ave, then just e on Stanley Rd. Int corridors. **Pets:** Accepted. 🏊 🛜 ✕ 🔋 🖥

◆◆◆ **Comfort Suites Airport** H

(336) 882-6666. **$94-$199.** 7619 Thorndike Rd 27409. I-40 exit 210 (SR 68), just s, then just w. Int corridors. **Pets:** Accepted.

🅑🅜 🏊 🛜 ✕ 🔋 🖥

◆◆◆ **Drury Inn & Suites-Greensboro** H

(336) 856-9696. **$79-$169.** 3220 Gate City Blvd 27407. I-40 exit 217, just s. Int corridors. **Pets:** Accepted. 🅑🅜 🏊 🛜 ✕ 🔋 🖥

◆◆ **Extended Stay America-Greensboro-Airport** H

(336) 454-0080. **$95-$110.** 7617 Thorndike Rd 27409. I-40 exit 210 (SR 68), just s, then just w. Int corridors. **Pets:** Accepted.

🏊 🛜 🔋 🖥

◆◆◆ **Fairfield Inn by Marriott Greensboro Airport** H

(336) 841-0140. **$84-$135.** 7615 Thorndike Rd 27409. I-40 exit 210 (SR 68), just s, then just w. Int corridors. **Pets:** Accepted.

🅑🅜 🏊 🛜 ✕ 🔋 🖥

♨ ◆◆◆◆ **Grandover Resort & Conference Center Golf & Spa** H

(336) 294-1800. **$165-$185.** 1000 Club Rd 27407. I-85 exit 118, 0.7 mi s on I-85 business route exit Guilford College Rd, 0.4 mi w, then 1.3 mi n on Grandover Pkwy. Int corridors. **Pets:** Accepted.

SAVE 🍴 🅑🅜 🏊 🖎 🛜 ✕ 🔋 🖥

◆◆◆ **Hawthorn Suites by Wyndham Greensboro** H

(336) 454-0078. **$89-$359.** 7623 Thorndike Rd 27409. I-40 exit 210 (SR 68), just s, then just w. Int corridors. **Pets:** Accepted.

🅑🅜 🛜 ✕ 🔋 🖥

◆◆◆ **Hilton Garden Inn** H

(336) 852-1491. **$89-$189.** 4307 Big Tree Way 27409. I-40 exit 214 or 214B, just ne on Wendover Ave, then just w. Int corridors. **Pets:** Medium. $50 one-time fee/room. Designated rooms, service with restrictions, crate. 🍴 🅑🅜 🛜 ✕ 🔋 🖥

◆◆◆ **Hilton Garden Inn - Greensboro Airport** H

(336) 881-1111. **$149-$399.** 238 NC Hwy 68 S 27409. I-40 exit 210, 0.8 mi s, then just w on Pai Park. Int corridors. **Pets:** Accepted.

🍴 🅑🅜 🛜 ✕ 🔋 🖥

◆◆◆ **Holiday Inn Express & Suites-Airport** H

(336) 882-0004. **$99-$129.** 645 S Regional Rd 27409. I-40 exit 210 (SR 68), just s, then just e. Int corridors. **Pets:** Accepted.

🏊 🛜 ✕ 🔋 🖥

◆◆◆ **Holiday Inn Express-I-40 at Wendover** H

(336) 854-0090. **Call for rates.** 4305 Big Tree Way 27409. I-40 exit 214 or 214B, just ne on Wendover Ave, then just w. Int corridors. **Pets:** Accepted. 🅑🅜 🏊 🛜 ✕ 🔋 🖥

◆◆◆ **Holiday Inn Greensboro Airport** H

(336) 668-0421. **$89-$109.** 6426 Burnt Poplar Rd 27409. I-40 exit 211, just n on Gallimore Dairy Rd, then just w. Int corridors. **Pets:** Accepted.

🍴 🏊 🛜 ✕ 🔋 🖥

◆◆◆ **Home2 Suites by Hilton Greensboro Airport** H

(336) 256-9680. **$99-$159.** 7801 National Service Rd 27409. I-40 exit 210 (SR 68), just s, then just w. Int corridors. **Pets:** Accepted.

🅑🅜 🛜 ✕ 🔋 🖥

♨ ◆◆◆◆ **Hyatt Place Greensboro** H

(336) 852-1443. **$79-$279.** 1619 Stanley Rd 27407. I-40 exit 214 or 214A, just sw on Wendover Ave, then just e. Int corridors. **Pets:** Accepted. SAVE 🅑🅜 🏊 🛜 ✕ 🔋 🖥

◆◆◆ **La Quinta Inn & Suites** H

(336) 316-0100. **$75-$317.** 1201 Lanada Rd 27407. I-40 exit 214 or 214A, just sw on Wendover Ave, then just e on Stanley Rd. Int corridors. **Pets:** Accepted. 🅑🅜 🏊 🛜 ✕ 🔋 🖥

◆◆◆ **Quality Inn & Suites-Airpark East** H

(336) 668-3638. **$70-$220.** 7067 Albert Pick Rd 27409. I-40 exit 210 (SR 68) westbound, just s, then just e; exit eastbound, just e. Int corridors. **Pets:** Medium. $25 one-time fee/pet. Designated rooms, service with restrictions, supervision. 🏊 🛜 🔋 🖥

♨ ◆◆ **Red Roof Inn Greensboro Coliseum** M

(336) 852-6560. **$51-$120, 3 day notice.** 2101 W Meadowview Rd 27403. I-40 exit 217, just n on Gate City Blvd, then just e. Ext corridors. **Pets:** Accepted. SAVE 🛜 ✕ 🔋 🖥

◆◆◆ **Residence Inn by Marriott-Greensboro Airport** H

(336) 632-4666. **$95-$200.** 7616 Thorndike Rd 27409. I-40 exit 210 (SR 68), just s, then just w. Int corridors. **Pets:** Accepted.

🅑🅜 🏊 🛜 ✕ 🔋 🖥

◆◆ **Sleep Inn-Airport** H

(336) 931-1272. **$79-$189.** 7 Sharps Airpark Ct 27409. I-40 exit 210 (SR 68) westbound, follow Regional Rd sign, then just n; exit eastbound, straight on Albert Pick Rd, then just n on Regional Rd. Int corridors. **Pets:** Dogs only. $20 daily fee/pet. Designated rooms, service with restrictions, supervision. 🅑🅜 🏊 🛜 🔋 🖥

GREENVILLE

Best Western Plus Suites-Greenville 🅷
(252) 752-2378. **$89-$186, 3 day notice.** 2310 NE Greenville Blvd 27858. Jct US 264 alternate route and SR 33, just e. Int corridors. **Pets:** Large, dogs only. $20 daily fee/room. No service, supervision.
[SAVE] ⬛ ⬛ ⬛ ⬛ ⬛ ⬛

Candlewood Suites 🅷
(252) 317-3000. **Call for rates.** 1055 Waterford Commons Dr 27834. Just e of US 264; jct Stantonsburg and B's Barbeque rds; just w of Pitt County Memorial Hospital. Int corridors. **Pets:** Accepted.
⬛ ⬛ ⬛ ⬛ ⬛ ⬛

Econo Lodge 🅜
(252) 752-7382. **$61-$130.** 920 Crosswinds St 27834. Jct US 264 alternate route, just s on US 13/SR 11, just w; behind Waffle House. Ext corridors. **Pets:** Accepted. ⬛ ⬛ ⬛ ⬛ ⬛

Hilton Greenville 🅷
(252) 355-5000. **$129-$249.** 207 SW Greenville Blvd 27834. Jct SR 11/903, 1 mi e on US 264 alternate route. Int corridors. **Pets:** Accepted.
⬛ ⬛ ⬛ ⬛ ⬛

Holiday Inn Greenville 🅷
(252) 355-8300. **Call for rates.** 203 SW Greenville Blvd 27834. Jct SR 11/903, 1 mi e on US 264A. Int corridors. **Pets:** Accepted.
⬛ ⬛ ⬛ ⬛ ⬛ ⬛ ⬛

In Town Suites 🅷
(252) 752-3411. **Call for rates.** 2111 W Arlington Blvd 27834. Jct US 13/SR 11, 0.4 mi w on Stantonsburg Rd, then just s. Int corridors. **Pets:** Accepted. ⬛ ⬛ ⬛ ⬛

Residence Inn by Marriott Greenville 🅷
(252) 364-8999. **$108-$171.** 1820 W 5th St 27834. Jct 5th St (SR 43); across from north entrance Vidant Medical Center. Int corridors. **Pets:** Accepted. ⬛ ⬛ ⬛ ⬛ ⬛ ⬛

GROVER

The Inn of the Patriots 🅱🅱 ❀
(704) 937-2940. **$125-$185, 7 day notice.** 301 Cleveland Ave 28073. On SR 226. Int corridors. **Pets:** Small, other species. $50 daily fee/pet. Service with restrictions, crate. [SAVE] ⬛ ⬛ ⬛ ⬛

HAVELOCK

Holiday Inn Express & Suites 🅷
(252) 447-9000. **Call for rates.** 103 Branchside Dr 28532. Jct SR 101, 1 mi w on US 70. Int corridors. **Pets:** Accepted.
⬛ ⬛ ⬛ ⬛ ⬛ ⬛

HENDERSON

Budget Host Inn 🅜
(252) 492-2013. **Call for rates.** 1727 N Garnett St 27536. I-85 exit 215, just e, then just w on US 158. Ext corridors. **Pets:** Accepted. ⬛ ⬛

Red Roof PLUS+ Henderson 🅷
(252) 438-6300. **$75-$115.** 200 Simmons Dr 27536. I-85 exit 212, just w on Ruin Creek Rd, 0.5 mi n on N Cooper Dr, then just e. Int corridors. **Pets:** Accepted. ⬛ ⬛ ⬛ ⬛

Sleep Inn 🅷
(252) 433-9449. **$90-$110.** 18 Market St 27537. I-85 exit 212, just w on Ruin Creek Rd, then just se on Zeb Robinson Rd. Int corridors. **Pets:** Accepted. ⬛ ⬛ ⬛ ⬛

HENDERSONVILLE

Best Western Hendersonville Inn 🅜
(828) 692-0521. **$80-$299.** 105 Sugarloaf Rd 28792. I-26 exit 49A, just e on US 64. Ext corridors. **Pets:** Accepted.
[SAVE] ⬛ ⬛ ⬛ ⬛ ⬛ ⬛

Econo Lodge 🅜
(828) 693-8800. **$66-$170.** 206 Mitchelle Dr 28792. I-26 exit 49B, just w on US 64, just s on Orr Camp Dr, then just e. Ext corridors. **Pets:** Other species. $15 daily fee/pet. Service with restrictions.
⬛ ⬛ ⬛ ⬛ ⬛

Mountain Inn & Suites 🅷
(828) 692-7772. **Call for rates.** 755 Upward Rd 28731. I-26 exit 53, just e. Int corridors. **Pets:** Accepted. ⬛ ⬛ ⬛ ⬛ ⬛

Mountain Lodge 🅷
(828) 693-9910. **Call for rates.** 755 Upward Rd 28731. I-26 exit 53, just e. Int corridors. **Pets:** Accepted. ⬛ ⬛ ⬛ ⬛ ⬛ ⬛

Ramada 🅷
(828) 697-0006. **$55-$175.** 150 Sugarloaf Rd 28792. I-26 exit 49A, just e on US 64, then just s. Int corridors. **Pets:** Accepted.
⬛ ⬛ ⬛ ⬛

HICKORY

Baymont Inn & Suites Hickory 🅜
(828) 304-0410. **$49-$79.** 1120 13th Ave Dr SE 28602. I-40 exit 125, just s on Lenoir Rhyne Blvd, then 0.4 mi w. Ext corridors. **Pets:** Small. $20 daily fee/room. Service with restrictions, supervision.
⬛ ⬛ ⬛ ⬛

Best Western Hickory 🅷 ❀
(828) 323-1150. **$92-$103.** 1520 13th Ave Dr SE 28602. I-40 exit 125, just s on Lenoir Rhyne Blvd, then just e. Ext/int corridors. **Pets:** Large, other species. $20 one-time fee/pet. Designated rooms, service with restrictions, supervision. [SAVE] ⬛ ⬛ ⬛ ⬛

Crowne Plaza 🅷
(828) 323-1000. **Call for rates.** 1385 Lenoir Rhyne Blvd SE 28602. I-40 exit 125, just s. Ext/int corridors. **Pets:** Other species. $50 one-time fee/room. Designated rooms, service with restrictions, crate.
⬛ ⬛ ⬛ ⬛ ⬛ ⬛ ⬛

Red Roof Inn Hickory 🅜
(828) 323-1500. **$39-$79.** 1184 Lenoir Rhyne Blvd 28602. I-40 exit 125, just n. Ext corridors. **Pets:** Accepted. ⬛ ⬛ ⬛ ⬛

HIGHLANDS

Highlands Inn Lodge 🅷
(828) 526-5899. **Call for rates.** 96 Log Cabin Ln 28741. Jct US 64, just s on SR 106 (Dillard Rd), just w. Ext/int corridors. **Pets:** Accepted.
⬛ ⬛ ⬛ ⬛ ⬛

Mitchell's Lodge & Cottages 🅜 ❀
(828) 526-2267. **$69-$300, 90 day notice.** 264 Dillard Rd 28741. Jct US 64, just s on SR 106. Ext corridors. **Pets:** Small. $25 one-time fee/pet. Designated rooms, service with restrictions.
⬛ ⬛ ⬛ ⬛ ⬛

The Park on Main 🅷
(828) 526-4502. **$189-$489, 14 day notice.** 205 Main 28741. Just w on US 64; downtown. Ext/int corridors. **Pets:** Accepted.
⬛ ⬛ ⬛ ⬛ ⬛

HILLSBOROUGH

Holiday Inn Express 🅷
(919) 644-7997. **Call for rates.** 202 Cardinal Dr 27278. I-85 exit 164, just se, then just s; I-40 exit 261, 1.2 mi n, then just w. Int corridors. **Pets:** Medium. $25 daily fee/pet. Designated rooms, no service, supervision. ⬛ ⬛ ⬛ ⬛ ⬛ ⬛

HUNTERSVILLE

Best Western Plus Huntersville Inn & Suites Near Lake Norman 🅷
(704) 875-7880. **$80-$119.** 13830 Statesville Rd 28078. I-77 exit 23, just e, then s on US 21. Int corridors. **Pets:** Accepted.
[SAVE] ⬛ ⬛ ⬛ ⬛ ⬛ ⬛

▼▼ Candlewood Suites H

(704) 895-3434. **Call for rates.** 16530 Northcross Dr 28078. I-77 exit 25, just w on SR 73, then just s. Int corridors. **Pets:** Accepted.

▼▼ Hampton Inn & Suites-Huntersville H

(704) 947-5510. **$109-$229.** 10305 Wilmington St 28078. I-77 exit 23, just e, then just n on US 21. Int corridors. **Pets:** Accepted.

▼▼▼ Residence Inn by Marriott-Lake Norman H

(704) 584-0000. **$89-$217.** 16830 Kenton Dr 28078. I-77 exit 25, 1 mi w on SR 73, then just n. Int corridors. **Pets:** Accepted.

JACKSONVILLE

▼▼ Baymont Inn & Suites Jacksonville H

(910) 347-6500. **$89-$160, 3 day notice.** 474 Western Blvd 28546. Jct US 17, just n. Ext corridors. **Pets:** Medium, other species. $15 daily fee/pet. Designated rooms, service with restrictions, crate.

▼▼▼ Candlewood Suites H

(910) 333-0494. **Call for rates.** 119 Penny Ln 28546. Jct Western Blvd, just n on US 17 business route, just w. Int corridors. **Pets:** Accepted.

▲▲▲ ▼▼▼▼ Home2 Suites by Hilton H ☙

(910) 355-3500. **$99-$169.** 139 Circuit Ln 28546. Jct US 17, 0.4 mi w on Western Blvd, just s. Int corridors. **Pets:** Medium, dogs only. $75 one-time fee/pet. Service with restrictions, crate.

▼▼▼▼ Staybridge Suites H

(910) 353-2513. **$89-$169.** 110 Cobia Ct 28546. From US 17, 1.5 mi w on Western Blvd (SR 53), just s on Marlin Dr to Tarpon Tr. Int corridors. **Pets:** Large, other species. $75 deposit/pet. Service with restrictions, supervision.

▼▼ Suburban Extended Stay Hotel-Camp Lejeune H

(910) 346-7759. **$39-$89.** 1323 Lejeune Blvd 28540. On SR 24 business route, just e of US 17. Int corridors. **Pets:** Accepted.

▼▼▼ TownePlace Suites by Marriott Jacksonville H

(910) 478-9795. **$65-$160.** 400 Northwest Cir 28546. Jct US 17, 2 mi w on Western Blvd, just s. Int corridors. **Pets:** Accepted.

JONESVILLE

▲▲▲ ▼▼▼▼ Best Western Yadkin Valley Inn & Suites H

(336) 835-6000. **$90-$140.** 1713 NC Hwy 67 28642. I-77 exit 82, just e. Int corridors. **Pets:** Accepted.

▲▲▲ ▼▼ Comfort Inn M ☙

(336) 835-9400. **$75-$130.** 1633 NC Hwy 67 28642. I-77 exit 82, just w on SR 67. Ext corridors. **Pets:** Medium. $15 daily fee/pet. Service with restrictions, supervision.

KANNAPOLIS

▼▼▼ Comfort Inn & Suites H

(704) 795-4888. **$99-$209.** 3033 Cloverleaf Pkwy 28083. I-85 exit 58, just n on US 29, just e on Cloverleaf Plaza, then just s. Int corridors. **Pets:** Small. $25 daily fee/pet. Service with restrictions, supervision.

KILL DEVIL HILLS

▼▼▼ Comfort Inn North Oceanfront H

(252) 441-6333. **$119-$359.** 1601 S Virginia Dare Tr 27948. SR 12, at MM 9.5. Int corridors. **Pets:** Accepted.

▼▼▼ First Flight Retreat Condominiums CO

(252) 489-4747. **Call for rates.** 815 S Virginia Dare Tr 27948. SR 12, at MM 8.5. Int corridors. **Pets:** Medium, dogs only. $125 one-time fee/pet. Designated rooms, no service, supervision.

▼▼ John Yancey Oceanfront Inn M

(252) 441-7141. **$59-$359, 3 day notice.** 2009 S Virginia Dare Tr 27948. SR 12, at MM 10.3. Ext/int corridors. **Pets:** Dogs only. $20 daily fee/pet. Designated rooms, service with restrictions, supervision.

▼▼▼ Quality Inn Carolina Oceanfront H

(252) 480-2600. **$52-$340.** 401 N Virginia Dare Tr 27948. SR 12, at MM 8.2. Ext corridors. **Pets:** Accepted.

▲▲▲ ▼▼▼▼ Ramada Plaza Nags Head Oceanfront H ☙

(252) 441-2151. **$89-$240, 3 day notice.** 1701 S Virginia Dare Tr 27948. SR 12, at MM 9.5. Int corridors. **Pets:** $30 daily fee/room. Designated rooms, service with restrictions, supervision.

▲▲▲ ▼▼▼ Sea Ranch Resort H

(252) 441-7126. **Call for rates.** 1731 N Virginia Dare Tr 27948. SR 12, at MM 7.5. Ext/int corridors. **Pets:** Medium, dogs only. $40 daily fee/pet. Designated rooms, service with restrictions, supervision.

▲▲▲ ▼▼▼ Travelodge-Nags Head Beach Hotel H ☙

(252) 441-0411. **$70-$210, 3 day notice.** 804 N Virginia Dare Tr 27948. SR 12, at MM 8.1. Ext/int corridors. **Pets:** Other species. $25 daily fee/pet. Designated rooms, service with restrictions.

LAURINBURG

▼▼ Quality Inn M

(910) 277-0080. **$69-$130.** 14 Jameson Inn Ct 28352. US 74 Bypass exit 183, just n on US 15/401 Bypass, then just e. Ext corridors. **Pets:** Accepted.

LELAND

▲▲▲ ▼▼▼ Best Western Plus Westgate Inn & Suites H

(910) 371-2858. **$70-$389.** 1120 Towne Lake Dr 28451. Jct US 74/76, 2 mi s on US 17. Int corridors. **Pets:** Medium, dogs only. $20 daily fee/room. Designated rooms, service with restrictions, supervision.

▼▼▼ Holiday Inn Express Leland - Wilmington Area H

(910) 383-3300. **Call for rates.** 1020 Grandiflora Dr 28451. Jct US 74/76, 2 mi s on US 17, just w. Int corridors. **Pets:** Accepted.

LILLINGTON

▼▼ Microtel Inn & Suites by Wyndham Lillington H

(910) 893-2626. **$70.** 300 E Cornelius Harnett Blvd 27546. Jct US 401/SR 210, just ne on US 421/SR 27. Int corridors. **Pets:** Accepted.

LUMBERTON

▲▲▲ ▼▼ Best Western Lumberton M

(910) 618-9799. **$90-$180.** 201 Jackson Ct 28358. I-95 exit 22, just e, then just s. Ext corridors. **Pets:** Medium. $10 daily fee/pet. Service with restrictions, supervision.

MAGGIE VALLEY

▼▼ ▼▼ **Microtel Inn & Suites by Wyndham Maggie Valley** 🅗
(828) 926-8554. **$55-$180.** 3777 Soco Rd 28751. Jct US 276, 4 mi w on US 19. Int corridors. **Pets:** Accepted. 🔣🏊📶✕🔌💻

MARION

▼▼ ▼▼ **Comfort Inn** 🅗
(828) 652-4888. **$100-$180.** 178 Hwy 70 W 28752. I-40 exit 85, 5 mi n; jct US 221 N Bypass and 70. Int corridors. **Pets:** Small. $45 deposit/pet. Service with restrictions, supervision. 🔣🏊📶🔌💻

MARS HILL

▼▼ ▼▼ **Comfort Inn** 🅗
(828) 689-9000. **$90-$199.** 167 J F Robinson Ln 28754. US 19/23 exit 11. Int corridors. **Pets:** Accepted. 🔣🏊📶✕🔌💻

MOCKSVILLE

▼▼ ▼▼ **Quality Inn** 🅜
(336) 751-7310. **$70-$110.** 1500 Yadkinville Rd 27028. I-40 exit 170, just s on US 601. Ext corridors. **Pets:** Accepted. 🏊📶🔌💻

MOORESVILLE

▼▼▼▼ **Candlewood Suites Mooresville/Lake Norman** 🅗
(704) 360-4899. **Call for rates.** 3247 Charlotte Hwy 28117. I-77 exit 33, 0.4 mi ne on US 21. Int corridors. **Pets:** Medium. $15 daily fee/pet. Service with restrictions. 🔣📶✕🔌💻

▼▼ ▼▼ **Holiday Inn Express Hotel & Suites** 🅗
(704) 662-6900. **$94-$139.** 130 Norman Station Blvd 28117. I-77 exit 36, just e on SR 150, then just s. Int corridors. **Pets:** Accepted. 🔣🏊📶✕🔌💻

▼▼ ▼▼ **TownePlace Suites by Marriott Charlotte Mooresville** 🅗
(704) 659-8600. **$75-$156.** 139 Gateway Blvd 28117. I-77 exit 33, just ne on US 21, then just w. Int corridors. **Pets:** Accepted. 🔣🏊📶✕🔌💻

MOREHEAD CITY

▼▼ ▼▼ **Econo Lodge Crystal Coast** 🅜
(252) 247-2940. **$51-$150.** 3410 Bridges St 28557. Jct US 70, just n on 35th St. Ext corridors. **Pets:** Accepted. 📶🔌💻

▼▼▼▼ **Holiday Inn Express Hotel & Suites** 🅗
(252) 247-5001. **Call for rates.** 5063 Executive Dr 28557. Jct US 70 and SR 24. Int corridors. **Pets:** Accepted. 🏊📶✕🔌💻

▼▼ ▼▼ **Quality Inn** 🅜
(252) 247-3434. **$70-$169.** 3100 Arendell St 28557. 2 mi w on US 70. Ext corridors. **Pets:** Accepted. 🏊📶🔌💻

MORGANTON

🅐🅐🅐 ▼▼ ▼▼ **Comfort Inn & Suites** 🅗
(828) 430-4000. **$100-$200.** 1273 Burkemont Ave 28655. I-40 exit 103, just s. Int corridors. **Pets:** Medium. $25 one-time fee/pet. Designated rooms, service with restrictions, supervision. 🅂🄰🅅🄴🔣🏊📶✕🔌💻

▼▼ ▼▼ **Quality Inn** 🅗
(828) 437-0171. **$80-$170.** 2400 S Sterling St 28655. I-40 exit 105 (SR 18), just s. Ext corridors. **Pets:** Small. $35 deposit/pet. No service, supervision. 🔣🏊📶🔌💻

▼▼ ▼▼ **Sleep Inn** 🅗
(828) 433-9000. **$76-$150.** 2400A S Sterling St 28655. I-40 exit 105 (SR 18), just s. Int corridors. **Pets:** Other species. $35 one-time fee/room. Service with restrictions, crate. 📶✕🔌💻

MORRISVILLE

▼▼▼▼ **Holiday Inn Express** 🅗
(919) 653-2260. **Call for rates.** 1014 Airport Blvd 27560. I-40 exit 284 or 284A, just s. Int corridors. **Pets:** Accepted. 🔣🏊📶✕🔌💻

▼▼▼▼ **Holiday Inn-Raleigh-Durham Airport** 🅗
(919) 465-1910. **Call for rates.** 930 Airport Blvd 27560. I-40 exit 284 or 284A, 0.5 mi s. Int corridors. **Pets:** Accepted. 🍴🔣🏊📶🔌💻

🅐🅐🅐 ▼▼▼▼ **Hyatt House Raleigh Durham Airport** 🅗
(919) 388-5355. **$79-$239.** 10962 Chapel Hill Rd 27560. I-40 exit 283A, 1 mi s on SR 540 exit 69, then just e on SR 54. Int corridors. **Pets:** Accepted. 🅂🄰🅅🄴🍴🔣🏊📶✕🔌💻

🅐🅐🅐 ▼▼▼▼ **Hyatt Place Raleigh-Durham Airport** 🅗
(919) 405-2400. **$99-$259.** 200 Airgate Dr 27560. I-40 exit 284 or 284B, just n, just w on Pleasant Grove Church Rd, then just s. Int corridors. **Pets:** Accepted. 🅂🄰🅅🄴🔣🏊📶✕🔌💻

▼▼ ▼▼ **La Quinta Inn & Suites Raleigh Durham Airport South** 🅗
(919) 481-3600. **$67-$170.** 1001 Aerial Center Pkwy 27560. I-40 exit 284 or 284A, just s, then just e; in Aerial Center Park. Int corridors. **Pets:** Accepted. 🔣🏊📶🔌💻

▼▼▼▼ **La Quinta Inn & Suites (Raleigh-Durham Int'l Airport)** 🅗
(919) 461-1771. **$75-$196.** 1001 Hospitality Ct 27560. I-40 exit 284 or 284A, just s, just e on Aerial Center Pkwy, then just ne; in Aerial Center Park. Int corridors. **Pets:** Accepted. 🔣🏊📶✕🔌💻

🅐🅐🅐 ▼▼▼▼ **Residence Inn by Marriott Raleigh-Durham Airport** 🅗
(919) 467-8689. **$85-$203.** 2020 Hospitality Ct 27560. I-40 exit 284 or 284A, just s on Airport Blvd, just e on Aerial Center Pkwy, then just ne. Int corridors. **Pets:** Other species. $100 one-time fee/room. Designated rooms, service with restrictions, supervision. 🅂🄰🅅🄴🄴🄲🄾🔣🏊📶✕🔌💻

▼▼▼▼ **Staybridge Suites Raleigh Durham Airport** 🅗
(919) 468-0180. **Call for rates.** 1012 Airport Blvd 27560. I-40 exit 284 or 284A, just s; enter between Hampton Inn-RDU and Holiday Inn Express. Int corridors. **Pets:** Accepted. 🔣📶🔌💻

MOUNT AIRY

▼▼▼▼ **Holiday Inn Express & Suites** 🅗
(336) 719-1731. **Call for rates.** 1320 EMS Dr 27030. Jct US 52, 0.5 mi s on US 601, then just w. Int corridors. **Pets:** Medium. $25 daily fee/pet. Designated rooms, service with restrictions, supervision. 🔣🏊📶✕🔌💻

MOUNT OLIVE

▼▼▼▼ **Sleep Inn & Suites Mount Olive** 🅗
(919) 658-1002. **$100-$150.** 203 NC Hwy 55 W 28365. Jct US 117, just w. Int corridors. **Pets:** Accepted. 🔣🏊📶✕🔌💻

MURPHY

🅐🅐🅐 ▼▼▼▼ **Best Western of Murphy** 🅜 ❀
(828) 837-3060. **$79-$149.** 1522 Andrews Rd 28906. US 74, 19 and 129 exit Andrews Rd. Ext corridors. **Pets:** Large, other species. $10 daily fee/room. Designated rooms, service with restrictions. 🅂🄰🅅🄴🔣🏊📶🔌💻

NAGS HEAD

▼▼▼▼ **Comfort Inn Oceanfront South** 🅗
(252) 441-6315. **$79-$489.** 8031 S Old Oregon Inlet Rd 27959. SR 12, at MM 17. Int corridors. **Pets:** Other species. $25 daily fee/room. Designated rooms, service with restrictions, supervision. 🔣🏊📶✕🔌💻

▼ **Dolphin Oceanfront Motel** Ⓜ
(252) 441-7488. **$99-$399, 30 day notice.** 8017 S Old Oregon Inlet Rd
27959. SR 12, at MM 16.5. Ext corridors. **Pets:** Accepted.
🛌 🛜 ✖ 🎫 🛗 💻

🅰🅰🅰 ▼▼ **Sea Foam Motel** Ⓜ
(252) 441-7320. **Call for rates.** 7111 S Virginia Dare Tr 27959. SR 12,
at MM 16.5. Ext corridors. **Pets:** Accepted.
[SAVE] 🛌 🛜 ✖ 🛗 💻

NEW BERN

▼▼ **Bridge Pointe Hotel & Marina** Ⓗ
(252) 636-3637. **Call for rates.** 101 Howell Rd 28562. US 70 Bypass
exit 417, just w on US 70 business route, then just s. Int corridors.
Pets: Accepted. 🛗 🛌 🛜 ✖ 🛗 💻

▼▼▼ **Candlewood Suites** Ⓗ
(252) 638-8166. **$109-$129.** 3465 Dr ML King Jr Blvd 28562. US 70
Bypass, exit Jacksonville/US 17, 0.5 mi s. Int corridors. **Pets:** Accepted.
🍴 🛗 🛜 ✖ 🛗 💻

▼▼▼ **Comfort Suites New Bern** Ⓗ
(252) 649-1717. **$100-$179.** 1006 Old Cherry Point Rd 28560. On US
70, just s of jct US 17/SR 55; behind Ruby Tuesday's. Int corridors.
Pets: Accepted. 🛌 🛜 ✖ 🛗 💻

▼▼▼ **DoubleTree by Hilton New Bern Riverfront** Ⓗ
(252) 638-3585. **$129-$189.** 100 Middle St 28560. Downtown. Int corridors. **Pets:** Accepted. 🍴 🛗 🛌 🛜 ✖ 🛗 💻

OCEAN ISLE BEACH

🅰🅰🅰 ▼▼ **The Islander Inn** Ⓗ
(910) 575-7000. **$69-$209, 3 day notice.** 57 W First St 28469. SR 904,
just s. Int corridors. **Pets:** Accepted.
[SAVE] 🛗 🛌 🛜 ✖ 🛗 💻

OCRACOKE (Restaurants p. 620)

▼▼ **The Anchorage Inn** Ⓜ
(252) 928-1101. **Call for rates.** 205 Irvin Garrish Hwy (SR 12) 27960.
From Cedar Island Ferry, just n. Ext corridors. **Pets:** Other species. $25
daily fee/room. Designated rooms, service with restrictions, supervision.
🛌 ✖ 🛜 ✖ 🛗 💻

ORIENTAL

▼▼▼ **Oriental Marina & Inn** 🅲🅾
(252) 249-1818. **$109-$239, 3 day notice.** 103 Wall St 28571. Jct SR
55 (Broad St), just ne on Hodges St. Ext corridors. **Pets:** Other species. $50 one-time fee/room. Service with restrictions, supervision.
🍴 🛌 🛜 🛗 💻

OXFORD

▼▼ **Comfort Inn & Suites** Ⓗ
(919) 692-1000. **$89-$149.** 1000 MLK Jr Ave 27565. I-85 exit 204, just
e. Int corridors. **Pets:** Medium. $25 daily fee/pet. Designated rooms,
service with restrictions, supervision. 🛗 🛌 🛜 🛗 💻

PEMBROKE

▼▼▼ **Holiday Inn Express** Ⓗ
(910) 521-1311. **Call for rates.** 605 Redmond Rd 28372. Jct SR 710,
just se on SR 711, then just s. Int corridors. **Pets:** Accepted.
🛗 🛌 🛜 ✖ 🛗 💻

PINEHURST

🅰🅰🅰 ▼▼▼ **Homewood Suites by Hilton-Olmsted Village**
near Pinehurst Ⓗ
(910) 255-0300. **Call for rates.** 250 Central Park Ave 28374. Jct SR 5
and 211, just n; in Olmsted Village. Int corridors. **Pets:** Accepted.
[SAVE] 🛗 🛌 🛜 ✖ 🛗 💻

PLYMOUTH

▼▼▼ **Holiday Inn Express** Ⓗ
(252) 793-4700. **Call for rates.** 840 US Hwy 64 W 27962. Jct SR 32 S,
1 mi w. Ext/int corridors. **Pets:** Accepted.
🛗 🛌 🛜 ✖ 🛗 💻

RALEIGH (Restaurants p. 620)

🅰🅰🅰 ▼▼▼ **Aloft Raleigh** Ⓗ
(919) 828-9900. **$169-$269.** 2100 Hillsborough St 27607. I-440 exit 3,
2.1 mi e. Int corridors. **Pets:** Accepted.
[SAVE] 🎫 🛗 🛜 ✖ 🛗 💻

▼▼ **Candlewood Suites-Crabtree** Ⓗ
(919) 789-4840. **Call for rates.** 4433 Lead Mine Rd 27612. I-440 exit 7
or 7B, just w on Glenwood Ave (US 70), then just n. Int corridors.
Pets: Accepted. 🛗 🛜 ✖ 🛗 💻

▼▼ **Comfort Inn & Suites Crabtree** Ⓗ
(919) 782-1112. **$79-$134.** 6209 Glenwood Ave 27612. I-440 exit 7 or
7B, 2.5 mi w on US 70. Int corridors. **Pets:** Accepted.
🛌 🛜 🛗 💻

▼▼ **Extended Stay America West - Raleigh/North**
Raleigh Ⓗ
(919) 829-7271. **$70-$80.** 911 Wake Towne Dr 27609. I-440 exit 10
(Wake Forest Rd), just s, then w. Int corridors. **Pets:** Accepted.
🛜 🛗 💻

▼▼▼ **Fairfield Inn & Suites by Marriott Raleigh Crabtree**
Valley Ⓗ
(919) 881-9800. **$95-$155.** 2201 Summit Park Ln 27612. I-440 exit 7 or
7B, just w on US 70, just s on Blue Ridge Rd, then just e. Int corridors.
Pets: Large. $75 one-time fee/room. Designated rooms, service with
restrictions, crate. 🛗 🛌 🛜 ✖ 🛗 💻

🅰🅰🅰 ▼▼▼▼ **Hilton North Raleigh Midtown** Ⓗ
(919) 872-2323. **$129-$229.** 3415 Wake Forest Rd 27609. I-440 exit 10
(Wake Forest Rd), 0.4 mi n. Int corridors. **Pets:** Accepted.
[SAVE] 🍴 🛗 🛌 🛜 ✖ 🛗 💻

▼▼▼ **Holiday Inn Express & Suites near NC**
State/Southwest Ⓗ
(919) 854-0001. **Call for rates.** 3741 Thistledown Dr 27606. I-40 exit
295, just n on Gorman St, then just e. Int corridors. **Pets:** Accepted.
🍴 🛗 🛌 🛜 ✖ 🛗 💻

▼▼▼ **Holiday Inn Express Hotel & Suites** Ⓗ
(919) 570-5550. **Call for rates.** 11400 Common Oaks Dr 27614. Jct SR
98, 1.2 mi s on US 1, then just w. Int corridors. **Pets:** Small. $25 daily
fee/pet. Designated rooms, service with restrictions, supervision.
🛗 🛌 🛜 ✖ 🛗 💻

🅰🅰🅰 ▼▼▼▼ **Hyatt House Raleigh North Hills** Ⓗ
(919) 363-0771. **$139-$309.** 160 Park at North Hills St 27609. I-440 exit
8B, just n on Six Forks Rd, then just ne. Int corridors. **Pets:** Accepted.
[SAVE] 🛗 🛜 ✖ 🛗 💻

🅰🅰🅰 ▼▼▼▼ **Hyatt Place North Raleigh - Midtown** Ⓗ
(919) 877-9997. **$69-$179.** 1105 Navaho Dr 27609. I-440 exit 10 (Wake
Forest Rd), just n, then just w. Int corridors. **Pets:** Accepted.
[SAVE] 🛌 🛜 ✖ 🛗 💻

🅰🅰🅰 ▼▼▼▼ **Hyatt Place Raleigh West** Ⓗ
(919) 233-2205. **$109-$249.** 710 Corporate Center Dr 27607. I-40 exit
290, just e on SR 54 (Chapel Hill Rd). Int corridors. **Pets:** Medium,
dogs only. $75 one-time fee/pet. Designated rooms, service with restric-
tions, crate. [SAVE] 🛗 🛌 🛜 ✖ 🛗 💻

▼▼▼ **La Quinta Inn & Suites Raleigh (Crabtree)** Ⓗ
(919) 785-0071. **$71-$202.** 2211 Summit Park Ln 27612. I-440 exit 7 or
7B, just w on US 70, just s on Blue Ridge Rd, then just e. Int corridors.
Pets: Accepted. 🛗 🛌 🛜 🛗 💻

Ramada-Blue Ridge H
(919) 832-4100. **$79-$109.** 1520 Blue Ridge Rd 27607. I-40 exit 289, 2 mi e on Wade Ave exit Blue Ridge Rd, then just s; I-440 exit 4 or 4B, just w on Wade Ave exit Blue Ridge Rd, then just s. Int corridors. **Pets:** $25 one-time fee/pet. Designated rooms, service with restrictions, supervision.

Red Roof PLUS+ Raleigh NCSU- Convention Center H
(919) 833-6005. **$59-$150.** 1813 S Saunders St 27603. I-40 exit 298B, just n. Int corridors. **Pets:** Accepted.

Residence Inn by Marriott Raleigh Crabtree Valley H
(919) 279-3000. **$116-$202.** 2200 Summit Park Ln 27612. I-440 exit 7 or 7B, just w on US 70, just s on Blue Ridge Rd, then just e. Int corridors. **Pets:** Accepted.

Residence Inn by Marriott Raleigh-Durham Airport/Brier Creek H
(919) 472-1005. **$79-$175.** 10600 Little Brier Creek Ln 27617. I-540 exit 4B, 0.5 mi w on US 70, just s on TW Alexander Dr, then just e. Int corridors. **Pets:** Accepted.

Residence Inn by Marriott-Raleigh Midtown H
(919) 878-6100. **$99-$148.** 1000 Navaho Dr 27609. I-440 exit 10 (Wake Forest Rd), just n, then w. Ext corridors. **Pets:** Accepted.

REIDSVILLE

Days Inn of Reidsville M
(336) 342-2800. **$64-$149.** 2205 Barnes St 27320. US 29 exit 150 (Barnes St), just e. Ext corridors. **Pets:** Accepted.

ROANOKE RAPIDS

Baymont Inn & Suites Roanoke Rapids M
(252) 533-0022. **$49-$80.** 101 S Old Farm Rd 27870. I-95 exit 173, 0.5 mi w on US 158, then just s. Ext corridors. **Pets:** Accepted.

Best Western Roanoke Rapids Hotel & Suites H
(252) 536-2300. **$74-$129.** 136 Sheraton Dr 27870. I-95 exit 171, just n on SR 125, then just e. Int corridors. **Pets:** Accepted.

Hilton Garden Inn-Roanoke Rapids H
(252) 519-2333. **$109-$149.** 111 Carolina Crossroads Pkwy 27870. I-95 exit 171, just s on SR 125, then just n. Int corridors. **Pets:** Accepted.

Quality Inn M
(252) 537-9927. **$80-$130.** 1914 Julian R Allsbrook Hwy 27870. I-95 exit 173, just w. Ext corridors. **Pets:** Small, other species. $15 one-time fee/room. Designated rooms, service with restrictions, crate.

ROBBINSVILLE

Microtel Inn & Suites by Wyndham Robbinsville H
(828) 479-6772. **$65-$95.** 111 Rodney Orr Bypass (US 129) 28771. Center of downtown. Int corridors. **Pets:** Accepted.

ROCKY MOUNT

Candlewood Suites H
(252) 467-2550. **$85-$115.** 688 English Rd 27804. I-95 exit 138, 1 mi e on US 64 exit 466, just n on Winstead Ave, then just w. Int corridors. **Pets:** Accepted.

Comfort Inn H
(252) 937-7765. **$94-$179.** 200 Gateway Blvd 27804. I-95 exit 138, 1 mi e on US 64 exit 466, just s on Winstead Ave, just e on Curtis Ellis Dr, then just ne. Int corridors. **Pets:** Accepted.

Country Inn & Suites By Carlson H
(252) 442-0500. **$89-$129, 14 day notice.** 672 English Rd 27804. I-95 exit 138, 1 mi e on US 64 exit 466, just n on Winstead Ave, then just w. Int corridors. **Pets:** Accepted.

Residence Inn by Marriott Rocky Mount H
(252) 451-5600. **$97-$177.** 230 Gateway Blvd 27804. I-95 exit 138, 1 mi e on US 64 exit 466, just s on Winstead Ave, just e on Curtis Ellis Dr, then just ne. Int corridors. **Pets:** Accepted.

ROXBORO

Hampton Inn H
(336) 599-8800. **$119-$169.** 920 Durham Rd 27573. Jct US 158, just n on US 501. Int corridors. **Pets:** Accepted.

Innkeeper M
(336) 599-3800. **Call for rates.** 906 Durham Rd 27573. Jct US 158, just n on US 501. Ext/int corridors. **Pets:** Accepted.

SALISBURY

Hampton Inn H
(704) 637-8000. **$119-$159.** 1001 Klumac Rd 28147. I-85 exit 75, just n on US 601, then just sw. Int corridors. **Pets:** Accepted.

SALUDA

The Oaks Bed & Breakfast BB
(828) 749-2000. **$170-$199, 14 day notice.** 339 Greenville St 28773. I-26 exit 59, 1.1 mi sw, 0.5 mi w on US 176, then cross railway tracks. Ext/int corridors. **Pets:** Accepted.

SANFORD

Baymont Inn & Suites Sanford M
(919) 708-7400. **$49-$80.** 2614 S Horner Blvd 27330. US 1 exit 69A, 4.1 mi s on US 421 and SR 87. Ext corridors. **Pets:** Accepted.

SCOTLAND NECK

Scotland Neck Inn M
(252) 826-5141. **$80.** 308 S Main St 27874. Jct SR 125 S, just s on US 258. Int corridors. **Pets:** Accepted.

SELMA

Days Inn H
(919) 965-4000. **$65-$75.** 115 US 70A 27576. I-95 exit 97, just e, then just n. Int corridors. **Pets:** Medium, other species. $15 deposit/pet. Service with restrictions, crate.

Quality Inn M
(919) 965-5200. **$63-$110.** 1705 Industrial Park Dr 27576. I-95 exit 97, just w, then just s. Ext corridors. **Pets:** Accepted.

SMITHFIELD

Baymont Inn & Suites Smithfield M
(919) 989-5901. **$49-$80.** 125 S Equity Dr 27577. I-95 exit 95, just w on US 70 business route, just n on Outlet Center Dr, then just w. Ext corridors. **Pets:** Accepted.

AAA ▼▼ Super 8 H ❀
(919) 989-8988. **$59-$84.** 735 Outlet Center Dr 27577. I-95 exit 95, just w on US 70 business route, then just n. Int corridors. **Pets:** Other species. $15 daily fee/room. Service with restrictions, supervision.
SAVE ⅃M ⊇ 🛜

SNEADS FERRY
▼▼ Quality Inn & Suites Sneads Ferry H
(910) 327-8282. **$90-$230.** 1565 NC Hwy 210 28460. Jct US 17, 5 mi e. Int corridors. **Pets:** Medium. $35 daily fee/pet. Designated rooms, service with restrictions, crate. ⅃M ⊇ 🛜 ☒ 🛏 🖵

SOUTHERN PINES
AAA ▼▼ Best Western Pinehurst Inn H ❀
(910) 692-0640. **$90-$125, 3 day notice.** 1675 US Hwy 1 S 28387. Jct US 15/501, 0.5 mi n. Ext corridors. **Pets:** Dogs only. $20 deposit/pet. Service with restrictions. SAVE ⊇ 🛜 🛏 🖵

▼▼ Econo Lodge Inn & Suites H
(910) 692-2063. **$70-$105.** 408 W Morganton Rd 28387. US 1 exit Morganton Rd, just w. Int corridors. **Pets:** Medium. $15 daily fee/pet. Designated rooms, service with restrictions, supervision. 🛜 🛏 🖵

**AAA ▼▼▼ Residence Inn by Marriott-Pinehurst/
Southern Pines H ❀**
(910) 693-3400. **$101-$153.** 105 Brucewood Rd 28387. Jct US 1, 1.2 mi n on US 15/501, then just e. Int corridors. **Pets:** Medium, other species. $100 one-time fee/room, $25 daily fee/room. Service with restrictions, crate. SAVE ⊇ 🛜 ☒ 🛏 🖵

SOUTHPORT *(Restaurants p. 620)*
▼▼▼ Comfort Suites H ❀
(910) 454-7444. **$85-$210.** 4963 Southport Supply Rd 28461. Jct SR 87, 1.8 mi n. Int corridors. **Pets:** $25 daily fee/room. Designated rooms, service with restrictions, supervision. ⅃M ⊇ 🛜 ☒ 🛏 🖵

STATESVILLE
AAA ▼▼ Best Western Statesville Inn M ❀
(704) 881-0111. **$80-$175.** 1121 Morland Dr 28677. I-77 exit 49A, just e on US 70. Ext corridors. **Pets:** Small. $20 daily fee/pet. Designated rooms, service with restrictions, supervision. SAVE ⊇ 🛜 🛏 🖵

AAA ▼▼▼ Comfort Inn & Suites-Statesville H
(704) 873-2044. **$99-$159.** 1214 Greenland Dr 28677. I-77 exit 49A, just e on US 70, then just s. Int corridors. **Pets:** Accepted.
SAVE ⅃M ⊇ 🛜 ☒ 🛏 🖵

**AAA ▼▼▼ Courtyard by Marriott Statesville
Mooresville/Lake Norman H**
(704) 768-2400. **$107-$183.** 1530 Cinema Dr 28625. I-77 exit 49B, just e on Salisbury Rd, 0.6 mi n on Folger Dr, then just e. Int corridors.
Pets: Accepted. SAVE ⅃M ⊇ 🛜 ☒ 🛏 🖵

▼▼ Quality Inn & Suites M
(704) 878-2721. **$70-$130.** 715 Sullivan Rd 28677. I-40 exit 151, just s on US 21. Ext corridors. **Pets:** Accepted. ⊇ 🛜 🛏 🖵

AAA ▼▼ Ramada H
(704) 878-9691. **$50-$115.** 1215 E Garner Bagnal Blvd 28677. I-77 exit 49A, just e on US 70. Int corridors. **Pets:** Accepted.
SAVE 🍴 ⊇ 🛜 🛏 🖵

AAA ▼▼ Red Roof PLUS+ Statesville M
(704) 878-2051. **$54-$149.** 1508 E Broad St 28625. I-77 exit 50, just e, then just s on Middleton St. Ext corridors. **Pets:** Accepted.
SAVE ⅃M 🛜 ☒ 🛏 🖵

TARBORO
AAA ▼▼▼ Best Western Tarboro Hotel H
(252) 824-0700. **$80-$95.** 102 Market Center Dr 27886. US 64 Bypass exit 485, just s on US 258. Int corridors. **Pets:** Accepted.
SAVE ⅃M ⊇ 🛜 🛏 🖵

THOMASVILLE
**▼▼ Microtel Inn & Suites by Wyndham Thomasville/High
Point/Lexington H**
(336) 474-4515. **$55-$120.** 959 Lake Rd 27360. I-85 exit 102, just w, then just s. Int corridors. **Pets:** Medium, dogs only. $20 daily fee/room. Designated rooms, service with restrictions, supervision.
🍴 🛜 🛏 🖵

WAKE FOREST
▼▼▼ Candlewood Suites H
(919) 554-6901. **$149-$159.** 12050 Retail Dr 27587. US 1 exit 125, just w on SR 98 (Durham Rd), then just s. Int corridors. **Pets:** Accepted.
⅃M 🛜 🛏 🖵

▼▼▼ Hampton Inn H
(919) 554-0222. **$109-$189.** 12318 Wake Union Church Rd 27587. Jct SR 98 (Durham Rd), 0.5 mi n on US 1, 0.5 mi w. Int corridors.
Pets: Accepted. ⊇ 🛜 ☒ 🛏 🖵

WAYNESVILLE *(Restaurants p. 620)*
▼ Motel 6 Waynesville #8668 M
(828) 454-9667. **Call for rates.** 79 Liner Cove Rd 28786. I-40 exit 27 to US 23/74 exit 104 (Liner Cove Rd). Ext corridors. **Pets:** Accepted.
🍴 ⅃M ⊇ 🛜 🛏

AAA ▼▼▼ The Waynesville Inn Golf Resort & Spa H
(828) 456-3551. **$88-$229.** 176 Country Club Dr 28786. US 23 S/74 W exit 100, 0.6 mi s on Hazelwood Ave, then 0.3 mi e on Virginia Ave. Ext/int corridors. **Pets:** Accepted.
SAVE 🍴 ⅃M ⊇ ☒ 🛜 ☒ 🛏 🖵

▼▼▼ The Yellow House on Plott Creek Road BB
(828) 452-0991. **Call for rates.** 89 Oakview Dr 28786. US 23/74 exit 100 eastbound, 1.3 mi nw on Plott Creek Rd; exit 100 westbound, just se, just w on Sulphur Springs Rd, then 1.4 mi nw on Plott Creek Rd. Ext/int corridors. **Pets:** Accepted. 🍴 ⅃M 🛜 ☒ 🛏 🖵

WILLIAMSTON
▼▼▼ Holiday Inn Express H
(252) 799-0100. **Call for rates.** 1071 Cantle Ct 27892. US 64 exit 512. Int corridors. **Pets:** Accepted. ⅃M ⊇ 🛜 ☒ 🛏 🖵

WILMINGTON
AAA ▼▼▼ Best Western Plus Coastline Inn H ❀
(910) 763-2800. **$109-$239.** 503 Nutt St 28401. Jct Market St, just w on Front St, just s on Red Cross St, then just w. Ext corridors.
Pets: Large, dogs only. $50 deposit/room, $20 daily fee/room. Designated rooms, service with restrictions, crate.
SAVE ⅃M 🛜 ☒ 🛏 🖵

**AAA ▼▼▼ Best Western Plus Wilmington/Wrightsville
Beach H ❀**
(910) 799-4292. **$90-$190.** 5345 Market St 28405. Jct SR 132, just s on US 17 business route. Int corridors. **Pets:** Large. $20 daily fee/room. Designated rooms, service with restrictions, crate.
SAVE ⊇ 🛜 ☒ 🛏 🖵

▼▼ MainStay Suites H
(910) 392-1741. **$71-$189.** 5229 Market St 28405. Jct SR 132, just s on US 17 business route. Int corridors. **Pets:** Accepted.
⅃M 🛜 🛏 🖵

Residence Inn by Marriott Wilmington Landfall H

(910) 256-0098. **$97-$229.** 1200 Culbreth Dr 28405. Jct US 17 business route, 2.4 mi e on US 74, 0.4 mi n on Military Cutoff Rd, then just e. Int corridors. **Pets:** Accepted.

Staybridge Suites Wilmington East H

(910) 202-8500. **$89-$299.** 5010 New Centre Dr 28403. Jct SR 132, 0.5 mi s on US 17 business route, just e. Int corridors. **Pets:** $75 one-time fee/room. Designated rooms, service with restrictions, crate.

TownePlace Suites by Marriott Wilmington/Wrightsville Beach H ❖

(910) 332-3326. **$68-$177.** 305 Eastwood Rd 28403. Jct US 17 business route, just e on US 74. Int corridors. **Pets:** Medium, other species. $75 one-time fee/room. Service with restrictions, crate.

WILSON

Country Inn & Suites By Carlson H

(252) 281-5501. **$75-$150.** 4910 Hayes Pl 27893. I-95 exit 121, just w, then just s. Int corridors. **Pets:** Other species. $20 daily fee/room. Service with restrictions, crate.

Microtel Inn by Wyndham Wilson H

(252) 234-0444. **$50-$100.** 5013 Hayes Pl 27896. I-95 exit 121, just w, then just n. Int corridors. **Pets:** Large, other species. $10 daily fee/pet. Designated rooms, supervision.

Sleep Inn H

(252) 234-2900. **$76-$126.** 5011 Hayes Pl 27896. I-95 exit 121, just w. Int corridors. **Pets:** Medium, dogs only. $20 one-time fee/pet. Designated rooms, service with restrictions, supervision.

WINDSOR

The Inn at Grays Landing CI

(252) 794-2255. **$70-$140.** 401 S King St 27983. US 17, just w on SR 308. Int corridors. **Pets:** Accepted.

WINSTON-SALEM

Days Inn-North M

(336) 744-5755. **$59-$75.** 5218 Germanton Rd 27105. US 52 exit 114, just n on SR 8. Ext corridors. **Pets:** Accepted.

Embassy Suites by Hilton-Winston-Salem H

(336) 724-2300. **$109-$299.** 460 N Cherry St 27101. I-40 business route exit 5C (Cherry St), just n. Int corridors. **Pets:** Accepted.

Fairfield Inn & Suites by Marriott Winston-Salem Hanes Mall H

(336) 714-3000. **$76-$135.** 1680 Westbrook Plaza Dr 27103. I-40 exit 189 (Stratford Rd), 0.5 mi n, just w, then just s. Int corridors. **Pets:** Accepted.

The Hawthorne Inn & Conference Center H

(336) 777-3000. **Call for rates.** 420 High St 27101. I-40 business route exit 5C (Cherry St) eastbound, just e; exit westbound, just w on 1st St, then just s on Marshall St. Int corridors. **Pets:** Accepted.

The Kimpton Cardinal Hotel H

(336) 724-1009. **$119-$459.** 51 E 4th St 27101. I-40 business route exit 5D, 0.4 mi n on Main St. Int corridors. **Pets:** Accepted.

La Quinta Inn & Suites Winston-Salem H

(336) 765-8777. **$67-$323.** 2020 Griffith Rd 27103. I-40 exit 189 (Stratford Rd), just s, just e on Hanes Mall Blvd, then just s. Int corridors. **Pets:** Accepted.

Quality Inn H

(336) 767-9009. **$67-$75.** 5719 University Pkwy 27105. US 52 exit 115B, 0.4 mi w. Ext corridors. **Pets:** Accepted.

Quality Inn-Coliseum H

(336) 767-8240. **$65-$130.** 531 Akron Dr 27105. US 52 exit 112, just e. Int corridors. **Pets:** Accepted.

Residence Inn by Marriott Winston-Salem H

(336) 759-0777. **$119-$187.** 7835 North Point Blvd 27106. US 52 exit 115B, 2 mi s on University Pkwy, then just e. Ext corridors. **Pets:** Accepted.

Sleep Inn-Hanes Mall H

(336) 774-8020. **$71-$150.** 1985 Hampton Inn Ct 27103. I-40 exit 189 (Stratford Rd), just s, just e on Hanes Mall Blvd, then just n. Int corridors. **Pets:** Accepted.

The Winston-Salem Hotel & Spa H

(336) 723-2911. **Call for rates.** 3050 University Pkwy 27105. I-40 business route exit 5C (Cherry St), 3 mi n. Int corridors. **Pets:** Accepted.

WRIGHTSVILLE BEACH

Summer Sands Suites M ❖

(910) 256-4175. **Call for rates.** 104 S Lumina Ave 28480. US 76, just e of causeway. Ext corridors. **Pets:** Dogs only. $100 deposit/room, $15 daily fee/room. Designated rooms, service with restrictions, crate.

NORTH DAKOTA

BEULAH

AmericInn Lodge & Suites of Beulah H

(701) 873-2220. **$119-$186.** 2100 2nd Ave NW 58523. Jct SR 49/200, 1.2 mi s. Int corridors. **Pets:** Accepted.

BISMARCK

Americas Best Value Inn & Suites M

(701) 223-8060. **$65-$100.** 1505 Interchange Ave 58501. I-94 exit 159 (US 83), just se. Int corridors. **Pets:** $10 daily fee/pet. Designated rooms, service with restrictions, supervision.

Candlewood Suites H

(701) 751-8900. **Call for rates.** 4400 Skyline Crossings 58503. I-94 exit 159 (US 83), 1.7 mi n, then just e. Int corridors. **Pets:** Accepted.

Comfort Inn H

(701) 223-1911. **$79-$159.** 1030 E Interstate Ave 58503. I-94 exit 159 (US 83), 0.3 mi nw. Int corridors. **Pets:** Accepted.

Comfort Suites H

(701) 223-4009. **$85-$165.** 929 Gateway Ave 58503. I-94 exit 159 (US 83), 0.3 mi nw. Int corridors. **Pets:** Accepted.

Country Suites By Carlson H

(701) 258-4200. **Call for rates.** 3205 N 14th St 58503. I-94 exit 159 (US 83), 0.5 mi n, then just e. Int corridors. **Pets:** Accepted.

▼▼ **Days Inn-Bismarck** H
(701) 223-9151. **$89-$90.** 1300 E Capitol Ave 58501. I-94 exit 159 (US 83), just s. Int corridors. **Pets:** Accepted.

▼▼ **Kelly Inn** M
(701) 223-8001. **Call for rates.** 1800 N 12th St 58501. I-94 exit 159 (US 83), 0.3 mi s. Int corridors. **Pets:** Accepted.

▼▼▼ **La Quinta Inn & Suites Bismarck** H
(701) 751-3313. **$93-$284.** 2240 N 12th St 58501. I-94 exit 159 (US 83), just s. Int corridors. **Pets:** Accepted.

▼▼▼ **Radisson Hotel Bismarck** H
(701) 255-6000. **Call for rates.** 605 E Broadway Ave 58501. Jct 6th St; center. Int corridors. **Pets:** Accepted.

∅ ▼▼▼ **Ramkota Hotel & Convention Center** H ❀
(701) 258-7700. **$119-$129.** 800 S 3rd St 58504. Just s of jct I-94 business loop (Bismarck Expwy) and S 3rd St. Int corridors. **Pets:** $10 daily fee/room. Designated rooms, service with restrictions, supervision.

▼▼▼ **Residence Inn by Marriott Bismarck** H
(701) 258-6088. **$107-$296.** 3421 N 14th St 58503. I-94 exit 159 (US 83), 1 m n on State St, just e on Calgary Ave, then just s. Int corridors. **Pets:** Accepted.

∅ ▼▼▼ **Super 8** M
(701) 255-1314. **$55-$115, 3 day notice.** 1124 E Capitol Ave 58501. I-94 exit 159 (US 83), just s. Int corridors. **Pets:** Accepted.

▼ ▼ **Super 8 Bismarck North** H
(701) 751-2550. **$70-$130.** 1405 Skyline Way 58503. I-94 exit 159 (US 83), 1.7 mi n, just e, then just s. Int corridors. **Pets:** Other species. $10 daily fee/pet. Designated rooms, service with restrictions, crate.

BOTTINEAU

∅ ▼▼ **Super 8 of Bottineau** H
(701) 228-2125. **$43-$95.** 1007 11th St E 58318. 0.5 mi e on SR 5. Int corridors. **Pets:** Accepted.

CARRINGTON

▼▼ **Carrington Inn & Suites** M
(701) 652-3982. **$79-$98.** 101 4th Ave S 58421. Jct US 52 and 281, 0.5 mi s on US 52; just s of jct SR 200. Int corridors. **Pets:** Medium. $20 daily fee/pet. Designated rooms, service with restrictions, supervision.

CASSELTON

▼ ▼ **Days Inn & Governors Conference Center** H
(701) 347-4524. **$73-$140.** 2050 Governors Dr 58012. I-94 exit 331, just n on SR 18. Int corridors. **Pets:** Dogs only. $15 daily fee/pet. Designated rooms, service with restrictions, supervision.

DICKINSON

▼▼▼ **Astoria Hotel & Event Center** H
(701) 456-5000. **Call for rates.** 363 15th St W 58601. I-90 exit 61 (SR 22), just n, then w. Int corridors. **Pets:** Accepted.

▼ ▼ **Comfort Inn** H
(701) 264-7300. **$89-$171.** 493 Elks Dr 58601. I-94 exit 61 (SR 22), just n, then w. Int corridors. **Pets:** Accepted.

▼▼▼ **Holiday Inn Express Hotel & Suites** H
(701) 456-8000. **Call for rates.** 103 14th St W 58601. I-94 exit 61 (SR 22), just n, then just e. Int corridors. **Pets:** Accepted.

▼▼▼▼ **La Quinta Inn & Suites** H
(701) 456-2500. **$93-$268.** 552 12th St W 58601. I-94 exit 61 (SR 22), just s, then just w. Int corridors. **Pets:** Accepted.

▼ ▼ **Microtel Inn & Suites by Wyndham Dickinson** H
(701) 456-2000. **$130-$190.** 1597 6th Ave W 58601. I-94 exit 61 (SR 22), just n, then w. Int corridors. **Pets:** Accepted.

▼▼ **Quality Inn & Suites-Dickinson** H
(701) 225-9510. **Call for rates.** 71 Museum Dr 58601. I-94 exit 61 (SR 22), just s, then just e. Int corridors. **Pets:** Accepted.

▼▼ **Ramada Grand Dakota Hotel** H
(701) 483-5600. **$91-$209.** 532 15th St W 58601. I-94 exit 61 (SR 22), just n, then w. Int corridors. **Pets:** Accepted.

FARGO

▼ ▼ **AmericInn Hotel & Suites Fargo South-45th Street** H
(701) 235-4699. **Call for rates.** 4325 23rd Ave S 58104. I-94 exit 348 (45th St SW), just se. Int corridors. **Pets:** Accepted.

▼▼ **AmericInn Lodge & Suites of Fargo** H
(701) 234-9946. **Call for rates.** 1423 35th St S 58103. I-29 exit 64 (13th Ave S), just e, just s on 34th St SW, then just w. Int corridors. **Pets:** $10 daily fee/pet. Designated rooms, service with restrictions.

▼ ▼ **Baymont Inn & Suites Fargo** H
(701) 235-3333. **$79-$149, 3 day notice.** 3333 13th Ave S 58103. I-29 exit 64 (13th Ave S), 0.3 mi e. Int corridors. **Pets:** Accepted.

∅ ▼▼▼ **Best Western Plus Kelly Inn & Suites** H ❀
(701) 282-2143. **$110-$289.** 1767 44th St S 58103. I-94 exit 348 (45th St SW), just n, then just e on 18th Ave. Ext/int corridors. **Pets:** Medium. Service with restrictions, supervision.

▼ ▼ **Biltmore Hotel and Suites on Main** H
(701) 281-9700. **Call for rates.** 3800 Main Ave 58103. I-29 exit 65, just sw on US 10. Ext/int corridors. **Pets:** Accepted.

▼▼▼ **Candlewood Suites** H
(701) 235-8200. **$115-$189.** 1831 NDSU Research Park Dr 58102. I-29 exit 67 (19th Ave), 1.6 mi e. Int corridors. **Pets:** Other species. $25 one-time fee/pet. Service with restrictions, crate.

∅ ▼▼▼ **ClubHouse Hotel & Suites** H
(701) 282-5777. **Call for rates.** 4400 15th Ave S 58103. I-94 exit 348 (45th St S), 0.6 mi n. Ext/int corridors. **Pets:** Accepted.

▼ ▼ **Country Inn & Suites By Carlson** H
(701) 234-0565. **Call for rates.** 3316 13th Ave S 58103. I-29 exit 64 (13th Ave S), 0.3 mi e. Int corridors. **Pets:** Accepted.

▼▼ Days Inn West Acres ℍ ❀
(701) 235-5566. **$80-$149.** 3431 14th Ave SW 58103. I-29 exit 64 (13th Ave S), just e, just s on 34th St S, then just w. Int corridors. **Pets:** Other species. $15 daily fee/pet. Service with restrictions.
🔊 ⛁ 📶 ⊠ 🛏 🖨

▼▼ Fargo Inn & Suites ℍ
(701) 282-6300. **Call for rates.** 1025 38th St SW 58103. I-29 exit 64 (13th Ave S), just n on west frontage road (38th St SW). Int corridors. **Pets:** Accepted. 🔊 📶 ⊠ 🛏 🖨

▼▼▼ Home2 Suites by Hilton ℍ
(701) 492-4502. **Call for rates.** 1652 44th St S 58103. I-94 exit 348, 0.5 mi n on 45th St, then just e on 17th Ave. Int corridors. **Pets:** Accepted. 🔊 📶 ⊠ 🛏 🖨

▼▼ Kelly Inn 13th Avenue ℍ
(701) 277-8821. **$90-$155, 5 day notice.** 4207 13th Ave SW 58103. I-29 exit 64 (13th Ave S), 0.4 mi w. Ext/int corridors. **Pets:** Medium. Service with restrictions, supervision. 🔊 ⛁ 📶 ⊠ 🛏 🖨

▼▼▼ La Quinta Inn & Suites Fargo ℍ
(701) 499-2000. **$88-$229.** 2355 46th St S 58104. I-94 exit 348 (45th St SW), just s, then just w. Int corridors. **Pets:** Accepted.
🍴 🔊 ⛁ 📶 ⊠ 🛏 🖨

▼▼ MainStay Suites ℍ
(701) 277-4627. **$59-$219.** 1901 44th St SW 58103. I-94 exit 348 (45th St SW), just n, then just e. Int corridors. **Pets:** Accepted.
🍴 🔊 ⛁ 📶 ⊠ 🛏 🖨

▼▼▼ Red Roof Inn Fargo ℍ
(701) 281-8240. **$55-$200.** 1921 44th St SW 58103. I-94 exit 348 (45th St SW), just n, just e on 19th Ave S, then just s. Int corridors. **Pets:** Accepted. 🔊 ⛁ 📶 ⊠ 🛏 🖨

▼▼▼ Residence Inn by Marriott Fargo ℍ
(701) 282-2240. **$91-$261.** 4335 23rd Ave S 58104. I-94 exit 348, just s on 45th St, then just e. Int corridors. **Pets:** Other species. $100 one-time fee/room. Service with restrictions, supervision.
🔊 📶 ⊠ 🛏 🖨

GRAND FORKS

▼▼▼ Baymont Inn & Suites Grand Forks ℍ
(701) 757-2345. **$90-$165.** 951 S 42nd St 58201. I-29 exit 140, just e on DeMers Ave, then just s. Int corridors. **Pets:** Accepted.
🔊 📶 ⊠ 🛏 🖨

ⒶⒶⒶ ▼▼▼ Best Western Harvest Inn & Suites ℍ
(701) 775-5000. **$85-$170.** 3350 32nd Ave S 58201. I-29 exit 138, 0.4 mi e on 32nd Ave S, then just n. Int corridors. **Pets:** Accepted.
SAVE ECO ⛁ 📶 ⊠ 🛏 🖨

ⒶⒶⒶ ▼▼ Days Inn - Columbia Mall ℍ
(701) 775-0060. **$75-$115.** 3101 S 34th St 58201. I-29 exit 138, 0.4 mi e on 32nd Ave S, then just n. Int corridors. **Pets:** Small. $10 daily fee/pet. Service with restrictions, supervision.
SAVE ⛁ 📶 ⊠ 🛏 🖨

▼▼ Ramada Inn ℍ
(701) 775-3951. **$79-$139.** 1205 N 43rd St 58203. I-29 exit 141, just e on US 2 (Gateway Dr), then just s. Int corridors. **Pets:** Accepted.
🍴 🔊 ⛁ 📶 ⊠ 🛏 🖨

▼▼▼ Staybridge Suites Grand Forks ℍ
(701) 772-9000. **Call for rates.** 1175 42nd St S 58201. I-29 exit 140, just e on DeMers Ave, then 0.3 mi s. Int corridors. **Pets:** Accepted.
🔊 ⛁ 📶 ⊠ 🛏 🖨

JAMESTOWN

▼▼ Quality Inn & Suites ℍ
(701) 252-3611. **$85-$139.** 507 25th St SW 58401. I-94 exit 258 (US 281), just se. Int corridors. **Pets:** Accepted.
🍴 ⛁ 📶 ⊠ 🛏 🖨

▼▼ Super 8 Jamestown ℍ
(701) 252-4715. **$70-$80.** 2623 Hwy 281 S 58401. I-94 exit 258 (US 281), just s. Int corridors. **Pets:** Accepted. 📶 ⊠ 🛏 🖨

MANDAN

▼▼ Baymont Inn & Suites Mandan Bismarck Area ℍ
(701) 663-7401. **$69-$159.** 2611 Old Red Tr 58554. I-94 exit 152, just n on Sunset Dr, then just w. Int corridors. **Pets:** Accepted.
🍴 🔊 ⛁ 📶 ⊠ 🛏 🖨

MINOT

▼▼ Baymont Inn & Suites ℍ ❀
(701) 837-1700. **$67-$169.** 1609 35th Ave SW 58701. US 83 (S Broadway) exit 37th Ave SW, 0.8 mi w to 16th St SW, then just n. Int corridors. **Pets:** Designated rooms, service with restrictions, supervision.
🔊 📶 ⊠ 🛏 🖨

ⒶⒶⒶ ▼▼ Best Western Kelly Inn ℍ
(701) 852-4300. **$82-$199.** 1510 26th Ave SW 58701. US 2 and 52 Bypass, at 16th St SW. Ext/int corridors. **Pets:** Accepted.
SAVE ⛁ 📶 ⊠ 🛏 🖨

▼▼▼ Candlewood Suites ℍ
(701) 858-7700. **$65-$140.** 900 37th Ave SW 58701. US 83, 0.6 mi s of US 2 and 52 Bypass, then just w. Int corridors. **Pets:** Accepted.
🍴 🔊 📶 ⊠ 🛏 🖨

▼▼ Comfort Inn ℍ ❀
(701) 852-2201. **$74-$165.** 1515 22nd Ave SW 58701. US 2 and 52 Bypass, at 16th St SW. Int corridors. **Pets:** Medium. $10 daily fee/room. Designated rooms, service with restrictions, supervision.
🔊 ⛁ 📶 ⊠ 🛏 🖨

▼▼▼ Comfort Suites ℍ
(701) 852-9700. **$80-$199.** 601 22th Ave SW 58701. Just w of S Broadway (US 83). Int corridors. **Pets:** Accepted.
🔊 ⊠ 📶 ⊠ 🛏 🖨

▼▼▼ Country Inn & Suites By Carlson ℍ
(701) 837-1900. **$80-$130.** 1900 22nd Ave SW 58701. Just w of 16th St SW. Int corridors. **Pets:** Accepted. 🔊 📶 ⊠ 🛏 🖨

▼ Days Inn Minot ℍ
(701) 852-3646. **$80-$154.** 2100 4th St SW 58701. Jct US 2 and 52 Bypass, just n. Int corridors. **Pets:** Accepted. ⛁ 📶 ⊠ 🛏 🖨

▼▼▼ Holiday Inn Riverside Minot ℍ
(701) 852-2504. **Call for rates.** 2200 Burdick Expwy E 58701. 1.3 mi e on US 2 business route (Burdick Expwy E). Int corridors. **Pets:** $50 daily fee/room. Designated rooms, service with restrictions.
🍴 🔊 ⛁ 📶 ⊠ 🛏 🖨

ⒶⒶⒶ ▼▼▼ Hyatt House Minot ℍ
(701) 838-7300. **$89-$249.** 2301 Landmark Dr NW 58703. 0.4 mi ne of jct US 83 Bypass and 21st Ave NW. Int corridors. **Pets:** Medium, dogs only. $75 one-time fee/room. Designated rooms, service with restrictions, crate. SAVE 🍴 🔊 📶 ⊠ 🛏 🖨

▼▼▼ La Quinta Inn & Suites ℍ
(701) 837-7900. **$82-$328.** 1605 35th Ave SW 58701. US 83 (S Broadway) exit 37th Ave SW, 0.8 mi w to 16th St SW, then just n. Int corridors. **Pets:** Accepted. 🔊 📶 ⊠ 🛏 🖨

▼▼▼ Microtel Inn & Suites by Wyndham Minot ℍ
(701) 839-2200. **$99-$150.** 414 37th Ave SW 58701. 1.5 mi n on US 83, just w. Int corridors. **Pets:** Dogs only. $15 daily fee/pet. Designated rooms, service with restrictions. 🔊 📶 ⊠ 🛏 🖨

▼▼▼ Souris Valley Suites ℍ
(701) 858-7300. **$109-$199.** 800 37th Ave SW 58701. 0.4 mi w of S Broadway (US 83). Int corridors. **Pets:** $25 one-time fee/pet. Service with restrictions, crate. 🔊 📶 ⊠ 🛏 🖨

▼▼▼▼ **Staybridge Suites** 🅷
(701) 852-0852. **Call for rates.** 3009 S Broadway 58701. US 83, just s of US 2 and 52 Bypass. Int corridors. **Pets:** Accepted.
[icons]

STANLEY
▼▼ **Microtel Inn & Suites by Wyndham Stanley** 🅷
(701) 628-4090. **$144-$149.** 901 Jarard St 58784. US 2 exit SR 8, just nw. Int corridors. **Pets:** Other species. $30 one-time fee/room. Service with restrictions, supervision. [icons]

VALLEY CITY
▼▼ **AmericInn Lodge & Suites Valley City** 🅷
(701) 845-5551. **$90-$140.** 280 Winter Show Rd SW 58072. I-94 exit 292, just ne. Int corridors. **Pets:** Accepted.
[icons]

WAHPETON
▼▼ **Baymont Inn & Suites** 🅷
(701) 642-5000. **$75-$135.** 1800 Two Ten Dr 58075. 1 mi n on SR 210 Bypass. Int corridors. **Pets:** Accepted.
[icons]

WATFORD CITY
AAA ▼▼▼ **Roosevelt Inn & Suites** 🅷
(701) 842-3686. **$89-$144.** 600 2nd Ave SW 58854. US 85, 0.3 mi w. Int corridors. **Pets:** Other species. $15 daily fee/pet. Designated rooms, service with restrictions, supervision.
[icons]

WEST FARGO
AAA ▼▼▼ **Element Fargo** 🅷 🐾
(701) 478-5333. **$119-$299.** 925 19th Ave E 58078. I-94 exit 347 (9th St E), just ne. Int corridors. **Pets:** Small, dogs only. $35 one-time fee/room. Designated rooms, service with restrictions, supervision.
[icons]

▼▼▼ **Microtel Inn & Suites by Wyndham West Fargo** 🅷 🐾
(701) 282-2100. **$69-$159.** 705 23rd Ave E 58078. I-94 exit 347 (Veterans Blvd), just sw. Int corridors. **Pets:** Other species. Designated rooms, service with restrictions, crate. [icons]

WILLISTON
AAA ▼▼▼ **Best Western Plus Williston Hotel & Suites** 🅷
(701) 572-8800. **$99-$189.** 4201 4th Ave W 58801. 2 blks w of US 2 and 85 Bypass, just n of Sloulin Field International Airport. Int corridors. **Pets:** Other species. $20 one-time fee/pet. Service with restrictions, supervision. [icons]

▼▼▼ **Candlewood Suites** 🅷 🐾
(701) 572-3716. **$130-$220.** 3716 6th Ave W 58801. 1.3 mi n on US 2 and 85 Bypass, just w. Int corridors. **Pets:** $5 daily fee/pet. Service with restrictions, crate. [icons]

▼▼ **El Rancho Motor Hotel** 🅷
(701) 572-6321. **Call for rates.** 1623 2nd Ave W 58801. 1 mi n on US 2 and 85 Bypass. Ext/int corridors. **Pets:** Dogs only. Designated rooms, service with restrictions, supervision. [icons]

▼▼▼ **Hawthorn Suites by Wyndham Williston** 🅷
(701) 577-3701. **$99-$155.** 3701 4th Ave W 58801. 1.3 mi n on US 2 and 85 Bypass, just w. Int corridors. **Pets:** $5 daily fee/pet. Service with restrictions. [icons]

▼▼▼ **MainStay Suites of Williston** 🅷
(701) 572-5793. **$99-$169.** 200 26th St E 58801. Just w of 2nd Ave W. Int corridors. **Pets:** Small. $75 one-time fee/room. Service with restrictions, supervision. [icons]

▼▼▼ **Microtel Inn & Suites by Wyndham Williston** 🅷
(701) 577-4900. **$99-$139, 3 day notice.** 3820 4th Ave W 58801. 1.3 mi n on US 2 and 85 Bypass, just w. Int corridors. **Pets:** Accepted.
[icons]

OHIO

AKRON
AAA ▼▼▼ **Red Roof Inn Akron** Ⓜ
(330) 644-7748. **$54-$119.** 2939 S Arlington Rd 44312. I-77 exit 120, just n. Ext corridors. **Pets:** Accepted. [icons]

▼▼▼ **Residence Inn by Marriott Akron South Green** 🅷
(330) 644-2111. **$77-$369.** 897 Arlington Ridge E 44312. I-77 exit 120, just s. Int corridors. **Pets:** Accepted. [icons]

ALLIANCE
▼▼▼ **Holiday Inn Express Hotel & Suites** 🅷
(330) 821-6700. **$100-$200.** 2341 W State St 44601. 2 mi w on US 62. Int corridors. **Pets:** Other species. $20 daily fee/pet. Service with restrictions, crate. [icons]

ATHENS
▼▼▼ **The Ohio University Inn & Conference Center** 🅷
(740) 593-6661. **Call for rates.** 331 Richland Ave 45701. 1 mi w on US 33 and 50. Int corridors. **Pets:** Accepted.
[icons]

AUSTINBURG
▼▼▼ **Sleep Inn & Suites** 🅷 🐾
(440) 275-6800. **$94-$254.** 9350 Center Rd 44010. I-90 exit 223, just n. Int corridors. **Pets:** Other species. $25 daily fee/pet. Designated rooms, service with restrictions, supervision.
[icons]

AUSTINTOWN
AAA ▼▼▼ **Austintown Super 8** Ⓜ
(330) 793-7788. **$60-$83.** 5280 76 Dr 44515. I-80 exit 223, just s on SR 46. Int corridors. **Pets:** $10 daily fee/pet. Designated rooms, service with restrictions, supervision. [icons]

AAA ▼▼▼ **Best Western Meander Inn** 🅷
(330) 544-2378. **$72-$99.** 870 N Canfield-Niles Rd 44515. I-80 exit 223, 0.3 mi s on SR 46. Int corridors. **Pets:** Large, other species. $10 daily fee/pet. Service with restrictions, supervision.
[icons]

▼▼▼ **Comfort Inn** Ⓜ
(330) 792-9740. **$73-$140.** 5425 Clarkins Dr 44515. I-80 exit 223B, just n. Ext corridors. **Pets:** Accepted. [icons]

AAA ▼▼▼ **Sleep Inn** 🅷
(330) 544-5555. **$75-$156.** 5555 Interstate Blvd 44515. I-80 exit 223, just s on SR 46. Int corridors. **Pets:** Other species. $10 daily fee/pet. Designated rooms, service with restrictions.
[icons]

BATAVIA

▼▼ **Hampton Inn-Cincinnati Eastgate** �H
(513) 752-8584. **$129-$169.** 858 Eastgate North Dr 45245. I-275 exit 63B (SR 32), 0.4 mi e to Eastgate Mall exit, then just s. Int corridors. **Pets:** Accepted. 🈁 🛰 🅗 💻

🅐🅐🅐 ▼▼▼ **Holiday Inn & Suites Cincinnati Eastgate** 🅗
(513) 752-4400. **Call for rates.** 4501 Eastgate Blvd 45245. I-275 exit 63B (SR 32), 0.4 mi e to Eastgate Mall exit, then just n. Int corridors. **Pets:** $25 one-time fee/room. 〔SAVE〕 ⑪ 🅶M 🛏 🛰 🗙 🅗 💻

BEACHWOOD

🅐🅐🅐 ▼▼▼ **Aloft Beachwood** 🅗
(216) 595-0900. **$89-$399.** 1010 Eaton Blvd 44122. I-271 exit 28B, 0.5 mi w on Harvard Rd, just n on Richmond Rd, then just w. Int corridors. **Pets:** Accepted. 〔SAVE〕 🅶M 🛰 🗙 🅗 💻

▼▼▼ **DoubleTree by Hilton Hotel-Cleveland East/Beachwood** 🅗
(216) 464-5950. **$99-$229.** 3663 Park East Dr 44122. I-271 exit 29, just w on Chagrin Blvd, then just n. Int corridors. **Pets:** Medium. $75 one-time fee/room. Designated rooms, service with restrictions, crate. ⑪ 🅶M 🛏 🛰 🗙 🅗 💻

🅐🅐🅐 ▼▼▼ **Embassy Suites by Hilton** 🅗
(216) 765-8066. **$109-$399.** 3775 Park East Dr 44122. I-271 exit 29, just w on Chagrin Blvd. Int corridors. **Pets:** Accepted. 〔SAVE〕 ⑪ 🅶M 🛏 🅗 💻

▼▼▼ **Homewood Suites by Hilton** 🅗
(216) 464-9600. **$109-$209.** 25725 Central Pkwy 44122. I-271 exit 29, just w on Chagrin Blvd, then just n on Enterprise Pkwy. Int corridors. **Pets:** Accepted. 🅶M 🛏 🛰 🅗 💻

▼▼▼ **Residence Inn by Marriott Cleveland-Beachwood** 🅗
(216) 831-3030. **$71-$246.** 3628 Park East Dr 44122. I-271 exit 29, just w on Chagrin Blvd. Int corridors. **Pets:** Accepted. 🅶M 🛏 🛰 🗙 💻

BEAVERCREEK

▼▼▼ **Residence Inn by Marriott Beavercreek** 🅗
(937) 427-3914. **$92-$220.** 2779 Fairfield Commons Blvd 45431. I-675 exit 17, just s on N Fairfield Rd, just w on Pentagon Rd, then just s. Int corridors. **Pets:** Accepted. 🅶M 🛏 🛰 🗙 🅗 💻

BELLVILLE

▼▼ **Comfort Inn Splash Harbor** 🅗
(419) 886-4000. **$79-$290.** 855 Comfort Plaza Dr 44813. I-71 exit 165, 0.3 mi e on SR 97. Int corridors. **Pets:** Accepted. 🅶M 🛏 🗙 🛰 🅗 💻

▼▼ **Quality Inn & Suites - Conference Center** 🅗
(419) 886-7000. **$74-$300.** 1000 Comfort Plaza Dr 44813. I-71 exit 165, 0.3 mi e on SR 97. Int corridors. **Pets:** Accepted. 🅶M 🛏 🗙 🛰 🅗 💻

BERLIN

🅐🅐🅐 ▼▼▼ **Berlin Grande Hotel** 🅗
(330) 403-3050. **$129-$279.** 4787 Township Rd 366 44610. SR 39, just n on US 62. Int corridors. **Pets:** Large, dogs only. $25 daily fee/pet. Designated rooms, service with restrictions, crate. 〔SAVE〕 🅶M 🛏 🛰 🗙 🅗 💻

BLUE ASH

▼ **Extended Stay America-Cincinnati-Blue Ash-Kenwood Road** 🅗
(513) 469-8900. **$65-$80.** 11145 Kenwood Rd 45242. I-71 exit 15, 0.5 mi w on Pfeiffer Rd, then 1.3 mi n. Int corridors. **Pets:** Accepted. ⑪ 🅶M 🛰 🅗 💻

▼▼ **Hawthorn Suites by Wyndham** 🅗
(513) 733-0100. **$89-$219.** 10665 Techwood Cir 45242. I-275 exit 47, 1.9 mi s, just e on Creek Rd, then just s. Int corridors. **Pets:** $25 daily fee/room. Service with restrictions, crate. 🅶M 🛰 🗙 🅗 💻

🅐🅐🅐 ▼▼▼ **Hyatt Place Cincinnati/Blue Ash** 🅗
(513) 489-3666. **$79-$199.** 11435 Reed Hartman Hwy 45241. I-275 exit 47, 0.8 mi s. Int corridors. **Pets:** Accepted. 〔SAVE〕 ⑪ 🅶M 🛏 🛰 🗙 💻

▼▼▼ **Residence Inn by Marriott-Blue Ash** 🅗
(513) 530-5060. **$99-$297.** 11401 Reed Hartman Hwy 45241. I-275 exit 47, 0.8 mi s. Ext/int corridors. **Pets:** Accepted. ⑪ 🅶M 🛏 🗙 🛰 🗙 🅗 💻

🅐🅐🅐 ▼▼▼ **TownePlace Suites by Marriott Blue Ash** 🅗
(513) 469-8222. **$53-$197.** 4650 Cornell Rd 45241. I-275 exit 47, 0.9 mi s on Reed Hartman Hwy, then just w. Int corridors. **Pets:** Accepted. 〔SAVE〕 🅶M 🛏 🛰 🗙 🅗 💻

BOWLING GREEN

▼▼▼ **Holiday Inn Express & Suites Bowling Green** 🅗
(419) 353-5500. **Call for rates.** 2150 E Wooster St 43402. I-75 exit 181, just e. Int corridors. **Pets:** Accepted. 🅶M 🛏 🛰 🗙 🅗 💻

BROOKLYN

▼▼ **Extended Stay America Cleveland-Brooklyn** 🅗
(216) 267-7799. **$85-$105.** 10300 Cascade Crossing 44144. I-480 exit 13, just s. Int corridors. **Pets:** Accepted. 🅶M 🛰 🗙 🅗 💻

BROOK PARK

🅐🅐🅐 ▼▼▼ **Best Western Airport Inn & Suites Cleveland** 🅗
(216) 267-9364. **$89-$299.** 16501 Snow Rd 44142. I-71 exit 237, just e. Int corridors. **Pets:** Accepted. 〔SAVE〕 🅶M 🛏 🛰 🗙 🅗 💻

BRYAN

▼ **Plaza Motel** 🅜
(419) 636-3159. **Call for rates.** 1604 S Main St 43506. 1.3 mi s on US 127 and SR 15. Ext corridors. **Pets:** Accepted. ⑪ 🛰 🗙 🅗 💻

BUCYRUS

▼▼▼ **Hideaway Country Inn** 🅒🅘
(419) 562-3013. **$169-$599, 75 day notice.** 1601 SR 4 44820. 4.5 mi s. Ext/int corridors. **Pets:** Accepted. ⑪ 🅶M 🛰 🗙 🅗 💻

▼▼▼ **Holiday Inn Express & Suites Bucyrus** 🅗
(419) 562-5664. **Call for rates.** 1575 N Sandusky Ave 44820. US 30 exit SR 100 S/19 (Sandusky Ave), just s. Int corridors. **Pets:** Accepted. 🅶M 🛰 🗙 🅗 💻

CADIZ

▼▼ **Microtel Inn & Suites by Wyndham** 🅗
(740) 942-1161. **$72-$125.** 620 Lincoln Ave 43907. US 22 exit US 250 E, just s. Int corridors. **Pets:** Small, dogs only. $25 daily fee/pet. Service with restrictions, crate. 🅶M 🛰 🗙 🅗 💻

CALDWELL

▼▼ **Microtel Inn & Suites by Wyndham** 🅗 🐾
(740) 732-4200. **$69-$139.** 44266 Fairground Rd 43724. I-77 exit 25, just e. Int corridors. **Pets:** Large, other species. $25 one-time fee/pet. Service with restrictions, crate. 🅶M 🛰 🗙 🅗 💻

CAMBRIDGE

⚏⚏ Comfort Inn 🅷 ❀
(740) 435-3200. **$114-$169.** 2327 Southgate Pkwy 43725. I-70 exit 178, just n on SR 209. Int corridors. **Pets:** $25 daily fee/pet. Service with restrictions, crate. (SAVE) ⓜ 🏊 🛜 ✕ 🔌 ▭

⚏⚏ Microtel Inn & Suites by Wyndham 🅷
(740) 435-8080. **$90-$110.** 8779 Georgetown Rd 43725. I-70 exit 178, just ne. Int corridors. **Pets:** Accepted. ⓜ 🛜 ✕ 🔌 ▭

⚏⚏ Salt Fork Lodge & Conference Center 🅷
(740) 435-9050. **Call for rates.** US Rt 22 E 43725. I-77 exit 47 (US 22/Cambridge), 13.2 mi e; in 17,000 acre state park. Ext/int corridors. **Pets:** Accepted. 🍴 ⓜ 🏊 ✕ 🌀 ✕ 🔌 ▭

CANTON

⚏⚏ Comfort Inn-Hall of Fame 🅷
(330) 492-1331. **$75-$299.** 5345 Broadmoor Cir NW 44709. I-77 exit 109, 0.5 mi e on Everhard Rd. Int corridors. **Pets:** Small, other species. $25 daily fee/pet. Designated rooms, service with restrictions, crate. (SAVE) 🍴 ⓜ 🏊 🛜 ✕ 🔌 ▭

⚏⚏⚏ Courtyard by Marriott 🅷
(330) 494-6494. **$79-$289.** 4375 Metro Cir NW 44720. I-77 exit 109, just w. Int corridors. **Pets:** Other species. Service with restrictions, supervision. (SAVE) 🍴 ⓜ 🏊 🛜 ✕ 🔌 ▭

⚏⚏⚏ Hyatt Place Canton 🅷
(330) 244-1700. **$99-$299.** 5421 Whipple Ave NW 44720. I-77 exit 109 southbound; exit 109B northbound. Int corridors. **Pets:** Accepted. (SAVE) 🍴 ⓜ 🛜 ✕ 🔌 ▭

⚏⚏ La Quinta Inn & Suites Canton 🅷
(330) 492-0151. **$70-$350.** 5335 Broadmoor Cir NW 44709. I-77 exit 109, 0.5 mi e on Everhard Rd. Int corridors. **Pets:** Accepted. ⓜ 🏊 🛜 ✕ 🔌 ▭

⚏⚏ Red Roof Inn Canton Ⓜ
(330) 499-1970. **$50-$140.** 5353 Inn Circle Ct NW 44720. I-77 exit 109, just w on Everhard Rd. Ext corridors. **Pets:** Accepted. (SAVE) ⓜ 🛜 ✕ 🔌 ▭

⚏⚏⚏ Residence Inn by Marriott 🅷
(330) 493-0004. **$80-$277.** 5280 Broadmoor Cir NW 44709. I-77 exit 109, 0.5 mi e on Everhard Rd. Int corridors. **Pets:** Accepted. ⓜ 🏊 🛜 ✕ 🔌 ▭

⚏⚏⚏ Staybridge Suites Canton 🅷
(330) 966-6620. **Call for rates.** 3879 Everhard Rd NW 44709. I-77 exit 109, 0.4 mi e. Int corridors. **Pets:** Accepted. ⓜ 🛜 ✕ 🔌 ▭

CARROLLTON

⚏⚏ Carrollton Days Inn 🅷
(330) 627-9314. **$94-$125, 3 day notice.** 1111 Canton Rd 44615. On SR 43, 0.5 mi n of SR 39. Int corridors. **Pets:** Accepted. ⓜ 🏊 🛜 ✕ 🔌 ▭

⚏⚏ Microtel Inn & Suites by Wyndham 🅷
(330) 627-1133. **$74-$119.** 1030 Canton Rd NW 44615. On SR 43, 0.5 mi n of SR 39. Int corridors. **Pets:** Accepted. ⓜ 🛜 ✕ 🔌 ▭

CEDARVILLE

⚏⚏ Hearthstone Inn & Suites 🅷
(937) 766-3000. **Call for rates.** 10 S Main St 45314. I-70 exit 54, 11 mi s. Int corridors. **Pets:** Accepted. 🛜 ✕ 🔌 ▭

CHERRY GROVE

⚏⚏⚏ Best Western Clermont Ⓜ
(513) 528-7702. **$80-$200.** 4004 Williams Dr 45255. I-275 exit 65, just w, then just s. Ext corridors. **Pets:** Large, other species. $20 daily fee/room. Service with restrictions, crate. (SAVE) 🏊 🛜 🔌 ▭

CINCINNATI

⚏⚏⚏ 21c Museum Hotel Cincinnati 🅷 ❀
(513) 578-6600. **Call for rates.** 609 Walnut St 45202. Between 6th and 7th sts. Int corridors. **Pets:** Medium, other species. $150 one-time fee/pet. Designated rooms, service with restrictions, crate.
🍴 ⓜ ✕ 🛜 ✕ 🔌 ▭

⚏⚏⚏ The Cincinnatian Hotel 🅷
(513) 381-3000. **$179-$399.** 601 Vine St 45202. Corner of 6th and Vine sts; entrance on 6th St. Int corridors. **Pets:** Accepted.
(SAVE) 🍴 ⓜ ✕ 🛜 ✕ 🔌 ▭

⚏⚏⚏ Holiday Inn Express Cincinnati West 🅷
(513) 574-6000. **$104-$299.** 5505 Rybolt Rd 45248. I-74 exit 11, just s. Int corridors. **Pets:** Large. $25 one-time fee/room. Designated rooms, service with restrictions, supervision.
(SAVE) ⓜ 🏊 🛜 ✕ 🔌 ▭

⚏⚏⚏ Hyatt Regency Cincinnati 🅷
(513) 579-1234. **$109-$359.** 151 W 5th St 45202. At Hyatt-Saks Fifth Avenue Center. Int corridors. **Pets:** Accepted.
(SAVE) ⒺⒸⓄ 🍴 ⓜ 🏊 🛜 ✕ 🔌 ▭

⚏⚏⚏ Residence Inn by Marriott Cincinnati Downtown/ The Phelps 🅷
(513) 651-1234. **$110-$519.** 506 E Fourth St 45202. Just e of downtown. Int corridors. **Pets:** Accepted. 🍴 🛜 ✕ 🔌 ▭

⚏⚏⚏ The Westin Cincinnati 🅷
(513) 621-7700. **$109-$759.** 21 E 5th St 45202. Between Vine and Walnut sts. Int corridors. **Pets:** Accepted.
(SAVE) 🍴 ⓜ 🏊 ✕ 🌀 ✕ 🔌 ▭

CIRCLEVILLE

⚏⚏ Holiday Inn Express Hotel & Suites 🅷
(740) 420-7711. **Call for rates.** 23911 US Hwy 23 S 43113. Jct US 22, 1.2 mi s. Int corridors. **Pets:** Medium. $30 daily fee/pet. Service with restrictions, supervision. ⓜ 🏊 🛜 ✕ 🔌 ▭

CLEVELAND *(Restaurants p. 620)*

⚏⚏⚏ Aloft Hotel Cleveland Downtown 🅷
(216) 400-6469. **$119-$399.** 1111 W 10th St 44113. Jct Front Ave; in Warehouse District. Int corridors. **Pets:** Accepted.
(SAVE) 🍴 ⓜ 🛜 ✕ 🔌 ▭

⚏⚏⚏ Cleveland Airport Marriott 🅷
(216) 252-5333. **$67-$296.** 4277 W 150th St 44135. I-71 exit 240, just s. Int corridors. **Pets:** Accepted.
(SAVE) 🍴 ⓜ 🏊 🌀 ✕ 🔌 ▭

⚏⚏⚏ Drury Plaza Hotel Cleveland Downtown 🅷
(216) 357-3100. **$120-$320.** 1380 E 6th St 44114. Btween St. Clair and Rockwell aves. Int corridors. **Pets:** Accepted. ⓜ 🛜 ✕ 🔌 ▭

⚏⚏⚏ Hilton Garden Inn Cleveland Downtown 🅷
(216) 658-6400. **$139-$329.** 1100 Carnegie Ave 44115. I-71/77 exit E 9th St, just w. Int corridors. **Pets:** Accepted.
(SAVE) ⓜ 🏊 🛜 🔌 ▭

⚏⚏⚏ Hyatt Regency Cleveland at The Arcade 🅷
(216) 575-1234. **$89-$329.** 420 Superior Ave E 44114. Just e of Public Square. Int corridors. **Pets:** Accepted.
(SAVE) ⒺⒸⓄ 🍴 ⓜ 🛜 ✕ 🔌 ▭

⚏⚏⚏ The Kimpton Schofield Hotel 🅷 🐾
(216) 357-3250. **Call for rates.** 2000 E 9th St 44115. Jct Euclid Ave. Int corridors. **Pets:** Other species. Designated rooms, no service, crate.
🍴 ⓜ 🌀 ✕

◆◆ La Quinta Inn-Cleveland Airport North H
(216) 251-8500. **$68-$191.** 4222 W 150th St 44135. I-71 exit 240, just n. Int corridors. **Pets:** Accepted. 🍴 ♿ 🛜 ✕ 🔌 💻

◆ ◆◆◆ Metropolitan at the 9, Autograph Collection H 🐾
(216) 239-1200. **$116-$494.** 2017 E 9th St 44115. Just n of jct Prospect Ave. Int corridors. **Pets:** Medium, dogs only. $100 one-time fee/room.
SAVE 🍴 ♿ 🛜 ✕

◆◆◆ Residence Inn by Marriott H
(216) 443-9043. **$101-$318.** 527 Prospect Ave E 44115. Between E 9th and Ontario sts. Int corridors. **Pets:** Accepted.
♿ 🛜 ✕ 🔌 💻

◆ ◆◆◆ The Ritz-Carlton, Cleveland H
(216) 623-1300. **Call for rates.** 1515 W 3rd St 44113. In Tower City Center (3rd St side). Int corridors. **Pets:** Accepted.
SAVE 🔌 🍴 ♿ 🏊 ✕ 🛜 ✕ 🔌 💻

◆ ◆◆◆ The Westin Cleveland Downtown Hotel H
(216) 771-7700. **$149-$999.** 777 St. Clair Ave NE 44114. Jct E 6th St. Int corridors. **Pets:** Accepted. SAVE 🍴 ♿ 🛜 ✕ 🔌 💻

CLYDE

◆◆ Red Roof Inn Clyde H
(419) 547-6660. **$80-$175.** 1363 W McPherson Hwy 43410. 1 mi w on SR 20. Int corridors. **Pets:** Accepted. ♿ 🏊 🛜 ✕ 🔌 💻

COLUMBUS

◆ ◆◆ Best Western Port Columbus H 🐾
(614) 337-8400. **$69-$199.** 1450 Airpointe Dr 43219. I-670 exit 9 (Johnstown Rd) eastbound; exit 9 (Cassady Ave) westbound, just n. Int corridors. **Pets:** Medium, other species. $20 daily fee/pet. Designated rooms, service with restrictions, supervision.
SAVE 🍴 ♿ 🏊 🛜 ✕ 🔌 💻

◆◆ Candlewood Suites Polaris H
(614) 436-6600. **Call for rates.** 8515 Lyra Dr 43240. I-71 exit 121, just w on Polaris Pkwy. Int corridors. **Pets:** Accepted.
♿ 🏊 🛜 🔌 💻

◆ ◆◆◆ DoubleTree by Hilton Hotel Columbus-Worthington H
(614) 885-3334. **Call for rates.** 175 Hutchinson Ave 43235. I-270 exit 23, just n on US 23, just e on Dimension Dr, then just s on High Cross Blvd. Int corridors. **Pets:** Accepted.
SAVE 🍴 ♿ 🏊 🛜 ✕ 🔌 💻

◆◆◆ Drury Inn & Suites-Columbus Convention Center H
(614) 221-7008. **$110-$200.** 88 E Nationwide Blvd 43215. 0.3 mi n on US 23. Int corridors. **Pets:** Accepted. ♿ 🏊 🛜 ✕ 🔌 💻

◆◆◆ Extended Stay America-Columbus-Easton H
(614) 428-6022. **$90-$115.** 4200 Stelzer Rd 43230. I-270 exit 32, just w on Morse Rd, then just n. Int corridors. **Pets:** Accepted. 🛜 ✕ 🔌

◆◆◆ Extended Stay America Columbus/Polaris H
(614) 431-5522. **$95-$125.** 8555 Lyra Dr 43240. I-71 exit 121, just w on Polaris Pkwy. Int corridors. **Pets:** Accepted. ♿ 🏊 🛜 🔌

◆◆◆ German Village Guest House BB
(614) 437-9712. **Call for rates.** 748 Jaeger St 43206. I-70 exit 100B, just s on S 3rd St, 0.4 mi e on E Sycamore St, then just s. Int corridors. **Pets:** Accepted. 🛜 ✕ 🔌 💻

◆ ◆◆ ◆◆ Hilton Columbus at Easton H
(614) 414-5000. **$179-$339.** 3900 Chagrin Dr 43219. I-270 exit 33, 0.5 mi w. Int corridors. **Pets:** Medium, dogs only. $50 one-time fee/room. Service with restrictions, supervision.
SAVE 🔌 🍴 ♿ 🏊 ✕ 🛜 ✕ 🔌 💻

◆◆ ◆◆◆ Hilton Columbus Downtown H
(614) 384-8600. **$159-$319.** 401 N High St 43215. Jct Nationwide Blvd, just n. Int corridors. **Pets:** Accepted.
🔌 🍴 ♿ 🏊 ✕ 🛜 ✕ 🔌 💻

◆ ◆◆◆ Holiday Inn Columbus Downtown Capitol Square H
(614) 221-3281. **Call for rates.** 175 E Town St 43215. I-70 exit 100B, 0.3 mi n on 4th St. Int corridors. **Pets:** Accepted.
SAVE 🍴 ♿ 🏊 🛜 ✕ 🔌 💻

◆ ◆◆◆ Hyatt Place Columbus/OSU H
(614) 280-1234. **$109-$299.** 795 Yard St 43212. US 31 exit Goodale Blvd, just w. Int corridors. **Pets:** Accepted.
SAVE 🍴 ♿ 🏊 🛜 ✕ 🔌 💻

◆ ◆◆◆ Hyatt Place Columbus/Worthington H
(614) 846-4355. **$79-$189.** 7490 Vantage Dr 43235. I-270 exit 23, 0.4 mi n on US 23, just e on Dimension Dr, then just s. Int corridors. **Pets:** Dogs only. $75 one-time fee/room. Service with restrictions.
SAVE 🍴 ♿ 🏊 🛜 ✕ 🔌 💻

◆ ◆◆◆ Hyatt Regency Columbus H
(614) 463-1234. **$99-$349.** 350 N High St 43215. 0.3 mi n on US 23. Int corridors. **Pets:** Accepted.
SAVE ECO 🍴 ♿ 🏊 🛜 ✕ 🔌 💻

◆◆ ◆◆ La Quinta Inn & Suites Columbus West-Hilliard H
(614) 878-8844. **$93-$189.** 5510 Trabue Rd 43228. I-70 exit 91 eastbound; exit 91B westbound, just n on Renner Rd, then just e. Int corridors. **Pets:** Accepted. ♿ 🏊 🛜 ✕ 🔌

◆ ◆◆◆ Le Meridien Columbus, The Joseph H
(614) 227-0100. **$229-$499.** 620 N High St 43215. Between Russell St and Poplar Ave; in Short North District. Int corridors. **Pets:** Accepted.
SAVE 🍴 ♿ ✕ 🛜 ✕ 🔌 💻

◆ ◆◆◆ Magnuson Grand North Hotel H
(614) 888-8230. **$79-$119.** 888 E Dublin Granville Rd 43229. I-71 exit 117, 0.5 mi w on SR 161. Int corridors. **Pets:** Accepted.
SAVE 🍴 ♿ 🏊 ✕ 🛜 🔌 💻

◆ ◆◆ Red Roof PLUS+ Columbus Downtown-Convention Center H
(614) 224-6539. **$79-$249.** 111 E Nationwide Blvd 43215. Jct 3rd St. Int corridors. **Pets:** Accepted. SAVE ♿ 🛜 ✕ 🔌 💻

◆ ◆◆ Red Roof PLUS+ Columbus-The Ohio State University H
(614) 267-9941. **$77-$125.** 441 Ackerman Rd 43202. SR 315 exit Ackerman Rd, 0.6 mi e. Ext corridors. **Pets:** Accepted.
SAVE ♿ 🛜 ✕ 🔌 💻

◆◆◆ Residence Inn by Marriott H
(614) 436-3955. **$88-$271.** 8865 Lyra Dr 43240. I-71 exit 121, 0.3 mi w on Polaris Pkwy, then just n. Int corridors. **Pets:** Accepted.
♿ 🛜 ✕ 🔌 💻

◆◆◆ Residence Inn by Marriott H
(614) 222-2610. **$107-$275.** 36 E Gay St 43215. Between High and S 3rd sts. Int corridors. **Pets:** Accepted. ♿ 🛜 ✕ 🔌 💻

▼▼▼▼ **Residence Inn by Marriott** H
(614) 885-0799. **$72-$219.** 7300 Huntington Park Dr 43235. I-270 exit 23, 0.4 mi n on US 23, 0.3 mi e on E Campus View Blvd, then 0.5 mi s. Int corridors. **Pets:** Accepted. 🚗 ⊿ 🛜 ✕ 🛢 🖥

▼▼▼▼ **Residence Inn by Marriott Easton** H
(614) 414-1000. **$118-$293.** 3999 Easton Loop W 43219. I-270 exit 33, 0.8 mi w, then just n. Int corridors. **Pets:** Accepted.
🚗 ⊿ 🛜 ✕ 🛢 🖥

🅰🅰🅰 ▼▼▼▼ **Sheraton Columbus at Capitol Square** H
(614) 365-4500. **$129-$224.** 75 E State St 43215. Corner of State and 3rd sts. Int corridors. **Pets:** Accepted.
🆂🅰🆅🅴 🄴🄲🄾 🍴 🚗 🛜 ✕ 🛢 🖥

🅰🅰🅰 ▼▼▼▼ **TownePlace Suites by Marriott** H
(614) 885-1557. **$64-$169.** 7272 Huntington Park Dr 43235. I-270 exit 23, 0.4 mi n, 0.3 mi e on E Campus View Blvd, then 0.3 mi s. Int corridors. **Pets:** Accepted. 🆂🅰🆅🅴 🄴🄲🄾 ⊿ 🛜 ✕ 🛢 🖥

🅰🅰🅰 ▼▼▼▼ **The Varsity Inn South** M
(614) 291-2983. **$69-$199.** 1445 Olentangy River Rd 43212. SR 315 exit King Ave southbound; exit Lane Ave northbound, 1 mi s. Ext corridors. **Pets:** $10 one-time fee/room. Designated rooms, service with restrictions, supervision. 🆂🅰🆅🅴 🚗 ⊿ 🛜 🛢 🖥

🅰🅰🅰 ▼▼▼▼ **The Westin Columbus** H 🐾
(614) 228-3800. **$149-$499.** 310 S High St 43215. Corner of Main and High sts. Int corridors. **Pets:** Very small. Service with restrictions, supervision. 🆂🅰🆅🅴 🍴 🆂🄾 ✕ 🛢 🖥

CONNEAUT

▼▼ **Days Inn of Conneaut** H
(440) 593-6000. **$70-$199.** 600 Days Blvd 44030. I-90 exit 241, 0.3 mi n. Int corridors. **Pets:** Accepted. 🍴 🚗 ⊿ 🛜 🛢 🖥

CUYAHOGA FALLS

🅰🅰🅰 ▼▼▼▼ **Sheraton Suites Akron-Cuyahoga Falls** H 🐾
(330) 929-3000. **$119-$369.** 1989 Front St 44221. SR 8 exit Broad Blvd, just w. Int corridors. **Pets:** Medium, other species. Designated rooms, service with restrictions, crate.
🆂🅰🆅🅴 🍴 🚗 ⊿ 🛜 ✕ 🛢 🖥

DANVILLE

▼▼▼▼ **The White Oak Inn** BB
(740) 599-6107. **$155-$275, 14 day notice.** 29683 Walhonding Rd (SR 715) 43014. 3.6 mi w on US 62, 1.3 mi se on US 36, then 2.7 mi e on SR 715. Ext/int corridors. **Pets:** Accepted. 🔌 🍴 🛜 ✕ 🎣

DAYTON

🅰🅰🅰 ▼▼▼▼ **Crowne Plaza Dayton** H
(937) 224-0800. **Call for rates.** 33 E 5th St 45402. 5th and Jefferson sts; downtown. Int corridors. **Pets:** Medium, dogs only. $75 one-time fee/room. Service with restrictions, crate.
🆂🅰🆅🅴 🍴 🚗 ⊿ 🛜 ✕ 🛢 🖥

▼▼▼▼ **Drury Inn & Suites-Dayton North** H
(937) 454-5200. **$95-$180.** 6616 Miller Ln 45414. I-75 exit 59 (Wyse Rd/Benchwood Rd), just w on Benchwood Rd, then just n. Int corridors. **Pets:** Accepted. 🚗 ⊿ 🛜 ✕ 🛢 🖥

▼▼▼▼ **Residence Inn by Marriott Dayton North** H
(937) 890-2244. **$99-$276.** 7227 York Center Dr 45414. I-75 exit 59 (Wyse Rd/Benchwood Rd), just w on Benchwood Rd, 0.6 mi n on Miller Ln, then just w. Int corridors. **Pets:** Accepted.
🚗 ⊿ 🛜 ✕ 🛢 🖥

▼▼▼▼ **TownePlace Suites by Marriott Dayton North** H
(937) 898-5700. **$76-$193.** 3642 Maxton Rd 45414. I-75 exit 59 (Wyse Rd/Benchwood Rd), just w on Wyse Rd, then 0.5 mi n on Miller Ln. Int corridors. **Pets:** Accepted. 🚗 🛜 ✕ 🛢 🖥

DELAWARE

🅰🅰🅰 ▼▼▼▼ **Baymont Inn & Suites Delaware** H
(740) 363-3510. **$90-$140.** 1720 Columbus Pike 43015. I-270 exit 23, 11 mi n on US 23. Int corridors. **Pets:** Small. $20 daily fee/pet. Designated rooms, service with restrictions, supervision.
🆂🅰🆅🅴 🚗 ⊿ 🛜 ✕ 🛢 🖥

▼▼▼ **Pacer Inn & Suites Motel** M
(740) 362-0050. **$60-$300.** 259 S Sandusky St 43015. Jct US 23, 0.7 mi w. Ext/int corridors. **Pets:** Medium, dogs only. $25 daily fee/pet. Designated rooms, service with restrictions, supervision.
🛜 ✕ 🛢 🖥

DELPHOS

▼▼▼ **Microtel Inn & Suites by Wyndham Delphos** H
(567) 765-1500. **$69-$83.** 480 Moxie Ln 45833. US 30 exit 5th St, 0.5 mi s. Int corridors. **Pets:** Accepted. 🍴 🚗 🛜 ✕ 🛢 🖥

DUBLIN

▼▼▼▼ **Drury Inn & Suites-Columbus Northwest** H
(614) 798-8802. **$100-$180.** 6170 Parkcenter Cir 43017. I-270 exit 15 (Tuttle Crossing Blvd), 0.3 mi e, then just n on Blazer Pkwy. Int corridors. **Pets:** Accepted. 🚗 ⊿ 🛜 ✕ 🛢 🖥

▼▼▼▼ **Dublin Homewood Suites by Hilton** H
(614) 791-8675. **$129-$199.** 5300 Parkcenter Ave 43017. I-270 exit 15 (Tuttle Crossing Blvd), just e, just n on Blazer Pkwy, then just e. Int corridors. **Pets:** Accepted. 🚗 ⊿ 🛜 🛢 🖥

▼▼▼▼ **Extended Stay America (Columbus/Tuttle)** H
(614) 760-0245. **$90-$115.** 5530 Tuttle Crossing Blvd 43016. I-270 exit 15 (Tuttle Crossing Blvd), 0.3 mi w. Int corridors. **Pets:** Accepted.
🍴 🚗 🛜 ✕ 🛢 🖥

▼▼▼▼ **Holiday Inn Express Dublin** H
(614) 793-5500. **Call for rates.** 5500 Tuttle Crossing Blvd 43016. I-270 exit 15 (Tuttle Crossing Blvd), just w. Int corridors. **Pets:** Medium. $35 one-time fee/room. Service with restrictions.
🚗 ⊿ 🛜 ✕ 🛢 🖥

🅰🅰🅰 ▼▼▼▼ **Hyatt Place Columbus/Dublin** H
(614) 799-1913. **$89-$229.** 6161 Parkcenter Cir 43017. I-270 exit 15 (Tuttle Crossing Blvd), just e on Tuttle Pkwy, then just n on Blazer Pkwy. Int corridors. **Pets:** Accepted.
🆂🅰🆅🅴 🍴 🚗 ⊿ 🛜 ✕ 🛢 🖥

🅰🅰🅰 ▼▼▼ **Red Roof PLUS+ Columbus/Dublin** M
(614) 764-3993. **$59-$199.** 5125 Post Rd 43017. I-270 exit 17A, just ne. Ext corridors. **Pets:** Accepted. 🆂🅰🆅🅴 🚗 🛜 ✕ 🛢 🖥

▼▼▼▼ **Residence Inn by Marriott Columbus Dublin** H
(614) 389-6600. **$89-$207.** 6364 Frantz 43017. I-270 exit 17A. Int corridors. **Pets:** Other species. $100 one-time fee/room. Service with restrictions, crate. 🚗 ⊿ 🛜 ✕ 🛢 🖥

🅰🅰🅰 ▼▼▼▼ **Sonesta ES Suites Dublin** H
(614) 791-0403. **Call for rates.** 435 Metro Pl S 43017. I-270 exit 17A, 0.5 mi e on SR 161, 0.5 mi s on Frantz Rd, then just w. Ext/int corridors. **Pets:** Accepted. 🆂🅰🆅🅴 🚗 ⊿ 🛜 ✕ 🛢 🖥

FAIRBORN

🅰🅰🅰 ▼▼▼▼ **Holiday Inn Dayton/Fairborn** H
(937) 426-7800. **Call for rates.** 2800 Presidential Dr 45324. I-675 exit 17 (N Fairfield Rd), just w. Int corridors. **Pets:** Medium. $75 one-time fee/pet. Designated rooms, service with restrictions, crate.
🆂🅰🆅🅴 🍴 🚗 ⊿ 🛜 ✕ 🛢 🖥

▼▼▼▼ **Homewood Suites by Hilton Dayton-Fairborn** H
(937) 429-0600. **$99-$329.** 2750 Presidential Dr 45324. I-675 exit 17 (N Fairfield Rd), just w, then just s on Colonel Glenn Hwy. Ext/int corridors. **Pets:** Accepted. ⊿ 🛜 ✕ 🛢 🖥

FAIRLAWN

Extended Stay America-Akron-Copley H
(330) 666-3177. **$70-$100.** 170 Montrose West Ave 44321. I-77 exit 137B, 0.3 mi w on SR 18, then 0.5 mi s. Int corridors. **Pets:** Accepted.

Hilton Akron/Fairlawn H ✿
(330) 867-5000. **$119-$249.** 3180 W Market St 44333. I-77 exit 137A, 2 mi e on SR 18. Int corridors. **Pets:** Medium, dogs only. $50 one-time fee/room. Designated rooms, service with restrictions, supervision.

Homewood Suites by Hilton Akron/Fairlawn H
(330) 664-6000. **Call for rates.** 210 Springside Dr 44333. I-77 exit 137A, just e, then n. Int corridors. **Pets:** Accepted.

Residence Inn by Marriott Akron/Fairlawn H
(330) 664-7800. **$89-$336.** 4080 Embassy Pkwy 44333. I-77 exit 137B, 0.3 mi w on SR 18. Int corridors. **Pets:** Accepted.

FINDLAY

Country Inn & Suites By Carlson H
(419) 422-4200. **Call for rates.** 903 Interstate Dr 45840. I-75 exit 159, just w. Int corridors. **Pets:** Dogs only. $25 one-time fee/room. Service with restrictions, supervision.

Drury Inn & Suites H
(419) 422-9700. **$100-$155.** 820 Trenton Ave 45840. I-75 exit 159, just e. Int corridors. **Pets:** Accepted.

Extended Stay America Findlay-Tiffin Ave H
(419) 425-9696. **$100-$120.** 2355 Tiffin Ave 45840. 3 mi e on US 224. Int corridors. **Pets:** Accepted.

Holiday Inn Express Hotel & Suites Findlay H
(419) 420-1776. **Call for rates.** 941 Interstate Dr 45840. I-75 exit 159, just w. Int corridors. **Pets:** Medium, dogs only. $25 one-time fee/pet. Designated rooms, service with restrictions, crate.

Quality Inn M ✿
(419) 423-4303. **$75-$134.** 1020 Interstate Ct 45840. I-75 exit 159, just w. Ext corridors. **Pets:** Small, dogs only. $15 daily fee/pet. Service with restrictions, supervision.

TownePlace Suites by Marriott Findlay H
(419) 425-9545. **$73-$171.** 2501 Tiffin Ave 45840. 3 mi e on US 224. Int corridors. **Pets:** Accepted.

FOSTORIA

Best Western Fostoria Inn & Suites H
(419) 436-3600. **$85-$240.** 1690 N County Line Rd 44830. SR 12, 2 mi n on SR 23. Int corridors. **Pets:** Accepted.

FRANKLIN

Drury Inn & Suites Middletown H
(513) 425-6650. **$90-$135.** 3320 Village Dr 45005. I-75 exit 32, just w on SR 122. Int corridors. **Pets:** Accepted.

FREMONT

Comfort Inn & Suites H ✿
(419) 355-9300. **$129-$300.** 840 Sean Dr 43420. I-80/90 exit 91, 2 mi s on SR 53. Int corridors. **Pets:** Other species. $25 one-time fee/pet. Service with restrictions, supervision.

GAHANNA

Candlewood Suites Columbus Airport H
(614) 863-4033. **Call for rates.** 590 Taylor Rd 43230. I-270 exit 37, 0.4 mi e, 0.6 mi s on Morrison Rd, then just e. Int corridors. **Pets:** Accepted.

TownePlace Suites by Marriott Columbus Airport H
(614) 861-1400. **$80-$208.** 695 Taylor Rd 43230. I-270 exit 37, just e, 0.6 mi s on Morrison Rd, then just e. Int corridors. **Pets:** Accepted.

GALLIPOLIS

Super 8 M
(740) 446-8080. **$74-$86, 3 day notice.** 321 Upper River Rd 45631. On SR 7, jct US 35. Int corridors. **Pets:** Accepted.

GENEVA

Motel 6 #4476 H
(440) 466-1168. **$60-$130.** 1715 S Broadway 44041. I-90 exit 218, just n. Ext/int corridors. **Pets:** Accepted.

GROVE CITY

Best Western Executive Inn M
(614) 875-7770. **$90-$136.** 4026 Jackpot Rd 43123. I-71 exit 100, just e. Ext corridors. **Pets:** Small, dogs only. $10 daily fee/pet. Designated rooms, service with restrictions, supervision.

Drury Inn & Suites-Columbus South H
(614) 875-7000. **$95-$180.** 4109 Parkway Centre Dr 43123. I-71 exit 100, just e. Int corridors. **Pets:** Accepted.

La Quinta Inn Grove City H
(614) 539-6200. **$93-$214.** 3962 Jackpot Rd 43123. I-71 exit 100, just e. Int corridors. **Pets:** Accepted.

HARRISON

Best Western Plus Whitewater Inn H ✿
(513) 845-4970. **$89-$159.** 391 Comfort Dr 45030. I-74 exit 1, just n on New Haven Rd, then just e on Biggs Blvd. Int corridors. **Pets:** Medium, dogs only. $20 daily fee/pet. Designated rooms, service with restrictions, crate.

HILLIARD

Homewood Suites by Hilton-Columbus H
(614) 529-4100. **$94-$149.** 3841 Park Mill Run Dr 43026. I-270 exit 13 southbound; exit 13A northbound, 0.4 mi e on Fishinger Blvd. Int corridors. **Pets:** Accepted.

HOLIDAY CITY

Holiday Inn Express Hotel & Suites Bryan/ Montpelier H
(419) 485-0008. **Call for rates.** 13399 SR 15 43543. I-80/90 exit 13, just s. Int corridors. **Pets:** Accepted.

HOLLAND

Extended Stay America Toledo-Holland H
(419) 861-1133. **$60-$80.** 6155 W Trust Dr 43528. I-475 exit 8, 0.5 mi e to Holland-Sylvania Rd, then just n. Int corridors. **Pets:** Accepted.

HUBER HEIGHTS

▼▼▼ Holiday Inn Express Hotel & Suites 🄷
(937) 235-2000. **Call for rates.** 5612 Merily Way 45424. I-70 exit 36, just se on SR 202. Int corridors. **Pets:** Accepted.
🔊 🛌 📶 ⊠ 🔌 🖥

HUDSON

⊛ ▼▼▼ Clarion Inn and Conference Center 🄷
(330) 653-9191. **$65-$499.** 6625 Dean Memorial Pkwy 44236. SR 8 exit 15 southbound; exit 14A northbound. Int corridors. **Pets:** Small. $10 daily fee/pet. Service with restrictions, supervision.
SAVE 🍴 🔊 🛌 ⊠ 📶 🔌 🖥

HURON

▼▼ Motel 6 Huron 🄼
(419) 433-7829. **Call for rates.** 601 Rye Beach Rd 44839. SR 2 exit Rye Beach, 2.5 mi w on US 6. Int corridors. **Pets:** Accepted.
🔊 🛌 📶 ⊠ 🔌 🖥

⊛ ▼▼▼ Sawmill Creek Resort 🄷
(419) 433-3800. **$129-$219, 3 day notice.** 400 Sawmill Creek W 44839. SR 2 exit Rye Beach, 0.5 mi w on US 6. Int corridors. **Pets:** Small, dogs only. $25 one-time fee/pet. Service with restrictions, crate.
SAVE 🍴 🔊 🛌 ⊠ 📶 ⊠ 🔌 🖥

INDEPENDENCE

⊛ ▼▼▼ Hyatt Place Cleveland/Independence 🄷
(216) 328-1060. **$89-$209.** 6025 Jefferson Dr 44131. I-77 exit 155 (Rockside Rd), just w, then just n. Int corridors. **Pets:** Accepted.
SAVE 🍴 🔊 🛌 📶 ⊠ 🔌 🖥

▼▼▼ Residence Inn by Marriott 🄷
(216) 520-1450. **$88-$417.** 5101 W Creek Rd 44131. I-77 exit 155 (Rockside Rd), just w, then just n. Ext/int corridors. **Pets:** Other species. $100 one-time fee/room. Service with restrictions, crate.
🔊 🛌 📶 ⊠ 🔌 🖥

JACKSON

▼▼ Days Inn 🄷
(740) 286-3464. **$78-$88.** 972 E Main St 45640. Just s of SR 93. Int corridors. **Pets:** Accepted. 📶 🔌 🖥

▼▼ Red Roof Inn Jackson, OH 🄼
(740) 288-1200. **$72-$107.** 1000 Acy Ave 45640. US 35 exit McCarty Ln, just nw. Int corridors. **Pets:** Accepted. 📶 🔌

KENWOOD

⊛ ▼▼▼ Best Western Plus Hannaford Inn & Suites 🄷
(513) 936-0525. **$109-$309.** 5900 E Galbraith Rd 45236. I-71 exit 12, 0.5 mi e, then 0.3 mi n. Int corridors. **Pets:** Accepted.
SAVE 🛌 📶 ⊠ 🔌 🖥

KINSMAN

▼▼▼ Dream Horse Guesthouse 🄱🄱
(330) 876-0428. **$75-$145, 14 day notice.** 9532 SR 7 44428. 0.5 mi n on SR 7. Int corridors. **Pets:** Other species. $20 daily fee/pet. No service, supervision. 🍴 📶 ⊠ 🔌 🖥

LIMA

▼▼▼ Country Inn & Suites By Carlson 🄷
(419) 999-9992. **Call for rates.** 804 S Leonard Ave 45804. I-75 exit 125A southbound; exit 125 northbound, just w. Int corridors.
Pets: Accepted. 🍴 🛌 📶 ⊠ 🔌 🖥

⊛ ▼▼▼ Holiday Inn & Suites Lima 🄷
(419) 879-4000. **Call for rates.** 803 S Leonard Ave 45804. I-75 exit 125, just w. Int corridors. **Pets:** Accepted.
SAVE 🍴 🔊 🛌 📶 ⊠ 🔌 🖥

⊛ ▼▼▼ Howard Johnson Lima 🄷
(419) 222-0004. **$79-$269.** 1920 Roschman Ave 45804. I-75 exit 125, just e. Int corridors. **Pets:** Dogs only. $25 daily fee/room. Service with restrictions, supervision. SAVE 🍴 🔊 🛌 ⊠ 📶 🔌 🖥

▼▼▼ Wingate by Wyndham Downtown Lima 🄷
(419) 228-7000. **$89-$125.** 175 W Market St 45801. Jct Elizabeth St; downtown. Int corridors. **Pets:** Accepted. 📶 🔌 🖥

LOGAN

▼▼▼ The Inn & Spa At Cedar Falls 🄲🄸 ❀
(740) 380-7489. **$129-$339, 30 day notice.** 21190 SR 374 43138. 9.5 mi s on SR 664, 1 mi e. Ext corridors. **Pets:** Large, dogs only. $50 one-time fee/room. Designated rooms, crate.
🍴 📶 ⊠ 🐾 🔌 🖥

MANSFIELD

⊛ ▼▼▼ Best Western Richland Inn-Mansfield 🄷 ❀
(419) 756-6670. **$89-$230.** 180 E Hanley Rd 44903. I-71 exit 169, jct SR 13. Int corridors. **Pets:** Other species. $15 daily fee/pet. Service with restrictions. SAVE 🍴 🔊 🛌 📶 ⊠ 🔌 🖥

▼▼ La Quinta Inn & Suites Mansfield 🄷
(419) 774-0005. **$75-$379.** 120 Stander Ave 44903. I-71 exit 169, just e. Int corridors. **Pets:** Accepted. 🔊 🛌 📶 ⊠ 🔌 🖥

▼▼▼ Quality Inn & Suites 🄷
(419) 529-1000. **$84-$350.** 500 N Trimble Rd 44906. Jct US 30, just s. Int corridors. **Pets:** $20 one-time fee/room. Service with restrictions, crate. 🔊 🛌 ⊠ 📶 🔌 🖥

MARIETTA

▼▼▼ Comfort Suites Marietta 🄷
(740) 376-1600. **$89-$179.** 202 Cherry Tree Ln 45750. I-77 exit 1, just e. Int corridors. **Pets:** $25 daily fee/pet. Service with restrictions, supervision. 🍴 🔊 📶 ⊠ 🔌 🖥

▼▼ The Lafayette Hotel 🄷
(740) 373-5522. **$80-$210.** 101 Front St 45750. I-77 exit 1; downtown. Int corridors. **Pets:** $50 deposit/room. Service with restrictions.
🍴 📶 ⊠ 🔌 🖥

▼▼ Quality Inn Marietta 🄷
(740) 374-8190. **$64-$149.** 700 Pike St 45750. I-77 exit 1, just e. Int corridors. **Pets:** Accepted. 🍴 🛌 📶 🔌 🖥

MASON

⊛ ▼▼▼ Hyatt Place Cincinnati-Northeast 🄷
(513) 754-0003. **$79-$199.** 5070 Natorp Blvd 45040. I-71 exit 19, 0.5 mi w. Int corridors. **Pets:** Accepted.
SAVE 🍴 🔊 🛌 📶 ⊠ 🔌 🖥

⊛ ▼▼▼ TownePlace Suites by Marriott Cincinnati Northeast/Mason 🄷
(513) 774-0610. **$45-$219.** 9369 Waterstone Blvd 45249. I-71 exit 19, just e on Mason-Montgomery Rd, then 0.9 mi n on Fields-Ertel and Union Cemetery rds. Int corridors. **Pets:** Accepted.
SAVE ECO 🍴 🔊 🛌 📶 ⊠ 🔌 🖥

MAUMEE

▼▼▼ Country Inn & Suites By Carlson, Toledo 🄷 ❀
(419) 893-8576. **Call for rates.** 541 W Dussel Dr 43537. I-475 exit 6, just e. Int corridors. **Pets:** $25 one-time fee/pet. Designated rooms, service with restrictions, supervision. 🔊 🛌 📶 ⊠ 🔌 🖥

▼▼▼ Extended Stay America-Toledo-Maumee 🄷
(419) 891-1211. **$70-$105.** 542 W Dussel Dr 43537. I-475 exit 6, just e. Int corridors. **Pets:** Accepted. 🛌 📶 ⊠ 🔌 🖥

Homewood Suites by Hilton Toledo/Maumee H
(419) 897-0980. **Call for rates.** 1410 Arrowhead Rd 43537. I-475 exit 6, just e. Int corridors. **Pets:** Accepted.

Red Roof Inn Toledo - Maumee M
(419) 893-0292. **$54-$100.** 1570 Reynolds Rd 43537. I-80/90 exit 59, just s. Ext/int corridors. **Pets:** Accepted.

Residence Inn by Marriott Toledo Maumee H
(419) 891-2233. **$93-$229.** 1370 Arrowhead Dr 43537. I-475 exit 6, just e. Int corridors. **Pets:** Accepted.

MAYFIELD HEIGHTS
Staybridge Suites Cleveland East H
(440) 442-9200. **Call for rates.** 6103 Landerhaven Dr 44124. I-271 exit 32, just e on Cedar Rd, 0.7 mi n on Lander Rd, then just e. Int corridors. **Pets:** Accepted.

MEDINA
Quality Inn & Suites H
(330) 723-4994. **$70-$500.** 2850 Medina Rd 44256. I-71 exit 218, just e. Int corridors. **Pets:** Other species. $20 daily fee/pet. Service with restrictions, crate.

MENTOR
Best Western Plus Lawnfield Inn & Suites H
(440) 205-7378. **$89-$159.** 8434 Mentor Ave 44060. I-90 exit 195, 1.5 mi n to US 20 (Mentor Ave), then just e. Int corridors. **Pets:** Accepted.

Residence Inn by Marriott H
(440) 392-0800. **$100-$284.** 5660 Emerald Ct 44060. Jct SR 2 and Heisley Rd, just s. Int corridors. **Pets:** Accepted.

Super 8 H
(440) 951-8558. **$47-$210.** 7325 Palisades Pkwy 44060. On SR 306, just s of SR 2. Int corridors. **Pets:** Accepted.

MIAMISBURG
Homewood Suites by Hilton-Dayton South H
(937) 432-0000. **$144-$164.** 3100 Contemporary Ln 45342. I-75 exit 44, just e on SR 725, just se on Prestige Plaza Dr, then just s. Int corridors. **Pets:** Accepted.

MIDDLEBURG HEIGHTS
Comfort Inn-Cleveland Airport H
(440) 234-3131. **$69-$354.** 17550 Rosbough Blvd 44130. I-71 exit 235, 0.3 mi w to Engle Rd, then 0.3 mi n. Int corridors. **Pets:** Accepted.

Days Inn Cleveland Airport South M
(440) 243-2277. **$69-$81.** 7233 Engle Rd 44130. I-71 exit 235, just w. Ext corridors. **Pets:** Accepted.

Extended Stay America Cleveland-Middleburg Heights H
(440) 243-7024. **$85-$125.** 17552 Rosbough Blvd 44130. I-71 exit 235, 0.3 mi w to Engle Rd, then 0.3 mi n. Int corridors. **Pets:** Accepted.

Red Roof Inn Cleveland - Airport Middleburg Heights H
(440) 243-2441. **$59-$150.** 17555 Bagley Rd 44130. I-71 exit 235, just w, then just s. Ext/int corridors. **Pets:** Accepted.

Sonesta ES Suites Cleveland Airport H
(440) 234-6688. **Call for rates.** 17525 Rosbough Blvd 44130. I-71 exit 235, just w on Bagley Rd, then just n on Engle Rd. Ext/int corridors. **Pets:** Accepted.

TownePlace Suites by Marriott Cleveland Airport H
(440) 816-9300. **$75-$208.** 7325 Engle Rd 44130. I-71 exit 235, just w on Bagley Rd, then just s. Int corridors. **Pets:** Accepted.

MILAN
Country Inn & Suites By Carlson H
(419) 499-4911. **Call for rates.** 11600 Milan Rd 44846. I-80/90 exit 118, just n. Int corridors. **Pets:** Accepted.

Motel 6-4016 M
(419) 499-8001. **Call for rates.** 11406 Milan Rd 44846. I-80/90 exit 118, 1.5 mi n. Int corridors. **Pets:** Accepted.

Red Roof Inn Sandusky-Milan H
(419) 499-4347. **$54-$175.** 11303 US 250 Milan Rd 44846. I-80/90 exit 118, 0.5 mi n. Int corridors. **Pets:** Accepted.

Super 8 H
(419) 499-4671. **$49-$180.** 11313 US 250 Milan Rd 44846. I-80/90 exit 118, 0.5 mi n. Ext/int corridors. **Pets:** Medium, dogs only. Designated rooms, supervision.

MILFORD
Homewood Suites by Hilton H
(513) 248-4663. **$129-$199.** 600 Chamber Dr 45150. I-275 exit 59 southbound; exit 59A northbound, 0.5 mi w on Milford Pkwy, then 0.5 mi s. Int corridors. **Pets:** Accepted.

MILLERSBURG
Comfort Inn Millersburg H
(330) 674-7400. **$90-$220.** 1102 Glen Dr 44654. SR 39, 0.5 mi s on S Clay St. Int corridors. **Pets:** Dogs only. $20 daily fee/pet. Designated rooms, service with restrictions, supervision.

Hotel Millersburg H
(330) 674-1457. **$89-$249, 3 day notice.** 35 W Jackson St 44654. Just w of jct SR 83; downtown. Int corridors. **Pets:** Accepted.

MOUNT VERNON
Comfort Inn H
(740) 392-6886. **$110-$220.** 150 Howard St 43050. Jct SR 13, just s. Int corridors. **Pets:** Accepted.

Holiday Inn Express H
(740) 392-1900. **Call for rates.** 11555 Upper Gilchrist Rd 43050. 2.6 mi e on US 36, then just s. Int corridors. **Pets:** Accepted.

NAPOLEON
Comfort Inn & Suites H
(419) 592-5599. **$79-$144.** 590 Bonaparte Dr 43545. Jct US 6 and 24 exit 40, just n on SR 108. Int corridors. **Pets:** Accepted.

NEWCOMERSTOWN
Hampton Inn by Hilton H
(740) 498-9800. **$99-$179.** 200 Morris Crossing 43832. I-77 exit 65, 0.8 mi w. Int corridors. **Pets:** Accepted.

NEW PHILADELPHIA

Best Western Dutch Valley Inn H
(330) 339-6500. **$80-$120.** 161 Bluebell Dr SW 44663. I-77 exit 81, 0.7 mi e. Int corridors. **Pets:** Accepted.

NEWTON FALLS

Econo Lodge M
(330) 872-0988. **$55-$140.** 4248 SR 5 44444. I-80 exit 209, just w. Ext corridors. **Pets:** Accepted.

NILES

Residence Inn by Marriott Youngstown/Warren-Niles H
(330) 505-3655. **$80-$229.** 5555 Youngstown-Warren Rd 44446. I-80 exit 227, 2.6 mi w on US 422. Int corridors. **Pets:** Accepted.

NORTH OLMSTED

Candlewood Suites Cleveland/North Olmsted H
(440) 716-0584. **Call for rates.** 24741 Country Club Blvd 44070. I-480 exit 6B westbound; exit 6 eastbound, just n on SR 252. Int corridors. **Pets:** Accepted.

Extended Stay America-North Olmsted H
(440) 777-8585. **$80-$120.** 24851 Country Club Blvd 44070. I-480 exit 6B westbound; exit 6 eastbound, just n on SR 252. Int corridors. **Pets:** Accepted.

La Quinta Inn & Suites Cleveland Airport West H
(440) 734-4477. **$67-$152.** 25105 Country Club Blvd 44070. I-480 exit 6B westbound; exit 6 eastbound, just n on SR 252. Int corridors. **Pets:** Accepted.

OBERLIN

The Hotel at Oberlin H ❖
(440) 775-7001. **$119-$309.** 10 E College St 44074. On SR 58; jct College and Main sts; center. Int corridors. **Pets:** Dogs only. $75 one-time fee/room. Service with restrictions, crate.

OREGON

Comfort Inn East H
(419) 691-8911. **$86-$170.** 2930 Navarre Ave 43616. I-280 exit 7, 0.6 mi e on SR 2 (Navarre Ave). Int corridors. **Pets:** $15 one-time fee/pet. Designated rooms, service with restrictions, supervision.

Sleep Inn & Suites H
(419) 697-7800. **$81-$191.** 1761 Meijer Cir 43616. I-280 exit 6 (Curtice Rd), just w. Int corridors. **Pets:** $15 one-time fee/pet. Designated rooms, service with restrictions, supervision.

PAINESVILLE

Quail Hollow Resort H
(440) 497-1100. **Call for rates.** 11080 Concord-Hambden Rd 44077. I-90 exit 200, 0.3 mi s on SR 44, then just e on Auburn Rd. Int corridors. **Pets:** Accepted.

PERRYSBURG

Candlewood Suites Perrysburg H
(419) 872-6161. **Call for rates.** 27350 Lake Vue Dr 43551. I-75 exit 193, just e. Int corridors. **Pets:** Accepted.

PIQUA

Comfort Inn Miami Valley Centre Mall H
(937) 778-8100. **Call for rates.** 987 E Ash St, Suite 171 45356. I-75 exit 82, just w. Int corridors. **Pets:** Small, other species. $20 daily fee/pet. Designated rooms, service with restrictions, supervision.

PORT CLINTON

Best Western Port Clinton H
(419) 734-2274. **$79-$210.** 1734 E Perry St 43452. 1.7 mi e on SR 163, w of jct SR 2. Ext/int corridors. **Pets:** Accepted.

Quality Inn H
(419) 732-2929. **$60-$340.** 1723 E Perry St 43452. 1.5 mi e on SR 163, w of jct SR 2. Int corridors. **Pets:** Accepted.

Travelodge Port Clinton M
(419) 734-0769. **$69-$190.** 1811 E Perry St 43452. SR 163, 1.8 mi e to jct SR 2, then w. Ext/int corridors. **Pets:** Large, other species. $50 deposit/room. Service with restrictions, supervision.

PORTSMOUTH

Quality Inn M
(740) 353-3232. **$80-$135.** 5100 Old Scioto Tr 45662. 3.8 mi n of downtown. Int corridors. **Pets:** Small, dogs only. $25 one-time fee/pet. Service with restrictions, supervision.

REYNOLDSBURG

Fairfield Inn & Suites by Marriott Columbus East H
(614) 864-4555. **$80-$182.** 2826 Taylor Rd Ext 43068. I-70 exit 112B eastbound; exit 112 westbound, just n, then just e. Int corridors. **Pets:** Accepted.

RICHFIELD

Days Inn & Suites Richfield H
(330) 659-6151. **$79-$300.** 4742 Brecksville Rd 44286. I-80 exit 173, just s; I-77 exit 145, 0.5 mi n. Int corridors. **Pets:** Other species. $50 one-time fee/room. Designated rooms, service with restrictions, supervision.

ROSSFORD

Country Inn & Suites By Carlson, Toledo South H
(419) 872-9900. **Call for rates.** 9790 Clark Dr 43460. I-75 exit 195A, just e. Int corridors. **Pets:** Small. $25 daily fee/pet. Designated rooms, service with restrictions, crate.

Staybridge Suites Toledo - Rossford - Perrysburg H
(419) 872-3700. **Call for rates.** 9749 Clark Dr 43460. I-75 exit 195A, just e. Int corridors. **Pets:** Medium, other species. $75 one-time fee/pet. Service with restrictions.

ST. CLAIRSVILLE

Americas Best Value Inn St. Clairsville/Wheeling M
(740) 695-5038. **$79-$169, 7 day notice.** 51260 National Rd 43950. I-70 exit 218, 0.5 mi ne on US 40. Ext corridors. **Pets:** Other species. $10 one-time fee/room. Designated rooms, service with restrictions.

Candlewood Suites St. Clairsville H
(740) 695-9200. **Call for rates.** 67689 Mall Ring Rd 43950. I-70 exit 218, just s. Int corridors. **Pets:** Medium. $75 one-time fee/room. Service with restrictions, crate.

Red Roof Inn St Clairsville-Wheeling West M
(740) 695-4057. **$49-$125.** 68301 Red Roof Ln 43950. I-70 exit 218, just n. Ext corridors. **Pets:** Accepted.

Residence Inn Wheeling-St. Clairsville H
(740) 695-9320. **$69-$296.** 50694 Ohio Valley Pl 43950. I-70 exit 218, just s. Int corridors. **Pets:** Accepted.

SANDUSKY

Knights Inn Sandusky M
(419) 621-9000. **$50-$125.** 2405 Cleveland Rd 44870. US 6, 2 mi e of Cedar Point Cswy. Ext corridors. **Pets:** Accepted.

La Quinta Inn Sandusky-Cedar Point M
(419) 626-6766. **$67-$449.** 3304 Milan Rd 44870. US 250, 2 mi n of SR 2. Int corridors. **Pets:** Accepted.

South Shore Inn M
(419) 626-4436. **Call for rates.** 2047 Cleveland Rd 44870. US 6, just e of Cedar Point Cswy. Ext/int corridors. **Pets:** Accepted.

SEAMAN

Comfort Inn M
(937) 386-2511. **$90-$115.** 55 Stern Dr 45679. Jct SR 32 and 247. Int corridors. **Pets:** Accepted.

SEVILLE

Comfort Inn H
(330) 769-4949. **$85-$330.** 4949 Park Ave W 44273. I-76/US 224 exit 2, just n. Int corridors. **Pets:** Medium. $25 one-time fee/pet. Designated rooms, service with restrictions, crate.

Hawthorn Suites by Wyndham H
(330) 769-5025. **$79-$279, 3 day notice.** 5025 Park Ave W 44273. I-76/US 224 exit 2, just n. Int corridors. **Pets:** Accepted.

Super 8-Seville H
(330) 769-8880. **$60-$250.** 6116 Speedway Dr 44273. Jct US 224 and Lake Rd, just s. Int corridors. **Pets:** Accepted.

SHARONVILLE

Drury Inn & Suites-Cincinnati Sharonville H
(513) 771-5601. **$95-$155.** 2265 E Sharon Rd 45241. I-75 exit 15, just e. Int corridors. **Pets:** Accepted.

Residence Inn by Marriott H
(513) 771-2525. **$144-$316.** 11689 Chester Rd 45246. I-75 exit 15, just w on Sharon Rd, then 1 mi n. Ext corridors. **Pets:** $100 one-time fee/room. Service with restrictions.

Sonesta ES Suites Cincinnati H
(513) 772-8888. **Call for rates.** 2670 E Kemper Rd 45241. I-275 exit 44, just s. Int corridors. **Pets:** Accepted.

SPRINGFIELD

Courtyard by Marriott Springfield Downtown H
(937) 322-3600. **$79-$157.** 100 S Fountain Ave 45502. I-70 exit 54, 2 mi n on SR 72 (Limestone St), just w on Main St, then just s; downtown. Int corridors. **Pets:** Other species. $75 one-time fee/room. Service with restrictions, crate.

STEUBENVILLE

Microtel Inn & Suites by Wyndham Steubenville H
(740) 282-1800. **$69-$129.** 875 University Blvd 43952. Jct US 22 and SR 7, just sw, then just s on Buckeye st. Int corridors. **Pets:** Accepted.

STRASBURG

Ramada Limited Dover/Strasburg H
(330) 878-1400. **$79-$105.** 509 S Wooster Ave 44680. I-77 exit 87, 0.4 mi n on US 250 and SR 21. Int corridors. **Pets:** Medium. $15 daily fee/room. Service with restrictions, supervision.

STREETSBORO

TownePlace Suites by Marriott H 🐾
(330) 422-1855. **$72-$208.** 795 Mondial Pkwy 44241. I-80 exit 187, 0.8 mi s. Int corridors. **Pets:** Other species. $25 daily fee/pet. Service with restrictions.

TIFFIN

Holiday Inn Express Tiffin H
(419) 443-5100. **$99-$159, 7 day notice.** 78 Shaffer Park Dr 44883. US 224, just n on Market St, then just w. Int corridors. **Pets:** Accepted.

TIPP CITY

La Quinta Inn & Suites Dayton North-Tipp City H
(937) 667-1574. **$67-$152.** 19 Weller Dr 45371. I-75 exit 68, just w. Int corridors. **Pets:** Accepted.

TOLEDO

Park Inn by Radisson Hotel Toledo H
(419) 241-3000. **Call for rates.** 101 N Summit St 43604. Between Jefferson and Monroe sts; downtown. Int corridors. **Pets:** Accepted.

TROY

Holiday Inn Express Hotel & Suites H
(937) 332-1700. **Call for rates.** 60 Troy Town Dr 45373. I-75 exit 74, just w. Int corridors. **Pets:** Accepted.

Residence Inn by Marriott H
(937) 440-9303. **$80-$215.** 87 Troy Town Dr 45373. I-75 exit 74, just w. Int corridors. **Pets:** Accepted.

VAN WERT

Comfort Inn H
(419) 232-6040. **$90-$139.** 840 N Washington St 45891. US 127, s of jct US 30 and 224. Int corridors. **Pets:** Accepted.

VERMILION

Holiday Inn Express H
(440) 967-8770. **$109-$350.** 2417 SR 60 44089. Jct SR 2 and 60. Int corridors. **Pets:** Medium. $35 one-time fee/pet. Service with restrictions, supervision.

WAPAKONETA

Best Western Wapakoneta Inn H
(419) 738-2050. **$90-$130.** 1008 Lunar Dr 45895. I-75 exit 111, just w. Int corridors. **Pets:** Accepted.

WARREN

♦♦ Fairfield Inn by Marriott-Warren/Niles H
(330) 544-5774. **$79-$217.** 1860 Niles-Cortland Rd 44484. Jct US 422 and SR 46, 1 mi n on SR 46. Int corridors. **Pets:** Accepted.

WASHINGTON COURT HOUSE

♦♦♦ Holiday Inn Express Washington Court House Jeffersonville Southwest H
(740) 335-9310. **Call for rates.** 101 Courthouse Pkwy 43160. Jct US 35, 0.4 mi sw on US 62. Int corridors. **Pets:** Accepted.

WAUSEON

♦♦♦ ♦♦ Best Western Del Mar M
(419) 335-1565. **$82-$146.** 8319 SR 108 43567. I-80/90 exit 34, just s. Ext corridors. **Pets:** Other species. $17 daily fee/room. Service with restrictions.

WEST CHESTER

♦♦♦ Residence Inn by Marriott Cincinnati North/West Chester H
(513) 341-4040. **$45-$255.** 6240 Muhlhauser Rd 45069. I-75 exit 19, just w on Union Centre Blvd, then just n. Int corridors. **Pets:** Other species. $100 one-time fee/room. Designated rooms, service with restrictions.

♦♦♦ Staybridge Suites Cincinnati North H
(513) 874-1900. **$99-$250.** 8955 Lakota Dr W 45069. I-75 exit 19, just w on Union Centre Blvd, then 0.5 mi n. Int corridors. **Pets:** Other species. $75 one-time fee/room. Service with restrictions, crate.

WESTLAKE

♦♦♦ DoubleTree by Hilton Cleveland/Westlake H
(440) 871-6000. **$109-$189.** 1100 Crocker Rd 44145. I-90 exit 156, just n. Int corridors. **Pets:** Accepted.

♦♦ Extended Stay America Cleveland-Westlake H
(440) 899-4160. **$95-$125.** 30360 Clemens Rd 44145. I-90 exit 156, just n. Int corridors. **Pets:** Accepted.

♦♦♦ ♦♦♦ Hyatt Place Cleveland Westlake Crocker Park H 🐾
(440) 871-3100. **$79-$269.** 2020 Crocker Rd 44145. I-90 exit 156, 0.7 mi s. Int corridors. **Pets:** Medium, dogs only. $75 one-time fee/room. Service with restrictions.

♦♦♦ ♦♦♦ Red Roof Inn Cleveland - Westlake M
(440) 892-7920. **$55-$120.** 29595 Clemens Rd 44145. I-90 exit 156, just n. Ext corridors. **Pets:** Accepted.

♦♦♦ ♦♦♦ Sonesta ES Suites Cleveland Westlake H
(440) 892-2254. **Call for rates.** 30100 Clemens Rd 44145. I-90 exit 156, just n. Ext corridors. **Pets:** Accepted.

♦♦♦ ♦♦♦ TownePlace Suites by Marriott Cleveland Westlake H
(440) 892-4275. **$64-$418.** 25052 Sperry Dr 44145. I-90 exit 159, just n. Int corridors. **Pets:** Accepted.

WILLOUGHBY

♦♦♦ ♦♦♦ Red Roof Inn Cleveland East - Willoughby M
(440) 946-9872. **$55-$109.** 4166 SR 306 44094. I-90 exit 193, just s. Ext corridors. **Pets:** Accepted.

WILMINGTON

♦♦♦ Hampton Inn & Suites by Hilton Wilmington H
(937) 382-4400. **$109-$174.** 201 Holiday Dr 45177. 1.5 mi e on US 22. Int corridors. **Pets:** Accepted.

♦♦♦ Holiday Inn Wilmington & Roberts Conference Centre H
(937) 283-3200. **Call for rates.** 123 Gano Rd 45177. I-71 exit 50, just w. Int corridors. **Pets:** Accepted.

ZANESVILLE

♦♦♦ ♦♦♦ Best Western B. R. Guest H
(740) 453-6300. **$80-$150.** 4929 East Pike 43701. I-70 exit 160, just s. Int corridors. **Pets:** Accepted.

♦♦♦ ♦♦♦ Comfort Inn H
(740) 454-4144. **$120-$250.** 500 Monroe St 43701. I-70 exit 155, just e on Elberon Ave to light, then just n on Underwood St. Int corridors. **Pets:** Large, other species. $20 daily fee/pet. Designated rooms, service with restrictions, supervision.

OKLAHOMA

ADA

♦♦ Raintree Inn H
(580) 332-6262. **$66-$79.** 1100 N Mississippi Ave 74820. Just e of jct J A Richardson Rd. Ext corridors. **Pets:** Accepted.

ALTUS

♦♦ Days Inn Altus H
(580) 482-9300. **$59-$103.** 2804 N Main St 73521. 2 mi n on US 283. Ext corridors. **Pets:** Other species. Service with restrictions, supervision.

♦♦♦ Hampton Inn & Suites Altus H
(580) 482-1273. **$94-$159.** 3601 N Main St 73521. 2.2 mi n on US 283. Int corridors. **Pets:** Accepted.

ARDMORE

♦♦ Lexington Inn H
(580) 223-7525. **Call for rates.** 136 Holiday Dr 73401. I-35 exit 31A, just ne. Int corridors. **Pets:** Medium. $10 daily fee/room. Service with restrictions, crate.

♦♦ Quality Hotel H
(580) 223-7130. **$70-$133.** 2705 W Broadway 73401. I-35 exit 31A, just e. Ext corridors. **Pets:** Accepted.

♦♦ Red Roof Inn Ardmore H
(580) 223-7976. **$64-$132.** 2432 Veterans Blvd 73401. I-35 exit 33, just e. Ext corridors. **Pets:** Accepted.

ATOKA

Comfort Inn & Suites H
(580) 889-8999. **$87-$145.** 1502 S Mississippi Ave 74525. Just s of center. Int corridors. **Pets:** Accepted. [SAVE] 🛜 ⊠ 🛏 🖥

Super 8 Atoka H
(580) 889-7381. **$63-$69.** 2101 S Mississippi Ave 74525. 1 mi s. Ext corridors. **Pets:** Accepted. 🍴 🛬 🛜 🛏 🖥

BARTLESVILLE

Candlewood Suites H ✿
(918) 766-0044. **Call for rates.** 3812 SE Washington Pl 74006. Just s of jct US 60. Int corridors. **Pets:** Medium, other species. $50 one-time fee/pet. Service with restrictions, crate. [&M] 🛜 ⊠ 🛏 🖥

Motel 6 Bartlesville #4870 H
(918) 333-2100. **Call for rates.** 2696 SE Washington Blvd 74006. 1.4 mi s of jct US 60. Int corridors. **Pets:** Accepted.
🍴 [&M] 🛜 🛏 🖥

BIG CABIN

Super 8-Big Cabin M
(918) 783-5888. **$55-$120.** 30954 S Hwy 69 74301. I-44 exit 283, just ne. Ext/int corridors. **Pets:** Accepted. 🍴 🛬 🛜 🛏 🖥

BLACKWELL

Best Western Blackwell Inn H
(580) 363-1300. **$100-$119.** 4545 W White Ave 74631. I-35 exit 222, just ne. Int corridors. **Pets:** Accepted.
[SAVE] [&M] 🛬 🛜 ⊠ 🛏 🖥

Econo Lodge Blackwell H
(580) 363-7000. **$53-$68.** 1201 N 44th St 74631. I-35 exit 222, just ne. Int corridors. **Pets:** Accepted. [SAVE] 🛬 🛜 ⊠ 🛏 🖥

BROKEN ARROW

Clarion Hotel H
(918) 258-7085. **$70-$139.** 2600 N Aspen Ave 74012. Just s of jct SR 51. Int corridors. **Pets:** Accepted. 🛬 🛜 🛏 🖥

Homewood Suites by Hilton Tulsa South H
(918) 392-7700. **$84-$134.** 4900 W Madison Pl 74012. Just ne of jct 71st St and Garnett Ave. Int corridors. **Pets:** Accepted.
[&M] 🛬 🛜 ⊠ 🛏 🖥

Quality Inn H
(918) 258-8585. **$60-$70.** 2301 W Concord St 74012. Just sw of jct SR 51 and Aspen Ave (145th St). Ext/int corridors. **Pets:** Accepted.
🛬 🛜 🛏 🖥

TownePlace Suites by Marriott H
(918) 355-9600. **$96-$127.** 2251 N Stonewood Cir 74012. Just ne of jct SR 51 and Elm Pl. Int corridors. **Pets:** Large, other species. $150 one-time fee/pet, $10 daily fee/pet. Service with restrictions, supervision.
[&M] 🛬 🛜 ⊠ 🛏 🖥

CATOOSA

Hampton Inn & Suites-Catoosa H
(918) 739-3939. **$104-$159.** 100 McNabb Field Rd 74015. I-44 exit 240A, just ne. Int corridors. **Pets:** Accepted.
[&M] 🛬 🛜 ⊠ 🛏 🖥

La Quinta Inn & Suites H
(918) 739-4600. **$86-$525.** 2009 S Cherokee St 74015. I-44 exit 240A, just n. Int corridors. **Pets:** Accepted.
[SAVE] [&M] 🛬 🛜 ⊠ 🛏 🖥

CHICKASHA

Hampton Inn H
(405) 320-5955. **$109-$209.** 3004 S 4th St 73018. I-44 exit 80, 0.4 mi e. Int corridors. **Pets:** Accepted. 🍴 [&M] 🛜 ⊠ 🛏 🖥

Quality Inn Chickasha H
(405) 224-4890. **$70-$120.** 2101 S 4th St 73018. I-44 exit 80, just nw. Ext/int corridors. **Pets:** Other species. $35 one-time fee/pet. Designated rooms, service with restrictions, crate. [SAVE] 🍴 🛬 🛜 🛏 🖥

CLAREMORE

Comfort Inn Claremore H
(918) 343-3297. **$75-$100.** 1720 S Lynn Riggs Blvd 74017. 1.6 mi s on SR 66. Int corridors. **Pets:** Accepted. 🛬 🛜 ⊠ 🛏 🖥

Microtel Inn & Suites by Wyndham Claremore H
(918) 343-2868. **$70-$75.** 10600 E Mallard Lake Rd 74017. 2.6 mi s on SR 66. Int corridors. **Pets:** $15 daily fee/pet. Service with restrictions.
[SAVE] 🍴 🛬 🛜 ⊠ 🛏 🖥

Super 8 H
(918) 341-2323. **$65-$93.** 1100 E Will Rogers Blvd 74017. I-44 exit 255, just w. Ext/int corridors. **Pets:** Accepted. 🍴 🛜 ⊠ 🛏 🖥

CLINTON

Holiday Inn Express H
(580) 323-1950. **$110-$135.** 2000 Boulevard of Champions 73601. I-40 exit 65A, 0.5 mi nw. Int corridors. **Pets:** Other species. $20 daily fee/room. Designated rooms, service with restrictions, supervision.
🍴 [&M] 🛜 ⊠ 🛏 🖥

La Quinta Inn & Suites H
(580) 547-4128. **$81-$174.** 2715 Chapman Rd 73601. I-40 exit 65, 0.5 mi sw. Int corridors. **Pets:** Accepted. [&M] 🛜 ⊠ 🛏 🖥

DURANT

Choctaw Lodge H
(580) 920-0160. **$79-$369.** 4617 S 9th Ave 74701. US 75 exit Choctaw Rd, just e. Int corridors. **Pets:** Medium, other species. $50 deposit/room. Service with restrictions, crate. 🛜 ⊠ 🖥

EDMOND

Best Western Edmond Inn & Suites H
(405) 216-0300. **$86-$105.** 2700 E 2nd St 73034. I-35 exit 141, 1.1 mi w. Int corridors. **Pets:** Accepted. [SAVE] 🍴 🛬 🛜 ⊠ 🛏 🖥

La Quinta Inn & Suites Edmond H
(405) 513-5353. **$86-$196.** 200 Meline Dr 73034. I-35 exit 141, just w. Int corridors. **Pets:** Accepted. 🍴 [&M] 🛬 🛜 ⊠ 🛏 🖥

Sleep Inn & Suites H
(405) 844-3000. **$76-$118.** 3608 S Broadway Extension 73013. John Kilpatrick Tpke, 1.5 mi n on US 77. Int corridors. **Pets:** Medium, other species. $15 daily fee/pet. Designated rooms, service with restrictions, supervision. [&M] 🛬 🛜 ⊠ 🛏 🖥

ELK CITY

Holiday Inn Express & Suites H
(580) 303-4556. **Call for rates.** 2101 E 3rd St 73644. I-40 exit 40, just n. Int corridors. **Pets:** Medium. $25 daily fee/pet. Designated rooms, service with restrictions, supervision. [SAVE] [&M] 🛜 ⊠ 🛏 🖥

Sleep Inn & Suites H
(580) 303-4574. **$65-$102.** 2710 E Hwy 66 73644. I-40 exit 41, just nw. Int corridors. **Pets:** Accepted. [&M] 🛜 ⊠ 🛏 🖥

EL RENO

AAA ▼◆◆ **Best Western Hensley's** 🅗
(405) 262-6490. **$105-$115.** 2701 S Country Club Rd 73036. I-40 exit 123, just s. Ext corridors. **Pets:** Small, dogs only. $25 deposit/room, $10 daily fee/pet. Supervision. [SAVE] ⊇ ⊛ 🖩 💻

AAA ▼◆◆ **Motel 6 El Reno #4267** 🅗
(405) 262-6060. **$70-$90.** 1506 Domino Dr 73036. I-40 exit 123, just ne. Int corridors. **Pets:** Accepted. [SAVE] ⊇ ⊛ 🖩

ENID

▼◆◆ **Baymont Inn & Suites-Enid** 🅗
(580) 234-6800. **$79.** 3614 W Owen K Garriott Rd 73703. 2 mi w of jct US 81. Int corridors. **Pets:** Accepted. 🛆 ⊇ ⊛ 🖩 💻

FAIRVIEW

AAA ▼◆◆ **Best Western Plus Fairview Inn & Suites** 🅗
(580) 227-2880. **$109-$119.** 802 N Main St 73737. Center. Int corridors. **Pets:** Accepted. [SAVE] 🍴 🛆 ⊛ ✕ 🖩 💻

GLENPOOL

AAA ▼◆◆ **Best Western Glenpool/Tulsa** 🅗 ✿
(918) 322-5201. **$80-$90.** 14831 S Casper St 74033. I-44 exit 224, 9.5 mi s on US 75. Ext corridors. **Pets:** Large. $15 one-time fee/pet. Designated rooms, service with restrictions, supervision.
[SAVE] ⊇ ⊛ 🖩 💻

▼◆◆ **Comfort Inn & Suites Glenpool** 🅗
(918) 995-2225. **$85-$155.** 12119 N Casper St 74033. Just se of jct US 75 and 121st St. Int corridors. **Pets:** Accepted.
🛆 ⊛ ✕ 🖩 💻

GROVE

AAA ▼◆◆ **Best Western TimberRidge Inn** 🅗
(918) 786-6900. **$98-$107.** 120 W 18th St 74344. Just w of jct US 59. Ext/int corridors. **Pets:** $20 daily fee/room. Designated rooms, service with restrictions, supervision. [SAVE] ⊇ ⊛ ✕ 🖩 💻

GUTHRIE

▼◆◆ **Americas Best Value Inn** 🅗
(405) 282-8831. **Call for rates.** 2323 Territorial Tr 73044. I-35 exit 157, just sw. Int corridors. **Pets:** Accepted. 🍴 ⊇ ⊛ ✕ 🖩 💻

▼◆◆ **Holiday Inn Express** 🅗
(405) 293-6464. **Call for rates.** 2227 E Oklahoma Ave 73044. I-35 exit 157, just s. Int corridors. **Pets:** Dogs only. $25 daily fee/pet. Designated rooms, service with restrictions, crate. 🛆 ⊇ ⊛ ✕ 🖩 💻

GUYMON

AAA ▼◆◆ **Best Western Plus Guymon Hotel & Suites** 🅗
(580) 338-0800. **$95-$105.** 1102 NE 6th St 73942. Just s of jct US 64. Int corridors. **Pets:** Accepted.
[SAVE] 🍴 🛆 ⊇ ⊠ ⊛ ✕ 🖩 💻

▼◆◆ **Comfort Inn & Suites** 🅗
(580) 338-0831. **$90-$125.** 501 Hwy 54 E 73942. Just s of jct US 64. Int corridors. **Pets:** Accepted. 🍴 🛆 ⊇ ⊛ ✕ 🖩 💻

▼◆◆ **Holiday Inn Express Hotel & Suites Guymon** 🅗
(580) 338-4208. **Call for rates.** 701 SE Hwy 3 73942. Jct US 54/412, just e. Int corridors. **Pets:** Accepted.
🍴 🛆 ⊇ ⊛ ✕ 🖩 💻

HENRYETTA

▼◆◆ **Green Country Inn** Ⓜ
(918) 652-9988. **$58-$85.** 2004 Old Hwy 75 W 74437. I-40 exit 237, just ne. Ext corridors. **Pets:** Small. $10 daily fee/pet. Designated rooms, service with restrictions, supervision. ⊇ ⊛ 🖩

IDABEL

▼◆◆ **Comfort Suites** 🅗
(580) 286-9393. **$100-$174.** 400 SE Lincoln Rd 74745. Just s of jct US 70 and 259. Int corridors. **Pets:** Accepted.
🍴 🛆 ⊇ ⊛ ✕ 🖩 💻

▼◆◆ **Super 8** 🅗
(580) 286-2888. **$66-$90.** 401 NE Lincoln Rd 74745. Just s of jct US 70 and 259. Ext corridors. **Pets:** Accepted. ⊇ ⊛ 🖩 💻

LAWTON

AAA ▼◆◆ **Best Western Plus Lawton Hotel & Convention Center** 🅗 ✿
(580) 353-0200. **$71-$200.** 1125 E Gore Blvd 73501. I-44 exit 37, just e. Ext/int corridors. **Pets:** Medium, dogs only. $20 daily fee/pet. Designated rooms, service with restrictions, supervision.
[SAVE] 🍴 ⊇ ⊛ 🖩 💻

▼◆◆ **Homewood Suites** 🅗
(580) 357-9800. **$109-$149.** 415 SE Interstate Dr 73501. I-44 exit 37, just sw. Int corridors. **Pets:** Accepted. 🍴 🛆 ⊛ 🖩 💻

AAA ▼◆◆ **Sleep Inn & Suites** 🅗 ✿
(580) 353-5555. **$65-$92.** 421 SE Interstate Dr 73501. I-44 exit 37, just sw. Int corridors. **Pets:** Medium, dogs only. $25 one-time fee/room. Service with restrictions, supervision. [SAVE] 🛆 ⊇ ⊛ ✕ 🖩 💻

LOCUST GROVE

AAA ▼◆◆ **Best Western Locust Grove Inn & Suites** 🅗
(918) 479-8082. **$89-$200.** 106 Holiday Ln 74352. Just nw of jct US 412 and SR 82. Int corridors. **Pets:** Medium, other species. $25 one-time fee/pet. Designated rooms, service with restrictions, supervision.
[SAVE] ⊇ ⊛ ✕ 🖩 💻

MADILL

AAA ▼◆◆ **Best Western Plus Sand Bass Inn & Suites** 🅗
(580) 677-9890. **$94-$140.** 827 S 1st St 73446. Just s on US 70 from jct US 377. Int corridors. **Pets:** Medium, dogs only. $20 daily fee/pet. Service with restrictions, crate. [SAVE] 🛆 ⊛ ✕ 🖩 💻

MCALESTER

▼◆◆ **AmericInn Lodge & Suites of McAlester** 🅗
(918) 426-1300. **Call for rates.** 609 S George Nigh Expwy 74501. 1 mi s on US 69. Int corridors. **Pets:** Accepted.
🛆 ⊇ ⊛ ✕ 🖩 💻

AAA ▼◆◆ **Best Western Inn of McAlester** 🅗
(918) 426-0115. **$61-$92.** 1215 George Nigh Expwy 74502. 3 mi s on US 69. Ext corridors. **Pets:** Accepted. [SAVE] ⊇ 🖩 💻

▼◆◆ **Candlewood Suites** 🅗
(918) 426-4171. **$89-$99.** 425 S George Nigh Expwy 74501. 2 mi e on US 69. Int corridors. **Pets:** Accepted. 🛆 ⊛ ✕ 🖩 💻

▼◆◆ **Comfort Suites** 🅗
(918) 302-0001. **$69-$139.** 650 S George Nigh Expwy 74501. 1.2 mi s on US 69. Int corridors. **Pets:** Accepted. ⊇ ⊛ ✕ 🖩 💻

▼◆◆ **Econo Lodge** Ⓜ
(918) 426-4420. **$52-$59.** 731 S George Nigh Expwy 74501. 1.5 mi s on US 69. Ext corridors. **Pets:** Accepted. 🍴 ⊛ 🖩 💻

▼▼ **Happy Days Hotel** H
(918) 429-0910. **Call for rates.** 1400 S George Nigh Expwy 74501. 3.3 mi s on US 69. Int corridors. **Pets:** Accepted. 🛋️ 📶 ✕ 🛏️ 🖥️

▼▼ **Oak Tree Inn** H
(918) 420-5002. **Call for rates.** 530 S George Nigh Expwy 74501. Just e of jct US 69. Int corridors. **Pets:** Accepted. 🍴 📶 ✕ 🛏️ 🖥️

MIAMI
AAA ▼▼▼ **Holiday Inn Express & Suites** H
(918) 542-7424. **Call for rates.** 509 Henley St 74354. I-44 exit 313, just w. Int corridors. **Pets:** Accepted.
SAVE 🍴 🔊 🛋️ 📶 ✕ 🛏️ 🖥️

MIDWEST CITY
AAA ▼▼ **Hawthorn Suites by Wyndham** H
(405) 737-7777. **$75-$129, 3 day notice.** 5701 Tinker Diagonal 73110. I-40 exit 156A (Sooner Rd), just n. Int corridors. **Pets:** Medium, other species. $15 daily fee/pet. Designated rooms, service with restrictions, crate. SAVE 🔊 🛋️ 📶 🛏️ 🖥️

AAA ▼▼▼ **La Quinta Inn & Suites Oklahoma City-Midwest City** H
(405) 733-1339. **$104-$174.** 5653 Tinker Diagonal 73110. I-40 exit 156A (Sooner Rd), just n. Int corridors. **Pets:** Accepted.
SAVE 🛋️ 📶 🛏️ 🖥️

AAA ▼▼▼ **Sheraton Midwest City Hotel at the Reed Conference Center** H
(405) 455-1800. **$99-$149.** 5750 Will Rogers Rd 73110. I-40 exit 156A (Sooner Rd), just ne. Int corridors. **Pets:** Accepted.
SAVE 🍴 🛋️ 📶 ✕ 🛏️ 🖥️

MOORE *(Restaurants p. 620)*
AAA ▼▼▼ **Best Western Greentree Inn & Suites** H
(405) 912-8882. **$89-$119.** 1811 N Moore Ave 73160. I-35 exit 118, just n on west frontage road. Int corridors. **Pets:** Dogs only. $10 daily fee/pet. Service with restrictions, supervision. SAVE 🛋️ 📶 🛏️ 🖥️

MUSKOGEE
▼▼ **Comfort Inn** H
(918) 682-3724. **$84-$126.** 3133 Azalea Park Dr 74401. Just sw of jct US 62 and 69. Int corridors. **Pets:** Accepted.
🍴 🔊 🛋️ 📶 ✕ 🛏️ 🖥️

▼▼▼ **Home2 Suites by Hilton Muskogee** H
(918) 910-5444. **Call for rates.** 2819 Military Blvd 74401. Just se of jct US 62 and 69. Int corridors. **Pets:** Small. $75 one-time fee/pet. Service with restrictions, supervision. 🍴 🔊 📶 ✕ 🛏️ 🖥️

▼▼▼ **Quality Inn & Suites** H
(918) 687-9000. **$75-$90.** 3031 Military Blvd 74401. Just se of jct US 62 and 69. Int corridors. **Pets:** Accepted. 🛋️ 📶 ✕ 🛏️ 🖥️

NORMAN
AAA ▼▼▼ **Best Western Plus Norman** H 🐾
(405) 801-2100. **$119-$299.** 3100 Medical Park Pl 73072. I-35 exit 112, just sw. Int corridors. **Pets:** Large, other species. $10 daily fee/pet. Designated rooms, service with restrictions, crate.
SAVE 🍴 🔊 📶 ✕ 🛏️ 🖥️

▼▼ **Days Inn Norman** M
(405) 360-1234. **$50-$156.** 2543 W Main St 73069. I-35 exit 109, just e. Ext/int corridors. **Pets:** Accepted. 📶 🛏️ 🖥️

▼▼▼ **Embassy Suites by Hilton Norman-Hotel & Conference Center** H
(405) 364-8040. **$129-$209.** 2501 Conference Dr 73069. Jct 24th Ave NW and Robinson St, 0.7 mi n on 24th Ave NW. Int corridors.
Pets: Accepted. ECO 🍴 🔊 🛋️ 📶 ✕ 🛏️ 🖥️

▼▼▼ **La Quinta Inn & Suites Norman** H
(405) 579-4000. **$67-$244.** 930 Ed Noble Dr 73072. I-35 exit 108B (Lindsey St), just nw. Int corridors. **Pets:** Accepted.
🔊 🛋️ 📶 ✕ 🛏️ 🖥️

▼▼▼▼ **Quality Inn & Suites** H
(405) 701-4011. **$70-$254.** 2841 S Classen Blvd 73071. Just n of jct SR 9. Int corridors. **Pets:** Accepted. 🍴 🛋️ 📶 ✕ 🛏️ 🖥️

OKLAHOMA CITY
▼▼▼ ▼▼▼ **21c Museum Hotel Oklahoma City** H
(405) 982-6900. **$169-$429.** 900 W Main St 73106. I-40 exit 149, 0.6 mi n, then just e. Int corridors. **Pets:** Accepted.
🍴 🔊 📶 ✕ 🛏️

AAA ▼▼▼ ▼▼▼ **Ambassador Oklahoma City, Autograph Collection** H
(405) 600-6200. **$171-$240.** 1200 N Walker Ave 73103. Jct 12th St. Int corridors. **Pets:** Accepted. SAVE 🍴 🔊 📶 ✕ 🛏️ 🖥️

▼▼ **Americas Best Value Inn-Oklahoma City/I-35 North** H
(405) 478-0400. **Call for rates.** 12001 N I-35 Service Rd 73131. I-35 exit 137 (122nd St), just sw. Ext corridors. **Pets:** Accepted.
🍴 🛋️ 📶 🛏️ 🖥️

▼▼▼ **Baymont Inn & Suites** H
(405) 943-4400. **$59-$80.** 4240 W I-40 Service Rd 73108. I-40 exit 145 (Meridian Ave), just e on south frontage road. Ext/int corridors.
Pets: Dogs only. $10 daily fee/pet. Service with restrictions, supervision.
🛋️ 📶 ✕ 🛏️ 🖥️

▼▼▼ **Baymont Inn & Suites Oklahoma City** H
(405) 752-7070. **$63-$119.** 13500 Plaza Terr 73120. John Kilpatrick Tpke exit May Ave, just e on south frontage road. Int corridors.
Pets: Accepted. 🛋️ 📶 🛏️ 🖥️

▼▼ **Baymont Inn & Suites Oklahoma City Edmond** H
(405) 478-7282. **Call for rates.** 4625 NE 120th St 73131. I-35 exit 137 (122nd St), just sw. Int corridors. **Pets:** Medium. $20 daily fee/pet. Designated rooms, service with restrictions, supervision.
🛋️ 📶 🛏️ 🖥️

AAA ▼▼▼ **Best Western Plus Saddleback Inn & Conference Center** H
(405) 947-7000. **$89-$159.** 4300 SW 3rd St 73108. I-40 exit 145 (Meridian Ave), just ne. Ext/int corridors. **Pets:** Medium. $15 daily fee/room. Designated rooms, service with restrictions, crate.
SAVE 🍴 🔊 🛋️ ✕ 📶 ✕ 🛏️ 🖥️

AAA ▼▼▼ **Broadway Inn & Suites** H
(405) 848-1919. **$89-$110.** 6101 N Santa Fe 73118. I-44 exit 127, just e on 63rd St, then just s. Int corridors. **Pets:** Medium. $20 daily fee/pet. Service with restrictions, crate. SAVE 🍴 🛋️ 📶 ✕ 🛏️ 🖥️

▼▼ **Candlewood Suites Hotel** H
(405) 680-8770. **Call for rates.** 4400 W River Park Dr 73108. I-40 exit 145 (Meridian Ave), 1.1 mi s. Int corridors. **Pets:** Large, other species. $75 one-time fee/room. Service with restrictions, crate.
🔊 📶 🛏️ 🖥️

▼▼▼ **Colcord Hotel** H
(405) 601-4300. **Call for rates.** 15 N Robinson Ave 73102. Jct Sheridan and Robinson aves. Int corridors. **Pets:** Accepted.
ECO 🍴 🔊 📶 ✕ 🛏️

▼▼▼ **Comfort Inn** H
(405) 631-3111. **Call for rates.** 7601 CA Henderson Blvd 73139. I-240 exit 2A, just s. Int corridors. **Pets:** Accepted. 🛋️ 📶 🛏️ 🖥️

▼▼▼ **Country Inn & Suites By Carlson** H
(405) 286-3555. **Call for rates.** 13501 Memorial Park Dr 73120. Just sw of jct Memorial Rd and Memorial Park Ln. Int corridors.
Pets: Accepted. 🍴 🛋️ 📶 ✕ 🛏️ 🖥️

Courtyard by Marriott Oklahoma City Downtown H
(405) 232-2290. $146-$220. 2 W Reno Ave 73102. Jct Gaylord Blvd and Reno Ave. Int corridors. **Pets:** Accepted.

Embassy Suites by Hilton H
(405) 682-6000. $109-$199. 1815 S Meridian Ave 73108. I-40 exit 145 (Meridian Ave), 1 mi s. Int corridors. **Pets:** Accepted.

Embassy Suites by Hilton Oklahoma City Downtown/Medical Center H
(405) 239-3900. $129-$219. 741 N Phillips Ave 73104. I-235 exit 1D (Lincoln Blvd), just e, then just n. Int corridors. **Pets:** Accepted.

Holiday Inn Hotel & Suites Oklahoma City North H
(405) 286-4777. $70-$175. 6200 N Robinson Ave 73118. I-44 exit 127, just w on 63rd St, then just s. Int corridors. **Pets:** Accepted.

Home2 Suites by Hilton Oklahoma City Quail Springs H
(405) 792-2420. $109-$159. 5500 NW 135th St 73142. John Kilpatrick Tpke exit MacArthur Blvd, just se. Int corridors. **Pets:** Accepted.

Home2 Suites by Hilton Oklahoma City South H
(405) 536-4663. $99-$169. 1001 Straka Terrace 73139. I-240 exit 2A, just s. Int corridors. **Pets:** $75 one-time fee/room. Service with restrictions, crate.

Homewood Suites Oklahoma City-West H
(405) 789-3600. $119-$199. 6920 W Reno Ave 73127. Just e of jct Rockwell Ave. Int corridors. **Pets:** Medium, dogs only. $100 one-time fee/room. Service with restrictions, crate.

Hyatt Place Oklahoma City Airport H
(405) 682-3900. $69-$189. 1818 S Meridian Ave 73108. I-40 exit 145 (Meridian Ave), 1 mi s. Int corridors. **Pets:** Medium, dogs only. $75 one-time fee/room. Service with restrictions, supervision.

La Quinta Inn & Suites OKC North-Quail Springs H
(405) 755-7000. $84-$251. 3003 W Memorial Rd 73134. John Kilpatrick Tpke exit May Ave, just nw. Int corridors. **Pets:** Accepted.

Quality Inn H
(405) 632-6666. $65-$75. 7800 CA Henderson Blvd 73139. I-240 exit 2A, just s. Ext corridors. **Pets:** Accepted.

Renaissance Oklahoma City Convention Center, Hotel & Spa H
(405) 228-8000. $143-$250. 10 N Broadway Ave 73102. Jct Sheridan and Broadway aves. Int corridors. **Pets:** Small, dogs only. $50 one-time fee/room. Service with restrictions, supervision.

Residence Inn by Marriott Bricktown H
(405) 601-1700. $168-$253. 400 E Reno Ave 73104. Just se of jct Joe Carter Ave; in Bricktown. Int corridors. **Pets:** Accepted.

Residence Inn by Marriott Oklahoma City South-Crossroads Mall H
(405) 634-9696. $108-$173. 1111 E I-240 Service Rd 73149. I-240 exit 4C eastbound, 0.4 mi nw; exit 5 westbound, 0.8 mi nw. Int corridors. **Pets:** Accepted.

Sheraton Oklahoma City Downtown Hotel H
(405) 235-2780. $119-$259. 1 N Broadway Ave 73102. Jct Sheridan and Broadway aves. Int corridors. **Pets:** Accepted.

Skirvin Hilton H
(405) 272-3040. $149-$299. 1 Park Ave 73102. Corner of N Broadway and Park aves. Int corridors. **Pets:** Accepted.

Sleep Inn & Suites H
(405) 478-9898. $74-$134. 12024 N I-35 Service Rd 73131. I-35 exit 137 (122nd St), just e. Int corridors. **Pets:** Accepted.

Sonesta ES Suites Oklahoma City H
(405) 942-4500. Call for rates. 4361 W Reno Ave 73107. I-40 exit 145 (Meridian Ave), 0.3 mi n, then just e. Ext corridors. **Pets:** Accepted.

SpringHill Suites by Marriott H
(405) 604-0200. $91-$160. 510 S MacArthur Blvd 73128. I-40 exit 144, just ne. Int corridors. **Pets:** Accepted.

Staybridge Suites H
(405) 429-4400. Call for rates. 4411 SW 15th St 73108. I-40 exit 145 (Meridian Ave), 1 mi se. Int corridors. **Pets:** Accepted.

TownePlace Suites by Marriott H
(405) 600-9988. $113-$186. 4601 SW 15th St 73128. I-40 exit 145 (Meridian Ave), 1 mi sw. Int corridors. **Pets:** Other species. $100 one-time fee/pet. Service with restrictions.

Wyndham Garden Hotel Oklahoma City Airport H
(405) 685-4000. $89-$155. 2101 S Meridian Ave 73108. I-40 exit 145 (Meridian Ave), 1.3 mi s. Int corridors. **Pets:** Accepted.

OKMULGEE

Best Western Okmulgee H
(918) 756-9200. $84-$89. 3499 N Wood Dr 74447. Just n of jct US 75 and SR 56. Int corridors. **Pets:** Medium. $10 daily fee/pet. Designated rooms, service with restrictions, supervision.

OWASSO

Candlewood Suites H
(918) 272-4334. Call for rates. 11699 E 96th St N 74055. 0.4 mi nw of jct US 169. Int corridors. **Pets:** Accepted.

Quality Inn & Suites H
(918) 272-2000. Call for rates. 7653 N Owasso Expwy 74055. Just ne of jct US 169 and 76th St. Ext/int corridors. **Pets:** Accepted.

TownePlace Suites by Marriott Tulsa North/Owasso H
(918) 376-4400. $98-$171. 9355 N Owasso Expwy 74055. Just se of jct US 169 and 96th St. Int corridors. **Pets:** Accepted.

PERRY

Holiday Inn Express H
(580) 336-5050. $89-$139. 3002 W Fir St 73077. I-35 exit 186, just w. Int corridors. **Pets:** Accepted.

PONCA CITY

Comfort Inn & Suites H ❀
(580) 765-2322. **$84-$140.** 3101 N 14th St 74604. I-35 exit 214, 3 mi n on US 77. Int corridors. **Pets:** $10 daily fee/pet. Service with restrictions, crate. SAVE

POTEAU

Holiday Inn Express & Suites-Poteau H
(918) 649-0123. **Call for rates.** 201 Hillview Pkwy 74953. Just ne of jct US 59/271 and SR 112. Int corridors. **Pets:** Other species. $25 one-time fee/room. Service with restrictions, supervision.

PRYOR

Comfort Inn & Suites H
(918) 476-6660. **$84-$155.** 307 Mid America Dr 74361. 5 mi s on US 69. Int corridors. **Pets:** Accepted. SAVE

Holiday Inn Express & Suites H
(918) 476-5400. **$109-$159.** 271 Mid America Dr 74361. 5 mi s on US 69. Int corridors. **Pets:** Accepted.

SHAWNEE

La Quinta Inn & Suites Shawnee H
(405) 275-7930. **$67-$192.** 5401 Enterprise Ct 74804. I-40 exit 186, just ne. Int corridors. **Pets:** Accepted. SAVE

STILLWATER

Best Western Plus Cimarron Hotel & Suites H
(405) 372-2878. **$90-$150.** 315 N Husband St 74074. Just w of jct Hall of Fame Ave and Main St. Int corridors. **Pets:** Accepted.
SAVE

Holiday Inn & Suites H
(405) 372-2445. **Call for rates.** 715 S Country Club Rd 74074. Just s of jct SR 51. Int corridors. **Pets:** Accepted.

Home2 Suites by Hilton H
(405) 372-2550. **Call for rates.** 306 E Hall of Fame Ave 74075. Just w of jct US 177 (Perkins Rd). Int corridors. **Pets:** Accepted.

Residence Inn by Marriott H
(405) 707-0588. **$113-$180.** 800 S Murphy St 74074. Just s of jct SR 51. Int corridors. **Pets:** Accepted.

Wyndham Garden Stillwater H
(405) 377-7010. **$81-$189.** 600 E McElroy Rd 74075. 1 mi n on US 177 (Perkins Rd). Int corridors. **Pets:** Accepted.
SAVE

STROUD

Cattle Country Lodge H
(918) 968-9515. **Call for rates.** 1200 N 8th Ave 74079. I-44 exit 179, just ne. Ext corridors. **Pets:** Accepted.

TAHLEQUAH

Days Inn & Suites Tahlequah H
(918) 456-7800. **$72-$139.** 701 Holiday Dr 74464. 1.2 mi e on SR 51 from jct US 62. Int corridors. **Pets:** Accepted.

THACKERVILLE

The Inn at WinStar H
(580) 276-4487. **Call for rates.** 21943 Red River Rd 73459. I-35 exit 1, 1.2 mi n on E Service Rd. Int corridors. **Pets:** Accepted.

TULSA *(Restaurants p. 620)*

Aloft Tulsa H
(918) 949-9000. **Call for rates.** 6716 S 104th E Ave 74133. Just nw of jct US 169 and 71st St. Int corridors. **Pets:** Accepted.
SAVE

Aloft-Tulsa Downtown H
(918) 947-8200. **$116-$125.** 200 Civic Center 74103. Just w of jct Denver Ave and 4th St. Int corridors. **Pets:** Accepted.
SAVE

Ambassador Hotel Tulsa, Autograph Collection H ❀
(918) 587-8200. **$180-$261.** 1324 S Main St 74119. Jct 14th St. Int corridors. **Pets:** Medium. $50 one-time fee/room. Service with restrictions, crate. SAVE

Best Western-Airport H
(918) 438-0780. **$75-$129.** 222 N Garnett Rd 74116. I-244 exit 14 (Garnett Rd), just s. Ext corridors. **Pets:** Accepted.
SAVE

Best Western Plus Downtown Tulsa H
(918) 794-6000. **$89-$149.** 707 S Houston Ave 74127. Just s of jct 7th St. Int corridors. **Pets:** Accepted. SAVE

Candlewood Suites H
(918) 294-9000. **Call for rates.** 10008 E 73rd St S 74133. Just sw of jct 71st St and 101st E Ave. Int corridors. **Pets:** Accepted.

Comfort Inn Midtown H
(918) 488-8777. **$81-$126.** 4530 E Skelly Dr 74135. I-44 exit 229 (Yale Ave), just sw. Int corridors. **Pets:** Accepted.

Country Inn & Suites By Carlson Tulsa Central H
(918) 663-1000. **Call for rates.** 3209 S 79th E Ave 74145. I-44 exit 231 (31st St) eastbound; exit 232 (Memorial Dr) westbound, just sw. Int corridors. **Pets:** Accepted. SAVE

Crowne Plaza Tulsa-Southern Hills H
(918) 492-5000. **Call for rates.** 7902 S Lewis Ave 74136. I-44 exit 227 (Lewis Ave), 3 mi s. Int corridors. **Pets:** Accepted.

DoubleTree by Hilton Hotel Tulsa Downtown H
(918) 587-8000. **$109-$219.** 616 W 7th St 74127. Jct 7th St and Houston Ave. Int corridors. **Pets:** Accepted.

DoubleTree by Hilton Hotel Tulsa-Warren Place H
(918) 495-1000. **$89-$189.** 6110 S Yale Ave 74136. I-44 exit 229 (Yale Ave), 1.3 mi s. Int corridors. **Pets:** Accepted.

Embassy Suites by Hilton Hotel H
(918) 622-4000. **$119-$199.** 3332 S 79th E Ave 74145. I-44 exit 231 (31st St) eastbound; exit 232 (Memorial Dr) westbound, just sw. Int corridors. **Pets:** $50 one-time fee/room. Service with restrictions, supervision.

Holiday Inn & Suites H
(918) 994-5000. **Call for rates.** 10020 E 81st St 74133. Just w of jct US 169. Int corridors. **Pets:** Accepted.

Holiday Inn Tulsa City Center H
(918) 585-5898. **$84-$169.** 17 W 7th St 74119. Jct Boulder Ave. Int corridors. **Pets:** Accepted. SAVE

Home2 Suites by Hilton Tulsa Hills H
(918) 970-6800. **Call for rates.** 6910 S Olympia Ave 74132. Just ne of jct US 75 and 71st St. Int corridors. **Pets:** Accepted.
⊗ ⊗ ⊗ ⊗ ⊗ ⊗

Hyatt Place Tulsa/South Medical District H
(918) 491-4010. **$84-$199.** 7037 S Zurich Ave 74136. I-44 exit 229 (Yale Ave), 3 mi s to 71st St, then just e. Int corridors. **Pets:** Accepted.
⊗ ⊗ ⊗ ⊗ ⊗ ⊗ ⊗

Hyatt Regency Tulsa H
(918) 234-1234. **$89-$289.** 100 E 2nd St 74103. Jct 2nd St and Boston Ave; downtown. Int corridors. **Pets:** Accepted.
⊗ ⊗ ⊗ ⊗ ⊗ ⊗ ⊗ ⊗

La Quinta Inn & Suites Tulsa Airport/Expo Square H
(918) 949-3600. **$82-$174.** 23 N 67th E Ave 74115. I-244 exit 11 (Sheridan Rd), just se. Int corridors. **Pets:** Accepted.
⊗ ⊗ ⊗ ⊗ ⊗ ⊗

La Quinta Inn & Suites Tulsa Central H
(918) 665-2630. **$86-$196.** 6030 E Skelly Dr 74135. I-44 exit 230, just s. Int corridors. **Pets:** Accepted. ⊗ ⊗ ⊗ ⊗ ⊗

Ramada H
(918) 828-9128. **$80-$90, 3 day notice.** 8175 E Skelly Dr 74129. I-44 exit 231 (31st St) eastbound; exit 232 (Memorial Dr) westbound, just ne. Int corridors. **Pets:** Accepted. ⊗ ⊗ ⊗ ⊗ ⊗

Red Roof Inn-Tulsa M
(918) 622-6776. **$50-$149.** 4717 S Yale Ave 74135. I-44 exit 229 (Yale Ave), just s. Ext corridors. **Pets:** Accepted. ⊗ ⊗ ⊗

Renaissance Tulsa Hotel & Convention Center H
(918) 307-2600. **$81-$167.** 6808 S 107th E Ave 74133. Just ne of jct US 169 and 71st St. Int corridors. **Pets:** Accepted.
⊗ ⊗ ⊗ ⊗ ⊗ ⊗ ⊗ ⊗ ⊗

Residence Inn by Marriott H
(918) 250-4850. **$106-$147.** 11025 E 73rd St 74133. Just se of jct US 169 and 71st St. Int corridors. **Pets:** Medium. $100 deposit/room. Service with restrictions, crate. ⊗ ⊗ ⊗ ⊗ ⊗ ⊗

Rodeway Inn & Suites H
(918) 628-0900. **$53-$132.** 1737 S 101st E Ave 74128. I-44 exit 233 eastbound; exit 233B westbound, follow signs. Int corridors. **Pets:** Other species. $15 daily fee/pet. No service, supervision.
⊗ ⊗ ⊗ ⊗ ⊗

Sleep Inn & Suites Tulsa Central H
(918) 663-2777. **$70-$120.** 8021 E 33rd St S 74145. I-44 exit 231 (31st St) eastbound; exit 232 (Memorial Dr) westbound, just sw. Int corridors. **Pets:** Accepted. ⊗ ⊗ ⊗ ⊗ ⊗ ⊗

Staybridge Suites H
(918) 461-2100. **Call for rates.** 11111 E 73rd St 74133. Just se of jct US 169 and 71st St. Int corridors. **Pets:** Accepted.
⊗ ⊗ ⊗ ⊗ ⊗ ⊗

Wyndham Tulsa H
(918) 627-5000. **$99-$109.** 10918 E 41st St 74146. Just e of US 169. Int corridors. **Pets:** Other species. $75 daily fee/pet. Service with restrictions, supervision. ⊗ ⊗ ⊗ ⊗ ⊗ ⊗

WEATHERFORD

Best Western Plus - Weatherford H
(580) 772-3325. **$90-$185.** 525 E Main St 73096. I-40 exit 82, 0.5 mi n. Ext corridors. **Pets:** Accepted. ⊗ ⊗ ⊗ ⊗ ⊗

WEST SILOAM SPRINGS

Best Western Stateline Lodge H
(918) 422-4444. **$89-$97.** 273 S Hwy 59 74338. Jct US 59 and 412. Int corridors. **Pets:** Accepted. ⊗ ⊗ ⊗ ⊗ ⊗ ⊗

WOODWARD

Northwest Inn H
(580) 256-7600. **$89-$99.** Hwy 270 S & 1st St 73802. 1.4 mi s of jct US 183, 270 and 412. Ext/int corridors. **Pets:** Accepted.
⊗ ⊗ ⊗ ⊗ ⊗ ⊗ ⊗

YUKON

Best Western Plus Yukon H
(405) 265-2995. **$115-$128.** 11440 W I-40 Service Rd 73099. I-40 exit 138, just sw. Ext/int corridors. **Pets:** Accepted.
⊗ ⊗ ⊗ ⊗

Comfort Suites H
(405) 577-6500. **$89-$181.** 11424 NW 4th St 73099. I-40 exit 138, just nw. Int corridors. **Pets:** Accepted. ⊗ ⊗ ⊗ ⊗ ⊗

La Quinta Inn & Suites Oklahoma City-Yukon H
(405) 494-7600. **$90-$185.** 11500 W I-40 73099. I-40 exit 138, just s. Int corridors. **Pets:** Accepted. ⊗ ⊗ ⊗ ⊗ ⊗ ⊗ ⊗

OREGON

ALBANY

Best Western Plus Prairie Inn H ❀
(541) 928-5050. **$100-$250.** 1100 Price Rd SE 97322. I-5 exit 233, just e on Santiam Hwy (US 20), then just n. Int corridors. **Pets:** Dogs only. $20 daily fee/pet. Designated rooms, service with restrictions, supervision. ⊗ ⊗ ⊗ ⊗ ⊗ ⊗ ⊗

Comfort Suites-Linn County Fairgrounds and Expo H
(541) 928-2053. **$95-$269.** 100 Opal Ct NE 97322. I-5 exit 234A southbound; exit 234 northbound, just se. Int corridors. **Pets:** Accepted.
⊗ ⊗ ⊗ ⊗ ⊗ ⊗ ⊗

Holiday Inn Express Hotel & Suites H
(541) 928-8820. **Call for rates.** 105 Opal Ct NE 97322. I-5 exit 234A southbound; exit 234 northbound, just se. Int corridors. **Pets:** Dogs only. $20 daily fee/room. Service with restrictions, supervision.
⊗ ⊗ ⊗ ⊗ ⊗ ⊗ ⊗

Motel 6 #4124 M
(541) 926-4233. **Call for rates.** 2735 E Pacific Blvd 97321. I-5 exit 234B southbound; exit 234 northbound, 0.5 mi w. Ext corridors. **Pets:** Accepted. ⊗ ⊗ ⊗

Phoenix Inn Suites-Albany H
(541) 926-5696. **Call for rates.** 3410 Spicer Rd SE 97322. I-5 exit 233, just se. Int corridors. **Pets:** Accepted. ⊗ ⊗ ⊗ ⊗ ⊗

▼ **Rodeway Inn** **M**
(541) 926-0170. **$66-$115.** 1212 SE Price Rd 97322. I-5 exit 233, just e on Santiam Hwy (US 20), then just n. Ext corridors. **Pets:** Small, dogs only. Service with restrictions, supervision. 🖥 🖨

ASHLAND
▼▼▼ **Ashland Chanticleer Inn** **BB**
(541) 482-1919. **$165-$215, 31 day notice.** 120 Gresham St 97520. Just se of downtown on SR 99 (E Main St), just s; jct Pearl St. Int corridors. **Pets:** Dogs only. $20 daily fee/pet. Designated rooms, service with restrictions, supervision. 🖥🌀 🖨 🖥 ☎

▼▼▼ **Ashland Hills Hotel & Suites** **H**
(541) 482-8310. **Call for rates.** 2525 Ashland St 97520. I-5 exit 14, just e on SR 66 (Ashland St). Int corridors. **Pets:** Accepted.
🖨 🖥 🖨 🖨 🖥

▼▼▼ **Ashland Springs Hotel** **H** 🐾
(541) 488-1700. **$89-$299, 3 day notice.** 212 E Main St 97520. Corner of 1st St; center. Int corridors. **Pets:** Medium. $25 one-time fee/room. Designated rooms, service with restrictions, supervision.
🍴 🖥🌀 🖨 🖥 🖨 🖥

🅰 ▼▼▼ **Best Western Bard's Inn** **H** 🐾
(541) 482-0049. **$170-$290.** 132 N Main St 97520. From Downtown Plaza, just nw on SR 99 (N Main St). Ext/int corridors. **Pets:** $20 daily fee/pet. Designated rooms, service with restrictions, supervision.
🖥 🖥🌀 🖨 🖨 🖥 🖨 🖥

🅰 ▼▼▼ **Best Western Windsor Inn** **H**
(541) 488-2330. **$90-$150.** 2520 Ashland St 97520. I-5 exit 14, just e on SR 66 (Ashland St). Ext corridors. **Pets:** Accepted.
🖥 🖨 🖨 🖥 🖨 🖥

▼▼▼ **Callahan's Lodge** **CI**
(541) 482-1299. **Call for rates.** 7100 Old Hwy 99 S 97520. I-5 exit 6 (Mt. Ashland), just e; 8 mi s of town. Int corridors. **Pets:** $20 one-time fee/room. Crate. 🍴 🖥🌀 🖨 🖥 🖨 🖥

▼▼▼ **Comfort Inn & Suites Ashland** **H** 🐾
(541) 482-6932. **Call for rates.** 434 S Valley View Rd 97520. I-5 exit 19, just sw. Int corridors. **Pets:** $10 daily fee/pet. Designated rooms, service with restrictions, supervision. 🖥🌀 🖨 🖨 🖥 🖨 🖥

🅰 ▼▼▼ **Flagship Inn of Ashland** **M**
(541) 482-2641. **Call for rates.** 1193 Siskiyou Blvd 97520. I-5 exit 14, 1.3 mi w on SR 66 (Ashland St), then just n. Ext corridors.
Pets: Accepted. 🖥 🖨 🖨 🖨 🖥 🖨 🖥

🅰 ▼▼▼ **Holiday Inn Express Hotel & Suites** **H**
(541) 201-0202. **$89-$199.** 565 Clover Ln 97520. I-5 exit 14, just e on SR 66 (Ashland St), then just s. Int corridors. **Pets:** Accepted.
🖥 🖥🌀 🖨 🖨 🖨 🖥 🖥

🅰 ▼▼▼ **Plaza Inn & Suites At Ashland Creek** **H** 🐾
(541) 488-8900. **$99-$389.** 98 Central Ave 97520. From Downtown Plaza, just nw on SR 99 (N Main St), just ne on Helman St, then just e. Int corridors. **Pets:** Medium. $25 daily fee/pet. Designated rooms, service with restrictions, supervision.
🖥 🍴 🖥🌀 🖨 🖥 🖨 🖥

🅰 ▼▼▼ **Timbers Motel of Ashland** **M**
(541) 482-4242. **$60-$135, 3 day notice.** 1450 Ashland St 97520. I-5 exit 14, 1.2 mi w on SR 66 (Ashland St). Ext corridors. **Pets:** Dogs only. Designated rooms, service with restrictions, crate.
🖥 🖨 🖨 🖥 🖨 🖥

ASTORIA *(Restaurants p. 620)*
▼▼▼ **Astoria Holiday Inn Express Hotel & Suites** **H**
(503) 325-6222. **Call for rates.** 204 W Marine Dr 97103. On US 30; west side of town. Int corridors. **Pets:** $20 daily fee/pet. Designated rooms, service with restrictions, supervision.
🍴 🖥🌀 🖨 🖨 🖥 🖨 🖥

🅰 ▼▼▼ **Best Western Astoria Bayfront Hotel** **H** 🐾
(503) 325-2205. **$130-$350.** 555 Hamburg Ave 97103. On US 101/30; at east end of Youngs Bay Bridge. Int corridors. **Pets:** Large, dogs only. $15 daily fee/pet. Designated rooms, service with restrictions, supervision. 🖥 🍴 🖨 🖨 🖥 🖨 🖥 🖨 🖥

▼▼▼ **Clementine's Bed & Breakfast** **BB** 🐾
(503) 325-2005. **Call for rates.** 847 Exchange St 97103. At 8th and Exchange sts; in historic downtown. Int corridors. **Pets:** $20 one-time fee/pet. Designated rooms, no service, supervision.
🍴 🖥🌀 🖨 🖥 ☎ 🖥 🖥

▼▼▼ **Comfort Suites Columbia River** **H**
(503) 325-2000. **$109-$314.** 3420 Leif Erickson Dr 97103. 2.5 mi e of Astoria Bridge on US 30. Int corridors. **Pets:** Accepted.
🍴 🖨 🖥 🖥🌀 🖨 🖥 🖨 🖥

BAKER CITY
🅰 ▼▼▼ **Best Western Sunridge Inn** **H** 🐾
(541) 523-6444. **$101-$120.** 1 Sunridge Ln 97814. I-84 exit 304, just w. Int corridors. **Pets:** Large. $20 daily fee/room. Designated rooms, service with restrictions, crate. 🖥 🖨 🍴 🖨 🖥🌀 🖨 🖥 🖨 🖥

▼▼▼ **Geiser Grand Hotel** **H** 🐾
(541) 523-1889. **$119-$299, 7 day notice.** 1996 Main St 97814. I-84 exit 304, 0.9 mi w on Campbell St, then 0.3 mi s; downtown. Int corridors. **Pets:** Other species. $15 daily fee/pet. Service with restrictions.
🍴 🖥🌀 🖨 🖥 🖨 🖥

▼ **Motel 6** **M**
(541) 523-3431. **Call for rates.** 175 Campbell St 97814. I-84 exit 304, just e. Ext corridors. **Pets:** Accepted. 🍴 🖥🌀 🖥 🖨 🖥 🖨

BANDON
🅰 ▼▼▼ **Bandon Inn** **M** 🐾
(541) 347-4417. **$84-$279.** 355 US 101 97411. Center. Ext corridors. **Pets:** Medium. $15 daily fee/pet. Designated rooms, service with restrictions, supervision. 🖥 🍴 🖥🌀 🖨 🖥 🖨 🖥 🖨 🖥

🅰 ▼▼▼ **Best Western Inn at Face Rock** **H** 🐾
(541) 347-9441. **$129-$199.** 3225 Beach Loop Dr 97411. 1 mi s on US 101, 0.8 mi w on Seabird Rd, just s. Ext corridors. **Pets:** Medium, dogs only. $20 daily fee/pet. Designated rooms, service with restrictions, supervision. 🖥 🍴 🖥🌀 🖨 🖥 🖨 🖥 🖨 🖥 🖨

BEAVERTON
▼▼▼ **Comfort Inn & Suites** **H**
(503) 643-9100. **$95-$404.** 13455 SW Tualatin Valley Hwy 97005. SR 217 exit 2A (Canyon Rd/SR 8), 1 mi w. Int corridors. **Pets:** Small, dogs only. $10 daily fee/pet. Service with restrictions, supervision.
🖨 🖥🌀 🖥 🖨 🖥

🅰 ▼▼▼ **DoubleTree by Hilton-Portland/Beaverton** **H**
(503) 614-8100. **Call for rates.** 15402 NW Cornell Rd 97006. US 26 exit 65, just ne. Int corridors. **Pets:** Accepted.
🖥 🍴 🖥🌀 🖨 🖥 🖨 🖥 🖨 🖥

▼▼▼ **Homewood Suites by Hilton** **H**
(503) 614-0900. **$129-$299.** 15525 NW Gateway Ct 97006. US 26 exit 65, just sw on NW Cornell Rd, just s on NW 158th Ave, just se on NW Waterhouse Ave, then just e. Int corridors. **Pets:** Accepted.
🖥🌀 🖨 🖥 🖨 🖥

BEND *(Restaurants p. 620)*
▼▼ **Bend Three Sisters Inn & Suites** **M** 🐾
(541) 382-1515. **Call for rates.** 721 NE 3rd St 97701. Jct US 20 and Business Rt US 97 (NE 3rd St), just s. Ext corridors. **Pets:** Other species. $10 daily fee/pet. Designated rooms, service with restrictions, crate. 🖨 🖥🌀 🖥 🖨 🖥

▼▼▼ Holiday Inn Express & Suites 🔢
(541) 317-8500. **Call for rates.** 20615 Grandview Dr 97701. On US 97; north end of town. Int corridors. **Pets:** Accepted.
🍴 ♿ 🛏 📶 ✖ 🔌 💻

◆◆ La Quinta Inn Bend 🔢
(541) 388-2227. **$75-$306.** 61200 SE 3rd St (Business Rt US 97) 97702. From south end of jct US 97 and Business Rt 97 (NE 3rd St), 0.5 mi n; south end of town. Int corridors. **Pets:** Accepted.
🍴 🛏 📶 ✖ 🔌 💻

◆◆ My Place Hotel Bend 🔢
(541) 213-2108. **Call for rates.** 550 SW Bond St 97702. US 97 exit 139 (Reed Market Rd), 0.4 mi w, then 1 mi nw; in Old Mill District. Int corridors. **Pets:** Accepted. ♿ 📶 ✖ 🔌 💻

(AAA) ▼▼▼ The Oxford Hotel 🔢
(541) 382-8436. **Call for rates.** 10 NW Minnesota Ave 97701. Jct NW Minnesota Ave and NW Lava Rd; downtown. Int corridors.
Pets: Accepted. 🆂 ⬅ 🍴 ♿ ✖ 📶 ✖ 🔌 💻

(AAA) ▼▼▼ Riverhouse on the Deschutes 🔢
(541) 389-3111. **$129-$209.** 3075 N US 97 Business 97703. US 97 exit 137 (Revere Ave) northbound, just n on NE Division St, then just n; exit 136 (Butler Market Rd) southbound, just w. Ext/int corridors.
Pets: Accepted. 🆂 🍴 🛏 ✖ 📶 ✖ 🔌 💻

▼▼▼ Tetherow Lodges 🔢
(541) 388-2582. **Call for rates.** 61240 Skyline Ranch Rd 97702. US 97 exit 139 (Reed Market Rd), 4 mi sw; at Tetherow Golf Club. Int corridors. **Pets:** Accepted. 🍴 ✖ 📶 ✖ 🔌 💻

◆◆ TownePlace Suites by Marriott 🔢
(541) 382-5006. **$103-$209.** 755 SW 13th Pl 97702. US 97 exit 138 (Downtown/Mt Bachelor Dr), 1.6 mi sw on NW Colorado Ave. Int corridors. **Pets:** Accepted. ⬅ ♿ 🛏 📶 ✖ 🔌 💻

BOARDMAN
▼▼▼ River Lodge & Grill 🔢
(541) 481-6800. **Call for rates.** 6 Marine Dr 97818. I-84 exit 164, 0.4 mi n on Main St, then 0.6 mi e. Int corridors. **Pets:** Accepted.
🍴 ♿ 🛏 ✖ 📶 ✖ 🔌 💻

BROOKINGS
(AAA) ▼▼▼ Best Western Beachfront Inn 🔢
(541) 469-7779. **$169-$219.** 16008 Boat Basin Rd 97415. US 101 exit Benham Ln, 0.6 mi w; 1.2 mi s of Chetco River Bridge. Ext corridors.
Pets: Accepted. 🆂 ♿ 🛏 📶 🐾 🔌 💻

(AAA) ▼▼▼ Westward Inn Ⓜ
(541) 469-7471. **$69-$169, 3 day notice.** 1026 Chetco Ave (US 101) 97415. On US 101; just n of downtown. Ext corridors. **Pets:** Medium, dogs only. Designated rooms, service with restrictions, supervision.
🆂 ♿ 📶 ✖ 🔌 💻

▼▼ Wild Rivers Motorlodge Ⓜ ✤
(541) 469-5361. **$69-$119.** 437 Chetco Ave (US 101) 97415. On US 101; just n of Chetco River Bridge. Ext corridors. **Pets:** $10 daily fee/ pet. Designated rooms, service with restrictions, supervision.
♿ 📶 🔌 💻

BURNS
(AAA) ▼▼▼ Americas Best Value Inn Ⓜ
(541) 573-1700. **$66-$85.** 999 Oregon Ave (US 395/20) 97720. 1 mi w on US 395/20 from jct SR 78. Ext/int corridors. **Pets:** Small, dogs only. $100 deposit/room, $10 daily fee/pet. Designated rooms, service with restrictions, supervision. 🆂 ⬅ 📶 ✖ 🔌 💻

CANNON BEACH
▼▼ Ecola Creek Lodge Ⓜ
(503) 436-2776. **$79-$244, 7 day notice.** 208 E 5th St 97110. US 101 exit Ecola State Park northbound, just w; north end of downtown. Ext corridors. **Pets:** Accepted. 🍴 📶 ✖ 🐾 🔌 💻

▼▼▼ Inn at Cannon Beach 🔢
(503) 436-9085. **Call for rates.** 3215 S Hemlock St 97110. US 101 exit Tolovana Park, just w on Warren Way, then just n. Ext corridors.
Pets: Accepted. 🍴 📶 ✖ 🐾 🔌 💻

▼▼▼ The Ocean Lodge 🔢
(503) 436-2241. **Call for rates.** 2864 S Pacific St 97110. US 101 exit Tolovana Park, just w on Warren Way, just n on S Hemlock St, just w on W Chisana St, then just n. Ext/int corridors. **Pets:** Accepted.
♿ 📶 ✖ 🔌 💻

(AAA) ▼▼▼ Surfsand Resort 🔢
(503) 436-2274. **$119-$469, 3 day notice.** 148 W Gower St 97110. US 101 exit Cannon Beach (2nd exit); downtown. Ext corridors.
Pets: Accepted. 🆂 🍴 ♿ 🛏 ✖ 📶 ✖ 🐾 🔌 💻

▼▼▼ Tolovana Inn Ⓒ
(503) 436-2211. **$89-$495, 7 day notice.** 3400 S Hemlock St 97145. US 101 exit Tolovana Park, just w on Warren Way, then just s. Ext corridors. **Pets:** Accepted. 🛏 ✖ 📶 ✖ 🐾 🔌 💻

CANYONVILLE
▼▼▼ Holiday Inn Express & Suites Canyonville 🔢
(541) 839-4200. **Call for rates.** 200 Creekside Dr 97417. I-5 exit 99, just w. Int corridors. **Pets:** Medium, dogs only. $15 daily fee/pet. Designated rooms, no service, supervision. ♿ ⬅ 📶 ✖ 🔌 💻

CASCADE LOCKS
(AAA) ▼▼▼ Best Western Plus Columbia River Inn 🔢
(541) 374-8777. **$129-$244.** 735 WaNaPa St (US 30) 97014. I-84 exit 44 eastbound, 0.4 mi ne; exit westbound, 1.4 mi nw. Int corridors.
Pets: $20 daily fee/room. Designated rooms, service with restrictions, supervision. 🆂 ♿ ⬅ 📶 ✖ 🔌 💻

CENTRAL POINT
▼▼ La Quinta Inn & Suites Central Point - Medford 🔢
(541) 665-4141. **$75-$224.** 1777 Larue Dr 97502. I-5 exit 33, just se. Int corridors. **Pets:** Accepted. ♿ ⬅ 📶 ✖ 🔌 💻

▼▼ Super 8 Inn & Suites 🔢
(541) 664-5888. **$80-$124.** 4999 Biddle Rd 97502. I-5 exit 33, 0.5 mi e. Int corridors. **Pets:** Accepted. ♿ ⬅ 📶 🔌 💻

CLACKAMAS
▼▼ Comfort Suites 🔢
(503) 723-3450. **$105-$140.** 15929 SE McKinley Ave 97015. I-205 exit 12 northbound; exit 12B southbound, just w. Int corridors. **Pets:** Other species. $15 daily fee/room. Designated rooms, service with restrictions, supervision. 🍴 ⬅ ✖ 📶 ✖ 🔌 💻

CLATSKANIE
(AAA) ▼▼▼ Clatskanie River Inn 🔢
(503) 728-9000. **Call for rates.** 600 E Columbia River Hwy (US 30) 97016. On US 30, just e. Int corridors. **Pets:** Accepted.
🆂 ⬅ 📶 ✖ 🔌 💻

COOS BAY
(AAA) ▼▼▼ Best Western Plus Holiday Hotel 🔢 🐾
(541) 269-5111. **$126-$186.** 411 N Bayshore Dr 97420. On US 101; just n of downtown. Ext corridors. **Pets:** Dogs only. $15 daily fee/pet. Supervision. 🆂 ♿ ⬅ 📶 ✖ 🔌 💻

◇ ▽▽▽ **Red Lion Hotel Coos Bay** H
(541) 267-4141. **$89-$156.** 1313 N Bayshore Dr 97420. On US 101; 0.5 mi n of downtown. Ext corridors. **Pets:** Accepted.
[SAVE] [icons]

CORVALLIS

◇ ▽▽▽ **Best Western Corvallis** H
(541) 758-8571. **$150-$280.** 925 NW Garfield Ave 97330. Jct SR 34 and US 20, 0.3 mi w on NW Harrison Blvd, 1 mi n on NW 9th St, then just w. Int corridors. **Pets:** Accepted.
[SAVE] [icons]

◇ ▽▽▽ **Comfort Suites Corvallis** H ❀
(541) 753-4320. **$139-$400.** 1730 NW 9th St 97330. Jct SR 34 and US 20, 0.3 mi w on NW Harrison Blvd, 1.1 mi n. Int corridors. **Pets:** Dogs only. $25 daily fee/pet. Designated rooms, service with restrictions, supervision. [SAVE] [icons]

▽ **Econo Lodge Corvallis** H
(541) 758-9125. **$62-$199.** 935 NW Garfield Ave 97330. Jct SR 34 and US 20, 0.3 mi w on NW Harrison Blvd, 1 mi n on NW 9th St, then just w. Int corridors. **Pets:** Very small, dogs only. $20 daily fee/pet. Designated rooms, service with restrictions, supervision.
[icons]

◇ ▽▽▽ **Holiday Inn Express On The River** H
(541) 752-0800. **$129-$299.** 781 NE 2nd St 97330. Jct SR 34 and US 20, 0.4 mi n. Int corridors. **Pets:** Dogs only. $25 daily fee/room. Designated rooms, service with restrictions, supervision.
[SAVE] [icons]

▽ **Rodeway Inn Willamette River** M
(541) 752-9601. **$60-$250.** 345 NW 2nd St 97330. Between NW Harrison Blvd and NW Van Buren St; downtown. Ext/int corridors. **Pets:** Dogs only. $15 daily fee/pet. Designated rooms, service with restrictions, supervision. [icons]

COTTAGE GROVE

◇ ▽▽▽ **Best Western Cottage Grove Inn** H
(541) 942-1000. **$96-$169.** 1601 Gateway Blvd 97424. I-5 exit 174, just sw. Int corridors. **Pets:** Large, other species. $15 daily fee/pet. Service with restrictions, supervision. [SAVE] [icons]

CRESCENT

◇ ▽▽▽ **Woodsman Country Lodge** M
(541) 433-2710. **Call for rates.** 136740 US 97 N 97733. Center. Ext corridors. **Pets:** Accepted. [SAVE] [icons]

CRESWELL

▽▽▽ **Comfort Inn & Suites** H
(541) 895-4025. **$94-$249.** 247 Melton Rd 97426. I-5 exit 182, just ne. Int corridors. **Pets:** Accepted. [icons]

ENTERPRISE *(Restaurants p. 620)*

▽▽ **Eagle's View Inn & Suites** H
(541) 426-2700. **$91-$129.** 1200 Highland Ave 97828. On SR 82, 1 mi e of downtown. Int corridors. **Pets:** Dogs only. $30 one-time fee/room. Designated rooms, supervision. [icons]

▽▽ **Ponderosa Motel** M
(541) 426-3186. **$76-$91.** 102 E Greenwood St 97828. At S River (SR 82) and Greenwood sts. Ext corridors. **Pets:** Dogs only. $20 one-time fee/pet. Designated rooms, service with restrictions, supervision.
[icons]

▽ **Wilderness Inn** M
(541) 426-4535. **$63-$85.** 301 W North St 97828. On SR 82; just w of downtown. Ext corridors. **Pets:** Dogs only. $10 one-time fee/pet. Designated rooms, service with restrictions, supervision. [icons]

EUGENE *(Restaurants p. 620)*

◇ ▽▽▽ **Americas Best Value Inn** M
(541) 343-0730. **$49-$149.** 1140 W 6th Ave 97402. I-5 exit 194B, 3.5 mi w on I-105, then 0.3 mi w on SR 99 N (6th Ave). Ext corridors. **Pets:** Accepted. [SAVE] [icons]

◇ ▽▽▽ **Best Western Greentree Inn** H
(541) 485-2727. **$109-$200.** 1759 Franklin Blvd 97403. I-5 exit 194B southbound to I-105 exit University of Oregon, 0.9 mi e; exit 192 northbound, 1.2 mi w. Ext/int corridors. **Pets:** Accepted.
[SAVE] [icons]

◇ ▽▽▽ **Best Western New Oregon** H
(541) 683-3669. **$116-$210.** 1655 Franklin Blvd 97403. I-5 exit 194B southbound to I-105 exit University of Oregon, 0.9 mi e; exit 192 northbound, 1.2 mi w. Ext corridors. **Pets:** Medium. $20 daily fee/pet. Designated rooms, service with restrictions, crate.
[icons]

◇ ▽▽▽ **Candlewood Suites - Eugene Springfield** H
(541) 683-8000. **$99-$399.** 3005 Franklin Blvd 97403. I-5 exit 191 (Glenwood Blvd), 0.7 mi n, then just w. Int corridors. **Pets:** Large, dogs only. $75 one-time fee/room. Service with restrictions, supervision.
[SAVE] [icons]

▽▽▽ **Excelsior Inn & Ristorante Italiano** CI
(541) 342-6963. **$135-$300.** 754 E 13th Ave 97401. I-5 exit 194B southbound, 1.3 mi w on I-105 exit 2 (Coburg Rd), 1.5 mi s, follow signs to University of Oregon, just e on Broadway/Franklin Blvd, just s on Patterson St, then just e; exit 192 northbound, 1.5 mi w, then just s on Alder St. Int corridors. **Pets:** Accepted. [icons]

◇ ▽▽▽ **Hilton Eugene** H
(541) 342-2000. **$119-$389.** 66 E 6th Ave 97401. At 6th Ave and Oak St; center. Int corridors. **Pets:** Accepted.
[SAVE] [icons]

◇ ▽▽▽ **Inn at the 5th** H
(541) 743-4099. **$199-$459.** 205 E 6th Ave 97401. Jct Pearl St; downtown. Int corridors. **Pets:** Accepted.
[SAVE] [icons]

▽▽▽ **La Quinta Inn & Suites Eugene** H
(541) 344-8335. **$92-$378.** 155 Day Island Rd 97401. I-5 exit 194B, 1.3 mi w on I-105 exit 2 (Coburg Rd), straight through jct Coburg Rd to Southwood Ln, just w, then 0.5 mi se on Country Club Rd, follow signs for Autzen Stadium. Int corridors. **Pets:** Accepted.
[icons]

▽▽▽ **Red Lion Inn & Suites Eugene** H
(541) 345-2331. **Call for rates.** 599 E Broadway 97401. I-5 exit 194B southbound, 1.3 mi w on I-105 exit 2 (Coburg Rd), then 1.7 mi s, follow signs to University of Oregon, U-turn at Alder St; exit 192 northbound, 1.9 mi w. Int corridors. **Pets:** Accepted. [icons]

▽▽▽ **Residence Inn by Marriott Eugene Springfield** H
(541) 342-7171. **$158-$257.** 25 Club Rd 97401. I-5 exit 194B, 1.3 mi w on I-105 exit 2 (Coburg Rd), straight through jct Coburg Rd to Southwood Ln, just w, then se on Country Club Rd, follow signs for Autzen Stadium. Int corridors. **Pets:** Accepted. [icons]

◇ ▽▽▽ **Valley River Inn** H ❀
(541) 743-1000. **Call for rates.** 1000 Valley River Way 97401. I-5 exit 194B, 2.5 mi w on I-105 exit 1, follow signs for Valley River Center. Int corridors. **Pets:** $46 one-time fee/room. Designated rooms, service with restrictions, supervision. [SAVE] [icons]

FLORENCE

◇ ▽▽▽ **Best Western Pier Point Inn** H
(541) 997-7191. **$139-$249.** 85625 US 101 S 97439. Jct SR 126, 1.1 mi s. Ext/int corridors. **Pets:** Medium. $20 one-time fee/pet. Designated rooms, service with restrictions, supervision.
[SAVE] [icons]

Ocean Breeze Motel M
(541) 997-2642. **$69-$130.** 85165 US 101 S 97439. Jct SR 126, 2 mi s. Ext corridors. **Pets:** Dogs only. $15 daily fee/pet. Designated rooms, supervision.

FOREST GROVE

Best Western University Inn & Suites H
(503) 992-8888. **$120-$275.** 3933 Pacific Ave 97116. East end of town on SR 8. Int corridors. **Pets:** Medium. $20 daily fee/pet. Designated rooms, service with restrictions, supervision.

GEARHART (Restaurants p. 621)

Gearhart By The Sea CO
(503) 738-8331. **Call for rates.** 1157 N Marion Ave 97138. US 101 exit City Center, 1 mi w. Ext corridors. **Pets:** Very small, dogs only. $15 daily fee/pet. Designated rooms, service with restrictions, supervision.

GLENEDEN BEACH

Salishan Spa & Golf Resort H
(541) 764-2371. **Call for rates.** 7760 US 101 N 97388. Just e of US 101; center. Ext corridors. **Pets:** Accepted.

GOLD BEACH

Gold Beach Inn M
(541) 247-7091. **Call for rates.** 29346 Ellensburg Ave (US 101) 97444. On US 101; center. Ext corridors. **Pets:** Accepted.

Gold Beach Resort H
(541) 247-7066. **Call for rates.** 29232 Ellensburg Ave 97444. On US 101; south end of town. Ext/int corridors. **Pets:** Large, dogs only. $20 daily fee/pet. Designated rooms, service with restrictions, supervision.

GRANTS PASS (Restaurants p. 621)

Bestway Inn M
(541) 479-2952. **Call for rates.** 1253 NE 6th St 97526. I-5 exit 58, 0.9 mi s on SR 99. Ext corridors. **Pets:** Medium, dogs only. $15 daily fee/pet. Designated rooms, service with restrictions, supervision.

Best Western Grants Pass Inn H
(541) 476-1117. **$89-$180.** 111 NE Agness Ave 97526. I-5 exit 55, just nw. Ext corridors. **Pets:** Accepted.

Best Western Inn at the Rogue H
(541) 582-2200. **$90-$155.** 8959 Rogue River Hwy 97527. I-5 exit 48, just nw. Int corridors. **Pets:** Other species. $25 daily fee/room. Designated rooms, service with restrictions, supervision.

Holiday Inn Express Grants Pass H
(541) 471-6144. **Call for rates.** 105 NE Agness Ave 97526. I-5 exit 55, just nw. Int corridors. **Pets:** Other species. $10 daily fee/pet. Designated rooms, service with restrictions, supervision.

Knights Inn Motel M
(541) 479-5595. **$69-$98.** 104 SE 7th St 97526. I-5 exit 58, 1.7 mi s on SR 99, just e on G St, then just n. Ext corridors. **Pets:** Accepted.

La Quinta Inn & Suites Grants Pass H
(541) 472-1808. **$86-$251.** 243 NE Morgan Ln 97526. I-5 exit 58, 0.4 mi s on SR 99, just e on Hillcrest Dr to SR 99 N, then just n. Int corridors. **Pets:** Accepted.

Motel 6-#253 M
(541) 474-1331. **$61-$145.** 1800 NE 7th St 97526. I-5 exit 58, just s on SR 99. Ext corridors. **Pets:** Accepted.

Redwood Hyperion Suites H
(541) 476-0878. **$109-$418.** 815 NE 6th St 97526. I-5 exit 58, 1.2 mi s on SR 99. Ext corridors. **Pets:** Designated rooms, service with restrictions, supervision.

Riverside Inn H
(541) 476-6873. **Call for rates.** 986 SW 6th St 97526. I-5 exit 58, 2.5 mi s on SR 99. Ext corridors. **Pets:** Other species. $25 daily fee/room. Designated rooms, service with restrictions, supervision.

Super 8-Grants Pass H
(541) 474-0888. **$57-$97.** 1949 NE 7th St 97526. I-5 exit 58, 0.4 mi s on SR 99, just e on Hillcrest Dr to SR 99 N, then just n. Int corridors. **Pets:** Accepted.

Travelodge M
(541) 479-6611. **$70-$89.** 1950 NW Vine St 97526. I-5 exit 58, just s on SR 99. Ext corridors. **Pets:** Medium. $10 daily fee/pet. Designated rooms, service with restrictions, supervision.

GRESHAM

Days Inn & Suites H
(503) 465-1515. **$62-$117.** 24124 SE Stark St 97030. I-84 exit 16, 1.5 mi s on NE 238th and NE 242nd drs, then just w. Int corridors. **Pets:** Accepted.

Quality Inn Gresham H
(503) 907-1777. **$95-$223.** 2752 NE Hogan Dr 97030. I-84 exit 16, 1.8 mi s on NE 238th, NE 242nd and NE Hogan drs. Int corridors. **Pets:** Small, dogs only. $35 daily fee/pet. Service with restrictions, supervision.

Super 8 H
(503) 661-5100. **$70-$110.** 121 NE 181st Ave 97230. I-84 exit 13, 1.3 mi s. Int corridors. **Pets:** Large, dogs only. $10 daily fee/pet. Service with restrictions, supervision.

HERMISTON

Comfort Inn & Suites Hermiston H
(541) 564-5911. **$107-$195.** 77514 SR 207 97838. I-84 exit 182, just n. Int corridors. **Pets:** Other species. $20 daily fee/pet. Service with restrictions, supervision.

Oak Tree Inn H
(541) 567-2330. **Call for rates.** 1110 SE 4th St 97838. 0.4 mi s on US 395, just w. Int corridors. **Pets:** Accepted.

Oxford Suites Hermiston H
(541) 564-8000. **Call for rates.** 1050 N 1st St 97838. I-84 exit 188 (US 395), 7.8 mi nw. Int corridors. **Pets:** Accepted.

HILLSBORO

Extended Stay America-Portland-Beaverton H
(503) 439-1515. **$100-$140.** 18665 NW Eider Ct 97006. US 26 exit 64, 0.7 mi s on NW 185th Ave, then just w. Int corridors. **Pets:** Accepted.

Larkspur Landing Hillsboro H
(503) 681-2121. **Call for rates.** 3133 NE Shute Rd 97124. US 26 exit 61, 1.1 mi s. Int corridors. **Pets:** Accepted.

▼▼▼ **Residence Inn by Marriott Portland Hillsboro/Brookwood** 🅷 ❀

(503) 844-7777. **$150-$309.** 3160 NE Brookwood Pkwy 97124. US 26 exit 61, 1.2 mi s. Int corridors. **Pets:** Medium. $100 one-time fee/room. Service with restrictions, crate. 🍴 Ⓜ 🛋 🤽 🌐 ✕ 🗋 💻

▼▼▼ **Residence Inn by Marriott-Portland West/Hillsboro** 🅷

(503) 531-3200. **$170-$306.** 18855 NW Tanasbourne Dr 97124. US 26 exit 64, just s on NW 185th Ave, then just w. Ext/int corridors. **Pets:** Accepted. 🍴 Ⓜ 🛋 🤽 🌐 ✕ 🗋 💻

▼▼▼ **TownePlace Suites by Marriott-Portland Hillsboro** 🅷

(503) 268-6000. **$119-$181.** 6550 NE Brighton St 97124. US 26 exit 62A westbound; exit 62 eastbound, 1 mi s on Cornelius Pass Rd, 0.7 mi w on NE Cornell Rd, just n on NW 229th Ave, then just w. Ext corridors. **Pets:** Accepted. 🍴 🤽 🌐 ✕ 🗋 💻

HINES

⟨AAA⟩ ▼▼▼ **Best Western Rory & Ryan Inns** 🅷

(541) 573-5050. **$110-$150.** 534 US 20 N 97738. On US 20 (Central Oregon Hwy), south edge of town. Int corridors. **Pets:** Dogs only. $15 daily fee/pet. Designated rooms, service with restrictions, supervision. 🆂🅰🆅🅴 🤽 🌐 ✕ 🗋 💻

▼▼ **Rory & Ryan Inns** 🅷

(541) 573-3370. **Call for rates.** 504 US 20 N 97738. On US 20 (Central Oregon Hwy). Int corridors. **Pets:** Medium, dogs only. $10 daily fee/pet. Designated rooms, service with restrictions, supervision. 🤽 🌐 ✕ 🗋 💻

HOOD RIVER

⟨AAA⟩ ▼▼▼ **Best Western Plus Hood River Inn** 🅷 ❀

(541) 386-2200. **$140-$240.** 1108 E Marina Way 97031. I-84 exit 64, just ne. Int corridors. **Pets:** Medium, dogs only. $15 daily fee/pet. Designated rooms, service with restrictions, supervision. 🆂🅰🆅🅴 🍴 🤽 🅧 🌐 ✕ 🗋 💻

▼▼▼ **Columbia Gorge Hotel & Spa** 🅷

(541) 386-5566. **Call for rates.** 4000 Westcliff Dr 97031. I-84 exit 62, just nw of overpass. Int corridors. **Pets:** Accepted. 🍴 🌐 ✕ 🗋

⟨AAA⟩ ▼▼▼ **Hampton Inn & Suites by Hilton Hood River** 🅷 ❀

(541) 436-1600. **$149-$309.** 1 Nichols Pkwy 97031. I-84 exit 63, just ne. Int corridors. **Pets:** $20 daily fee/room. Designated rooms, service with restrictions, supervision. 🆂🅰🆅🅴 🍴 Ⓜ 🌐 ✕ 🗋 💻

⟨AAA⟩ ▼▼▼ **Sunset Motel** Ⓜ

(541) 386-6322. **$79-$159, 3 day notice.** 2300 Cascade Ave 97031. I-84 exit 62, 0.7 mi se. Ext corridors. **Pets:** Accepted. 🆂🅰🆅🅴 🍴 🌐 ✕ 🗋 💻

JACKSONVILLE

⟨AAA⟩ ▼▼▼ **Jacksonville Inn** 🅲

(541) 899-1900. **$159-$465, 3 day notice.** 175 E California St 97530. Between 3rd and 4th sts; in historic district; center. Ext/int corridors. **Pets:** Accepted. 🆂🅰🆅🅴 🍴 🌐 ✕ 🗋 💻

▼▼▼ **Jacksonville's Magnolia Inn** 🅱🅱 ❀

(541) 899-0255. **$124-$179, 7 day notice.** 245 N 5th St 97530. At 5th (SR 238) and D sts; in historic district. Int corridors. **Pets:** Dogs only. $25 one-time fee/room. Supervision. Ⓜ 🌐 ✕ 🆆

⟨AAA⟩ ▼▼▼ **Wine Country Inn** 🅲 ❀

(541) 899-2050. **Call for rates.** 830 N 5th St 97530. 0.5 mi ne of downtown; in historic district. Ext/int corridors. **Pets:** Large, other species. $25 daily fee/pet. Designated rooms, service with restrictions, supervision. 🆂🅰🆅🅴 🍴 Ⓜ 🌐 ✕ 🆉 🗋 💻

JOHN DAY

⟨AAA⟩ ▼▼▼ **Best Western John Day Inn** Ⓜ

(541) 575-1700. **$105-$180.** 315 W Main St 97845. Just w of jct US 26 and 395. Ext corridors. **Pets:** Dogs only. $15 one-time fee/room. Designated rooms, service with restrictions, crate. 🆂🅰🆅🅴 🤽 🌐 ✕ 🗋 💻

⟨AAA⟩ ▼▼ **Dreamers Lodge** Ⓜ

(541) 575-0526. **$59-$120.** 144 N Canyon Blvd 97845. Just n of jct US 26 and 395; downtown. Ext corridors. **Pets:** Medium, dogs only. $10 daily fee/pet. Service with restrictions, supervision. 🆂🅰🆅🅴 🌐 ✕ 🗋 💻

JOSEPH

⟨AAA⟩ ▼▼▼ **Mountain View Motel & RV Park** Ⓜ

(541) 432-2982. **$55-$75.** 83450 Joseph Hwy 97846. 1.8 mi n of downtown; on SR 82. Ext corridors. **Pets:** Accepted. 🆂🅰🆅🅴 🍴 🌐 ✕ 🆉 🗋 💻

KLAMATH FALLS

⟨AAA⟩ ▼▼▼ **Cimarron Inn Klamath Falls** Ⓜ ❀

(541) 882-4601. **Call for rates.** 3060 S 6th St 97603. 0.4 mi w on S 6th St (SR 39) from jct SR 140 E/39 S and SR 39 N/US 97 business route. Ext corridors. **Pets:** Small. $25 one-time fee/pet. Designated rooms, service with restrictions, supervision. 🆂🅰🆅🅴 🤽 🌐 ✕ 🗋 💻

⟨AAA⟩ ▼▼ **Golden West Motel** Ⓜ ❀

(541) 882-1758. **$49-$79.** 6402 S 6th St 97603. On S 6th St (SR 39); east edge of town. Ext corridors. **Pets:** Dogs only. $10 one-time fee/room. Supervision. 🆂🅰🆅🅴 🍴 🌐 ✕ 🗋 💻

⟨AAA⟩ ▼▼▼ **Running Y Ranch Resort** 🅷 ❀

(541) 850-5500. **$119-$289.** 5500 Running Y Rd 97601. Jct US 97, 7.5 mi nw on SR 140. Int corridors. **Pets:** Other species. $25 daily fee/pet. Designated rooms, service with restrictions, crate. 🆂🅰🆅🅴 🎬 🍴 Ⓜ 🛋 🅧 🌐 ✕ 🗋 💻

▼▼ **Shilo Inn Suites Hotel Klamath Falls** 🅷 ❀

(541) 885-7980. **Call for rates.** 2500 Almond St 97601. Jct US 97 and Campus Dr; 1.7 mi n of city center. Int corridors. **Pets:** Dogs only. $75 deposit/room, $15 daily fee/room. Designated rooms, service with restrictions, crate. 🍴 Ⓜ 🛋 🅧 🌐 ✕ 🗋 💻

LA GRANDE

⟨AAA⟩ ▼▼▼ **America's Best Value Sandman Inn** 🅷

(541) 963-3707. **$89-$149.** 2410 E 'R' Ave 97850. I-84 exit 261, just s on Island Ave, just e on N Albany St, then just n. Int corridors. **Pets:** Accepted. 🆂🅰🆅🅴 Ⓜ 🤽 ✕ 🗋 💻

LAKE OSWEGO

▼▼ **Lakeshore Inn** 🅷 ❀

(503) 636-9679. **$89-$219, 3 day notice.** 210 N State St 97034. Jct N State St and Foothills Rd; downtown. Ext corridors. **Pets:** Dogs only. $15 daily fee/pet. Designated rooms, service with restrictions, crate. 🍴 🤽 🌐 ✕ 🗋 💻

▼▼▼ **Phoenix Inn Suites-Lake Oswego** 🅷

(503) 624-7400. **Call for rates.** 14905 SW Bangy Rd 97035. I-5 exit 292B northbound; exit 292 southbound, just s. Int corridors. **Pets:** Accepted. Ⓜ 🤽 🌐 ✕ 🗋 💻

▼▼▼ **Residence Inn by Marriott-Portland South** 🅷

(503) 684-2603. **$140-$240.** 15200 SW Bangy Rd 97035. I-5 exit 292B northbound; exit 292 southbound, just e, then 0.3 mi s. Ext corridors. **Pets:** Accepted. 🍴 🤽 🌐 ✕ 🗋 💻

LAKEVIEW

⟨AAA⟩ ▼▼▼ **Best Western Skyline Motor Lodge** Ⓜ

(541) 947-2194. **$106-$160.** 414 N G St 97630. Jct US 395 and SR 140. Ext corridors. **Pets:** Accepted. 🆂🅰🆅🅴 🤽 🌐 ✕ 🗋 💻

AAA ▼ Interstate 8 Motel M
(541) 947-3341. **$66-$72.** 354 N K St 97630. On SR 140, 0.3 mi w of jct US 395. Ext corridors. **Pets:** Large, dogs only. $100 deposit/room, $10 daily fee/pet. Designated rooms, service with restrictions, supervision. 🏷 🛜 ✕ 🔌 💻

LA PINE
AAA ▼▼ Best Western Newberry Station H
(541) 536-5130. **$115-$180.** 16515 Reed Rd 97739. Just off US 97; north end of town. Int corridors. **Pets:** Accepted.
🏷 🍴 🛜 ✕ 🔌 💻

LEBANON
AAA ▼▼▼ Best Western Premier Boulder Falls Inn H 🐾
(541) 451-1000. **$129-$329.** 505 Mullins Dr 97355. US 20 (Main St), just w. Int corridors. **Pets:** Other species. $20 daily fee/pet. Service with restrictions, crate. 🏷 🍴 ⛎ 🛜 ✕ 🔌 💻

LINCOLN CITY
AAA ▼▼▼ The Coho Oceanfront Lodge H 🐾
(541) 994-3684. **$99-$299.** 1635 NW Harbor Ave 97367. US 101 exit N 17th St, just w. Ext corridors. **Pets:** Small, dogs only. $25 daily fee/pet. Designated rooms, service with restrictions, supervision.
🏷 🍴 ⛎ ⛎ ✕ 🛜 ✕ 🐾 🔌 💻

▼▼ Comfort Inn & Suites H
(541) 994-8155. **$99-$319.** 136 NE US 101 97367. Just n of D River. Int corridors. **Pets:** Accepted. ⛎ ⛎ 🛜 ✕ 🔌 💻

AAA ▼▼▼ Inn at Wecoma H 🐾
(541) 994-2984. **$89-$289.** 2945 NW US 101 97367. Just s of NW 30th St; north of downtown. Int corridors. **Pets:** Small, dogs only. $15 daily fee/pet. Designated rooms, service with restrictions, supervision.
🏷 ⛎ ✕ 🛜 ✕ 🔌 💻

AAA ▼▼▼ Liberty Inn H
(541) 994-1777. **Call for rates.** 4990 NE Logan Rd 97367. 0.3 mi n of US 101; north end of downtown. Int corridors. **Pets:** $20 daily fee/room. Designated rooms, service with restrictions, supervision.
🏷 ⛎ 🛜 ✕ 🔌 💻

▼▼ Looking Glass Inn H 🐾
(541) 996-3996. **Call for rates.** 861 SW 51st St 97367. US 101, just w on 51st St; south end of town. Ext corridors. **Pets:** Dogs only. $15 daily fee/pet. Designated rooms, service with restrictions, crate.
🛜 ✕ 🐾 🔌 💻

▼ Motel 6-#4172 H
(541) 996-9900. **$49-$129.** 3517 NW US 101 97367. North end of downtown. Int corridors. **Pets:** Accepted. 🍴 ⛎ 🛜 🔌

▼▼▼ Shearwater Inn H 🐾
(541) 994-4121. **Call for rates.** 120 NW Inlet Ct 97367. From US 101, just w on NW 2nd Dr, just s. Int corridors. **Pets:** Medium, dogs only. $15 daily fee/pet. Designated rooms, service with restrictions, crate.
⛎ 🛜 ✕ 🐾 🔌 💻

MADRAS
AAA ▼▼▼ Inn at Cross Keys Station H
(541) 475-5800. **$90-$186.** 66 NW Cedar St 97741. On US 26; north end of town. Int corridors. **Pets:** Medium, dogs only. $30 deposit/pet. Designated rooms, service with restrictions, supervision.
🏷 🍴 ⛎ ⛎ 🛜 ✕ 🔌 💻

▼▼▼ Quality Inn M
(541) 475-6141. **$75-$150.** 12 SW 4th St 97741. On US 97/26 S; at B and 4th sts; downtown. Ext corridors. **Pets:** Accepted.
⛎ ⛎ 🛜 ✕ 🔌 💻

MCMINNVILLE *(Restaurants p. 621)*
▼▼▼ Comfort Inn & Suites H
(503) 472-1700. **$100-$290.** 2520 SE Stratus Ave 97128. Jct SR 99 W; 2.3 mi ne on SR 18; across from Willamette Valley Medical Center. Int corridors. **Pets:** Accepted. 🍴 ⛎ ⛎ 🛜 ✕ 🔌 💻

AAA ▼▼ GuestHouse Vineyard Inn H
(503) 472-4900. **Call for rates.** 2035 S SR 99 W 97128. Jct SR 99 W and 18. Int corridors. **Pets:** Accepted.
🏷 🍴 ⛎ 🛜 ✕ 🔌 💻

AAA ▼▼▼ Red Lion Inn & Suites McMinnville H
(503) 472-1500. **Call for rates.** 2535 NE Cumulus Ave 97128. Jct SR 99 W; 2.3 mi ne on SR 18. Int corridors. **Pets:** Accepted.
🏷 🍴 ⛎ 🛜 ✕ 🔌 💻

MEDFORD *(Restaurants p. 621)*
AAA ▼▼▼ Best Western Horizon Inn H
(541) 779-5085. **$86-$139.** 1154 E Barnett Rd 97504. I-5 exit 27 (Barnett Rd), just e. Ext corridors. **Pets:** Accepted.
🏷 ⛎ ⛎ 🛜 🔌 💻

AAA ▼▼ Candlewood Suites Medford Airport H
(541) 772-2800. **Call for rates.** 3548 Heathrow Way 97504. I-5 exit 33, 1.5 mi se via E Pine St and Biddle Rd, just w on O'Hare Pkwy, then just n. Int corridors. **Pets:** Accepted. 🏷 ⛎ 🛜 ✕ 🔌 💻

AAA ▼▼ Comfort Inn North Medford H
(541) 772-9500. **$104-$195.** 2280 Biddle Rd 97504. I-5 exit 30 southbound, just ne on Crater Lake Hwy, follow signs to Biddle Rd/Airport, then just n; exit northbound, follow signs to Biddle Rd/Airport, just ne. Int corridors. **Pets:** Small, dogs only. $150 deposit/room, $10 daily fee/pet. Designated rooms, service with restrictions.
🏷 ⛎ ⛎ 🛜 ✕ 🔌 💻

AAA ▼▼ Comfort Inn South H
(541) 772-8000. **$109-$194.** 60 E Stewart Ave 97501. I-5 exit 27 (Barnett Rd), just w on Garfield St, 0.4 mi n on S Pacific Hwy, then just e. Int corridors. **Pets:** Other species. $20 daily fee/pet. Designated rooms, service with restrictions, supervision.
🏷 ⛎ ⛎ 🛜 ✕ 🔌 💻

AAA ▼▼▼ Homewood Suites by Hilton H 🐾
(541) 779-9800. **$119-$189.** 2010 Hospitality Way 97504. I-5 exit 27 (Barnett Rd), 0.4 mi e, just s on Ellendale Dr, then just w. Int corridors. **Pets:** Medium, other species. $50 one-time fee/room. Service with restrictions, supervision. 🏷 ⛎ ⛎ 🛜 🔌 💻

▼▼ Inn at the Commons H
(541) 779-5811. **Call for rates.** 200 N Riverside Ave 97501. I-5 exit 27 (Barnett Rd), 0.4 mi w on Garfield St, then 1.7 mi n on S Pacific Hwy. Ext corridors. **Pets:** Accepted. 🍴 ⛎ ⛎ 🛜 ✕ 🔌 💻

AAA ▼▼ Ramada Medford and Convention Center H
(541) 779-3141. **$77-$125.** 2250 Biddle Rd 97504. I-5 exit 30 southbound, just ne on Crater Lake Hwy, follow signs to Biddle Rd/Airport, then just s; exit northbound, follow signs to Biddle Rd/Airport, just s. Int corridors. **Pets:** $20 daily fee/room. Designated rooms, service with restrictions, supervision. 🏷 🍴 ⛎ 🛜 🔌 💻

▼▼ Rogue Regency Inn & Suites H
(541) 770-1234. **Call for rates.** 2300 Biddle Rd 97504. I-5 exit 30 southbound, just ne on Crater Lake Hwy, follow signs to Biddle Rd/Airport, then just n; exit northbound, follow signs to Biddle Rd/Airport, then just n. Int corridors. **Pets:** Accepted.
🍴 ⛎ ✕ 🛜 ✕ 🔌 💻

▼▼ Shilo Inn-Medford H 🐾
(541) 770-5151. **Call for rates.** 2111 Biddle Rd 97504. I-5 exit 30 southbound, just ne on Crater Lake Hwy, follow signs to Biddle Rd/Airport, then just s; exit northbound, follow signs to Biddle Rd/Airport, then just s. Int corridors. **Pets:** Dogs only. $75 deposit/room, $15 daily fee/room. Designated rooms, service with restrictions, crate.
⛎ 🛜 ✕ 🔌 💻

MERLIN

◆◆ Morrison's Rogue River Lodge CA

(541) 476-3825. **Call for rates.** 8500 Galice Rd 97532. I-5 exit 61, 12 mi w on Merlin-Galice Rd. Ext/int corridors. **Pets:** Accepted.

MYRTLE POINT

◆◆◆ ◆◆ Myrtle Trees Motel M

(541) 572-5811. **$83-$97.** 1010 8th St (SR 42) 97458. On SR 42, just s of center. Ext corridors. **Pets:** Small, dogs only. $25 daily fee/pet. Designated rooms, service with restrictions, supervision.

NEWBERG

◆◆◆◆ ◆◆◆◆ The Allison Inn & Spa H ❀

(503) 554-2525. **$405-$1255, 3 day notice.** 2525 Allison Ln 97132. Jct Portland Rd (SR 99), 1 mi n on Springbrook Rd; north of center. Int corridors. **Pets:** Dogs only. $75 one-time fee/pet. Designated rooms, service with restrictions, supervision.

◆◆◆ ◆◆ Best Western Newberg Inn H

(503) 537-3000. **$139-$179.** 2211 Portland Rd 97132. Northeast of center. Int corridors. **Pets:** Medium. $20 daily fee/pet. Designated rooms, service with restrictions, supervision.

◆◆◆ ◆◆ Travelodge Suites H

(503) 537-5000. **$80-$144.** 2816 Portland Rd 97132. North end on SR 99 W; behind Finnigan's Restaurant. Int corridors. **Pets:** Medium, dogs only. $15 daily fee/pet. Designated rooms, service with restrictions, supervision.

NEWPORT (Restaurants p. 621)

◆◆◆ ◆◆◆◆ Best Western Agate Beach Inn H

(541) 265-9411. **$98-$215.** 3019 N Coast Hwy (US 101) 97365. Jct US 20, 1.5 mi n on US 101. Int corridors. **Pets:** Medium. $20 daily fee/room. Designated rooms, no service, supervision.

◆◆◆◆ Elizabeth Street Inn H ❀

(541) 265-9400. **$200-$340.** 232 SW Elizabeth St 97365. Jct US 20, 0.5 mi s on US 101, just w on SW Falls St, just n. Int corridors. **Pets:** Large, dogs only. $25 one-time fee/room. Designated rooms, service with restrictions, supervision.

◆◆◆◆ Hallmark Resort Newport H

(541) 265-2600. **$129-$219.** 744 SW Elizabeth St 97365. Jct US 20, 0.7 mi s on US 101, just w on SW Bay St. Ext/int corridors. **Pets:** Accepted.

◆◆◆ ◆◆◆◆ The Landing at Newport CO

(541) 574-6777. **$119-$429.** 890 SE Bay Blvd 97365. Jct US 101, 0.5 mi e on US 20, 0.3 mi s on Moore Dr. Ext corridors. **Pets:** Accepted.

◆◆ ◆◆ La Quinta Inn & Suites Newport H

(541) 867-7727. **$82-$290.** 45 SE 32nd St 97365. US 101, just s of Yaquina Bay Bridge, just e. Int corridors. **Pets:** Accepted.

◆◆ ◆◆ Newport Belle Riverboat Bed & Breakfast BB

(541) 867-6290. **Call for rates.** 2126 SE Marine Science Dr, Dock H 97365. South end of Yaquina Bay Bridge, follow signs to Marine Science Center, around traffic circle exit at boat ramp, then just w; moored at Dock H. Ext corridors. **Pets:** Small, dogs only. $20 one-time fee/room. Designated rooms, service with restrictions, supervision.

◆◆ ◆◆ Shilo Inn Suites Oceanfront Hotel-Newport H ❀

(541) 265-7701. **Call for rates.** 536 SW Elizabeth St 97365. Jct US 20, 0.5 mi s on US 101, just w on SW Falls St. Ext/int corridors. **Pets:** Dogs only. $75 deposit/room, $15 daily fee/room. Designated rooms, service with restrictions, crate.

◆◆◆ ◆◆ The Whaler Motel M

(541) 265-9261. **$124-$214.** 155 SW Elizabeth St 97365. Jct US 20, just s on US 101, 0.4 mi w on SW 2nd St. Ext corridors. **Pets:** Dogs only. $10 daily fee/pet. Designated rooms, supervision.

NORTH BEND

◆◆◆ ◆◆◆◆ The Mill Casino & Hotel H

(541) 756-8800. **$113-$185.** 3201 Tremont Ave (US 101) 97459. 0.7 mi n of Coos Bay on US 101; on bayfront. Int corridors. **Pets:** Accepted.

◆◆ ◆◆ Quality Inn & Suites at Coos Bay H

(541) 756-3191. **$79-$200.** 1503 Virginia Ave 97459. 0.5 mi w of US 101. Ext/int corridors. **Pets:** Accepted.

OAKRIDGE

◆◆◆ ◆◆ Best Western Oakridge Inn H

(541) 782-2212. **$100-$115.** 47433 SR 58 97463. West end of town. Ext corridors. **Pets:** Small. $15 daily fee/pet. Designated rooms, service with restrictions, supervision.

◆◆◆ ◆◆ Cascade Motel M ❀

(541) 782-2489. **$55-$82.** 47487 SR 58 97463. West end of town. Ext corridors. **Pets:** Small, dogs only. $10 one-time fee/room. Service with restrictions, supervision.

ONTARIO

◆◆◆ ◆◆◆◆ Holiday Inn Express & Suites H

(541) 889-7100. **Call for rates.** 212 SE 10th St 97914. I-84 exit 376A, just se. Int corridors. **Pets:** Accepted.

◆◆ ◆◆ Sleep Inn H

(541) 881-0007. **$79-$120.** 1221 SE 1st Ave 97914. I-84 exit 376B, just ne. Int corridors. **Pets:** Accepted.

OREGON CITY

◆◆◆ ◆◆ Best Western Plus Rivershore Hotel H ❀

(503) 655-7141. **$140-$180.** 1900 Clackamette Dr 97045. I-205 exit 9, just n. Int corridors. **Pets:** Dogs only. $10 daily fee/pet. Designated rooms, service with restrictions, supervision.

PACIFIC CITY

◆◆◆◆ Inn at Cape Kiwanda H ❀

(503) 965-7001. **Call for rates.** 33105 Cape Kiwanda Dr 97135. Just w on Pacific Ave, 1 mi n. Ext corridors. **Pets:** Dogs only. $20 daily fee/pet. Designated rooms, service with restrictions, supervision.

◆◆◆ ◆◆ Pacific City Inn M

(503) 965-6464. **Call for rates.** 35280 Brooten Rd 97135. Center. Ext corridors. **Pets:** Accepted.

PENDLETON

◆◆◆ ◆◆◆ Best Western Pendleton Inn H

(541) 276-2135. **$104-$165.** 400 SE Nye Ave 97801. I-84 exit 210 (SR 11), just se. Int corridors. **Pets:** Other species. $20 one-time fee/pet. Designated rooms, service with restrictions, supervision.

▼▼▼ Holiday Inn Express H
(541) 966-6520. **Call for rates.** 600 SE Nye Ave 97801. I-84 exit 210 (SR 11), just se. Int corridors. **Pets:** Accepted.
⬛ ⬛ ⬛ ⬛ ⬛ ⬛ ⬛

⟨AAA⟩ ▼▼▼ Oxford Suites Pendleton H
(541) 276-6000. **Call for rates.** 2400 SW Court Pl 97801. I-84 exit 209, just n on SW Emigrant Ave, just nw on SW 20th St, then just sw to SW Court Pl. Int corridors. **Pets:** Accepted.
⬛ ⬛ ⬛ ⬛ ⬛ ⬛ ⬛

⟨AAA⟩ ♦ Travelodge M ☙
(541) 276-7531. **$59-$139.** 411 SW Dorion Ave 97801. I-84 exit 209, 0.9 mi ne on SW Frazer Ave, then just nw on SW 4th St. Ext corridors. **Pets:** Medium, dogs only. $12 daily fee/pet. Designated rooms, service with restrictions. ⬛ ⬛ ⬛ ⬛ ⬛ ⬛

PORTLAND *(Restaurants p. 621)*

⟨AAA⟩ ▼▼▼ Aloft Portland Airport at Cascade Station H ☙
(503) 200-5678. **$100-$300.** 9920 NE Cascades Pkwy 97220. I-205 exit 24A northbound; exit 24 southbound, 0.5 mi w on Airport Way, 0.5 mi s on NE Mt Hood Ave, then just e. Int corridors. **Pets:** Small. Designated rooms, service with restrictions, supervision.
⬛ ⬛ ⬛ ⬛ ⬛ ⬛ ⬛ ⬛ ⬛ ⬛

⟨AAA⟩ ▼▼▼ The Benson Hotel, a Coast Hotel H ☙
(503) 228-2000. **$189-$529, 3 day notice.** 309 SW Broadway 97205. At SW Broadway and Oak St. Int corridors. **Pets:** Other species. $25 one-time fee/room. Designated rooms, no service, supervision.
⬛ ⬛ ⬛ ⬛ ⬛ ⬛

⟨AAA⟩ ▼▼ Best Western Inn at the Meadows H
(503) 286-9600. **$110-$318.** 1215 N Hayden Meadows Dr 97217. I-5 exit 306B, just e. Int corridors. **Pets:** Accepted.
⬛ ⬛ ⬛ ⬛ ⬛

⟨AAA⟩ ▼▼▼ Best Western Pony Soldier Inn-Airport H
(503) 256-1504. **$105-$113.** 9901 NE Sandy Blvd 97220. I-205 exit 23A, just e. Int corridors. **Pets:** Accepted.
⬛ ⬛ ⬛ ⬛ ⬛ ⬛ ⬛

⟨AAA⟩ ▼▼▼ Candlewood Suites-Portland Airport H
(503) 255-4003. **$89-$199.** 11250 NE Holman St 97220. I-205 exit 24B northbound; exit 24 southbound, 0.4 mi e on Airport Way, then just sw. Int corridors. **Pets:** Accepted. ⬛ ⬛ ⬛ ⬛ ⬛ ⬛ ⬛

▼▼▼ Courtyard by Marriott Portland City Center H
(503) 505-5000. **$129-$271.** 550 SW Oak St 97204. At SW Oak St and SW 6th Ave. Int corridors. **Pets:** Large, dogs only. $50 one-time fee/room. Designated rooms, service with restrictions, crate.
⬛ ⬛ ⬛ ⬛ ⬛ ⬛

⟨AAA⟩ ▼▼▼ DoubleTree by Hilton Portland H
(503) 281-6111. **Call for rates.** 1000 NE Multnomah St 97232. I-5 exit 302A, just e, just s on 9th Ave, then just e; I-84 exit Lloyd Center westbound. Int corridors. **Pets:** Accepted.
⬛ ⬛ ⬛ ⬛ ⬛ ⬛ ⬛ ⬛ ⬛ ⬛

⟨AAA⟩ ▼▼▼▼ The Heathman Hotel H
(503) 241-4100. **$259-$409, 3 day notice.** 1001 SW Broadway 97205. At SW Broadway and Salmon St. Int corridors. **Pets:** Accepted.
⬛ ⬛ ⬛ ⬛ ⬛ ⬛

⟨AAA⟩ ▼▼▼ Hilton Portland & Executive Tower H ☙
(503) 226-1611. **$179-$399.** 921 SW 6th Ave 97204. I-405 exit 1B (6th Ave); at 6th Ave and Taylor St. Int corridors. **Pets:** Large, other species. $60 one-time fee/room. Designated rooms, service with restrictions, crate. ⬛ ⬛ ⬛ ⬛ ⬛ ⬛ ⬛ ⬛

⟨AAA⟩ ▼▼▼ Holiday Inn Express Hotel & Suites at Jantzen Beach H
(503) 283-8000. **$104-$325.** 2300 N Hayden Island Dr 97217. I-5 exit 308, 0.6 mi w. Int corridors. **Pets:** Accepted.
⬛ ⬛ ⬛ ⬛ ⬛ ⬛ ⬛ ⬛

▼▼▼ Holiday Inn Portland Airport Hotel & Convention Center H
(503) 256-5000. **Call for rates.** 8439 NE Columbia Blvd 97220. I-205 exit 23B, 0.5 mi w. Int corridors. **Pets:** Accepted.
⬛ ⬛ ⬛ ⬛ ⬛ ⬛ ⬛

⟨AAA⟩ ▼▼▼ Hospitality Inn H
(503) 244-6684. **$85-$135.** 10155 SW Capitol Hwy 97219. I-5 exit 295 southbound, just e; exit 294 northbound, 1 mi n on SW Barbur Blvd, then just e. Int corridors. **Pets:** Medium, dogs only. $10 daily fee/pet. Designated rooms, service with restrictions, supervision.
⬛ ⬛ ⬛ ⬛ ⬛

⟨AAA⟩ ▼▼▼ Hotel deLuxe H
(503) 219-2094. **Call for rates.** 729 SW 15th Ave 97205. I-5 to I-405 exit Salmon St northbound, just n on 14th Ave, w on Morrison St, then s; exit Couch St/Burnside St southbound; at SW 15th Ave and Yamhill St. Int corridors. **Pets:** Accepted. ⬛ ⬛ ⬛ ⬛ ⬛ ⬛

⟨AAA⟩ ▼▼▼ Hotel Lucia H ☙
(503) 225-1717. **$199-$459.** 400 SW Broadway 97205. At SW Broadway and Stark St. Int corridors. **Pets:** Other species. $45 one-time fee/room. Service with restrictions, supervision. ⬛ ⬛ ⬛ ⬛ ⬛

⟨AAA⟩ ▼▼▼ Hotel Modera H
(503) 484-1084. **Call for rates.** 515 SW Clay St 97201. Between 5th and 6th sts. Int corridors. **Pets:** Accepted.
⬛ ⬛ ⬛ ⬛ ⬛ ⬛ ⬛

⟨AAA⟩ ▼▼▼ Hyatt House Portland/Downtown H
(503) 241-2775. **Call for rates.** 2080 SW River Dr 97201. At SW River Dr and SW River Pkwy. Int corridors. **Pets:** Medium, dogs only. $75 one-time fee/room. Service with restrictions, crate.
⬛ ⬛ ⬛ ⬛ ⬛ ⬛

⟨AAA⟩ ▼▼▼ Hyatt Place Portland Airport/Cascade Station H
(503) 288-2808. **$109-$279.** 9750 NE Cascades Pkwy 97220. I-205 exit 24A northbound; exit 24 southbound, 0.5 mi w on Airport Way, 0.5 mi s on NE Mt Hood Ave, then just e. Int corridors. **Pets:** Accepted.
⬛ ⬛ ⬛ ⬛ ⬛ ⬛

⟨AAA⟩ ▼▼▼ Kimpton Hotel Monaco Portland H ☙
(503) 222-0001. **Call for rates.** 506 SW Washington St 97204. At SW 5th Ave and SW Washington St. Int corridors. **Pets:** Other species. Designated rooms, service with restrictions, crate.
⬛ ⬛ ⬛ ⬛ ⬛ ⬛ ⬛ ⬛

⟨AAA⟩ ▼▼▼ ▼▼▼ Kimpton Hotel Vintage Portland H
(503) 228-1212. **Call for rates.** 422 SW Broadway 97205. At Broadway and Washington St. Int corridors. **Pets:** Accepted.
⬛ ⬛ ⬛ ⬛ ⬛ ⬛

⟨AAA⟩ ▼▼▼ Kimpton RiverPlace Hotel H ☙
(503) 228-3233. **$189-$950.** 1510 SW Harbor Way 97201. At Naito Pkwy and SW Harbor Way. Int corridors. **Pets:** Other species. Service with restrictions, crate. ⬛ ⬛ ⬛ ⬛ ⬛ ⬛ ⬛

▼▼ ▼▼ La Quinta Inn & Suites Portland Airport H
(503) 382-3820. **$97-$251.** 11207 NE Holman St 97220. I-205 exit 24B northbound; exit 24 southbound, 0.4 mi e on Airport Way, then just sw. Int corridors. **Pets:** Accepted. ⬛ ⬛ ⬛ ⬛ ⬛ ⬛

▼▼ ▼▼ La Quinta Inn & Suites Portland NW H
(503) 497-9044. **$86-$273.** 4319 NW Yeon Ave 97210. I-5 to I-405 exit 3 (US 30), 2.5 mi w. Int corridors. **Pets:** Accepted.
⬛ ⬛ ⬛ ⬛ ⬛ ⬛

@@@ ▼▼▼▼ **The Mark Spencer Hotel** 🅗 ❀
(503) 224-3293. **$169-$369.** 409 SW 11th Ave 97205. At SW Stark St and SW 11th Ave. Int corridors. **Pets:** Other species. $25 daily fee/pet. Designated rooms, service with restrictions, crate.
[SAVE] [ECO] [❄] [🌐] [✕] [❚] [▦]

@@@ ▼▼▼▼ **The Nines, A Luxury Collection Hotel** 🅗
(503) 222-9996. **Call for rates.** 525 SW Morrison St 97204. At SW Morrison St and SW 5th Ave. Int corridors. **Pets:** Accepted.
[SAVE] [ECO] [❄] [♿] [🌐] [✕]

@@@ ▼▼▼▼ **Oxford Suites Portland-Jantzen Beach** 🅗
(503) 283-3030. **Call for rates.** 12226 N Jantzen Dr 97217. I-5 exit 308, just e on Hayden Island Dr. Int corridors. **Pets:** Accepted.
[SAVE] [❄] [♿] [▨] [🌐] [✕] [❚] [▦]

@@@ ▼▼▼ **Park Lane Suites and Inn** 🅜
(503) 226-6288. **Call for rates.** 809 SW King Ave 97205. I-405 exit Couch St/Burnside St southbound, 0.5 mi w on Burnside St, then just s; exit Everett St northbound, 0.3 mi w on Glisan St, just s on NW 21st Ave, just w on Burnside St, then just s. Ext corridors. **Pets:** Accepted.
[SAVE] [❄] [♿] [🌐] [✕] [❚] [▦]

▼▼▼ **The Portlander Inn** 🅗
(503) 345-0300. **$77-$162.** 10350 N Vancouver Way 97217. I-5 exit 307, follow signs for Marine Dr E, just ne, then 0.7 mi se. Int corridors. **Pets:** Medium, dogs only. $20 daily fee/room. Designated rooms, service with restrictions, supervision. [❄] [▨] [🌐] [✕] [❚] [▦]

@@@ ▼▼▼ **Ramada Portland South I-205** 🅗
(503) 252-7400. **$71-$161.** 9707 SE Stark St 97216. I-205 exit 21A southbound; exit 20 northbound, just e on Washington St, just n on SE 99th Ave, then just w. Int corridors. **Pets:** Accepted.
[SAVE] [❄] [♿] [🌐] [✕] [❚] [▦]

▼▼▼▼ **Red Lion Hotel on the River Jantzen Beach-Portland** 🅗
(503) 283-4466. **$99-$299.** 909 N Hayden Island Dr 97217. I-5 exit 308, just ne. Int corridors. **Pets:** Accepted.
[ECO] [❄] [▨] [♿] [🌐] [✕] [❚] [▦]

▼▼▼ **Red Lion Hotel Portland Airport** 🅗
(503) 255-6722. **Call for rates.** 7101 NE 82nd Ave 97220. I-205 exit 24A northbound; exit 24 southbound, 1.3 mi w on NE Airport Way, then 0.5 mi s. Int corridors. **Pets:** Accepted. [❄] [▨] [🌐] [✕] [❚] [▦]

▼▼▼ **Residence Inn by Marriott Portland Airport at Cascade Station** 🅗
(503) 284-1800. **$132-$231.** 9301 NE Cascades Pkwy 97220. I-205 exit 24A northbound; exit 24 southbound, 0.5 mi w on Airport Way, 0.5 mi s on NE Mt Hood Ave, then just w. Int corridors. **Pets:** Accepted.
[❄] [♿] [▨] [🌐] [✕] [❚] [▦]

▼▼▼ **Residence Inn by Marriott Portland Downtown at RiverPlace** 🅗
(503) 552-9500. **$153-$323.** 2115 SW River Pkwy 97201. At SW Moody Ave and SW River Pkwy; on Willamette River Waterfront. Int corridors.
Pets: Accepted. [❄] [♿] [▨] [🌐] [✕] [❚] [▦]

▼▼▼ **Residence Inn by Marriott Portland Downtown/Lloyd Center** 🅗
(503) 288-1400. **$134-$265.** 1710 NE Multnomah St 97232. I-5 exit 302A, 0.8 mi e on Weidler St, then just s on 15th Ave; I-84 exit 1 (Lloyd Center) westbound, just n on 13th St, then just e. Ext corridors.
Pets: Accepted. [❄] [▨] [🌐] [✕] [❚] [▦]

▼▼▼ **Residence Inn by Marriott Portland Downtown/Pearl District** 🅗
(503) 220-1339. **$174-$330.** 1150 NW 9th Ave 97209. Between NW Marshall and NW Northrup sts. Int corridors. **Pets:** Accepted.
[❄] [♿] [🌐] [✕] [❚] [▦]

▼▼▼▼ **Residence Inn by Marriott-Portland North Harbour** 🅗
(503) 285-9888. **$117-$244.** 1250 N Anchor Way 97217. I-5 exit 307, follow signs to Marine Dr E, then just n. Int corridors. **Pets:** Accepted.
[♿] [▨] [🌐] [✕] [❚] [▦]

@@@ ▼▼▼▼ **River's Edge Hotel & Spa** 🅗
(503) 802-5800. **$159-$499.** 0455 SW Hamilton Ct 97239. I-5 exit 298 northbound, just s on SW Corbett Ave, e on SW Richardson Ct, 0.3 mi n on Macadam Ave (SR 43), then just e; exit 299A southbound, follow signs for Johns Landing/Lake Oswego, 0.8 mi s, then just e. Int corridors. **Pets:** Accepted. [SAVE] [ECO] [❄] [♿] [▨] [🌐] [✕] [❚] [▦]

@@@ ▼▼▼ ▼▼▼ **Sentinel** 🅗 ❀
(503) 224-3400. **$229-$499.** 614 SW 11th Ave 97205. At SW 11th Ave and Alder St. Int corridors. **Pets:** Other species. $45 one-time fee/pet. Supervision. [SAVE] [❄] [♿] [🌐] [✕] [❚] [▦]

@@@ ▼▼▼▼ **Sheraton Portland Airport Hotel** 🅗 ❀
(503) 281-2500. **$169-$319.** 8235 NE Airport Way 97220. I-205 exit 24A northbound; exit 24 southbound, 1.5 mi w. Int corridors. **Pets:** Medium, other species. Designated rooms, no service, supervision.
[SAVE] [❄] [♿] [▨] [🌐] [✕] [❚] [▦]

▼▼▼▼ **Staybridge Suites Portland-Airport** 🅗
(503) 262-8888. **Call for rates.** 11936 NE Glenn Widing Dr 97220. I-205 exit 24B northbound; exit 24 southbound, 0.7 mi e, then just nw. Int corridors. **Pets:** Accepted. [❄] [♿] [▨] [🌐] [✕] [❚] [▦]

▼▼ **University Place Hotel & Conference Center** 🅗
(503) 221-0140. **Call for rates.** 310 SW Lincoln St 97201. I-5 to I-405 exit 4th Ave, just n, then just e. Ext/int corridors. **Pets:** Accepted.
[❄] [▨] [🌐] [✕] [❚] [▦]

@@@ ▼▼▼ ▼▼▼ **The Westin Portland** 🅗 ❀
(503) 294-9000. **$179-$799.** 750 SW Alder St 97205. At Park Ave and SW Alder St. Int corridors. **Pets:** Medium, dogs only. Designated rooms, service with restrictions, supervision.
[SAVE] [◀] [❄] [♿] [📵] [✕] [❚] [▦]

PRINEVILLE *(Restaurants p. 621)*

▼▼ **Stafford Inn** 🅗
(541) 447-7100. **Call for rates.** 1773 NE 3rd St 97754. 1 mi e on US 26. Int corridors. **Pets:** Accepted. [▨] [🌐] [❚] [▦]

PROSPECT

▼▼ **Prospect Historic Hotel, Motel & Dinner House** 🅜 ❀
(541) 560-3664. **$80-$225.** 391 Mill Creek Dr 97536. Jct SR 62, 0.7 mi e of MM 43, 0.3 mi s on 1st St, then just w. Ext/int corridors. **Pets:** Other species. $20 one-time fee/pet. Designated rooms, service with restrictions, supervision. [❄] [🌐] [✕] [❚] [▦]

REDMOND

▼▼▼ **Comfort Suites Redmond Airport** 🅗
(541) 504-8900. **$124-$369.** 2243 SW Yew Ave 97756. US 97 exit 124 (Yew Ave/Airport Way/Redmond Airport), just nw; 2 mi s of jct SR 126. Int corridors. **Pets:** $28 one-time fee/room. Service with restrictions, supervision. [❄] [♿] [▨] [🌐] [✕] [❚] [▦]

@@@ ▼▼▼▼ **The Lodge At Eagle Crest, A Holiday Inn Resort** 🅗
(541) 923-2453. **$139-$239, 3 day notice.** 1522 Cline Falls Rd 97756. 4.5 mi w of center on SR 126, 1 mi s. Int corridors. **Pets:** Accepted.
[SAVE] [◀] [❄] [♿] [▨] [🌐] [✕] [❚] [▦]

@@@ ▼▼▼▼ **Sleep Inn & Suites** 🅗
(541) 504-1500. **$124-$249.** 1847 N Hwy 97 97756. US 97 exit 119, 0.6 mi s on Business Rt US 97; 1 mi n of downtown. Int corridors. **Pets:** Medium, other species. $25 one-time fee/pet. Service with restrictions, supervision. [SAVE] [❄] [♿] [▨] [🌐] [✕] [❚] [▦]

REEDSPORT *(Restaurants p. 621)*

AAA **WWW** **Best Western Salbasgeon Inn & Suites of Reedsport** **H**

(541) 271-4831. **$99-$138.** 1400 US 101 S 97467. Jct SR 38, 0.4 mi s. Ext corridors. **Pets:** Medium, dogs only. $25 daily fee/pet. Designated rooms, service with restrictions, supervision.

[SAVE] [icons]

ROCKAWAY BEACH

W **Silver Sands Oceanfront Motel** **H**

(503) 355-2206. **Call for rates.** 215 S Pacific St 97136. US 101, just w on SW 2nd Ave. Ext corridors. **Pets:** Accepted.

[icons]

ROSEBURG *(Restaurants p. 621)*

AAA **WWW** **Best Western Garden Villa Inn** **M**

(541) 672-1601. **$120-$150.** 760 NW Garden Valley Blvd 97470. I-5 exit 125, just nw. Ext corridors. **Pets:** Accepted.

[SAVE] [icons]

WWW **Holiday Inn Express** **H**

(541) 673-7517. **$91-$220.** 375 W Harvard Blvd 97470. I-5 exit 124, just se. Ext/int corridors. **Pets:** $15 daily fee/pet. Designated rooms, supervision. [icons]

W **Motel 6-#4108** **H**

(541) 464-8000. **$61-$121.** 3100 NW Aviation Dr 97470. I-5 exit 127, just se. Int corridors. **Pets:** Accepted. [icons]

AAA **W** **Quality Inn** **M**

(541) 673-5561. **$85-$220.** 427 NW Garden Valley Blvd 97470. I-5 exit 125, just se. Ext corridors. **Pets:** Accepted.

[SAVE] [icons]

AAA **W** **Shady Oaks Motel** **M**

(541) 672-2608. **$45-$79.** 2954 Old Hwy 99 S 97471. I-5 exit 120, 0.5 mi n. Ext corridors. **Pets:** Dogs only. $10 daily fee/pet. Designated rooms, service with restrictions, supervision. [SAVE] [icons]

WWW **Sleep Inn & Suites** **H**

(541) 464-8338. **$100-$180.** 2855 NW Edenbower Blvd 97471. I-5 exit 127, just sw. Int corridors. **Pets:** Accepted.

[icons]

W W **Super 8** **H**

(541) 672-8880. **$69-$100.** 3200 NW Aviation Dr 97470. I-5 exit 127, just ne. Int corridors. **Pets:** $10 daily fee/pet. Designated rooms, service with restrictions, supervision. [icons]

AAA **WWW** **Travelodge Roseburg** **M**

(541) 672-4836. **$80-$95.** 315 W Harvard Ave 97470. I-5 exit 124, just se. Ext corridors. **Pets:** $10 daily fee/pet. Designated rooms, supervision. [SAVE] [icons]

WWW **Windmill Inn of Roseburg** **H**

(541) 673-0901. **Call for rates.** 1450 NW Mulholland Dr 97470. I-5 exit 125, just e, then just n. Int corridors. **Pets:** Dogs only. $15 one-time fee/room. Designated rooms, service with restrictions, supervision.

[icons]

ST. HELENS

AAA **WWW** **Best Western Oak Meadows Inn** **H**

(503) 397-3000. **Call for rates.** 585 S Columbia River Hwy (US 30) 97051. South end of town. Int corridors. **Pets:** Accepted.

[SAVE] [icons]

SALEM *(Restaurants p. 621)*

AAA **WWW** **Best Western Pacific Highway Inn** **H**

(503) 390-3200. **$95-$135.** 4646 Portland Rd NE 97305. I-5 exit 258, 0.3 mi e. Ext corridors. **Pets:** Accepted. [SAVE] [icons]

AAA **WWW** **Best Western Plus Mill Creek Inn** **H** ❁

(503) 585-3332. **$159-$229.** 3125 Ryan Dr SE 97301. I-5 exit 253, just w on Mission St (SR 22), just n on Hawthorne Ave SE, then just w. Int corridors. **Pets:** Dogs only. $20 daily fee/room. Service with restrictions, supervision. [SAVE] [icons]

WWW **Comfort Suites Airport** **H**

(503) 585-9705. **$105-$321.** 630 Hawthorne Ave SE 97301. I-5 exit 253, just w on Mission St (SR 22), 0.3 mi n on Hawthorne Ave SE, then just e; in Creekside Corporate Center (private drive). Int corridors. **Pets:** Accepted. [icons]

AAA **WWW** **DoubleTree by Hilton Salem-Oregon** **H**

(503) 581-7004. **$129-$229.** 1590 Weston Ct NE 97301. I-5 exit 256, just w on Market St, then just s. Int corridors. **Pets:** Accepted.

[SAVE] [icons]

AAA **WWW** **La Quinta Inn & Suites Salem** **H**

(503) 391-7000. **$86-$361.** 890 Hawthorne Ave SE 97301. I-5 exit 253, just w on Mission St (SR 22), then just n. Int corridors. **Pets:** Accepted.

[SAVE] [icons]

WWW **Phoenix Inn Suites-South Salem** **H**

(503) 588-9220. **Call for rates.** 4370 Commercial St SE 97302. I-5 exit 252, 1.5 mi w on Kuebler Blvd, then 0.7 mi n. Int corridors. **Pets:** Accepted. [icons]

WWWW **Residence Inn by Marriott** **H**

(503) 585-6500. **$125-$204.** 640 Hawthorne Ave SE 97301. I-5 exit 253, just w on Mission St (SR 22), 0.3 mi n on Hawthorne Ave SE, then just e; on Creekside Corporate Center (private drive). Int corridors. **Pets:** Accepted. [icons]

WWW **Super 8 Salem** **H**

(503) 370-8888. **$55-$130.** 1288 Hawthorne Ave NE 97301. I-5 exit 256, just w on Market St, then just s. Int corridors. **Pets:** Accepted.

[icons]

SANDY

AAA **WWW** **Best Western Sandy Inn** **H** ❁

(503) 668-7100. **$115-$180.** 37465 US 26 97055. West side of town. Int corridors. **Pets:** Large, dogs only. $20 daily fee/pet. Service with restrictions, supervision. [SAVE] [icons]

SEASIDE

AAA **WWWW** **Best Western Ocean View Resort** **H**

(503) 738-3334. **$139-$349.** 414 N Prom 97138. US 101 exit 1st Ave, just w, just n on Necanicum Dr, then just w on 4th Ave. Ext/int corridors. **Pets:** Accepted. [SAVE] [icons]

AAA **W** **Coast River Inn** **M**

(503) 738-8474. **$59-$219, 3 day notice.** 800 S Holladay Dr 97138. US 101, just nw. Ext corridors. **Pets:** Other species. $10 daily fee/pet. Service with restrictions. [SAVE] [icons]

AAA **WWW** **Comfort Inn & Suites by Seaside Convention Center/Boardwalk** **H**

(503) 738-3011. **$90-$430.** 545 Broadway St 97138. US 101, just w on Ave A; downtown. Int corridors. **Pets:** Medium, dogs only. $25 one-time fee/pet. Designated rooms, service with restrictions, supervision.

[SAVE] [icons]

WWW **Ebb-Tide Oceanfront Inn** **H** 🐾

(503) 738-8371. **$79-$289.** 300 N Prom 97138. US 101 exit 1st Ave, 0.4 mi w, just n on Columbia St, then just w on 2nd Ave. Ext/int corridors. **Pets:** Dogs only. $15 daily fee/pet. Designated rooms, service with restrictions, crate. [icons]

WWW **Hillcrest Inn** **M**

(503) 738-6273. **Call for rates.** 118 N Columbia St 97138. US 101 exit Broadway St, 0.4 mi w, then just n. Ext corridors. **Pets:** Accepted.

[icons]

◆◆ **Hi-Tide Oceanfront Inn** M
(503) 738-8414. **$79-$259.** 30 Ave G 97138. US 101 exit Ave G, 0.6 mi
w. Ext corridors. **Pets:** Accepted.

◆◆◆ ◆◆ **Holiday Inn Express Hotel & Suites-Seaside**
Convention Center H
(503) 717-8000. **$89-$499.** 34 N Holladay Dr 97138. US 101 exit
Broadway St, just w, then just n. Int corridors. **Pets:** Medium, dogs only.
$25 daily fee/pet. Designated rooms, service with restrictions, supervi-
sion.

◆◆◆ ◆◆ **Inn at Seaside** H ✿
(503) 738-9581. **Call for rates.** 441 2nd Ave 97138. US 101 exit 1st
Ave, just w. Ext/int corridors. **Pets:** Other species. $15 daily fee/pet.
Service with restrictions.

◆◆◆ **Inn At The Shore** M
(503) 738-3113. **Call for rates.** 2275 S Prom 97138. US 101 exit Ave
U, just w. Ext corridors. **Pets:** Accepted.

◆◆ **River Inn at Seaside** H ✿
(503) 717-5744. **Call for rates.** 531 Ave A 97138. US 101, just w;
downtown. Int corridors. **Pets:** Other species. $20 daily fee/pet. Service
with restrictions.

◆◆◆ ◆◆ **Rivertide Suites Hotel** H ✿
(503) 717-1100. **$79-$449, 3 day notice.** 102 N Holladay Dr 97138. US
101, just w on Broadway St, just n. Int corridors. **Pets:** Large, dogs
only. $25 daily fee/pet. Designated rooms, service with restrictions,
supervision.

◆◆◆ ◆◆ **Seashore Inn...on the Beach** H
(503) 738-6368. **Call for rates.** 60 N Prom 97138. US 101 exit 1st Ave,
0.4 mi w. Ext/int corridors. **Pets:** Accepted.

◆◆ **The Seaside Oceanfront Inn** H
(503) 738-6403. **$99-$399, 5 day notice.** 580 Beach Dr 97138. US 101
exit Ave G, 0.6 mi w, then just n. Int corridors. **Pets:** Dogs only. $25
one-time fee/room. Designated rooms, supervision.

SISTERS *(Restaurants p. 621)*

◆◆◆ ◆◆ **Best Western Ponderosa Lodge** M ✿
(541) 549-1234. **$150-$280.** 500 US 20 W 97759. Jct SR 242, 1.3 mi w
on US 20; at Barclay Dr. Ext corridors. **Pets:** Large, dogs only. $15
daily fee/room. Designated rooms, supervision.

◆◆◆ ◆◆◆ **FivePine Lodge & Spa** CA ✿
(541) 549-5900. **$159-$419, 7 day notice.** 1021 Desperado Tr 97759.
Jct US 20 and SR 126, just e on US 20; east end of town. Ext/int corridors. **Pets:** $25 daily fee/room. Designated rooms, service with restric-
tions, crate.

SPRINGFIELD

◆◆◆ ◆◆ **Best Western Grand Manor Inn** H
(541) 726-4769. **$116-$224.** 971 Kruse Way 97477. I-5 exit 195A, just
se. Int corridors. **Pets:** Accepted.

◆◆◆◆ **Comfort Suites Springfield** H ✿
(541) 746-5359. **$109-$269.** 969 Kruse Way 97477. I-5 exit 195, just
se. Int corridors. **Pets:** Dogs only. $25 one-time fee/room. Designated
rooms, service with restrictions, supervision.

◆◆◆◆ **Holiday Inn Eugene-Springfield** H ✿
(541) 284-0707. **Call for rates.** 919 Kruse Way 97477. I-5 exit 195A,
just se. Int corridors. **Pets:** Dogs only. $20 one-time fee/room. Desig-
nated rooms, service with restrictions, supervision.

◆◆◆◆ **Holiday Inn Express Hotel & Suites** H
(541) 746-8471. **Call for rates.** 3480 Hutton St 97477. I-5 exit 195A,
just se. Int corridors. **Pets:** Accepted.

◆◆ **Motel 6-#418** M
(541) 741-1105. **$61-$115.** 3752 International Ct 97477. I-5 exit 195A,
just e on Beltline Rd, just nw on Gateway St, then just n. Ext corridors.
Pets: Accepted.

◆◆ **Quality Inn & Suites** H
(541) 726-9266. **$79-$329.** 3550 Gateway St 97477. I-5 exit 195A, just
e on Beltline Rd, then just nw. Int corridors. **Pets:** Accepted.

◆◆ **Village Inn** M
(541) 747-4546. **Call for rates.** 1875 Mohawk Blvd 97477. I-5 exit
194A, 2.5 mi e on SR 126 exit Mohawk Blvd, then just n. Ext corridors.
Pets: $25 one-time fee/room. Service with restrictions, supervision.

SUNRIVER

◆◆◆ ◆◆◆ **Sunriver Resort** H ✿
(541) 593-1000. **Call for rates.** 17600 Center Dr 97707. US 97 exit 153
(S Century Dr), 1.5 mi w to Abbott Dr, then 0.6 mi w. Ext corridors.
Pets: Other species. $75 one-time fee/room. Designated rooms, service
with restrictions, crate.

SUTHERLIN

◆◆◆ ◆◆◆ **Best Western Plus Hartford**
Lodge H ✿
(541) 459-1424. **$109-$139.** 150 Myrtle St 97479. I-5 exit 136, just ne.
Ext corridors. **Pets:** Large. $20 daily fee/pet. Designated rooms, service
with restrictions, crate.

◆◆◆◆ **GuestHouse Inn & Suites Sutherlin** H
(541) 459-6800. **Call for rates.** 1400 Hospitality Way 97479. I-5 exit
136, just se. Int corridors. **Pets:** Accepted.

SWEET HOME

◆◆◆ ◆◆ **Sweet Home Inn** M
(541) 367-5137. **$89-$175.** 805 Long St 97386. Just se of jct US 20
and SR 228, just s on 10th Ave, just w; jct Terrace Ln. Ext corridors.
Pets: Medium, dogs only. $15 daily fee/pet. Designated rooms, service
with restrictions, supervision.

THE DALLES

◆◆◆ **Celilo Inn Columbia Gorge** M
(541) 769-0001. **Call for rates.** 3550 E 2nd St 97058. I-84 exit 87
(Dufur/Bend), just s on US 197, just w on US 30, then 0.8 mi e on
Frontage Rd/E 2nd St. Ext corridors. **Pets:** Accepted.

◆◆ **Comfort Inn Columbia Gorge** H
(541) 298-2800. **$105-$350.** 351 Lone Pine Dr 97058. I-84 exit 87, just
nw. Int corridors. **Pets:** Accepted.

◆◆ **Cousins' Country Inn** M
(541) 298-5161. **Call for rates.** 2114 W 6th St 97058. I-84 exit 83 eastbound, just nw; exit 84 westbound, just nw on W 2nd St, just sw on
Webber St, then just n. Ext corridors. **Pets:** Accepted.

◆◆ **The Dalles Inn** H ✿
(541) 296-9107. **$79-$199.** 112 W 2nd St 97058. I-84 exit 84 eastbound, 0.6 mi se; exit 85 westbound, 0.8 mi nw; at Liberty and W 2nd
sts; downtown. Ext/int corridors. **Pets:** Dogs only. $12 daily fee/pet.
Designated rooms, service with restrictions, crate.

▼▼▼ Fairfield Inn & Suites by Marriott The Dalles [H] ❀

(541) 769-0753. **$113-$145.** 2014 W 7th St 97058. I-84 exit 83 eastbound, just nw on W 6th St, then just sw on Walnut St; exit 84 westbound, 0.3 mi nw on W 2nd St, just sw on Webber St, 0.3 mi nw on W 6th St, then just sw on Walnut St. Int corridors. **Pets:** Other species. $75 daily fee/pet. Designated rooms, service with restrictions, crate.

[&M] [📶] [✕] [🛢] [💻]

TIGARD

△△△▽ ▼▼▼ DoubleTree by Hilton Portland - Tigard [H]

(503) 624-9000. **$99-$229.** 9575 SW Locust St 97223. SR 217 exit 5 (Greenburg Rd), just ne, then just e. Int corridors. **Pets:** Accepted.

[SAVE] [🍴] [&M] [🏊] [📶] [✕] [🛢] [💻]

TROUTDALE

▼▼▼ Comfort Inn Columbia Gorge-Gateway [H]

(503) 492-2900. **Call for rates.** 1000 NW Graham Rd 97060. I-84 exit 17 eastbound, e on Frontage Rd, then just n; exit westbound, just n. Int corridors. **Pets:** Accepted. [🍴] [📶] [✕] [🛢] [💻]

▼ Motel 6-Portland Troutdale-#407 [M]

(503) 665-2254. **$61-$81.** 1610 NW Frontage Rd 97060. I-84 exit 17 eastbound, just sw; exit westbound, just w on Frontage Rd, then just sw. Ext corridors. **Pets:** Accepted. [🍴] [&M] [🏊] [📶] [🛢]

TUALATIN

△△△▽ ▼▼▼ Comfort Inn & Suites [H] ❀

(503) 612-9952. **$110-$250.** 7640 SW Warm Springs St 97062. I-5 exit 289, just w on Nyberg St, just s on Martinazzi Ave, then just e; just behind Fred Meyer. Int corridors. **Pets:** Medium, dogs only. $25 daily fee/pet. Designated rooms, service with restrictions, supervision.

[SAVE] [🍴] [&M] [🏊] [📶] [✕] [🛢] [💻]

WELCHES

△△△▽ ▼▼▼ Best Western Premier Collection Resort at The Mountain [H] ❀

(503) 622-3101. **$99-$599.** 68010 E Fairway Ave 97067. 0.6 mi s of US 26 on E Welches Rd. Ext corridors. **Pets:** Medium. $10 one-time fee/room. Designated rooms, service with restrictions, crate.

[SAVE] [🍴] [🏊] [✕] [📶] [✕] [🛢] [💻]

WHITE CITY

▼▼▼ Brookside Inn & Suites [H]

(541) 826-0800. **$92-$159.** 2020 Leigh Way 97503. I-5 exit 30, 5.6 mi ne on Crater Lake Hwy (SR 62), then just w. Int corridors. **Pets:** Other species. $15 one-time fee/room. Designated rooms, service with restrictions, supervision. [&M] [🏊] [📶] [✕] [🛢] [💻]

WILSONVILLE *(Restaurants p. 621)*

▼▼▼ GuestHouse Inn & Suites [H]

(503) 682-9000. **$90-$110.** 8855 SW Citizens Dr 97070. I-5 exit 283, just e on Wilsonville Rd, just n on Town Center Loop W, then just w. Int corridors. **Pets:** Other species. $15 daily fee/room. Service with restrictions, supervision. [🍴] [&M] [🏊] [📶] [✕] [🛢] [💻]

▼▼▼ Holiday Inn-Wilsonville [H]

(503) 682-2211. **Call for rates.** 25425 SW 95th Ave 97070. I-5 exit 286, just w on Boones Ferry Rd, then just se. Int corridors. **Pets:** Accepted.

[🍴] [🏊] [📶] [✕] [🛢] [💻]

△△△▽ ▼▼▼ La Quinta Inn Wilsonville [H]

(503) 682-3184. **$97-$262.** 8815 SW Sun Pl 97070. I-5 exit 286, just e on Elligsen Rd, just n on Parkway Ave, then just w. Int corridors. **Pets:** Accepted. [SAVE] [🍴] [&M] [🏊] [📶] [✕] [🛢] [💻]

WOODBURN

△△△▽ ▼▼▼ Best Western Woodburn Inn [H]

(503) 982-6515. **$120-$160.** 2980 Tom Tennant Dr 97071. I-5 exit 271, just e on Hillsboro-Silverton Hwy NE (SR 214), just n on Evergreen Rd, then just w. Int corridors. **Pets:** Medium, dogs only. $10 deposit/pet, $10 daily fee/pet. Designated rooms, service with restrictions, supervision. [SAVE] [&M] [🏊] [📶] [✕] [🛢] [💻]

▼▼▼ La Quinta Inn & Suites Woodburn [H]

(503) 982-1727. **$75-$235.** 120 Arney Rd NE 97071. I-5 exit 271, just nw. Int corridors. **Pets:** Accepted. [🍴] [🏊] [📶] [✕] [🛢] [💻]

▼▼▼ Super 8-Woodburn [H]

(503) 981-8881. **$55-$101.** 821 Evergreen Rd 97071. I-5 exit 271, just e on Hillsboro-Silverton Hwy (SR 214), then just s. Int corridors. **Pets:** Medium. $10 daily fee/pet. Designated rooms, service with restrictions, supervision. [🍴] [🏊] [📶] [💻]

YACHATS

△△△▽ ▼▼▼ The Adobe Resort [H]

(541) 547-3141. **Call for rates.** 1555 US 101 N 97498. 0.5 mi n; just w of US 101. Int corridors. **Pets:** Accepted.

[SAVE] [🍴] [&M] [🏊] [✕] [📶] [✕] [🎾] [🛢] [💻]

△△△▽ The Dublin House [M]

(541) 547-3703. **$64-$150, 3 day notice.** 251 W 7th St 97498. US 101 at 7th St; center. Ext corridors. **Pets:** Accepted.

[SAVE] [🍴] [&M] [🏊] [📶] [🎾] [🛢] [💻]

▼▼ Fireside Motel [M] ❀

(541) 547-3636. **$80-$200.** 1881 US 101 N 97498. 0.6 mi n; just w of US 101. Ext corridors. **Pets:** Other species. $14 daily fee/pet. Supervision. [&M] [📶] [✕] [🎾] [🛢] [💻]

PENNSYLVANIA

ABBOTTSTOWN

▼▼▼ The Altland House Inn and Suites [CI]

(717) 259-9535. **Call for rates.** 1 Center Square 17301. Jct SR 194 and US 30; on circle. Int corridors. **Pets:** $15 one-time fee/pet. Service with restrictions. [🍴] [📶] [✕] [🛢] [💻]

ADAMSTOWN

▼▼▼▼ Adamstown Inns & Cottages [BB]

(717) 484-0800. **$129-$450, 14 day notice.** 144 W Main St 19501. Center. Ext/int corridors. **Pets:** Accepted.

[&M] [📶] [✕] [🎾] [🛢] [💻]

AKRON

▼▼▼ Boxwood Inn [BB]

(717) 859-3466. **Call for rates.** 1320 Diamond St 17501. SR 272, 0.4 mi se on Main St to Diamond St, 0.3 mi s. Ext/int corridors.
Pets: Accepted. [🍴] [📶] [✕] [🎾] [🛢] [💻]

ALLENTOWN

▼▼▼ Allentown Comfort Suites [H]

(610) 437-9100. **$94-$247.** 3712 Hamilton Blvd 18103. I-78 exit 54 (Hamilton Blvd), just n. Int corridors. **Pets:** Medium. $50 one-time fee/pet. Designated rooms, service with restrictions, supervision.

[🍴] [📶] [✕] [🛢] [💻]

▼▼▼ Comfort Inn Lehigh Valley-West [H]

(610) 391-0344. **$89-$204.** 7625 Imperial Way 18106. I-78 exit 49B (SR 100), just n. Int corridors. **Pets:** Accepted. [🍴] [📶] [✕] [🛢] [💻]

◆◆ **Days Hotel Allentown Airport/Lehigh Valley** H
(610) 266-1000. **$80-$149.** 3400 Airport Rd 18109. On SR 987 N (Airport Rd), 0.5 mi n of jct US 22. Int corridors. **Pets:** Accepted.
🅼 🖥 🛜 ✕ 🔌 🖥

◆◆ **Staybridge Suites Allentown Bethlehem
Airport** H
(610) 443-5000. **Call for rates.** 1787-A Airport Rd 18109. US 22 exit Airport Rd S, 0.3 mi s. Int corridors. **Pets:** Accepted.
🅼 🖥 🛜 ✕ 🔌 🖥

ALTOONA

◆◆◆ **Clarion Inn & Suites** H 🐾
(814) 944-9661. **$100-$230.** 3306 Pleasant Valley Blvd 16602. I-99/US 220 exit 32, 0.5 mi w, then just n. Int corridors. **Pets:** Medium. $75 one-time fee/room. Designated rooms, service with restrictions, crate.
🛜 ✕ 🔌 🖥

◆◆ **Days Inn & Suites** H
(814) 944-4499. **$79-$129.** 458 Sabbath Rest Rd 16601. I-99 exit 39, just w. Int corridors. **Pets:** Accepted. 🍴 🛜 🔌 🖥

◆ **Motel 6 #1415** M
(814) 946-7601. **$51-$115.** 1500 Sterling St 16602. I-99/US 220 exit 31 (Plank Rd), just w. Ext corridors. **Pets:** Accepted. 🖥 🛜

◆ **Super 8 Altoona** M
(814) 942-5350. **$68-$100.** 3535 Fairway Dr 16602. I-99/US 220 exit 32, just w. Int corridors. **Pets:** Accepted. 🍴 🛜 🔌 🖥

AUDUBON

◆◆◆ ◆◆◆ **Homewood Suites by Hilton** H
(610) 539-7300. **$149-$209.** 681 Shannondell Blvd 19403. US 422 exit S Trooper Rd, 1.2 mi n. Int corridors. **Pets:** Accepted.
SAVE 🖥 🅼 🖥 🛜 🔌 🖥

BARKEYVILLE

◆◆ **Quality Inn-Barkeyville** M
(814) 786-7901. **$85-$105.** 137 Gibb Rd 16038. I-80 exit 29, just n on SR 8. Ext corridors. **Pets:** Accepted. 🅼 🛜 🔌 🖥

BARNESVILLE

◆◆ **MainStay Suites Barnesville/Frackville** H 🐾
(570) 773-5252. **$49-$145.** 1252 Morea Rd 18214. I-81 exit 131A southbound; exit 131B northbound, just s. Int corridors. **Pets:** $10 daily fee/pet. Service with restrictions, crate. 🍴 🅼 🛜 🔌 🖥

BARTONSVILLE

◆◆◆ ◆◆ **Baymont Inn & Suites** H 🐾
(570) 476-1500. **$90-$299.** 116 Turtlewalk Ln 18321. I-80 exit 302B, 0.4 mi n. Int corridors. **Pets:** Other species. $10 daily fee/room. Designated rooms, service with restrictions.
SAVE 🍴 🅼 🖥 ✕ 🛜 🔌 🖥

BEAVER FALLS

◆◆◆◆ **Park Inn by Radisson Beaver Falls** H
(724) 846-3700. **Call for rates.** 7195 Eastwood Rd 15010. I-76 (Pennsylvania Tpke) exit 13, just n. Int corridors. **Pets:** Accepted.
🍴 🅼 🖥 ✕ 🛜 ✕ 🔌 🖥

BEDFORD

◆◆◆ ◆◆◆ ◆◆◆ **Omni Bedford Springs Resort &
Spa** H
(814) 623-8100. **$129-$599, 7 day notice.** 2138 Business Rt 220 15522. I-70/76 (Pennsylvania Tpke) exit 146, 3.9 mi s. Int corridors. **Pets:** Accepted. SAVE 🍴 🅼 🖥 ✕ 🛜 ✕ 🔌 🖥

◆◆ **Quality Inn Bedford** H
(814) 623-5188. **$94-$229.** 4407 Business Rt 220 N 15522. I-70/76 (Pennsylvania Tpke) exit 146, just n. Ext/int corridors. **Pets:** Medium, other species. $15 one-time fee/room. Designated rooms, service with restrictions, crate. 🍴 🖥 🛜 🔌 🖥

◆◆ **Travelodge Bedford** H 🐾
(814) 623-9006. **$50-$100.** 4517 Business Rt 220 15522. I-70/76 (Pennsylvania Tpke) exit 146, 0.3 mi n. Ext/int corridors. **Pets:** Large. $50 deposit/room, $15 daily fee/room. Service with restrictions, supervision.
🍴 🖥 ✕ 🛜 🔌 🖥

BENSALEM

◆◆◆ ◆◆◆ **Best Western Plus Philadelphia
Bensalem** H
(215) 638-1500. **$93-$193.** 3499 Street Rd 19020. I-276 (Pennsylvania Tpke) exit 351, just s on US 1, then 0.3 mi e on SR 132. Int corridors. **Pets:** Medium. $20 daily fee/pet. Designated rooms, service with restrictions, supervision. SAVE 🍴 🅼 🖥 🛜 🔌 🖥

◆◆ **Extended Stay America-Philadelphia/Bensalem** H
(215) 633-6900. **$100-$125.** 3216 Tillman Dr 19020. I-95 exit 37 (SR 132), 2.5 mi w, then just s; I-276 (Pennsylvania Tpke) exit 351, 0.9 mi on US 1, 1.4 mi e, then just s. Int corridors. **Pets:** Accepted.
🅼 🛜 🔌 🖥

BENTLEYVILLE

◆◆◆ ◆◆ **Best Western Garden Inn** H
(724) 239-4321. **$99-$119.** 101 Gosai Dr 15314. I-70 exit 32B, just s. Int corridors. **Pets:** Other species. $20 one-time fee/room. Designated rooms, service with restrictions, supervision.
SAVE 🖥 🅼 🖥 🛜 🔌 🖥

BERWYN

◆◆◆ ◆◆◆ **Residence Inn by Marriott
Philadelphia-Valley Forge** H
(610) 640-9494. **$140-$307.** 600 W Swedesford Rd 19312. US 202 exit Paoli/SR 252, 1 mi n. Ext corridors. **Pets:** Accepted.
SAVE ECO 🅼 🖥 🛜 ✕ 🔌 🖥

BETHEL

◆◆◆ ◆◆ **Comfort Inn-Bethel/Midway** H
(717) 933-8888. **$75-$119.** 41 Diner Dr 19507. I-78 exit 16, just w. Int corridors. **Pets:** Accepted. SAVE 🅼 🖥 🛜 ✕ 🔌 🖥

BETHEL PARK

◆◆◆ **Crowne Plaza Hotel & Suites Pittsburgh
South** H
(412) 833-5300. **$119-$179.** 164 Ft Couch Rd 15241. 1 mi n on US 19. Int corridors. **Pets:** Large. $45 one-time fee/room. Designated rooms, service with restrictions, crate. 🍴 🅼 🖥 🛜 ✕ 🔌 🖥

BETHLEHEM

◆◆◆ ◆◆ **Best Western Lehigh Valley Hotel &
Conference Center** H
(610) 866-5800. **$89-$189.** 300 Gateway Dr 18017. US 22 exit Center St and SR 512. Ext/int corridors. **Pets:** Large. $25 daily fee/room. Designated rooms, service with restrictions, supervision.
SAVE 🍴 🖥 🛜 ✕ 🔌 🖥

◆◆◆ **Comfort Suites University** H
(610) 882-9700. **$100-$239.** 120 W 3rd St 18015. SR 378 exit 3rd St; jct W 3rd and Brodhead sts; center. Int corridors. **Pets:** Large, other species. $20 daily fee/pet. Designated rooms, service with restrictions.
🍴 🛜 ✕ 🔌 🖥

◆◆◆ **Historic Hotel Bethlehem** H 🐾
(610) 625-5000. **Call for rates.** 437 Main St 18018. SR 378 S exit 3 (City Center), just n on 3rd Ave, 0.3 mi e on Union Blvd, then 0.3 mi s. Int corridors. **Pets:** Medium. $75 one-time fee/pet. Designated rooms, service with restrictions, supervision. 🍴 🅼 🛜 ✕ 🔌 🖥

Homewood Suites - Allentown/Bethlehem Airport H
(610) 264-7500. **$149-$219.** 2031 Avenue C 18017. US 22 exit SR 378/Schoenersville Rd, follow signs for Schoenersville Rd, then 0.7 mi n. Int corridors. **Pets:** Accepted.

Hyatt Place Bethlehem H
(610) 625-0500. **$139-$249.** 45 W North St 18018. SR 378 exit 2 (Eighth Ave), just s, 0.7 mi w on Broad St, just n on Main St, then just w. Int corridors. **Pets:** Medium, dogs only. $75 one-time fee/room. Service with restrictions, supervision.

Residence Inn by Marriott Allentown Bethlehem/Lehigh Valley Airport H
(610) 317-2662. **$116-$301.** 2180 Motel Dr 18018. US 22 exit Airport Rd S, 0.8 mi se on Catasauqua Rd. Int corridors. **Pets:** Accepted.

The View Inn & Suites H
(610) 865-6300. **$60-$150.** 3191 Highfield Dr 18020. US 22 exit SR 191, just s. Ext/int corridors. **Pets:** Medium, other species. $30 daily fee/pet. Designated rooms, service with restrictions.

Wydnor Hall Inn BB
(610) 867-6851. **Call for rates.** 3612 Old Philadelphia Pike 18015. I-78 exit 60, 0.3 mi s to Center Valley Pkwy, 2.3 mi e to SR 378, 1.5 mi n to Black River Rd, just w to Old Philadelphia Pike, then 0.3 mi s. Int corridors. **Pets:** Accepted.

BIRD-IN-HAND

Amish Country Motel M
(717) 768-8396. **$91-$124.** 3013 Old Philadelphia Pike (Rt 340) 17505. On SR 340, 1 mi e. Ext corridors. **Pets:** Small, other species. $100 deposit/pet, $50 one-time fee/pet. Designated rooms, service with restrictions, crate.

BLAKESLEE

Best Western Inn at Blakeslee-Pocono H
(570) 646-6000. **$99-$140.** 107 Parkside Ave 18610. I-80 exit 284, just n. Int corridors. **Pets:** Accepted.

BLOOMSBURG

Econo Lodge H
(570) 387-0490. **$60-$190.** 189 Columbia Mall Dr 17815. I-80 exit 232 (SR 42), just n. Int corridors. **Pets:** Medium, dogs only. $15 daily fee/pet. Service with restrictions, crate.

The Inn at Turkey Hill CI
(570) 387-1500. **$145-$255.** 991 Central Rd 17815. I-80 exit 236 eastbound; exit 236A westbound, just s. Ext/int corridors. **Pets:** Other species. $20 daily fee/room. Designated rooms, service with restrictions, supervision.

BLUE MOUNTAIN

Kenmar Motel M
(717) 423-5915. **Call for rates.** 17788 Cumberland Hwy 17240. I-76 (Pennsylvania Tpke) exit 201, just e on SR 997 N. Ext corridors. **Pets:** Accepted.

BRADFORD

Best Western Plus Bradford Inn H
(814) 362-4501. **$110-$170.** 100 Davis St S 16701. US 219 exit Forman St southbound, just w to Davis St, then 0.3 mi s; exit Elm St northbound, just w. Int corridors. **Pets:** $10 daily fee/pet. Designated rooms, service with restrictions, crate.

Comfort Inn-Bradford H
(814) 368-6772. **$90-$160.** 76 Elm St 16701. US 219 exit Forman St southbound, just w to Davis St, then 0.3 mi s; exit Elm St northbound, just w. Int corridors. **Pets:** Accepted.

The Lodge at Glendorn CI
(814) 362-6511. **$475-$1075, 30 day notice.** 1000 Glendorn Dr 16701. US 219 exit Forman St, just s on Mechanic St, then 4.3 mi w on W Corydon St. Ext/int corridors. **Pets:** Accepted.

BREEZEWOOD

Best Western Plaza Inn M
(814) 735-4352. **$93-$119.** 16407 Lincoln Hwy 15533. I-76 (Pennsylvania Tpke) exit 161, just w on US 30; I-70 exit 147. Ext corridors. **Pets:** Accepted.

BURNHAM

Quality Inn & Suites of Lewistown M
(717) 248-4961. **$76-$299.** 13015 Ferguson Valley Rd 17009. US 322 exit Burnham, just w. Ext corridors. **Pets:** Accepted.

BUTLER

Locust Brook Lodge BB
(724) 283-8453. **Call for rates.** 179 Eagle Mill Rd 16001. 5 mi w on US 422 to jct Eagle Mill Rd, 0.8 mi s; I-79 exit 99, 10 mi e on US 422 to jct Eagle Mill Rd, then 0.8 mi s. Ext/int corridors. **Pets:** Accepted.

CAMP HILL

Radisson Hotel Harrisburg H
(717) 763-7117. **$99-$189.** 1150 Camp Hill Bypass 17011. Jct US 11, 15 and Erford Rd. Int corridors. **Pets:** Accepted.

CARLISLE

Best Western Carlisle H
(717) 243-6200. **$79-$149.** 1155 Harrisburg Pike 17013. I-76 (Pennsylvania Tpke) exit 226, just s. Int corridors. **Pets:** Medium. $15 daily fee/pet. Designated rooms, service with restrictions, supervision.

Comfort Inn PA Turnpike-I-81 H
(717) 706-3400. **$89-$249.** 77 Shady Ln 17013. I-76 exit 226, just s. Int corridors. **Pets:** Accepted.

Comfort Suites Downtown Carlisle H
(717) 960-1000. **$109-$279.** 10 S Hanover St 17013. I-81 exit 47, 0.8 mi n on SR 34, just s of square; downtown. Int corridors. **Pets:** Accepted.

Country Inn & Suites By Carlson - Carlisle, PA H
(717) 241-4900. **Call for rates.** 1529 Commerce Ave 17015. I-81 exit 44 (Plainfield Rd), s on SR 465 (Allen Rd), then left. Int corridors. **Pets:** Accepted.

Days Inn Carlisle-South H
(717) 258-4147. **$79-$209.** 101 Alexander Spring Rd 17015. I-81 exit 45, just sw. Int corridors. **Pets:** Other species. $15 daily fee/pet. Designated rooms, service with restrictions, supervision.

Fairfield Inn & Suites by Marriott Carlisle H
(717) 243-2080. **$94-$208.** 1528 E Commerce Ave 17015. I-81 exit 44 (Plainfield Rd), just s, then just e. Int corridors. **Pets:** Other species. $75 deposit/room.

AAA ▼▼▼▼ **Hampton Inn by Hilton Carlisle** H

(717) 240-0200. **$114-$199.** 1164 Harrisburg Pike 17013. I-76 (Pennsylvania Tpke) exit 226, just n; I-81 exit 52 (US 11) southbound; exit 52B northbound, 0.8 mi s. Int corridors. **Pets:** Accepted.

[SAVE] 🍴 👤 🏊 🛜 ✕ 🛢 🖥

AAA ▼▼▼▼ **Pheasant Field Bed & Breakfast** BB ❀

(717) 258-0717. **$135-$255, 7 day notice.** 150 Hickorytown Rd 17015. I-76 (Pennsylvania Tpke) exit 226, 0.4 mi n on US 11, 2.3 mi right on S Middlesex Rd, 0.4 mi left on Ridge Dr, then right. Ext/int corridors. **Pets:** Medium. $25 daily fee/pet. Designated rooms, service with restrictions, supervision. [SAVE] 🍴 🛜 ✕ 📠 🛢 🖥

AAA ▼▼▼▼ **Residence Inn by Marriott Harrisburg Carlisle** H ❀

(717) 610-9050. **$94-$207.** 1 Hampton Ct 17013. I-76 (Pennsylvania Tpke) exit 226, just n; I-81 exit 52 (US 11) southbound; exit 52B northbound, 0.8 mi s. Int corridors. **Pets:** $50 one-time fee/room. Designated rooms, service with restrictions, crate.

[SAVE] 👤 👤 🛜 ✕ 🛢 🖥

▼▼ **Sleep Inn Carlisle** H

(717) 249-8863. **$99-$210.** 5 E Garland Dr 17013. I-81 exit 47 northbound; exit 47A southbound, just ne. Int corridors. **Pets:** Other species. $15 daily fee/pet. Designated rooms, service with restrictions, crate.

👤 👤 🛜 🛢 🖥

CHADDS FORD

▼▼▼ **Brandywine River Hotel** H

(610) 388-1200. **$129-$169.** 1609 Baltimore Pike, Bldg 300 19317. Jct US 1 (Baltimore Pike) and SR 100, 2 mi w of US 202 (Wilmington Pike). Int corridors. **Pets:** Dogs only. $45 daily fee/pet. Designated rooms, service with restrictions, crate. 🛜 ✕ 🛢 🖥

CHALK HILL

▼▼ **The Lodge at Chalk Hill** M

(724) 438-8880. **Call for rates.** 2920 National Pike Rd 15421. 0.5 mi on US 40. Ext corridors. **Pets:** Accepted. 🍴 🛜 🛢 🖥

CHAMBERSBURG

AAA ▼▼ **Best Western Chambersburg** H

(717) 262-4994. **$79-$99.** 211 Walker Rd 17201. I-81 exit 16, just w on US 30, then just n. Int corridors. **Pets:** Other species. $15 daily fee/pet. Designated rooms, service with restrictions, supervision.

[SAVE] 👤 🛜 🛢 🖥

▼▼ **Candlewood Suites** H

(717) 263-2800. **Call for rates.** 231 Walker Rd 17201. I-81 exit 16, just w on US 30, then just n. Int corridors. **Pets:** Accepted.

👤 🛜 ✕ 🛢 🖥

▼▼ **Country Inn & Suites By Carlson** H ❀

(717) 261-0900. **Call for rates.** 399 Bedington Blvd 17201. I-81 exit 17 (Walker Rd), 0.6 mi s, then just w. Int corridors. **Pets:** Medium. $15 one-time fee/room. Designated rooms, no service, supervision.

👤 👤 🛜 ✕ 🛢 🖥

▼▼ **Sleep Inn & Suites** H

(717) 263-0596. **$60-$140.** 1435 Doron Dr 17202. I-81 exit 20, just w. Int corridors. **Pets:** Large, other species. $15 daily fee/pet. Designated rooms, service with restrictions, supervision.

🍴 👤 🏊 🛜 🛢 🖥

CHESTER

AAA ▼▼▼▼ **Best Western Plus Philadelphia Airport South at Widener University** H

(610) 872-8100. **$110-$170.** 1450 Providence Ave (SR 320) 19013. I-95 exit 6, just e to SR 320, follow signs. Int corridors. **Pets:** Accepted.

[SAVE] 🛜 ✕ 🛢 🖥

CLARION

▼▼ **Comfort Inn-Clarion** H

(814) 226-5230. **$75-$140.** 129 Dolby St 16214. I-80 exit 62, 0.6 mi n on SR 68. Int corridors. **Pets:** Accepted. 👤 👤 🛜 🛢 🖥

▼▼ **Park Inn By Radisson - Clarion** H

(814) 226-8850. **$99-$139.** 45 Holiday Inn Rd 16214. I-80 exit 62, 0.5 mi n on SR 68. Int corridors. **Pets:** Accepted.

🍴 👤 👤 🛜 ✕ 🛢 🖥

CLARKS SUMMIT

▼▼▼ **Ramada Clarks Summit-Scranton** H ❀

(570) 586-2730. **$72-$130.** 820 Northern Blvd 18411. I-81 exit 194; I-476 (Pennsylvania Tpke) exit 131, 0.3 mi w on US 6 and 11. Int corridors. **Pets:** Medium. $20 daily fee/pet. Designated rooms, service with restrictions, crate. 👤 👤 🛜 🛢 🖥

CLEARFIELD

AAA ▼▼▼▼ **Best Western Plus Clearfield** H

(814) 768-1049. **$89-$115.** 14424 Clearfield Shawville Hwy (Rt 879) 16830. I-80 exit 120, just s. Int corridors. **Pets:** Large, other species. $20 daily fee/room. Designated rooms, service with restrictions, supervision. [SAVE] 👤 👤 🛜 🛢 🖥

▼▼ **Super 8-Clearfield** M

(814) 768-7580. **$68-$79.** 14597 Clearfield Shawville Hwy (Rt 879) 16830. I-80 exit 120, just s. Int corridors. **Pets:** Other species. $5 daily fee/room. Service with restrictions, supervision. 🛜 🛢 🖥

CONSHOHOCKEN

AAA ▼▼▼▼ **Residence Inn by Marriott Philadelphia/Conshohocken** H

(610) 828-8800. **$100-$219.** 191 Washington St 19428. I-76 (Schuylkill Expwy) exit 332 (SR 23), 0.3 mi over Fayette Bridge to Elm St, then just se along river. Int corridors. **Pets:** Other species. $75 one-time fee/room. Service with restrictions. [SAVE] 👤 👤 🛜 ✕ 🛢 🖥

CORAOPOLIS

▼▼▼▼ **Embassy Suites by Hilton Pittsburgh International Airport** H

(412) 269-9070. **$189-$309.** 550 Cherrington Pkwy 15108. Business I-376 Loop exit Thorn Run Rd. Int corridors. **Pets:** Accepted.

🍴 👤 👤 🛜 🛢 🖥

▼▼▼ **Hampton Inn Pittsburgh Airport** H

(412) 264-0020. **$109-$159.** 8514 University Blvd 15108. Jct Business I-376 Loop, 0.5 mi n. Int corridors. **Pets:** Accepted.

👤 🛜 ✕ 🛢 🖥

AAA ▼▼▼▼ **Hyatt Regency Pittsburgh International Airport** H

(724) 899-1234. **$99-$359.** 1111 Airport Blvd 15231. I-376 exit 53 (Airport Blvd), just n. Int corridors. **Pets:** Accepted.

[SAVE] [ECO] 🍴 👤 👤 ✕ 🛜 🛢 🖥

▼▼▼▼ **La Quinta Inn Pittsburgh Airport** H

(412) 269-0400. **$82-$169.** 8507 University Blvd 15108. Jct I-376 Business route, 1 mi n. Int corridors. **Pets:** Accepted. 👤 🛜 🛢 🖥

AAA ▼▼▼▼ **Sheraton Pittsburgh Airport Hotel** H

(412) 262-2400. **Call for rates.** 1160 Thorn Run Rd 15108. Business I-376 Loop exit Thorn Run Rd. Int corridors. **Pets:** Accepted.

[SAVE] 🍴 👤 👤 🛜 ✕ 🛢 🖥

COUDERSPORT

▼▼ **Westgate Inn** H

(814) 274-0400. **$82-$129.** 307 Rt 6 W 16915. On US 6, 1 mi w. Int corridors. **Pets:** Small, dogs only. $15 daily fee/pet. Designated rooms, service with restrictions, crate. 🛜 🛢 🖥

CRANBERRY TOWNSHIP

▼▼▼ Candlewood Suites 🅗 🐾
(724) 591-8666. **Call for rates.** 20036 Rt 19 16066. I-76 (Pennsylvania Tpke) exit 28, I-79 exit 76 northbound; exit 78 southbound. Int corridors. **Pets:** Large, other species. $25 daily fee/room. Service with restrictions.
🅑🅜 🛜 ✕ 🔌 🖥

AAA ▼▼▼ DoubleTree Cranberry 🅗
(724) 776-6900. **$119-$239.** 910 Sheraton Dr 16066. I-76 (Pennsylvania Tpke) exit 28, 0.5 mi s on US 19; I-79 exit 76 (US 19) northbound; exit 78 southbound. Int corridors. **Pets:** Accepted.
🆂🅰🆅🅴 🍴 🅑🅜 🏊 🛜 ✕ 🔌 🖥

▼▼ Holiday Inn Express Cranberry Township 🅗
(724) 772-1000. **Call for rates.** 20003 Rt 19 16066. I-76 (Pennsylvania Tpke) exit 28; I-79 exit 76 northbound; exit 78 southbound, just s. Int corridors. **Pets:** Accepted. 🅑🅜 🛜 ✕ 🔌 🖥

AAA ▼▼▼ Hyatt Place Pittsburgh/Cranberry 🅗
(724) 779-7900. **$84-$229.** 136 Emeryville Dr 16066. I-76 (Pennsylvania Tpke) exit 28; I-79 exit 76 northbound, 0.7 mi n on US 19, then just w on Marguerite Dr. Int corridors. **Pets:** Accepted.
🆂🅰🆅🅴 🍴 🅑🅜 🏊 🛜 ✕ 🔌 🖥

AAA ▼▼▼ Pittsburgh Marriott North 🅗
(724) 772-3700. **$93-$296.** 100 Cranberry Woods Dr 16066. I-79 exit 78 to Cranberry Woods Dr. Int corridors. **Pets:** Medium, dogs only. $75 one-time fee/room. Designated rooms, service with restrictions, supervision. 🆂🅰🆅🅴 🍴 🅑🅜 🏊 🛜 ✕ 🔌 🖥

▼▼▼ Quality Inn 🅗
(724) 772-0600. **$88-$171.** 30 St. Francis Way 16066. I-76 (Pennsylvania Tpke) exit 28, 0.3 mi n on US 19; I-79 exit 76 northbound; exit 78 southbound, 0.5 mi n on US 19. Ext/int corridors. **Pets:** Accepted.
🅑🅜 🏊 🛜 ✕ 🔌 🖥

▼▼▼ Residence Inn by Marriott Pittsburgh Cranberry Township 🅗
(724) 779-1000. **$87-$355.** 1308 Freedom Rd 16066. I-76 (Pennsylvania Tpke) exit 76, 0.5 mi n on US 19, then 0.3 mi w; I-79 exit 78 southbound, 0.5 mi w. Int corridors. **Pets:** Accepted.
🔵 🅑🅜 🏊 ✕ 🛜 🔌 🖥

DANVILLE

AAA ▼▼▼ Best Western Plus Danville Inn 🅗
(570) 275-5750. **$80-$159.** 79 Old Valley School Rd 17821. I-80 exit 224, just s. Int corridors. **Pets:** Accepted.
🆂🅰🆅🅴 🅑🅜 🏊 🛜 ✕ 🔌 🖥

AAA ▼▼ Danville Super 8 🎝
(570) 275-4640. **$65-$136, 3 day notice.** 35 Sheraton Rd 17821. I-80 exit 224, just sw on SR 54. Ext corridors. **Pets:** Accepted.
🆂🅰🆅🅴 🅑🅜 🛜 🔌 🖥

DELMONT

▼▼ Super 8 🅗
(724) 468-4888. **$70-$190.** 180 Sheffield Dr 15626. SR 66, just s of US 22. Int corridors. **Pets:** $10 daily fee/pet. Designated rooms, service with restrictions, supervision. 🅑🅜 🛜 🔌 🖥

DENVER

▼▼▼ Comfort Inn Lancaster County North 🅗
(717) 336-7541. **$100-$185.** 1 Denver Rd 17517. I-76 (Pennsylvania Tpke) exit 286, 1 mi w to SR 272, then just s. Int corridors. **Pets:** Other species. $10 one-time fee/pet. Supervision.
🍴 🅑🅜 🏊 🛜 ✕ 🔌 🖥

▼▼ Red Roof Inn Denver 🅗
(717) 336-4649. **$40-$160.** 2017 N Reading Rd 17517. I-76 (Pennsylvania Tpke) exit 286, 1 mi w to SR 272, then just s. Int corridors. **Pets:** Accepted. 🍴 🛜 ✕ 🔌 🖥

DICKSON CITY

▼▼▼ Residence Inn by Marriott-Scranton 🅗
(570) 343-5121. **$85-$282.** 947 Viewmont Dr 18519. I-81 exit 190, just e, follow signs to Viewmont Dr. Int corridors. **Pets:** Accepted.
🅑🅜 🏊 🛜 ✕ 🔌 🖥

DONEGAL

▼▼ Days Inn at Donegal 🅗
(724) 593-7536. **$84-$89.** 3620 Rt 31 15628. I-70/76 (Pennsylvania Tpke) exit 91, just e. Ext/int corridors. **Pets:** Medium, dogs only. $20 daily fee/pet. Designated rooms, service with restrictions, supervision.
🅑🅜 🏊 🛜 ✕ 🔌 🖥

DU BOIS

AAA ▼▼▼ Best Western Inn & Conference Center 🅗
(814) 371-6200. **$80-$140.** 82 N Park Pl 15801. I-80 exit 97 eastbound, 2.5 mi e on DuBois Ave (US 219/SR 255), then just s; exit 101 westbound, 2.7 mi w on DuBois Ave (US 219/SR 255), then just s on US 219. Int corridors. **Pets:** $12 daily fee/pet. Service with restrictions.
🆂🅰🆅🅴 🅑🅜 🛜 🔌 🖥

DUNMORE

AAA ▼▼▼ Quality Inn Scranton 🅗
(570) 348-6101. **$79-$179.** 1226 Oneill Hwy 18512. I-81 exit 188 (Throop), just e at SR 347 N (Oneill Hwy). Int corridors. **Pets:** Medium. $20 daily fee/pet. Designated rooms, service with restrictions, supervision. 🆂🅰🆅🅴 🅑🅜 🛜 🔌 🖥

▼▼▼ Sleep Inn & Suites 🅗
(570) 961-1116. **$89-$179.** 102 Monahan Ave 18512. I-81 exit 188 (Throop), just e at SR 347 N (Oneill Hwy), then just s. Int corridors. **Pets:** Medium, other species. $15 daily fee/pet. Designated rooms, service with restrictions, crate. 🅑🅜 🏊 🛜 🔌 🖥

EAST NORRITON

AAA ▼▼▼ Hyatt House Philadelphia/Plymouth Meeting 🅗
(610) 313-9990. **$94-$249.** 501 E Germantown Pike 19401. I-476 exit 20, 2.5 mi w. Int corridors. **Pets:** Accepted.
🆂🅰🆅🅴 🍴 🅑🅜 🏊 🛜 ✕ 🔌 🖥

EASTON

▼▼▼ Grand Eastonian Suites Hotel 🅗
(610) 258-6350. **$109-$239.** 140 N Northampton St 18042. US 22 exit 4th St (SR 611), just e to 3rd St, just s to downtown square, then just e towards river. Int corridors. **Pets:** Medium. $25 daily fee/room. Designated rooms, service with restrictions, crate.
🍴 🅑🅜 🏊 🛜 ✕ 🔌 🖥

▼▼▼ The Lafayette Inn 🅱🅱 🐾
(610) 253-4500. **$139-$229.** 525 W Monroe St 18042. US 22 exit 4th St (SR 611), just n on 3rd St, 0.3 mi ne on College Ave, then 0.3 mi n on Cattell St to jct Monroe St. Ext/int corridors. **Pets:** $20 daily fee/room. Designated rooms, service with restrictions, supervision.
🔵 🛜 ✕ 🔌 🖥

AAA ▼▼▼ TownePlace Suites by Marriott-Bethlehem/Easton 🅗
(610) 829-2000. **$87-$256.** 3800 Easton-Nazareth Hwy 18045. SR 33 exit SR 248 (Easton-Nazareth Hwy), 0.6 mi w. Int corridors.
Pets: Accepted. 🆂🅰🆅🅴 🅑🅜 🏊 🛜 ✕ 🔌 🖥

EAST STROUDSBURG

AAA ▼▼▼ Budget Inn & Suites 🅗
(570) 424-5451. **$69-$139.** 320 Greentree Dr 18301. I-80 exit 308, just se. Ext/int corridors. **Pets:** Accepted. 🆂🅰🆅🅴 🍴 🅑🅜 🛜 🔌 🖥

▼▼ Super 8 East Stroudsburg **M**
(570) 424-7411. **$55-$145.** 340 Greentree Dr 18301. I-80 exit 308, just se. Int corridors. **Pets:** $10 daily fee/pet. Designated rooms, service with restrictions, crate. 🔲M 🛜 🔲 🔲 🔲

EBENSBURG
▼▼▼▼ Quality Inn **H**
(814) 472-6100. **$99-$175.** 111 Cook Rd 15931. Jct US 219, just e on US 22. Int corridors. **Pets:** Medium, dogs only. $15 daily fee/pet. Designated rooms, service with restrictions, supervision.
🔲 🛜 🔲 🔲 🔲

ELIZABETHTOWN
🔷 ▼▼ Holiday Inn Express Elizabethtown (Hershey Area) **H** ❀
(717) 367-4000. **$131-$175.** 147 Merts Dr 17022. SR 283 exit Elizabethtown/Rheems. Int corridors. **Pets:** Large, other species. $25 daily fee/pet. Designated rooms, service with restrictions, crate.
🔲 🔲 🔲M 🔲 🔲 🔲 🔲

ERIE *(Restaurants p. 621)*
🔷 ▼▼▼▼ Courtyard by Marriott Erie Bayfront **H**
(814) 636-1005. **$145-$391.** 2 Sassafras Pier 16507. I-90 exit 22B to Bayfront Connector; I-79 to Bayfront Pkwy. Int corridors.
Pets: Accepted. 🔲 🔲 🔲M 🛜 🔲 🔲 🔲

▼▼▼▼ Homewood Suites by Hilton **H**
(814) 866-8292. **$124-$199.** 2084 Interchange Rd 16565. I-79 exit 180, just e; in Pavilion Marketplace. Int corridors. **Pets:** Medium, other species. $75 one-time fee/room. Service with restrictions, crate.
🔲M 🔲 🛜 🔲 🔲 🔲

▼▼▼▼ La Quinta Inn & Suites **H**
(814) 864-1812. **$75-$202.** 7820 Perry Hwy 16509. I-90 exit 27, just n. Int corridors. **Pets:** Accepted. 🔲M 🔲 🛜 🔲 🔲 🔲

🔷 ▼▼ Microtel Inn by Wyndham Erie **M**
(814) 864-1010. **$59-$129.** 8100 Peach St 16509. I-90 exit 24, just s. Int corridors. **Pets:** Medium. $10 daily fee/pet. Service with restrictions, crate. 🔲 🔲M 🛜 🔲

🔷 ▼▼ Red Roof Inn Erie **M**
(814) 868-5246. **$49-$170.** 7865 Perry Hwy 16509. I-90 exit 27, just n on SR 97. Ext/int corridors. **Pets:** Accepted.
🔲 🔲M 🛜 🔲 🔲 🔲

🔷 ▼▼▼▼ Sheraton Erie Bayfront Hotel **H**
(814) 454-2005. **$119-$459.** 55 West Bay Dr 16507. I-90 exit 22B to Bayfront Connector; I-79 to Bayfront Pkwy. Int corridors.
Pets: Accepted. 🔲 🔲 🔲M 🔲 🔲 🛜 🔲 🔲 🔲

▼▼▼▼ TownePlace Suites by Marriott Erie **H**
(814) 866-7100. **$76-$286.** 2090 Interchange Rd 16565. I-79 exit 180, just e; in Pavilion Marketplace. Int corridors. **Pets:** Medium, other species. $100 one-time fee/room. Service with restrictions.
🔲M 🔲 🛜 🔲 🔲 🔲

▼▼▼▼ Wingate by Wyndham **H**
(814) 860-3050. **$109-$179.** 8060 Old Oliver Rd 16509. I-90 exit 24, just s on Peach St, just w, just n, then just e. Int corridors.
Pets: Accepted. 🔲M 🔲 🛜 🔲 🔲 🔲

ESSINGTON
🔷 ▼▼▼▼ Red Roof PLUS+ Philadelphia Airport **M**
(610) 521-5090. **$85-$109.** 49 Industrial Hwy 19029. I-95 exit 9A, 0.3 mi sw on SR 291. Ext corridors. **Pets:** Accepted.
🔲 🔲M 🛜 🔲 🔲 🔲

▼▼▼▼ Wyndham Garden Hotel Philadelphia Airport **H**
(610) 521-2400. **$89-$265.** 45 Industrial Hwy 19029. I-95 exit 9A, 0.3 mi sw on SR 291. Int corridors. **Pets:** Accepted.
🔲 🔲M 🔲 🛜 🔲 🔲 🔲

FARMINGTON
▼▼▼ Historic Summit Inn **H**
(724) 438-8594. **Call for rates.** 101 Skyline Dr 15437. On US 40; center. Int corridors. **Pets:** Accepted.
🔲 🔲M 🔲 🔲 🛜 🔲 🔲 🔲

🔷 ▼▼▼▼ Nemacolin Woodlands Resort **H**
(724) 329-8555. **$209-$869, 3 day notice.** 1001 Lafayette Dr 15437. On US 40. Ext/int corridors. **Pets:** Accepted.
🔲 🔲 🔲 🔲M 🔲 🔲 🛜 🔲 🔲

FOGELSVILLE
🔷 ▼▼▼▼ The Center at Holiday Inn **H**
(610) 391-1000. **Call for rates.** 7736 Adrienne Dr 18031. I-78 exit 49A, 0.3 mi s on SR 100. Int corridors. **Pets:** $40 one-time fee/room. Designated rooms, service with restrictions, crate.
🔲 🔲 🔲M 🔲 🛜 🔲 🔲 🔲

▼▼▼▼ Glasbern **CI**
(610) 285-4723. **Call for rates.** 2141 Packhouse Rd 18051. I-78 exit 49B (SR 100), 0.3 mi n to 1st traffic light, 0.3 mi w on Main St, 0.6 mi n on Church St, then 0.8 mi ne. Ext/int corridors. **Pets:** Accepted.
🔲 🔲M 🔲 🛜 🔲 🔲

▼▼▼ Sleep Inn **H**
(610) 395-6603. **$85-$190.** 327 Star Rd 18106. I-78 exit 49A, 0.3 mi s on SR 100, e at traffic light, then n on service road. Int corridors.
Pets: Accepted. 🔲M 🛜 🔲 🔲

▼▼▼ Staybridge Suites-Allentown West **H**
(610) 841-5100. **Call for rates.** 327 Star Rd 18106. I-78 exit 49A, 0.3 mi s on SR 100, e at traffic light, then n on service road. Int corridors.
Pets: Accepted. 🔲M 🔲 🛜 🔲 🔲 🔲

FORT WASHINGTON
🔷 ▼▼▼▼ Best Western Fort Washington Inn **H**
(215) 542-7930. **$81-$135.** 285 Commerce Dr 19034. I-276 (Pennsylvania Tpke) exit 339 (SR 309 S), just w on Pennsylvania Ave, just n to Commerce Dr, then 0.3 mi e. Int corridors. **Pets:** Accepted.
🔲 🔲 🔲 🛜 🔲 🔲

FRANKLIN (VENANGO COUNTY)
▼▼▼ Knights Inn **H**
(814) 432-2101. **$64-$130.** 847 Allegheny Blvd 16323. 2 mi n on SR 8. Int corridors. **Pets:** Accepted. 🔲M 🛜 🔲 🔲

GETTYSBURG *(Restaurants p. 621)*
▼▼ 1863 Inn of Gettysburg **H**
(717) 334-6211. **$105-$345, 7 day notice.** 516 Baltimore St 17325. Jct US 15 business route and SR 97. Ext/int corridors. **Pets:** Other species. $20 daily fee/room. Designated rooms, service with restrictions, supervision. 🔲M 🔲 🛜 🔲 🔲 🔲

▼▼▼▼ Battlefield Bed & Breakfast **BB**
(717) 334-8804. **Call for rates.** 2264 Emmitsburg Rd 17325. 3.8 mi s on Steinwehr Ave/Emmitsburg Rd from jct Baltimore St. Int corridors.
Pets: Accepted. 🔲 🛜 🔲 🔲 🔲

🔷 ▼▼ Country Inn & Suites By Carlson **H**
(717) 337-9518. **$89-$319.** 1857 Gettysburg Village Dr 17325. US 15 exit SR 97, just e. Int corridors. **Pets:** $35 daily fee/room. Designated rooms, service with restrictions, crate.
🔲 🔲M 🔲 🛜 🔲 🔲 🔲

▼▼▼ Inn at Cemetery Hill **M** ❀
(717) 334-9281. **$89-$250.** 613 Baltimore St 17325. On SR 97; at US 15 business route. Ext/int corridors. **Pets:** Other species. $20 daily fee/room. Designated rooms, service with restrictions. 🛜 🔲 🔲 🔲

▼▼ Quality Inn & Suites **H**
(717) 337-2400. **$84-$269.** 871 York Rd 17325. 1 mi e on US 30. Int corridors. **Pets:** Accepted. 🔲 🛜 🔲 🔲 🔲

▼▼ Quality Inn Gettysburg Battlefield Ⓜ
(717) 334-1103. **$74-$213.** 380 Steinwehr Ave 17325. 1 mi s on US 15 business route; just s of jct SR 134. Ext/int corridors. **Pets:** Dogs only. Service with restrictions. 🅿️ 🛜 ❌ 🔒 🖥️

AAA ▼▼ Super 8 Ⓜ
(717) 337-1400. **$49-$209.** 869 York Rd 17325. 1 mi e on US 30. Int corridors. **Pets:** Large, other species. $12 daily fee/pet. Service with restrictions, crate. 🆂🅰️🆅🅴 🛜 ❌ 🔒 🖥️

AAA ▼▼▼ Wyndham Gettysburg Ⓗ
(717) 339-0020. **$119-$229.** 95 Presidential Cir 17325. US 15 exit York St, just e on US 30. Int corridors. **Pets:** Accepted.
🆂🅰️🆅🅴 🍴 ♿ 🏊 🛜 ❌ 🔒 🖥️

GIBSONIA

▼▼ Quality Inn & Suites Pittsburgh-Gibsonia Ⓜ
(724) 444-8700. **$80-$190.** 5137 William Flynn Hwy 15044. I-76 (Pennsylvania Tpke) exit 39, just n. Ext corridors. **Pets:** Large, other species. $15 daily fee/pet. Service with restrictions, supervision. 🛜 🔒 🖥️

GLEN MILLS

▼▼▼ The Inn at Grace Winery 🅱️🅱️ ❀
(610) 459-4711. **Call for rates.** 50 Sweetwater Rd 19342. US 1, 2 mi w on Valley Rd, 0.6 mi s. Ext/int corridors. **Pets:** Dogs only. $35 daily fee/pet. Designated rooms, service with restrictions.
🍴 🏊 🛜 ❌ 🔒 🖥️

GORDONVILLE

AAA ▼▼ Harvest Drive Family Inn Ⓜ
(717) 768-7186. **Call for rates.** 3368 Harvest Dr 17529. 0.5 mi w on SR 340, 0.7 mi s on Clearview Rd, then just w. Ext corridors. **Pets:** Dogs only. $25 daily fee/room. Designated rooms, service with restrictions, crate. 🆂🅰️🆅🅴 🍴 🛜 ❌ 🔒 🖥️

AAA ▼▼ Motel 6-Lancaster #4174 Ⓜ
(717) 687-3880. **Call for rates.** 2959 Lincoln Hwy E 17529. On US 30 (Lincoln Hwy); center. Int corridors. **Pets:** Accepted.
🆂🅰️🆅🅴 🛜 ❌ 🖥️

GRANTVILLE

▼▼ Days Inn Grantville-Hershey Ⓜ
(717) 469-0631. **$90-$170.** 252 Bow Creek Rd 17028. I-81 exit 80, 0.3 mi s. Ext corridors. **Pets:** Accepted. ♿ 🛜 🔒 🖥️

AAA ▼▼▼ Holiday Inn Harrisburg-Hershey Area, I-81 Ⓗ
(717) 469-0661. **$99-$229.** 604 Station Rd 17028. I-81 exit 80, just w. Int corridors. **Pets:** Dogs only. $25 one-time fee/room. Designated rooms, service with restrictions, supervision.
🆂🅰️🆅🅴 🍴 ♿ 🏊 🛜 ❌ 🔒 🖥️

GREENCASTLE

AAA ▼▼ Comfort Inn Ⓗ
(717) 597-8164. **$80-$190.** 50 Pine Dr 17225. I-81 exit 3, just s on US 11. Int corridors. **Pets:** Other species. $15 daily fee/pet. Designated rooms, service with restrictions, supervision.
🆂🅰️🆅🅴 🍴 🛜 ❌ 🔒 🖥️

GREENSBURG

▼▼▼ Ramada Hotel and Conference Center Greensburg Ⓗ ❀
(724) 836-6060. **$85-$119.** 100 Ramada Inn Dr 15601. I-76 (Pennsylvania Tpke) exit 75, 5.6 mi on US 119 N, 3 mi e on US 30, then just n. Int corridors. **Pets:** Other species. Service with restrictions, supervision.
🍴 ♿ 🏊 🛜 ❌ 🔒 🖥️

GREEN TREE

AAA ▼▼▼ DoubleTree by Hilton Pittsburgh-Green Tree Ⓗ
(412) 922-8400. **$89-$190.** 500 Mansfield Ave 15205. I-376 exit 67, 1.1 mi nw to Mansfield Ave. Int corridors. **Pets:** Accepted.
🆂🅰️🆅🅴 🍴 ♿ 🏊 🛜 ❌ 🔒 🖥️

▼▼▼ Hampton Inn Pittsburgh Green Tree Ⓗ
(412) 922-0100. **$109-$159.** 555 Trumbull Dr 15205. I-376 exit 67; jct US 22 and 30, 1 mi nw via Mansfield Ave. Int corridors. **Pets:** Other species. Service with restrictions. 🍴 ♿ 🏊 🛜 🔒 🖥️

HALLSTEAD

AAA ▼▼▼ Colonial Brick Inn & Suites Ⓜ
(570) 879-2162. **$98-$140.** 25161 SR 11 18822. I-81 exit 230 (Great Bend-Hallstead), just w. Int corridors. **Pets:** Dogs only. $10 one-time fee/pet. Designated rooms, service with restrictions, supervision.
🆂🅰️🆅🅴 🛜 🔒 🖥️

HAMBURG

▼▼▼ Microtel Inn & Suites by Wyndham Hamburg Ⓗ
(610) 562-4234. **$77-$93.** 50 Industrial Dr 19526. I-78 exit 29B, 0.3 mi n on SR 61, then just e. Int corridors. **Pets:** Accepted.
🍴 ♿ 🛜 🔒 🖥️

HAMLIN

▼▼▼ Comfort Inn-Pocono Lakes Region Ⓗ
(570) 689-4148. **$89-$220.** 117 Twin Rocks Rd 18427. I-84 exit 17, just n on SR 191. Int corridors. **Pets:** Accepted. ♿ 🛜 🔒 🖥️

HARMARVILLE

▼▼▼ TownePlace Suites by Marriott Ⓗ
(412) 423-1900. **$95-$183.** 2785 Freeport Rd 15238. I-76 (Pennsylvania Tpke) exit 48, just s. Int corridors. **Pets:** Accepted.
♿ 🛜 ❌ 🔒 🖥️

HARRISBURG

AAA ▼▼▼ Best Western Plus Harrisburg East Inn & Suites Ⓜ
(717) 985-1600. **$79-$189.** 1344 Eisenhower Blvd 17111. I-76 (Pennsylvania Tpke) exit 247, just n. Int corridors. **Pets:** Accepted.
🆂🅰️🆅🅴 🍴 ♿ 🛜 ❌ 🔒 🖥️

AAA ▼▼▼ Best Western Premier The Central Hotel & Conference Center Ⓗ
(717) 561-2800. **$99-$189.** 800 E Park Dr 17111. I-83 exit 48, just e on Union Deposit Rd, then 0.5 mi s. Int corridors. **Pets:** Accepted.
🆂🅰️🆅🅴 🍴 ♿ 🏊 🛜 ❌ 🔒 🖥️

▼▼▼ Candlewood Suites Harrisburg Ⓗ
(717) 652-7800. **Call for rates.** 504 N Mountain Rd 17112. I-81 exit 72B, 0.4 mi n. Int corridors. **Pets:** Accepted. ♿ 🏊 🛜 🔒 🖥️

▼▼▼ Candlewood Suites Harrisburg-Hershey Ⓗ
(717) 561-9400. **Call for rates.** 413 Portview Dr 17111. I-83 exit 45, 0.7 mi on Paxton St, then 0.4 mi s. Int corridors. **Pets:** Accepted.
🍴 ♿ 🛜 ❌ 🔒 🖥️

AAA ▼▼▼ Comfort Inn Harrisburg/Hershey Ⓗ
(717) 657-2200. **$69-$199.** 5680 Allentown Blvd 17112. I-81 exit 72, just s on N Mountain Rd, then just w on US 22. Int corridors.
Pets: Accepted. 🆂🅰️🆅🅴 ♿ 🏊 🛜 ❌ 🔒 🖥️

AAA ▼▼▼ Hilton Harrisburg Ⓗ
(717) 233-6000. **$199-$269.** One N 2nd St 17101. Jct Market St; downtown. Int corridors. **Pets:** Accepted.
🆂🅰️🆅🅴 🍴 ♿ 🏊 🛜 🔒 🖥️

Holiday Inn Express Harrisburg East 🅷
(717) 561-8100. **Call for rates.** 4021 Union Deposit Rd 17109. I-83 exit 48, just w. Int corridors. **Pets:** Accepted. 🔳🔳🔳🔳🔳🔳🔳

La Quinta Inn & Suites Harrisburg Hershey 🅷
(717) 566-7666. **$71-$306.** 265 N Hershey Rd 17112. I-81 exit 77, just s. Int corridors. **Pets:** Accepted. 🔳🔳🔳🔳🔳

Ramada Harrisburg 🅷
(717) 652-7180. **$64-$139.** 300 N Mountain Rd 17112. I-81 exit 72 southbound; exit 72B northbound, just s. Int corridors. **Pets:** Accepted. 🔳🔳🔳🔳🔳🔳🔳

Red Lion Hotel Harrisburg Hershey 🅷 ❀
(717) 939-7841. **$89-$179.** 4751 Lindle Rd 17111. I-283 exit 2, just e. Int corridors. **Pets:** Other species. $15 one-time fee/room. Designated rooms, service with restrictions, crate.
🔳🔳🔳🔳🔳🔳🔳🔳

Red Roof Inn Harrisburg - Hershey 🅼
(717) 939-1331. **$50-$126.** 950 Eisenhower Blvd 17111. I-283 exit 2, just e. Ext/int corridors. **Pets:** Accepted. 🔳🔳🔳🔳🔳

Red Roof Inn Harrisburg North 🅼
(717) 657-1445. **$49-$126.** 400 Corporate Cir 17110. I-81 exit 69 (Progress Ave), just n. Ext/int corridors. **Pets:** Accepted.
🔳🔳🔳🔳🔳🔳

Residence Inn by Marriott Harrisburg-Hershey 🅷
(717) 561-1900. **$101-$307.** 4480 Lewis Rd 17111. US 322 exit Penhar Dr, just e. Ext/int corridors. **Pets:** $100 one-time fee/room. Designated rooms, service with restrictions. 🔳🔳🔳🔳🔳🔳

Sheraton Harrisburg Hershey 🅷 ❀
(717) 564-5511. **$129-$249.** 4650 Lindle Rd 17111. I-283 exit 2, just e. Int corridors. **Pets:** Medium, dogs only. Designated rooms, service with restrictions, supervision. 🔳🔳🔳🔳🔳🔳🔳🔳🔳

Staybridge Suites Harrisburg 🅷
(717) 233-3304. **Call for rates.** 920 Wildwood Park Dr 17110. I-81 exit 67A/B, just w. Int corridors. **Pets:** Accepted.
🔳🔳🔳🔳🔳🔳🔳

TownePlace Suites by Marriott Harrisburg Hershey 🅷
(717) 558-0200. **$95-$256.** 450 Friendship Rd 17111. I-83 exit 45, 0.7 mi on Paxton St, then 0.3 mi s. Int corridors. **Pets:** Accepted.
🔳🔳🔳🔳🔳🔳🔳

HAWLEY

The Settlers Inn at Bingham Park 🅲🅸 ❀
(570) 226-2993. **$166-$276, 3 day notice.** 4 Main Ave 18428. On Main Ave (US 6), 0.3 mi w. Int corridors. **Pets:** Dogs only. $25 daily fee/pet. Designated rooms, service with restrictions, crate. 🔳🔳🔳🔳

HAZLETON

Ramada Inn Hazleton 🅷
(570) 455-2061. **$70-$100.** 1221 N Church St 18202. I-80 exit 262, 6 mi s on SR 309. Ext/int corridors. **Pets:** Accepted.
🔳🔳🔳🔳🔳

Red Roof Inn & Suites Hazleton 🅷
(570) 454-2494. **$85-$98.** 1341 N Church St 18202. I-80 exit 262, 6 mi s on SR 309. Ext/int corridors. **Pets:** Accepted.
🔳🔳🔳🔳🔳

Residence Inn by Marriott-Hazleton 🅷
(570) 455-9555. **$99-$186.** 1 Station Circle Dr 18202. I-81 exit 143, just s on SR 924 S; at Humboldt Station, just e on Commerce Dr. Int corridors. **Pets:** Accepted. 🔳🔳🔳🔳🔳🔳🔳🔳

HERSHEY

Days Inn Hershey 🅷 ❀
(717) 534-2162. **$110-$300.** 350 W Chocolate Ave 17033. On US 422; center. Int corridors. **Pets:** Large, dogs only. $15 daily fee/pet. Designated rooms, service with restrictions, crate.
🔳🔳🔳🔳🔳🔳🔳🔳

Hampton Inn & Suites Hershey 🅷
(717) 533-8400. **$119-$269.** 749 E Chocolate Ave 17033. 0.9 mi e on US 422. Int corridors. **Pets:** Accepted.
🔳🔳🔳🔳🔳🔳🔳🔳

Holiday Inn Express - Hershey/Hummelstown 🅷
(717) 583-0500. **$99-$259.** 610 Walton Ave 17036. Just nw of jct US 322, 422 and SR 39 (Hersheypark Dr); just off Hersheypark Dr. Int corridors. **Pets:** Accepted. 🔳🔳🔳🔳🔳🔳🔳🔳

The Milton Hotel 🅼 ❀
(717) 533-5665. **$89-$229.** US 422 & Sipe Ave 17033. Jct US 322, just e. Ext/int corridors. **Pets:** $20 daily fee/room. Designated rooms, service with restrictions. 🔳🔳🔳🔳🔳🔳🔳

HORSHAM

Days Inn-Horsham/Philadelphia 🅷
(215) 674-2500. **$59-$99.** 245 Easton Rd 19044. I-276 (Pennsylvania Tpke) exit 343 (SR 611), 1 mi n. Int corridors. **Pets:** Accepted.
🔳🔳🔳

Extended Stay America-Philadelphia/Horsham 🅷
(215) 784-9045. **$100-$120.** 114 Welsh Rd 19044. I-276 (Pennsylvania Tpke) exit 343 (SR 611), s toward Jenkintown, 0.6 mi w on Maryland Rd, 0.5 mi sw on Computer Ave, then just n. Int corridors.
Pets: Accepted. 🔳🔳🔳🔳

Residence Inn by Marriott-Willow Grove 🅷
(215) 443-7330. **$104-$292.** 3 Walnut Grove Dr 19044. I-276 (Pennsylvania Tpke) exit 343, 1 mi n on Easton Rd, then 1.3 mi w on Dresher Rd. Ext/int corridors. **Pets:** Accepted.
🔳🔳🔳🔳🔳🔳🔳

HUNTINGDON

Comfort Inn 🅷
(814) 643-1600. **$99-$169.** 100 S 4th St 16652. I-99 exit 48, 8.8 mi on SR 453, then 9.8 mi on US 22 and S 4th St; just off US 22. Int corridors. **Pets:** Accepted. 🔳🔳🔳🔳🔳

Huntingdon Motor Inn 🅼
(814) 643-1133. **Call for rates.** 6920 Motor Inn Dr 16652. On US 22 (William Penn Hwy) at SR 26. Ext corridors. **Pets:** Small. $10 daily fee/pet. Designated rooms, service with restrictions, supervision.
🔳🔳🔳

The Mill Stone Manor 🅼
(814) 643-0108. **Call for rates.** 11979 William Penn Hwy 16652. On US 22 (William Penn Hwy); 3 mi n of downtown. Ext/int corridors.
Pets: Accepted. 🔳🔳🔳🔳🔳

INDIANA (INDIANA COUNTY)

Park Inn by Radisson 🅷
(724) 463-3561. **$109-$159.** 1395 Wayne Ave 15701. US 422 exit Wayne Ave, 1 mi n. Ext/int corridors. **Pets:** Small. $30 one-time fee/pet. Designated rooms, service with restrictions, crate.
🔳🔳🔳🔳🔳🔳🔳

JOHNSTOWN

Holiday Inn Downtown 🅷
(814) 535-7777. **Call for rates.** 250 Market St 15901. Corner of Market and Vine sts; downtown. Int corridors. **Pets:** Accepted.
🔳🔳🔳🔳🔳🔳🔳

▼▼▼ Quality Inn & Suites H
(814) 266-3678. **$125-$215.** 455 Theatre Dr 15904. US 219 exit Elton
(SR 756), just e. Int corridors. **Pets:** Accepted.
🏊 📶 ✕ 🛏 💻

▼▼ Sleep Inn H
(814) 262-9292. **$95-$160.** 453 Theatre Dr 15904. US 219 exit Elton
(SR 756), just e. Int corridors. **Pets:** Accepted. 📶 ✕ 🛏 💻

AAA ▼▼▼ Super 8 Johnstown H
(814) 535-5600. **$60-$200.** 627 Solomon Run Rd 15904. US 219 exit
Galleria Dr, just w. Int corridors. **Pets:** Accepted.
SAVE 🍴 📶 ✕ 🛏 💻

JONES MILLS
▼▼ Log Cabin Lodge & Suites M
(724) 593-8200. **Call for rates.** 288 Rt 711 15646. I-76 (Pennsylvania
Tpke) exit 91, 2 mi on SR 31 E, then just s. Ext corridors.
Pets: Accepted. ⌖M 📶 🛏 💻

JONESTOWN
AAA ▼▼▼ Comfort Inn Lebanon Valley-Ft. Indiantown
Gap M
(717) 865-8080. **$63-$188.** 16 Marsanna Ln 17038. I-81 exit 90, just w.
Int corridors. **Pets:** Accepted. SAVE ⌖M 🏊 📶 ✕ 🛏 💻

▼▼ Days Inn Lebanon/Fort Indiantown Gap H 🐾
(717) 865-4064. **$89-$189.** 3 Everest Ln 17038. I-81 exit 90, just e. Int
corridors. **Pets:** Medium. $10 daily fee/pet. Designated rooms, service
with restrictions, supervision. 🍴 ⌖M 📶 🛏 💻

KING OF PRUSSIA
AAA ▼▼▼ DoubleTree by Hilton Philadelphia Valley
Forge H
(610) 337-1200. **$119-$219.** 301 W Dekalb Pike 19406. I-76 (Pennsylvania Tpke) exit 326 (Valley Forge Rd), 1.4 mi ne on US 202 N. Int
corridors. **Pets:** Accepted. SAVE 🍴 ⌖M 🏊 📶 ✕ 🛏 💻

AAA ▼▼▼ Hyatt House Philadelphia/King of
Prussia H
(610) 265-0300. **$109-$349.** 240 Mall Blvd 19406. I-76 (Pennsylvania
Tpke) exit 326 (Valley Forge Rd), 1 mi n of jct US 202 on Gulph Rd.
Int corridors. **Pets:** Accepted. SAVE ⌖M 🏊 📶 ✕ 🛏 💻

AAA ▼▼▼ Hyatt Place Philadelphia/King of
Prussia H
(484) 690-3000. **$99-$349.** 440 American Ave 19406. I-76 (Pennsylvania Tpke) exit 326 (Valley Forge Rd); Schuylkill Expwy exit 328A (Mall
Blvd), 1.3 mi n on N Gulph Rd, 1 mi ne on 1st Ave, then just e. Int
corridors. **Pets:** Accepted. SAVE 🍴 ⌖M 🏊 📶 ✕ 🛏 💻

AAA ▼▼▼ Sheraton Valley Forge H
(484) 238-1800. **$129-$359.** 480 N Gulph Rd 19406. I-76 (Pennsylvania
Tpke) exit 326 (Valley Forge Rd), 0.5 mi w. Int corridors.
Pets: Accepted. SAVE 🍴 ⌖M 🏊 📶 ✕ 🛏 💻

KITTANNING
▼▼ Quality Inn Royle M 🐾
(724) 543-1159. **$90-$159.** 405 Butler Rd 16201. SR 28 exit US 422 W.
Ext/int corridors. **Pets:** Medium. $15 daily fee/pet. Designated rooms,
service with restrictions, crate. ⌖M 📶 ✕ 🛏 💻

KULPSVILLE
▼▼▼ Holiday Inn Lansdale H
(215) 368-3800. **Call for rates.** 1750 Sumneytown Pike 19443. I-476
(Pennsylvania Tpke NE Ext) exit 31, just e. Int corridors.
Pets: Accepted. 🍴 ⌖M 🏊 📶 ✕ 🛏 💻

LAMAR
▼▼ Quality Inn Mill Hall H
(570) 726-4901. **$79-$189.** 31 Hospitality Ln 17751. I-80 exit 173, just n
on SR 64. Int corridors. **Pets:** $10 daily fee/room. Designated rooms,
service with restrictions, supervision. 🏊 📶 🛏 💻

LANCASTER
▼▼▼ Eden Resort & Suites H 🐾
(717) 569-6444. **$109-$219.** 222 Eden Rd 17601. Jct US 30 (Lincoln
Hwy) and SR 272 (Oregon Pike). Ext/int corridors. **Pets:** Large, other
species. $20 daily fee/pet. Designated rooms, service with restrictions,
crate. 🍴 ⌖M 🏊 ✕ 📶 ✕ 🛏 💻

AAA ▼▼▼ Hawthorn Suites by Wyndham H
(717) 290-7100. **$90-$170.** 2045 Lincoln Hwy 17602. Jct US 30 (Lincoln
Hwy). Int corridors. **Pets:** Medium, dogs only. $100 deposit/room, $50
one-time fee/room. Designated rooms, service with restrictions, crate.
SAVE ⌖M 📶 ✕ 🛏 💻

LANGHORNE
AAA ▼▼▼ Red Roof Inn Philadelphia Oxford
Valley M
(215) 750-6200. **$59-$140.** 3100 Cabot Blvd W 19047. I-95 exit 46A
(Oxford Valley Rd), just e off US 1 N; 0.5 mi n of Sesame Place. Ext
corridors. **Pets:** Accepted. SAVE 🍴 ⌖M 📶 ✕ 🛏 💻

AAA ▼▼▼ Residence Inn by Marriott Philadelphia
Langhorne H
(215) 946-6500. **$89-$362.** 15 E Cabot Blvd 19047. I-95 exit 46A
(Oxford Valley Rd), just e off US 1 N; 0.5 mi n of Sesame Place. Int
corridors. **Pets:** Accepted. SAVE ⌖M 🏊 📶 ✕ 🛏 💻

LEBANON (LEBANON COUNTY)
▼▼▼ Berry Patch Bed and Breakfast BB
(717) 865-7219. **$135-$239, 14 day notice.** 115 Moore Rd 17046. I-81
exit 90, 2.8 mi s on SR 72, 1 mi e on New Bunker Hill St, 0.8 mi s on
S Lancaster St, then just e, follow signs. Ext/int corridors.
Pets: Accepted. 🍴 📶 ✕ 🐾 🛏

LEHIGHTON
AAA ▼▼▼ Country Inn & Suites By Carlson H
(610) 379-5066. **$99-$300.** 1619 Interchange Rd 18235. I-476 (Pennsylvania Tpke NE Ext) exit 74 (US 209), just w. Int corridors.
Pets: Accepted. SAVE ⌖M 🏊 📶 ✕ 🛏 💻

LINCOLN FALLS
▼▼▼ Morgan Century Farm BB
(570) 924-4909. **Call for rates.** 7043 Rt 154 18616. Just w on SR 87,
0.6 mi s; in village. Ext/int corridors. **Pets:** Medium. $15 one-time fee/
pet. Designated rooms, service with restrictions, supervision.
🍴 📶 ✕ 🐾 🛏 💻

LIONVILLE
▼▼▼ Clarion Hotel H
(610) 363-1100. **$100-$200.** 815 N Pottstown Pike 19341. I-76 (Pennsylvania Tpke) exit 312, 2 mi s on SR 100. Int corridors.
Pets: Accepted. 🍴 ⌖M 🏊 📶 ✕ 🛏 💻

▼▼▼ Comfort Suites Exton H
(610) 594-4770. **$94-$239.** 700 W Uwchlan Ave 19341. I-76 (Pennsylvania Tpke) exit 312, 1 mi s on SR 100. Int corridors. **Pets:** Small. $50
daily fee/pet. Service with restrictions, supervision.
⌖M 🏊 📶 ✕ 🛏 💻

▼▼ Extended Stay America-Philadelphia/Exton H
(610) 524-7185. **$95-$120.** 877 N Pottstown Pike (Rt 100) 19353. I-76
(Pennsylvania Tpke) exit 312, 1.8 mi s. Int corridors. **Pets:** Accepted.
📶 🛏 💻

▼▼ **Fairfield Inn by Marriott Philadelphia West Chester/Exton** H
(610) 524-8811. **$70-$207.** 5 N Pottstown Pike 19341. I-76 (Pennsylvania Tpke) exit 312, 0.5 mi s; jct SR 113 and 100. Int corridors. **Pets:** Accepted. ⓈⓂ ⌒ ⌒ ⓍⓁⒹⒾ

▼▼▼ **Hampton Inn Exton/Downingtown** H 🐾
(610) 363-5555. **$99-$199.** 4 N Pottstown Pike 19341. I-76 (Pennsylvania Tpke) exit 312, 0.5 mi s; jct SR 113 and 100. Int corridors. **Pets:** Other species. Service with restrictions, crate.
⌒ ⌒ Ⓧ Ⓘ Ⓓ

▼▼ **Residence Inn by Marriott Philadelphia Great Valley/Exton** H
(610) 594-9705. **$97-$254.** 10 N Pottstown Pike 19341. I-76 (Pennsylvania Tpke) exit 312, 1 mi s on SR 100. Int corridors. **Pets:** Other species. $100 one-time fee/room. Service with restrictions.
ⒼⓂ ⌒ ⌒ Ⓧ Ⓘ Ⓓ

LITITZ

◈◈◈ ▼▼▼▼ **Holiday Inn Express & Suites** H
(717) 625-2366. **Call for rates.** 101 Crosswinds Dr 17543. 1.4 mi s on SR 501 (Lititz Pike), just w on Trolley Run Rd. Int corridors. **Pets:** Accepted. ⓢⓐⓥⓔ ⒼⓂ ⌒ ⌒ Ⓧ Ⓘ Ⓓ

LOCK HAVEN

◈◈◈ ▼▼▼ **Best Western Lock Haven** H 🐾
(570) 748-3297. **$119-$199.** 101 E Walnut St 17745. US 220 exit 111 (SR 120 W), just w. Int corridors. **Pets:** Other species. $12 daily fee/pet. Service with restrictions, crate. ⓢⓐⓥⓔ ⒼⓂ ⌒ Ⓘ Ⓓ

MALVERN

▼▼▼ **The Desmond Hotel and Conference Center Malvern** H
(610) 296-9800. **Call for rates.** 1 Liberty Blvd 19355. US 202 exit SR 29 N, 0.5 mi w. Int corridors. **Pets:** Accepted.
Ⓨ ⌒ ⌒ Ⓧ Ⓘ Ⓓ

▼▼ **Extended Stay America Malvern** H
(610) 695-9200. **$105-$140.** 8 E Swedesford Rd 19355. Just w of US 202 and SR 29 N. Int corridors. **Pets:** Accepted. ⌒ ⌒ Ⓧ Ⓘ

▼▼ **Extended Stay America-Philadelphia Great Valley** H
(610) 240-0455. **$100-$125.** 300 Morehall Rd (SR 29) 19355. US 202 exit SR 29 N. Int corridors. **Pets:** Accepted. ⒼⓂ ⌒ Ⓘ Ⓓ

▼▼▼ **Homewood Suites by Hilton** H 🐾
(610) 296-3500. **Call for rates.** 12 E Swedesford Rd 19355. US 202 exit SR 29, follow signs. Int corridors. **Pets:** Other species. $50 one-time fee/room. Service with restrictions, supervision.
ⒼⓂ ⌒ ⌒ Ⓧ Ⓘ Ⓓ

◈◈◈ ▼▼▼▼ **Sheraton Great Valley Hotel** H
(610) 524-5500. **Call for rates.** 707 E Lancaster Ave 19355. Jct US 202 and 30 E. Int corridors. **Pets:** Accepted.
ⓢⓐⓥⓔ Ⓨ ⒼⓂ ⌒ ⌒ Ⓧ Ⓘ Ⓓ

◈◈◈ ▼▼▼▼ **Sonesta ES Suites Malvern** H
(610) 296-4343. **Call for rates.** 20 Morehall Rd 19355. Jct US 30 and SR 29, just nw. Ext/int corridors. **Pets:** Accepted.
ⓢⓐⓥⓔ ⌒ ⌒ Ⓧ Ⓘ Ⓓ

MANSFIELD

◈◈◈ ▼▼▼ **Comfort Inn** H
(570) 662-3000. **$119-$169.** 300 Gateway Dr 16933. Jct US 6 and 15. Int corridors. **Pets:** Accepted. ⓢⓐⓥⓔ ⒼⓂ ⌒ Ⓧ Ⓘ Ⓓ

MARIENVILLE

▼ **The Forest Lodge & Campground** M
(814) 927-8790. **$79, 14 day notice.** 44078 Rt 66 16239. 6 mi n of town. Ext/int corridors. **Pets:** Accepted. ⌒ Ⓧ Ⓘ Ⓓ

MARS

▼▼▼▼ **Comfort Inn Cranberry Township** H
(724) 772-2700. **$99-$179.** 924 Sheraton Dr 16046. I-76 (Pennsylvania Tpke) exit 28; I-79 exit 76 (US 19) northbound; exit 78 southbound, 0.5 mi s on US 19. Int corridors. **Pets:** Accepted. ⒼⓂ ⌒ Ⓧ Ⓘ Ⓓ

▼▼ **Super 8-Cranberry** H
(724) 776-9700. **$90-$230.** 929 Sheraton Dr 16046. I-76 (Pennsylvania Tpke) exit 28; I-79 exit 76 (US 19) northbound; exit 78 southbound, 0.5 mi s on US 19. Int corridors. **Pets:** Small. $20 daily fee/pet. Service with restrictions, supervision. ⓈⓂ ⌒ Ⓧ Ⓘ

MATAMORAS

◈◈◈ ▼▼▼▼ **Best Western Inn at Hunt's Landing** H
(570) 491-2400. **$109-$209.** 120 Rt 6 & 209 18336. I-84 exit 53, just s. Int corridors. **Pets:** Accepted. ⓢⓐⓥⓔ Ⓨ ⌒ Ⓧ ⌒ Ⓧ Ⓘ Ⓓ

MEADVILLE

▼▼ **Quality Inn Meadville** M
(814) 333-8883. **$80-$170.** 17259 Conneaut Lake Rd 16335. I-79 exit 147B, just w on US 322. Ext/int corridors. **Pets:** $20 daily fee/pet. Service with restrictions, supervision. ⒼⓂ ⌒ Ⓘ Ⓓ

MECHANICSBURG

▼▼ **Comfort Inn Mechanicsburg/Harrisburg South** H
(717) 766-3700. **$104-$169.** 1012 Wesley Dr 17055. I-76 (Pennsylvania Tpke) exit 236, 1 mi n to Wesley Dr exit, then just w. Int corridors. **Pets:** Accepted. ⒼⓂ ⌒ ⌒ Ⓧ Ⓘ Ⓓ

▼▼▼ **Country Inn & Suites by Carlson Harrisburg West** H
(717) 796-0300. **$99-$179, 7 day notice.** 4943 Gettysburg Rd 17055. US 15 exit Rossmoyne Rd/Wesley Dr. Int corridors. **Pets:** Medium, dogs only. $25 one-time fee/pet. Service with restrictions, supervision.
ⒼⓂ ⌒ ⌒ Ⓧ Ⓘ Ⓓ

▼▼▼ **Hampton Inn-Harrisburg West** H
(717) 691-1300. **$109-$169.** 4950 Ritter Rd 17055. I-76 (Pennsylvania Tpke) exit 236, 1 mi n to Rossmoyne Rd exit. Int corridors. **Pets:** Accepted. ⒼⓂ ⌒ ⌒ Ⓧ Ⓘ Ⓓ

▼▼▼ **Holiday Inn Express Harrisburg SW-Mechanicsburg** H
(717) 790-0924. **$99-$249.** 6325 Carlisle Pike 17050. Jct Carlisle Pike and US 11, 1 mi w on US 11. Int corridors. **Pets:** Medium. $25 daily fee/room. Service with restrictions, crate.
Ⓨ ⒼⓂ ⌒ Ⓧ Ⓘ Ⓓ

▼▼▼ **Homewood Suites by Hilton-Harrisburg West** H
(717) 697-4900. **$129-$229.** 5001 Ritter Rd 17055. I-76 (Pennsylvania Tpke) exit 236, 1 mi n to Rossmoyne Rd exit. Int corridors. **Pets:** Accepted. ⒺⒸⓄ ⒼⓂ ⌒ ⌒ Ⓧ Ⓘ Ⓓ

▼▼ **La Quinta Inn & Suites** H
(717) 790-1520. **$75-$145.** 350 Bentcreek Blvd 17050. I-81 exit 57, 1 mi e on SR 114. Int corridors. **Pets:** Accepted.
ⒼⓂ ⌒ ⌒ Ⓧ Ⓘ Ⓓ

▼▼ **Motel 6** M
(717) 766-0238. **Call for rates.** 381 Cumberland Pkwy 17055. I-76 (Pennsylvania Tpke) exit 236, just s, then exit Cumberland Pkwy. Ext corridors. **Pets:** Other species. Service with restrictions, supervision.
Ⓨ ⌒ ⌒ Ⓘ

▼▼ **Park Inn by Radisson Harrisburg West** 🅷
(717) 697-0321. **Call for rates.** 5401 Carlisle Pike 17050. Jct Carlisle Pike and US 11, just w. Ext/int corridors. **Pets:** Accepted.
🍴 🛗 ⊠ 🛜 ⊠ 🛠 💻

▼▼▼ **TownePlace Suites by Marriott** 🅷
(717) 691-1400. **$85-$265.** 4915 Ritter Rd 17055. I-76 exit 236, 1 mi n to Rossmoyne Rd exit. Int corridors. **Pets:** Accepted.
🛗ᴹ 🛜 ⊠ 🛠 💻

▼▼▼ **Wingate by Wyndham Mechanicsburg/Harrisburg West** 🅷
(717) 766-2710. **$109-$209.** 385 Cumberland Pkwy 17055. I-76 (Pennsylvania Tpke) exit 236, just s. Int corridors. **Pets:** $25 daily fee/pet. Service with restrictions, crate. 🛗ᴹ 🛗 🛜 ⊠ 🛠 💻

MEDIA
▼▼ **Quality Inn** Ⓜ
(610) 565-5800. **$95-$251.** 4 S New Middletown Rd 19063. US 1, just s on SR 352. Ext corridors. **Pets:** Accepted. 🛗ᴹ 🛜 🛠 💻

MERCER
▼▼▼ **Candlewood Suites Grove City** 🅷
(724) 748-6900. **Call for rates.** 37 Holiday Blvd 16137. I-79 exit 113, just w on SR 208. Int corridors. **Pets:** Accepted.
🛗ᴹ 🛜 ⊠ 🛠 💻

MIFFLINVILLE
▼▼ **Super 8 - Mifflinville** Ⓜ
(570) 759-6778. **$65-$140.** 450 W 3rd St 18631. I-80 exit 242 (SR 339), just n. Ext corridors. **Pets:** Accepted. 🛗ᴹ 🛜 🛠 💻

MILFORD
▼▼▼ **Hotel Fauchère** 🅷 🐾
(570) 409-1212. **$140-$594, 7 day notice.** 401 Broad St 18337. In historic downtown. Int corridors. **Pets:** $25 daily fee/pet. Designated rooms, service with restrictions, crate. 🍴 🛗ᴹ 🛜 ⊠ 🛠 💻

MILROY
🆎 ▼▼ **Best Western Nittany Inn Milroy** 🅷
(717) 667-9595. **$79-$110.** 5 Commerce Dr 17063. US 322 exit Milroy, just e. Int corridors. **Pets:** Large, dogs only. $20 daily fee/pet. Service with restrictions, supervision. 🆂🅰🆅🅴 🍴 🛗 🛜 ⊠ 🛠 💻

MONACA
▼▼▼ **Hampton Inn Beaver Valley/Pittsburgh** 🅷
(724) 774-5580. **$134-$154.** 202 Fairview Dr 15061. I-376 exit 39, just n. Int corridors. **Pets:** Medium, other species. Designated rooms, service with restrictions, supervision. 🛗ᴹ 🛜 🛜 🛠 💻

▼▼ **Holiday Inn Express Hotel & Suites-Center Township** 🅷
(724) 728-5121. **Call for rates.** 105 Stone Quarry Rd 15061. I-376 exit 39 (SR 18 N/Frankfort Rd), just n. Int corridors. **Pets:** Accepted.
🛗ᴹ 🛜 🛜 ⊠ 🛠 💻

MONROEVILLE
🆎 ▼▼▼ **DoubleTree by Hilton Hotel Pittsburgh - Monroeville Convention Center** 🅷
(412) 373-7300. **$109-$229.** 101 Mall Blvd 15146. I-76 (Pennsylvania Tpke) exit 57, 2 mi w on US 22. Int corridors. **Pets:** Accepted.
🆂🅰🆅🅴 🍴 🛗ᴹ 🛜 🛜 🛠 💻

▼▼ **Extended Stay America Pittsburgh-Monroeville** 🅷
(412) 856-8400. **$105-$140.** 3851 Northern Pike 15146. I-76 (Pennsylvania Tpke) exit 57, 1.2 mi w on Business Rt US 22. Int corridors. **Pets:** Accepted. 🛗ᴹ 🛜 ⊠ 🛠 💻

▼▼▼ **Hampton Inn Monroeville/Pittsburgh** 🅷
(412) 380-4000. **$109-$179.** 3000 Mosside Blvd 15146. I-76 (Pennsylvania Tpke) exit 57; I-376 exit 84A, 0.3 mi s on SR 48. Int corridors. **Pets:** Accepted. 🛗ᴹ 🛜 🛜 ⊠ 🛠 💻

🆎 ▼▼ **Red Roof PLUS+ Pittsburgh East - Monroeville** Ⓜ
(412) 856-4738. **$52-$157.** 2729 Mosside Blvd 15146. I-76 (Pennsylvania Tpke) exit 57; I-376 exit 84A, 0.8 mi s on SR 48. Ext corridors. **Pets:** Accepted. 🆂🅰🆅🅴 🛗ᴹ 🛜 ⊠ 🛠 💻

MONTGOMERYVILLE
▼▼▼ **Quality Inn Montgomeryville** 🅷
(215) 361-3600. **$79-$179.** 678 Bethlehem Pike 18936. Jct SR 463 and US 202, 0.3 mi n on SR 309. Int corridors. **Pets:** Accepted.
🛗ᴹ 🛜 ⊠ 🛠 💻

🆎 ▼▼▼ **Residence Inn by Marriott Philadelphia/Montgomeryville** 🅷
(267) 468-0111. **$63-$246.** 1110 Bethlehem Pike 19454. I-276 (Pennsylvania Tpke) exit 339, 6.5 mi n on SR 309. Int corridors. **Pets:** $75 one-time fee/room. Service with restrictions, crate.
🆂🅰🆅🅴 🛗ᴹ 🛜 🛜 ⊠ 🛠 💻

MOON RUN
▼▼▼ **Candlewood Suites** 🅷
(412) 787-7770. **$109-$159.** 100 Chauvet Dr 15275. I-376 exit 59 (Robinson Town Center Blvd), just s. Int corridors. **Pets:** Accepted.
🍴 🛗ᴹ 🛜 ⊠ 🛠 💻

▼▼▼ **Homewood Suites** 🅷
(412) 490-0440. **Call for rates.** 2000 GSK Dr 15108. I-376 exit 59 (Montour Run Rd), 0.9 mi w, then just w to Fedex Dr; jct Montour Run Rd and Fedex Dr. Int corridors. **Pets:** Accepted.
🍴 🛗ᴹ 🛜 ⊠ 🛠 💻

🆎 ▼▼▼ **Hyatt Place Pittsburgh Airport** 🅷
(412) 494-0202. **$79-$259.** 6011 Campbells Run Rd 15205. I-376 exit 60B (Crafton/SR 60 S), just w. Int corridors. **Pets:** Small, dogs only. $75 one-time fee/pet. Service with restrictions, supervision.
🆂🅰🆅🅴 🛗ᴹ 🛜 🛜 ⊠ 🛠 💻

🆎 ▼▼▼ **Pittsburgh Airport Marriott** 🅷 🐾
(412) 788-8800. **$87-$313.** 777 Aten Rd 15108. I-376 exit 58 (Montour Run Rd), just n. Int corridors. **Pets:** Other species. $75 one-time fee/room. Service with restrictions, supervision.
🆂🅰🆅🅴 🍴 🛗ᴹ 🛜 🛜 ⊠ 💻

▼▼▼ **Residence Inn by Marriott Pittsburgh Airport Coraopolis** 🅷
(412) 787-3300. **$84-$237.** 1500 Park Lane Dr 15275. I-376 exit 58 (Montour Run Rd), just w on Cliff Mine Dr to Summit Park Dr, just s to Park Lane Dr, then just e. Ext/int corridors. **Pets:** Accepted.
🛗ᴹ 🛜 ⊠ 🛜 ⊠ 🛠 💻

▼▼▼ **TownePlace Suites Pittsburgh Airport/Robinson Township** 🅷
(412) 494-4000. **$93-$167.** 1006 Sutherland Dr 15205. I-376 exit 59, 0.5 mi ne on Robinson Town Centre Blvd, just n on Park Manor Blvd, then just w. Int corridors. **Pets:** Accepted. 🛗ᴹ 🛜 ⊠ 🛠 💻

MORGANTOWN
▼▼▼ **Holiday Inn** 🅷
(610) 286-3000. **$101-$126.** 6170 Morgantown Rd 19543. I-76 (Pennsylvania Tpke) exit 298, just s on SR 10. Int corridors. **Pets:** Other species. $25 daily fee/pet. Designated rooms, no service, supervision.
🍴 🛗ᴹ 🛜 🛜 ⊠ 🛠 💻

MORRISVILLE

Quality Inn & Suites NJ State Capital Area H
(215) 428-2600. **$80-$209.** 7 S Pennsylvania Ave 19067. US 1 exit Pennsylvania Ave, just n. Int corridors. **Pets:** Accepted.
SAVE ⑤M 🛜 ⨉ 🖥 🖵

MOUNTVILLE

MainStay Suites H
(717) 285-2500. **$75-$220.** 314 Primrose Ln 17554. US 30 (Lincoln Hwy) exit Mountville, just n on Stoney Battery Rd, just w on Highland Dr, then just s. Int corridors. **Pets:** Other species. $100 deposit/pet, $15 daily fee/pet. Service with restrictions, supervision.
SAVE 🍴 ⑤M 🛜 ⨉ 🖥 🖵

NEW COLUMBIA

Holiday Inn Express H
(570) 568-1100. **$99-$229.** 160 Commerce Park Dr 17856. I-80 exit 210A (US 15/New Columbia), just s. Int corridors. **Pets:** Medium, other species. $20 daily fee/pet. Designated rooms, service with restrictions, crate. SAVE ⑤M 🛜 ⨉ 🖥 🖵

NEW CUMBERLAND

Best Western Plus New Cumberland Inn & Suites H
(717) 774-4440. **$91-$145.** 702 Limekiln Rd 17070. I-83 exit 40A, just w. Int corridors. **Pets:** Accepted. SAVE ⑤M 🛜 🖥 🖵

Clarion Hotel & Conference Center Harrisburg West H
(717) 774-2721. **Call for rates.** 148 Sheraton Dr 17070. I-83 exit 40A, just se. Int corridors. **Pets:** Medium. $25 daily fee/room. Designated rooms, service with restrictions, supervision.
🍴 ⑤M 🛜 ⨉ 🖥 🖵

Days Inn Harrisburg South H
(717) 774-4156. **$65-$135.** 353 Lewisberry Rd 17070. I-83 exit 39A, just ne. Int corridors. **Pets:** Accepted. 🍴 🛜 ⨉ 🖥 🖵

Holiday Inn Express New Cumberland H
(717) 774-6400. **$109-$189.** 190 Beacon Hill Blvd 17070. I-83 exit 40A, just ne. Int corridors. **Pets:** Accepted. 🍴 ⑤M 🛜 ⨉ 🖥 🖵

NEW HOPE

1870 Wedgwood Inn of New Hope BB
(215) 862-2570. **Call for rates.** 111 W Bridge St (SR 179) 18938. 0.5 mi w of SR 32; downtown. Int corridors. **Pets:** Accepted.
🛜 ⨉ 🖥 🖵

Aaron Burr House Inn & Conference Center BB 🐾
(215) 862-3937. **Call for rates.** 80 W Bridge St (SR 179) 18938. 0.5 mi w of SR 32; at W Bridge and Chestnut sts. Int corridors. **Pets:** Medium, dogs only. $25 daily fee/pet. Designated rooms, service with restrictions.
🛜 ⨉ 🐾 🖥

PHILADELPHIA *(Restaurants p. 621)*

Aloft Philadelphia Airport H 🐾
(267) 298-1700. **$129-$299.** 4301 Island Ave 19153. I-95 and SR 291 exit 13 northbound; exit 15 southbound. Int corridors. **Pets:** Medium, dogs only. Service with restrictions, crate.
SAVE 🍴 ⑤M 🛜 ⨉ 🖥 🖵

Four Points by Sheraton Philadelphia Airport H 🐾
(215) 492-0400. **Call for rates.** 4105 Island Ave 19153. Jct I-95 and SR 291 exit 13 northbound; exit 15 southbound. Int corridors. **Pets:** Medium, dogs only. Service with restrictions, crate.
SAVE 🍴 ⑤M 🛜 ⨉ 🖥 🖵

The Franklin Hotel at Independence Park H
(215) 925-0000. **$111-$626.** 401 Chestnut St 19106. Jct 4th St. Int corridors. **Pets:** Accepted. SAVE 🍴 ⑤M 🛜 ⨉ 🖥 🖵

Hawthorn Suites by Wyndham Philadelphia Airport H
(215) 492-1611. **$129-$229.** 4630 Island Ave 19153. I-95 exit 13 northbound; exit 15 southbound, 0.5 mi e; just e of SR 291. Ext corridors. **Pets:** Accepted. SAVE ⑤M 🛜 ⨉ 🖥 🖵

Hilton Philadelphia at Penn's Landing H
(215) 928-1234. **Call for rates.** 201 S Columbus Blvd 19106. Jct S Columbus Blvd and Dock St. Int corridors. **Pets:** Accepted.
SAVE 🍴 ⑤M 🛜 ⨉ 🛜 ⨉ 🖥 🖵

Home2 Suites by Hilton Philadelphia Convention Center H
(215) 627-1850. **$139-$399.** 1200 Arch St 19107. Between Market and Arch sts. Int corridors. **Pets:** Accepted. ⑤M 🛜 ⨉ 🖥 🖵

Hotel Palomar-Philadelphia H
(215) 563-5006. **$179-$549, 3 day notice.** 117 S 17th St 19103. Corner of 17th and Samson sts. Int corridors. **Pets:** Accepted.
SAVE ECO 🍴 ⑤M 🛜 ⨉ 🖥 🖵

Hyatt at The Bellevue H
(215) 893-1234. **$119-$449, 3 day notice.** 200 S Broad St 19102. Between Walnut and Locust sts. Int corridors. **Pets:** Accepted.
SAVE 🍴 ⑤M ⨉ 🛜 ⨉ 🖥 🖵

Kimpton Hotel Monaco Philadelphia H
(215) 925-2111. **$179-$549, 3 day notice.** 433 Chestnut St 19106. Jct 5th and Chestnut sts. Int corridors. **Pets:** Accepted.
SAVE 🍴 ⑤M 🛜 ⨉ 🖥 🖵

Le Méridien Philadelphia H
(215) 422-8200. **$149-$699.** 1421 Arch St 19102. Between Broad and 15th sts. Int corridors. **Pets:** Accepted.
SAVE 🍴 ⑤M 🛜 ⨉ 🖥 🖵

Loews Philadelphia Hotel H
(215) 627-1200. **Call for rates.** 1200 Market St 19107. Corner of 12th and Market sts. Int corridors. **Pets:** Accepted.
SAVE 🍴 ⑤M 🛜 ⨉ 🛜 ⨉ 🖥 🖵

Residence Inn by Marriott Center City Philadelphia H
(215) 557-0005. **$106-$451.** 1 E Penn Square 19107. Jct Market and Juniper sts. Int corridors. **Pets:** Accepted.
SAVE ⑤M 🛜 ⨉ 🖥 🖵

Residence Inn by Marriott Philadelphia Airport H
(215) 921-8011. **$133-$291.** 3701 Island Ave 19153. I-95 exit 13 northbound, just n; exit 14 southbound, 0.8 mi w. Int corridors. **Pets:** Medium, other species. $75 one-time fee/pet. Service with restrictions. 🍴 ⑤M 🛜 ⨉ 🖥 🖵

The Rittenhouse H 🐾
(215) 546-9000. **Call for rates.** 210 W Rittenhouse Square 19103. Jct W Rittenhouse Square and Walnut St. Int corridors. **Pets:** $150 one-time fee/room. Supervision. 🍴 ⑤M 🛜 ⨉ 🛜 ⨉ 🖥 🖵

The Ritz-Carlton Philadelphia H
(215) 523-8000. **Call for rates.** Ten Avenue of the Arts 19102. On Broad St; between Market and Chestnut sts. Int corridors.
Pets: Accepted. 🍴 ⑤M ⨉ 🐾 ⨉ 🖥 🖵

Sheraton Philadelphia Downtown H

(215) 448-2000. **$129-$399.** 201 N 17th St 19103. Jct 17th and Race sts. Int corridors. **Pets:** Accepted.

Sheraton Philadelphia University City Hotel H

(215) 387-8000. **Call for rates.** 3549 Chestnut St 19104. I-76 (Schuylkill Expwy) exit 345, 0.5 mi w; jct 36th St; at University of Pennsylvania. Int corridors. **Pets:** Large, dogs only. Service with restrictions, supervision.

Sheraton Suites Philadelphia Airport H

(215) 365-6600. **Call for rates.** 4101 Island Ave 19153. Jct I-95 and SR 291 exit 13 northbound; exit 13 southbound. Int corridors. **Pets:** Accepted.

Sofitel Philadelphia H

(215) 569-8300. **$160-$600.** 120 S 17th St 19103. Jct Sansom and 17th sts. Int corridors. **Pets:** Accepted.

The Warwick Hotel Rittenhouse Square H 🐾

(215) 735-6000. **$109-$699.** 220 S 17th St 19103. Between Walnut and Locust sts; main entrance on 17th St. Int corridors. **Pets:** Medium, dogs only. $100 deposit/pet, $50 one-time fee/pet. Service with restrictions, crate.

The Westin Philadelphia H

(215) 563-1600. **$179-$799.** 99 S 17th St at Liberty Pl 19103. Between Market and Chestnut sts. Int corridors. **Pets:** Accepted.

The Windsor Suites H 🐾

(215) 981-5678. **Call for rates.** 1700 Benjamin Franklin Pkwy 19103. At 17th St and Benjamin Franklin Pkwy. Int corridors. **Pets:** Other species. Designated rooms, service with restrictions, crate.

PINE GROVE

Comfort Inn H

(570) 345-8031. **$55-$169.** 433 Suedberg Rd 17963. I-81 exit 100, just e. Int corridors. **Pets:** Other species. $10 daily fee/pet. Designated rooms, service with restrictions, supervision.

Hampton Inn Pine Grove H

(570) 345-4505. **$129-$229.** 481 Suedberg Rd 17963. I-81 exit 100, just w. Int corridors. **Pets:** Large, other species. $25 daily fee/pet. Designated rooms, service with restrictions, supervision.

PITTSBURGH

DoubleTree by Hilton Hotel & Suites Pittsburgh Downtown H

(412) 281-5800. **$159-$289.** One Bigelow Square 15219. Jct Bigelow Square and 6th St; just n of Grant St. Int corridors. **Pets:** Accepted.

Fairmont Pittsburgh H

(412) 773-8800. **$219-$599.** 510 Market St 15222. Between Market St and 5th Ave; in cultural district. Int corridors. **Pets:** Accepted.

Hampton Inn University Center/Pittsburgh H

(412) 681-1000. **$129-$199.** 3315 Hamlet St 15213. I-376 exit 72A, 0.6 mi e, then e. Int corridors. **Pets:** Medium. $50 one-time fee/room. Designated rooms, service with restrictions, crate.

Home2 Suites by Hilton Pittsburgh/McCandless H

(412) 630-8400. **$109-$159.** 8630 Duncan Ave 15237. I-279 exit 4, 7 mi n on US 19 Truck Babcock, then left to Duncan Ave. Int corridors. **Pets:** Accepted.

Homewood Suites by Hilton Pittsburgh Downtown H

(412) 232-0200. **Call for rates.** 1410 Smallman St 15222. Jct 14th st, just e. Int corridors. **Pets:** Accepted.

Hotel Indigo Pittsburgh East Liberty H

(412) 665-0555. **$129-$259.** 123 N Highland Ave 15206. Jct Penn Ave, just n. Int corridors. **Pets:** Accepted.

Hyatt House Pittsburgh/Bloomfield/Shadyside H

(412) 621-9900. **$139-$399.** 5335 Baum Blvd 15224. Jct Liberty Ave. Int corridors. **Pets:** Medium, dogs only. $75 one-time fee/room. Designated rooms, service with restrictions, supervision.

Hyatt House Pittsburgh-South Side H

(412) 390-2477. **$139-$289.** 2795 S Water St 15203. I-376 exit 72A, right on 2nd Ave, then just s. Int corridors. **Pets:** Accepted.

Hyatt Place Pittsburgh-North Shore H

(412) 321-3000. **$129-$399.** 260 N Shore Dr 15212. I-279/376 exit 70B (Fort Duquesne Blvd), exit 6C, stay right, n on 6th St/Roberto Clemente Bridge (which becomes Federal St), w on W General Robinson St, s on Mazeroski Way, then just w. Int corridors. **Pets:** Accepted.

Omni William Penn Hotel H 🐾

(412) 281-7100. **Call for rates.** 530 William Penn Pl 15219. Jct 6th St and William Penn Pl. Int corridors. **Pets:** Other species. $50 one-time fee/room. Service with restrictions, crate.

Renaissance Pittsburgh Hotel H

(412) 562-1200. **$122-$523.** 107 Sixth St 15222. I-376 E exit 70B (Liberty Ave), just e, then just n. Int corridors. **Pets:** Accepted.

Residence Inn by Marriott Pittsburgh University/Medical Center H

(412) 621-2200. **$89-$336.** 3896 Bigelow Blvd 15213. On SR 380. Int corridors. **Pets:** Accepted.

Residence Inn by Marriott-Wilkins H 🐾

(412) 816-1300. **$100-$275.** 3455 William Penn Hwy 15235. I-76 (Pennsylvania Tpke) exit 57, 3.5 mi n. Int corridors. **Pets:** Large, other species. $100 one-time fee/room. Service with restrictions.

Sheraton Pittsburgh Hotel at Station Square H

(412) 261-2000. **$159-$425.** 300 W Station Square Dr 15219. I-376 exit Grant St, south end of Smithfield Street Bridge. Int corridors. **Pets:** Accepted.

The Westin Convention Center Pittsburgh H

(412) 281-3700. **$149-$379.** 1000 Penn Ave 15222. Jct 10th St; at Liberty Center. Int corridors. **Pets:** Accepted.

Wyndham Grand Pittsburgh Downtown H
(412) 391-4600. **$99-$459.** 600 Commonwealth Pl 15222. Jct I-279/376/SR 885; in Gateway Center. Int corridors. **Pets:** Accepted.

PITTSTON
Comfort Inn Pittston H ❖
(570) 655-1234. **$79-$189.** 400 Hwy 315 18640. I-81 exit 175 northbound, 1 mi n; exit 175B southbound, just w; in Pittston Crossings Plaza. Int corridors. **Pets:** Medium. $15 daily fee/pet. Designated rooms, service with restrictions, supervision.

PLYMOUTH MEETING
Homewood Suites by Hilton Philadelphia-Plymouth Meeting H
(610) 828-9600. **$124-$229.** 200 Lee Dr 19462. I-276 exit 333, 0.3 mi s, 0.8 mi w on Chemical Rd, 0.6 mi n on Gallagher Rd, then 0.6 mi e on Davis Dr. Int corridors. **Pets:** Other species. $25 daily fee/pet. Service with restrictions, crate.

POCONO MANOR
Pocono Manor Resort & Spa H
(570) 839-7111. **$99-$199.** 1 Manor Dr 18349. I-380 exit 3, just e on SR 314, follow signs for 1.3 mi. Int corridors. **Pets:** Accepted.

POTTSTOWN
Comfort Inn & Suites H
(610) 326-5000. **$94-$244.** 99 Robinson St 19464. SR 100, 1 mi n of jct US 422. Int corridors. **Pets:** Accepted.

QUAKERTOWN
Quality Inn & Suites H
(215) 538-3000. **$89-$299.** 1905 John Fries Hwy (SR 663) 18951. I-476 (Pennsylvania Tpke) exit 44, just e. Ext corridors. **Pets:** Large, other species. $10 daily fee/room. Service with restrictions, crate.

READING
DoubleTree by Hilton Reading H
(610) 375-8000. **Call for rates.** 701 Penn St 19601. Jct N 8th St, just w. Int corridors. **Pets:** Accepted.

RONKS
La Quinta Inn & Suites H
(717) 392-8100. **$81-$269.** 25 Eastbrook Rd 17572. Jct US 30 (Lincoln Hwy), just n on SR 896. Int corridors. **Pets:** Accepted.

ROYERSFORD
Staybridge Suites Royersford/Valley Forge H
(610) 792-9300. **$139-$229.** 88 Anchor Pkwy 19468. I-422 exit Royersford, just n. Int corridors. **Pets:** Accepted.

SAYRE
Best Western Grand Victorian Inn H ❖
(570) 888-7711. **$99-$109.** 255 Spring St 18840. SR 17 exit 61, just s. Int corridors. **Pets:** Large. $10 daily fee/pet. Designated rooms, service with restrictions, supervision.

SCRANTON
Hilton Scranton & Conference Center H ❖
(570) 343-3000. **$109-$239.** 100 Adams Ave 18503. I-81 exit 185, just w of jct Lackawanna Ave, Jefferson Ave and Spruce St; downtown. Int corridors. **Pets:** Large, other species. $25 deposit/room, $50 one-time fee/room. Designated rooms, service with restrictions.

Radisson Lackawanna Station Hotel Scranton H
(570) 342-8300. **Call for rates.** 700 Lackawanna Ave 18503. I-81 exit 185; jct Lackawanna Ave, Jefferson Ave and Spruce St; downtown. Int corridors. **Pets:** Medium. $75 one-time fee/room. Service with restrictions, crate.

TownePlace Suites by Marriott Scranton Wilkes-Barre H
(570) 207-8500. **$71-$197.** 26 Radcliffe Dr 18507. I-81 exit 182 northbound; exit 182A southbound, 0.5 mi se on Montage Mountain Rd, then just se to Glenmaura Blvd. Int corridors. **Pets:** Other species. $100 one-time fee/room. Service with restrictions, supervision.

SELINSGROVE
Comfort Inn H ❖
(570) 374-8880. **$94-$175.** 613 N Susquehanna Tr 17870. US 11 and 15, just n of US 522. Int corridors. **Pets:** Medium, other species. $25 daily fee/pet. Designated rooms, service with restrictions.

SHAMOKIN DAM
Econo Lodge Inn & Suites H
(570) 743-1111. **$74-$159.** 3249 N Susquehanna Tr 17876. US 11 and 15, just n of jct SR 61. Ext corridors. **Pets:** Accepted.

SHILLINGTON
Best Western Plus Reading Inn & Suites H
(610) 777-7888. **$109-$179.** 2299 Lancaster Pike 19607. I-76 (Pennsylvania Tpke) exit 286, 9 mi n on US 222. Int corridors. **Pets:** Other species. $50 deposit/room, $14 daily fee/room. Designated rooms, service with restrictions, supervision.

SHIPPENSBURG *(Restaurants p. 622)*
Best Western Shippensburg Hotel H
(717) 532-5200. **$79-$189.** 125 Walnut Bottom Rd 17257. I-81 exit 29, 0.5 mi w on SR 174. Int corridors. **Pets:** Medium, other species. $10 daily fee/pet. Designated rooms, service with restrictions, crate.

Holiday Inn Express & Suites Shippensburg H
(717) 532-1100. **Call for rates.** 120 Walnut Bottom Rd 17257. I-81 exit 29, 0.6 mi w on SR 174. Int corridors. **Pets:** Large. $25 one-time fee/pet. Service with restrictions, supervision.

SMOKETOWN
Mill Stream Country Inn H
(717) 299-0931. **Call for rates.** 170 Eastbrook Rd 17576. Jct SR 340, 0.3 mi s on SR 896. Ext corridors. **Pets:** Accepted.

SOMERSET
Budget Host Inn M
(814) 445-7988. **$50-$95, 3 day notice.** 799 N Center Ave 15501. I-70/76 (Pennsylvania Tpke) exit 110, 0.3 mi s. Ext corridors. **Pets:** Very small. $10 daily fee/pet. Designated rooms, service with restrictions, supervision.

♨♨ ▼▼▼▼ Comfort Inn 🄷
(814) 445-9611. **$100-$150.** 202 Harmon St 15501. I-70/76 (Pennsylvania Tpke) exit 110, just s. Int corridors. **Pets:** Medium. $35 one-time fee/room. Designated rooms, service with restrictions, supervision.
🆂🅰🆅🄴 ➰ 📶 ⛁ 💻

▼▼ Glades Pike Inn 🄱🄱
(814) 443-4978. **$75-$125, 7 day notice.** 2684 Glades Pike Rd 15501. I-70/76 (Pennsylvania Tpke) exit 110, 6 mi w on SR 31; exit 91, 13 mi e on SR 31. Int corridors. **Pets:** Accepted. 🍽 ⊠ 📶 ⛒ ☎

STARLIGHT

▼▼ The Inn at Starlight Lake 🄲🄸
(570) 798-2519. **Call for rates.** 289 Starlight Lake Rd 18461. Off SR 370, 1 mi n, follow signs. Ext/int corridors. **Pets:** Accepted.
🍽 ⊠ 📶 ⛒ 🎿 🎱 ☎

STATE COLLEGE

▼▼▼ Comfort Suites 🄷 🐾
(814) 235-1900. **$94-$509.** 132 Village Dr 16803. SR 26, 1.1 mi on US 322 W (Atherton St), just ne; center. Int corridors. **Pets:** Other species. $25 one-time fee/room. Designated rooms, service with restrictions, supervision. ➰ 📶 ⛒ ⛁ 💻

▼▼▼ Days Inn Penn State 🄷 🐾
(814) 238-8454. **$104-$270.** 240 S Pugh St 16801. Just e of SR 26 northbound; 0.4 mi n of jct US 322 business route; downtown. Int corridors. **Pets:** $10 daily fee/room. Service with restrictions, supervision.
🍽 ➰ 📶 ⛒ ⛁ 💻

♨♨ ▼ Nittany Budget Motel 🄼
(814) 238-0015. **$49-$275.** 2070 Cato Ave 16801. SR 26, 2.6 mi s of jct US 322 business route. Ext corridors. **Pets:** Dogs only. $5 daily fee/pet. Service with restrictions, crate. 🆂🅰🆅🄴 📶 ⛁

▼▼ Quality Inn Penn State 🄼
(814) 234-1600. **$79-$349.** 1274 N Atherton St 16803. US 322 business route, 1 mi w of jct SR 26. Int corridors. **Pets:** Accepted.
📶 ⛒ ⛁ 💻

▼▼▼ Residence Inn by Marriott State College 🄷
(814) 235-6960. **$98-$388.** 1555 University Dr 16801. US 322 business route, 1.5 mi e of jct SR 26. Int corridors. **Pets:** Accepted.
➰ 📶 ⛒ ⛁ 💻

TANNERSVILLE

▼▼ The Chateau Resort & Conference Center 🄷
(570) 629-5900. **Call for rates.** 475 Camelback Rd 18372. I-80 exit 299, 1 mi w on Sullivan Tr, then 1.7 mi, follow signs to Camelback Ski area or Camelback Beach Water Park. Int corridors. **Pets:** Accepted.
🍽 🛗 ➰ ⊠ 📶 ⛒ ⛁ 💻

TREVOSE

▼▼▼ Comfort Inn Trevose 🄷
(215) 638-4554. **$82-$190.** 2779 Lincoln Hwy N 19053. I-276 (Pennsylvania Tpke) exit 351, 0.5 mi s. Int corridors. **Pets:** Accepted.
➰ 📶 ⛒ ⛁ 💻

♨♨ ▼▼▼ Red Roof Inn Philadelphia Trevose 🄼
(215) 244-9422. **$63-$99.** 3100 Lincoln Hwy 19053. I-276 (Pennsylvania Tpke) exit 351, 0.5 mi s on US 1 at US 132. Ext corridors.
Pets: Accepted. 🆂🅰🆅🄴 🍽 📶 ⊠ ⛁ 💻

TUNKHANNOCK

▼▼▼ Comfort Inn & Suites Tunkhannock 🄷
(570) 836-4100. **$99-$199.** 5 N Eaton Rd 18657. 0.4 mi s; just across bridge. Int corridors. **Pets:** Accepted. 🍽 🛗 📶 ⊠ ⛁ 💻

UNIONTOWN

▼▼▼ Park Inn by Radisson Uniontown 🄷 🐾
(724) 437-2816. **$99-$179.** 700 W Main St 15401. 1.8 mi w on US 40. Int corridors. **Pets:** Medium. $25 one-time fee/pet. Designated rooms, service with restrictions, supervision.
🍽 🛗 ➰ ⊠ 📶 ⛒ ⛁ 💻

UPPER BLACK EDDY

▼▼ The Bridgeton House on the Delaware 🄱🄱
(610) 982-5856. **$189-$329.** 1525 River Rd 18972. On SR 32; center. Int corridors. **Pets:** Accepted. 🍽 📶 ⛒ ⛁ 💻

WARREN

▼▼▼ Holiday Inn of Warren 🄷
(814) 726-3000. **Call for rates.** 210 Ludlow St 16365. Jct US 6, just n on US 62 N (Ludlow St). Int corridors. **Pets:** Dogs only. $40 one-time fee/room. Designated rooms, service with restrictions, supervision.
🍽 🛗 ➰ 📶 ⛒ 💻

▼▼ Quality Inn & Suites 🄼
(814) 723-8881. **Call for rates.** 204 Struthers St 16365. 1.5 mi w on US 6 exit Ludlow St, w on Allegheny Ave, then s. Ext/int corridors.
Pets: Accepted. 🛗 📶 ⊠ ⛁ 💻

WARRINGTON

♨♨ ▼▼▼ Homewood Suites Warrington 🄷
(215) 343-1300. **$149-$279.** 2650 Kelly Rd 18976. 2.4 mi s of jct US 202 and SR 611. Int corridors. **Pets:** Accepted.
🆂🅰🆅🄴 ⛗ 🛗 📶 ⛁ 💻

WASHINGTON

▼▼▼ Candlewood Suites Washington North 🄷
(724) 873-7300. **Call for rates.** 255 Meadowland Blvd 15301. I-79 exit 41, just e. Int corridors. **Pets:** Accepted. 🍽 🛗 📶 ⊠ ⛁ 💻

▼▼ Comfort Inn Meadowlands 🄷
(724) 746-9700. **$97-$176.** 237 Meadowlands Blvd 15301. I-79 exit 41, just e. Int corridors. **Pets:** Accepted. 🛗 ➰ 📶 ⛁ 💻

▼▼▼ DoubleTree by Hilton Hotel Pittsburgh-Meadow Lands 🄷
(724) 222-6200. **$99-$159.** 340 Racetrack Rd 15301. I-79 exit 41, 0.5 mi e. Int corridors. **Pets:** Accepted. 🍽 🛗 ➰ 📶 ⊠ ⛁ 💻

♨♨ ▼▼▼ Hyatt Place Pittsburgh South/Meadows Racetrack & Casino 🄷 🐾
(724) 222-7777. **$99-$329.** 212 Racetrack Rd 15301. I-79 exit 41, just e. Int corridors. **Pets:** Medium, dogs only. $75 one-time fee/room. Service with restrictions, crate. 🆂🅰🆅🄴 ⛗ 🍽 🛗 📶 ⊠ ⛁ 💻

♨♨ ▼▼ Ramada 🄷
(724) 225-9750. **$82-$89.** 1170 W Chestnut St 15301. I-70 exit 15, 0.5 mi e on US 40. Ext/int corridors. **Pets:** Medium. $35 daily fee/pet. Designated rooms, service with restrictions, supervision.
🆂🅰🆅🄴 🍽 🛗 ➰ 📶 ⛁ 💻

♨♨ ▼▼ Red Roof Inn Washington, PA 🄼
(724) 228-5750. **$50-$105.** 1399 W Chestnut St 15301. I-70 exit 15, just e on US 40. Ext/int corridors. **Pets:** Accepted.
🆂🅰🆅🄴 🛗 📶 ⊠ ⛁ 💻

WEST CHESTER (Restaurants p. 622)

♨♨ ▼▼ Brinton Hotel & Suites 🄷
(484) 301-9232. **Call for rates.** 1516 Wilmington Pike 19382. 0.9 mi n of jct US 1 and 202. Int corridors. **Pets:** Accepted.
🆂🅰🆅🄴 🍽 📶 ⊠ ☎ ⛁ 💻

▼▼ Centerstone West Chester Inn H
(610) 692-1900. Call for rates. 943 S High St 19382. 1.5 mi s on US 202 and 322; jct US 322 business route. Int corridors. Pets: Accepted.
🍴 ♿ 🛏 📶 ✕ 🔋 💻

WEST HAZLETON
▼▼▼ Candlewood Suites H
(570) 459-1600. $80-$110. 9 Bowman's Mill Rd 18202. I-81 exit 145 southbound; exit SR 93 S northbound to Tom Hicken Rd. Int corridors. Pets: Large, other species. $10 daily fee/pet. Service with restrictions, crate. 🍴 ♿ 📶 🔋 💻

WEST READING
▼▼▼ Candlewood Suites H
(610) 898-1910. $85-$135. 55 S 3rd Ave 19611. Jct Penn Ave. Int corridors. Pets: Large. $75 one-time fee/pet. Service with restrictions, crate. ♿ 📶 🔋 💻

WHITE HAVEN
▼▼ Comfort Inn-Pocono Mountain H ❀
(570) 443-8461. $74-$259. Rt 940 at I-80 & 476 18661. I-476 exit 95, just e; I-80 exit 277 (Lake Harmony). Int corridors. Pets: Medium. $15 daily fee/pet. Designated rooms, service with restrictions, crate.
🍴 🛏 ✕ 📶 🔋 💻

WILKES-BARRE
AAA ▼▼ Best Western Plus Genetti Hotel & Conference Center H ❀
(570) 823-6152. $99-$179. 77 E Market St 18701. Jct Washington St; downtown. Int corridors. Pets: $15 daily fee/pet. Designated rooms, service with restrictions, supervision.
SAVE 🍴 ♿ 🛏 📶 ✕ 🔋 💻

AAA ▼▼ Days Inn H
(570) 826-0111. $65-$111. 760 Kidder St 18702. I-81 exit 170B to exit 1 (SR 309 S business route), just w; I-76 (Pennsylvania Tpke) exit 105 to exit 1 (SR 115 N). Int corridors. Pets: Accepted.
SAVE ♿ 📶 🔋 💻

AAA ▼▼ Econo Lodge Arena H
(570) 823-0600. $70-$100. 1075 Wilkes-Barre Township Blvd 18702. I-81 exit 165 southbound; exit 165B northbound, on SR 309 business route. Int corridors. Pets: Accepted. SAVE ♿ 📶 🔋 💻

▼▼ Extended Stay America Wilkes-Barre Hwy 315 H
(570) 970-2500. $100-$140. 1067 Hwy 315 18702. I-81 exit 170B to exit 1 (SR 309 S business route), 0.3 mi n. Int corridors.
Pets: Accepted. 🍴 ♿ 📶 ✕ 🔋 💻

AAA ▼▼ Host Inn All Suites H
(570) 270-4678. $99-$199. 860 Kidder St 18702. I-81 exit 170B to exit 1 (SR 309 S business route), 0.5 mi w. Int corridors. Pets: Other species. $20 daily fee/pet. Service with restrictions, crate.
SAVE ♿ 🛏 📶 ✕ 🔋 💻

▼▼ Quality Inn & Suites Conference Center H ❀
(570) 824-8901. $61-$169. 880 Kidder St 18702. I-81 exit 170B to exit 1 (SR 309 S business route) off expressway, 0.5 mi w. Ext corridors. Pets: $20 daily fee/pet. Service with restrictions, crate.
🍴 ✕ 🔋 💻

AAA ▼▼ Red Roof Inn Wilkes-Barre Arena M
(570) 829-6422. $49-$120. 1035 Hwy 315 18702. I-81 exit 170B to exit 1 (SR 309 S business route) to SR 315, just n. Ext corridors.
Pets: Accepted. SAVE 🍴 ♿ 📶 ✕ 🔋 💻

▼▼▼ The Woodlands Inn, an Ascend Hotel Collection Member H
(570) 824-9831. $109-$310. 1073 Hwy 315 18702. I-81 exit 170B to exit 1 (SR 309 S business route), 0.3 mi n. Int corridors.
Pets: Accepted. 🍴 🛏 ✕ 📶 ✕ 🔋 💻

WILLIAMSPORT
AAA ▼▼▼ Best Western Williamsport Inn H
(570) 326-1981. $79-$259. 1840 E 3rd St 17701. I-180 exit 25 (Faxon St), 0.5 mi e. Ext corridors. Pets: Accepted.
SAVE 🍴 ♿ 🛏 📶 ✕ 🔋 💻

▼▼ Candlewood Suites Williamsport H
(570) 601-9100. Call for rates. 1836 E 3rd St 17701. I-180 exit 25 (Faxon St), 0.5 mi e. Int corridors. Pets: Accepted.
♿ 🛏 📶 ✕ 🔋 💻

▼▼ Comfort Inn H
(570) 601-9300. $80-$239. 1959 E 3rd St 17701. I-180 exit 23A westbound; exit 23 eastbound, just w. Int corridors. Pets: Dogs only. $25 daily fee/pet. Designated rooms, supervision.
♿ 🛏 📶 ✕ 🔋 💻

▼▼ Genetti Hotel & Suites H
(570) 326-6600. $129-$229, 30 day notice. 200 W 4th St 17701. Jct William St; downtown. Ext/int corridors. Pets: Dogs only. $15 daily fee/pet. Designated rooms, service with restrictions.
🍴 ♿ 🛏 📶 🔋 💻

▼▼ Residence Inn by Marriott Williamsport H
(570) 505-3140. $91-$188. 150 W Church St 17701. I-180 exit 27B eastbound; exit 26 westbound; just w of Market St; downtown. Int corridors. Pets: Accepted. ♿ 📶 ✕ 🔋 💻

▼▼ TownePlace Suites by Marriott Williamsport H
(570) 567-7467. $69-$191. 10 W Church St 17701. I-180 exit 27B eastbound; exit 26 westbound; at Market St; downtown. Int corridors.
Pets: Accepted. ♿ 📶 ✕ 🔋 💻

WYOMISSING
▼▼▼ Crowne Plaza Reading Hotel H
(610) 376-3811. $109-$199. 1741 W Papermill Rd 19610. US 422 exit Papermill Rd. Int corridors. Pets: Small, other species. $25 daily fee/pet. Designated rooms, service with restrictions, supervision.
🍴 ♿ 🛏 📶 ✕ 🔋 💻

▼▼ Homewood Suites-Reading/Wyomissing H
(610) 736-3100. $129-$214. 2801 Papermill Rd 19610. US 422 exit Papermill Rd, 1.8 mi nw; US 222 exit Spring Ridge Rd. Int corridors. Pets: Large. $75 one-time fee/pet. Service with restrictions.
♿ 🛏 📶 ✕ 🔋 💻

▼▼ The Inn at Reading Hotel & Conference Center H
(610) 372-7811. $89-$199. 1040 N Park Rd 19610. US 222 exit N Wyomissing Blvd, just n, then 0.3 mi e. Int corridors. Pets: Small. $15 daily fee/room. Designated rooms, service with restrictions, crate.
🍴 ♿ 🛏 📶 ✕ 🔋 💻

WYSOX
▼▼ Comfort Inn H
(570) 265-5691. $85-$159. 898 Golden Mile Rd 18854. On US 6 E. Int corridors. Pets: Other species. $25 one-time fee/room. Designated rooms, service with restrictions, supervision.
♿ 🛏 📶 ✕ 🔋 💻

YORK
▼▼ Comfort Inn & Suites H
(717) 699-1919. $99-$163. 2250 N George St 17402. I-83 exit 22, just n. Int corridors. Pets: Accepted. ♿ 📶 ✕ 🔋 💻

AAA ▼▼▼ Heritage Hills Golf Resort and Conference Center H
(717) 755-0123. Call for rates. 2700 Mount Rose Ave 17402. I-83 exit 18, 1 mi e on SR 124. Int corridors. Pets: Large. $35 daily fee/room. Service with restrictions, crate.
SAVE 🍴 ♿ ✕ 📶 ✕ 🔋 💻

▼▼▼▼ **Home2 Suites by Hilton York** �H
(717) 747-0360. **Call for rates.** 212 Pauline Dr 17402. I-83 exit 16B, just s. Int corridors. **Pets:** Large, other species. $75 one-time fee/room. Designated rooms, service with restrictions, crate.
🍽 ⓜ 🛜 ✕ 🛢 💻

▼▼▼▼ **Towneplace Suites by Marriott York** �H
(717) 840-1180. **$106-$250.** 2789 Concord Rd 17402. I-83 exit 21A northbound; exit 21 southbound, 3.5 mi e on US 30, then just s on SR 24. Int corridors. **Pets:** Accepted. ⓜ 🛜 ✕ 🛢 💻

▼▼▼▼ **Wyndham Garden York** �H 🐾
(717) 846-9500. **$109-$189, 7 day notice.** 2000 Loucks Rd 17408. I-83 exit 21B, 2.5 mi w on US 30, then just n; exit 22 southbound, 0.5 mi s on SR 181, 2.2 mi w on US 30, then just n. Int corridors. **Pets:** Other species. $25 daily fee/room. Designated rooms, service with restrictions, crate. 🍽 ⓜ 🛁 🛜 ✕ 🛢 💻

RHODE ISLAND

COVENTRY
▼▼▼▼ **La Quinta Inn & Suites Coventry/Providence** �H
(401) 821-3322. **$97-$273.** 4 Universal Blvd 02816. I-95 exit 7, just ne. Int corridors. **Pets:** Accepted. 🍽 ⓜ 🛁 🛜 ✕ 🛢 💻

EAST PROVIDENCE
▼▼ **Extended Stay America East Providence** �H
(401) 272-1661. **$105-$145.** 1000 Warren Ave 02914. I-195 exit 8 eastbound, just e; exit 6 westbound, 1.1 mi e. Int corridors. **Pets:** Accepted.
🍽 ⓜ 🛜 ✕ 🛢 💻

MIDDLETOWN
▼▼▼▼ **Homewood Suites by Hilton Newport/Middletown** �H 🐾
(401) 848-2700. **$109-$489.** 348 W Main Rd 02842. On SR 114, 0.3 mi s of jct SR 138. Int corridors. **Pets:** Medium, other species. $75 one-time fee/room. Designated rooms, service with restrictions, crate.
ⓜ 🛁 🛜 ✕ 🛢 💻

🔵🔵🔵 ▼▼▼▼ **Howard Johnson Inn-Newport** �H 🐾
(401) 849-2000. **$69-$500.** 351 W Main Rd 02842. On SR 114, 0.3 mi s of jct SR 138. Int corridors. **Pets:** Other species. $12 daily fee/pet. Designated rooms, service with restrictions, supervision.
SAVE 🍽 ⓜ 🛁 ✕ 🛜 ✕ 🛢 💻

🔵🔵🔵 ▼▼▼▼ **Residence Inn by Marriott-Newport/Middletown** �H 🐾
(401) 845-2005. **$88-$563, 3 day notice.** 325 W Main Rd 02842. On SR 114, 0.3 mi s of jct SR 138. Int corridors. **Pets:** Other species. $75 one-time fee/room. Designated rooms, service with restrictions.
SAVE 🍽 ⓜ 🛁 🛜 ✕ 🛢 💻

NEWPORT *(Restaurants p. 622)*
🔵🔵🔵 ▼▼▼▼ **Beech Tree Inn** BB
(401) 847-9794. **Call for rates.** 34 Rhode Island Ave 02840. Just e of SR 114; 0.8 mi s of jct SR 138. Int corridors. **Pets:** Other species. $25 daily fee/pet. Service with restrictions. SAVE 🛜 ✕ 🛢

🔵🔵🔵 ▼▼▼▼▼ **Cliffside Inn** BB 🐾
(401) 847-1811. **$170-$560.** 2 Seaview Ave 02840. Just s of Memorial Blvd via Cliff Ave. Ext/int corridors. **Pets:** Small, dogs only. $50 one-time fee/room. Designated rooms, service with restrictions, crate.
SAVE 🛜 ✕ 🛢 💻

▼▼▼ **Mainstay Hotel & Conference Center** �H
(401) 849-9880. **Call for rates.** 151 Admiral Kalbfus Rd 02840. SR 138; from Newport Bridge, 2nd exit. Int corridors. **Pets:** Accepted.
🍽 🛁 🛜 ✕ 🛢 💻

🔵🔵🔵 ▼▼▼▼ **Mill Street Inn** �H 🐾
(401) 849-9500. **Call for rates.** 75 Mill St 02840. Just e of Thames St; between Spring and Corne sts; downtown. Int corridors. **Pets:** Medium, dogs only. $50 one-time fee/pet. Designated rooms, service with restrictions, crate. SAVE 🛜 ✕ 🛢

▼▼▼▼ **Pelham Court Hotel** CO
(401) 619-4950. **Call for rates.** 14 Pelham St 02840. Just n of Memorial Blvd (SR 138A) via Spring St, then just w. Ext/int corridors. **Pets:** Accepted. 🛜 ✕ 🛢 💻

🔵🔵🔵 ▼▼▼▼ **The Vanderbilt Grace** �H 🐾
(401) 846-6200. **Call for rates.** 41 Mary St 02840. Just n of Thames St; downtown. Int corridors. **Pets:** Dogs only. $150 daily fee/room. Designated rooms, service with restrictions, crate.
SAVE 🍽 ⓜ 🛁 ✕ 🛜 ✕ 💻

NORTH KINGSTOWN
▼▼▼ **Hamilton Village Inn** M
(401) 295-0700. **$102-$159, 7 day notice.** 642 Boston Neck Rd 02852. SR 1A, 1.3 mi s of jct SR 102. Ext corridors. **Pets:** Large. Designated rooms, service with restrictions, supervision. 🍽 🛜 ✕ 🛢 💻

▼▼▼▼ **TownePlace Suites by Marriott Providence/North Kingstown** �H
(401) 667-7500. **$82-$368.** 55 Gate Rd 02852. Jct SR 403, just n on US 1, then just e. Int corridors. **Pets:** Accepted.
🍽 🛁 🛜 ✕ 🛢 💻

PROVIDENCE *(Restaurants p. 622)*
🔵🔵🔵 ▼▼▼▼ **Hotel Providence** �H 🐾
(401) 861-8000. **$159-$299.** 139 Mathewson St 02903. Corner of Westminster St. Int corridors. **Pets:** Dogs only. $75 one-time fee/room. Service with restrictions, supervision. SAVE ECO 🍽 🛜 ✕ 🛢 💻

▼▼▼▼ **Omni Providence Hotel** �H 🐾
(401) 598-8000. **$159-$299.** One W Exchange St 02903. I-95 exit 22A, just e. Int corridors. **Pets:** Small. $50 one-time fee/room. Service with restrictions. ECO 🍽 ⓜ 🛁 🛜 ✕ 🛢 💻

🔵🔵🔵 ▼▼▼▼ **Providence Marriott Downtown** �H
(401) 272-2400. **$121-$348.** 1 Orms St 02904. I-95 exit 23 to state offices. Int corridors. **Pets:** Accepted.
SAVE ECO 🍽 ⓜ 🛁 🛜 ✕ 🛢 💻

SMITHFIELD
🔵🔵🔵 ▼▼▼ **All Seasons Inn & Suites** �H
(401) 232-2400. **$100-$220, 7 day notice.** 355 George Washington Hwy 02917. I-295 exit 8B, 0.3 mi n on SR 7, then 0.6 mi e on SR 116. Int corridors. **Pets:** Accepted. SAVE 🍽 ⓜ 🛁 🛜 ✕ 🛢 💻

🔵🔵🔵 ▼▼▼ **Hampton Inn & Suites Providence/Smithfield** �H
(401) 232-9200. **$159-$259.** 945 Douglas Pike 02917. I-295 exit 8B, 0.6 mi nw on SR 7. Int corridors. **Pets:** Accepted.
SAVE 🍽 ⓜ 🛁 🛜 ✕ 🛢 💻

WARWICK *(Restaurants p. 622)*

Best Western Airport Inn 🅷
(401) 737-7400. **$75-$179.** 2138 Post Rd 02886. I-95 exit 13, e to US 1, then just ne. Int corridors. **Pets:** Medium. $20 daily fee/pet. Designated rooms, service with restrictions, supervision.

Comfort Inn-Airport 🅷
(401) 732-0470. **$73-$229.** 1940 Post Rd 02886. I-95 exit 13, e to US 1, then 0.5 mi n. Int corridors. **Pets:** Medium. $50 one-time fee/pet. Service with restrictions, supervision.

Crowne Plaza Hotel at the Crossings 🅷
(401) 732-6000. **Call for rates.** 801 Greenwich Ave 02886. I-95 exit 12A southbound; exit 12 northbound, 0.3 mi se on SR 5. Int corridors. **Pets:** Accepted.

Extended Stay America-Providence-Airport 🅷
(401) 732-6667. **$85-$125.** 268 Metro Center Blvd 02886. I-95 exit 12A, 0.4 mi e on SR 113, 0.4 mi n on SR 5, then 0.4 mi e. Int corridors. **Pets:** $25 daily fee/pet. Service with restrictions, crate.

Extended Stay America Providence-Warwick 🅷
(401) 732-2547. **$80-$120.** 245 W Natick Rd 02886. I-295 exit 2 northbound, just sw; exit 3A southbound, 1.1 mi e on SR 37, 2 mi s on SR 2, then just sw. Int corridors. **Pets:** Accepted.

Hampton Inn & Suites Providence-Warwick Airport 🅷
(401) 739-8888. **$99-$199.** 2100 Post Rd 02886. I-95 exit 13, e to US 1, then just n. Int corridors. **Pets:** Accepted.

Holiday Inn Express Hotel & Suites 🅷
(401) 736-5000. **Call for rates.** 901 Jefferson Blvd 02886. I-95 exit 13, 0.4 mi on Airport Connector Rd exit Jefferson Blvd. Int corridors. **Pets:** Accepted.

Homewood Suites by Hilton Warwick 🅷
(401) 738-0008. **Call for rates.** 33 International Way 02886. I-95 exit 13, 0.4 mi n on Jefferson Blvd, 0.5 mi nw on Kilvert St, then 0.4 mi sw on Metro Center Blvd. Int corridors. **Pets:** Accepted.

NYLO Providence/Warwick 🅷
(401) 734-4460. **$139-$309.** 400 Knight St 02886. Jct SR 5, just ne. Int corridors. **Pets:** Accepted.

Residence Inn by Marriott Providence-Warwick 🅷
(401) 737-7100. **$99-$415.** 500 Kilvert St 02886. I-95 exit 13 to Jefferson Blvd, 0.4 mi n, then 0.6 mi w. Ext corridors. **Pets:** Accepted.

WATCH HILL

Ocean House 🅷
(401) 584-7000. **Call for rates.** 1 Bluff Ave 02891. Jct SR 1A, 0.4 mi sw via Westerly Rd. Int corridors. **Pets:** Accepted.

WESTERLY

Shelter Harbor Inn 🅲🅸
(401) 322-8883. **Call for rates.** 10 Wagner Rd 02891. 4 mi ne of jct SR 78 on US 1. Ext/int corridors. **Pets:** Accepted.

The Weekapaug Inn 🅷
(401) 637-7600. **Call for rates.** 25 Spray Rock Rd 02891. SR 1A, 1 mi s on Noyes Neck Rd, just e on Shawmut Ave, then just s. Int corridors. **Pets:** Accepted.

WEST GREENWICH

Residence Inn by Marriott Providence/Coventry 🅷
(401) 828-1170. **$87-$271.** 725 Centre of New England Blvd 02817. I-95 exit 7, just ne. Int corridors. **Pets:** Accepted.

WEST WARWICK

Extended Stay America Providence-West Warwick 🅷
(401) 885-3161. **$80-$120.** 1235 Division Rd 02893. I-95 exit 8A northbound, just s on SR 2, then just w; exit 8 southbound, just s on SR 2, then just w. Int corridors. **Pets:** Accepted.

SpringHill Suites by Marriott Providence West Warwick 🅷
(401) 822-1244. **$93-$290.** 14 James P Murphy Industrial Hwy 02893. I-95 exit 8 southbound, just nw; exit 8B northbound, just n on Old Quaker Ln, then 0.5 mi nw. Int corridors. **Pets:** Accepted.

WYOMING

Stagecoach House Inn 🅱🅱
(401) 539-9600. **$110-$199.** 1136 Main St (SR 138) 02898. I-95 exit 3B northbound, 0.7 mi nw; exit southbound, 0.4 mi nw. Ext/int corridors. **Pets:** Dogs only. $25 daily fee/pet. Designated rooms, service with restrictions, supervision.

SOUTH CAROLINA

AIKEN

Clarion Inn 🅼
(803) 648-0999. **$79-$119.** 155 Colony Pkwy/Whiskey Rd 29803. Jct US 1/78 and SR 19 (Whiskey Rd), 1.8 mi s on SR 19 (Whiskey Rd). Ext corridors. **Pets:** Accepted.

Quality Inn & Suites 🅼
(803) 641-1100. **$75-$135.** 3608 Richland Ave W 29801. Jct US 1/78 and SR 19 (Whiskey Rd), 2.9 mi w on US 1/78. Ext corridors. **Pets:** $20 deposit/pet. Service with restrictions.

TownePlace Suites by Marriott Aiken 🅷
(803) 641-7373. **$94-$160.** 1008 Monterey Dr 29803. Jct US 1/78 and SR 19 (Whiskey Rd), 3 mi s on SR 19 (Whiskey Rd). Int corridors. **Pets:** Large. $100 one-time fee/room. Service with restrictions, supervision.

ANDERSON

Baymont Inn & Suites Anderson/Clemson 🅼
(864) 375-9800. **$59-$110.** 128 Interstate Blvd 29621. I-85 exit 19B, just n, then just se. Ext corridors. **Pets:** Accepted.

▼▼▼ Country Inn & Suites By Carlson 🄷
(864) 622-2200. **$90-$500.** 116 Interstate Blvd 29621. I-85 exit 19B, just n, then just se. Int corridors. **Pets:** Accepted.

🛆🅼 🛍️ 🛜 ✖️ 🔋 🖥️

▼▼ Days Inn 🄼
(864) 375-0375. **$69-$150.** 1007 Smith Mill Rd 29625. I-85 exit 19A, just se. Ext corridors. **Pets:** Accepted. 🛆🅼 🛍️ 🛜 🔋 🖥️

▼▼ Howard Johnson Anderson 🄼
(864) 225-3721. **$49-$135.** 3430 Clemson Blvd 29621. I-85 exit 19A northbound, 2.9 mi se on US 76/SR 28 (Clemson Blvd); exit 21 southbound, 2.6 mi s on US 178. Ext corridors. **Pets:** $15 daily fee/room. Service with restrictions, crate. 🛍️ 🛜 🔋 🖥️

▼▼ InTown Suites 🄷
(864) 226-1112. **Call for rates.** 151 Civic Center Blvd 29625. I-85 exit 19A, 2.2 mi se on US 76, then 0.6 mi s. Int corridors. **Pets:** Small. $5 daily fee/pet. Service with restrictions, supervision.

🍴 🛍️ 🛜 ✖️ 🔋 🖥️

▼▼ Super 8 🄷
(864) 225-8384. **$59-$115.** 3302 Cinema Ave 29621. I-85 exit 19A northbound, 2.8 mi se on US 76/SR 28 (Clemson Blvd); exit 21 southbound, 2.5 mi s on US 178. Int corridors. **Pets:** Accepted.

🛜 🔋 🖥️

BEAUFORT

▼▼▼ The Beaufort Inn 🄱🄱
(843) 379-4667. **$129-$379.** 809 Port Republic St 29902. Between Scott and West sts; downtown; in historic district. Ext/int corridors. **Pets:** Accepted. 🍴 🛜 ✖️ 🔋 🖥️

▼▼ Quality Inn at Town Center 🄼
(843) 524-2144. **$65-$110.** 2001 Boundary St 29902. Jct US 21/SR 170, 1 mi e. Ext corridors. **Pets:** Accepted. 🍴 🛍️ 🛜 🔋 🖥️

BENNETTSVILLE

▼▼ Quality Inn 🄼
(843) 479-1700. **$85-$200.** 213 US Hwy 15 & 401 Bypass E 29512. Jct SR 38/Broad St, just ne on US 15/401/SR 9. Ext corridors. **Pets:** Medium. $25 daily fee/pet. Service with restrictions, crate.

🛍️ 🛜 🔋 🖥️

BLUFFTON *(Restaurants p. 622)*

ⒶⒶⒶ ▼▼▼ Candlewood Suites 🄷
(843) 705-9600. **Call for rates.** 5 Young Clyde Ct 29909. I-95 exit 8 (US 278), 7.2 mi e to Okatie Center Blvd S, then just s. Int corridors. **Pets:** Other species. $75 one-time fee/room. No service, crate.

🆂🅰️🆅🅴 🛆🅼 🛍️ 🛜 ✖️ 🔋 🖥️

▼▼▼ Holiday Inn Express Hotel & Suites 🄷 ❁
(843) 757-2002. **Call for rates.** 35 Bluffton Rd 29910. Jct US 278 (William Hilton Pkwy)/SR 46 (Bluffton Rd), just se; in Kittie's Crossing Shopping Center. Int corridors. **Pets:** Medium, dogs only. Designated rooms, service with restrictions, crate. 🛆🅼 🛍️ 🛜 ✖️ 🔋 🖥️

ⒶⒶⒶ ▼▼▼▼ Montage Palmetto Bluff 🄲🄰
(843) 706-6500. **$275-$590, 7 day notice.** 477 Mount Pelia Rd 29910. Jct US 278/SR 170, 4.4 mi sw on SR 170, 2.2 mi e on SR 46 (Bluffton Rd) to Palmetto Bluff Rd; check-in at gatehouse. Ext corridors. **Pets:** Accepted. 🆂🅰️🆅🅴 🍴 🛍️ ✖️ 🛜 ✖️ 🔋 🖥️

CAMDEN

▼▼▼ Comfort Inn & Suites 🄷
(803) 425-1010. **$94-$199.** 220 Wall St 29020. I-20 exit 98, just n on US 521. Int corridors. **Pets:** Small. $25 daily fee/room. Designated rooms, service with restrictions, supervision.

🛆🅼 🛍️ 🛜 ✖️ 🔋 🖥️

CHARLESTON *(Restaurants p. 622)*

ⒶⒶⒶ ▼▼▼ Best Western Sweetgrass Inn 🄼 ❁
(843) 571-6100. **$70-$300.** 1540 Savannah Hwy 29407. US 17, 3.6 mi w of Ashley River Bridge; jct I-526 W terminus and US 17, 1.7 mi e. Ext corridors. **Pets:** $20 daily fee/room. Service with restrictions, supervision. 🆂🅰️🆅🅴 🛍️ 🛜 ✖️ 🔋 🖥️

ⒶⒶⒶ ▼▼▼ Days Inn Historic District 🄼 ❁
(843) 722-8411. **$109-$260.** 155 Meeting 29401. Between Cumberland and S Market sts. Ext corridors. **Pets:** Other species. $20 daily fee/pet. Designated rooms, service with restrictions.

🆂🅰️🆅🅴 🍴 🛍️ 🛜 ✖️ 🔋 🖥️

▼▼ Hawthorn Suites by Wyndham 🄷
(843) 225-4411. **$99-$299, 3 day notice.** 2455 Savannah Hwy 29414. I-526 exit US 17 (terminus), 1.3 mi w on US 17. Int corridors. **Pets:** Small. $50 one-time fee/pet. Designated rooms, service with restrictions, supervision. 🛆🅼 🛍️ 🛜 ✖️ 🔋 🖥️

▼▼▼ Holiday Inn Express Charleston Downtown Ashley River 🄷
(843) 722-4000. **Call for rates.** 250 Spring St 29403. I-26 exit 221A (US 17), 1.2 mi sw; just e of Ashley River. Int corridors. **Pets:** Accepted. 🍴 🛍️ 🛜 ✖️ 🔋 🖥️

ⒶⒶⒶ ▼▼▼ The Inn at Middleton Place 🄲🄸
(843) 556-0500. **$149-$749, 3 day notice.** 4290 Ashley River Rd 29414. I-526 exit 11B (Ashley River Rd/SR 61), 2.8 mi nw on Paul Cantrell Blvd/Glenn McConnell Pkwy to Bees Ferry Rd, 1.8 mi ne to Ashley River Rd/SR 61, then 9.2 mi nw, follow signs to historic plantations; adjacent to Middleton Place, National Historic Landmark. Ext corridors. **Pets:** Accepted. 🆂🅰️🆅🅴 🍴 🛍️ 🛜 ✖️ 🔋 🖥️

ⒶⒶⒶ ▼▼▼ John Rutledge House Inn 🄱🄱 ❁
(843) 723-7999. **$239-$415, 3 day notice.** 116 Broad St 29401. Corner of King St. Int corridors. **Pets:** Medium, dogs only. $25 daily fee/pet. Designated rooms, service with restrictions. 🆂🅰️🆅🅴 🛜 ✖️ 🔋

ⒶⒶⒶ ▼▼▼ Kings Courtyard Inn 🄷 ❁
(843) 723-7000. **$189-$325, 3 day notice.** 198 King St 29401. Between Market St and Horlbeck Alley. Ext/int corridors. **Pets:** Medium, dogs only. $25 daily fee/room. Designated rooms, service with restrictions.

🆂🅰️🆅🅴 🛜 ✖️ 🔋

ⒶⒶⒶ ▼▼▼ Residence Inn by Marriott Charleston Downtown/Riverview 🄷 ❁
(843) 571-7979. **$134-$269.** 90 Ripley Point Dr 29407. US 17, just over Ashley River Bridge to Albermarle Rd, just s. Int corridors. **Pets:** Medium. $100 one-time fee/room. Service with restrictions. 🆂🅰️🆅🅴 🛆🅼 🛍️ 🛜 ✖️ 🔋 🖥️

▼▼▼ Sleep Inn-Charleston 🄷
(843) 556-6959. **$80-$220.** 1524 Savannah Hwy 29407. US 17, 3.6 mi w of Ashley River Bridge; I-526 exit US 17 (terminus), 1.7 mi e. Int corridors. **Pets:** $20 daily fee/room. Service with restrictions, crate. 🛜 ✖️ 🔋 🖥️

CHERAW

▼▼ Quality Inn 🄼
(843) 537-5625. **$99-$129.** 885 Chesterfield Hwy 29520. Jct US 1/52/SR 9, 1.6 mi w on SR 9. Ext corridors. **Pets:** Accepted.

🛍️ 🛜 🔋 🖥️

CLEMSON

▼▼ Comfort Inn-Clemson 🄷
(864) 653-3600. **$99-$460.** 1305 Tiger Blvd 29631. Jct SR 133 (College Ave) and US 76/123, 0.5 mi e. Int corridors. **Pets:** Accepted.

🛍️ 🛜 ✖️ 🔋 🖥️

CLINTON

▼▼ Quality Inn 🄼
(864) 833-5558. **$64-$86.** 105 Trade St 29325. I-26 exit 52, just n. Ext corridors. **Pets:** Accepted. 🛆🅼 🛍️ 🛜 🔋 🖥️

COLUMBIA *(Restaurants p. 622)*

▼▼▼ **Candlewood Suites Columbia-Fort Jackson** H
(803) 727-1299. **Call for rates.** 921 Atlas Rd 29209. I-77 exit 9A (Garners Ferry Rd), 0.9 mi se to Atlas Rd, then just sw. Int corridors. **Pets:** Accepted. 🍴 ᴸM ⊠ 📶 📦 💻

△△△ ▼▼▼ **Comfort Inn Columbia** H
(803) 798-5101. **$76-$160.** 911 Bush River Rd 29210. I-26 exit 108A, just e. Int corridors. **Pets:** Medium. $15 daily fee/pet. Designated rooms, service with restrictions, supervision.
🆅 🍴 ⊠ 📶 ⊠ 📦 💻

△△△ ▼▼▼ **Fairfield Inn & Suites by Marriott Columbia Northeast** H ✿
(803) 760-1700. **$93-$143.** 120 Blarney Dr 29223. I-77 exit 17 (Two Notch Rd), just s on US 1, just w on Daulton Dr, then just n; I-20 exit 74 (Two Notch Rd), 0.5 mi n on US 1, just w on Daulton Dr, then just n. Int corridors. **Pets:** Other species. $50 one-time fee/pet. Designated rooms, service with restrictions.
🆅 🍴 ᴸM ⊠ 📶 ⊠ 📦 💻

▼▼▼ **Hampton Inn Harbison** H
(803) 749-6999. **$109-$249.** 101 Woodcross Dr 29212. I-26 exit 103 (Harbison Blvd), just ne, then se. Int corridors. **Pets:** Accepted.
ᴸM ⊠ 📶 ⊠ 📦 💻

△△△ ▼▼▼ **Hyatt Place Columbia/Downtown/The Vista** H ✿
(803) 978-2013. **$109-$429.** 819 Gervais St 29201. Jct US 1/21, 0.3 mi nw; downtown; in Vista Historic District. Int corridors. **Pets:** Medium, dogs only. $175 one-time fee/room. Designated rooms, service with restrictions, supervision. 🆅 ᴸM 📶 ⊠ 📦 💻

▼▼▼ **La Quinta Inn & Suites Columbia NE/Ft. Jackson Area** H
(803) 736-6400. **$67-$119.** 1538 Horseshoe Dr 29223. I-20 exit 74 (Two Notch Rd), just n on US 1, then just w; I-77 exit 17 (Two Notch Rd), 0.6 mi s on US 1, then just w. Int corridors. **Pets:** Accepted.
🍴 ⊠ 📶 📦 💻

▼▼▼ **La Quinta Inn-Maingate Ft. Jackson** H
(803) 783-5410. **$79-$163.** 7333 Garners Ferry Rd 29209. I-77 exit 9A (Garners Ferry Rd), just se. Int corridors. **Pets:** Accepted.
⊠ ⊠ 📦 💻

△△△ ▼▼▼ **Red Roof Inn Columbia East Ft. Jackson** M
(803) 736-0850. **$50-$80.** 7431 Nates Rd 29223. I-20 exit 74 (Two Notch Rd), just n on US 1, then just e; I-77 exit 17 (Two Notch Rd), 0.5 mi s on US 1, then just e. Ext corridors. **Pets:** Accepted.
🆅 📶 ⊠ 📦 💻

▼▼▼ **Residence Inn by Marriott Columbia Northeast** H
(803) 788-8850. **$116-$187.** 2320 Legrand Rd 29223. I-77 exit 19, just ne on Farrow Rd (SR 555), just e on Rabon Rd, then just s. Int corridors. **Pets:** Accepted. ᴸM ⊠ 📶 ⊠ 📦 💻

△△△ ▼▼▼ **Sheraton Columbia Downtown Hotel** H
(803) 988-1400. **$199-$499.** 1400 Main St 29201. Jct Washington St; center of downtown. Int corridors. **Pets:** Accepted.
🆅 🍴 📶 ⊠ 📦 💻

▼▼▼ **Staybridge Suites Columbia** H
(803) 451-5900. **Call for rates.** 1913 Huger St 29201. I-126 exit 3B (US 21/Huger St), just s. Int corridors. **Pets:** Accepted.
🍴 ᴸM ⊠ 📶 ⊠ 📦 💻

▼▼▼ **TownePlace Suites by Marriott Columbia Northwest/Harbison** H
(803) 749-7552. **$88-$138.** 438 Columbiana Dr 29212. I-26 exit 103 (Harbison Blvd), just sw, then 0.9 mi nw. Int corridors. **Pets:** Accepted.
ᴸM 📶 ⊠ 📦 💻

DILLON

▼▼ **Quality Inn** M
(843) 774-0222. **$85-$170.** 817 Radford Blvd 29536. I-95 exit 193, just se on SR 9. Ext corridors. **Pets:** Accepted. ⊠ 📶 📦 💻

DUNCAN

▼▼ **Baymont Inn & Suites Duncan/Spartanburg** M
(864) 433-8405. **$49-$119.** 1546 E Main St 29334. I-85 exit 63, 0.4 mi se on SR 290. Ext corridors. **Pets:** Accepted. ᴸM ⊠ 📶 📦 💻

△△△ ▼▼▼ **Holiday Inn Express & Suites** H
(864) 486-9191. **$109-$179.** 275 Frontage Rd 29334. I-85 exit 63, just nw on SR 290, just ne on S Main St, then just se. Int corridors. **Pets:** Medium, dogs only. $50 daily fee/pet. Designated rooms, service with restrictions, supervision. 🆅 ᴸM ⊠ 📶 ⊠ 📦 💻

EASLEY

▼▼ **Baymont Inn & Suites Easley/Greenville** M
(864) 306-9000. **$59-$200.** 211 Dayton School Rd 29642. Jct US 123/SR 93, 0.6 mi e on US 123; jct US 123/SR 153, 1.4 mi w. Ext corridors. **Pets:** Accepted. ⊠ 📶 📦 💻

FLORENCE

▼▼ **Baymont Inn & Suites** M
(843) 468-9994. **$69-$175, 3 day notice.** 1826 W Lucas St 29501. I-95 exit 164, just e on US 52. Ext corridors. **Pets:** Medium, other species. $15 one-time fee/pet. Designated rooms, service with restrictions, supervision. ⊠ 📶 📦 💻

△△△ ▼▼▼ **Best Western Inn** M
(843) 678-9292. **$117-$130.** 1808 W Lucas St 29501. I-95 exit 164, just se. Ext corridors. **Pets:** Other species. $20 one-time fee/pet, $10 daily fee/pet. Designated rooms, service with restrictions, supervision.
🆅 ⊠ 📶 📦 💻

▼▼▼ **Home2 Suites by Hilton** H
(843) 664-9008. **Call for rates.** 900 Woody Jones Blvd 29501. I-95 exit 160A, just e to W Radio Rd, then 0.4 mi s. Int corridors.
Pets: Accepted. ᴸM 📶 ⊠ 📦 💻

▼▼▼ **La Quinta Inn & Suites Florence** H
(843) 629-1111. **$86-$372.** 2123 W Lucas St 29501. I-95 exit 164, 0.4 mi nw. Int corridors. **Pets:** Accepted. ᴸM ⊠ 📶 ⊠ 📦 💻

△△△ ▼▼▼ **Quality Inn & Suites** M
(843) 664-2400. **$100-$200.** 150 Dunbarton Dr 29501. I-95 exit 160A, just e, then just n. Ext corridors. **Pets:** Other species. $20 one-time fee/pet. Service with restrictions. 🆅 ᴸM ⊠ 📶 📦 💻

△△△ ▼▼▼ **Red Roof Inn-Florence Civic Center** M
(843) 678-9000. **$45-$180.** 2690 David McLeod Blvd 29501. I-95 exit 160A, just e on service road. Ext corridors. **Pets:** Accepted.
🆅 📶 ⊠ 📦

▼▼▼ **Residence Inn by Marriott Florence** H
(843) 468-2800. **$111-$187.** 2660 Hospitality Blvd 29501. I-95 exit 160A, just e, then s. Int corridors. **Pets:** Accepted.
ᴸM ⊠ 📶 ⊠ 📦 💻

△△△ ▼▼▼ **Super 8** M
(843) 661-7267. **$59-$200.** 1832 1/2 W Lucas St 29501. I-95 exit 164, just se. Ext corridors. **Pets:** Small, other species. $10 daily fee/pet. Designated rooms, service with restrictions, supervision.
🆅 ⊠ 📶 📦 💻

▼▼▼ **TownePlace Suites by Marriott Florence, SC** H
(843) 407-9400. **$105-$150.** 2650 Hospitality Blvd 29501. I-95 exit 160A, just e, then s. Int corridors. **Pets:** Accepted.
ᴸM 📶 ⊠ 📦 💻

FOLLY BEACH *(Restaurants p. 622)*

▼▼▼▼ Tides Folly Beach H
(843) 588-6464. **Call for rates.** 1 Center St 29439. Terminus of SR 171; center. Ext corridors. **Pets:** Accepted.

GREENVILLE *(Restaurants p. 622)*

◈◈◈ ▼▼▼▼ Aloft Greenville Downtown H
(864) 297-6100. **$169-$469.** 5 N Laurens St 29601. Jct Richardson St; downtown. Int corridors. **Pets:** Accepted.

◈◈◈ ▼▼▼ Best Western Greenville Airport Inn M
(864) 297-5353. **$88-$124.** 5009 Pelham Rd 29615. I-85 exit 54 (Pelham Rd), just se. Ext corridors. **Pets:** Accepted.

▼▼▼▼ Drury Inn & Suites-Greenville H
(864) 288-4401. **$99-$199.** 10 Carolina Point Pkwy 29607. I-85 exit 51A (Woodruff Rd), just se; I-385 exit 35 (Woodruff Rd), 0.6 mi nw. Int corridors. **Pets:** Accepted.

▼▼▼ Extended Stay America-Greenville Airport H
(864) 213-9698. **$80-$100.** 3715 Pelham Rd 29615. I-85 exit 54 (Pelham Rd), 0.5 mi w. Int corridors. **Pets:** Accepted.

▼▼▼▼ Home2 Suites by Hilton Greenville Airport H
(864) 288-0000. **$129-$189.** 20 Beacon Dr 29615. I-85 exit 54 (Pelham Rd), 0.6 mi w to Beacon Dr, then just s. Int corridors. **Pets:** Accepted.

◈◈◈ ▼▼▼▼ Hyatt Place Greenville/Haywood H
(864) 232-3000. **$99-$299.** 40 W Orchard Park Dr 29615. I-385 exit 39 (Haywood Rd), just n, then w. Int corridors. **Pets:** Accepted.

◈◈◈ ▼▼▼▼ Hyatt Regency Greenville H
(864) 235-1234. **$149-$329.** 220 N Main St 29601. Just n of center. Int corridors. **Pets:** Medium, dogs only. $125 one-time fee/room. Service with restrictions, supervision.

▼▼▼ La Quinta Inn & Suites Greenville Haywood H
(864) 233-3018. **$86-$204.** 65 W Orchard Park Dr 29615. I-385 exit 39 (Haywood Rd), just n, then w. Int corridors. **Pets:** Accepted.

▼▼▼ La Quinta Inn Greenville (Woodruff Rd) M
(864) 297-3500. **$67-$130.** 31 Old Country Rd 29607. I-85 exit 51A (Woodruff Rd), just nw on SR 146; I-385 exit 37, just sw on Roper Mountain Rd, then 0.9 mi se. Ext/int corridors. **Pets:** Accepted.

◈◈◈ ▼▼▼ Red Roof Inn-Greenville M
(864) 297-4458. **$59-$89.** 91 Vision Ct 29607. I-85 exit 48A, just se to Millennium Blvd, then just nw. Ext corridors. **Pets:** Accepted.

◈◈◈ ▼▼▼▼ Residence Inn by Marriott Greenville-Spartanburg Airport H 🐾
(864) 627-0001. **$123-$241.** 120 Milestone Way 29615. I-85 exit 54 (Pelham Rd), 0.6 mi w to Milestone Way, then just n. Int corridors. **Pets:** Small. $100 one-time fee/room. Service with restrictions.

▼▼▼▼ Staybridge Suites Greenville/Spartanburg H
(864) 288-4448. **Call for rates.** 31 Market Point Dr 29607. I-85 exit 51A (Woodruff Rd), 0.5 mi se to Miller Rd, 0.5 mi s to S Oak Forest Dr, then just nw; I-385 exit 35 (Woodruff Rd), nw to Miller Rd, 0.5 mi s to S Oak Forest Dr, then just nw. Int corridors. **Pets:** Accepted.

▼▼▼ TownePlace Suites by Marriott Greenville Haywood Mall H
(864) 675-1670. **$109-$197.** 75 Mall Connector Rd 29607. I-385 exit 39 (Haywood Rd), just s to Woods Crossing Rd, just se to Mall Connector Rd, then just s. Int corridors. **Pets:** Other species. $100 one-time fee/room. Service with restrictions, crate.

◈◈◈ ▼▼▼▼ The Westin Poinsett H
(864) 421-9700. **$139-$399.** 120 S Main St 29601. Just s of center. Int corridors. **Pets:** Accepted.

◈◈◈ ▼▼▼▼ Wyndham Garden Greenville Airport Hotel H
(864) 288-3500. **$79-$150.** 47 Fisherman Ln 29615. I-85 exit 54 (Pelham Rd), 0.6 mi w to Beacon Dr, then just s. Int corridors. **Pets:** Accepted.

GREENWOOD

▼ Days Inn Greenwood M
(864) 223-1819. **$55-$82.** 233 Birchtree Dr 29649. Jct US 25 Bypass/25 business route, just se on US 25 business route. Int corridors. **Pets:** Small, dogs only. $15 daily fee/pet. Designated rooms, service with restrictions, crate.

▼▼ Quality Inn M
(864) 229-5329. **$76-$81.** 719 Bypass Hwy 25 NE 29646. Jct US 25 Bypass NE/221, just se. Ext corridors. **Pets:** Accepted.

GREER

◈◈◈ ▼▼▼▼ Holiday Inn Express Hotel & Suites Greenville Airport H
(864) 213-9331. **Call for rates.** 2681 Dry Pocket Rd 29650. I-85 exit 54 (Pelham Rd), just w to The Parkway, just n to Parkway E, then just se. Int corridors. **Pets:** Accepted.

▼▼ MainStay Suites-Greenville H
(864) 987-5566. **$64-$149.** 2671 Dry Pocket Rd 29650. I-85 exit 54 (Pelham Rd), just w to The Parkway, just n to Parkway E, then just se. Int corridors. **Pets:** Accepted.

HARDEEVILLE

▼▼▼ Holiday Inn Express & Suites H
(843) 784-2800. **$89-$229.** 145 Independence Blvd 29927. I-95 exit 8, just w. Int corridors. **Pets:** Medium, other species. $35 one-time fee/room. Designated rooms, service with restrictions, crate.

HILTON HEAD ISLAND *(Restaurants p. 622)*

◈◈◈ ▼▼▼ Best Western Ocean Breeze Inn M 🐾
(843) 715-4116. **$89-$199, 3 day notice.** 11 Lemoyne Ave 29928. Sea Pines Cir, 1.1 mi se on Pope Ave to Coligny Plaza then 0.5 mi to Lemoyne Ave; follow road to terminus; in South Forest Beach area. Ext corridors. **Pets:** Medium. $45 daily fee/room. Designated rooms, crate.

◈◈◈ ▼▼▼▼ Omni Hilton Head Oceanfront Resort H 🐾
(843) 842-8000. **$99-$499, 3 day notice.** 23 Ocean Ln 29928. Jct US 278 business route/Queens Folly Rd, 0.9 mi se to Ocean Ln, just sw; in Palmetto Dunes Plantation. Ext/int corridors. **Pets:** Medium, dogs only. $150 one-time fee/room. Designated rooms, service with restrictions, supervision.

◈◈◈ ▼▼▼ Red Roof Inn-Hilton Head M
(843) 686-6808. **$50-$150.** 5 Regency Pkwy 29928. 9 mi e of J Wilton Graves Bridge on US 278 business route; between Shipyard Plantation and Palmetto Dunes. Ext corridors. **Pets:** Accepted.

(AAA) ▼▼▼▼ Sonesta Resort Hilton Head Island **H** ❀

(843) 842-2400. **$129-$399, 3 day notice.** 130 Shipyard Dr 29928. Jct US 278 business route/Shipyard Dr, 1.3 mi se; in Shipyard Plantation. Int corridors. **Pets:** Small, dogs only. $150 one-time fee/room. Designated rooms, service with restrictions, crate.

SAVE ECO ⬛ ⬛ ⬛ ⬛ ⬛ ⬛ ⬛ ⬛

(AAA) ▼▼▼▼ The Westin Hilton Head Island Resort & Spa **H** ❀

(843) 681-4000. **$109-$599, 5 day notice.** Two Grasslawn Ave 29928. 5.6 mi e of J Wilton Graves Bridge on US 278 business route to Coggins Point Rd, just e, follow signs; in Port Royal Plantation. Int corridors. **Pets:** Small, dogs only. $150 one-time fee/room. Service with restrictions, supervision. SAVE ⬛ ⬛ ⬛ ⬛ ⬛ ⬛ ⬛ ⬛ ⬛

IRMO

(AAA) ▼▼▼ Hyatt Place Columbia/Harbison **H**

(803) 407-1560. **$79-$199.** 1130 Kinley Rd 29063. I-26 exit 102B, just e on SR 60, then just n. Int corridors. **Pets:** Medium, dogs only. $75 one-time fee/room. Service with restrictions.

SAVE ⬛ ⬛ ⬛ ⬛ ⬛ ⬛ ⬛

▼▼▼ Residence Inn by Marriott Columbia Northwest/Harbison **H**

(803) 749-7575. **$98-$183.** 944 Lake Murray Blvd 29063. I-26 exit 102A, just w on SR 60. Int corridors. **Pets:** Accepted.

⬛ ⬛ ⬛ ⬛ ⬛

KIAWAH ISLAND

▼▼▼ Kiawah Island Golf Resort-Courtside Villas **CO**

(843) 768-2121. **Call for rates.** 1401 Shipwatch Rd 29455. Just e of main gate to Kiawah Beach Dr, just s; in West Beach Village area. Ext corridors. **Pets:** Accepted. ⬛ ⬛ ⬛ ⬛ ⬛ ⬛

▼▼▼ Kiawah Island Golf Resort-Fairway Oaks Villas **CO**

(843) 768-2121. **Call for rates.** 1301 Kiawah Beach Dr 29455. Just e of main gate, just s; in West Beach Village area. Ext corridors. **Pets:** Accepted. ⬛ ⬛ ⬛ ⬛ ⬛ ⬛

▼▼▼ Kiawah Island Golf Resort-Mariners Watch Villas **CO**

(843) 768-2121. **Call for rates.** 4200 Sea Forest Dr 29455. 1.6 mi e of main gate, just s; in East Beach Village area. Ext corridors. **Pets:** Accepted. ⬛ ⬛ ⬛ ⬛ ⬛ ⬛

▼▼▼ Kiawah Island Golf Resort-Parkside Villas **CO**

(843) 768-2121. **Call for rates.** 4501 Park Lake Dr 29455. 2 mi e of main gate, just s; in East Beach Village area. Ext corridors. **Pets:** Accepted. ⬛ ⬛ ⬛ ⬛ ⬛ ⬛

▼▼▼ Kiawah Island Golf Resort-Seascape Villas **CO**

(843) 768-2121. **Call for rates.** 3510 Shipwatch Rd 29455. Just e of main gate, just s; in West Beach Village area. Ext corridors. **Pets:** Accepted. ⬛ ⬛ ⬛ ⬛ ⬛ ⬛

▼▼▼ Kiawah Island Golf Resort-Tennis Club Villas **CO**

(843) 768-2121. **Call for rates.** 4659 Tennis Club Ln 29455. 2.2 mi e of main gate, just s; at Roy Barth Tennis Center. Ext corridors. **Pets:** Accepted. ⬛ ⬛ ⬛ ⬛ ⬛ ⬛

▼▼▼ Kiawah Island Golf Resort-Turtle Cove Villas **CO**

(843) 768-2121. **Call for rates.** 5501 Green Dolphin Way 29455. 2.4 mi e of main gate, just se; at Roy Barth Tennis Center. Ext corridors. **Pets:** Accepted. ⬛ ⬛ ⬛ ⬛ ⬛ ⬛

▼▼▼ Kiawah Island Golf Resort-Turtle Point Villas **CO**

(843) 768-2121. **Call for rates.** 4901 Green Dolphin Way 29455. 2.4 mi e of main gate, just se; at Roy Barth Tennis Center and Turtle Point Golf Club. Ext corridors. **Pets:** Accepted.

⬛ ⬛ ⬛ ⬛ ⬛ ⬛

▼▼▼ Kiawah Island Golf Resort-Windswept Villas **CO**

(843) 768-2121. **Call for rates.** 4300 Sea Forest Dr 29455. 1.6 mi e of main gate, just s; in East Beach Village area. Ext corridors. **Pets:** Accepted. ⬛ ⬛ ⬛ ⬛ ⬛ ⬛ ⬛

LANCASTER

▼▼▼ Quality Inn **M**

(803) 283-1188. **$80.** 114 Commerce Blvd 29720. Jct US 521, 1.3 mi w on SR 9 Bypass, just n. Ext corridors. **Pets:** Accepted.

⬛ ⬛ ⬛ ⬛

LANDRUM

▼▼▼ The Red Horse Inn Cottages **CA** ❀

(864) 909-1575. **$210-$320, 30 day notice.** 45 Winstons Chase Ct 29356. Jct SR 14/414, 1.5 mi w on SR 414 to Campbell Rd, 0.7 mi n. Ext corridors. **Pets:** $25 daily fee/pet. Designated rooms, no service, crate. ⬛ ⬛ ⬛ ⬛ ⬛ ⬛

LATTA

(AAA) ▼▼▼ Best Western Executive Inn **H**

(843) 752-5060. **$99-$129.** 1534 Hwy 38 W 29565. I-95 exit 181B, just nw. Int corridors. **Pets:** Accepted. SAVE ⬛ ⬛ ⬛ ⬛ ⬛

LEXINGTON

▼▼▼ Quality Inn & Suites **M**

(803) 359-3099. **$70-$140.** 328 W Main St 29072. I-20 exit 58 (US 1), 3.5 mi w. Ext corridors. **Pets:** Accepted. ⬛ ⬛ ⬛ ⬛

LITTLE RIVER

(AAA) ▼▼▼ Holiday Inn Express Hotel & Suites-North Myrtle Beach **H**

(843) 281-9400. **Call for rates.** 722 Hwy 17 N 29566. Jct SR 9/US 17, 1 mi e; at Coquina Harbor. Int corridors. **Pets:** Medium. $25 daily fee/pet. Designated rooms, service with restrictions, crate.

SAVE ⬛ ⬛ ⬛ ⬛ ⬛

MANNING

(AAA) ▼▼▼ Baymont Inn & Suites **M**

(803) 473-5334. **$59-$129.** 2284 Raccoon Rd 29102. I-95 exit 119 (SR 261), just se, then s. Ext corridors. **Pets:** Accepted.

SAVE ⬛ ⬛ ⬛ ⬛

MOUNT PLEASANT *(Restaurants p. 623)*

(AAA) ▼▼▼ Days Inn Patriots Point **M**

(843) 881-1800. **$79-$126, 3 day notice.** 261 Johnnie Dodds Blvd 29464. Just e of base of Arthur Ravenel Jr Bridge on US 17 (Johnnie Dodds Blvd). Ext corridors. **Pets:** Small, dogs only. $25 daily fee/pet. Designated rooms, service with restrictions, supervision.

SAVE ⬛ ⬛ ⬛ ⬛ ⬛

(AAA) ▼▼▼ Hampton Inn-Patriots Point **H**

(843) 881-3300. **$109-$239.** 255 Sessions Way 29464. Just ne of base of Arthur Ravenel Jr Bridge to McGrath Darby Blvd, just s. Int corridors. **Pets:** Accepted. SAVE ⬛ ⬛ ⬛ ⬛ ⬛

▼▼▼ Homewood Suites by Hilton **H**

(843) 881-6950. **$129-$249.** 1998 Riviera Dr 29464. I-526 exit 32 (Georgetown/US 17 N), 1.4 mi ne on US 17, 1 mi se on SR 517 (Isle of Palms Connector), then just sw. Int corridors. **Pets:** Accepted. ⬛ ⬛ ⬛ ⬛ ⬛

(AAA) ▼▼▼ Red Roof PLUS+ Mt. Pleasant Patriot Point **M**

(843) 884-1411. **$59-$179.** 301 Johnnie Dodds Blvd 29464. Just e of base of Arthur Ravenel Jr Bridge on US 17 (Johnnie Dodds Blvd), just s on McGrath Darby Blvd. Ext corridors. **Pets:** Accepted. SAVE ⬛ ⬛ ⬛ ⬛

Residence Inn by Marriott Charleston Mt. Pleasant H
(843) 881-1599. **$134-$285.** 1116 Isle of Palms Connector 29464. I-526 exit 30 (Georgetown/US 17 N), 1.4 mi ne on US 17 to SR 517 (Isle of Palms Connector), then just se. Int corridors. **Pets:** Accepted.

Sleep Inn Mt. Pleasant H
(843) 856-5000. **$79-$220.** 299 Wingo Way 29464. Just ne of base of Arthur Ravenel Jr Bridge to McGrath Darby Blvd, just n. Int corridors. **Pets:** Accepted.

MULLINS

Quality Inn H
(843) 423-0516. **$80-$200.** 2693 E Hwy 76 29574. Jct US 501/76, just e. Int corridors. **Pets:** Accepted.

MYRTLE BEACH (Restaurants p. 623)

Best Western Plus Myrtle Beach Hotel H
(843) 213-1440. **$59-$189.** 9551 N Kings Hwy 29572. Jct SR 22, 1.4 mi sw. Int corridors. **Pets:** Accepted.

Comfort Suites H
(843) 448-4884. **$79-$309.** 710 Frontage Rd E 29577. Jct US 17 Bypass, just se on US 501, just ne. Int corridors. **Pets:** Medium, dogs only. $20 daily fee/pet. Designated rooms, service with restrictions, crate.

La Quinta Inn & Suites Myrtle Beach At 48th Avenue H
(843) 449-5231. **$67-$372.** 4709 N Kings Hwy 29577. Jct 48th Ave N and US 17 business route. Int corridors. **Pets:** Accepted.

La Quinta Inn & Suites Myrtle Beach Broadway Area H
(843) 916-8801. **$67-$367.** 1561 21st Ave N 29577. Jct US 17 Bypass, just se. Int corridors. **Pets:** Accepted.

Mermaid Inn M
(843) 712-2480. **Call for rates.** 5400 N Ocean Blvd 29577. Between 53 Ave N and Hampton Cir. Ext corridors. **Pets:** Dogs only. $20 daily fee/room. Designated rooms, service with restrictions, crate.

Ocean Park Resort H
(843) 448-1915. **$54-$213, 365 day notice.** 1905 S Ocean Blvd 29577. Jct 20th Ave S. Int corridors. **Pets:** Accepted.

Patricia Grand Resort Hotel H
(843) 448-8453. **$61-$224.** 2710 N Ocean Blvd 29577. Jct 27th Ave N. Ext corridors. **Pets:** Small, dogs only. $20 daily fee/pet. Designated rooms, service with restrictions, crate.

Red Roof Inn Myrtle Beach Hotel - Market Commons H
(843) 626-4444. **$39-$280.** 2801 S Kings Hwy 29577. Between 27th Ave S and 29th Ave S on US 17 business route. Int corridors. **Pets:** Accepted.

Westgate Myrtle Beach Oceanfront Resort H
(843) 448-4481. **Call for rates.** 415 S Ocean Blvd 29577. Jct 6th Ave S, just ne. Int corridors. **Pets:** Medium. $100 deposit/room, $170 one-time fee/room. Designated rooms, service with restrictions, supervision.

NORTH CHARLESTON (Restaurants p. 623)

Aloft Charleston Airport & Convention Center H
(843) 566-7300. **$139-$259.** 4875 Tanger Outlet Blvd 29418. I-26 exit 213 westbound; exit 213A eastbound, follow signs to Tanger Outlet Mall. Int corridors. **Pets:** Accepted.

Candlewood Suites H
(843) 797-3535. **$119-$169.** 2177 Northwoods Blvd 29406. I-26 exit 209A eastbound; exit 209B (Ashley Phosphate Rd) westbound, just e, then just n. Int corridors. **Pets:** Accepted.

Embassy Suites by Hilton Hotel Airport-Convention Center North Charleston H
(843) 747-1882. **$159-$289.** 5055 International Blvd 29418. I-26 exit 213 westbound; exit 213A eastbound, just s, then w; I-526 exit 10 (International Blvd), 0.4 mi e. Int corridors. **Pets:** Accepted.

Home2 Suites by Hilton Charleston Airport/Convention Center H
(843) 744-4202. **$99-$269.** 3401 W Montague Ave 29418. I-26 exit 213 westbound; exit 213A eastbound, 0.9 mi sw; I-526 exit 16. Int corridors. **Pets:** Large. $75 one-time fee/room. Service with restrictions.

Residence Inn by Marriott Charleston Airport H ❀
(843) 266-3434. **$120-$224.** 5035 International Blvd 29418. I-26 exit 213 westbound; exit 213A eastbound, just s; I-526 exit 16 (International Blvd), 0.7 mi e. Int corridors. **Pets:** Other species. $100 one-time fee/room. Service with restrictions.

Staybridge Suites North Charleston H
(843) 377-4600. **$159-$299.** 7329 Mazyck Rd 29406. I-26 exit 209A eastbound; exit 209B (Ashley Phosphate Rd) westbound, just w to Mazyck Rd, then just s. Int corridors. **Pets:** Accepted.

ORANGEBURG

Baymont Inn & Suites Orangeburg M
(803) 937-6684. **$79-$85.** 3583 St Matthews Rd 29118. I-26 exit 145A (US 601), 0.5 mi sw. Ext corridors. **Pets:** Accepted.

RICHBURG

Motel 6 H
(803) 789-7770. **Call for rates.** 2912 Parkway Blvd 29729. I-77 exit 65, just w on SR 9. Int corridors. **Pets:** Accepted.

RIDGELAND

Quality Inn & Suites M
(843) 726-2121. **$69-$124.** 221 James L Taylor Rd 29936. I-95 exit 21 (US 336), just nw. Ext/int corridors. **Pets:** Other species. $10 daily fee/pet. Service with restrictions, supervision.

ROCK HILL

Comfort Suites H
(803) 326-3300. **$109-$269.** 1323 Old Springdale Rd 29730. I-77 exit 79, just e on Dave Lyle Blvd, just s on Galleria Blvd, then just e. Int corridors. **Pets:** Accepted.

Hampton Inn Rock Hill H
(803) 325-1100. **$124-$234.** 2111 Tabor Dr 29730. I-77 exit 79, just e on Dave Lyle Blvd, just n on Galleria Blvd, then just w. Int corridors. **Pets:** Accepted.

WWWW TownePlace Suites by Marriott Rock Hill ⛔ ❀
(803) 327-0700. **$109-$177.** 2135 Tabor Dr 29730. I-77 exit 79, just e on Dave Lyle Blvd, just n on Galleria Blvd, then just w. Int corridors. **Pets:** $75 one-time fee/room. Designated rooms, service with restrictions, supervision. 🆓 🍴 🐾 📶 ✕ 🛏 🖥

WWWW Wingate by Wyndham ⛔
(803) 324-9000. **$79-$209.** 760 Galleria Blvd 29730. I-77 exit 79, just e on Dave Lyle Blvd, then just s. Int corridors. **Pets:** Accepted.
🆓 🐾 📶 ✕ 🛏 🖥

SANTEE
WWWW Holiday Inn Santee ⛔
(803) 854-9800. **Call for rates.** 139 Bradford Blvd 29142. I-95 exit 98 (SR 6), just nw, then just sw. Int corridors. **Pets:** Small, other species. $20 daily fee/room. Designated rooms, service with restrictions, supervision. 🍴 🆓 🐾 📶 ✕ 🛏 🖥

AAA WW Super 8 Ⓜ
(803) 854-3456. **$51-$100.** 9125 Old Hwy 6 29142. I-95 exit 98 (SR 6), 0.4 mi se. Ext corridors. **Pets:** Accepted. 🆓 🐾 📶 🛏 🖥

SENECA
WW Quality Inn Ⓜ
(864) 888-8300. **$75-$199.** 226 Hi-Tech Rd 29678. Jct SR 28 and US 76/123, 0.9 mi w on US 76/123, just se. Ext corridors. **Pets:** Accepted.
🆓 🐾 📶 🛏 🖥

SIMPSONVILLE *(Restaurants p. 623)*
WW Comfort Suites ⛔
(864) 757-1552. **$120-$290.** 3971 Grandview Dr 29680. I-385 exit 26, just s on Fairview Rd, then 0.5 mi se along Service Rd. Int corridors. **Pets:** Accepted. 🍴 🆓 🐾 📶 ✕ 🛏 🖥

WWWW Days Inn Ⓜ
(864) 963-7701. **$70-$90.** 45 Ray E Talley Ct 29680. I-385 exit 27, just s, then just se. Ext corridors. **Pets:** Accepted. 🐾 📶 🛏 🖥

WWWW Quality Inn Ⓜ
(864) 963-2777. **$74-$100.** 3755 Grandview Dr 29680. I-385 exit 27, just s. Ext corridors. **Pets:** Accepted. 🐾 📶 🛏 🖥

SPARTANBURG
WWWW Holiday Inn Express Hotel & Suites ⛔
(864) 699-7777. **$135-$195, 14 day notice.** 895 Spartan Blvd 29301. I-26 exit 21B (US 29), just e to W Blackstock Rd, then 0.7 mi n. Int corridors. **Pets:** Accepted. 🆓 🐾 📶 ✕ 🛏 🖥

SUMMERVILLE *(Restaurants p. 624)*
AAA WWWW Wyndham
Garden-Charleston/Summerville ⛔
(843) 875-3300. **$89-$169.** 120 Holiday Dr 29483. I-26 exit 199A, just w on US 17 alternate route to Holiday Dr, then just n. Int corridors.
Pets: Accepted. 🆓 🐾 📶 ✕ 🛏 🖥

SUMTER
WWWW Candlewood Suites ⛔
(803) 469-4000. **Call for rates.** 2541 Broad St 29150. 1.1 mi w of jct US 76/378/521. Int corridors. **Pets:** Accepted.
🆓 🐾 📶 ✕ 🛏 🖥

WALTERBORO
AAA WWWW Best Western of Walterboro Ⓜ ❀
(843) 538-3600. **$99-$119.** 1428 Sniders Hwy 29488. I-95 exit 53 (SR 63), just e. Ext corridors. **Pets:** $15 daily fee/pet. Designated rooms, service with restrictions, supervision. 🆓 🐾 📶 🛏 🖥

AAA WW Super 8 Ⓜ
(843) 538-5383. **$62-$65.** 1972 Bells Hwy 29488. I-95 exit 57 (SR 64), just nw. Ext corridors. **Pets:** Accepted. 🆓 🍴 🐾 📶 🛏 🖥

WEST COLUMBIA *(Restaurants p. 624)*
WW Quality Inn Ⓜ
(803) 791-5160. **$70-$120.** 2516 Augusta Rd 29169. I-26 exit 111B (US 1 N), just e. Ext/int corridors. **Pets:** Accepted. 🐾 📶 🛏 🖥

WINNSBORO
WW Americas Best Value Inn Winnsboro Ⓜ
(803) 635-1447. **$65-$105.** 1894 US Hwy 321 Bypass 29180. I-77 exit 34 (SR 34), 6.5 mi w; jct US 321/SR 34/213. Ext corridors.
Pets: Small. $15 daily fee/pet. Designated rooms, service with restrictions, supervision. 🐾 📶 🛏 🖥

YEMASSEE
AAA WWWW Best Western Point South Ⓜ
(843) 726-8101. **$75-$120.** 3536 Point South Dr 29945. I-95 exit 33 (US 17), just ne. Ext corridors. **Pets:** Accepted.
🆓 🐾 📶 🛏 🖥

SOUTH DAKOTA

ABERDEEN
WW AmericInn Lodge & Suites of Aberdeen ⛔
(605) 225-4565. **Call for rates.** 301 Centennial St 57401. 2.2 mi e on US 12, just n. Int corridors. **Pets:** Accepted.
🆓 🐾 ✕ 📶 ✕ 🛏 🖥

AAA WWWW Best Western Ramkota Hotel ⛔ ❀
(605) 229-4040. **$115-$170.** 1400 8th Ave NW 57401. 1.5 mi nw on US 281. Ext/int corridors. **Pets:** Medium. Service with restrictions, crate.
🆓 🈁 🍴 🆓 🐾 📶 ✕ 🛏 🖥

WWWW Holiday Inn Express Hotel & Suites ⛔
(605) 725-4000. **Call for rates.** 3310 7th Ave SE 57401. 2.1 mi e on US 12. Int corridors. **Pets:** Accepted. 🆓 🐾 📶 ✕ 🛏 🖥

WWWW My Place Hotel-Aberdeen ⛔
(605) 262-4600. **$75-$110.** 410 S Harvard St 57401. 1.9 mi e on US 12, then just n. Int corridors. **Pets:** Large. $10 daily fee/room. Service with restrictions, supervision. 🆓 📶 ✕ 🛏 🖥

WWWWW TownePlace Suites by Marriott ⛔
(605) 725-3500. **$104-$229.** 402 Norwood St S 57401. Between 3rd and 6th aves SE. Int corridors. **Pets:** Accepted.
🆓 🐾 📶 ✕ 🛏 🖥

BOX ELDER
AAA WWWW Residence Inn by Marriott ⛔
(605) 791-9600. **$49-$355.** 581 Watiki Way 57719. I-90 exit 61 (Elk Vale Rd), just s, then just e. Int corridors. **Pets:** Accepted.
🆓 🆓 📶 ✕ 🛏 🖥

BRANDON
WWWW Holiday Inn Express & Suites ⛔ ❀
(605) 582-2901. **$99-$164.** 1103 N Splitrock Blvd 57005. I-90 exit 406, just s. Int corridors. **Pets:** Other species. $15 daily fee/pet. Service with restrictions, crate. 🆓 🐾 📶 ✕ 🛏 🖥

BROOKINGS

▼▼ Brookings Days Inn H
(605) 692-9471. $74-$99. 2500 E 6th St S 57006. I-29 exit 134, just w. Int corridors. Pets: Small, dogs only. $15 daily fee/pet. Designated rooms, service with restrictions, supervision. 🍴 📶 ✕ 🛗 💻

▼▼ Brookings Super 8 H
(605) 692-6920. $71-$125. 3034 Lefevre Dr 57006. I-29 exit 132, just e. Int corridors. Pets: Accepted. 🏊 📶 ✕ 🛗 💻

▼▼▼ Holiday Inn Express Hotel & Suites H
(605) 692-9060. $120-$180. 3020 Lefevre Dr 57006. I-29 exit 132, just se. Int corridors. Pets: Medium, dogs only. $20 daily fee/pet. Designated rooms, service with restrictions, supervision.
♿ 🏊 📶 ✕ 🛗 💻

▼▼ My Place Hotel-Brookings H
(605) 696-3150. $89-$99. 711 32nd Ave 57006. I-29 exit 132, just e. Int corridors. Pets: Accepted. ♿ 📶 ✕ 🛗 💻

CHAMBERLAIN

▼▼ AmericInn Lodge & Suites of Chamberlain H
(605) 734-0985. Call for rates. 1981 E King St 57325. I-90 exit 265, just e. Int corridors. Pets: Accepted.
🍴 ♿ 🏊 ✕ 📶 🛗 💻

◈ ▼▼▼ Best Western Lee's Motor Inn M
(605) 234-5575. $70-$130. 220 W King Ave 57325. US 16 and I-90 business loop; downtown. Ext/int corridors. Pets: Medium, other species. $10 one-time fee/pet. Designated rooms, service with restrictions, supervision. SAVE 🏊 📶 ✕ 💻

CUSTER CITY

▼▼ Bavarian Inn M
(605) 673-2802. Call for rates. 855 N 5th St 57730. 1 mi n on US 16 and 385. Ext/int corridors. Pets: $25 daily fee/pet. Service with restrictions, supervision. ♿ 🏊 📶 ✕ 🛗 💻

▼▼▼ Best Western Buffalo Ridge Inn H
(605) 673-2275. $70-$155. 310 W Mt. Rushmore Rd 57730. 0.7 mi w on US 16. Ext/int corridors. Pets: Accepted.
SAVE ♿ 🏊 📶 ✕ 🛗 💻

▼▼ Rock Crest Lodge and Cabins CA
(605) 673-4323. Call for rates. 15 W Mt. Rushmore Rd 57730. US 16, 0.5 mi w. Ext/int corridors. Pets: Accepted. 🏊 📶 ✕ 🛗 💻

◈ ▼▼▼ Super 8-Custer H 🐾
(605) 673-2200. $80-$220. 535 W Mt. Rushmore Rd 57730. US 16, 0.8 mi w. Int corridors. Pets: $15 daily fee/room. Designated rooms, service with restrictions, supervision. SAVE ♿ 🏊 📶 ✕ 🛗 💻

DEADWOOD

◈ ▼▼▼▼ Cadillac Jack's Gaming Resort H 🐾
(605) 578-1500. $39-$469. 360 Main St 57732. 0.6 mi n on US 85. Int corridors. Pets: Other species. $25 daily fee/pet. Designated rooms, service with restrictions. SAVE 🍴 ♿ 📶 ✕ 🛗 💻

▼▼▼▼ Comfort Inn & Suites H
(605) 578-7550. $74-$579. 225 Cliff St 57732. 1 mi s on US 85 S. Int corridors. Pets: Accepted. 🍴 ♿ 🏊 ✕ 📶 ✕ 🛗 💻

◈ ▼▼▼ Deadwood Gulch Gaming Resort H
(605) 578-1294. Call for rates. 304 Cliff St 57732. 0.7 mi s on US 85 S. Ext/int corridors. Pets: Dogs only. $500 deposit/room, $20 one-time fee/pet. Designated rooms, service with restrictions.
SAVE 🍴 ♿ 📶 ✕ 🛗 💻

◈ ▼▼▼ First Gold Hotel & Gaming H
(605) 578-9777. $89-$379, 60 day notice. 270 Main St 57732. 0.7 mi n on US 85. Ext/int corridors. Pets: Medium. $25 one-time fee/room. Designated rooms, service with restrictions, supervision.
SAVE 🍴 ♿ 📶 ✕ 🛗 💻

▼▼▼ Holiday Inn Express Hotel & Suites H
(605) 578-3330. Call for rates. 22 Lee St 57732. Jct Main St; center. Int corridors. Pets: Accepted. ♿ 🏊 📶 ✕ 🛗 💻

▼▼▼ Holiday Inn Resort Deadwood Mountain Grand H
(605) 559-0386. Call for rates. 1906 Deadwood Mountain Dr 57732. Jct US 14 and Pine St; downtown. Int corridors. Pets: Accepted.
🍴 ♿ 🏊 ✕ 📶 ✕ 🛗 💻

▼▼▼▼ The Hotel by Gold Dust H
(605) 559-1400. Call for rates. 25 Lee St 57732. Jct Main St; center. Int corridors. Pets: Medium, dogs only. $35 one-time fee/room. Designated rooms, service with restrictions, crate. ♿ 📶 ✕ 🛗 💻

▼▼▼▼ The Lodge at Deadwood H 🌸
(605) 584-4800. $89-$799. 100 Pine Crest Ln 57732. Jct US 14, 1 mi n on US 85. Ext/int corridors. Pets: Dogs only. Service with restrictions.
🍴 🏊 📶 ✕ 🛗 💻

FAITH

▼ Prairie Vista Inn M
(605) 967-2343. Call for rates. 204 E 1st St 57626. On US 212; east end of town. Int corridors. Pets: Accepted. ♿ 📶 🛗 💻

FAULKTON

▼ Faulkton Inn M
(605) 598-4567. Call for rates. 700 Main St 57438. On US 212; center. Int corridors. Pets: Accepted. 📶 ✕ 🛗 💻

FORT PIERRE

▼▼▼ AmericInn Lodge & Suites of Pierre/Fort Pierre H
(605) 223-2358. Call for rates. 312 Island Dr 57532. Jct US 14 and SR 34, just w of Missouri River Bridge, just s. Int corridors. Pets: Accepted. ♿ 🏊 📶 ✕ 🛗 💻

▼▼ My Place Hotel - Pierre/Fort Pierre H
(605) 494-2090. Call for rates. 209 E Hustan Ave 57532. Jct US 14 and SR 34, just w of Missouri River Bridge, just s. Int corridors. Pets: Accepted. ♿ 📶 ✕ 🛗 💻

FREEMAN

▼ Freeman Country Inn M
(605) 925-4888. $80-$124. 1019 S Hwy 81 57029. On US 81, just s. Int corridors. Pets: Accepted. ♿ 📶 ✕ 🛗

HILL CITY

◈ ▼▼▼ Best Western Golden Spike Inn & Suites H
(605) 574-2577. $110-$250. 601 E Main St 57745. Just n on US 16 and 385. Ext/int corridors. Pets: Accepted.
SAVE 🍴 ♿ 🏊 📶 ✕ 🛗 💻

▼ Hill City Super 8 M
(605) 574-4141. $66-$230. 109 Main St 57745. On US 16 and 385; center. Int corridors. Pets: Accepted. 📶 ✕ 💻

▼ Lantern Inn M
(605) 574-2582. Call for rates. 580 E Main St 57745. On US 16 and 385; north side of town. Ext corridors. Pets: Accepted.
🏊 📶 ✕ 🛗

◍ 🔷🔷 **Mount Rushmore Lodge at Palmer Gulch** 🄷
(605) 574-2525. **$85-$750, 10 day notice.** 12620 SR 244 57745. On SR 244, 5 mi w of Mt. Rushmore. Int corridors. **Pets:** Accepted.
[SAVE] 🍽 🛗 🛏 ⊠ 📶 ⊠ 🔲 🖥

HOT SPRINGS

◍ 🔷🔷 **Baymont Inn & Suites** 🄷
(605) 745-7378. **$72-$216.** 737 S 6th St 57747. 0.5 mi se off US 18 and 385. Int corridors. **Pets:** Accepted.
[SAVE] 🛗 🛏 📶 ⊠ 🔲 🖥

◍ 🔷 **Dollar Inn Hot Springs** Ⓜ 🐾
(605) 745-3182. **Call for rates.** 402 Battle Mountain Ave 57747. 1 mi n on US 385. Ext corridors. **Pets:** Other species. $5 daily fee/pet. Designated rooms, supervision. [SAVE] 📶 ⊠ 🔲 🖥

◍ 🔷🔷 **Hills Inn** Ⓜ
(605) 745-3130. **$59-$250.** 640 S 6th St 57747. 0.5 mi se off US 18 and 385. Ext corridors. **Pets:** Accepted. [SAVE] 🛏 📶 ⊠ 🔲 🖥

🔷 **Motel 6** 🄷
(605) 745-6666. **Call for rates.** 541 Indianapolis Ave 57747. US 18 and 385, just w; jct S 6th St. Int corridors. **Pets:** Accepted.
🍽 🛗 🛏 📶 🔲

◍ 🔷🔷 **Stay USA Hotel and Suites** 🄷
(605) 745-4411. **$58-$280.** 1401 Hwy 18 Bypass 57747. Jct US 18 and 385, 0.7 mi w on US 18 Bypass. Int corridors. **Pets:** Accepted.
[SAVE] 🛗 📶 ⊠ 🔲 🖥

🔷 **Super 8-Hot Springs** 🄷
(605) 745-3888. **$44-$90.** 800 Mammoth St 57747. Jct US 18 and 385, 1 mi w on US 18 Bypass. Int corridors. **Pets:** $10 daily fee/pet. Designated rooms, service with restrictions, supervision. 🛗 📶 🔲 🖥

HURON

◍ 🔷🔷 **Best Western Of Huron** 🄷
(605) 352-2000. **$93-$99.** 2000 Dakota Ave S 57350. 1.3 mi s on SR 37. Ext/int corridors. **Pets:** Accepted. [SAVE] 🛗 📶 🔲 🖥

KEYSTONE

🔷 **Holy Smoke Resort** 🄲🄰
(605) 666-4616. **$70-$295, 14 day notice.** 24105 Hwy 16A 57751. On US 16A, 2 mi n. Ext corridors. **Pets:** Dogs only. $10 daily fee/pet. Service with restrictions, crate. 🍽 📶 ⊠ 🎴 🔲 🖥

🔷🔷 **Mt. Rushmore's Washington Inn & Suites** 🄷
(605) 666-5070. **Call for rates.** 231 Winter St 57751. On US 16A; downtown. Ext/int corridors. **Pets:** Other species. Designated rooms, service with restrictions, crate. 🍽 🛗 🛏 📶 ⊠ 🔲

🔷🔷 **Mt. Rushmore's White House Resort** 🄷
(605) 666-4917. **$70-$129, 3 day notice.** 115 Swanzey St 57751. Just e of jct US 16A and SR 40. Ext/int corridors. **Pets:** Other species. Designated rooms, service with restrictions, crate.
🍽 🛗 🛏 📶 ⊠ 🔲

🔷🔷 **Powder House Lodge** 🄲🄰
(605) 666-4646. **$90-$529, 3 day notice.** 24125 Hwy 16A 57751. On US 16A, 1.5 mi n. Ext corridors. **Pets:** Accepted.
⊟ 🍽 🛗 🛏 📶 ⊠ 🔲 🖥

MADISON

🔷🔷 **AmericInn Lodge & Suites Madison** 🄷
(605) 256-3076. **Call for rates.** 504 10th St SE 57042. SR 34, 0.5 mi se; south side of town. Int corridors. **Pets:** Accepted.
🛗 🛏 📶 ⊠ 🔲 🖥

MITCHELL

🔷🔷 **AmericInn Lodge & Suites** 🄷
(605) 996-9700. **$90-$150.** 1421 S Burr St 57301. I-90 exit 332, just n. Int corridors. **Pets:** Accepted. 🛏 📶 ⊠ 🔲 🖥

🔷🔷 **Days Inn of Mitchell** 🄷
(605) 996-6208. **$74-$129.** 1506 S Burr St 57301. I-90 exit 332, just n. Int corridors. **Pets:** Dogs only. $10 daily fee/pet. Designated rooms, service with restrictions, supervision. 🛗 🛏 📶 🔲 🖥

🔷🔷🔷 **Hampton Inn** 🄷
(605) 995-1575. **$134-$177.** 1920 Highland Way 57301. I-90 exit 332, just se. Int corridors. **Pets:** Accepted. 🛗 🛏 📶 ⊠ 🔲 🖥

🔷🔷🔷 **Kelly Inn & Suites** 🄷
(605) 995-0500. **$79-$145.** 1010 Cabela Dr 57301. I-90 exit 332, just sw. Ext/int corridors. **Pets:** Service with restrictions, supervision.
🛗 🛏 📶 ⊠ 🔲 🖥

MOBRIDGE

🔷 **Wrangler Inn** 🄷
(605) 845-3641. **$85-$159.** 820 W Grand Crossing 57601. 0.5 mi w on US 12. Ext/int corridors. **Pets:** Accepted.
🍽 🛏 ⊠ 📶 ⊠ 🔲 🖥

MURDO

◍ 🔷🔷 **Best Western Graham's** Ⓜ
(605) 669-2441. **$79-$199.** 301 W 5th St 57559. On I-90 business loop, 0.5 mi w of jct US 83; I-90 exit 191 or 192. Ext corridors. **Pets:** Large, other species. $20 one-time fee/room. Designated rooms, service with restrictions, supervision. [SAVE] 🛗 🛏 📶 ⊠ 🔲 🖥

◍ 🔷🔷 **Range Country Lodging** 🄷
(605) 669-2425. **$89-$159.** 302 W 5th St 57559. I-90 business loop, 0.5 mi w of jct US 83 exit 192 or 191. Ext/int corridors. **Pets:** Accepted.
[SAVE] ⊟ 🛗 🛏 📶 🔲 🖥

OACOMA

🔷🔷 **Howard Johnson Inn & Suites** 🄷
(605) 234-4222. **$70-$160.** 203 E Hwy 16 57365. I-90 exit 260, just n, then just e. Int corridors. **Pets:** Accepted.
🍽 🛗 📶 ⊠ 🔲 🖥

🔷🔷 **Quality Inn** 🄷
(605) 734-5593. **$79-$199.** 100 W Hwy 16 57365. I-90 exit 260, just n. Int corridors. **Pets:** Accepted. 🍽 🛏 📶 ⊠ 🔲 🖥

PIERRE

🔷🔷 **Baymont Inn & Suites Pierre** Ⓜ
(605) 224-4140. **$55-$70.** 713 W Sioux Ave 57501. 0.8 mi w on US 14/83 and SR 34. Int corridors. **Pets:** Accepted. 📶 ⊠ 🔲 🖥

◍ 🔷🔷🔷 **ClubHouse Hotel & Suites** 🄷
(605) 494-2582. **Call for rates.** 808 W Sioux Ave 57501. 1 mi w on US 14/83. Ext/int corridors. **Pets:** Accepted.
[SAVE] 🍽 🛗 ⊠ 📶 ⊠ 🔲 🖥

🔷🔷🔷 **Ramkota Hotel & Conference Center-Pierre** 🄷
(605) 224-6877. **Call for rates.** 920 W Sioux Ave 57501. 1 mi w on US 14/83. Ext/int corridors. **Pets:** Accepted.
🍽 🛗 🛏 ⊠ 📶 ⊠ 🔲 🖥

🔷🔷 **Super 8** Ⓜ
(605) 224-1617. **$55-$68.** 320 W Sioux Ave 57501. 0.3 mi w on US 14/83 and SR 34. Int corridors. **Pets:** Accepted. 📶 🔲 🖥

RAPID CITY

▼▼▼ Americas Best Value Inn 🄷
(605) 343-5434. **$70-$260.** 620 Howard St 57701. I-90 exit 58 (Haines Ave), just nw. Int corridors. **Pets:** Large, other species. $15 daily fee/room. Service with restrictions, supervision. 🛇🔲🍴📶🔲🔲🔲

🄰🄰🄰' ▼▼▼ AmericInn Lodge & Suites Rapid City 🄷
(605) 343-8424. **$44-$399, 3 day notice.** 1632 Rapp St 57701. I-90 exit 59 (LaCrosse St), just s, then just w on Eglin St. Int corridors. **Pets:** Accepted. 🆂🅰🆅🅴🔲🔲🔲🔲🔲🔲

▼▼▼ Baymont Inn & Suites 🄷
(605) 791-5151. **$54-$374.** 4040 Cheyenne Blvd 57703. I-90 exit 61 (Elk Vale Rd), just s. Int corridors. **Pets:** Accepted. 🍴🔲📶🔲🔲🔲

🄰🄰🄰' ▼▼▼ Best Western Ramkota Hotel 🄷 🐾
(605) 343-8550. **$100-$230.** 2111 N LaCrosse St 57701. I-90 exit 59 (LaCrosse St), just n. Ext/int corridors. **Pets:** Other species. Designated rooms, service with restrictions, crate. 🆂🅰🆅🅴🍴🔲📶🔲🔲🔲

🄰🄰🄰' ▼▼▼ Country Inn & Suites By Carlson 🄷
(605) 394-0017. **Call for rates.** 2321 N LaCrosse St 57701. I-90 exit 59 (LaCrosse St), just n. Int corridors. **Pets:** Accepted. 🆂🅰🆅🅴🔲📶🔲🔲🔲

▼▼▼ GrandStay Residential Suites Hotel 🄷
(605) 341-5100. **Call for rates.** 660 Disk Dr 57701. I-90 exit 58 (Haines Ave), just n, then just w. Int corridors. **Pets:** Accepted. 🔲🔲🔲📶🔲🔲🔲

▼▼▼ Holiday Inn-Rushmore Plaza 🄷
(605) 348-4000. **Call for rates.** 505 N 5th St 57701. I-90 exit 58 (Haines Ave), 1.3 mi s. Int corridors. **Pets:** Accepted. 🍴🔲🔲🔲📶🔲🔲🔲

🄰🄰🄰' ▼▼▼ The Hotel Alex Johnson, Curio Collection by Hilton 🄷
(605) 342-1210. **$89-$289.** 523 6th St 57701. I-90 exit 57 (I-190/US 16 W/Mt. Rushmore), 1.8 mi s, just e on SR 44 (Omaha St), then just s; jct St Joseph St. Int corridors. **Pets:** Accepted. 🆂🅰🆅🅴🍴📶🔲🔲🔲

🄰🄰🄰' ▼▼▼ Howard Johnson Inn & Suites 🄷
(605) 737-4656. **$79-$459.** 950 North St 57701. I-90 exit 57 (I-190 S/US-16 W Mt. Rushmore); exit 1C, just e. Int corridors. **Pets:** Small, dogs only. $10 daily fee/pet. Designated rooms, supervision. 🆂🅰🆅🅴🔲🔲📶🔲🔲🔲

🄰🄰🄰' ▼▼▼ La Quinta Inn & Suites 🄷
(605) 718-7000. **$67-$526.** 1416 N Elk Vale Rd 57701. I-90 exit 61 (Elk Vale Rd), just s. Int corridors. **Pets:** Accepted. 🆂🅰🆅🅴🍴📶🔲🔲🔲

▼ Lazy U Motel 🄼
(605) 343-4242. **Call for rates.** 2215 Mt. Rushmore Rd 57701. 1 mi s on US 16. Ext corridors. **Pets:** Accepted. 📶🔲🔲

🄰🄰🄰' ▼▼ Microtel Inn & Suites by Wyndham Rapid City 🄷
(605) 348-2523. **$53-$191.** 1740 Rapp St 57701. I-90 exit 59 (LaCrosse St), just se. Int corridors. **Pets:** Other species. $10 daily fee/pet. Service with restrictions, crate. 🆂🅰🆅🅴🔲🔲📶🔲🔲🔲

▼▼▼ The Rushmore Hotel 🄷
(605) 348-8300. **$89-$369.** 445 Mt. Rushmore Rd 57701. On I-90 business loop; jct Main St; center. Int corridors. **Pets:** Accepted. 🍴🔲📶🔲🔲🔲

▼▼ Super 8 LaCrosse St 🄼
(605) 348-8070. **$44-$115.** 2124 LaCrosse St 57701. I-90 exit 59 (LaCrosse St), just n. Int corridors. **Pets:** Accepted. 🔲📶🔲🔲🔲

▼▼ Travelodge-Rapid City 🄷
(605) 343-5383. **$49-$159.** 2505 Mt. Rushmore Rd 57701. 1.3 mi s on US 16. Ext corridors. **Pets:** Accepted. 🔲🔲📶🔲🔲🔲

SIOUX FALLS

🄰🄰🄰' ▼▼▼ Best Western Empire Towers 🄷
(605) 361-3118. **$90-$140.** 4100 W Shirley Pl 57106. I-29 exit 77 (41st St), just ne. Int corridors. **Pets:** Accepted.
🆂🅰🆅🅴🔲📶🔲🔲🔲

🄰🄰🄰' ▼▼▼ Best Western Plus Ramkota Hotel 🄷
(605) 336-0650. **$100-$140.** 3200 W Maple St 57107. I-29 exit 81 (Airport/Russell St), just e. Ext/int corridors. **Pets:** Accepted.
🆂🅰🆅🅴🍴🔲🔲🔲📶🔲🔲🔲

▼▼▼ Candlewood Suites Sioux Falls 🄷
(605) 361-5100. **Call for rates.** 2725 S Carolyn Ave 57106. I-29 exit 77, just e; then just n. Int corridors. **Pets:** Accepted.
🔲📶🔲🔲🔲

▼▼ Center Inn 🄼
(605) 334-9002. **Call for rates.** 900 E 20th St 57105. I-90 exit 399 (Cliff Ave), 5 mi s, then just w. Int corridors. **Pets:** Accepted.
🔲📶🔲🔲

▼▼▼ ClubHouse Hotel & Suites 🄷 🐾
(605) 361-8700. **Call for rates.** 2320 S Louise Ave 57106. I-29 exit 78 (26th St), just e. Ext/int corridors. **Pets:** Service with restrictions, supervision. 🍴🔲🔲🔲📶🔲🔲🔲

▼▼▼ Comfort Suites by Choice Hotels 🄷
(605) 362-9711. **$90-$170.** 3208 S Carolyn Ave 57106. I-29 exit 77 (41st St), just e, then n. Int corridors. **Pets:** Large. $10 daily fee/pet. Designated rooms, service with restrictions, supervision.
🔲🔲📶🔲🔲🔲

▼▼ Dakotah Lodge 🄼
(605) 332-2000. **Call for rates.** 3200 W Russell St 57107. I-29 exit 81 (Airport/Russell St), just e. Int corridors. **Pets:** Accepted.
🍴🔲🔲🔲📶🔲🔲🔲

▼▼▼ Home2 Suites by Hilton 🄷
(605) 332-5461. **Call for rates.** 1120 S Grange 57105. Between 18th and 19th sts. Int corridors. **Pets:** Accepted.
🍴🔲📶🔲🔲🔲

▼▼▼ Homewood Suites by Hilton 🄷
(605) 338-8585. **$129-$179.** 3620 W Avera Dr 57108. I-229 exit 1C (Louise Ave), just s. Int corridors. **Pets:** Accepted.
🔲🔲📶🔲🔲

▼▼▼ La Quinta Inn and Suites 🄷
(605) 275-4555. **$97-$196.** 4521 W 41st St 57106. I-29 exit 77, just w. Int corridors. **Pets:** Accepted. 🔲📶🔲🔲🔲

▼▼▼ My Place Hotel - Sioux Falls 🄷
(605) 271-9988. **$60-$120.** 3005 S Carolyn Ave 57106. I-29 exit 77, just e, then just n. Int corridors. **Pets:** Accepted. 🔲📶🔲🔲🔲

▼▼▼ Quality Inn & Suites 🄷
(605) 336-1900. **$100-$180.** 5410 N Granite Ln 57107. I-29 exit 83 (SR 38), just e, then 0.3 mi n. Int corridors. **Pets:** Accepted.
🔲🔲📶🔲🔲🔲

▼▼▼ Red Roof Inn Sioux Falls 🄼
(605) 361-1864. **$59-$299.** 3500 S Gateway Blvd 57106. I-29 exit 77 (41st St), just w, then s. Int corridors. **Pets:** Accepted.
📶🔲🔲🔲

▼▼▼ Residence Inn by Marriott 🄷
(605) 361-2202. **$89-$261.** 4509 W Empire Pl 57106. I-29 exit 77 (41st St), 0.5 mi se. Int corridors. **Pets:** Accepted.
🔲🔲📶🔲🔲🔲

AAA **▼▼▼▼** **Sheraton Sioux Falls** **H** ❀
(605) 331-0100. **Call for rates.** 1211 N West Ave 57104. I-29 exit 81 (Airport/Russell St), 1.3 mi e. Int corridors. **Pets:** Dogs only. $40 one-time fee/pet. Supervision. [SAVE] ⬚⬚⬚⬚⬚⬚⬚⬚⬚

▼▼▼▼ **Staybridge Suites** **H**
(605) 361-2298. **$109-$179.** 2505 S Carolyn Ave 57106. I-29 exit 78 (26th St), just se. Int corridors. **Pets:** Large, other species. $35 one-time fee/pet, $15 daily fee/pet. Designated rooms, service with restrictions, crate. ⬚⬚⬚⬚⬚⬚

▼▼▼ **Super 8 Sioux Falls** **H**
(605) 338-8881. **$70-$100.** 2616 E 10th St 57103. I-229 exit 6, just e. Int corridors. **Pets:** Medium. $10 daily fee/pet. Designated rooms, service with restrictions, supervision. ⬚⬚⬚⬚⬚⬚

▼▼ **TownePlace Suites by Marriott** **H**
(605) 361-2626. **$67-$172.** 4545 W Homefield Dr 57106. I-29 exit 78 (26th St), just w. Int corridors. **Pets:** Accepted.
⬚⬚⬚⬚⬚⬚

SPEARFISH
▼▼ **Bell's Motor Lodge Motel** **M**
(605) 642-3812. **$40-$78.** 230 N Main St 57783. 0.5 mi s of center. Ext corridors. **Pets:** Small. $3 daily fee/pet. Designated rooms, supervision. ⬚⬚⬚⬚

AAA **▼▼▼** **Best Western Black Hills Lodge** **H**
(605) 642-7795. **$69-$199.** 540 E Jackson Blvd 57783. I-90 exit 12, just w. Ext/int corridors. **Pets:** Accepted. [SAVE] ⬚⬚⬚⬚⬚

▼▼▼ **Days Inn** **H** ❀
(605) 642-7101. **$54-$295.** 240 Ryan Rd 57783. I-90 exit 10, 1.2 mi s. Ext/int corridors. **Pets:** Large, other species. $10 daily fee/pet. Designated rooms, service with restrictions, crate. ⬚⬚⬚⬚⬚⬚

▼▼▼▼ **Holiday Inn Hotel & Convention Center** **H** ❀
(605) 642-4683. **$89-$219.** 305 N 27th St 57783. I-90 exit 14 (Spearfish Canyon), just n. Ext/int corridors. **Pets:** $100 deposit/room, $25 one-time fee/room. Designated rooms, service with restrictions, supervision. ⬚⬚⬚⬚⬚⬚⬚⬚

AAA **▼▼▼** **Quality Inn** **H**
(605) 642-2337. **$70-$370.** 2725 1st Ave 57783. I-90 exit 14 (Spearfish Canyon), just n. Int corridors. **Pets:** Small, other species. $10 daily fee/pet. Designated rooms, service with restrictions, supervision. [SAVE] ⬚⬚⬚⬚⬚⬚

▼▼ **Super 8-Spearfish** **H**
(605) 642-4721. **$55-$175.** 440 Heritage Dr 57783. I-90 exit 14 (Spearfish Canyon), just s, just e, then just s. Int corridors. **Pets:** Other species. $10 daily fee/pet. Designated rooms, supervision.
⬚⬚⬚⬚

STURGIS
AAA **▼▼▼** **Best Western Sturgis Inn** **H**
(605) 347-3604. **$79-$149.** 2431 Junction Ave 57785. I-90 exit 32, just n. Ext/int corridors. **Pets:** Accepted.
[SAVE] ⬚⬚⬚⬚⬚⬚

▼▼▼▼ **Holiday Inn Express & Suites-Sturgis** **H**
(605) 347-4140. **Call for rates.** 2721 Lazelle St 57785. I-90 exit 30 (US 14A), just s. Int corridors. **Pets:** Other species. $20 one-time fee/room. Designated rooms, service with restrictions.
⬚⬚⬚⬚⬚⬚

SUMMERSET
▼▼ **Ramada-Summerset/Rapid City West** **H**
(605) 787-4844. **$59-$275.** 7900 Stagestop Rd 57718. I-90 exit 48, just w. Int corridors. **Pets:** Accepted. ⬚⬚⬚⬚⬚⬚

VERMILLION
AAA **▼▼▼** **Best Western Vermillion Inn** **H** ❀
(605) 624-8333. **$129-$169, 3 day notice.** 701 W Cherry St 57069. I-29 exit 26 (SR 50), 7.5 mi w on Business Rt SR 50. Int corridors. **Pets:** Medium. $20 daily fee/pet. Designated rooms, service with restrictions, supervision. ⬚⬚⬚⬚⬚⬚

WALL
AAA **▼▼▼** **Best Western Plains Motel** **M** ❀
(605) 279-2145. **$83-$181.** 712 Glenn St 57790. I-90 exit 110, just n. Ext corridors. **Pets:** Other species. $20 daily fee/room. Designated rooms, service with restrictions, supervision.
[SAVE] ⬚⬚⬚⬚⬚⬚

AAA **▼▼** **Econo Lodge** **M**
(605) 279-2121. **$50-$200.** 804 Glenn St 57790. I-90 exit 110, just n. Ext corridors. **Pets:** Designated rooms, service with restrictions, supervision. [SAVE] ⬚⬚⬚⬚⬚

WATERTOWN
▼▼▼ **Country Inn & Suites By Carlson** **H**
(605) 886-8900. **Call for rates.** 3400 8th Ave SE 57201. I-29 exit 177 (US 212), just w. Int corridors. **Pets:** Accepted.
⬚⬚⬚⬚⬚⬚

▼▼▼ **Days Inn** **H**
(605) 886-3500. **$70-$95.** 2900 9th Ave SE 57201. I-29 exit 177 (US 212), 0.5 mi w. Ext/int corridors. **Pets:** Accepted.
⬚⬚⬚⬚⬚⬚

▼▼▼ **Holiday Inn Express Hotel & Suites** **H**
(605) 882-3636. **Call for rates.** 3901 9th Ave SE 57201. I-29 exit 177 (US 212), just e. Int corridors. **Pets:** Accepted.
⬚⬚⬚⬚⬚⬚

▼▼▼ **Quality Inn & Suites** **H** ❀
(605) 886-3010. **$94-$189.** 800 35th Street Cir 57201. I-29 exit 177 (US 212), just w. Ext/int corridors. **Pets:** Other species. $20 one-time fee/room. Designated rooms, service with restrictions, supervision.
⬚⬚⬚⬚⬚

▼▼▼ **Ramkota Hotel** **H** ❀
(605) 886-8011. **$90-$180.** 1901 9th Ave SW 57201. I-29 exit 177 (US 212), 4 mi w. Int corridors. **Pets:** Designated rooms, service with restrictions, supervision. ⬚⬚⬚⬚⬚⬚⬚

WINNER
▼▼▼ **Holiday Inn Express Hotel & Suites Winner** **H**
(605) 842-2255. **$117-$127.** 1360 E Hwy 44 57580. Just ne of jct US 18 and 183. Int corridors. **Pets:** Very small. $25 daily fee/room. Service with restrictions, supervision. ⬚⬚⬚⬚⬚⬚

YANKTON
AAA **▼▼▼** **Best Western Kelly Inn** **H** ❀
(605) 665-2906. **$110-$130.** 1607 E Hwy 50 57078. On US 50, 1.8 mi e. Ext/int corridors. **Pets:** Other species. Service with restrictions, supervision. [SAVE] ⬚⬚⬚⬚⬚⬚⬚

AAA **▼▼** **Days Inn** **M**
(605) 665-8717. **$65-$80.** 2410 Broadway Ave 57078. US 81, 1.7 mi n. Int corridors. **Pets:** Dogs only. $10 one-time fee/pet. Designated rooms, service with restrictions, crate. [SAVE] ⬚⬚⬚⬚⬚

▼▼ **Lewis & Clark Resort** **M**
(605) 665-2680. **$75-$145, 30 day notice.** 43496 Shore Dr 57078. 4 mi w on SR 52; in Lewis and Clark State Park, just w of marina. Ext corridors. **Pets:** Accepted. ⬚⬚⬚⬚⬚⬚⬚⬚

ALCOA

▼▼ Candlewood Suites Knoxville Airport/Alcoa 🄷
(865) 233-4411. **Call for rates.** 176 Cusick Rd 37701. US 129, just e.
Int corridors. **Pets:** Accepted. 🄼 ⊃ 📶 🄷 🖳

▼▼ La Quinta Inn & Suites Knoxville Airport 🄷
(865) 984-9350. **$79-$154.** 126 Cusick Rd 37701. US 129, just e. Int
corridors. **Pets:** Accepted. 🄲 🄼 ⊃ 📶 ✕ 🄷 🖳

▼▼ MainStay Suites 🄷 🐾
(865) 379-7799. **$65-$220.** 361 Fountain View Cir 37701. US 129, just
n on SR 35, just se on Associates Blvd, then just w. Int corridors.
Pets: Other species. $25 one-time fee/room. Service with restrictions.
🄲 🄼 ⊃ 📶 ✕ 🄷 🖳

▼▼ Quality Inn 🄷
(865) 984-6800. **$80-$160.** 206 Corporate Pl 37701. US 129, just s. Int
corridors. **Pets:** Accepted. 🄼 ⊃ 📶 🄷 🖳

BRENTWOOD (Restaurants p. 624)

▼▼ Candlewood Suites 🄷
(615) 309-0600. **Call for rates.** 5129 Virginia Way 37027. I-65 exit 74B
(SR 254 W), 0.3 mi s on Franklin Rd (US 31), 1.2 mi w on Maryland
Way, just s on Ward Circle, then just s. Int corridors. **Pets:** Accepted.
🄼 📶 ✕ 🄷 🖳

ⒶⒶⒶ ▼▼▼ Hyatt Place Nashville/Brentwood 🄷
(615) 661-9477. **$94-$209.** 202 Summit View Dr 37027. I-65 exit 74A,
just e. Int corridors. **Pets:** Medium, dogs only. $75 one-time fee/pet.
Service with restrictions, supervision.
SAVE 🍽 🄼 ⊃ 📶 ✕ 🄷 🖳

ⒶⒶⒶ ◆ Residence Inn by Marriott
Nashville-Brentwood 🄷
(615) 371-0100. **$114-$239.** 206 Ward Cir 37027. I-65 exit 74B, 0.3 mi
s on Franklin Rd (US 31), then 0.5 mi w on Maryland Way. Ext/int corridors. **Pets:** Other species. $100 one-time fee/room. Service with restric-
tions, crate. SAVE ⊃ ✕ 📶 ✕ 🄷 🖳

▼▼ Sleep Inn 🄷
(615) 376-2122. **$100-$170.** 1611 Galleria Blvd 37027. I-65 exit 69, just
w, then just n. Int corridors. **Pets:** Medium, other species. $20 daily
fee/pet. Designated rooms, service with restrictions, supervision.
🄼 ⊃ 📶 ✕ 🄷 🖳

BULLS GAP

▼▼ Quality Inn 🄷
(423) 235-9111. **$75-$170.** 50 Speedway Ln 37711. I-81 exit 23, just w.
Int corridors. **Pets:** $15 daily fee/pet. Service with restrictions, crate.
🍽 🄼 ⊃ 📶 🄷 🖳

CHATTANOOGA (Restaurants p. 624)

ⒶⒶⒶ ▼▼ Best Western Heritage Inn 🄼
(423) 899-3311. **$70-$80.** 7641 Lee Hwy 37421. I-75 exit 7B northbound; exit 7 southbound, just w. Ext corridors. **Pets:** Medium, dogs
only. $50 deposit/room, $15 daily fee/room. Designated rooms, service
with restrictions, crate. SAVE 🍽 ⊃ 📶 ✕ 🄷 🖳

ⒶⒶⒶ ▼▼ Best Western Royal Inn 🄼
(423) 821-6840. **$64-$129.** 3644 Cummings Hwy 37419. I-24 exit 174,
0.4 mi s. Ext corridors. **Pets:** Accepted. SAVE ⊃ 📶 🄷 🖳

ⒶⒶⒶ ▼▼ Chattanooga Choo-Choo 🄷
(423) 266-5000. **$139-$229.** 1400 Market St 37402. I-24 exit 178
(Broad St) eastbound; exit Market St westbound, 0.5 mi n. Ext/int corridors. **Pets:** Accepted. SAVE ECO 🄼 ⊃ 📶 ✕ 🄷 🖳

▼▼ Comfort Inn Downtown-Lookout Mountain 🄷
(423) 265-0077. **$79-$199.** 2420 Williams St 37408. I-24 exit 178 (Market St), just s. Int corridors. **Pets:** Accepted.
🍽 🄼 ⊃ 📶 🄷 🖳

▼▼ Country Inn & Suites By Carlson, Chattanooga I-24
West 🄷
(423) 825-6100. **Call for rates.** 3725 Modern Industries Blvd 37419.
I-24 exit 174, just s. **Pets:** $25 one-time fee/pet. Service
with restrictions, supervision. 🄼 ⊃ 📶 ✕ 🄷 🖳

ⒶⒶⒶ ▼▼ Days Inn-Lookout Mountain 🄼
(423) 821-6044. **$59-$89.** 3801 Cummings Hwy 37419. I-24 exit 174,
just n. Ext corridors. **Pets:** Medium. $10 daily fee/pet. Designated
rooms, service with restrictions, supervision.
SAVE 🄼 ⊃ 📶 ✕ 🄷 🖳

▼▼ Econo Lodge-Hamilton Mall Area 🄼
(423) 499-9550. **$60-$70.** 7421 Bonny Oaks Dr 37421. I-75 exit 7B
northbound; exit 7 southbound, just w. Ext corridors. **Pets:** Accepted.
⊃ 📶 🄷 🖳

▼ Extended Stay America-Chattanooga-Airport 🄷
(423) 892-1315. **$60-$70.** 6240 Airpark Dr 37421. SR 153 exit 1 (Lee
Hwy), 0.3 mi s to Vance Rd, then just w to cul-de-sac. Ext corridors.
Pets: Accepted. 🍽 🄼 📶 🄷 🖳

ⒶⒶⒶ ▼▼▼ Homewood Suites by Hilton 🄷
(423) 510-8020. **Call for rates.** 2250 Center St 37421. I-75 exit 5
(Shallowford Rd), 0.5 mi w. Int corridors. **Pets:** Accepted.
SAVE 🄼 ⊃ 📶 ✕ 🄷 🖳

▼▼ Howard Johnson Chattanooga Lookout
Mountain 🄼
(423) 821-1499. **$79-$180.** 3109 Parker Ln 37419. I-24 exit 175, just s.
Ext corridors. **Pets:** Accepted. ⊃ 📶 🄷 🖳

ⒶⒶⒶ ▼▼▼ La Quinta Inn & Suites 🄷
(423) 551-4100. **$90-$213.** 311 Browns Ferry Rd 37419. I-24 exit 175,
just n. Int corridors. **Pets:** Accepted. SAVE 🄼 📶 ✕ 🄷 🖳

▼▼ La Quinta Inn Chattanooga/Hamilton Place 🄼
(423) 855-0011. **$67-$137.** 7015 Shallowford Rd 37421. I-75 exit 5
(Shallowford Rd), just w. Ext corridors. **Pets:** Accepted.
🄼 ⊃ 📶 🄷 🖳

▼▼ MainStay Suites-Chattanooga 🄷
(423) 485-9424. **$99-$169.** 7030 Amin Dr 37421. I-75 exit 5 (Shallowford Rd), just w, then s. Int corridors. **Pets:** Accepted.
🄼 📶 🄷 🖳

▼▼▼ The Read House Historic Inn & Suites 🄷
(423) 266-4121. **Call for rates.** 827 Broad St 37402. US 27 exit 1A,
just e; downtown. Int corridors. **Pets:** Accepted.
🍽 🄼 ⊃ 📶 ✕ 🄷 🖳

▼▼ Red Roof Inn Chattanooga Lookout Mountain 🄼
(423) 821-7162. **$59-$159.** 30 Birmingham Hwy 37419. I-24 exit 174,
just s. Ext/int corridors. **Pets:** Accepted. ⊃ 📶 🄷 🖳

▼▼▼ Residence Inn by Marriott Chattanooga near
Hamilton Place 🄷
(423) 468-7700. **$123-$203.** 2340 Center St 37421. I-75 exit 5 (Shallowford Rd), 0.5 mi w to Lee Hwy, then just n. Int corridors.
Pets: Medium. $75 one-time fee/room. Service with restrictions.
🄲 🄼 ⊃ 📶 ✕ 🄷 🖳

▼▼ Stadium Inn 🄷
(423) 265-3151. **$67-$180.** 100 W 21st St 37408. I-24 exit 178 (Broad
St) eastbound; exit Market St westbound, US 11 to Lookout Mountain,
w to 20th St, w to Williams St, then w. Int corridors. **Pets:** Accepted.
🍽 🄼 ⊃ 📶 ✕ 🄷 🖳

▼▼▼▼ Staybridge Suites H
(423) 267-0900. **Call for rates.** 1300 Carter St 37402. US 27 N exit 1A (Dr Martin Luther King Blvd), just e to Carter St, then 0.3 mi s. Int corridors. **Pets:** Accepted. ECO ⊞ ⚫M ⇌ 🛜 ✕ 🛏 🖵

▼▼▼▼ Staybridge Suites-Hamilton Place H
(423) 826-2700. **Call for rates.** 7015 Shallowford Rd 37421. I-75 exit 5 (Shallowford Rd), just w. Int corridors. **Pets:** Accepted.
⚫M ⇌ 🛜 ✕ 🛏 🖵

▼▼ Studio 6 M
(423) 892-1500. **$80-$170.** 7324 Shallowford Rd 37421. I-75 exit 5 (Shallowford Rd), just e. Ext corridors. **Pets:** Accepted.
⇌ 🛜 🛏 🖵

▼▼▼▼ TownePlace Suites by Marriott Chattanooga near Hamilton Place H
(423) 834-9444. **$99-$150.** 7010 McCutcheon Rd 37421. I-75 exit 5 (Shallowford Rd), 0.5 mi w to Lee Hwy, then just n. Int corridors. **Pets:** Accepted. ⅋⅋ ⚫M ⇌ 🛜 ✕ 🛏 🖵

CLARKSVILLE

▲▲▲ ▼▼▼▼ Best Western Plus Atrium & Suites Clarksville H
(931) 919-4998. **$119-$129.** 275 Alfred Thun Rd 37040. I-24 exit 4, just ne. Int corridors. **Pets:** Accepted. SAVE ⅋⅋ 🛜 ✕ 🛏 🖵

▼▼▼▼ Candlewood Suites H
(931) 906-0900. **Call for rates.** 3050 Clay Lewis Rd 37040. I-24 exit 4, just s. Int corridors. **Pets:** Accepted. ⚫M 🛜 ✕ 🛏 🖵

▼▼▼▼ Home2 Suites by Hilton Clarksville/Ft. Campbell H
(931) 645-7771. **$99-$179.** 3020 Mr. C Dr 37040. I-24 exit 4, just sw. Int corridors. **Pets:** Accepted. ⚫M 🛜 ✕ 🛏 🖵

▼▼▼▼ La Quinta Inn & Suites Clarksville H
(931) 906-0606. **$97-$235.** 251 Holiday Dr 37040. I-24 exit 4, just se. Int corridors. **Pets:** Accepted. ⚫M ⇌ 🛜 ✕ 🛏 🖵

▼▼ MainStay Suites H
(931) 648-3400. **$68-$139.** 115 Fairbrook Pl 37043. I-24 exit 4, just sw. Int corridors. **Pets:** Accepted. ⚫M ⇌ 🛜 ✕ 🛏 🖵

▲▲▲ ▼▼▼ Quality Inn-Exit 4 H 🐾
(931) 648-4848. **$84-$104.** 3095 Wilma Rudolph Blvd 37040. I-24 exit 4, just se. Ext corridors. **Pets:** Medium, other species. $25 one-time fee/room, $15 daily fee/pet. Designated rooms, service with restrictions, crate. SAVE ⅋⅋ ⇌ ✕ 🛏 🖵

▼▼ Red Roof Inn Clarksville M
(931) 905-1555. **$50-$119.** 197 Holiday Dr 37040. I-24 exit 4, just s. Ext corridors. **Pets:** Accepted. ⇌ 🛜 🛏 🖵

CLEVELAND

▼▼▼ Baymont Inn & Suites Cleveland H
(423) 614-5583. **$69-$79.** 360 Paul Huff Pkwy 37312. I-75 exit 27, 0.8 mi e. Ext corridors. **Pets:** Accepted. ⚫M ⇌ 🛜 🛏 🖵

▼▼▼▼ Clarion Inn H
(423) 559-1001. **$59-$114.** 185 James Asbury Dr NW 37312. I-75 exit 27, just w, then just s. Ext corridors. **Pets:** Accepted.
⚫M ⇌ 🛜 🛏 🖵

▲▲▲ ▼▼▼ Comfort Inn & Suites-Cleveland H
(423) 339-1000. **$75-$170.** 107 Interstate Dr NW 37312. I-75 exit 25, just w, then just s. Int corridors. **Pets:** Accepted.
SAVE ⇌ 🛜 ✕ 🛏 🖵

▲▲▲ ▼▼▼ Douglas Inn & Suites H
(423) 559-5579. **$55-$115.** 2600 Westside Dr NW 37312. I-75 exit 25, just e, then just n. Ext/int corridors. **Pets:** Accepted.
SAVE ⚫M 🛜 🛏 🖵

▼▼▼ Quality Inn H
(423) 478-5265. **$66-$75.** 153 James Asbury Dr 37312. I-75 exit 27, just w, then just s. Ext/int corridors. **Pets:** $10 daily fee/pet. Service with restrictions, supervision. ⇌ 🛜 🛏 🖵

▲▲▲ ▼▼▼▼ Wingate by Wyndham H
(423) 478-1212. **$99-$129.** 110 Interstate Dr 37312. I-75 exit 25, just w, then just s. Int corridors. **Pets:** Medium. $25 deposit/room. Designated rooms, service with restrictions, supervision.
SAVE ⚫M ⇌ 🛜 ✕ 🛏 🖵

CLINTON

▼▼▼▼ Country Inn & Suites By Carlson H
(865) 457-4311. **Call for rates.** 710 Park Pl 37716. I-75 exit 122, just w. Int corridors. **Pets:** $35 one-time fee/room. Designated rooms, service with restrictions, crate. ⚫M ⇌ 🛜 🛏 🖵

▼▼▼▼ Holiday Inn Express Hotel & Suites H 🐾
(865) 457-2233. **$99-$189.** 111 Hillvale Rd 37716. I-75 exit 122, just w. Int corridors. **Pets:** Other species. $25 one-time fee/room. Designated rooms, service with restrictions. ⊞ ⚫M ⇌ 🛜 ✕ 🛏 🖵

COLLIERVILLE

▼▼▼▼ Hampton Inn by Hilton Collierville H
(901) 854-9400. **$129-$169.** 1280 W Poplar Ave 38017. 0.9 mi w of jct CR 175 on US 72. Int corridors. **Pets:** Accepted.
⚫M ⇌ 🛜 ✕ 🛏 🖵

COOKEVILLE

▲▲▲ ▼▼▼ Best Western Thunderbird Motel H
(931) 526-7115. **$71-$89.** 900 S Jefferson Ave 38501. I-40 exit 287, just n. Ext corridors. **Pets:** Accepted. SAVE ⅋⅋ ⚫M ⇌ 🛜 🛏 🖵

▼▼▼▼ Country Inn & Suites By Carlson Cookeville H
(931) 525-6668. **$99-$189.** 1151 S Jefferson Ave 38506. I-40 exit 287, just s. Int corridors. **Pets:** Other species. $15 daily fee/pet. Designated rooms, service with restrictions, crate. ⚫M ⇌ 🛜 ✕ 🛏 🖵

▼▼▼▼ La Quinta Inn & Suites H
(931) 520-3800. **$86-$191.** 1131 S Jefferson Ave 38506. I-40 exit 287, just s. Int corridors. **Pets:** Accepted. ⚫M ⇌ 🛜 ✕ 🛏 🖵

▲▲▲ ▼▼▼ Red Roof Inn Cookeville-Tennessee Tech. M
(931) 528-2020. **$50-$125.** 1292 S Walnut Ave 38501. I-40 exit 287, just n. Ext corridors. **Pets:** Accepted. SAVE ⚫M ⇌ 🛜 🛏 🖵

CORDOVA

▼▼▼ Microtel Inn & Suites by Wyndham H
(901) 213-4141. **$60-$100.** 2423 N Germantown Pkwy 38018. I-40 exit 16 or 16A, just s, then just w on Rock Creek Cove. Int corridors. **Pets:** Medium. $150 deposit/pet, $25 daily fee/pet. Designated rooms, service with restrictions, supervision. 🛜 🛏 🖵

COUNCE *(Restaurants p. 624)*

▼▼▼ Pickwick Landing State Resort Park Inn H
(731) 689-3135. **$74-$88.** 120 Playground Loop 38326. Jct SR 128, just se on SR 57, then just e; in state park. Int corridors. **Pets:** Accepted.
⅋⅋ ⚫M ⇌ ✕ 🛜 ✕ 🛏 🖵

CROSSVILLE

AAA ▼▼▼ **Quality Inn Crossville** 🅷
(931) 484-1551. **$74-$254.** 4035 Hwy 127 N 38571. I-40 exit 317 (US 127), just n. Int corridors. **Pets:** Small. $15 daily fee/pet. Designated rooms, service with restrictions, supervision.
[SAVE] [❚❶] 🏊 📶 📠 ☕

DANDRIDGE

▼▼ **Jefferson Inn** 🅷
(865) 940-5042. **Call for rates.** 127 Sharon Dr 37725. I-40 exit 417, just s. Int corridors. **Pets:** Accepted. 🏊 📶 📠 ☕

▼▼ **Super 8** 🅷
(865) 397-1200. **$60-$130.** 125 Sharon Dr 37725. I-40 exit 417, just s. Int corridors. **Pets:** Accepted. 🏊 📶 📠 ☕

DAYTON

AAA ▼▼ **Best Western Dayton** Ⓜ
(423) 775-6560. **$80-$135.** 7835 Rhea County Hwy 37321. 1 mi n on US 27. Ext corridors. **Pets:** Medium. $15 daily fee/pet. Service with restrictions, supervision. [SAVE] [❚❶] 🏊 📶 📠 ☕

DICKSON

AAA ▼▼ **Best Western Executive Inn** 🅷
(615) 446-0541. **$79-$130.** 2338 Hwy 46 S 37055. I-40 exit 172, just n. Ext corridors. **Pets:** Dogs only. $20 daily fee/pet. Service with restrictions, supervision. [SAVE] 🏊 📶 📠 ☕

▼▼▼ **Holiday Inn Express & Suites** 🅷
(615) 446-2781. **Call for rates.** 100 Barzani Blvd 37055. I-40 exit 172, just se. Int corridors. **Pets:** Accepted. 🅼 🏊 📶 ✕ 📠 ☕

DYERSBURG

▼▼ **Days Inn** 🅷
(731) 287-0888. **$61-$70.** 2600 Lake Rd 38024. I-155 exit 13, just s on SR 78. Int corridors. **Pets:** Very small, dogs only. $12 daily fee/pet. Designated rooms, service with restrictions, supervision.
🅼 📶 📠 ☕

▼▼ **Executive Inn & Suites** Ⓜ
(731) 287-0044. **Call for rates.** 2331 Lake Rd 38024. I-155 exit 13, 0.5 mi s on SR 78. Ext corridors. **Pets:** $15 daily fee/pet. Designated rooms, supervision. 📶 📠

▼▼▼ **Hampton Inn** 🅷
(731) 285-4778. **$85-$115.** 2750 Mall Loop Rd 38024. I-155 exit 13, just s on SR 78, then just e. Int corridors. **Pets:** Accepted.
🅼 🏊 📶 📠 ☕

▼▼▼ **Holiday Inn Express & Suites** 🅷
(731) 286-1021. **$104-$124.** 822 Reelfoot Dr 38024. I-155 exit 13, just s on SR 78, then just w. Int corridors. **Pets:** Accepted.
[❚❶] 🅼 🏊 📶 ✕ 📠 ☕

▼▼▼ **Sleep Inn & Suites** 🅷
(731) 287-0248. **$89-$99.** 824 Reelfoot Dr 38024. I-155 exit 13, just s on SR 78, then just w. Int corridors. **Pets:** Small. $12 daily fee/pet. Designated rooms, service with restrictions, supervision.
[❚❶] 🅼 🏊 📶 ✕ 📠 ☕

EAST RIDGE

▼▼▼ **Holiday Inn Express Hotel & Suites** 🅷
(423) 308-0111. **Call for rates.** 1441 N Smith Rd 37412. I-75 exit 1 southbound; exit 1B northbound, just w. Int corridors. **Pets:** Accepted.
🅼 🏊 📶 ✕ 📠 ☕

▼▼▼ **La Quinta Inn & Suites Chattanooga East Ridge** 🅷
(423) 760-3120. **Call for rates.** 6650 Ringgold Rd 37412. I-75 exit 1 (East Ridge), just e. Int corridors. **Pets:** Accepted.
[❚❶] 🅼 📶 ✕ 📠 ☕

FARRAGUT *(Restaurants p. 624)*

▼▼▼ **Clarion Inn & Suites** 🅷
(865) 671-1010. **$75-$220.** 11341 Campbell Lakes Dr 37934. I-40/75 exit 373 (Campbell Station Rd), just s. Int corridors. **Pets:** Accepted.
🅼 🏊 📶 ✕ 📠 ☕

AAA ▼▼▼ **Country Inn & Suites By Carlson, Knoxville West** 🅷
(865) 675-9800. **$79-$159.** 805 N Campbell Station Rd 37934. I-40/75 exit 373 (Campbell Station Rd), just n. Int corridors. **Pets:** Accepted.
[SAVE] 🅼 🏊 📶 ✕ 📠 ☕

▼▼▼ **Super 8 Knoxville West** 🅷
(865) 675-5566. **$59-$100.** 11748 Snyder Rd 37932. I-40/75 exit 373 (Campbell Station Rd), just ne. Ext corridors. **Pets:** Accepted.
[❚❶] 🅼 🏊 📶 📠 ☕

FAYETTEVILLE

AAA ▼▼▼ **Best Western Fayetteville Inn** 🅷
(931) 433-0100. **$95-$105.** 3021 Thornton Taylor Pkwy 37334. 0.7 mi e of US 431, on US 64 and 231 Bypass. Ext corridors. **Pets:** Accepted.
[SAVE] [❚❶] 🏊 📶 📠 ☕

FRANKLIN

AAA ▼▼▼ **Aloft Nashville-Cool Springs** 🅷
(615) 435-8700. **$129-$299.** 7109 S Springs Dr 37067. I-65 exit 68B, 0.4 mi w, 0.3 mi n on Mallory Ln, then just e. Int corridors. **Pets:** Accepted. [SAVE] 🅼 🏊 📶 ✕ 📠 ☕

▼▼▼ **Baymont Inn & Suites Franklin** Ⓜ
(615) 791-6675. **$78-$110.** 4206 Franklin Commons Ct 37067. I-65 exit 65, just e. Ext corridors. **Pets:** Accepted. 🅼 🏊 📶 📠 ☕

▼▼▼ **Best Western Franklin Inn** 🅷
(615) 790-0570. **$85-$125.** 1308 Murfreesboro Rd 37064. I-65 exit 65, just w. Ext corridors. **Pets:** Accepted. [SAVE] 🏊 📶 📠 ☕

▼▼▼ **Drury Plaza Hotel Franklin** 🅷
(615) 771-6778. **$119-$249.** 1874 W McEwen Dr 37067. I-65 exit 67, just w. Int corridors. **Pets:** Accepted. [❚❶] 🏊 📶 ✕ 📠 ☕

▼▼▼ **Embassy Suites by Hilton Nashville South/Cool Springs** 🅷
(615) 515-5151. **$139-$244.** 820 Crescent Centre Dr 37067. I-65 exit 68A, exit 68A to Carothers Rd. Int corridors. **Pets:** Large. $30 daily fee/room. Service with restrictions, crate.
[❚❶] 🅼 🏊 ✕ 📶 ✕ 📠 ☕

AAA ▼▼▼ **Hyatt Place Nashville/Franklin/Cool Springs** 🅷
(615) 771-8900. **$99-$249.** 650 Bakers Bridge Ave 37067. I-65 exit 69 (SR 441), 0.3 mi e to Carothers Pkwy, 0.5 mi s, then 0.3 mi w. Int corridors. **Pets:** Accepted. [SAVE] [❚❶] 🅼 🏊 📶 ✕ 📠 ☕

▼▼▼ **Residence Inn by Marriott Franklin Cool Springs** 🅷
(615) 778-0002. **$146-$269.** 2009 Meridian Blvd 37067. I-65 exit 68A, just e on Cool Springs Blvd, just n on Carothers Pkwy, then just w; in Meridian Cool Springs business park. Int corridors. **Pets:** Accepted.
🅼 🏊 📶 ✕ 📠 ☕

AAA ▼▼▼ **TownePlace Suites by Marriott Franklin Cool Springs** 🅷
(615) 861-1111. **$113-$197.** 7153 S Springs Dr 37067. I-65 exit 68B, just w, then just n. Int corridors. **Pets:** Accepted.

[SAVE] 🅼 📶 ✕ 📠 ☕

GALLATIN

▼▼ **Quality Inn of Gallatin** 🅷
(615) 451-4494. **$85-$95.** 1001 Village Green Crossing 37066. 2 mi s on US 31 E. Ext corridors. **Pets:** Accepted. 🏊 📶 📠 ☕

GATLINBURG

Cobbly Nob Rentals CA
(865) 436-5298. **Call for rates.** 3722 E Parkway 37738. Jct US 441, 10.3 mi n on US 321. Ext corridors. **Pets:** Accepted.

Motel 6 Gatlinburg Smoky Mountains #4767 M
(865) 436-7813. **Call for rates.** 309 Ownby St 37738. Traffic light 10 (Ski Mountain Rd), 0.4 mi n. Ext corridors. **Pets:** Accepted.

Outback Resort Rentals & Sales VH
(865) 430-9385. **$100-$450, 30 day notice.** 902 Street of Dreams Way 37738. Ext corridors. **Pets:** Medium. $75 one-time fee/pet. Service with restrictions, crate.

Westgate Smoky Mountain Resort & Spa CO
(865) 430-4800. **Call for rates.** 915 Westgate Resort 37738. Jct US 441, just e on Little Smoky Rd, then just s. Ext corridors. **Pets:** Accepted.

GERMANTOWN

Homewood Suites by Hilton-Germantown H
(901) 751-2500. **$119-$189.** 7855 Wolf River Blvd 38138. I-40 exit 16, 5.7 mi s on Germantown Pkwy, then just e. Int corridors. **Pets:** Accepted.

Hyatt Place Memphis/Germantown H
(901) 759-1174. **$99-$219.** 9161 Winchester Rd 38138. SR 177 (Germantown Pkwy), 3 mi e on US 72 (Poplar Ave), just s on Forest Hill Irene Rd, then just e. Int corridors. **Pets:** Medium, dogs only. $75 deposit/room. Designated rooms, no service, supervision.

Quality Inn & Suites-Germantown H
(901) 757-7800. **$79-$139.** 7787 Wolf River Blvd 38138. I-40 exit 16A, 5.7 mi s on Germantown Pkwy, then just w. Int corridors. **Pets:** Accepted.

Residence Inn by Marriott Memphis/Germantown H
(901) 752-0900. **$111-$181.** 9314 Poplar Pike 38138. SR 177 (Germantown Pkwy), 3 mi e on US 72 (Poplar Ave), just s on Forest Hill Irene Rd, then just e. Int corridors. **Pets:** Accepted.

GOODLETTSVILLE

Country Inn & Suites By Carlson H
(615) 851-4444. **$90-$350, 5 day notice.** 641 Wade Cir 37072. I-65 exit 96, just ne. Int corridors. **Pets:** Accepted.

GREENEVILLE

Quality Inn H
(423) 638-7511. **$90-$300.** 3160 E Andrew Johnson Hwy 37745. US 11 E Bypass, 3.6 mi ne. Int corridors. **Pets:** Accepted.

HENDERSONVILLE

Hyatt Place Nashville - Northeast H
(615) 826-4301. **$79-$209.** 330 E Main St 37075. US 31 E, 1 mi n. Int corridors. **Pets:** Accepted.

HUNTINGDON

Heritage Inn M
(731) 986-2281. **$77-$78.** 11790 Lexington St 38344. Jct US 70 Bypass, just n on SR 22 business route. Ext corridors. **Pets:** Small, dogs only. $20 daily fee/pet. Designated rooms, service with restrictions, supervision.

HURRICANE MILLS

Quality Inn H
(931) 296-4251. **$79-$180.** 15542 Hwy 13 S 37078. I-40 exit 143, just n. Ext corridors. **Pets:** Accepted.

JACKSON *(Restaurants p. 624)*

Best Western Carriage House Inn & Suites M
(731) 664-3030. **$96-$120.** 1936 Hwy 45 Bypass 38305. I-40 exit 80A, just s. Ext corridors. **Pets:** Accepted.

Hampton Inn & Suites H
(731) 427-6100. **$139-$189.** 150 Campbell Oaks Dr 38305. I-40 exit 83, just s on Campbell St, then just w. Int corridors. **Pets:** Accepted.

Residence Inn by Marriott Jackson H
(731) 935-4100. **$113-$187.** 126 Old Medina Crossing 38305. I-40 exit 83, just ne. Int corridors. **Pets:** Accepted.

JOHNSON CITY

Best Western Johnson City Hotel & Conference Center H
(423) 282-2161. **$79-$119.** 2406 N Roan St 37601. I-26 exit 20A westbound; exit 20 eastbound, just n. Ext/int corridors. **Pets:** Accepted.

Carnegie Hotel H
(423) 979-6400. **$135-$144.** 1216 W State of Franklin Rd 37604. I-26 exit 24, 2.2 mi se on US 321 S. Int corridors. **Pets:** Medium, dogs only. $50 daily fee/pet. Designated rooms, service with restrictions, supervision.

Comfort Suites H
(423) 610-0010. **$85-$369.** 3118 Browns Mill Rd 37604. I-26 exit 19, just e, then just n. Int corridors. **Pets:** Medium. $20 daily fee/pet. Designated rooms, service with restrictions, supervision.

DoubleTree by Hilton Hotel Johnson City H
(423) 929-2000. **$119-$149.** 211 Mockingbird Ln 37604. I-26 exit 20A westbound; exit 20 eastbound, just w on N Roan St. Int corridors. **Pets:** Accepted.

Holiday Inn-Johnson City H
(423) 282-4611. **$91-$210.** 101 W Springbrook Dr 37604. I-26 exit 20A westbound; exit 20 eastbound, just e on N Roan St, then just n. Int corridors. **Pets:** Accepted.

Quality Inn M
(423) 282-0488. **$63-$289.** 119 Pinnacle Dr 37615. I-26 exit 17, just w on CR 354, then just s. Ext corridors. **Pets:** Accepted.

Red Roof Inn-Johnson City M
(423) 282-3040. **$50-$100.** 210 Broyles Dr 37601. I-26 exit 20A westbound; exit 20 eastbound, just w on N Roan St. Ext corridors. **Pets:** Accepted.

Sleep Inn & Suites H
(423) 915-0081. **$70-$300.** 2020 Franklin Terrace Ct 37604. I-26 exit 19, just w, then just n, follow signs; entrance on Oakland Ave at light. Int corridors. **Pets:** Accepted.

Super 8 Motel Johnson City M
(423) 282-8818. **$54-$140.** 108 Wesley St 37601. I-26 exit 20A westbound; exit 20 eastbound, just e on N Roan St, then just s on E Spring Brook Dr. Int corridors. **Pets:** Accepted.

KIMBALL

Best Western Kimball Inn
(423) 837-2478. **$75-$110.** 205 Kimball Crossing 37347. I-24 exit 152B, 0.3 mi n. Int corridors. **Pets:** Dogs only. $15 daily fee/pet. Designated rooms, service with restrictions, supervision.

KINGSPORT

La Quinta Inn & Suites Kingsport Tri-Cities Airport
(423) 323-0500. **$71-$306.** 10150 Airport Pkwy 37663. I-81 exit 63, just e. Int corridors. **Pets:** Accepted.

Quality Inn
(423) 230-0534. **$94-$305.** 3004 Bay Meadow Pl 37664. I-26 exit 4, just n. Int corridors. **Pets:** Medium, dogs only. $20 daily fee/pet. Service with restrictions, crate.

Sleep Inn
(423) 279-1811. **$85-$340.** 200 Hospitality Pl 37663. I-81 exit 63, just s. Int corridors. **Pets:** Accepted.

KINGSTON

Motel 6 #4403
(865) 376-2069. **$43-$90.** 495 Gallaher Rd 37763. I-40 exit 356, just n. Ext corridors. **Pets:** Accepted.

KINGSTON SPRINGS

Quality Inn Kingston Springs
(615) 952-3961. **$79-$180.** 116 Luyben Hills Rd 37082. I-40 exit 188, just n. Ext corridors. **Pets:** Accepted.

KNOXVILLE *(Restaurants p. 624)*

Baymont Inn Knoxville/Cedar Bluff, TN
(865) 531-7444. **$74-$240.** 209 Market Place Blvd 37922. I-40/75 exit 378 (Cedar Bluff Rd), just s to N Peters Rd, then just w. Int corridors. **Pets:** Medium. $20 daily fee/pet. Designated rooms, service with restrictions, crate.

Best Western Knoxville Suites
(865) 687-9922. **$79-$110.** 5317 Pratt Rd 37912. I-75 exit 108 (Merchants Dr), just e, then n. Int corridors. **Pets:** Accepted.

Best Western Plus Strawberry Inn & Suites
(865) 544-7737. **$70-$169.** 7260 Saddlerack St 37914. I-40 exit 398 (Strawberry Plains Pike), just s, then just e. Int corridors. **Pets:** Other species. $15 daily fee/pet. Designated rooms, service with restrictions, supervision.

Candlewood Suites-Knoxville
(865) 777-0400. **$95-$125.** 10206 Parkside Dr 37922. I-40/75 exit 374 (Lovell Rd), 0.5 mi s, then 1 mi e. Int corridors. **Pets:** Medium. $25 daily fee/pet. Service with restrictions, crate.

The Clarion Inn
(865) 687-8989. **$58-$125.** 5634 Merchants Center Blvd 37912. I-75 exit 108 (Merchants Dr), just w, then just n. Int corridors. **Pets:** Accepted.

Country Inn & Suites By Carlson, West Knoxville/Cedar Bluff
(865) 693-4500. **Call for rates.** 9137 Cross Park Dr 37923. I-40/75 exit 378 (Cedar Bluff Rd), just e. Int corridors. **Pets:** Accepted.

Crowne Plaza Knoxville
(865) 522-2600. **$99-$399.** 401 W Summit Hill Dr 37902. Corner of Walnut St; downtown. Int corridors. **Pets:** Other species. $35 one-time fee/room. Service with restrictions.

Econo Lodge-North
(865) 687-5680. **$53-$129.** 5505 Merchants Center Blvd 37912. I-75 exit 108 (Merchants Dr), just w, then just n. Ext corridors. **Pets:** Accepted.

Extended Stay America Knoxville-Cedar Bluff
(865) 769-0822. **$60-$70.** 214 Langley Pl 37922. I-40/75 exit 378 (Cedar Bluff Rd), just s, then 1 mi w on N Peters Rd. Ext corridors. **Pets:** Accepted.

Extended Stay America Knoxville-West Hills
(865) 694-4178. **$60-$70.** 1700 Winston Rd 37919. I-40/75 exit 380 (West Hills), just w on Kingston Pike, then just s. Int corridors. **Pets:** Accepted.

Four Points by Sheraton Knoxville Cumberland House Hotel
(865) 971-4663. **$92-$499.** 1109 White Ave 37916. Jct 11th St. Int corridors. **Pets:** Accepted.

Hampton Inn & Suites Knoxville Papermill
(865) 693-5400. **$109-$159.** 601 N Weisgarber Rd 37919. I-40 exit 383 (Papermill Dr NW), just w. Int corridors. **Pets:** Accepted.

Hilton Knoxville Downtown
(865) 523-2300. **$119-$199.** 501 W Church Ave 37902. Between Locust and Walnut sts; downtown. Int corridors. **Pets:** Accepted.

Holiday Inn Express Knoxville-East
(865) 525-5100. **$105.** 730 Rufus Graham Rd 37924. I-40 exit 398 (Strawberry Plains Pike), just n. Int corridors. **Pets:** Other species. $30 daily fee/pet. Service with restrictions, crate.

Holiday Inn Knoxville West-Cedar Bluff

(865) 693-1011. **Call for rates.** 9134 Executive Park Dr 37923. I-40/75 exit 378 (Cedar Bluff Rd) eastbound; exit 378B westbound, just n to Executive Park Dr. Int corridors. **Pets:** Medium, dogs only. $35 one-time fee/room. Designated rooms, service with restrictions, crate.

Holiday Inn World's Fair Park

(865) 522-2800. **$95-$800.** 525 Henley St 37902. Corner of Clinch Ave; downtown. Int corridors. **Pets:** Medium, dogs only. $50 one-time fee/pet. Service with restrictions, crate.

Home2 Suites by Hilton Knoxville West
(865) 973-9444. **$99-$159.** 380 N Peters Rd 37922. I-40/75 exit 378 (Cedar Bluff Rd), just s, then just w. Int corridors. **Pets:** Accepted.

Homewood Suites by Hilton
(865) 777-0375. **$114-$189.** 10935 Turkey Dr 37922. I-40/75 exit 374 (Lovell Rd), just s to Parkside Dr, then 0.5 mi n on Snow Goose Dr. Int corridors. **Pets:** Accepted.

La Quinta Inn & Suites Knoxville Strawberry Plains
(865) 633-5100. **$81-$185.** 7210 Saddlerack St 37914. I-40 exit 398 (Strawberry Plains Pike), just s, just e on Region Ln, then just se on Shumard Ave. Int corridors. **Pets:** Accepted.

▼▼▼ La Quinta Inn & Suites Papermill **H**
(865) 321-1840. **$82-$257.** 1317 Kirby Rd 37909. I-40 exit 383 (Papermill Dr NW), just w. Int corridors. **Pets:** Accepted.
🍴 ⬆M 📶 ✕ 🛗 💻

AAA ▼▼▼ MainStay Suites Knoxville **H**
(865) 247-0222. **$64-$169.** 144 Merchants Dr 37912. I-75 exit 108 (Merchants Dr), just n. Int corridors. **Pets:** Small. $15 daily fee/pet. Designated rooms, no service, supervision. 💲 ⬆M 📶 🛗 💻

▼▼ Quality Inn Merchants Dr **M**
(865) 342-3701. **$60-$149.** 117 Cedar Ln 37912. I-75 exit 108 (Merchants Dr), just e. Ext corridors. **Pets:** Accepted.
⬆M 🏊 📶 🛗 💻

▼▼ Red Roof Inn & Suites Knoxville-East **H**
(865) 546-5700. **$49-$119.** 7525 Crosswood Blvd 37924. I-40 exit 398 (Strawberry Plains Pike), just n, then w. Int corridors. **Pets:** Accepted.
⬆M 🏊 📶 🛗 💻

▼▼ Red Roof Inn Knoxville-University of
Tennessee **M**
(865) 691-1664. **$50-$120.** 209 Advantage Pl 37922. I-40/75 exit 378 (Cedar Bluff Rd), just s to N Peters Rd, then w. Ext corridors.
Pets: Accepted. 📶 🛗 💻

▼▼▼ Residence Inn by Marriott Knoxville Cedar
Bluff **H**
(865) 539-5339. **$112-$180.** 215 Langley Pl 37922. I-40/75 exit 378 (Cedar Bluff Rd), just s, then 1 mi w on N Peters Rd. Int corridors.
Pets: Accepted. ⬆M 🏊 📶 ✕ 🛗 💻

▼▼▼ TownePlace Suites by Marriott Cedar Bluff **H**
(865) 693-5216. **$89-$169.** 205 Langley Pl 37922. I-40/75 exit 378 (Cedar Bluff Rd), just s, then 1 mi w on N Peters Rd. Int corridors.
Pets: Accepted. 🍴 ⬆M 📶 ✕ 🛗 💻

LAWRENCEBURG
▼▼ Americas Best Value Inn **M**
(931) 762-4467. **$75-$85.** 1940 N Locust Ave 38464. Jct US 43 and 64, 1.6 mi n. Ext corridors. **Pets:** Very small. $15 daily fee/pet. Designated rooms, service with restrictions, crate. ⬆M 🏊 📶 🛗 💻

LEBANON
▼▼ Econo Lodge **M**
(615) 444-1001. **$65-$100.** 829 S Cumberland St 37087. I-40 exit 238, just n. Ext corridors. **Pets:** Accepted. 🏊 📶 🛗 💻

▼▼ Sleep Inn & Suites-Lebanon/Nashville **H**
(615) 449-7005. **$84-$164.** 150 S Eastgate Ct 37090. I-40 exit 232, just n. Int corridors. **Pets:** Accepted. ⬆M 🏊 📶 ✕ 🛗 💻

LENOIR CITY
▼▼ Days Inn **H**
(865) 986-2011. **$50-$70.** 1110 Hwy 321 N 37771. I-75 exit 81, just e. Ext corridors. **Pets:** Accepted. 🍴 🏊 📶 🛗 💻

AAA ▼▼▼ Econo Lodge **H**
(865) 986-0295. **$69-$74.** 1211 Hwy 321 N 37771. I-75 exit 81, just w. Ext corridors. **Pets:** Small. $10 daily fee/pet. Service with restrictions, crate. 💲 ⬆M 🏊 📶 🛗

MANCHESTER
▼▼ Microtel Inn & Suites by Wyndham
Manchester **H**
(931) 723-7001. **$67-$225.** 201 Expressway Dr 37355. I-24 exit 114, just w, then just n. Int corridors. **Pets:** Accepted.
🍴 ⬆M 🏊 📶 ✕ 🛗 💻

AAA ▼▼▼ Sleep Inn & Suites **H**
(931) 954-0580. **$110-$350.** 84 Relco Dr 37355. I-24 exit 114, just e. Int corridors. **Pets:** Large. $20 daily fee/pet. Designated rooms, service with restrictions, supervision. 💲 ⬆M 🏊 📶 ✕ 🛗 💻

MARYVILLE
▼▼▼ LuxBury Inn & Suites **M**
(865) 983-9839. **Call for rates.** 805 Foothills Mall Dr 37801. Jct US 321 (Lamar Alexander Pkwy). Ext corridors. **Pets:** Accepted.
⬆M 📶 🛗 💻

MCKENZIE
AAA ▼▼▼ Best Western McKenzie **M**
(731) 352-1083. **$74-$79.** 16180 N Highland Ave 38201. Jct SR 22, 1 mi s on US 79. Ext corridors. **Pets:** Accepted.
💲 🏊 📶 🛗 💻

MCMINNVILLE
AAA ▼▼▼ Best Western Tree City Inn **H**
(931) 473-2159. **$80-$114.** 809 Sparta St 37110. Jct US 70 S Bypass and Red Rd, 1 mi s, follow signs. Ext corridors. **Pets:** Medium, dogs only. $10 daily fee/pet. Service with restrictions, crate.
💲 🏊 📶 🛗 💻

MEMPHIS *(Restaurants p. 624)*
▼▼ Baymont Inn & Suites Memphis East **H**
(901) 377-2233. **$59-$95.** 6020 Shelby Oaks Dr 38134. I-40 exit 12, just n, then just e. Int corridors. **Pets:** Accepted. 🏊 📶 🛗 💻

▼▼▼▼ Hampton Inn Memphis-Walnut Grove/Baptist
Hospital East **H**
(901) 747-3700. **$109-$149.** 33 Humphreys Center Dr 38120. I-240 exit 13 (Walnut Grove E), just e. Int corridors. **Pets:** Accepted.
⬆M 🏊 📶 ✕ 🛗 💻

▼▼▼▼ Hilton Memphis **H**
(901) 684-6664. **$109-$299.** 939 Ridge Lake Blvd 38120. I-240 exit 15 (Poplar Ave), just e, then n under overpass. Int corridors.
Pets: Accepted. 🍴 ⬆M 🏊 🍽 ✕ 🛗 💻

▼▼▼▼ Homewood Suites by Hilton Memphis-Poplar **H**
(901) 763-0500. **$139-$219.** 5811 Poplar Ave 38119. I-240 exit 15 (Poplar Ave), just e. Ext/int corridors. **Pets:** Medium. $50 one-time fee/room. Service with restrictions, supervision. 🏊 📶 ✕ 🛗 💻

▼▼▼▼ Homewood Suites by Hilton Southwind-Hacks
Cross **H**
(901) 758-5018. **$109-$299.** 3583 Hacks Cross Rd 38125. I-240 exit 16, 4 mi e on SR 385, then 1 mi n. Int corridors. **Pets:** Accepted.
⬆M 🏊 📶 ✕ 🛗 💻

AAA ▼▼▼▼ Hyatt Place-Memphis/Primacy
Parkway **H**
(901) 680-9700. **$89-$219.** 1220 Primacy Pkwy 38119. I-240 exit 15 (Poplar Ave), 0.5 mi e, s on Ridgeway Rd, just w, then just s. Int corridors. **Pets:** Medium, dogs only. $75 one-time fee/room. Designated rooms, service with restrictions, supervision.
💲 🍴 ⬆M 🏊 📶 ✕ 🛗 💻

AAA ▼▼▼▼ Hyatt Place Memphis/Wolfchase
Galleria **H**
(901) 371-0010. **$84-$189.** 7905 Giacosa Pl 38133. I-40 exit 16 or 16B, just n on Germantown Rd, then just w. Int corridors. **Pets:** Medium, dogs only. $75 one-time fee/room. Service with restrictions.
💲 ⬆M 🏊 📶 ✕ 🛗 💻

AAA ▼▼▼▼ La Quinta Inn & Suites Memphis
East-Sycamore View **H**
(901) 381-0044. **$82-$159.** 6069 Macon Cove 38134. I-40 exit 12, just s, then just w. Int corridors. **Pets:** Accepted.
💲 ⬆M 🏊 📶 ✕ 🛗 💻

Madison Hotel H
(901) 333-1200. **$189-$389, 3 day notice.** 79 Madison Ave 38103. Jct Main St, just w. Int corridors. **Pets:** Accepted.

Peabody Memphis H ✿
(901) 529-4000. **$219-$405, 3 day notice.** 149 Union Ave 38103. Jct 2nd St. Int corridors. **Pets:** Dogs only. $75 one-time fee/room. Designated rooms, service with restrictions.

Residence Inn by Marriott Memphis Downtown H
(901) 578-3700. **$157-$239.** 110 Monroe Ave 38103. Jct Main St. Int corridors. **Pets:** Other species. $125 one-time fee/room. Service with restrictions, supervision.

Residence Inn by Marriott Memphis East H
(901) 685-9595. **$125-$202.** 6141 Poplar Pike 38119. I-240 exit 15 (Poplar Ave), 0.5 mi e. Int corridors. **Pets:** Accepted.

Sheraton Memphis Downtown Hotel H
(901) 527-7300. **$129-$299.** 250 N Main St 38103. I-40 exit 1A westbound; exit 1 eastbound, just s. Int corridors. **Pets:** Accepted.

Staybridge Suites Memphis-Poplar Ave East H ✿
(901) 682-1722. **Call for rates.** 1070 Ridge Lake Blvd 38120. I-240 exit 15 (Poplar Ave), just e, then n under overpass. Int corridors. **Pets:** Large, other species. $75 daily fee/room. Designated rooms, service with restrictions, supervision.

The Westin Memphis Beale Street H ✿
(901) 334-5900. **$189-$399.** 170 Lt. George W. Lee Ave 38103. Jct S 3rd St. Int corridors. **Pets:** Medium. Designated rooms, service with restrictions, crate.

MILLINGTON

Plantation Oaks Suites & Inn M
(901) 872-8000. **Call for rates.** 6656 Hwy 51 N 38053. SR 385, 2.4 mi s. Ext/int corridors. **Pets:** Accepted.

MORRISTOWN

Best Western Plus Morristown Conference Center Hotel H ✿
(423) 587-2400. **$110-$200.** 130 Cracker Rd 37813. I-81 exit 8, just w. Int corridors. **Pets:** Medium. $20 daily fee/room. Service with restrictions, supervision.

Super 8 M
(423) 318-8888. **$50-$160.** 5400 S Davy Crockett Pkwy 37813. I-81 exit 8, just n. Int corridors. **Pets:** Dogs only. $9 daily fee/pet. Service with restrictions, supervision.

MOUNT JULIET

Quality Inn & Suites H
(615) 773-3600. **$70-$139.** 1000 Hershel Dr 37122. I-40 exit 226A eastbound; exit 226 westbound, just s. Int corridors. **Pets:** Accepted.

MURFREESBORO

Baymont Inn & Suites M
(615) 896-1172. **$69-$119.** 2230 Armory Dr 37129. I-24 exit 78B, just n. Ext corridors. **Pets:** Accepted.

Best Western Chaffin Inn M
(615) 895-3818. **$70-$150.** 168 Chaffin Pl 37129. I-24 exit 78B, just s. Ext corridors. **Pets:** Accepted.

DoubleTree by Hilton Hotel Murfreesboro H
(615) 895-5555. **$109-$189.** 1850 Old Fort Pkwy 37129. I-24 exit 78B, 0.6 mi ne. Int corridors. **Pets:** Accepted.

Hampton Inn & Suites H
(615) 890-2424. **$119-$189.** 325 N Thompson Ln 37129. I-24 exit 78B, just ne. Int corridors. **Pets:** Accepted.

Quality Inn Murfreesboro H
(615) 890-1006. **$80-$275.** 2135 S Church St 37130. I-24 exit 81, e on US 231 E. Int corridors. **Pets:** Accepted.

Residence Inn by Marriott-Murfreesboro H
(615) 225-9250. **$123-$177.** 1409 Conference Center Blvd 37129. I-24 exit 76, just e. Int corridors. **Pets:** Accepted.

NASHVILLE (Restaurants p. 624)

Aloft Nashville West End H
(615) 329-4200. **$179-$499.** 1719 West End Ave 37203. I-40 exit 209B (Broadway), 0.4 mi w. Int corridors. **Pets:** Accepted.

Comfort Inn Downtown H
(615) 255-9977. **$100-$350.** 1501 Demonbreun St 37203. I-40 exit 209B, just w. Ext corridors. **Pets:** Accepted.

Comfort Inn West H
(615) 356-0888. **$99-$249.** 412 White Bridge Pl 37209. I-40 exit 204B, just s. Int corridors. **Pets:** Small. $20 daily fee/pet. Service with restrictions.

Days Inn North M
(615) 228-3421. **$70-$104.** 3312 Dickerson Pike 37207. I-65 exit 90A (Dickerson Pike), just s. Ext corridors. **Pets:** $10 daily fee/pet. Designated rooms, service with restrictions, supervision.

Drury Inn & Suites-Nashville Airport H
(615) 902-0400. **$84-$224.** 555 Donelson Pike 37214. I-40 exit 216 (Donelson Pike), just n. Int corridors. **Pets:** Accepted.

Embassy Suites by Hilton Nashville Airport H
(615) 871-0033. **$99-$229.** 10 Century Blvd 37214. I-40 exit 215B northbound to exit 7 (Elm Hill Pike), 0.3 mi e to McGavock Pike, 0.3 mi s to Century Blvd, then 0.3 mi w. Int corridors. **Pets:** Accepted.

The Hermitage Hotel H
(615) 244-3121. **Call for rates.** 231 6th Ave N 37219. Corner of Union St. Int corridors. **Pets:** Accepted.

Hilton Garden Inn Nashville-Vanderbilt H
(615) 369-5900. **$139-$399.** 1715 Broadway 37203. Corner of 17th Ave S and Broadway; in West End. Int corridors. **Pets:** Accepted.

Hilton Nashville Downtown H ✿
(615) 620-1000. **$119-$499.** 121 4th Ave S 37201. Center. Int corridors. **Pets:** Medium, other species. $75 one-time fee/room. Service with restrictions, supervision.

Holiday Inn Express-Airport/Opryland Area H
(615) 883-1366. **Call for rates.** 1111 Airport Center Dr 37214. I-40 exit 216C (Donelson Pike N), 1 mi n, then 0.5 mi e. Int corridors.
Pets: Accepted. SAVE &M ⌐ ⇔ X ⊟ 🖵

Home2 Suites by Hilton-Nashville/Vanderbilt H
(615) 254-2170. **$189-$259.** 1800 Division St 37203. I-40 exit 209 (Demonbreun St), 0.5 mi w. Int corridors. **Pets:** Large, other species. $75 one-time fee/room. Designated rooms, service with restrictions, supervision. &M ⌐ ⊟ 🖵

Homewood Suites by Hilton Nashville Vanderbilt/ West End H
(615) 340-8000. **Call for rates.** 2400 West End Ave 37203. I-40 exit 209A (Broadway), 0.7 mi w. Int corridors. **Pets:** Accepted.
&M ⌐ X ⊟ 🖵

Homewood Suites Nashville Downtown H
(615) 742-5550. **$159-$449.** 706 Church St 37203. Jct 7th Ave N and Church St. Int corridors. **Pets:** Accepted. &M ⌐ X ⊟ 🖵

Hotel Indigo-Nashville Downtown H
(615) 891-6000. **$199-$469.** 301 Union St 37201. I-40 exit 209A (Church St), 0.8 mi e on Charlotte Ave, then just s. Int corridors.
Pets: Accepted. ⊓⊔ ⌐ X ⊟ 🖵

Hotel Preston H ❀
(615) 361-5900. **Call for rates.** 733 Briley Pkwy 37217. I-40 exit 215A (SR 155/Briley Pkwy), just s. Int corridors. **Pets:** Dogs only. $45 one-time fee/room. Designated rooms, service with restrictions, supervision.
SAVE ⊓⊔ &M ⌐ X ⊟ 🖵

Hutton Hotel H
(615) 340-9333. **Call for rates.** 1808 West End Ave 37203. I-40 W exit 209B (Broadway), 1 mi w. Int corridors. **Pets:** Accepted.
SAVE ECO ⊞ ⊓⊔ &M ⌐ X ⊟ 🖵

Hyatt Place Nashville Airport H
(615) 493-5200. **$95-$249.** 721 Royal Pkwy 37214. I-40 exit 216C (Donelson Pike), just n, then just e. Int corridors. **Pets:** Accepted.
SAVE ⊓⊔ &M ⌐ ⌐ X ⊟ 🖵

Hyatt Place Nashville Downtown H
(615) 687-9995. **$189-$799.** 301 3rd Ave S 37201. I-40 exit 210C, 0.6 mi n on 2nd Ave S, then w at Korean Veterans Blvd. Int corridors.
Pets: Accepted. SAVE ⊓⊔ ⌐ X ⊟ 🖵

Hyatt Place Nashville/Opryland H
(615) 872-0422. **$89-$229.** 220 Rudy Cir 37214. I-40 exit 215B (SR 155 N/Briley Pkwy), 5.3 mi n to exit 12 (McGavock Pike), just w, then 0.3 mi n on Music Valley Dr. Int corridors. **Pets:** Accepted.
SAVE ⊓⊔ &M ⌐ ⌐ X ⊟ 🖵

La Quinta Inn & Suites Nashville-Airport H
(615) 885-3100. **$82-$280.** 531 Donelson Pike 37214. I-40 exit 216C (Donelson Pike), 0.3 mi n. Int corridors. **Pets:** Accepted.
&M ⌐ ⌐ ⊟ 🖵

Loews Vanderbilt Hotel Nashville H ❀
(615) 320-1700. **$189-$549.** 2100 West End Ave 37203. I-40 exit 209B (Broadway), 1.3 mi w. Int corridors. **Pets:** $50 one-time fee/pet. Designated rooms. SAVE ECO ⊓⊔ &M ⌐ X ⊟ 🖵

Microtel Inn & Suites by Wyndham Nashville H
(615) 662-0004. **$62-$124.** 100 Coley Davis Ct 37221. I-40 exit 196, just se. Int corridors. **Pets:** Accepted.
SAVE &M ⌐ ⌐ X ⊟ 🖵

Omni Hotel H
(615) 782-5300. **Call for rates.** 250 5th Ave S 37203. I-40 exit 210C, just n to 2nd Ave, then w; enter from Korean Veterans Blvd, between 4th and 5th aves. Int corridors. **Pets:** Accepted.
⊓⊔ &M X ⌐ X ⊟ 🖵

Red Roof Inn Nashville Airport M
(615) 872-0735. **$69-$130.** 510 Claridge Dr 37214. I-40 exit 216C (Donelson Pike), 0.3 mi n. Ext corridors. **Pets:** Accepted.
SAVE &M ⌐ X ⊟ 🖵

Residence Inn by Marriott Nashville Airport H
(615) 889-8600. **$128-$215.** 2300 Elm Hill Pike 37214. I-40 exit 215B (SR 155 N/Briley Pkwy), 1.5 mi n. Ext corridors. **Pets:** Accepted.
SAVE ECO &M ⌐ ⌐ X ⊟ 🖵

Residence Inn by Marriott Nashville West End/Vanderbilt H
(615) 988-9920. **$148-$302.** 1801 Hayes St 37203. I-40 exit 209A westbound; exit 209B eastbound, 0.5 mi w. Int corridors. **Pets:** Other species. $100 one-time fee/room. Service with restrictions, crate.
SAVE &M ⌐ X ⊟ 🖵

Sheraton Music City Hotel H ❀
(615) 885-2200. **$100-$600.** 777 McGavock Pike 37214. I-40 exit 215B (SR 155 N/Briley Pkwy), 1 mi n to exit 7 (Elm Hill Pike), 0.5 mi e, then s. Int corridors. **Pets:** Small, dogs only. $200 one-time fee/room. Service with restrictions, supervision.
SAVE ⊓⊔ &M ⌐ X ⌐ X ⊟ 🖵

Sheraton Nashville Downtown Hotel H
(615) 259-2000. **$229-$575.** 623 Union St 37219. Corner of Union and 7th Ave N. Int corridors. **Pets:** Accepted.
SAVE ⊞ ⊓⊔ &M ⌐ X ⊟ 🖵

Super 8-West M
(615) 356-6005. **$50-$175.** 6924 Charlotte Pike 37209. I-40 exit 201B, just n. Ext corridors. **Pets:** Medium, dogs only. $25 daily fee/pet. Service with restrictions, supervision. SAVE ⌐ ⊟ 🖵

TownePlace Suites by Marriott Nashville Airport H ❀
(615) 232-3830. **$104-$209.** 2700 Elm Hill Pike 37214. I-40 exit 215B (SR 155 N/Briley Pkwy), 1 mi n to exit 7 (Elm Hill Pike), then just e. Int corridors. **Pets:** Other species. $100 one-time fee/room. Service with restrictions, crate. SAVE &M ⌐ ⌐ X ⊟ 🖵

NEWPORT

Best Western Newport Inn M
(423) 623-8713. **$70-$169.** 1015 Cosby Hwy 37821. I-40 exit 435, just w. Ext corridors. **Pets:** $10 deposit/pet. Service with restrictions, crate.
SAVE ⊓⊔ &M ⌐ ⊟ 🖵

Comfort Inn H
(423) 623-5355. **$53-$175.** 1149 Smokey Mountain Ln 37821. I-40 exit 432B, just n. Int corridors. **Pets:** Accepted. &M ⌐ ⌐ ⊟ 🖵

Motel 6 #4090 M
(423) 623-1850. **Call for rates.** 255 Heritage Blvd 37822. I-40 exit 435, just n. Int corridors. **Pets:** Accepted. &M ⌐ ⌐

OAK RIDGE

DoubleTree by Hilton Hotel Oak Ridge-Knoxville H
(865) 481-2468. **$89-$179.** 215 S Illinois Ave 37830. 0.3 mi se of SR 95 on SR 62 (Oak Ridge Hwy). Int corridors. **Pets:** Accepted.
ECO ⊓⊔ &M ⌐ ⌐ X ⊟ 🖵

▼▼ **Quality Inn** H

(865) 483-6809. **$70-$130.** 216 S Rutgers Ave 37830. Jct SR 95 and 62, 0.9 mi se on SR 62 (Oak Ridge Hwy) to Rutgers Ave, 0.7 mi n. Int corridors. **Pets:** Small. $20 daily fee/pet. Service with restrictions, supervision.

▼▼▼▼ **Staybridge Suites** H

(865) 298-0050. **Call for rates.** 420 S Illinois Ave 37830. Jct Lafayette St and SR 62 (Oak Ridge Hwy). Int corridors. **Pets:** Accepted.

OOLTEWAH

▼▼ **Super 8** M

(423) 238-5951. **$50-$70.** 8934 Lee Hwy 37363. I-75 exit 11, just w. Ext corridors. **Pets:** Accepted.

PARIS

▼▼ **Quality Inn Paris** H

(731) 642-2838. **$80-$160.** 1510 E Wood St 38242. Jct US 641, 2 mi n on US 79. Ext corridors. **Pets:** Accepted.

▼▼ **Super 8** H

(731) 644-7008. **$58-$95.** 1309 E Wood St 38242. Jct US 641, 1.5 mi n on US 79. Ext/int corridors. **Pets:** Accepted.

PIGEON FORGE *(Restaurants p. 624)*

▼▼ **Bear Creek Crossing by Eden Crest Vacation Rentals** CA

(865) 774-0059. **Call for rates.** 652 Wears Valley Rd 37863. Jct US 441, 1 mi s on US 321 at traffic light 3. Ext corridors. **Pets:** Accepted.

▼▼▼ **Black Bear Ridge by Eden Crest Vacation Rentals** CA

(865) 774-0059. **Call for rates.** 652 Wears Valley Rd 37863. Jct US 441, 1 mi s on US 321 at traffic light 3. Int corridors. **Pets:** Accepted.

▼▼▼ **Hampton Inn & Suites** H

(865) 428-1600. **$109-$189.** 2025 Parkway 37863. On US 441, at traffic light 0. Int corridors. **Pets:** Medium. $35 daily fee/room. Designated rooms, service with restrictions, crate.

AAA ▼▼▼ **La Quinta Inn & Suites** H

(865) 908-6633. **$67-$306.** 125 Community Center Dr 37863. Jct US 441, just w at traffic light 2B. Int corridors. **Pets:** Accepted.

▼▼ **Microtel Inn & Suites by Wyndham** H

(865) 453-1116. **$45-$160.** 2045 Parkway 37863. On US 441, just s of traffic light 0. Int corridors. **Pets:** Very small, dogs only. $15 daily fee/pet. Designated rooms, service with restrictions, crate.

AAA ▼▼▼ **RiverStone Resort & Spa** CO

(865) 908-0660. **$149-$499, 7 day notice.** 212 Dollywood Ln 37863. Jct US 441, just e at traffic light 8. Ext corridors. **Pets:** Small, dogs only. $25 daily fee/pet. No service, supervision.

▼▼▼ **Smoky Cove by Eden Crest Vacation Rentals** CA

(865) 774-0059. **Call for rates.** 652 Wears Valley Rd 37863. Jct US 441, 1 mi s on US 321 at traffic light 3. Ext corridors. **Pets:** Accepted.

▼▼ **Timbers Lodge** M

(865) 428-5216. **Call for rates.** 134 Wears Valley Rd E 37863. Jct US 441, just e at traffic light 3. Ext corridors. **Pets:** Accepted.

PIONEER

▼▼▼ **Comfort Inn** H

(423) 566-4400. **$84-$169.** 335 Howard Baker Hwy 37847. I-75 exit 141, just w. Int corridors. **Pets:** Accepted.

POWELL

▼▼▼ **Comfort Inn** H

(865) 938-5500. **$88-$170.** 7585 Barnett Way 37849. I-75 exit 112, 0.4 mi e on Emory Rd, then just w. Int corridors. **Pets:** Medium, other species. $25 daily fee/pet. Service with restrictions, crate.

▼▼▼ **Holiday Inn Express** H ❀

(865) 938-3800. **Call for rates.** 7520 Conner Rd 37849. I-75 exit 112, just e. Int corridors. **Pets:** Large. $35 one-time fee/room. Designated rooms, service with restrictions, supervision.

▼▼▼ **La Quinta Inn & Suites Knoxville North I-75** H

(865) 947-7500. **Call for rates.** 7534 Conner Rd 37849. I-75 exit 112, just e. Int corridors. **Pets:** Accepted.

▼▼ **Super 8 of Powell** M

(865) 938-5501. **$60-$145.** 323 E Emory Rd 37849. I-75 exit 112, just s. Ext corridors. **Pets:** Medium. $15 daily fee/pet. Designated rooms, service with restrictions, supervision.

ROGERSVILLE

▼▼▼ **Comfort Inn & Suites** H

(423) 272-8700. **$85-$230.** 128 James Richardson Ln 37857. US 11 W/SR 1/70, 1.6 mi w, just n. Int corridors. **Pets:** Other species. $25 daily fee/pet. Designated rooms, service with restrictions, supervision.

SEVIERVILLE

AAA ▼▼▼ **Baymont Inn & Suites Sevierville/Pigeon Forge** M

(865) 428-1000. **$50-$140.** 711 Parkway 37862. Jct US 411, 0.7 mi s. Ext corridors. **Pets:** Medium, dogs only. $20 deposit/pet, $20 daily fee/pet. Designated rooms, service with restrictions, supervision.

▼▼▼▼ **Blue Mountain Mist Country Inn & Cottages** BB

(865) 428-2335. **Call for rates.** 1811 Pullen Rd 37862. Jct US 411, 3.4 mi s on Veterans Blvd, 1.6 mi e on Jayell Rd, then just s. Ext/int corridors. **Pets:** Accepted.

▼▼ **Econo Lodge** M

(865) 429-7797. **$49-$200.** 680 Winfield Dunn Pkwy 37864. Jct US 411, 0.7 mi n on SR 66. Int corridors. **Pets:** Accepted.

▼▼ **La Quinta Inn & Suites Sevierville/Kodak** H

(865) 933-3339. **$68-$192.** 2428 Winfield Dunn Pkwy 37764. I-40 exit 407, 3.2 mi s on SR 66. Int corridors. **Pets:** Accepted.

▼▼ **Sleep Inn** H

(865) 429-0484. **$85-$180, 3 day notice.** 1020 Parkway 37862. On US 441, 1.2 mi s of jct US 411. Int corridors. **Pets:** Accepted.

SHELBYVILLE

AAA ▼▼▼ **Best Western Celebration Inn & Suites** H

(931) 684-2378. **$75-$250.** 724 Madison St 37160. Jct US 231 and 41. Ext corridors. **Pets:** Accepted.

AAA ▼▼▼ **Microtel Inn & Suites by Wyndham** H

(931) 684-8343. **$49-$139.** 1207 N Main St 37160. Jct US 231 and 41, 0.9 mi n. Int corridors. **Pets:** Accepted.

SMYRNA

▼▼▼ La Quinta Inn & Suites 🄷
(615) 220-8845. $92-$218. 2537 Highwood Blvd 37167. I-24 exit 66A, just w. Int corridors. Pets: Accepted.
🔌 ⓜ ⇌ 📶 ✕ 🔋 🖥

SWEETWATER (Restaurants p. 624)

▼▼▼ Quality Inn West 🄷
(423) 337-3353. $80-$110. 249 New Hwy 68 37874. I-75 exit 60, just e. Ext/int corridors. Pets: Accepted. ⇌ 📶 ✕ 🔋 🖥

TOWNSEND

🄰🄰🄰 ▼▼▼ Best Western Cades Cove Inn 🄼
(865) 448-9000. $80-$250. 7824 E Lamar Alexander Pkwy 37882. Jct SR 73, 0.7 mi s on US 321. Ext corridors. Pets: Dogs only. $20 daily fee/pet. Designated rooms, service with restrictions, supervision.
🆂🅰🆅🅴 ⓜ ⇌ 📶 ✕ 🔋 🖥

TULLAHOMA

▼▼ Baymont Inn & Suites Tullahoma 🄼
(931) 455-7891. $49-$270. 2113 N Jackson St 37388. 3 mi n on SR 41A (N Jackson St). Ext corridors. Pets: Very small, other species. $20 daily fee/pet. Designated rooms, service with restrictions, crate.
🍴 ⇌ 📶 🔋 🖥

WHITE HOUSE

▼▼▼ Hampton Inn 🄷
(615) 672-3993. $99-$189. 404 Hester Dr 37188. I-65 exit 108, just e, then just s. Int corridors. Pets: Accepted.
ⓜ ⇌ 📶 ✕ 🔋 🖥

🄰🄰🄰 ▼▼▼ Holiday Inn Express 🄷
(615) 672-7200. $140-$250. 206 Knight Cir 37188. I-65 exit 108, just e. Int corridors. Pets: Accepted. 🆂🅰🆅🅴 ⓜ ⇌ 📶 ✕ 🔋 🖥

WINCHESTER

🄰🄰🄰 ▼▼▼ Best Western Inn 🄼
(931) 967-9444. $83-$90. 1602 Dinah Shore Blvd 37398. Jct US 41A and 41 Bypass, just w. Ext corridors. Pets: Accepted.
🆂🅰🆅🅴 ⇌ 📶 🔋 🖥

TEXAS

ABILENE

▼▼▼ Comfort Inn & Suites 🄷
(325) 232-8801. $82-$119. 6350 Directors Pkwy 79606. US 83/84 S exit Antilley Rd, just w. Int corridors. Pets: Accepted.
⇌ 📶 ✕ 🔋 🖥

🄰🄰🄰 ▼▼▼ Days Inn 🄷
(325) 695-1262. $89-$109. 3950 Ridgemont Dr 79606. US 83/84 exit Buffalo Gap Rd to Ridgemont Dr, just w. Ext corridors. Pets: Accepted.
🆂🅰🆅🅴 ⇌ 📶 🔋 🖥

▼▼▼ MCM Elegante Suites 🄷
(325) 698-1234. $129-$349. 4250 Ridgemont Dr 79606. US 83/84 exit Buffalo Gap Rd, 1 mi s of W Frontage Rd to Ridgemont Dr, then 0.5 mi w. Ext/int corridors. Pets: Accepted. 🍴 ⇌ 📶 🔋 🖥

▼▼▼ Residence Inn by Marriott 🄷
(325) 677-8700. $89-$144. 1641 Musgrave Blvd 79601. I-20 exit 288; on N Frontage Rd. Int corridors. Pets: Accepted.
ⓜ ⇌ 📶 ✕ 🔋 🖥

🄰🄰🄰 ▼▼▼ Super 8 🄷
(325) 701-4779. $79-$119. 4397 Sayles Blvd 79605. US 83/84 exit Buffalo Gap Rd northbound, just e; exit southbound, just e to Industrial Blvd, 0.5 mi e to Sayles Blvd, then just s. Int corridors. Pets: Accepted.
🆂🅰🆅🅴 ⇌ 📶 🔋 🖥

▼▼▼ TownePlace Suites by Marriott Abilene Northeast 🄷
(325) 673-0400. $94-$130. 2141 Scottish Rd 79601. I-20 exit 290 eastbound; exit 288 westbound, continue on westbound frontage road, then just n on Musgrave Blvd. Int corridors. Pets: Other species. $100 one-time fee/room. Service with restrictions. ⓜ 📶 ✕ 🔋 🖥

ADDISON (Restaurants p. 624)

▼▼▼ Homewood Suites by Hilton 🄷
(972) 788-1342. $109-$164. 4451 Belt Line Rd 75001. Just e of jct Belt Line and Midway rds. Ext/int corridors. Pets: Accepted.
ⓜ ⇌ 📶 🔋 🖥

🄰🄰🄰 ▼▼▼ Hyatt House Dallas/Addison 🄷
(972) 661-3113. $79-$189. 4900 Edwin Lewis Dr 75001. Just n of jct Belt Line Rd and Quorum Dr to Edwin Lewis Dr, just w. Ext corridors. Pets: Accepted. 🆂🅰🆅🅴 🍴 📶 ✕ 🔋 🖥

▼▼▼ La Quinta Inn & Suites Dallas Addison Galleria 🄷
(972) 404-0004. $68-$202. 14925 Landmark Blvd 75254. Jct Belt Line Rd and Landmark Blvd, just s. Int corridors. Pets: Accepted.
⇌ 📶 ✕ 🔋 🖥

▼▼▼ Residence Inn by Marriott-Addison 🄷
(972) 866-9933. $98-$194. 14975 Quorum Dr 75254. Just s of jct Belt Line Rd and Quorum Dr. Ext/int corridors. Pets: Accepted.
⇌ 📶 ✕ 🔋 🖥

ALAMO

▼▼▼ La Quinta Inn & Suites Alamo At East McAllen 🄷
(956) 783-6955. $90-$196. 909 E Frontage Rd 78516. US 83 exit Alamo Rd. Int corridors. Pets: Accepted.
ⓜ ⇌ 📶 ✕ 🔋 🖥

ALPINE

▼▼▼ The Holland Hotel 🄷
(432) 837-2800. Call for rates. 209 W Holland Ave 79830. On US 90 eastbound and 6th St. Int corridors. Pets: Other species. $30 one-time fee/pet. Service with restrictions, supervision.
🍴 📶 ✕ 🅿 🔋 🖥

▼▼▼ The Maverick Inn 🄷
(432) 837-0628. $110-$140. 1200 E Holland Ave 79830. Just e of downtown. Ext corridors. Pets: $25 one-time fee/pet. Service with restrictions, crate. 📶 ✕ 🅿 🔋 🖥

▼▼▼ Oak Tree Inn 🄷
(432) 837-5711. Call for rates. 2407 E Holland Ave (Hwy 90/67) 79830. On US 90, 2 mi e. Int corridors. Pets: Accepted.
🍴 ⓜ 📶 ✕ 🔋 🖥

ALVARADO

▼▼ **Super 8** 🅷

(817) 790-7378. **$50-$90.** 5445 S I-35W 76009. I-35W exit 27A (US 67), just e to 1st traffic light, then 0.4 mi n on access road. Int corridors. **Pets:** Other species. $10 daily fee/pet. Service with restrictions, supervision. 🍴 ⑤M ➡ 📶 📠 💻

ALVIN *(Restaurants p. 624)*

▼▼ **Americas Best Value Inn & Suites** Ⓜ

(281) 331-0335. **Call for rates.** 1588 S Loop 35 77511. SR 35 Bypass, 0.5 mi sw of SR 6. Ext corridors. **Pets:** Accepted.
🍴 ➡ 📶 📠 💻

AMARILLO

▼▼ **Baymont Inn & Suites** 🅷

(806) 372-1425. **$59-$85.** 1700 I-40 E 79103. I-40 exit 71 (Ross-Osage), just e on south frontage road. Int corridors. **Pets:** Accepted.
➡ 📶 📠 💻

🔼 ▼▼ **Best Western Santa Fe** 🅷

(806) 372-1885. **$100-$190.** 4600 I-40 E 79103. I-40 exit 73 (Eastern St) eastbound; exit Bolton St westbound, U-turn on south frontage road. Int corridors. **Pets:** Large, dogs only. $20 daily fee/pet. Designated rooms, service with restrictions, supervision.

SAVE 🍴 ➡ 📶 ✕ 📠 💻

▼▼▼ **Country Inn & Suites By Carlson, I-40 West** 🅷

(806) 356-9977. **Call for rates.** 2000 Soncy Rd 79121. I-40 exit 64 (Soncy Rd), just n. Int corridors. **Pets:** Accepted.
🍴 ➡ 📶 ✕ 📠 💻

🔼 ▼▼ **Days Inn** 🅷

(806) 359-9393. **$60-$126.** 2102 S Coulter St 79106. I-40 exit 65 (Coulter St), just n. Ext corridors. **Pets:** Medium. $20 daily fee/pet. Service with restrictions, supervision. SAVE ➡ 📶 📠 💻

▼▼▼ **Drury Inn & Suites-Amarillo** 🅷

(806) 351-1111. **$89-$199.** 8540 W I-40 79106. I-40 exit 65 (Coulter St), 0.8 mi w; on north service road. Int corridors. **Pets:** Accepted.
⑤M ➡ 📶 ✕ 📠 💻

▼▼▼ **Holiday Inn Express & Suites** 🅷

(806) 335-2500. **Call for rates.** 9401 I-40 E 79118. I-40 exit 76 (Airport Blvd), just w on north frontage road. Int corridors. **Pets:** Accepted.
🍴 ⑤M ➡ 📶 ✕ 📠 💻

🔼 ▼▼ **Microtel Inn & Suites by Wyndham Amarillo** 🅷

(806) 372-8373. **$70-$109.** 1501 S Ross St 79102. I-40 exit 71 (Ross St/Osage St), just n. Int corridors. **Pets:** $20 one-time fee/pet. Designated rooms, service with restrictions, supervision.

SAVE ⑤M ➡ 📶 📠 💻

🔼 ▼▼ **Quality Inn Medical Center** 🅷

(806) 358-7861. **$59-$124.** 1610 S Coulter St 79106. I-40 exit 65 (Coulter St), 0.6 mi n. Ext/int corridors. **Pets:** Accepted.
SAVE 🍴 ➡ 📶 ✕ 📠 💻

▼▼▼ **Residence Inn by Marriott** 🅷

(806) 354-2978. **$108-$193.** 6700 I-40 W 79106. I-40 exit 66 (Bell St), 0.5 mi w on north frontage road. Int corridors. **Pets:** $100 one-time fee/room. Service with restrictions, crate.
🍴 ⑤M ➡ 📶 ✕ 📠 💻

ANGLETON

🔼 ▼▼ **Best Western Angleton Inn** 🅷

(979) 849-5822. **$113-$210.** 1809 N Velasco St 77515. Jct SR 35 and Business Rt SR 288, 1 mi n. Ext corridors. **Pets:** Medium. $25 one-time fee/pet. Service with restrictions, supervision. SAVE ➡ 📶 📠 💻

▼▼▼ **La Quinta Inn & Suites Angelton** 🅷

(979) 864-3383. **$108-$235.** 2400 W Mulberry St 77515. Jct SR 35 and 288; on northwest corner. Int corridors. **Pets:** Accepted.
🍴 ⑤M ➡ 📶 ✕ 📠 💻

ANTHONY

🔼 ▼▼▼ **Best Western Anthony/West El Paso** 🅷

(915) 886-3333. **$89-$145.** 9401 S Desert Blvd 79821. I-10 exit 0, just s. Ext corridors. **Pets:** Small. $20 daily fee/pet. Designated rooms, service with restrictions, supervision. SAVE ⑤M ➡ 📶 📠 💻

ARLINGTON

🔼 ▼▼▼ **Comfort Suites Six Flags in Arlington** 🅷

(817) 460-8700. **$99-$329.** 411 W Road To Six Flags Dr 76011. I-30 exit 27 (Cooper St) eastbound; exit 28 (Collins St) westbound, just s, then just e. Int corridors. **Pets:** Accepted.
SAVE ➡ 📶 📠 💻

▼▼ **Hawthorn Suites by Wyndham** 🅷

(817) 640-1188. **$109-$199.** 2401 Brookhollow Plaza Dr 76006. I-30 exit 30 (SR 360), just n to Lamar Blvd, just w to Brookhollow Plaza Dr, then just n. Ext corridors. **Pets:** Medium. $58 one-time fee/pet. Service with restrictions, crate. ➡ 📶 📠 💻

▼▼ **Holiday Inn Express Hotel & Suites Arlington Six Flags Area** 🅷

(817) 640-5454. **Call for rates.** 2451 E Randol Mill Rd 76011. I-30 exit 30 (SR 360), 0.4 mi s, then just w. Int corridors. **Pets:** Accepted.
➡ 📶 ✕ 📠 💻

🔼 ▼▼▼ **Hyatt Place Dallas/Arlington** 🅷

(817) 649-7676. **$79-$299.** 2380 E Road to Six Flags St 76011. I-30 exit 30 (SR 360), 0.5 mi s on southbound frontage road, then just w. Int corridors. **Pets:** Accepted. SAVE ➡ 📶 ✕ 📠 💻

▼▼▼ **La Quinta Inn & Suites Dallas/Arlington 6 Flags Dr** 🅷

(817) 640-4142. **$82-$361.** 825 N Watson Rd 76011. SR 360 exit Six Flags Dr northbound; exit Ave H/Lamar Blvd southbound; on southbound frontage road. Int corridors. **Pets:** Accepted. ➡ 📶 📠 💻

▼▼ **Sleep Inn Arlington Near Six Flags** 🅷

(817) 649-1010. **$45-$219.** 750 Six Flags Dr 76011. I-30 exit 30 (SR 360), 0.5 mi s. Int corridors. **Pets:** Accepted. ➡ 📶 📠 💻

AUSTIN *(Restaurants p. 624)*

🔼 ▼▼▼ **Aloft Austin at the Domain** 🅷

(512) 491-0777. **$149-$349.** 11601 Domain Dr 78758. Loop 1 (Mo-Pac Expwy) exit Burnett Rd/Duval Rd, just e; in The Domain. Int corridors. **Pets:** Accepted. SAVE ⑤M ➡ 📶 ✕ 📠 💻

🔼 ▼▼▼ **Best Western Plus Austin Airport Inn & Suites** 🅷

(512) 386-5455. **$129-$149.** 1805 Airport Commerce Dr 78741. Jct SR 71 (E Ben White Blvd) and Riverside Dr, just n; in Airport Commerce Park. Int corridors. **Pets:** Accepted.
SAVE 🍴 ⑤M ➡ 📶 ✕ 📠 💻

🔼 ▼▼▼ **Best Western Plus Austin City Hotel** 🅷

(512) 444-0561. **$140-$220.** 2200 S I-35 78704. I-35 exit 232A (Oltorf Blvd); on west side access road. Ext/int corridors. **Pets:** Accepted.
SAVE 🍴 ➡ 📶 ✕ 📠 💻

▼▼ **Candlewood Suites Austin Northwest** 🅷

(512) 338-1611. **Call for rates.** 9701 Stonelake Blvd 78759. Jct Capital of Texas Hwy (SR 360) and Stonelake Blvd, just s. Int corridors. **Pets:** Accepted. ⑤M ➡ ✕ 📠 💻

▼▼▼ **Candlewood Suites-South** H

(512) 444-8882. **Call for rates.** 4320 S I-35 78745. I-35 exit 230 (Ben White Blvd/SR 71) northbound; exit 231 (Woodward Rd) southbound; on southbound frontage road. Int corridors. **Pets:** Accepted.

🛆M 🛜 🛅 🖵

▼▼ **Clarion Inn Austin North** H

(512) 339-7311. **$79-$189.** 7928 Gessner Dr 78753. I-35 exit 240A, 0.4 mi w on US 183. Int corridors. **Pets:** Accepted.

🛆M 🕽 🛜 🛅 🖵

▼▼▼ **DoubleTree Suites by Hilton Hotel Austin** H

(512) 478-7000. **$184-$609.** 303 W 15th St 78701. Just nw of state capitol building. Int corridors. **Pets:** Accepted.

🍽 🕽 🕾 🗙 🛅 🖵

◈◈ ▼▼▼▼ **The Driskill** H

(512) 474-5911. **$179-$599.** 604 Brazos St 78701. Jct 6th St. Int corridors. **Pets:** Accepted. SAVE ECO 🍽 🛆M 🗙 🛜 🗙 🛅 🖵

▼▼▼▼ **Drury Inn & Suites-Austin North** H

(512) 467-9500. **$89-$219.** 6711 I-35 N 78752. I-35 exit 238A; on east frontage road. Int corridors. **Pets:** Accepted. 🕽 🛜 🗙 🛅 🖵

▼▼ **Econo Lodge** M

(512) 835-7070. **$70-$220.** 9102 Burnet Rd 78758. US 183 and Burnet Rd; on northeast corner. Ext corridors. **Pets:** Accepted. 🛜 🛅 🖵

▼▼▼ **Extended Stay America Austin Arboretum** H

(512) 231-1520. **$90-$115.** 10100 N Capital of Texas Hwy 78759. Jct Loop 1 (Mo-Pac Expwy) and Capital of Texas Hwy (SR 360), just w. Int corridors. **Pets:** Accepted. 🛆M 🛜 🛅 🖵

▼▼ **Extended Stay America Austin-Arboretum-North** H

(512) 833-0898. **$85-$115.** 2700 Gracy Farms Ln 78758. 2 mi n of US 183 on Loop 1 (Mo-Pac Expwy) exit Burnet Rd. Int corridors. **Pets:** Accepted. 🕽 🛜 🛅 🖵

▼▼ **Extended Stay America-Austin/Downtown/Town Lake** H

(512) 476-1818. **$135-$180.** 507 S 1st St 78704. I-35 exit 234B southbound; exit 234A northbound, 1.8 mi w on Cesar Chavez St/E 1st St, then 0.5 mi s. Int corridors. **Pets:** Accepted. 🛜 🛅 🖵

▼▼ **Extended Stay America Austin Northwest Lakeline Mall** H

(512) 258-3365. **$80-$105.** 13858 US Hwy 183 N 78750. Jct US 183 and SR 620; on southwest corner. Int corridors. **Pets:** Accepted.

🛆M 🛜 🛅 🖵

▼▼ **Extended Stay America (Austin/Northwest/Research Park)** H

(512) 219-6500. **$75-$105.** 12424 Research Blvd 78759. US 183 exit Oak Knoll Dr; on eastbound frontage road. Int corridors. **Pets:** Accepted. 🍽 🛆M 🕽 🛜 🗙 🛅 🖵

▼▼ **Extended Stay America Austin Southwest** H

(512) 892-4272. **$100-$125.** 5100 US Hwy 290 W 78735. I-35 exit 230; US 290 W exit Brodie Ln, 1 mi w. Int corridors. **Pets:** Accepted.

🛆M 🛜 🛅 🖵

◈◈◈ ▼▼▼▼▼ **Four Seasons Hotel Austin** H 🐾

(512) 478-4500. **Call for rates.** 98 San Jacinto Blvd 78701. Jct Congress Ave and Cesar Chavez St; 2 blks e on Lady Bird Lake Tr. Int corridors. **Pets:** Large. $100 one-time fee/pet. Service with restrictions, supervision. SAVE ⊟ 🍽 🛆M 🕽 🗙 🛜 🗙 🛅 🖵

▼▼▼ **Hampton Inn Northwest** H

(512) 349-9898. **$89-$199.** 3908 W Braker Ln 78759. 1 mi n of US 183 on Loop 1 (Mo-Pac Expwy) exit W Braker Ln. Int corridors. **Pets.** Accepted. 🍽 🛆M 🕽 🛜 🗙 🛅 🖵

◈◈◈ ▼▼▼ **Hilton Austin** H 🐾

(512) 482-8000. **$100-$999.** 500 E 4th St 78701. Jct 4th and Neches sts. Int corridors. **Pets:** Large, other species. $50 one-time fee/pet. Service with restrictions, supervision.

SAVE 🍽 🛆M 🕽 🗙 🛜 🗙 🛅 🖵

◈◈◈ ▼▼▼▼ **Hilton Austin Airport** H

(512) 385-6767. **$119-$209.** 9515 Hotel Dr 78719. SR 71; service road exit at airport. Int corridors. **Pets:** Accepted.

SAVE ECO 🍽 🛆M 🕽 🛜 🗙 🛅 🖵

▼▼▼ **Holiday Inn Express & Suites Austin Airport** H

(512) 386-7600. **Call for rates.** 7601 E Ben White Blvd 78741. I-35 exit 230B (Ben White Blvd/SR 71), 3.2 mi e. Int corridors. **Pets:** Accepted.

🍽 🛆M 🕽 🛜 🗙 🛅 🖵

▼▼▼ **Homewood Suites-Austin South/Airport** H

(512) 445-5050. **$119-$219.** 4143 Governor's Row 78744. I-35 exit 231 (Ben White Blvd/SR 71) southbound; exit 229 northbound; at Ben White Blvd. Int corridors. **Pets:** Accepted. 🛆M 🕽 🛜 🛅 🖵

▼▼▼ **Homewood Suites by Hilton Arboretum NW** H

(512) 349-9966. **$99-$229.** 10925 Stonelake Blvd 78759. US 183 N to Loop 1 (Mo-Pac Expwy), 1.5 mi n to Braker Ln; on northwest corner. Int corridors. **Pets:** Accepted. 🛆M 🕽 🛜 🗙 🛅 🖵

◈◈◈ ▼▼▼▼ **Hotel Ella** H

(512) 495-1800. **Call for rates.** 1900 Rio Grande St 78705. Jct Rio Grande St and Martin Luther King Jr Blvd. Int corridors.

Pets: Accepted. SAVE ⊟ 🍽 🛆M 🗙 🛜 🗙 🛅 🖵

◈◈◈ ▼▼▼▼ **Hotel Granduca Austin** H

(512) 306-6400. **$209-$399.** 320 S Capital of Texas Hwy 78746. Jct SR 360 and Bee Cave Rd, just n. Int corridors. **Pets:** Accepted.

SAVE 🍽 🛆M 🗙 🛜 🗙 🛅 🖵

◈◈◈ ▼▼▼▼ **Hyatt House Austin/Arboretum** H

(512) 342-8080. **$79-$425.** 10001 N Capital of Texas Hwy 78759. US 183, N Capital of Texas Hwy (SR 360), just e. Int corridors. **Pets:** $75 one-time fee/room. Service with restrictions.

SAVE 🕽 🛜 🗙 🛅 🖵

◈◈◈ ▼▼▼▼ **Hyatt Place Austin/Arboretum** H

(512) 231-8491. **$119-$309.** 3612 Tudor Blvd 78759. Jct US 183 and N Capital of Texas Hwy (SR 360), 1 blk e to Stonelake Blvd, 0.5 mi s to Tudor Blvd, then just e. Int corridors. **Pets:** Accepted.

SAVE 🕽 🛜 🗙 🛅 🖵

◈◈◈ ▼▼▼▼ **Hyatt Place Austin-North Central** H

(512) 323-2121. **$79-$219.** 7522 N I-35 78752. I-35 exit 240A; on west frontage road. Int corridors. **Pets:** Accepted.

SAVE 🛆M 🕽 🛜 🗙 🛅 🖵

◈◈◈ ▼▼▼▼ **Hyatt Regency Austin** H

(512) 477-1234. **$149-$459.** 208 Barton Springs Rd 78704. At south end of Congress Avenue Bridge; on south bank of Town Lake. Int corridors. **Pets:** Accepted.

SAVE ECO ⊟ 🍽 🛆M 🕽 🗙 🛜 🗙 🛅 🖵

◈◈◈ ▼▼▼▼ **Hyatt Regency Lost Pines Resort and Spa** H

(512) 308-1234. **$169-$639, 3 day notice.** 575 Hyatt Lost Pines Rd 78612. SR 71, 13 mi e of Austin-Bergstrom International Airport; 9 mi w of Bastrop. Int corridors. **Pets:** Accepted.

SAVE ECO 🍽 🛆M 🕽 🗙 🛜 🗙 🛅 🖵

◈◈◈ ▼▼▼▼ **InterContinental Stephen F. Austin Hotel** H

(512) 457-8800. **$199-$699, 3 day notice.** 701 Congress Ave 78701. Northeast corner of 7th St and Congress Ave. Int corridors.

Pets: Accepted. SAVE ⊟ 🍽 🛆M 🕽 🗙 🕾 🗙 🛅 🖵

▲▲▲ ▼▼▼ Kimpton Hotel Van Zandt H
(512) 542-5300. **Call for rates.** 605 Davis St 78701. I-35 exit 234A southbound; exit 234B northbound, jct Driskill and Davis sts, just s. Int corridors. **Pets:** Accepted. SAVE ⛥ 🖧 🖎 🗎 💻

▼▼▼ La Quinta Inn & Suites Austin Airport H
(512) 386-6800. **$75-$317.** 7625 E Ben White Blvd 78741. I-35 exit 230B (Ben White Blvd/SR 71), 8.8 mi e. Int corridors. **Pets:** Accepted. 🏊 🛜 🖎 🗎 💻

▼▼▼ La Quinta Inn & Suites Austin Mopac North H
(512) 832-2121. **$97-$317.** 11901 N Mo-Pac Expwy 78759. US 183, 2 mi n on Loop 1 (Mo-Pac Expwy) exit Duval Rd. Int corridors. **Pets:** Accepted. ⛥ 👬 🏊 🛜 🖎 🗎 💻

▲▲▲ ▼▼▼ La Quinta Inn & Suites Austin NW/Lakeline Mall H
(512) 568-3538. **$100-$279.** 10701 Lakeline Mall Dr 78717. Jct US 183 and Lakeline Dr, 0.5 mi e, then just s on Lake Creek Dr. Int corridors. **Pets:** Accepted. SAVE ⛥ 👬 🏊 🛜 🖎 🗎 💻

▼▼▼ La Quinta Inn & Suites Austin Southwest at Mopac H
(512) 899-3000. **$97-$372.** 4525 S Gaines Ranch Loop 78735. Jct Loop 1 (Mo-Pac Expwy), US 290 and SR 71 E; on southbound frontage road. Int corridors. **Pets:** Accepted. ⛥ 👬 🏊 🛜 🖎 🗎 💻

▼▼▼ La Quinta Inn & Suites Round Rock South H
(512) 246-2800. **$75-$251.** 150 Parker Dr 78728. I-35 exit 250; on west frontage road. Int corridors. **Pets:** Accepted. 🏊 🛜 🖎 🗎 💻

▲▲▲ ▼▼▼ Omni Austin Hotel Downtown H 🐾
(512) 476-3700. **Call for rates.** 700 San Jacinto Blvd 78701. At 8th St and San Jacinto Blvd. Int corridors. **Pets:** Small. $50 deposit/room. Service with restrictions, crate. SAVE ⛥ 👬 🏊 🖧 🖎 🗎 💻

▼▼▼ Omni Austin Hotel Southpark H
(512) 448-2222. **$139-$599.** 4140 Governor's Row 78744. I-35 exit 230B (Ben White Blvd/SR 71) southbound; exit 230 northbound; on east frontage road. Int corridors. **Pets:** Accepted. ⛥ 👬 🏊 🗶 🖧 🖎 🗎 💻

▼▼▼ Omni Barton Creek Resort & Spa H
(512) 329-4000. **Call for rates.** 8212 Barton Club Dr 78735. Jct Capital of Texas Hwy (SR 360) and FM 2244 (Bee Caves Rd), 1 mi w to Barton Creek Blvd, then 1.7 mi s. Int corridors. **Pets:** Accepted. ECO ⛥ 🏊 🗶 🖧 🖎 🗎 💻

▲▲▲ ▼▼▼ Quality Inn & Suites Airport H
(512) 385-1000. **$90-$400.** 2751 Hwy 71 E 78617. On SR 71, 0.5 mi e of airport. Int corridors. **Pets:** Small. $20 daily fee/pet. Designated rooms, service with restrictions, supervision. SAVE ⛥ 👬 🛜 🖎 🗎 💻

▼▼▼ Radisson Hotel & Suites Downtown-Austin H
(512) 478-9611. **$159-$699.** 111 E Cesar Chavez St 78701. At 1st St and Congress Ave. Int corridors. **Pets:** Accepted. ⛥ 🏊 🛜 🖎 🗎 💻

▲▲▲ ▼▼ Red Roof PLUS+ Austin South H
(512) 448-0091. **$69-$260.** 4701 S IH-35 78744. I-35 exit 230B (Ben White Blvd/SR 71) southbound; exit 229 (Stassney Rd) northbound; on northbound frontage road. Int corridors. **Pets:** Accepted. SAVE ⛥ 🏊 🛜 🖎 🗎 💻

▲▲▲ ▼▼▼ Renaissance Austin Hotel H
(512) 343-2626. **$160-$305.** 9721 Arboretum Blvd 78759. Jct US 183 and N Capital of Texas Hwy (SR 360); southwest corner. Int corridors. **Pets:** Accepted. SAVE ⛥ 👬 🏊 🗶 🖧 🖎 🗎 💻

▲▲▲ ▼▼▼ Residence Inn by Marriott Austin/Downtown/ Convention Center H
(512) 236-8008. **$179-$352.** 300 E 4th St 78701. Between Trinity St and San Jacinto Blvd. Int corridors. **Pets:** Accepted. SAVE ⛥ 🏊 🛜 🖎 🗎 💻

▼▼▼ Residence Inn by Marriott-Austin North/Parmer Lane H
(512) 977-0544. **$128-$218.** 12401 N Lamar Blvd 78753. I-35 exit 245, just w. Int corridors. **Pets:** Accepted. 👬 🏊 🛜 🖎 🗎 💻

▼▼▼ Residence Inn by Marriott Austin South H
(512) 912-1100. **$118-$193.** 4537 S I-35 78744. I-35 exit 229 (Stassney Rd) southbound; exit 230 (Ben White Blvd/SR 71) northbound; on northbound frontage road. Int corridors. **Pets:** Accepted. 🏊 🛜 🖎 🗎 💻

▼▼▼ Residence Inn by Marriott Austin-University Area H
(512) 469-7842. **$152-$250.** 1200 Barbara Jordan Blvd 78723. Just e of N I-35 (Frontage Rd). Int corridors. **Pets:** Accepted. 👬 🛜 🖎 🗎 💻

▲▲▲ ▼▼▼ Sheraton Austin at the Capitol H
(512) 478-1111. **$119-$399.** 701 E 11th St 78701. I-35 exit 234B, 0.3 mi w. Int corridors. **Pets:** Accepted. SAVE ⛥ 🏊 🖧 🖎 🗎 💻

▼▼▼ Sleep Inn & Suites Northeast H
(512) 524-5400. **$99-$309.** 8410 US 290 E 78724. Just n of US 290 E. Int corridors. **Pets:** Medium, other species. $25 daily fee/pet. Service with restrictions, crate. 👬 🛜 🖎 🗎 💻

▼▼▼ Staybridge Suites Austin Airport H
(512) 389-9767. **Call for rates.** 1611 Airport Commerce Dr 78741. Jct SR 71 (E Ben White Blvd) and Riverside Dr, just n. Int corridors. **Pets:** Accepted. ⛥ 👬 🏊 🛜 🖎 🗎 💻

▼▼▼ Staybridge Suites Austin Arboretum H
(512) 349-0888. **$129-$169.** 10201 Stonelake 78759. Jct N Capital of Texas Hwy (SR 360) and Stonelake Blvd, 1 blk n. Int corridors. **Pets:** Accepted. 👬 🏊 🛜 🖎 🗎 💻

▼▼▼ Staybridge Suites Austin Northwest H
(512) 336-7829. **Call for rates.** 13087 Hwy 183 N 78750. US 183 N exit Anderson Mill Rd, just n of exit on east frontage road; south of Anderson Mill Rd. Int corridors. **Pets:** Accepted. 👬 🏊 🛜 🖎 🗎 💻

▲▲▲ ▼▼▼ W Austin H
(512) 542-3600. **$199-$799.** 200 Lavaca St 78701. At Lavaca and 2nd sts. Int corridors. **Pets:** Accepted. SAVE ⭐ ⛥ 👬 🏊 🗶 🛜 🖎 🗎 💻

▲▲▲ ▼▼▼ Westin Austin at the Domain H
(512) 832-4197. **$199-$999.** 11301 Domain Dr 78758. Jct Braker Ln and Burnet Rd; on northwest corner; in The Domain. Int corridors. **Pets:** Accepted. SAVE ⛥ 👬 🏊 🖧 🖎 🗎 💻

▲▲▲ ▼▼▼ The Westin Austin Downtown H 🐾
(512) 391-2333. **$249-$1999.** 310 E 5th St 78701. Corner of San Jacinto Blvd and E 5th St. Int corridors. **Pets:** Dogs only. Supervision. SAVE ⛥ 👬 🗶 🖧 🖎 🗎 💻

▼▼▼ Wyndham Garden Hotel H
(512) 448-2444. **$89-$279.** 3401 I-35 S 78741. I-35 exit 231 (Woodward St) southbound; exit 230 (Ben White Blvd/SR 71) northbound; on northbound frontage road. Ext/int corridors. **Pets:** Accepted. ⛥ 👬 🏊 🛜 🖎 🗎 💻

BASTROP *(Restaurants p. 625)*

▼▼▼ Comfort Suites **H**

(512) 321-3377. **$90-$230.** 505 Agnes St 78602. SR 71 exit Hasler Blvd; on south frontage road. Int corridors. **Pets:** Medium, dogs only. $35 one-time fee/pet. Designated rooms, service with restrictions, supervision. 〔&M〕〔⤳〕〔奈〕〔✕〕〔🛢〕〔🖥〕

BAY CITY

▼▼▼ Comfort Suites **H**

(979) 245-9300. **$99-$130.** 5100 7th St 77414. On SR 35 (7th St), 2.2 mi e. Int corridors. **Pets:** Small, other species. $25 daily fee/pet. Designated rooms, service with restrictions, crate. 〔⤳〕〔奈〕〔✕〕〔🛢〕〔🖥〕

▼▼▼ La Quinta Inn & Suites Bay City **H**

(979) 323-9095. **$91-$196.** 5300 7th St 77414. On SR 35 (7th St), 3 mi e of downtown. Int corridors. **Pets:** Accepted.
〔&M〕〔⤳〕〔奈〕〔✕〕〔🛢〕〔🖥〕

BAYTOWN

▼▼▼ Comfort Suites **H**

(281) 421-9764. **$100-$180.** 7209 Garth Rd 77521. I-10 exit 792 (Garth Rd), just n. Int corridors. **Pets:** Accepted.
〔&M〕〔⤳〕〔奈〕〔✕〕〔🛢〕〔🖥〕

▼▼ La Quinta Inn & Suites Baytown East **H**

(281) 421-5566. **$79-$235.** 5215 I-10 E 77521. I-10 exit 792 (Garth Rd), just ne. Int corridors. **Pets:** Accepted. 〔&M〕〔⤳〕〔奈〕〔🛢〕〔🖥〕

BEAUMONT

▼▼▼ Holiday Inn Hotel & Suites Beaumont Plaza **H**

(409) 842-5995. **Call for rates.** 3950 I-10 S 77705. I-10 exit 848 (Walden Rd), just n. Int corridors. **Pets:** $50 daily fee/pet. Service with restrictions, supervision. 〔🍴〕〔&M〕〔⤳〕〔奈〕〔✕〕〔🛢〕〔🖥〕

▼▼▼ Homewood Suites by Hilton **H**

(409) 842-9990. **$129-$169.** 3745 IH-10 S 77705. I-10 exit 848 (Walden Rd); on eastbound frontage road. Int corridors. **Pets:** Accepted.
〔⊲〕〔&M〕〔⤳〕〔奈〕〔🛢〕〔🖥〕

BEE CAVE

▲▲▲ ▼▼▼ Sonesta Bee Cave Austin **H**

(512) 430-1125. **$109-$299.** 12525 Bee Cave Pkwy 78738. 0.5 mi n of jct US 71 and Bee Cave Rd. Int corridors. **Pets:** Medium. $100 one-time fee/room. Designated rooms, service with restrictions, crate.
〔SAVE〕〔🍴〕〔&M〕〔奈〕〔✕〕〔🛢〕〔🖥〕

BEEVILLE

▼▼▼ Holiday Inn Express Hotel & Suites Beeville **H**

(361) 358-7300. **Call for rates.** 2199 US 59 78102. Just n of US 181. Int corridors. **Pets:** Accepted. 〔🍴〕〔&M〕〔奈〕〔✕〕

BENBROOK

▼ Motel 6 #4051 **H**

(817) 249-8885. **Call for rates.** 8601 Benbrook Blvd (Hwy 377 S) 76126. I-20 exit 429A, 0.7 mi s. Int corridors. **Pets:** Accepted.
〔&M〕〔⤳〕〔奈〕〔🛢〕

BIG SPRING

▼▼▼ Holiday Inn Express **H**

(432) 263-5400. **Call for rates.** 1109 N Aylesford St 79720. I-20 exit 177, just s. Int corridors. **Pets:** Medium. $30 one-time fee/room. Service with restrictions, supervision. 〔&M〕〔⤳〕〔奈〕〔✕〕〔🛢〕〔🖥〕

▼▼▼ La Quinta Inn & Suites Big Spring **H**

(432) 264-0222. **$104-$213.** 1102 I-20 W 79720. I-20 exit 177, just nw. Int corridors. **Pets:** Accepted. 〔&M〕〔⤳〕〔奈〕〔✕〕〔🛢〕〔🖥〕

BOERNE

▲▲▲ ▼▼▼ Best Western Plus Boerne Inn & Suites **H**

(830) 249-1212. **$99-$159.** 36756 IH-10 W 78006. I-10 exit 539 (Johns Rd) westbound; exit 540 (Bandera Rd) eastbound, U-turn; on westbound frontage road. Int corridors. **Pets:** Accepted.
〔SAVE〕〔&M〕〔⤳〕〔奈〕〔✕〕〔🛢〕〔🖥〕

▼▼▼ Comfort Inn & Suites **H**

(830) 249-6800. **$89-$219.** 35000 I-10 W 78006. I-10 exit 540 (SR 46), just e to Norris Ln, then just s. Int corridors. **Pets:** Small. $25 one-time fee/pet. Designated rooms, service with restrictions, supervision.
〔⤳〕〔奈〕〔✕〕〔🛢〕〔🖥〕

▼▼▼ Fairfield Inn & Suites by Marriott San Antonio Boerne **H**

(830) 368-4167. **$93-$172.** 6 Cascade Caverns Rd 78006. I-10 exit 543 (Cascade Caverns Rd), just off westbound access road. Int corridors.
Pets: Accepted. 〔⤳〕〔奈〕〔✕〕〔🛢〕〔🖥〕

▼▼ Motel 6 **M**

(830) 249-3562. **Call for rates.** 1228 S Main St 78006. Jct US 83 and SR 46. Int corridors. **Pets:** Accepted. 〔奈〕〔✕〕〔🛢〕

BORGER

▲▲▲ ▼▼▼ Best Western Borger Inn **H**

(806) 274-7050. **$105-$155.** 206 S Cedar St 79007. Jct SR 136 and 207, just n. Int corridors. **Pets:** $20 daily fee/pet. Designated rooms, service with restrictions. 〔SAVE〕〔⤳〕〔奈〕〔🛢〕〔🖥〕

▼▼▼ Borger Ambassador Inn **H**

(806) 273-6000. **$99-$155.** 900 E 3rd St 79007. Corner of SR 152 and Florida St. Int corridors. **Pets:** Accepted.
〔🍴〕〔&M〕〔⤳〕〔✕〕〔奈〕〔✕〕〔🛢〕〔🖥〕

▼▼▼ Holiday Inn Express & Suites **H**

(806) 274-3333. **$99-$199.** 1351 W Wilson St 79007. Jct SR 136/152/ 207, 0.5 mi w. Int corridors. **Pets:** Accepted.
〔&M〕〔⤳〕〔奈〕〔✕〕〔🛢〕〔🖥〕

BOWIE

▲▲▲ ▼▼▼ Best Western Bowie Inn & Suites **H**

(940) 872-9595. **$90-$145.** 900 W US Hwy 287 S 76230. Just s of jct SR 59. Int corridors. **Pets:** Accepted.
〔SAVE〕〔🍴〕〔&M〕〔⤳〕〔奈〕〔✕〕〔🛢〕〔🖥〕

BRADY

▲▲▲ ▼▼▼ Best Western Brady Inn **H**

(325) 597-3997. **$100-$110.** 2200 S Bridge St 76825. 1.1 mi s on US 87/377. Ext corridors. **Pets:** Small. $10 daily fee/pet. Designated rooms, service with restrictions, supervision. 〔SAVE〕〔⤳〕〔奈〕〔✕〕〔🛢〕〔🖥〕

BRENHAM

▲▲▲ ▼▼▼ Best Western Inn of Brenham **H**

(979) 251-7791. **$90-$160.** 1503 Hwy 290 E 77833. Jct SR 36 and US 290, 1.3 mi e. Ext corridors. **Pets:** Large. $50 deposit/room, $20 daily fee/room. Designated rooms, service with restrictions, crate.
〔SAVE〕〔🍴〕〔⤳〕〔奈〕〔🛢〕〔🖥〕

▼▼ Comfort Suites **H**

(979) 421-8100. **$79-$165.** 2350 S Day St 77833. US 290 exit SR 36 S, just n on Business Rt SR 36. Int corridors. **Pets:** Accepted.
〔&M〕〔⤳〕〔奈〕〔✕〕〔🛢〕〔🖥〕

BROOKSHIRE

▼▼▼ La Quinta Inn & Suites Brookshire **H**

(281) 375-8888. **$67-$207.** 721 FM 1489 77423. I-10 exit 731; on south frontage road. Int corridors. **Pets:** Accepted. 〔⤳〕〔奈〕〔✕〕〔🛢〕〔🖥〕

BROWNFIELD

Best Western Caprock Inn ⛨
(806) 637-9471. $98-$125. 321 Lubbock Rd 79316. Jct US 385 and 82, just n. Ext corridors. Pets: Other species. $15 daily fee/pet. Service with restrictions. [icons]

BROWNSVILLE

La Quinta Inn & Suites Brownsville North ⛨
(956) 350-2118. $97-$181. 5051 North Expwy (US 77) 78520. US 77 exit Alton Gloor Rd southbound; exit Stillman Rd northbound U-turn; on southbound frontage road. Int corridors. Pets: Accepted.
[icons]

Residence Inn by Marriott Brownsville ⛨
(956) 350-8100. $76-$158. 3975 N Expwy 83 78520. US 77 and 83 exit Ruben Torres Sr Blvd (FM 802). Int corridors. Pets: Accepted.
[icons]

Staybridge Suites ⛨
(956) 504-9500. Call for rates. 2900 Pablo Kisel Blvd 78526. US 77 and 83 exit Ruben Torres Sr Blvd (FM 802), 0.8 mi n on frontage road to Pablo Kisel Blvd, then 0.5 mi e. Int corridors. Pets: Accepted.
[icons]

BRYAN

Best Western Premier Bryan College Station ⛨ ☀
(979) 731-5300. $104-$355. 1920 Austins Colony Pkwy 77803. SR 6 exit Briarcrest Dr; just n on east frontage road. Int corridors. Pets: Medium. $20 daily fee/room. Designated rooms, service with restrictions, crate. [icons]

Candlewood Suites College Station ⛨
(979) 704-6198. Call for rates. 3021 Plaza Centre Ct 77802. 0.7 mi e of jct SR 6. Int corridors. Pets: Accepted.
[icons]

LaSalle Hotel ⛨
(979) 822-2000. $125-$152, 30 day notice. 120 S Main St 77803. SR 6 exit W William Joel Bryan Pkwy, 2.2 mi w to Main St, then 2 blks s. Int corridors. Pets: Accepted. [icons]

BUDA

Comfort Suites Buda-Austin South ⛨
(512) 295-8600. $109-$229. 15295 IH-35 #800 78610. I-35 exit 221; on east frontage road. Int corridors. Pets: Accepted.
[icons]

BURKBURNETT

Best Western Red River Inn ⛨
(940) 569-9707. $89-$139. 1008 Sheppard Rd 76354. I-44 exit 12, just e. Int corridors. Pets: $30 one-time fee/room. Service with restrictions, crate. [icons]

BURLESON

La Quinta Inn & Suites ⛨
(817) 447-6565. $67-$192. 225 E Alsbury Blvd 76028. I-35W exit 38 (E Alsbury Blvd), just e. Int corridors. Pets: Accepted.
[icons]

BURNET

Best Western Post Oak Inn Ⓜ
(512) 756-4747. $89-$163. 908 Buchanan Dr 78611. Jct US 281 and FM 29, 1 mi w. Ext corridors. Pets: Medium, other species. $15 daily fee/pet. Service with restrictions, crate.
[icons]

Comfort Inn & Suites ⛨
(512) 756-1789. $84-$204. 810 S Water St (US 281) 78611. Jct US 281 and FM 29, 0.5 mi s. Int corridors. Pets: Small. $10 daily fee/pet. Designated rooms, service with restrictions, supervision.
[icons]

Log Country Cove Ⓥ Ⓗ
(512) 756-9132. Call for rates. 617 Log Country Cove 78611. Jct FM 1431 and 2342, 2 mi n; Park Rd 4 and FM 2342, 3 mi s. Ext corridors. Pets: Accepted. [icons]

CAMERON

Budget Host Inn & Suites ⛨
(254) 605-0610. Call for rates. 102 Lafferty Ave 76520. US 77/190, 0.5 mi s. Int corridors. Pets: Medium. $25 daily fee/pet. Designated rooms, service with restrictions, supervision.
[icons]

CANTON

Best Western Canton Inn ⛨
(903) 567-6591. $90-$100. 2251 N Trade Days Blvd 75103. Jct I-20 and SR 19 exit 527. Ext corridors. Pets: Other species. $5 daily fee/pet. Service with restrictions, supervision.
[icons]

CANYON

Best Western Palo Duro Canyon Inn & Suites ⛨
(806) 655-1818. $90-$96. 2801 4th Ave 79015. I-27 exit 106, 1.6 mi w. Int corridors. Pets: Accepted. [icons]

Holiday Inn Express Hotel & Suites ⛨
(806) 655-4445. Call for rates. 2901 4th Ave 79015. I-27 exit 106, 1.5 mi w. Int corridors. Pets: Accepted.
[icons]

CARRIZO SPRINGS

Best Western Plus Carrizo Springs Inn & Suites ⛨
(830) 876-2500. $80-$100. 2474 N 1st St (US 83) 78834. Just n of US 83, 0.7 mi n of US 277. Int corridors. Pets: Accepted.
[icons]

CEDAR PARK

Candlewood Suites ⛨
(512) 986-4825. Call for rates. 1100 Cottonwood Creek Tr 78613. Jct SR 183A and CR 1431, 1 mi e. Int corridors. Pets: Accepted.
[icons]

La Quinta Inn & Suites Austin-Cedar Park ⛨
(512) 528-9300. $67-$262. 1010 E Whitestone Blvd 78613. Jct SR 183A and CR 1431; on southwest corner. Int corridors. Pets: Accepted.
[icons]

CENTER

Best Western Plus Classic Inn & Suites ⛨
(936) 591-0002. $70-$85. 210 Moffett Dr 75935. Jct US 96 and SR 87, just n. Int corridors. Pets: Accepted. [icons]

CHILDRESS

Days Inn Childress Ⓜ
(940) 937-0622. $50-$79. 2220 Ave F NW 79201. 1.8 mi w on US 287 from jct US 62/83. Int corridors. Pets: Accepted.
[icons]

Red Roof Inn Childress ⛨
(940) 937-6353. $89-$109. 1801 Ave F NW (Hwy 287) 79201. Jct US 62/83, just s. Ext corridors. Pets: Accepted. [icons]

Super 8 Childress **M**
(940) 937-8825. **$62-$82.** 411 Ave F NE (Hwy 287 S) 79201. Jct US 83/287, 1.5 mi e. Ext corridors. **Pets:** Accepted.

CLARENDON

Best Western Plus Red River Inn **H**
(806) 874-0160. **$109-$129.** 902 W 2nd St 79226. Jct US 287 and SR 70. Int corridors. **Pets:** Accepted.

CLEAR LAKE CITY

Candlewood Suites-Houston-Clear Lake **H**
(281) 461-3060. **Call for rates.** 2737 Bay Area Blvd 77058. I-45 exit 26 (Bay Area Blvd), 3.7 mi e. Int corridors. **Pets:** Accepted.

Residence Inn by Marriott Houston NASA/Clear Lake **H**
(281) 486-2424. **$110-$189.** 525 Bay Area Blvd 77058. I-45 exit 26 (Bay Area Blvd), 1.2 mi e. Ext/int corridors. **Pets:** Accepted.

CLEBURNE

Quality Inn **H**
(817) 641-4702. **$69-$109.** 2117 N Main St 76033. On SR 174, just s of jct US 67. Int corridors. **Pets:** Accepted.

CLEVELAND

Best Western Cleveland Inn & Suites **H**
(281) 659-2700. **$69-$139.** 708 US Hwy 59 S 77328. US 59 exit SR 105; northwest corner. Int corridors. **Pets:** Accepted.

Holiday Inn Express & Suites **H**
(281) 592-7500. **Call for rates.** 600 Hwy 59 S 77327. US 59 exit Cleveland/Conroe northbound; exit Cleveland southbound; on northbound frontage road. Int corridors. **Pets:** Accepted.

CLUTE

TownePlace Suites by Marriott **H**
(979) 388-9300. **$117-$176.** 1003 W Hwy 332 77531. On SR 288/332, just w of jct Business Rt SR 288. Int corridors. **Pets:** Accepted.

COLLEGE STATION

Aloft College Station **H**
(979) 704-6400. **$89-$499.** 1150 University Dr E 77840. SR 6 exit University Dr E/FM 60. Int corridors. **Pets:** Accepted.

Best Western Plus College Station Inn & Suites **H**
(979) 704-6444. **$100-$129.** 950 Arrington Rd 77845. 0.8 mi nw of jct SR 6 (Texas 6 Frontage Rd) and SR 40 (William D Fitch Pkwy). Int corridors. **Pets:** Accepted.

Hawthorn Suites by Wyndham **H**
(979) 695-9500. **$99-$169.** 1010 University Dr E 77840. SR 6 exit University Dr, 0.5 mi w. Int corridors. **Pets:** Accepted.

Hilton College Station & Conference Center **H**
(979) 693-7500. **$109-$229.** 801 University Dr E 77840. SR 6 exit University Dr, 1.1 mi w. Int corridors. **Pets:** Accepted.

Home2 Suites by Hilton College Station **H**
(979) 703-8288. **$129-$189.** 300 Texas Ave S 77840. Just n of jct SR 60. Int corridors. **Pets:** Medium. $125 one-time fee/room. Service with restrictions, crate.

Homewood Suites-College Station **H**
(979) 846-0400. **$119-$199.** 950 University Dr E 77840. Jct SR 6 and 60, 1.5 mi e. Int corridors. **Pets:** Accepted.

Hyatt Place College Station **H**
(979) 846-9800. **$99-$409.** 1100 University Dr E 77840. Jct University Dr and Texas Ave, 1 mi e. Int corridors. **Pets:** Accepted.

La Quinta Inn College Station **H**
(979) 696-7777. **$82-$262.** 607 Texas Ave 77840. Just s on jct SR 60 and 6 business route to Live Oak St, just e. Ext corridors. **Pets:** Accepted.

Manor Inn College Station **H**
(979) 764-9540. **Call for rates.** 2504 Texas Ave S 77840. 2.4 mi s of jct SR 60 (University Dr). Ext corridors. **Pets:** Accepted.

Residence Inn by Marriott College Station **H**
(979) 268-2200. **$134-$192.** 720 University Dr E 77840. Jct Texas Ave, 0.5 mi e. Int corridors. **Pets:** Accepted.

TownePlace Suites by Marriott **H**
(979) 260-8500. **$102-$177.** 1300 University Dr E 77840. SR 6 exit University Dr, 1 mi w. Ext corridors. **Pets:** Accepted.

CONROE

Baymont Inn & Suites-Conroe/Woodlands **H**
(936) 539-5100. **$69-$200.** 1506 Interstate 45 S 77304. I-45 exit 85 (Gladstell St) northbound; exit 84 (Frazier St) southbound. Int corridors. **Pets:** Accepted.

La Quinta Inn & Suites Conroe **H**
(936) 228-0790. **$97-$312.** 4006 Sprayberry Ln 77303. I-45 exit 91 (League Line Rd), just e. Int corridors. **Pets:** Accepted.

CORPUS CHRISTI

Best Western Corpus Christi **H**
(361) 883-5111. **$99-$399.** 300 N Shoreline Blvd 78401. Center of downtown. Int corridors. **Pets:** Large. $20 daily fee/room. Designated rooms, service with restrictions, supervision.

Best Western Padre Island **M**
(361) 949-2300. **$80-$249.** 14050 S Padre Island Dr 78418. On Park Rd 22. Ext corridors. **Pets:** Accepted.

Emerald Beach Hotel **H**
(361) 883-5731. **$119-$289.** 1102 S Shoreline Blvd 78401. 1.5 mi s on bay from downtown marina. Ext/int corridors. **Pets:** Large, other species. $100 one-time fee/room. Designated rooms, service with restrictions, supervision.

Homewood Suites by Hilton **H**
(361) 854-1331. **$109-$259.** 5201 Crosstown Expwy (SR 286) 78417. I-37 exit SR 358 E (Greenwood Dr), 0.6 mi e; on eastbound access road. Int corridors. **Pets:** Accepted.

▼▼▼ **La Quinta Inn & Suites Corpus Christi Airport** H
(361) 299-2600. **$79-$218.** 546 S Padre Island Dr 78405. SR 358 exit Old Brownsville Rd; on frontage road. Int corridors. **Pets:** Accepted.
🍴 🏃ᴹ ⇌ 🛜 ✕ 🛏 ▣

▼▼▼ **La Quinta Inn & Suites Northwest** H
(361) 241-4245. **$119-$273.** 10446 I-37 78410. I-37 exit 11A (McKinzie Rd); on northbound frontage road. Int corridors. **Pets:** Accepted.
🏃ᴹ 🛜 ✕ 🛏 ▣

▼▼▼ **La Quinta Inn Corpus Christi South** H
(361) 991-5730. **$67-$312.** 6225 S Padre Island Dr 78412. SR 358 exit Airline Rd. Ext corridors. **Pets:** Accepted. ⇌ 🛜 🛏 ▣

🌀 ▼▼▼ **Omni Corpus Christi Hotel** H 🐾
(361) 887-1600. **Call for rates.** 900 N Shoreline Blvd 78401. Downtown. Int corridors. **Pets:** Small. $50 one-time fee/room. Service with restrictions, supervision. SAVE 🍴 🏃ᴹ ⇌ ✕ 🆘 ✕ 🛏 ▣

▼▼▼ **Residence Inn by Marriott** H
(361) 985-1113. **$123-$213.** 5229 Blanche Moore Dr 78411. SR 358 E exit Everhart Rd, 0.3 mi e. Int corridors. **Pets:** Accepted.
⇌ 🛜 ✕ 🛏 ▣

▼▼▼ **Staybridge Suites** H
(361) 857-7766. **Call for rates.** 5201 Oakhurst Dr 78411. SR 358 exit Weber St. Int corridors. **Pets:** Accepted. 🏃ᴹ 🛜 ✕ 🛏 ▣

🌀 ▼▼▼ **Surfside Condominiums** CO
(361) 949-8128. **$140-$265, 3 day notice.** 15005 Windward Dr 78418. Park Rd 22 on N Padre Island Dr, jct Whitecap Blvd, 0.6 mi n to Windward Dr, then 0.8 mi w. Ext corridors. **Pets:** Accepted.
SAVE ⇌ 🛜 ✕ 🛏 ▣

▼▼▼ **TownePlace Suites by Marriott** H
(361) 991-2011. **$79-$152.** 6701 S Padre Island Dr 78412. SR 358 exit Airline Rd; on southeast access road. Int corridors. **Pets:** Accepted.
🏃ᴹ 🛜 ✕ 🛏 ▣

COTULLA
🌀 ▼▼▼ **Cowboy Inn** H
(830) 879-3100. **$50-$100.** 145 W FM 468 78014. I-35 exit 57 (FM 468), just w. Ext/int corridors. **Pets:** Accepted.
SAVE ⇌ 🛜 ✕ 🛏 ▣

▼▼▼ **La Quinta Inn & Suites** H
(830) 879-2200. **$67-$372.** 677 N Baylor St 78014. I-35 exit 67 (SR 468), just off northbound frontage road. Int corridors. **Pets:** Accepted.
🍴 🏃ᴹ 🛜 ✕ 🛏 ▣

▼▼ **Microtel Inn & Suites by Wyndham** H
(830) 483-4860. **$64-$85.** 499 I-35 N 78014. I-35 exit 66, just off southbound frontage road. Int corridors. **Pets:** Accepted.
🏃ᴹ 🛜 ✕ 🛏 ▣

CRESSON
🌀 ▼▼ **Scottish Inns** H
(817) 396-4480. **Call for rates.** 9120 E Hwy 377 76035. 0.4 mi s of jct US 377 and SR 171. Int corridors. **Pets:** Medium. $15 daily fee/pet. Designated rooms, no service, supervision.
SAVE 🍴 ⇌ 🛜 🛏 ▣

DALHART
🌀 ▼▼ **Best Western Nursanickel Hotel** H 🐾
(806) 244-5637. **$95-$199.** 102 Scott Ave (Hwy 87 S) 79022. Just s of jct US 54 and 87. Ext corridors. **Pets:** $10 daily fee/pet. Service with restrictions, supervision. SAVE ⇌ 🛜 🛏 ▣

🌀 ▼▼▼ **Super 8 Dalhart** M
(806) 249-8526. **$60-$65.** 403 Tanglewood Rd (Hwy 54 E) 79022. Jct US 87 and 54, 0.5 mi e. Int corridors. **Pets:** Medium. $50 deposit/pet. Designated rooms, supervision. SAVE 🛜 🛏 ▣

DALLAS *(Restaurants p. 625)*
🌀 ▼▼▼ **Aloft Downtown Dallas** H
(214) 761-0000. **$149-$399.** 1033 Young St 75202. Northeast corner of Griffin and Young sts. Int corridors. **Pets:** Accepted.
SAVE 🚪 🍴 ⇌ 🛜 ✕ 🛏 ▣

🌀 ▼▼▼ **Candlewood Suites Dallas Market Center** H
(214) 631-3333. **$99-$134.** 7930 N Stemmons Frwy 75247. I-35 exit 433B (Mockingbird Ln); on northbound frontage road. Int corridors. **Pets:** Large. $10 daily fee/pet. Service with restrictions.
SAVE ⇌ 🛜 ✕ 🛏 ▣

▼▼▼ **Candlewood Suites Dallas Park Central** H
(972) 669-9606. **Call for rates.** 12525 Greenville Ave 75243. I-635 exit 18A (Greenville Ave), just n, then just w on Amberton Pkwy. Int corridors. **Pets:** Accepted. 🏃ᴹ 🛜 🛏 ▣

🌀 ▼▼▼ **Comfort Inn & Suites Market Center** H
(214) 461-2677. **$89-$189.** 7138 N Stemmons Frwy 75247. I-35E exit 433B (Mockingbird Ln) northbound; exit 432B (Commonwealth Dr) southbound, turn under freeway, 0.7 mi on north access road. Int corridors. **Pets:** Other species. $20 daily fee/pet. Service with restrictions, supervision. SAVE 🍴 🛜 ✕ 🛏 ▣

🌀 ▼▼▼ **Embassy Suites by Hilton Hotel-Dallas/Love Field** H
(214) 357-4500. **Call for rates.** 3880 W Northwest Hwy 75220. Just se of jct Northwest Hwy (Loop 12) and Marsh Ln. Int corridors. **Pets:** Medium, dogs only. $50 one-time fee/room. Service with restrictions, crate. SAVE 🍴 ⇌ 🆘 🛏 ▣

🌀 ▼▼▼▼ **The Fairmont Dallas** H
(214) 720-2020. **Call for rates.** 1717 N Akard St 75201. Corner of Ross Ave and N Akard St. Int corridors. **Pets:** Accepted.
SAVE ECO 🚪 🍴 ⇌ 🆘 ✕ ▣

🌀 ▼▼▼▼ **The Highland Dallas, Curio Collection by Hilton** H 🐾
(214) 520-7969. **$129-$269.** 5300 E Mockingbird Ln 75206. US 75 exit 3 (Mockingbird Ln); on southeast corner. Int corridors. **Pets:** Other species. Service with restrictions.
SAVE ECO 🚪 🍴 ⇌ ✕ 🛜 ✕ ▣

▼▼▼ **Holiday Inn Dallas Market Center** H
(214) 219-3333. **Call for rates.** 4500 Harry Hines Blvd 75219. I-35E exit 430B (Market Center Blvd), just e. Int corridors. **Pets:** Accepted.
🍴 🏃ᴹ ⇌ 🛜 ✕ 🛏 ▣

▼▼▼ **Homewood Suites by Hilton - Dallas Park Central** H
(972) 437-6966. **$99-$189.** 9169 Markville Dr 75243. I-635 exit 18A (Greenville Ave S), just s, then just e. Int corridors. **Pets:** Accepted.
🍴 ⇌ 🛜 🛏 ▣

▼▼▼ **Homewood Suites Dallas Market Center** H
(214) 819-9700. **$109-$229.** 2747 N Stemmons Frwy 75207. I-35E exit 432A (Inwood Rd), just s. Int corridors. **Pets:** Medium, other species. $125 one-time fee/room. Service with restrictions, crate.
🏃ᴹ ⇌ 🛜 ✕ 🛏 ▣

▼▼▼▼ **The Hotel Crescent Court** H
(214) 871-3200. **$300-$5000.** 400 Crescent Ct 75201. Corner of Crescent Ct and McKinney Ave; uptown. Int corridors. **Pets:** Accepted.
🍴 ⇌ ✕ 🛜 ✕ ▣

▼▼▼ **Hotel Indigo Dallas Downtown** H
(214) 741-7700. **Call for rates.** 1933 Main St 75201. Jct Main and Harwood sts; on northwest corner. Int corridors. **Pets:** Accepted.
🛏 📶 ✕ 🅴 💻

◆◆◆ ▼▼▼▼ **Hotel St. Germain** CI
(214) 871-2516. **Call for rates.** 2516 Maple Ave 75201. I-35 exit 430A (Oak Lawn Ave), 0.5 mi e, then 1 mi s. Int corridors. **Pets:** Accepted.
SAVE ❙❙ 📶 ✕ 🅴

◆◆◆ ▼▼▼▼ **Hotel ZaZa** H
(214) 468-8399. **Call for rates.** 2332 Leonard St 75201. Jct Maple Ave/Routh St and McKinney Ave; southeast corner. Ext/int corridors.
Pets: Accepted. SAVE ◐ ❙❙ ➢ ✕ 📶 ✕ 🅴 💻

◆◆◆ ▼▼▼ **Hyatt House Dallas/Lincoln Park** H
(214) 696-1555. **$89-$299.** 8221 N Central Expwy 75225. US 75 exit 5A southbound; exit 4B northbound, just w on Caruth Haven to Lincoln Pl, then just n. Int corridors. **Pets:** Accepted.
SAVE ⬛M ➢ 📶 ✕ 🅴 💻

◆◆◆ ▼▼▼ **Hyatt House Dallas/Uptown** H
(214) 965-9990. **$89-$299.** 2914 Harry Hines Blvd 75201. I-35 exit 430A (Oak Lawn Ave), just n to Harry Hines Blvd, then 0.6 mi s. Int corridors. **Pets:** Accepted. SAVE ⬛M ➢ 📶 ✕ 🅴 💻

◆◆◆ ▼▼▼▼ **Hyatt Place Dallas-North/by the Galleria** H
(972) 716-2001. **$89-$249.** 5229 Spring Valley Rd 75254. Jct Dallas North Tollway, just e. Int corridors. **Pets:** Accepted.
SAVE ❙❙ ➢ 📶 ✕ 🅴 💻

◆◆◆ ▼▼▼▼ **Hyatt Place Dallas/Park Central** H
(972) 458-1224. **$69-$179.** 12411 N Central Expwy 75243. US 75 exit 8 (Coit Rd) southbound; exit 8B northbound, just e on Churchill Way; on southbound access road. Int corridors. **Pets:** Accepted.
SAVE ❙❙ ➢ 📶 ✕ 🅴 💻

◆◆◆ ▼▼▼▼ **Hyatt Regency Dallas at Reunion** H ❖
(214) 651-1234. **$99-$499.** 300 Reunion Blvd 75207. I-35E and US 77 exit Reunion Blvd, just e; I-30 exit Commerce St eastbound, just n. Int corridors. **Pets:** Medium. $100 daily fee/room. Designated rooms.
SAVE ECO ◐ ❙❙ ➢

◆◆◆ ▼▼▼▼ **The Joule** H
(214) 748-1300. **$269-$599.** 1530 Main St 75201. Between Akard and Ervay sts; center. Int corridors. **Pets:** Accepted. SAVE ❙❙ 📶 ✕

▼▼ ◆ **La Quinta Inn & Suites Dallas North Central** H
(214) 361-8200. **$86-$257.** 10001 N Central Expwy 75231. US 75 exit 6 (Walnut Hill Ln/Meadow Rd) northbound, 0.5 mi n to Meadow Rd, then U-turn under highway; exit 7 (Royal St/Meadow Rd) southbound, 1 mi s on feeder. Int corridors. **Pets:** Accepted.
❙❙ ⬛M ➢ 📶 ✕ 🅴 💻

◆◆◆ ▼▼▼▼ **Le Meridien Dallas by the Galleria** H
(972) 503-8700. **$179-$279.** 13402 Noel Rd 75240. Dallas Pkwy exit Alpha Rd, just e to Noel Rd, then just s. Int corridors. **Pets:** Accepted.
SAVE ❙❙ ➢ 📶 ✕ 🅴

◆◆◆ ▼▼▼▼ **Le Méridien Dallas, The Stoneleigh** H
(214) 871-7111. **$209-$499, 3 day notice.** 2927 Maple Ave 75201. I-35E exit 430A (Oak Lawn Ave), 0.5 mi e, then 1.2 mi s. Int corridors.
Pets: Accepted. SAVE ❙❙ ◉ ✕

◆◆◆ ▼▼▼▼ **Magnolia Hotel Dallas Downtown** H
(214) 915-6500. **$139-$359.** 1401 Commerce St 75201. Corner of Commerce and Akard sts. Int corridors. **Pets:** Accepted.
SAVE ❙❙ 📶 ✕ 🅴 💻

◆◆◆ ▼▼▼▼ **Magnolia Hotel Dallas Park Cities** H
(214) 750-6060. **Call for rates.** 6070 N Central Expwy 75206. US 75 exit 3 (Mockingbird Ln); on northbound frontage road. Int corridors.
Pets: Accepted. SAVE ❙❙ ➢ 📶 ✕ 🅴 💻

◆◆◆ ▼▼▼▼ **MCM Elegante Hotel & Suites** H
(214) 351-4477. **$99-$139, 7 day notice.** 2330 W Northwest Hwy 75220. I-35E exit 436, just e. Ext/int corridors. **Pets:** Dogs only. $75 one-time fee/room. Service with restrictions, supervision.
SAVE ❙❙ ➢ 📶 ✕ 🅴 💻

▼▼▼ **NYLO Dallas South Side** H
(214) 421-1080. **$146-$471.** 1325 S Lamar St 75215. I-30 exit 45B (Lamar St) eastbound, just s; exit 45 (Ervay St) westbound, continue through Griffin St to Akard St, just s to Bellview St, then just w. Int corridors. **Pets:** $50 one-time fee/pet. Service with restrictions.
◐ ❙❙ 📶 💻

▼▼▼ **Residence Inn by Marriott Dallas Central Expressway** H
(214) 750-8220. **$106-$175.** 10333 N Central Expwy 75231. US 75 exit 6 (Walnut Hill Ln/Meadow Rd) northbound, 0.5 mi n to Meadow Rd, U-turn under highway; exit 7 (Royal St/Meadow Rd) southbound, 1 mi s on access road. Ext/int corridors. **Pets:** Accepted.
❙❙ ➢ 📶 ✕ 🅴 💻

▼▼▼ **Residence Inn by Marriott-Dallas Market Center** H
(214) 631-2472. **$123-$202.** 6950 N Stemmons Frwy 75247. I-35E exit 432B (Commonwealth Ln), 0.6 mi n on northbound frontage road. Ext/Int corridors. **Pets:** Accepted. ❙❙ ➢ 📶 ✕ 🅴 💻

▼▼▼▼ **The Ritz-Carlton, Dallas** H
(214) 922-0200. **Call for rates.** 2121 McKinney Ave 75201. SR 366 (Woodall Rodgers Frwy) exit Pearl St, just sw to Olive St, then just nw. Int corridors. **Pets:** Accepted. ◐ ❙❙ ⬛M ➢ ◉ ✕ 🅴

▼▼▼▼ **Rosewood Mansion on Turtle Creek** H ❖
(214) 559-2100. **$270-$5000, 7 day notice.** 2821 Turtle Creek Blvd 75219. 2 mi nw, entrance on Gillespie St, just e of jct Gillespie St and Oak Lawn Ave. Int corridors. **Pets:** Large. $100 one-time fee/pet. Service with restrictions, supervision. ❙❙ ➢ ✕ ◉ ✕ 🅴

▼▼▼ **Staybridge Suites Dallas/Addison** H
(972) 726-9990. **$89-$249.** 16060 N Dallas Pkwy 75248. Dallas North Tollway exit Keller Springs, just e to Knoll Tr, then just s. Int corridors.
Pets: Accepted. ⬛M ➢ 📶 ✕ 🅴 💻

◆◆◆ ▼▼▼▼ **Warwick Melrose Dallas** H
(214) 521-5151. **Call for rates.** 3015 Oak Lawn Ave 75219. I-35E exit 430 (Oak Lawn Ave), 0.8 mi n; entrance off Cedar Springs, just n. Int corridors. **Pets:** Accepted. SAVE ❙❙ ◉ ✕ 🅴 💻

◆◆◆ ▼▼▼▼ **W Dallas Victory Hotel & Residences** H
(214) 397-4100. **$229-$499.** 2440 Victory Park Ln 75219. Southwest corner of Olive and N Houston sts; uptown Dallas; across from American Airlines Center. Int corridors. **Pets:** Accepted.
SAVE ❙❙ ⬛M ➢ ◉ ✕

◆◆◆ ▼▼▼▼ **The Westin Galleria, Dallas** H ❖
(972) 934-9494. **Call for rates.** 13340 Dallas Pkwy 75240. Just n of jct I-635 and N Dallas Pkwy. Int corridors. **Pets:** Medium, dogs only. Service with restrictions, crate. SAVE ❙❙ ➢ ◉ ✕ 💻

▼▼▼ **Wyndham Dallas Suites Park Central** H
(972) 233-7600. **$79-$324.** 7800 Alpha Rd 75240. I-635 exit 19C (Coit Rd) eastbound; exit 19B (Coit Rd) westbound, just n, then just w. Int corridors. **Pets:** Accepted. ❙❙ ➢ 📶 ✕ 🅴 💻

DECATUR

Baymont Inn & Suites H
(940) 627-3338. **$46-$109.** 600 W Hale Ave 76234. Just s of jct Business Rt US 380 and 287. Int corridors. **Pets:** $18 daily fee/pet. Designated rooms, service with restrictions, supervision.

Best Western Decatur Inn M
(940) 627-5982. **$59-$65.** 1801 S Hwy 287 76234. 0.6 mi s of jct Business Rt US 380. Ext corridors. **Pets:** Accepted.

Econo Lodge Decatur H
(940) 627-6919. **$62-$72.** 1709 S Hwy 287 76234. 0.6 mi s of jct Business Rt US 380. Ext corridors. **Pets:** Accepted.

DEL RIO

Best Western Inn of Del Rio M
(830) 775-7511. **$80-$99.** 810 Veterans Blvd 78840. Between E 6th and E 7th sts. Ext corridors. **Pets:** Accepted.

Ramada H
(830) 775-1511. **$69-$199.** 2101 Veterans Blvd 78840. 1.8 mi nw on US 90, 277 and 377. Ext/int corridors. **Pets:** Accepted.

DENISON

Best Western Plus Texoma Hotel & Suites H
(903) 327-8883. **$94-$124.** 810 N US Hwy 75 75020. US 75 exit 69 (Morton Rd); on northbound frontage road. Int corridors. **Pets:** Small. $25 one-time fee/room. Service with restrictions, supervision.

DENTON

Homewood Suites by Hilton-Denton H
(940) 382-0420. **$149-$199.** 2907 Shoreline Dr 76210. I-35E exit 462 (State School Rd), just w to Unicorn Lake, 0.4 mi n, then just w. Int corridors. **Pets:** Accepted.

DENVER CITY

Best Western Plus Denver City Hotel & Suites H
(806) 305-0330. **$100-$115.** 830 E Broadway St 79323. Just w of jct SR 214. Int corridors. **Pets:** Accepted.

DESOTO

TownePlace Suites by Marriott Dallas DeSoto H
(972) 780-9300. **$92-$132.** 2700 Travis St 75115. US 67 exit Cockrell Hill; on northbound service road. Int corridors. **Pets:** Accepted.

DILLEY

Best Western Plus Dilley Inn & Suites H
(830) 326-3220. **$130-$160.** 16491 S I-35 78017. I-35 exit 85, on northbound access road. Ext corridors. **Pets:** Accepted.

DONNA

Victoria Palms Inn & Suites H
(956) 782-3200. **$69-$155.** 602 N Victoria Rd 78537. US 83 exit Victoria Rd. Ext corridors. **Pets:** Accepted.

DRIPPING SPRINGS

Sleep Inn & Suites H
(512) 858-2400. **$119-$350.** 2720 E US Hwy 290 78620. On US 290, 2.5 mi e. Int corridors. **Pets:** Accepted.

DUMAS

Best Western Windsor Inn H
(806) 935-9644. **$89-$99.** 1701 S Dumas Ave 79029. US 287, 2 mi s of US 87 and SR 152. Ext corridors. **Pets:** Dogs only. $20 deposit/room, $10 daily fee/pet. Designated rooms, service with restrictions, crate.

Days Inn & Suites H
(806) 935-2222. **$75-$93.** 1610 S Dumas Ave 79029. Just s on US 287. Int corridors. **Pets:** Dogs only. $25 daily fee/pet. Service with restrictions, supervision.

DUNCANVILLE

Holiday Inn Express & Suites H
(972) 298-8000. **Call for rates.** 1035 Hwy 67 E 75137. US 67 exit Wheatland; on southbound frontage road. Int corridors. **Pets:** Accepted.

EAGLE PASS

Motel 6 H
(830) 757-8100. **Call for rates.** 2338 E Main St 78852. Between Bibb And Veterans aves. Int corridors. **Pets:** Accepted.

TownePlace Suites by Marriott Eagle Pass H
(830) 757-0077. **$90-$144.** 2033 N Veterans Blvd 78852. 1.5 mi n on Loop 431 (US 277). Int corridors. **Pets:** Accepted.

EDINBURG

Best Western Plus Edinburg Inn & Suites H
(956) 318-0442. **$84-$199.** 2708 S Bus Hwy 281 78539. US 281 exit Canton Ave, 1 mi w to Business Rt US 281. Ext corridors. **Pets:** Accepted.

ELMENDORF

Days Inn & Suites Braunig Lake H
(210) 633-1833. **$75-$100.** 13800 IH-37 S 78112. I-37 exit 130 (Donop Rd/Southton Rd), on northbound access lane. Ext corridors. **Pets:** Large, other species. $7 daily fee/pet. Service with restrictions, crate.

EL PASO

Best Western East El Paso Inn M
(915) 851-2882. **$75-$95.** 1570 FM 1110 Rd 79906. I-10 exit 42, just w. Int corridors. **Pets:** Accepted.

Best Western Plus El Paso Airport & Conference Center H
(915) 778-6411. **$125-$150.** 6655 Gateway W 79925. I-10 exit 25 (Airway Blvd), just w. Int corridors. **Pets:** Accepted.

Best Western Sunland Park Inn M
(915) 587-4900. **$71-$99.** 1045 Sunland Park Dr 79922. I-10 exit 13 (Sunland Park Dr), just s. Ext corridors. **Pets:** Accepted.

Candlewood Suites H
(915) 755-9000. **Call for rates.** 4631 Cohen Ave 79924. US 54 exit 28 (Diana Dr) northbound, 1 mi n, then just e; exit southbound, 1 mi s, U-turn under freeway, 1 mi n, then just e. Int corridors. **Pets:** Accepted.

▼▼ Chase Suites Hotel H

(915) 772-8000. **$79-$109.** 6791 Montana Ave 79925. I-10 exit 25 (Airway Blvd), 1 mi n, then just e. Ext corridors. **Pets:** Accepted.

🏊 📶 ✕ 🛄 💻

▼◆ Country Inn & Suites By Carlson El Paso Sunland H

(915) 833-2900. **$99-$149.** 900 Sunland Park Dr 79922. I-10 exit 13 (Sunland Park Dr), just s. Ext corridors. **Pets:** Accepted.

🍴 🏊 📶 ✕ 🛄 💻

▼▼▼ Embassy Suites by Hilton El Paso H

(915) 779-6222. **$119-$219.** 6100 Gateway Blvd E 79905. I-10 exit 24B (Geronimo Dr) eastbound; exit 24 westbound, 0.6 mi to Trowbridge, U-turn under interstate, then 0.5 mi e. Int corridors. **Pets:** Accepted.

🍴 ♿ 🏊 📶 ✕ 🛄 💻

▼▼▼ GuestHouse International Suites H

(915) 772-0395. **Call for rates.** 1940 Airway Blvd 79925. I-10 exit 25 (Airway Blvd), 1.2 mi n. Int corridors. **Pets:** Accepted.

🍴 ♿ 🏊 📶 ✕ 🛄 💻

◆ ▼▼▼ Holiday Inn Express El Paso-Central H

(915) 544-3333. **$79-$145.** 409 E Missouri St 79901. I-10 exit 19B westbound (downtown); exit 19 eastbound, just e. Int corridors.
Pets: Accepted. SAVE 🏊 📶 ✕ 🛄 💻

◆ ▼▼▼ Hyatt Place El Paso Airport H

(915) 771-0022. **$89-$215.** 6030 Gateway Blvd E 79905. I-10 exit 24B (Geronimo Dr) eastbound; exIt 24 westbound, 0.6 mi to Trowbridge Dr, then U-turn under interstate; on eastbound service road. Int corridors.
Pets: Accepted. SAVE 🍴 ♿ 🏊 📶 ✕ 🛄 💻

▼▼ La Quinta Inn & Suites El Paso East H

(915) 591-3300. **$67-$176.** 7944 Gateway Blvd E 79915. I-10 exit 28B, just s. Int corridors. **Pets:** Accepted. ♿ 🏊 📶 🛄 💻

▼▼ La Quinta Inn El Paso Lomaland H

(915) 591-2244. **$67-$130.** 11033 Gateway Blvd W 79935. I-10 exit 29 eastbound; exit 30 westbound, 1 mi w. Ext corridors. **Pets:** Accepted.

♿ 🏊 📶 🛄 💻

▼▼ Microtel Inn & Suites by Wyndham El Paso Airport H

(915) 772-3650. **$50-$98.** 2001 Airway Blvd 79925. I-10 exit 25 (Airway Blvd), 1.3 mi n. Int corridors. **Pets:** Small, other species. $100 deposit/pet, $5 daily fee/pet. Service with restrictions, supervision.

♿ 📶 ✕ 🛄 💻

▼▼▼ Residence Inn by Marriott El Paso H

(915) 771-0504. **$106-$198.** 6355 Gateway Blvd W 79925. I-10 exit 24B (Geronimo Dr) eastbound, n to Edgemere, then just e; exit 25 (Airway Blvd) westbound; on westbound frontage road. Int corridors.
Pets: Accepted. 🏊 📶 ✕ 🛄 💻

▼▼▼ Staybridge Suites Airport H

(915) 775-1212. **Call for rates.** 6680 Gateway Blvd E 79915. I-10 exit 25 (Airway Blvd) eastbound, just e; exit westbound, 0.5 mi w to Airway Blvd, then just sw. Int corridors. **Pets:** Accepted.

♿ 🏊 📶 ✕ 🛄 💻

▼▼▼ Wyndham El Paso Airport H

(915) 778-4241. **$90-$185, 3 day notice.** 2027 Airway Blvd 79925. I-10 exit 25 (Airway Blvd), 1.3 mi n. Int corridors. **Pets:** Small, dogs only. $25 one-time fee/room. Service with restrictions, crate.

🍴 🏊 📶 ✕ 🛄 💻

EMORY

◆ ▼▼▼ Best Western Plus Emory at Lake Fork Inn & Suites H

(903) 473-2022. **$100-$125.** 1026 E Lennon Dr 75440. On US 69, just s of jct SR 515. Int corridors. **Pets:** Accepted.

SAVE 🍴 📶 ✕ 🛄 💻

EULESS

▼▼▼ La Quinta Inn & Suites DFW Airport West - Euless H

(817) 836-4000. **$92-$184.** 431 Airport Frwy 76040. SR 183 exit Ector Dr; on eastbound frontage road. Int corridors. **Pets:** Accepted.

🍴 🏊 📶 ✕ 🛄 💻

FARMERS BRANCH

▼▼ Fairfield Inn & Suites by Marriott Dallas North by the Galleria H

(972) 661-9800. **$69-$125.** 13900 Parkside Center Blvd 75244. I-635 exit 23 (Midway Rd), 0.9 mi n to Spring Valley Rd, just w, then just s. Int corridors. **Pets:** Accepted. 🍴 🏊 📶 ✕ 🛄 💻

▼▼▼ Omni Dallas Hotel at Park West H

(972) 869-4300. **Call for rates.** 1590 LBJ Frwy 75234. I-635 exit 29 (Luna Rd), just s. Int corridors. **Pets:** Accepted.

🍴 🏊 ✕ 📺 ✕ 💻

▼▼▼ Sheraton Dallas Hotel by the Galleria H 🐾

(972) 661-3600. **$99-$999.** 4801 LBJ Frwy 75244. I-635 exit 22D (Dallas Pkwy) eastbound; exit 22B (Dallas Pkwy) westbound; on westbound frontage road. Int corridors. **Pets:** Medium. $75 one-time fee/pet. Service with restrictions, supervision.

SAVE 🍴 ♿ 🏊 📶 ✕ 🛄 💻

FLORESVILLE

◆ ▼◆ Best Western Floresville Inn M

(830) 393-0443. **$73-$93.** 1720 S 10th St 78114. US 181, just s of downtown. Ext corridors. **Pets:** Other species. $15 daily fee/pet. Service with restrictions, supervision. SAVE 🏊 📶 💻

▼▼▼ La Quinta Inn & Suites H

(830) 542-3077. **$86-$218.** 1910 10th St 78114. US 181, just s of downtown. Ext corridors. **Pets:** Accepted. 🍴 📶 ✕ 🛄 💻

FOREST HILL

◆ ▼▼▼ Best Western Plus Forest Hill Inn & Suites H

(817) 293-1667. **$80-$100.** 3230 Forest Hill Cir 76140. I-20/SE Loop 820 exit 440A (Wichita St), just s, then just e. Int corridors.
Pets: Accepted. SAVE ♿ 📶 ✕ 🛄 💻

▼▼▼ La Quinta Inn & Suites H

(817) 293-5800. **$79-$165.** 3346 Forest Hill Cir 76140. I-20 exit 440B (Forest Hill Cir), just s, then just w. Int corridors. **Pets:** Accepted.

🏊 📶 ✕ 🛄 💻

FORNEY

◆ ▼▼▼ Best Western Plus Christopher Inn & Suites H

(972) 552-1412. **$99-$119.** 752 Pinson Rd 75126. US 80 exit FM 740 (Pinson Rd), just ne. Int corridors. **Pets:** Large, dogs only. $20 daily fee/pet. Designated rooms, service with restrictions, crate.

SAVE 🏊 📶 ✕ 🛄 💻

FORT DAVIS

▼▼ Historical Prude Guest Ranch RA

(432) 426-3202. **Call for rates.** 6 mi n Hwy 118 79734. 4.5 mi n of jct SR 118 and 17. Ext corridors. **Pets:** Medium. $10 daily fee/room. Designated rooms, service with restrictions, supervision.

🍴 🏊 📶 ✕ 🎿 🅿 🛄 💻

FORT STOCKTON

Best Western Plus Fort Stockton Hotel 🅷 ❧
(432) 336-7000. **$120-$130.** 2115 W I-10 79735. I-10 exit 256, just s. Int corridors. **Pets:** Large, other species. $50 deposit/pet, $20 daily fee/pet. Designated rooms, service with restrictions, supervision.
[SAVE] [&M] [📶] [✕] [🛏] [💻]

Candlewood Suites 🅷
(432) 336-7700. **Call for rates.** 2469 I-10 W 79735. I-10 exit 257, just s. Int corridors. **Pets:** Accepted. [&M] [🖿] [📶] [✕] [🛏] [💻]

Days Inn 🅷
(432) 336-7500. **$69-$89.** 1408 N US Hwy 285 79735. I-10 exit 257, just s. Ext corridors. **Pets:** Accepted. [SAVE] [🖿] [📶] [🛏] [💻]

Sleep Inn & Suites 🅷
(432) 336-8338. **$104-$129.** 3401 W Dickinson Blvd 79735. I-10 exit 256, just e. Int corridors. **Pets:** Medium. $35 deposit/pet, $35 daily fee/pet. Designated rooms, service with restrictions, supervision.
[SAVE] [&M] [🖿] [📶] [✕] [🛏] [💻]

FORT WORTH

Candlewood Suites 🅷
(817) 838-8229. **Call for rates.** 5201 Endicott Ave 76137. I-820 exit 17B (Beach St), just s, then w. Int corridors. **Pets:** Accepted.
[📶] [🛏] [💻]

Candlewood Suites DFW Airport South Ⓜ
(817) 868-1900. **Call for rates.** 4200 Reggis Ct 76155. SR 360 exit Trinity Blvd, just e, then just n. Int corridors. **Pets:** Accepted.
[SAVE] [📶] [🛏] [💻]

Country Inn & Suites By Carlson, Fort Worth West 🅷
(817) 560-4200. **Call for rates.** 2730 S Cherry Ln 76116. I-30 exit 7A (Cherry Ln), just s. Int corridors. **Pets:** Accepted.
[🍴] [🖿] [📶] [✕] [🛏] [💻]

Courtyard by Marriott Fort Worth Downtown/Blackstone 🅷
(817) 885-8700. **$154-$242.** 601 Main St 76102. Center. Int corridors. **Pets:** Accepted. [SAVE] [🍴] [📶] [✕] [🛏] [💻]

Dallas Fort Worth Marriott Hotel & Golf Club at Champions Circle 🅷
(817) 961-0800. **$79-$221.** 3300 Championship Pkwy 76177. I-35W exit 70, 1.2 mi w on SR 114 to Championship Pkwy, then 0.4 mi s. Int corridors. **Pets:** Accepted. [🍴] [&M] [🖿] [✕] [📶] [✕] [🛏] [💻]

Holiday Inn Express Hotel & Suites 🅷
(817) 744-7755. **$99-$125.** 3541 NW Loop 820 76106. I-820 exit 10A (Azle Ave) eastbound; exit 10B westbound. Int corridors. **Pets:** Accepted. [&M] [🖿] [📶] [✕] [🛏] [💻]

Holiday Inn Express Hotel & Suites Fort Worth Downtown 🅷
(817) 698-9595. **Call for rates.** 1111 W Lancaster Ave 76102. I-30 exit 13B (Henderson St), just n. Int corridors. **Pets:** Accepted.
[SAVE] [🍴] [&M] [🖿] [📶] [✕] [🛏] [💻]

Homewood Suites Fort Worth Medical Center 🅷
(817) 921-0202. **$149-$229.** 2200 Charlie Ln 76104. I-30 exit 12B (Forest Park Blvd), just s. Int corridors. **Pets:** Accepted.
[📶] [✕] [🛏] [💻]

Hyatt Place Fort Worth/Historic Stockyards 🅷
(817) 626-6000. **$149-$409.** 132 E Exchange Ave 76164. In Historic Fort Worth Stockyards. Int corridors. **Pets:** Accepted.
[SAVE] [🖿] [📶] [✕] [🛏] [💻]

Hyatt Place Ft. Worth/Cityview 🅷
(817) 361-9797. **$99-$194.** 5900 Cityview Blvd 76132. I-20 exit 431 (Bryant Irvin Rd), just e on frontage road, then just s. Int corridors. **Pets:** Accepted. [SAVE] [🖿] [📶] [✕] [🛏] [💻]

La Quinta Inn & Suites Fort Worth North 🅷
(817) 222-2888. **$67-$224.** 4700 North Frwy 76137. I-35W exit 56A (Meacham Blvd); on northbound frontage road. Int corridors. **Pets:** Accepted. [🍴] [🖿] [📶] [🛏] [💻]

Omni Hotel 🅷
(817) 535-6664. **Call for rates.** 1300 Houston St 76102. Between 12th and 14th sts. Int corridors. **Pets:** Accepted.
[🍴] [&M] [🖿] [✕] [📶] [✕] [💻]

Radisson Hotel Fort Worth North Fossil Creek 🅷
(817) 625-9911. **$79-$179.** 2540 Meacham Blvd 76106. I-35W exit 56A (Meacham Blvd), just w. Int corridors. **Pets:** Accepted.
[🍴] [🖿] [📶] [✕] [🛏] [💻]

Residence Inn by Marriott Fort Worth Alliance Airport 🅷
(817) 750-7000. **$105-$180.** 13400 North Frwy 76177. I-35W exit 66, on northbound frontage road. Int corridors. **Pets:** Accepted.
[SAVE] [🖿] [📶] [✕] [🛏] [💻]

Residence Inn by Marriott-Fossil Creek 🅷
(817) 439-1300. **$120-$177.** 5801 Sandshell Dr 76137. I-35W exit 58 (Western Center Blvd) northbound, 0.7 mi s; exit southbound, first road to right through strip center, just s to Sandshell Dr, then 0.7 mi s. Int corridors. **Pets:** Accepted. [SAVE] [ECO] [&M] [🖿] [📶] [✕] [🛏] [💻]

Staybridge Suites West Fort Worth 🅷
(817) 935-6500. **$119-$159.** 229 Clifford Center Dr 76108. I-820 N exit 5A (Clifford Center Dr), just w. Int corridors. **Pets:** Accepted.
[🖿] [📶] [✕] [🛏] [💻]

The Worthington Renaissance Fort Worth Hotel 🅷
(817) 870-1000. **$176-$298.** 200 Main St 76102. Northwest corner of 2nd and Main sts. Int corridors. **Pets:** Accepted.
[🍴] [🖿] [✕] [📶] [✕] [🛏] [💻]

FREDERICKSBURG

Best Western Plus Fredericksburg 🅷
(830) 992-2929. **$220-$310.** 314 E Highway St 78624. Jct US 87 (Washington St) and US 290, 0.7 mi s to E Highway St, then just e. Int corridors. **Pets:** Medium. $20 daily fee/pet. Designated rooms, service with restrictions, supervision. [SAVE] [🖿] [📶] [✕] [🛏] [💻]

Dietzel Motel Ⓜ
(830) 997-3330. **Call for rates.** 1141 W US 290 78624. On US 290, 1 mi w; at US 87. Ext corridors. **Pets:** Accepted.
[🖿] [📶] [✕] [🛏] [💻]

Fredericksburg Econo Lodge Ⓜ
(830) 997-3437. **$46-$199.** 810 S Adams St 78624. Jct US 290 and SR 16 S, 1 mi s. Ext corridors. **Pets:** $15 daily fee/room. Service with restrictions, crate. [SAVE] [🖿] [📶] [🛏] [💻]

Fredericksburg Inn & Suites 🅷
(830) 997-0202. **$109-$269.** 201 S Washington St 78624. US 290 and 87 (Washington St), 3 blks s. Ext corridors. **Pets:** Accepted.
[SAVE] [🖿] [📶] [✕] [🛏] [💻]

▼▼▼▼ La Quinta Inn & Suites Fredericksburg 🅷
(830) 990-2899. **$104-$257.** 1465 E Main St 78624. 1 mi e of down-town. Int corridors. **Pets:** Accepted. 🛗 🛆 📶 ✕ 🔋 🖵

🔵 ▼▼▼ Sunset Inn & Suites 🅼
(830) 997-9581. **Call for rates.** 900 S Adams St 78624. 0.8 mi sw of jct US 290 and SR 16. Ext corridors. **Pets:** Accepted.
🅂🅰🅅🅴 🍽 📶 ✕ 🔋 🖵

▼▼▼ Windcrest Inn & Suites 🅷
(830) 997-9811. **Call for rates.** 908 S Adams St 78624. 0.8 mi sw on SR 16; 0.8 mi sw of jct US 87 and 290. Ext corridors. **Pets:** Accepted.
🛆 📶 🔋 🖵

FRISCO

🔵 ▼▼▼▼ Aloft Frisco 🅷
(972) 668-6011. **$49-$269.** 3202 Parkwood Blvd 75034. Dallas North Tollway exit Warren Pkwy, 0.5 mi e to Parkwood Blvd, then just s. Int corridors. **Pets:** Accepted. 🅂🅰🅅🅴 🛗 🛆 📶 ✕ 🔋 🖵

▼▼▼▼ Embassy Suites by Hilton Dallas-Frisco Hotel, Convention Center & Spa 🅷 🐾
(972) 712-7200. **$199-$269.** 7600 John Q Hammons Dr 75034. SR 121 exit Parkwood, just n. Int corridors. **Pets:** Large. $75 one-time fee/room. Designated rooms, service with restrictions, crate.
🍽 🛗 🛆 ✕ 🔊 ✕ 🔋 🖵

🔵 ▼▼▼▼ Hyatt House Frisco 🅷
(972) 668-4500. **$129-$699.** 2875 Parkwood Blvd 75034. Dallas North Tollway; exit Warren Pkwy, just e then just s. Int corridors. **Pets:** Medium, dogs only. $75 one-time fee/pet. Service with restrictions, supervision. 🅂🅰🅅🅴 🍽 🛗 🛆 📶 ✕ 🔋 🖵

🔵 ▼▼▼▼ Sheraton Stonebriar Dallas-Frisco 🅷
(972) 668-8700. **$139-$429.** 5444 State Hwy 121 75034. SR 121 exit Legacy Dr; northwest corner. Int corridors. **Pets:** Accepted.
🅂🅰🅅🅴 🍽 📶 ✕ 🔋 🖵

🔵 ▼▼▼▼ ▼▼▼▼ The Westin Stonebriar Hotel & Golf Club 🅷 🐾
(972) 668-8000. **$127-$389.** 1549 Legacy Dr 75034. 0.3 mi n of jct SR 121. Int corridors. **Pets:** Medium, dogs only. $200 deposit/room. Service with restrictions, supervision. 🅂🅰🅅🅴 🍽 🛗 🛆 ✕ 🔊 ✕ 🔋 🖵

GAINESVILLE

▼▼▼ La Quinta Inn & Suites Gainesville 🅷
(940) 665-5700. **$93-$229.** 4201 N I-35 76240. I-35 exit 501, just w on FM 1202, then just s on access road. Int corridors. **Pets:** Accepted.
🍽 🛆 📶 ✕ 🔋 🖵

GALVESTON

🔵 ▼▼▼ ▼▼▼ Hotel Galvez and Spa-A Wyndham Grand Hotel 🅷
(409) 765-7721. **$109-$429, 3 day notice.** 2024 Seawall Blvd 77550. Jct 21st St. Int corridors. **Pets:** Accepted.
🅂🅰🅅🅴 🍽 🛆 ✕ 📶 ✕ 🔋 🖵

▼▼▼▼ La Quinta Inn & Suites Galveston Seawall West 🅷
(409) 740-9100. **$68-$438.** 8710 Seawall Blvd 77554. Between 85th and 89th sts. Int corridors. **Pets:** Accepted.
🍽 🛗 🛆 📶 ✕ 🔋 🖵

🔵 ▼▼▼ ▼▼▼ TownePlace Suites by Marriott Galveston Island 🅷
(409) 497-2840. **$74-$201.** 9540 Seawall Blvd 77554. 5 mi w. Int corridors. **Pets:** Accepted. 🅂🅰🅅🅴 🛗 📶 ✕ 🔋 🖵

🔵 ▼▼▼ The Tremont House-A Wyndham Grand Hotel 🅷
(409) 763-0300. **$99-$429, 3 day notice.** 2300 Ship's Mechanic Row 77550. Broadway Ave, 0.4 mi n on 23rd St; just w to entrance; down-town. Int corridors. **Pets:** Accepted.
🅂🅰🅅🅴 🍽 🛗 📶 ✕ 🔋 🖵

GARLAND

🔵 ▼▼▼▼ Hyatt Place Dallas/Garland/Richardson at Firewheel Convention Center 🅷
(972) 414-3500. **$69-$219.** 5101 N President George Bush Hwy 75040. Jct N Garland Ave, just e on frontage road. Int corridors.
Pets: Accepted. 🅂🅰🅅🅴 🍽 🛗 🛆 📶 ✕ 🔋 🖵

▼▼▼ Quality Inn & Suites 🅷
(972) 303-1601. **$70-$103.** 1635 E I-30 at Bass Pro Rd 75043. I-30 exit 62 (Bass Pro Rd) eastbound, just s on Chaha Rd, over bridge to north frontage road. Ext corridors. **Pets:** Accepted. 🍽 🛆 📶 🔋 🖵

GATESVILLE

▼▼▼ Rodeway Inn 🅷
(254) 865-2281. **$79-$99.** 2501 E Main St 76528. Jct US 84 and SR 36, 0.5 mi w. Ext corridors. **Pets:** Accepted. 🛆 📶 🔋 🖵

GEORGETOWN *(Restaurants p. 625)*

🔵 ▼▼▼▼ Best Western Plus Georgetown Inn & Suites 🅷
(512) 868-8555. **$104-$135.** 600 San Gabriel Village Blvd 78626. I-35 exit 261A, 0.5 mi n on east frontage road, then just e. Int corridors.
Pets: Accepted. 🅂🅰🅅🅴 🍽 🛗 🛆 📶 ✕ 🔋 🖵

GEORGE WEST

🔵 ▼▼▼▼ Best Western George West Executive Inn 🅼
(361) 449-3300. **$80-$100.** 208 N Nueces St 78022. Just n of US 59 on US 281. Ext corridors. **Pets:** Accepted. 🅂🅰🅅🅴 🛆 📶 🔋 🖵

GRAND PRAIRIE

🔵 ▼▼▼▼ Hyatt Place Dallas/North Arlington/Grand Prairie 🅷
(972) 988-6800. **$94-$279.** 1542 N Hwy 360 75050. SR 360 exit K/J aves southbound, U-turn at Ave J; exit Lamar Dr northbound, just n on frontage road. Int corridors. **Pets:** Accepted.
🅂🅰🅅🅴 🛗 🛆 📶 ✕ 🔋 🖵

▼▼▼ Super 8 🅷
(972) 606-2800. **$59-$90.** 4020 S Great Southwest Pkwy 75052. I-20 exit 454 (Great Southwest Pkwy), just s. Ext corridors. **Pets:** Accepted.
🛆 📶 🔋 🖵

GRAPEVINE

▼▼▼ Embassy Suites by Hilton Outdoor World 🅷
(972) 724-2600. **$139-$259.** 2401 Bass Pro Dr 76051. SR 121 exit Bass Pro Dr, just w. Int corridors. **Pets:** Accepted.
🍽 🛆 🔊 ✕ 🔋 🖵

🔵 ▼▼▼▼ Hyatt Place Dallas/Grapevine 🅷
(972) 691-1199. **$69-$209.** 2220 Grapevine Mills Cir W 76051. SR 121 exit Bass Pro Dr, just w, then just e on SR 26. Int corridors.
Pets: Accepted. 🅂🅰🅅🅴 📶 ✕ 🔋 🖵

🔵 ▼▼▼▼ Hyatt Regency DFW 🅷
(972) 453-1234. **$99-$499.** 2334 N International Pkwy 75261. In Dallas-Fort Worth International Airport Terminal C area. Int corridors.
Pets: Accepted. 🅂🅰🅅🅴 🌿 🍽 🛗 🛆 📶 ✕ 🔋 🖵

▼▼ Super 8-Grapevine ⎈
(817) 329-7222. **$79-$149.** 250 E Hwy 114 76051. SR 114 exit Main St. Int corridors. **Pets:** Other species. $10 daily fee/pet. Designated rooms, service with restrictions, supervision. 🛏 📶 🅿 💻

GROOM
⚛ ▼ Chalet Inn Ⓜ
(806) 248-7524. **Call for rates.** I-40 FM 2300 79039. I-40 exit 113, just s. Ext corridors. **Pets:** Medium. $5 daily fee/pet. Service with restrictions, supervision. 🆂🅰🆅🅴 📶 🅿

GUN BARREL CITY
▼▼ Days Inn Gun Barrel City Ⓜ
(903) 887-8886. **$63-$99.** 2111 W Main St 75156. 4.1 mi e of jct SR 274 and 334. Ext corridors. **Pets:** Dogs only. $10 daily fee/pet. Service with restrictions, supervision. 🍴 🛏 📶 🅿 💻

HALLETTSVILLE
▼▼▼ Hotel Texas ⎈
(361) 798-5900. **Call for rates.** 1632 N Texana St 77964. Just s of CR 200. Int corridors. **Pets:** Accepted. 🛏 📶 ❎ 🅿 💻

HARLINGEN
▼▼ Quality Inn Harlingen ⎈
(956) 428-6888. **$64-$999.** 1002 S Expwy 83 78552. US 83 and 77 exit M St. Ext corridors. **Pets:** Very small, other species. $10 daily fee/pet. Designated rooms, service with restrictions, crate.
🅰🆅🅴 🛏 📶 🅿 💻

HEBBRONVILLE
⚛ ▼▼ Best Western Hebbronville Inn ⎈
(361) 527-3600. **$100-$130.** 37 E Hwy 359 78361. On CR 359, just e of SR 16. Int corridors. **Pets:** Accepted. 🆂🅰🆅🅴 🍴 🛏 📶 🅿 💻

HENDERSON
▼▼▼ Baymont Inn & Suites Henderson ⎈
(903) 657-7900. **$79-$110.** 410 Hwy 79 S 75654. Just n of jct US 259. Int corridors. **Pets:** Small. $50 deposit/pet, $10 daily fee/pet. Service with restrictions, supervision. 🍴 🛏 📶 ❎ 🅿 💻

HEREFORD
⚛ ▼▼ Best Western Red Carpet Inn ⎈
(806) 364-0540. **$80-$85.** 830 W 1st St 79045. Just w of jct US 385 and 60. Ext corridors. **Pets:** Medium. $5 daily fee/pet. Service with restrictions, crate. 🆂🅰🆅🅴 🛏 📶 🅿 💻

⚛ ▼▼ Holiday Inn Express ⎈
(806) 364-3322. **$139-$169.** 1400 W 1st St 79045. Just w of jct US 385 and 60. Int corridors. **Pets:** Medium. $20 daily fee/pet. Service with restrictions, supervision. 🆂🅰🆅🅴 🍴 🛏 📶 ❎ 🅿 💻

HEWITT
▼▼ Sleep Inn & Suites ⎈
(254) 420-3200. **$89-$500.** 209 Enterprise Blvd 76643. I-35 exit 328; on northwest corner. Int corridors. **Pets:** Accepted.
🍴 🆂🅼 🛏 📶 🅿 💻

HIDALGO
▼▼▼ Super 8 Hidalgo/McAllen Area ⎈
(956) 843-1234. **$60-$250.** 2520 N 10th St 78557. US 83 exit 10th St, 6 mi s. Int corridors. **Pets:** Accepted.
🍴 🆂🅼 🛏 📶 ❎ 🅿 💻

HILLSBORO
▼▼ Super 8 ⎈
(254) 580-0404. **$70-$126.** 1512 Hillview Dr 76645. I-35 exit 368A northbound; exit 368 southbound, just e. Int corridors. **Pets:** Accepted.
🆂🅼 🛏 📶 🅿 💻

HONDO
⚛ ▼▼▼ Best Western Hondo Inn ⎈
(830) 426-4466. **$89-$160.** 301 Hwy 90 E 78861. Just e of downtown. Int corridors. **Pets:** $25 daily fee/pet. Designated rooms, service with restrictions, supervision. 🆂🅰🆅🅴 🆂🅼 🛏 📶 ❎ 🅿 💻

HORSESHOE BAY
⚛ ▼▼▼ ▼▼ Horseshoe Bay Resort ⎈
(830) 598-8600. **Call for rates.** 200 Hi Cir N 78657. Jct US 281 and SR 2147, 6.6 mi w. Ext/int corridors. **Pets:** Accepted.
🆂🅰🆅🅴 🎗 🍴 🆂🅼 🛏 ❎ 📶 ❎ 🅿 💻

HOUSTON *(Restaurants p. 625)*
⚛ ▼▼▼ Aloft Houston by the Galleria ⎈
(713) 622-7010. **$89-$169.** 5415 Westheimer Rd 77056. I-610 exit 8C (Westheimer Rd) northbound; exit 9A (San Felipe Rd/Westheimer Rd) southbound, 0.8 mi w. Int corridors. **Pets:** Accepted.
🆂🅰🆅🅴 🆂🅼 🛏 📶 ❎ 🅿 💻

⚛ ▼▼▼ Best Western Plus Westchase Mini-Suites ⎈
(713) 782-1515. **$89-$239.** 2950 W Sam Houston Pkwy S 77042. Just w of Sam Houston Pkwy (Beltway 8) and Westheimer Rd; on southbound frontage road. Int corridors. **Pets:** Accepted.
🆂🅰🆅🅴 🛏 📶 ❎ 🅿 💻

▼▼ Candlewood Suites at CITYCENTRE - Energy Corridor ⎈
(713) 464-2677. **Call for rates.** 10503 Town & Country Way 77024. I-10 exit 755 eastbound, 1.2 mi on frontage road to Attingham Dr, just s to Town and Country Way, then just w; exit 756A westbound, U-turn under I-10, just e to Attingham Dr, just s to Town and Country Way, then just w. Int corridors. **Pets:** Accepted. 🆂🅼 📶 🅿 💻

⚛ ▼▼ Candlewood Suites Beltway 8 ⎈
(713) 244-0400. **$99.** 11280 Westheimer Rd 77042. Sam Houston Pkwy (Beltway 8) exit Westheimer Rd, 0.8 mi w. Int corridors. **Pets:** Medium. $75 one-time fee/room. Designated rooms, service with restrictions, supervision. 🆂🅰🆅🅴 🍴 🆂🅼 📶 ❎ 🅿 💻

▼▼ Candlewood Suites Houston by the Galleria ⎈
(713) 839-9411. **Call for rates.** 4900 Loop Central Dr 77081. I-610 exit 7 (Furnace Rd) southbound; exit 7 (Westpark Dr) northbound; on northbound frontage road. Int corridors. **Pets:** Accepted. 🍴 📶 🅿 💻

▼▼ Candlewood Suites-Westchase ⎈
(713) 780-7881. **Call for rates.** 4033 W Sam Houston Pkwy S 77042. Sam Houston Pkwy (Beltway 8) exit Westpark Dr; southeast corner of Westpark Dr and Sam Houston Pkwy (Beltway 8); on northbound frontage road. Int corridors. **Pets:** Accepted. 🆂🅼 📶 🅿 💻

▼▼▼ Candlewood Suites Willowbrook ⎈
(832) 237-7300. **Call for rates.** 8719 FM 1960 W 77070. Corner of Mills Rd and FM 1960 W; just w of Tomball Pkwy. Int corridors. **Pets:** Accepted. 🆂🅼 🛏 📶 🅿 💻

▼▼▼ Country Inn & Suites By Carlson, Houston Northwest ⎈
(832) 478-9937. **Call for rates.** 12915 FM 1960 Rd W 77065. US 290 exit FM 1960, just e. Int corridors. **Pets:** Medium. $25 one-time fee/pet. Service with restrictions, crate. 🆂🅼 🛏 📶 ❎ 🅿 💻

▼▼▼ Crowne Plaza Northwest Hotel ⎈
(713) 462-9977. **Call for rates.** 12801 Northwest Frwy 77040. Northwest on US 290 exit Hollister Rd, 0.7 mi e; on south service road. Ext/int corridors. **Pets:** Accepted. 🍴 🛏 📶 ❎ 🅿 💻

Crowne Plaza Suites Houston-Near Sugar Land H
(713) 995-0123. **$79-$169.** 9090 Southwest Frwy 77074. US 59 (Southwest Frwy) exit Beechnut St/Gessner Rd; on southbound frontage road. Int corridors. **Pets:** Accepted.

DoubleTree by Hilton Hotel Houston Downtown H
(713) 759-0202. **$189-$329.** 400 Dallas St 77002. At Dallas and Bagby sts. Int corridors. **Pets:** Medium. $50 one-time fee/pet. Service with restrictions, supervision.

DoubleTree Hotel and Suites by Hilton Hotel Houston by the Galleria H
(713) 961-9000. **$119-$899.** 5353 Westheimer Rd 77056. I-610 exit 8C (Westheimer Rd) northbound; exit 9A (San Felipe Rd/Westheimer Rd) southbound, 0.8 mi w. Int corridors. **Pets:** Medium. $200 deposit/room, $50 daily fee/pet. Service with restrictions, supervision.

Drury Inn & Suites-Houston Hobby H
(713) 941-4300. **$74-$169.** 7902 Mosley Rd 77061. I-45 exit 36 (Airport Blvd/College St) northbound, just w on Airport Blvd, then just n; exit southbound, follow frontage road to Mosley Rd. Int corridors.
Pets: Accepted.

Drury Inn & Suites-Houston Near the Galleria H
(713) 963-0700. **$79-$269.** 1615 West Loop S 77027. I-610 exit 9 (San Felipe Rd) northbound; exit 9A (San Felipe Rd/Westheimer Rd) southbound; on east frontage road. Int corridors. **Pets:** Accepted.

Drury Inn & Suites-Houston West H
(281) 558-7007. **$74-$169.** 1000 N Hwy 6 77079. I-10 exit 751 (Addicks Rd/SR 6), just n. Int corridors. **Pets:** Accepted.

Element by Westin Houston Vintage Park H
(281) 379-7300. **$129-$209.** 14555 Vintage Preserve Pkwy 77070. SR 249 exit Louetta Rd, just e to Chasewood Park, then just s. Int corridors. **Pets:** Accepted.

Embassy Suites by Hilton Houston Downtown H
(713) 739-9100. **$179-$499.** 1515 Dallas St 77010. Between Crawford and La Branch sts. Int corridors. **Pets:** Accepted.

Four Points by Sheraton Houston - CITYCENTRE H
(281) 501-4600. **$79-$349.** 10655 Katy Frwy 77024. I-10 exit 756A westbound; exit 755 eastbound; southeast corner of I-10 and Sam Houston Pkwy (Beltway 8). Ext/int corridors. **Pets:** Accepted.

Four Seasons Hotel Houston H
(713) 650-1300. **Call for rates.** 1300 Lamar St 77010. Jct Lamar and Austin sts. Int corridors. **Pets:** Accepted.

Hampton Inn-Brookhollow H ❀
(713) 939-7100. **$84-$169.** 12909 Northwest Frwy 77040. US 290 exit Hollister St; on eastbound access road. Int corridors. **Pets:** Medium, other species. Service with restrictions, supervision.

Hilton Houston North H
(281) 875-2222. **$79-$219.** 12400 Greenspoint Dr 77060. I-45 exit 61 (Greens Rd), 0.5 mi e. Int corridors. **Pets:** Accepted.

Hilton Houston Post Oak H
(713) 961-9300. **$89-$275.** 2001 Post Oak Blvd 77056. I-610 exit 8C (Westheimer Rd) northbound, just w; exit 9A (San Felipe Rd/Westheimer Rd) southbound; between San Felipe and Westheimer rds. Ext/int corridors. **Pets:** Accepted.

Hilton Houston Westchase H
(713) 974-1000. **$89-$229.** 9999 Westheimer Rd 77042. Sam Houston Pkwy (Beltway 8) exit Westheimer Rd/Briar Forest Dr northbound; exit Westheimer Rd/Richmond Ave southbound, 0.5 mi e. Int corridors.
Pets: Accepted.

Holiday Inn Express Hotel & Suites Memorial Area H
(713) 688-2800. **Call for rates.** 7625 Katy Frwy 77024. I-10 exit 762 (Silber Rd); on eastbound frontage road. Int corridors. **Pets:** Accepted.

Holiday Inn Houston Hobby Airport H
(713) 946-8900. **$99-$349.** 8611 Airport Blvd 77061. I-45 exit 36 (Airport Blvd/College St), 1.3 mi w. Int corridors. **Pets:** Accepted.

Holiday Inn Houston Intercontinental Airport H
(281) 449-2311. **Call for rates.** 15222 John F Kennedy Blvd 77032. Jct N Sam Houston Pkwy (Beltway 8) E and John F Kennedy Blvd. Int corridors. **Pets:** Accepted.

Homewood Suites by Hilton Houston Northwest Cy-Fair H
(832) 237-2000. **$99-$329.** 13110 Wortham Center Dr 77065. US 290 exit FM 1960/SR 6, just w on westbound frontage road, then just n. Int corridors. **Pets:** Accepted.

Homewood Suites by Hilton Near the Galleria H
(713) 439-1305. **$139-$209.** 2950 Sage Rd 77056. I-610 exit 8C (Westheimer Rd), just w to Sage Rd, then just s. Int corridors.
Pets: Accepted.

Homewood Suites by Hilton-Westchase H
(713) 334-2424. **$169-$199.** 2424 Rogerdale Rd 77042. Sam Houston Pkwy (Beltway 8) exit Westheimer Rd, just w to Rogerdale Rd, then just n. Int corridors. **Pets:** Accepted.

Hotel Derek H
(713) 961-3000. **$89-$899.** 2525 West Loop S 77027. I-610 exit 9A (San Felipe Rd/Westheimer Rd) southbound; exit 8C (Westheimer Rd) northbound. Int corridors. **Pets:** Accepted.

Hotel ICON, Autograph Collection H
(713) 224-4266. **$141-$288.** 220 Main St 77002. Between Travis and Main sts; entrance on Congress St. Int corridors. **Pets:** Accepted.

Hotel Indigo Houston at the Galleria H
(713) 621-8988. **Call for rates.** 5160 Hidalgo St 77056. I-610 exit 9A (San Felipe Rd/Westheimer Rd) southbound; exit 8C (Westheimer Rd) northbound, s to Post Oak, just e to Hidalgo St, then just s. Int corridors. **Pets:** Accepted.

Hotel ZaZa Houston Museum District H
(713) 526-1991. **Call for rates.** 5701 Main St 77005. US 59 (Southwest Frwy) exit Main St northbound, 0.5 mi s; exit Fannin St southbound, 0.5 mi s to Ewing St, then just w. Int corridors. **Pets:** Accepted.

Houston Marriott South at Hobby Airport H
(713) 943-7979. **$84-$200.** 9100 Gulf Frwy 77017. I-45 exit 36 (Airport Blvd/College St) southbound; exit 38 (Monroe Rd) northbound; on southbound frontage road. Int corridors. **Pets:** Accepted.

Hyatt House Houston/Galleria H
(713) 629-9711. **$99-$449.** 3440 Sage Rd 77056. I-610 exit 9A (San Felipe Rd/Westheimer Rd) southbound; exit 8C (Westheimer Rd) northbound, just w to Sage Rd, then 0.8 mi s. Int corridors. **Pets:** Accepted.

Hyatt House Houston-West/Energy Corridor H
(281) 646-9990. **$89-$359.** 15405 Katy Frwy (I-10) 77094. I-10 exit 751 (SR 6), just s to Grisby Rd, then just w. Int corridors. **Pets:** Medium. $75 one-time fee/room. Service with restrictions, supervision.

Hyatt Place Houston/Bush Airport H
(281) 820-6060. **$89-$219.** 300 Ronan Park Pl 77060. Sam Houston Pkwy (Beltway 8) exit Imperial Valley Dr westbound, 0.8 mi w on frontage road; exit Hardy Toll Rd eastbound, turn under parkway, 1.2 mi w; on west frontage road. Int corridors. **Pets:** Accepted.

Hyatt Place Houston Galleria H
(713) 626-7300. **$99-$399.** 5252 W Alabama St 77056. I-610 exit 8C (Westheimer Rd), 06 mi w, then just s; jct Sage Rd and W Alabama St. Int corridors. **Pets:** Accepted.

Hyatt Regency Houston H 🐾
(713) 654-1234. **$89-$399.** 1200 Louisiana St 77002. Between Polk and Dallas sts. Int corridors. **Pets:** Medium. $100 one-time fee/room. Service with restrictions.

Hyatt Regency North Houston H
(281) 249-1234. **$89-$399.** 425 N Sam Houston Pkwy E 77060. Sam Houston Pkwy (Beltway 8) exit Imperial Valley Dr westbound; exit Hardy Toll Rd eastbound; on westbound frontage road. Int corridors.
Pets: Accepted.

JW Marriott Houston Downtown H
(713) 237-1111. **$168-$428.** 806 Main St 77002. Jct 8th and Main sts. Int corridors. **Pets:** Accepted.

La Quinta Inn & Suites Energy Corridor H
(281) 668-1068. **$86-$482.** 2451 Shadow View Ln 77077. 2.5 mi w of Sam Houston Pkwy (Beltway 8) on Westheimer Rd, just n. Int corridors.
Pets: Accepted.

La Quinta Inn & Suites Houston Bush Intercontinental Airport South H
(281) 219-2000. **$75-$279.** 15510 John F Kennedy Blvd 77032. Sam Houston Pkwy (Beltway 8) exit John F Kennedy Blvd/Vickery Dr, just n. Int corridors. **Pets:** Accepted.

La Quinta Inn & Suites Houston Channelview H
(281) 452-4402. **$97-$229.** 5520 E Sam Houston Pkwy N 77015. Sam Houston Pkwy exit Woodforest Blvd. Int corridors. **Pets:** Accepted.

La Quinta Inn & Suites-Houston Clay Road H
(713) 939-1400. **$75-$339.** 4424 Westway Park Blvd 77041. Sam Houston Pkwy (Beltway 8) exit Clay Rd, just e. Int corridors. **Pets:** Accepted.

La Quinta Inn & Suites Houston Galleria Area H
(713) 355-3440. **$71-$807.** 1625 West Loop S 77027. I-610 exit 9 (San Felipe Rd) northbound; exit 9A (San Felipe Rd/Westheimer Rd) southbound; on northbound frontage road. Int corridors. **Pets:** Accepted.

La Quinta Inn & Suites Houston Hobby Airport H
(713) 490-1008. **$79-$356.** 8776 Airport Blvd 77061. I-45 exit 36 (Airport Blvd/College St), 1.3 mi w. Int corridors. **Pets:** Accepted.

La Quinta Inn & Suites Houston I-45/1960 H
(281) 784-1112. **$86-$334.** 415 FM 1960 Rd E 77073. I-45 exit 66 (FM 1960), just e. Int corridors. **Pets:** Accepted.

La Quinta Inn & Suites Houston-Normandy H
(713) 451-0009. **$79-$389.** 930 Normandy St 77015. I-10 exit 778B, just n. Int corridors. **Pets:** Accepted.

La Quinta Inn & Suites Houston-Westchase H
(281) 495-7700. **$86-$504.** 10850 Harwin Dr 77072. Sam Houston Pkwy (Beltway 8) exit Bellaire Blvd/Harwin Dr northbound; exit Westpark Dr/Harwin Dr southbound. Int corridors. **Pets:** Accepted.

La Quinta Inn & Suites Houston West Park 10 H
(281) 646-9200. **$75-$587.** 15225 Katy Frwy 77094. I-10 exit 748 (Barker Cypress Rd) eastbound, 2.6 mi on eastbound service road; exit 751 (SR 6) westbound, just s to Grisby Rd, then 0.5 mi w. Int corridors. **Pets:** Accepted.

Omni Houston Hotel H
(713) 871-8181. **Call for rates.** Four Riverway 77056. I-610 exit 10 (Woodway Dr), 0.3 mi w. Int corridors. **Pets:** Accepted.

Omni Houston Hotel Westside H 🐾
(281) 558-8338. **$99-$399.** 13210 Katy Frwy 77079. I-10 exit 753A (Eldridge St), just n. Int corridors. **Pets:** Medium. $50 one-time fee/room. Service with restrictions, crate.

Residence Inn by Marriott Houston by the Galleria H
(713) 840-9757. **$104-$231.** 2500 McCue Rd 77056. I-610 exit 8C (Westheimer Rd) northbound; exit 9A (San Felipe Rd/Westheimer Rd) southbound, just w to McCue Rd, then just n. Ext/int corridors.
Pets: Accepted.

Residence Inn by Marriott Houston Downtown/Convention Center H
(832) 366-1000. **$142-$288.** 904 Dallas St 77002. At Main St. Int corridors. **Pets:** Accepted.

Residence Inn by Marriott Houston Westchase H
(713) 974-5454. **$117-$208.** 9965 Westheimer Rd 77042. Sam Houston Pkwy (Beltway 8) exit Westheimer Rd, 0.7 mi e to Elmside Dr, then just s. Int corridors. **Pets:** Accepted.

Residence Inn by Marriott-West University H
(713) 661-4660. **$98-$209.** 2939 Westpark Dr 77005. US 59 (Southwest Frwy) exit Kirby Dr, just s, then just w. Int corridors. **Pets:** Accepted.

Residence Inn by Marriott Willowbrook H
(832) 237-2002. **$110-$199.** 7311 W Greens Rd 77064. SR 249 exit Greens Rd, just e. Int corridors. **Pets:** Accepted.

Royal Sonesta Hotel Houston H
(713) 627-7600. **$99-$399.** 2222 West Loop S 77027. I-610 exit 9 (San Felipe Rd) northbound; exit 9A (San Felipe Rd/Westheimer Rd) southbound. Int corridors. **Pets:** Accepted.

The St. Regis Houston H ❖
(713) 840-7600. **$200-$600.** 1919 Briar Oaks Ln 77027. I-610 exit 9A (San Felipe Rd/Westheimer Rd), 0.3 mi e. Int corridors. **Pets:** Medium, dogs only. Supervision. ⟦SAVE⟧ ⟦≣⟧ ⟦¶⟧ ⟦⊇⟧ ⟦✕⟧ ⟦⊠⟧ ⟦✕⟧ ⟦⊟⟧ ⟦⊒⟧

Sheraton Houston Brookhollow H ❖
(713) 688-0100. **$99-$179, 3 day notice.** 3000 North Loop W 77092. I-610 exit 13C (T C Jester Blvd); on southbound frontage road. Int corridors. **Pets:** Medium. Service with restrictions, supervision.
⟦SAVE⟧ ⟦¶⟧ ⟦&M⟧ ⟦⊇⟧ ⟦✕⟧ ⟦⊒⟧

Sheraton Houston West Hotel H
(281) 501-4200. **$79-$329.** 11191 Clay Rd 77041. Sam Houston Pkwy (Beltway 8) exit Clay Rd, just e. Int corridors. **Pets:** Accepted.
⟦SAVE⟧ ⟦¶⟧ ⟦&M⟧ ⟦⊇⟧ ⟦⊜⟧ ⟦✕⟧ ⟦⊒⟧

Sheraton North Houston Hotel H ❖
(281) 442-5100. **$289-$309.** 15700 John F Kennedy Blvd 77032. Sam Houston Pkwy (Beltway 8) exit John F Kennedy Blvd, just n. Int corridors. **Pets:** Medium. Service with restrictions, supervision.
⟦SAVE⟧ ⟦¶⟧ ⟦&M⟧ ⟦⊇⟧ ⟦⊜⟧ ⟦✕⟧ ⟦⊟⟧ ⟦⊒⟧

Sheraton Suites Houston Near The Galleria H ❖
(713) 586-2444. **$99-$399.** 2400 West Loop S 77027. I-610 exit 9 (San Felipe Rd) northbound; exit 9A (San Felipe Rd/Westheimer Rd) southbound. Int corridors. **Pets:** Medium, dogs only. Service with restrictions, crate. ⟦SAVE⟧ ⟦¶⟧ ⟦⊇⟧ ⟦⊜⟧ ⟦✕⟧ ⟦⊟⟧ ⟦⊒⟧

Sonesta ES Suites Houston H
(713) 355-8888. **Call for rates.** 5190 Hidalgo St 77056. I-610 exit 9A (San Felipe Rd/Westheimer Rd) southbound; exit 8C (Westheimer Rd) northbound, 0.4 mi w to Sage Rd, then just s. Int corridors.
Pets: Accepted. ⟦SAVE⟧ ⟦&M⟧ ⟦⊇⟧ ⟦⊜⟧ ⟦✕⟧ ⟦⊟⟧ ⟦⊒⟧

SpringHill Suites Marriott Houston I-45 H
(281) 872-2000. **$80-$173.** 15555 N Freeway 77090. I-45 exit 64 (Richey Rd), just s on southbound frontage road. Int corridors. **Pets:** Small, dogs only. $75 one-time fee/room. Service with restrictions, supervision. ⟦¶⟧ ⟦&M⟧ ⟦⊜⟧ ⟦✕⟧ ⟦⊟⟧ ⟦⊒⟧

Staybridge Suites H
(281) 897-8868. **Call for rates.** 18828 State Hwy 249 (Tomball Pkwy) 77070. SR 249 exit Grant Rd/Schroeder Rd; on northbound frontage road. Int corridors. **Pets:** Accepted. ⟦¶⟧ ⟦&M⟧ ⟦⊇⟧ ⟦⊜⟧ ⟦✕⟧ ⟦⊟⟧ ⟦⊒⟧

Staybridge Suites Houston West Energy Corridor H
(281) 759-7829. **Call for rates.** 1225 Eldridge Pkwy 77077. I-10 exit 753A (Eldridge Pkwy), 1.8 mi s. Int corridors. **Pets:** Accepted.
⟦⊇⟧ ⟦⊜⟧ ⟦✕⟧ ⟦⊟⟧ ⟦⊒⟧

TownePlace Suites by Marriott Houston I-10 West/Energy Corridor H
(281) 646-0058. **$72-$137.** 15155 Katy Frwy 77094. I-10 exit 751, just s on SR 6 to Grisby Rd, then w. Int corridors. **Pets:** Medium, other species. $150 one-time fee/room. Service with restrictions.
⟦SAVE⟧ ⟦¶⟧ ⟦⊇⟧ ⟦⊜⟧ ⟦✕⟧ ⟦⊟⟧ ⟦⊒⟧

TownePlace Suites by Marriott-Northwest Central H
(713) 690-4035. **$76-$158.** 12820 Northwest Frwy (US 290) 77040. US 290 exit Bingle Rd/43rd St eastbound; exit Bingle Rd/Pinemont Dr/43rd St westbound; on westbound frontage road. Int corridors.
Pets: Accepted. ⟦&M⟧ ⟦⊜⟧ ⟦✕⟧ ⟦⊟⟧ ⟦⊒⟧

The Westin Galleria, Houston H ❖
(713) 960-8100. **$79-$529.** 5060 W Alabama St 77056. I-610 exit 8C (Westheimer Rd) northbound; exit 9A (San Felipe Rd/Westheimer Rd) southbound, 0.5 mi w on Westheimer Rd to Sage Rd, just s, then just e. Int corridors. **Pets:** Medium, dogs only. Service with restrictions, supervision. ⟦SAVE⟧ ⟦¶⟧ ⟦⊇⟧ ⟦⊜⟧ ⟦✕⟧ ⟦⊟⟧ ⟦⊒⟧

Westin Houston Memorial City H
(281) 501-4300. **$129-$699.** 945 Gessner Rd 77024. I-10 exit 757 (Gessner Rd), just s. Int corridors. **Pets:** Accepted.
⟦SAVE⟧ ⟦¶⟧ ⟦&M⟧ ⟦⊇⟧ ⟦⊠⟧ ⟦⊜⟧ ⟦✕⟧ ⟦⊟⟧ ⟦⊒⟧

Westin Oaks Houston at the Galleria H
(713) 960-8100. **$79-$529.** 5011 Westheimer Rd 77056. I-610 exit 8C (Westheimer Rd) northbound; exit 9A (San Felipe Rd/Westheimer Rd) southbound. Int corridors. **Pets:** Accepted.
⟦SAVE⟧ ⟦¶⟧ ⟦⊇⟧ ⟦⊜⟧ ⟦✕⟧ ⟦⊟⟧ ⟦⊒⟧

Wyndham Houston West Energy Corridor H
(281) 558-5580. **$109-$499.** 14703 Park Row Blvd 77079. I-10 exit 751 (Addicks Rd/SR 6), just n. Int corridors. **Pets:** Small. $75 one-time fee/ room. Service with restrictions, supervision.
⟦SAVE⟧ ⟦¶⟧ ⟦&M⟧ ⟦⊇⟧ ⟦⊜⟧ ⟦✕⟧ ⟦⊟⟧ ⟦⊒⟧

HUMBLE

Best Western Plus Atascocita Humble Inn & Suites H
(281) 852-5665. **$110-$160.** 7730 FM 1960 Rd E 77346. Jct US 59 and FM 1960, 6.8 mi e. Int corridors. **Pets:** Accepted.
⟦SAVE⟧ ⟦¶⟧ ⟦&M⟧ ⟦⊇⟧ ⟦⊜⟧ ⟦✕⟧ ⟦⊟⟧ ⟦⊒⟧

HUNTSVILLE

Best Western Huntsville Inn & Suites H
(936) 295-9000. **$109-$169.** 201 W Hill Park Cir 77320. I-45 exit 116, just w on US 190. Ext corridors. **Pets:** Medium. $20 daily fee/pet. Service with restrictions, crate. ⟦SAVE⟧ ⟦⊇⟧ ⟦⊜⟧ ⟦⊟⟧ ⟦⊒⟧

HURST

Hyatt Place Ft. Worth/Hurst H
(817) 577-3003. **$99-$199.** 1601 Hurst Town Center Dr 76054. SR 183 exit Precinct Line Rd, just n to Thousand Oaks Dr, then just w. Int corridors. **Pets:** Accepted. ⟦SAVE⟧ ⟦&M⟧ ⟦⊇⟧ ⟦⊜⟧ ⟦✕⟧ ⟦⊟⟧ ⟦⊒⟧

INGLESIDE

Best Western Naval Station Inn M
(361) 776-2767. **$90-$170.** 2025 State Hwy 361 78362. Jct SR 1069, 1 mi e. Ext corridors. **Pets:** Accepted. ⟦SAVE⟧ ⟦¶⟧ ⟦⊇⟧ ⟦⊜⟧ ⟦⊟⟧ ⟦⊒⟧

IRVING

Aloft Las Colinas H
(972) 717-6100. **$109-$289.** 122 E John Carpenter Frwy 75062. SR 114 exit O'Connor Rd, just s. Int corridors. **Pets:** Accepted.
⟦SAVE⟧ ⟦&M⟧ ⟦⊇⟧ ⟦⊜⟧ ⟦✕⟧ ⟦⊟⟧ ⟦⊒⟧

Candlewood Suites Dallas/Las Colinas H
(972) 714-9990. **Call for rates.** 5300 Green Park Dr 75038. SR 114 exit Walnut Hill Ln, just s. Int corridors. **Pets:** Accepted.
⟦&M⟧ ⟦⊜⟧ ⟦⊟⟧ ⟦⊒⟧

Courtyard by Marriott-DFW Airport North H
(972) 929-4004. **$80-$208.** 4949 Regent Blvd 75063. I-635 exit 34 (Freeport Pkwy), 0.5 mi s, then 0.5 mi w. Int corridors. **Pets:** Accepted.
⟦¶⟧ ⟦⊇⟧ ⟦⊜⟧ ⟦✕⟧ ⟦⊟⟧ ⟦⊒⟧

DoubleTree by Hilton DFW Airport-North H
(972) 929-8181. **Call for rates.** 4441 W John Carpenter Frwy 75063. North off SR 114 exit Esters Blvd. Int corridors. **Pets:** Accepted.
⟦SAVE⟧ ⟦¶⟧ ⟦⊇⟧ ⟦⊜⟧ ⟦✕⟧ ⟦⊟⟧ ⟦⊒⟧

Four Seasons Resort and Club H ❖
(972) 717-0700. **Call for rates.** 4150 MacArthur Blvd 75038. SR 114 exit MacArthur Blvd, 1.5 mi s. Int corridors. **Pets:** Medium, other species. Service with restrictions, supervision.
⟦SAVE⟧ ⟦¶⟧ ⟦&M⟧ ⟦⊇⟧ ⟦⊠⟧ ⟦⊜⟧ ⟦✕⟧ ⟦⊟⟧ ⟦⊒⟧

Hyatt House Dallas/Las Colinas H
(972) 831-0909. **$89-$249.** 5901 N MacArthur Blvd 75039. SR 114 exit MacArthur Blvd; on northwest corner. Ext/int corridors. **Pets:** Accepted.
[SAVE] [icons]

Hyatt Place Dallas/Las Colinas H
(972) 550-7400. **$84-$399.** 5455 Green Park Dr 75038. SR 114 exit Walnut Hill Ln, just se. Int corridors. **Pets:** Accepted.
[SAVE] [icons]

La Quinta Inn & Suites Dallas DFW Airport North H
(972) 915-4022. **$71-$207.** 4850 W John Carpenter Frwy 75063. SR 114 exit Freeport Pkwy; on eastbound frontage road. Int corridors.
Pets: Accepted. [icons]

La Quinta Inn & Suites Dallas DFW Airport South/Irving H
(972) 252-6546. **$75-$207.** 4105 W Airport Frwy 75062-5997. SR 183 exit Esters Rd westbound; exit N Belt Line Rd eastbound; on westbound frontage road. Int corridors. **Pets:** Accepted.
[icons]

La Quinta Inn & Suites Dallas-Las Colinas H
(972) 261-4900. **$75-$240.** 4225 N MacArthur Blvd 75038. Southeast off SR 114 exit MacArthur Blvd, 1.4 mi s. Int corridors. **Pets:** Accepted.
[icons]

Motel 6 - #4728 DFW North M
(972) 915-3993. **Call for rates.** 7800 Heathrow Dr 75063. SR 114 exit Freeport Pkwy, just se. Int corridors. **Pets:** Accepted. [icons]

NYLO Irving/Las Colinas H
(972) 373-8900. **Call for rates.** 1001 Royal 75039. SR 114 exit MacArthur Blvd, just n, then just w. Int corridors. **Pets:** Accepted.
[SAVE] [icons]

Omni Mandalay Dallas at Las Colinas H
(972) 556-0800. **Call for rates.** 221 E Las Colinas Blvd 75039. SR 114 exit O'Connor Rd, just n, then just e. Int corridors. **Pets:** Accepted.
[icons]

Residence Inn by Marriott at Las Colinas H
(972) 580-7773. **$97-$202.** 950 W Walnut Hill Ln 75038. SR 114 exit MacArthur Blvd, 0.5 mi s, then just e. Ext corridors. **Pets:** Accepted.
[SAVE] [ECO] [icons]

Residence Inn by Marriott-DFW North H
(972) 871-1331. **$75-$193.** 8600 Esters Blvd 75063. SR 114 exit Esters Blvd, 0.9 mi n. Ext/int corridors. **Pets:** Accepted.
[icons]

Sheraton DFW Airport Hotel H
(972) 929-8400. **Call for rates.** 4440 W John Carpenter Frwy 75063. SR 114 exit Esters Blvd, just s. Int corridors. **Pets:** Accepted.
[SAVE] [icons]

The Westin Dallas Fort Worth Airport H
(972) 929-4500. **$109-$299.** 4545 W John Carpenter Frwy 75063. SR 114 exit Esters Blvd, just n. Int corridors. **Pets:** Accepted.
[SAVE] [icons]

JACKSONVILLE

Best Western Executive Inn H 🌸
(903) 586-0007. **$72-$100.** 1659 S Jackson St 75766. On US 69, 1.7 mi s of jct US 69 and 79. Int corridors. **Pets:** Medium, other species. $20 one-time fee/pet. Service with restrictions, crate.
[SAVE] [icons]

JASPER

Best Western Inn Of Jasper H 🌸
(409) 384-7767. **$97-$108.** 205 W Gibson St 75951. US 190 and SR 63, 0.5 mi w of jct US 96. Ext corridors. **Pets:** $10 daily fee/room. Service with restrictions, supervision. [SAVE] [icons]

JOHNSON CITY

Best Western Johnson City Inn M
(830) 868-4044. **$90-$140.** 107 S US Hwy 281 78636. Jct US 281 and 290 N. Ext corridors. **Pets:** Accepted.
[SAVE] [icons]

JUNCTION

Rodeway Inn H
(325) 446-4588. **$70-$85.** 184 Dos Rios Dr 76849. I-10 exit 456, just s on US 377. Ext corridors. **Pets:** Accepted. [icons]

KATY

Home2 Suites by Hilton Houston/Katy H
(281) 398-3500. **$109-$129.** 20985 Katy Frwy 77450. I-10 exit 746; on east frontage road. Int corridors. **Pets:** Accepted.
[icons]

Residence Inn by Marriott Houston Katy Mills H
(281) 391-7501. **$103-$175.** 25401 Katy Mills Pkwy 77494. I-10 exit 740 (Pin Oak Rd) westbound; exit 741 (Pin Oak Rd) eastbound, just s; on south side of Kay Mills Mall. Int corridors. **Pets:** Accepted.
[icons]

KAUFMAN

Best Western La Hacienda Inn M
(972) 962-6272. **$65-$150.** 200 E Hwy 175 75142. Just e of jct US 175 and SR 34. Ext corridors. **Pets:** Medium. $15 daily fee/pet. Designated rooms, no service, supervision. [SAVE] [icons]

KERRVILLE

La Quinta Inn Kerrville H
(830) 896-9200. **$71-$218.** 1940 Sidney Baker St 78028. I-10 exit 508 (SR 16), 0.4 mi s. Int corridors. **Pets:** Accepted.
[icons]

Quality Inn of Kerrville H
(830) 792-7700. **$59-$219.** 2001 Sidney Baker St 78028. I-10 exit 508 (SR 16), 0.4 mi s. Int corridors. **Pets:** Small. $10 daily fee/pet. Supervision. [icons]

Y. O. Ranch Hotel & Conference Center H
(830) 257-4440. **$79-$169.** 2033 Sidney Baker St 78028. I-10 exit 508 (SR 16), 0.3 mi s. Ext/int corridors. **Pets:** Accepted.
[SAVE] [icons]

KILGORE

Best Western Inn of Kilgore H
(903) 986-1195. **$95-$120.** 1411 US Hwy 259 N 75662. I-20 exit 589, 3.9 mi s. Ext corridors. **Pets:** Accepted. [SAVE] [icons]

KILLEEN

Candlewood Suites-Ft. Hood/Killeen H
(254) 501-3990. **Call for rates.** 2300 Florence Rd 76542. US 90 exit Jasper Rd, just s. Int corridors. **Pets:** Large. $75 one-time fee/room. Service with restrictions, crate. [icons]

Days Inn Killeen M
(254) 554-2727. **$69-$105.** 1602 E Central Texas Expwy 76541. US 190 exit Trimmier Rd. Ext corridors. **Pets:** Other species. $25 one-time fee/pet. Service with restrictions. [SAVE] [icons]

Hawthorn Suites by Wyndham H
(254) 634-7795. **$69-$169.** 1502 E Central Texas Expwy 76541. US 190 exit Trimmier Rd; on south frontage road. Int corridors. **Pets:** Other species. $25 one-time fee/pet. Service with restrictions.

Residence Inn by Marriott Killeen H
(254) 634-1020. **$82-$125.** 400 E Central Texas Expwy 76541. US 190 exit Fort Hood St/Jasper Rd (SR 195); on south frontage road. Int corridors. **Pets:** Accepted.

Shilo Inn Suites Hotel - Killeen H
(254) 699-0999. **Call for rates.** 3701 S WS Young Dr 76542. US 190 exit WS Young Dr, 1 mi s. Int corridors. **Pets:** Dogs only. $75 deposit/room, $15 daily fee/room. Designated rooms, service with restrictions, crate.

TownePlace Suites by Marriott H
(254) 554-8899. **$66-$103.** 2401 Florence Rd 76542. US 190 exit Trimmier Rd to Jasper Rd, on south frontage road, 1 blk e to Florence Rd, then just s. Int corridors. **Pets:** Accepted.

KINGSVILLE

Best Western Kingsville Inn M
(361) 595-5656. **$99-$130.** 2402 E King Ave 78363. 1.5 mi e on US 77 Bypass; opposite jct SR 141. Ext corridors. **Pets:** Small. $30 daily fee/pet. Service with restrictions, supervision.

KINGWOOD

Comfort Suites Kingwood - Humble Houston North H
(281) 359-4448. **$80-$200.** 22223 Hwy 59 N 77339. US 59 exit Kingwood Dr northbound; exit McClellan southbound. Int corridors. **Pets:** Small. $25 daily fee/pet. Service with restrictions, supervision.

KYLE

La Quinta Inn & Suites Kyle H
(512) 295-5599. **$108-$207.** 18869 IH-35 N 78640. I-35 exit 217; on east frontage road. Int corridors. **Pets:** Accepted.

LA GRANGE *(Restaurants p. 625)*

Best Western La Grange Inn & Suites H
(979) 968-6800. **$106-$129.** 600 E State Hwy 71 Bypass 78945. Jct US 77 and SR 71, just e on N Frontage Rd. Int corridors. **Pets:** Accepted.

LAKE JACKSON *(Restaurants p. 625)*

Candlewood Suites-Lake Jackson-Clute H
(979) 297-0011. **$190.** 506 Hwy 332 77566. Jct SR 288/332 and Plantation Dr, just n. Int corridors. **Pets:** Medium. $150 one-time fee/room. Designated rooms, service with restrictions, crate.

LAKEWAY *(Restaurants p. 626)*

Lakeway Resort & Spa H
(512) 261-6600. **Call for rates.** 101 Lakeway Dr 78734. Jct FM 620 and Lakeway Blvd W, 1.5 mi to Lakeway Dr, 2.1 mi n. Int corridors. **Pets:** Accepted.

LAREDO

Days Inn & Suites H
(956) 724-8221. **$90-$175.** 7060 N San Bernardo Ave 78041. I-35 exit 4 (San Bernardo Ave), just s; on southbound access road. Ext/int corridors. **Pets:** Accepted.

La Posada Hotel H
(956) 722-1701. **Call for rates.** 1000 Zaragoza St 78040. I-35 exit downtown; just e of International Bridge 1. Ext/int corridors.
Pets: Accepted.

La Quinta Inn & Suites Laredo Airport H
(956) 724-7222. **$67-$186.** 7220 Bob Bullock Loop 78041. I-35 exit 8 (Bob Bullock Loop E), 5.8 mi e. Int corridors. **Pets:** Accepted.

La Quinta Inn Laredo I-35 M
(956) 722-0511. **$67-$152.** 3610 Santa Ursula Ave 78041. I-35 exit 2 (Jefferson St); on southbound frontage road. Ext corridors.
Pets: Accepted.

Residence Inn by Marriott Laredo H
(956) 753-9700. **$91-$122.** 310 Lost Oaks Blvd 78041. I-35 exit 3B (Mann Rd), just n; on northbound frontage road. Int corridors.
Pets: Accepted.

Staybridge Suites-Laredo H
(956) 722-0444. **Call for rates.** 7010 Bob Bullock Loop 78041. US 83 exit on Loop 20 (Bob Bullock Loop); on west side. Int corridors.
Pets: Accepted.

LEWISVILLE

Motel 6 - #1288 H
(972) 436-5008. **$55-$75.** 1705 Lakepointe Dr 75057. I-35E exit 449 (Corporate Dr), just n on service road. Int corridors. **Pets:** Accepted.

Residence Inn by Marriott Dallas/Lewisville H
(972) 315-3777. **$85-$177.** 755 E Vista Ridge Mall Dr 75067. I-35E exit 448A (Round Grove Rd) southbound, 0.5 mi s on frontage road, then just w; exit 447B northbound, just w to Lake Vista, then just n. Int corridors. **Pets:** Accepted.

TownePlace Suites by Marriott Dallas Lewisville H
(972) 459-1275. **$93-$146.** 731 E Vista Ridge Mall Dr 75067. I-35 exit 447B northbound (SR 121); exit 448A southbound, just w to Lake Vista Dr, then just n. Int corridors. **Pets:** Large. $100 one-time fee/room. Service with restrictions.

LITTLEFIELD

Best Western Littlefield Inn & Suites H
(806) 385-3400. **$102-$199.** 2600 Hall Ave 79339. Just s of jct US 84 and 385. Int corridors. **Pets:** Accepted.

LIVE OAK

La Quinta Inn San Antonio I-35 North at Toepperwein H
(210) 657-5500. **$67-$240.** 12822 I-35 N 78233. I-35 exit 170B (Toepperwein Rd); on northbound access road. Ext/int corridors.
Pets: Accepted.

LIVINGSTON

Livingston Inn & Suites H
(936) 327-8500. **$86-$95.** 335 Hwy 59 Loop S 77351. Just s of jct US 59 and 190; on southbound frontage road. Int corridors. **Pets:** $100 deposit/room. Designated rooms, service with restrictions, crate.

LLANO

Best Western Llano H
(325) 247-4101. **$80-$145.** 901 W Young St 78643. 1 mi w on SR 71 and 29. Ext corridors. **Pets:** Accepted.

LONGVIEW

▼▼ Holiday Inn Express Hotel & Suites Longview South ℍ
(903) 247-3000. **Call for rates.** 900 S Access Rd 75602. I-20 exit 596, just s. Int corridors. **Pets:** Accepted. 🛎 📶 ✖ 🛗 💻

▼▼▼▼ La Quinta Inn & Suites Longview North ℍ
(903) 663-6611. **$88-$174.** 908 E Hawkins Pkwy 75605. Just w of jct US 259. Int corridors. **Pets:** Accepted. 🛎 📶 ✖ 🛗 💻

▼▼ Sleep Inn and Suites ℍ
(903) 212-6520. **$69-$130.** 615 City Center Way 75605. Jct Loop 281 and US 259, just e. Int corridors. **Pets:** Medium. $25 one-time fee/pet. Service with restrictions, supervision. 📶 ✖ 🛗 💻

▼▼▼▼ Staybridge Suites ℍ
(903) 212-3800. **Call for rates.** 3409 N Fourth St 75605. Just n of jct SR 281/Loop 281. Int corridors. **Pets:** Accepted. 📶 ✖ 🛗 💻

LUBBOCK

𝔸𝔸𝔸 ▼▼▼▼ Arbor Inn & Suites ℍ
(806) 722-2726. **$99-$299.** 5310 Englewood Ave 79424. Loop 289 exit 50th St, just w. Int corridors. **Pets:** Accepted.
SAVE 🅼 🛎 📶 ✖ 🛗 💻

▼▼▼▼ Baymont Inn & Suites Lubbock ℍ
(806) 792-5181. **$69-$220.** 3901 19th St 79410. Jct US 62/82 W and 19th St. Int corridors. **Pets:** Accepted.
🍴 🅼 🛎 📶 ✖ 🛗 💻

𝔸𝔸𝔸 ▼▼▼▼ Best Western Plus Lubbock Windsor Inn ℍ
(806) 762-8400. **$70-$250.** 5410 I-27 79404. I-27 exit 1B southbound; exit 1A (50th St) northbound. Int corridors. **Pets:** Other species. $15 daily fee/pet. Designated rooms, service with restrictions, supervision.
SAVE 🍴 🛎 📶 ✖ 🛗 💻

𝔸𝔸𝔸 ▼▼▼▼ Best Western Plus Tech Medical Center Inn ℍ
(806) 701-5299. **$100-$299.** 4703 N Loop 289 79416. 1 mi sw of jct N Loop 289 and Quaker Ave; on S Service Rd. Int corridors. **Pets:** Medium. $20 daily fee/pet. Designated rooms, service with restrictions, supervision. SAVE 🍴 🅼 📶 ✖ 🛗 💻

▼▼▼▼ Home2 Suites by Hilton - Lubbock ℍ
(806) 833-5000. **$109-$159.** 6004 Marsha Sharp Frwy 79407. Just w of jct Loop 289. Int corridors. **Pets:** Accepted. 🅼 📶 ✖ 🛗 💻

𝔸𝔸𝔸 ▼▼▼▼ Hyatt Place Lubbock ℍ
(806) 741-0200. **$109-$379.** 2309 Mac Davis Ln 79401. US 82 (Marsha Sharpe Frwy), just s on University Ave, then just e. Int corridors. **Pets:** Medium, dogs only. $75 one-time fee/pet. Service with restrictions, crate. SAVE 📶 ✖ 🛗 💻

▼▼▼▼ La Quinta Inn & Suites Lubbock North ℍ
(806) 749-1600. **$93-$229.** 5006 Auburn St 79416. 1 mi sw of jct Loop 289 N and Quaker Ave; on N Service Rd. Int corridors. **Pets:** Accepted.
🍴 🛎 📶 ✖ 🛗 💻

▼▼ La Quinta Inn & Suites Lubbock West Medical Center ℍ
(806) 792-0065. **$68-$301.** 4115 Marsha Sharp Frwy 79407. Jct US 62/82 and Quaker Ave, just se. Ext/int corridors. **Pets:** Accepted.
🛎 📶 ✖ 🛗 💻

▼▼▼▼ Staybridge Suites ℍ
(806) 765-8900. **Call for rates.** 2515 19th St 79410. Just sw of jct University Ave. Int corridors. **Pets:** Accepted.
🅼 🛎 📶 ✖ 🛗 💻

▼▼▼ Studio 6 ℍ
(806) 745-1963. **Call for rates.** 2551 S Loop 289 79423. Just w of jct University Ave; on south frontage road. Ext corridors. **Pets:** Other species. $10 daily fee/room. Service with restrictions, supervision.
🛎 📶 ✖ 🛗 💻

▼▼▼▼ TownePlace Suites by Marriott ℍ
(806) 799-6226. **$93-$142.** 5310 W Loop 289 79424. 0.5 mi s of jct US 62/82. Int corridors. **Pets:** Accepted. 🅼 🛎 📶 ✖ 🛗 💻

LUFKIN

𝔸𝔸𝔸 ▼▼▼▼ Best Western Plus Crown Colony Inn & Suites ℍ 🐾
(936) 634-3481. **$116-$149.** 3211 S 1st St 75901. 2 mi s of jct US 59 and Loop 287. Int corridors. **Pets:** Medium. $25 one-time fee/room. Designated rooms, service with restrictions, crate.
SAVE 🛎 📶 ✖ 🛗 💻

LULING

▼▼▼▼ Longhorn Inn & Suites ℍ
(830) 875-5442. **$109-$139, 3 day notice.** 4120 E Pierce St 78648. I-10 exit 632; on northwest corner. Int corridors. **Pets:** Accepted.
🍴 🅼 📶 ✖ 🛗 💻

MADISONVILLE

𝔸𝔸𝔸 ▼▼▼ Best Western Executive Inn & Suites ℍ
(936) 349-1700. **$110-$115.** 3307 E Main St 77864. I-45 exit 142, just e. Int corridors. **Pets:** $10 daily fee/pet. Service with restrictions, crate.
SAVE 🛎 📶 🛗 💻

MANSFIELD

𝔸𝔸𝔸 ▼▼▼ Best Western Plus Mansfield Inn & Suites ℍ
(817) 539-0707. **$99-$134.** 775 N Hwy 287 76063. US 287 exit Walnut Creek Rd; on southbound frontage road. Int corridors. **Pets:** Accepted.
SAVE 🍴 🛎 ✖ 🛗 💻

▼▼▼ Holiday Inn Express Hotel & Suites ℍ
(817) 453-8722. **Call for rates.** 201 Hwy 287 N 76063. US 287 exit Walnut Creek Rd, just s on frontage road. Int corridors. **Pets:** Accepted.
🛎 📶 ✖ 🛗 💻

▼▼▼▼ La Quinta Inn & Suites Mansfield ℍ
(817) 453-5040. **$86-$202.** 1503 Breckenridge Rd 76063. US 287 exit Walnut Creek Rd/Debbie Ln, 1.2 mi n to Debbie Ln, then just e. Int corridors. **Pets:** Accepted. 🛎 📶 ✖ 🛗 💻

MANVEL

𝔸𝔸𝔸 ▼▼▼ Best Western Plus Manvel Inn & Suites ℍ
(281) 489-2266. **$90-$115.** 19301 Hwy 6 77578. 1.3 mi e of jct SR 288. Int corridors. **Pets:** Accepted. SAVE 🍴 🅼 🛎 📶 ✖ 🛗 💻

MARBLE FALLS

𝔸𝔸𝔸 ▼▼▼ Best Western Marble Falls Inn Ⓜ
(830) 693-5122. **$80-$165.** 1403 N US Hwy 281 78654. 0.4 mi n of jct US 281 and FM 1431. Ext/int corridors. **Pets:** Accepted.
SAVE 🎬 🅼 🛎 📶 🛗 💻

▼▼▼ Quality Inn-Marble Falls Ⓜ
(830) 693-7531. **$80-$200.** 1206 US Hwy 281 N 78654. 0.3 mi n of jct US 281 and FM 1431. Ext corridors. **Pets:** Medium, other species. $10 daily fee/pet. Designated rooms, service with restrictions, supervision.
🛎 📶 🛗 💻

MARFA

▼▼▼ Hotel Paisano H ❀

(432) 729-3669. **Call for rates.** 207 N Highland Ave 79843. Jct US 90 and SR 17, 3 blks n. Int corridors. **Pets:** Other species. $20 daily fee/pet. Service with restrictions, supervision.

⟨¶⟩ ⟨≈⟩ ⟨≈⟩ ⟨✕⟩ ⟨⚷⟩ ⟨❚⟩ ⟨▣⟩

MARSHALL

◢◣◢ ▼▼ Best Western Executive Inn H

(903) 935-0707. **$70-$80.** 5201 E End Blvd S 75672. I-20 exit 617, 0.4 mi n on US 59. Ext corridors. **Pets:** Medium, dogs only. $15 daily fee/pet. Service with restrictions, supervision.

⟨SAVE⟩ ⟨¶⟩ ⟨≈⟩ ⟨≈⟩ ⟨❚⟩ ⟨▣⟩

▼▼ La Quinta Inn & Suites H

(903) 934-3080. **$86-$152.** 6015 E End Blvd S 75672. I-20 exit 617, just s. Int corridors. **Pets:** Accepted. ⟨¶⟩ ⟨≈⟩ ⟨✕⟩ ⟨❚⟩ ⟨▣⟩

MCALLEN

▼▼ Drury Inn-McAllen H

(956) 687-5100. **$79-$129.** 612 W Expwy 83 78501. US 83 exit 2nd St; on northwest frontage road. Int corridors. **Pets:** Accepted.

⟨≈⟩ ⟨≈⟩ ⟨✕⟩ ⟨❚⟩ ⟨▣⟩

▼▼▼ Drury Suites-McAllen H

(956) 682-3222. **$89-$179.** 300 W Expwy 83 78501. At US 83 and 6th St. Int corridors. **Pets:** Accepted. ⟨≈M⟩ ⟨≈⟩ ⟨≈⟩ ⟨✕⟩ ⟨❚⟩ ⟨▣⟩

▼ Motel 6 McAllen #212 M

(956) 687-3700. **$55-$75.** 700 W Expwy 83 78501. US 83 exit 2nd St; on northwest frontage road. Ext corridors. **Pets:** Accepted. ⟨≈⟩ ⟨⬡⟩

▼ Posada Ana Inn H

(956) 631-6700. **$90-$119.** 620 W Expwy 83 78501. US 83 exit 2nd St; on northwest frontage road. Int corridors. **Pets:** Accepted.

⟨≈⟩ ⟨✕⟩ ⟨❚⟩ ⟨▣⟩

▼▼▼ Residence Inn by Marriott H

(956) 994-8626. **$107-$169.** 220 W Expwy 83 78501. US 83 exit 2nd St, just w, then just n. Int corridors. **Pets:** Accepted.

⟨¶⟩ ⟨≈M⟩ ⟨≈⟩ ⟨✕⟩ ⟨≈⟩ ⟨✕⟩ ⟨❚⟩ ⟨▣⟩

▼▼▼ Staybridge Suites McAllen-Airport H

(956) 213-7829. **Call for rates.** 620 Wichita Ave 78503. 0.4 mi s of US 83, just e of S 10th St. Int corridors. **Pets:** Accepted.

⟨¶⟩ ⟨≈M⟩ ⟨≈⟩ ⟨≈⟩ ⟨✕⟩ ⟨❚⟩ ⟨▣⟩

MCKINNEY

◢◣◢ ▼▼▼ Sheraton McKinney Hotel H

(972) 549-4000. **$99-$209.** 1900 Gateway Blvd 75070. US 75 exit 38B (Frontage Road) northbound, just n to Gateway Blvd, then just e; exit 39 (El Dorado Pkwy) southbound, just e to Medical Center Dr, just s, then just w. Int corridors. **Pets:** Accepted. ⟨SAVE⟩ ⟨¶⟩ ⟨≈⟩ ⟨✕⟩ ⟨▣⟩

MEXIA

◢◣◢ ▼▼ Best Western Limestone Inn & Suites H

(254) 562-0200. **$80-$90.** 1314 E Milam St 76667. Just e of CR 1365 on US 84; east side of town. Int corridors. **Pets:** Small. $10 daily fee/pet. Service with restrictions, supervision.

⟨SAVE⟩ ⟨¶⟩ ⟨≈⟩ ⟨≈⟩ ⟨❚⟩ ⟨▣⟩

MIDLAND

▼▼ Baymont Inn & Suites Midland Center H

(432) 253-4000. **$89-$99.** 3100 US 158 E 79706. I-20 exit 138, just se. Int corridors. **Pets:** Accepted. ⟨¶⟩ ⟨≈M⟩ ⟨≈⟩ ⟨✕⟩ ⟨❚⟩ ⟨▣⟩

▼▼ Home2 Suites by Hilton H ❀

(432) 699-4040. **$99-$249.** 1401 Catalina Dr 79706. Just sw of jct Loop 250 and SR 191. Int corridors. **Pets:** Other species. $75 one-time fee/room. Service with restrictions, supervision. ⟨≈M⟩ ⟨≈⟩ ⟨✕⟩ ⟨❚⟩ ⟨▣⟩

▼▼▼ La Quinta Inn & Suites Midland North H

(432) 694-1200. **$130-$328.** 2606 N Loop 250 W 79707. 0.5 mi n of jct SR 158/191; on east frontage road. Int corridors. **Pets:** Accepted.

⟨¶⟩ ⟨≈M⟩ ⟨≈⟩ ⟨≈⟩ ⟨✕⟩ ⟨❚⟩ ⟨▣⟩

▼▼ Microtel Inn & Suites by Wyndham H

(432) 203-2100. **$74-$119.** 200 W Longview Rd 79701. I-20 exit 137, 1 mi w to S Baird St, then just n. Int corridors. **Pets:** Other species. $10 daily fee/pet. Designated rooms, service with restrictions, supervision.

⟨¶⟩ ⟨≈M⟩ ⟨≈⟩ ⟨✕⟩ ⟨❚⟩ ⟨▣⟩

▼▼▼ Residence Inn by Marriott Midland H

(432) 689-3511. **$83-$217.** 5509 Deauville Blvd 79706. Just w of jct Loop 250; on south frontage road. Int corridors. **Pets:** Medium, other species. $100 one-time fee/room. Service with restrictions, supervision.

⟨≈M⟩ ⟨≈⟩ ⟨≈⟩ ⟨✕⟩ ⟨❚⟩ ⟨▣⟩

MINERAL WELLS

◢◣◢ ▼▼ Best Western Club House Inn & Suites H ❀

(940) 325-2270. **$60-$160.** 4410 Hwy 180 E 76067. Jct US 180 and CR 1195; in East Mineral Wells. Int corridors. **Pets:** Other species. $15 daily fee/pet. Service with restrictions, supervision.

⟨SAVE⟩ ⟨¶⟩ ⟨≈M⟩ ⟨≈⟩ ⟨≈⟩ ⟨❚⟩ ⟨▣⟩

MISSION

▼▼▼ La Quinta Inn & Suites H

(956) 581-7772. **$93-$251.** 805 Travis St 78572. US 83 exit Bryan Rd; on eastbound access road. Int corridors. **Pets:** Accepted.

⟨¶⟩ ⟨≈⟩ ⟨≈⟩ ⟨✕⟩ ⟨❚⟩ ⟨▣⟩

MONTGOMERY

◢◣◢ ▼▼ Best Western Lake Conroe Inn H

(936) 588-3030. **$100-$135.** 14643 Hwy 105 77356. Just w of McCaleb Rd. Ext corridors. **Pets:** Medium. $20 daily fee/pet. Service with restrictions, supervision. ⟨SAVE⟩ ⟨≈M⟩ ⟨≈⟩ ⟨≈⟩ ⟨❚⟩ ⟨▣⟩

◢◣◢ ▼▼ ▼▼ La Torretta Lake Resort & Spa H

(936) 448-4400. **$149-$259, 3 day notice.** 600 La Torretta Blvd 77356. SR 105, 2.5 mi n on Walden Rd to La Torretta Blvd. Ext/int corridors. **Pets:** Accepted. ⟨SAVE⟩ ⟨⊟⟩ ⟨¶⟩ ⟨≈M⟩ ⟨≈⟩ ⟨✕⟩ ⟨≈⟩ ⟨✕⟩ ⟨❚⟩ ⟨▣⟩

MOUNT PLEASANT

◢◣◢ ▼▼ Best Western Mount Pleasant Inn M

(903) 577-7377. **$71-$100.** 102 E Burton Rd 75455. I-30 exit 162, just e. Ext corridors. **Pets:** Accepted. ⟨SAVE⟩ ⟨¶⟩ ⟨≈⟩ ⟨≈⟩ ⟨❚⟩ ⟨▣⟩

▼▼ Super 8 M

(903) 572-9808. **$50-$155.** 204 Lakewood Dr 75455. I-30 exit 162 eastbound; exit 162A westbound, just n, then just w. Ext corridors. **Pets:** Accepted. ⟨≈⟩ ⟨≈⟩ ⟨❚⟩ ⟨▣⟩

NACOGDOCHES

◢◣◢ ▼▼ Best Western Inn of Nacogdoches H

(936) 560-4900. **$70-$110.** 3428 South St 75964. US 59, just s of jct Loop 224 and US 59 business route. Ext corridors. **Pets:** Accepted.

⟨SAVE⟩ ⟨≈⟩ ⟨≈⟩ ⟨❚⟩ ⟨▣⟩

◢◣◢ ▼▼ Best Western Northpark Inn H ❀

(936) 560-1906. **$63-$160.** 4809 NW Stallings Dr 75964. Jct US 59 N and Loop 224 exit Westward Dr. Ext corridors. **Pets:** Small, dogs only. $15 daily fee/pet. Designated rooms, service with restrictions, supervision. ⟨SAVE⟩ ⟨≈⟩ ⟨≈⟩ ⟨❚⟩ ⟨▣⟩

▼▼▼ Holiday Inn Express Nacogdoches H

(936) 564-0100. **$100-$230.** 200 Holiday Ln 75964. US 59, just s of jct Loop 224 and US 59 business route. Int corridors. **Pets:** Accepted.

⟨¶⟩ ⟨≈M⟩ ⟨≈⟩ ⟨✕⟩ ⟨❚⟩ ⟨▣⟩

NASSAU BAY

▼▼▼▼ Hilton Houston NASA Clear Lake 🏠
(281) 333-9300. **$99-$189.** 3000 NASA Pkwy 77058. 2 mi e of NASA Bypass road. Int corridors. **Pets:** Accepted.
🍴 ♿ 🏊 📶 ✖ 🔌 💻

NAVASOTA

ⓐⓐⓐ ▼▼▼ Best Western Inn of Navasota 🏠 🐾
(936) 870-4100. **$90-$200.** 8965 Hwy 6 N 77868. Jct SR 6 and 90; on southeast corner. Int corridors. **Pets:** Medium. $20 daily fee/pet. Designated rooms, service with restrictions, supervision.
🆂🅰🆅🅴 🍴 🏊 📶 🔌 💻

ⓐⓐⓐ ▼▼▼ Comfort Inn & Suites 🏠
(936) 825-9464. **$80-$280.** 9345 State Hwy 6 Loop S 77868. SR 6 exit SR 105 and 90, 0.5 mi n on E Frontage Rd. Int corridors. **Pets:** Accepted. 🆂🅰🆅🅴 🏊 📶 ✖ 🔌 💻

NEW BRAUNFELS

▼▼▼ Americas Best Value Inn Ⓜ
(830) 625-3932. **$59-$259.** 808 S State Hwy 46 78130. I-35 exit 189 (SR 46), 0.4 mi e. Ext corridors. **Pets:** Accepted. 🏊 📶 🔌 💻

▼▼▼▼ La Quinta Inn & Suites New Braunfels 🏠
(830) 627-3333. **$79-$273.** 365 Hwy 46 S 78130. I-35 exit 189 (SR 46), just e. Int corridors. **Pets:** Accepted. 🏊 📶 ✖ 🔌 💻

▼▼ Ramada New Braunfels 🏠
(830) 625-8017. **$69-$179.** 1051 I-35 E 78130. I-35 exit 189 (SR 46); on southbound frontage road. Ext corridors. **Pets:** Accepted.
♿ 🏊 📶 🔌 💻

▼▼ Super 8-New Braunfels Ⓜ
(830) 629-1155. **$60-$190.** 510 Hwy 46 S 78130. I-35 exit 189 (SR 46), just e. Ext corridors. **Pets:** Small. $25 daily fee/pet. Service with restrictions. ♿ 🏊 📶 🔌 💻

ⓐⓐⓐ ▼▼▼ Wingate by Wyndham 🏠
(830) 515-4701. **$84-$179.** 245 FM 306 N 78130. I-35 exit 191 (FM 306), just w. Int corridors. **Pets:** Accepted.
🆂🅰🆅🅴 ♿ 🏊 📶 ✖ 🔌 💻

NEW CANEY

ⓐⓐⓐ ▼▼▼ Best Western Plus New Caney Inn & Suites 🏠
(281) 354-7222. **$85-$200.** 22033 N Hwy 59 77357. US 59 exit northbound Community Dr, just e; exit southbound FM 1314, make U-turn. Int corridors. **Pets:** Accepted. 🆂🅰🆅🅴 🍴 ♿ 🏊 📶 ✖ 🔌 💻

ⓐⓐⓐ ▼▼▼ La Quinta Inn & Suites-New Caney 🏠
(281) 354-1904. **$86-$187.** 22025 US Hwy 59 N 77357. US 59 exit northbound Community Dr, just e; exit southbound FM 1314, U-turn 1 mi n. Int corridors. **Pets:** Accepted. 🆂🅰🆅🅴 ♿ 🏊 📶 ✖ 🔌 💻

NORTH RICHLAND HILLS

ⓐⓐⓐ ▼▼▼ Quality Inn & Suites 🏠
(817) 656-8881. **$86-$100.** 8709 Airport Frwy 76180. SR 121/183 exit Precinct Line Rd eastbound; exit Bedford Euless Rd westbound; on westbound frontage road. Ext corridors. **Pets:** Accepted.
🆂🅰🆅🅴 🏊 📶 🔌 💻

ODESSA

▼▼▼ Comfort Suites 🏠
(432) 362-1500. **$79-$249.** 4801 E 50th St 79762. Jct JBS Pkwy and 52nd St, just s. Int corridors. **Pets:** Accepted. 🏊 📶 ✖ 🔌 💻

▼▼▼ Homewood Suites by Hilton 🏠
(432) 563-2323. **$159-$229.** 7221 Tres Hermanas Blvd 79765. Just s of jct SR 191 and Billy Hext Rd. Int corridors. **Pets:** Accepted.
♿ 📶 ✖ 🔌 💻

▼▼▼ Residence Inn by Marriott 🏠
(432) 563-2190. **$82-$187.** 7261 Tres Hermanas Blvd 79765. Just s of jct SR 191 and Billy Hext Rd. Int corridors. **Pets:** Other species. $100 one-time fee/room. Service with restrictions, supervision.
🍴 ♿ 📶 ✖ 🔌 💻

▼▼▼ TownePlace Suites by Marriott 🏠
(432) 362-1077. **$67-$186.** 4412 Tanglewood Ln 79762. Just nw of jct JBS Pkwy and 42nd St. Int corridors. **Pets:** Accepted.
♿ 🏊 📶 ✖ 🔌 💻

ORANGE

ⓐⓐⓐ ▼▼▼ Holiday Inn Express & Suites Orange 🏠
(409) 882-9222. **$109-$139.** 2655 I-10 E 77630. I-10 exit 877 eastbound; exit 876 westbound; on eastbound frontage road. Int corridors. **Pets:** Small. $25 daily fee/pet. Service with restrictions, supervision.
🆂🅰🆅🅴 🍴 ♿ 🏊 📶 ✖ 🔌 💻

▼▼▼ La Quinta Inn & Suites Orange 🏠
(409) 883-0011. **$86-$213.** 2220 Hwy 62 S 77630. I-10 exit 873, just s. Int corridors. **Pets:** Accepted. ♿ 🏊 📶 ✖ 🔌 💻

OZONA

ⓐⓐⓐ ▼▼▼ Hillcrest Inn & Suites Ⓜ
(325) 392-4000. **$70-$90.** 1204 Sheffield Rd/Loop 466 W 76943. I-10 exit 365, 2 blks n to Loop 466, then 1 mi w. Ext corridors.
Pets: Accepted. 🆂🅰🆅🅴 🍴 📶 🔌 💻

ⓐⓐⓐ ▼▼▼ Quality Inn Ⓜ
(325) 392-3791. **$120-$200.** 1307 Ave A 76943. I-10 exit 365; on westbound frontage road. Ext/int corridors. **Pets:** Accepted.
🆂🅰🆅🅴 🏊 📶 🔌 💻

PALESTINE

ⓐⓐⓐ ▼▼▼ Best Western Palestine Inn 🏠
(903) 723-4655. **$75-$83.** 1601 W Palestine Ave 75801. Jct US 287/SR 19, 0.7 mi sw on US 79. Ext corridors. **Pets:** Accepted.
🆂🅰🆅🅴 🏊 📶 🔌 💻

▼▼▼ Holiday Inn Express 🏠
(903) 723-4884. **Call for rates.** 1030 E Palestine Ave 75801. Jct US 79 and Loop 256, 0.3 mi s on US 79. Int corridors. **Pets:** Accepted.
🍴 ♿ 🏊 📶 ✖ 🔌 💻

▼▼▼ La Quinta Inn & Suites Palestine 🏠
(903) 723-1387. **$86-$225.** 3000 S Loop 256 75801. 1.8 mi e of jct US 79 and Loop 256. Int corridors. **Pets:** Accepted.
🔲 🍴 🏊 📶 ✖ 🔌 💻

PAMPA

▼▼ AmericInn Lodge & Suites of Pampa 🏠
(806) 665-4404. **Call for rates.** 1101 N Hobart St 79065. Just n of jct SR 70 and 152. Int corridors. **Pets:** Accepted.
🏊 📶 ✖ 🔌 💻

ⓐⓐⓐ ▼▼▼ Best Western Northgate Inn 🏠
(806) 665-0926. **$70-$99.** 2831 Perryton Pkwy 79065. 2.1 mi n of jct SR 70 and 152. Ext corridors. **Pets:** Medium, other species. $10 daily fee/room. Designated rooms, service with restrictions, supervision.
🆂🅰🆅🅴 📶 🔌 💻

PASADENA

▼▼▼ Residence Inn by Marriott 🏠
(832) 283-0450. **Call for rates.** 4711 E Sam Houston Pkwy S 77505. Beltway 8 exit Crenshaw Rd, just e. Int corridors. **Pets:** Accepted.
♿ 📶 ✖ 🔌 💻

PEARLAND

Best Western Pearland Inn [H]
(281) 997-2000. **$90-$250.** 1855 N Main St 77581. Jct Loop 8 S and SR 35, 1.5 mi s. Ext corridors. **Pets:** Accepted.

Comfort Suites Pearland-South Houston [H]
(713) 340-1705. **$99-$239.** 2806 Miller Ranch Rd 77584. SR 288 exit Shadow Creek Pkwy, just e. Int corridors. **Pets:** Small. $25 one-time fee/pet. Designated rooms, service with restrictions, crate.

La Quinta Inn & Suites Pearland [H]
(281) 412-5454. **$86-$471.** 9002 Broadway St 77584. Jct SR 288 and 518, 1.6 mi e. Int corridors. **Pets:** Accepted.

PEARSALL

Baymont Inn & Suites Pearsall [H]
(830) 334-4900. **$80-$110.** 1808 W Comal St 78061. I-35 exit 101, just e. Ext/int corridors. **Pets:** Very small. $10 daily fee/pet. Designated rooms, service with restrictions, supervision.

La Quinta Inn & Suites [H]
(830) 872-3277. **$67-$218.** 170 Medical Dr 78061. I-35 exit 101, just w; on southbound frontage road. Int corridors. **Pets:** Accepted.

PECOS

Best Western Swiss Clock Inn [H] 🐾
(432) 447-2215. **$111-$140.** 133 S Frontage Rd, I-20 79772. I-20 exit 40, just s. Ext corridors. **Pets:** Large, dogs only. $15 daily fee/pet. Designated rooms, service with restrictions, crate.

Fairfield Inn & Suites by Marriott Pecos [H]
(432) 447-2500. **$79-$159.** 92 Raul Florez Blvd 79772. I-20 exit Country Club Dr, just n. Int corridors. **Pets:** Medium, dogs only. $100 one-time fee/pet. Service with restrictions, supervision.

Knights Inn Laura Lodge Motel & Suites [M]
(432) 445-4924. **$99-$139.** 1000 E 3rd St 79772. I-20 exit 42, 1 mi nw to Business Rt I-20, then 0.5 mi e. Ext corridors. **Pets:** Small. $10 daily fee/pet. Designated rooms, service with restrictions, supervision.

Microtel Inn & Suites by Wyndham, Pecos [H]
(432) 447-0551. **$80-$98.** 5204 S Cedar St 79772. I-20 exit 42, just se. Int corridors. **Pets:** Dogs only. $25 daily fee/pet. Service with restrictions, supervision.

PERRYTON

Best Western Perryton Inn [H]
(806) 434-2850. **$95-$155.** 3505 S Main St (US 83) 79070. US 83, 2.2 mi s. Int corridors. **Pets:** $20 daily fee/pet. Designated rooms, service with restrictions.

PFLUGERVILLE

Best Western Plus Pflugerville [H]
(512) 600-3300. **$129-$189.** 16101 Impact Way 78660. Jct US 290 and SR 130/SR 45, exit 431, just e, then s. Int corridors. **Pets:** Accepted.

PHARR

Comfort Inn & Suites [H]
(956) 783-7777. **$86-$180.** 2706 N Cage Blvd 78577. On northboud frontage road. Int corridors. **Pets:** Medium. $10 daily fee/pet. Designated rooms, service with restrictions, supervision.

La Quinta Inn & Suites North [H]
(956) 782-8832. **$90-$214.** 4607 N Cage Blvd 78577. US 281 exit Nolana Loop, just w. Int corridors. **Pets:** Accepted.

La Quinta Inn & Suites Pharr [H]
(956) 787-2900. **$90-$219.** 4603 N Cage Blvd 78577. US 281 exit Nolana Loop, just w. Int corridors. **Pets:** Accepted.

PLAINVIEW

Holiday Inn Express Hotel & Suites [H]
(806) 296-9900. **Call for rates.** 4213 W 13th St 79072. I-27 exit 49 northbound, 0.5 mi nw; exit 50 southbound, 0.5 mi sw. Int corridors.
Pets: Accepted.

PLANO

Aloft Plano [H]
(214) 474-2520. **$99-$269.** 6853 N Dallas Pkwy 75024. Dallas North Tollway exit Spring Creek Pkwy/Tennyson Pkwy, just s of Tennyson Pkwy; on frontage road. Int corridors. **Pets:** Accepted.

Candlewood Suites-Plano [H]
(972) 618-5446. **$70-$180, 3 day notice.** 4701 Legacy Dr 75024. Jct SR 289 (Preston Rd) and Legacy Dr, just e. Int corridors.
Pets: Accepted.

Comfort Inn & Suites Plano [H]
(972) 881-1881. **$89-$169.** 700 Central Pkwy E 75074. Just e of US 75, 0.3 mi ne of jct FM 544; exit 29A northbound; exit 29 southbound, 0.5 mi s on frontage road, just e on 15th St, then 0.5 mi n on frontage road. Int corridors. **Pets:** Accepted.

Hilton Dallas/Plano Granite Park [H]
(469) 353-5000. **$99-$349.** 5805 Granite Pkwy 75024. Dallas Pkwy exit SR 121 (Sam Rayburn Tollway), on northbound frontage road. Int corridors. **Pets:** Accepted.

Homewood Suites by Hilton [H]
(972) 758-8800. **$99-$169.** 4705 Old Shepard Pl 75093. Jct Plano Pkwy and SR 289 (Preston Rd), 0.4 mi n, just e. Int corridors.
Pets: Accepted.

Hyatt Place Dallas/Plano [H]
(972) 378-3997. **$79-$239.** 3100 Dallas Pkwy 75093. Dallas Pkwy exit W Park Blvd northbound; exit Parker Rd southbound; on northbound frontage road. Int corridors. **Pets:** Accepted.

La Quinta Inn & Suites Dallas Plano West [H]
(972) 599-0700. **$71-$202.** 4800 W Plano Pkwy 75093. Just e of jct SR 289 (Preston Rd). Int corridors. **Pets:** Accepted.

Magnuson Park Suites Hotel [H]
(972) 578-2243. **Call for rates.** 640 Park Blvd E 75074. US 75 exit 29A northbound, just e, then 0.5 mi s on frontage road; exit 29 southbound, just e on 15th St, then 0.5 mi n on frontage road.
Pets: Accepted.

NYLO Plano at Legacy [H]
(972) 624-6990. **$99-$399, 3 day notice.** 8201 Preston Rd 75024. Just s of jct SR 121. Int corridors. **Pets:** Accepted.

▼▼ Quality Inn & Suites H

(972) 578-8555. $72-$100. 1600 N Central Expwy 75074. US 75 exit 29A northbound; exit 29 southbound; on northbound frontage road. Int corridors. Pets: Accepted. 📶 🛜 ✕ 🛏 🖥

AAA ▼▼ Residence Inn by Marriott Dallas Plano H

(972) 473-6761. $76-$213. 5001 Whitestone Ln 75024. North Dallas Tollway exit Spring Creek Pkwy, 1.9 mi e, then n on Preston Rd; between Spring Creek and Tennyson pkwys. Int corridors. Pets: Accepted. SAVE 🍴 📶 🛜 ✕ 🛏 🖥

AAA ▼▼ Staybridge Suites Plano/Richardson H

(972) 612-8180. Call for rates. 301 Silverglen Dr 75075. George Bush Toll Rd exit Coit Rd, n to Mapleshade Ln, just e, then just s. Int corridors. Pets: Accepted. SAVE ⛹M 📶 🛜 ✕ 🛏 🖥

▼▼ TownePlace Suites by Marriott H

(972) 943-8200. $98-$166. 5005 Whitestone Ln 75024. Dallas North Tollway exit Spring Creek Pkwy, 1.9 mi e, just n on SR 289 (Preston Rd) to Whitestone Ln, then just w. Int corridors. Pets: Accepted. 🍴 📶 🛜 ✕ 🛏 🖥

PORT ARANSAS

▼▼ Beachgate CondoSuites & Motel CO

(361) 749-5900. $50-$670, 30 day notice. 2000 On the Beach Dr 78373. Between beach markers 8 and 9; street access on Anchor Rd off 11th St. Ext/int corridors. Pets: Accepted. 📶 🛜 ✕ 🛏 🖥

▼▼ Island Hotel Port Aransas M

(361) 749-8200. Call for rates. 2607 Hwy 361 78373. Just n of Paradise Dr. Ext corridors. Pets: Accepted. 🍴 🛜 ✕ 🛏 🖥

▼▼▼ Plantation Suites & Conference Center M

(361) 749-3866. Call for rates. 1909 Hwy 361 78373. On SR 361, 0.4 mi s; on Mustang Island. Ext corridors. Pets: Accepted. 🍴 📶 🛜 ✕ 🛏 🖥

PORTLAND

AAA ▼▼ Best Western Plus Northshore Inn H 🐾

(361) 777-3100. $120-$160. 1707 State Hwy 181 78374. US 181 exit Buddy Ganem Dr; on south frontage road. Int corridors. Pets: Large, other species. $50 deposit/pet. Service with restrictions, supervision. SAVE 📶 🛜 🛏 🖥

AAA ▼▼ La Quinta Inn & Suites H

(361) 777-2777. $119-$290. 201 Buddy Ganem Dr 78374. US 181 exit Buddy Ganem Dr; on south frontage road. Int corridors. Pets: Accepted. SAVE ⛹M 🛜 ✕ 🛏 🖥

▼▼▼▼ TownePlace Suites Corpus Christi Portland H

(361) 777-2003. $98-$196. 109 Esplanade Dr 78374. US 181 exit Wildcat Dr; on northbound frontage road. Int corridors. Pets: Accepted. 🍴 ⛹M 🛜 ✕ 🛏 🖥

PORT LAVACA

AAA ▼▼ Best Western Port Lavaca Inn H

(361) 553-6800. $109-$139. 2202 N Hwy 35 77979. Jct US 87 and SR 35, 2.5 mi e. Int corridors. Pets: Large. $20 daily fee/pet. Designated rooms, service with restrictions, supervision. SAVE 📶 🛜 🛏 🖥

AAA ▼▼ La Quinta Inn & Suites Port Lavaca H

(361) 552-8800. $86-$198. 910 Hwy 35 N 77979. Jct US 87 and SR 35, 2 mi e. Int corridors. Pets: Accepted. SAVE ⛹M 📶 🛜 ✕ 🛏 🖥

POST

AAA ▼▼ Best Western Post Inn H

(806) 495-9933. $87-$92. 1011 N Broadway 79356. 1 mi n on US 84. Int corridors. Pets: Accepted. SAVE 🍴 📶 🛜 🛏 🖥

RANCHO VIEJO

▼▼▼ Rancho Viejo Resort & Country Club H

(956) 350-4000. Call for rates. 1 Rancho Viejo Dr 78575. US 77/83 exit Rancho Viejo. Ext corridors. Pets: Accepted. 🍴 📶 ✕ 🛜 ✕ 🛏 🖥

RAYMONDVILLE

▼▼▼ La Quinta Inn & Suites Raymondville H

(956) 689-4000. $67-$186. 128 N Expwy 77 78580. US 77, jct FM 186; on southbound access road. Int corridors. Pets: Accepted. ⛹M 📶 🛜 ✕ 🛏 🖥

RICHARDSON

AAA ▼▼ Hyatt House Dallas/Richardson H

(972) 671-8080. $69-$199. 2301 N Central Expwy 75080. US 75 exit 26 (Campbell Rd), 0.5 mi w to Collins Blvd, then 0.6 mi n. Int corridors. Pets: Accepted. SAVE 🍴 📶 🛜 ✕ 🛏 🖥

AAA ▼▼ Hyatt Regency North Dallas/Richardson H

(972) 619-1234. $89-$249. 701 E Campbell Rd 75081. US 75 exit 26 (Campbell Rd) southbound; exit northbound; on frontage road. Int corridors. Pets: Accepted. SAVE 🍴 📶 🛜 ✕ 🛏 🖥

AAA ▼▼ Renaissance Dallas-Richardson Hotel H

(972) 367-2000. $89-$198. 900 E Lookout Dr 75082. US 75 exit 27A (Gallatin Pkwy/Renner Rd) northbound; exit 26 (Gallatin Pkwy/Campbell Rd) southbound, just e. Int corridors. Pets: Accepted. SAVE 🍴 📶 ✕ 🛜 ✕ 🛏 🖥

AAA ▼▼ Residence Inn by Marriott Dallas Richardson H

(972) 669-5888. $98-$201. 1040 Waterwood Dr 75082. US 75 exit 26 (Campbell Rd), just e to Greenville Ave, 0.4 mi n to Glenville Rd, then just w. Int corridors. Pets: Accepted. SAVE ECO 🍴 📶 🛜 ✕ 🛏 🖥

RICHLAND HILLS

▼▼▼ La Quinta Inn & Suites Fort Worth NE Mall H

(817) 595-4442. $86-$229. 653 NE Loop 820 76118. I-820 exit 23, just s of Glenview Dr. Int corridors. Pets: Accepted. ⛹M 📶 🛜 ✕ 🛏 🖥

ROANOKE

▼▼ Comfort Suites Near Alliance H

(817) 490-1455. $105-$299. 801 W Byron Nelson Blvd 76262. I-35 exit 70 (SR 114), 2 mi e. Int corridors. Pets: Accepted. ⛹M 📶 🛜 ✕ 🛏 🖥

ROBSTOWN

▼▼▼ Days Inn M

(361) 387-8600. $90-$165. 650 Hwy 77 S 78380. Just n of jct CR 892 (Lincoln Ave) and US 77. Ext corridors. Pets: Small. $10 daily fee/pet. Service with restrictions, supervision. 🍴 📶 🛜 🛏 🖥

ROCKDALE

▼▼ Days Inn-Rockdale, TX M

(512) 446-5800. $70-$115. 221 N US Hwy 77 76567. Jct US 77 and 79, just n. Int corridors. Pets: Accepted. ⛹M 🛜 ✕ 🛏 🖥

ROCKPORT

▼▼ Blue Wave Inn M

(361) 729-6379. $65-$160. 1212 Laurel St 78382. Jct Laurel St and Business Rt SR 35; center. Ext corridors. Pets: Medium, dogs only. $15 daily fee/pet. Service with restrictions, supervision. 📶 🛜 🛏 🖥

ROCKWALL *(Restaurants p. 626)*

⬙⬙⬙ Best Western Plus Rockwall Inn & Suites H
(972) 722-3265. **$100-$169.** 996 E I-30 75087. I-30 exit 68; on westbound frontage road. Int corridors. **Pets:** Accepted.
[SAVE] [&M] [🛏] [📶] [✕] [🛎] [💻]

⬙⬙ La Quinta Inn & Suites Rockwall H
(972) 771-1685. **$82-$394.** 689 E I-30 75087. I-30 exit 67 (Ridge Rd) westbound; exit 67B (Horizon Rd) eastbound; on eastbound frontage road. Int corridors. **Pets:** Accepted. [&M] [🛏] [📶] [✕] [🛎] [💻]

ROSENBERG

⬙⬙⬙ La Quinta Inn & Suites Rosenberg H
(832) 595-6111. **$97-$268.** 28332 Southwest Frwy 77471. Jct US 59 and SR 36; on southbound frontage road. Int corridors. **Pets:** Accepted.
[🍴] [🛏] [📶] [✕] [🛎] [💻]

ROUND ROCK *(Restaurants p. 626)*

⬙⬙ Best Western Executive Inn H
(512) 255-3222. **$84-$149.** 1851 N I-35 78664. I-35 exit 253 northbound; exit 253A southbound, U-turn. Ext corridors. **Pets:** Medium. $10 daily fee/pet. Designated rooms, service with restrictions.
[SAVE] [&M] [🛏] [📶] [🛎] [💻]

⬙⬙ Candlewood Suites Round Rock H
(512) 828-0899. **Call for rates.** 521 S I-35 78664. I-35 exit 252A, just n; on northbound frontage road. Int corridors. **Pets:** Accepted.
[🍴] [📶] [✕] [🛎] [💻]

⬙⬙⬙ Hampton Inn Austin-Round Rock H
(512) 248-9100. **$109-$189.** 110 Dell Way 78664. I-35 exit 251; on east frontage road. Int corridors. **Pets:** Accepted.
[&M] [🛏] [📶] [✕] [🛎] [💻]

⬙⬙⬙ Homewood Suites by Hilton H
(512) 341-9200. **$119-$289.** 2201 S Mays St 78664. I-35 exit 251, just n on east frontage road to Hesters Crossing, then just e. Int corridors. **Pets:** Accepted. [🍴] [&M] [🛏] [📶] [✕] [🛎] [💻]

⬙⬙⬙ Residence Inn by Marriott Austin Round Rock H
(512) 733-2400. **$104-$188.** 2505 S I-35 78664. I-35 exit 250 southbound; exit 251 northbound; on east frontage road. Int corridors. **Pets:** Accepted. [&M] [🛏] [📶] [✕] [🛎] [💻]

ROUND TOP

⬙⬙⬙ The Prairie by Rachel Ashwell BB
(979) 836-4975. **Call for rates.** 5808 Wagner Rd 78954. Jct SR 237 and FM 1457, 5.8 mi e to Neumann Rd, just n. Ext/int corridors. **Pets:** Accepted. [🍴] [✕] [📶] [✕] [🅿] [🛎] [💻]

ROWLETT

⬙⬙⬙ Comfort Suites Lake Ray Hubbard H
(972) 463-9595. **$79-$139.** 8701 E I-30 75088. I-30 exit 64 (Dalrock Rd), just n. Int corridors. **Pets:** Accepted.
[&M] [🛏] [📶] [✕] [🛎] [💻]

SALADO *(Restaurants p. 626)*

⬙⬙⬙ Days Inn Salado H
(254) 947-4001. **$80-$81.** 10825 S I-35 76571. I-35 exit 286; on E Frontage Rd. Int corridors. **Pets:** Accepted.
[SAVE] [&M] [🛏] [📶] [✕] [🛎] [💻]

SAN ANGELO

⬙⬙ Days Inn San Angelo H
(325) 653-6111. **$60-$72.** 3017 W Loop 306 76904. Loop 306 exit College Hills Blvd, just s. Ext corridors. **Pets:** Medium. $15 daily fee/pet. Designated rooms, service with restrictions.
[SAVE] [🍴] [🛏] [📶] [🛎] [💻]

⬙⬙ Microtel Inn and Suites by Wyndham San Angelo H
(325) 227-4866. **$75-$159.** 4649 W Houston Harte Expwy 76905. Loop 306 and Arden St; on east frontage road. Int corridors. **Pets:** Accepted.
[🍴] [&M] [📶] [✕] [🛎] [💻]

⬙⬙⬙ Staybridge Suites H
(325) 653-1500. **Call for rates.** 1355 Knickerbocker Rd 76904. US 87 S, 1 mi w. Int corridors. **Pets:** Accepted. [&M] [🛏] [📶] [✕] [🛎] [💻]

SAN ANTONIO

⬙⬙⬙ Aloft San Antonio Airport H 🐾
(210) 541-8881. **$89-$309.** 838 NW Loop 410 78216. I-410 exit Blanco Rd, just s. Int corridors. **Pets:** Small, dogs only. Designated rooms, service with restrictions, supervision. [SAVE] [🛏] [📶] [✕] [🛎] [💻]

⬙⬙⬙ Arbor House Suites Bed & Breakfast BB
(210) 472-2005. **$129-$207, 14 day notice.** 109 Arciniega St 78205. Just s of E Nueva St; between S Presa and S St. Mary's sts; near La Villita Historic District; in King William Historic District. Ext/int corridors. **Pets:** Small, other species. $25 daily fee/pet. Designated rooms, service with restrictions, supervision. [SAVE] [🍴] [📶] [✕] [🛎] [💻]

⬙⬙⬙ Best Western Plus San Antonio East Inn & Suites H
(210) 661-8669. **$90-$190.** 8669 I-10 E 78219. I-10 exit 585 (Converse Rd); on westbound frontage road. Int corridors. **Pets:** Accepted.
[SAVE] [&M] [🛏] [📶] [🛎] [💻]

⬙⬙ Candlewood Suites Hotel H
(210) 615-0550. **Call for rates.** 9350 I-10 W 78230. I-10 W exit 561 (Wurzbach Rd), between Wurzbach Rd and Medical Dr; on eastbound frontage road. Int corridors. **Pets:** Accepted.
[&M] [🛏] [📶] [✕] [🛎] [💻]

⬙⬙⬙ Candlewood Suites San Antonio Downtown H
(210) 226-7700. **Call for rates.** 1024 S Laredo St 78204. I-10/35 exit Laredo St; on frontage road. Int corridors. **Pets:** Accepted.
[🛏] [📶] [✕] [🛎] [💻]

⬙⬙⬙ Candlewood Suites San Antonio NW SeaWorld Area H
(210) 523-7666. **Call for rates.** 9502 Amelia Pass 78254. Loop 1604 at Braun Rd; on northbound frontage road. Int corridors. **Pets:** Accepted.
[SAVE] [🛏] [📶] [🛎] [💻]

⬙⬙⬙ Candlewood Suites Stone Oak Area H
(210) 545-2477. **Call for rates.** 21103 Encino Commons Blvd 78259. US 281 exit Evans Rd; on northbound frontage road. Int corridors. **Pets:** Accepted. [&M] [🛏] [📶] [✕] [🛎] [💻]

⬙⬙ Comfort Inn & Suites H
(210) 733-8080. **$69-$279.** 6039 IH-10 W 78201. I-10 exit 565B eastbound; exit 565C (Vance Jackson Rd) westbound; on westbound frontage road. Int corridors. **Pets:** Accepted. [🛏] [📶] [✕] [🛎] [💻]

⬙⬙⬙ Comfort Inn & Suites Airport H
(210) 249-2000. **$99-$174.** 8640 Crownhill Blvd 78209. I-410 exit Airport Blvd, just off eastbound frontage road; just e of Broadway Ave. Int corridors. **Pets:** Small. $25 one-time fee/pet. Service with restrictions, crate. [SAVE] [&M] [🛏] [📶] [✕] [🛎] [💻]

⬙⬙⬙ Country Inn & Suites by Carlson Medical Center San Antonio H
(210) 781-4550. **Call for rates.** 8318 I-10 W 78230. I-10 exit 561 (Callaghan Rd); on eastbound frontage road. Int corridors. **Pets:** Accepted.
[🛏] [📶] [✕] [🛎] [💻]

⬙⬙⬙ Crockett Hotel H 🐾
(210) 225-6500. **$109-$309.** 320 Bonham St 78205. Center. Int corridors. **Pets:** $60 one-time fee/pet. Service with restrictions, supervision.
[SAVE] [🛏] [📶] [✕] [🛎] [💻]

▼▼▼ Drury Inn & Suites Northeast 🅗
(210) 657-1107. **$79-$169.** 4900 Crestwind Dr 78239. I-35 exit 165 (Walzem Rd); on northbound access road. Int corridors. **Pets:** Accepted.

▼▼▼ Drury Inn & Suites-San Antonio Airport 🅗
(210) 308-8100. **$79-$169.** 95 NE Loop 410 78216. I-410 exit 21A (Jones Maltsberger Rd), 1.8 mi w of airport. Int corridors.
Pets: Accepted.

▼▼▼ Drury Inn & Suites San Antonio-La Cantera 🅗
(210) 696-0800. **$89-$179.** 15806 IH-10 W 78249. I-10 exit Loop 1604; on eastbound access road. Int corridors. **Pets:** Accepted.

▼▼▼ Drury Inn & Suites-San Antonio North 🅗
(210) 404-1600. **$79-$139.** 801 N Loop 1604 E 78232. Jct Loop 1604 and US 281, just w. Int corridors. **Pets:** Accepted.

▼▼▼ Drury Inn & Suites-San Antonio Northwest 🅗
(210) 561-2510. **$89-$189.** 9806 I-10 W 78230. I-10 exit 561 (Wurzbach Rd); on southeast corner. Int corridors. **Pets:** Accepted.

▼▼▼ Drury Inn & Suites-San Antonio Riverwalk 🅗
(210) 212-5200. **$119-$249.** 201 N St. Mary's St 78205. Just s of College St. Int corridors. **Pets:** Accepted.

▼▼▼ Drury Plaza Hotel-San Antonio Riverwalk 🅗
(210) 270-7799. **$119-$249.** 105 S St. Mary's St 78205. Jct Commerce, St. Mary's and Market sts. Int corridors. **Pets:** Accepted.

▼▼▼ Drury Plaza San Antonio North 🅗
(210) 494-2420. **$89-$189.** 823 N Loop 1604 E 78232. Jct Loop 1604 and US 281, just w. Int corridors. **Pets:** Accepted.

▼▼ Econo Lodge Downtown South 🅗
(210) 927-4800. **$54-$229.** 606 Division Ave 78214. I-35 exit 152A (Division Ave), on northbound frontage road. Ext corridors. **Pets:** Accepted.

▼▼ Econo Lodge Inn & Suites Downtown Northeast Ⓜ
(210) 229-9220. **$60-$150.** 2755 N PanAm Expwy 78208. I-35 exit 159B (Walters Rd); on southbound access road. Ext corridors.
Pets: Accepted.

◉◉◉ ▼▼▼ Econo Lodge Inn & Suites Fiesta Park Ⓜ
(210) 690-5500. **$60-$170.** 13575 I-10 W 78249. I-10 exit 557 westbound; exit 558 eastbound; on westbound frontage road. Ext corridors.
Pets: Accepted.

◉◉◉ ▼▼▼▼ Eilan Hotel and Spa, Autograph Collection 🅗
(210) 598-2900. **$159-$281.** 17103 La Cantera Pkwy 78256. I-10 exit 554 (La Cantera Pkwy), just w; in Eilan office/shopping complex. Int corridors. **Pets:** Accepted.

◉◉◉ ▼▼ El Tropicano Riverwalk 🅗
(210) 223-9461. **$99-$169.** 110 Lexington Ave 78205. 0.3 mi s of jct Lexington Ave and I-35. Int corridors. **Pets:** Accepted.

◉◉◉ ▼▼▼▼ Emily Morgan Hotel-DoubleTree by Hilton 🅗
(210) 225-5100. **Call for rates.** 705 E Houston St 78205. Just n of Bonham St. Int corridors. **Pets:** Medium, other species. $50 one-time fee/room. Service with restrictions, crate.

▼▼ Extended Stay America-San Antonio-Colonnade 🅗
(210) 694-1229. **$80-$110.** 4331 Spectrum One 78230. I-10 exit 561 (Wurzbach Rd), just nw. Int corridors. **Pets:** Accepted.

▼▼▼ The Fairmount Hotel 🅗
(210) 224-8800. **Call for rates.** 401 S Alamo St 78205. Opposite convention center and Hemisfair Plaza. Ext/int corridors. **Pets:** Accepted.

◉◉◉ ▼▼▼▼ Grand Hyatt San Antonio 🅗 🐾
(210) 224-1234. **$139-$389.** 600 E Market St 78205. I-37 exit 141A (Market St); between S Alamo St and I-37. Int corridors. **Pets:** Medium, dogs only. $100 one-time fee/room. Service with restrictions, crate.

▼▼▼ Hilton San Antonio Hill Country Hotel & Spa 🅗
(210) 509-9800. **$99-$249.** 9800 Westover Hills Blvd 78251. Between Loop 410 and 1604, just off CR 151. Int corridors. **Pets:** Accepted.

◉◉◉ ▼▼▼▼ The Historic Menger Hotel 🅗
(210) 223-4361. **$129-$295.** 204 Alamo Plaza 78205. Just s of the Alamo. Int corridors. **Pets:** Accepted.

▼▼ Holiday Inn Express-San Antonio Airport 🅗
(210) 308-6700. **$99-$149.** 91 NE Loop 410 78216. Loop 410 exit 21A (Jones Maltsberger Rd) eastbound; exit 20B westbound; between San Pedro Ave and Jones Maltsberger Rd; on westbound access road. Int corridors. **Pets:** Accepted.

◉◉◉ ▼▼▼▼ Holiday Inn San Antonio International Airport 🅗
(210) 349-9900. **Call for rates.** 77 NE Loop 410 78216. I-410 exit 20B (McCullough St); on westbound access road. Int corridors.
Pets: Accepted.

▼▼▼ Home2 Suites by Hilton 🅗
(210) 342-0400. **$109-$169.** 94 NE Loop 410 78216. I-410 exit Jones Maltsberger; on eastbound frontage road. Int corridors. **Pets:** Accepted.

▼▼▼ Home2 Suites by Hilton San Antonio Downtown-Riverwalk 🅗
(210) 354-4366. **Call for rates.** 603 Navarro St 78205. Jct E Houston St. Int corridors. **Pets:** Accepted.

▼▼▼ Homewood Suites Lackland AFB /Seaworld 🅗
(210) 509-7770. **$149-$289.** 215 Richland Hills Dr 78245. I-410 exit 9A (SeaWorld), just w; on westbound frontage road. Int corridors.
Pets: Accepted.

▼▼▼ Homewood Suites San Antonio 🅗
(210) 804-0100. **Call for rates.** 8531 Broadway St 78217. I-410 exit Broadway, just n. Int corridors. **Pets:** Accepted.

▼▼▼ Homewood Suites Stone Oak 🅗 🐾
(210) 497-8200. **$109-$229.** 125 North Loop 1604 W 78232. On Loop 1604, just e of US 281; on eastbound frontage road. Int corridors.
Pets: Medium, dogs only. $100 one-time fee/room. Service with restrictions.

◉◉◉ ▼▼▼▼ Hotel Contessa 🅗
(210) 229-9222. **Call for rates.** 306 W Market St 78205. Corner of Navarro and Market sts. Int corridors. **Pets:** Accepted.

▼▼▼ Hotel Havana 🅒🅘
(210) 222-2008. **Call for rates.** 1015 Navarro St 78205. Just s of N St. Mary's St. Int corridors. **Pets:** Accepted.

▼▼▼ Hotel Indigo at the Alamo 🄷

(210) 933-2000. **Call for rates.** 105 N Alamo Plaza 78205. I-37 exit 141 (Commerce St), just s. Int corridors. **Pets:** Other species. $75 one-time fee/room. Service with restrictions. 🍴 📶 ⊠ 📋

▼▼▼ Hotel Indigo Riverwalk 🄷

(210) 527-1900. **Call for rates.** 830 N St. Mary's St 78205. Just n of Navarro St. Int corridors. **Pets:** Accepted.
🍴 🛠 🈂️ 📶 ⊠ 📋

🆂 ▼▼▼ Hyatt Place San Antonio Airport/Quarry Market 🄷

(210) 930-2333. **$94-$209.** 7615 Jones Maltsberger Rd 78216. US 281 exit Jones Maltsberger Rd; on Loop 410. Int corridors. **Pets:** Accepted.
🆂 🛠 🈂️ 📶 ⊠ 📋

🆂 ▼▼▼ Hyatt Place San Antonio North Stone Oak 🄷

(210) 545-2810. **$79-$189.** 1610 E Sonterra Blvd 78258. US 281 exit Sonterra Blvd, just w. Int corridors. **Pets:** Accepted.
🆂 🍴 🛠 🈂️ 📶 ⊠ 📋

🆂 ▼▼▼ Hyatt Place San Antonio-Northwest/Medical Center 🄷

(210) 561-0099. **$84-$209.** 4303 Hyatt Place Dr 78230. I-10 exit 561 (Wurzbach Rd), 0.5 mi on westbound access road. Int corridors.
Pets: Accepted. 🆂 🛠 🈂️ 📶 ⊠ 📋

🆂 ▼▼▼ Hyatt Place San Antonio/Riverwalk 🄷

(210) 227-6854. **$119-$279.** 601 S St. Mary's St 78205. I-35 exit 155B (Cesar E Chavez Blvd), 0.9 mi e. Int corridors. **Pets:** Accepted.
🆂 🍴 🛠 🈂️ 📶 ⊠ 📋

🆂 ▼▼▼▼ Hyatt Regency Hill Country Resort and Spa 🄷

(210) 647-1234. **$149-$439, 3 day notice.** 9800 Hyatt Resort 78251. Between Loop 410 and 1604, just off CR 151 exit Hyatt Resort Dr. Int corridors. **Pets:** Accepted.
🆂 🌱 🍴 🛠 🈂️ ⊠ 📶 📋

🆂 ▼▼▼ Hyatt Regency San Antonio 🄷

(210) 222-1234. **$149-$389.** 123 Losoya St 78205. Between College and Crockett sts. Int corridors. **Pets:** Accepted.
🆂 🌱 🍴 🈂️ 📶 ⊠ 📋

▼▼▼ La Quinta Inn & Suites 🄷

(210) 447-8000. **$67-$284.** 11155 W Loop 1604 N 78023. Just w of Bandera Rd. Int corridors. **Pets:** Accepted.
🛠 🈂️ 📶 ⊠ 📋

▼▼▼ La Quinta Inn & Suites Riverwalk 🄷

(210) 222-9181. **$115-$339.** 303 Blum St 78202. 0.5 mi ne. Ext/int corridors. **Pets:** Accepted. 🛠 🈂️ 📶 ⊠ 📋

▼▼▼ La Quinta Inn & Suites San Antonio Airport 🄷

(210) 342-3738. **$82-$229.** 850 Halm Blvd 78216. I-410 exit 21A (Jones Maltsberger Rd); on eastbound frontage road. Int corridors.
Pets: Accepted. 🛠 🈂️ 📶 ⊠ 📋

▼▼▼ La Quinta Inn & Suites San Antonio Downtown 🄷

(210) 212-5400. **$86-$339.** 100 Cesar E Chavez Blvd 78204. I-35 exit 155B (Cesar E Chavez Blvd), 3 blks e of jct E Flores St. Int corridors.
Pets: Accepted. 🍴 🛠 🈂️ 📶 📋

▼▼ La Quinta Inn & Suites San Antonio North Stone Oak 🄷

(210) 497-0506. **$93-$350.** 1017 N Loop E 78258. Jct Loop 1604 and US 281, just w. Int corridors. **Pets:** Accepted.
🛠 🈂️ 📶 ⊠ 📋

🆀 ▼▼▼ La Quinta Inn San Antonio Brooks City Base 🄷

(210) 337-7171. **$82-$196.** 3180 Goliad Rd 78223. I-37 exit 135 (Brooks City Base/SE Military Dr), just w of interstate. Int corridors.
Pets: Accepted. 🆂 🛠 🈂️ 📶 ⊠ 📋

▼▼ La Quinta Inn San Antonio Lackland 🄷

(210) 674-3200. **$67-$229.** 6511 Military Dr W 78227. Sw of jct US 90 and Military Dr W. Ext corridors. **Pets:** Accepted. 🈂️ 📶 📋

▼▼ La Quinta Inn San Antonio Market Square 🄷

(210) 271-0001. **$75-$471.** 900 Dolorosa St 78207. I-10/35 exit 155B (Cesar E Chavez Blvd), just n on Santa Rosa St, then just w on Nueva St. Ext corridors. **Pets:** Accepted. 🈂️ 📶 📋

▼▼ La Quinta Inn San Antonio SeaWorld/Ingram Park 🄷

(210) 680-8883. **$67-$284.** 7134 NW Loop 410 78238. I-410 exit 10 (Culebra Rd); on eastbound access road. Ext corridors. **Pets:** Accepted.
🈂️ 📶 📋

🆀 ▼▼▼▼ Marriott Plaza San Antonio 🄷

(210) 229-1000. **$124-$215.** 555 S Alamo St 78205. Opposite convention center and Hemisfair Plaza. Int corridors. **Pets:** Accepted.
🆂 🍴 🛠 🈂️ 📶 📋

🆀 ▼▼▼▼ Mokara Hotel & Spa 🄷

(210) 396-5800. **$279-$509.** 212 W Crockett St 78205. Between St. Mary's and Navarro sts; on River Walk. Int corridors. **Pets:** Accepted.
🆂 🍴 🛠 🈂️ 📶 ⊠ 📋

▼ Motel 6 - #651 🄼

(210) 673-9020. **$55-$105.** 2185 SW Loop 410 78227. I-410 exit 7 (Marbach Rd), 0.7 mi w; on westbound access road. Ext corridors.
Pets: Accepted. 🈂️ 📶 📋

▼▼ Motel 6 - Medical Center South - #4429 🄷

(210) 616-0030. **Call for rates.** 7500 Louis Pasteur Dr 78229. I-410 exit 14C (Babcock Rd), 1 mi nw, then 0.5 mi n. Int corridors.
Pets: Accepted. 🛠 📶 ⊠ 📋

🆀 ▼▼▼ Omni La Mansión del Rio 🄷

(210) 518-1000. **Call for rates.** 112 College St 78205. Just s on River Walk. Ext/int corridors. **Pets:** Accepted.
🆂 🍴 🛠 🈂️ 📶 📋

🆀 ▼▼▼ Omni San Antonio Hotel at the Colonnade 🄷

(210) 691-8888. **Call for rates.** 9821 Colonnade Blvd 78230. I-10 exit 561 (Wurzbach Rd); on westbound frontage road. Int corridors.
Pets: Accepted. 🆂 🍴 🛠 🈂️ 📶 ⊠ 📋

▼▼▼ Pear Tree Inn San Antonio Airport 🄷

(210) 366-9300. **$79-$169.** 143 NE Loop 410 78216. I-410 exit 21 (Jones Maltsberger Rd); on westbound frontage road. Int corridors.
Pets: Accepted. 🛠 🈂️ 📶 ⊠ 📋

🆀 ▼▼▼ Pear Tree Inn San Antonio NW Medical Center 🄷

(210) 691-9550. **$90-$160.** 9411 Wurzbach Rd 78240. I-10 exit 561 (Wurzbach Rd); on eastbound access road. Int corridors.
Pets: Accepted. 🆂 🛠 🈂️ 📶 📋

🆀 ▼▼ Red Roof Inn San Antonio Lackland 🄷

(210) 675-4120. **$60-$160.** 6861 Hwy 90 W 78227. Ne of jct US 90 and Military Dr W; access via Renwick St, off Military Dr, just n of jct US 90. Ext corridors. **Pets:** Accepted. 🆂 🈂️ 📶 ⊠ 📋

▼▼ Red Roof Inn San Antonio (NW-SeaWorld) 🄷

(210) 509-3434. **$49-$189.** 6880 NW Loop 410 78238. I-410 exit 11 (Alamo Downs Pkwy); on eastbound frontage road. Ext/int corridors.
Pets: Accepted. 🛠 🈂️ 📶 ⊠ 📋

Red Roof PLUS+ San Antonio Downtown - Riverwalk H
(210) 229-9973. **$69-$250.** 1011 E Houston St 78205. I-37 exit 141 (Commerce St) northbound; exit 141B southbound. Int corridors.
Pets: Accepted.

Residence Inn by Marriott Alamo Plaza H
(210) 212-5555. **$115-$234.** 425 Bonham St 78205. I-37 and US 281 exit Commerce St, just w to Bowie St, then 4 blks n. Int corridors.
Pets: Accepted.

Residence Inn by Marriott North San Antonio H
(210) 490-1333. **$117-$197.** 1115 N SR 1604 E 78232. Loop 1604, just w of US 281; on westbound frontage road. Int corridors.
Pets: Accepted.

Residence Inn by Marriott San Antonio Airport/Alamo Heights H
(210) 805-8118. **$98-$172.** 1014 NE Loop 410 78209. Loop 410 exit Broadway St, 0.4 mi e on eastbound access road. Ext corridors.
Pets: Accepted.

Residence Inn by Marriott San Antonio Downtown/ Market Square H
(210) 231-6000. **$120-$228.** 628 S Santa Rosa Blvd 78204. I-10/35 exit 155B (Cesar E Chavez Blvd), 0.5 mi e. Int corridors. **Pets:** Accepted.

Residence Inn by Marriott San Antonio Northwest at The RIM H
(210) 561-0200. **$116-$191.** 5707 Rim Pass Dr 78257. I-10 exit 556B (La Cantera Pkwy); on westbound access road; just s of The Rim Shopping Complex. Int corridors. **Pets:** Medium, dogs only. $100 one-time fee/pet. Designated rooms, service with restrictions, crate.

Residence Inn by Marriott SeaWorld/Lackland AFB H
(210) 509-3100. **$91-$176.** 2838 Cinema Ridge 78238. I-410 exit 10 (Ingram Rd); on eastbound frontage road. Int corridors. **Pets:** Accepted.

Sheraton Gunter H 🐾
(210) 227-3241. **$119-$399.** 205 E Houston St 78205. Center. Int corridors. **Pets:** Medium, dogs only. Designated rooms, service with restrictions, crate.

Staybridge Suites Downtown Convention Center H
(210) 444-2700. **Call for rates.** 123 Hoefgen Ave 78205. In Historic Sunset Station. Int corridors. **Pets:** Accepted.

Staybridge Suites NW Near Six Flags Fiesta H
(210) 691-3443. **Call for rates.** 6919 N Loop 1604 W 78249. Loop 1604 exit La Cantera Pkwy; on westbound frontage road. Int corridors.
Pets: Accepted.

Staybridge Suites San Antonio-Airport H 🐾
(210) 341-3220. **Call for rates.** 66 NE Loop 410 78216. I-410 exit 20B (McCullough St); on eastbound access road. Int corridors.
Pets: Medium, other species. $50 one-time fee/pet. Service with restrictions, crate.

Staybridge Suites San Antonio NW-Colonnade H
(210) 558-9009. **Call for rates.** 4320 Spectrum One 78230. I-10 exit 561 (Wurzbach Rd), 0.3 mi w; off westbound access road. Int corridors.
Pets: Accepted.

Staybridge Suites San Antonio-Stone Oak H
(210) 497-0100. **Call for rates.** 808 N Loop 1604 E 78232. On Loop 1604, 0.4 mi w of US 281. Int corridors. **Pets:** Accepted.

Staybridge Suites-SeaWorld San Antonio H
(210) 767-1100. **Call for rates.** 10919 Town Center Dr 78251. SR 151 exit Westover Hills, just off northbound access road. Int corridors.
Pets: Accepted.

Super 8 on Roland H
(210) 798-5500. **$79-$120.** 302 Roland Ave 78210. I-10 exit 577 (Roland Ave); on eastbound access road. Ext corridors. **Pets:** Medium. $25 daily fee/pet. Designated rooms, service with restrictions.

TownePlace Suites by Marriott Airport H
(210) 308-5510. **$80-$139.** 214 NE Loop 410 78216. I-410 exit 21A (Jones Maltsberger Rd); on eastbound frontage road. Int corridors.
Pets: Accepted.

TownePlace Suites by Marriott San Antonio Downtown H
(210) 271-3444. **$99-$160.** 409 E Houston St 78205. 1 blk w of Broadway St. Int corridors. **Pets:** Accepted.

TownePlace Suites by Marriott San Antonio Northwest H
(210) 694-5100. **$71-$118.** 5014 Prue Rd 78240. I-10 exit 560 (Huebner Rd) westbound; exit 559 eastbound, 1 blk sw to Fredericksburg Rd, then just n. Int corridors. **Pets:** Accepted.

The Westin Riverwalk, San Antonio H
(210) 224-6500. **$179-$489.** 420 W Market St 78205. 2 blks w of Navarro St. Int corridors. **Pets:** Accepted.

Wyndham Garden River Walk Museum Reach H
(210) 515-4555. **$127-$200.** 103 9th St 78215. Jct 9th and N St. Mary's sts. Int corridors. **Pets:** Other species. $25 daily fee/pet. Service with restrictions, crate.

The Wyndham San Antonio Riverwalk Hotel H 🐾
(210) 354-2800. **$99-$249.** 111 Pecan St E 78205. Corner of Pecan and Soledad sts. Int corridors. **Pets:** Medium. $50 one-time fee/pet. Service with restrictions, supervision.

SAN MARCOS

Embassy Suites by Hilton-San Marcos Hotel, Spa and Conference Center H
(512) 392-6450. **$159-$229.** 1001 E McCarty Ln 78666. I-35 exit 201; on east frontage road. Int corridors. **Pets:** Accepted.

La Quinta Inn San Marcos H
(512) 392-8800. **$67-$251.** 1619 I-35 N 78666. I-35 exit 206 southbound, 0.5 mi s; on west frontage road; exit northbound, 1 mi n to turnaround to west frontage road, then 1.5 mi s. Ext/int corridors.
Pets: Accepted.

SCHERTZ

Fairfield Inn & Suites by Marriott H
(210) 658-1466. **$81-$147.** 5008 Corridor Loop Rd 78154. I-35 exit 175 (Natural Bridge Cavern Rd); just off northbound frontage road. Int corridors. **Pets:** Accepted.

La Quinta Inn & Suites H

(210) 655-2700. **$67-$207.** 17650 Four Oaks Ln 78154. I-35 exit 175 CR 3009 (Natural Bridge Cavern Rd), just w. Int corridors.
Pets: Accepted. 🛜 ⊠ 🔋 💻

SCHULENBURG

Best Western Plus Schulenburg Inn & Suites H

(979) 743-2030. **$110-$140.** 101 Huser Blvd 78956. I-10 exit 674, just s. Int corridors. **Pets:** Other species. $20 daily fee/pet. Designated rooms, service with restrictions, supervision.
SAVE 🛗 🛌 🛜 ⊠ 🔋 💻

SEABROOK

Best Western Plus Seabrook Suites H

(281) 291-9090. **$109-$159.** 5755 Bayport Blvd 77586. 1.5 mi n on SR 146. Int corridors. **Pets:** Accepted. SAVE 🛌 🛜 ⊠ 🔋 💻

SEGUIN

La Quinta Inn & Suites Seguin H

(830) 372-0567. **$75-$284.** 1501 Hwy 46 N 78155. I-10 exit 607 (SR 46), just off westbound frontage road. Int corridors. **Pets:** Accepted.
🛗 🛌 🛜 ⊠ 🔋 💻

Super 8 of Seguin H

(830) 379-6888. **$69-$140.** 1525 N Hwy 46 78155. I-10 exit 607 (SR 46); on eastbound frontage road. Ext corridors. **Pets:** Accepted.
🛜 🔋 💻

SEMINOLE

Best Western Plus Seminole Hotel & Suites H

(432) 955-6200. **$95-$125.** 308 S Main St (US 385) 79360. Just s of jct US 62/180. Int corridors. **Pets:** Medium. $20 daily fee/pet. Designated rooms, service with restrictions, crate.
SAVE 🛗 🛗 🛜 ⊠ 🔋 💻

SHAMROCK

Best Western Plus Shamrock Inn & Suites H

(806) 256-1001. **$110-$170.** 1802 N Main St 79079. I-40 exit 163, just n. Int corridors. **Pets:** Accepted. SAVE 🛗 🛌 🛜 ⊠ 🔋 💻

SHERMAN

La Quinta Inn & Suites Sherman H

(903) 870-1122. **$68-$150.** 2912 N US 75 75090. US 75 exit 63; on southbound frontage road. Int corridors. **Pets:** Accepted.
🛗 🛌 🛜 🔋 💻

Quality Suites of Sherman H

(903) 893-0499. **$74-$114.** 2900 Michelle Dr 75090. US 75 exit 63, 0.3 mi s of jct US 82. Int corridors. **Pets:** Accepted.
🛗 🛌 🛜 ⊠ 🔋 💻

SINTON

Best Western Sinton M

(361) 364-2882. **$95-$130.** 8108 US Hwy 77 78387. 0.5 mi s of SR 188. Ext corridors. **Pets:** Accepted. SAVE 🛌 🛜 🔋 💻

SONORA

Best Western Sonora Inn H

(325) 387-9111. **$82-$91.** 270 Hwy 277 N 76950. I-10 exit 400, just s. Ext corridors. **Pets:** Other species. $10 daily fee/pet. Service with restrictions, crate. SAVE 🛗 🛌 🛜 ⊠ 🔋 💻

SOUTH PADRE ISLAND

The Inn at South Padre H

(956) 761-5658. **Call for rates.** 1709 Padre Blvd 78597. 0.9 mi n of Queen Isabella Cswy; corner of W Palm St. Int corridors.
Pets: Accepted. 🛗 🛌 🛜 ⊠ 🔋 💻

Isla Grand Beach Resort H

(956) 761-6511. **Call for rates.** 500 Padre Blvd 78597. 0.3 mi n of Queen Isabella Cswy. Ext/int corridors. **Pets:** Accepted.
🛗 🛌 ⊠ 🛜 ⊠ 🔋 💻

La Copa Inn Beach Hotel H

(956) 761-6000. **Call for rates.** 350 Padre Blvd 78597. Just s of Queen Isabella Cswy. Int corridors. **Pets:** Accepted.
🛗 🛌 🛜 ⊠ 🔋 💻

La Quinta Inn & Suites South Padre Beach H

(956) 772-7000. **$67-$417.** 7000 Padre Blvd 78597. 3 mi n of Queen Isabella Cswy. Int corridors. **Pets:** Accepted.
🛗 🛗 🛌 🛜 ⊠ 🔋 💻

The Ramada South Padre Island H

(956) 761-4744. **$60-$400.** 6200 Padre Blvd 78597. 3 mi n of Queen Isabella Cswy. Ext corridors. **Pets:** Accepted.
SAVE 🛗 🛗 🛌 🛜 🔋 💻

Super 8 H

(956) 761-6300. **$69-$280.** 4205 Padre Blvd 78597. 2.7 mi n of Queen Isabella Cswy. Ext corridors. **Pets:** Medium. $25 daily fee/pet. Service with restrictions, supervision. SAVE 🛌 🛜 ⊠ 🔋 💻

STAFFORD

Residence Inn by Marriott Houston/Sugar Land H

(281) 277-0770. **$97-$173.** 12703 Southwest Frwy 77477. US 59 exit Corporate Dr southbound; exit Airport Blvd/Kirkwood Rd northbound; on northbound service road. Int corridors. **Pets:** Accepted.
🛌 🛜 ⊠ 🔋 💻

Sleep Inn & Suites M

(281) 494-2900. **$89-$150.** 4810 Alpine Dr 77477. US 59 exit Corporate Dr southbound; exit Alternate Rt 90/Stafford northbound, just n on northbound frontage road, then just e. Int corridors. **Pets:** Medium, other species. $25 one-time fee/pet. Designated rooms, service with restrictions, supervision. 🛗 🛗 🛌 🛜 🔋 💻

Staybridge Suites Stafford H

(281) 302-6535. **Call for rates.** 11101 Fountain Lake Dr 77477. US 59 exit Kirkwood Rd, just nw. Int corridors. **Pets:** Large. $75 one-time fee/room. Service with restrictions, supervision.
🛗 🛌 🛜 ⊠ 🔋 💻

STANTON

Comfort Inn H

(432) 756-1100. **$69-$179.** 3414 W I-20 79782. I-20 exit 156, just se. Int corridors. **Pets:** Accepted. 🛗 🛗 🛌 🛜 ⊠ 🔋 💻

SUGAR LAND

Drury Inn & Suites-Houston/Sugar Land H

(281) 277-9700. **$74-$169.** 13770 Southwest Frwy 77478. US 59 exit Dairy Ashford Rd/Sugar Creek Blvd; on north frontage road. Int corridors. **Pets:** Accepted. 🛗 🛌 🛜 ⊠ 🔋 💻

Hyatt Place Houston/Sugar Land H

(281) 491-0300. **$99-$239.** 16730 Creek Bend Dr 77478. Jct US 59 and SR 6, just n on SR 6 to Fluor Daniel Dr, just e. Int corridors. **Pets:** Medium, dogs only. $75 one-time fee/pet. Service with restrictions, crate. SAVE 🛗 🛗 🛌 🛜 ⊠ 🔋 💻

SULPHUR SPRINGS

Best Western Trail Dust Inn & Suites H
(903) 885-7515. **$80-$90.** 1521 Shannon Rd E 75482. I-30 exit 127; on eastbound frontage road. Ext corridors. **Pets:** Accepted.

SWEETWATER

Best Western Plus Sweetwater Inn & Suites H
(325) 236-6512. **$100-$115.** 300 NW Georgia Ave 79556. I-20 exit 244, just nw. Int corridors. **Pets:** Accepted.

Microtel Inn & Suites by Wyndham Sweetwater H
(325) 235-2000. **$98-$129.** 9416 N I-20 79556. I-20 exit 242, just ne. Int corridors. **Pets:** Accepted.

TEMPLE

Days Inn H
(254) 774-9223. **$65-$79.** 1104 N General Bruce Dr 76504. I-35 exit 302 (Nugent Ave), just w. Ext corridors. **Pets:** Medium, dogs only. $10 daily fee/pet. Service with restrictions, supervision.

TEXARKANA

Courtyard by Marriott H
(903) 334-7400. **$76-$94.** 5001 N Cowhorn Creek Loop 75503. I-30 exit 222 (Summerhill Rd), just w on frontage road, then just n. Int corridors. **Pets:** Accepted.

Fairfield Inn & Suites by Marriott H
(903) 838-1000. **$72-$88.** 4209 Mall Dr 75503. I-30 exit 219; on eastbound frontage road. Int corridors. **Pets:** Accepted.

Residence Inn by Marriott Texarkana H
(430) 200-0742. **$83-$121.** 3900 St Michael Dr 75503. I-30 exit 220B (Richmond Rd); on westbound frontage road. Int corridors. **Pets:** $100 one-time fee/room. Service with restrictions, crate.

TownePlace Suites by Marriott H
(903) 334-8800. **$76-$118.** 5020 N Cowhorn Creek Loop 75503. I-30 exit 222 (Summerhill Rd), w on frontage road, then just n. Int corridors. **Pets:** Accepted.

THE COLONY

Comfort Suites H
(972) 668-5555. **$84-$300.** 4796 Memorial Dr 75056. SR 121 exit Blair Oaks southbound; exit Main St northbound, just n to Memorial Dr, then just e. Int corridors. **Pets:** Accepted.

Residence Inn by Marriott-Plano/Frisco/The Colony H ❖
(214) 469-1155. **$97-$157.** 6600 Cascades Ct 75056. SR 121 exit Spring Creek Pkwy; on southwest frontage road. Int corridors. **Pets:** Other species. $100 one-time fee/room. Service with restrictions, crate.

THE WOODLANDS

Drury Inn & Suites-Houston/The Woodlands H
(281) 362-7222. **$99-$209.** 28099 I-45 N 77380. I-45 exit 77 (Research Forest Dr/Tamina Rd) southbound; on southbound frontage road. Int corridors. **Pets:** Accepted.

Hilton Garden Inn-Houston/The Woodlands H
(281) 364-9300. **$109-$269.** 9301 Six Pines Dr 77380. I-45 exit 77 (Lake Woodlands Dr/Research Forest Dr/Tamina Rd), 0.4 mi w on Lake Woodlands Dr, then just n. Int corridors. **Pets:** Accepted.

Hyatt Place Houston/The Woodlands H ❖
(281) 298-4600. **$119-$399.** 1909 Research Forest Dr 77380. I-45 exit 77 (Research Forest Dr), 0.8 mi w. Int corridors. **Pets:** Large, dogs only. $75 one-time fee/room. Service with restrictions, supervision.

La Quinta Inn & Suites-The Woodlands South H
(281) 681-9188. **$93-$317.** 24868 I-45 N 77386. I-45 exit 73 (Rayford Rd/Sawdust Rd) northbound on frontage road; exit 73 southbound, just e on Rayford Rd, then just s on Oakhurst Dr. Int corridors. **Pets:** Accepted.

Residence Inn by Marriott Lake Front H
(281) 292-3252. **$135-$264.** 1040 Lake Front Cir 77380. I-45 exit 79 (College Park Dr/Needham Rd) northbound; exit 77 (Research Forest Dr/Tamina Rd) southbound; just off southbound frontage road. Int corridors. **Pets:** Accepted.

The Westin at The Woodlands H
(281) 419-4300. **$179-$399, 3 day notice.** 2 Waterway Square 77380. Jct I-45 and Woodlands Pkwy, just w, then just n on Woodloch Forest Dr. Int corridors. **Pets:** Accepted.

The Woodlands Waterway Marriott Hotel & Convention Center H
(281) 367-9797. **$187-$330.** 1601 Lake Robbins Dr 77380. I-45 exit 76B (Woodlands Pkwy) northbound, 1.6 mi w to Six Pines, then just n; exit 77 (Research Forest Dr/Tamina Rd) southbound, 0.5 mi w. Int corridors. **Pets:** Accepted.

THREE RIVERS

Best Western Inn-Three Rivers H
(361) 786-2000. **$89-$139.** 900 N Harborth Ave 78071. I-37 exit 72 (US 281), 1.8 mi s; jct US 281 and SR 72. Ext corridors. **Pets:** Accepted.

TYLER

Best Western Plus Southpark Inn & Suites H
(903) 534-8800. **$89-$160.** 120 W Rieck Rd 75703. Jct US 69 and W Rieck Rd, just w. Int corridors. **Pets:** Accepted.

Candlewood Suites H
(903) 509-4131. **Call for rates.** 315 E Rieck Rd 75703. 1.1 mi s of jct Loop 323 and US 69 to Rieck Rd, just e. Int corridors. **Pets:** Accepted.

Holiday Inn South Broadway H
(903) 561-5800. **Call for rates.** 5701 S Broadway Ave 75703. 1.1 mi s of jct Loop 323 and US 69. Int corridors. **Pets:** $50 one-time fee/pet. Service with restrictions, supervision.

Residence Inn by Marriott - Tyler Texas H
(903) 787-5899. **$104-$164.** 350 W Heritage Dr 75703. Jct Loop 323 and US 69, 2.8 mi s, just w. Int corridors. **Pets:** Accepted.

Staybridge Suites - Tyler University Area H ❖
(903) 566-1100. **$130-$170.** 2759 McDonald Rd 75701. Jct SE Loop 323 and SR 64, 1 mi s. Int corridors. **Pets:** Large, other species. $75 one-time fee/pet. Designated rooms, service with restrictions, supervision.

UNIVERSITY PARK

The Lumen H

(214) 219-2400. **Call for rates.** 6101 Hillcrest Ave 75205. Just n of jct Mockingbird Ln and Hillcrest Ave. Int corridors. **Pets:** Accepted.

VAN HORN

Econo Lodge H

(432) 283-2211. **$77-$110.** 1601 W Broadway St 79855. I-10 exit 138, 0.5 mi e on Business Rt I-10. Ext corridors. **Pets:** Small. $25 daily fee/pet. Designated rooms, service with restrictions, supervision.

Economy Inn M

(432) 283-2754. **Call for rates.** 1500 W Broadway St 79855. I-10 exit 138, 0.5 mi e on US 80. Ext corridors. **Pets:** Accepted.

Hampton Inn H

(432) 283-0088. **$119-$139.** 1921 SW Frontage Rd 79855. I-10 exit 138, just w on S Frontage Rd. Int corridors. **Pets:** Accepted.

VEGA

Americas Best Value Inn & Suites Country Inn M

(806) 267-2131. **$79-$99, 3 day notice.** 1800 W Vega Blvd 79092. 0.5 mi w on US 40 business loop. Ext corridors. **Pets:** Medium. $10 daily fee/pet. Designated rooms, service with restrictions, supervision.

VERNON

Hampton Inn H

(940) 552-2100. **$109-$124.** 4131 Western Trail Dr 76384. Jct US 287 and 70; on W Frontage Rd. Int corridors. **Pets:** Very small. Service with restrictions, supervision.

Holiday Inn Express Hotel & Suites H

(940) 552-0200. **Call for rates.** 700 Hillcrest Dr 76384. Jct US 287 and 70; on W Frontage Rd. Int corridors. **Pets:** Accepted.

The Hotel Vernon H

(940) 552-5417. **Call for rates.** 1615 US Hwy 287 E 76384. Jct Main St, just e. Ext/int corridors. **Pets:** Accepted.

VICTORIA *(Restaurants p. 626)*

Baymont Inn & Suites H

(361) 894-8909. **$80-$129.** 8107 NE Zac Lentz Pkwy 77904. Jct US 77 (Frontage Rd) and Invitational Dr. Int corridors. **Pets:** Accepted.

Best Western Plus Victoria Inn & Suites H 🐾

(361) 485-2300. **$90-$95.** 8106 NE Zac Lentz Pkwy 77904. Jct Zac Lenz Pkwy and Invitational Dr. Int corridors. **Pets:** Small. $40 daily fee/pet. Designated rooms, service with restrictions, crate.

Candlewood Suites H

(361) 578-0236. **$89-$164.** 7103 N Navarro St 77904. Jct US 77 and Navarro St, just s. Int corridors. **Pets:** Other species. $25 one-time fee/room. Service with restrictions.

Comfort Inn & Suites H

(361) 894-6480. **$89-$105.** 6603 NE Zac Lentz Pkwy 77904. Jct NE Zac Lentz Pkwy and US 77. Int corridors. **Pets:** $50 one-time fee/pet, $15 daily fee/pet. Service with restrictions, supervision.

La Quinta Inn Victoria H

(361) 572-3585. **$67-$130.** 7603 N Navarro St (US 77 N) 77904. 4 mi n; at Loop 463. Ext corridors. **Pets:** Accepted.

Lone Star Inn & Suites H

(361) 579-0225. **Call for rates.** 1907 US 59 N 77905. US 59 exit Bloomington (SR 185); on northeast corner. Ext corridors. **Pets:** Medium. $15 daily fee/pet. Service with restrictions, supervision.

WACO

Hilton-Waco H

(254) 754-8484. **$125-$199.** 113 S University Parks Dr 76701. I-35 exit 335B, 0.5 mi w. Int corridors. **Pets:** Accepted.

Residence Inn by Marriott H

(254) 714-1386. **$130-$203.** 501 S University Parks Dr 76706. I-35 exit 335B, just w. Int corridors. **Pets:** Accepted.

Super 8 Waco Mall H

(254) 776-3194. **$55-$130.** 6624 Woodway Dr 76712. Jct US 84 and SR 6; on southwest corner. Ext corridors. **Pets:** Small. $10 daily fee/pet. Designated rooms, service with restrictions, supervision.

TownePlace Suites by Marriott Waco South H

(254) 420-3000. **$97-$167.** 5621 Legend Lake Pkwy 76712. Jct I-35 and SR 6, just sw; behind Baylor Medical Center. Ext corridors. **Pets:** Accepted.

WASHINGTON

The Inn at Dos Brisas CI

(979) 277-7750. **Call for rates.** 10000 Champion Dr 77880. US 290 exit Chapel Hill to FM 1155, 6.5 mi n. Ext corridors. **Pets:** Accepted.

WEATHERFORD

Best Western Plus Cutting Horse Inn & Suites H

(817) 599-3300. **$105-$140.** 210 Alford Dr 76086. I-20 exit 408, just s on SR 171, then just w. Int corridors. **Pets:** Accepted.

Hampton Inn H

(817) 599-4800. **$99-$169.** 2524 S Main St 76087. I-20 exit 408, just s. Int corridors. **Pets:** Accepted.

WEBSTER *(Restaurants p. 626)*

Best Western Webster Hotel NASA H

(281) 338-6000. **$79-$119.** 889 W Bay Area Blvd 77598. I-45 exit 26 (Bay Area Blvd), just e. Int corridors. **Pets:** Accepted.

Comfort Suites H

(281) 554-5400. **$99-$195.** 16931 N Texas Ave 77598. I-45 exit 26 (Bay Area Blvd), 0.5 mi e to Texas Ave, then just s. Int corridors. **Pets:** Accepted.

Staybridge Suites Houston/Clear Lake H

(281) 338-0900. **Call for rates.** 501 W Texas Ave 77598. I-45 exit 26 (Bay Area Blvd), right, then left at 3rd light. Int corridors. **Pets:** Accepted.

WICHITA FALLS

Baymont Inn & Suites Wichita Falls H

(940) 691-7500. **$52-$99.** 4510 Kell Blvd 76309. US 82/277 exit McNeil Ave, just w. Int corridors. **Pets:** Accepted.

Comfort Inn-Wichita Falls H
(940) 766-3300. **$70-$349.** 1317 Kenley Ave 76303. I-44 exit 2, just w. Int corridors. **Pets:** Medium. $15 daily fee/pet. Service with restrictions, supervision.

La Quinta Inn Event Center North H
(940) 322-6971. **$67-$213.** 1128 Central Frwy N 76306. I-44 exit 2 (Maurine St), just w. Ext corridors. **Pets:** Accepted.

WILLIS

Best Western Willis H
(936) 856-1906. **$80-$130.** 12323 IH-45 N 77318. I-45 exit 94, just s on frontage road to Old Montgomery Hwy, just sw to Western Rd, then just s. Ext corridors. **Pets:** Medium. $20 daily fee/pet. Service with restrictions, supervision.

WYLIE

Best Western Plus Wylie Inn H
(972) 429-1771. **$109-$139.** 2011 Hwy 78 N 75098. 1.8 mi ne of SR 2514 (Ballard St); downtown. Int corridors. **Pets:** Other species. Supervision.

ZAPATA

Best Western Inn by the Lake H
(956) 765-8403. **$95-$106.** 1896 S US Hwy 83 78076. On US 83, 0.5 mi se. Ext corridors. **Pets:** Accepted.

UTAH

AMERICAN FORK

Holiday Inn Express & Suites American Fork H
(801) 763-8500. **Call for rates.** 712 S Utah Valley Dr 84003. I-15 exit 276, 0.3 mi n on S 500 E, just e on E 620 S, then 0.3 mi s. Int corridors. **Pets:** Accepted.

BEAVER

Best Western Butch Cassidy Inn M
(435) 438-2438. **$74-$129.** 161 S Main St 84713. I-15 exit 109, 1.8 mi e. Ext corridors. **Pets:** Accepted.

Best Western Paradise Inn H
(435) 438-2455. **$79-$199.** 314 W 1425 N 84713. I-15 exit 112, just e. Ext corridors. **Pets:** Accepted.

BLANDING

Super 8 M
(435) 678-3880. **$60-$113.** 755 S Main St 84511. On US 191 (Main St). Int corridors. **Pets:** Accepted.

BOULDER

Boulder Mountain Lodge H
(435) 335-7460. **$120-$325, 31 day notice.** 20 N Hwy 12 84716. Just s. Ext/int corridors. **Pets:** $15 daily fee/pet. Designated rooms, service with restrictions, supervision.

BRIGHAM CITY

Crystal Inn Brigham City H
(435) 723-0440. **Call for rates.** 480 Westland Dr 84302. I-15 exit 362, 1 mi e to S 500 W, then just n. Int corridors. **Pets:** Accepted.

BRYCE CANYON CITY

Best Western Plus Ruby's Inn H
(435) 834-5341. **$69-$149.** 26 S Main St 84764. On SR 63, 1 mi s of SR 12. Ext/int corridors. **Pets:** Accepted.

Bryce View Lodge M
(435) 834-5180. **$60-$140.** 105 E Center St 84764. 1 mi s of SR 12. Ext corridors. **Pets:** Accepted.

CAINEVILLE

Rodeway Inn Capitol Reef M
(435) 456-9900. **$116.** 25 E SR 24 84775. West end of town. Ext corridors. **Pets:** Accepted.

CEDAR CITY

Americas Best Value Inn H
(435) 867-4700. **$47-$99, 7 day notice.** 333 N 1100 W 84720. I-15 exit 59, just e. Int corridors. **Pets:** Large. $10 daily fee/room. Designated rooms, service with restrictions, crate.

Comfort Inn & Suites H
(435) 865-0003. **$85-$209.** 1288 S Main St 84720. I-15 exit 57, just e, then just n. Int corridors. **Pets:** Accepted.

El Rey Inn & Suites H
(435) 586-6518. **$59-$199.** 80 S Main St 84720. I-15 exit 57, 2 mi n; center. Ext corridors. **Pets:** Accepted.

Holiday Inn Express Hotel & Suites H
(435) 865-7799. **Call for rates.** 1555 S Old Hwy 91 84720. I-15 exit 57, just e, then s. Int corridors. **Pets:** Accepted.

La Quinta Inn & Suites Del Sol H
(435) 865-0005. **$97-$240.** 1377 S Main St 84720. I-15 exit 57, just e. Int corridors. **Pets:** Accepted.

Motel 6 of Cedar City - 4041 M
(435) 586-9200. **Call for rates.** 1620 W 200 N 84720. I-15 exit 59, just w. Int corridors. **Pets:** Accepted.

Quality Inn M
(435) 586-2082. **$75-$110.** 250 N 1100 W 84720. I-15 exit 59, just e. Ext corridors. **Pets:** Large. $10 daily fee/room. Designated rooms, service with restrictions, crate.

CIRCLEVILLE

Butch Cassidy's Hideout M
(435) 577-2008. **Call for rates.** 339 S Hwy 89 84723. Just s of center. Ext corridors. **Pets:** Accepted.

COALVILLE

Best Western Holiday Hills H
(435) 336-4444. **$89-$140.** 500 W 120 S 84017. I-80 exit 162, just w. Int corridors. **Pets:** $20 daily fee/room. Designated rooms, service with restrictions, supervision.

COTTONWOOD HEIGHTS

Residence Inn by Marriott Salt Lake City-Cottonwood H
(801) 453-0430. **$84-$333.** 6425 S 3000 E 84121. I-215 S exit 6 (6200 S), 0.4 mi s, then just e. Int corridors. **Pets:** Large, other species. $100 one-time fee/room. Designated rooms, service with restrictions, crate.

DELTA

Days Inn M
(435) 864-3882. **$80.** 527 E Topaz Blvd 84624. Jct US 6 and 50. Ext corridors. **Pets:** Accepted.

ESCALANTE

Rainbow Country Bed & Breakfast BB
(435) 826-4567. **Call for rates.** 585 E 300 S 84726. Just s of SR 12; east end of town. Int corridors. **Pets:** $10 daily fee/pet. Service with restrictions, supervision.

FARMINGTON

Hampton Inn & Suites Salt Lake City-Farmington H
(801) 451-7999. **Call for rates.** 332 Park Ln 84025. I-15 exit 324 (Lagoon Park), 0.3 mi e on Park Ln. Int corridors. **Pets:** Medium, dogs only. $25 one-time fee/room. Service with restrictions, supervision.

Hyatt Place Salt Lake City-Farmington/Station Park H
(801) 683-4444. **Call for rates.** 222 N Union Ave 84025. I-15 exit 324 (US 89) northbound; exit 325 (Park Ln) southbound; 0.3 mi sw, then just se; follow signs to Station Park. Int corridors. **Pets:** Accepted.

FILLMORE

Best Western Paradise Inn & Resort M
(435) 743-6895. **$85-$115.** 905 N Main St 84631. I-15 exit 167, just e. Ext corridors. **Pets:** $15 daily fee/pet. Designated rooms, service with restrictions, crate.

GREEN RIVER

Holiday Inn Express H
(435) 564-4439. **Call for rates.** 1845 E Main St 84525. I-70 exit 164, 1.7 mi nw. Int corridors. **Pets:** Accepted.

Super 8 M
(435) 564-8888. **$75-$90.** 1248 E Main St 84525. I-70 exit 164, 1.3 mi n. Int corridors. **Pets:** Accepted.

HOLLADAY

Hyatt Place Salt Lake City-Cottonwood H
(801) 890-1280. **$84-$199.** 3090 E 6200 S 84121. I-215 exit 6 (6200 S), 0.3 mi s; at base of Big Cottonwood Canyon. Int corridors. **Pets:** Large, dogs only. $75 one-time fee/room. Service with restrictions, supervision.

HUNTSVILLE

Jackson Fork Inn CI
(801) 745-0051. **$120, 3 day notice.** 7345 E 900 S 84317. I-15 exit 344 (12th St), 12 mi e. Int corridors. **Pets:** $20 one-time fee/room. Designated rooms, service with restrictions, supervision.

KANAB

Best Western Red Hills M ✿
(435) 644-2675. **$80-$230.** 125 W Center St 84741. Center. Ext/int corridors. **Pets:** Medium. $20 daily fee/room. Designated rooms, service with restrictions, supervision.

Canyons Boutique Hotel H
(435) 644-8660. **Call for rates.** 190 N 300 W 84741. North end of town. Int corridors. **Pets:** Accepted.

Comfort Suites H
(435) 644-8200. **$99-$209.** 150 W Center St 84741. Center. Int corridors. **Pets:** Accepted.

Holiday Inn Express Hotel & Suites H
(435) 644-3100. **Call for rates.** 217 S 100 E 84741. On US 89; jct 200 S. Int corridors. **Pets:** Accepted.

LA VERKIN

Best Western Plus Zion West Hotel H
(435) 635-0277. **$89-$440.** 44 W 500 N 84745. Jct SR 17, just e. Int corridors. **Pets:** Accepted.

LAYTON

Hampton Inn by Hilton Layton H ✿
(801) 775-8800. **$119-$129.** 1700 N Woodland Park Dr 84041. I-15 exit 332 (Antelope Dr), 0.3 mi e, then just s. Int corridors. **Pets:** Other species. Service with restrictions, supervision.

Home2 Suites by Hilton Layton H
(801) 820-9222. **$99-$159.** 803 W Heritage Park Blvd 84041. I-15 exit 332 (Antelope Dr), 0.6 mi e to 700 W, then 0.5 mi s. Int corridors. **Pets:** Medium. $75 one-time fee/pet. Designated rooms, service with restrictions, crate.

TownePlace Suites by Marriott Layton H
(801) 779-2422. **$85-$219.** 1743 Woodland Park Dr 84041. I-15 exit 332 (Antelope Dr), 0.3 mi se. Int corridors. **Pets:** Accepted.

LEHI

Best Western Timpanogos Inn H
(801) 768-1400. **$79-$149.** 195 S 850 E 84043. I-15 exit 279, just w, then just s. Int corridors. **Pets:** Accepted.

Home2 Suites by Hilton Lehi-Thanksgiving Point H
(801) 753-5430. **Call for rates.** 3051 W Club House Dr 84043. I-15 exit 284, 0.5 mi w. Int corridors. **Pets:** Accepted.

Hyatt Place Salt Lake City-Lehi H
(385) 345-8300. **$89-$289.** 3700 N Outlet Pkwy 84043. I-15 exit 284 (Highland), 0.3 mi e to Triumph Blvd, just n, then just w. Int corridors. **Pets:** Accepted.

LOGAN

Best Western Plus Weston Inn H
(435) 752-5700. **$90-$205.** 250 N Main St 84321. 0.3 mi n of center. Ext corridors. **Pets:** Large. $15 daily fee/room. Designated rooms, service with restrictions, supervision.

Holiday Inn Express & Suites Logan H
(435) 752-3444. **$89-$399.** 2235 N Main St 84341. 2.8 mi n of center. Int corridors. **Pets:** Accepted.

La Quinta Inn & Suites H
(435) 752-0707. **$79-$273.** 853 S Hwy 89 and 91 84321. 2 mi s of center. Int corridors. **Pets:** Accepted. 🔣🅼🏊📶❌🚪🖥

MANTI

Manti Country Village Motel M
(435) 835-9300. **$69-$99.** 145 N Main St 84642. On US 89 (Main St), just n of center. Ext corridors. **Pets:** Accepted. 📶❌🚪

MIDVALE

Hawthorn Suites by Wyndham Midvale H
(801) 567-0111. **$89-$259.** 6990 S Park Centre Dr 84121. I-15 exit 297 (7200 S), 2.4 mi e on 7200 S (Fort Union Blvd) to 1300 E, just e, then just s. Int corridors. **Pets:** Accepted. 📶❌🚪🖥

Park Inn by Radisson Midvale H
(801) 566-4141. **Call for rates.** 280 W 7200 S 84047. I-15 exit 297 (7200 S), just e. Int corridors. **Pets:** Accepted.
🆂🅰🆅🅴 🔣🅼🏊📶❌🚪🖥

Staybridge Suites Midvale H
(801) 871-0871. **Call for rates.** 747 W Blue Vista Ln 84047. I-15 exit 297 (7200 S), 0.4 mi w, then just s. Int corridors. **Pets:** Accepted.
🔣🅼📶❌🚪🖥

MIDWAY

Homestead Resort H
(435) 654-1102. **Call for rates.** 700 N Homestead Dr 84049. I-80 exit 146 (US 40), 13 mi s to River Rd traffic light, 2.9 mi w to roundabout, 1.2 mi w, follow signs to Homestead Dr, then 0.4 mi s. Ext/int corridors.
Pets: Accepted. 🆂🅰🆅🅴 🍴🏊❌📶❌🚪🖥

MOAB *(Restaurants p. 626)*

Big Horn Lodge M
(435) 259-6171. **$60-$140.** 550 S Main St 84532. 0.5 mi s. Ext corridors. **Pets:** $50 daily fee/pet. Designated rooms, service with restrictions, supervision. 🆂🅰🆅🅴 🍴🏊❌🚪🖥

The Gonzo Inn H 🐾
(435) 259-2515. **Call for rates.** 100 W 200 S 84532. Just w of 200 S and S Main St. Ext/int corridors. **Pets:** Other species. $30 daily fee/room. Service with restrictions, supervision.
🆂🅰🆅🅴 🏊📶❌🚪🖥

Homewood Suites by Hilton Moab H 🐾
(435) 259-7000. **Call for rates.** 132 N Main St 84532. Downtown. Int corridors. **Pets:** Medium, dogs only. $50 one-time fee/room. Service with restrictions, supervision. 🆂🅰🆅🅴 🔣🅼📶❌🚪🖥

La Quinta Inn & Suites Moab H
(435) 259-8700. **$75-$372.** 815 S Main St 84532. 0.8 mi s. Int corridors. **Pets:** Accepted. 🏊❌📶❌🚪🖥

Motel 6 Moab #4119 M
(435) 259-6686. **$59-$199.** 1089 N Main St 84532. 1.5 mi n. Int corridors. **Pets:** Accepted. 🍴🏊📶❌

Red Cliffs Lodge - Moab's National Park Experience R A
(435) 259-2002. **$99-$340, 30 day notice.** Milepost 14 Hwy 128 84532. 2.3 mi n to jct US 191 and SR 128, 14 mi e to MM 14. Ext corridors.
Pets: Accepted. 🆂🅰🆅🅴 🍴🏊❌📶❌🚪🖥

Red Stone Inn M
(435) 259-3500. **Call for rates.** 535 S Main St 84532. 0.5 mi s. Int corridors. **Pets:** Accepted. 🆂🅰🆅🅴 📶❌🚪🖥

Silver Sage Inn M
(435) 259-4420. **$45-$135.** 840 S Main St 84532. 0.9 mi s of the center. Int corridors. **Pets:** Medium. $10 daily fee/pet. Service with restrictions, supervision. 🆂🅰🆅🅴 📶❌🚪🖥

Sorrel River Ranch Resort & Spa H 🐾
(435) 259-4642. **$399-$2050, 45 day notice.** Mile 17 Hwy 128 84532. 17 mi e of jct US 191 and SR 128; at MM 17. Ext corridors.
Pets: Medium, other species. $100 one-time fee/pet. Designated rooms, service with restrictions, crate.
🔌🍴🔣🅼🏊❌📶❌🚪🖥

MONUMENT VALLEY

Goulding's Lodge & Tours H
(435) 727-3231. **$91-$325, 3 day notice.** 1000 Main St 84536. 2 mi w of US 163; 0.5 mi n of Arizona border. Ext corridors. **Pets:** $25 daily fee/pet. Service with restrictions, supervision.
🍴🏊📶❌🚪🖥

MURRAY

Crystal Inn Midvalley-Murray H
(801) 685-9300. **Call for rates.** 818 E Winchester St 84107. I-215 exit 9 (Union Park Ave), 1.2 mi nw via 6600 S. Int corridors.
Pets: Accepted. 🔣🅼🏊📶🚪🖥

Home2 Suites by Hilton Salt Lake City-Murray H
(801) 288-1234. **Call for rates.** 4927 S State St 84107. I-15 exit 300 (5300 S), 0.6 mi e, then 0.6 mi n. Int corridors. **Pets:** Accepted.
🍴🔣🅼📶❌🚪🖥

Residence Inn by Marriott Salt Lake City-Murray H
(801) 262-4200. **$104-$395.** 171 E 5300 S 84107. I-15 exit 300 (5300 S), 0.8 mi e. Int corridors. **Pets:** Accepted.
🍴🔣🅼📶❌🚪🖥

NEPHI

Best Western Paradise Inn of Nephi M
(435) 623-0624. **$90-$125.** 1025 S Main St 84648. I-15 exit 222, 0.5 mi n. Ext corridors. **Pets:** Accepted. 🆂🅰🆅🅴 🏊📶❌🚪🖥

NORTH SALT LAKE

Best Western Plus CottonTree Inn H
(801) 292-7666. **$93-$199.** 1030 N 400 E 84054. I-15 exit 315 (Woods Cross), just e to Onion St, then just s. Int corridors. **Pets:** Accepted.
🆂🅰🆅🅴 🔣🅼🏊📶❌🚪🖥

OGDEN

Best Western Plus High Country Inn H 🐾
(801) 394-9474. **$79-$299.** 1335 W 12th St 84404. I-15 exit 344 (12th St), just e. Ext/int corridors. **Pets:** Other species. $10 daily fee/room. Designated rooms, service with restrictions, crate.
🆂🅰🆅🅴 🍴🔣🅼🏊📶❌🚪🖥

Comfort Suites Ogden H
(801) 621-2545. **$99-$174.** 2250 S 1200 W 84401. I-15 exit 343 (21st St), 0.3 mi e. Int corridors. **Pets:** Other species. $25 one-time fee/room. Designated rooms, service with restrictions, crate.
🍴🔣🅼🏊📶❌🚪🖥

Holiday Inn Express & Suites Ogden H
(801) 392-5000. **$89-$199.** 2245 S 1200 W 84401. I-15 exit 343 (21st St), 0.3 mi e. Int corridors. **Pets:** Medium, other species. $25 one-time fee/room. Designated rooms, service with restrictions, supervision.
🔣🅼🏊📶❌🚪🖥

Sleep Inn Ogden H
(801) 731-6500. **$65-$144.** 1155 S 1700 W 84404. I-15 exit 344 (12th St), just w. Int corridors. **Pets:** Accepted. 🆂🅰🆅🅴 📶🚪🖥

OREM

▼▼▼▼ Holiday Inn Express & Suites Orem H
(801) 655-1515. **Call for rates.** 1290 W University Pkwy 84058. I-15 exit 269 (University Pkwy), 0.5 mi w. Int corridors. **Pets:** Accepted.
〔&M〕〔⟲〕〔✕〕〔📶〕〔✕〕〔🛏〕〔☕〕

AAA ▼▼▼▼ TownePlace Suites by Marriott Orem H
(801) 225-4477. **$72-$186.** 873 N 1200 W 84057. I-15 exit 272 (800 N), just e. Int corridors. **Pets:** Other species. $40 daily fee/pet. Service with restrictions, supervision. 〔SAVE〕〔¶¶〕〔&M〕〔⟲〕〔✕〕〔📶〕〔✕〕〔🛏〕〔☕〕

PARK CITY

AAA ▼▼▼ Best Western Plus Landmark Inn & Pancake House H 🐾
(435) 649-7300. **$99-$259.** 6560 N Landmark Dr 84098. I-80 exit 145 (Kimball Jct), 0.3 mi s, then 0.3 mi nw. Int corridors. **Pets:** Medium. $10 daily fee/pet. Designated rooms, service with restrictions, supervision.
〔SAVE〕〔¶¶〕〔&M〕〔⟲〕〔✕〕〔📶〕〔✕〕〔🛏〕〔☕〕

▼▼▼▼ Holiday Inn Express & Suites Park City H
(435) 658-1600. **Call for rates.** 1501 W Ute Blvd 84098. I-80 exit 145 (Kimball Jct), just s to Ute Blvd, then 0.3 mi e. Int corridors.
Pets: Accepted. 〔&M〕〔⟲〕〔✕〕〔📶〕〔🛏〕〔☕〕

AAA ▼▼▼▼ Hyatt Centric Park City H
(435) 940-1234. **$139-$799, 7 day notice.** 3551 N Escala Ct 84098. I-80 exit 145 (Kimball Jct), 3 mi sw on SR 224 (Park Ave), then 0.8 mi w; at Canyons. Int corridors. **Pets:** Accepted.
〔SAVE〕〔ECO〕〔¶¶〕〔&M〕〔⟲〕〔✕〕〔📶〕〔✕〕〔🛏〕〔☕〕

AAA ▼▼▼▼ Hyatt Place Park City H
(435) 776-1234. **$69-$339.** 4377 N Hwy 224 84060. I-80 exit 145 (Kimball Jct), 2.3 mi e. Int corridors. **Pets:** Accepted.
〔SAVE〕〔¶¶〕〔&M〕〔📶〕〔✕〕〔🛏〕〔☕〕

AAA ▼▼▼▼ Montage Deer Valley H
(435) 604-1300. **$265-$1500, 90 day notice.** 9100 Marsac Ave 84060. I-80 exit 145 (Kimball Jct), at roundabout, take Marsac Ave exit, 2 mi s to Guardsman Connection, then 2 mi sw. Int corridors. **Pets:** Accepted.
〔SAVE〕〔¶¶〕〔&M〕〔⟲〕〔✕〕〔📶〕〔✕〕〔🛏〕〔☕〕

AAA ▼▼▼▼ St. Regis Deer Valley H
(435) 940-5700. **$299-$1299, 14 day notice.** 2300 Deer Valley Dr E 84060. I-80 exit 145 (Kimball Jct), 6 mi s to Deer Valley Dr, 1 mi se to roundabout, take third exit (Deer Valley Dr), then 1.2 mi se. Int corridors. **Pets:** Accepted. 〔SAVE〕〔¶¶〕〔&M〕〔⟲〕〔✕〕〔📶〕〔✕〕〔🛏〕〔☕〕

▼▼▼ ▼▼▼ Washington School House Hotel, A Luxury Boutique Hotel H
(435) 649-3800. **Call for rates.** 543 Park Ave 84060. I-80 exit 145 (Kimball Jct), 6 mi se to Kearns Blvd and SR 224 (Park Ave), then 1.2 mi s; downtown. Int corridors. **Pets:** Accepted. 〔⟲〕〔📶〕〔✕〕〔🛏〕

PRICE

▼▼ ▼▼ Ramada Price H
(435) 637-8880. **$81-$99.** 838 Westwood Blvd 84501. US 6 exit 240 (Business Loop), just e. Int corridors. **Pets:** Accepted.
〔¶¶〕〔&M〕〔⟲〕〔📶〕〔✕〕〔🛏〕〔☕〕

PROVO

▼▼ ▼▼ Baymont Inn & Suites Provo River H
(801) 373-7044. **$79-$137.** 2230 N University Pkwy 84604. I-15 exit 269 (University Pkwy), 3.2 mi e, then just n; in CottonTree Square. Int corridors. **Pets:** Accepted. 〔⟲〕〔📶〕〔✕〕〔🛏〕〔☕〕

AAA ▼▼▼▼ Hampton Inn Provo H 🐾
(801) 377-6396. **$109-$269.** 1511 S 40 E 84601. I-15 exit 263 (University Ave), just e. Int corridors. **Pets:** Service with restrictions, supervision. 〔SAVE〕〔&M〕〔⟲〕〔📶〕〔✕〕〔🛏〕〔☕〕

▼▼▼ ▼▼ Ramada Provo Towne Centre H
(801) 374-9750. **$75-$169.** 1460 S University Ave 84601. I-15 exit 263 (University Ave), just e. Int corridors. **Pets:** Accepted.
〔¶¶〕〔⟲〕〔📶〕〔✕〕〔🛏〕〔☕〕

▼▼▼ ▼▼ Residence Inn by Marriott Provo H
(801) 374-1000. **$84-$307.** 252 W 2230 N 84604. I-15 exit 269 (University Pkwy), 3.2 mi e to W 2230 N, then 0.3 mi n. Int corridors.
Pets: Accepted. 〔&M〕〔⟲〕〔📶〕〔✕〕〔🛏〕〔☕〕

▼▼▼ Sleep Inn H
(801) 377-6597. **$70-$182.** 1505 S 40 E 84606. I-15 exit 263 (University Ave), just e. Int corridors. **Pets:** Accepted.
〔⟲〕〔📶〕〔✕〕〔🛏〕〔☕〕

RICHFIELD

AAA ▼▼▼ Best Western Richfield Inn H
(435) 893-0100. **$75-$100.** 1275 N Main St 84701. I-70 exit 40, just s. Int corridors. **Pets:** Small. $15 deposit/pet. Designated rooms, service with restrictions, supervision. 〔SAVE〕〔&M〕〔⟲〕〔📶〕〔✕〕〔🛏〕〔☕〕

▼▼▼ Comfort Inn H
(435) 893-0119. **$90-$146.** 1070 W 1250 S 84701. I-70 exit 37, just e. Int corridors. **Pets:** Accepted. 〔⟲〕〔📶〕〔✕〕〔🛏〕〔☕〕

▼▼▼ ▼▼ Holiday Inn Express & Suites H
(435) 896-8552. **Call for rates.** 20 W 1400 N 84701. I-70 exit 40, just s. Int corridors. **Pets:** Accepted.
〔📧〕〔¶¶〕〔&M〕〔⟲〕〔📶〕〔✕〕〔🛏〕〔☕〕

▼▼▼ Super 8 M
(435) 896-9204. **$55-$105, 3 day notice.** 1377 N Main St 84701. I-70 exit 40, just s. Ext/int corridors. **Pets:** Accepted. 〔📶〕〔🛏〕〔☕〕

ROOSEVELT

▼▼▼ Americas Best Value Inn Roosevelt-Ballard M
(435) 722-4644. **Call for rates.** 2203 E Hwy 40 84066. 1 mi e of downtown on US 40. Ext corridors. **Pets:** Accepted. 〔¶¶〕〔📶〕〔🛏〕〔☕〕

AAA ▼▼▼▼ Best Western Plus Landmark Hotel Roosevelt-Ballard H
(435) 725-1800. **$110-$160.** 2477 E Hwy 40 84066. 1.2 mi e of downtown on US 40. Int corridors. **Pets:** Accepted.
〔SAVE〕〔&M〕〔📶〕〔✕〕〔🛏〕〔☕〕

ST. GEORGE

▼▼ ▼▼ America's Best Inn & Suites M
(435) 652-3030. **Call for rates.** 245 N Red Cliffs Dr 84790. I-15 exit 8, just e. Ext corridors. **Pets:** Accepted. 〔⟲〕〔📶〕〔🛏〕〔☕〕

AAA ▼▼▼▼ Best Western Coral Hills H
(435) 673-4844. **$99-$239.** 125 E St. George Blvd 84770. I-15 exit 8, 1 mi w. Ext/int corridors. **Pets:** Large, dogs only. $20 daily fee/room. Designated rooms, service with restrictions, supervision.
〔SAVE〕〔ECO〕〔📧〕〔⟲〕〔📶〕〔✕〕〔🛏〕〔☕〕

AAA ▼▼▼ Crystal Inn St. George H
(435) 688-7477. **$89-$229.** 1450 S Hilton Dr 84770. I-15 exit 6 (Bluff St), just w. Int corridors. **Pets:** Other species. $35 one-time fee/room. Designated rooms, service with restrictions, supervision.
〔SAVE〕〔¶¶〕〔⟲〕〔✕〕〔📶〕〔✕〕〔🛏〕〔☕〕

AAA ▼▼▼ Fairfield Inn by Marriott M
(435) 673-6066. **$76-$197.** 1660 S Convention Center Dr 84790. I-15 exit 6 (Bluff St), just e. Int corridors. **Pets:** Medium, other species. $30 one-time fee/pet. Designated rooms, service with restrictions, supervision. 〔SAVE〕〔⟲〕〔📶〕〔✕〕〔🛏〕〔☕〕

▼▼ ▼▼ **Green Valley Boutique Hotel and Spa** H ❀
(435) 628-8060. **$119-$169, 7 day notice.** 1871 W Canyon View Dr 84770. Jct Bluff and S Main sts, 4 mi sw via Hilton Dr to Dixie Dr, then just w to Canyon View Dr. Ext corridors. **Pets:** Dogs only. $500 deposit/room, $5 daily fee/pet. Designated rooms, service with restrictions, crate. ⊞ 🄼 🚗 ⊠ 🟍 ⊠ 🔋 🖵

🛸 ▼▼ **Howard Johnson Inn** M
(435) 628-8000. **$89-$179.** 1040 S Main St 84770. I-15 exit 6 (Bluff St), just w, then just e. Ext corridors. **Pets:** Small, dogs only. $10 daily fee/pet. Service with restrictions, crate. 🆂🅰🆅🅴 🄼 🚗 🛜 ⊠ 🔋 🖵

▼▼ **La Quinta Inn & Suites - St. George** H
(435) 674-2664. **$86-$268.** 91 E 2680 S 84790. I-15 exit 4, just e on Brigham Rd. Int corridors. **Pets:** Accepted.
⊞ 🄼 🚗 🛜 ⊠ 🔋 🖵

▼▼ **Quality Inn St. George** H
(435) 628-4481. **$67-$189.** 1165 S Bluff St 84770. I-15 exit 6 (Bluff St), just w. Ext corridors. **Pets:** Accepted. 🚗 🛜 ⊠ 🔋 🖵

▼▼ **St. George Inn & Suites** H
(435) 673-6661. **$69-$129.** 1221 S Main St 84770. I-15 exit 6 (Bluff St), just w. Ext corridors. **Pets:** Other species. $25 daily fee/room. Designated rooms, service with restrictions, crate. 🚗 ⊠ 🛜 🔋 🖵

▼▼ **Seven Wives Inn** BB
(435) 628-3737. **$115-$200, 7 day notice.** 217 N 100 W 84770. I-15 exit 8, 2.1 mi w, then n. Ext/int corridors. **Pets:** Accepted.
🚗 🛜 ⊠ 🔋

▼▼ **TownePlace Suites by Marriott** H
(435) 986-9955. **$77-$318.** 251 S 1470 E 84790. I-15 exit 8, just e. Int corridors. **Pets:** Accepted. 🄼 🚗 🛜 ⊠ 🔋 🖵

▼▼ **Wingate by Wyndham** H
(435) 673-9608. **$99-$199.** 144 W Brigham Rd, Bldg G 84790. I-15 exit 4, just w. Int corridors. **Pets:** Accepted. 🄼 🚗 ⊠ 🔋 🖵

SALINA

🛸 ▼▼ **Scenic Hills Super 8** M
(435) 529-7483. **$60-$83.** 375 E 1620 S 84654. I-70 exit 56, just n. Ext corridors. **Pets:** Accepted. 🆂🅰🆅🅴 🚗 🛜 🔋 🖵

SALT LAKE CITY

▼▼ **Candlewood Suites Airport** H
(801) 359-7500. **Call for rates.** 2170 W North Temple 84116. I-80 exit 118, 0.3 mi n, then 0.7 mi w. Int corridors. **Pets:** Accepted.
🛜 ⊠ 🔋 🖵

▼▼ **Crystal Inn Hotel & Suites Salt Lake City Downtown** H
(801) 328-4466. **Call for rates.** 230 W 500 S 84101. Cross streets 500 S and 200 W. Int corridors. **Pets:** Large, other species. $25 one-time fee/room. Designated rooms, service with restrictions, crate.
🄼 🚗 ⊠ 🛜 🔋 🖵

🛸 ▼▼ **DoubleTree by Hilton Salt Lake City Airport** H
(801) 539-1515. **$100-$299.** 5151 Wiley Post Way 84116. I-80 exit 114 (Wright Brothers Dr), just n off ramp, then 0.5 mi w. Int corridors.
Pets: Accepted. 🆂🅰🆅🅴 ⊞ 🄼 🚗 🛜 ⊠ 🔋 🖵

▼▼ **DoubleTree Suites by Hilton Salt Lake City Downtown** H
(801) 359-7800. **$99-$299.** 110 W 600 S 84101. Jct 600 S and S West Temple. Int corridors. **Pets:** Accepted.
⊞ 🄼 🚗 🛜 ⊠ 🔋 🖵

▼▼ **Hilton Salt Lake City Center** H
(801) 328-2000. **$92-$319.** 255 S West Temple 84101. Just s of S West Temple and 200 S. Int corridors. **Pets:** Accepted.
⊞ 🄼 🚗 🟍 ⊠ 🔋 🖵

▼▼ **Holiday Inn & Suites Airport West** H
(801) 741-1800. **Call for rates.** 5001 W Wiley Post Way 84116. I-80 exit 114 (Wright Brothers Dr), then 0.4 mi w. Int corridors. **Pets:** Accepted. ⊞ 🄼 🚗 🛜 ⊠ 🔋 🖵

▼▼ **Holiday Inn Express & Suites Airport East** H
(801) 741-1500. **Call for rates.** 200 N 2100 W 84116. I-80 exit 218, 0.3 mi e, 0.8 mi n, then just e. Int corridors. **Pets:** Accepted.
🄼 🚗 🛜 ⊠ 🔋 🖵

▼▼ **Home2 Suites by Hilton Salt Lake City-East** H
(801) 384-5785. **Call for rates.** 2350 S Foothill Dr 84109. I-80 exit 129 (Foothill Dr/Parleys Way), 0.6 mi n. Int corridors. **Pets:** Accepted.
🄼 🛜 ⊠ 🔋 🖵

🛸 ▼▼ **Hyatt House Salt Lake City Downtown** H
(801) 359-4020. **$99-$359.** 140 S 300 W 84101. I-15 exit 307 (400 S) southbound; exit 306 (600 S) northbound; jct 100 S and 300 W, just s. Int corridors. **Pets:** Accepted. 🆂🅰🆅🅴 ⊞ 🄼 🛜 ⊠ 🔋 🖵

🛸 ▼▼ **Hyatt Place Salt Lake City Airport** H
(801) 363-1400. **$70-$200.** 52 N Tommy Thompson Rd 84116. I-80 exit 114 (Wright Brothers Dr), just n off ramp, just e, then just se. Int corridors. **Pets:** Medium. $75 one-time fee/room. Service with restrictions, crate. 🆂🅰🆅🅴 ⊞ 🄼 🛜 ⊠ 🔋 🖵

🛸 ▼▼ **Hyatt Place Salt Lake City Downtown-The Gateway** H
(801) 456-6300. **$79-$459.** 55 N 400 W 84101. Jct W North Temple and 400 W, then just s. Int corridors. **Pets:** Accepted.
🆂🅰🆅🅴 🄼 🚗 🛜 ⊠ 🔋 🖵

🛸 ▼▼ ▼▼ **Kimpton Hotel Monaco** H
(801) 595-0000. **Call for rates.** 15 W 200 S 84101. Jct 200 S and Main St. Int corridors. **Pets:** Accepted.
🆂🅰🆅🅴 🄴🄲🄾 ⊞ 🄼 ⊠ 🟍 ⊠ 🔋

▼▼ **Radisson Hotel Salt Lake City Downtown** H
(801) 531-7500. **Call for rates.** 215 W South Temple 84101. Cross streets 200 S and W South Temple. Int corridors. **Pets:** Accepted.
🄴🄲🄾 ⊞ 🄼 🚗 ⊠ 🛜 ⊠ 🔋 🖵

▼▼ **Residence Inn by Marriott Salt Lake City Airport** H
(801) 532-4101. **$61-$326.** 4883 W Douglas Corrigan Way 84116. I-80 exit 114 (Wright Brothers Dr), just n off ramp. Int corridors.
Pets: Accepted. 🄼 🚗 ⊠ 🔋 🖵

▼▼ **Residence Inn by Marriott Salt Lake City Downtown** H
(801) 355-3300. **$58-$681.** 285 W 300 S (Broadway) 84101. At 300 W and 300 S. Int corridors. **Pets:** Accepted.
🄼 🚗 🛜 ⊠ 🔋 🖵

🛸 ▼▼ **Sheraton Salt Lake City Hotel** H ❀
(801) 401-2000. **$79-$399.** 150 W 500 S 84101. Jct 200 W and 500 S. Int corridors. **Pets:** Medium, other species. Service with restrictions, supervision. 🆂🅰🆅🅴 ⊞ 🄼 🚗 🛜 ⊠ 🔋 🖵

SANDY

🛸 ▼▼ **Best Western Plus CottonTree Inn Salt Lake City-Sandy** H ❀
(801) 523-8484. **$124-$179.** 10695 S Auto Mall Dr 84070. I-15 exit 293 (10600 S), 0.3 mi e, then just s. Int corridors. **Pets:** Other species. $25 daily fee/room. Designated rooms, service with restrictions, supervision.
🆂🅰🆅🅴 🄼 🚗 🛜 ⊠ 🔋 🖵

(AAA) ▼▼▼▼ **Holiday Inn Express & Suites Sandy** H
(801) 495-1317. **Call for rates.** 10680 S Auto Mall Dr 84070. I-15 exit
293 (10600 S), 0.3 mi e, then just s. Int corridors. **Pets:** Accepted.
SAVE &M 🍴 🛏 🛜 ✕ 🛗 💻

(AAA) ▼▼▼▼ **Hyatt House Salt Lake City-Sandy** H
(801) 304-5700. **$94-$249.** 9685 S Monroe St 84070. I-15 exit 295
(9000 S), 0.3 mi e to Frontage Rd, then 1 mi s. Int corridors.
Pets: Accepted. SAVE 🍴 &M 🛏 🛜 ✕ 🛗 💻

▼▼▼▼ **Residence Inn by Marriott Sandy** H
(801) 561-5005. **$94-$255.** 270 W 10000 S 84070. I-15 exit 293 (10600
S), 0.4 mi e to State St, 0.7 mi n to 10000 S, then 0.3 mi w. Int corridors. **Pets:** Accepted. 🍴 &M 🛏 🛜 ✕ 🛗 💻

SOUTH JORDAN

▼▼▼▼ **Home2 Suites by Hilton South Jordan** H
(801) 446-8800. **Call for rates.** 10704 S River Front Park 84095. I-15
exit 293 (10600 S), 1 mi w, then just s. Int corridors. **Pets:** Accepted.
&M 🛜 ✕ 🛗 💻

SPANISH FORK

▼ **Western Inn** H
(801) 798-9400. **Call for rates.** 632 Kirby Ln 84660. I-15 exit 257B, on
US 6. Int corridors. **Pets:** Accepted. 🛜 ✕ 🛗

SPRINGDALE

▼▼▼▼ **Hampton Inn & Suites Springdale Zion National
Park** H
(435) 627-9191. **$161-$313.** 1127 Zion Park Blvd 84767. 2 mi s of Zion
National Park entrance. Int corridors. **Pets:** Accepted.
&M 🛜 ✕ 🛗 💻

▼▼▼▼ **Holiday Inn Express Zion National Park** H
(435) 772-3200. **Call for rates.** 1215 Zion Park Blvd 84767. 2 mi s of
Zion National Park entrance. Int corridors. **Pets:** Accepted.
🛏 🛜 ✕ 🛗 💻

SPRINGVILLE

(AAA) ▼▼ **Best Western Mountain View Inn** H
(801) 489-3641. **$75-$215.** 1455 N 1750 W 84663. I-15 exit 261, just e.
Int corridors. **Pets:** Other species. $20 daily fee/room. Designated
rooms, service with restrictions, supervision.
SAVE &M 🛏 🛜 ✕ 🛗 💻

TOOELE

▼▼▼ **Comfort Inn & Suites Tooele** H
(801) 250-3600. **$104-$209.** 8580 N Hwy 36 84074. I-80 exit 99, just s.
Int corridors. **Pets:** Accepted. &M 🛏 🛜 ✕ 🛗 💻

▼▼▼ **Holiday Inn Express & Suites Tooele** H
(435) 833-0500. **Call for rates.** 1531 N Main St 84074. I-80 exit 99, 11
mi s. Int corridors. **Pets:** Accepted. &M 🛏 🛜 ✕ 🛗 💻

TORREY

▼▼ **Red Sands Hotel** H
(435) 425-3688. **Call for rates.** 670 E SR 24 84775. 0.3 mi w of jct SR
12 and 24. Int corridors. **Pets:** Accepted.
&M 🛏 🛜 ✕ 🛗 💻

▼ **The Rim Rock Inn & Restaurants** M
(435) 425-3398. **Call for rates.** 2523 E Hwy 24 84775. 2.5 mi ne of jct
SR 12 and 24. Ext corridors. **Pets:** $10 daily fee/room. Designated
rooms, service with restrictions, supervision. 🍴 🛜 ✕

TREMONTON

▼▼▼ **Hampton Inn by Hilton Tremonton** H
(435) 257-6000. **$119-$169.** 2145 W Main St 84337. I-84 exit 40, 0.4
mi e. Int corridors. **Pets:** Accepted.
🔌 🍴 &M 🛏 🛜 ✕ 🛗 💻

▼▼ **Western Inn Tremonton** H
(435) 257-3399. **Call for rates.** 2301 W Main St 84337. I-84 exit 40,
just e. Int corridors. **Pets:** Accepted. 🍴 🛜 ✕ 🛗

VERNAL

(AAA) ▼▼▼ **Best Western Dinosaur Inn** M
(435) 789-2660. **$76-$250.** 251 E Main St 84078. 0.3 mi e of downtown
on US 40. Ext corridors. **Pets:** Accepted.
SAVE 🍴 🛏 🛜 ✕ 🛗 💻

▼▼▼ **Comfort Inn & Suites Vernal** H 🐾
(435) 789-6066. **$69-$249.** 2500 W 1500 S 84078. On US 40 and 191,
3 mi sw of downtown. Int corridors. **Pets:** Large, other species. $10
daily fee/pet. Designated rooms, service with restrictions, supervision.
🍴 &M 🛜 ✕ 🛗 💻

▼▼▼ **Holiday Inn Express & Suites
Vernal-Dinosaurland** H
(435) 789-4654. **Call for rates.** 1515 W US 40 84078. 1.8 mi w of
downtown. Int corridors. **Pets:** Accepted. &M 🛜 ✕ 🛗 💻

▼▼▼ **TownePlace Suites by Marriott Vernal** H
(435) 789-8050. **$89-$167.** 1219 W Hwy 40 84078. 1.3 mi w of downtown. Int corridors. **Pets:** Other species. $50 one-time fee/room. Service
with restrictions. 🍴 &M 🛏 🛜 ✕ 🛗 💻

WASHINGTON

▼▼▼ **Holiday Inn Express & Suites** H
(435) 986-1313. **Call for rates.** 2450 N Town Center Dr 84780. I-15 exit
16, just e. Int corridors. **Pets:** Accepted.
🍴 &M 🛏 🛜 ✕ 🛗 💻

WENDOVER

(AAA) ▼▼▼ **Best Western Plus Wendover Inn** H
(435) 665-2215. **Call for rates.** 685 E Wendover Blvd 84083. I-80 exit
2, east end of town. Int corridors. **Pets:** Large. $10 daily fee/pet. Desig-
nated rooms, service with restrictions, supervision.
SAVE &M 🛏 🛜 ✕ 🛗 💻

WEST VALLEY CITY

▼▼▼ **Crystal Inn Salt Lake City-West Valley City** H
(801) 736-2000. **Call for rates.** 2254 W City Center Ct 84119. I-215
exit 18 (3500 S), just e, then 0.3 mi n. Int corridors. **Pets:** Accepted.
&M 🛏 🛜 ✕ 🛗 💻

▼▼▼ **Holiday Inn Express & Suites West Valley
City** H
(801) 517-4000. **Call for rates.** 3036 S Decker Lake Dr 84119. I-215
exit 18A (3500 S), just e, 0.6 mi n, then just w. Int corridors.
Pets: Accepted. 🍴 &M 🛏 ✕ 🛜 ✕ 🛗 💻

▼▼▼ **Home2 Suites by Hilton West Valley City** H
(801) 679-8222. **$99-$189.** 4028 Parkway Blvd 84120. I-15 exit 305A
(West Valley/2100 S), 4.2 mi w on SR 201 exit 13 (Bangerter Hwy), 1.2
mi s to Parkway Blvd, then 0.3 mi w. Int corridors. **Pets:** Accepted.
🍴 &M 🛏 🛜 ✕ 🛗 💻

▼▼ **La Quinta Inn Salt Lake City West** H
(801) 954-9292. **$67-$323.** 3540 S 2200 W 84119. I-215 exit 18 (3500
S), just e, then just s. Int corridors. **Pets:** Accepted.
&M 🛏 🛜 ✕ 🛗 💻

▼▼ **My Place Hotel West Valley City** H
(801) 869-8484. **Call for rates.** 3074 S Decker Lake Dr 84119. I-215
exit 18A (3500 S), just e, 0.6 mi n, then just w. Int corridors.
Pets: Accepted. 🍴 &M 🛜 ✕ 🛗 💻

▼▼▼ **Staybridge Suites West Valley City** H

(801) 746-8400. **Call for rates.** 3038 S Decker Lake Dr 84119. I-215 exit 18A (3500 S), just e, 0.6 mi n, then just w. Int corridors. **Pets:** Accepted. 🍽 🛗 ➿ ⊠ 📶 ⊠ 🛄 🖥

▼▼▼ **TownePlace Suites by Marriott West Valley City** H

(801) 307-3300. **$81-$229.** 5473 W High Market Dr 84120. I-80 exit 113 (5600 S), 4.7 mi s, then just e; I-15 exit 305A/B (SR 201), 6.5 mi w, exit 11, 1 mi s, then just e. Int corridors. **Pets:** Accepted.
🛗 📶 ⊠ 🛄 🖥

WOODS CROSS

▼▼ **Comfort Inn & Suites Salt Lake City-Woods Cross** H

(801) 298-3900. **$65-$290.** 2437 S Wildcat Way 84010. I-15 exit 315, just e, then 0.8 mi n on frontage road. Int corridors. **Pets:** Other species. $20 daily fee/pet. Designated rooms, service with restrictions.
🍽 🛗 ➿ 📶 ⊠ 🛄 🖥

▼▼ **Hampton Inn Salt Lake City North/Woods Cross** H

(801) 296-1211. **$99-$179.** 2393 S 800 W 84087. I-15 exit 315, just w, then just n. Int corridors. **Pets:** Accepted.
🍽 🛗 ➿ 📶 ⊠ 🛄 🖥

VERMONT

ALBURG

▼▼ **Ransom Bay Inn & Restaurant** BB

(802) 796-3399. **Call for rates.** 4 Center Bay Rd 05440. Jct SR 78, 0.5 mi s on US 2, then just e. Int corridors. **Pets:** Accepted.
🍽 📶 ⊠ 🐾 🍸

BENNINGTON

▼ **The Harwood Hill** M

(802) 442-6278. **$90-$145.** 864 Harwood Hill Rd 05201. Jct SR 9, 1.2 mi n on US 7, then 1.7 mi n on Historic SR 7A. Ext corridors. **Pets:** Accepted. 📶 ⊠ 🛄 🖥

▼ **Knotty Pine Motel** M

(802) 442-5487. **$90-$125.** 130 Northside Dr 05201. Jct SR 9, 1.2 mi n on US 7, then just n on Historic SR 7A. Ext corridors. **Pets:** Dogs only. Designated rooms, service with restrictions, supervision.
➿ 📶 ⊠ 🛄 🖥

BRANDON

▼▼ **Brandon Motor Lodge** M

(802) 247-9594. **Call for rates.** 2095 Franklin St 05733. 2 mi s on US 7. Ext corridors. **Pets:** Accepted. ECO 🍽 ➿ ⊠ 📶 ⊠ 🛄

▼▼▼ **The Lilac Inn** CI

(802) 247-5463. **$155-$245, 30 day notice.** 53 Park St 05733. Just e on SR 73. Int corridors. **Pets:** Dogs only. $35 one-time fee/room. Service with restrictions, supervision. ECO 📶 ⊠ 🍸

BURLINGTON

AAA ▼▼▼ **Hilton Burlington** H 🐾

(802) 658-6500. **$119-$309.** 60 Battery St 05401. At Battery and College sts; just n of ferry terminal; center. Int corridors. **Pets:** Dogs only. $50 deposit/room. Designated rooms, service with restrictions, supervision. SAVE 🍽 🛗 ➿ 📶 ⊠ 🛄 🖥

▼▼▼ **Hotel Vermont** H

(802) 651-0080. **Call for rates.** 41 Cherry St 05401. Just e of Battery St. Int corridors. **Pets:** Accepted. 🍽 🛗 ⊠ 📶 ⊠ 🛄

CAVENDISH

▼▼▼ **The Pointe at Castle Hill Resort & Spa** H

(802) 226-7688. **Call for rates.** 2940 SR 103 05142. On SR 103, just n of jct SR 131. Int corridors. **Pets:** Accepted.
🍽 🛗 ➿ ⊠ 📶 ⊠ 🛄 🖥

COLCHESTER

▼▼ **Days Inn Colchester** H

(802) 655-0900. **$70-$180.** 124 College Pkwy 05446. I-89 exit 15 northbound, just e on SR 15; exit 16 southbound, 1.1 mi s on US 7, then 1 mi e on SR 15. Int corridors. **Pets:** Dogs only. $200 deposit/room, $10 daily fee/pet. Designated rooms, service with restrictions, crate.
🍽 🛗 ➿ 📶 ⊠ 🛄 🖥

▼▼▼ **Hampton Inn by Hilton & Vermont Event Center** H

(802) 655-6177. **$89-$279.** 42 Lower Mountain View Dr 05446. I-89 exit 16, just n on US 7. Int corridors. **Pets:** Large, other species. Designated rooms, service with restrictions, supervision.
ECO 🍽 🛗 ➿ 📶 ⊠ 🛄 🖥

▼ **Motel 6 #1407** H

(802) 654-6860. **$55-$155.** 74 S Park Dr 05446. I-89 exit 16, just s on US 7. Int corridors. **Pets:** Accepted. ➿ 📶 ⊠ 🛄

▼▼▼ **Residence Inn by Marriott, Burlington-Colchester** H

(802) 655-3100. **$123-$344.** 71 Rathe Rd 05446. I-89 exit 16, 0.6 mi n on US 2 W/7 N, then just w. Int corridors. **Pets:** $150 one-time fee/ room. Service with restrictions, crate.
🍽 🛗 ➿ 📶 ⊠ 🛄 🖥

ESSEX JUNCTION

▼▼ **Baymont Inn & Suites Burlington/Essex Junction** H

(802) 872-5200. **$69-$299.** 27 Susie Wilson Rd 05452. I-89 exit 15 northbound, 2 mi e, then just n. Int corridors. **Pets:** Dogs only. $200 deposit/room, $10 daily fee/pet. Designated rooms, service with restrictions, crate. 🍽 🛗 ➿ 📶 ⊠ 🛄 🖥

▼▼▼ **The Essex Resort & Spa** H 🐾

(802) 878-1100. **$119-$349.** 70 Essex Way 05452. SR 289 exit 10, 0.3 mi s. Int corridors. **Pets:** Other species. $45 daily fee/pet. Designated rooms, service with restrictions.
ECO 🍽 🛗 ➿ ⊠ 📶 ⊠ 🛄 🖥

FAIRFAX

AAA ▼▼▼ **The Inn at Buck Hollow Farm** BB

(802) 849-2400. **$125-$145, 14 day notice.** 2150 Buck Hollow Rd 05454. 6 mi n of jct SR 104 via Buck Hollow Rd. Int corridors. **Pets:** Dogs only. $20 daily fee/pet. Designated rooms, service with restrictions, crate. SAVE 🍽 ➿ 📶 ⊠ 🍸

JAMAICA

▼▼▼ **Three Mountain Inn** CI

(802) 874-4140. **$199-$360, 21 day notice.** 3732 VT 100 05343. On SR 30; center. Ext/int corridors. **Pets:** Accepted.
🍽 ➿ 📶 ⊠ 🛄 🖥

KILLINGTON

▼▼▼ **Killington Mountain Lodge Hotel & Conference Center** H

(802) 422-4302. **Call for rates.** 2617 Killington Rd 05751. 2.7 mi s from jct SR 100/US 4. Int corridors. **Pets:** Accepted.
➿ ⊠ 📶 ⊠ 🛄 🖥

LUDLOW

▼▼▼ **Andrie Rose Inn** BB
(802) 228-4846. **Call for rates.** 13 Pleasant St 05149. Corner of Depot St; center. Int corridors. **Pets:** Accepted. ⊤⊤ 🛜 ✕ 🖋 🖨

MANCHESTER CENTER *(Restaurants p. 626)*

▼▼ **Casablanca Motel** CA ❖
(802) 362-2145. **$72-$209, 14 day notice.** 5927 Main St 05255. Jct SR 11/30, 1 mi on Historic SR 7A. Ext corridors. **Pets:** Dogs only. $15 daily fee/pet. Designated rooms, service with restrictions.
ECO ⊤⊤ 🛜 ✕ 🖋 🖨 🖳

▲▲▲ ▼▼ **Chalet Motel** M
(802) 362-1622. **$100-$180, 14 day notice.** 1875 Depot St 05255. On SR 11/30, 0.4 mi e of jct US 7. Ext corridors. **Pets:** $10 daily fee/pet. Designated rooms, service with restrictions.
SAVE ⊤⊤ 🛜 ✕ 🖋 🖨 🖳

▲▲▲ ▼▼▼ **Manchester View Fine Lodging** M ❖
(802) 362-2739. **$90-$350, 14 day notice.** 77 High Meadows Way 05255. On Historic SR 7A, 2 mi n of jct SR 11/30 N, then just e. Ext/int corridors. **Pets:** Small, dogs only. $20 daily fee/pet. Designated rooms, service with restrictions, supervision.
SAVE ⊤⊤ 🛜 🛜 🛜 ✕ 🖋 🖨 🖳

MANCHESTER VILLAGE

▲▲▲ ▼▼▼▼ **The Equinox, A Luxury Collection Golf Resort & Spa** H
(802) 362-4700. **$189-$699, 14 day notice.** 3567 Main St 05254. 1.3 mi s on Historic SR 7A, from jct SR 11/30. Int corridors.
Pets: Accepted. SAVE ECO ⊤⊤ 🛜 🛜 ✕ 🛜 ✕ 🖋 🖨 🖳

▲▲▲ ▼▼▼▼ **The Inns at Equinox** CI
(802) 362-4700. **Call for rates.** 3567 Main St 05254. Jct SR 11/30, 1.3 mi s on Historic SR 7A; at The Equinox, A Luxury Collection Golf Resort & Spa. Ext/int corridors. **Pets:** Accepted.
SAVE ⊤⊤ ✕ 🛜 ✕ 🖋 🖨 🖳

▲▲▲ ▼▼▼▼ **Taconic, A Kimpton Hotel** H ❖
(802) 362-0147. **$269-$699, 3 day notice.** 3835 Main St 05254. On Historic SR 7A, 1 mi s of jct SR 11/30. Ext/int corridors. **Pets:** Other species. Designated rooms, service with restrictions, supervision.
SAVE ⊤⊤ 🛜 🛜 ✕ 🛜 ✕ 🖋

MIDDLEBURY

▼▼▼ **Middlebury Inn** CI ❖
(802) 388-4961. **$139-$229.** 14 Court Square 05753. On US 7; center. Ext/int corridors. **Pets:** Other species. $35 one-time fee/room. Designated rooms, service with restrictions, supervision.
ECO ⊤⊤ 🛜 ✕ 🖋 🖳

▼▼▼ **Swift House Inn** CI ❖
(802) 388-9925. **Call for rates.** 25 Stewart Ln 05753. 0.3 mi n on US 7 from jct SR 125 W. Ext/int corridors. **Pets:** Medium, dogs only. $50 daily fee/pet. Designated rooms, service with restrictions, supervision.
ECO 🖪 ⊤⊤ 🛜 ✕ 🖋 🖳

MORRISVILLE

▲▲▲ ▼▼▼ **Sunset Motor Inn** M
(802) 888-4956. **$105-$145, 7 day notice.** 160 Vt Rt 15 W 05661. Jct SR 100, just w. Ext/int corridors. **Pets:** Other species. $100 deposit/room. Designated rooms, service with restrictions, crate.
SAVE ⊤⊤ 🛜 🛜 ✕ 🖋 🖳

NORTH HERO

▼▼▼ **Shore Acres Inn** CI
(802) 372-8722. **Call for rates.** 237 Shore Acres Dr 05474. 0.5 mi s on US 2. Ext/int corridors. **Pets:** Dogs only. $25 deposit/pet, $5 daily fee/pet. Service with restrictions, supervision.
⊤⊤ ✕ 🛜 ✕ 🖋 🖨

RANDOLPH

▲▲▲ ▼▼▼ **Three Stallion Inn** BB
(802) 728-5575. **$98-$170, 15 day notice.** 665 Stock Farm Rd 05060. I-89 exit 4 (SR 66), 2 mi w; jct SR 12, just e on SR 66, then just s. Ext/int corridors. **Pets:** Dogs only. $25 one-time fee/pet. Designated rooms, supervision. SAVE ⊤⊤ 🛜 ✕ 🛜 ✕ 🖨 🖳

RIPTON

▼▼▼ **The Chipman Inn** BB
(802) 388-2390. **$169-$289, 7 day notice.** 1233 Rt 125 05766. Jct US 7, 4.4 mi e on SR 125. Int corridors. **Pets:** Medium. $25 daily fee/pet. Designated rooms, service with restrictions, supervision.
⊤⊤ 🛜 🛜 ✕ 🅦 🛜

RUTLAND

▼▼▼ **Holiday Inn Rutland/Killington** H
(802) 775-1911. **$119-$229.** 476 Holiday Dr 05701. 2.4 mi s on US 7 from US 4 W, 0.4 mi n on US 7 from US 4 E. Int corridors.
Pets: Accepted. ⊤⊤ 🛜 🛜 🛜 ✕ 🖨 🖳

ST. ALBANS

▼▼ **La Quinta Inn & Suites St. Albans** H
(802) 524-3300. **$104-$273.** 813 Fairfax Rd 05478. I-89 exit 19, just w on Interstate Access Rd, then just s. Int corridors. **Pets:** Accepted.
⊤⊤ 🛜 🛜 ✕ 🖨 🖳

ST. JOHNSBURY

▼▼▼ **Comfort Inn & Suites Near Burke Mountain** H ❖
(802) 748-1500. **$174-$349.** 703 US Rt 5 S 05819. I-91 exit 20, just sw. Int corridors. **Pets:** Dogs only. $30 daily fee/pet. Service with restrictions, crate. ECO ⊤⊤ 🛜 🛜 ✕ 🛜 ✕ 🖨 🖳

▼▼ **Fairbanks Inn** M
(802) 748-5666. **Call for rates.** 401 Western Ave 05819. I-91 exit 21, 0.8 mi e on US 2. Ext corridors. **Pets:** Other species. $25 daily fee/pet. Designated rooms, service with restrictions, supervision.
⊤⊤ 🛜 🛜 ✕ 🖨 🖳

SHAFTSBURY

▼ **Serenity Motel** CA
(802) 442-6490. **Call for rates.** 4379 Rt 7A 05262. Jct SR 67, 3.3 mi n on Historic SR 7A. Ext corridors. **Pets:** Accepted.
⊤⊤ 🛜 ✕ 🖨 🖳

SHELBURNE

▼▼ **Days Inn Shelburne** H
(802) 985-3334. **$50-$209.** 3229 Shelburne Rd 05482. I-189 exit 13 (I-189/US 7), 2.8 mi s. Ext/int corridors. **Pets:** Medium, dogs only. $25 daily fee/pet. Designated rooms, service with restrictions, supervision.
🛜 ✕ 🖨 🖳

SOUTH BURLINGTON

▲▲▲ ▼▼▼ **Best Western Plus Windjammer Inn & Conference Center** H ❖
(802) 863-1125. **$99-$249.** 1076 Williston Rd 05403. I-89 exit 14E, 0.3 mi e on US 2. Int corridors. **Pets:** Large, dogs only. $10 daily fee/pet. Designated rooms, service with restrictions, supervision.
SAVE ECO ⊤⊤ 🛜 🛜 🛜 ✕ 🖨 🖳

▲▲▲ ▼▼▼ **DoubleTree by Hilton Hotel Burlington** H
(802) 658-0250. **$169-$269.** 1117 Williston Rd 05403. I-89 exit 14E, 0.6 mi e on US 2. Int corridors. **Pets:** Medium. $25 daily fee/room. Designated rooms, service with restrictions, supervision.
SAVE ECO ⊤⊤ 🛜 🛜 🛜 ✕ 🖨 🖳

▼▼▼▼ Green Mountain Suites Hotel H ❀
(802) 860-1212. **$149-$489, 3 day notice.** 401 Dorset St 05403. I-89 exit 14E, just e on US 2, then 0.8 mi s. Int corridors. **Pets:** Medium, dogs only. $25 daily fee/pet. Designated rooms, service with restrictions, supervision. ⬛ 🈁 ⅃M 🏊 🛜 ✖ 🔋 🖥

▼▼▼▼ Homewood Suites by Hilton South
        Burlington H
(802) 652-4400. **Call for rates.** 5 Dorset St 05403. I-89 exit 14E, just e on US 2, then s. Int corridors. **Pets:** Accepted.
⬛ 🈁 ⅃M 🛜 ✖ 🔋 🖥

▼▼◇ La Quinta Inn & Suites South Burlington H
(802) 865-3400. **$68-$357.** 1285 Williston Rd 05403. I-89 exit 14E, 0.5 mi e on US 2. Int corridors. **Pets:** Accepted. 🏊 🛜 ✖ 🔋 🖥

◇◇◇ ▼▼▼▼ Sheraton Burlington Hotel H
(802) 865-6600. **$99-$459.** 870 Williston Rd 05403. I-89 exit 14W, just w on US 2. Int corridors. **Pets:** Accepted.
SAVE ECO 🈁 ⅃M 🏊 🛜 ✖ 🔋 🖥

SOUTH WOODSTOCK
▼▼▼▼ Kedron Valley Inn CI
(802) 457-1473. **Call for rates.** 4778 South Rd 05071. Jct US 4, 5 mi s. Ext/int corridors. **Pets:** Other species. $15 daily fee/pet. Designated rooms, service with restrictions. 🈁 ⅃M 🛜 ✖ 🔋 🖥

SPRINGFIELD
▼▼▼▼ Holiday Inn Express H
(802) 885-4516. **Call for rates.** 818 Charlestown Rd 05156. I-91 exit 7, just w on SR 11 (Charlestown Rd). Int corridors. **Pets:** Accepted.
🈁 ⅃M 🏊 🛜 ✖ 🔋 🖥

STOWE
▼▼▼ Commodores Inn H
(802) 253-7131. **$118-$198, 3 day notice.** 823 S Main St 05672. Jct SR 108, 0.8 mi s on SR 100. Int corridors. **Pets:** Other species. $10 daily fee/room. Designated rooms. 🈁 🏊 ✖ 🛜 ✖ 🔋 🖥

▼▼▼▼ Golden Eagle Resort M
(802) 253-4811. **$119-$249.** 511 Mountain Rd 05672. Jct SR 100, 0.5 mi w on SR 108. Ext corridors. **Pets:** Dogs only. $25 daily fee/pet. Designated rooms, service with restrictions, crate.
ECO 🈁 🏊 ✖ 🛜 ✖ 🔋 🖥

▼▼ Hob Knob Inn & Lounge M
(802) 253-8549. **$90-$160, 15 day notice.** 2364 Mountain Rd 05672. Jct SR 100, 2.5 mi w on SR 108. Ext/int corridors. **Pets:** Dogs only. $20 daily fee/pet. Designated rooms, service with restrictions.
ECO 🈁 🏊 🛜 ✖ 🔋 🖥

▼▼ Snowdrift Motel M
(802) 253-7629. **$96-$200, 7 day notice.** 2135 Mountain Rd 05672. Jct SR 100, 2.1 mi w on SR 108. Ext/int corridors. **Pets:** Dogs only. $20 daily fee/pet. Designated rooms, service with restrictions, crate.
🏊 ✖ 🛜 ✖ 🔋 🖥

◇◇◇ ▼▼▼▼ Stoweflake Mountain Resort &
        Spa H
(802) 253-7355. **$259-$489, 15 day notice.** 1746 Mountain Rd 05672. Jct SR 100, 1.4 mi w on SR 108. Int corridors. **Pets:** Accepted.
SAVE 🈁 ⅃M 🏊 ✖ 🛜 ✖ 🔋 🖥

◇◇◇ ▼▼▼▼ ▼▼▼▼ Stowe Mountain Lodge H 🐾
(802) 760-4755. **$199-$829, 14 day notice.** 7412 Mountain Rd 05672. Jct SR 100, 7.3 mi w on SR 108. Int corridors. **Pets:** Large, dogs only. $125 one-time fee/pet. Service with restrictions, supervision.
SAVE ECO 🈁 ⅃M 🏊 ✖ 🛜 ✖ 🔋 🖥

▼▼ Sun & Ski Inn and Suites M
(802) 253-7159. **Call for rates.** 1613 Mountain Rd 05672. Jct SR 100, 1.7 mi w on SR 108. Ext/int corridors. **Pets:** Accepted.
🈁 🏊 ✖ 🛜 ✖ 🔋 🖥

◇◇◇ ▼▼▼▼ Topnotch Resort H ❀
(802) 253-8585. **Call for rates.** 4000 Mountain Rd 05672. Jct SR 100, 4.2 mi w on SR 108. Ext/int corridors. **Pets:** Dogs only. $25 daily fee/pet. Designated rooms, service with restrictions, supervision.
SAVE ⬛ 🈁 🏊 ✖ 🛜 ✖ 🔋 🖥

▼▼▼▼ Trapp Family Lodge H ❀
(802) 253-8511. **$195-$950, 14 day notice.** 700 Trapp Hill Rd 05672. Jct SR 100, 2.1 mi w on SR 108, 1.4 mi s on Luce Hill Rd, follow signs. Int corridors. **Pets:** Medium, dogs only. $50 daily fee/pet. Designated rooms, service with restrictions, crate.
ECO 🈁 ⅃M 🏊 ✖ 🛜 ✖ 🔋 🖥

SWANTON
◇◇◇ ▼▼▼ Swanton Motel M
(802) 868-4284. **$79-$122.** 112 Grand Ave (US 7) 05488. I-89 exit 21, 0.8 mi w on SR 78, then 0.5 mi s. Ext corridors. **Pets:** Accepted.
SAVE 🈁 🏊 🛜 ✖ 🔋 🔋 🖥

VERGENNES
◇◇◇ ▼▼▼▼ Strong House Inn CI ❀
(802) 877-3337. **$140-$340, 14 day notice.** 94 W Main St 05491. 0.6 mi s on SR 22A. Int corridors. **Pets:** Dogs only. $35 one-time fee/pet. Designated rooms, service with restrictions, supervision.
SAVE 🈁 ⅃M 🛜 ✖ 🖥

WARREN
▼▼▼ ▼▼▼ The Pitcher Inn, Relais & Chateaux CI
(802) 496-6350. **Call for rates.** 275 Main St 05674. Center. Ext/int corridors. **Pets:** Accepted. 🈁 ✖ 🛜 ✖ 🔋 🖥

WATERBURY
◇◇◇ ▼▼▼▼ The Old Stagecoach Inn BB
(802) 244-5056. **$110-$170, 14 day notice.** 18 N Main St 05676. I-89 exit 10, just s on SR 100, then just e. Ext/int corridors. **Pets:** Other species. $20 daily fee/room. Designated rooms, service with restrictions, supervision. SAVE 🛜 ✖ 🔋 🔋 🖥

WEST DOVER
▼▼▼ ▼▼▼ The Hermitage Inn CI
(802) 464-3511. **$125-$325, 21 day notice.** 25 Handle Rd 05356. Jct SR 9, 3 mi n on SR 100, 3 mi w on Coldbrook Rd. Ext/int corridors. **Pets:** Accepted. 🈁 ⅃M ✖ 🛜 ✖ 🔋 🖥

WESTMORE
▼▼▼ WilloughVale Inn & Cottages on Lake
        Willoughby CI
(802) 525-4123. **Call for rates.** 793 SR 5A 05860. Jct SR 16 and 5A, just s. Ext/int corridors. **Pets:** Accepted. 🈁 ✖ 🛜 ✖ 🔋 🖥

WILLISTON
◇◇◇ ▼▼▼ Sonesta ES Suites Burlington H
(802) 878-2001. **$89-$329.** 35 Hurricane Ln 05495. I-89 exit 12, just s on SR 2A, then just e. Ext corridors. **Pets:** Accepted.
SAVE 🈁 🏊 🛜 ✖ 🔋 🖥

WOODSTOCK
▼▼▼ 506 on the River Inn H ❀
(802) 457-5000. **$179-$489, 14 day notice.** 1653 W Woodstock Rd (US 4) 05091. 2 mi w of center on US 4. Int corridors. **Pets:** Dogs only. $250 deposit/room. Designated rooms, service with restrictions, crate.
🈁 ⅃M 🛜 ✖ 🔋

▼▼▼ The Shire Woodstock M
(802) 457-2211. **Call for rates.** 46 Pleasant St 05091. 0.4 mi e on US 4; downtown. Ext/int corridors. **Pets:** Accepted. 🛜 ✖ 🔋

AAA ▼▼▼▼ **Woodstock Inn & Resort** H
(802) 457-1100. **$169-$1299, 14 day notice.** 14 The Green 05091. On US 4; center. Int corridors. **Pets:** Accepted.
[SAVE] [ECO] [icons]

VIRGINIA

ABINGDON

▼ **Super 8 Motel Abingdon** H
(276) 676-3329. **$60-$70.** 298 Town Center Dr 24210. I-81 exit 17, just ne. Int corridors. **Pets:** Dogs only. $20 daily fee/pet. Designated rooms, service with restrictions. [icons]

ALEXANDRIA *(Restaurants p. 626)*

▼▼ **Candlewood Suites Alexandria-Ft. Belvoir** H ❀
(703) 780-1111. **Call for rates.** 8847 Richmond Hwy 22309. I-95/495 exit 177A, 7.2 mi s on US 1. Int corridors. **Pets:** Other species. $150 one-time fee/room. Service with restrictions, crate.
[icons]

▼▼ **Comfort Inn & Suites Alexandria** H ❀
(703) 922-9200. **$99-$199.** 5716 S Van Dorn St 22310. I-95/495 exit 173, 2 mi e of jct I-395 and 495. Int corridors. **Pets:** Small, dogs only. $50 daily fee/pet. Service with restrictions, supervision.
[icons]

▼▼ **Comfort Inn Landmark** H
(703) 642-3422. **$99-$209.** 6254 Duke St 22312. I-395 exit 3B, just w. Int corridors. **Pets:** Accepted. [icons]

▼▼ **Extended Stay America-Washington DC-Alexandria-Eisenhower Ave** H
(703) 329-3399. **$120-$145.** 200 Bluestone Rd 22304. I-95/495 exit 176B, 1 mi s on Eisenhower Ave. Int corridors. **Pets:** Accepted.
[icons]

AAA ▼▼▼▼ **Hilton Alexandria Mark Center** H
(703) 845-1010. **$99-$259.** 5000 Seminary Rd 22311. I-395 exit 4, just w. Int corridors. **Pets:** Accepted.
[SAVE] [icons]

AAA ▼▼▼▼ **Holiday Inn Hotel & Suites-Alexandria Old Town** H
(703) 548-6300. **$89-$399.** 625 First St 22314. George Washington Memorial Pkwy, just e of jct First and Washington sts. Int corridors. **Pets:** Accepted. [SAVE] [ECO] [icons]

AAA ▼▼▼▼ **Hotel Monaco Alexandria-a Kimpton Hotel** H
(703) 549-6080. **$116-$1500.** 480 King St 22314. On SR 7; between S Pitt and S Royal sts; just sw of City Hall. Int corridors. **Pets:** Accepted.
[SAVE] [ECO] [icons]

AAA ▼▼▼▼ **Kimpton Morrison House** H ❀
(703) 838-8000. **$125-$509.** 116 S Alfred St 22314. Jct King and S Alfred sts, just s. Int corridors. **Pets:** Other species. Designated rooms, service with restrictions. [SAVE] [ECO] [icons]

AAA ▼▼▼ **Lorien Hotel & Spa-a Kimpton Hotel** H
(703) 894-3434. **$134-$799.** 1600 King St 22314. Between Harvard and Peyton sts. Int corridors. **Pets:** Accepted.
[SAVE] [ECO] [icons]

AAA ▼▼▼ **Red Roof PLUS+ Washington DC-Alexandria** H
(703) 960-5200. **$70-$200.** 5975 Richmond Hwy 22303. I-95/495 exit 177A, 0.5 mi s on US 1. Ext corridors. **Pets:** Accepted.
[SAVE] [icons]

AAA ▼▼▼▼ **Residence Inn by Marriott Alexandria-Old Town/Duke St.** H
(703) 548-5474. **$114-$292.** 1456 Duke St 22314. I-95/495 exit 176B, 0.5 mi n on SR 241, then 0.7 mi e on SR 236. Int corridors. **Pets:** Accepted. [SAVE] [icons]

▼▼▼ **Residence Inn by Marriott Alexandria Old Town South at Carlyle** H
(703) 549-1155. **$104-$241.** 2345 Mill Rd 22314. I-95/495 exit 176B, 0.3 mi n on Eisenhower Ave, then just w. Int corridors. **Pets:** Accepted.
[ECO] [icons]

AAA ▼▼▼▼ **Sheraton Suites Old Town Alexandria** H ❀
(703) 836-4700. **$95-$325.** 801 N St. Asaph St 22314. Just e of Washington St. Int corridors. **Pets:** Medium, dogs only. Designated rooms, service with restrictions, supervision.
[SAVE] [ECO] [icons]

▼▼ **TownePlace Suites by Marriott Alexandria-Fort Belvoir** H
(703) 619-6060. **$85-$189.** 8632 Woodlawn Ct 22309. I-95/495 exit 177A, 6.7 mi s on US 1. Int corridors. **Pets:** Accepted.
[icons]

AAA ▼▼▼▼ **The Westin Alexandria** H
(703) 253-8600. **$119-$499.** 400 Courthouse Square 22314. I-95/495 exit 176B, just n on Telegraph Rd (SR 241 N), 0.4 mi e on SR 236, then just s on Dulany St. Int corridors. **Pets:** Accepted.
[SAVE] [icons]

ALTAVISTA

▼▼ **Comfort Inn** H
(434) 369-4000. **$60-$200.** 1558 Main St 24517. US 29 business route, jct US 29. Int corridors. **Pets:** Accepted. [icons]

▼▼ **Days Inn** H
(434) 369-4070. **$75-$200.** 1557 Main St 24517. US 29 business route; jct US 29. Int corridors. **Pets:** Accepted. [icons]

APPOMATTOX

▼ **Super 8** M
(434) 352-2339. **$65-$70.** 7571 Richmond Hwy 24522. US 460, just w of jct US 26. Int corridors. **Pets:** Accepted. [icons]

ARLINGTON *(Restaurants p. 626)*

AAA ▼▼▼▼ **Arlington Court Suites Hotel, A Clarion Collection** H
(703) 524-4000. **$119-$389.** 1200 N Courthouse Rd 22201. 1.5 mi sw of Theodore Roosevelt Bridge, just n off US 50. Int corridors. **Pets:** Accepted. [SAVE] [icons]

AAA ▼▼▼▼ **Hyatt Place - Arlington** H
(703) 243-2494. **$89-$369.** 2401 Wilson Blvd 22201. Jct Wilson Blvd and N Adams St. Int corridors. **Pets:** Accepted.
[SAVE] [icons]

Hyatt Regency Crystal City at Reagan National Airport H
(703) 418-1234. **$89-$429.** 2799 Jefferson Davis Hwy 22202. 2 mi s of 14th St Bridge on US 1, jct SR 233; entrance just e of US 1 on Clark St. Int corridors. **Pets:** Accepted.
SAVE ⛔ 🛗 🚗 📶 ⚔ 🔌 📺

Le Méridien Arlington H ❀
(703) 351-9170. **Call for rates.** 1121 N 19th St 22209. I-66 exit 73, just sw of Key Bridge. Int corridors. **Pets:** Medium. $25 daily fee/pet. Designated rooms, service with restrictions, supervision.
SAVE ⛔ 🛗 📶 ❌

Residence Inn by Marriott Arlington Ballston H
(703) 310-1999. **$124-$314.** 650 N Quincy St 22203. I-66 exit 71, 0.9 mi s on N Glebe Rd (SR 120), then just n. Int corridors.
Pets: Accepted. 🔌 🛗 📶 ❌ ⚔ 📺

Residence Inn by Marriott Arlington Capital View H ❀
(703) 415-1300. **$109-$292.** 2850 S Potomac Ave 22202. 2 mi s of 14th St Bridge on US 1; just s of jct SR 233. Int corridors.
Pets: Medium. $200 one-time fee/room. Designated rooms, service with restrictions. SAVE ⛔ 🛗 🚗 📶 ❌ ⚔ 📺

Residence Inn by Marriott Arlington Courthouse H
(703) 312-2100. **$128-$359.** 1401 N Adams St 22201. Jct Clarendon Blvd and N Adams St. Int corridors. **Pets:** Accepted.
ECO 🛗 🚗 📶 ❌ ⚔ 📺

Residence Inn by Marriott Arlington Rosslyn H ❀
(703) 812-8400. **$125-$323.** 1651 N Oak St 22209. I-66 exit 73, 0.3 mi s on Fort Myer Dr, 0.3 mi w on Wilson Blvd to N Pierce St, then 2 blks e on Clarendon Blvd. Int corridors. **Pets:** Medium, other species. $100 one-time fee/pet. Service with restrictions, crate.
🛗 📶 ❌ ⚔ 📺

Residence Inn by Marriott-Pentagon City H
(703) 413-6630. **$112-$303.** 550 Army Navy Dr 22202. I-395 exit 8C, 1 mi s of 14th St Bridge. Int corridors. **Pets:** Accepted.
SAVE ECO ⛔ 🛗 🚗 📶 ❌ ⚔ 📺

Sheraton Pentagon City Hotel H
(703) 521-1900. **$89-$499.** 900 S Orme St 22204. I-395 exit 8A; at SR 27 and 244; 1.3 mi s of 14th St Bridge. Int corridors. **Pets:** Accepted.
SAVE ⛔ 🛗 🚗 📶 ❌ ⚔ 📺

The Westin Arlington Gateway H
(703) 717-6200. **Call for rates.** 801 N Glebe Rd 22203. I-66 exit 71, just e on Fairfax Dr to Vermont Ave; just n of jct N Glebe Rd (SR 120) and Wilson Blvd. Int corridors. **Pets:** Accepted.
SAVE ECO ⛔ 🛗 🚗 📶 ❌ ⚔ 📺

The Westin Crystal City H
(703) 486-1111. **Call for rates.** 1800 Jefferson Davis Hwy 22202. I-395 exit 8C, 1.4 mi s of 14th St Bridge on US 1; entrance corner of Eads St. Int corridors. **Pets:** Accepted. SAVE ⛔ 🛗 📶 ❌ ⚔ 📺

ASHBURN (Restaurants p. 627)

Aloft Dulles Airport North H
(703) 723-6969. **$89-$239.** 22390 Flagstaff Plaza 20148. On Loudoun County Pkwy (CR 607), just s of jct SR 267 (Toll Rd) exit 1. Int corridors. **Pets:** Accepted. SAVE ECO ⛔ 🛗 🚗 📶 ⚔ 🔌 📺

Homewood Suites by Hilton/Dulles North H
(703) 723-7500. **$89-$169.** 44620 Waxpool Rd 20147. 1.7 mi w of jct SR 28 and Waxpool Rd (CR 625); SR 7, 3.4 mi s on Loudoun County Pkwy (CR 607), 0.3 mi w. Int corridors. **Pets:** Accepted.
🛗 🚗 📶 ⚔ 📺

BLACKSBURG

Comfort Inn Blacksburg H
(540) 951-1500. **$99-$259.** 3705 S Main St 24060. 3.5 mi s on US 460; jct US 460 Bypass. Int corridors. **Pets:** Accepted.
SAVE 🚗 📶 ⚔ 📺

Days Inn Blacksburg H
(540) 951-1330. **$75-$180.** 3503 Holiday Ln 24060. 3.8 mi s on US 460; jct US 460 Bypass. Ext corridors. **Pets:** $20 daily fee/pet. Designated rooms, no service, crate. 🚗 📶 ⚔ 📺

BRISTOL

Holiday Inn Hotel & Suites H
(276) 466-4100. **Call for rates.** 3005 Linden Dr 24202. I-81 exit 7, just w. Int corridors. **Pets:** Accepted.
ECO ⛔ 🛗 🚗 📶 ❌ ⚔ 📺

Motel 6 #4125 M
(276) 466-6060. **Call for rates.** 21561 Clear Creek Rd 24202. I-81 exit 7, 0.3 mi w. Int corridors. **Pets:** Accepted. 🛗 📶

BUCHANAN

Wattstull Inn M
(540) 254-1551. **Call for rates.** 130 Arcadia Rd 24066. I-81 exit 168, just e on SR 614. Ext corridors. **Pets:** Accepted.
SAVE ⛔ 🚗 📶 ⚔ 📺

CAPE CHARLES (Restaurants p. 627)

Shore Stay Suites M
(757) 331-4090. **$89-$169.** 26406 Lankford Hwy 23310. On US 13. Ext corridors. **Pets:** $25 one-time fee/pet. Designated rooms, service with restrictions, crate. ECO 🛗 📶 ❌ ⚔ 📺

CENTREVILLE

Extended Stay America-Washington DC-Centreville/Manassas H
(703) 988-9955. **$95-$115.** 5920 Fort Dr 20121. I-66 exit 53, 0.9 mi s on SR 28; off SR 28, 0.3 mi s of jct US 29. Int corridors.
Pets: Accepted. 🛗 📶 ⚔

CHANTILLY (Restaurants p. 627)

Extended Stay America Washington DC-Chantilly-Airport H
(703) 263-7200. **$100-$115.** 4506 Brookfield Corporate Dr 20151. I-66 exit 53, 3 mi n on SR 28; jct US 50, 1 mi s of SR 28. Int corridors.
Pets: Accepted. ⛔ 🛗 📶 ⚔

Holiday Inn Chantilly-Dulles Expo Center H
(703) 815-6060. **Call for rates.** 4335 Chantilly Shopping Center 20151. I-66 exit 53, 3 mi n on SR 28; 1 mi s of jct US 50 and SR 28. Int corridors. **Pets:** Accepted. ⛔ 🛗 🚗 📶 ❌ ⚔ 📺

Hyatt Place Chantilly/Dulles Airport-South H
(703) 961-8160. **$64-$199.** 4994 Westone Plaza Dr 20151. I-66 exit 53, 2 mi n on SR 28, then just w on Westfields Blvd; 1.7 mi s of jct SR 28 and US 50. Int corridors. **Pets:** Accepted.
SAVE 🛗 🚗 📶 ❌ ⚔ 📺

Residence Inn by Marriott Chantilly Dulles South H
(703) 263-7900. **$78-$197.** 14440 Chantilly Crossing Ln 20151. Jct SR 28, just w on US 50. Int corridors. **Pets:** Accepted.
ECO 🛗 🚗 📶 ❌ ⚔ 📺

Staybridge Suites Hotel Chantilly/Dulles International Airport H
(703) 435-8090. **$99-$299.** 3860 Centerview Dr 20151. Jct SR 28, just e on US 50. Int corridors. **Pets:** Accepted. ECO 🛗 📶 ⚔ 📺

▼▼ **TownePlace Suites by Marriott-Chantilly Dulles South** 🄷

(703) 709-0453. **$78-$151.** 14036 Thunderbolt Pl 20151. Jct SR 28, just e on US 50. Int corridors. **Pets:** Accepted.

[ECO] 🛜 ⊠ 🛏 🖵

🄰🄰🄰 ▼▼▼ **Wingate by Wyndham Dulles Airport-Chantilly** 🄷

(571) 203-0999. **$79-$250.** 3940 Centerview Dr 20151. Jct SR 28, just e on US 50. Int corridors. **Pets:** Accepted.

[SAVE] ♿ 🛜 ⊠ 🛏 🖵

CHARLES CITY

▼▼▼ **Edgewood Plantation Bed & Breakfast** 🄱🄱

(804) 829-2962. **Call for rates.** 4800 John Tyler Memorial Hwy 23030. Jct SR 609, just e on SR 5. Ext/int corridors. **Pets:** Small, dogs only. $15 one-time fee/room. Designated rooms, service with restrictions, crate. 🛜 ⊠ 🛏 🖵

CHARLOTTESVILLE

▼▼ **Cavalier Inn at the University of Virginia** 🄷

(434) 296-8111. **Call for rates.** 105 N Emmet St 22903. Jct US 29 (Emmet St) and 250 Business, 1.3 mi s on US 29 business route. Ext/int corridors. **Pets:** Accepted. [ECO] ♿ 🛜 ⊠ 🛏 🖵

🄰🄰🄰 ▼▼▼ **DoubleTree by Hilton Hotel Charlottesville** 🄷 ❀

(434) 973-2121. **$129-$239.** 990 Hilton Heights Rd 22901. I-64 exit 118B (US 29/Emmet St), 4 mi n of jct US 250 Bypass. Int corridors. **Pets:** Other species. $50 one-time fee/room. Designated rooms, service with restrictions, crate. [SAVE] [ECO] ♿ 🛜 🛏 🖵

▼▼▼ **Fairfield Inn & Suites by Marriott** 🄷

(434) 964-9411. **$99-$181.** 577 Branchlands Blvd 22901. US 29 (Emmet St), 1.3 mi n of US 250 Bypass. Int corridors. **Pets:** Accepted.

🛜 ⊠ 🛏 🖵

▼▼▼ **Graduate Charlottesville** 🄷

(434) 295-4333. **Call for rates.** 1309 W Main St 22903. US 29 (Emmet St), 1 mi e on US 250 (University Ave). Int corridors. **Pets:** Accepted.

♿ 🛜 ⊠ 🛏 🖵

▼▼▼ **Holiday Inn-Monticello/Charlottesville** 🄷

(434) 977-5100. **Call for rates.** 1200 5th St SW 22902. I-64 exit 120, just n on SR 631. Int corridors. **Pets:** Accepted.

♿ 🛜 🛏 🖵

🄰🄰🄰 ▼▼▼ **Hyatt Place Charlottesville** 🄷

(434) 995-5200. **$79-$299.** 2100 Bond St 22901. Jct US 250 Bypass, 0.4 mi n on US 29. Int corridors. **Pets:** Medium, dogs only. $75 one-time fee/room. Service with restrictions, supervision.

[SAVE] ♿ 🛜 ⊠ 🛏 🖵

▼▼ **La Quinta Inn & Suites Charlottesville-UVA Medical** 🄷

(434) 293-6188. **$97-$427.** 1803 Emmet St 22901. Jct US 250 Bypass, just n on US 29 (Emmet St). Int corridors. **Pets:** Accepted.

♿ 🛜 ⊠ 🛏 🖵

▼▼▼ **Omni Charlottesville Hotel** 🄷 🐾

(434) 971-5500. **$179-$339.** 212 Ridge McIntire Rd 22903. I-64 exit 120, 2.3 mi n on SR 631; downtown. Int corridors. **Pets:** Small, other species. $50 one-time fee/room. Designated rooms, service with restrictions. [ECO] ♿ 🛜 ⊠ 🛏 🖵

▼▼▼ **Residence Inn by Marriott** 🄷

(434) 923-0300. **$121-$264.** 1111 Millmont St 22903. I-64 exit 118B (US 29/Emmet St), 2.5 mi n on US 29/250 E, just s on Barracks Rd, then just se. Int corridors. **Pets:** Accepted.

[ECO] ♿ 🛜 ⊠ 🛏 🖵

CHESAPEAKE

🄰🄰🄰 ▼▼▼ **Aloft Chesapeake** 🄷

(757) 410-9562. **$89-$269.** 1454 Crossways Blvd 23320. I-64 exit 289B (Greenbrier Pkwy), just s to Jarman Rd (at Crossways Center) to Crossways Blvd, then 0.7 mi n. Int corridors. **Pets:** Accepted.

[SAVE] [ECO] ♿ 🛜 ⊠ 🛏 🖵

▼▼▼ **Candlewood Suites** 🄷

(757) 405-3030. **Call for rates.** 4809 Market Pl 23321. I-664 exit 11A (SR 337 W), just w. Int corridors. **Pets:** Large, dogs only. $100 one-time fee/pet. Designated rooms, service with restrictions, crate.

[ECO] ♿ 🛜 🛏 🖵

▼▼▼ **Comfort Inn & Suites** 🄷

(757) 673-8585. **$60-$300.** 3355 S Military Hwy 23323. I-64 exit 296A, just n on George Washington Memorial Hwy N (US 17 Bypass), then just e on US 460 and 13. Int corridors. **Pets:** Accepted.

♿ 🛜 ⊠ 🛏 🖵

▼▼▼ **Hampton Inn & Suites** 🄷

(757) 819-5230. **$79-$299.** 1421 N Battlefield Blvd 23320. I-64 exit 290B, just s; jct Coastal Way. Int corridors. **Pets:** Accepted.

♿ 🛜 ⊠ 🛏 🖵

▼▼▼ **Hampton Inn Chesapeake/Greenbrier** 🄷

(757) 420-1550. **$79-$209.** 701A Woodlake Dr 23320. I-64 exit 289A (Greenbrier Pkwy), just n. Int corridors. **Pets:** Accepted.

♿ 🛜 🛏 🖵

🄰🄰🄰 ▼▼▼ **Hyatt Place-Chesapeake/Greenbrier** 🄷

(757) 312-0020. **$124-$229.** 709 Eden Way N 23320. I-64 exit 289B (Greenbrier Pkwy), 1 mi s; in Towne Place at Greenbrier. Int corridors. **Pets:** Accepted. [SAVE] [ECO] ♿ 🛜 ⊠ 🛏 🖵

🄰🄰🄰 ▼▼▼ **The Marriott Hotel Chesapeake** 🄷

(757) 523-1500. **$84-$161.** 725 Woodlake Dr 23320. I-64 exit 289A (Greenbrier Pkwy), n to Woodlake Dr, then just e. Int corridors. **Pets:** Accepted. [SAVE] [ECO] ♿ 🛜 ⊠ 🛏 🖵

🄰🄰🄰 ▼▼▼ **Red Roof Inn Chesapeake Conference Center** 🄷

(757) 523-0123. **$50-$120.** 724 Woodlake Dr 23320. I-64 exit 289A (Greenbrier Pkwy), just n to Woodlake Dr, then just e. Ext corridors. **Pets:** Accepted. [SAVE] ♿ 🛜 ⊠ 🛏 🖵

▼▼▼ **Residence Inn by Marriott, Chesapeake-Greenbrier** 🄷

(757) 502-7300. **$110-$194.** 1500 Crossways Blvd 23320. I-64 exit 289B (Greenbrier Pkwy), just s to Jarman Rd (at Crossways Center) to Crossways Blvd, then 0.6 mi n. Int corridors. **Pets:** Accepted.

[ECO] ♿ 🛜 ⊠ 🛏 🖵

▼▼▼ **Staybridge Suites Greenbrier** 🄷

(757) 420-2525. **Call for rates.** 709 Woodlake Dr 23320. I-64 exit 289A (Greenbrier Pkwy), just n. Int corridors. **Pets:** Accepted.

♿ 🛜 🛏 🖵

🄰🄰🄰 ▼▼▼ **Studios & Suites 4 Less** 🄷

(757) 484-5800. **$69-$119.** 3235 Western Branch Blvd 23321. I-664 exit 9B northbound; exit 8B southbound, 1 mi s on US 17. Int corridors. **Pets:** Accepted. [SAVE] ♿ 🛜 🛏 🖵

CHESTER

🄰🄰🄰 ▼▼▼ **Fairfield Inn by Marriott** 🄷

(804) 778-7500. **$89-$129.** 12400 Redwater Creek Rd 23831. I-95 exit 61B, just w of jct SR 10. Int corridors. **Pets:** Accepted.

[SAVE] ♿ 🛜 ⊠ 🛏 🖵

🄰🄰🄰 ▼▼▼ **Hyatt Place Richmond/Chester** 🄷

(804) 530-4600. **$89-$199.** 13148 Kingston Ave 23836. I-206 exit 15D, just w, I-95 exit 61A, 4.5 mi e; in River's Bend. **Pets:** Accepted. [SAVE] ⊟ ♿ 🛜 ⊠ 🛏 🖵

▼▼▼ Residence Inn by Marriott 🅷
(804) 530-5501. **$123-$170.** 800 Bermuda Hundred Rd 23836. I-295 exit 15, just w; in River's Bend. Int corridors. **Pets:** Accepted.
🅴🅲🅾 ⓖM 🔁 🛜 ⊠ 🚻 💻

CHESTERFIELD

AAA ▼▼▼ La Quinta Inn Richmond South 🅷
(804) 743-0770. **$67-$213.** 9040 Pams Ave 23237. I-95 exit 64, just w. Int corridors. **Pets:** Accepted. SAVE ⓖM 🛜 🚻 💻

AAA ▼▼▼ Sleep Inn Richmond 🅷
(804) 275-8800. **$64-$114.** 2321 Willis Rd 23237. I-95 exit 64, just w. Int corridors. **Pets:** Accepted. SAVE ⓖM 🛜 🚻 💻

CHINCOTEAGUE (Restaurants p. 627)

AAA ▼▼▼ Americas Best Value Inn & Suites Ⓜ
(757) 336-6562. **$50-$210, 10 day notice.** 6151 Maddox Blvd 23336. Just e of Chincoteague Cswy. Ext corridors. **Pets:** Medium, dogs only. $15 daily fee/pet. Designated rooms, service with restrictions, crate.
SAVE 🔁 🛜 🚻 💻

CHRISTIANSBURG

AAA ▼▼▼ Econo Lodge Ⓜ
(540) 382-6161. **$55-$160.** 2430 Roanoke St 24073. I-81 exit 118, just w on US 11/460. Ext corridors. **Pets:** Small. $15 daily fee/pet. Designated rooms, service with restrictions, supervision.
SAVE ⓖM 🔁 🛜 🚻 💻

▼▼▼ Hampton Inn Christiansburg/Blacksburg 🅷
(540) 381-5874. **$169-$189.** 380 Arbor Dr 24073. I-81 exit 118B, 4 mi w on US 460 Bypass, just n on Peppers Ferry Rd, then just w. Int corridors. **Pets:** Accepted. 🔁 🛜 ⊠ 🚻 💻

AAA ▼▼▼▼ Quality Inn Ⓜ 🐾
(540) 382-2055. **$80-$160.** 50 Hampton Blvd 24073. I-81 exit 118C, just e. Ext corridors. **Pets:** Other species. $10 daily fee/room. Designated rooms, service with restrictions. SAVE 🔁 🛜 🚻 💻

CLARKSVILLE

AAA ▼▼▼ Magnuson Hotel On The Lake Clarksville 🅷
(434) 374-5023. **$90-$130, 3 day notice.** 103 Second St 23927. US 58 business route, just n; downtown. Int corridors. **Pets:** Other species. $100 deposit/pet, $20 daily fee/pet. Designated rooms, service with restrictions, crate. SAVE ⓖM 🔁 🛜 🚻 💻

COLLINSVILLE

▼▼ Quality Inn-Dutch Inn Hotel & Convention Center 🅷
(276) 647-3721. **$69-$310.** 2360 Virginia Ave 24078. Jct US 58, 3 mi n on US 220 business route. Ext corridors. **Pets:** Accepted.
🍴 🔁 🛜 🚻 💻

COLONIAL HEIGHTS

▼▼▼ Candlewood Suites 🅷
(804) 526-0111. **Call for rates.** 15820 Woods Edge Rd 23834. I-95 exit 58 northbound; exit 58B southbound, just w. Int corridors.
Pets: Accepted. 🍴 ⓖM 🛜 🚻 💻

COVINGTON

AAA ▼▼▼ Magnuson Hotel Covington 🅷
(540) 962-4951. **Call for rates.** 820 E Madison St 24426. I-64 exit 16, just n. Ext corridors. **Pets:** Accepted. SAVE 🍴 🔁 🛜 🚻 💻

CULPEPER

▼▼ Quality Inn Ⓜ
(540) 825-4900. **$65-$130.** 890 Willis Ln 22701. 2 mi s on Main St (US 29 business route); jct US 29, just e. Ext corridors. **Pets:** Dogs only. $15 daily fee/pet. Designated rooms, service with restrictions, supervision. 🔁 🛜 🚻 💻

DAHLGREN

▼▼ Quality Inn Dahlgren 🅷
(540) 663-3060. **Call for rates.** 4661 James Madison Pkwy 22485. From US 301, 2 mi s of entrance to US Navy Surface Weapons Center; 4 mi s of Potomac River Bridge. Int corridors. **Pets:** Accepted.
🍴 ⓖM 🔁 🛜 ⊠ 🚻 💻

DANVILLE

▼▼ Comfort Inn & Suites 🅷
(434) 793-2000. **$90-$240.** 100 Tower Dr 24540. Jct US 29 business route/SR 86, just w on US 58 business route. Int corridors.
Pets: Accepted. 🍴 🔁 🛜 ⊠ 🚻 💻

▼▼▼ Courtyard by Marriott 🅷
(434) 791-2661. **$118-$164.** 2136 Riverside Dr 24540. Jct US 29 business route/SR 86, 0.5 mi e on US 58 business route. Int corridors.
Pets: Accepted. ⓖM 🔁 🛜 ⊠ 🚻 💻

DOSWELL

AAA ▼▼▼ Centerstone Inn Doswell 🅷
(804) 876-3321. **$69-$139.** 16102 Theme Park Way 23047. I-95 exit 98, just e on SR 30; entrance to theme park. Ext corridors. **Pets:** Small. $10 daily fee/room. Service with restrictions, crate.
SAVE 🍴 🔁 ⊠ 🛜 🚻 💻

AAA ▼▼▼ Days Inn Kings Dominion 🅷
(804) 612-8680. **$55-$155.** 16220 International St 23047. I-95 exit 98, just e on SR 30. Int corridors. **Pets:** $25 daily fee/pet. Designated rooms, service with restrictions, supervision. SAVE 🔁 🛜 🚻 💻

▼▼▼ La Quinta Inn & Suites Doswell - Kings Dominion 🅷
(804) 876-6900. **$67-$317.** 16280 International St 23047. I-95 exit 98, just e on SR 30. Int corridors. **Pets:** Accepted.
🍴 ⓖM 🔁 🛜 ⊠ 🚻 💻

DUBLIN

▼▼▼ Holiday Inn Express 🅷
(540) 674-1600. **Call for rates.** 4428 Cleburne Blvd 24084. I-81 exit 98, just e. Int corridors. **Pets:** Accepted.
🍴 ⓖM 🔁 🛜 ⊠ 🚻 💻

AAA ▼▼▼ Sleep Inn & Suites 🅷
(540) 674-4099. **$70-$160.** 5094 State Park Rd 24084. I-81 exit 101, just e. Int corridors. **Pets:** $10 daily fee/pet. Designated rooms, service with restrictions, crate. SAVE 🅴🅲🅾 🍴 ⓖM 🔁 🛜 🚻 💻

DUMFRIES (Restaurants p. 627)

▼▼ Comfort Inn Dumfries near Quantico Main Gate North 🅷
(703) 445-8070. **$85-$199.** 16931 Old Stage Rd 22025. I-95 exit 152B, 0.4 mi w on SR 234. Int corridors. **Pets:** Medium, other species. $50 one-time fee/pet. Designated rooms, service with restrictions, supervision. ⓖM 🔁 🛜 ⊠ 🚻 💻

EMPORIA

AAA ▼▼▼ Best Western Emporia 🅷
(434) 634-3200. **$87-$99.** 1100 W Atlantic St 23847. I-95 exit 11B, just w on US 58. Ext corridors. **Pets:** Accepted. SAVE 🔁 🛜 🚻 💻

▼▼▼ **Country Inn & Suites By Carlson Emporia** **H**
(434) 336-0001. **Call for rates.** 107 Sadler Ln 23847. I-95 exit 11A, just
e on US 58. Int corridors. **Pets:** $20 daily fee/room. Designated rooms,
service with restrictions, crate. 🔥 🏊 🛜 ✕ 🛏 💻

🅰 ▼▼ **Days Inn-Emporia** **H**
(434) 634-9481. **$62-$75.** 921 W Atlantic St 23847. I-95 exit 11B, just w
on US 58. Ext corridors. **Pets:** $10 daily fee/pet. Designated rooms,
service with restrictions, supervision. (SAVE) ⌦ 🏊 🛜 🛏 💻

🅰 ▼▼▼ **Hampton Inn by Hilton** **H**
(434) 634-9200. **$99-$129.** 898 Wiggins Rd 23847. I-95 exit 11B, just w
on US 58. Int corridors. **Pets:** Accepted.
(SAVE) (ECO) 🔥 🏊 🛜 ✕ 🛏 💻

🅰 ▼▼▼ **Sleep Inn** **H**
(434) 348-3900. **$89-$150.** 899 Wiggins Rd 23847. I-95 exit 11B, just e
on US 58, then just s. Int corridors. **Pets:** $15 daily fee/pet. Designated
rooms, service with restrictions, supervision. (SAVE) 🔥 🛜 🛏 💻

EXMORE
▼▼▼ **Holiday Inn Express & Suites** **H**
(757) 442-5522. **Call for rates.** 3446 Lankford Hwy 23350. On US 13.
Int corridors. **Pets:** Accepted. 🔥 🏊 🛜 ✕ 🛏 💻

FAIRFAX *(Restaurants p. 627)*
▼▼ **Candlewood Suites Fairfax-Washington, D.C.** **H**
(703) 359-4490. **Call for rates.** 11400 Random Hills Rd 22030. I-66 exit
57A, 0.5 mi e on US 50, just s on Waples Mill Rd, then 0.4 mi w. Int
corridors. **Pets:** Accepted. ⌦ 🔥 🛜 ✕ 🛏 💻

▼▼ **Comfort Inn University Center** **H**
(703) 591-5900. **$63-$170.** 11180 Fairfax Blvd 22030. I-66 exit 57A, 0.8
mi se on US 50; 0.5 mi nw of jct US 29 and US 50. Int corridors.
Pets: Accepted. (ECO) ⌦ 🏊 🛜 ✕ 🛏 💻

▼▼ **Extended Stay America Washington
DC-Fairfax** **H**
(703) 359-5000. **$105-$125.** 3997 Fair Ridge Dr 22033. I-66 exit 57B,
1.2 mi w on US 50. Int corridors. **Pets:** Accepted.
⌦ 🔥 🏊 🛜 ✕ 🛏

▼▼ **Extended Stay America-Washington DC-Fairfax-Fair
Oaks** **M**
(703) 273-3444. **$95-$115.** 12104 Monument Dr 22033. I-66 exit 57B,
0.8 mi w on US 50, 0.3 mi s on SR 620 (W Ox Rd), then just se. Ext
corridors. **Pets:** Accepted. 🔥 🛜 🛏

▼▼ **Extended Stay America Washington DC-Falls
Church-Merrifield** **H**
(703) 204-0088. **$115-$145.** 8281 Willow Oaks Corporate Dr 22031.
I-495 exit 50A, just w on US 50 to Gallows Rd, then just s. Ext corridors. **Pets:** Accepted. ⌦ 🔥 🛜 🛏

🅰 ▼▼▼ **Hyatt House Falls Church/Merrifield** **H**
(571) 327-2277. **$99-$369.** 8296 Glass Alley 22031. I-495 exit 50A, just
w to SR 650, 0.5 mi n on SR 650, then just w on US 29. Int corridors.
Pets: Accepted. (SAVE) ⌦ 🔥 🛜 ✕ 🛏 💻

🅰 ▼▼▼ **Residence Inn by Marriott Fairfax
City** **H**
(703) 267-2525. **$104-$197.** 3565 Chain Bridge Rd 22030. I-66 exit 60,
0.5 mi s on SR 123; jct US 29/50. Int corridors. **Pets:** Accepted.
(SAVE) 🔥 🏊 🛜 ✕ 🛏 💻

🅰 ▼▼▼ **Residence Inn by Marriott-Fair Lakes** **H**
(703) 266-4900. **$90-$171.** 12815 Fair Lakes Pkwy 22033. I-66 exit 55
(SR 286/Fairfax County Pkwy N), just w. Int corridors. **Pets:** Large.
$150 one-time fee/room. Service with restrictions.
(SAVE) (ECO) 🔥 🏊 🛜 ✕ 🛏 💻

FALLS CHURCH *(Restaurants p. 627)*
▼▼ **Comfort Inn Arlington Boulevard** **H**
(703) 534-9100. **$104-$189.** 6111 Arlington Blvd 22044. 0.8 mi e of jct
SR 7. Int corridors. **Pets:** Accepted. 🏊 🛜 ✕ 🛏 💻

▼▼▼ **Homewood Suites by Hilton-Falls Church** **H**
(703) 560-6644. **$109-$259.** 8130 Porter Rd 22042. I-495 exit 50A, just
w to SR 650, then 0.4 mi n on SR 650. Int corridors. **Pets:** Accepted.
🔥 ⌦ 🛜 ✕ 🛏 💻

🅰 ▼▼▼ **Residence Inn by Marriott
Fairfax-Merrifield** **H**
(703) 573-5200. **$91-$239.** 8125 Gatehouse Rd 22042. I-495 exit 50A,
just w to SR 650 N. Int corridors. **Pets:** Accepted.
(SAVE) 🔥 🏊 🛜 ✕ 🛏 💻

▼▼▼ **TownePlace Suites by Marriott-Falls Church** **H**
(703) 237-6172. **$92-$211.** 205 Hillwood Ave 22046. I-495 exit 50B, 2.5
mi e on US 50, 0.6 mi n on Annandale Rd (CR 649), then e; just s of
US 29. Int corridors. **Pets:** Accepted.
(ECO) 🔥 ⌦ 🛜 ✕ 🛏 💻

🅰 ▼▼▼▼ **The Westin Tysons Corner** **H**
(703) 893-1340. **Call for rates.** 7801 Leesburg Pike 22043. I-495 exit
47B, just e on SR 7. Int corridors. **Pets:** Accepted.
(SAVE) (ECO) ⌦ 🏊 🛜 ✕ 💻

FANCY GAP
▼▼ **Doe Run Lodging at Groundhog Mountain** **CO**
(276) 398-4099. **$70-$165, 7 day notice.** 27 Buck Hollar Rd 24328.
Blue Ridge Parkway at milepost 189.2; 10 mi n from US 52. Ext corridors. **Pets:** Accepted. ⌦ 🛜 🛏 💻

FARMVILLE
▼▼ **Comfort Inn-Farmville** **H**
(434) 392-8163. **$90-$169.** 2108 S Main St 23901. Jct US 460 Bypass
and US 15. Int corridors. **Pets:** Accepted. 🏊 🛜 🛏 💻

FREDERICKSBURG *(Restaurants p. 627)*
🅰 ▼▼▼ **Best Western Fredericksburg** **H**
(540) 371-5050. **$69-$129.** 2205 Plank Rd 22401. I-95 exit 130A (SR
3), 0.3 mi e. Ext corridors. **Pets:** $10 daily fee/pet. Designated rooms,
service with restrictions, crate.
(SAVE) (ECO) 🔥 🏊 🛜 ✕ 🛏 💻

🅰 ▼▼▼ **Candlewood Suites** **H**
(540) 376-7244. **Call for rates.** 4821 Crossings Ct 22407. I-95 exit
126B northbound; exit 126 southbound, just s on US 1/17 (Jefferson
Davis Hwy). Int corridors. **Pets:** Accepted. (SAVE) 🔥 🛜 🛏 💻

▼▼▼ **Country Inn & Suites By Carlson, Fredericksburg
South** **H** 🐾
(540) 898-1800. **$79-$179.** 5327 Jefferson Davis Hwy 22408. I-95 exit
126 southbound; exit 126A northbound; just n on US 1. Int corridors.
Pets: Medium. $10 daily fee/pet. Service with restrictions, crate.
🏊 🛜 ✕ 🛏 💻

🅰 ▼▼▼ **Fredericksburg Hospitality House Hotel &
Conference Center** **H**
(540) 786-8321. **$79-$169.** 2801 Plank Rd 22401. I-95 exit 130B (SR
3), just e; in Central Park shopping complex. Int corridors.
Pets: Accepted. (SAVE) ⌦ 🔥 🏊 🛜 ✕ 🛏 💻

🅰 ▼▼▼ **Homewood Suites by Hilton at Celebrate
Virginia** **H**
(540) 786-9700. **$129-$299.** 1040 Hospitality Ln 22401. I-95 exit 130B
(SR 3), just w to Carl D Silver Pkwy, then 2 mi n. Int corridors.
Pets: Medium, dogs only. $75 one-time fee/room. Designated rooms,
service with restrictions, supervision. (SAVE) 🔥 🏊 🛜 🛏 💻

AAA ♦♦♦ **Hyatt Place Fredericksburg at Mary Washington** H
(540) 654-3333. **$79-$269.** 1241 Jefferson Davis Hwy 22401. On US 1/17; jct College Ave; in Eagle Village. Int corridors. **Pets:** Small, dogs only. $75 one-time fee/room. Designated rooms, service with restrictions, crate. 🖫 🍴 🛏ᴹ 🛜 ⊠ 🔋 💻

♦♦♦ **Quality Inn Fredericksburg** M
(540) 373-0000. **$67-$95.** 543 Warrenton Rd 22406. I-95 exit 133, just n on US 17. Ext corridors. **Pets:** Accepted. 🛜 ⊠ 🔋 💻

♦♦♦ **Residence Inn by Marriott** H
(540) 786-9222. **$120-$200.** 60 Towne Centre Blvd 22407. I-95 exit 130B (SR 3), just w to Mall Dr, then just s. Int corridors. **Pets:** Accepted. 🛏ᴹ 🛜 ⊠ 🔋 💻

GLADE SPRING

♦ **Econo Lodge Glade Spring** M
(276) 429-5191. **$65-$200.** 33361 Lee Hwy 24340. I-81 exit 29, just e. Ext corridors. **Pets:** Accepted. 🍴 🛜 🔋

GLEN ALLEN

AAA ♦♦♦ **Aloft Richmond West** H
(804) 433-1888. **$139-$249.** 3939 Duckling Dr 23060. I-64 exit 178B, just w on W Broad St; in West Broad Village. Int corridors. **Pets:** Accepted. 🖫 📶 🍴 🛏ᴹ 🛜 ⊠ 🔋 💻

AAA ♦♦♦ **Best Western Plus Glen Allen Inn** H
(804) 266-3500. **$119-$189.** 8507 Brook Rd 23060. I-95 exit 83B, 0.5 mi w to Brook Rd, then just n. Int corridors. **Pets:** Accepted.
🖫 🍴 🛏ᴹ 🛜 🔋 💻

♦♦♦ **Candlewood Suites Richmond-West** H
(804) 364-2000. **Call for rates.** 4120 Tom Leonard Dr 23060. I-64 exit 178, just w on W Broad St. Int corridors. **Pets:** Accepted.
🛏ᴹ 🛜 🔋 💻

♦♦♦ **Candlewood Suites Virginia Center Commons** H
(804) 262-2240. **$85-$200, 3 day notice.** 10609 Telegraph Rd 23059. I-295 exit 43C, 1.7 mi n to JEB Stuart Pkwy, then just w; I-95 exit 86B (SR 656/Elmont), just w, then 1 mi s. Int corridors. **Pets:** Medium. $25 daily fee/pet. Designated rooms, service with restrictions, crate. 🛏ᴹ 🛜 🔋 💻

♦♦♦ **Comfort Suites-Innsbrook** H
(804) 217-9200. **$92-$159.** 4051 Innslake Dr 23060. I-64 exit 178B, just e on W Broad St to Cox Rd, then just n. Int corridors. **Pets:** Other species. $20 daily fee/pet. Designated rooms, service with restrictions, crate. 🅴🅲🅾 🛏ᴹ 🛜 ⊠ 🔋 💻

AAA ♦♦♦ **Hyatt Place Richmond/Innsbrook** H
(804) 747-9644. **$79-$179.** 4100 Cox Rd 23060. I-64 exit 178B, 0.5 mi e to Dominion Blvd, then just n. Int corridors. **Pets:** $75 one-time fee/ pet. Service with restrictions. 🖫 🅴🅲🅾 🛏ᴹ 🛜 ⊠ 🔋 💻

AAA ♦♦♦ **TownePlace Suites by Marriott** H
(804) 747-5253. **$81-$156.** 4231 Park Place Ct 23060. I-64 exit 178B, just e on W Broad St to Cox Rd, then just n to Innslake Dr. Int corridors. **Pets:** $100 one-time fee/room. Service with restrictions.
🖫 🅴🅲🅾 🍴 🛏ᴹ 🛜 ⊠ 🔋 💻

♦♦♦♦ **Wyndham Virginia Crossings Hotel & Conference Center** H
(804) 727-1400. **$99-$259.** 1000 Virginia Center Pkwy 23059. I-295 exit 43C, just n on US 1, then 1 mi e. Int corridors. **Pets:** Medium, dogs only. $50 one-time fee/room. Designated rooms, service with restrictions, supervision. 🍴 🛏ᴹ 🛜 ⊠ 🛜 ⊠ 🔋 💻

GLOUCESTER

♦♦ **Quality Inn** H
(804) 695-1900. **$89-$169.** 6639 Forest Hill Ave 23061. US 17, just s. Int corridors. **Pets:** Accepted. 🛏ᴹ 🛜 🔋 💻

GRETNA

♦♦♦ **Hampton Inn Gretna/Altavista/Chatham** H
(434) 656-9000. **Call for rates.** 200 McBride Ln 24557. US 29, just e on SR 40. Int corridors. **Pets:** Accepted. 🍴 🛏ᴹ 🛜 🔋 💻

GRUNDY

♦♦♦ **Comfort Inn** H
(276) 935-5050. **$135-$220.** 22006 Riverside Dr 24614. On US 460 business route, 0.5 mi e. Int corridors. **Pets:** Accepted.
🛏ᴹ 🛜 🔋 💻

HAMPTON (Restaurants p. 627)

♦♦♦ **Candlewood Suites** H
(757) 766-8976. **Call for rates.** 401 Butler Farm Rd 23666. I-64 exit 261B (Hampton Roads Center Pkwy) eastbound; exit 262B (Magruder Blvd) westbound, just n. Int corridors. **Pets:** Accepted.
🅴🅲🅾 🍴 🛏ᴹ 🛜 ⊠ 🔋 💻

HARRISONBURG

♦♦ **Candlewood Suites Harrisonburg** H
(540) 437-1400. **Call for rates.** 1560 Country Club Rd 22802. I-81 exit 247, just e. Int corridors. **Pets:** Accepted. 🅴🅲🅾 🛜 🔋 💻

♦♦♦ **Comfort Inn** H
(540) 433-6066. **$89-$299.** 1440 E Market St 22801. I-81 exit 247A, just e. Int corridors. **Pets:** Medium. $15 daily fee/room. Service with restrictions, supervision. 🅴🅲🅾 🛏ᴹ 🛜 🔋 💻

♦♦♦ **Harrisonburg Econo Lodge** M
(540) 433-2576. **$75-$230.** 1703 E Market St 22801. I-81 exit 247A, 0.5 mi e on US 33. Ext/int corridors. **Pets:** Accepted. 🛏ᴹ 🛜 🔋 💻

♦♦♦ **Microtel Inn & Suites by Wyndham** H
(540) 437-3777. **$69-$300.** 85 Pleasant Valley Rd 22801. I-81 exit 243, just w. Int corridors. **Pets:** Accepted. 📶 🛜 ⊠ 🔋 💻

♦♦♦ **Ramada** H
(540) 434-9981. **$74-$298.** 91 Pleasant Valley Rd 22801. I-81 exit 243, just w, then just n on US 11. Ext corridors. **Pets:** Accepted.
🛏ᴹ 🛜 🔋 💻

AAA ♦♦♦ **Residence Inn by Marriott Harrisonburg** H
(540) 437-7426. **$127-$223.** 1945 Deyerle Ave 22801. I-81 exit 245, just e. Int corridors. **Pets:** Other species. $100 one-time fee/room. Service with restrictions, crate. 🖫 🛏ᴹ 🛜 ⊠ 🔋 💻

AAA ♦♦♦ **Sleep Inn & Suites** H
(540) 433-7100. **$87-$229.** 1891 Evelyn Byrd Ave 22801. I-81 exit 247A, 0.5 mi e on US 33 to University Blvd, 0.3 mi s to Evelyn Byrd Ave, then just w. Int corridors. **Pets:** Accepted.
🖫 🅴🅲🅾 🛜 🔋 💻

AAA ♦♦♦ **Super 8** M
(540) 433-8888. **$60-$200, 3 day notice.** 3330 S Main St 22801. I-81 exit 243, just e, then just s on US 11. Int corridors. **Pets:** Small. $10 daily fee/pet. Designated rooms, service with restrictions, supervision.
🖫 🛜 🔋

AAA ♦♦♦ **The Village Inn** H
(540) 434-7355. **Call for rates.** 4979 S Valley Pike 22801. I-81 exit 240 southbound, 0.6 mi w on SR 257, then 1.5 mi n on US 11; exit 243 northbound, just w to US 11, then 1.7 mi s. Ext corridors. **Pets:** Other species. $15 daily fee/pet. Designated rooms, service with restrictions, crate. 🖫 🅴🅲🅾 🍴 🛏ᴹ 🛜 🔋 💻

HERNDON *(Restaurants p. 627)*

◆◆ **Candlewood Suites Washington Dulles-Herndon** H
(703) 793-7100. **Call for rates.** 13845 Sunrise Valley Dr 20171. SR 267 (Dulles Toll Rd) exit 9A, 1.1 m s on SR 28, 0.3 mi e on Frying Pan Rd (CR 608), then 0.6 mi nw. Int corridors. **Pets:** Accepted.
⬚ ⬚ ⬚ ⬚ ⬚ ⬚

◆◆ ◆◆◆◆ **Hilton Washington Dulles Airport** H
(703) 478-2900. **$89-$249.** 13869 Park Center Rd 20171. SR 267 (Dulles Toll Rd) exit 9, 3 mi s on SR 28; at McLearen Rd (SR 668). Int corridors. **Pets:** Accepted.
⬚ ⬚ ⬚ ⬚ ⬚ ⬚ ⬚ ⬚ ⬚

◆◆ ◆◆◆ **Hyatt House Herndon** H
(703) 437-5000. **$79-$269.** 467 Herndon Pkwy 20170. SR 267 (Dulles Toll Rd) exit 11 (SR 286/Fairfax County Pkwy), just n to Spring St exit, just s to CR 606 (Herndon Pkwy), then just w. Int corridors.
Pets: Accepted. ⬚ ⬚ ⬚ ⬚ ⬚ ⬚ ⬚ ⬚

◆◆ ◆◆◆ **Hyatt Place Herndon/Dulles Airport-East** H
(571) 643-0905. **$74-$239.** 13711 Sayward Blvd 20171. SR 267 (Dulles Toll Rd) exit 9A, 1.1 mi s on SR 28, 0.3 mi e on Frying Pan Rd (CR 608), then 1.2 mi nw on Sunrise Valley Dr. Int corridors.
Pets: Accepted. ⬚ ⬚ ⬚ ⬚ ⬚ ⬚ ⬚ ⬚

◆◆ ◆◆◆ **Hyatt Regency Dulles** H
(703) 713-1234. **$65-$319.** 2300 Dulles Corner Blvd 20171. SR 267 (Dulles Toll Rd) exit 9A, 1.1 mi s on SR 28, 0.3 mi e on Frying Pan Rd (CR 608), then 1.2 mi nw on Sunrise Valley Dr. Int corridors.
Pets: Accepted. ⬚ ⬚ ⬚ ⬚ ⬚ ⬚ ⬚ ⬚ ⬚

◆◆◆ **Residence Inn by Marriott-Herndon/Reston** H
(703) 435-0044. **$85-$193.** 315 Elden St 20170. 0.4 mi w on CR 606 (Herndon Pkwy) from jct SR 286 (Fairfax County Pkwy). Ext corridors.
Pets: Accepted. ⬚ ⬚ ⬚ ⬚ ⬚ ⬚

◆◆ ◆◆◆ **Sheraton Herndon Dulles Airport Hotel** H 🐾
(571) 643-0950. **$89-$249.** 13715 Sayward Blvd 20171. SR 267 (Dulles Toll Rd) exit 9A, 1.1 mi s on SR 28, 0.3 mi e on Frying Pan Rd (CR 608), then 1.2 mi nw on Sunrise Valley Dr. Int corridors. **Pets:** Medium, dogs only. Service with restrictions, crate.
⬚ ⬚ ⬚ ⬚ ⬚ ⬚ ⬚

◆◆◆ **Staybridge Suites Herndon Dulles** H
(703) 713-6800. **Call for rates.** 13700 Coppermine Rd 20171. SR 267 (Dulles Toll Rd) exit 9A, 1.1 mi s on SR 28, 0.3 mi e on Frying Pan Rd (CR 608), 0.7 mi nw on Sunrise Valley Dr, then just e. Ext corridors.
Pets: Accepted. ⬚ ⬚ ⬚ ⬚ ⬚ ⬚

◆◆◆ **The Westin Washington Dulles Airport** H
(703) 793-3366. **$79-$299.** 2520 Wasser Terrace 20171. SR 267 (Dulles Toll Rd) exit 9A, 1.1 mi s on SR 28, 0.3 mi e on Frying Pan Rd (CR 608), then 0.6 mi nw. Int corridors. **Pets:** Accepted.
⬚ ⬚ ⬚ ⬚ ⬚ ⬚ ⬚ ⬚ ⬚

HILLSVILLE

◆◆◆ **Quality Inn** H
(276) 728-2120. **$89-$199.** 85 Airport Rd 24343. I-77 exit 14, just w on US 58 and 221. Ext corridors. **Pets:** Accepted. ⬚ ⬚ ⬚ ⬚

HOPEWELL

◆◆ **Candlewood Suites** H
(804) 541-0200. **Call for rates.** 5113 Plaza Dr 23860. I-295 exit 9B (SR 36), just w. Int corridors. **Pets:** Accepted. ⬚ ⬚ ⬚ ⬚ ⬚

◆◆◆ **Fairfield Inn & Suites by Marriott** H
(804) 458-2600. **$89-$120.** 3952 Courthouse Rd 23860. I-295 exit 9A (SR 36), just e. Int corridors. **Pets:** Accepted.
⬚ ⬚ ⬚ ⬚ ⬚ ⬚

HUDDLESTON

◆◆ **Mariners Landing** CO
(540) 297-4900. **Call for rates.** 1217 Graves Harbor Tr 24104. On SR 626; on Smith Mountain Lake. Ext/int corridors. **Pets:** Accepted.
⬚ ⬚ ⬚ ⬚ ⬚ ⬚ ⬚ ⬚

IRVINGTON

◆◆ ◆◆◆◆ **The Tides Inn** H ❖
(804) 438-5000. **$210-$395, 7 day notice.** 480 King Carter Dr 22480. 0.3 mi w of SR 200. Ext/int corridors. **Pets:** Dogs only. $35 daily fee/pet. Designated rooms, service with restrictions.
⬚ ⬚ ⬚ ⬚ ⬚ ⬚ ⬚ ⬚

KESWICK

◆◆ ◆◆◆◆ **Keswick Hall and Golf Club** H 🐾
(434) 979-3440. **$249-$1500, 7 day notice.** 701 Club Dr 22947. I-64 exit 129, just n. Int corridors. **Pets:** Other species. $75 one-time fee/pet. Service with restrictions. ⬚ ⬚ ⬚ ⬚ ⬚ ⬚ ⬚

LEBANON

◆◆ **Lebanon Super 8** M
(276) 889-1800. **$64-$70.** 71 Townview Dr 24266. Just e on SR 654 from US 19 Bypass. Int corridors. **Pets:** Medium. $10 daily fee/pet. Service with restrictions, supervision. ⬚ ⬚ ⬚ ⬚ ⬚

LEESBURG *(Restaurants p. 628)*

◆◆ ◆◆ **Best Western Leesburg Hotel & Conference Center** H
(703) 777-9400. **$89-$154.** 726 E Market St 20176. Off SR 7 business route, just w of jct US 15. Int corridors. **Pets:** Medium. $25 daily fee/pet. Designated rooms, service with restrictions, crate.
⬚ ⬚ ⬚ ⬚ ⬚ ⬚ ⬚

◆◆ ◆◆◆ **Lansdowne Resort & Spa** H
(703) 729-8400. **Call for rates.** 44050 Woodridge Pkwy 20176. SR 7, 3.6 mi w of jct SR 28; 4.4 mi e of jct US 15. Int corridors.
Pets: Accepted. ⬚ ⬚ ⬚ ⬚ ⬚ ⬚ ⬚ ⬚ ⬚

LEXINGTON

◆◆ ◆◆ **Best Western Lexington Inn** M
(540) 458-3020. **$80-$200.** 850 N Lee Hwy 24450. I-64 exit 55, just s on US 11; I-81 exit 191, 1.6 mi w. Ext corridors. **Pets:** Accepted.
⬚ ⬚ ⬚ ⬚

◆◆ ◆◆◆ **Best Western Plus Inn at Hunt Ridge** H
(540) 464-1500. **$85-$250.** 25 Willow Spring Rd 24450. I-64 exit 55, just n on US 11 to SR 39; I-81 exit 191, 0.6 mi w. Int corridors.
Pets: Accepted. ⬚ ⬚ ⬚ ⬚ ⬚ ⬚ ⬚

◆◆ ◆◆ **Comfort Inn-Virginia Horse Center** H
(540) 463-7311. **$85-$225.** 62 Comfort Way 24450. I-64 exit 55, just s on US 11; I-81 exit 191, 0.6 mi w. Int corridors. **Pets:** Accepted.
⬚ ⬚ ⬚ ⬚

◆◆◆ **Holiday Inn Express** H ❖
(540) 463-7351. **$79-$275, 3 day notice.** 880 N Lee Hwy 24450. I-64 exit 55, just s on US 11; I-81 exit 191, 1 mi w. Int corridors.
Pets: Other species. $25 one-time fee/room. Service with restrictions, supervision. ⬚ ⬚ ⬚ ⬚ ⬚ ⬚

◆◆ ◆◆ **Howard Johnson Inn** H
(540) 463-9181. **$69-$120.** 2836 N Lee Hwy 24450. I-81 exit 195, just s on US 11. Int corridors. **Pets:** Accepted. ⬚ ⬚ ⬚ ⬚ ⬚

◆◆ ◆◆ **Motel 6** M
(540) 463-7371. **Call for rates.** 65 Econo Ln 24450. I-81 exit 191, just o on US 11. Ext corridors. **Pets:** Accepted. ⬚ ⬚

Quality Inn & Suites H
(540) 463-6400. **$85-$219.** 2814 N Lee Hwy 24450. I-81 exit 195, just sw on US 11. Int corridors. **Pets:** Medium. $10 daily fee/pet. Designated rooms, service with restrictions, supervision.
[SAVE] [icons]

Sleep Inn & Suites H
(540) 463-6000. **$89-$290.** 95 Maury River Rd 24450. I-64 exit 55, just n. Int corridors. **Pets:** Medium. $20 daily fee/pet. Designated rooms, service with restrictions, supervision.
[SAVE] [icons]

Super 8 Lexington M
(540) 463-7858. **$75-$189.** 1139 N Lee Hwy 24450. I-64 exit 55, just n. Int corridors. **Pets:** Medium. $10 daily fee/pet. Designated rooms, service with restrictions, supervision. [SAVE] [icons]

LORTON

Comfort Inn Gunston Corner H
(703) 643-3100. **$99-$134.** 8180 Silverbrook Rd 22079. I-95 exit 163, just w. Int corridors. **Pets:** Accepted. [icons]

LOW MOOR

Oak Tree Inn M
(540) 965-0090. **Call for rates.** 123 Westvaco Rd 24457. I-64 exit 21, just s. Int corridors. **Pets:** Accepted. [icons]

LURAY

Best Western Intown of Luray M
(540) 743-6511. **$75-$160.** 410 W Main St 22835. 0.3 mi w on US 211 business route. Ext corridors. **Pets:** Medium. $20 daily fee/pet. No service, crate. [SAVE] [icons]

Days Inn-Luray M
(540) 743-4521. **$80-$120.** 138 Whispering Hill Rd 22835. US 211 Bypass, 1.7 mi e of jct US 340. Ext/int corridors. **Pets:** Accepted.
[icons]

LYNCHBURG

Best Western of Lynchburg M
(434) 237-2986. **$80-$130.** 2815 Candlers Mountain Rd 24502. Jct US 29 and 460. Ext corridors. **Pets:** Large, dogs only. $15 daily fee/room. Designated rooms, service with restrictions, supervision.
[SAVE] [icons]

The Craddock Terry Hotel and Event Center H
(434) 455-1500. **$149-$299.** 1312 Commerce St 24504. US 29 business route exit 1A (Main St), just w. Int corridors. **Pets:** Accepted.
[SAVE] [ECO] [icons]

Extended Stay America - Lynchburg - University Blvd M
(434) 239-8863. **$95-$125.** 1910 University Blvd 24502. US 460 exit Candlers Mountain Rd/University Blvd. Int corridors. **Pets:** Accepted.
[icons]

Holiday Inn Downtown Lynchburg H
(434) 528-2500. **Call for rates.** 601 Main St 24504. US 29 business route exit 1A (Main St), 0.7 mi w. Int corridors. **Pets:** Accepted.
[icons]

Holiday Inn Express H
(434) 237-7771. **Call for rates.** 5600 Seminole Ave 24502. US 460 exit Candlers Mountain Rd, 0.3 mi w; US 29 business route exit Candlers Mountain Rd. Int corridors. **Pets:** Accepted. [icons]

La Quinta Inn & Suites Lynchburg at Liberty University H
(434) 847-8655. **$90-$383.** 3320 Candlers Mountain Rd 24502. US 29 exit US 501, just e. Int corridors. **Pets:** Accepted.
[icons]

Microtel & Suites by Wyndham Lynchburg H
(434) 239-2300. **$109-$169.** 5704 Seminole Ave 24502. US 460 exit Candlers Mountain Rd, 0.3 mi w; US 29 business route exit Candlers Mountain Rd. Int corridors. **Pets:** Accepted. [icons]

MANASSAS *(Restaurants p. 628)*

Best Western Battlefield Inn H 🐾
(703) 361-8000. **$109-$129.** 10820 Balls Ford Rd 20109. I-66 exit 47A westbound; exit 47 eastbound, just s on SR 234 business route. Ext corridors. **Pets:** Dogs only. $10 daily fee/pet. Service with restrictions, supervision. [SAVE] [icons]

Candlewood Suites Manassas H
(703) 530-0550. **$99-$199.** 11220 Balls Ford Rd 20109. I-66 exit 47A westbound; exit 47 eastbound, just s on SR 234 business route, then 0.7 mi w. Int corridors. **Pets:** Accepted. [icons]

Comfort Suites Manassas H
(703) 686-1100. **$99-$219.** 7350 Williamson Blvd 20109. I-66 exit 47A westbound; exit 47 eastbound, 0.5 mi s on SR 234 business route, then just e. Int corridors. **Pets:** Medium. $50 one-time fee/room. Designated rooms, service with restrictions, supervision.
[icons]

La Quinta Inn & Suites Manassas H
(703) 393-9966. **$71-$295.** 6950 Nova Way 20109. I-66 exit 47 eastbound; exit 47B westbound, just n on SR 234, then just e. Int corridors. **Pets:** Accepted. [icons]

Red Roof PLUS+ Washington DC-Manassas M
(703) 335-9333. **$69-$150.** 10610 Automotive Dr 20109. I-66 exit 47A westbound; exit 47 eastbound, just s on SR 234 business route, then just e on Balls Ford Rd. Ext corridors. **Pets:** Accepted.
[SAVE] [icons]

Residence Inn by Marriott Manassas Battlefield Park H
(703) 330-8808. **$101-$153.** 7345 Williamson Blvd 20109. I-66 exit 47A westbound; exit 47 eastbound, 0.5 mi s on SR 234 business route, then just e. Int corridors. **Pets:** Accepted.
[SAVE] [icons]

MARTINSVILLE

Baymont Inn & Suites Martinsville H
(276) 638-0478. **$49-$109.** 378 Commonwealth Blvd W 24112. Jct US 220 business route, just e. Int corridors. **Pets:** Accepted.
[icons]

Hampton Inn H
(276) 647-4700. **$119-$349.** 50 Hampton Dr 24112. Jct US 58, 2.5 mi n on US 220 business route. Int corridors. **Pets:** Accepted.
[icons]

MAX MEADOWS

Super 8 M
(276) 637-4141. **$55-$125.** 194 Ft. Chiswell Rd 24360. I-77/81 exit 80, just e. Ext corridors. **Pets:** Accepted. [icons]

MCLEAN

Staybridge Suites Tysons McLean Hotel (Washington, D.C. area) H
(703) 448-5400. **$99-$399.** 6845 Old Dominion Dr 22101. I-495 exit 46B, 2 mi n on SR 123, then 0.3 mi e on SR 309. Int corridors. **Pets:** Large, other species. $75 one-time fee/room. Service with restrictions. [SAVE] [icons]

MECHANICSVILLE

◆◆◆ **Hampton Inn** 🅷

(804) 559-0559. **$145-$189.** 7433 Bell Creek Rd 23111. I-295 exit 37A (US 360 E) to Bell Creek Rd, just n. Int corridors. **Pets:** Small. Designated rooms, service with restrictions, crate.

🔲 🛂 🛜 ✕ 🔲 🖵

◆◆◆ **Holiday Inn**
Express-Richmond-Mechanicsville 🅷

(804) 559-0022. **$89-$139.** 7441 Bell Creek Rd 23111. I-295 exit 37A (US 360 E) to Bell Creek Rd, just n. Int corridors. **Pets:** Accepted.

🔲 🛂 🛜 ✕ 🔲 🖵

MIDDLEBURG *(Restaurants p. 628)*

🛰 ◆◆◆◆ **Salamander Resort & Spa** 🅷

(540) 326-4000. **$235-$575, 3 day notice.** 500 N Pendleton St 20117. Off US 50, just n. Int corridors. **Pets:** Accepted.

SAVE 🔲 🔲 ✕ 🔲 ✕ 🔲 🖵

MIDLOTHIAN

◆◆◆ **La Quinta Inn & Suites -**
Richmond-Chesterfield 🅷

(804) 794-4999. **$86-$192.** 1301 Huguenot Rd 23113. Just n of jct US 60 and SR 147. Int corridors. **Pets:** Accepted.

🔲 🛜 ✕ 🔲 🖵

MINT SPRING

◆◆ **Days Inn-Staunton** 🅼

(540) 337-3031. **$70-$140.** 372 White Hill Rd 24401. I-81 exit 217, just e on SR 654. Ext corridors. **Pets:** Accepted. 🔲 🛂 🛜 🔲 🖵

MOUNTAIN LAKE

◆◆◆◆ **Mountain Lake Lodge** 🅷 ❀

(540) 626-7121. **Call for rates.** 115 Hotel Cir 24136. Jct US 460, 6.6 mi n on SR 700; caution, steep narrow paved mountain road. Ext/int corridors. **Pets:** Medium, dogs only. $75 one-time fee/pet. Designated rooms, service with restrictions, crate.

🔲 🛂 ✕ 🛜 ✕ 🔲 🔲 🖵

MOUNT JACKSON

🛰 ◆◆◆ **Super 8 - Mt. Jackson** 🅼

(540) 477-2911. **$68-$76.** 250 Conicville Blvd 22842. I-81 exit 273, just e. Ext corridors. **Pets:** Accepted. SAVE 🛂 🛜 🔲 🖵

◆◆◆◆ **The Widow Kip's** 🅱🅱 ❀

(540) 477-2400. **$120-$145, 5 day notice.** 355 Orchard Dr 22842. I-81 exit 273, 1.5 mi s on US 11, just w on SR 263, then just sw on SR 698. **Pets:** Other species. $20 daily fee/pet. Supervision.

ECO 🔲 🛂 🛜 ✕ 🔲 🖵

NEW CHURCH

◆◆◆◆ **The Garden & The Sea Inn** 🅱🅱

(757) 894-9097. **Call for rates.** 4188 Nelson Rd 23415. US 13, 0.3 mi n, just w on CR 710 (Nelson Rd). Int corridors. **Pets:** Accepted.

ECO 🛂 🛜 ✕ 🔲 🔲 🖵

NEWPORT NEWS *(Restaurants p. 628)*

◆◆ **Mulberry Inn & Plaza** 🅷

(757) 887-3000. **Call for rates.** 16890A Warwick Blvd 23603. I-64 exit 250A (SR 105/Ft Eustis Blvd S), s to US 60, then 0.3 mi w. Ext/int corridors. **Pets:** Accepted. ECO 🔲 🛂 🛜 🔲 🖵

◆◆◆◆ **Residence Inn by Marriott Newport News**
Airport 🅷

(757) 842-6214. **$104-$187.** 531 St. Johns Rd 23602. I-64 exit 255A, just s on Jefferson Ave to Freedom Way, then just nw. Int corridors. **Pets:** Accepted. 🔲 🛂 🛜 ✕ 🔲 🖵

◆◆ **Super 8 Motel Newport News** 🅷

(757) 825-1422. **$50-$100.** 6105 Jefferson Ave 23605. On US 17, just nw of jct Mercury Blvd (US 258). Int corridors. **Pets:** Small. $15 daily fee/pet. Designated rooms, service with restrictions, supervision.

🛜 🔲 🖵

NORFOLK *(Restaurants p. 628)*

🛰 ◆◆◆ **Best Western Plus Holiday Sands Inn &**
Suites 🅷 ❀

(757) 583-2621. **$79-$230.** 1330 E Ocean View Ave 23503. US 60, 4 mi e of Hampton Roads Bridge Tunnel. Ext corridors. **Pets:** Large, dogs only. $20 daily fee/room. Designated rooms, service with restrictions, supervision. SAVE ECO 🔲 🛂 🛜 ✕ 🔲 🖵

◆◆◆◆ **Candlewood Suites Norfolk Airport** 🅷

(757) 605-4001. **Call for rates.** 5600 Lowery Rd 23502. I-264 exit 13B (US 13/Military Hwy), 1.3 mi n, then just w. Int corridors. **Pets:** Accepted. 🛂 🛜 🔲 🖵

◆◆◆◆ **DoubleTree Hotel Norfolk Airport** 🅷

(757) 466-8000. **$109-$239.** 1500 N Military Hwy 23502. I-64 exit 281 (Military Hwy), just s; jct US 13 and SR 165. Int corridors. **Pets:** Accepted. ECO 🔲 🛂 🛜 ✕ 🔲 🖵

◆◆◆◆ **La Quinta Inn & Suites Norfolk Airport** 🅷

(757) 466-7001. **$67-$163.** 1387 N Military Hwy 23502. I-64 exit 281 (Military Hwy), just s. Int corridors. **Pets:** Accepted.

🔲 🛂 🛜 ✕ 🔲 🖵

🛰 ◆◆◆ **Page House Inn Bed &**
Breakfast 🅱🅱 ❀

(757) 625-5033. **$160-$245, 14 day notice.** 323 Fairfax Ave 23507. I-264 exit 9, 1.4 mi n on Waterside Dr to Olney Rd, just w to Mowbray Arch, then just s; in Ghent Historic District. Int corridors. **Pets:** Small, dogs only. $35 daily fee/pet. Designated rooms, service with restrictions, supervision. SAVE 🛜 ✕ 🔲

◆◆◆◆ **Residence Inn by Marriott Downtown** 🅷

(757) 842-6216. **$110-$168.** 227 W Brambleton Ave 23510. Jct Duke St; downtown. Int corridors. **Pets:** Accepted.

ECO 🛂 🛜 ✕ 🔲 🖵

◆◆◆◆ **Residence Inn by Marriott Norfolk Airport** 🅷

(757) 333-3000. **$103-$191.** 1590 N Military Hwy 23502. I-64 exit 281B (Military Hwy); jct Lake Wright Dr. Int corridors. **Pets:** Accepted.

ECO 🛂 🛜 ✕ 🔲 🖵

🛰 ◆◆◆◆ **Sheraton Norfolk Waterside Hotel** 🅷

(757) 622-6664. **$109-$189.** 777 Waterside Dr 23510. I-264 exit 9 (Waterside Dr); downtown. Int corridors. **Pets:** Accepted.

SAVE ECO 🔲 🛂 🛜 ✕ 🔲 🖵

🛰 ◆◆◆◆ **Wyndham Garden Norfolk Downtown** 🅷

(757) 627-5555. **$79-$279.** 700 Monticello Ave 23510. Jct Brambleton Ave and St Pauls Blvd; downtown. Int corridors. **Pets:** Medium. $100 one-time fee/room. Service with restrictions, crate.

SAVE 🔲 🛂 🛜 ✕ 🔲 🖵

NORTON

◆◆ **Super 8-Norton** 🅼

(276) 679-0893. **$57-$64.** 425 Wharton Ln 24273. Jct US 58 and 23. Int corridors. **Pets:** $10 daily fee/pet. Service with restrictions, crate.

🛜 🔲 🖵

ONANCOCK *(Restaurants p. 628)*

🛰 ◆◆ **1890 Spinning Wheel Bed &**
Breakfast 🅱🅱 ❀

(757) 787-7311. **$110-$135, 5 day notice.** 31 North St 23417. Just n of jct Market (SR 179) and North sts. Int corridors. **Pets:** Large, dogs only. $10 daily fee/pet. Designated rooms, service with restrictions, supervision. SAVE ECO 🛜 ✕ 🔲 🔲

ORANGE

◆◆◆◆ Comfort Inn & Suites 🄷

(540) 672-3121. **$89-$269.** 334 Caroline St 22960. On US 15, just s of downtown. Int corridors. **Pets:** Accepted.

🍴 🕹M 🛋 📶 ✕ 🔋 💻

PETERSBURG *(Restaurants p. 628)*

◆◆ Comfort Inn-Petersburg South 🄷

(804) 732-2000. **$70-$131.** 12001 S Crater Rd 23805. I-95 exit 45, just n on US 301. Int corridors. **Pets:** Small, other species. $25 one-time fee/pet, $10 daily fee/pet. Designated rooms, service with restrictions, supervision. 🕹M 🛋 🔋 💻

POUNDING MILL

◆◆◆ Claypool Hill Holiday Inn Express Hotel & Suites 🄷

(276) 596-9880. **Call for rates.** 180 Clay Dr 24637. 0.5 mi e of US 19/460. Int corridors. **Pets:** Accepted. 🛋 📶 ✕ 🔋 💻

◆ Claypool Hill Super 8 🄼

(276) 964-9888. **$63-$100.** 12367 Governor GC Peery Hwy 24637. 0.3 mi w on US 19/460. Int corridors. **Pets:** Accepted. 📶 ✕ 🔋 💻

PRINCE GEORGE

◆◆◆ ◆◆ Baymont Inn & Suites Prince George 🄷

(804) 452-0022. **$69-$100.** 5380 Oaklawn Blvd 23875. I-295 exit 9B (SR 36), just w. Int corridors. **Pets:** Accepted.

🆂🅰🆅🅴 🍴 🕹M 🛋 📶 🔋 💻

RADFORD

◆◆◆ ◆◆◆ Best Western Radford Inn 🄷

(540) 639-3000. **$79-$209.** 1501 Tyler Ave 24141. I-81 exit 109, 2.7 mi nw on SR 177. Int corridors. **Pets:** Medium, other species. $10 daily fee/room. Designated rooms, service with restrictions, supervision.

🆂🅰🆅🅴 🍴 🛋 ✕ 📶 🔋 💻

◆◆◆ Comfort Inn & Suites 🄷

(540) 639-3333. **$70-$210.** 2331 Tyler Rd 24073. I-81 exit 109, just w. Int corridors. **Pets:** Medium, dogs only. $15 daily fee/pet. Designated rooms, service with restrictions, supervision.

🍴 🛋 📶 ✕ 🔋 💻

◆◆◆ ◆◆ La Quinta Inn Radford 🄼

(540) 633-6800. **$70-$273.** 1450 Tyler Ave 24141. I-81 exit 109, 2.6 mi w on SR 177. Int corridors. **Pets:** Accepted.

🆂🅰🆅🅴 🍴 📶 ✕ 🔋 💻

◆ Super 8-Radford 🄼

(540) 731-9355. **$59-$99.** 1600 Tyler Ave 24141. I-81 exit 109, just w. Int corridors. **Pets:** Accepted. 🍴 📶 🔋 💻

RAPHINE

◆◆◆ ◆◆ Comfort Inn & Suites 🄼

(540) 377-2604. **Call for rates.** 584 Oakland Cir 24472. I-81 exit 205, just sw. Int corridors. **Pets:** Medium. $15 daily fee/pet. Designated rooms, service with restrictions, supervision. 🆂🅰🆅🅴 🍴 🛋 📶 🔋

RESTON

◆◆ Extended Stay America Washington DC-Reston 🄼

(703) 707-9700. **$110-$130.** 12190 Sunset Hills Rd 20190. SR 267 (Dulles Toll Rd) exit 12 (Reston Pkwy), just n, then just w. Ext corridors. **Pets:** Accepted. 📶 🔋

◆◆◆ ◆◆◆◆ Hyatt Regency Reston 🄷

(703) 709-1234. **$129-$399.** 1800 Presidents St 20190. SR 267 (Dulles Toll Rd) exit 12 (Reston Pkwy); center. Int corridors. **Pets:** Accepted.

🆂🅰🆅🅴 🅴🅲🅾 🍴 🕹M 🛋 📶 ✕ 🔋 💻

◆◆◆ ◆◆◆◆ Sheraton Reston Hotel 🄷

(703) 620-9000. **Call for rates.** 11810 Sunrise Valley Dr 20191. SR 267 (Dulles Toll Rd) exit 12 (Reston Pkwy), just s. Int corridors. **Pets:** Accepted. 🆂🅰🆅🅴 🍴 🕹M 🛋 📶 ✕ 🔋 💻

◆◆◆ ◆◆◆◆ The Westin Reston Heights 🄷

(703) 391-9000. **Call for rates.** 11750 Sunrise Valley Dr 20191. SR 267 (Dulles Toll Rd) exit 12 (Reston Pkwy), just s. Int corridors. **Pets:** Accepted. 🆂🅰🆅🅴 ➔ 🍴 🕹M 🛋 📶 ✕ 💻

RICHMOND *(Restaurants p. 628)*

◆◆◆ ◆◆◆◆ The Berkeley Hotel 🄷

(804) 780-1300. **$149-$329.** 1200 E Cary St 23219. Just s of state Capitol; jct 12th St. Int corridors. **Pets:** Accepted.

🆂🅰🆅🅴 🍴 🕹M 📶 ✕ 🔋 💻

◆◆ Candlewood Suites 🄷

(804) 271-0016. **Call for rates.** 4301 Commerce Rd 23234. I-95 exit 69, just n. Int corridors. **Pets:** Accepted. 🕹M 📶 ✕ 🔋 💻

◆◆ Extended Stay America North Chesterfield Arboretum 🄷

(804) 272-1800. **$75-$105.** 241 Arboretum Pl 23236. Jct Powhite Pkwy (SR 76) and Midlothian Tpke (US 60), just w. Int corridors. **Pets:** Accepted. 🕹M 📶 🔋 💻

◆◆◆ Fairfield Inn & Suites by Marriott Northwest 🄷

(804) 545-4200. **$94-$134.** 9937 Mayland Dr 23233. I-64 exit 180B, just n on Gaskins Rd. Int corridors. **Pets:** Accepted.

🕹M 🛋 📶 ✕ 🔋 💻

◆◆◆ ◆◆◆ Four Points by Sheraton Richmond 🄷

(804) 323-1144. **Call for rates.** 9901 Midlothian Tpke 23235. 1 mi w of Powhite Pkwy (SR 76). Int corridors. **Pets:** Accepted.

🆂🅰🆅🅴 🅴🅲🅾 🍴 🕹M 🛋 📶 ✕ 💻

◆◆◆ Holiday Inn Express 🄷

(804) 934-9300. **Call for rates.** 9933 Mayland Dr 23233. I-64 exit 180B, just n to Mayland Dr, then just w. Int corridors. **Pets:** Accepted.

🕹M 🛋 📶 ✕ 🔋 💻

◆◆◆ Holiday Inn Express Midlothian Turnpike 🄷

(804) 320-8900. **Call for rates.** 8710 Midlothian Tpke 23235. Jct Powhite Pkwy (SR 76) and Midlothian Tpke (US 60), just e. Int corridors. **Pets:** Accepted. 🕹M 🛋 📶 ✕ 🔋 💻

◆◆◆ ◆◆◆ Hyatt Place Richmond Airport 🄷

(804) 549-4865. **$104-$299.** 4401 S Laburnum Ave 23231. I-64 exit 195, just s; in White Oak Village. Int corridors. **Pets:** Accepted.

🆂🅰🆅🅴 🕹M 🛋 📶 ✕ 🔋 💻

◆◆◆ ◆◆◆ Hyatt Place Richmond/Arboretum 🄷

(804) 560-1566. **$59-$169.** 201 Arboretum Pl 23236. Jct Powhite Pkwy (SR 76) and Midlothian Tpke (US 60), just w. Int corridors. **Pets:** Accepted. 🆂🅰🆅🅴 🍴 🕹M 🛋 📶 ✕ 🔋 💻

◆◆◆ Omni Richmond Hotel 🄷

(804) 344-7000. **Call for rates.** 100 S 12th St 23219. I-95 exit 74A (I-195) exit Canal St; in James Center. Int corridors. **Pets:** Accepted.

🅴🅲🅾 ➔ 🍴 🕹M 📶 ✕ 🔋 💻

◆◆◆ Residence Inn by Marriott Northwest 🄷

(804) 762-9852. **$107-$146.** 3940 Westerre Pkwy 23233. I-64 exit 180, n on Gaskins Rd to W Broad St. Int corridors. **Pets:** Accepted.

🕹M 🛋 📶 ✕ 🔋 💻

◆◆◆ ◆◆◆ Residence Inn by Marriott Richmond Downtown 🄷

(804) 225-5550. **$144-$245.** 14 S 14th St 23219. Jct E Cary St; in Historic Shockoe Slip District. Int corridors. **Pets:** Accepted.

🆂🅰🆅🅴 🍴 🕹M 📶 ✕ 🔋 💻

The Westin Richmond H ❀
(804) 282-8444. **$149-$299.** 6631 W Broad St 23230. I-64 exit 183 eastbound; exit 183B westbound; in Reynolds Crossing. Int corridors. **Pets:** Medium, dogs only. Designated rooms, service with restrictions, supervision. SAVE ECO 🍽 ᴧM 🛏 ✕ 🛜 ✕ 🛢 🖵

ROANOKE

Best Western Plus Inn at Valley View H
(540) 362-2400. **$85-$225.** 5050 Valley View Blvd 24012. I-581 exit 3E, just e, then just s via shopping center exit. Int corridors. **Pets:** Accepted. SAVE ᴧM 🛏 🛜 ✕ 🛢 🖵

Comfort Inn Airport H 🐾
(540) 527-2020. **$89-$210.** 5070 Valley View Blvd 24012. I-81 exit 143 to I-581 exit 3, just e to Hershberger Rd. Int corridors. **Pets:** Medium. $25 one-time fee/room. Service with restrictions, supervision.
🛏 🛜 ✕ 🛢 🖵

Days Inn M
(540) 366-0341. **$70-$135.** 8118 Plantation Rd 24019. I-81 exit 146, just e on SR 115. Ext/int corridors. **Pets:** $15 one-time fee/room. Supervision. SAVE 🍽 🛏 🛜 🛢 🖵

Fairfield Inn & Suites by Marriott Roanoke North H
(540) 362-4200. **$104-$164.** 7944 Plantation Rd 24019. I-81 exit 146, just e. Int corridors. **Pets:** Accepted. 🛏 🛜 ✕ 🛢 🖵

Holiday Inn Roanoke Valley View H
(540) 362-4500. **Call for rates.** 3315 Ordway Dr 24017. I-581 exit 3W, just w to Ordway Dr, then 0.6 mi n via service road. Int corridors. **Pets:** Accepted. ECO 🍽 🛏 🛜 🛢 🖵

Holiday Inn Tanglewood/Roanoke H
(540) 774-4400. **$99-$149, 15 day notice.** 4468 Starkey Rd 24018. I-581 exit US 220 (Franklin Rd/Salem), 0.8 mi s on SR 419 (Electric Rd). Int corridors. **Pets:** $35 one-time fee/room. Designated rooms, service with restrictions, supervision.
SAVE ECO 🍽 🛏 🛜 🛢 🖵

Hyatt Place Roanoke Airport/Valley View Mall H
(540) 366-4700. **$99-$249.** 5040 Valley View Blvd 24012. I-581 exit 3E, just e, then just s via shopping center exit. Int corridors. **Pets:** Large, other species. $75 one-time fee/room. Designated rooms, service with restrictions. SAVE ᴧM 🛏 🛜 ✕ 🛢 🖵

MainStay Suites Roanoke Airport H
(540) 527-3030. **$79-$250.** 5080 Valley View Blvd 24012. I-581 exit 3E, just n. Int corridors. **Pets:** Medium, dogs only. $25 one-time fee/room. Designated rooms, service with restrictions, crate. 🛜 🛢 🖵

Residence Inn by Marriott Roanoke Airport H
(540) 265-1119. **$107-$157.** 3305 Ordway Dr NW 24017. I-581 exit 3W, just s. Int corridors. **Pets:** Accepted. ᴧM 🛏 🛜 ✕ 🛢 🖵

Sheraton Roanoke Hotel & Conference Center H
(540) 563-9300. **$79-$229.** 2801 Hershbarger Rd 24017. I-581 exit 3W, just w to Ordway Dr, then just n via service road. Int corridors. **Pets:** Accepted. SAVE ECO 🍽 ᴧM 🛏 ✕ 🛜 ✕ 🛢 🖵

Super 8 M
(540) 563-8888. **$58-$99, 3 day notice.** 6616 Thirlane Rd 24019. I-581 exit 25, s on SR 117 (Peters Creek Rd), then just w. Int corridors. **Pets:** Medium. $10 daily fee/pet. Designated rooms, service with restrictions, supervision. SAVE 🛜 🛢 🖵

ROCKY MOUNT

Comfort Inn-Rocky Mount H
(540) 489-4000. **$86-$165.** 1730 N Main St 24151. 1.5 mi n on US 220 business route. Int corridors. **Pets:** Accepted. 🛏 🛜 🛢 🖵

Holiday Inn Express Hotel & Suites H
(540) 489-5001. **Call for rates.** 395 Old Franklin Tpke 24151. US 220 S, just e on SR 40. Int corridors. **Pets:** Accepted.
🛏 🛜 ✕ 🛢 🖵

SALEM

Baymont Inn & Suites Salem Roanoke Area H ❀
(540) 562-1912. **$62-$199.** 179 Sheraton Dr 24153. I-81 exit 141, 0.4 mi e on SR 419. Int corridors. **Pets:** Other species. Designated rooms, service with restrictions, crate. SAVE 🍽 🛏 🛜 ✕ 🛢 🖵

Comfort Suites Inn at Ridgewood Farm H ❀
(540) 375-4800. **$80-$200.** 2898 Keagy Rd 24153. I-81 exit 141, 4.7 mi s on SR 419, then just w. Int corridors. **Pets:** $25 daily fee/room. Designated rooms, service with restrictions, crate. 🛏 🛜 ✕ 🛢 🖵

La Quinta Inn Roanoke Salem H
(540) 562-2717. **$86-$301.** 140 Sheraton Dr 24153. I-81 exit 141, 0.5 mi se on SR 419. Int corridors. **Pets:** Accepted.
🛏 🛜 ✕ 🛢 🖵

Quality Inn M
(540) 387-1600. **$70-$200.** 151 Wildwood Rd 24153. I-81 exit 137, 0.3 mi e on SR 112. Ext corridors. **Pets:** Accepted. 🛏 🛜 🛢 🖵

SANDSTON

Candlewood Suites Richmond Airport H ❀
(804) 652-1888. **Call for rates.** 5400 Audubon Dr 23231. I-64 exit 197A (Sandston-RIC Airport), 1 mi w. Int corridors. **Pets:** Large. $75 one-time fee/pet. Service with restrictions, supervision.
ECO 🍽 ᴧM 🛜 ✕ 🛢 🖵

Holiday Inn Express H
(804) 222-1499. **Call for rates.** 491 International Center Dr 23150. I-64 exit 197A (Sandston-RIC Airport), just s to Audubon Dr, then just n. Int corridors. **Pets:** Accepted. ᴧM 🛏 🛜 ✕ 🛢 🖵

SOUTH BOSTON

The Berry Hill Resort and Conference Center H
(434) 517-7000. **Call for rates.** 3105 River Rd S 24592. Jct US 58, 1.2 mi n on US 501, 0.6 mi w on Edmunds St, 2.3 mi nw on Berry Hill Rd, then 1 mi sw on SR 659. Ext/int corridors. **Pets:** Accepted.
🍽 ᴧM 🛏 ✕ 🛜 ✕ 🛢 🖵

Days Inn & Suites South Boston H
(434) 575-4000. **$70-$109.** 1074 Bill Tuck Hwy 24592. Jct US 501, just e on US 58. Int corridors. **Pets:** $20 daily fee/pet. Service with restrictions, supervision. ᴧM 🛏 🛜 🛢 🖵

Super 8 M
(434) 572-8868. **$56-$119, 3 day notice.** 1040 Bill Tuck Hwy 24592. Jct US 501, just e on US 58. Int corridors. **Pets:** Accepted. 🛜 🛢 🖵

SOUTH HILL

Comfort Inn & Suites H
(434) 447-2200. **$64-$139.** 250 Thompson St 23970. I-85 exit 12A, just n. Int corridors. **Pets:** Medium. $20 daily fee/room.
SAVE ᴧM 🛜 ✕ 🛢 🖵

Fairfield Inn & Suites by Marriott South Hill I-85 H
(434) 447-6800. **$100-$152.** 150 Arnold Dr 23970. I-85 exit 12A, just e on US 58. Int corridors. **Pets:** Accepted.
ECO ᴧM 🛏 🛜 ✕ 🛢 🖵

Quality Inn H
(434) 447-2600. **$59-$89.** 918 E Atlantic St 23970. I-85 exit 12B, just w. Ext corridors. **Pets:** Other species. $20 one-time fee/room. Service with restrictions. 🛜 🛢 🖵

SPRINGFIELD (Restaurants p. 628)

Homewood Suites by Hilton Springfield H
(703) 866-6045. $99-$259. 7010 Old Keene Mill Rd 22150. I-95 exit 169A, just nw of SR 644; jct I-395 and 495, 0.8 mi s. Int corridors.
Pets: Accepted.

Residence Inn by Marriott Springfield Old Keene Mill H
(703) 644-0020. $93-$244. 6412 Backlick Rd 22150. I-95 exit 169A, just nw of SR 644; jct I-395 and 495, 0.8 mi s. Int corridors.
Pets: Accepted.

TownePlace Suites by Marriott Springfield H
(703) 569-8060. $91-$206. 6245 Brandon Ave 22150. I-95 exit 169B, just nw of SR 644; jct I-395 and 495, 0.8 mi s. Int corridors.
Pets: Accepted.

STAFFORD (Restaurants p. 628)

Best Western Aquia/Quantico Inn H
(540) 659-0022. $71-$109. 2868 Jefferson Davis Hwy 22554. I-95 exit 143A, jct US 1 and SR 610. Ext corridors. **Pets:** Accepted.

Quality Inn & Suites H
(540) 657-5566. $93-$159. 28 Greenspring Dr 22554. I-95 exit 143B, just w on Garrisonville Rd. Int corridors. **Pets:** Medium. $20 daily fee/pet. Service with restrictions, crate.

Red Roof Inn & Suites Stafford H
(540) 659-4330. $69-$179. 153 Garrisonville Rd 22554. I-95 exit 143B, just w. Int corridors. **Pets:** Accepted.

Staybridge Suites Stafford/Quantico H
(540) 720-2111. **Call for rates.** 2996 Jefferson Davis Hwy 22554. I-95 exit 143A, just n on US 1. Int corridors. **Pets:** Accepted.

Suburban Extended Stay Hotel-Quantico H
(540) 288-9051. $64-$119. 3097 Jefferson Davis Hwy 22554. I-95 exit 143A, 0.7 mi n on US 1. Int corridors. **Pets:** Large, other species. $25 one-time fee/pet. Service with restrictions, crate.

TownePlace Suites by Marriott Quantico-Stafford H
(540) 657-1990. $104-$177. 2772 Jefferson Davis Hwy 22554. I-95 exit 143A, just s on US 1. Int corridors. **Pets:** Accepted.

STAUNTON

Best Western Staunton Inn H
(540) 885-1112. $89-$150. 92 Rowe Rd 24401. I-81 exit 222, just e on US 250. Int corridors. **Pets:** Accepted.

Comfort Inn H
(540) 886-5000. $99-$219. 1302 Richmond Ave 24401. I-81 exit 222, just w on US 250. Int corridors. **Pets:** Accepted.

Econo Lodge Staunton M
(540) 885-5158. $64-$109. 1031 Richmond Ave 24401. I-81 exit 222, 0.7 mi w on US 250. Ext/int corridors. **Pets:** Medium. $10 daily fee/pet. Designated rooms, service with restrictions, supervision.

Holiday Inn Staunton Conference Center H
(540) 248-6020. $99-$289. 152 Fairway Ln 24401. I-81 exit 225, 0.3 mi w on SR 262. Int corridors. **Pets:** Accepted.

Red Roof Inn-Staunton M
(540) 885-3117. $69-$110. 42 Sangers Ln 24401. I-81 exit 222, just e on US 250. Ext corridors. **Pets:** Accepted.

Sleep Inn H
(540) 887-6500. $95-$150. 222 Jefferson Hwy 24401. I-81 exit 222, just e on US 250. Int corridors. **Pets:** Accepted.

Stonewall Jackson Hotel & Conference Center H 🐾
(540) 885-4848. **Call for rates.** 24 S Market St 24401. Between Beverley and Johnson sts; downtown. Int corridors. **Pets:** Large, other species. $50 one-time fee/room. Designated rooms, service with restrictions, supervision.

STEPHENS CITY

Comfort Inn-Stephens City H
(540) 869-6500. $79-$150. 167 Town Run Ln 22655. I-81 exit 307, just se. Int corridors. **Pets:** Medium. $10 daily fee/pet. Designated rooms, service with restrictions, supervision.

STERLING

Best Western Dulles Airport Inn M
(703) 471-8300. $69-$189. 45440 Holiday Dr 20166. 1.7 mi n on SR 28 from jct SR 267 (Dulles Toll Rd), just e on SR 846, just s on Shaw Rd. Ext corridors. **Pets:** Accepted.

Candlewood Suites Washington Dulles/Sterling H
(703) 674-2288. $99-$109. 45520 Severn Way 20166. 1.3 mi s on SR 28 from jct SR 7, 0.3 mi e on Nokes Blvd, 0.4 mi s on Atlantic Blvd. Int corridors. **Pets:** Accepted.

Hampton Inn by Hilton-Dulles/Cascades H
(703) 450-9595. $89-$209. 46331 McClellan Way 20165. 1.7 mi e on SR 7 from jct SR 28, 0.5 mi n on SR 1794 (Cascades Pkwy) to Palisade Pkwy, just e, then 0.4 mi s on Whitfield Pl. Int corridors. **Pets:** Accepted.

Hawthorn Suites by Wyndham Dulles Sterling H
(703) 444-2111. $79-$179. 21123 Whitfield Pl 20165. 1.7 mi e on SR 7 from jct SR 28, 0.5 mi n on SR 1794 (Cascades Pkwy) to Palisades Pkwy, just e, then just s. Int corridors. **Pets:** Accepted.

Holiday Inn Washington Dulles International Airport H
(703) 471-7411. **Call for rates.** 45425 Holiday Dr 20166. 1.7 mi n on SR 28 from jct SR 267 (Dulles Toll Rd), just e on SR 846, just s on Shaw Rd. Int corridors. **Pets:** Accepted.

Hyatt House Sterling/Dulles Airport North H
(703) 435-9002. $74-$199. 45520 Dulles Plaza 20166. 1 mi n on SR 28 from jct SR 267 (Dulles Toll Rd), just e on CR 606. Int corridors.
Pets: Accepted.

Hyatt Place Sterling/Dulles Airport-North H
(703) 444-3909. $69-$199. 21481 Ridgetop Cir 20166. 1.3 mi e on SR 7 from jct SR 28. Int corridors. **Pets:** Accepted.

Residence Inn by Marriott Dulles Airport @ Dulles 28 Centre H
(703) 421-2000. $104-$186. 45250 Monterey Pl 20166. SR 28 exit CR 625 (Waxpool Rd), just w, just n on Pacific Blvd, then just e on Commercial Dr. Int corridors. **Pets:** Accepted.

▼▼ **Suburban Extended Stay Hotel Washington-Dulles/Sterling** H
(703) 674-2299. **$74-$229.** 45510 E Severn Way 20166. 1.3 mi s on SR 28 from jct SR 7, 0.3 mi e on Nokes Blvd, then 0.4 mi s on Atlantic Blvd. Int corridors. **Pets:** Accepted. 📶 🛅 🖥

▼▼ **TownePlace Suites by Marriott at Dulles Airport** H
(703) 707-2017. **$75-$133.** 22744 Holiday Park Dr 20166. 1.7 mi n on SR 28 from jct SR 267 (Dulles Toll Rd), just e on SR 846, just s on Shaw Rd. Int corridors. **Pets:** Accepted.
🌿 🍽 ♿ 📶 ✕ 🛅 🖥

STONY CREEK

▼▼▼ **Hampton Inn-Stony Creek** H
(434) 246-5500. **$89-$149.** 10476 Blue Star Hwy 23882. I-95 exit 33, 0.3 mi s on SR 301. Int corridors. **Pets:** Large, other species. Designated rooms, service with restrictions, supervision.
♿ 🏊 📶 ✕ 🛅 🖥

▼▼▼ **Sleep Inn & Suites** H
(434) 246-5100. **$90-$130.** 11019 Blue Star Hwy 23882. I-95 exit 33, 0.3 mi s on SR 301. Int corridors. **Pets:** Accepted.
♿ 🏊 📶 ✕ 🛅 🖥

STRASBURG

▼▼▼ **Hotel Strasburg** CI
(540) 465-9191. **Call for rates.** 213 S Holliday St 22657. I-81 exit 298, 2.2 mi s on US 11, then just s. Int corridors. **Pets:** Accepted.
🍽 📶 ✕

▼▼ **The Ramada Strasburg** H
(540) 465-2444. **$69-$149.** 21 Signal Knob Dr 22657. I-81 exit 298, just e. Int corridors. **Pets:** Accepted. 🍽 🏊 ✕ 📶 🛅 🖥

SUFFOLK

▼▼▼ **TownePlace Suites by Marriott** H
(757) 483-5177. **$74-$138.** 8050 Harbour View Blvd 23435. I-664 exit 8A (College Dr), just n. Int corridors. **Pets:** Accepted.
🌿 ♿ 🏊 📶 ✕ 🛅 🖥

TAPPAHANNOCK

▼▼▼ **The Essex Inn** BB
(804) 443-9900. **$139-$199, 7 day notice.** 203 Duke St 22560. 0.3 mi s on US 17, just e. Ext/int corridors. **Pets:** Accepted.
🌿 📶 ✕ 🛅 🖥

THORNBURG

▼▼▼ **Holiday Inn Express & Suites** H
(540) 604-9690. **$85-$190.** 6415 Dan Bell Ln 22565. I-95 exit 118, just w. Int corridors. **Pets:** Other species. $25 one-time fee/room. Designated rooms, service with restrictions, supervision.
🍽 ♿ 🏊 ✕ 📶 ✕ 🛅 🖥

TROUTVILLE

▼▼▼ **Comfort Inn** H
(540) 992-5600. **$99-$175.** 2545 Lee Hwy S 24175. I-81 exit 150A, just s on US 11. Int corridors. **Pets:** Medium. $25 one-time fee/room. Service with restrictions, crate. 🏊 📶 🛅 🖥

▼▼▼ **Quality Inn** H
(540) 992-5335. **$70-$140.** 3139 Lee Hwy S 24175. I-81 exit 150A, just ne on US 11. Ext/int corridors. **Pets:** Accepted. 🏊 📶 🛅 🖥

TYSONS CORNER

▼▼▼ **Crowne Plaza Tysons Corner** H
(703) 893-2100. **Call for rates.** 1960 Chain Bridge Rd 22102. I-495 exit 46A, 0.5 mi s on SR 123, just nw on International Dr, then just sw on Greensboro Dr. Int corridors. **Pets:** Accepted.
🌿 🍽 ♿ 🏊 📶 ✕ 🛅 🖥

▼▼ **Extended Stay America-Washington, DC-Tysons Corner** H
(703) 356-6300. **$120-$160.** 8201 Old Courthouse Rd 22182. I-495 exit 47A, 0.6 mi w on SR 7, then just s on Gallows Rd. Int corridors. **Pets:** Accepted. 🍽 ♿ 📶 🛅

🌀 ▼▼▼ **Hyatt Regency Tysons Corner Center** H
(703) 893-1234. **$129-$459.** 7901 Tysons One Pl 22102. I-495 exit 46A, just s on SR 123. Int corridors. **Pets:** Small, dogs only. $100 one-time fee/pet. Designated rooms, service with restrictions, supervision.
[SAVE] 🍽 ♿ 📶 ✕ 🛅 🖥

🌀 ▼▼▼ **Residence Inn by Marriott-Tysons Corner** H
(703) 893-0120. **$79-$237.** 8616 Westwood Center Dr 22182. I-495 exit 47A, 1.9 mi w on SR 7, then just s. Ext corridors. **Pets:** Accepted.
[SAVE] 🏊 📶 ✕ 🛅 🖥

▼▼▼ **Residence Inn by Marriott Tysons Corner Mall** H
(703) 917-0800. **$78-$239.** 8400 Old Courthouse Rd 22182. I-495 exit 46A, 1.1 mi s on SR 123; 0.3 mi s of jct SR 7 and 123. Int corridors. **Pets:** Other species. $75 one-time fee/room. Service with restrictions.
♿ 🏊 📶 ✕ 🛅 🖥

🌀 ▼▼▼▼ **The Ritz-Carlton, Tysons Corner** H
(703) 506-4300. **$189-$799.** 1700 Tysons Blvd 22102. I-495 exit 46A, 0.3 mi sw on SR 123, then just nw; I-495 Express Lanes exit Jones Branch Dr. Int corridors. **Pets:** Accepted.
[SAVE] 🌿 🍽 ♿ 🏊 ✕ 🔊 ✕ 🛅 🖥

🌀 ▼▼▼ **Sheraton Tysons Hotel** H
(703) 448-1234. **$79-$349.** 8661 Leesburg Pike 22182. SR 7, just e of jct SR 267 (Dulles Toll Rd). Int corridors. **Pets:** Accepted.
[SAVE] 🌿 🍽 🍽 ♿ 🏊 📶 ✕ 🛅 🖥

VIRGINIA BEACH *(Restaurants p. 628)*

▼▼▼ **Candlewood Suites** H
(757) 213-1500. **$59-$249.** 4437 Bonney Rd 23462. I-264 exit 17B (Independence Blvd/Pembroke area), just n to Bonney Rd, then just e. Int corridors. **Pets:** Medium, other species. $75 one-time fee/pet. Service with restrictions, crate. 🌿 ♿ 📶 🛅 🖥

▼▼▼ **Clarion Inn & Suites** H ❀
(757) 961-8190. **$79-$349.** 2604 Atlantic Ave 23451. I-264 0.5 mi n of terminus; jct Atlantic Ave and 26th St. Int corridors. **Pets:** Small, dogs only. $15 daily fee/room. Designated rooms, service with restrictions, crate. 🍽 ♿ 🏊 📶 ✕ 🖥

🌀 ▼▼▼ **DoubleTree by Hilton Hotel Virginia Beach** H ❀
(757) 422-8900. **$109-$289.** 1900 Pavilion Dr 23451. I-264 exit 22 (Birdneck Rd), just e. Int corridors. **Pets:** Large, dogs only. $25 daily fee/pet. Designated rooms, service with restrictions, supervision.
[SAVE] 🌿 🍽 ♿ 🏊 📶 ✕ 🛅 🖥

▼▼▼ **The Founders Inn and Spa** H
(757) 424-5511. **Call for rates.** 5641 Indian River Rd 23464. I-64 exit 286B, just e; on campus of Christian Broadcasting Network & Regent University. Int corridors. **Pets:** Accepted.
🌿 ✕ 🍽 ♿ 🏊 ✕ 📶 ✕ 🛅 🖥

▼▼▼ **Homewood Suites by Hilton** H
(757) 552-0080. **$119-$399.** 5733 Cleveland St 23462. I-264 exit 15 (Newtown Rd N), just n. Int corridors. **Pets:** Accepted.
🌿 ♿ 🏊 ✕ 📶 🛅 🖥

▼▼▼ **La Quinta Inn & Suites Virginia Beach** H
(757) 428-2203. **$67-$383.** 2800 Pacific Ave 23451. I-264 0.5 mi n of terminus. Int corridors. **Pets:** Accepted. ♿ 🏊 📶 🛅 🖥

Quality Inn M
(757) 460-5566. **$79-$149.** 5189 Shore Dr 23455. Just w of Independence Blvd (SR 225); at Gate 5 of the Naval Amphibious Base. Ext corridors. **Pets:** Accepted. (SAVE) 🏊 🛜 🔒 💻

Residence Inn by Marriott Virginia Beach Oceanfront H 🐾
(757) 425-1141. **$121-$376, 3 day notice.** 3217 Atlantic Ave 23451. I-264 1.5 mi n of terminus; jct 33rd St. Int corridors. **Pets:** $100 one-time fee/room. Service with restrictions, crate.
(ECO) (&M) 🏊 🛜 ✕ 🔒 💻

Sheraton Virginia Beach Oceanfront Hotel H
(757) 425-9000. **$99-$499, 3 day notice.** 3501 Atlantic Ave 23451. I-264 1 mi n of terminus; jct 36th St. Int corridors. **Pets:** Accepted.
(SAVE) (ECO) (¶¶) (&M) 🏊 ✕ 🛜 ✕ 🔒 💻

TownePlace Suites by Marriott H
(757) 490-9367. **$69-$187.** 5757 Cleveland St 23462. I-64 exit 284B to I-264 exit Newtown Rd N. Int corridors. **Pets:** Accepted.
(SAVE) (ECO) 🏊 🛜 ✕ 🔒 💻

The Westin Virginia Beach Town Center H
(757) 557-0550. **$109-$399.** 4535 Commerce St 23462. I-264 exit 17B (Independence Blvd), just n, then just e. Int corridors. **Pets:** Accepted.
(SAVE) (ECO) (¶¶) (&M) 🏊 🛜 ✕ 🔒 💻

Wyndham Virginia Beach Oceanfront H
(757) 428-7025. **$69-$319, 3 day notice.** 5700 Atlantic Ave 23451. I-264 2.2 mi n of terminus. Int corridors. **Pets:** Accepted.
(ECO) (¶¶) (&M) 🏊 ✕ 🛜 ✕ 🔒 💻

WARSAW

Quality Inn Warsaw H
(804) 333-1700. **$90-$150.** 4522 Richmond Rd 22572. US 360, just w of town. Int corridors. **Pets:** Accepted. (&M) 🏊 🛜 ✕ 🔒 💻

WASHINGTON

Middleton Inn BB
(540) 675-2020. **Call for rates.** 176 Main St 22747. 0.5 mi w on US 211 business route. Ext/int corridors. **Pets:** Accepted.
(SAVE) (¶¶) 🛜 ✕ 🔒 💻

WAYNESBORO

Best Western Plus Waynesboro Inn & Suites Conference Center H
(540) 942-1100. **$105-$160.** 109 Apple Tree Ln 22980. I-64 exit 94, just n. Int corridors. **Pets:** Accepted. (SAVE) (ECO) 🏊 🛜 ✕ 🔒 💻

Comfort Inn Waynesboro H
(540) 932-3060. **$104-$169.** 15 Windigrove Dr 22980. I-64 exit 94, 0.5 mi n on US 340, then just e. Int corridors. **Pets:** Small, dogs only. $10 daily fee/pet. Service with restrictions, supervision. 🏊 🔒 💻

Days Inn Waynesboro M
(540) 943-1101. **$70-$135.** 2060 Rosser Ave 22980. I-64 exit 94, 0.5 mi n on US 340. Ext corridors. **Pets:** Accepted. (SAVE) 🏊 🛜 🔒 💻

The Iris Inn & Cabins BB
(540) 943-1991. **$159-$349, 7 day notice.** 191 Chinquapin Dr 22980. I-64 exit 96, just s on SR 624, then just e. Ext/int corridors.
Pets: Accepted. (ECO) ⊟ (¶¶) 🛜 ✕ 🐾 🔒 💻

Quality Inn Waynesboro M
(540) 942-1171. **$72-$120.** 640 W Broad St 22980. I-64 exit 96, 3 mi w on SR 624; jct US 250 and 340. Ext/int corridors. **Pets:** Accepted.
(SAVE) 🏊 🛜 🔒 💻

Residence Inn by Marriott Waynesboro H 🐾
(540) 943-7426. **$136-$190.** 44 Windigrove Dr 22980. I-64 exit 94, 0.5 mi n on US 340, then just e. Int corridors. **Pets:** Medium, other species. $150 one-time fee/pet. Service with restrictions, supervision.
🏊 🛜 ✕ 🔒 💻

WILLIAMSBURG *(Restaurants p. 629)*

Colonial Capital Bed & Breakfast BB
(757) 645-4525. **Call for rates.** 501 Richmond Rd 23185. Just w of Colonial Williamsburg and College of William and Mary. Int corridors. **Pets:** Accepted. 🛜 ✕

Colonial Williamsburg Hotels-Williamsburg Lodge H
(757) 220-7976. **$119-$269, 3 day notice.** 310 S England St 23185. Just s of jct Francis St and restored area. Int corridors. **Pets:** Dogs only. $50 daily fee/room. Designated rooms, service with restrictions, supervision. (ECO) (¶¶) (&M) 🏊 ✕ 🛜 ✕ 🔒 💻

Colonial Williamsburg-Woodlands Hotel & Suites H
(757) 220-7960. **$119-$269, 3 day notice.** 105 Visitor Center Dr 23185. I-64 exit 238, s on SR 143 to SR 132. Int corridors. **Pets:** Accepted.
(ECO) (¶¶) (&M) 🏊 ✕ 🛜 ✕ 🔒 💻

Fort Magruder Hotel & Conference Center H 🐾
(757) 220-2250. **Call for rates.** 6945 Pocahontas Tr 23185. US 60, 0.8 mi e of jct SR 5 and 31. Int corridors. **Pets:** Medium. $50 one-time fee/room. Designated rooms, service with restrictions, supervision.
(SAVE) (ECO) (¶¶) (&M) 🏊 ✕ 🛜 ✕ 🔒 💻

Residence Inn by Marriott Williamsburg H
(757) 941-2000. **$84-$223.** 1648 Richmond Rd 23185. US 60, just w of jct Bypass Rd. Int corridors. **Pets:** Accepted.
(SAVE) (&M) 🏊 🛜 ✕ 🔒 💻

Super 8-Williamsburg/Historic Area M
(757) 229-0500. **$40-$75.** 304 2nd St 23185. I-64 exit 242 (SR 199 W), 0.6 mi w to SR 143, 1.6 mi w to SR 162, then just w. Ext corridors.
Pets: Small, dogs only. $20 daily fee/pet. Service with restrictions, supervision. (SAVE) 🏊 🛜 🔒 💻

Westgate Historic Williamsburg H
(757) 229-6220. **Call for rates.** 1324 Richmond Rd 23185. Jct Richmond and Bypass rds, just e. Ext/int corridors. **Pets:** Large, dogs only. $100 deposit/room, $170 one-time fee/room. Designated rooms, service with restrictions, supervision.
(SAVE) (ECO) (&M) 🏊 ✕ 🛜 ✕ 🔒 💻

Williamsburg Inn H
(757) 220-7978. **$379-$499, 3 day notice.** 136 E Francis St 23185. In Colonial Williamsburg restored area. Int corridors. **Pets:** Accepted.
(¶¶) (&M) 🏊 ✕ 🛜 ✕ 🔒 💻

WINCHESTER

Aloft Winchester H
(540) 678-8899. **$119-$249.** 1055 Millwood Pike 22602. I-81 exit 313, just e. Int corridors. **Pets:** Accepted.
(SAVE) (ECO) 🏊 🛜 ✕ 🔒 💻

Best Western Lee-Jackson Inn & Conference Center H
(540) 662-4154. **$74-$75.** 711 Millwood Ave 22601. I-81 exit 313B, just nw on US 17/50/522. Ext corridors. **Pets:** Medium. $8 daily fee/pet. Designated rooms, service with restrictions, crate.
(SAVE) (¶¶) 🏊 🛜 🔒 💻

Candlewood Suites H
(540) 667-8323. **Call for rates.** 1135 Millwood Pike 22602. I-81 exit 313 northbound; exit 313A southbound, just se. Int corridors.
Pets: Accepted. (ECO) 🛜 🔒 💻

▼▼▼▼ Country Inn & Suites By Carlson �H
(540) 869-7657. **Call for rates.** 141 Kernstown Commons Blvd 22602.
I-81 exit 310, just w. Int corridors. **Pets:** Accepted.
🔲 🛒 🛜 ✖ 🔋 💻

◇◇◇ ▼▼▼ Econo Lodge North 🅼
(540) 662-4700. **$65-$90.** 1593 Martinsburg Pike 22603. I-81 exit 317,
0.3 mi sw on US 11. Int corridors. **Pets:** Medium. $10 daily fee/pet.
Designated rooms, no service, supervision. 🆂🅰🆅🅴 🛜 🔋 💻

◇◇◇ ▼▼▼ Red Roof Inn - Winchester 🅼
(540) 667-5000. **$50-$80.** 991 Millwood Pike 22602. I-81 exit 313 northbound; exit 313A southbound, just se on US 50/17. Ext corridors.
Pets: Accepted. 🆂🅰🆅🅴 🛜 🔋

▼▼▼▼ TownePlace Suites by Marriott Winchester �H
(540) 722-2722. **$82-$113.** 170 Getty Ln 22602. I-81 exit 315, just e. Int
corridors. **Pets:** Accepted. 🛒 🛜 ✖ 🔋 💻

WOODBRIDGE

▼▼▼▼ Homewood Suites by Hilton Woodbridge �H
(703) 590-0100. **$109-$209.** 2650 Neabsco Common Pl 22191. I-95 exit
156A, 0.3 mi e on CR 784, then just w on Neabsco Mills Rd. Int corridors. **Pets:** Large, dogs only. $100 one-time fee/pet. Designated rooms,
service with restrictions. 🔲 🛜 ✖ 🔋 💻

▼▼▼▼ Residence Inn by Marriott Potomac Mills �H
(703) 490-4020. **$116-$197.** 14301 Crossing Pl 22192. I-95 exit 158B
(Prince William Pkwy), 0.5 mi sw. Int corridors. **Pets:** Accepted.
🔲 🛒 🛜 ✖ 🔋 💻

WOODSTOCK

▼▼▼ Comfort Inn Woodstock �H
(540) 459-7600. **$99-$189.** 1011 Motel Dr 22664. I-81 exit 283, just e.
Int corridors. **Pets:** Other species. $20 daily fee/pet. Service with
restrictions, supervision. 🛒 🛜 ✖ 🔋 💻

WYTHEVILLE

◇◇◇ ▼▼▼ Best Western Wytheville Inn �H ☙
(276) 228-7300. **$84-$146.** 355 Nye Rd 24382. I-77 exit 41, just e. Int
corridors. **Pets:** $10 daily fee/pet. Designated rooms, service with
restrictions, supervision. 🆂🅰🆅🅴 🛒 🛜 ✖ 🔋 💻

▼▼▼▼ Comfort Inn �H
(276) 637-4281. **$90-$210.** 2594 E Lee Hwy 24382. I-77/81 exit 80, just
w. Int corridors. **Pets:** Accepted. 🔲 🛒 🛜 🔋 💻

▼▼ Days Inn 🅼
(276) 228-5500. **$55-$140.** 150 Malin Dr 24382. I-77/81 exit 73, just w.
Ext corridors. **Pets:** $15 daily fee/room. Designated rooms, service with
restrictions, supervision. 🛜 🔋 💻

▼▼▼▼ La Quinta Inn Wytheville �H
(276) 228-7400. **$92-$185.** 1800 E Main 24382. I-77/81 exit 73, just w.
Int corridors. **Pets:** Accepted. 🛒 🛜 ✖ 🔋 💻

▼▼▼▼ Red Roof Inn & Suites- Wytheville 🅼
(276) 223-1700. **$50-$149.** 1900 E Main St 24382. I-77/81 exit 73, just
w. Ext corridors. **Pets:** Accepted. 🍴 🛒 🛜 🔋 💻

YORKTOWN

▼▼▼▼ Candlewood Suites-Yorktown �H
(757) 952-1120. **Call for rates.** 329 Commonwealth Dr 23693. I-64 exit
256B, just n, then just e. Int corridors. **Pets:** Accepted.
🔲 🛒 🛜 ✖ 🔋 💻

▼▼▼ Red Roof Inn Yorktown �H
(757) 283-1111. **$60-$120.** 4531 George Washington Memorial Hwy
23692. I-64 exit 256B, 0.8 mi ne on Victory Blvd (SR 171), then 2.4 mi
n on US 17. Int corridors. **Pets:** Accepted. 🛒 🛜 ✖ 🔋 💻

▼▼▼▼ Staybridge Suites �H 🐾
(757) 251-6644. **Call for rates.** 401 Commonwealth Dr 23693. I-64 exit
256B, just n, then just e. Int corridors. **Pets:** Medium. $75 one-time
fee/pet. Designated rooms, service with restrictions, crate.
🅴🅲🅾 🔲 🛒 🛜 ✖ 🔋 💻

◇◇◇ ▼▼▼ TownePlace Suites by Marriott �H
(757) 874-8884. **$59-$125.** 200 Cybernetics Way 23693. I-64 exit 256B,
e to Kiln Creek Pkwy. Int corridors. **Pets:** Accepted.
🆂🅰🆅🅴 🅴🅲🅾 🔲 🛒 🛜 ✖ 🔋 💻

ZION CROSSROADS

◇◇◇ ▼▼▼ Best Western Plus Crossroads Inn &
Suites �H
(540) 832-1700. **$135-$147.** 135 Wood Ridge Terr 22942. I-64 exit 136,
just n. Int corridors. **Pets:** Medium. $20 daily fee/room. Designated
rooms, service with restrictions, supervision.
🆂🅰🆅🅴 🅴🅲🅾 🔲 🛒 🛜 ✖ 🔋 💻

WASHINGTON

AIRWAY HEIGHTS

◇◇◇ ▼▼▼ Days Inn & Suites Spokane Airport �H
(509) 244-0222. **$78-$200.** 1215 S Garfield Rd 99001. I-90/US 2 exit
277 to US 2, 4 mi w. Int corridors. **Pets:** Accepted.
🆂🅰🆅🅴 🔲 🛜 🔋 💻

ANACORTES

▼▼ Fidalgo Country Inn �H
(360) 293-3494. **Call for rates.** 7645 SR 20 98221. Jct Fidalgo Bay Rd.
Ext/int corridors. **Pets:** Accepted. 🔲 🛒 🛜 ✖ 🔋 💻

▼▼ Islands Inn 🅼
(360) 293-4644. **Call for rates.** 3401 Commercial Ave 98221. Just s of
downtown. Ext corridors. **Pets:** Accepted.
🍴 🛒 🛜 ✖ 🔋 💻

◇◇◇ ▼▼▼ Majestic Inn & Spa �H ☙
(360) 299-1400. **$129-$399, 3 day notice.** 419 Commercial Ave 98221.
At 5th Ave; downtown. Int corridors. **Pets:** Small, dogs only. $50 one-
time fee/room. Designated rooms, service with restrictions, supervision.
🆂🅰🆅🅴 🍴 🛜 ✖ 🔋 💻

ARLINGTON

◇◇◇ ▼▼▼ Best Western Plus
Arlington/Marysville �H 🐾
(360) 363-4321. **$105-$199.** 3721 172nd St NE 98223. I-5 exit 206, 0.4
mi e. Int corridors. **Pets:** Other species. $20 daily fee/pet. Designated
rooms, service with restrictions, crate. 🆂🅰🆅🅴 🔲 🛜 ✖ 🔋 💻

▼▼▼▼ Medallion Hotel �H
(360) 657-0500. **$99-$129.** 16710 Smokey Point Blvd 98223. I-5 exit
206, just e on 172nd St NE, then just s. Int corridors. **Pets:** Accepted.
🍴 🔲 🛒 🛜 ✖ 🔋 💻

ASHFORD

▼▼ Alexander's Lodge ▣
(360) 569-2300. **Call for rates.** 37515 SR 706 E 98304. 1 mi w of
Nisqually entrance to Mount Rainier National Park. Ext/int corridors.
Pets: Accepted. 🍴 🛜 ✕ 🏊 🧺 🔋 💻

AUBURN

**AAA ▼▼▼ Best Western Plus Mountain View Auburn
Inn** ▣
(253) 887-7600. **$135-$145.** 401 8th St SW 98001. SR 18 exit C St,
just s, then just w. Int corridors. **Pets:** Accepted.
🆂 🛥 ✕ 🛜 ✕ 🔋 💻

▼▼ Comfort Inn-Auburn ▣
(253) 333-8888. **$79-$189.** 1 16th St NE 98002. SR 167 exit 15th St
NW, 0.8 mi e, then just n on A St NE. Int corridors. **Pets:** Accepted.
🍴 🛥 🛜 🔋 💻

▼▼▼ La Quinta Inn & Suites Auburn ▣
(253) 804-9999. **$93-$284.** 225 6th St SE 98002. SR 18 exit Auburn
Way N, just sw. Int corridors. **Pets:** Accepted. 🛥 🛜 ✕ 🔋 💻

BAINBRIDGE ISLAND

**AAA ▼▼▼ Best Western Plus Bainbridge Island
Suites** ▣ 🐾
(206) 855-9666. **$170-$190.** 350 NE High School Rd 98110. 0.8 mi n of
ferry dock on SR 305, just w. Int corridors. **Pets:** Medium, dogs only.
$20 daily fee/room. Designated rooms, service with restrictions, supervi-
sion. 🆂 🍴 🛜 ✕ 🔋 💻

BELLEVUE

**AAA ▼▼▼ Embassy Suites by Hilton Seattle -
Bellevue** ▣
(425) 644-2500. **$99-$299.** 3225 158th Ave SE 98008. I-90 exit 11
westbound; exit 11A (SE Eastgate Way/156th Ave SE) eastbound, just
ne. Int corridors. **Pets:** Medium. $75 one-time fee/pet. Service with
restrictions, supervision. 🆂 🍴 🛥 🛥 🛜 ✕ 🔋 💻

**▼▼ Extended Stay
America-Seattle-Bellevue-Downtown** ▣
(425) 453-8186. **$110-$180.** 11400 Main St 98004. I-405 exit 13A, just
e on NE 4th St, just s on 116th Ave NE, then just w. Int corridors.
Pets: Accepted. 🍴 🛥 🛜 ✕ 🔋 💻

**AAA ▼▼▼ Fairfield Inn & Suites by Marriott Seattle
Bellevue/Redmond** ▣
(425) 869-6548. **$97-$292.** 14595 NE 29th Pl 98007. I-405 exit 14 (SR
520), 2.3 mi e to 148th Ave NE (north exit), then just nw. Int corridors.
Pets: Accepted. 🆂 🛥 🛥 🛜 ✕ 🔋 💻

AAA ▼▼▼ Hilton Bellevue ▣
(425) 455-1300. **$149-$425.** 300 112th Ave SE 98004. I-405 exit 12,
just nw. Int corridors. **Pets:** Accepted.
🆂 🟢 🍴 🛥 🛥 🛜 ✕ 🔋 💻

AAA ▼▼▼ Hotel Bellevue ▣
(425) 454-4424. **Call for rates.** 11200 SE 6th St 98004. I-405 exit 12,
0.4 mi nw. Int corridors. **Pets:** Accepted.
🆂 🍴 🛥 🛥 ✕ 🛜 ✕ 🔋 💻

AAA ▼▼▼ Hyatt House Seattle/Bellevue ▣
(425) 747-2705. **$99-$359.** 3244 139th Ave SE 98005. I-90 exit 11
westbound, 0.9 mi w, just n; exit 10B eastbound, just n, 0.7 mi e, then
just n. Int corridors. **Pets:** Accepted.
🆂 🍴 🛥 🛥 🛜 ✕ 🔋 💻

AAA ▼▼▼ Hyatt Regency Bellevue ▣
(425) 462-1234. **$159-$399.** 900 Bellevue Way NE 98004. I-405 exit
13B, 1.5 mi w on NE 8th St. Int corridors. **Pets:** Accepted.
🆂 🔷 🍴 🛥 🛥 🛜 ✕ 🔋 💻

AAA ▼▼▼ La Residence Suite Hotel ▣
(425) 455-1475. **$139-$229.** 475 100th Ave NE 98004. I-405 exit 13B,
0.9 mi w on NE 8th St, then just s. Int corridors. **Pets:** Accepted.
🆂 🍴 🛜 ✕ 🔋 💻

AAA ▼▼▼ Red Lion Hotel Bellevue ▣
(425) 455-5240. **$89-$209.** 11211 Main St 98004. I-405 exit 12, 0.4 mi
n on 114th St. Int corridors. **Pets:** Accepted.
🆂 🍴 🛥 🛜 ✕ 🔋 💻

▼▼▼ Residence Inn by Marriott Seattle Bellevue ▣
(425) 882-1222. **$128-$355.** 14455 NE 29th Pl 98007. I-405 exit 14 (SR
520), 2.3 mi e to 148th Ave NE (north exit), then just nw. Ext corridors.
Pets: Accepted. 🍴 🛥 🛥 🛜 ✕ 🔋 💻

**▼▼▼ Residence Inn by Marriott Seattle
Bellevue/Downtown** ▣
(425) 637-8500. **$119-$302.** 605 114th Ave SE 98004. I-405 exit 12,
just nw. Int corridors. **Pets:** Accepted.
🍴 🛥 🛥 🛜 ✕ 🔋 💻

AAA ▼▼▼ Sheraton Bellevue Hotel ▣ 🐾
(425) 455-3330. **$109-$399.** 100 112th Ave NE 98004. I-405 exit 12
northbound; exit 13 southbound, just s. Int corridors. **Pets:** Medium,
other species. $250 one-time fee/room. Service with restrictions, super-
vision. 🆂 🍴 🛥 🛜 ✕ 🔋 💻

AAA ▼▼▼ The Westin Bellevue ▣
(425) 638-1000. **$169-$389.** 600 Bellevue Way NE 98004. I-405 exit
13B, 1.5 mi w on NE 8th St, then just s. Int corridors. **Pets:** Accepted.
🆂 🍴 🛥 🛥 ✕ 🛜 ✕ 🔋 💻

BELLINGHAM *(Restaurants p. 629)*

AAA ▼▼▼ Baymont Inn & Suites ▣ 🐾
(360) 671-6200. **$79-$124.** 125 E Kellogg Rd 98226. I-5 exit 256A, 1
mi ne via Meridian St. Int corridors. **Pets:** Dogs only. $10 daily fee/
room. Designated rooms, service with restrictions, supervision.
🆂 🍴 🛥 🛥 🛜 ✕ 🔋 💻

AAA ▼▼▼ Best Western Plus Heritage Inn ▣ 🐾
(360) 647-1912. **$120-$220.** 151 E McLeod Rd 98226. I-5 exit 256A,
just se. Int corridors. **Pets:** Large, other species. $20 daily fee/room.
Designated rooms, service with restrictions, crate.
🆂 🟢 🛥 🛥 🛜 ✕ 🔋 💻

AAA ▼▼▼ The Chrysalis Inn & Spa ▣ 🐾
(360) 756-1005. **$179-$359.** 804 10th St 98225. I-5 exit 250, 1.3 mi nw
on Old Fairhaven Pkwy, 0.6 mi n via 12th and 11th sts, just w on Taylor
Ave, then just n. Int corridors. **Pets:** Medium, dogs only. $50 one-time
fee/room. Designated rooms, service with restrictions, supervision.
🆂 🍴 🛥 🛜 ✕ 🔋 💻

AAA ▼▼ Econo Lodge Inn & Suites ▣
(360) 671-4600. **$69-$189.** 3750 Meridian St 98225. I-5 exit 256A, just
sw. Ext corridors. **Pets:** Dogs only. $10 daily fee/pet. Designated rooms,
service with restrictions, supervision. 🆂 🛥 🛜 🔋 💻

**AAA ▼▼▼ Four Points by Sheraton Bellingham Hotel
& Conference Center** ▣
(360) 671-1011. **$119-$379.** 714 Lakeway Dr 98229. I-5 exit 253 (Lakeway Dr), just se. Int corridors. **Pets:** Accepted.
🆂 🍴 🛥 🛥 🛜 ✕ 🔋 💻

AAA ▼▼▼ Holiday Inn Express-Bellingham ▣
(360) 671-4800. **$89-$209.** 4160 Meridian St 98226. I-5 exit 256A, 0.7
mi e. Int corridors. **Pets:** Small, other species. $15 daily fee/pet. Desig-
nated rooms, service with restrictions, supervision.
🆂 🍴 🛥 🛥 🛜 🔋 💻

**AAA ▼▼▼ Home2 Suites by Hilton, Bellingham
Airport** ▣
(360) 734-3111. **$139-$229.** 805 Home Ln 98226. I-5 exit 257, just n.
Int corridors. **Pets:** Accepted. 🆂 🍴 🛥 🛥 ✕ 🛜 ✕ 🔋 💻

▼▼▼▼ **Hotel Bellwether** 🅷 ❀
(360) 392-3100. **$189-$590.** One Bellwether Way 98225. I-5 exit 253 (Lakeway Dr), 0.9 mi nw via Lakeway Dr and E Holly St, just w on Bay St, 0.6 mi n via W Chestnut St and Roeder Ave, then just w. Int corridors. **Pets:** Dogs only. $25 daily fee/pet. Designated rooms, service with restrictions, crate. 🄴 ⑪ 🖫ᴹ 🛜 ✕ 🔋 🖵

ⒶⒶⒶ ▼▼▼▼ **Oxford Suites Bellingham** 🅷
(360) 676-1400. **Call for rates.** 4051 Meridian St 98226. I-5 exit 256A, just ne. Int corridors. **Pets:** Accepted.
🆂🅰🆅🅴 🄴 ⑪ 🖫ᴹ ✕ 🛜 ✕ 🔋 🖵

ⒶⒶⒶ ▼▼▼▼ **SpringHill Suites by Marriott Bellingham** 🅷 ❀
(360) 714-9600. **$93-$166.** 4040 Northwest Ave 98226. I-5 exit 257, just n. Int corridors. **Pets:** Medium, dogs only. $20 daily fee/room. Designated rooms, service with restrictions, crate.
🆂🅰🆅🅴 ⑪ 🖫ᴹ 🛜 ✕ 🖵

ⒶⒶⒶ ▼▼▼▼ **TownePlace Suites by Marriott Bellingham** 🅷 ❀
(360) 714-9700. **$95-$193.** 4050 Northwest Ave 98226. I-5 exit 257, just n. Int corridors. **Pets:** Medium, dogs only. $20 daily fee/room. Designated rooms, service with restrictions, crate.
🆂🅰🆅🅴 🖫ᴹ 🛜 ✕ 🔋 🖵

BLAINE

ⒶⒶⒶ ▼▼▼▼ **Semiahmoo Resort, Golf and Spa** 🅷 ❀
(360) 318-2000. **$139-$269, 5 day notice.** 9565 Semiahmoo Pkwy 98230. I-5 exit 270, 9.5 mi nw on Semiahmoo Spit. Int corridors. **Pets:** Medium, dogs only. $50 daily fee/room. Designated rooms, supervision. 🆂🅰🆅🅴 🄴 ⑪ 🖫ᴹ ⤳ ✕ 🛜 ✕ 🔋 🖵

BOTHELL

▼▼ ▼▼ **Country Inn & Suites By Carlson** 🅷
(425) 485-5557. **Call for rates.** 19333 N Creek Pkwy 98011. I-405 exit 24, just e. Int corridors. **Pets:** Other species. $50 one-time fee/room. Designated rooms, service with restrictions, crate.
🄴🄲🄾 ⑪ 🖫ᴹ ⤳ 🛜 ✕ 🔋 🖵

▼▼ ▼▼ **Extended Stay America-Seattle-Bothell-West** 🅷
(425) 402-4252. **$95-$140.** 923 228th St SE 98021. I-405 exit 26, just sw. Int corridors. **Pets:** Accepted. ⑪ 🖫ᴹ 🛜 🔋

▼▼▼▼ **Residence Inn by Marriott Seattle NE** 🅷
(425) 485-3030. **$130-$271.** 11920 NE 195th St 98011. I-405 exit 24, 0.4 mi ne. Ext corridors. **Pets:** Accepted.
⑪ 🖫ᴹ ⤳ 🛜 ✕ 🔋 🖵

BREMERTON

ⒶⒶⒶ ▼▼ ▼▼ **Super 8-Bremerton** 🅷
(360) 377-8881. **$70-$80.** 5068 Kitsap Way 98312. SR 3 exit Kitsap Way, just ne; 4.2 mi w of ferry terminal. Int corridors. **Pets:** Medium, other species. $10 daily fee/pet. Designated rooms, service with restrictions, supervision. 🆂🅰🆅🅴 🖫ᴹ 🛜 ✕ 🔋 🖵

BURLINGTON

▼▼▼▼ **Candlewood Suites-Burlington** 🅷
(360) 755-3300. **Call for rates.** 1866 S Burlington Blvd 98233. I-5 exit 229, just e on George Hopper Dr, then just s. Int corridors. **Pets:** Accepted. 🖫ᴹ 🛜 ✕ 🔋 🖵

▼▼▼▼ **Fairfield Inn & Suites by Marriott Burlington** 🅷
(360) 757-2717. **$107-$167.** 9384 Old Hwy 99 N 98233. I-5 exit 232, just ne. Int corridors. **Pets:** Accepted.
🄴 🖫ᴹ ⤳ 🛜 ✕ 🔋 🖵

CAMAS

ⒶⒶⒶ ▼▼ ▼▼ **Camas Hotel** 🅷 ❀
(360) 834-5722. **Call for rates.** 405 NE 4th Ave 98607. Jct NE Cedar St; downtown. Int corridors. **Pets:** Medium, dogs only. $30 one-time fee/room. Designated rooms, service with restrictions, crate.
🆂🅰🆅🅴 ⑪ 🛜 ✕ 🔋 🖵

CASHMERE

ⒶⒶⒶ ▼ **Village Inn Motel** 🅼
(509) 782-3522. **$59-$99, 3 day notice.** 229 Cottage Ave 98815. On Business Rt US 2 and 97; downtown. Ext corridors. **Pets:** Dogs only. $20 daily fee/pet. Designated rooms, service with restrictions, supervision. 🆂🅰🆅🅴 🛜 ✕ 🔋

CENTRALIA

▼ **Motel 6 - #394** 🅼
(360) 330-2057. **$55-$105.** 1310 Belmont Ave 98531. I-5 exit 82, just w on Harrison Ave, then just n. Ext corridors. **Pets:** Accepted.
⑪ ⤳ 🆂🅰 ✕ 🔋

▼▼ ▼▼ **Peppermill Empress Inn** 🅷
(360) 330-9441. **Call for rates.** 1233 Alder St 98531. I-5 exit 81 (Mellen St), just ne. Int corridors. **Pets:** Accepted.
⑪ ⤳ 🛜 ✕ 🔋 🖵

CHEHALIS

ⒶⒶⒶ ▼▼▼▼ **Best Western Plus Park Place Inn & Suites** 🅷
(360) 748-4040. **$129-$290.** 201 SW Interstate Ave 98532. I-5 exit 76, just se. Int corridors. **Pets:** Accepted.
🆂🅰🆅🅴 ⑪ 🖫ᴹ ⤳ ✕ 🛜 ✕ 🔋 🖵

▼▼▼▼ **Holiday Inn Express & Suites Chehalis** 🅷
(360) 740-1800. **Call for rates.** 730 NW Liberty Pl 98532. I-5 exit 77, just ne. Int corridors. **Pets:** Accepted. ⑪ ⤳ 🛜 ✕ 🔋 🖵

CHELAN

ⒶⒶⒶ ▼▼▼▼ **Lakeside Lodge & Suites** 🅷
(509) 682-4396. **$99-$329, 7 day notice.** 2312 W Woodin Ave 98816. West end of town. Ext corridors. **Pets:** Accepted.
🆂🅰🆅🅴 🖫ᴹ ⤳ 🛜 ✕ 🔋 🖵

CHEWELAH

ⒶⒶⒶ ▼ **Nordlig Motel** 🅼
(509) 935-6704. **$72-$77.** 101 W Grant Ave 99109. North edge of town on US 395. Ext corridors. **Pets:** Dogs only. $10 one-time fee/room. Designated rooms, service with restrictions, supervision.
🆂🅰🆅🅴 🖫ᴹ 🛜 ✕ 🔋

CLARKSTON

ⒶⒶⒶ ▼▼ ▼▼ **Best Western RiverTree Inn** 🅼 ❀
(509) 758-9551. **$110-$115.** 1257 Bridge St 99403. 0.9 mi w of Snake River Bridge on US 12. Ext corridors. **Pets:** Medium, dogs only. $20 one-time fee/room. Designated rooms, service with restrictions, supervision. 🆂🅰🆅🅴 🖫ᴹ ⤳ ✕ 🛜 ✕ 🔋 🖵

▼▼ ▼▼ **Quality Inn & Suites Conference Center** 🅷
(509) 758-9500. **$95-$235.** 700 Port Dr 99403. Just w of Snake River Bridge on US 12, then 0.3 mi n via 5th St. Int corridors. **Pets:** $10 daily fee/pet. Designated rooms, service with restrictions, supervision.
⑪ 🖫ᴹ ⤳ ✕ 🛜 ✕ 🔋 🖵

CLE ELUM

ⒶⒶⒶ ▼▼ ▼▼ ▼▼ **Suncadia Resort** 🅷
(509) 649-6460. **Call for rates.** 3600 Suncadia Tr 98922. I-90 exit 80, 2 mi n, then 0.3 mi w. Int corridors. **Pets:** Accepted.
🆂🅰🆅🅴 ⑪ 🖫ᴹ ⤳ ✕ 🛜 ✕ 🔋 🖵

▼▼ Timber Lodge Inn **M**

(509) 674-5966. **$72-$104.** 301 W 1st St 98922. I-90 exit 84 eastbound, 1 mi ne; exit westbound, just w; downtown. Int corridors.
Pets: Accepted. ⬛M 🛜 ⊠ 🛄

COLFAX

ΔΔΔ ▼▼▼ Best Western Wheatland Inn **H**

(509) 397-0397. **$103-$180.** 701 N Main St 99111. 0.6 mi n of down-town. Int corridors. **Pets:** Small, dogs only. $20 daily fee/pet. Desig-nated rooms, service with restrictions, supervision.
SAVE 🍴 ⬛M ⊃ 🛜 ⊠ 🛄 🖥

CONCRETE

ΔΔΔ ▼▼▼ Ovenell's Heritage Inn and Log Cabins **CA**

(360) 853-8494. **$115-$250, 3 day notice.** 46276 Concrete Sauk Valley Rd 98237. 0.5 mi w of downtown on SR 20, 3 mi se. Ext corridors.
Pets: Dogs only. $15 daily fee/pet. Designated rooms, service with restrictions, supervision. SAVE 🍴 🛜 ⊠ 🛅 🛄 🖥

COULEE DAM

ΔΔΔ ▼▼▼ Columbia River Inn **M**

(509) 633-2100. **$118-$129.** 10 Lincoln Ave 99116. On SR 155 at visitor center. Ext corridors. **Pets:** $25 deposit/pet. Supervision.
SAVE 🍴 ⊃ ⊠ 🛜 ⊠ 🛄

DAYTON

ΔΔΔ ▼▼▼ Best Western Plus Dayton Hotel & Suites **H** 🐾

(509) 382-4790. **$109-$199.** 507 E Main St 99328. Just e of downtown. Int corridors. **Pets:** Medium, dogs only. $20 one-time fee/pet. No ser-vice, supervision. SAVE 🍴 ⬛M 🛜 ⊠ 🛄 🖥

▼▼▼ The Weinhard Hotel **H**

(509) 382-4032. **$129-$185, 7 day notice.** 235 E Main St 99328. Downtown. Int corridors. **Pets:** Dogs only. $20 one-time fee/pet. Super-vision. 🛜 ⊠ 🛄

DEER HARBOR

▼▼ Deer Harbor Inn **CI**

(360) 376-4110. **Call for rates.** 33 Inn Ln 98243. In Deer Harbor; 7 mi sw of ferry landing; 3.5 mi sw of Westsound. Ext/int corridors.
Pets: Accepted. 🍴 🛜 ⊠ 🐾 🛅 🛄 🖥

EASTSOUND *(Restaurants p. 629)*

▼▼ Landmark Orcas Island **CO**

(360) 376-2423. **Call for rates.** 67 Main St 98245. In Eastsound; between N Beach and Orcas rds; downtown. Ext corridors.
Pets: Accepted. 🍴 🛜 ⊠ 🐾 🛄 🖥

▼▼ Outlook Inn on Orcas Island **H**

(360) 376-2200. **$89-$240, 8 day notice.** 171 Main St 98245. In East-sound; between N Beach and Orcas rds; downtown. Ext/int corridors.
Pets: Accepted. 🍴 ⬛M 🛜 ⊠ 🐾 🛄 🖥

ΔΔΔ ▼▼▼▼ Turtleback Farm Inn **BB**

(360) 376-4914. **$125-$260, 15 day notice.** 1981 Crow Valley Rd 98245. In Eastsound; 4 mi sw of Eastsound on Orcas Rd. Int corridors.
Pets: Medium, dogs only. Designated rooms, service with restrictions, supervision. SAVE 🍴 🛜 ⊠ 🐾 🌊 🛅 🛄 🖥

EAST WENATCHEE

ΔΔ ▼▼ Cedars Inn, East Wenatchee **H**

(509) 886-8000. **Call for rates.** 80 Ninth St NE 98802. Just e of SR 28. Int corridors. **Pets:** Small, dogs only. $15 daily fee/pet. Designated rooms, service with restrictions, supervision.
SAVE ⬛M ⊃ 🛜 🛄 🖥

EATONVILLE

ΔΔΔ ▼▼ Mill Village Motel **M**

(360) 832-3200. **$110-$150.** 210 Center St E 98328. Just e of jct SR 161. Ext corridors. **Pets:** Small, dogs only. $20 one-time fee/pet. Ser-vice with restrictions, supervision. SAVE 🛜 ⊠ 🛄 🖥

EDMONDS

ΔΔΔ ▼▼▼ Best Western Plus Edmonds Harbor Inn **H** 🐾

(425) 771-5021. **$120-$200.** 130 W Dayton St 98020. Just s at Port of Edmonds. Ext/int corridors. **Pets:** Medium. $20 daily fee/room. Desig-nated rooms, supervision.
SAVE 🍴 ⬛M 🏊 ⊠ 🛜 ⊠ 🛄 🖥

ELLENSBURG

ΔΔΔ ▼▼▼ Best Western Plus Ellensburg Hotel **H**

(509) 925-4244. **$100-$220.** 211 W Umptanum Rd 98926. I-90 exit 109, just n, then just w. Int corridors. **Pets:** Accepted.
SAVE ⬛M ⊃ 🛜 ⊠ 🛄 🖥

ΔΔΔ ▼▼▼ Days Inn **H**

(509) 933-1500. **$70-$265.** 901 Berry Rd 98926. I-90 exit 109, just s. Int corridors. **Pets:** Accepted. SAVE ⬛M ⊃ 🛜 🛄 🖥

▼▼ Econo Lodge **M**

(509) 925-9844. **$63-$315.** 1390 N Dollarway Rd 98926. I-90 exit 106, just n. Ext corridors. **Pets:** Accepted. 🛜 ⊠ 🛄

▼▼ Ellensburg Comfort Inn **H**

(509) 925-7037. **$105-$225.** 1722 Canyon Rd 98926. I-90 exit 109, just n. Int corridors. **Pets:** Accepted. ⊃ 🛜 🛄 🖥

▼▼▼ Holiday Inn Express **H**

(509) 962-9400. **Call for rates.** 1620 Canyon Rd 98926. I-90 exit 109, just n. Int corridors. **Pets:** Accepted.
⊟ ⬛M ⊃ 🛜 ⊠ 🛄 🖥

ELMA

▼▼ Stay Beyond Inn & Suites Elma **H**

(360) 482-6868. **Call for rates.** 800 E Main St 98541. Just ne of jct US 12 and SR 8. Int corridors. **Pets:** Accepted.
🍴 ⬛M 🛜 ⊠ 🛄 🖥

EPHRATA

ΔΔΔ ▼▼▼ Best Western Rama Inn **H** 🐾

(509) 754-7111. **$79-$159.** 1818 Basin St SW 98823. On SR 28; west end of town. Int corridors. **Pets:** Large, other species. $20 one-time fee/room. Service with restrictions, supervision.
SAVE ⬛M ⊃ 🛜 ⊠ 🛄 🖥

EVERETT *(Restaurants p. 629)*

ΔΔΔ ▼▼ Best Western Cascadia Inn **H**

(425) 258-4141. **$99-$169.** 2800 Pacific Ave 98201. I-5 exit 193 north-bound; exit 194 southbound, just w. Int corridors. **Pets:** Medium, dogs only. $20 daily fee/pet. Designated rooms, service with restrictions, supervision. SAVE ⬛M ⊃ 🛜 ⊠ 🛄 🖥

ΔΔΔ ▼▼▼ Best Western Plus Navigator Inn & Suites **H**

(425) 347-2555. **$129-$229.** 10210 Evergreen Way 98204. I-5 exit 189, 1 mi w on SR 526 to Evergreen Way, then 1.6 mi s. Int corridors.
Pets: Accepted. SAVE 🍴 ⬛M ⊃ 🛜 ⊠ 🛄 🖥

▼▼▼ Delta Hotels by Marriott **H**

(425) 339-2000. **Call for rates.** 3105 Pine St 98201. I-5 exit 193 north-bound; exit 194 southbound, just sw. Int corridors. **Pets:** Accepted.
🍴 ⬛M ⊃ 🛜 ⊠ 🛄 🖥

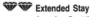 Extended Stay
America-Seattle-Everett-Silverlake H
(425) 337-1341. **$100-$140.** 1431 112th St SE 98208. I-5 exit 189, 1.5 mi se on 19th Ave SE, then 0.3 mi w. Int corridors. **Pets:** Accepted.

Inn at Port Gardner H
(425) 252-6779. **Call for rates.** 1700 W Marine View Dr 98201. I-5 exit 193 northbound, 1.2 mi w on Pacific Ave, then 1.2 mi n; exit 194 southbound, 1.2 mi w on Everett Ave, then 1 mi n; in Everett Marina Village. Int corridors. **Pets:** Accepted.

La Quinta Inn Everett H
(425) 347-9099. **$67-$163.** 12619 4th Ave W 98204. I-5 exit 186, just nw. Int corridors. **Pets:** Accepted.

Quality Inn & Suites H
(425) 609-4550. **$94-$189.** 101 128th St SE 98208. I-5 exit 186, just ne. Int corridors. **Pets:** Accepted.

FEDERAL WAY

Best Western Plus Evergreen Inn & Suites H
(253) 529-4000. **$129-$199.** 32124 25th Ave S 98003. I-5 exit 143, just sw. Int corridors. **Pets:** Accepted.

Clarion Hotel Federal Way H
(253) 941-6000. **$109-$229.** 31611 Pete von Reichbauer Way S 98003. I-5 exit 143, 0.5 mi w on 320th St, then just n. Int corridors. **Pets:** Accepted.

Comfort Inn Federal Way-Seattle H
(253) 529-0101. **$99-$249.** 31622 Pacific Hwy S 98003. I-5 exit 143, 0.5 mi w on 320th St, just n on 20th Ave, then just w on 316th Pl. Int corridors. **Pets:** Accepted.

Quality Inn & Suites H
(253) 835-4141. **$50-$219.** 1400 S 348th St 98003. I-5 exit 142B, 0.5 mi w. Int corridors. **Pets:** Accepted.

FERNDALE

Silver Reef Hotel Casino Spa H
(360) 383-0777. **Call for rates.** 4876 Haxton Way 98248. I-5 exit 260, 3.6 mi w on Slater Rd. Int corridors. **Pets:** Accepted.

FIFE

Emerald Queen Hotel & Casino H
(253) 922-2000. **$99-$159.** 5700 Pacific Hwy E 98424. I-5 exit 137, just ne. Int corridors. **Pets:** Small, dogs only. $25 one-time fee/room. Designated rooms, service with restrictions, supervision.

Extended Stay America-Tacoma-Fife H
(253) 926-6316. **$85-$115.** 2820 Pacific Hwy E 98424. I-5 exit 136B northbound; exit 136 southbound, just nw. Int corridors. **Pets:** Accepted.

FORKS

Manitou Lodge BB
(360) 374-6295. **Call for rates.** 813 Kilmer Rd 98331. 7.7 mi sw on SR 110 (LaPush Rd), 0.7 mi w on Mora Rd, then 0.8 mi n. Ext/int corridors. **Pets:** Accepted.

Miller Tree Inn Bed & Breakfast BB
(360) 374-6806. **$150-$265, 7 day notice.** 654 E Division St 98331. 0.3 mi e of US 101 (S Forks Ave). Ext/int corridors. **Pets:** Other species. $10 daily fee/pet. Designated rooms, service with restrictions.

FRIDAY HARBOR

Argyle House Bed & Breakfast BB 🐾
(360) 378-4084. **$110-$250, 14 day notice.** 685 Argyle Ave 98250. In Friday Harbor; 0.3 mi e of jct Spring St. Ext/int corridors. **Pets:** Dogs only. $25 one-time fee/room. Supervision.

Earthbox Inn & Spa H 🐾
(360) 378-4000. **$174-$447, 10 day notice.** 410 Spring St 98250. In Friday Harbor; 0.5 mi w of ferry dock. Ext corridors. **Pets:** Dogs only. $15 daily fee/pet. Designated rooms, service with restrictions, supervision.

Friday Harbor House H
(360) 378-8455. **Call for rates.** 130 West St 98250. In Friday Harbor; just w of Spring St. Ext/int corridors. **Pets:** Accepted.

Friday Harbor Suites H
(360) 378-3031. **$140-$390, 7 day notice.** 680 Spring St 98250. In Friday Harbor; 0.7 mi w of ferry dock. Int corridors. **Pets:** Accepted.

GIG HARBOR

Best Western Wesley Inn & Suites H 🐾
(253) 858-9690. **$129-$259.** 6575 Kimball Dr 98335. SR 16 exit City Center, just e on Pioneer Way, then 0.3 mi s. Int corridors. **Pets:** Medium, other species. $20 daily fee/pet. Designated rooms, service with restrictions, supervision.

The Inn at Gig Harbor H
(253) 858-1111. **Call for rates.** 3211 56th St NW 98335. SR 16 exit Olympic Dr, just w, then 0.4 mi n. Int corridors. **Pets:** Other species. $10 daily fee/room. Designated rooms, service with restrictions, supervision.

ILWACO

Heidi's Inn Ilwaco M
(360) 642-2387. **Call for rates.** 126 E Spruce St 98624. Downtown. Ext corridors. **Pets:** Other species. $8 daily fee/pet. Service with restrictions, supervision.

ISSAQUAH

Homewood Suites by Hilton Seattle/Issaquah H
(425) 391-4000. **$149-$349.** 1484 Hyla Ave NW 98027. I-90 exit 15, just s, then just w. Int corridors. **Pets:** Accepted.

KALALOCH

Kalaloch Lodge CA
(360) 962-2271. **$186-$345, 3 day notice.** 157151 Hwy 101 98331. In Kalaloch; at MM 157. Ext/int corridors. **Pets:** Accepted.

KELSO

Best Western Aladdin Inn H
(360) 425-9660. **$99-$179.** 310 Long Ave 98626. I-5 exit 39, 1.1 mi w via Allen and W Main sts, then just n on 5th Ave NW. Int corridors. **Pets:** Medium, dogs only. $20 daily fee/pet. Designated rooms, service with restrictions, supervision.

Motel 6-#43 M
(360) 425-3229. **$55-$85.** 106 Minor Rd 98626. I-5 exit 39, just ne. Ext corridors. **Pets:** Accepted.

Red Lion Hotel & Conference Center Kelso/Longview H
(360) 636-4400. **Call for rates.** 510 Kelso Dr 98626. I-5 exit 39, 0.3 mi se. Int corridors. **Pets:** Accepted.

▼▼ Super 8 - Kelso H

(360) 423-8880. **$73-$91.** 250 Kelso Dr 98626. I-5 exit 39, just se. Int corridors. **Pets:** Accepted. 🍴 🛁M 🛏 🛜 🛗 📺

KENNEWICK

◈ ▼▼▼▼ Best Western Plus Kennewick Inn H ❀

(509) 586-1332. **$119-$159.** 4001 W 27th Ave 99337. I-82 exit 113 (US 395), 0.8 mi n. Int corridors. **Pets:** Other species. $15 one-time fee/room. Supervision. SAVE 🛁M 🛏 ✕ 🛜 ✕ 🛗 📺

▼▼ Clover Island Inn H ❀

(509) 586-0541. **Call for rates.** 435 Clover Island Dr 99336. US 395 exit Port of Kennewick, 1 mi e on Columbia Dr, then 0.7 mi n. Int corridors. **Pets:** Other species. $10 one-time fee/room. Designated rooms, service with restrictions, supervision.
🍴 🛏 ✕ 🛜 ✕ 🛗 📺

▼▼ Comfort Inn Kennewick H

(509) 783-8396. **$80-$184.** 7801 W Quinault Ave 99336. 0.5 mi s on N Columbia Center Blvd from SR 240. Int corridors. **Pets:** Medium, dogs only. $15 daily fee/pet. Designated rooms, service with restrictions, supervision. 🍴 🛏 🛜 ✕ 🛗 📺

▼▼▼ Fairfield Inn by Marriott H

(509) 783-2164. **$93-$155.** 7809 W Quinault Ave 99336. 0.5 mi s on N Columbia Center Blvd from SR 240. Int corridors. **Pets:** Other species. $15 daily fee/pet. Service with restrictions, crate.
🍴 🛏 ✕ 🛜 ✕ 🛗 📺

◈ ▼▼▼ Kennewick Super 8 H

(509) 736-6888. **$65-$100, 3 day notice.** 626 N Columbia Center Blvd 99336. 1.1 mi s of SR 240. Int corridors. **Pets:** $15 daily fee/room. Designated rooms, service with restrictions, supervision.
SAVE 🛁M 🛏 🛜 ✕ 🛗 📺

▼▼ Quality Inn Kennewick H

(509) 735-6100. **$66-$199.** 7901 W Quinault Ave 99336. 0.5 mi s on Columbia Center Blvd from SR 240. Int corridors. **Pets:** Accepted.
🍴 🛏 🛜 ✕ 🛗 📺

▼▼ Red Lion Hotel Columbia Center H

(509) 783-0611. **Call for rates.** 1101 N Columbia Center Blvd 99336. SR 240, 0.5 mi s. Int corridors. **Pets:** Accepted.
🍴 🛏 🛜 ✕ 🛗 📺

▼▼▼▼ Red Lion Inn & Suites Kennewick Convention Center H

(509) 396-9979. **Call for rates.** 602 N Young St 99336. 1 mi s of SR 240 on N Columbia Center Blvd, just e. Int corridors. **Pets:** Accepted.
🍴 🛏 🛜 ✕ 🛗 📺

KENT

▼▼ Comfort Inn Kent H

(253) 872-2211. **$95-$229.** 22311 84th Ave S 98032. SR 167 exit 84th Ave S, just n. Int corridors. **Pets:** Accepted.
🍴 🛏 🛜 ✕ 🛗 📺

◈ ▼▼▼ Red Lion Inn & Suites Kent H

(253) 520-6670. **$179-$299, 3 day notice.** 25100 74th Ave S 98032. I-5 exit 149, 2.5 mi se via Kent Des Moines Rd (SR 516) to 74th Ave S. Int corridors. **Pets:** Accepted. SAVE 🍴 🛁M 🛏 ✕ 🛜 ✕ 🛗

▼▼▼▼ TownePlace Suites by Marriott-Seattle Southcenter H

(253) 796-6000. **$91-$187.** 18123 72nd Ave S 98032. I-405 exit 1 (SR 181), 1.6 mi s on W Valley Hwy, just e on S 180th St, then just s. Ext corridors. **Pets:** Accepted. 🍴 🛁M 🛏 🛜 ✕ 🛗 📺

KIRKLAND

◈ ▼▼▼▼ The Heathman Hotel H ❀

(425) 284-5800. **$169-$349, 7 day notice.** 220 Kirkland Ave 98033. I-405 exit 18 (NE 85th St), 1 mi w, just s on 3rd St, then just w. Int corridors. **Pets:** Designated rooms, service with restrictions, crate.
SAVE 🍴 🛁M 🛜 ✕ 🛗 📺

▼▼▼ La Quinta Inn & Suites Seattle Bellevue/Kirkland H

(425) 828-6585. **$90-$280.** 10530 NE Northup Way 98033. I-405 exit 14 (SR 520 W) via exit 108th Ave, just n, then just w. Int corridors.
Pets: Accepted. 🍴 🛁M 🛏 🛜 ✕ 🛗 📺

◈ ▼▼▼▼ Woodmark Hotel & Still Spa H ❀

(425) 822-3700. **$197-$329.** 1200 Carillon Point 98033. On Lake Washington Blvd, 1 mi n of SR 520. Int corridors. **Pets:** $35 one-time fee/pet. Designated rooms, service with restrictions, supervision.
SAVE 🍴 🛁M ✕ 🛜 ✕ 🛗 📺

LACEY

◈ ▼▼▼▼ Best Western Plus Lacey Inn & Suites H ❀

(360) 456-5655. **$132-$200.** 8326 Quinault Dr NE 98516. I-5 exit 111 (Marvin Rd), just ne. Int corridors. **Pets:** Medium, dogs only. $20 daily fee/room. Designated rooms, service with restrictions, supervision.
SAVE 🛏 🛜 ✕ 🛗 📺

▼▼ Candlewood Suites H

(360) 491-1698. **$140-$299.** 4440 3rd Ave SE 98503. I-5 exit 108 northbound, just n; exit 109 southbound, just s on Martin Ave E, just e on College Way, then just s. Int corridors. **Pets:** Accepted.
🍴 🛜 🛗 📺

LA CONNER

▼▼ La Conner Country Inn H

(360) 466-1500. **Call for rates.** 107 S 2nd St 98257. Jct 2nd and Morris sts; downtown. Ext/int corridors. **Pets:** Accepted.
🍴 🛜 ✕ 🛗 📺

LANGLEY (Restaurants p. 629)

▼▼▼ The Inn at Langley H

(360) 221-3033. **Call for rates.** 400 1st St 98260. Between Anthes and Park aves. Ext corridors. **Pets:** Accepted.
🍴 🛁M 🛜 ✕ 🅰 🛗

LEAVENWORTH

▼▼ Alpine Rivers Inn H

(509) 548-8888. **Call for rates.** 1505 Alpensee Strasse 98826. US 2, just n. Ext corridors. **Pets:** Accepted.
🍴 🛁M 🛏 ✕ 🛜 ✕ 🛗 📺

▼▼ Der Ritterhof Motor Inn H

(509) 548-5845. **$84-$129.** 190 US 2 98826. 0.3 mi w; downtown. Ext corridors. **Pets:** Accepted. 🛁M 🛏 🛜 ✕ 🛗 📺

▼▼ Howard Johnson Express Inn - Leavenworth H

(509) 548-4326. **$81-$165.** 405 W US Hwy 2 98826. West end of town. Ext corridors. **Pets:** Accepted. 🛁M 🛏 🛜 ✕ 🛗 📺

◈ ▼▼▼ Icicle Village Resort H ❀

(509) 548-7000. **$129-$429.** 505 W US 2 98826. West side of town. Int corridors. **Pets:** $20 daily fee/pet. Designated rooms, service with restrictions, supervision. SAVE 🍴 🛏 ✕ 🛜 ✕ 🛗 📺

▼▼ Obertal Inn M ❀

(509) 548-5204. **$99-$325, 3 day notice.** 922 Commercial St 98826. From US 2, just s on 9th St, just nw. Ext corridors. **Pets:** Other species. $18 daily fee/pet. Service with restrictions. 🛜 ✕ 🛗 📺

LIBERTY LAKE

Best Western Plus Liberty Lake Inn H
(509) 755-1111. **$129-$229.** 1816 N Pepper Ln 99019. I-90 exit 296 (Liberty Lake), just n. Int corridors. **Pets:** Accepted.

LONG BEACH

Anchorage Cottages CA
(360) 642-2351. **$89-$136, 30 day notice.** 2209 Boulevard N 98631. Just w of SR 103; north end of downtown. Ext corridors. **Pets:** Other species. $10 daily fee/pet. Designated rooms, no service, supervision.

Best Western Long Beach Inn H
(360) 642-8988. **$90-$199.** 500 Ocean Beach Blvd 98631. On SR 103; downtown. Int corridors. **Pets:** Dogs only. $20 daily fee/room. Designated rooms, service with restrictions, supervision.

The Breakers CO
(360) 642-4414. **Call for rates.** 210 26th St NW 98631. Just w of SR 103; north end of downtown. Ext corridors. **Pets:** Accepted.

Rodeway Inn & Suites M
(360) 642-3714. **$75-$150.** 115 3rd St SW 98631. Just off SR 103; downtown. Ext corridors. **Pets:** Dogs only. $7 daily fee/pet. Service with restrictions, supervision.

LYNNWOOD

Courtyard by Marriott Seattle North-Lynnwood-Everett H
(425) 670-0500. **$92-$184.** 4220 Alderwood Mall Blvd 98036. I-5 exit 181A northbound, just w on 44th Ave W, then just n; exit 181 (SR 524 W) southbound, 0.5 mi w on 196th St SW, just s on 44th Ave W, then just e. Int corridors. **Pets:** Accepted.

Embassy Suites by Hilton Hotel Seattle North/Lynnwood H
(425) 775-2500. **$119-$259.** 20610 44th Ave W 98036. I-5 exit 181A northbound, just se; exit 181 (SR 524 W) southbound, 0.5 mi w on 196th St SW, then 0.6 mi s. Int corridors. **Pets:** Accepted.

Hampton Inn & Suites by Hilton Seattle-North/Lynnwood H
(425) 771-1888. **$119-$269.** 19324 Alderwood Mall Pkwy 98036. I-5 exit 181B northbound, 0.6 mi n; exit 181 (SR 524 E) southbound, 0.5 mi e on 196th St SE, then just n. Int corridors. **Pets:** Accepted.

Homewood Suites by Hilton Seattle/Lynnwood H
(425) 670-8943. **$109-$259.** 18123 Alderwood Mall Pkwy 98037. I-5 exit 183, 0.4 mi w on 164th St SW, then 1.2 mi se. Int corridors. **Pets:** Accepted.

La Quinta Inn Lynnwood H
(425) 775-7447. **$81-$268.** 4300 Alderwood Mall Blvd 98036. I-5 exit 181A northbound, just w; exit 181 (SR 524 W) southbound, 0.5 mi w on 196th St SW, just s on 44th Ave SW, then just e. Int corridors. **Pets:** Accepted.

Residence Inn by Marriott-Seattle North/Lynnwood H
(425) 771-1100. **$122-$227.** 18200 Alderwood Mall Pkwy 98037. I-5 exit 183, 0.4 mi w on 164th St SW, then 1.2 mi se. Ext corridors. **Pets:** Accepted.

MARYSVILLE

Holiday Inn Express Hotel & Suites-Marysville H
(360) 530-1234. **Call for rates.** 8606 36th Ave NE 98270. I-5 exit 200, just se. Int corridors. **Pets:** Accepted.

MOCLIPS

Ocean Crest Resort and Restaurant H
(360) 276-4465. **$87-$237, 4 day notice.** 4651 SR 109 98562. South edge of town. Ext corridors. **Pets:** Other species. $15 daily fee/pet. Designated rooms, service with restrictions, supervision.

MONROE

Best Western Sky Valley Inn H
(360) 794-3111. **$109-$229.** 19233 SR 2 98272. West end of town. Int corridors. **Pets:** Accepted.

Evergreen Inn & Suites H
(360) 863-1900. **$119-$199.** 19103 SR 2 98272. West end of town. Int corridors. **Pets:** Accepted.

MORTON

Seasons Motel M
(360) 496-6835. **$110-$150.** 200 Westlake Ave 98356. Jct of US 12 and SR 7. Ext corridors. **Pets:** Small, dogs only. $20 one-time fee/pet. Service with restrictions, supervision.

MOSES LAKE

AmeriStay Inn & Suites H
(509) 764-7500. **Call for rates.** 1157 N Stratford Rd 98837. I-90 exit 179, 1 mi n to SR 17, 2.8 mi nw; exit Stratford Rd, just e. Int corridors. **Pets:** Accepted.

Best Western Plus Lake Front Hotel H
(509) 765-9211. **$120-$140.** 3000 Marina Dr 98837. I-90 exit 176, just nw. Int corridors. **Pets:** Accepted.

Comfort Suites Moses Lake H
(509) 765-3731. **$120-$240.** 1700 E Kittleson Rd 98837. I-90 exit 179, just nw. Int corridors. **Pets:** Small, dogs only. $25 daily fee/pet. Designated rooms, service with restrictions, supervision.

Inn at Moses Lake H
(509) 766-7000. **$95-$200.** 1741 E Kittleson Rd 98837. I-90 exit 179, just nw. Int corridors. **Pets:** Other species. $10 daily fee/pet. Designated rooms, service with restrictions, supervision.

Quality Inn H
(509) 765-8886. **$80-$210.** 449 Melva Ln 98837. I-90 exit 176, just n. Int corridors. **Pets:** Other species. $10 daily fee/pet. Service with restrictions, supervision.

Ramada Moses Lake H
(509) 766-1000. **$38-$160.** 1745 E Kittleson Rd 98837. I-90 exit 179, just n. Int corridors. **Pets:** Accepted.

MOUNT RAINIER NATIONAL PARK

Alta Crystal Resort at Mt Rainier H
(360) 663-2500. **$179-$339, 30 day notice.** 68317 SR 410 E 98022. 2 mi outside northeast entrance. Ext corridors. **Pets:** Dogs only. $50 one-time fee/pet. Designated rooms, service with restrictions, supervision.

MOUNT VERNON

⟡ ▼▼ Best Western College Way Inn 🅗
(360) 424-4287. **$98-$163.** 300 W College Way 98273. I-5 exit 227, just w. Ext corridors. **Pets:** Medium. $20 daily fee/pet. Designated rooms, service with restrictions, supervision. 🆂 🖼 🛜 ✖ 🔋 💻

⟡ ▼▼ Quality Inn-Mount Vernon 🅗
(360) 428-7020. **$79-$270.** 1910 Freeway Dr 98273. I-5 exit 227, just w on College Way, then just n. Ext corridors. **Pets:** Accepted.
🆂 🖼 🛜 🔋 💻

⟡ ▼▼ Tulip Inn Ⓜ ☙
(360) 428-5969. **$75-$119.** 2200 Freeway Dr 98273. I-5 exit 227, just w on College Way, then just n. Ext corridors. **Pets:** Small, dogs only. $10 daily fee/pet. Designated rooms, service with restrictions, supervision.
🆂 🛜 ✖ 🔋 💻

MUKILTEO

⟡ ▼▼▼ Staybridge Suites Seattle North-Everett 🅗
(425) 493-9500. **Call for rates.** 9600 Harbour Pl 98275. Jct Paine Field Blvd and SR 525 (Mukilteo Speedway). Int corridors. **Pets:** Accepted.
🆂 🖼 🛜 ✖ 🔋 💻

▼▼ TownePlace Suites by Marriott-Mukilteo 🅗 ☙
(425) 551-5900. **$107-$173.** 8521 Mukilteo Speedway 98275. Just se of jct 84th St SW and SR 525 (Mukilteo Speedway). Ext corridors.
Pets: Other species. $10 daily fee/room. Service with restrictions, crate.
🖼 🛜 ✖ 🔋 💻

OAK HARBOR

⟡ ▼▼ Best Western Plus Harbor Plaza & Conference Center 🅗
(360) 679-4567. **$110-$149.** 33175 SR 20 98277. Just n of town. Int corridors. **Pets:** Accepted. 🆂 🖼 🛜 ✖ 🔋 💻

▼▼ Candlewood Suites-Oak Harbor 🅗
(360) 279-2222. **Call for rates.** 33221 SR 20 98277. Just n of town. Int corridors. **Pets:** Accepted. 🖼 🛜 ✖ 🔋 💻

OCEAN PARK

▼ Ocean Park Resort Ⓜ
(360) 665-4585. **Call for rates.** 25904 R St 98640. Just e of SR 103; downtown. Ext corridors. **Pets:** Accepted.
🍴 🖼 🛜 ✖ 🎞 ☒ 🔋 💻

OCEAN SHORES

⟡ ▼▼ Best Western Lighthouse Suites Inn 🅗 ☙
(360) 289-2311. **$121-$260.** 491 Damon Rd NW 98569. Just w of main entrance to town; north end of downtown. Int corridors. **Pets:** Large, dogs only. $20 daily fee/room. Designated rooms, service with restrictions, crate. 🆂 🍴 🖼 🛜 ✖ 🎞 🔋 💻

▼▼ The Canterbury Inn 🅒 ☙
(360) 289-3317. **$86-$298.** 643 Ocean Shores Blvd NW 98569. 0.3 mi s of Chance A La Mer Blvd. Int corridors. **Pets:** Medium, dogs only. $150 deposit/room, $15 daily fee/pet. Designated rooms, supervision.
🖼 🛜 ✖ 🎞 🔋 💻

▼▼ The Polynesian Condominium Resort 🅒
(360) 289-3361. **$139-$429, 3 day notice.** 615 Ocean Shores Blvd NW 98569. 0.3 mi s of Chance A La Mer Blvd. Ext/int corridors. **Pets:** Other species. $15 daily fee/pet. Designated rooms, service with restrictions, supervision. 🍴 🖼 🛜 ✖ 🎞 🔋 💻

OLYMPIA

▼▼▼ Hotel RL Olympia 🅗
(360) 943-4000. **$89-$199.** 2300 Evergreen Park Dr SW 98502. I-5 exit 104, 0.7 mi w on US 101, just n on Cooper Point Rd N, 0.7 mi e on S Evergreen Park Dr SW, then just n on Lakeridge Way SW. Int corridors.
Pets: Accepted. 🄴 🍴 🖼 🛜 ✖ 🔋

▼▼▼ TownePlace Suites by Marriott Olympia 🅗
(360) 753-8770. **$75-$195.** 900 Capitol Way S 98501. I-5 exit 105 (City Center) northbound; exit 105A southbound, 0.4 mi w on 14th Ave, then 0.5 mi n; downtown. Int corridors. **Pets:** Accepted.
🍴 🖼 🛜 🛜 ✖ 🔋 💻

OMAK

⟡ ▼▼▼ Best Western Plus Peppertree Inn at Omak 🅗
(509) 422-2088. **$99-$299.** 820 Koala Dr 98841. US 97, just n of Riverside Dr. Int corridors. **Pets:** Accepted.
🆂 🖼 🛜 🛜 ✖ 🔋 💻

⟡ ▼▼ Omak Inn LLC 🅗
(509) 826-3822. **$70-$140.** 912 Koala Dr 98841. On US 97, just n of Riverside Dr. Int corridors. **Pets:** Accepted.
🆂 🄴 🖼 🛜 ✖ 🔋 💻

OTHELLO

⟡ ▼▼ Quality Inn Othello 🅗
(509) 488-5671. **$90-$145.** 1020 E Cedar St 99344. Just off Main St; jct 10th St. Int corridors. **Pets:** Accepted.
🆂 🍴 🖼 🛜 🔋 💻

PACIFIC

▼▼ Quality Inn & Suites 🅗
(253) 288-1916. **Call for rates.** 415 Ellingson Rd 98047. SR 167 exit Algona/Pacific, just se. Int corridors. **Pets:** Accepted.
🍴 🖼 ✖ 🛜 ✖ 🔋 💻

PACKWOOD

▼▼ Cowlitz River Lodge Ⓜ
(360) 494-4444. **$110-$150, 3 day notice.** 13069 US 12 98361. East end of town. Ext corridors. **Pets:** Small, dogs only. $20 one-time fee/pet. Service with restrictions, supervision. 🍴 🛜 ✖ 🔋 💻

⟡ ▼▼ Crest Trail Lodge 🅗
(360) 494-4944. **Call for rates.** 12729 US 12 98361. West end of town. Int corridors. **Pets:** Small, dogs only. $20 one-time fee/pet. Designated rooms, service with restrictions, supervision.
🆂 🍴 🛜 ✖ 🔋 💻

PASCO

⟡ ▼▼▼ Best Western Plus Pasco Inn & Suites 🅗 ☙
(509) 543-7722. **$130-$180.** 2811 N 20th Ave 99301. I-182 exit 12B, just n. Int corridors. **Pets:** $15 one-time fee/room. Service with restrictions, supervision. 🆂 🍴 🖼 ✖ 🛜 ✖ 🔋 💻

▼▼▼ Holiday Inn Express Pasco/Tri-Cities at TRAC 🅗
(509) 543-7000. **Call for rates.** 4525 Convention Pl 99301. I-182 exit 9 (Rd 68), just n, then just e. Int corridors. **Pets:** Accepted.
🖼 🖼 🛜 ✖ 🔋 💻

▼▼ My Place Hotel Pasco 🅗
(509) 545-2186. **Call for rates.** 6830 Rodeo Dr 99301. I-182 exit 9 (Rd 68), just n, then just e. Int corridors. **Pets:** Accepted.
🍴 🖼 🛜 ✖ 🔋 💻

▼▼▼ Red Lion Hotel Pasco 🅗
(509) 547-0701. **Call for rates.** 2525 N 20th Ave 99301. I-182 exit 12B, just n. Int corridors. **Pets:** Other species. $15 one-time fee/room. Service with restrictions, crate. 🄴 🍴 🖼 🛜 ✖ 🔋 💻

▼▼ **Sleep Inn Pasco** H
(509) 545-9554. **$100-$193.** 9930 Bedford St 99301. I-182 exit 7, just ne. Int corridors. **Pets:** Accepted. 🍴 ➔ 🛰 ✕ 🔒 💻

PORT ANGELES

♨ ▼▼ **Days Inn** H
(360) 452-4015. **$69-$139.** 1510 E Front St 98362. Jct Alder St; on east side. Ext corridors. **Pets:** Dogs only. $25 daily fee/pet. Designated rooms, service with restrictions, supervision. 📖 ➔ 🛰 🔒 💻

▼▼ **Red Lion Hotel Port Angeles** H
(360) 452-9215. **Call for rates.** 221 N Lincoln St 98362. On US 101 westbound; at ferry landing. Ext/int corridors. **Pets:** Accepted.
🍴 ➔ 🛰 ✕ 🔒 💻

♨ ▼▼ **Super 8 Port Angeles** M
(360) 452-8401. **$56-$174.** 2104 E 1st St 98362. 1.8 mi e of downtown, just s of US 101; jct Del Guzzi Dr. Int corridors. **Pets:** Accepted.
📖 🛰 ✕ 🔒 💻

PORT ORCHARD

♨ ▼▼ **Comfort Inn Port Orchard** M
(360) 895-2666. **$94-$170.** 1121 Bay St 98366. SR 16 exit Tremont St, 0.9 mi e to Sidney Ave, 1.2 mi n to Bay St, then just e. Ext corridors. **Pets:** Dogs only. $25 daily fee/pet. Designated rooms, service with restrictions, supervision. 📖 🍴 ♿ 🛰 ✕ 🔒 💻

PORT TOWNSEND

♨ ▼▼ **Bishop Victorian Hotel** H 🐾
(360) 385-6122. **$135-$275, 3 day notice.** 714 Washington St 98368. Corner of Washington and Quincy sts. Int corridors. **Pets:** Dogs only. $20 daily fee/pet. Designated rooms, supervision.
📖 🍴 🛰 ✕ 🎿 🔒 💻

▼▼ **Harborside Inn** H
(360) 385-7909. **Call for rates.** 330 Benedict St 98368. Just s of SR 20; between Jefferson and Washington sts. Ext corridors.
Pets: Accepted. 🍴 ➔ 🛰 ✕ 🎿 🔒 💻

▼▼ **Old Consulate Inn** BB 🐾
(360) 385-6753. **$120-$230, 7 day notice.** 313 Walker St 98368. Jct Washington St; on the bluff. Int corridors. **Pets:** Dogs only. $25 one-time fee/room. Designated rooms, service with restrictions, supervision.
🍴 🛰 ✕ 🎿 🎿 🎿

♨ ▼▼ **The Swan Hotel** M 🐾
(360) 385-1718. **$110-$325, 3 day notice.** 222 Monroe St 98368. Jct Water St; downtown. Ext corridors. **Pets:** Dogs only. $20 daily fee/pet. Designated rooms, service with restrictions, supervision.
📖 🍴 🛰 ✕ 🎿 🔒 💻

POULSBO

▼▼ **GuestHouse International Inn & Suites** H
(360) 697-4400. **$89-$179.** 19801 7th Ave NE 98370. SR 3, 1.4 mi e on SR 305, then just s; just n from jct NE Liberty Rd. Int corridors. **Pets:** $40 daily fee/pet. Service with restrictions, supervision.
🛰 🔒 💻

♨ ▼▼ **Poulsbo Inn & Suites** M
(360) 779-3921. **$104-$135, 7 day notice.** 18680 SR 305 NE 98370. SR 3, 2.3 mi e. Ext corridors. **Pets:** Small. $25 daily fee/pet. Designated rooms, service with restrictions, crate.
📖 🍴 ➔ ✕ 🛰 🔒 💻

PROSSER

♨ ▼▼ **Best Western Plus The Inn at Horse Heaven** H
(509) 786-7977. **$112-$162.** 259 Merlot Dr 99350. I-82 exit 80, just s. Int corridors. **Pets:** Accepted. 📖 ♿ ➔ ✕ 🛰 🔒 💻

PULLMAN

▼▼ **Hilltop Inn** H 🐾
(509) 332-0928. **$116-$219, 3 day notice.** 928 NW Olsen St 99163. 1.6 mi e on SR 270 from US 195. Int corridors. **Pets:** Medium, other species. $25 daily fee/pet. Designated rooms, service with restrictions, supervision. 🍴 ♿ ➔ 🛰 ✕ 🔒 💻

▼▼ **Holiday Inn Express & Suites Pullman** H 🐾
(509) 334-4437. **$129-$289.** 1190 SE Bishop Blvd 99163. Jct US 195 business route, 0.5 mi s, 1 mi e on SR 270. Int corridors. **Pets:** Medium, dogs only. $20 daily fee/pet. Designated rooms, service with restrictions. 🔌 ♿ ➔ 🛰 ✕ 🔒 💻

♨ ▼▼ **Residence Inn by Marriott Pullman** H
(509) 332-4400. **$95-$177.** 1255 NE North Fairway Rd 99163. Jct Grand Ave and Stadium Way, 1 mi se to N Fairway Rd, then 0.6 mi ne. Int corridors. **Pets:** Accepted. 📖 🍴 ♿ 🛰 ✕ 🔒 💻

PUYALLUP

♨ ▼▼ **Best Western Premier Plaza Hotel & Conference Center** H
(253) 848-1500. **$139-$249.** 620 S Hill Park Dr 98373. SR 512 exit S Hill Park Dr southbound; exit 9th St SW northbound, just w. Int corridors. **Pets:** Accepted. 📖 🍴 ♿ 🛰 ✕ 🔒 💻

▼▼ **Holiday Inn Express Hotel & Suites** H
(253) 848-4900. **Call for rates.** 812 S Hill Park Dr 98373. SR 512 exit S Hill Park Dr southbound; exit 9th St SW northbound, just w. Int corridors. **Pets:** Accepted. 🍴 ➔ 🛰 ✕ 🔒 💻

QUINAULT

▼▼ **Lake Quinault Lodge** H
(360) 288-2900. **Call for rates.** 345 S Shore Rd 98575. 2.2 mi ne of US 101 and S Shore Rd. Ext/int corridors. **Pets:** Accepted.
🍴 ➔ ✕ 🛰 ✕ 🎿 🎿 🔒 💻

REDMOND

♨ ▼▼ **Hyatt House Seattle/Redmond** H
(425) 497-2000. **$99-$409.** 15785 Bear Creek Pkwy NE 98052. I-405 exit 14 (SR 520), 4.5 mi e to W Lake Sammamish Pkwy, just n to Leary Way, just e to Bear Creek Pkwy, then just n. Int corridors. **Pets:** Accepted. 📖 🍴 ♿ ➔ 🛰 ✕ 🔒 💻

▼▼ **Residence Inn by Marriott Seattle East / Redmond** H
(425) 497-9226. **$126-$340.** 7575 164th Ave NE 98052. I-405 exit 14 (SR 520), 4.5 mi e to W Lake Sammamish Pkwy, just n to Leary Way, just e to Bear Creek Pkwy, just s to NE 74th Ave, just w to 164th Ave NE, then just n; center. Int corridors. **Pets:** Accepted.
♻ ♿ ➔ 🛰 ✕ 🔒 💻

♨ ▼▼ **Seattle Marriott Redmond** H
(425) 498-4000. **$116-$318.** 7401 164th Ave NE 98052. I-405 exit 14 (SR 520), 4.5 mi e to W Lake Sammamish Pkwy, just n to Leary Way, just e to Bear Creek Pkwy, just s to NE 74th Ave, then just w. Int corridors. **Pets:** Accepted. 📖 ♻ 🍴 ♿ ➔ 🛰 ✕ 🔒 💻

RENTON (Restaurants p. 629)

♨ ▼▼ **Larkspur Landing Renton** H
(425) 235-1212. **$119-$369.** 1701 E Valley Rd 98057. SR 167 exit E Valley Rd, 1 mi nw. Int corridors. **Pets:** Accepted.
📖 🛰 ✕ 🔒 💻

♨ ▼▼ **TownePlace Suites by Marriott Seattle South/Renton** H
(425) 917-2000. **$107-$193.** 300 SW 19th St 98057. SR 167 exit E Valley Rd, 1 mi nw, then just w. Int corridors. **Pets:** Accepted.
📖 🍴 ♿ ➔ 🛰 🔒 💻

RICHLAND

▼▼▼ Holiday Inn Express & Suites ㅐ
(509) 737-8000. **Call for rates.** 1970 Center Pkwy 99352. Just s on Columbia Center Blvd from SR 240, then just w. Int corridors.
Pets: Accepted. 〔⫶〕 ⬚ᴹ ⊇ 奈 ⊠ 🗎 💻

△△△ ▼▼▼ TownePlace Suites by Marriott Richland-Columbia Point ㅐ
(509) 943-9800. **$105-$168.** 591 Columbia Point Dr 99352. I-182 exit 5B, just n to Columbia Point Dr, then 0.8 mi e. Int corridors.
Pets: Accepted. 〔SAVE〕 ⊇ ⊠ 奈 ⊠ 🗎 💻

RITZVILLE

△△△ ▼▼▼ Best Western Bronco Inn ㅐ
(509) 659-5000. **$104-$115.** 105 W Galbreath Way 99169. I-90 exit 221, cross overpass, then second left. Int corridors. **Pets:** Medium. $20 daily fee/room. Designated rooms, service with restrictions, supervision.
〔SAVE〕 ⊖ ⊇ 奈 ⊠ 🗎 💻

△△△ ▼▼▼ Cedars Inn & Suites Ritzville ㅐ
(509) 659-1007. **Call for rates.** 1513 Smitty's Blvd 99169. I-90 exit 221, just n. Int corridors. **Pets:** Accepted. 〔SAVE〕 ⬚ᴹ ⊇ 奈 🗎

SEATAC

▼▼ Clarion Hotel ㅐ
(206) 242-0200. **$87-$303.** 3000 S 176th St 98188. Jct SR 518, 1.2 mi s on International Blvd (SR 99) then just e. Int corridors.
Pets: Accepted. 〔⫶〕 ⬚ᴹ ⊇ 奈 ⊠ 🗎 💻

△△△ ▼▼ Coast Gateway Hotel ㅐ
(206) 248-8200. **Call for rates.** 18415 International Blvd (SR 99) 98188. Jct SR 518, 1.7 mi s. Int corridors. **Pets:** Accepted.
〔SAVE〕 〔⫶〕 奈 ⊠ 🗎 💻

△△△ ▼▼▼ DoubleTree by Hilton Hotel Seattle Airport ㅐ
(206) 246-8600. **$99-$369.** 18740 International Blvd (SR 99) 98188. Jct SR 518, 1.7 mi s. Int corridors. **Pets:** Accepted.
〔SAVE〕 〔ECO〕 〔⫶〕 ⊇ 𝕤̄ ⊠ 🗎 💻

△△△ ▼▼▼ Hilton Seattle Airport & Conference Center ㅐ
(206) 244-4800. **$99-$369.** 17620 International Blvd (SR 99) 98188. Jct SR 518, 1.3 mi s. Int corridors. **Pets:** Accepted.
〔SAVE〕 〔ECO〕 ⊖ 〔⫶〕 ⬚ᴹ ⊇ 𝕤̄ ⊠ 🗎 💻

▼▼▼ Holiday Inn Express Hotel & Suites-Seattle Sea-Tac Airport ㅐ
(206) 824-3200. **Call for rates.** 19621 International Blvd (SR 99) 98188. Jct SR 518, 2.5 mi s. Int corridors. **Pets:** Accepted.
〔⫶〕 奈 ⊠ 🗎 💻

△△△ ▼▼▼ Radisson Hotel Seattle Airport ㅐ
(206) 244-6666. **Call for rates.** 18118 International Blvd (SR 99) 98188. Jct SR 518, 1.5 mi s. Int corridors. **Pets:** Accepted.
〔SAVE〕 〔ECO〕 〔⫶〕 ⬚ᴹ ⊇ 奈 ⊠ 🗎 💻

△△△ ▼▼ Red Roof Inn Seattle Airport-SeaTac ㅐ
(206) 248-0901. **$59-$289.** 16838 International Blvd (SR 99) 98188. Jct SR 518, 0.8 mi s. Int corridors. **Pets:** Accepted.
〔SAVE〕 〔⫶〕 奈 ⊠ 🗎 💻

SEATTLE (Restaurants p. 629)

△△△ ▼▼▼ ▼▼ The Edgewater ㅐ
(206) 728-7000. **$179-$529.** 2411 Alaskan Way, Pier 67 98121. On waterfront at Pier 67; at base of Wall St. Int corridors. **Pets:** Other species. $25 daily fee/room. Designated rooms, service with restrictions, crate. 〔SAVE〕 〔⫶〕 奈 ⊠ 🗎 💻

△△△ ▼▼▼ ▼▼ Fairmont Olympic Hotel ㅐ
(206) 621-1700. **Call for rates.** 411 University St 98101. Corner of 4th Ave and University St. Int corridors. **Pets:** Accepted.
〔SAVE〕 〔ECO〕 〔⫶〕 ⊇ ⊠ 𝕤̄ ⊠ 🗎 💻

△△△ ▼▼▼ ▼▼ Four Seasons Hotel Seattle ㅐ
(206) 749-7000. **Call for rates.** 99 Union St 98101. Southwest corner of 1st Ave and Union St. Int corridors. **Pets:** Accepted.
〔SAVE〕 ⊖ 〔⫶〕 ⬚ᴹ ⊇ ⊠ 奈 ⊠

△△△ ▼▼▼ ▼▼ Grand Hyatt Seattle ㅐ
(206) 774-1234. **$179-$499, 3 day notice.** 721 Pine St 98101. Corner of 7th Ave and Pine St. Int corridors. **Pets:** Accepted.
〔SAVE〕 〔ECO〕 〔⫶〕 ⬚ᴹ ⊠ 奈 ⊠ 🗎 💻

△△△ ▼▼▼ Homewood Suites by Hilton Seattle Convention Center/Pike Street ㅐ
(206) 682-8282. **$149-$389.** 1011 Pike St 98101. I-5 exit 165 northbound to Pike St via 6th Ave; exit Union St southbound to Pike St. Int corridors. **Pets:** Accepted. 〔SAVE〕 〔⫶〕 ⬚ᴹ ⊇ ⊠ 奈 🗎 💻

▼▼▼ Homewood Suites by Hilton-Seattle Downtown ㅐ
(206) 281-9393. **$159-$399.** 206 Western Ave W 98119. Just w of Seattle Center; at jct 2nd Ave W. Int corridors. **Pets:** Accepted.
〔⫶〕 奈 ⊠ 🗎 💻

△△△ ▼▼▼ ▼▼ Hotel 1000 ㅐ
(206) 957-1000. **Call for rates.** 1000 1st Ave 98104. Corner of 1st Ave and Madison St. Int corridors. **Pets:** Accepted.
〔SAVE〕 ⊖ 〔⫶〕 ⬚ᴹ 奈 ⊠ 🗎 💻

△△△ ▼▼▼ ▼▼ Hotel Max ㅐ 🐾
(206) 728-6299. **Call for rates.** 620 Stewart St 98101. Corner of 7th Ave and Stewart St. Int corridors. **Pets:** Medium, other species. $45 one-time fee/room. Designated rooms, service with restrictions.
〔SAVE〕 ⊖ 〔⫶〕 ⬚ᴹ 奈 ⊠ 🗎 💻

△△△ ▼▼▼ Hotel Nexus Seattle ㅐ
(206) 365-0700. **Call for rates.** 2140 N Northgate Way 98133. I-5 exit 173, just nw. Ext corridors. **Pets:** Accepted.
〔SAVE〕 ⬚ᴹ ⊇ 奈 ⊠ 🗎 💻

▼▼▼ Hotel Sorrento ㅐ
(206) 622-6400. **Call for rates.** 900 Madison St 98104. I-5 exit Madison St, just e; jct 9th Ave. Int corridors. **Pets:** Accepted.
〔⫶〕 ⬚ᴹ 奈 ⊠ 💻

△△△ ▼▼▼ Hyatt House Seattle/Downtown ㅐ
(206) 727-1234. **$169-$399.** 201 5th Ave N 98109. Just n of jct E Denny Way. Int corridors. **Pets:** Accepted.
〔SAVE〕 〔⫶〕 ⬚ᴹ 奈 ⊠ 🗎 💻

△△△ ▼▼▼ ▼▼ Hyatt Olive 8 ㅐ
(206) 695-1234. **$169-$499.** 1635 8th Ave 98101. Between Olive Way and Pine St. Int corridors. **Pets:** Accepted.
〔SAVE〕 〔ECO〕 〔⫶〕 ⬚ᴹ ⊇ ⊠ 奈 ⊠ 🗎 💻

△△△ ▼▼▼ ▼▼ Kimpton Alexis Hotel Seattle ㅐ
(206) 624-4844. **Call for rates.** 1007 1st Ave 98104. Corner of Madison St and 1st Ave. Int corridors. **Pets:** Accepted.
〔SAVE〕 〔ECO〕 ⊖ 〔⫶〕 ⬚ᴹ ⊠ 𝕤̄ ⊠ 🗎 💻

△△△ ▼▼▼ ▼▼ Kimpton Hotel Monaco Seattle ㅐ
(206) 621-1770. **Call for rates.** 1101 4th Ave 98101. Corner of 4th Ave and Spring St. Int corridors. **Pets:** Accepted.
〔SAVE〕 〔ECO〕 〔⫶〕 ⬚ᴹ ⊠ 𝕤̄ ⊠ 🗎 💻

△△△ ▼▼▼ ▼▼ Kimpton Hotel Vintage Seattle ㅐ
(206) 624-8000. **Call for rates.** 1100 5th Ave 98101. Corner of Spring St and 5th Ave. Int corridors. **Pets:** Accepted.
〔SAVE〕 〔ECO〕 ⊖ 〔⫶〕 ⊠ 𝕤̄ ⊠ 🗎 💻

▼▼▼ **La Quinta Inn & Suites Seattle Downtown** 🅷
(206) 624-6820. **$97-$416.** 2224 8th Ave 98121. Corner of 8th Ave and
Blanchard St. Int corridors. **Pets:** Accepted. 🍴 📶 ⊠ 🛎 💻

▼▼▼ **The Maxwell Hotel** 🅷
(206) 286-0629. **Call for rates.** 300 Roy St 98109. Jct 3rd Ave N; just
n of Seattle Center. Int corridors. **Pets:** Accepted.
🍴 ♿ 🏊 📶 ⊠ 🛎 💻

🅰🅰🅰 ▼▼▼ **Motif Seattle** 🅷
(206) 971-8000. **Call for rates.** 1415 5th Ave 98101. Between Pike and
Union sts. Int corridors. **Pets:** Accepted.
SAVE ⊟ 🍴 📶 ⊠ 🛎 💻

🅰🅰🅰 ▼▼▼▼ **Pan Pacific Hotel Seattle** 🅷 ❀
(206) 264-8111. **$225-$585.** 2125 Terry Ave 98121. Just s of jct E
Denny Way. Int corridors. **Pets:** Other species. $50 one-time fee/room.
Designated rooms, supervision. SAVE 🍴 ⊠ 📶 ⊠ 💻

🅰🅰🅰 ▼▼▼ ▼▼▼ **Renaissance Seattle Hotel** 🅷
(206) 583-0300. **$153-$331.** 515 Madison St 98104. Corner of Madison
St and 6th Ave. Int corridors. **Pets:** $50 one-time fee/room. Service with
restrictions, crate. SAVE 🍴 ♿ 📶 ⊠ 🛎 💻

▼▼▼ **Residence Inn by Marriott Seattle Downtown/Lake**
Union 🅷
(206) 624-6000. **$158-$388.** 800 Fairview Ave N 98109. I-5 exit 167
(Mercer St), just nw; south end of Lake Union. Int corridors.
Pets: Accepted. 🍴 ♿ 🏊 📶 ⊠ 🛎 💻

▼▼▼ **Residence Inn by Marriott - Seattle/University**
District 🅷
(206) 322-8887. **$134-$221.** 4501 12th Ave NE 98105. I-5 exit 169, just
e on NE 45th St. **Pets:** $100 one-time fee/room. Service
with restrictions, supervision. 🍴 📶 ⊠ 🛎 💻

🅰🅰🅰 ▼▼▼ **The Roosevelt Hotel** 🅷 ❀
(206) 621-1200. **$185-$425.** 1531 7th Ave 98101. Corner of 7th Ave
and Pine St. Int corridors. **Pets:** Medium, dogs only. $45 one-time fee/
pet. No service. SAVE 🍴 📶 ⊠ 🛎 💻

🅰🅰🅰 ▼▼▼ **Sheraton Seattle Hotel** 🅷
(206) 621-9000. **$169-$500.** 1400 6th Ave 98101. Between Pike and
Union sts. Int corridors. **Pets:** Medium, dogs only. Designated rooms,
supervision. SAVE 🄴🄲🄾 🍴 ♿ 🏊 📶 ⊠ 💻

▼▼▼ **Staybridge Suites - Seattle - Fremont** 🅷
(206) 632-1015. **Call for rates.** 3926 Aurora Ave N 98103. 2 mi n of
downtown; just n of Aurora bridge. Int corridors. **Pets:** Medium, dogs
only. $75 one-time fee/room. Designated rooms, service with restric-
tions, supervision. 🍴 ♿ 📶 ⊠ 🛎 💻

▼▼▼ **Thompson Seattle** 🅷
(206) 623-4600. **Call for rates.** 110 Stewart St 98101. Corner of 1st
Ave and Stewart St. Int corridors. **Pets:** Accepted.
🍴 ♿ 📶 ⊠ 🛎

▼▼ **University Inn** 🅷
(206) 632-5055. **Call for rates.** 4140 Roosevelt Way NE 98105. I-5 exit
169, just e on NE 45th St, then just s. Int corridors. **Pets:** Accepted.
🍴 🏊 📶 ⊠ 🛎 💻

🅰🅰🅰 ▼▼▼ ▼▼▼ **The Westin Seattle** 🅷
(206) 728-1000. **$169-$529.** 1900 5th Ave 98101. Corner of 5th Ave
and Stewart St. Int corridors. **Pets:** Accepted.
SAVE 🄴🄲🄾 🍴 ♿ 🏊 📶 ⊠ 💻

🅰🅰🅰 ▼▼▼ ▼▼▼ **W Seattle** 🅷
(206) 264-6000. **$169-$799.** 1112 4th Ave 98101. Corner of 4th Ave
and Seneca St. Int corridors. **Pets:** Accepted.
SAVE 🄴🄲🄾 ⊟ 🍴 ♿ 📶 ⊠ 🛎 💻

SEQUIM

▼▼▼ **Juan de Fuca Cottages** 🅲🅰
(360) 683-4433. **$120-$350, 14 day notice.** 182 Marine Dr 98382. US
101 exit Sequim Ave, 4.9 mi nw on Sequim/Dungeness Ave, 0.7 mi nw
on E Anderson Rd, then 1.3 mi nw. Ext corridors. **Pets:** Accepted.
🍴 📶 ⊠ 🎿 📷 🛎 💻

▼▼ **Quality Inn & Suites at Olympic National Park** 🅷
(360) 683-2800. **$104-$289.** 134 River Rd 98382. US 101 exit River
Rd, just nw. Int corridors. **Pets:** Accepted.
🄴🄲🄾 ♿ 🏊 📶 ⊠ 🛎 💻

SHELTON

🅰🅰🅰 ▼▼▼ **Little Creek Casino Resort** 🅷
(360) 427-7711. **$59-$299.** 91 W SR 108 98584. Jct US 101 and SR
108. Int corridors. **Pets:** Accepted.
SAVE 🍴 ♿ 🏊 ⊠ 📶 🛎 💻

▼▼ **Super 8 of Shelton** 🄼
(360) 426-1654. **$61-$91.** 2943 Northview Cir 98584. US 101 exit
Wallace-Kneeland Blvd, just se. Int corridors. **Pets:** Accepted.
🍴 📶 🛎 💻

SILVERDALE

🅰🅰🅰 ▼▼▼ **Best Western Plus Silverdale Beach**
Hotel 🅷
(360) 698-1000. **$99-$179.** 3073 NW Bucklin Hill Rd 98383. SR 3 exit
Newberry Hill Rd, just e, 1 mi n on Silverdale Way, then just e. Int corridors. **Pets:** Accepted. SAVE 🍴 🏊 ⊠ 📶 🛎 💻

🅰🅰🅰 ▼▼▼ **Oxford Inn Silverdale** 🅷
(360) 692-7777. **Call for rates.** 9734 NW Silverdale Way 98383. SR 3
exit Newberry Hill Rd, just e, then 1 mi n. Int corridors. **Pets:** Accepted.
SAVE 🍴 ♿ 📶 ⊠ 🛎 💻

🅰🅰🅰 ▼▼▼ **Oxford Suites Silverdale** 🅷
(360) 698-9550. **Call for rates.** 9550 NW Silverdale Way 98383. SR 3
exit Newberry Hill Rd, just e, then 0.9 mi n. Int corridors.
Pets: Accepted. SAVE 🍴 ♿ 🏊 ⊠ 📶 ⊠ 🛎 💻

SNOHOMISH

🅰🅰🅰 ▼▼▼ **Inn At Snohomish** 🄼
(360) 568-2208. **$81-$160.** 323 2nd St 98290. Just e; corner of Pine St.
Ext corridors. **Pets:** Other species. $50 deposit/room. Designated
rooms, service with restrictions, crate. SAVE 🍴 📶 🛎 💻

SNOQUALMIE

▼▼ ▼▼ **Salish Lodge & Spa** 🅷 🐾
(425) 888-2556. **Call for rates.** 6501 Railroad Ave SE 98065. I-90 exit
25 eastbound, 3.6 mi ne on Snoqualmie Pkwy, then 0.4 mi n; exit 31
westbound, 7 mi nw via SR 202. Int corridors. **Pets:** Dogs only. $65
one-time fee/pet. Designated rooms, service with restrictions.
🍴 ⊠ ⊠ 🛎 💻

SOAP LAKE

▼▼ **Notaras Lodge** 🄼
(509) 246-0462. **Call for rates.** 236 E Main Ave 98851. Just w of SR
17. Ext corridors. **Pets:** Accepted. 📶 ⊠ 🛎 💻

▼▼ **Soap Lake Natural Spa & Resort** 🄼
(509) 246-1132. **Call for rates.** 226 E Main Ave 98851. Just w of SR
17. Ext/int corridors. **Pets:** Accepted. 📶 ⊠ 🛎 💻

SPOKANE (Restaurants p. 629)

🅰🅰🅰 ▼▼▼ **Apple Tree Inn** 🄼
(509) 466-3020. **$44-$79.** 9508 N Division St 99218. Jct US 2 and 395,
just n. Ext/int corridors. **Pets:** Small, dogs only. $10 daily fee/pet. Des-
ignated rooms, service with restrictions, supervision.
SAVE 🏊 📶 🛎

Best Western Plus City Center H 🐾
(509) 623-9727. **$96-$190.** 33 W Spokane Falls Blvd 99201. I-90 exit 281 (Division St), 0.5 mi n, then just w. Int corridors. **Pets:** Large, dogs only. $15 daily fee/pet. Designated rooms, service with restrictions.

Best Western Plus Peppertree Airport Inn H
(509) 624-4655. **$99-$299.** 3711 S Geiger Blvd 99224. I-90 exit 276 (Geiger Field), 1.3 mi n, 0.8 mi s, 0.4 mi e, then just s. Int corridors. **Pets:** Accepted.

The Davenport Tower, Autograph Collection H
(509) 455-8888. **$135-$229.** 111 S Post St 99201. Center. Int corridors. **Pets:** Dogs only. $50 one-time fee/pet. Designated rooms, service with restrictions, supervision.

DoubleTree by Hilton Spokane City Center H
(509) 455-9600. **$109-$219.** 322 N Spokane Falls Ct 99201. I-90 exit 281 (Division St), just n; downtown. Int corridors. **Pets:** $25 one-time fee/room. Designated rooms, service with restrictions, crate.

The Historic Davenport Hotel, Autograph Collection H
(509) 455-8888. **$169-$271.** 10 S Post St 99201. Downtown. Int corridors. **Pets:** Dogs only. $50 one-time fee/pet. Designated rooms, service with restrictions, supervision.

Holiday Inn Express-Downtown H 🐾
(509) 328-8505. **$159-$219.** 801 N Division St 99202. I-90 exit 281 (Division St), 0.8 mi n. Ext/int corridors. **Pets:** Other species. Designated rooms, service with restrictions, supervision.

Hotel RL Spokane at the Park H
(509) 326-8000. **Call for rates.** 303 W North River Dr 99201. I-90 exit 281 (Division St), 1.5 mi n on US 195, then just w. Int corridors. **Pets:** Accepted.

The Madison Inn by Riversage H
(509) 474-4200. **Call for rates.** 15 W Rockwood Blvd 99204. I-90 exit 281 (Division St) eastbound, just e to Cowley St, 0.4 mi s, then just w; exit westbound, just n to 2nd Ave, just w to Browne St, 0.5 mi s to 9th Ave, then just e. Int corridors. **Pets:** Accepted.

Oxford Suites-Downtown Spokane H
(509) 353-9000. **Call for rates.** 115 W North River Dr 99201. I-90 exit 281 (Division St), 1 mi n, then just n. Int corridors. **Pets:** Accepted.

Quality Inn Downtown 4th Avenue H
(509) 838-6101. **$89-$248.** 110 E 4th Ave 99202. I-90 exit 281 (Division St), just n to 2nd Ave, just w to Browne St, just s to 4th Ave W, then just e. Int corridors. **Pets:** Accepted.

Quality Inn Oakwood H 🐾
(509) 467-4900. **$89-$365.** 7919 N Division St 99208. I-90 exit 281 (Division St), 6.5 mi n. Int corridors. **Pets:** Medium. $30 one-time fee/room. Designated rooms, service with restrictions, supervision.

Ramada at Spokane Airport H
(509) 838-5211. **$105-$125.** 8909 Airport Dr 99224. I-90 exit 277B eastbound; exit 277 westbound, 3.4 mi n. Int corridors. **Pets:** Medium, dogs only. $10 daily fee/pet. Designated rooms, service with restrictions, supervision.

Ramada North Spokane H
(509) 467-7111. **$95-$230.** 7111 N Division St 99208. I-90 exit 281 (Division St), 4.4 mi n. Int corridors. **Pets:** Accepted.

Red Lion River Inn-Spokane H
(509) 326-5577. **Call for rates.** 700 N Division St 99202. I-90 exit 281 (Division St), 1 mi n; downtown. Int corridors. **Pets:** Accepted.

Super 8 Airport West M
(509) 838-8800. **$70-$84.** 11102 W Westbow Blvd 99224. I-90 exit 272 (Medical Lake Rd), just s. Int corridors. **Pets:** Accepted.

Wingate by Wyndham Spokane Airport H
(509) 838-3226. **$103-$189.** 2726 S Flint Rd 99201. I-90 exit 277B eastbound; exit 277 westbound, 3 mi w, then just s. Int corridors. **Pets:** Large, other species. $10 daily fee/room. Designated rooms, service with restrictions, crate.

SPOKANE VALLEY (Restaurants p. 629)

Comfort Inn & Suites at Spokane Valley H
(509) 926-7432. **$94-$363.** 12415 E Mission Ave 99216. I-90 exit 289 (N Pines Rd), just se. Int corridors. **Pets:** Accepted.

Holiday Inn Express-Valley H
(509) 927-7100. **$119-$209.** 9220 E Mission Ave 99206. I-90 exit 287, just s. Ext/int corridors. **Pets:** Accepted.

La Quinta Inn & Suites Spokane Valley H
(509) 893-0955. **$71-$251.** 3808 N Sullivan Rd 99216. I-90 exit 291B, 1.5 mi n. Int corridors. **Pets:** Accepted.

Mirabeau Park Hotel & Convention Center H
(509) 924-9000. **$95-$159.** 1100 N Sullivan Rd 99037. I-90 exit 291B, just s. Int corridors. **Pets:** Accepted.

My Place Hotel - Spokane Valley H
(509) 228-6105. **Call for rates.** 16106 E Indiana Ave 99216. I-90 exit N Sullivan Rd, just n, then just e. Int corridors. **Pets:** Accepted.

Oxford Suites Spokane Valley H
(509) 847-1000. **Call for rates.** 15015 E Indiana Ave 99216. I-90 exit 291A eastbound; exit 291B westbound, just nw. Int corridors. **Pets:** Accepted.

Quality Inn Valley Suites H
(509) 928-5218. **$89-$200.** 8923 E Mission Ave 99212. I-90 exit 287, just n. Int corridors. **Pets:** Accepted.

Residence Inn by Marriott H
(509) 892-9300. **$128-$194.** 15915 E Indiana Ave 99216. I-90 exit 291 westbound, just e; exit 291B eastbound, just n, then just e. Int corridors. **Pets:** Accepted.

Super 8 M
(509) 928-4888. **$58-$122.** 2020 N Argonne Rd 99212. I-90 exit 287, just n. Int corridors. **Pets:** Other species. $50 deposit/room, $15 one-time fee/room. Service with restrictions, supervision.

STEVENSON

Skamania Lodge H 🐾
(509) 427-7700. **Call for rates.** 1131 SW Skamania Lodge Way 98648. 1 mi w on SR 14, just n on Rock Creek Dr, then just w. Int corridors. **Pets:** Other species. $75 one-time fee/room. Designated rooms, service with restrictions.

SUMNER

▼▼▼ Holiday Inn Express Sumner 🅷
(253) 299-0205. **Call for rates.** 2500 136th Ave Ct E 98390. SR 167 exit 24th St, just se. Int corridors. **Pets:** Accepted.
🍴 ᵫ ⩘ 🛜 ⌧ 🔌 ▣

SUNNYSIDE

◈◈▷ ▼▼▼ Best Western Plus Grapevine Inn 🅷
(509) 839-6070. **$90-$140.** 1849 Quail Ln 98944. I-82 exit 69, just n, then just w. Int corridors. **Pets:** Accepted.
ⓢ ᵫ ⩘ 🛜 ⌧ 🔌 ▣

SUQUAMISH

◈◈▷ ▼▼▼▼ Suquamish Clearwater Casino Resort 🅷
(360) 598-8700. **$109-$289.** 15347 Suquamish Way 98392. SR 3 exit SR 305, 6.2 mi se. Int corridors. **Pets:** Dogs only. $200 deposit/room. Designated rooms, service with restrictions, crate.
ⓢ ☎ 🍴 ᵫ ⩘ ⌧ 🛜 🔌 ▣

TACOMA

◈◈▷ ▼▼▼ Best Western Plus Tacoma Dome Hotel 🅷
(253) 272-7737. **$129-$199.** 2611 East E St 98421. I-5 exit 133 (City Center), follow E 26th St/Tacoma Dome lanes, just n on E 26th St, then just e. Int corridors. **Pets:** Accepted.
ⓢ ☎ 🍴 ᵫ 🛜 ⌧ 🔌 ▣

▼▼▼ Holiday Inn Express & Suites - Tacoma Downtown 🅷
(253) 272-2434. **$129-$139.** 2102 S C St 98402. I-5 exit 133 (City Center) to I-705 N exit S 21st St (SR 509), just w, then just s; downtown. Int corridors. **Pets:** Accepted. 🍴 ᵫ 🛜 ⌧ 🔌 ▣

◈◈▷ ▼▼▼ Hotel Murano 🅷
(253) 238-8000. **$129-$329.** 1320 Broadway Plaza 98402. I-5 exit 133 (City Center) to I-705 N exit A St, just w on 11th St, then just s; downtown. Int corridors. **Pets:** Accepted.
ⓢ ☎ 🍴 🛜 ⌧ 🔌 ▣

▼▼ La Quinta Inn & Suites Tacoma Seattle 🅷
(253) 383-0146. **$86-$253.** 1425 E 27th St 98421. I-5 exit 135 southbound; exit 134 northbound, just n. Int corridors. **Pets:** Accepted.
🍴 ᵫ 🛜 ⌧ 🔌 ▣

▼▼▼ Shilo Inn & Suites - Tacoma 🅷 🐾
(253) 475-4020. **Call for rates.** 7414 S Hosmer St 98408. I-5 exit 129, just se. Int corridors. **Pets:** Dogs only. $75 deposit/room, $15 daily fee/room. Designated rooms, service with restrictions, crate.
🍴 ᵫ ⌧ 🛜 ⌧ 🔌 ▣

TUKWILA

▼▼▼ Embassy Suites by Hilton Hotel 🅷
(425) 227-8844. **$119-$309.** 15920 W Valley Hwy 98188. I-405 exit 1 (SR 181), just s. Int corridors. **Pets:** Accepted.
🍴 ᵫ 🛜 🔌 ▣

▼▼▼ Homewood Suites by Hilton Seattle Airport - Tukwila 🅷
(206) 433-8000. **$129-$319.** 6955 Fort Dent Way 98188. I-405 exit 1 (SR 181), just ne. Ext/int corridors. **Pets:** Accepted.
🍴 ᵫ 🛜 ⌧ 🔌 ▣

▼▼▼ Residence Inn by Marriott-Seattle South 🅷
(425) 226-5500. **$148-$266.** 16201 W Valley Hwy 98188. I-405 exit 1 (SR 181), just s. Ext corridors. **Pets:** Large. $75 one-time fee/room. Service with restrictions. ᵫ ᵫ 🛜 ⌧ 🔌 ▣

TUMWATER

◈◈▷ ▼▼▼ Best Western Tumwater-Olympia Inn 🅷
(360) 956-1235. **$119-$139.** 5188 Capitol Blvd 98501. I-5 exit 102, just e. Int corridors. **Pets:** Large, dogs only. $20 daily fee/room. Designated rooms, service with restrictions, supervision. ⓢ 🛜 ⌧ 🔌 ▣

▼▼▼ Comfort Inn Conference Center 🅷
(360) 352-0691. **$95-$175.** 1620 74th Ave SW 98501. I-5 exit 101, just se. Int corridors. **Pets:** Accepted. 🍴 ᵫ 🛜 ⌧ 🔌 ▣

▼▼▼ Extended Stay America - Olympia/Tumwater 🅷
(360) 754-6063. **$85-$115.** 1675 Mottman Rd SW 98512. I-5 exit 104, 0.6 mi nw on US 101, just s on Crosby Blvd, then just se. Int corridors. **Pets:** Accepted. 🍴 🛜 🔌

▼▼▼ La Quinta Inn & Suites Tumwater/Olympia 🅷
(360) 352-5433. **$101-$240.** 4600 Capitol Blvd SE 98501. I-5 exit 102, just e on Trosper Rd, then 0.4 mi n. Int corridors. **Pets:** Accepted.
🍴 🛜 ⌧ 🔌 ▣

UNION

▼▼▼ Alderbrook Resort & Spa 🅷
(360) 898-2200. **Call for rates.** 7101 E SR 106 98592. Just e of town. Ext/int corridors. **Pets:** Accepted.
☎ 🍴 ᵫ ⌧ 🛜 ⌧ 🔌 ▣

UNION GAP

◈◈▷ ▼▼ Best Western Plus Ahtanum Inn 🅷
(509) 248-9700. **$99-$139.** 2408 Rudkin Rd 98903. I-82 exit 36, just n. Ext/int corridors. **Pets:** Accepted. ⓢ ᵫ 🛜 🔌 ▣

◈◈▷ ▼ Super 8 Yakima 🅷
(509) 248-8880. **$71-$99.** 2605 S Rudkin Rd 98903. I-82 exit 36, just s. Int corridors. **Pets:** $20 daily fee/pet. Designated rooms, service with restrictions, supervision. ⓢ ᵫ 🛜 ⌧ 🔌 ▣

VANCOUVER *(Restaurants p. 629)*

◈◈▷ ▼▼▼▼ Best Western Plus Vancouver Mall Drive Hotel & Suites 🅷
(360) 256-0707. **$109-$229.** 9420 NE Vancouver Mall Dr 98662. I-205 exit 30A northbound, 0.5 mi e on SR 500, just n on NE Gher Rd, then 0.7 mi sw on NE Fourth Plain Blvd; exit 30 (Vancouver Mall Dr) southbound, just ne on NE Fourth Plain Blvd. Int corridors. **Pets:** Accepted.
ⓢ 🍴 ᵫ ⌧ 🛜 ⌧ 🔌 ▣

▼▼▼ Candlewood Suites Vancouver - Camas 🅷
(360) 216-1111. **$119-$289.** 2010 SE 192nd Ave 98683. SR 14 exit 10, 1.5 mi n. Int corridors. **Pets:** Medium, dogs only. $150 one-time fee/room. Designated rooms, service with restrictions, supervision.
🍴 🛜 ⌧ 🔌 ▣

▼▼▼ Comfort Inn & Suites Downtown Vancouver 🅷
(360) 696-0411. **$82-$407.** 401 E 13th St 98660. I-5 exit 1C (E Mill Plain Blvd), just w, just s on C St, then just e. Int corridors. **Pets:** Accepted. ᵫ ᵫ ⌧ 🛜 ⌧ 🔌 ▣

▼▼▼ Comfort Suites 🅷
(360) 253-3100. **$87-$319.** 4714 NE 94th Ave 98662. I-205 exit 30 (SR 500 W), 0.6 mi w to Thurston Way, just n to Vancouver Mall Dr, then 0.5 mi e; southeast edge of Westfield Shopping Center. Int corridors. **Pets:** Accepted. 🍴 ᵫ 🛜 ⌧ 🔌 ▣

◈◈▷ ▼▼▼ DoubleTree by Hilton Vancouver 🅷
(360) 891-9777. **$129-$209.** 12712 SE 2nd Cir 98684. I-205 exit 28 (E Mill Plain Blvd), 0.8 mi e, then just n on SE 126th Ave. Int corridors. **Pets:** Accepted. ⓢ 🍴 ᵫ 🛜 ⌧ 🔌 ▣

Hilton Vancouver Washington H ❖
(360) 993-4500. **$119-$292.** 301 W 6th St 98660. I-5 exit 1C (E Mill Plain Blvd) southbound, 0.3 mi w, then 0.3 mi s on W Columbia St; exit 1B northbound, 0.5 mi sw, follow signs to City Center/6th St. Int corridors. **Pets:** Large. $35 one-time fee/room. Service with restrictions, crate. SAVE ECO ⛽ 🏋 🏊 📶 ✕ 🚪 💻

Homewood Suites by Hilton Vancouver/Portland H
(360) 750-1100. **$129-$179.** 701 SE Columbia Shores Blvd 98661. SR 14 exit 1, just s. Ext/int corridors. **Pets:** Accepted.
🏋 🏊 📶 ✕ 🚪 💻

Quality Inn & Suites H
(360) 696-0516. **$77-$202.** 7001 NE Hwy 99 98665. I-5 exit 4, 0.5 mi se. Int corridors. **Pets:** Other species. $10 daily fee/pet. Service with restrictions, supervision. 🏋 🏊 📶 ✕ 🚪 💻

Quality Inn & Suites H
(360) 574-6000. **$69-$259.** 13207 NE 20th Ave 98686. I-5 exit 7, just e; I-205 exit 36, just w. Int corridors. **Pets:** $10 daily fee/pet. Designated rooms, service with restrictions, supervision.
🏋 🏊 📶 ✕ 🚪 💻

Residence Inn by Marriott Portland North/Vancouver H
(360) 253-4800. **$119-$208.** 8005 NE Parkway Dr 98662. I-205 exit 30 (SR 500 W), 0.5 mi w to Thurston Way, just n to NE Parkway Dr, then just w. Ext corridors. **Pets:** Other species. $75 one-time fee/room. Service with restrictions. 🏋 🏊 📶 ✕ 🚪 💻

Shilo Inn & Suites-Salmon Creek H ❖
(360) 573-0511. **Call for rates.** 13206 Hwy 99 98686. I-5 exit 7, just e; I-205 exit 36, just w. Int corridors. **Pets:** Dogs only. $75 deposit/room, $15 daily fee/room. Designated rooms, service with restrictions, crate.
🏊 ✕ 📶 ✕ 🚪 💻

Staybridge Suites Vancouver-Portland Metro Area H
(360) 891-8282. **Call for rates.** 7301 NE 41st St 98662. I-205 exit 30 (SR 500 W), 1.5 mi w to NE Andresen Rd, just n to NE 40th St, just e to NE 72nd St, just n to NE 41st St, then just e. Int corridors.
Pets: Accepted. 🏋 🏋 🏊 📶 ✕ 🚪 💻

TownePlace Suites by Marriott Portland Vancouver H
(360) 260-9000. **$123-$189.** 17717 SE Mill Plain Blvd 98683. SR 14 exit 8, 1.7 mi n on SE 164th Ave, then 0.5 mi e. Int corridors.
Pets: Accepted. 🏋 🏋 📶 ✕ 🚪 💻

VASHON

The Swallow's Nest Guest Cottages CA ❖
(206) 463-2646. **$125-$390, 160 day notice.** 6030 SW 248th St 98070. North end Ferry Landing, 7.8 mi s on Vashon Hwy; south end (Tahlequah) Ferry Landing, 5.8 mi n on Vashon Hwy, 1.4 mi e on Quartermaster Dr, 1.5 mi s on Dockton Rd, 0.4 mi s on 75th Ave, then 1 mi e. Ext corridors. **Pets:** Other species. $20 daily fee/pet. Designated rooms, service with restrictions, supervision. 🏋 📶 ✕ 🏋 🚪 💻

WALLA WALLA

Best Western Plus Walla Walla Suites Inn H
(509) 525-4700. **$89-$125.** 7 E Oak St 99362. US 12 exit 2nd Ave, just s. Int corridors. **Pets:** Dogs only. $10 daily fee/pet. Service with restrictions. SAVE 🏋 🏊 📶 ✕ 🚪 💻

Holiday Inn Express H
(509) 525-6200. **Call for rates.** 1433 W Pine St 99362. US 12 exit Pendleton/Prescott. Int corridors. **Pets:** Accepted.
SAVE 🏋 🏊 📶 ✕ 🚪 💻

Marcus Whitman Hotel & Conference Center H
(509) 525-2200. **Call for rates.** 6 W Rose St 99362. At N 2nd Ave and W Rose St; downtown. Int corridors. **Pets:** Accepted.
SAVE 🏋 🏋 📶 ✕ 🚪 💻

Quality Inn & Suites H
(509) 525-2522. **$74-$199.** 520 N 2nd Ave 99362. US 12 exit 2nd Ave, 0.3 mi s. Int corridors. **Pets:** Accepted. 🏊 📶 ✕ 🚪 💻

WENATCHEE

Coast Wenatchee Center Hotel H ❖
(509) 662-1234. **$93-$205.** 201 N Wenatchee Ave 98801. Jct 2nd St; downtown. Int corridors. **Pets:** Designated rooms, service with restrictions, supervision. 🏋 🏋 🏊 📶 ✕ 🚪 💻

Holiday Inn Express H
(509) 663-6355. **Call for rates.** 1921 N Wenatchee Ave 98801. Northwest side of town. Int corridors. **Pets:** Accepted.
🏋 🏊 📶 ✕ 🚪 💻

La Quinta Inn & Suites Wenatchee H
(509) 664-6565. **$70-$268.** 1905 N Wenatchee Ave 98801. Northwest side of town. Int corridors. **Pets:** Accepted. 🏊 📶 ✕ 🚪 💻

Red Lion Hotel Wenatchee H
(509) 663-0711. **$99-$299.** 1225 N Wenatchee Ave 98801. Just nw of downtown. Int corridors. **Pets:** Accepted. 🏋 🏊 📶 ✕ 🚪 💻

Super 8 Wenatchee H
(509) 662-3443. **$55-$160.** 1401 N Miller St 98801. 1.5 mi n on US 2. Int corridors. **Pets:** Small, dogs only. $50 deposit/room, $20 daily fee/pet. Designated rooms, service with restrictions, supervision.
SAVE 🏊 📶 ✕ 🚪 💻

WESTPORT

Chateau Westport Resort H
(360) 268-9101. **Call for rates.** 710 W Hancock St 98595. Just w of SR 105 Spur N; 1.5 mi n of Twin Harbors State Park. Int corridors.
Pets: Accepted. 🏋 🏊 ✕ 📶 ✕ 🏋 🚪 💻

WINTHROP

River Run Inn M
(509) 996-2173. **Call for rates.** 27 Rader Rd 98862. 0.5 mi w on SR 20. Ext corridors. **Pets:** Other species. $15 daily fee/pet. Designated rooms, service with restrictions, supervision.
🏋 🏋 🏊 📶 ✕ 🚪 💻

Winthrop Inn M ❖
(509) 996-2217. **$89-$165, 7 day notice.** 960 Hwy 20 98862. 0.9 mi e. Int corridors. **Pets:** Dogs only. $15 daily fee/pet. Designated rooms, service with restrictions, supervision. SAVE 🏋 🏊 📶 ✕ 🚪

WOODINVILLE

Willows Lodge H
(425) 424-3900. **Call for rates.** 14580 NE 145th St 98072. I-405 exit 20B (NE 124th St), 0.7 mi e, 1.2 mi n on 132nd Ave NE, 0.6 mi e on NE 143rd Pl, then just e. Int corridors. **Pets:** Accepted.
🌐 🏋 ✕ 📶 ✕ 🚪 💻

WOODLAND

Best Western Woodland Inn H
(360) 225-1000. **$90-$160.** 1380 Atlantic Ave 98674. I-5 exit 21, just ne. Int corridors. **Pets:** Large, dogs only. $15 daily fee/pet. Designated rooms, service with restrictions, supervision.
SAVE 🏋 🏊 📶 🚪 💻

Lewis River Inn M ❖
(360) 225-6257. **$100-$140.** 1100 Lewis River Rd 98674. I-5 exit 21, just e. Ext corridors. **Pets:** Dogs only. Designated rooms, service with restrictions, supervision. 🏋 📶 🚪 💻

YAMIKA

AAA ♦♦ **Best Western Plus Yakima Hotel** 🅷
(509) 453-8898. **$109-$119.** 1614 N 1st St 98901. I-82 exit 31, just s.
Int corridors. **Pets:** Dogs only. $15 daily fee/room. Designated rooms,
service with restrictions, crate.

[SAVE] [🍽] [&M] [➔] [☎] [✕] [📶] [💻]

AAA ♦♦♦ **Fairfield Inn & Suites by Marriott**
Yakima 🅷
(509) 452-3100. **$107-$166.** 137 N Fair Ave 98901. I-82 exit 33A eastbound, 0.4 mi w to N 10th St, then just ne; exit 33 westbound, 0.6 mi
w to N 9th St, then just ne. Int corridors. **Pets:** Accepted.

[SAVE] [&M] [➔] [☎] [✕] [📶] [💻]

WW ♦♦♦ **Holiday Inn Downtown Yakima** 🅷
(509) 494-7000. **$139-$209, 7 day notice.** 802 E Yakima Ave 98901.
I-82 exit 33 westbound; exit 33B eastbound, 0.8 mi w. Int corridors.
Pets: Accepted. [🍽] [&M] [➔] [☎] [✕] [📶] [💻]

AAA ♦♦♦ **Oxford Inn Yakima** 🅷
(509) 457-4444. **Call for rates.** 1603 E Yakima Ave 98901. I-82 exit 33
westbound, just e; exit 33B eastbound. Int corridors. **Pets:** Accepted.
[SAVE] [➔] [☎] [📶] [💻]

AAA ♦♦♦ **Oxford Suites Yakima** 🅷
(509) 457-9000. **Call for rates.** 1701 E Yakima Ave 98901. I-82 exit 33
westbound; exit 33B eastbound. Int corridors. **Pets:** Accepted.
[SAVE] [🍽] [&M] [➔] [☎] [✕] [📶] [💻]

WEST VIRGINIA

BARBOURSVILLE

WW ♦♦ **Barboursville Holiday Inn & Suites** 🅷
(304) 733-3338. **$109-$139.** 3551 Rt 60 E 25504. I-64 exit 20, just s.
Int corridors. **Pets:** Accepted. [🍽] [☎] [✕] [📶] [💻]

AAA ♦♦♦ **Best Western Huntington Mall Inn** 🅼
(304) 736-9772. **$90-$140.** 3441 US 60 E 25504. I-64 exit 20A eastbound; exit 20 westbound, 0.3 mi s. Int corridors. **Pets:** Other species.
$15 one-time fee/room. Service with restrictions.
[SAVE] [➔] [☎] [📶] [💻]

WW ♦♦ **Comfort Inn by Choice Hotels** 🅷
(304) 733-2122. **$95-$140.** 249 Mall Rd 25504. I-64 exit 20, 0.4 mi n.
Int corridors. **Pets:** Accepted. [🍽] [&M] [➔] [☎] [✕] [📶] [💻]

BECKLEY

WW ♦♦ **Country Inn & Suites By Carlson** 🅷
(304) 252-5100. **$99-$199, 7 day notice.** 2120 Harper Rd 25801.
I-64/77 exit 44, just w on SR 3. Int corridors. **Pets:** Accepted.
[&M] [➔] [✕] [☎] [📶] [💻]

WW ♦♦ **Econo Lodge** 🅼
(304) 255-2161. **$55-$89.** 1909 Harper Rd 25801. I-64/77 exit 44, 0.3
mi e on SR 3. Ext/int corridors. **Pets:** Accepted. [☎] [📶] [💻]

AAA ♦♦♦ **Fairfield Inn & Suites by Marriott** 🅷
(304) 252-8661. **$73-$160.** 125 Hylton Ln 25801. I-64/77 exit 44, just e.
Int corridors. **Pets:** Large. $30 one-time fee/room. Designated rooms,
service with restrictions, supervision. [SAVE] [➔] [☎] [✕] [📶] [💻]

WW ♦♦ **Travelodge** 🅼
(304) 252-0671. **$53-$80.** 1939 Harper Rd 25801. I-64/77 exit 44, just e
on SR 3. Ext/int corridors. **Pets:** Other species. $10 daily fee/pet. Ser-
vice with restrictions, crate. [☎] [💻]

BERKELEY SPRINGS

AAA ♦♦♦ **Best Western Berkeley Springs Inn** 🅼
(304) 258-9400. **$85-$94.** 1776 Valley Rd 25411. 1.1 mi s on US 522.
Int corridors. **Pets:** Medium. $20 daily fee/room. Designated rooms,
service with restrictions, crate. [SAVE] [🍽] [➔] [☎] [✕] [📶] [💻]

BRADLEY

AAA ♦♦ **Days Inn** 🅼
(304) 877-6455. **$69-$100.** 127 Ontario Dr 25880. I-64/77 exit 48, 1 mi
ne on US 19. Int corridors. **Pets:** Small. $15 one-time fee/pet. Supervi-
sion. [SAVE] [➔] [☎] [📶] [💻]

BRIDGEPORT

AAA ♦♦♦ **Best Western Plus Bridgeport Inn** 🅷
(304) 842-5411. **$90-$100.** 100 Lodgeville Rd 26330. I-79 exit 119, just
e on US 50. Int corridors. **Pets:** Accepted.
[SAVE] [🍽] [➔] [☎] [📶] [💻]

WWW ♦♦♦ **Hawthorn Suites by Wyndham** 🅷
(304) 848-8700. **$100-$129.** 75 Southview Dr 26330. I-79 exit 124, just
w. Int corridors. **Pets:** Medium. $100 one-time fee/pet. Service with
restrictions, supervision. [🍽] [&M] [☎] [✕] [📶] [💻]

WWW ♦♦♦ **TownePlace Suites by Marriott-Bridgeport**
Clarksburg 🅷
(304) 842-3600. **$81-$224.** 101 Platinum Dr 26330. I-79 exit 119, just w
on US 50. Int corridors. **Pets:** Accepted. [➔] [☎] [✕] [📶] [💻]

BRUCETON MILLS

WW ♦♦ **Microtel Inn & Suites by Wyndham**
Hazelton 🅼 ❀
(304) 379-7900. **$74-$129.** 886 Casteel Rd 26525. I-68 exit 29 (Hazelton), just n. Int corridors. **Pets:** Other species. $15 daily fee/pet. Desig-
nated rooms, service with restrictions, crate. [🍽] [☎] [✕] [📶] [💻]

BUCKHANNON

WW ♦♦ **Microtel Inn & Suites by Wyndham,**
Buckhannon 🅷
(304) 460-2525. **$91-$134.** 2 Northridge Dr 26201. US 19, just n. Int
corridors. **Pets:** Accepted. [☎] [✕] [📶] [💻]

CHARLESTON

AAA ♦♦♦ **Charleston Residence Inn by Marriott** 🅷
(304) 345-4200. **$107-$252.** 200 Hotel Cir 25311. I-64/77 exit 99, just e.
Int corridors. **Pets:** Medium. $100 one-time fee/room.
[SAVE] [🍽] [➔] [☎] [✕] [📶] [💻]

WWW ♦♦♦ **Country Inn & Suites By Carlson South** 🅷
(304) 925-4300. **Call for rates.** 105 Alex Ln 25304. I-77 exit 95, just s
on SR 61. Int corridors. **Pets:** Dogs only. $25 deposit/pet. Designated
rooms, service with restrictions, crate. [🍽] [➔] [☎] [✕] [📶] [💻]

WWW ♦♦♦ **Motel 6 Charleston** 🅷
(304) 345-9779. **$60-$109.** 1010 Washington St E 25301. I-64/77 exit
100, 0.3 mi w. Int corridors. **Pets:** Accepted. [➔] [☎] [📶] [💻]

AAA ♦♦♦ **Red Roof Inn Charleston-Kanawha City,**
WV 🅼
(304) 925-6953. **$54-$89.** 6305 SE MacCorkle Ave 25304. I-77 exit 95,
just s on SR 61. Ext corridors. **Pets:** Accepted. [SAVE] [☎] [✕] [📶]

CHESTER

▼▼▼ **Mountaineer Casino Racetrack & Resort** 🅗
(304) 387-8000. **Call for rates.** 1420 Mountaineer Circle (Rt 2) 26034. On SR 2, 6 mi s. Int corridors. **Pets:** Accepted.
🍴 ⬛ ➿ ✕ 🛜 📞 💻

COMFORT

▼▼ **Oak Tree Inn** 🅜
(304) 837-3377. **Call for rates.** 129 Deanna Ave 25049. 1 mi s on SR 3; entrance at V-Mart. Int corridors. **Pets:** Accepted.
🛜 ✕ 📞 💻

CROSS LANES

▼▼ **Comfort Inn Charleston West** 🅜
(304) 776-8070. **$94-$269.** 102 Racer Dr 25313. I-64 exit 47, just s. Int corridors. **Pets:** Accepted. 🍴 ➿ 🛜 ✕ 📞 💻

DANIELS

🅐🅐🅐 ▼▼▼ **The Resort at Glade Springs** 🅗
(304) 763-2000. **$89-$199, 7 day notice.** 255 Resort Dr 25832. I-64 exit 125, 1.5 mi w on SR 307, then 2.8 mi w on US 19. Ext/int corridors. **Pets:** Accepted. 🆂🅰🆅🅴 🍴 ➿ ✕ 🛜 📞 💻

DAVIS

▼▼▼ **Black Bear Resort** 🅒🅐
(304) 866-4391. **$110-$275, 14 day notice.** 247 Lodge Dr 26260. 4.5 mi s on SR 32. Ext corridors. **Pets:** Accepted.
➿ ✕ 🛜 ✕ 📞 💻

EDRAY

🅐🅐🅐 ▼▼▼ **Marlinton Motor Inn** 🅜
(304) 799-4711. **Call for rates.** 21507 Seneca Tr N 24954. Center. Ext corridors. **Pets:** Accepted. 🆂🅰🆅🅴 🍴 ➿ 🛜 📞 💻

FAIRMONT

▼▼ **Clarion Inn Fairmont** 🅗
(304) 366-5500. **$65-$140.** 930 E Grafton Rd 26554. I-79 exit 137, just e. Int corridors. **Pets:** Accepted. 🍴 ⬛ ➿ 🛜 ✕ 📞 💻

▼▼ **Days Inn Fairmont** 🅜
(304) 366-5995. **$64-$99.** 166 Middletown Rd 26554. I-79 exit 132, just se on US 250, then just s. Ext/int corridors. **Pets:** Accepted.
🛜 📞 💻

▼▼ **Super 8** 🅜
(304) 363-1488. **$72-$119.** 2208 Pleasant Valley Rd 26554. I-79 exit 133, just e. Int corridors. **Pets:** $10 deposit/pet. Service with restrictions, crate. 🛜 📞 💻

FALLING WATERS

▼▼▼ **Quality Inn Spring Mills-Martinsburg North** 🅗
(304) 274-6100. **$79-$109.** 1220 TJ Jackson Dr 25419. I-81 exit 20, just w. Int corridors. **Pets:** Other species. $20 one-time fee/pet. Designated rooms, service with restrictions, supervision.
🍴 ➿ 🛜 ✕ 📞 💻

FROST

▼▼▼ **The Inn at Mountain Quest** 🅒🅘
(304) 799-7267. **Call for rates.** 303 Mountain Quest Ln 24954. On SR 92, 0.4 mi n. Ext corridors. **Pets:** Accepted. 🍴 ✕ 🛜 ✕

GASSAWAY

▼▼ **Microtel Inn & Suites by Wyndham Gassaway/Sutton** 🅜
(304) 364-6100. **$59-$80.** 115 Reston Pl 26624. I-79 exit 62, just w. Int corridors. **Pets:** Dogs only. $20 daily fee/pet. Designated rooms, service with restrictions, crate. 🍴 🛜 ✕ 📞 💻

HARPERS FERRY

▼▼ **Clarion Hotel** 🅗
(304) 535-6302. **$104-$209.** 4328 William L Wilson Frwy 25425. Just w on US 340. Int corridors. **Pets:** Medium, dogs only. $50 one-time fee/room. Designated rooms, service with restrictions, crate.
🍴 ➿ 🛜 ✕ 📞 💻

HUNTINGTON

▼▼▼ **Holiday Inn Hotel & Suites** 🅗
(304) 523-8880. **Call for rates.** 800 3rd Ave 25701. I-64 exit 11, 3 mi n on SR 10, then 0.9 mi w; downtown. Int corridors. **Pets:** Medium. $25 daily fee/pet. Designated rooms, service with restrictions, supervision.
🍴 ⬛ ➿ 🛜 ✕ 📞 💻

🅐🅐🅐 ▼▼◆ **Red Roof Inn Huntington** 🅗
(304) 733-3737. **$60-$90.** 5190 US Rt 60 E 25705. I-64 exit 15, just s. Ext corridors. **Pets:** Accepted. 🆂🅰🆅🅴 🛜 ✕ 📞

▼◆▼ **Super 8** 🅗
(304) 525-1410. **$88-$120.** 3090 16th Street Rd 25701. I-64 exit 11, just n. Int corridors. **Pets:** Accepted. ➿ ✕ 🛜 📞 💻

▼◆▼ **TownePlace Suites by Marriott Huntington** 🅗
(304) 525-4877. **$69-$406.** 157 Kinetic Dr 25701. I-64 exit 11, just n. Int corridors. **Pets:** Accepted. ➿ 🛜 ✕ 📞 💻

HURRICANE

🅐🅐🅐 ▼◆◆ **Red Roof Inn Charleston West-Hurricane, WV** 🅗
(304) 757-6392. **$58-$90.** 500 Putnam Village Dr 25526. I-64 exit 39, just n on SR 34, then just e. Ext corridors. **Pets:** Accepted.
🆂🅰🆅🅴 🛜 ✕ 📞 💻

KEYSER

🅐🅐🅐 ▼▼ **Keyser Inn** 🅜
(304) 788-0913. **$64-$87.** 51 Josie Dr 26726. On US 220, 2.3 mi s. Int corridors. **Pets:** Small. $25 one-time fee/room. Designated rooms, service with restrictions, supervision. 🆂🅰🆅🅴 🛜 ✕ 📞 💻

◆▼ **Microtel Inn & Suites by Wyndham Keyser** 🅗
(304) 597-1400. **$90-$140, 3 day notice.** 70 N Tornado Way 26726. On US 220, 2.1 mi s. Int corridors. **Pets:** Accepted. 🛜 ✕ 📞 💻

LEWISBURG

▼▼▼ **Lewisburg Holiday Inn Express Hotel & Suites** 🅗
(304) 645-5750. **Call for rates.** 222 Hunter Ln 24901. I-64 exit 169, just s. Int corridors. **Pets:** Accepted. ➿ 🛜 ✕ 📞 💻

🅐🅐🅐 ▼▼▼ **Quality Inn Lewisburg Conference Center** 🅗
(304) 645-7722. **$75-$176.** 540 N Jefferson St 24901. I-64 exit 169, just s on US 219. Ext corridors. **Pets:** Medium. $50 daily fee/pet. Designated rooms, service with restrictions, supervision.
🆂🅰🆅🅴 🍴 ➿ 🛜 ✕ 📞 💻

▼▼ **Super 8** 🅜
(304) 647-3188. **$68-$145.** 550 N Jefferson St 24901. I-64 exit 169, just s on US 219. Int corridors. **Pets:** Other species. $11 daily fee/pet. Designated rooms, service with restrictions, supervision.
🛜 ✕ 📞 💻

MARTINSBURG

▼▼▼ **Holiday Inn Martinsburg** 🅗
(304) 267-5500. **$109-$169.** 301 Foxcroft Ave 25401. I-81 exit 13, just e on W King St (CR 15). Int corridors. **Pets:** Accepted.
🍴 ➿ 🛜 ✕ 📞 💻

◆ Knights Inn-Martinsburg ⓜ
(304) 267-2211. $60-$65. 1997 Edwin Miller Blvd 25404. I-81 exit 16E, 0.4 mi e on SR 9. Ext corridors. Pets: Accepted. 🛜 ⊠ 🛏

MINERAL WELLS
◆◆◆ Comfort Suites Parkersburg South Ⓗ ☙
(304) 489-9600. $89-$234. 167 Elizabeth Pike 26150. I-77 exit 170, 0.3 mi se. Ext/int corridors. Pets: Other species. $20 daily fee/pet. Designated rooms, service with restrictions, crate.
🍴 ⌇ 🛜 ⊠ 🛏 💻

◆◆◆ Holiday Inn Express Hotel & Suites Parkersburg/
   Mineral Wells Ⓗ
(304) 489-4111. Call for rates. 80 Old Nicholette Rd 26150. I-77 exit 170, just w. Int corridors. Pets: Accepted.
🚹ᴹ ⌇ 🛜 ⊠ 🛏 💻

MORGANTOWN
◆◆ Microtel Inn & Suites by Wyndham,
   Morgantown Ⓗ
(304) 292-0055. $80-$220. 15 Lawless Rd 26505. I-79 exit 152, just w. Int corridors. Pets: Accepted. 🛜 ⊠ 🛏 💻

◆◆ Quality Inn-Morgantown ⓜ
(304) 296-9364. $84-$249. 225 Comfort Inn Dr 26508. I-68 exit 1, 0.3 mi n on US 119. Int corridors. Pets: Large, other species. $25 daily fee/pet. Designated rooms, service with restrictions.
🍴 🚹ᴹ ⌇ 🛜 ⊠ 🛏 💻

⚑ ◆◆◆ Residence Inn by Marriott
   Morgantown Ⓗ
(304) 599-0237. $94-$395. 1046 Willowdale Rd 26505. I-79 exit 155, 2 mi s on US 19, then 0.9 mi e on SR 705. Int corridors. Pets: Accepted.
ⓢᴀᴠᴇ 🍴 ⌇ 🛜 ⊠ 🛏 💻

◆◆ Super 8 Morgantown Ⓗ
(304) 296-4000. $61-$295. 603 Venture Dr 26508. I-68 exit 7, just n. Int corridors. Pets: Accepted. 🛜 ⊠ 🛏 💻

OAK HILL
⚑ ◆◆◆ Holiday Lodge Hotel and Conference
   Center Ⓗ ☙
(304) 465-0571. $69-$159. 340 Oyler Ave 25901. US 19 exit Oyler Ave, just w. Int corridors. Pets: Medium, dogs only. $25 daily fee/room. Designated rooms, service with restrictions, supervision.
ⓢᴀᴠᴇ 🍴 🚹ᴹ ⌇ 🏊 🛜 ⊠ 🛏 💻

PARKERSBURG
◆◆◆ The Blennerhassett Ⓗ ☙
(304) 422-3131. $123-$246. 320 Market St 26101. Between 4th and 5th sts; downtown. Int corridors. Pets: Dogs only. $50 one-time fee/room. Designated rooms, crate. 🍴 🛜 ⊠ 🛏 💻

◆◆◆ Hampton Inn & Suites Ⓗ ☙
(304) 428-0555. Call for rates. 920 Emerson Ave 26104. I-77 exit 179, 4.1 mi w on SR 68. Int corridors. Pets: Other species. Service with restrictions, crate. 🍴 🚹ᴹ 🛜 ⊠ 🛏 💻

⚑ ◆◆ Red Roof Inn Parkersburg ⓜ
(304) 485-1741. $48-$89. 3714 E 7th St 26104. I-77 exit 176, just w on US 50. Ext corridors. Pets: Accepted. ⓢᴀᴠᴇ 🛜 ⊠ 🛏 💻

PHILIPPI
⚑ ◆ Mountaineer Inn ⓜ
(304) 457-5888. $65-$125. 14928 Barbour County Hwy 26416. 2.5 mi s on US 250. Int corridors. Pets: Small, dogs only. $20 daily fee/pet. Service with restrictions, supervision. ⓢᴀᴠᴇ 🛜 🛏

PRINCETON
⚑ ◆◆ Days Inn ⓜ
(304) 425-8100. $65-$170, 3 day notice. 347 Meadowfield Ln 24740. I-77 exit 9, 0.3 mi w on US 460, just s on Ambrose Ln, then just e. Ext corridors. Pets: Accepted. ⓢᴀᴠᴇ ⌇ 🛜 🛏 💻

⚑ ◆◆◆ Holiday Inn Express Princeton Ⓗ
(304) 425-8156. $105-$180. 805 Oakvale Rd 24740. I-77 exit 9, just w. Int corridors. Pets: Accepted. ⓢᴀᴠᴇ ⌇ 🛜 ⊠ 🛏 💻

◆◆ Quality Inn ⓜ
(304) 487-6101. $65-$105. 136 Ambrose Ln 24740. I-77 exit 9, 0.3 mi w on US 460. Int corridors. Pets: Accepted. 🛜 🛏 💻

◆◆ Sleep Inn & Suites Ⓗ
(304) 431-2800. $94-$121. 1015 Oakvale Rd 24740. I-77 exit 9, just w on US 460, then just n via service road. Int corridors. Pets: Accepted.
⌇ 🛜 🛏 💻

RIPLEY
◆◆◆ Holiday Inn Express & Suites Ripley Ⓗ
(304) 372-4444. $135-$250, 3 day notice. 110 Memorial Dr 25271. I-77 exit 138, e on US 33, then s on New Stone Ridge Rd. Int corridors. Pets: $25 daily fee/pet. Service with restrictions, supervision.
🚹ᴹ ⌇ 🛜 ⊠ 🛏 💻

◆ Ripley Super 8 ⓜ
(304) 372-8880. $64-$69. 102 Duke Dr 25271. I-77 exit 138, just e on US 33. Int corridors. Pets: Accepted. 🛜 🛏 💻

ROANOKE
⚑ ◆◆◆◆ Stonewall Resort Ⓗ
(304) 269-7400. $159-$299, 3 day notice. 940 Resort Dr 26447. I-79 exit 91, just e. Int corridors. Pets: Accepted.
ⓢᴀᴠᴇ 🍴 🚹ᴹ ⌇ 🏊 🛜 ⊠ 🛏 💻

SHEPHERDSTOWN
◆◆ Quality Inn Shepherdstown ⓜ
(304) 876-3160. $88-$120. 70 Maddex Square Dr 25443. Just w on SR 45; center. Int corridors. Pets: Accepted. 🛜 🛏 💻

SOUTH CHARLESTON
⚑ ◆◆◆ Holiday Inn & Suites Charleston
   West Ⓗ ☙
(304) 744-4641. $109-$179. 400 2nd Ave SW 25303. I-64 exit 56, just nw. Int corridors. Pets: Other species. $25 daily fee/pet. Service with restrictions, crate. ⓢᴀᴠᴇ 🍴 ⌇ 🛜 🛏 💻

SUMMERSVILLE
◆◆ Econo Lodge Ⓗ
(304) 872-6900. $65-$80. 1203 S Broad St 26651. US 19 and Broad St; 0.6 mi s of jct SR 39. Ext corridors. Pets: Other species. $10 daily fee/pet. Designated rooms, service with restrictions, supervision.
🛜 ⊠ 🛏 💻

◆◆◆ Hampton Inn Ⓗ
(304) 872-7100. $110-$140. 5400 Webster Rd 26651. Just s on SR 41 from US 19. Int corridors. Pets: Accepted.
🚹ᴹ ⌇ 🛜 ⊠ 🛏 💻

◆◆◆ La Quinta Inn & Suites Ⓗ
(304) 872-0555. $86-$204. 106 Merchants Walk 26651. US 19, just w. Int corridors. Pets: Accepted. ⌇ 🛜 ⊠ 🛏 💻

⚑ ◆◆◆ Quality Inn ⓜ
(304) 872-6500. $59-$100. 903 Industrial Dr N 26651. US 19, 1.9 mi n of jct SR 39. Int corridors. Pets: Other species. $10 daily fee/pet. Designated rooms, service with restrictions, supervision.
ⓢᴀᴠᴇ ⌇ 🏊 🛜 ⊠ 🛏 💻

▼▼▼ Sleep Inn of Summersville [M]
(304) 872-4500. $70-$145. 701 Professional Park Dr 26651. US 19, 1.7 mi n of jct SR 39. Int corridors. Pets: Other species. $10 daily fee/pet. Designated rooms, service with restrictions, supervision.
[SAVE] [icons]

▼ Super 8-Summersville [M]
(304) 872-4888. $65-$90. 306 Merchants Walk 26651. US 19, just n. Int corridors. Pets: Other species. $15 one-time fee/pet. [icons]

TRIADELPHIA
▼▼▼ Comfort Inn & Suites-Wheeling [H]
(304) 547-0610. $75-$150. 675 Fort Henry Rd 26059. I-70 exit 11, just n. Int corridors. Pets: Accepted. [icons]

▼▼▼ Hawthorn Suites by Wyndham [H]
(304) 218-2500. $109-$149. 20 Bob Wise Dr 26059. I-70 exit 10 (Cabela Dr), just w. Int corridors. Pets: Accepted.
[icons]

▼▼ Suburban Extended Stay [H] 🐾
(304) 547-1037. $59-$129. 40 Robinson Dr 26059. I-70 exit 10 (Cabela Dr), just w. Int corridors. Pets: Other species. Service with restrictions.
[icons]

VIENNA
▼▼▼ Wingate by Wyndham [H]
(304) 295-5501. $115-$149. 1502 Grand Central Ave 26105. I-77 exit 179, 3.9 mi w on SR 68. Int corridors. Pets: Accepted.
[icons]

WEIRTON
▼▼▼ Holiday Inn [H]
(304) 723-5522. $109-$199. 350 Three Springs Dr 26062. 4.5 mi e on US 22 exit Three Springs Dr. Int corridors. Pets: $25 daily fee/pet. Service with restrictions, supervision. [icons]

WESTON
▼▼▼ Holiday Inn Express Hotel & Suites [H]
(304) 269-3550. Call for rates. 215 Staunton Dr 26452. I-79 exit 99, just e. Int corridors. Pets: Large. $25 daily fee/pet. Service with restrictions, crate. [icons]

▼▼▼ Quality Inn [H]
(304) 269-7000. $93-$109. 2906 US Hwy 33 E 26452. I-79 exit 99, just e. Ext corridors. Pets: Medium. $15 daily fee/pet. Designated rooms, service with restrictions, supervision. [SAVE] [icons]

▼▼ Weston Super 8 [H]
(304) 269-1086. $67-$83. 100 Market Place Mall, Suite 12 26452. I-79 exit 99, just e. Int corridors. Pets: Accepted. [icons]

WHITE HALL
▼▼▼ Red Roof Inn Fairmont [H]
(304) 366-6800. $65-$110. 42 Spencer Dr 26554. I-79 exit 132, 0.3 mi s on US 250, just w, then just s. Ext corridors. Pets: Accepted.
[SAVE] [icons]

WISCONSIN

ADAMS
▼▼ Adams Inn Hotel [H]
(608) 339-6088. Call for rates. 2188 SR 13 53910. Just s of town. Int corridors. Pets: Accepted. [icons]

ALGOMA
▼ Scenic Shore Inn [M]
(920) 487-3214. $65-$79, 3 day notice. 2221 Lake St 54201. Jct SR 54, 0.8 mi s on SR 42. Ext corridors. Pets: Medium, dogs only. $5 daily fee/pet. Designated rooms, service with restrictions, supervision.
[icons]

ANTIGO
▼▼▼ Holiday Inn Express & Suites Antigo [H]
(715) 627-7500. Call for rates. 2407 Neva Rd 54409. Just ne of jct SR 64 E and US 45. Int corridors. Pets: Accepted.
[icons]

▼▼ Super 8-Antigo [M]
(715) 623-4188. $74-$100. 535 Century Ave 54409. On US 45, at jct SR 64 E. Int corridors. Pets: Accepted. [icons]

APPLETON (Restaurants p. 629)
▼▼ Candlewood Suites [H]
(920) 739-8000. Call for rates. 4525 W College Ave 54914. US 41 exit 137 (SR 125), just w. Int corridors. Pets: Accepted.
[icons]

▼▼ Country Inn & Suites By Carlson [H]
(920) 830-3240. Call for rates. 355 Fox River Dr 54913. US 41 exit 137 (SR 125), just nw. Int corridors. Pets: Accepted.
[icons]

▼▼ Extended Stay America-Appleton-Fox Cities [H]
(920) 830-9596. $65-$125. 4141 Boardwalk Ct 54915. US 41 exit 137 (SR 125), just w on College Ave, then just s on Nicolet Rd. Int corridors. Pets: Accepted. [icons]

▼▼ La Quinta Inn & Suites Appleton College Avenue [H]
(920) 734-7777. $93-$334. 3800 W College Ave 54914. US 41 exit 137 (SR 125), just e. Int corridors. Pets: Accepted.
[icons]

▼▼▼ Residence Inn by Marriott [H]
(920) 954-0570. $94-$428. 310 Metro Dr 54913. US 41 exit 137 (SR 125), just nw on Mall Dr. Int corridors. Pets: Accepted.
[icons]

ARKDALE
▼▼▼ Northern Bay Resort [CO]
(608) 339-2090. $95-$403, 30 day notice. 1844 20th Ave 54613. 2.9 mi w on SR 21, 3 mi s on CR Z, 0.9 mi w on Czech Ave, then 0.4 mi se. Int corridors. Pets: Accepted. [icons]

BALDWIN
▼▼ AmericInn Lodge & Suites of Baldwin [H]
(715) 684-5888. Call for rates. 500 Baldwin Plaza Dr 54002. I-94 exit 19 (US 63), just ne. Int corridors. Pets: Medium, dogs only. $15 daily fee/pet. Designated rooms, service with restrictions, crate.
[icons]

BEAVER DAM
▼▼ Super 8 [H]
(920) 887-8880. $64-$96. 711 Park Ave 53916. US 151 exit 132 (SR 33), just w. Int corridors. Pets: Accepted. [icons]

BELOIT

▼▼▼▼ Fairfield Inn & Suites by Marriott H
(608) 365-2200. **$85-$224.** 2784 Milwaukee Rd 53511. I-90 exit 185A, just sw; at I-43 and SR 81. Int corridors. **Pets:** Other species. $20 daily fee/pet. Service with restrictions, crate. 🔥M 🛏 🛜 ✖ 🍴 💻

▲▲▲ ▼▼▼▼ Ironworks Hotel H
(608) 362-5500. **$149-$309.** 500 Pleasant St 53511. Downtown. Int corridors. **Pets:** Dogs only. $20 daily fee/pet. Service with restrictions, crate. 🅢🅐🅥🅔 🍴 🔥M 🛜 ✖ 🍴 💻

▼▼ Quality Inn H
(608) 362-2666. **$80-$190.** 2786 Milwaukee Rd 53511. I-90 exit 185A, just w; at I-43 and SR 81. Int corridors. **Pets:** Accepted.
🛏 🛜 ✖ 🍴 💻

▼▼ Rodeway Inn M
(608) 364-4000. **$62-$80.** 2956 Milwaukee Rd 53511. I-90 exit 185A, 0.3 mi w. Ext/int corridors. **Pets:** Accepted. 🍴 🛜 ✖ 🍴 💻

BERLIN

▼▼ Magnuson Countryside Lodge M
(920) 361-4411. **Call for rates.** 227 Ripon Rd 54923. On SR 49; at CR F. Int corridors. **Pets:** Accepted. 🛜 ✖ 🍴 💻

BIRCHWOOD

▼▼ Cobblestone Bed & Breakfast BB
(715) 354-3494. **$119-$185, 8 day notice.** 319 S Main St 54817. Just s of SR 48; center. Int corridors. **Pets:** Accepted. 🛜 ✖ 🐾

BLACK RIVER FALLS

▲▲▲ ▼▼▼ Best Western Arrowhead Lodge & Suites H
(715) 284-9471. **$60-$110.** 600 Oasis Rd 54616. I-94 exit 116 (SR 54), just ne. Int corridors. **Pets:** Other species. $20 daily fee/room. Designated rooms, service with restrictions, supervision.
🅢🅐🅥🅔 🍴 🛏 🛜 ✖ 🍴 💻

▼▼▼▼ Comfort Inn & Suites H
(715) 284-0888. **$70-$204.** W10170 Hwy 54 E 54615. I-94 exit 116 (SR 54), just nw. Int corridors. **Pets:** Accepted.
🍴 🛏 🛜 ✖ 🍴 💻

▼▼ Days Inn H
(715) 284-4333. **$60-$140.** 919 Hwy 54 E 54615. I-94 exit 116 (SR 54), just w. Int corridors. **Pets:** Other species. $15 daily fee/room. Designated rooms, service with restrictions, supervision.
🛏 🛜 ✖ 🍴 💻

BROOKFIELD

▲▲▲ ▼▼▼▼ Country Inn & Suites By Carlson, Milwaukee-West H
(262) 782-1400. **Call for rates.** 1250 S Moorland Rd 53005. I-94 exit 301A (Moorland Rd), just se. Int corridors. **Pets:** Accepted.
🅢🅐🅥🅔 🍴 🔥M 🛏 🛜 ✖ 🍴 💻

▼▼▼▼ Extended Stay America-Milwaukee/Brookfield H
(262) 782-9300. **$75-$140.** 325 N Brookfield Rd 53045. I-94 exit 297, 1.1 mi e on US 18, then just e. Int corridors. **Pets:** Accepted.
🛜 ✖ 🍴

▼▼▼ La Quinta Inn Milwaukee West-Brookfield H
(262) 782-9100. **$67-$185.** 20391 W Bluemound Rd 53045. I-94 exit 297, just e on US 18. Int corridors. **Pets:** Other species. Service with restrictions. 🛜 ✖ 🍴 💻

▲▲▲ ▼▼▼ Quality Inn-Milwaukee/Brookfield H ❀
(262) 785-0500. **$70-$150.** 20150 W Bluemound Rd 53045. I-94 exit 297, just e on US 18. Ext/int corridors. **Pets:** Other species. $10 daily fee/pet. Designated rooms, service with restrictions, crate.
🅢🅐🅥🅔 🛏 🛜 ✖ 🍴 💻

▲▲▲ ▼▼▼▼ Residence Inn by Marriott Milwaukee-Brookfield H
(262) 782-5990. **$98-$244.** 950 S Pinehurst Ct 53005. I-94 exit 301A (Moorland Rd), just s. Ext corridors. **Pets:** $100 one-time fee/room. Service with restrictions, crate. 🅢🅐🅥🅔 🛏 🛜 ✖ 🍴 💻

▲▲▲ ▼▼▼▼ Sheraton Milwaukee Brookfield H
(262) 364-1100. **$89-$249.** 375 S Moorland Rd 53005. I-94 exit 301B (Moorland Rd), just n. Int corridors. **Pets:** Accepted.
🅢🅐🅥🅔 🍴 🔥M 🛏 🛜 ✖ 🍴 💻

▲▲▲ ▼▼▼▼ TownePlace Suites by Marriott Brookfield H
(262) 784-8450. **$109-$240.** 600 N Calhoun Rd 53005. I-94 exit 297 eastbound, 2.1 mi e on US 18; exit 301B (Moorland Rd) westbound, 1.5 mi n, then 0.4 mi w on US 18. Int corridors. **Pets:** Accepted.
🅢🅐🅥🅔 🔥M 🛏 🛜 ✖ 🍴 💻

BROWN DEER

▼▼ Candlewood Suites Milwaukee North H
(414) 355-3939. **Call for rates.** 4483 W Schroeder Dr 53223. Just nw of jct SR 100 and 57. Int corridors. **Pets:** Accepted.
🔥M 🛜 ✖ 🍴 💻

BURLINGTON

▼▼ AmericInn Lodge & Suites Burlington H
(262) 534-2125. **$80-$200.** 2709 Browns Lake Dr 53105. 3 mi n on SR 36 and 83; jct CR W. Int corridors. **Pets:** Medium, dogs only. $25 daily fee/pet. Designated rooms, service with restrictions, supervision.
🍴 🛏 🛜 ✖ 🍴 💻

CADOTT

▼▼ Countryside Motel M
(715) 289-4000. **$70-$130.** 545 Lavorata Rd 54727. SR 29 exit 91 (SR 27), just s. Int corridors. **Pets:** Small, dogs only. $10 daily fee/pet. Designated rooms, service with restrictions, supervision. 🛜 ✖

CHIPPEWA FALLS

▼▼ AmericInn Hotel & Suites of Chippewa Falls H
(715) 723-5711. **Call for rates.** 11 W South Ave 54729. 2 mi s on SR 124. Int corridors. **Pets:** Dogs only. $10 daily fee/room. Designated rooms, service with restrictions, supervision.
🍴 🔥M 🛏 🛜 ✖ 🍴 💻

CLINTONVILLE

▼▼ Cobblestone Inn & Suites H
(715) 823-2000. **Call for rates.** 175 Waupaca St 54929. Jct US 45 and CR C. Int corridors. **Pets:** Other species. $25 one-time fee/room. Service with restrictions, supervision. 🔥M 🛜 ✖ 🍴 💻

COLUMBUS

▼▼ Super 8-Columbus H
(920) 623-8800. **$68-$130.** 219 Industrial Dr 53925. US 151 exit 118 (SR 16/60), just ne. Int corridors. **Pets:** Accepted.
🔥M 🛏 🛜 ✖ 🍴 💻

CRANDON

▲▲▲ ▼▼▼▼ Best Western Crandon Inn & Suites H
(715) 478-4000. **$100-$130.** 9075 E Pioneer St 54520. 0.5 mi e on US 8 and SR 32. Int corridors. **Pets:** Medium. $20 one-time fee/room, $5 daily fee/room. Designated rooms, service with restrictions, supervision.
🅢🅐🅥🅔 🍴 🔥M 🛏 ✖ 🛜 ✖ 🍴 💻

DE FOREST

▼▼ Comfort Inn & Suites H
(608) 846-9100. **$79-$209.** 5025 County Rd V 53532. I-90/94 exit 126 (CR V), just w. Int corridors. **Pets:** Accepted.
🔥M 🛏 🛜 ✖ 🍴 💻

▼▼▼ Holiday Inn Express 🄷
(608) 846-8686. **$114-$224.** 7184 Morrisonville Rd 53532. I-90/94 exit 126 (CR V), just e. Int corridors. **Pets:** Accepted.
🄴🄲🄾 🛗 🛏 🛜 ✕ 🔌 💻

DELAFIELD *(Restaurants p. 629)*

▼▼▼ Americlnn of Delafield 🄷
(262) 646-3300. **Call for rates.** 2412 Milwaukee St 53018. I-94 exit 287, just nw on Golf Rd. Int corridors. **Pets:** Accepted.
🛜 ✕ 🔌 💻

🄰🄰🄰 ▼▼▼▼▼ The Delafield Hotel 🄷 🐾
(262) 646-1600. **$179-$249.** 415 Genesee St 53018. I-94 exit 285, 0.4 mi n on CR C (Genesee St). Int corridors. **Pets:** Other species. $35 one-time fee/pet. Service with restrictions, supervision.
🅂🄰🅅🄴 🍽 🛜 ✕ 🔌 💻

▼▼ La Quinta Inn & Suites Milwaukee Delafield 🄷
(262) 395-1162. **$71-$312.** 2801 Hillside Dr 53018. I-94 exit 287, just s on SR 83, then just e. Int corridors. **Pets:** Accepted.
🛏 🛜 ✕ 🔌 💻

DE PERE

▼▼▼ Kress Inn, an Ascend Hotel Collection Member 🄷
(920) 403-5100. **$99-$899.** 300 Grant St 54115. US 41 exit 163 (Main Ave), 1 mi e, then just s on 3rd St. Int corridors. **Pets:** Accepted.
🛜 ✕ 🔌 💻

DODGEVILLE

🄰🄰🄰 ▼▼▼ Best Western Quiet House & Suites 🄷
(608) 935-7739. **$99-$300.** 1130 N Johns St 53533. On US 18, just e of jct SR 23. Int corridors. **Pets:** Accepted.
🅂🄰🅅🄴 🛏 🛜 ✕ 🔌 💻

▼▼ Super 8 of Dodgeville 🄷
(608) 935-3888. **$60-$85, 3 day notice.** 1308 Johns St 53533. Just n of US 18. Int corridors. **Pets:** Dogs only. $50 deposit/pet. Supervision.
🄴🄲🄾 🛗 🛜 ✕ 🔌 💻

EAU CLAIRE

▼▼▼ Americlnn Hotel & Suites of Eau Claire 🄷 🐾
(715) 874-4900. **Call for rates.** 6200 Texaco Dr 54703. I-94 exit 59, just n on US 12. Int corridors. **Pets:** Dogs only. $20 daily fee/pet. Designated rooms, service with restrictions. 🛗 🛏 🛜 ✕ 🔌 💻

🄰🄰🄰 ▼▼▼▼▼ Best Western Plus Eau Claire Conference Center 🄷
(715) 838-9989. **$100-$120.** 3340 Mondov Rd 54701. I-94 exit 65, just n. Int corridors. **Pets:** $20 daily fee/room. Designated rooms, service with restrictions, supervision.
🅂🄰🅅🄴 🍽 🛗 🛏 ✕ 🛜 🔌 💻

▼▼▼ Clarion Hotel Campus Area 🄷 🐾
(715) 835-2211. **$89-$169.** 2703 Craig Rd 54701. I-94 exit 65, 1.3 mi n on SR 37; just w of jct US 12. Int corridors. **Pets:** Medium. $15 daily fee/room. Service with restrictions, supervision.
🍽 🛗 🛏 🛜 ✕ 🔌 💻

▼▼ Econo Lodge 🄷
(715) 833-8818. **$70-$200.** 4608 Royal Dr 54701. I-94 exit 68, just n on SR 93, just w on Golf Rd, then just s. Int corridors. **Pets:** Accepted.
🍽 🛗 🛜 ✕ 🔌 💻

▼▼ Quality Inn & Suites 🄷
(715) 833-9798. **$75-$204.** 3117 Craig Rd 54701. I-94 exit 65, 0.8 mi n on SR 37; just s of jct US 12. Int corridors. **Pets:** Accepted.
🛗 🛏 🛜 ✕ 🔌 💻

▼▼ Sleep Inn & Suites Conference Center 🄷
(715) 874-2900. **$64-$214.** 5872 N 33rd Ave 54703. SR 29 exit 69 (CR T), just sw. Int corridors. **Pets:** Other species. $15 daily fee/room. Designated rooms, service with restrictions, crate.
🍽 🛗 🛏 ✕ 🛜 ✕ 🔌 💻

EGG HARBOR

🄰🄰🄰 ▼▼▼ The Shallows Resort 🄼
(920) 868-3458. **$85-$450, 30 day notice.** 7353 Horseshoe Bay Rd 54209. On CR G, 2.5 mi s. Ext corridors. **Pets:** Medium, dogs only. $20 daily fee/pet. Service with restrictions, supervision.
🅂🄰🅅🄴 🍽 🛏 ✕ 🛜 ✕ 🔌 💻

ELKHORN

▼▼ Americlnn Lodge & Suites of Elkhorn 🄷
(262) 723-7799. **Call for rates.** 210 E Commerce Ct 53121. I-43 exit 25, just s. Int corridors. **Pets:** Accepted.
🍽 🛗 🛏 🛜 ✕ 🔌 💻

FISH CREEK

▼▼ Julie's Park Cafe & Motel 🄼
(920) 868-2999. **Call for rates.** 4020 Hwy 42 54212. On SR 42, 0.3 mi n. Ext corridors. **Pets:** Accepted. 🍽 🛜 ✕ 🔌 💻

FITCHBURG

▼▼▼ Candlewood Suites 🄷 🐾
(608) 271-3400. **Call for rates.** 5421 Caddis Bend 53711. US 12/18 exit 260A (Fish Hatchery/CR D), 1.5 mi s. Int corridors. **Pets:** Medium. $25 daily fee/pet. Service with restrictions.
🛗 🛏 🛜 ✕ 🔌 💻

▼▼▼ Wyndham Garden 🄷
(608) 274-7200. **$104-$180.** 2969 Cahill Main 53711. US 12/18 exit 260A (Fish Hatchery/CR D), 1.5 mi s at CR PD (McKee Rd). Int corridors. **Pets:** Accepted. 🍽 🛗 🛏 🛜 ✕ 🔌 💻

FOND DU LAC

▼▼ Comfort Inn by Choice Hotels Fond du Lac 🄷
(920) 921-4000. **$89-$349.** 77 Holiday Ln 54937. US 41 exit 97 (Military Rd), just sw. Int corridors. **Pets:** Accepted.
🛏 ✕ 🛜 ✕ 🔌 💻

▼▼ Holiday Inn Fond du Lac 🄷
(920) 923-1440. **$109-$419.** 625 W Rolling Meadows Dr 54937. US 41 exit 97 (Military Rd), just sw. Int corridors. **Pets:** Designated rooms, service with restrictions, supervision.
🄴🄲🄾 🍽 🛏 ✕ 🛜 ✕ 🔌 💻

▼▼ Super 8-FOND DU LAC 🄷
(920) 922-1088. **$55-$225, 3 day notice.** 391 N Pioneer Rd 54935. US 41 exit 99 (SR 23/Johnson St), just n on east frontage road (CR VV). Int corridors. **Pets:** Accepted. 🛜 ✕ 🔌 💻

FORT ATKINSON

▼▼▼ Holiday Inn Express Hotel & Suites 🄷
(920) 563-3600. **$124-$229.** 1680 Madison Ave 53538. Jct SR 26 Bypass and US 12. Int corridors. **Pets:** Medium. $30 one-time fee/room. Designated rooms, service with restrictions, crate.
🛗 🛏 ✕ 🛜 ✕ 🔌 💻

FRANKLIN

🄰🄰🄰 ▼▼▼ Staybridge Suites Milwaukee Airport South 🄷 🐾
(414) 761-3800. **$99-$199.** 9575 S 27th St 53132. I-94 exit 322 (Ryan Rd), 0.6 mi w; jct 27th St. Int corridors. **Pets:** Medium, dogs only. $7 daily fee/pet. Service with restrictions, supervision.
🅂🄰🅅🄴 🄴🄲🄾 🍽 🛗 🛏 🛜 ✕ 🔌 💻

GERMANTOWN

▼▼▼ **Holiday Inn Express Milwaukee NW-Germantown** 🅗

(262) 255-1100. **Call for rates.** W177 N9675 Riversbend Ln 53022. US 41 and 45 exit CR Q (County Line Rd), just w. Int corridors. **Pets:** Accepted. 🅛🖘🖿⊠🔔🖲

🔺 ▼▼▼ **Super 8-Germantown/Milwaukee** 🅗

(262) 255-0880. **$69-$85.** N96 W17490 County Line Rd 53022. US 41 and 45 exit CR Q (County Line Rd), just w. Int corridors. **Pets:** Dogs only. $10 daily fee/pet. Service with restrictions, supervision. 🅢🖘🖘⊠🔔🖲

GLENDALE

▼▼▼ **La Quinta Inn & Suites Milwaukee Bayshore Area** 🅗

(414) 962-6767. **$82-$235.** 5423 N Port Washington Rd 53217. I-43 exit 78A (Silver Spring Dr), just se. Int corridors. **Pets:** Accepted. 🅛🖘🖘⊠🔔🖲

▼▼▼ **La Quinta Inn Milwaukee Glendale Hampton Ave** 🅗

(414) 964-8484. **$67-$185.** 5110 N Port Washington Rd 53217. I-43 exit 78A (Silver Spring Dr), 0.4 mi se. Int corridors. **Pets:** Accepted. 🖘⊠🔔🖲

GRAFTON

🔺 ▼▼▼ **Comfort Inn & Suites Milwaukee-Grafton** 🅗

(262) 387-1180. **$84-$229.** 1415 N Port Washington Rd 53024. I-43 exit 92 (SR 60), just w, then just s. Int corridors. **Pets:** Medium. $20 daily fee/pet. Designated rooms, service with restrictions, crate. 🅢🍴🅛🖘🖘⊠🔔🖲

GREEN BAY

🔺 ▼▼▼ **Aloft Green Bay** 🅗

(920) 884-0800. **$99-$499.** 465 Pilgrim Way 54304. US 41 exit 163B, just e. Int corridors. **Pets:** Accepted. 🅢🔲🍴🅛🖘🖘⊠🔔🖲

🔺 ▼▼▼ **AmericInn Lodge & Suites Green Bay East** 🅗

(920) 964-0177. **$80-$160.** 2628 Manitowoc Rd 54311. I-43 exit 181, just w. Int corridors. **Pets:** Dogs only. $20 one-time fee/pet. Designated rooms, service with restrictions, supervision. 🅢🅛🖘🖘⊠🔔🖲

▼▼▼ **AmericInn Lodge of Green Bay West** 🅗

(920) 434-9790. **Call for rates.** 2032 Velp Ave 54303. US 41 exit 170, 0.3 mi w. Int corridors. **Pets:** $15 daily fee/pet. Designated rooms, service with restrictions, supervision. 🖘🖘⊠🔔🖲

▼▼ **Baymont Inn & Suites-Green Bay** 🅗

(920) 494-7887. **$59-$395.** 2840 S Oneida St 54304. US 41 exit 164 (Oneida St), just e. Int corridors. **Pets:** Accepted. 🖘⊠🔔🖲

🔺 ▼ **Bay Motel** 🅜

(920) 494-3441. **$55-$79.** 1301 S Military Ave 54304. US 41 exit 167 (Lombardi Ave), 0.4 mi e to Marlee Ln, then 0.6 mi n. Ext corridors. **Pets:** Accepted. 🅢🍴🖘⊠🔔🖲

🔺 ▼▼▼ **Best Western Green Bay Inn Conference Center** 🅗

(920) 499-3161. **$89-$425.** 780 Armed Forces Dr 54304. US 41 exit 167 (Lombardi Ave), 1.4 mi e to Holmgren Way, then just s. Int corridors. **Pets:** Small, dogs only. $25 daily fee/pet. Designated rooms, service with restrictions, supervision. 🅢🍴🖘🖘⊠🔔🖲

▼▼▼ **Country Inn & Suites By Carlson Green Bay North** 🅗

(920) 884-2000. **Call for rates.** 2308 Lineville Rd 54313. US 41 exit Lineville Rd, 1 mi w. Int corridors. **Pets:** Accepted. 🅛🖘⊠🔔🖲

▼▼ **Country Inn & Suites By Carlson Green Bay-Stadium District** 🅗

(920) 336-6600. **$129-$189, 3 day notice.** 2945 Allied St 54304. US 41 exit 164 (Oneida St), just nw. Int corridors. **Pets:** Medium, other species. $15 daily fee/room. Designated rooms, service with restrictions, supervision. 🍴🅛🖘🖘⊠🔔🖲

▼▼ **Extended Stay Airport** 🅗

(920) 499-3600. **Call for rates.** 1639 Commanche Ave 54313. US 41 exit 165, 1 mi w on SR 172, then just s. Int corridors. **Pets:** Accepted. 🖘⊠🔔🖲

▼▼ **Hawthorn Suites by Wyndham Green Bay** 🅗

(920) 435-2222. **$69-$299.** 335 W St. Joseph St 54301. SR 172 exit Riverside Dr, 1.1 mi n on SR 57, then just e. Ext corridors. **Pets:** Other species. $150 one-time fee/room. Service with restrictions. 🖘🖘⊠🔔🖲

🔺 ▼▼▼ **Hyatt Regency Green Bay** 🅗

(920) 432-1234. **$85-$399.** 333 Main St 54301. Between Adams and Madison sts; downtown. Int corridors. **Pets:** Accepted. 🅢🍴🅛🖘⊠🖘⊠🔔🖲

▼▼ **Microtel Inn & Suites by Wyndham Green Bay** 🅗

(920) 338-9000. **$70-$570.** 3031 Allied St 54304. US 41, exit 164 (Oneida St), just sw. Int corridors. **Pets:** Accepted. 🖘🖘⊠🔔🖲

▼▼ **Quality Inn & Suites Downtown** 🅗

(920) 437-8771. **$69-$339.** 321 S Washington St 54301-4214. On east side of Fox River, just s of Walnut St (SR 29); downtown. Int corridors. **Pets:** Medium. $20 one-time fee/room. Designated rooms, service with restrictions, crate. 🖘⊠🖘⊠🔔🖲

▼▼ **Super 8-Airport Stadium** 🅗

(920) 494-2042. **$68-$345.** 2868 S Oneida St 54304. US 41 exit 164 (Oneida St), just e. Int corridors. **Pets:** Accepted. 🖘⊠🔔🖲

HAYWARD

▼▼ **AmericInn of Hayward** 🅗

(715) 634-2700. **$89-$295.** 15601 US Hwy 63 N 54843. Just n of jct SR 77. Int corridors. **Pets:** Medium, dogs only. $10 daily fee/pet. Designated rooms, service with restrictions, supervision. 🅛🖘🖘⊠🔔🖲

▼▼▼ **Comfort Suites** 🅗

(715) 634-0700. **$119-$290.** 15586 CR B 54843. 0.5 mi s of jct SR 27. Int corridors. **Pets:** Accepted. 🅛🖘⊠🖘⊠🔔🖲

🔺 ▼▼ **The Flat Creek Inn & Suites** 🅗

(715) 634-4100. **$89-$165.** 10290 Hwy 27 S 54843. 0.7 mi s of jct US 63. Int corridors. **Pets:** Dogs only. $15 daily fee/room. Service with restrictions, crate. 🅢🍴🅛🖘🖘⊠🔔🖲

HILLSBORO

🔺 ▼▼ **Hotel Hillsboro** 🅗

(608) 489-3000. **$80-$133.** 1235 Water Ave (SR 33) 54634. Jct SR 80/82 and 33, just n. Int corridors. **Pets:** Large. $15 one-time fee/room. Designated rooms, service with restrictions. 🅢🍴🅛🖘🖘⊠🔔🖲

HUDSON

▼▼▼ **Comfort Suites** 🅗

(715) 690-2500. **$100-$180.** 2620 Center Dr 54016. I-94 exit 2 (CR F), just se. Int corridors. **Pets:** Accepted. 🅛🖘⊠🔔🖲

▼▼ Quality Inn **H**

(715) 386-6355. **$85-$130.** 811 Dominion Dr 54016. I-94 exit 2 (CR F), 1 mi w on south frontage road (Crest View Dr). Int corridors. **Pets:** Accepted. 🍴 🛜 ✕ 🖥 💻

HURLEY

▼▼ Days Inn of Hurley **H**

(715) 561-3500. **$79-$140.** 13355 N US Hwy 51 54534. On US 51, 0.4 mi s of jct US 2. Int corridors. **Pets:** Accepted.

🍴 🛜 ✕ 🖥 💻

JACKSON

▼▼ Comfort Inn & Suites of Jackson **H**

(262) 677-1133. **$94-$184.** W227 N 16890 Tillie Lake Ct 53037. US 41 exit 64 (SR 60), 2.9 mi e; jct US 45. Int corridors. **Pets:** Accepted.

🍴 ♿ 🛜 ✕ 🖥 💻

JANESVILLE

▼▼ Econo Lodge-Janesville **H**

(608) 754-0251. **$63-$149.** 3520 Milton Ave 53545. I-90 exit 171A, just sw via Frontage Rd. Int corridors. **Pets:** Accepted.

♿ 🛜 ✕ 🖥 💻

JOHNSON CREEK

▼▼ Comfort Suites by Choice Hotels-Johnson Creek **H**

(920) 699-2800. **$90-$175.** 725 Paradise Ln 53038. I-94 exit 267 (SR 26), 1.4 mi n, 1.6 mi w on River Dr, 0.8 mi s on CR Y, then just w. Int corridors. **Pets:** Dogs only. $15 daily fee/pet. Service with restrictions, crate. 🍴 ♿ 🛜 ✕ 🖥 💻

KENOSHA

▼▼ Candlewood Suites **H**

(262) 842-5000. **Call for rates.** 10200 74th St 53142. SR 50 exit 104th Ave, just n. Int corridors. **Pets:** Accepted. ♿ 🛜 ✕ 🖥 💻

▼▼▼ Comfort Inn & Suites by Choice Hotels **H**

(262) 857-3450. **$90-$199.** 7206 122nd Ave 53142. I-94 exit 344 (SR 50), just nw. Int corridors. **Pets:** Accepted.

♿ 🛜 ✕ 🖥 💻

AAA ▼▼▼ Wyndham Garden - Kenosha Harborside **H**

(262) 658-3281. **$119-$169.** 5125 6th Ave 53140. Just ne of jct SR 32 and 158; downtown. Int corridors. **Pets:** Accepted.

SAVE ♿ 🛜 ✕ 🖥 💻

KOHLER

AAA ▼▼▼ Inn on Woodlake **H** 🐾

(920) 452-7800. **$109-$299, 7 day notice.** 705 Woodlake Rd 53044. I-43 exit 126, 0.5 mi w on SR 23, 0.5 mi s on CR Y and Highland Dr; in Woodlake Shopping Center. Int corridors. **Pets:** Medium, dogs only. $100 one-time fee/room. Designated rooms, service with restrictions, supervision. SAVE 🛜 ✕ 🖥 💻

LA CROSSE

AAA ▼▼▼ AmericInn Hotel & Conference Center La Crosse Riverfront **H**

(608) 781-7000. **$110-$230.** 1835 Rose St 54603. I-90 exit 3, 1 mi s on US 53. Int corridors. **Pets:** Accepted.

SAVE 🍴 ♿ 🛜 ✕ 🖥 💻

AAA ▼▼▼▼ The Charmant Hotel **H**

(608) 519-8800. **$139-$439.** 101 State St 54601. Jct 2nd St N, just w; downtown. Int corridors. **Pets:** Accepted. SAVE 🍴 ♿ 🛜 ✕ 🖥

▼▼ GrandStay Hotel & Suites La Crosse **H**

(608) 796-1615. **$100-$270.** 525 Front St N 54601. I-90 exit 3; downtown. Int corridors. **Pets:** Medium. $200 deposit/room, $20 daily fee/pet. Service with restrictions. ♿ 🛜 ✕ 🛜 ✕ 🖥 💻

▼▼ Holiday Inn Hotel & Suites **H**

(608) 784-4444. **Call for rates.** 200 Pearl St 54601. Downtown. Int corridors. **Pets:** Accepted. 🍴 ♿ 🛜 🛜 ✕ 🖥 💻

▼▼ Home2 Suites by Hilton **H**

(608) 881-6666. **$109-$209.** 210 Jay St 54601. Between King and Cass sts; downtown. Int corridors. **Pets:** Accepted.

🍴 ♿ 🛜 ✕ 🖥 💻

▼▼ Radisson Hotel La Crosse **H**

(608) 784-6680. **$129-$399.** 200 Harborview Plaza 54601. Just w of US 53; downtown. Int corridors. **Pets:** Accepted.

🍴 ♿ 🛜 🛜 ✕ 🖥 💻

▼▼ Settle Inn **H**

(608) 781-5100. **Call for rates.** 2110 Rose St 54603. I-90 exit 3, 0.9 mi s on US 53. Int corridors. **Pets:** Small, dogs only. $15 daily fee/pet. Designated rooms, service with restrictions, supervision.

♿ 🛜 ✕ 🖥 💻

LAKE GENEVA

AAA ▼▼ ▼▼ Grand Geneva Resort & Spa **H** 🐾

(262) 248-8811. **$139-$449, 3 day notice.** 7036 Grand Geneva Way 53147. On SR 50, just e of jct US 12. Int corridors. **Pets:** Small, dogs only. $65 daily fee/pet. Designated rooms, service with restrictions.

SAVE ECO 🍴 ♿ 🛜 ✕ 🖥 💻

LAND O'LAKES

▼▼ Sunrise Lodge **CA** 🐾

(715) 547-3684. **Call for rates.** 5894 W Shore Dr 54540. 2 mi s on US 45, 2.8 mi e on CR E, then 1 mi n. Ext corridors. **Pets:** Other species. Service with restrictions. 🍴 ✕ 🛜 ✕ 🖥 💻

LODI

▼▼ Quality Inn & Suites **H**

(608) 592-1450. **$75-$204.** W 9250 Prospect Dr 53555. I-90/94 exit 119, just w. Int corridors. **Pets:** Accepted.

🍴 ♿ 🛜 ✕ 🖥 💻

MADISON

▼▼▼ AmericInn Madison West **H**

(608) 662-1990. **Call for rates.** 516 Grand Canyon Dr 53719. US 12 and 14 exit 255 (Gammon Rd), just n, then 0.5 mi e on Odana Rd. Int corridors. **Pets:** $30 daily fee/pet. Designated rooms, service with restrictions, supervision. ♿ 🛜 🛜 ✕ 🖥 💻

▼▼ Baymont Inn & Suites Madison West **H**

(608) 831-7711. **$75-$450.** 8102 Excelsior Dr 53717. US 12 and 14 exit 253 (Old Sauk Rd), just w, then 0.4 mi n. Int corridors. **Pets:** Accepted. ♿ ✕ 🛜 ✕ 🖥 💻

AAA ▼▼▼ Best Western East Towne Suites **H**

(608) 244-2020. **$89-$159.** 4801 Annamark Dr 53704. I-90/94 exit 135A (US 151) southbound; exit 135C (US 151/High Crossing Blvd) northbound, just sw. Int corridors. **Pets:** Other species. $20 daily fee/pet. Service with restrictions, crate. SAVE ♿ 🛜 🛜 ✕ 🖥 💻

AAA ▼▼▼ Best Western West Towne Suites **H** 🐾

(608) 833-4200. **$100-$200.** 650 Grand Canyon Dr 53719. US 12 and 14 exit 255 (Gammon Rd), just e on Odana Rd, then just sw. Int corridors. **Pets:** Medium. $50 deposit/room, $20 daily fee/room. Designated rooms, service with restrictions, supervision.

SAVE 🍴 ♿ 🛜 ✕ 🖥 💻

▼▼▼ **Clarion Suites at the Alliant Energy Center** H ❀

(608) 284-1234. **$89-$339.** 2110 Rimrock Rd 53713. US 12 and 18 exit 262 (Rimrock Rd), just nw. Int corridors. **Pets:** $25 deposit/pet. Designated rooms, service with restrictions, crate.

⦗❜⦘⦗♿M⦘⦗➥⦘⦗🛜⦘⦗✕⦘⦗🛏⦘⦗💻⦘

▼▼▼ **Comfort Inn of Madison Downtown** H

(608) 255-7400. **$84-$305.** 722 John Nolen Dr 53713. US 12 and 18 exit 263 (John Nolen Dr), just n. Int corridors. **Pets:** Accepted.

⦗♿M⦘⦗➥⦘⦗🛜⦘⦗✕⦘⦗🛏⦘⦗💻⦘

▼▼▼ **Comfort Suites-Madison** H

(608) 836-3033. **$95-$289.** 1253 John Q Hammons Dr 53717. US 12 and 14 exit 252 (Greenway Blvd), just sw. Int corridors. **Pets:** Accepted.

⦗ECO⦘⦗♿M⦘⦗➥⦘⦗✕⦘⦗🛜⦘⦗✕⦘⦗🛏⦘⦗💻⦘

ⓐⓐⓐ ▼▼ **Days Inn & Suites** H 🐾

(608) 223-1800. **$72-$150.** 4402 E Broadway Service Rd 53716. US 12 and 18 exit 266 (US 51), just ne. Int corridors. **Pets:** Large. $50 deposit/room, $20 daily fee/room. Designated rooms, service with restrictions, supervision. ⦗SAVE⦘⦗ECO⦘⦗♿M⦘⦗➥⦘⦗🛜⦘⦗✕⦘⦗🛏⦘⦗💻⦘

ⓐⓐⓐ ▼▼▼ **Econo Lodge of Madison** H

(608) 241-4171. **$59-$200.** 4726 E Washington Ave 53704. I-90/94 exit 135A (US 151), just w. Int corridors. **Pets:** Small. $10 daily fee/pet. Designated rooms, service with restrictions, supervision.

⦗SAVE⦘⦗♿M⦘⦗🛜⦘⦗✕⦘⦗🛏⦘⦗💻⦘

ⓐⓐⓐ ▼▼▼ **The Edgewater** H ❀

(608) 535-8200. **$159-$599, 3 day notice.** 1001 Wisconsin Pl 53703. On Lake Mendota, 0.3 mi n of Capitol Square. Int corridors. **Pets:** Dogs only. $100 one-time fee/pet. Designated rooms.

⦗SAVE⦘⦗🔌⦘⦗❜⦘⦗♿M⦘⦗✕⦘⦗📶⦘⦗✕⦘⦗🛏⦘⦗💻⦘

▼▼▼ **Extended Stay America Old Sauk Rd** H

(608) 833-2121. **$95-$165.** 45 Junction Ct 53717. US 12 and 14 exit 253 (Old Sauk Rd), just w. Int corridors. **Pets:** Accepted.

⦗♿M⦘⦗➥⦘⦗🛜⦘⦗✕⦘⦗🛏⦘

ⓐⓐⓐ ▼▼▼ **Graduate Madison** H

(608) 257-4391. **Call for rates.** 601 Langdon St 53703. Just e of jct Lake St; downtown. Int corridors. **Pets:** Accepted.

⦗SAVE⦘⦗❜⦘⦗♿M⦘⦗🛜⦘⦗✕⦘⦗🛏⦘⦗💻⦘

ⓐⓐⓐ ▼▼▼ **Hilton Madison Monona Terrace** H ❀

(608) 255-5100. **$179-$499.** 9 E Wilson St 53703. 2 blks e of Capitol Square; downtown. Int corridors. **Pets:** $30 daily fee/room. Service with restrictions, crate. ⦗SAVE⦘⦗ECO⦘⦗🔌⦘⦗❜⦘⦗♿M⦘⦗➥⦘⦗🛜⦘⦗✕⦘⦗🛏⦘⦗💻⦘

ⓐⓐⓐ ▼▼▼ **Homewood Suites by Hilton** H

(608) 271-0600. **$99-$209.** 479 Commerce Dr 53719. US 12/14 exit 255 (Gammon Rd), just s, 1.1 mi w on Watts Rd, then just n. Int corridors. **Pets:** Accepted. ⦗SAVE⦘⦗♿M⦘⦗➥⦘⦗🛜⦘⦗✕⦘⦗🛏⦘⦗💻⦘

ⓐⓐⓐ ▼▼▼ **HotelRED** H

(608) 819-8228. **$99-$999.** 1501 Monroe St 53711. Downtown. Int corridors. **Pets:** Accepted. ⦗SAVE⦘⦗❜⦘⦗♿M⦘⦗🛜⦘⦗✕⦘⦗🛏⦘⦗💻⦘

ⓐⓐⓐ ▼▼▼ **Hyatt Place Madison/Downtown** H

(608) 257-2700. **$109-$309.** 333 W Washington Ave 53703. 2 1/2 blks sw of Capitol Square; downtown. Int corridors. **Pets:** Medium, dogs only. $75 one-time fee/pet. Service with restrictions, supervision.

⦗SAVE⦘⦗ECO⦘⦗❜⦘⦗♿M⦘⦗➥⦘⦗🛜⦘⦗✕⦘⦗🛏⦘⦗💻⦘

▼▼▼ **La Quinta Inn & Suites Madison American Center** H

(608) 245-0123. **$79-$378.** 5217 E Terrace Dr 53718. US 151 exit 98B, just nw on Ameican Pkwy, then just sw. Int corridors. **Pets:** Accepted.

⦗❜⦘⦗♿M⦘⦗➥⦘⦗🛜⦘⦗✕⦘⦗🛏⦘⦗💻⦘

▼▼▼ **Residence Inn by Marriott Madison East** H

(608) 244-5047. **$98-$417.** 4862 Hayes Rd 53704. I-90/94 exit 135A (US 151), just sw to Hayes Rd, then just ne. Int corridors. **Pets:** Medium. $50 one-time fee/pet. Service with restrictions, supervision. ⦗➥⦘⦗🛜⦘⦗✕⦘⦗🛏⦘⦗💻⦘

ⓐⓐⓐ ▼▼▼ **Sheraton Madison Hotel** H

(608) 251-2300. **$129-$279.** 706 John Nolen Dr 53713. US 12/18 exit 263 (John Nolen Dr), just n. Int corridors. **Pets:** Accepted.

⦗SAVE⦘⦗ECO⦘⦗❜⦘⦗♿M⦘⦗➥⦘⦗🛜⦘⦗✕⦘⦗🛏⦘⦗💻⦘

▼▼▼ **Sleep Inn & Suites** H

(608) 221-8100. **$79-$199.** 4802 Tradewinds Pkwy 53718. US 12 and 18 exit 266 (US 51), 0.5 mi se, then 0.6 mi on Dutch Mill Rd. Int corridors. **Pets:** Accepted. ⦗♿M⦘⦗➥⦘⦗✕⦘⦗🛜⦘⦗✕⦘⦗🛏⦘⦗💻⦘

▼▼▼ **Staybridge Suites** H

(608) 241-2300. **Call for rates.** 3301 City View Dr 53718. I-90/94 exit 135C (US 151/High Crossing Blvd), 0.4 mi e. Int corridors. **Pets:** Large, other species. $50 deposit/room. Designated rooms, service with restrictions, supervision. ⦗❜⦘⦗♿M⦘⦗➥⦘⦗🛜⦘⦗✕⦘⦗🛏⦘⦗💻⦘

▼▼ **Super 8-Madison** H

(608) 258-8882. **$60-$140.** 1602 W Beltline Hwy 53713. US 12 and 18 exit 260B (CR D), just w on N Frontage Rd. Int corridors. **Pets:** Medium. $10 daily fee/room. Service with restrictions, crate.

⦗♿M⦘⦗➥⦘⦗🛜⦘⦗✕⦘⦗🛏⦘⦗💻⦘

MANITOWOC

▼▼ **AmericInn Lodge & Suites of Manitowoc** H

(920) 684-3344. **Call for rates.** 5020 Hecker Rd 54220. I-43 exit 149, just sw. Int corridors. **Pets:** Accepted. ⦗❜⦘⦗➥⦘⦗🛜⦘⦗✕⦘⦗🛏⦘⦗💻⦘

▼▼▼ **Holiday Inn Manitowoc** H

(920) 682-6000. **$149-$249.** 4601 Calumet Ave 54220. I-43 exit 149, just e. Int corridors. **Pets:** Other species. $150 deposit/room. Service with restrictions, supervision. ⦗❜⦘⦗♿M⦘⦗➥⦘⦗🛜⦘⦗✕⦘⦗🛏⦘⦗💻⦘

▼▼ **Quality Inn by Choice Hotels** H

(920) 683-0220. **$85-$169.** 2200 S 44th St 54220. I-43 exit 149, just e. Int corridors. **Pets:** Accepted. ⦗🛜⦘⦗✕⦘⦗🛏⦘⦗💻⦘

MARINETTE

▼▼▼ **Country Inn & Suites By Carlson** H

(715) 732-3400. **Call for rates.** 2020 Old Peshtigo Ct 54143. Jct Cleveland Ave, 1 mi s of downtown. Int corridors. **Pets:** Accepted.

⦗♿M⦘⦗➥⦘⦗🛜⦘⦗✕⦘⦗🛏⦘⦗💻⦘

MARSHFIELD

ⓐⓐⓐ ▼▼▼ **Hotel Marshfield, BW Premier Collection** H

(715) 387-2700. **$99-$169, 3 day notice.** 2700 S Central Ave 54449. Jct US 10 and SR 13, 1.3 mi n. Int corridors. **Pets:** Accepted.

⦗SAVE⦘⦗🔌⦘⦗❜⦘⦗♿M⦘⦗✕⦘⦗🛜⦘⦗✕⦘⦗🛏⦘⦗💻⦘

MAUSTON

ⓐⓐⓐ ▼▼▼ **Best Western Park Oasis Inn** H

(608) 847-6255. **$90-$160.** 1006 SR 82 E 53948. I-90/94 exit 69, just se. Int corridors. **Pets:** Other species. $50 deposit/room, $5 daily fee/pet. Designated rooms, service with restrictions, supervision.

⦗SAVE⦘⦗❜⦘⦗➥⦘⦗🛜⦘⦗✕⦘⦗🛏⦘⦗💻⦘

▼▼ **Quality Inn** H

(608) 847-5959. **$74-$229.** 1001 Gateway Ave 53948. I-90/94 exit 69, just ne. Int corridors. **Pets:** Accepted. ⦗➥⦘⦗🛜⦘⦗✕⦘⦗🛏⦘⦗💻⦘

▼▼ **Super 8** M

(608) 847-2300. **$74-$135.** 1001A Hwy 82 E 53948. I-90/94 exit 69, just ne. Int corridors. **Pets:** Other species. $10 daily fee/pet. Service with restrictions, supervision. ⦗♿M⦘⦗➥⦘⦗🛜⦘⦗✕⦘⦗🛏⦘⦗💻⦘

MEDFORD

▼▼▼ **Boarders Inn & Suites** H

(715) 748-2330. **$84-$120.** 435 S 8th St 54451. On SR 13, 0.5 mi s of jct SR 64. Int corridors. **Pets:** Dogs only. $30 one-time fee/room. Designated rooms, service with restrictions, supervision.

⊇ 🤶 ✕ 🛅 💻

▼▼ **Woodlands Inn & Suites** M

(715) 748-3995. **Call for rates.** 854 N 8th St 54451. On SR 13, 0.6 mi n of jct SR 64. Int corridors. **Pets:** Accepted. ⊇ 🤶 ✕ 🛅 💻

MENOMONIE

▼▼ **Menomonie Motel 6** M

(715) 235-6901. **$55-$85.** 2100 Stout St 54751. I-94 exit 41 (SR 25), just se. Int corridors. **Pets:** Accepted. ♿M 🤶 ✕ 🛅

MERRILL

▼▼ **AmericInn Lodge & Suites of Merrill** H

(715) 536-7979. **Call for rates.** 3300 E Main St 54452. US 51 exit 208, 0.5 mi w on SR 64. Int corridors. **Pets:** Accepted.

♿M ⊇ 🤶 ✕ 🛅 💻

MIDDLETON

◿◿◿ ▼▼▼ **Residence Inn by Marriott-Madison West/Middleton** H

(608) 662-1100. **$94-$296.** 8400 Market St 53562. US 12/14 exit 252 (Greenway Blvd), just w, then just n; in Greenway Station. Int corridors. **Pets:** Accepted. [SAVE] ♿M ⊇ 🤶 ✕ 🛅 💻

▼▼▼ **Staybridge Suites** H

(608) 664-5888. **Call for rates.** 7790 Elmwood Ave 53562. US 12/14 exit 251A (University Ave), just se. Int corridors. **Pets:** Accepted.

♿M ⊇ 🤶 ✕ 🛅 💻

MILWAUKEE

◿◿◿ ▼▼▼ **Aloft Milwaukee Downtown** H 🐾

(414) 226-0122. **$79-$299.** 1230 N Old World 3rd St 53212. I-43 exit 73A, just se. Int corridors. **Pets:** Medium, dogs only. Designated rooms, service with restrictions, supervision.

[SAVE] 🍴 ♿M ⊇ 🤶 ✕ 🛅 💻

▼▼▼ **Ambassador Hotel** H

(414) 345-5000. **$129-$399.** 2308 W Wisconsin Ave 53233. I-94 exit 308 (US 41), just n to Wisconsin Ave (US 18) exit, then 1.5 mi e; jct N 24th St. Int corridors. **Pets:** Accepted. 🍴 🤶 ✕ 💻

◿◿◿ ▼▼▼ **Comfort Suites at Park Place** H

(414) 979-0250. **$99-$259.** 10831 W Park Pl 53224. US 41/45 exit 47B (Good Hope Rd), just e. Int corridors. **Pets:** Medium, dogs only. $15 daily fee/room. Service with restrictions, supervision.

[SAVE] ♿M ⊇ 🤶 ✕ 🛅 💻

◿◿◿ ▼▼ **Days Inn & Suites Milwaukee** H

(414) 265-5629. **$60-$150.** 1840 N 6th St 53212. I-43 exit 73A, just se to 6th St, then 0.4 mi n. Int corridors. **Pets:** Accepted.

[SAVE] 🤶 ✕ 🛅 💻

◿◿◿ ▼▼▼ **Hilton Milwaukee City Center** H 🐾

(414) 271-7250. **$99-$399.** 509 W Wisconsin Ave 53203. Jct 5th St. Int corridors. **Pets:** Large. $50 one-time fee/pet. Service with restrictions, crate. [SAVE] [ECO] 🔌 🍴 ♿M 🤶 ✕ 🛅 💻

▼▼▼ **Holiday Inn Express & Suites Milwaukee Airport**

(414) 563-4000. **Call for rates.** 1400 W Zellman Ct 53221. I-94 exit 319 (College Ave/CR ZZ), 0.4 mi e to S 13th St, then just s. Int corridors. **Pets:** Accepted. [ECO] ⊇ 🤶 ✕ 🛅 💻

▼▼▼▼ **Home2 Suites By Hilton Milwaukee Airport** H

(414) 481-2900. **Call for rates.** 5880 S Howell Ave 53207. I-94 exit 318 (Airport), 1.1 mi e to Howell Ave (SR 38), then 0.5 mi s. Int corridors. **Pets:** Accepted. ♿M 🤶 ✕ 🛅 💻

◿◿◿ ▼▼▼ **Hyatt Place Milwaukee Airport** H

(414) 744-3600. **$93-$225.** 200 W Grange Ave 53207. I-94 exit 318 (Airport), 1.1 mi e, just n on Howell Ave (SR 38), then just w. Int corridors. **Pets:** Medium, dogs only. $75 one-time fee/room. Service with restrictions, supervision. [SAVE] ♿M 🤶 ✕ 🛅 💻

◿◿◿ ▼▼▼ **Hyatt Place Milwaukee-West** H

(414) 462-3500. **$93-$225.** 11777 W Silver Spring Dr 53225. US 45 exit 46 (Silver Spring Dr), just w. Int corridors. **Pets:** Medium, dogs only. $75 one-time fee/pet. Service with restrictions, supervision.

[SAVE] 🍴 ♿M ⊇ 🤶 ✕ 🛅 💻

◿◿◿ ▼▼▼ ▼▼▼ **The Iron Horse Hotel** H

(414) 374-4766. **$159-$509.** 500 W Florida St 53204. Jct 6th St. Int corridors. **Pets:** Accepted. [SAVE] 🍴 ♿M 🤶 ✕ 🛅 💻

◿◿◿ ▼▼▼ ▼▼▼ **The Pfister Hotel** H 🐾

(414) 273-8222. **Call for rates.** 424 E Wisconsin Ave 53202. Corner of E Wisconsin Ave and Jefferson St. Int corridors. **Pets:** Dogs only. $100 one-time fee/room. Service with restrictions, supervision.

[SAVE] [ECO] 🔌 🍴 ♿M ⊇ 🎱 ✕ 🛅 💻

◿◿◿ ▼▼▼ **The Plaza Hotel Milwaukee** H

(414) 276-2101. **$99-$299.** 1007 N Cass St 53202. Jct E State St. Int corridors. **Pets:** Other species. $50 one-time fee/room. Designated rooms, service with restrictions. [SAVE] 🍴 🤶 ✕ 🛅 💻

MINOCQUA

▼▼▼ **AmericInn of Minocqua** H 🐾

(715) 356-3730. **$79-$189.** 700 Hwy 51 54548. On US 51; downtown. Int corridors. **Pets:** Other species. $10 daily fee/room. Service with restrictions, supervision. [ECO] ⊇ ✕ 🤶 🛅 💻

◿◿◿ ▼▼▼ **Best Western Plus Concord Inn** H 🐾

(715) 356-1800. **$155-$180.** 320 Front St 54548. On US 51; downtown. Int corridors. **Pets:** Medium, dogs only. $10 daily fee/pet. Designated rooms, service with restrictions, supervision.

[SAVE] ⊇ 🤶 ✕ 🛅 💻

MONROE

▼▼▼ **Gasthaus Motel** M

(608) 328-8395. **Call for rates.** 685 30th St 53566. 1.5 mi s on SR 69. Ext corridors. **Pets:** Accepted. ♿M 🤶 ✕ 🛅 💻

▼▼ **Super 8 of Monroe** H

(608) 325-1500. **$73-$78.** 500 6th St 53566. On SR 69 S, 0.5 mi s of jct SR 81/11. Int corridors. **Pets:** Accepted.

[ECO] ♿M ⊇ 🤶 ✕ 🛅 💻

NEILLSVILLE

▼▼▼ **Super 8-Neillsville** H

(715) 743-8080. **$80-$100.** 1000 E Division St 54456. On US 10; jct Boon Blvd and Division St. Int corridors. **Pets:** Accepted.

♿M ⊇ 🤶 ✕ 🛅 💻

NEW BERLIN

▼▼ **La Quinta Inn & Suites Milwaukee SW New Berlin** H

(262) 717-0900. **$79-$240.** 15300 W Rock Ridge Rd 53151. I-43 exit 57 (Moorland Rd), just se. Int corridors. **Pets:** Accepted.

♿M ⊇ 🤶 ✕ 🛅 💻

NEW GLARUS

Chalet Landhaus Inn H
(608) 527-5234. **$99-$199.** 801 SR 69 53574. On SR 69. Int corridors.
Pets: Large, other species. $25 daily fee/room. Service with restrictions, supervision. SAVE [icons]

NEW LONDON

AmericInn Lodge & Suites of New London H
(920) 982-5700. **$79-$210.** 1404 N Shawano St 54961. US 45 exit US 54, just n. Int corridors. **Pets:** Medium. $20 one-time fee/pet. Designated rooms, service with restrictions, supervision.
[icons]

OAK CREEK

Comfort Suites Milwaukee Airport H
(414) 570-1111. **$89-$279.** 6362 S 13th St 53154. I-94 exit 319 (College Ave), just e on CR 22, then just s. Int corridors. **Pets:** Accepted.
[icons]

La Quinta Inn Milwaukee Airport / Oak Creek H
(414) 762-2266. **$67-$191.** 7141 S 13th St 53154. I-94 exit 320 (Rawson Ave), just se. Int corridors. **Pets:** Accepted. [icons]

OCONOMOWOC

Staybridge Suites Milwaukee West H
(262) 200-2900. **Call for rates.** 1141 Blue Ribbon Dr 53066. I-94 exit 282 (SR 67), just s. Int corridors. **Pets:** Accepted.
[icons]

ONALASKA

Holiday Inn Express H
(608) 783-6555. **$109-$149.** 9409 Hwy 16 54650. I-90 exit 5, 1 mi e. Int corridors. **Pets:** Small, cats only. Designated rooms, no service, supervision. [icons]

Stoney Creek Hotel & Conference Center H
(608) 781-3060. **Call for rates.** 3060 S Kinney Coulee Rd 54650. I-90 exit 5, just se. Int corridors. **Pets:** Large, dogs only. $25 daily fee/pet. Designated rooms, service with restrictions, crate.
[icons]

OSCEOLA

River Valley Inn & Suites H
(715) 294-4060. **Call for rates.** 1030 Cascade St 54020. Just n on SR 35. Int corridors **Pets:** Accepted. [icons]

OSHKOSH

AmericInn Lodge & Suites Oshkosh H
(920) 232-0300. **Call for rates.** 1495 W South Park Ave 54902. US 41 exit 116 (SR 44), 0.4 mi e. Int corridors. **Pets:** Accepted.
[icons]

Comfort Suites by Choice Hotels at Oshkosh H
(920) 230-7378. **$95-$870.** 400 S Koeller St 54902. US 41 exit 117 (9th Ave), just e. Int corridors. **Pets:** Accepted.
[icons]

Fairfield Inn & Suites by Marriott Oshkosh H
(920) 233-8504. **$79-$207.** 1800 S Koeller St 54902. US 41 exit 117 (9th Ave), 0.8 mi s on east frontage road. Int corridors. **Pets:** Accepted.
[icons]

Holiday Inn Express & Suites H
(920) 303-1300. **Call for rates.** 2251 Westowne Ave 54904. US 41 exit 119, 0.4 mi w of jct SR 21. Int corridors. **Pets:** Other species. $10 one-time fee/pet. Service with restrictions, crate.
[icons]

La Quinta Inn Oshkosh H
(920) 233-4190. **$67-$405.** 1886 Rath Ln 54902. US 41 exit 119, jct SR 21. Int corridors. **Pets:** Accepted. [icons]

PEWAUKEE

The Wildwood Lodge H
(262) 506-2000. **Call for rates.** N14 24121 W Tower Pl 53072. I-94 exit 294 (SR 164 N/CR J), just nw. Int corridors. **Pets:** Accepted.
[icons]

PLATTEVILLE

Mound View Inn H
(608) 348-9518. **$79-$299.** 1755 E Business Hwy 151 53818. On US 151 exit 21, just w. Int corridors. **Pets:** Accepted. [icons]

PLEASANT PRAIRIE

La Quinta Inn Pleasant Prairie Kenosha H
(262) 857-7911. **$68-$180.** 7540 118th Ave 53158. I-94 exit 344 (SR 50), just e. Int corridors. **Pets:** Accepted.
[icons]

PLOVER

AmericInn of Plover/Stevens Point H
(715) 342-1244. **Call for rates.** 1501 American Dr 54467. I-39 exit 153 (CR B), just nw. Int corridors. **Pets:** Accepted.
[icons]

PORTAGE

Comfort Suites H
(608) 745-4717. **$79-$189.** N5780 Kinney Rd 53901. I-90/94 exit 108A (SR 78), just sw. Int corridors. **Pets:** Medium, dogs only. $20 daily fee/pet. Service with restrictions, supervision.
[icons]

Super 8-Portage H
(608) 742-8330. **$59-$85.** 3000 New Pinery Rd 53901. I-39 exit 92, just s. Int corridors. **Pets:** Dogs only. $11 daily fee/pet. Designated rooms, no service, supervision. [icons]

PRAIRIE DU CHIEN

Super 8-Prairie Du Chien H
(608) 326-8777. **$52-$110.** 1930 S Marquette Rd 53821. On US 18, 1.9 mi e of jct SR 27 N. Ext/int corridors. **Pets:** Accepted.
[icons]

RICHLAND CENTER

The Center Lodge H
(608) 647-8988. **$74-$90.** 100 Foundry Dr 53581. 0.9 mi e on US 14. Int corridors. **Pets:** Accepted. [icons]

RIVER FALLS

Econo Lodge H
(715) 425-8388. **$84-$134.** 1207 Saint Croix St 54022. On SR 65, 0.5 mi w jct SR 35. Int corridors. **Pets:** Dogs only. $15 daily fee/room. Service with restrictions, supervision. SAVE [icons]

ROTHSCHILD

Best Western Plus Wausau/Rothschild Hotel H
(715) 355-8900. **$110-$160.** 803 Industrial Park Ave 54474. I-39 exit 185 (Business Rt US 51), just w. Int corridors. **Pets:** Medium, dogs only. $20 daily fee/pet. Designated rooms, service with restrictions, supervision. SAVE [icons]

Grand Lodge by Stoney Creek H
(715) 241-6300. **Call for rates.** 805 Creske Ave 54474. I-39 exit 185 (Business Rt US 51), just se. Int corridors. **Pets:** Accepted.
[icons]

▼▼▼ Holiday Inn Hotel & Suites 🅷
(715) 355-1111. **$119-$159, 3 day notice.** 1000 Imperial Ave 54474. I-39 exit 185 (Business Rt US 51), just se. Int corridors. **Pets:** Accepted. 🍽 ⓜ 🛁 🛜 ✕ 📵 💻

▼▼ 💎 Stoney Creek Hotel and Conference Center 🅷 🐾
(715) 355-6858. **$79-$129.** 1100 Imperial Ave 54474. I-39 exit 185 (Business Rt US 51), just e. Int corridors. **Pets:** Medium, dogs only. $25 daily fee/pet. Service with restrictions, crate. ⓜ 🛁 ✕ 🛜 ✕ 📵 💻

SHEBOYGAN

▼▼▼▼ GrandStay Residential Suites Hotel 🅷
(920) 208-8000. **Call for rates.** 708 Niagara Ave 53081. Jct N 7th St; downtown. Int corridors. **Pets:** $25 daily fee/room. Designated rooms, service with restrictions, crate. ⓜ 🛁 🛜 ✕ 📵 💻

▼▼ 💎 La Quinta Inn Sheboygan 🅷
(920) 457-2321. **$67-$246.** 2932 Kohler Memorial Dr 53081. I-43 exit 126, 1 mi e on SR 23. Int corridors. **Pets:** Accepted. 🛜 ✕ 📵 💻

▼▼ Quality Inn 🅷
(920) 457-7724. **$84-$224.** 4332 N 40th St 53083. I-43 exit 128, 0.3 mi e on Business Rt SR 42. Int corridors. **Pets:** Medium, dogs only. $15 daily fee/pet. Designated rooms, supervision. 🛁 🛜 ✕ 📵 💻

SHEBOYGAN FALLS

▼▼▼▼ The Rochester Inn, A Historic Hotel 🅱🅱 🐾
(920) 467-3123. **$100-$175, 21 day notice.** 504 Water St 53085. Just e of downtown via CR PP. Int corridors. **Pets:** Small, dogs only. Designated rooms, service with restrictions, crate. 🛜 ✕ 📵 💻

SIREN

🅰🅰🅰 ▼▼ 💎 Best Western Northwoods Lodge 🅷
(715) 349-7800. **$90-$170.** 23986 SR 35 S 54872. On SR 35, jct SR 70 W and CR B E. Int corridors. **Pets:** Accepted. SAVE ⓜ 🛁 🛜 ✕ 📵 💻

SISTER BAY

▼▼ 💎 Country House Resort 🅼 🐾
(920) 854-4551. **$82-$193, 14 day notice.** 2468 Sunnyside Rd 54234. Jct SR 42 and 57, 0.3 mi s on SR 42 to Highland Ave, then just w. Ext corridors. **Pets:** Large, dogs only. $20 daily fee/pet. Designated rooms, service with restrictions, supervision. ECO 🛁 ✕ 🛜 ✕ 📵 💻

▼ 💎 Sister Bay Inn 🅼
(920) 854-4242. **$68-$129, 14 day notice.** 10490 SR 57 54234. Jct SR 42, 0.5 mi se. Ext/int corridors. **Pets:** Accepted. 🛁 🛜 ✕ 📵 💻

SPARTA

💎 ▼▼ Country Inn & Suites By Carlson 🅷
(608) 269-3110. **Call for rates.** 737 Avon Rd 54656. I-90 exit 25 (SR 27), just n. Int corridors. **Pets:** Accepted. ⓜ 🛁 🛜 ✕ 📵 💻

▼▼ Super 8 Sparta 🅷
(608) 269-8489. **$79-$135.** 716 Avon Rd 54656. I-90 exit 25 (SR 27), just n. Int corridors. **Pets:** Other species. $10 daily fee/pet. Service with restrictions, crate. 🛁 🛜 ✕ 📵 💻

SPOONER

🅰🅰🅰 ▼▼ 💎 Best Western Spooner Riverplace 🅷
(715) 635-9770. **$90-$200.** 101 W Maple St 54801. Jct SR 70 and US 63. Int corridors. **Pets:** Accepted. SAVE 🛁 ✕ 🛜 ✕ 📵 💻

STEVENS POINT

▼▼▼▼ Country Inn & Suites By Carlson 🅷
(715) 345-7000. **$109-$139.** 301 Division St N 54481. I-39 exit 161 (US 51 business route), 0.6 mi s. Int corridors. **Pets:** Medium. $25 one-time fee/room. No service, supervision. 🛁 🛜 ✕ 📵 💻

🅰🅰🅰 ▼▼▼▼ Holiday Inn Express 🅷
(715) 344-0000. **$89-$149.** 1100 Amber Ave 54482. I-39 exit 158 (US 10), 1 mi e, then just n. Int corridors. **Pets:** Accepted. SAVE ⓜ 🛁 🛜 ✕ 📵 💻

▼▼ 💎 La Quinta Inn & Suites Stevens Point 🅷
(715) 344-1900. **$67-$196.** 4917 Main St 54481. I-39 exit 158B (US 10), just sw. Int corridors. **Pets:** Accepted. ⓜ 🛁 🛜 ✕ 📵 💻

STURGEON BAY

🅰🅰🅰 ▼▼ 💎 Best Western Maritime Inn 🅷
(920) 743-7231. **$70-$145.** 1001 N 14th Ave 54235. 1 mi n on Business Rt SR 42/57; jct N 14th Ave. Int corridors. **Pets:** Accepted. SAVE 🛁 🛜 ✕ 📵 💻

SUN PRAIRIE

🅰🅰🅰 ▼▼ 💎 Quality Inn & Suites-Sun Prairie 🅷
(608) 834-9889. **$80-$169.** 105 Business Park Dr 53590. US 151 exit 103 (CR N), just n. Int corridors. **Pets:** Medium, dogs only. $15 daily fee/pet. Designated rooms, service with restrictions, supervision. SAVE 🍽 ⓜ 🛁 🛜 ✕ 📵 💻

SUPERIOR

🅰🅰🅰 ▼▼▼▼ Best Western Bridgeview Hotel 🅷
(715) 392-8174. **$83-$280.** 415 Hammond Ave 54880. 0.8 mi n at south end of Blatnik Bridge. Int corridors. **Pets:** Accepted. SAVE ⓜ 🛁 🛜 ✕ 📵 💻

TOMAH

▼▼ AmericInn Lodge & Suites of Tomah 🅷
(608) 372-4100. **Call for rates.** 750 Vandervort St 54660. I-94 exit 143 (SR 21), just e. Int corridors. **Pets:** Accepted. ⓜ 🛁 🛜 ✕ 📵 💻

🅰🅰🅰 ▼▼ 💎 Best Western Tomah Hotel 🅷 🐾
(608) 372-3211. **$89-$149.** 1017 E McCoy Blvd 54660. I-94 exit 143 (SR 21), just e. Int corridors. **Pets:** Medium, dogs only. $15 daily fee/pet. Designated rooms, service with restrictions, supervision. SAVE 🍽 ⓜ 🛁 ✕ 🛜 ✕ 📵 💻

▼▼ Econo Lodge 🅷
(608) 372-9100. **$54-$185.** 2005 N Superior Ave 54660. I-94 exit 143 (SR 21), just w. Ext/int corridors. **Pets:** Accepted. ⓜ 🛁 🛜 ✕ 📵 💻

🅰🅰🅰 ▼▼ Lark Inn 🅼
(608) 372-5981. **$60-$129.** 229 N Superior Ave 54660. I-94 exit 143 (SR 21), 1.5 mi s on US 12; I-90 exit 41, 2 mi n on US 12. Ext/int corridors. **Pets:** Dogs only. $8 daily fee/pet. SAVE ⓜ 🛁 ✕ 📵 💻

▼▼ Microtel Inn & Suites by Wyndham 🅷
(608) 374-2050. **$61-$70.** 115 W Andres St 54660. I-94 exit 143 (SR 21), just nw. Int corridors. **Pets:** Accepted. ⓜ 🛜 ✕ 📵 💻

▼▼ 💎 Quality Inn Tomah 🅷
(608) 372-6600. **$69-$239.** 305 Wittig Rd 54660. I-94 exit 143 (SR 21), just w. Int corridors. **Pets:** Accepted. 🛁 🛜 ✕ 📵 💻

TWO RIVERS

🅰🅰🅰 ▼▼ 💎 Lighthouse Inn on Lake Michigan 🅷
(920) 793-4524. **$97-$166.** 1515 Memorial Dr 54241. 0.3 mi s on SR 42. Int corridors. **Pets:** Accepted. SAVE 🍽 🛁 ✕ 🛜 ✕ 📵 💻

VERONA

▼▼▼ **Holiday Inn Express Hotel & Suites Madison-Verona** 🄷

(608) 497-4500. **$120-$500.** 515 W Verona Ave 53593. US 18 and 151 exit 76, 0.6 mi ne. Int corridors. **Pets:** Accepted.

🕭ᴹ ⊇ 🛜 ⊠ 🔋 🖵

WATERFORD

▼▼ **Baymont Inn & Suites-Waterford** 🄷

(262) 534-4100. **$69-$250.** 750 Fox Ln 53185. On SR 36, 1 mi s of jct SR 164. Int corridors. **Pets:** Accepted. 🕭ᴹ ⊇ 🛜 ⊠ 🔋 🖵

WAUKESHA

▼▼ **Baymont Inn & Suites Waukesha** 🄷

(262) 547-7770. **$69-$90.** 2111 E Moreland Blvd 53186. I-94 exit 297, 0.9 mi sw on US 18 (E Moreland Ave). Int corridors. **Pets:** Accepted.

⊇ 🛜 ⊠ 🔋 🖵

🄰🄰🄰 ▼▼ **Best Western Waukesha Grand** 🄷

(262) 524-9300. **$80-$140.** 2840 N Grandview Blvd 53072. I-94 exit 293, just s on CR T. Int corridors. **Pets:** Accepted.

SAVE ⊇ 🛜 ⊠ 🔋 🖵

▼▼ **Super 8-Waukesha** 🄷

(262) 786-6015. **$66-$100.** 2510 Plaza Ct 53186. I-94 exit 297, just w on CR JJ (Bluemound Rd). Int corridors. **Pets:** Medium. $10 daily fee/pet. Designated rooms, service with restrictions, supervision.

🕭ᴹ 🛜 ⊠ 🔋 🖵

WAUPACA

▼▼▼ **Comfort Suites at Foxfire** 🄷

(715) 942-0500. **$99-$189.** 199 Foxfire Dr 54981. Jct US 10/SR 49/54 and CR QQ, 0.7 mi sw. Int corridors. **Pets:** Medium. $15 daily fee/pet. Service with restrictions, supervision. 🕭ᴹ ⊇ 🛜 ⊠ 🔋 🖵

▼▼ **Ramada Waupaca** 🄷

(715) 258-9212. **$100-$150.** 110 Grand Seasons Dr 54981. Jct US 10/SR 49/54 and CR QQ, just w. Int corridors. **Pets:** Accepted.

🍴 🕭ᴹ ⊇ ⊠ 🛜 ⊠ 🔋 🖵

WAUPUN

▼▼▼ **AmericInn Hotel & Suites-Waupun** 🄷

(920) 345-1140. **$95-$200.** 204 Shaler Dr 53963. US 151 exit 146, just sw. Int corridors. **Pets:** Accepted. 🕭ᴹ 🛜 ⊠ 🔋 🖵

▼ **Inn Town Motel** 🄼

(920) 324-4211. **Call for rates.** 27 S State St 53963. US 151 exit 146 (SR 49), 1 mi w on Main St, then just s. Ext corridors. **Pets:** Accepted.

🍴 🕭ᴹ 🛜 ⊠ 🔋 🖵

WAUSAU

🄰🄰🄰 ▼▼▼▼ **Jefferson Street Inn** 🄷 ❀

(715) 845-6500. **$129-$169, 3 day notice.** 201 Jefferson St 54403. Jct N 2nd St; center. Int corridors. **Pets:** Medium. $30 daily fee/pet. Designated rooms, service with restrictions, crate.

SAVE ECO 🍴 🕭ᴹ ⊇ 🛜 ⊠ 🔋 🖵

▼▼ **Super 8** 🄷

(715) 848-2888. **$47-$90.** 2006 Stewart Ave W 54401. US 51 exit SR 52, just se. Int corridors. **Pets:** Dogs only. $10 daily fee/pet. Designated rooms, service with restrictions, supervision. ⊇ 🛜 ⊠ 🔋 🖵

WAUTOMA

▼▼ **Super 8-Wautoma** 🄷

(920) 787-4811. **$73-$175.** W7607 SR 21/73 54982. On SR 21 and 73, 1.5 mi e. Int corridors. **Pets:** Accepted. ⊇ 🛜 ⊠ 🔋 🖵

WAUWATOSA

▼▼ **Extended Stay America-Milwaukee-Wauwatosa** 🄷

(414) 443-1909. **$95-$150.** 11121 W North Ave 53226. US 45 exit 42A, just n. Int corridors. **Pets:** Accepted. 🛜 ⊠ 🔋

▼▼ **Holiday Inn Express Milwaukee West-Medical Center** 🄷

(414) 778-0333. **Call for rates.** 11111 W North Ave 53226. US 45 exit 42A, just n on SR 100, then just w. Int corridors. **Pets:** Accepted.

🕭ᴹ 🛜 ⊠ 🔋 🖵

WISCONSIN RAPIDS

▼▼ **Sleep Inn & Suites** 🄷 ❀

(715) 424-6800. **$79-$154.** 4221 8th St S 54494. 1.3 mi s on SR 13 from jct SR 54. Int corridors. **Pets:** Medium, dogs only. $25 daily fee/pet. Service with restrictions, supervision.

🕭ᴹ ⊇ 🛜 ⊠ 🔋 🖵

WITTENBERG

🄰🄰🄰 ▼▼ **Best Western Wittenberg Inn** 🄷

(715) 253-3755. **$84-$250.** W17267 Red Oak Ln 54499. SR 29 exit 198, just se. Int corridors. **Pets:** Other species. $20 daily fee/room. Designated rooms, service with restrictions, crate.

SAVE 🕭ᴹ ⊇ 🛜 ⊠ 🔋 🖵

WYOMING

AFTON

▼ **Lazy B Motel** 🄼

(307) 885-3187. **$82-$110.** 219 S Washington St (US 89) 83110. US 89; downtown. Ext corridors. **Pets:** Large, dogs only. $7 daily fee/pet. Service with restrictions, supervision. 🕭ᴹ ⊇ 🛜 ⊠ 🔋 🖵

BUFFALO

▼▼ **Buffalo Inn** 🄷 ❀

(307) 684-7000. **Call for rates.** 100 Flatiron Dr 82834. On US 16, between I-25 and 90. Int corridors. **Pets:** Large, other species. $10 daily fee/pet. Designated rooms, service with restrictions, supervision.

🕭ᴹ 🛜 ⊠ 🔋 🖵

🄰🄰🄰 ▼▼ **Comfort Inn** 🄷

(307) 684-9564. **$79-$184.** 65 US Hwy 16 E 82834. I-25 exit 299 (US 16), just e; I-90 exit 58, 1.3 mi w. Ext/int corridors. **Pets:** Large, other species. $10 daily fee/pet. Designated rooms, supervision.

SAVE 🕭ᴹ ⊇ 🛜 ⊠ 🔋 🖵

▼▼▼ **Hampton Inn & Suites** 🄷

(307) 684-8899. **$99-$319.** 85 US Hwy 16 E 82834. I-90 exit 58, 1.6 mi w. Int corridors. **Pets:** Accepted. 🕭ᴹ ⊇ 🛜 ⊠ 🔋 🖵

🄰🄰🄰 ▼▼▼ **The Occidental Hotel** 🄷

(307) 684-0451. **$75-$285, 14 day notice.** 10 N Main St 82834. Center. Int corridors. **Pets:** Other species. $10 daily fee/pet. Designated rooms, service with restrictions, supervision. SAVE 🍴 🛜 ⊠ 🛇

▼ **Rodeway Inn** 🄼

(307) 684-5505. **$49-$130.** 610 E Hart St 82834. I-25 exit 299 (US 16), just w; I-90 exit 58, 1.3 mi w. Ext corridors. **Pets:** Accepted.

⊇ 🛜 🔋 🖵

CASPER (Restaurants p. 629)

◆◆◆ Days Inn Casper 🏠 ❀
(307) 234-1159. **$90-$98, 3 day notice.** 301 E 'E' St 82601. I-25 exit 188A (Center St), just s, then just e. Int corridors. **Pets:** Dogs only. $15 one-time fee/pet. Service with restrictions, supervision.

◆◆◆ MainStay Suites Casper 🏠
(307) 472-7829. **$79-$209.** 551 Granite Peak Dr 82609. I-25 exit 182 (Hat Six Rd), just s, then just w. Int corridors. **Pets:** Accepted.

◆◆ Quality Inn & Suites Casper 🏠
(307) 266-2400. **$90-$190.** 821 N Poplar St 82601. I-25 exit 188B (N Poplar St), just e. Int corridors. **Pets:** Accepted.

◁AAA▷ ◆◆◆ Ramkota Hotel & Conference Center 🏠 ❀
(307) 266-6000. **Call for rates.** 800 N Poplar St 82601. I-25 exit 188B (N Poplar St), just ne. Int corridors. **Pets:** Other species. Designated rooms.

◆◆ Super 8 Casper West 🏠
(307) 266-3480. **$95-$109.** 3838 CY Ave 82604. I-25 exit 188B (N Poplar St), 1.5 mi s to CY Ave, then 1.7 mi w. Int corridors. **Pets:** Accepted.

CHEYENNE

◁AAA▷ ◆◆◆ Best Western Plus Frontier Inn 🏠 ❀
(307) 638-8891. **$119-$219.** 8101 Hutchins Dr 82007. I-80 exit 367, just n. Int corridors. **Pets:** Other species. $20 daily fee/room. Designated rooms, service with restrictions, supervision.

◆◆◆ Candlewood Suites 🏠
(307) 634-6622. **$119-$179.** 2335 Tura Pkwy 82001. I-25 exit 9, just e on I-80 business loop/US 30, then just n. Int corridors. **Pets:** Accepted.

◆◆◆ Days Inn Cheyenne 🏠
(307) 778-8877. **$90-$290.** 2360 W Lincolnway 82001. I-25 exit 9, just e. Int corridors. **Pets:** Accepted.

◆◆ La Quinta Inn Cheyenne 🏠
(307) 632-7117. **$75-$369.** 2410 W Lincolnway 82009. I-25 exit 9, just e. Int corridors. **Pets:** Accepted.

◆◆ My Place Hotel - Cheyenne 🏠
(307) 634-1400. **Call for rates.** 1920 W Lincolnway 82001. I-25 exit 9, 0.6 mi e. Int corridors. **Pets:** Accepted.

◁AAA▷ ◆◆◆◆ Nagle Warren Mansion B & B BB ❀
(307) 637-3333. **$158-$192, 3 day notice.** 222 E 17th St 82001. I-80 exit 362, 1.2 mi n on I-25 business loop/US 85/87 business route, then just e; jct House St; downtown. Int corridors. **Pets:** Medium. $25 daily fee/pet. Designated rooms, service with restrictions, supervision.

◆◆ Oak Tree Inn Cheyenne 🏠
(307) 778-6620. **Call for rates.** 1625 Stillwater Ave 82009. I-25 exit 12, 0.8 mi se to Yellowstone Rd, 0.3 mi n to Dell Range Blvd, 1.2 mi e, then just se. Ext/int corridors. **Pets:** Accepted.

◆◆◆ Quality Inn of Cheyenne 🏠 ❀
(307) 638-7202. **$89-$299.** 2245 Etchepare Dr 82007. I-25 exit 7, just w. Int corridors. **Pets:** Other species. $15 one-time fee/room. Designated rooms, service with restrictions, supervision.

◆◆◆ Super 8 Cheyenne M
(307) 635-8741. **$69-$94.** 1900 W Lincolnway 82001. I-25 exit 9, 0.7 mi e. Int corridors. **Pets:** Accepted.

◁AAA▷ ◆◆◆ TownePlace Suites by Marriott Cheyenne Southwest/Downtown Area 🏠 ❀
(307) 634-0400. **$113-$195.** 1710 W Lincolnway 82001. I-25 exit 9 (US 30 W/Lincolnway), 0.8 mi ne. Int corridors. **Pets:** Other species. $50 one-time fee/room. Service with restrictions, crate.

CODY

◆◆◆ The Cody 🏠
(307) 587-5915. **Call for rates.** 232 W Yellowstone Ave 82414. 2 mi w on US 14/16/20. Int corridors. **Pets:** Accepted.

◁AAA▷ ◆ Cody Motor Lodge M
(307) 527-6291. **Call for rates.** 1455 Sheridan Ave 82414. Just w on US 14/16/20 and SR 120. Int corridors. **Pets:** Accepted.

DUBOIS

◁AAA▷ ◆◆◆ The Longhorn Ranch Lodge and RV Resort M
(307) 455-2337. **$89-$169, 3 day notice.** 5810 US Hwy 26 82513. Jct US 26 and 287, 3 mi e. Ext corridors. **Pets:** Other species. $10 daily fee/pet. Service with restrictions, supervision.

◆ Rocky Mountain Lodge M
(307) 455-2844. **Call for rates.** 1349 W Ramshorn St 82513. 1.6 mi w on US 26 and 287. Ext corridors. **Pets:** Other species. $10 deposit/pet. Designated rooms, supervision.

EVANSTON

◁AAA▷ ◆◆◆ Best Western Dunmar Inn 🏠
(307) 789-3770. **$110-$140.** 1601 Harrison Dr 82930. I-80 exit 3 (Harrison Dr), just n. Ext corridors. **Pets:** Accepted.

◁AAA▷ ◆◆◆ Holiday Inn Express & Suites Evanston 🏠
(307) 789-7999. **$99-$169.** 1965 Harrison Dr 82930. I-80 exit 3 (Harrison Dr), just n. Int corridors. **Pets:** Medium, dogs only. $25 daily fee/room. Designated rooms, service with restrictions, supervision.

EVANSVILLE

◆◆◆ Comfort Inn 🏠
(307) 237-8100. **$99-$174.** 269 Miracle St 82636. I-25 exit 185, just n to Lathrop Rd, then just e. Int corridors. **Pets:** Accepted.

◆◆◆ Sleep Inn & Suites Casper East 🏠
(307) 235-3100. **$101-$150.** 6733 Bonanza Rd 82636. I-25 exit 182, just n on Hat Six Rd. Int corridors. **Pets:** Accepted.

GILLETTE

◆◆ Arbuckle Lodge 🏠
(307) 685-6363. **Call for rates.** 1400 S Garner Lake Rd 82718. I-90 exit 129, just e. Int corridors. **Pets:** Accepted.

◆◆◆ Candlewood Suites 🏠
(307) 682-6100. **Call for rates.** 904 Country Club Rd 82718. I-90 exit 126, 0.5 mi s, then just e. Int corridors. **Pets:** Accepted.

◁AAA▷ ◆◆◆ Comfort Inn & Suites of Gillette 🏠
(307) 685-2223. **$89-$270.** 1607 W 2nd St 82716. I-90 exit 124, 0.3 mi ne, then just se. Int corridors. **Pets:** Accepted.

▼▼▼ Holiday Inn Express & Suites ⊞
(307) 686-9576. **Call for rates.** 1908 Cliff Davis Dr 82718. I-90 exit 126, just s to Boxelder Rd, then just e to Cliff Davis Dr. Int corridors. **Pets:** Accepted. 🛒 🛜 ✕ 🔌 💻

GRAND TETON NATIONAL PARK

▼▼▼ Headwaters Lodge & Cabins at Flagg Ranch ⊠
(307) 543-2861. **Call for rates.** Hwy 89 83013. 25 mi n of jct US 89/191; 2.5 mi s of Yellowstone National Park south entrance. Ext corridors. **Pets:** Accepted. 🍴 🔌 🛜 ✕ 🐾 🌀 🔌 💻

▼▼▼ Jackson Lake Lodge ⊞
(307) 543-2811. **Call for rates.** US Hwy 89 83013. 5 mi nw of jct US 26, 89 and 191. Ext/int corridors. **Pets:** Accepted.
🌿 🍴 🔌 🛒 🛜 ✕ 🐾 🌀 🔌 💻

⊛ ▼▼▼ Signal Mountain Lodge ⊞
(307) 543-2831. **$200-$469, 7 day notice.** 1 Inner Park Rd 83013. Jct US 26, 89 and 191, 3 mi s on Teton Park Rd. Ext corridors.
Pets: Accepted. 💾 🌿 🍴 🔌 ✕ 🛜 ✕ 🌀 🔌 💻

▼▼▼ Togwotee Mountain Lodge ⊞
(307) 543-2847. **$179-$259.** 27655 Hwy US 26 & 287 83013. 16.5 mi e of Moran; 38 mi nw of Dubois. Ext/int corridors. **Pets:** Accepted.
🍴 🔌 ✕ 🛜 ✕ 🔌 💻

GREEN RIVER

▼▼▼ Hampton Inn & Suites by Hilton Green River ⊞
(307) 875-5300. **$109-$184.** 1055 Wild Horse Canyon Rd 82935. I-80 exit 89, 0.4 mi s, then 0.5 mi n. Int corridors. **Pets:** Medium. $100 deposit/room. Service with restrictions, supervision.
🍴 🔌 🛒 🛜 ✕ 🔌 💻

HULETT

▼ Hulett Motel Ⓜ
(307) 467-5220. **Call for rates.** 202 Main St 82720. On SR 24 (Main St), north end of town. Ext corridors. **Pets:** Accepted.
🍴 🛜 ✕ 🔌 💻

JACKSON

⊛ ▼▼▼ 49'er Inn and Suites Quality Inn ⊞
(307) 733-7550. **$115-$309.** 330 W Pearl St 83001. 0.3 mi e of US 89 and 191 (W Broadway Ave) and Pearl St. Ext/int corridors. **Pets:** $50 deposit/room, $10 one-time fee/pet. Service with restrictions, supervision. 💾 🔌 🛜 ✕ 🔌 💻

⊛ ▼▼▼ Antler Inn Ⓜ
(307) 733-2535. **$90-$300, 4 day notice.** 43 W Pearl St 83001. Just w of S Cache and W Pearl sts; just s of Town Square. Ext/int corridors.
Pets: Dogs only. Supervision. 💾 ✕ 🛜 ✕ 🔌 💻

⊛ ▼▼▼ Cowboy Village Resort ⊠ 🐾
(307) 733-3121. **$99-$289.** 120 S Flat Creek Dr 83001. 0.4 mi w of Town Square to Flat Creek Dr, then just s. Ext corridors. **Pets:** Large, dogs only. No service, supervision.
💾 🔌 🛒 ✕ 🛜 🔌 💻

⊛ ▼▼▼ Elk Country Inn Ⓜ
(307) 733-2364. **$76-$328.** 480 W Pearl Ave 83001. 0.4 mi w of Towne Square; just e of jct US 89/191 (W Broadway Ave) and Pearl Ave. Ext/int corridors. **Pets:** Accepted. 💾 🔌 ✕ 🛜 ✕ 🔌 💻

▼▼▼ Homewood Suites Jackson Hole ⊞
(307) 739-0808. **$149-$439.** 260 N Millward St 83001. 0.3 mi n of US 89 and 191 (W Broadway Ave) and N Millward St; just nw of Town Square. Int corridors. **Pets:** Accepted. 🔌 ✕ 🛜 ✕ 🔌 💻

▼▼▼ Snow King Hotel ⊞
(307) 733-5200. **$125-$599, 14 day notice.** 400 E Snow King Ave 83001. 0.4 mi s of E Broadway. Ext/int corridors. **Pets:** Accepted.
🍴 🔌 🛒 ✕ 🛜 ✕ 🔌 💻

KEMMERER

⊛ ▼▼▼ Best Western Plus Fossil Country Inn & Suites ⊞
(307) 877-3388. **$99-$149.** 760 US 30/189 83101. Jct US 30 and 189. Int corridors. **Pets:** Accepted. 💾 🔌 🛒 🛜 ✕ 🔌 💻

LANDER

▼▼▼ Holiday Inn Express & Suites Lander ⊞
(307) 332-4005. **Call for rates.** 1002 11th St 82520. 1 mi w on US 287, just w on Lincoln St. Int corridors. **Pets:** Accepted.
🔌 🛒 🛜 ✕ 🔌 💻

⊛ ▼▼▼ The Inn at Lander ⊞
(307) 332-2847. **$125.** 260 Grand View Dr 82520. Jct US 287 and SR 789. Int corridors. **Pets:** Medium. $25 daily fee/pet. Designated rooms, service with restrictions, supervision.
💾 🔌 🛒 🛜 ✕ 🔌 💻

⊛ ▼▼▼ Rodeway Inn & Suites Pronghorn Lodge Ⓜ
(307) 332-3940. **$70-$125, 3 day notice.** 150 E Main St 82520. Just n of jct US 287 and SR 789. Ext corridors. **Pets:** Accepted.
💾 🍴 🔌 🛜 🔌 💻

LARAMIE

▼▼▼ AmericInn Lodge & Suites of Laramie ⊞
(307) 745-0777. **Call for rates.** 4712 E Grand Ave 82070. I-80 exit 316 (Grand Ave), just n. Int corridors. **Pets:** Accepted.
🍴 🔌 🛒 🛜 ✕ 🔌 💻

⊛ ▼▼▼ Best Western Laramie Inn & Suites ⊞
(307) 745-5700. **$120-$180.** 1767 N Banner Rd 82072. I-80 exit 310 (Curtis St), just n. Int corridors. **Pets:** Medium. $20 daily fee/pet. Designated rooms, service with restrictions, supervision.
💾 🍴 🛒 🛜 ✕ 🔌 💻

▼▼▼ Days Inn ⊞
(307) 745-5678. **$91-$170.** 1368 N McCue St 82072. I-80 exit 310 (Curtis St), 0.3 mi e, then just s. Int corridors. **Pets:** Accepted.
🍴 🛒 🛜 🔌 💻

▼▼▼ Hampton Inn ⊞
(307) 742-0125. **$85-$214.** 3715 E Grand Ave 82070. I-80 exit 316 (Grand Ave), 2.2 mi nw to Boulder Dr. Int corridors. **Pets:** Service with restrictions, supervision. 🔌 🛒 🛜 🔌 💻

▼▼▼ Holiday Inn ⊞
(307) 721-9000. **Call for rates.** 204 S 30th St 82070. I-80 exit 316 (Grand Ave), 2.5 mi w to 30th St. Int corridors. **Pets:** Accepted.
🍴 🔌 🛒 🛜 ✕ 🔌 💻

LITTLE AMERICA

⊛ ▼▼▼ Little America Hotel Ⓜ
(307) 875-2400. **Call for rates.** I-80, exit 68 82929. I-80 exit 68, just n. Ext/int corridors. **Pets:** Accepted. 💾 🍴 🛒 🛜 ✕ 🔌 💻

LUSK

⊛ ▼▼▼ Best Western Pioneer Ⓜ
(307) 334-2640. **$89-$299.** 731 S Main St 82225. Just n of jct US 20/85. Ext corridors. **Pets:** Accepted.
💾 🔌 🛒 🛜 ✕ 🔌 💻

PAINTER

▼▼ Hunter Peak Ranch ⊠
(307) 587-3711. **$150-$215, 91 day notice.** 4027 Crandall Rd 82414. SR 296, 5 mi s of US 212; 40 mi n of SR 120. Ext corridors.
Pets: Dogs only. $20 daily fee/pet. No service, supervision.
🍴 🛜 ✕ 🐾 🌀 🛒 🔌 💻

PINEDALE

▼▼▼ Baymont Inn & Suites ⊞
(307) 367-8300. **$59-$144.** 1424 W Pine St 82941. On US 191 (W Pine St), 1 mi w of downtown. Int corridors. **Pets:** Accepted.
🅰 🖢ᴹ ➰ 📶 ✕ 🛏 🖵

⨁ ▼▼▼ Best Western Pinedale Inn ⊞
(307) 367-6869. **$79-$149.** 864 W Pine St 82941. On US 191 (W Pine St), 0.5 mi w of downtown. Int corridors. **Pets:** Accepted.
SAVE ➰ 📶 ✕ 🛏 🖵

⨁ ▼▼▼ Hampton Inn & Suites ⊞ ❀
(307) 367-6700. **$99-$189.** 55 Bloomfield Ave 82941. On US 191 (W Pine St), 1.2 mi w of downtown. Int corridors. **Pets:** Medium. $35 one-time fee/pet. Designated rooms, service with restrictions, crate.
SAVE 🍽 🖢ᴹ ➰ 📶 ✕ 🛏 🖵

POWELL

▼▼ Americas Best Value Inn Ⓜ
(307) 754-5117. **Call for rates.** 777 E 2nd St 82435. 0.3 mi e on US 14A. Ext corridors. **Pets:** Accepted. 🍽 ➰ 📶 🛏 🖵

RAWLINS

⨁ ▼▼▼ Best Western CottonTree Inn Rawlins ⊞
(307) 324-2737. **$119-$179.** 2221 W Spruce St 82301. I-80 exit 211, just n. Ext/int corridors. **Pets:** Accepted.
SAVE 🍽 🖢ᴹ ➰ 📶 ✕ 🛏 🖵

⨁ ▼▼▼ Comfort Inn & Suites ⊞
(307) 324-3663. **$115-$155.** 2366 E Cedar St 82301. I-80 exit 215 (Cedar St), 1 mi w. Int corridors. **Pets:** Dogs only. $20 one-time fee/pet. Designated rooms, service with restrictions, supervision.
SAVE 🍽 🖢ᴹ ➰ 📶 ✕ 🛏 🖵

▼▼▼ Hampton Inn by Hilton Rawlins ⊞
(307) 324-2320. **$89-$199.** 406 Airport Rd 82301. I-80 exit 215 (Cedar St), 0.8 mi nw. Int corridors. **Pets:** Accepted.
🍽 🖢ᴹ ➰ 📶 ✕ 🛏 🖵

⨁ ▼▼▼ Pronghorn Inn & Suites ⊞
(307) 324-5588. **Call for rates.** 812 Locust St 82301. I-80 exit 214, 0.4 mi n on Higley Blvd, then just e. Int corridors. **Pets:** Accepted.
SAVE 🍽 📶 ✕ 🛏 🖵

RIVERTON

▼▼ Comfort Inn & Suites ⊞
(307) 856-8900. **$84-$179.** 2020 N Federal Blvd 82501. 1.5 mi ne on US 26/SR 789. Int corridors. **Pets:** Accepted.
🖢ᴹ ➰ 📶 ✕ 🛏 🖵

▼▼▼ Hampton Inn & Suites Riverton ⊞ ❀
(307) 856-3500. **$109-$189.** 2500 N Federal Blvd (US 26) 82501. 2 mi ne on US 26/SR 789. Int corridors. **Pets:** Medium. Service with restrictions, supervision. ⊟ 🍽 🖢ᴹ ➰ 📶 ✕ 🛏 🖵

⨁ ▼▼▼ Wind River Hotel & Casino ⊞
(307) 856-3964. **$80-$149.** 10269 Hwy 789 82501. 3 mi s from jct US 26. Int corridors. **Pets:** Accepted. SAVE 🍽 🖢ᴹ 📶 ✕ 🛏 🖵

ROCK SPRINGS

▼▼▼ Hampton Inn by Hilton Rock Springs ⊞
(307) 382-9222. **Call for rates.** 1901 Dewar Dr 82901. I-80 exit 102 (Dewar Dr), 0.5 mi se. Int corridors. **Pets:** Accepted.
🖢ᴹ ➰ 📶 ✕ 🛏 🖵

▼▼▼ Holiday Inn Express & Suites Rock Springs ⊞
(307) 362-9200. **Call for rates.** 1660 Sunset Dr 82901. I-80 exit 102 (Dewar Dr), just e, then 0.5 mi sw. Int corridors. **Pets:** Accepted.
🖢ᴹ 📶 ✕ 🛏 🖵

▼▼▼ Holiday Inn Rock Springs ⊞
(307) 382-9200. **Call for rates.** 1675 Sunset Dr 82901. I-80 exit 102 (Dewar Dr), just e, then 0.7 mi sw. Ext/int corridors. **Pets:** Accepted.
🍽 🖢ᴹ ➰ 📶 ✕ 🛏 🖵

▼▼▼ My Place Hotel Rock Springs ⊞
(307) 362-5977. **Call for rates.** 700 Gateway Blvd 82901. I-80 exit 102 (Dewar Dr), just se, then 0.6 mi n. Int corridors. **Pets:** Accepted.
🍽 🖢ᴹ 📶 ✕ 🛏 🖵

SHERIDAN (Restaurants p. 629)

⨁ ▼ Americas Best Value Inn Ⓜ
(307) 672-9757. **$76-$116.** 580 E 5th St 82801. I-90 exit 23 (5th St), 0.4 mi w. Ext corridors. **Pets:** Other species. Designated rooms, service with restrictions, supervision. SAVE 📶 🛏 🖵

⨁ ▼▼▼ Best Western Sheridan Center Ⓜ ❀
(307) 674-7421. **$89-$210.** 612 N Main St 82801. I-90 exit 23 (5th St), 1 mi w, then just s. Ext/int corridors. **Pets:** Other species. $20 one-time fee/room. Designated rooms, service with restrictions, supervision.
SAVE ⊟ 🍽 ➰ 📶 ✕ 🛏 🖵

▼▼▼ Candlewood Suites ⊞
(307) 675-2100. **Call for rates.** 1709 Sugarland Dr 82801. I-90 exit 25, just w, then just n. Int corridors. **Pets:** Accepted. 🖢ᴹ 📶 🛏 🖵

⨁ ▼▼▼ Holiday Inn Atrium & Convention Center ⊞
(307) 672-8931. **Call for rates.** 1809 Sugarland Dr 82801. I-90 exit 25, just w on Brundage, then just n. Int corridors. **Pets:** Accepted.
SAVE 🍽 🖢ᴹ ➰ ✕ 📶 ✕ 🖵

▼ Super 8 Sheridan Ⓜ
(307) 672-9725. **$52-$169.** 2435 N Main St 82801. I-90 exit 20, 0.7 mi n. Int corridors. **Pets:** Accepted. 🍽 📶 ✕ 🛏 🖵

SUNDANCE

⨁ ▼▼▼ Best Western Inn at Sundance ⊞ ❀
(307) 283-2800. **$99-$199.** 2719 E Cleveland St 82729. I-90 exit 189, just n, then just w; 1.5 mi ne of SR 585. Int corridors. **Pets:** Other species. $20 daily fee/pet. Supervision.
SAVE 🍽 🖢ᴹ ➰ 📶 ✕ 🛏 🖵

TETON VILLAGE

⨁ ▼▼▼▼ Four Seasons Resort & Residences Jackson Hole ⊞ ❀
(307) 732-5000. **$400-$1900, 30 day notice.** 7680 Granite Loop Rd 83025. At base of Jackson Hole Mountain Resort. Int corridors. **Pets:** Medium, dogs only. Service with restrictions, supervision.
SAVE 🍽 🖢ᴹ ➰ ✕ 📶 ✕ 🖵

⨁ ▼▼▼▼ Teton Mountain Lodge & Spa ⊞
(307) 734-7111. **$139-$3500, 30 day notice.** 3385 Cody Ln 83025. At base of Jackson Hole Mountain Resort; Upper Village. Int corridors. **Pets:** Accepted. SAVE 🍽 🖢ᴹ ➰ ✕ 📶 ✕ 🛏 🖵

THERMOPOLIS

▼▼ Days Inn Hot Springs Convention Center ⊞ ❀
(307) 864-3131. **$77-$149.** 115 E Park St 82443. In Hot Springs State Park. Ext/int corridors. **Pets:** Other species. $15 daily fee/pet. Service with restrictions, supervision. 🍽 ➰ ✕ 📶 🛏 🖵

TORRINGTON

▼ Americas Best Value Inn Ⓜ
(307) 532-7118. **Call for rates.** 1548 S Main St 82240. Just s of jct US 26 (W Valley Rd) and 85 (Main St). Int corridors. **Pets:** Accepted.
➰ 📶 🛏 🖵

Holiday Inn Express & Suites H
(307) 532-7600. **Call for rates.** 1700 E Valley Rd 82240. On US 26 (E Valley Rd), 0.4 mi e of US 85 (Main St). Int corridors. **Pets:** Accepted.
SAVE 🔥M 🛏 📶 ✖ 📱 ☕

WRIGHT
Wright Hotel H
(307) 464-6060. **$129-$139, 3 day notice.** 300 Reata Dr 82732. Just w of jct SR 59 and 387. Int corridors. **Pets:** $25 daily fee/pet. Designated rooms, service with restrictions, supervision.
🍴 🔥M 📶 ✖ 📱 ☕

YELLOWSTONE NATIONAL PARK
Elephant Head Lodge CA
(307) 587-3980. **$150-$370, 30 day notice.** 1170 N Fork Hwy 82414. 11.7 mi e of Yellowstone National Park east gate on US 14/16/20. Ext corridors. **Pets:** Other species. $25 one-time fee/pet. Service with restrictions, supervision.
SAVE 🍴 ✖ 📶 ✖ 🍽 📺 💤 📱 ☕

Shoshone Lodge CA
(307) 587-4044. **Call for rates.** 349 North Fork Hwy 82190. 3.5 mi e of Yellowstone National Park east gate on US 14/16/20. Ext corridors.
Pets: Accepted. 🍴 📶 ✖ 🍽 💤 📱 ☕

Canadian Hotels

AIRDRIE

(AA) ◆◆ Best Western Airdrie H
(403) 948-3838. **$125-$200.** 121 Edmonton Tr SE T4B 1S2. Hwy 2 exit Airdrie/Irricana, just w, then 0.5 mi (0.9 km) s. Ext/int corridors. **Pets:** Dogs only. $10 daily fee/pet. Designated rooms, service with restrictions, supervision. [SAVE] [○] [🍽] [📶] [✕] [📁] [💻]

(AA) ◆◆◆ Comfort Inn & Suites Airdrie H
(403) 948-3411. **$100-$143.** 133 Sierra Springs Dr SE T4B 3G7. Hwy 2 exit 282 (Yankee Valley Blvd), just w. Int corridors. **Pets:** Medium, other species. $20 daily fee/pet. Designated rooms, service with restrictions, supervision. [SAVE] [&M] [🛆] [📶] [✕] [📁] [💻]

◆◆◆ Hampton Inn & Suites Airdrie H
(403) 980-4477. **$109-$169.** 52 E Lake Ave NE T4A 2G8. Hwy 2 exit E Airdrie, 0.8 mi (1.3 km) n. Int corridors. **Pets:** Accepted.
[&M] [📶] [✕] [📁] [💻]

◆◆◆ Holiday Inn Express & Suites Airdrie-Calgary North H
(403) 912-1952. **$109-$169.** 64 E Lake Ave NE T4A 2G8. Hwy 2 exit E Airdrie, 0.8 mi (1.3 km) n. Int corridors. **Pets:** Large. $15 daily fee/pet. Designated rooms, no service, supervision.
[○] [&M] [🛆] [📶] [✕] [📁] [💻]

◆◆ Super 8 Airdrie H
(403) 948-4188. **$120-$130.** 815 E Lake Blvd T4A 2G4. Hwy 2 exit E Airdrie, just e. Int corridors. **Pets:** Other species. $25 one-time fee/room. Designated rooms, service with restrictions, supervision.
[📶] [✕] [📁] [💻]

◆◆◆◆ Wingate by Wyndham Airdrie H
(587) 775-6171. **$99-$159.** 513 Gateway Rd NE T4B 0J6. Hwy 2 exit Airdrie, just w, then just s. Int corridors. **Pets:** Accepted.
[🍽] [📶] [✕] [📁] [💻]

BANFF (Restaurants p. 630)

◆◆ Banff Ptarmigan Inn H
(403) 762-2207. **$99-$269, 3 day notice.** 337 Banff Ave T1L 1B1. Between Moose and Elk sts. Int corridors. **Pets:** Accepted.
[🍽] [🛆] [📶] [✕] [🅰🅲] [📁] [💻]

◆◆◆◆ Banff Rocky Mountain Resort H
(403) 762-5531. **Call for rates.** 1029 Banff Ave T1L 1A2. Jct Banff Ave and Tunnel Mountain Rd; just s of Trans-Canada Hwy 1. Ext corridors.
Pets: Accepted. [🍽] [🛆] [📶] [✕] [🅰🅲] [📁] [💻]

(AA) ◆◆◆ Best Western Plus Siding 29 Lodge H
(403) 762-5575. **$120-$369.** 453 Marten St T1L 1B3. 0.6 mi (1 km) ne, just off Banff Ave. Int corridors. **Pets:** Accepted.
[SAVE] [🛆] [📶] [✕] [📁] [💻]

◆◆◆◆ Buffalo Mountain Lodge H
(403) 762-2400. **$179-$349, 3 day notice.** 700 Tunnel Mountain Rd T1L 1B3. Jct Banff Ave and Wolf St, 1 mi (1.6 km) ne. Ext corridors.
Pets: Accepted. [○] [🍽] [📶] [✕] [🅰🅲] [📁] [💻]

◆◆◆ Castle Mountain Chalets CA
(403) 762-3868. **$160-$400, 7 day notice.** Bow Valley Pkwy (Hwy 1A) & Hwy 93 S T1L 1B5. 20 mi (32 km) w on Trans-Canada Hwy 1 to jct Castle Mountain, 0.6 mi (1 km) ne on Hwy 1A (Bow Valley Pkwy). Ext corridors. **Pets:** Accepted. [📶] [✕] [🅰🅲] [🐾] [📁] [💻]

(AA) ◆◆◆ Douglas Fir Resort & Chalets CO ❀
(403) 762-5591. **Call for rates.** 525 Tunnel Mountain Rd T1L 1B2. Jct Banff Ave and Wolf St, 1 mi (1.6 km) ne. Ext/int corridors. **Pets:** Large, dogs only. $25 daily fee/pet. Designated rooms, service with restrictions, crate. [SAVE] [🛆] [📶] [✕] [📁] [💻]

(AA) ◆◆◆ ◆◆◆ The Fairmont Banff Springs H ❀
(403) 762-2211. **Call for rates.** 405 Spray Ave T1L 1J4. Just s on Banff Ave over the bridge, 0.3 mi (0.5 km) e. Int corridors. **Pets:** $39 daily fee/pet. Service with restrictions, crate.
[SAVE] [ECO] [🍽] [🛆] [✕] [📶] [✕] [📁] [💻]

◆◆◆ Hidden Ridge Resort CO
(403) 762-3544. **$129-$329, 3 day notice.** 901 Hidden Ridge Way T1L 1B7. Jct Banff Ave and Wolf St, 1 mi (1.6 km) ne. Ext corridors.
Pets: Accepted. [✕] [📶] [✕] [📁] [💻]

◆◆◆ Irwin's Mountain Inn H
(403) 762-4566. **$229-$299.** 429 Banff Ave T1L 1B2. N of Rabbit St. Int corridors. **Pets:** Other species. $25 daily fee/pet. Designated rooms, no service, supervision. [🍽] [✕] [📶] [✕] [📁] [💻]

(AA) ◆◆◆ Johnston Canyon Resort CA
(403) 762-2971. **Call for rates.** Hwy 1A T1L 1A9. 15 mi (24 km) nw on Hwy 1A (Bow Valley Pkwy). Ext corridors. **Pets:** Accepted.
[SAVE] [ECO] [🍽] [📶] [✕] [🅰🅲] [🐾] [📁] [💻]

◆◆ Red Carpet Inn H
(403) 762-4184. **Call for rates.** 425 Banff Ave T1L 1B6. Between Beaver and Rabbit sts. Int corridors. **Pets:** Accepted. [📶] [✕] [📁] [💻]

(AA) ◆◆◆◆ The Rimrock Resort Hotel H ❀
(403) 762-3356. **$188-$488, 3 day notice.** 300 Mountain Ave T1L 1J2. 2.4 mi (4 km) s via Sulphur Mountain Rd; adjacent to Upper Hot Springs Pool. Int corridors. **Pets:** $40 daily fee/pet. Designated rooms, service with restrictions, crate.
[SAVE] [🍽] [&M] [🛆] [✕] [📶] [✕] [📁] [💻]

BONNYVILLE

(AA) ◆◆◆ Best Western Bonnyville Inn & Suites H
(780) 826-6226. **$140-$170.** 5401 43rd St T9N 0H3. Hwy 28, just n at 44th St. Int corridors. **Pets:** Accepted.
[SAVE] [🍽] [&M] [📶] [✕] [📁] [💻]

◆◆◆ Comfort Inn & Suites Bonnyville H
(780) 826-2020. **$95-$189.** 5404 Lakeland Rd T9N 0B2. Hwy 28, just n at 44th St. Int corridors. **Pets:** Medium. $10 daily fee/pet. Designated rooms, service with restrictions, crate.
[🍽] [&M] [✕] [📶] [✕] [📁] [💻]

BROOKS

◆◆ Heritage Inn Hotel & Convention Centre Brooks H
(403) 362-6666. **$121-$180.** 1217 2nd St W T1R 1P7. Trans-Canada Hwy 1 exit Hwy 873, 0.5 mi (0.8 km) s. Int corridors. **Pets:** Accepted.
[🍽] [📶] [📁] [💻]

◆◆◆ Ramada Brooks H
(403) 362-6440. **$140-$170.** 1319 2nd St W T1R 1P7. Trans-Canada Hwy 1 exit Hwy 873, 0.5 mi (0.8 km) s. Ext/int corridors.
Pets: Accepted. [ECO] [&M] [🛆] [✕] [📶] [✕] [📁] [💻]

CALGARY

(AA) ◆◆◆ Calgary Marriott Downtown H
(403) 266-7331. **$92-$302.** 110 9th Ave SE T2G 5A6. Jct 9th Ave and Centre St; adjacent to TELUS Convention Centre. Int corridors.
Pets: Accepted. [SAVE] [ECO] [🍽] [&M] [🛆] [s◎] [✕] [📁] [💻]

(AA) ◆◆◆ Calgary Westways Guest House BB ❀
(403) 229-1758. **$110-$189, 4 day notice.** 216 25th Ave SW T2S 0L1. 1.1 mi (1.7 km) s on Hwy 2A (Macleod Tr), just w. Int corridors.
Pets: Other species. $10 daily fee/pet. [SAVE] [📶] [✕]

Carriage House Inn H ❀
(403) 253-1101. **$145-$369.** 9030 Macleod Tr S T2H 0M4. On Hwy 2A
(Macleod Tr); corner of 90th Ave SW. Int corridors. **Pets:** $20 daily fee/
pet. Designated rooms, service with restrictions, crate.
[SAVE] [ECO] [▮] [▭] [▦] [◈] [⊠] [▯] [▭]

Clarion Hotel & Conference Centre Calgary
Airport H
(403) 291-4666. **$89-$219.** 2120 16th Ave NE T2E 1L4. Just e of jct
Hwy 2 (Deerfoot Tr) and 16th Ave NE (Trans-Canada Hwy 1). Int corridors. **Pets:** Other species. $25 one-time fee/pet. Designated rooms,
service with restrictions, supervision.
[SAVE] [ECO] [▮] [▭] [&M] [▦] [◈] [⊠] [▯] [▭]

Coast Plaza Hotel & Conference Centre H
(403) 248-8888. **$109-$289, 3 day notice.** 1316 33rd St NE T2A 6B6.
Just s of jct 16th Ave (Trans-Canada Hwy 1) and 36th St NE, just w on
12th Ave NE. Int corridors. **Pets:** Accepted.
[SAVE] [ECO] [▮] [▭] [▦] [◈] [⊠] [▯] [▭]

Days Inn Calgary Northwest H
(403) 288-7115. **$113-$189.** 4420 16th Ave NW T3B 0M4. On 16th Ave
NW (Trans-Canada Hwy 1) at 43rd St NW. Int corridors.
Pets: Accepted. [ECO] [▦] [⊠] [▯] [▭]

Delta Calgary Airport In-Terminal
Hotel H ❀
(403) 291-2600. **$112-$244.** 2001 Airport Rd NE T2E 6Z8. At Calgary
International Airport. Int corridors. **Pets:** Small, other species. $35 daily
fee/room. Designated rooms, supervision.
[SAVE] [ECO] [▮] [▭] [&M] [▦] [◈] [⊠] [▯] [▭]

Delta Calgary Downtown H ❀
(403) 266-1980. **$100-$301.** 209 4th Ave SE T2G 0C6. Jct 1st St SE
and 4th Ave SE. Int corridors. **Pets:** Medium. $35 one-time fee/room.
Service with restrictions, crate.
[SAVE] [ECO] [▮] [▭] [&M] [▦] [◈] [⊠] [▯] [▭]

Delta Calgary South H
(403) 278-5050. **$85-$182.** 135 Southland Dr SE T2J 5X5. On Hwy 2A
(Macleod Tr); corner of Southland Dr. Int corridors. **Pets:** Accepted.
[ECO] [▮] [&M] [▭] [▦] [⊠] [▯] [▭]

Econo Lodge South M
(403) 252-4401. **$95-$190.** 7505 Macleod Tr SW T2H 0L8. Corner of
Hwy 2A (Macleod Tr) and 75th Ave SW. Ext/int corridors.
Pets: Accepted. [SAVE] [ECO] [▭] [▦] [▯] [▭]

Executive Royal Hotel North Calgary H
(403) 291-2003. **Call for rates.** 2828 23rd St NE T2E 8T4. Barlow Tr
NE, just w; at 27th Ave NE. Int corridors. **Pets:** Accepted.
[ECO] [▮] [&M] [▦] [⊠] [▯] [▭]

The Fairmont Palliser H ❀
(403) 262-1234. **$169-$699.** 133 9th Ave SW T2P 2M3. Jct 9th Ave SW
and 1st St SW. Int corridors. **Pets:** Medium. $25 daily fee/room. Service
with restrictions, supervision. [SAVE] [ECO] [▮] [▭] [▦] [◈] [⊠] [▭]

Holiday Inn Calgary-Airport H
(403) 230-1999. **Call for rates.** 1250 McKinnon Dr NE T2E 7T7. 0.6 mi
(1 km) e of jct Hwy 2 (Deerfoot Tr) and 16th Ave NE (Trans-Canada
Hwy 1). Int corridors. **Pets:** Accepted.
[▮] [&M] [▭] [▦] [⊠] [▯] [▭]

Holiday Inn Calgary-Macleod Trail
South H ❀
(403) 287-2700. **$119-$289.** 4206 Macleod Tr S T2G 2R7. Corner of
42nd Ave SW and Macleod Tr S. Int corridors. **Pets:** $20 one-time fee/
room. Designated rooms, service with restrictions.
[SAVE] [ECO] [▮] [&M] [▭] [▦] [⊠] [▯] [▭]

Holiday Inn Express Hotel & Suites
Calgary-South H
(403) 225-3000. **$130-$300.** 12025 Lake Fraser Dr SE (Macleod Tr S)
T2J 7G5. Hwy 2 (Deerfoot Tr) exit Anderson Rd W, just s on Macleod
Tr, just e on Lake Fraser Gate, then 0.4 mi (0.7 km) n. Int corridors.
Pets: $20 one-time fee/pet, $3 daily fee/pet. Designated rooms, service
with restrictions, supervision. [▭] [▦] [⊠] [▯] [▭]

Homewood Suites Calgary Airport H ❀
(403) 453-7888. **$119-$189.** 1000 2021 100th Ave NE T3J 0R3. Hwy 2
(Deerfoot Tr) exit 266, 1.1 mi (1.8 km) e on Airport Tr NE, then just n
on 19th St NE. Int corridors. **Pets:** Other species. $75 one-time fee/
room. Designated rooms, service with restrictions, crate.
[&M] [▦] [⊠] [▯] [▭]

Hotel Arts H
(403) 266-4611. **Call for rates.** 119 12th Ave SW T2R 0G8. At 1st St
SW; center. Int corridors. **Pets:** Accepted.
[▮] [&M] [▭] [▦] [⊠] [▯] [▭]

Hotel Blackfoot H ❀
(403) 252-2253. **$129-$299.** 5940 Blackfoot Tr SE T2H 2B5. At 58th
Ave SE. Int corridors. **Pets:** Other species. $25 one-time fee/pet. Ser-
vice with restrictions. [ECO] [▮] [&M] [▭] [▦] [◈] [⊠] [▯] [▭]

Hotel Le Germain Calgary H ❀
(403) 264-8990. **$209-$799.** 899 Centre St SW T2G 1B8. Corner of 1st
St SW and 9th Ave SW; center. Int corridors. **Pets:** Large. $30 one-time
fee/room. [SAVE] [▮] [▭] [▦] [◈] [⊠] [▭]

Hyatt Regency Calgary H ❀
(403) 717-1234. **$149-$709.** 700 Centre St SE T2G 5P6. Corner of
Centre St and 7th Ave SW. Int corridors. **Pets:** Small. $100 one-time
fee/room. Supervision. [SAVE] [▮] [&M] [▭] [▦] [◈] [⊠] [▯] [▭]

Lakeview Signature Inn H
(403) 735-3336. **$140-$310, 3 day notice.** 2622 39th Ave NE T1Y 7J9.
Barlow Tr NE, just e. Int corridors. **Pets:** Medium. $100 one-time fee/
room. Service with restrictions, supervision.
[ECO] [&M] [▭] [▦] [⊠] [▯] [▭]

Residence Inn by Marriott Calgary
Airport H
(403) 278-1000. **$95-$212.** 2530 48th Ave NE T3J 4V8. Just n of jct
Barlow Tr NE and McKnight Blvd NE. Int corridors. **Pets:** Accepted.
[SAVE] [▮] [&M] [▭] [▦] [⊠] [▯] [▭]

Residence Inn by Marriott Calgary
South H ❀
(587) 349-8633. **$136-$200.** 3710 Market St SE T3M 2P2. Hwy 2
(Deerfoot Tr) exit Seton Blvd SE, just e. Int corridors. **Pets:** Medium.
$75 one-time fee/room. Service with restrictions, crate.
[SAVE] [&M] [▦] [⊠] [▯] [▭]

Sandman Hotel Downtown Calgary H
(403) 237-8626. **Call for rates.** 888 7th Ave SW T2P 3J3. Corner of
7th Ave SW and 8th St SW. Int corridors. **Pets:** Accepted.
[ECO] [▮] [▭] [▦] [⊠] [▯] [▭]

Sandman Hotel Suites & Spa Calgary Airport H
(403) 219-2475. **Call for rates.** 25 Hopewell Way NE T3J 4V7. Just n
of jct Barlow Tr and McKnight Blvd. Int corridors. **Pets:** Accepted.
[ECO] [▮] [&M] [▭] [▦] [⊠] [▯] [▭]

Service Plus Inn & Suites Calgary H ❀
(403) 256-5352. **$139-$159.** 3503 114th Ave SE T2Z 3X2. South end of
Barlow Tr, just w. Int corridors. **Pets:** $15 daily fee/pet. Service with
restrictions, supervision. [SAVE] [▭] [▦] [⊠] [▯] [▭]

Sheraton Cavalier Hotel H ❀
(403) 291-0107. **$129-$409.** 2620 32nd Ave NE T1Y 6B8. Barlow Tr at
32nd Ave NE. Int corridors. **Pets:** Medium. Service with restrictions,
supervision. [SAVE] [ECO] [▮] [▭] [▦] [◈] [⊠] [▯] [▭]

ⓐ ▼▼▼ **Sheraton Suites Calgary Eau Claire** H ❖
(403) 266-7200. **$149-$789.** 255 Barclay Parade SW T2P 5C2. At 3rd St SW and 2nd Ave SW. Int corridors. **Pets:** Designated rooms, service with restrictions, supervision.
SAVE ECO ▦ 🍴 &M ≈ ☒ 📶 ☒ 🛄 ▣

ⓐ ▼▼▼ **Staybridge Suites Calgary Airport** H
(403) 204-7829. **$129-$199.** 2825 Sunridge Way NE T1Y 7K7. Trans-Canada Hwy 1 exit Barlow Tr NE, just n, then just e. Int corridors. **Pets:** Large. $75 one-time fee/room. Designated rooms, service with restrictions, supervision. SAVE 🍴 &M ≈ ☞ ☒ 🛄 ▣

ⓐ ▼▼▼ **Travelodge Calgary University** H
(403) 289-6600. **$109-$189.** 2227 Banff Tr NW T2M 4L2. 16th Ave NW (Trans-Canada Hwy 1) and Banff Tr NW. Int corridors. **Pets:** Accepted.
SAVE ECO ≈ ☞ ☒ 🛄 ▣

ⓐ ▼▼▼ **The Westin Calgary** H
(403) 266-1611. **$129-$399.** 320 4th Ave SW T2P 2S6. Corner of 4th Ave SW and 3rd St. Int corridors. **Pets:** Accepted.
SAVE 🍴 &M ≈ ☒ ☞ ☒ 🛄 ▣

▼▼▼ **Wingate by Wyndham Calgary** H ❖
(403) 514-0099. **$169-$399.** 400 Midpark Way SE T2X 3S4. Hwy 2A (Macleod Tr), 0.3 mi (0.5 km) e on Sun Valley Blvd SE, just n on Midpark Blvd SE, then just s. Int corridors. **Pets:** $25 daily fee/pet. Service with restrictions, supervision. ECO &M ≈ ☞ ☒ 🛄 ▣

ⓐ ▼▼▼ **Wyndham Garden Calgary Airport** H ❖
(403) 516-2266. **$90-$174.** 11 Freeport Cres NE T3J 0T4. Hwy 2 (Deerfoot Tr) exit 266, just ne. Int corridors. **Pets:** Medium, other species. $25 daily fee/pet. Designated rooms, service with restrictions, supervision. SAVE 🍴 ☒ ☞ ☒ 🛄 ▣

CAMROSE

ⓐ ▼▼▼ **Best Western Plus Camrose Resort & Casino** H
(780) 679-2376. **Call for rates.** 3201 48th Ave T4V 0K9. Hwy 13 (48th Ave), just s of Correction Line Rd; eastern approach to city. Int corridors. **Pets:** Accepted. SAVE 🍴 &M ≈ ☞ ☒ 🛄 ▣

▼▼▼ **Canalta Hotel Camrose** H
(780) 672-7303. **Call for rates.** 4710 73rd St T4V 0E5. Hwy 13 (48th Ave), just s. Int corridors. **Pets:** Accepted. ≈ ☞ ☒ 🛄 ▣

▼▼ **Norsemen Inn** H
(780) 672-9171. **$104-$129.** 6505 48th Ave T4V 3K3. Hwy 13 (48th Ave) at 65th St; west end of town. Int corridors. **Pets:** Other species. $20 daily fee/room. Service with restrictions. 🍴 ☞ ☒ 🛄 ▣

▼▼▼ **Ramada Inn Camrose** H
(780) 672-5220. **$140-$200.** 4702 73rd St T4V 0E5. Hwy 13 (48th Ave), just s. Int corridors. **Pets:** Accepted. ≈ ☞ ☒ 🛄 ▣

CANMORE

ⓐ ▼▼▼ **Banff Boundary Lodge** CO
(403) 678-9555. **$109-$279.** 1000 Harvie Heights Rd T1W 2W2. Trans-Canada Hwy 1 exit 86, just n. Ext corridors. **Pets:** $25 daily fee/room. Designated rooms, no service, crate.
SAVE 🍴 ☞ ☒ ☒ 🛄 ▣

ⓐ ▼▼▼ **Best Western Pocaterra Inn** H
(403) 678-4334. **$140-$355.** 1725 Mountain Ave T1W 2W1. Trans-Canada Hwy 1 exit 86, 1.3 mi (2.1 km) e. Int corridors. **Pets:** Accepted.
SAVE &M ≈ ☒ ☞ ☒ 🛄 ▣

▼▼ **Canadian Rockies Chalets** CO
(403) 678-3799. **Call for rates.** 1206 Bow Valley Tr T1W 1N6. Trans-Canada Hwy 1 exit 89, 0.9 mi (1.5 km) se. Ext corridors.
Pets: Accepted. ☞ ☒ ☒ 🛄 ▣

ⓐ ▼▼▼ **Coast Canmore Hotel & Conference Centre** H
(403) 678-3625. **$119-$399.** 511 Bow Valley Tr T1W 1N7. Trans-Canada Hwy 1 exit 89, 1.4 mi (2.2 km) s. Int corridors. **Pets:** Accepted.
SAVE ECO 🍴 &M ≈ ☞ ☒ 🛄 ▣

▼▼ **Days Inn Canmore** H
(403) 678-5488. **$120-$250.** 1602 2nd Ave T1W 1M8. Trans-Canada Hwy 1 exit 89, 1.3 mi (2.1 km) e. Int corridors. **Pets:** Accepted.
🍴 ☞ ☒ 🛄 ▣

▼▼▼ **Fire Mountain Lodge** CO
(403) 609-9949. **Call for rates.** 121 Kananaskis Way T1W 2X2. Trans-Canada Hwy 1 exit 89, 1 mi (1.6 km) s. Ext corridors. **Pets:** Accepted.
☞ ☒ 🛄 ▣

▼▼▼ **Mystic Springs Chalets & Hot Pools** CO
(403) 609-0333. **$209-$429.** 140 Kananaskis Way T1W 2X2. Trans-Canada Hwy 1 exit 89, 1.1 mi (1.8 km) s. Ext corridors.
Pets: Accepted. ECO ≈ ☒ ☞ ☒ 🛄 ▣

▼▼ **Quality Resort-Chateau Canmore** H
(403) 678-6699. **$95-$299.** 1720 Bow Valley Tr T1W 2X3. Trans-Canada Hwy 1 exit 86, 0.5 mi (0.8 km) s. Int corridors. **Pets:** $15 daily fee/pet. Designated rooms, service with restrictions.
🍴 ≈ ☒ ☞ ☒ 🛄 ▣

▼▼ **Ramada Inn & Suites Canmore** H
(403) 609-4656. **$89-$399.** 1402 Bow Valley Tr T1W 1N5. Trans-Canada Hwy 1 exit 89, 1 mi (1.6 km) se. Int corridors. **Pets:** Accepted.
&M ≈ ☞ ☒ 🛄 ▣

ⓐ ▼▼▼ **Rocky Mountain Ski Lodge** M
(403) 678-5445. **$109-$239.** 1711 Bow Valley Tr T1W 2T8. Trans-Canada Hwy 1 exit 86, 0.5 mi (0.8 km) s. Ext corridors. **Pets:** Medium. $15 daily fee/pet. Designated rooms, service with restrictions, supervision. SAVE ECO ☒ ☞ ☒ 🛄 ▣

▼▼ **Solara Resort & Spa** CO
(403) 609-3600. **$159-$709, 7 day notice.** 187 Kananaskis Way T1W 0A3. Trans-Canada Hwy 1 exit 89, 1.2 mi (2 km) s. Int corridors.
Pets: Accepted. 🍴 ☒ ☞ ☒ 🛄 ▣

CLAIRMONT

▼▼ **Ramada Clairmont/Grande Prairie** H
(780) 814-7448. **$139-$239.** 7201 99th St T0H 0W0. Jct Hwy 43 and 2, just n. Ext/int corridors. **Pets:** Accepted. 🍴 ☞ 🛄 ▣

CLARESHOLM

▼▼ **Bluebird Motel** M
(403) 625-3395. **Call for rates.** 5505 1st St W T0L 0T0. 0.3 mi (0.5 km) n on Hwy 2. Ext corridors. **Pets:** Accepted. ☞ ☒ 🛄 ▣

▼ **Motel 6 Claresholm** H
(403) 625-4646. **Call for rates.** 11 Alberta Rd (Hwy 2) T0L 0T0. North end of town. Int corridors. **Pets:** Accepted. 🍴 &M ☞ 🛄

COCHRANE

▼▼▼ **Days Inn & Suites Cochrane** H
(403) 932-5588. **$99-$180.** 5 West Side Dr T4C 1M1. Jct Hwy 1A and 22, 0.4 mi (0.6 km) s, just e on Quigley Dr, then just s. Int corridors.
Pets: Accepted. ≈ ☞ 🛄 ▣

ⓐ ▼▼▼ **Super 8 Cochrane** H
(403) 932-1410. **$120-$160.** 11 West Side Dr T4C 1M1. Jct Hwy 1A and 22, 0.4 mi (0.6 km) s, just e on Quigley Dr, then just s. Int corridors. **Pets:** Other species. $15 daily fee/pet. Designated rooms, service with restrictions, crate. SAVE ☒ ☞ ☒ 🛄 ▣

COLD LAKE

(AAA) ▼▼▼▼ Best Western Cold Lake Inn 🅷
(780) 594-4888. **$139-$249.** 4815 52nd St T9M 1P1. Corner of 55th Ave (Hwy 26 and 55) and 52nd St; south end of city. Ext/int corridors. **Pets:** Accepted. [SAVE] 🍴 🕭M 🏊 📶 ☒ 🛢 🖵

DEAD MAN'S FLATS

▼▼▼▼ Copperstone Resort Hotel 🅲🅾
(403) 678-0303. **Call for rates.** 250 2nd Ave T1W 2W4. Trans-Canada Hwy 1 exit 98, just n on 2nd St, then just e. Int corridors. **Pets:** Accepted. 📶 ☒ 🛢 🖵

DRAYTON VALLEY

(AAA) ▼▼▼▼ Best Western Plus Executive Residency Drayton Valley 🅷
(780) 621-2378. **$150-$180.** 2252 50th St T7A 1R5. Just n on Hwy 39; south end of town. Int corridors. **Pets:** Accepted.
[SAVE] 🕭M 📶 ☒ 🛢 🖵

▼▼▼▼ Holiday Inn Express Hotel & Suites 🅷
(780) 515-9888. **Call for rates.** 5001 Brougham Dr T7A 0A1. Hwy 22 exit Drayton Valley, 1.5 mi (2.4 km) n. Int corridors. **Pets:** Accepted.
🕭M 📶 ☒ 🛢 🖵

▼▼ Lakeview Inn & Suites 🅷
(780) 542-3200. **Call for rates.** 4302 50th St T7A 1M4. Hwy 22 exit Drayton Valley, 1.5 mi (2.4 km) n. Int corridors. **Pets:** Accepted.
🍴 📶 ☒ 🛢 🖵

▼▼▼▼ Ramada Drayton Valley 🅷
(780) 514-7861. **$140.** 2051 50th St T7A 1S5. Just n on Hwy 39; south end of town. Ext/int corridors. **Pets:** Accepted.
🅴🅲🅾 🕭M 🏊 📶 ☒ 🛢 🖵

DRUMHELLER

▼▼▼▼ Canalta Jurassic Hotel 🅷
(403) 823-7700. **Call for rates.** 1103 Hwy 9 S T0J 0Y0. Hwy 9, southeast access to town. Ext/int corridors. **Pets:** Accepted.
🅴🅲🅾 📶 ☒ 🛢 🖵

▼▼▼▼ Inn and Spa at Heartwood 🅲🅸
(403) 823-6495. **$135-$225, 3 day notice.** 320 N Railway Ave E T0J 0Y4. Jct Hwy 9 and 575 (S Railway Ave SE), just n, just e. Ext/int corridors. **Pets:** Accepted. 📶 ☒ 🛢 🖵

▼▼▼▼ Ramada Inn & Suites 🅷
(403) 823-2028. **$160-$220.** 680 2nd St SE T0J 0Y0. Jct Hwy 9 and 575 (S Railway Ave SE), just ne. Ext/int corridors. **Pets:** Accepted.
🅴🅲🅾 🕭M 🏊 📶 ☒ 🛢 🖵

▼▼▼▼ Super 8 Drumheller 🅷
(403) 823-8887. **$140-$255.** 600-680 2nd St SE T0J 0Y0. Jct Hwy 9 and 575 (S Railway Ave SE), just ne. Ext/int corridors. **Pets:** Accepted.
🅴🅲🅾 🏊 📶 ☒ 🛢 🖵

EDMONTON

(AAA) ▼▼▼ Best Western Cedar Park Inn 🅷
(780) 434-7411. **$119-$139.** 5116 Gateway Blvd T6H 2H4. Hwy 2 (Gateway Blvd) at 51st Ave. Int corridors. **Pets:** Accepted.
[SAVE] 🍴 🕭M 📶 ☒ 🛢 🖵

(AAA) ▼▼▼ Best Western Plus Westwood Inn 🅷
(780) 483-7770. **$109-$129.** 18035 Stony Plain Rd T5S 1B2. Hwy 16A (Stony Plain Rd) at 180th St. Int corridors. **Pets:** Accepted.
[SAVE] 🍴 🏊 📶 ☒ 🛢 🖵

(AAA) ▼▼▼ Comfort Inn West 🅷
(780) 484-4415. **$99-$180.** 17610 100th Ave T5S 1S9. At 176th St. Int corridors. **Pets:** Accepted. [SAVE] 🅴🅲🅾 🍴 📶 ☒ 🛢 🖵

▼▼▼▼ Continental Inn 🅷
(780) 484-7751. **$120-$145.** 16625 Stony Plain Rd T5P 4A8. On Hwy 16A (Stony Plain Rd) at 166th St. Int corridors. **Pets:** Medium. $200 deposit/pet. Service with restrictions, supervision.
🍴 📶 ☒ 🛢 🖵

(AAA) ▼▼▼▼ Delta Edmonton Centre Suite Hotel 🅷
(780) 429-3900. **$80-$187.** 10222 102nd St NW T5J 4C5. At 102nd St NW and 103rd Ave NW. Int corridors. **Pets:** Accepted.
[SAVE] 🅴🅲🅾 🍴 🕭M 📶 ☒ 🛢 🖵

(AAA) ▼▼▼▼ Delta Edmonton South Hotel and Conference Centre 🅷
(780) 434-6415. **$113-$175.** 4404 Gateway Blvd T6H 5C2. Jct Hwy 2 (Gateway Blvd) and Whitemud Dr. Int corridors. **Pets:** Accepted.
[SAVE] 🅴🅲🅾 🍴 🕭M 🏊 📶 ☒ 🛢 🖵

▼▼▼▼ DoubleTree by Hilton West Edmonton 🅷
(780) 484-0821. **$139-$169.** 16615 109th Ave T5P 4K8. 1 mi (1.6 km) n of jct Hwy 2 (170th St) and 16A (Stony Plain Rd). Int corridors.
Pets: Accepted. 🅴🅲🅾 🍴 🕭M 📶 ☒ 🛢 🖵

▼▼▼▼ Executive Royal Hotel West Edmonton 🅷
(780) 484-6000. **$124-$200, 7 day notice.** 10010 178th St T5S 1T3. Corner of 178th St and 100th Ave. Int corridors. **Pets:** Accepted.
🅴🅲🅾 🍴 📶 ☒ 🛢 🖵

(AAA) ▼▼▼▼▼ The Fairmont Hotel Macdonald 🅷 🐾
(780) 424-5181. **$189-$489.** 10065 100th St T5J 0N6. Just s of Jasper Ave. Int corridors. **Pets:** Other species. $25 daily fee/room. Service with restrictions, supervision. [SAVE] 🅴🅲🅾 🍴 🕭M 🏊 📶 ☒ 🖵

▼▼▼▼ Fantasyland Hotel 🅷
(780) 444-3000. **Call for rates.** 17700 87th Ave T5T 4V4. At 178th St; in West Edmonton Mall, at southwest end. Int corridors. **Pets:** Accepted.
🅴🅲🅾 🍴 🕭M 📶 ☒ 🛢 🖵

(AAA) ▼▼▼ Four Points by Sheraton Edmonton South 🅷 🐾
(780) 465-7931. **Call for rates.** 7230 Argyll Rd T6C 4A6. Hwy 2 (Gateway Blvd), 2.3 mi (3.7 km) e at 63rd Ave (which becomes Argyll Rd); at 75th St. Int corridors. **Pets:** $25 daily fee/pet. Designated rooms, service with restrictions, supervision.
[SAVE] 🍴 🕭M 🏊 📶 ☒ 🛢 🖵

▼▼▼▼ Holiday Inn & Suites, West Edmonton 🅷
(780) 444-3110. **$129-$249.** 11330 170th St T5S 2X1. Between 113th and 114th aves. Int corridors. **Pets:** Accepted.
🍴 🕭M 🏊 📶 ☒ 🛢 🖵

▼▼▼▼ Holiday Inn Express Edmonton Downtown 🅷
(780) 423-2450. **Call for rates.** 10010 104th St T5J 0Z1. Corner of 100th Ave; center. Int corridors. **Pets:** $30 one-time fee/room. Designated rooms, service with restrictions, supervision.
🅴🅲🅾 🕭M 🏊 ☒ 📶 🛢 🖵

▼▼▼▼ Metterra Hotel on Whyte 🅷
(780) 465-8150. **Call for rates.** 10454 82nd Ave (Whyte Ave) T6E 4Z7. Just e of 105th St. Int corridors. **Pets:** Accepted.
🕭M 📶 ☒ 🛢 🖵

▼▼▼▼ Quality Inn West Edmonton 🅷 🐾
(780) 484-8000. **$114-$230.** 17803 Stony Plain Rd NW T5S 1B4. Jct Hwy 16A (Stony Plain Rd) and 178th St. Int corridors. **Pets:** Medium, other species. $20 one-time fee/room. Designated rooms, service with restrictions, supervision. 🕭M 📶 ☒ 🛢 🖵

(AAA) ▼▼▼▼ Radisson Hotel Edmonton South 🅷
(780) 437-6010. **$119-$349.** 4440 Gateway Blvd NW T6H 5C2. Between Whitemud Dr and 45th Ave. Int corridors. **Pets:** Accepted.
[SAVE] 🅴🅲🅾 🍴 🕭M 🏊 ☒ 📶 ☒ 🛢 🖵

▼▼▼ Ramada Inn Edmonton South 🅷
(780) 434-3431. **$92-$160.** 5359 Calgary Tr NW T6H 4J9. Just n of 51st Ave. Int corridors. **Pets:** Accepted. 🍴 🕭M 📶 ☒ 🛢 🖵

(CAA) ▼▼▼ **Sawridge Inn Edmonton South** 🅷
(780) 438-1222. **$109-$189, 15 day notice.** 4235 Gateway Blvd T6J 5H2. Just s of Whitemud Dr. Int corridors. **Pets:** Other species. $20 daily fee/pet. Designated rooms, service with restrictions, crate.
SAVE ECO 🍽 ⅙M 📶 ⊠ 🅱 💻

(CAA) ▼▼▼ **Staybridge Suites West Edmonton** 🅷
(780) 484-6223. **$152-$190.** 16929 109 Ave NW T5P 4P6. Hwy 216 (Anthony Henday Dr) exit 21. Int corridors. **Pets:** Accepted.
SAVE ⅙M 📶 ⊠ 🅱 💻

▼▼ **Super 8 Edmonton South** 🅷
(780) 433-8688. **$120-$134.** 3610 Gateway Blvd T6J 7H8. Jct 36th Ave. Int corridors. **Pets:** Accepted. ⅙M ⅏ 📶 ⊠ 🅱 💻

▼▼▼ **The Sutton Place Hotel Edmonton** 🅷
(780) 428-7111. **Call for rates.** 10235 101st St T5J 3E9. Jct 102nd Ave and 101st St. Int corridors. **Pets:** Accepted.
ECO 🍽 ⅏ 📶 ⊠ 🅱 💻

▼▼▼ **Varscona Hotel on Whyte** 🅷
(780) 434-6111. **Call for rates.** 8208 106th St T6E 6R9. Corner of 82nd Ave (Whyte Ave) and 106th St. Int corridors. **Pets:** Accepted.
ECO 🍽 ⅙M 📶 ⊠ 🅱 💻

▼▼ **West Edmonton Mall Inn** 🅷
(780) 444-9378. **Call for rates.** 17504 90th Ave T5T 6L6. From Whitemud Dr exit 170th St N, just w. Int corridors. **Pets:** Accepted.
⅙M 📶 ⊠ 🅱 💻

(CAA) ▼▼▼▼ **The Westin Edmonton** 🅷 🐾
(780) 426-3636. **$129-$329.** 10135 100th St T5J 0N7. Jct 101st Ave. Int corridors. **Pets:** Medium. Designated rooms, service with restrictions, supervision. SAVE ECO 🍽 ⅙M ⅏ ⊠ 📶 ⊠ 🅱 💻

▼▼▼ **Wingate Inn Edmonton West** 🅷
(780) 443-1000. **$129-$249.** 18220 100th Ave T5S 2V2. From Anthony Henday Dr, 0.9 mi (1.5 km) e; at 182nd St. Int corridors.
Pets: Accepted. 🍽 ⅙M ⅏ 📶 🅱 💻

EDSON

(CAA) ▼▼▼ **Best Western High Road Inn** 🅷
(780) 712-2378. **$136-$170.** 300 52nd St T7E 1V8. On 2nd Ave; center. Int corridors. **Pets:** Accepted. SAVE 🍽 ⅙M 📶 🅱 💻

▼▼▼ **Lakeview Inn & Suites Edson Airport West** 🅷
(780) 723-7508. **Call for rates.** 528 63rd St T7E 1M1. Hwy 16, west end of town. Int corridors. **Pets:** Accepted. ECO ⅙M 📶 🅱 💻

▼▼▼ **Ramada Edson** 🅷
(780) 723-9797. **$74-$119.** 4536 2nd Ave T7E 1C3. 0.6 mi (1 km) e on Hwy 16. Int corridors. **Pets:** Accepted. 📶 ⊠ 🅱 💻

FORT MACLEOD

▼▼ **Sunset Motel** Ⓜ
(403) 553-4448. **Call for rates.** 104 Hwy 3 W T0L 0Z0. 0.6 mi (1 km) w on Hwy 2 and 3. Ext corridors. **Pets:** Accepted. 📶 🅱 💻

FORT MCMURRAY

(CAA) ▼▼▼▼ **Best Western Plus Sawridge Suites** 🅷
(780) 799-4552. **$185-$299.** 410 Taiganova Cres T9H 4W1. Hwy 63 exit Taiganova Cres, then 0.6 mi (1 km) e. Int corridors. **Pets:** Accepted.
SAVE 🍽 📶 ⊠ 🅱 💻

▼▼▼ **Clearwater Suite Hotel** 🅷
(780) 799-7676. **Call for rates.** 4 Haineault St T9H 1L6. Hwy 63 (Sakitawaw Tr) exit Hardin St, just n, just e on Franklin Ave, then just s. Int corridors. **Pets:** Accepted. ECO ⅙M ⊠ 📶 ⊠ 🅱 💻

▼▼ **Merit Hotel & Suites** 🅷
(780) 714-9444. **Call for rates.** 8200 Franklin Ave T9H 2H9. Hwy 63 (Sakitawaw Tr) exit King St, 0.6 mi (1 km) n. Int corridors.
Pets: Accepted. 🍽 ⅏ 📶 ⊠ 🅱 💻

▼▼ **Vantage Inn & Suites** 🅷
(780) 713-4111. **$143-$161.** 200 Parent Way T9H 5E6. 3.1 mi (5 km) s on Hwy 63 (Sakitawaw Tr). Int corridors. **Pets:** $20 daily fee/pet. Designated rooms, service with restrictions, supervision.
ECO ⅙M 📶 🅱 💻

FORT SASKATCHEWAN

▼▼▼▼ **The Kanata** 🅷
(780) 998-2770. **Call for rates.** 9820 86th Ave T8L 4P4. Just sw of jct Hwy 15/21 and 101st St. Int corridors. **Pets:** Medium, dogs only. $15 daily fee/pet. Designated rooms, service with restrictions, crate.
🍽 ⅙M 📶 ⊠ 🅱 💻

▼▼ **Super 8 Hotel-Fort Saskatchewan** 🅷
(780) 998-2898. **$118-$138.** 8750 84th St T8L 4P5. Just e of jct Hwy 15/21. Int corridors. **Pets:** Accepted. 🍽 ⅏ 📶 🅱 💻

FOX CREEK

▼▼▼ **Comfort Inn & Suites** 🅷
(780) 622-3311. **Call for rates.** 317 1st Ave T0H 1P0. Hwy 43, just n. Int corridors. **Pets:** Accepted. 🍽 ⅙M 📶 ⊠ 🅱 💻

▼▼ **Super 8** 🅷
(780) 622-8333. **$119-$149.** 206 Highway Ave T0H 1P0. Hwy 46, town center. Ext/int corridors. **Pets:** Accepted. 🍽 📶 ⅍ 🅱 💻

GRANDE PRAIRIE

(CAA) ▼▼▼ **Best Western Grande Prairie Hotel & Suites** 🅷
(780) 402-2378. **$149-$199.** 10745 117th Ave T8V 7N6. Corner of Hwy 43 (100th Ave) and 117th Ave. Int corridors. **Pets:** Medium. $20 daily fee/room. Designated rooms, service with restrictions, supervision.
SAVE ECO 🍽 ⅙M ⅏ 📶 🅱 💻

▼▼▼▼ **Holiday Inn Hotel & Suites** 🅷
(780) 402-6886. **$150-$275.** 9816 107th St T8V 8E7. Jct Hwy 43 (100th Ave) and 40 (108th St). Int corridors. **Pets:** Accepted.
ECO 🍽 ⅙M ⊠ 📶 ⊠ 🅱 💻

▼▼ **Motel 6 Grande Prairie #5709** 🅷
(780) 830-7744. **Call for rates.** 15402 101st St T8V 0P7. Jct Hwy 2 and 43 (100th Ave), just s. Int corridors. **Pets:** Accepted.
ECO 🍽 ⅙M ⅍ 🅱 💻

▼▼ **Paradise Inn & Conference Centre Grande Prairie Airport** 🅷
(780) 539-6000. **Call for rates.** 11201 100th Ave T8V 5M6. 1.8 mi (2.9 km) w on Hwy 2. Int corridors. **Pets:** $25 daily fee/room. Designated rooms, service with restrictions, supervision. ECO 🍽 📶 🅱 💻

▼▼▼ **Podollan Inn & Spa** 🅷
(780) 830-2000. **Call for rates.** 10612 99th Ave T8V 8E8. Jct Hwy 43 (100th Ave) and 40 (108th St), just e. Int corridors. **Pets:** Accepted.
🍽 📶 ⊠ 🅱 💻

▼▼▼▼ **Pomeroy Hotel & Conference Centre** 🅷
(780) 532-5221. **Call for rates.** 11633 100th St T8V 3Y4. Jct Hwy 43 (100th Ave) and 116th Ave. Int corridors. **Pets:** Accepted.
ECO 🍽 ⅙M ⅏ ⊠ 📶 ⊠ 🅱 💻

▼▼▼ **Quality Inn & Suites** 🅷
(780) 831-2999. **$139-$274.** 11710 102nd St T8V 7S7. 102nd St at 117th Ave. Int corridors. **Pets:** Other species. $30 one-time fee/pet. Designated rooms, service with restrictions, crate.
ECO ⅙M ⅏ 📶 🅱 💻

▼▼ **Service Plus Inns and Suites** H
(780) 538-3900. **Call for rates.** 10810 107A Ave T8V 7A9. 1.4 mi (2.2 km) w on Hwy 2, just n. Int corridors. **Pets:** Accepted.

▼▼ **Stanford Hotel** H
(780) 539-5678. **Call for rates.** 11401 100th Ave T8V 5M6. Jct Hwy 2 and 43 (100th Ave), just e of 116th St. Ext/int corridors. **Pets:** Accepted.

▼▼ **Stonebridge Hotel** H
(780) 539-5561. **$129-$169.** 12102 100th St T8V 5P1. 100th St at 121st Ave. Int corridors. **Pets:** Accepted.

▼▼ **Super 8** H
(780) 532-8288. **$137-$147.** 10050 116th Ave T8V 4K5. 102nd St at 117th Ave. Int corridors. **Pets:** Accepted.

GRIMSHAW
▼▼▼ **Pomeroy Inn & Suites** H
(780) 332-2000. **$119-$235.** 4311 51st St T0H 1W0. On Hwy 2; south end of town. Int corridors. **Pets:** Accepted.

HIGH LEVEL
ⒸⒶ ▼▼▼ **Best Western Plus Mirage Hotel & Resort** H
(780) 821-1000. **$90-$150.** 9616 Hwy 58 T0H 1Z0. Jct Hwy 35 and 58; north end of town. Ext/int corridors. **Pets:** Accepted.

▼▼ **Super 8 High Level** H
(780) 841-3448. **$140-$160.** 9502 114th Ave T0H 1Z0. Hwy 35, just se; south end of town. Ext/int corridors. **Pets:** Other species. $25 one-time fee/room. Designated rooms, service with restrictions, supervision.

HIGH PRAIRIE
▼▼▼ **Peavine Inn & Suites** H
(780) 523-2398. **Call for rates.** 3905 51st Ave T0G 1E0. Hwy 2, just n; east end of town. Ext/int corridors. **Pets:** Accepted.

HIGH RIVER
▼▼ **Heritage Inn Hotel & Convention Centre** H
(403) 652-3834. **$132-$188.** 1104 11th Ave SE T1V 1M4. Hwy 2 exit 194B, 0.8 mi (1.3 km) w. Int corridors. **Pets:** Accepted.

▼▼▼ **Ramada Inn & Suites High River** H
(403) 603-3183. **$60-$195.** 1512 13th Ave SE T1V 2B1. Hwy 2 exit 194B, just w. Int corridors. **Pets:** Accepted.

▼▼ **Super 8** H
(403) 652-4448. **$125-$170.** 1601 13th Ave SE T1V 2B1. Hwy 2 exit 194B, just w. Int corridors. **Pets:** Accepted.

INNISFAIL
ⒸⒶ ▼▼▼ **Days Inn Innisfail** H
(403) 227-4405. **$129-$159.** 5010 40th Ave T4G 1Z1. Hwy 2 exit Hwy 54 (Innisfail/Caroline), just w. Int corridors. **Pets:** Medium, dogs only. $20 daily fee/pet. Designated rooms, service with restrictions, supervision.

JASPER
ⒸⒶ ▼▼▼ **Best Western Jasper Inn & Suites** H ❀
(780) 852-4461. **$108-$275, 3 day notice.** 98 Geikie St T0E 1E0. Corner of Geikie and Bonhomme sts. Ext/int corridors. **Pets:** Dogs only. $20 daily fee/pet. Designated rooms, service with restrictions.

▼▼ **Chateau Jasper** H
(780) 852-5644. **$163-$365.** 96 Geikie St T0E 1E0. Corner of Juniper and Geikie sts. Int corridors. **Pets:** Accepted.

▼▼▼ **The Crimson Jasper** H
(780) 852-3394. **Call for rates.** 200 Connaught Dr T0E 1E0. 0.3 mi (0.5 km) e. Int corridors. **Pets:** Accepted.

ⒸⒶ ▼▼▼ **The Fairmont Jasper Park Lodge** H ❀
(780) 852-3301. **Call for rates.** 1 Old Lodge Rd T0E 1E0. 3 mi (4.8 km) ne via Hwy 16, 2 mi (3.2 km) se off highway via Maligne Rd, follow signs. Ext corridors. **Pets:** $50 daily fee/room. Service with restrictions, supervision.

▼▼ **Lobstick Lodge** H
(780) 852-4431. **Call for rates.** 94 Geikie St T0E 1E0. Corner of Geikie and Juniper sts. Int corridors. **Pets:** Accepted.

▼▼ **Marmot Lodge** M
(780) 852-4471. **Call for rates.** 86 Connaught Dr T0E 1E0. 1 mi (1.6 km) ne. Ext corridors. **Pets:** Accepted.

▼▼ **Patricia Lake Bungalows** CA
(780) 852-3560. **$110-$410, 7 day notice.** Pyramid Lake Rd T0E 1E0. 3 mi (4.8 km) nw via Pyramid Lake Rd. Ext corridors. **Pets:** Accepted.

▼▼ **Pyramid Lake Resort** H
(780) 852-4900. **$134-$269.** Pyramid Lake Rd T0E 1E0. From Connaught Dr, 3.8 mi (6 km) nw. Ext corridors. **Pets:** Accepted.

ⒸⒶ ▼▼▼ **Sawridge Inn & Conference Centre Jasper** H
(780) 852-5111. **$123-$402, 3 day notice.** 76 Connaught Dr T0E 1E0. 1.1 mi (1.7 km) e. Int corridors. **Pets:** Accepted.

▼▼ **Sunwapta Falls Rocky Mountain Lodge** CA
(780) 852-4852. **Call for rates.** Hwy 93 T0E 1E0. 34.7 mi (55 km) s on Icefields Pkwy (Hwy 93). Ext corridors. **Pets:** Accepted.

▼▼ **Tonquin Inn** M 🐾
(780) 852-4987. **$145-$275.** 100 Juniper St T0E 1E0. Corner of Juniper and Geikie sts. Ext corridors. **Pets:** Medium. $25 one-time fee/pet. Designated rooms, service with restrictions, crate.

KANANASKIS
▼▼▼ **Delta Lodge at Kananaskis** H
(403) 591-7711. **$95-$292, 3 day notice.** 1 Centennial Dr, Kananaskis Village T0L 2H0. Trans-Canada Hwy 1, 14.7 mi (23.5 km) s on Hwy 40 (Kananaskis Tr), 1.8 mi (3 km) on Kananaskis Village access road, follow signs. Int corridors. **Pets:** Accepted.

LAC LA BICHE
▼▼▼ **Ramada Inn & Suites Lac La Biche** H
(780) 623-2250. **$50-$145.** 9305 100 St T0A 2C0. Jct Hwy 36 and 55, just n. Int corridors. **Pets:** Accepted.

LACOMBE

(CAA) ▼▼▼ **Best Western Plus Lacombe Inn & Suites** H ❀

(403) 782-3535. **$159-$174.** 4751 63rd St T4L 1K7. Hwy 2 exit 422, 1.5 mi (2.5 km) e. Int corridors. **Pets:** Large, dogs only. $50 deposit/room, $20 daily fee/pet. Designated rooms, service with restrictions, supervision. SAVE ⏹ ⏹ ⏹ ⏹ ⏹ ⏹ ⏹

LAKE LOUISE

(CAA) ▼▼▼ ▼▼▼ **The Fairmont Chateau Lake Louise** H

(403) 522-3511. **$309-$749, 7 day notice.** 111 Lake Louise Dr T0L 1E0. 1.8 mi (3 km) up the hill from the village. Int corridors. **Pets:** Accepted. SAVE ECO ⏹ ⏹ ⏹ ⏹ ⏹ ⏹ ⏹

▼▼▼ **Lake Louise Inn** H ❀

(403) 522-3791. **Call for rates.** 210 Village Rd T0L 1E0. Just w of 4-way stop. Ext/int corridors. **Pets:** $50 one-time fee/room. Designated rooms, service with restrictions, supervision. ⏹ ⏹ ⏹ ⏹ ⏹ ⏹ ⏹ ⏹

LEDUC

▼▼▼▼ **Wingate by Wyndham Leduc Edmonton Airport** H

(587) 783-7179. **$80-$139.** 7120 Sparrow Dr T9E 8A5. Hwy 2 exit 522 (Airport Rd), just e, then 1.2 mi (1.9 km) s. Int corridors. **Pets:** Accepted. ⏹ ⏹ ⏹ ⏹ ⏹ ⏹

LETHBRIDGE

(CAA) ▼▼▼▼ **Best Western Plus Service Inn & Suites** H

(403) 329-6844. **$150-$170.** 209 41st St S T1J 1Z3. Hwy 3 (Crowsnest Tr), just s on 43rd St S. Int corridors. **Pets:** Accepted. SAVE ⏹ ⏹ ⏹ ⏹ ⏹

(CAA) ▼▼▼ **Coast Lethbridge Hotel & Conference Centre** H

(403) 327-5701. **$134-$164.** 526 Mayor Magrath Dr S T1J 3M2. Hwy 3 (Crowsnest Tr) exit Mayor Magrath Dr S, just s. Int corridors. **Pets:** Accepted. SAVE ⏹ ⏹ ⏹ ⏹ ⏹

▼▼▼ **Comfort Inn** H

(403) 320-8874. **$99-$179.** 3226 Fairway Plaza Rd S T1K 7T5. Hwy 3 (Crowsnest Tr) exit Mayor Magrath Dr S, 1.8 mi (3 km) s, then just e on 24th Ave. Int corridors. **Pets:** Accepted. ⏹ ⏹ ⏹ ⏹

▼▼▼ **Days Inn Lethbridge** H

(403) 327-6000. **$103-$108.** 100 3rd Ave S T1J 4L2. Corner of 3rd Ave and Scenic Dr; center. Ext/int corridors. **Pets:** Accepted. ECO ⏹ ⏹ ⏹ ⏹

▼▼▼▼ **Holiday Inn Express Hotel & Suites Lethbridge** H

(403) 394-9292. **$135-$159.** 120 Stafford Dr S T1J 4W4. Hwy 3 (Crowsnest Tr) exit Stafford Dr, just s; downtown. Int corridors. **Pets:** $25 one-time fee/room. Designated rooms, service with restrictions, supervision. ⏹ ⏹ ⏹ ⏹

(CAA) ▼▼▼▼ **Holiday Inn Hotel Lethbridge** H

(403) 380-5050. **$139-$199.** 2375 Mayor Magrath Dr S T1K 7M1. Hwy 3 (Crowsnest Tr) exit Mayor Magrath Dr S, 1.8 mi (3 km) s, then just e on 22nd St. Int corridors. **Pets:** Accepted. SAVE ECO ⏹ ⏹ ⏹ ⏹ ⏹ ⏹

▼▼▼ **Lethbridge Lodge Hotel and Conference Centre** H

(403) 328-1123. **Call for rates.** 320 Scenic Dr T1J 4B4. Jct 4th Ave S; center. Int corridors. **Pets:** Accepted. ECO ⏹ ⏹ ⏹ ⏹ ⏹

▼▼▼ **Motel 6 Lethbridge** M

(403) 328-4436. **Call for rates.** 1142 Mayor Magrath Dr S T1K 2P8. Hwy 3 (Crowsnest Tr) exit Mayor Magrath Dr S, 1 mi (1.6 km) s. Ext corridors. **Pets:** Accepted. ⏹ ⏹ ⏹ ⏹

▼▼ **Quality Inn & Suites** H

(403) 331-6440. **$112-$185.** 4070 2nd Ave S T1J 3Z2. Hwy 3 (Crowsnest Tr), just s on WT Hill Blvd, just e. Int corridors. **Pets:** Accepted. ⏹ ⏹ ⏹ ⏹

▼▼ **Sandman Hotel Lethbridge** H

(403) 328-1111. **Call for rates.** 421 Mayor Magrath Dr S T1J 3L8. Hwy 3 (Crowsnest Tr) exit Mayor Magrath Dr S, just s. Int corridors. **Pets:** Accepted. ECO ⏹ ⏹ ⏹ ⏹ ⏹ ⏹

LLOYDMINSTER

▼▼▼ **Days Hotel & Suites Lloydminster** H

(780) 875-4404. **$160-$169.** 5411 44th St T9V 0A9. 0.5 mi (0.8 km) w on Hwy 16 from jct Hwy 17. Int corridors. **Pets:** Accepted. ⏹ ⏹ ⏹ ⏹ ⏹ ⏹ ⏹

▼▼▼▼ **Hampton Inn by Hilton-Lloydminster** H

(780) 874-1118. **$109-$209.** 8288 44 St T9V 2G8. Hwy 16 exit 80 Ave, just n. Int corridors. **Pets:** Accepted. ⏹ ⏹ ⏹ ⏹ ⏹ ⏹

▼▼▼ **Holiday Inn Hotel & Suites** H

(780) 870-5050. **$139-$199.** 5612 44th T9V 0B6. Jct Hwy 16 and 17, 0.6 mi (1 km) w. Int corridors. **Pets:** Accepted. ⏹ ⏹ ⏹ ⏹ ⏹ ⏹ ⏹

(CAA) ▼▼▼ **Ramada Inn Lloydminster** H

(780) 871-6940. **$109-$179.** 5610 44th T9V 0B6. Jct Hwy 16 and 17, 0.6 mi (1 km) w. Int corridors. **Pets:** Accepted. SAVE ⏹ ⏹ ⏹

MEDICINE HAT

(CAA) ▼▼▼ **Best Western Plus Sun Country** H

(403) 527-3700. **$109-$129.** 722 Redcliff Dr T1A 5E3. Just w of Trans-Canada Hwy 1, access on 7th St SW. Ext/int corridors. **Pets:** Accepted. SAVE ECO ⏹ ⏹ ⏹ ⏹ ⏹ ⏹

(CAA) ▼▼▼ **Comfort Inn & Suites** H ❀

(403) 504-1700. **$79-$259.** 2317 Trans-Canada Way SE T1B 4E9. Trans-Canada Hwy 1, just n on Dunmore Rd, just w. Int corridors. **Pets:** Other species. $25 daily fee/pet. Designated rooms, service with restrictions, supervision. SAVE ECO ⏹ ⏹ ⏹ ⏹ ⏹ ⏹

▼▼▼▼ **Hampton Inn & Suites by Hilton Medicine Hat** H

(403) 548-7818. **Call for rates.** 2510 Box Springs Blvd T1C 0C8. Trans-Canada Hwy 1 exit Boundary Rd NE, then 0.9 mi (1.5 km) s. Int corridors. **Pets:** Accepted. ⏹ ⏹ ⏹ ⏹

▼▼▼▼ **Holiday Inn Express Hotel & Suites** H

(403) 504-5151. **Call for rates.** 9 Strachan Bay SE T1B 4Y2. Trans-Canada Hwy 1, just s on Dunmore Rd, just e; east end of city. Int corridors. **Pets:** Accepted. ECO ⏹ ⏹ ⏹ ⏹ ⏹ ⏹ ⏹

▼▼ **Home Inn Express Medicine Hat** H

(403) 527-1749. **Call for rates.** 20 Strachan Ct SE T1B 4R7. Trans-Canada Hwy 1, just s on Dunmore Rd, just w; southeast end of city. Int corridors. **Pets:** Accepted. ECO ⏹ ⏹ ⏹

(CAA) ▼▼▼▼ **Medicine Hat Lodge Resort, Casino & Spa** H

(403) 529-2222. **$139-$159.** 1051 Ross Glen Dr SE T1B 3T8. Trans-Canada Hwy 1 exit Dunmore Rd, just ne. Int corridors. **Pets:** Accepted. SAVE ⏹ ⏹ ⏹ ⏹ ⏹ ⏹ ⏹

MORLEY

(CAA) ▼▼▼▼ **Stoney Nakoda Resort & Casino** H

(403) 881-2830. **$89-$199.** Jct Trans-Canada Hwy 1 and Hwy 40 T0L 1N0. Jct Hwy 40, just s. Int corridors. **Pets:** Accepted. SAVE ⏹ ⏹ ⏹ ⏹ ⏹ ⏹

NISKU

(CAA) ◈◈◈ **Four Points by Sheraton Edmonton International Airport** H

(780) 770-9099. **$99-$149.** 403 11th Ave T9E 7N2. Hwy 2 exit Edmonton International Airport/Nisku Business Park (10th Ave), 0.5 mi (0.9 km) e. Int corridors. **Pets:** $15 one-time fee/pet. Designated rooms, service with restrictions, supervision. SAVE ⫽ ⟨M⟩ ⟨⟩ ⟨X⟩ ⟨⟩ ⟨⟩

OKOTOKS

(CAA) ◈◈◈ **Best Western Plus Okotoks Inn & Suites** H ✿

(403) 995-6262. **$149-$194.** 100 Southbank Rd T1S 0N3. Hwy 2 exit 209 (Hwy 7), 2.7 mi (4.5 km) w. Int corridors. **Pets:** Other species. $20 daily fee/pet. Designated rooms, service with restrictions, supervision.

SAVE ⫽ ⟨⟩ ⟨X⟩ ⟨⟩ ⟨⟩

OLDS

(CAA) ◈◈◈ **Best Western of Olds** H

(403) 556-5900. **$113-$179.** 4520 46th St T4H 1P7. Hwy 2 exit 340B (Hwy 27), 3 mi (5 km) w. Int corridors. **Pets:** Accepted.

SAVE ⫽ ⟨⟩ ⟨⟩ ⟨⟩ ⟨⟩

◈◈◈ **Pomeroy Inn & Suites at Olds College** H ✿

(403) 556-8815. **Call for rates.** 4601 46 Ave T4H 1P5. Hwy 22/27, just e of Bergen Rd. Int corridors. **Pets:** Other species. $25 one-time fee/pet, $5 daily fee/pet. Service with restrictions, crate.

⫽ ⟨M⟩ ⟨⟩ ⟨X⟩ ⟨⟩ ⟨⟩

◈◈◈ **Ramada Olds** H

(403) 507-8349. **$130-$170.** 500 6700 46th St T4H 0A2. Hwy 2 exit 340B (Hwy 27), 4.2 mi (7 km) w. Int corridors. **Pets:** Accepted.

⫽ ⟨M⟩ ⟨X⟩ ⟨⟩ ⟨⟩ ⟨⟩

PINCHER CREEK

◈◈ **Heritage Inn & Hotel Convention Centre Pincher Creek** H

(403) 627-5000. **$125-$269.** 919 Waterton Ave (Hwy 6) T0K 1W0. Jct Hwy 785, just s. Int corridors. **Pets:** Accepted.

⫽ ⟨⟩ ⟨⟩ ⟨X⟩ ⟨⟩ ⟨⟩

◈◈◈ **Ramada Inn & Suites** H

(403) 627-3777. **$140-$205.** 1132 Table Mountain St T0K 1W0. Hwy 3 (Crowsnest Tr), 1.3 mi (2.1 km) s on Hwy 6. Int corridors. **Pets:** Other species. $15 daily fee/pet. Designated rooms, service with restrictions, supervision. ECO ⟨⟩ ⟨⟩ ⟨X⟩ ⟨⟩ ⟨⟩

RED DEER (Restaurants p. 630)

◈◈ **Baymont Inn & Suites and Conference Center** H

(403) 346-8841. **$85-$240.** 4311 49th Ave T4N 5Y7. Hwy 2 exit 394 (Gaetz Ave), 2.6 mi (4.2 km) n. Int corridors. **Pets:** Accepted.

ECO ⫽ ⟨⟩ ⟨X⟩ ⟨⟩ ⟨⟩ ⟨⟩

(CAA) ◈◈◈ **Best Western Plus Red Deer Inn & Suites** H

(403) 346-3555. **$120-$186.** 6839 66th St T4P 3T5. Hwy 2 exit 401 (67th St), just e. Int corridors. **Pets:** Accepted.

SAVE ECO ⟨M⟩ ⟨⟩ ⟨⟩ ⟨X⟩ ⟨⟩ ⟨⟩

◈◈◈ **Comfort Inn & Suites** H

(403) 348-0025. **$120-$189.** 6846 66th St T4P 3T5. Hwy 2 exit 401 (67th St), just e. Int corridors. **Pets:** Accepted. ⟨⟩ ⟨⟩ ⟨⟩ ⟨⟩

(CAA) ◈◈◈ **Microtel Inn & Suites by Wyndham Red Deer** H

(403) 967-0320. **$107-$175.** 126 Leva Ave T4E 1B9. Hwy 2 exit 391 (Gasoline Alley), just w. Int corridors. **Pets:** Accepted.

SAVE ⟨M⟩ ⟨⟩ ⟨X⟩ ⟨⟩ ⟨⟩

◈ **Motel 6 Red Deer** H

(403) 340-1749. **Call for rates.** 900-5001 19th St T4R 3R1. Hwy 2 exit 394 (Gaetz Ave), just w; in Southpointe Common Shopping District. Int corridors. **Pets:** Accepted. ECO ⟨⟩ ⟨⟩

(CAA) ◈◈◈ **Quality Inn & Conference Centre** H ✿

(403) 343-8800. **$108-$179.** 7150 50th Ave T4N 6A5. Hwy 2 exit 401 (67th St), 1.7 mi (2.9 km) e, then 0.5 mi (0.8 km) w. Int corridors. **Pets:** Small, dogs only. $15 daily fee/pet. Designated rooms, service with restrictions, supervision. SAVE ⫽ ⟨⟩ ⟨⟩ ⟨X⟩ ⟨⟩ ⟨⟩

(CAA) ◈◈◈ **Ramada Red Deer Hotel & Suites** H

(403) 342-4445. **$118-$145.** 6853 66th St T4P 3T5. Hwy 2 exit 401 (67th St), just e. Int corridors. **Pets:** Small, dogs only. $15 daily fee/room. Designated rooms, service with restrictions, supervision.

SAVE ⟨⟩ ⟨⟩ ⟨X⟩ ⟨⟩ ⟨⟩

◈◈◈ **Sandman Hotel Red Deer** H

(403) 343-7400. **$139-$179.** 2818 Gaetz Ave T4R 1M4. 1 mi (1.6 km) n on Hwy 2A (Gaetz Ave). Int corridors. **Pets:** Accepted.

ECO ⫽ ⟨⟩ ⟨⟩ ⟨⟩ ⟨⟩

(CAA) ◈◈◈ **Sheraton Red Deer Hotel** H ✿

(403) 346-2091. **$149-$299.** 3310 50th Ave T4N 3X9. 1.3 mi (2 km) n on Hwy 2A (Gaetz Ave). Int corridors. **Pets:** Medium, dogs only. Service with restrictions, supervision.

SAVE ⫽ ⟨M⟩ ⟨⟩ ⟨X⟩ ⟨⟩ ⟨X⟩ ⟨⟩ ⟨⟩

(CAA) ◈◈◈ **TownePlace Suites by Marriott Red Deer** H

(403) 341-3589. **$97-$161.** 6822 66th St T4P 3T5. Hwy 2 exit 401 (67th St), just e. Int corridors. **Pets:** Medium, other species. $30 daily fee/room. Crate. SAVE ⟨M⟩ ⟨⟩ ⟨X⟩ ⟨⟩ ⟨⟩

RIMBEY

(CAA) ◈◈◈ **Best Western Rimstone Ridge Hotel** H

(403) 843-2999. **$126-$225.** 5501 50th Ave T0C 2J0. Jct Hwy 20 and 20A (50th Ave), 1.2 mi (2 km) w; west end of town. Int corridors. **Pets:** Medium, dogs only. $20 daily fee/pet. Designated rooms, service with restrictions, supervision. SAVE ⫽ ⟨⟩ ⟨⟩ ⟨X⟩ ⟨⟩ ⟨⟩

ROCKY MOUNTAIN HOUSE

(CAA) ◈◈◈ **Best Western Rocky Mountain House Inn & Suites** H ✿

(403) 844-3100. **$139-$169.** 4407 41st Ave T4T 1A5. Hwy 11 and 22, just w on 42nd Ave, just s; east end of town. Int corridors. **Pets:** Large, other species. $20 daily fee/pet. Service with restrictions.

SAVE ECO ⟨M⟩ ⟨⟩ ⟨⟩ ⟨⟩ ⟨⟩

◈◈ **Canalta Rocky Mountain House** H

(403) 846-0088. **Call for rates.** 4406 41st Ave T4T 1J6. Hwy 11 and 22, just w on 42nd Ave, just s; east end of town. Ext/int corridors. **Pets:** Accepted. ECO ⟨M⟩ ⟨⟩ ⟨⟩ ⟨X⟩ ⟨⟩ ⟨⟩

ST. ALBERT

(CAA) ◈◈◈ **Best Western Plus The Inn at St. Albert** H

(780) 470-3800. **$140-$180.** 460 St. Albert Tr T8N 5J9. Hwy 2 (St. Albert Tr), just w at Lennox Dr. Int corridors. **Pets:** Accepted.

SAVE ⟨⟩ ⟨⟩ ⟨X⟩ ⟨⟩ ⟨⟩

ST. PAUL

◈◈ **Canalta Hotel** H

(780) 645-5581. **$129-$139.** 5008 43rd St T0A 3A2. Jct Hwy 29 and 40 st, 0.5 mi (0.8 km) w. Ext/int corridors. **Pets:** Accepted.

⫽ ⟨M⟩ ⟨X⟩ ⟨⟩ ⟨X⟩ ⟨⟩ ⟨⟩

SHERWOOD PARK

Days Inn & Suites Sherwood Park H
(780) 570-8080. **$125-$145.** 201 Palisades Way T8H 0N3. Hwy 16 exit
403 (Sherwood Dr), 0.9 mi (1.5 km) s. Int corridors. **Pets:** Other species. $20 daily fee/room. Service with restrictions, supervision.
SAVE ⊞ ᬀ ⬚ ⬚ ⬚

Holiday Inn Express & Suites H
(780) 417-3388. **Call for rates.** 11 Portage Ln T8H 2R7. Hwy 16 exit
Broadmoor Blvd, 0.6 mi (1 km) s. Int corridors. **Pets:** Accepted.
ECO ᬀ ⬚ ⬚ ⬚ ⬚

Ramada-Edmonton East/Sherwood Park H
(780) 467-6727. **$125-$150.** 30 Broadway Blvd T8H 2A2. Hwy 16 exit
Broadmoor Blvd, 1.2 mi (2 km) s. Int corridors. **Pets:** Accepted.
ᬀ ⬚ ⬚ ⬚

SLAVE LAKE

Holiday Inn Express H ❀
(780) 849-4819. **$109-$199.** 1551 Main St SE T0G 2A0. Hwy 2, just s.
Int corridors. **Pets:** Other species. $25 daily fee/pet. Designated rooms,
supervision. ᬀ ⬚ ⬚ ⬚

Lakeview Inns & Suites H
(780) 849-9500. **$108-$148.** 1550 Holmes Tr SE T0G 2A3. Hwy 2, just
n; east end of town. Int corridors. **Pets:** Large, other species. $100
deposit/room. Service with restrictions, supervision.
ECO ᬀ ⬚ ⬚ ⬚

SPRUCE GROVE

Travelodge Inn & Suites Spruce Grove H
(780) 962-6050. **$70-$124.** 20 Westgrove Dr T7X 3X3. Hwy 16A, just n.
Int corridors. **Pets:** Accepted. ECO ᬀ ⬚ ⬚ ⬚

STETTLER

Ramada Inn & Suites H
(403) 742-6555. **$50-$160.** 6711 49th Ave T0C 2L1. Jct Hwy 56 and 11,
0.7 mi (1.2 km) w. Int corridors. **Pets:** Accepted.
ᬀ ⬚ ⬚ ⬚ ⬚

STONY PLAIN

Best Western Sunrise Inn & Suites H
(780) 968-1716. **$120-$180.** 3101 43rd Ave T7Z 1L1. Hwy 16A (Township Rd 530), just s at S Park Dr, just e. Int corridors. **Pets:** Accepted.
SAVE ᬀ ᬀ ⬚ ᬀ ⬚ ⬚ ⬚

Motel 6 Stony Plain H
(780) 968-5123. **Call for rates.** 66 Boulder Blvd T7Z 1V7. Just off Hwy
16A (Township Rd 530). Int corridors. **Pets:** Accepted.
ECO ᬀ ⬚ ⬚ ⬚

Ramada Inn & Suites H
(780) 963-0222. **$120-$121.** 3301 43rd Ave T7Z 1L1. Hwy 16A (Township Rd 530), just s on S Park Dr, just e. Ext/int corridors.
Pets: Accepted. ⬚ ᬀ ⬚ ᬀ ⬚ ⬚

Travelodge Stony Plain H
(780) 963-1161. **$90-$118.** 74 Boulder Blvd T7Z 1V7. Hwy 16A exit N
35th St, just n, then just e. Int corridors. **Pets:** Dogs only. $15 daily
fee/pet. Designated rooms, service with restrictions, supervision.
SAVE ECO ⬚ ᬀ ⬚ ⬚ ⬚

STRATHMORE

Best Western Strathmore Inn H
(403) 934-5777. **$99-$169.** 550 Hwy 1 T1P 1M6. Jct Trans-Canada
Hwy 1 and 817; center. Int corridors. **Pets:** Accepted.
SAVE ᬀ ᬀ ⬚ ⬚ ⬚

Days Inn & Suites H
(403) 934-1134. **$140-$170.** 400 Ranch Market T1P 0B2. Trans-Canada
Hwy 1, just n at Lakeside Blvd (Centre St). Int corridors. **Pets:** Medium.
$15 daily fee/pet. Service with restrictions, supervision.
SAVE ᬀ ᬀ ⬚ ᬀ ⬚ ⬚ ⬚

Travelodge Strathmore H ❀
(403) 901-0000. **$139-$170.** 350 Ridge Rd T1P 1B5. Just n of Trans-
Canada Hwy 1; at Ridge Rd. Int corridors. **Pets:** Other species. $15
daily fee/pet. Designated rooms, service with restrictions, supervision.
ᬀ ᬀ ⬚ ⬚ ⬚

SYLVAN LAKE

**Best Western Plus Chateau Inn Sylvan
Lake** H
(403) 887-7788. **$144-$170.** 5027 Lakeshore Dr T4S 1R3. Jct Hwy 11
and 781 (50th St), 1.9 mi (3.1 km) n, just e. Int corridors. **Pets:** Other
species. $20 daily fee/room. Designated rooms, service with restrictions.
SAVE ᬀ ᬀ ⬚ ⬚ ⬚

TABER

Heritage Inn Hotel & Convention Centre Taber H
(403) 223-4424. **$90-$144.** 4830 46th Ave T1G 2A4. Jct Hwy 3 and 36
S, 1.5 mi (2.5 km) se. Int corridors. **Pets:** Accepted.
⬚ ᬀ ᬀ ⬚ ⬚ ⬚

THREE HILLS

Best Western Diamond Inn H
(403) 443-7889. **$119-$145.** 351 7th Ave N T0M 2A0. Jct Hwy 21/27
and 583, 1.1 mi (1.9 km) w. Int corridors. **Pets:** Other species. $15
one-time fee/pet. Designated rooms, service with restrictions, crate.
SAVE ᬀ ⬚ ⬚ ⬚

VALLEYVIEW

Western Valley Inn M
(780) 524-4000. **$120-$180.** 5402 Highway St T0H 3N0. Just w of jct
Hwy 43 and 49. Ext corridors. **Pets:** Medium. $20 daily fee/pet. Service
with restrictions, supervision. SAVE ⬚ ᬀ ⬚ ⬚

VEGREVILLE

Hotello by Pomeroy H
(780) 632-2878. **Call for rates.** 6529 Hwy 16A W T9C 0A3. Jct Hwy
16A and 67th St, just e. Int corridors. **Pets:** Accepted.
⬚ ᬀ ᬀ ⬚ ⬚

Vegreville Pomeroy Inn & Suites H
(780) 632-2094. **Call for rates.** 6359 Hwy 16A W T9C 0A3. Hwy 16A,
just w of 60 St. Int corridors. **Pets:** Accepted. ᬀ ᬀ ⬚ ⬚ ⬚

WAINWRIGHT

Best Western Wainwright Inn & Suites H
(780) 845-9934. **$160-$180.** 1209 27th St T9W 0A2. Jct Hwy 14 and
41, just e. Int corridors. **Pets:** Accepted.
SAVE ⬚ ᬀ ᬀ ⬚ ⬚

Ramada Wainwright H
(780) 842-5010. **$99-$160.** 1510 27th St T9W 0A4. 0.3 mi (0.5 km) nw
of jct Hwy 14 and 41. Ext/int corridors. **Pets:** Accepted.
ᬀ ᬀ ⬚ ⬚ ⬚

WATERTON PARK

Aspen Village Inn M
(403) 859-2255. **Call for rates.** 111 Windflower Ave T0K 2M0. Center.
Ext corridors. **Pets:** Accepted. SAVE ᬀ ⬚ ⬚ ⬚ ⬚

Bayshore Inn Resort & Spa M
(403) 859-2211. **$144-$349, 3 day notice.** 111 Waterton Ave T0K 2M0.
Center. Ext/int corridors. **Pets:** Accepted.
⬚ ᬀ ᬀ ⬚ ⬚

Waterton Lakes Resort H
(403) 859-2150. **Call for rates.** 101 Clematis Ave T0K 2M0. Center.
Ext/int corridors. **Pets:** Accepted.

WESTEROSE

Village Creek Country Inn H
(780) 586-0006. **Call for rates.** 15 Village Dr, RR 2 T0C 2V0. Hwy 2
exit 482, 17.5 mi (28 km) w on Hwy 13; in Village at Pigeon Lake. Ext/
int corridors. **Pets:** Accepted.

WESTLOCK

Quality Inn & Suites H
(780) 349-4102. **$104-$170.** 10520 100th St T7P 2C6. Jct Hwy 18 and
44, just e. Ext/int corridors. **Pets:** Accepted.

Ramada Inn & Suites Westlock H
(780) 349-2245. **$80-$140.** 11311 100 St T7P 2R8. Jct Hwy 18 and 115
Ave, just w. Ext/int corridors. **Pets:** Accepted.

WETASKIWIN

Best Western Wayside Inn H
(780) 312-7300. **$130-$150.** 4103 56th St T9A 1V2. On Hwy 2A, just n
of jct Hwy 13 W. Int corridors. **Pets:** Medium, other species. $50
deposit/room, $5 daily fee/room. Designated rooms, service with restric-
tions, crate.

Super 8 Wetaskiwin H
(780) 361-3808. **$125-$145.** 3820 56th St T9A 2B2. On Hwy 2A, just s
of jct Hwy 13 W. Int corridors. **Pets:** Accepted.

WHITECOURT

Holiday Inn Express & Suites Whitecourt H
(780) 778-2512. **Call for rates.** 4721 49th St T7S 1N5. Hwy 43, just n
on 51st St, just e. Int corridors. **Pets:** Accepted.

The Kanata H
(780) 706-3390. **Call for rates.** 3315 33rd St T7S 0A2. Hwy 43, just n
on 35th St, then just e. Ext/int corridors. **Pets:** Accepted.

Microtel Inn & Suites by Wyndham H
(780) 396-0990. **$109-$189.** 4915 49th Ave T7S 1N5. Hwy 43, just n on
51st St, then just e. Int corridors. **Pets:** $30 one-time fee/room. Desig-
nated rooms, service with restrictions, crate.

Super 8 H
(780) 778-8908. **$140.** 4121 Kepler St T7S 0A3. On Hwy 43, just e of
Hwy 32. Int corridors. **Pets:** Accepted.

BRITISH COLUMBIA

ABBOTSFORD

Best Western Bakerview Inn M
(604) 859-1341. **$109-$169.** 1821 Sumas Way V2S 4L5. Trans-Canada
Hwy 1 exit 92 (Town Centre), just n on Hwy 11. Ext corridors.
Pets: Accepted.

ALDERGROVE

**Best Western Plus Country Meadows
Inn** H
(604) 856-9880. **$119-$359.** 3070 264th St V4W 3E1. Trans-Canada
Hwy 1 exit 73 (264th St/Aldergrove), 3.1 mi (5 km) s on 264th St (Hwy
13). Int corridors. **Pets:** Accepted.

BRENTWOOD BAY

Brentwood Bay Resort & Spa H
(250) 544-2079. **$149-$899, 7 day notice.** 849 Verdier Ave V8M 1C5.
Jct Brentwood Dr and Verdier Ave. Ext corridors. **Pets:** $30 daily fee/
pet. Designated rooms, service with restrictions, supervision.

BURNABY

Accent Inns H
(604) 473-5000. **Call for rates.** 3777 Henning Dr V5C 6N5. Trans-
Canada Hwy 1 exit 28 (Grandview Hwy), just n on Boundary Rd. Ext
corridors. **Pets:** Medium. $20 daily fee/room. Designated rooms, service
with restrictions, supervision.

**Best Western Plus Kings Inn & Conference
Center** M
(604) 438-1383. **$119-$159.** 5411 Kingsway V5H 2G1. Trans-Canada
Hwy 1 exit 29 (Willingdon Ave), 1.9 mi (3 km) s to Kingsway, then 1.2
mi (2 km) e. Ext corridors. **Pets:** Accepted.

**Delta Burnaby Hotel and Conference
Centre** H
(604) 453-0750. **$125-$252.** 4331 Dominion St V5G 1B2. Trans-Canada
Hwy 1 exit 29 (Willingdon Ave), just w on Canada Way, then n on Sumner St. Int corridors. **Pets:** Dogs only. $20 daily fee/room. Designated
rooms, service with restrictions, supervision.

Element Vancouver Metrotown H
(604) 568-3696. **$189-$349.** 5988 Willingdon Ave V5H 2A7. Trans-
Canada Hwy 1 exit 29 (Willingdon Ave), 2 mi (3.3 km) s. Int corridors.
Pets: Accepted.

Executive Hotels & Resorts H
(604) 298-2010. **Call for rates.** 4201 Lougheed Hwy V5C 3Y6. Trans-
Canada Hwy 1, exit 29 (Willingdon Ave N) to Lougheed Hwy, 0.6 mi (1
km) w. Int corridors. **Pets:** Accepted.

Hilton Vancouver Metrotown H
(604) 438-1200. **$119-$284.** 6083 McKay Ave V5H 2W7. Trans-Canada
Hwy 1 exit 29 (Willingdon Ave), 1.8 mi (3 km) s to Kingsway, then just
e. Int corridors. **Pets:** Accepted.

Holiday Inn Express Metrotown H
(604) 438-1881. **Call for rates.** 4405 Central Blvd V5H 4M3. Trans-
Canada Hwy 1 exit 29 (Willingdon Ave), 3.1 mi (5 km) s to Central
Blvd, then just e. Int corridors. **Pets:** Accepted.

CAMPBELL RIVER

Best Western Austrian Chalet H
(250) 923-4231. **$114-$169.** 462 S Island Hwy V9W 1A5. 2 mi (3.2 km)
s on Island Hwy 19A. Ext/int corridors. **Pets:** Other species. $20 one-
time fee/room. Designated rooms, service with restrictions, supervision.

▼▼▼▼ Comfort Inn & Suites-Campbell River H ❀
(250) 914-5117. **$110-$220.** 1351 Shoppers Row V9W 2C9. Corner of Spit Rd and Shoppers Row; downtown. Int corridors. **Pets:** $20 daily fee/room. Designated rooms, service with restrictions, supervision.

&M 🛜 ✕ 🛄 ⛾

▼▼▼ Ocean Resort M
(250) 923-4281. **Call for rates.** 4384 S Island Hwy V9H 1E8. 11 mi (18 km) s on Island Hwy 19A. Int corridors. **Pets:** Accepted.

⏏ ✕ 🛜 ✕ ✕ 🛄 ⛾

CASTLEGAR

▼▼▼ Canadas Best Value Inn & Suites Castlegar H
(250) 365-2177. **$90-$122.** 1935 Columbia Ave V1N 2W8. Jct Hwy 3A and 3B, just s. Ext/int corridors. **Pets:** Accepted.

⏏ 🛜 ✕ 🛄 ⛾

▼▼▼ Super 8-Castlegar H
(250) 365-2700. **$125-$155.** 651 18th St V1N 2N1. Jct Hwy 3, just n on Hwy 22. Int corridors. **Pets:** Accepted.

🅴 ⏏ 🛀 🛜 ✕ 🛄 ⛾

CHASE

▼ Chase Country Inn Motel M
(250) 679-3333. **Call for rates.** 576 Coburn St V0E 1M0. Jct Trans-Canada Hwy 1 and Coburn St. Ext corridors. **Pets:** Accepted.

⏏ &M 🛜 ✕ 🛄 ⛾

Ⓐ ▼▼▼▼ Quaaout Lodge & Spa, Talking Rock Golf H ❀
(250) 679-3090. **$116-$215.** 1663 Little Shuswap Lake Rd V0E 1M0. Trans-Canada Hwy 1 exit Squilax Bridge, 1.5 mi (2.5 km) w; on Little Shuswap Lake Rd. Int corridors. **Pets:** Other species. $15 daily fee/room. Designated rooms, service with restrictions, supervision.

🆂🅰🆅🅴 ⏏ &M 🛀 ✕ 🛜 ✕ 🛄 ⛾

CHEMAINUS

Ⓐ ▼▼▼▼ Best Western Plus Chemainus Inn H ❀
(250) 246-4181. **$143-$175.** 9573 Chemainus Rd V0R 1K5. Trans-Canada Hwy 1 exit Henry Rd, 0.9 mi (1.4 km) e. Int corridors. **Pets:** Other species. $20 daily fee/pet. Designated rooms, service with restrictions, supervision. 🆂🅰🆅🅴 🅴🅲🅾 &M 🛀 ✕ 🛜 ✕ 🛄 ⛾

CHETWYND

▼▼▼ Days Inn Chetwynd M
(250) 788-3344. **$60-$135.** 4401 53rd Ave V0C 1J0. Hwy 96, south of town. Int corridors. **Pets:** Accepted. 🛜 🛄 ⛾

▼▼▼ Lakeview Inns & Suites H
(250) 788-3000. **Call for rates.** 4820 N Access Rd V0C 1J0. Hwy 29 and 97, just n on 48th St, just e. Int corridors. **Pets:** Accepted.

🅴🅲🅾 &M 🛜 🛄 ⛾

▼▼▼▼ Pomeroy Inn & Suites H
(250) 788-4800. **Call for rates.** 5200 N Access Rd V0C 1J0. Hwy 29 and 97, just n on 52nd St. Int corridors. **Pets:** Accepted.

&M 🛀 🛜 ✕ 🛄 ⛾

CHILLIWACK

Ⓐ ▼▼▼ Best Western Rainbow Country Inn H
(604) 795-3828. **$110-$300.** 43971 Industrial Way V2R 3A4. Trans-Canada Hwy 1 exit 116 (Lickman Rd). Int corridors. **Pets:** Small, other species. $200 deposit/room, $10 daily fee/pet. Designated rooms, service with restrictions, supervision.

🆂🅰🆅🅴 🅴🅲🅾 ⏏ &M 🛀 🛜 ✕ 🛄 ⛾

▼▼▼▼ The Coast Chilliwack Hotel H
(604) 792-5552. **Call for rates.** 45920 First Ave V2P 7K1. Trans-Canada Hwy 1 exit 119, 1.8 mi (2.9 km) n on Vedder Rd, then just e. Int corridors. **Pets:** Accepted. 🅴🅲🅾 ⏏ 🛀 ✕ 🛜 ✕ 🛄 ⛾

Ⓐ ▼▼▼ Travelodge Hotel Chilliwack H
(604) 792-4240. **$89-$149, 3 day notice.** 45466 Yale Rd W V2R 3Z8. Trans-Canada Hwy 1 exit 119, just n. Int corridors. **Pets:** Accepted.

🆂🅰🆅🅴 🅴🅲🅾 ⏏ &M 🛀 🛜 ✕ 🛄 ⛾

CHRISTINA LAKE

▼▼▼ New Horizon Motel M
(250) 447-9312. **Call for rates.** 2037 Hunter Frontage Rd (Hwy 3) V0H 1E2. Just e on Hwy 3. Ext corridors. **Pets:** Accepted.

🅴🅲🅾 ⏏ &M 🛜 ✕ 🛄

COMOX

▼▼▼ Port Augusta Inn & Suites M
(250) 339-2277. **Call for rates.** 2082 Comox Ave V9M 1P8. Hwy 19A (Cliffe Ave), follow signs to Comox Ave, 2.5 mi (4 km) e. Ext/int corridors. **Pets:** Medium. $10 daily fee/pet. Service with restrictions, supervision. ⏏ &M 🛀 🛜 ✕ 🛄 ⛾

COQUITLAM

Ⓐ ▼▼▼ Best Western Chelsea Inn H
(604) 525-7777. **$109-$139.** 725 Brunette Ave V3K 6A6. Trans-Canada Hwy 1 exit 40B (Brunette Ave N). Int corridors. **Pets:** $20 daily fee/pet. Designated rooms, service with restrictions.

🆂🅰🆅🅴 ⏏ &M 🛀 🛜 ✕ 🛄 ⛾

Ⓐ ▼▼▼▼ Best Western Plus Coquitlam Inn Convention Centre H
(604) 931-9011. **$139-$209.** 319 North Rd V3K 3V8. Trans-Canada Hwy 1 exit 37 (Cariboo Rd/Gaglardi Way), 1.2 mi (2 km) e on Lougheed Hwy (Hwy 7), then just s. Ext/int corridors. **Pets:** Medium, dogs only. $25 daily fee/room. Designated rooms, service with restrictions, supervision. 🆂🅰🆅🅴 🅴🅲🅾 ⏏ &M 🛀 ✕ 🛜 ✕ 🛄 ⛾

COURTENAY

▼▼▼ Anco Inn M
(250) 334-2451. **$80-$110.** 1885 Cliffe Ave V9N 2K9. Just s of Hwy 19A Connector. Ext corridors. **Pets:** Small. $20 daily fee/pet. Designated rooms, service with restrictions, supervision.

⏏ &M 🛀 🛜 🛄 ⛾

Ⓐ ▼▼▼▼ Best Western The Westerly Hotel & Convention Centre H
(250) 338-7741. **$129-$199.** 1590 Cliffe Ave V9N 2K4. Corner of Cliffe Ave and Island Hwy 19A N. Int corridors. **Pets:** Large, dogs only. $15 daily fee/pet. Designated rooms, service with restrictions, supervision.

🆂🅰🆅🅴 🅴🅲🅾 ⏏ &M 🛀 ✕ 🛜 ✕ 🛄 ⛾

▼▼▼▼ Crown Isle Resort & Golf Community H
(250) 703-5050. **$139-$279, 7 day notice.** 399 Clubhouse Dr V9N 9G3. Island Hwy 19A N, 0.9 mi (1.5 km) n on Comox Ave, 1.6 mi (2.5 km) ne on Ryan Rd to Crowne Isle Dr, then e, follow signs. Ext corridors. **Pets:** Other species. $25 one-time fee/room. Designated rooms, service with restrictions, crate. ⏏ &M ✕ 🛜 ✕ 🛄 ⛾

▼▼▼▼ Holiday Inn Express & Suites Comox Valley H ❀
(778) 225-0010. **$125-$225.** 2200 Cliffe Ave V9N 2L4. 0.6 mi (1.1 km) s on Island Hwy 19A S. Int corridors. **Pets:** Other species. $15 deposit/pet. Designated rooms, service with restrictions, supervision.

⏏ &M 🛀 🛜 ✕ 🛄 ⛾

▼▼▼▼ Kingfisher Oceanside Resort & Spa H
(250) 338-1323. **$110-$200.** 4330 S Island Hwy V9N 9R9. 3.8 mi (6 km) s on Island Hwy 19A S, follow signs. Ext corridors. **Pets:** Accepted. ⏏ &M 🛀 ✕ 🛜 ✕ ✕ 🛄 ⛾

▼▼▼ Travelodge Courtenay M
(250) 334-4491. **$93-$155.** 2605 Cliffe Ave V9N 2L8. 0.8 mi (1.2 km) s on Island Hwy 19A S. Ext corridors. **Pets:** Accepted.

🅴🅲🅾 🛀 🛜 ✕ 🛄 ⛾

CRANBROOK

Best Western Cranbrook Hotel H
(250) 417-4002. **$149-$219.** 1019 Cranbrook St N V1C 3S4. Hwy 3 and 95; center. Int corridors. **Pets:** Accepted.

Days Inn Cranbrook H
(250) 426-6683. **$109-$163.** 600 Cranbrook St N V1C 3R7. Corner of 6th St and Cranbrook St N. Int corridors. **Pets:** Accepted.

Heritage Inn Hotel & Convention Centre Cranbrook H
(250) 489-4301. **$100-$185.** 803 Cranbrook St N V1C 3S2. Hwy 3 and 95, just n of 6th St N. Int corridors. **Pets:** Accepted.

St. Eugene Golf Resort & Casino H
(250) 420-2000. **Call for rates.** 7731 Mission Rd V1C 7E5. Hwy 3 exit Kimberley/Airport (Hwy 95A) to Mission Rd, 2.8 mi (4.5 km) n. Int corridors. **Pets:** Accepted.

DAWSON CREEK

Dawson Creek Super 8 H
(250) 782-8899. **$146-$170.** 1440 Alaska Ave V1G 1Z5. Jct Hwy 2 and 49, 0.5 mi (0.8 km) ne. Int corridors. **Pets:** Accepted.

Pomeroy Inn & Suites H
(250) 782-3700. **Call for rates.** 540 Hwy 2 V1G 0A4. Jct Hwy 49, 1.6 mi (2.6 km) s on 8th St (Hwy 2), just e; south end of town. Int corridors. **Pets:** Accepted.

Stonebridge Hotel Dawson Creek H
(250) 782-6226. **Call for rates.** 500 Hwy 2 V1G 0A4. Jct Hwy 49, 1.6 mi (2.6 km) s on 8th St (Hwy 2), just e; south end of town. Int corridors. **Pets:** Accepted.

DELTA

The Coast Tsawwassen Inn H ❀
(604) 943-8221. **$122-$275.** 1665 56th St V4L 2B2. Jct Hwy 17 and 56th St, 0.6 mi (1 km) s. Int corridors. **Pets:** Other species. $15 daily fee/pet. Service with restrictions, supervision.

DUNCAN

Best Western Cowichan Valley Inn H
(250) 748-2722. **$119-$180.** 6474 Trans-Canada Hwy V9L 6C6. 1.8 mi (3 km) n. Int corridors. **Pets:** Accepted.

FAIRMONT HOT SPRINGS

Fairmont Hot Springs Resort H
(250) 345-6070. **$145-$225, 3 day notice.** 5225 Fairmont Resort Rd V0B 1L1. 1 mi (1.6 km) e off Hwy 93 and 95. Ext/int corridors.
Pets: Accepted.

FERNIE

Best Western Plus Fernie Mountain Lodge H
(250) 423-5500. **$181-$265.** 1622 7th Ave V0B 1M0. Jct Hwy 3 and 7th Ave; east end of town. Int corridors. **Pets:** Accepted.

Park Place Lodge H
(250) 423-6871. **Call for rates.** 742 Hwy 3 V0B 1M0. At 7th St. Int corridors. **Pets:** Accepted.

FORT NELSON

Lakeview Inn & Suites H
(250) 233-5001. **$137-$147.** 4507 50th Ave S V0C 1R0. Just off Hwy 97 (Alaska Hwy); at 44th St. Int corridors. **Pets:** Large, other species. $25 daily fee/room. Service with restrictions, crate.

FORT ST. JOHN

Holiday Inn Express Fort St. John H
(250) 787-7737. **Call for rates.** 9504 Alaska Rd V1J 6L5. Just s on Hwy 97 (AK Hwy). Int corridors. **Pets:** Accepted.

Microtel Inn & Suites by Wyndham H
(250) 794-3100. **$101-$219.** 8407 93 St V1J 6Y3. Just s on Hwy 97 (Alaska Hwy). Int corridors. **Pets:** Large. $20 daily fee/room. Designated rooms, service with restrictions, crate.

Northern Grand Hotel H
(250) 787-0521. **Call for rates.** 9830 100th Ave V1J 1Y5. Center. Int corridors. **Pets:** Accepted.

Pomeroy Hotel & Conference Centre H
(250) 262-3233. **Call for rates.** 11308 Alaska Rd V1J 5T5. Just w on Hwy 97 (Alaska Hwy). Int corridors. **Pets:** Accepted.

Pomeroy Inn & Suites H ❀
(250) 262-3030. **Call for rates.** 9320 Alaska Rd V1J 6L5. Just s on Hwy 97 (Alaska Hwy). Int corridors. **Pets:** Other species. $25 one-time fee/room, $5 daily fee/room. Service with restrictions, crate.

Super 8-Fort St. John H ❀
(250) 785-7588. **$159-$160.** 9500 W Alaska Rd V1J 6L5. Just s on Hwy 97 (Alaska Hwy). Int corridors. **Pets:** Medium. $25 daily fee/pet. Designated rooms, service with restrictions, supervision.

FORT STEELE

Bull River Guest Ranch RA
(250) 429-3760. **Call for rates.** 2975 Bull River Rd V1C 4H7. Hwy 93 and 95, 12.9 mi (21.4 km) se of town on Ft Steele-Wardner Rd, 7.2 mi (12 km) ne on gravel road; Hwy 3 and 93, 24.6 mi (41 km) e of Cranbrook, 5 mi (8.2 km) n on Ft Steele-Wardner Rd, 7.2 mi (12 km) ne on gravel road. Ext corridors. **Pets:** Accepted.

GALIANO ISLAND

Galiano Oceanfront Inn & Spa H ❀
(250) 539-3388. **Call for rates.** 134 Madrona Dr V0N 1P0. From Sturdies Bay Ferry Terminal, just ne on Sturdies Bay Rd. Ext/int corridors. **Pets:** Other species. $50 one-time fee/room. Designated rooms, service with restrictions.

GOLD BRIDGE

Tyax Wilderness Resort & Spa H
(250) 238-2221. **Call for rates.** 1 Tyaughton Lake Rd V0K 1P0. 5 mi (8 km) n from Tyaughton Lake turnoff, follow signs. Int corridors. **Pets:** Accepted.

GOLDEN (Restaurants p. 630)

Best Western Mountainview Inn H
(250) 344-2333. **$130-$240.** 1024 11th St N V0A 1H2. Just w of jct Hwy 95 and Trans-Canada Hwy 1; on S Service Rd. Int corridors. **Pets:** Accepted.

Days Inn Golden M
(250) 344-2216. **$89-$179.** 1416 Golden View Rd V0A 1H1. On Trans-Canada Hwy 1, 1 mi (1.6 km) e of jct Hwy 95. Ext corridors. **Pets:** Accepted.

GRAND FORKS

ⒶⒶ ▼▼▼ Western Traveller Motel Ⓜ

(250) 442-5566. **$74-$144.** 1591 Central Ave V0H 1H0. West end of town on Hwy 3. Ext corridors. **Pets:** Medium, dogs only. $10 daily fee/ pet. Designated rooms, no service, supervision.

🆂🅰🆅🅴 ⓵🅼 🛜 🔲

HARRISON HOT SPRINGS

▼▼▼ Harrison Beach Hotel Ⓗ ❀

(604) 796-1111. **$104-$254, 3 day notice.** 160 Esplanade Ave V0M 1K0. Just w; on lakefront. Int corridors. **Pets:** Other species. $25 daily fee/room. Designated rooms, service with restrictions, crate.

🍽 ⓵🅼 ⏩ ⌧ 🛜 ⌧ 🛢 🔲

ⒶⒶ ▼▼▼ Harrison Hot Springs Resort & Spa Ⓗ

(604) 796-2244. **$119-$429, 3 day notice.** 100 Esplanade Ave V0M 1K0. Jct Hwy 9 (Hot Springs Rd) and Esplanade Ave, just w. Int corridors. **Pets:** Accepted.

🆂🅰🆅🅴 🄴🄲🄾 🍽 ⓵🅼 ⏩ ⌧ 🛜 ⌧ 🛢 🔲

HOPE

ⒶⒶ ▼ Alpine Motel Ⓜ

(604) 869-9931. **$85-$135.** 505 Old Hope-Princeton Way V0X 1L0. Trans-Canada Hwy 1 exit 173 westbound; exit 170 eastbound, just n from lights. Ext corridors. **Pets:** Small. $50 deposit/room, $10 daily fee/ room. No service, supervision. 🆂🅰🆅🅴 🛜 ⌧ 🛢 🔲

ⒶⒶ ▼ Best Continental Motel Ⓜ

(604) 869-9726. **$64-$83.** 860 Fraser Ave V0X 1L0. Trans-Canada Hwy 1 exit 170 to downtown; at Fort St. Ext corridors. **Pets:** Accepted.

🆂🅰🆅🅴 🛜 🛢 🔲

▼▼ Heritage Inn Ⓜ

(604) 869-7166. **$105-$135.** 570 Old Hope-Princeton Way V0X 1L0. Trans-Canada Hwy 1 exit 173 westbound; exit 170 eastbound, just n from lights. Ext corridors. **Pets:** Other species. $20 daily fee/pet. Designated rooms, service with restrictions, supervision.

⓵🅼 🛜 ⌧ 🛢 🔲

ⒶⒶ ▼▼▼ Travelodge Hope Ⓜ

(604) 869-9951. **$90-$110.** 350 Old Hope-Princeton Way V0X 1L0. Trans-Canada Hwy 1 exit 173 westbound; exit 170 eastbound, just n from lights. Int corridors. **Pets:** Small, dogs only. $25 one-time fee/room. Designated rooms, service with restrictions, supervision.

🆂🅰🆅🅴 ⓵🅼 ⏩ 🛜 ⌧ 🛢 🔲

HUDSON'S HOPE

▼▼ Sigma Inn & Suites Ⓗ

(250) 783-2300. **$139-$159.** 9006 Clark Ave V0C 1V0. Hwy 29, north end of town. Int corridors. **Pets:** Accepted. 🍽 🛜 ⌧ 🛢 🔲

INVERMERE

ⒶⒶ ▼▼▼ Best Western Invermere Inn Ⓗ

(250) 342-9246. **$129-$180.** 1310 7th Ave V0A 1K0. Hwy 93 and 95 exit Invermere, 1.8 mi (3 km) w; center. Int corridors. **Pets:** Accepted.

🆂🅰🆅🅴 🍽 🛜 🛢 🔲

▼▼▼ Copperpoint Resort Ⓗ

(250) 341-4000. **$119-$195.** 760 Cooper Rd V0A 1K2. Hwy 93 and 95, just w. Int corridors. **Pets:** $25 daily fee/pet. Designated rooms, no service, supervision. 🍽 ⏩ ⌧ 🛜 ⌧ 🛢 🔲

KAMLOOPS

▼▼ Accent Inns Ⓜ

(250) 374-8877. **Call for rates.** 1325 Columbia St W V2C 6P4. Trans-Canada Hwy 1 exit 370 (Summit Dr) westbound; exit 369 (Columbia St) eastbound, at Notre Dame Dr. Ext corridors. **Pets:** Accepted.

🄴🄲🄾 ⓵🅼 ⏩ 🛜 ⌧ 🛢 🔲

ⒶⒶ ▼▼▼▼ Best Western Plus Kamloops Hotel Ⓗ ❀

(250) 374-7878. **$145-$195.** 660 Columbia St W V2C 1L1. Trans-Canada Hwy 1 exit 369 (Columbia St) eastbound; exit 370 (Summit Dr) westbound to Columbia St via City Centre, 1.1 mi (1.8 km) n. Int corridors. **Pets:** Medium, other species. $20 one-time fee/room. Designated rooms, service with restrictions, supervision.

🆂🅰🆅🅴 🄴🄲🄾 ⏩ 🛜 ⌧ 🛢 🔲

▼▼ Canadas Best Value Inn and Suites Ⓜ

(250) 374-8100. **$68-$189.** 1200 Rogers Way V1S 1N5. Trans-Canada Hwy 1 exit 368 (Hillside Ave), just s. Ext corridors. **Pets:** Medium. $20 daily fee/pet. Designated rooms, service with restrictions, supervision.

⏩ 🛜 ⌧ 🛢 🔲

▼▼▼ The Coast Kamloops Hotel & Conference Centre Ⓗ

(250) 828-6660. **$109-$199.** 1250 Rogers Way V1S 1N5. Trans-Canada Hwy 1 exit 368 (Hillside Ave), just s. Int corridors. **Pets:** Accepted.

🄴🄲🄾 🍽 ⏩ ⌧ 🛜 ⌧ 🛢 🔲

ⒶⒶ ▼▼▼ Comfort Inn & Suites Ⓗ ❀

(250) 372-0987. **$124-$209.** 1810 Rogers Pl V1S 1T7. Trans-Canada Hwy 1 exit 368 (Hillside Ave), just s. Int corridors. **Pets:** Dogs only. $20 daily fee/room. Designated rooms, service with restrictions, supervision.

🆂🅰🆅🅴 ⏩ 🛜 ⌧ 🛢 🔲

ⒶⒶ ▼▼▼▼ DoubleTree by Hilton Kamloops Ⓗ

(250) 851-0026. **$109-$159.** 339 St. Paul St V2C 2J5. Between 3rd and 4th Aves; downtown. Int corridors. **Pets:** Accepted.

🆂🅰🆅🅴 🄴🄲🄾 🍽 ⌧ 🛜 ⌧ 🛢 🔲

ⒶⒶ ▼▼▼▼ Hampton Inn by Hilton Ⓗ ❀

(250) 571-7897. **$109-$179.** 1245 Rogers Way V1S 1R9. Trans-Canada Hwy 1 exit 368 (Hillside Ave), just s via Hillside Way. Int corridors. **Pets:** Other species. $20 daily fee/room. Designated rooms, service with restrictions, supervision. 🆂🅰🆅🅴 🄴🄲🄾 ⓵🅼 ⏩ 🛜 ⌧ 🛢 🔲

ⒶⒶ ▼▼▼▼ Holiday Inn & Suites Ⓗ

(250) 376-8288. **$99-$169.** 675 Tranquille Rd V2B 3H7. Trans-Canada Hwy 1 exit 374 (Jasper Ave), 2.5 mi (4 km) w on Halston Connector Rd, 1.8 mi (3 km) s on 8th St to Fortune Dr, then just s. Int corridors. **Pets:** Other species. $20 daily fee/pet. Designated rooms, service with restrictions, supervision. 🆂🅰🆅🅴 🍽 ⓵🅼 ⏩ 🛜 ⌧ 🛢 🔲

▼▼▼ Holiday Inn Express Kamloops Ⓗ

(250) 372-3474. **Call for rates.** 1550 Versatile Dr V1S 1X4. Trans-Canada Hwy 1 exit 367 (Pacific Way), just w. Int corridors. **Pets:** Accepted. ⏩ 🛜 ⌧ 🛢 🔲

ⒶⒶ ▼▼▼▼ Pacific Inn & Suites Ⓗ 🐾

(250) 372-0952. **Call for rates.** 1820 Rogers Pl V1S 1T7. Trans-Canada Hwy 1 exit 368 (Hillside Ave), just w. Int corridors. **Pets:** Dogs only. $20 daily fee/room. Designated rooms, service with restrictions, supervision. 🆂🅰🆅🅴 🍽 ⓵🅼 ⏩ 🛜 ⌧ 🛢 🔲

ⒶⒶ ▼▼▼ Quality Inn Ⓜ

(250) 851-0111. **$79-$189.** 1860 Rogers Pl V1S 1T7. Trans-Canada Hwy 1 exit 368 (Hillside Ave). Int corridors. **Pets:** Other species. $10 daily fee/pet. Service with restrictions. 🆂🅰🆅🅴 ⓵🅼 ⏩ 🛜 ⌧ 🛢 🔲

▼▼ Ramada Kamloops Ⓗ

(250) 374-0358. **$109-$179.** 555 W Columbia St V2C 1K7. Trans-Canada Hwy 1 exit 369 (Columbia St) eastbound; exit 370 (Summit Dr) westbound to Columbia St via City Centre, 1.1 mi (1.8 km) n. Int corridors. **Pets:** Accepted. 🄴🄲🄾 🍽 🛜 ⌧ 🛢 🔲

▼▼ Ranchland Inn Ⓜ

(250) 828-8787. **$79-$125.** 2357 Trans-Canada Hwy 1 E V2C 4A8. 2.8 mi (4.5 km) e on Trans-Canada Hwy 1 exit River Rd, just w on service access road. Ext corridors. **Pets:** Accepted. 🍽 ⓵🅼 🛜 🛢 🔲

(AA) ▽▽ Scott's Inn & Restaurant M ❀
(250) 372-8221. Call for rates. 551 11th Ave V2C 3Y1. Trans-Canada
Hwy 1 exit City Center (from eastern approach), 0.5 mi (0.9 km) w on
Battle St, then just s. Ext corridors. Pets: Medium, dogs only. $10 daily
fee/pet. Designated rooms, service with restrictions, supervision.
SAVE ⊞ ♿ ⊿ 🛜 ✕ 🔋 💻

(AA) ▽▽ The Thompson Hotel 🏨
(250) 374-1999. Call for rates. 650 Victoria St V2C 2B4. Between 6th
and 7th aves; downtown. Int corridors. Pets: Accepted.
SAVE ECO ⊞ ⊿ ✕ 🛜 ✕ 🔋 💻

KELOWNA
▽▽ Accent Inns 🏨
(250) 862-8888. Call for rates. 1140 Harvey Ave V1Y 6E7. Corner of
Hwy 97 N (Harvey Ave) and Gordon Dr. Ext corridors. Pets: Accepted.
ECO ♿ ⊿ 🛜 🔋 💻

(AA) ▽▽▽ Best Western Plus Kelowna Hotel &
Suites 🏨 ❀
(250) 860-1212. $140-$250. 2402 Hwy 97 N V1X 4J1. 0.6 mi (1 km) s
of jct Hwy 97 N (Harvey Ave) and 33; corner of Leckie Rd. Int corridors. Pets: $20 daily fee/pet. Designated rooms, service with restric-
tions, crate. SAVE ECO ⊞ ♿ ⊿ ✕ 🛜 ✕ 🔋 💻

(AA) ▽▽▽ Comfort Suites 🏨 ❀
(250) 861-1110. $142-$349. 2656 Hwy 97 N V1X 4J4. Jct Hwy 97 N
(Harvey Ave) and 33, 0.5 mi (0.9 km) n. Int corridors. Pets: $25 daily
fee/pet. Designated rooms, service with restrictions, supervision.
SAVE ECO ♿ ⊿ 🛜 ✕ 🔋 💻

▽▽▽ Delta Grand Okanagan Resort & Conference
Centre 🏨
(250) 763-4500. $149-$362, 3 day notice. 1310 Water St V1Y 9P3.
Hwy 97 (Harvey Ave), 0.6 mi (1 km) w along Water St. Int corridors.
Pets: Accepted. ECO ⊞ ♿ ⊿ ✕ 🛜 ✕ 🔋 💻

▽▽▽ Fairfield Inn & Suites by Marriott
Kelowna 🏨 ❀
(250) 763-2800. $85-$191. 1655 Powick Rd V1X 4L1. Just s of jct Hwy
97 N (Harvey Ave) and 33. Int corridors. Pets: $15 daily fee/pet. Desig-
nated rooms, service with restrictions, supervision.
ECO ♿ ⊿ 🛜 ✕ 🔋 💻

(AA) ▽▽▽ Four Points by Sheraton Kelowna
Airport 🏨
(250) 807-2000. $129-$389. 5505 Airport Way V1V 3C3. Hwy 97 (Harvey Ave), just w. Int corridors. Pets: Accepted.
SAVE ⊞ ♿ 🛜 ✕ 🔋 💻

(AA) ▽▽▽ Holiday Inn Express Kelowna Conference
Centre 🏨
(250) 763-0500. Call for rates. 2429 Hwy 97 N V1X 4J2. 0.6 mi (1 km)
s of jct Hwy 97 N (Harvey Ave) and 33. Int corridors. Pets: Large. $20
daily fee/room. Designated rooms, service with restrictions, supervision.
SAVE ECO ♿ ⊿ 🛜 ✕ 🔋 💻

▽▽ Kelowna Inn & Suites M
(250) 762-2533. Call for rates. 1070 Harvey Ave V1Y 8S4. Corner of
Hwy 97 N (Harvey Ave) and Gordon Dr. Ext/int corridors.
Pets: Accepted. ECO ⊿ ♿ 🛜 🔋 💻

▽▽▽ Ramada Hotel & Conference Centre 🏨 ❀
(250) 860-9711. $119-$229. 2170 Harvey Ave V1Y 6G8. Hwy 97 N
(Harvey Ave) at Dilworth Dr. Ext/int corridors. Pets: Other species. $15
daily fee/room. Designated rooms, service with restrictions, supervision.
⊞ ♿ ⊿ 🛜 ✕ 🔋 💻

▽▽▽ The Royal Anne Hotel 🏨
(250) 763-2277. $89-$500. 348 Bernard Ave V1Y 6N5. Between Pan-
dosy and Water sts; downtown. Int corridors. Pets: Medium. $100
deposit/room, $20 daily fee/room. Designated rooms, service with
restrictions, supervision. 🛜 ✕ 🔋 💻

▽▽ Super 8 Kelowna M
(250) 762-8222. $81-$145. 2592 Hwy 97 N V1X 4J4. Jct Hwy 33, just n
on Harvey Ave (Hwy 97 N). Ext corridors. Pets: Dogs only. $10 daily
fee/pet. Designated rooms, service with restrictions, supervision.
ECO ♿ ⊿ 🛜 🔋 💻

KIMBERLEY
▽▽▽ Trickle Creek Lodge 🏨
(250) 427-5175. Call for rates. 500 Stemwinder Dr V1A 2Y6. From
Gerry Sorensen Way, follow signs. Int corridors. Pets: Accepted.
⊞ ⊿ ✕ 🛜 ✕ 🔋 💻

LANGLEY
(AA) ▽▽▽ Best Western Plus Langley Inn 🏨
(604) 530-9311. $132-$192. 5978 Glover Rd V3A 4H9. Trans-Canada
Hwy 1 exit 66 (232nd St), 3.6 mi (6 km) se on Hwy 10, follow signs. Int
corridors. Pets: Small, dogs only. $15 daily fee/pet. Designated rooms,
service with restrictions, supervision.
SAVE ⊞ ♿ ⊿ 🛜 ✕ 🔋 💻

(AA) ▽▽ Coast Hotel & Convention Centre 🏨
(604) 530-1500. $112-$169, 3 day notice. 20393 Fraser Hwy V3A 7N2.
Trans-Canada Hwy 1 exit 58 (200th St/Langley City), 3.9 mi (6.3 km) s
on 200th St, then just e. Int corridors. Pets: Accepted.
SAVE ECO ⊞ ♿ 🛜 🔋 💻

▽▽ Days Inn & Suites Langley 🏨
(604) 539-0100. $99-$169. 20250 Logan Ave V3A 4L6. Trans-Canada
Hwy 1 exit 58 (200th St/Langley City), 3.9 mi (6.3 km) s on 200th St,
then just e. Int corridors. Pets: Medium, dogs only. $15 daily fee/room.
Designated rooms, service with restrictions, supervision.
ECO ♿ 🛜 ✕ 🔋 💻

(AA) ▽▽▽ Holiday Inn Express Hotel & Suites
Langley 🏨
(604) 882-2000. $115-$499. 8750 204th St V1M 2Y5. Trans-Canada
Hwy 1 exit 58 (200th St/Langley City), just e on 88th Ave. Int corridors.
Pets: Small. $20 daily fee/pet. Designated rooms, service with restric-
tions, supervision. SAVE ECO ⊞ ♿ ⊿ 🛜 ✕ 🔋 💻

MADEIRA PARK
▽▽▽ Painted Boat Resort Spa & Marina CO
(604) 883-2456. $215-$565, 3 day notice. 12849 Lagoon Rd V0N 2H0.
Hwy 101, just w on Gonzales Rd, just s, follow signs. Ext corridors.
Pets: Accepted. ⊞ ⊿ ✕ 🛜 ✕ ♿ 🔋 💻

▽▽▽ Sunshine Coast Resort & Marina CA ❀
(604) 883-9177. $129-$219, 21 day notice. 12695 Sunshine Coast Hwy
V0N 2H0. Just n of Madeira Park Rd, follow signs. Ext/int corridors.
Pets: Large, other species. $20 daily fee/pet. Supervision.
⊞ ♿ ✕ 🛜 ✕ 🔋 💻

MAPLE RIDGE
(AA) ▽▽ Best Western Maple Ridge 🏨
(604) 467-1511. $109-$139. 21650 Lougheed Hwy V2X 2S1. 1.2 mi (2
km) w on Lougheed Hwy (Hwy 7). Int corridors. Pets: Accepted.
SAVE ⊿ ✕ 🛜 ✕ 🔋 💻

(AA) ▽▽ Quality Inn M
(604) 463-5111. $89-$600. 21735 Lougheed Hwy V2X 2S2. 1.2 mi (2
km) w on Lougheed Hwy (Hwy 7). Ext corridors. Pets: Accepted.
SAVE ⊞ ♿ 🛜 🔋 💻

MERRITT
(AA) ▽▽ Quality Inn Merritt M
(250) 378-4253. $96-$186. 4025 Walters St V1K 1K1. Hwy 5 exit 290,
0.6 mi (1 km) w. Ext corridors. Pets: Accepted.
SAVE ⊞ ♿ ⊿ 🛜 ✕ 🔋 💻

CAA ❖❖❖ **Ramada Limited** M

(250) 378-3567. **$80-$149.** 3571 Voght St V1K 1C5. Hwy 5 exit 290, just w. Ext corridors. **Pets:** Accepted.

[SAVE] ⊛ ⊠ 📶 ⊠ 🛎 🖵

❖❖ **Super 8 Merritt** M

(250) 378-9422. **$75-$150.** 3561 Voght St V1K 1C5. Hwy 5 exit 290, just w. Ext corridors. **Pets:** Accepted. 🍴 ⊛ 📶 🛎 🖵

MISSION

CAA ❖❖❖ **Best Western Plus Mission City Lodge** H ❖

(604) 820-5500. **$110-$150.** 32281 Lougheed Hwy V2V 1A3. Just w of Hwy 11; corner of Lougheed Hwy (Hwy 7) and Hurd St. Int corridors. **Pets:** Medium, dogs only. $15 daily fee/pet. Designated rooms, service with restrictions, supervision.

[SAVE] 🍴 ♿ ⊛ ⊠ 📶 ⊠ 🛎 🖵

NANAIMO

CAA ❖❖❖ **Best Western Dorchester Hotel** H ❖

(250) 754-6835. **$129-$199.** 70 Church St V9R 5H4. Hwy 19A (Island Hwy) to Comox Rd; downtown. Int corridors. **Pets:** Medium. $25 daily fee/pet. Service with restrictions, crate.

[SAVE] [ECO] 🍴 📶 ⊠ 🛎 🖵

CAA ❖❖❖ **Best Western Northgate Inn** H

(250) 390-2222. **$109-$399.** 6450 Metral Dr V9T 2L8. Hwy 19A (Island Hwy), just w on Aulds Rd, just s. Int corridors. **Pets:** Accepted.

[SAVE] 📶 ⊠ 🛎 🖵

❖❖ **Days Inn Nanaimo Harbourview** H

(250) 754-8171. **$100-$140.** 809 Island Hwy S V9R 5K1. Hwy 19A (Island Hwy), 1.3 mi (2 km) s. Int corridors. **Pets:** Medium. $15 daily fee/pet. Designated rooms, service with restrictions, supervision.

🍴 ♿ ⊛ 📶 ⊠ 🛎 🖵

CAA ❖❖❖ **Inn on Long Lake** H

(250) 758-1144. **Call for rates.** 4700 Island Hwy N V9T 1W6. 3.1 mi (5 km) n on Hwy 19A (Island Hwy) from Departure Bay Ferry Terminal. Ext corridors. **Pets:** Accepted.

[SAVE] [ECO] 🍴 ⊠ 📶 ⊠ 🛎 🖵

❖❖ **Travelodge Nanaimo** H

(250) 754-6355. **$100-$150.** 96 Terminal Ave N V9S 4J2. Between Terminal Ave N and Stewart Ave. Int corridors. **Pets:** Accepted.

[ECO] 📶 ⊠ 🛎 🖵

NELSON

CAA ❖❖❖ **Best Western Plus Baker Street Inn & Convention Centre** H

(250) 352-3525. **$150-$220.** 153 Baker St V1L 4H1. Jct Hwy 3A and 6. Int corridors. **Pets:** Medium. $20 deposit/pet. Designated rooms, service with restrictions, supervision. [SAVE] [ECO] 🍴 ♿ 📶 ⊠ 🛎 🖵

❖ **North Shore Inn** M

(250) 352-6606. **$74-$114.** 687 Hwy 3A V1L 5P7. 1.9 mi (3 km) n on Hwy 3A via Nelson Bridge. Int corridors. **Pets:** Accepted.

📶 ⊠ 🛎

NORTH VANCOUVER

CAA ❖❖❖ **Pinnacle Hotel at the Pier** H ❖

(604) 986-7437. **$149-$399.** 138 Victory Ship Way V7L 0B1. Corner of Esplanade St and Lonsdale Ave. Int corridors. **Pets:** Other species. $75 daily fee/room. Designated rooms, service with restrictions.

[SAVE] [ECO] 🍴 ⊛ ⊠ 📶 ⊠ 🛎 🖵

OAK BAY

CAA ❖❖❖❖ **Oak Bay Beach Hotel** H

(250) 598-4556. **$219-$284.** 1175 Beach Dr V8S 2N4. In Oak Bay district. Int corridors. **Pets:** Accepted. [SAVE] 🍴 ⊠ 📶 ⊠ 🛎 🖵

OSOYOOS

CAA ❖❖❖ **Best Western Plus Sunrise Inn** H

(250) 495-4000. **$119-$280.** 5506 Main St V0H 1V0. Jct Hwy 97, 1.9 mi (3 km) on Hwy 3 (Main St). Int corridors. **Pets:** Small, other species. $20 daily fee/pet. Service with restrictions, crate.

[SAVE] [ECO] 🍴 ♿ ⊛ 📶 ⊠ 🛎 🖵

CAA ❖❖❖ **The Coast Osoyoos Beach Hotel** H

(250) 495-6525. **$79-$539, 14 day notice.** 7702 Main St V0H 1V0. Jct Hwy 97, 1.2 mi (2 km) e. Ext/int corridors. **Pets:** Dogs only. $10 daily fee/pet. Designated rooms, service with restrictions.

[SAVE] [ECO] ⊛ 📶 ⊠ 🛎 🖵

❖❖❖ **Spirit Ridge Vineyard Resort & Spa** CO

(250) 495-5445. **Call for rates.** 1200 Rancher Creek Rd V0H 1V6. Hwy 97 S, e on Hwy 3 (Main St), cross bridge, left on 45th St, then 0.9 mi (1.5 km) e. Ext/int corridors. **Pets:** Accepted.

[ECO] 🍴 ♿ ⊛ ⊠ 📶 ⊠ 🛎 🖵

❖❖❖ **Watermark Beach Resort** CO

(250) 495-5500. **$107-$476.** 15 Park Pl V0H 1V0. Corner of Park Pl and Main St; downtown. Ext/int corridors. **Pets:** Accepted.

[ECO] 🍴 ♿ ⊛ ⊠ 📶 ⊠ 🛎 🖵

PARKSVILLE

❖❖ **Arbutus Grove Motel** M

(250) 248-6422. **Call for rates.** 1182 E Island Hwy V9P 1W3. Island Hwy 19 exit 46 (Parksville), 1 mi (1.6 km) n on Hwy 19A. Ext corridors. **Pets:** Accepted. 📶 ⊠ 🛎 🖵

❖❖❖ **Oceanside Village Resort** CA

(250) 248-8961. **Call for rates.** 1080 Resort Dr V9P 2E3. Island Hwy 19 exit 46 (Parksville), 1.8 mi (2.5 km) n on Hwy 19A. Ext corridors. **Pets:** $20 daily fee/room. Designated rooms, no service, crate.

⊛ 📶 ⊠ 🛎 🖵

CAA ❖❖❖ **Quality Resort Bayside** H

(250) 248-8333. **$99-$199.** 240 Dogwood St V9P 2H5. Island Hwy 19 exit 51 (Parksville/Coombs), 1.3 mi (2 km) e, then 0.6 mi (1 km) n on Hwy 19A. Int corridors. **Pets:** Accepted.

[SAVE] 🍴 ♿ ⊛ 📶 🛎 🖵

❖❖ **Tigh-Na-Mara Seaside Spa Resort & Conference Centre** H

(250) 248-2072. **Call for rates.** 1155 Resort Dr V9P 2E3. Island Hwy 19 exit 46 (Parksville), 1.3 mi (2 km) n on Hwy 19A. Ext corridors. **Pets:** Accepted. 🍴 ⊛ ⊠ 📶 ⊠ 🐾 🛎 🖵

❖❖ **Travelodge Parksville** H

(250) 248-2232. **$89-$149.** 424 W Island Hwy V9P 1K8. Island Hwy 19 exit 51 (Parksville/Coombs), 1.3 mi (2 km) e, then n on Hwy 19A. Int corridors. **Pets:** Accepted. [ECO] ♿ ⊛ 📶 ⊠ 🛎 🖵

❖ **V.I.P. Motel** M

(250) 248-3244. **$69-$109.** 414 W Island Hwy V9P 1K8. Island Hwy 19 exit 51 (Parksville/Coombs), 1.3 mi (2 km) e, then just n on Hwy 19A. Ext corridors. **Pets:** Accepted. 📶 ⊠ 🛎 🖵

PENDER ISLANDS

❖❖❖ **Poets Cove Resort & Spa** H

(250) 629-2100. **$250-$550, 3 day notice.** 9801 Spalding Rd V0N 2M3. From Otter Bay Ferry Terminal, follow signs to South Pender Island, 10 mi (16 km) s; Otter Bay Rd to Bidwell Harbour Rd to Canal Rd. Ext/int corridors. **Pets:** Large, other species. $50 one-time fee/room. Service with restrictions, supervision. 🍴 ⊛ ⊠ 📶 ⊠ 🐾 🛎 🖵

PENTICTON

CAA ❖❖❖ **Best Western Inn at Penticton** H ❖

(250) 493-0311. **$109-$239.** 3180 Skaha Lake Rd V2A 6G4. From downtown, 2.5 mi (4 km) s. Ext corridors. **Pets:** Medium, dogs only. $15 deposit/pet. Designated rooms, service with restrictions, supervision. [SAVE] [ECO] ⊛ ⊠ 📶 ⊠ 🛎 🖵

▼▼ **Coast Penticton Hotel** H
(250) 492-0225. **Call for rates.** 950 Westminster Ave W V2A 1L2. Hwy 97 (Eckhardt Ave W), just n to Westminster Ave W, just e. Ext/int corridors. **Pets:** Accepted. 🍴 ⊠ 🛜 ⊠ 🛇 📺

▼▼ **Days Inn & Conference Centre Penticton** H
(250) 493-6616. **$104-$199.** 152 Riverside Dr V2A 5Y4. Hwy 97, just n. Int corridors. **Pets:** Accepted.
🍽 🍴 🐾 ⊠ ⊠ 🛜 ⊠ 🛇 📺

▼▼▼ **Penticton Lakeside Resort, Convention Centre & Casino** H
(250) 493-8221. **$141-$261.** 21 Lakeshore Dr W V2A 7M5. Main St at Lakeshore Dr W. Int corridors. **Pets:** Accepted.
🍽 🍴 🐾 ⊠ ⊠ 🛜 ⊠ 🛇 📺

▼▼ **Ramada Inn & Suites** H 🐾
(250) 492-8926. **$99-$304.** 1050 Eckhardt Ave W V2A 2C3. 0.8 mi (1.2 km) w on Hwy 97. Ext/int corridors. **Pets:** $15 daily fee/pet. Designated rooms, service with restrictions, crate.
🍽 🍴 🐾 ⊠ ⊠ 🛜 ⊠ 🛇 📺

PITT MEADOWS
▼▼ **Ramada Inn Pitt Meadows** H
(604) 460-9859. **$93-$235.** 19267 Lougheed Hwy V3Y 2J5. Jct Lougheed Hwy (Hwy 7) and Harris Rd. Int corridors. **Pets:** Accepted.
🐾 ⊠ 🛜 ⊠ 🛇 📺

PORT ALBERNI
Ⓐ ▼▼▼ **Best Western Plus Barclay Hotel** H
(250) 724-7171. **$110-$170.** 4277 Stamp Ave V9Y 7X8. Johnston Rd (Hwy 4), just s on Gertrude St. Int corridors. **Pets:** Accepted.
🅂🅰🅅🅴 🍴 ⊠ ⊠ 🛜 ⊠ 🛇 📺

Ⓐ ▼▼▼ **The Hospitality Inn** H
(250) 723-8111. **$99-$159.** 3835 Redford St V9Y 3S2. 2 mi (3.2 km) sw of jct Hwy 4 via City Centre/Port Alberni south route. Int corridors.
Pets: Accepted. 🅂🅰🅅🅴 🍽 🍴 ⊠ ⊠ 🛜 ⊠ 🛇 📺

▼▼ **Riverside Motel** M
(250) 724-9916. **Call for rates.** 5065 Roger St V9Y 3Y9. Johnston Rd (Hwy 4), just s on Gertrude St, just w. Ext corridors. **Pets:** Accepted.
🍴 🛜 ⊠ 🛇 📺

▼▼ **Somass Motel and RV** M
(250) 724-3236. **Call for rates.** 5279 River Rd V9Y 6Z3. 0.5 mi (0.8 km) nw on River Rd from jct Johnston Rd (Hwy 4). Ext corridors.
Pets: Accepted. ⊠ 🛜 ⊠ 🛇 📺

PORT HARDY
▼ **Airport Inn** H
(250) 949-9434. **Call for rates.** 4030 Byng Rd V0N 2P0. Hwy 19, 3.1 mi (5 km) ne, follow signs. Int corridors. **Pets:** Accepted.
🍴 🛜 ⊠ 🎞 🛇 📺

▼▼ **Quarterdeck Inn & Marina** H
(250) 902-0455. **$110-$165.** 6555 Hardy Bay Rd V0N 2P0. Hwy 19, 0.9 mi (1.5 km) n. Int corridors. **Pets:** Accepted.
🍴 🐾 🛜 ⊠ 🎞 🛇 📺

POWELL RIVER
▼▼ **Powell River Town Centre Hotel** H
(604) 485-3000. **Call for rates.** 4660 Joyce Ave V8A 3B6. 0.5 mi (0.8 km) e on Duncan St (Westview-Powell Ferry Terminal), 0.6 mi (1 km) n. Int corridors. **Pets:** Accepted. 🍴 🐾 🛜 ⊠ 🛇 📺

PRINCE GEORGE
▼ **Bon Voyage Inn** M
(250) 964-2333. **Call for rates.** 4222 Hwy 16 W V2N 5N7. Jct Hwy 16 and Kimball Rd, just s. Ext corridors. **Pets:** Other species. $10 daily fee/room. Service with restrictions, supervision. 🛜 🛇 📺

▼▼ **Carmel Inn** M
(250) 564-6339. **Call for rates.** 1502 Hwy 97 S V2L 5L9. Jct Hwy 97 and Trans-Canada Hwy 16 (Yellowhead Hwy), 0.6 mi (1 km) e. Ext corridors. **Pets:** Accepted. 🍴 🛜 🛇 📺

▼▼▼ **Sandman Signature Hotel & Suites Prince George** H
(250) 645-7263. **Call for rates.** 2990 Recreation Place Dr V2N 0B2. Hwy 16, just w on Ferry Ave, just s. Int corridors. **Pets:** Other species. $20 daily fee/pet. Designated rooms, service with restrictions, supervision. 🍴 🛜 ⊠ 🛇 📺

PRINCE RUPERT
▼▼ **Inn on the Harbour** H
(250) 624-9107. **Call for rates.** 720 1st Ave W V8J 3V6. Corner of 6th St. Int corridors. **Pets:** Accepted. 🐾 🛜 ⊠ 🛇 📺

PRINCETON
Ⓐ ▼▼ **Canadas Best Value Princeton Inn & Suites** M
(250) 295-3537. **Call for rates.** 169 Hwy 3 V0X 1W0. Hwy 3, just n on Vermilion Ave. Ext corridors. **Pets:** Accepted.
🅂🅰🅅🅴 🐾 ⊠ 🛜 ⊠ 🛇 📺

QUADRA ISLAND
▼▼ **Taku Resort & Marina** M
(250) 285-3031. **Call for rates.** 616 Taku Rd V0P 1H0. From Campbell River Ferry Terminal, 4.1 mi (6.6 km) n on West Rd, just e on Heriot Bay Rd, follow signs to Heriot Bay. Ext corridors. **Pets:** Accepted.
⊠ 🛜 ⊠ 🎞 🎞 🛇 📺

▼▼ **Tsa-Kwa-Luten Lodge** H
(250) 285-2042. **$135-$165, 3 day notice.** 1 Lighthouse Rd V0P 1N0. From Campbell River Ferry Terminal, just se on Green Rd, 0.6 mi (1 km) e on Noble Rd, 1.8 mi (2.9 km) se on Cape Mudge Rd to Joyce Rd, 0.6 mi (1 km) sw, then 1.4 mi (2.2 km) s. Ext/int corridors. **Pets:** Other species. Designated rooms, supervision.
🍽 🍴 🐾 ⊠ 🛰 ⊠ 🎞 🔲 🛇 📺

QUALICUM BEACH
▼▼▼ **Qualicum Beach Inn** H 🐾
(250) 752-6914. **$199-$499.** 2690 Island Hwy W V9K 1G8. Hwy 19 exit 60 (Qualicum Beach/Port Alberni), 2.5 mi (4 km) on Memorial Ave; jct Hwy 19A; entrance on Elizabeth St. Int corridors. **Pets:** Dogs only. $20 daily fee/pet. Designated rooms. 🍴 ⊠ ⊠ 🛜 ⊠ 🛇 📺

QUESNEL
Ⓐ ▼▼ **Best Western Plus Tower Inn** H 🐾
(250) 992-2201. **$118-$138.** 500 Reid St V2J 2M9. Hwy 97, just e on Shepherd Ave; downtown. Int corridors. **Pets:** Medium, dogs only. $20 daily fee/room. Designated rooms, service with restrictions, supervision.
🅂🅰🅅🅴 🍴 🛜 ⊠ 🛇 📺

Ⓐ ▼▼ **Quality Inn & Suites** H
(250) 992-7247. **$89-$189.** 753 Front St V2J 2L2. Hwy 97, 0.6 mi (1 km) n of Carson Ave. Int corridors. **Pets:** Accepted.
🅂🅰🅅🅴 🍴 🛜 ⊠ 🛇 📺

Ⓐ ▼ **Travelodge Quesnel** M
(250) 992-7071. **$80.** 524 Front St V2J 2K6. Hwy 97, 0.5 mi (0.8 km) n of Carson Ave. Ext corridors. **Pets:** Accepted.
🅂🅰🅅🅴 🍽 🐾 🛜 🛇 📺

RADIUM HOT SPRINGS
Ⓐ ▼▼▼ **Best Western Plus Prestige Inn Radium Hot Springs** H
(250) 347-2300. **$129-$249.** 7493 Main St W V0A 1M0. Jct Hwy 93 and 95. Int corridors. **Pets:** Accepted. 🅂🅰🅅🅴 🍴 🐾 🛜 ⊠ 🛇 📺

ⓐⓐ ▼ **Bighorn Motel** Ⓜ
(250) 347-9111. **$70-$80.** 4881 St. Mary's St E V0A 1M0. Jct Hwy 93 and 95, just s on Main St W, just w. Ext corridors. **Pets:** Accepted.

[SAVE] 🛜 ✕ ☎ 🔒 ▣

REVELSTOKE

ⓐⓐ ▼▼▼ **Best Western Plus Revelstoke** Ⓗ ❀
(250) 837-2043. **$199-$299.** 1925 Laforme Blvd V0E 2S0. Trans-Canada Hwy 1, just n. Int corridors. **Pets:** Large, other species. $20 daily fee/room. Designated rooms, service with restrictions, supervision.

[SAVE] 🛦 🖳 ✕ 🔒 ▣

ⓐⓐ ▼▼▼ **Coast Hillcrest Hotel** Ⓗ
(250) 837-3322. **$129-$249, 3 day notice.** 2100 Oak Dr V0E 2S0. 2.7 mi (4.3 km) e on Trans-Canada Hwy 1, 0.6 mi (1 km) sw. Int corridors. **Pets:** Accepted. [SAVE] [ECO] ▥ 🛦 ✕ 🛜 ✕ 🔒 ▣

RICHMOND

▼▼ **Accent Inns** Ⓗ
(604) 273-3311. **Call for rates.** 10551 St Edwards Dr V6X 3L8. Hwy 99 exit 39 (Bridgeport Rd/Airport) northbound; exit 39A (Richmond/Airport) southbound to St Edwards Dr. Ext corridors. **Pets:** Accepted.

[ECO] ▥ ✕ 🛜 🔒 ▣

ⓐⓐ ▼▼▼ **Best Western Plus Abercorn Inn** Ⓗ ❀
(604) 270-7576. **$109-$309.** 9260 Bridgeport Rd V6X 1S1. Hwy 99 exit 39 (Bridgeport Rd/Airport) northbound; exit 39A (Richmond/Airport) southbound. Int corridors. **Pets:** $20 daily fee/pet. Designated rooms, service with restrictions, supervision.

[SAVE] [ECO] ▥ 🛦 🛜 ✕ 🔒 ▣

ⓐⓐ ▼▼ ▼▼ **The Fairmont Vancouver Airport** Ⓗ ❀
(604) 207-5200. **$249-$949.** 3111 Grant McConachie Way V7B 0A6. In Vancouver International Airport. Int corridors. **Pets:** $25 daily fee/room. Designated rooms, service with restrictions, supervision.

[SAVE] [ECO] ▥ 🛦 🖳 ✕ 🔒 ▣

ⓐⓐ ▼▼▼ **Hilton Vancouver Airport** Ⓗ
(604) 273-6336. **$229-$489.** 5911 Minoru Blvd V6X 4C7. Corner of Minoru Blvd and Westminster Hwy. Int corridors. **Pets:** Accepted.

[SAVE] [ECO] ▥ 🛦 🖳 🛜 ✕ 🔒 ▣

▼▼▼ **Holiday Inn Express Vancouver-Airport** Ⓗ
(604) 273-8080. **Call for rates.** 9351 Bridgeport Rd V6X 1S3. Hwy 99 exit 39 (Bridgeport Rd/Airport) northbound; exit 39A (Richmond/Airport) southbound. Int corridors. **Pets:** Accepted.

[ECO] 🖳 🛜 ✕ 🔒 ▣

▼▼▼ **Holiday Inn Vancouver Airport-Richmond** Ⓗ
(604) 821-1818. **Call for rates.** 10720 Cambie Rd V6X 1K8. Hwy 99 exit 39A (Bridgeport Rd/Airport) northbound to St Edwards Dr, 0.6 mi (1 km) n; exit 39B (No. 4 Rd) southbound, just e. Int corridors. **Pets:** Accepted. [ECO] ▥ 🖳 🛜 ✕ 🔒 ▣

▼▼▼ **Hotel at River Rock** Ⓗ
(604) 247-8900. **$269-$459.** 8811 River Rd V6X 3P8. Hwy 99 exit 39 (Bridgeport Rd/Airport) northbound; exit 39A (Richmond/Airport) southbound, just w on Bridgeport Rd, then just n on Great Canadian Way. Int corridors. **Pets:** Accepted. ▥ 🖳 🛜 ✕ 🔒 ▣

ⓐⓐ ▼▼▼ **Pacific Gateway Hotel at Vancouver Airport** Ⓗ
(604) 278-1241. **$149-$499.** 3500 Cessna Dr V7B 1C7. Just s of island airport interchange; at Russ Baker Way. Int corridors. **Pets:** Accepted.

[SAVE] [ECO] ▥ 🖳 🛦 🛜 ✕ 🔒 ▣

ⓐⓐ ▼▼ ▼▼ **River Rock Casino Resort** Ⓗ
(604) 247-8900. **$209-$459.** 8811 River Rd V6X 3P8. Hwy 99 exit 39 (Bridgeport Rd/Airport) northbound; exit 39A (Richmond/Airport) southbound, just w on Bridgeport Rd, then just n on Great Canadian Way. Int corridors. **Pets:** Accepted.

[SAVE] ▥ 🖳 🛦 ✕ 🛜 ✕ 🔒 ▣

▼▼ **Sandman Hotel Vancouver Airport** Ⓗ
(604) 303-8888. **Call for rates.** 3233 St Edwards Dr V6X 3K4. Hwy 99 exit 39 (Bridgeport Rd/Airport) northbound; exit 39A (Richmond/Airport) southbound to St Edwards Dr. Int corridors. **Pets:** Accepted.

[ECO] ▥ 🛦 🛜 🔒 ▣

ⓐⓐ ▼▼▼ **Sheraton Vancouver Airport Hotel** Ⓗ ❀
(604) 273-7878. **$199-$549.** 7551 Westminster Hwy V6X 1A3. Corner of Minoru Blvd and Westminster Hwy. Int corridors. **Pets:** $20 daily fee/pet. Service with restrictions, crate.

[SAVE] [ECO] ▥ 🛦 🛜 ☒ ✕ 🔒 ▣

ⓐⓐ ▼▼ ▼▼ **Travelodge Hotel Vancouver Airport** Ⓗ
(604) 278-5155. **$70-$181.** 3071 St Edwards Dr V6X 3K4. Hwy 99 exit 39 (Bridgeport Rd/Airport) northbound to St Edwards Dr; exit 39A (Richmond/Airport) southbound. Int corridors. **Pets:** Accepted.

[SAVE] [ECO] ▥ 🛦 🛜 🔒 ▣

ⓐⓐ ▼▼▼ **Vancouver Airport Marriott** Ⓗ
(604) 276-2112. **$150-$347.** 7571 Westminster Hwy V6X 1A3. Corner of Minoru Blvd and Westminster Hwy. Int corridors. **Pets:** Accepted.

[SAVE] ▥ 🛦 🛜 ✕ 🔒 ▣

ⓐⓐ ▼▼▼ **The Westin Wall Centre Vancouver Airport** Ⓗ
(604) 303-6565. **$149-$549.** 3099 Corvette Way V6X 4K3. Hwy 99 exit 39 (Bridgeport Rd/Airport) northbound; exit 39A (Richmond/Airport) southbound, just w to No. 3 Rd. Int corridors. **Pets:** Accepted.

[SAVE] ▥ 🛦 🛦 ✕ ☒ ✕ 🔒 ▣

ROSSLAND

▼ **Casa Alpina** Ⓜ
(250) 362-7364. **$89-$99, 7 day notice.** 1199 Nancy Greene Hwy V0G 1Y0. 0.6 mi (1 km) w on Hwy 3B; jct Hwy 22. Ext corridors. **Pets:** Accepted. ▥ 🛜 🔒 ▣

SALMON ARM

▼▼ **Comfort Inn & Suites** Ⓗ
(250) 832-7711. **$119-$299.** 1090 22nd St NE V1E 2V5. Trans-Canada Hwy 1, access via 30th St NE, just w on 11th Ave NE. Int corridors. **Pets:** Large, other species. $15 daily fee/pet. Designated rooms, service with restrictions, supervision. [ECO] 🛦 🛜 ✕ 🔒 ▣

▼▼ **Podollan Inn** Ⓗ ❀
(250) 832-6025. **$99-$350.** 1460 Trans-Canada Hwy NE V1E 4N1. At 14th St and 9th Ave NE. Ext/int corridors. **Pets:** Other species. $15 daily fee/pet. Designated rooms, service with restrictions.

▥ 🛦 🛜 ✕ 🔒 ▣

SALT SPRING ISLAND

▼▼ **Harbour House Hotel** Ⓗ
(250) 537-5571. **Call for rates.** 121 Upper Ganges Rd V8K 2S2. 0.6 mi (1 km) n on Lower Ganges Rd, just e, towards Long Harbour Ferry Terminal. Ext/int corridors. **Pets:** Accepted.

[ECO] 🛦 🛜 ✕ 🔒 ▣

SICAMOUS

ⓐⓐ ▼▼▼ **Best Western Sicamous Inn** Ⓜ ❀
(250) 836-4117. **$135-$175.** 806 Trans-Canada Hwy 1 V0E 2V0. Jct Trans-Canada Hwy 1 and 97; at east end of town. Ext/int corridors. **Pets:** Large, dogs only. $20 daily fee/room. Designated rooms, service with restrictions, supervision. [SAVE] 🛦 🛜 ✕ 🔒 ▣

SIDNEY

ⓐⓐ ▼▼▼ **Best Western Plus Emerald Isle Motor Inn** Ⓗ
(250) 656-4441. **$129-$199.** 2306 Beacon Ave V8L 1X2. Hwy 17 exit 28 (Sidney), just e. Int corridors. **Pets:** Small, dogs only. $15 daily fee/pet. Designated rooms, service with restrictions, supervision.

[SAVE] [ECO] ▥ 🛦 🛜 ✕ 🔒 ▣

▼▼ The Cedarwood Inn & Suites 🅷

(250) 656-5551. **Call for rates.** 9522 Lochside Dr V8L 1N8. Hwy 17 exit 26, just e on McTavish Rd, then 0.8 mi (1.4 km) n. Ext corridors. **Pets:** Accepted. 🍽 🛗 📶 ⊗ 🎬 🔋 🖥

Ⓐ ▼▼ The Sidney Pier Hotel & Spa 🅷 🐾

(250) 655-9445. **$144-$344.** 9805 Seaport Pl V8L 4X3. Hwy 17 exit 28 (Beacon Ave), 0.6 mi (1 km) e. Int corridors. **Pets:** Small, dogs only. $50 one-time fee/room. Designated rooms, service with restrictions, supervision. 🆂 🅴 🍽 🛗 ⊗ 📶 ⊗ 🔋 🖥

SMITHERS

▼▼ Aspen Inn & Suites Ⓜ

(250) 847-4551. **Call for rates.** 4628 Yellowhead Hwy V0J 2N0. 0.9 mi (1.5 km) w on Hwy 16. Ext corridors. **Pets:** Accepted.
🍽 🛗 🏊 📶 ⊗ 🔋 🖥

SOOKE

Ⓐ ▼▼▼ Best Western Premier Prestige Oceanfront Resort 🅷

(250) 642-0805. **$120-$300.** 6929 W Coast Rd V9Z 0V1. 1 mi (1.6 km) w on Hwy 14. Int corridors. **Pets:** Accepted.
🆂 🍽 🛗 🏊 ⊗ 📶 ⊗ 🔋 🖥

▼▼▼ Sooke Harbour Resort and Marina 🅲🅾

(250) 642-3236. **$199-$259, 3 day notice.** 6971 W Coast Rd V9Z 0V1. 1 mi (1.6 km) w on Hwy 14. Ext corridors. **Pets:** Accepted.
📶 ⊗ 🎬 🔋 🖥

SQUAMISH

Ⓐ ▼▼ Mountain Retreat Hotel & Suites 🅷

(604) 815-0883. **Call for rates.** 38922 Progress Way V8B 0K5. 0.9 mi (1.5 km) n on Hwy 99; at Industrial Way. Int corridors. **Pets:** Accepted.
🆂 🍽 🏊 📶 ⊗ 🔋 🖥

SUMMERLAND

▼▼ Summerland Motel Ⓜ

(250) 494-4444. **$69-$170, 5 day notice.** 2107 Tait St V0H 1Z4. 3.1 mi (5 km) s on Hwy 97 (32nd St). Ext corridors. **Pets:** Accepted.
🍽 🏊 📶 ⊗ 🔋 🖥

SUN PEAKS

▼▼ Coast Sundance Lodge 🅷

(250) 578-0200. **Call for rates.** 3160 Creekside Way V0E 5N0. Hwy 5, 19.5 mi (31 km) ne on Todd Mountain Rd, follow signs to village. Int corridors. **Pets:** Accepted.
🅴 🍽 🛗 ⊗ 📶 ⊗ 🎬 🔋 🖥

▼▼ Hearthstone Lodge 🅷

(250) 578-6969. **Call for rates.** 3170 Creekside Way V0E 5N0. Hwy 5, 19.4 mi (31 km) ne on Todd Mountain Rd, follow signs to village. Int corridors. **Pets:** Accepted.
🅴 🍽 🛗 ⊗ 📶 ⊗ 🎬 🔋 🖥

▼▼ Heffley Boutique Inn 🅷

(250) 578-8343. **$129-$429, 30 day notice.** 3185 Creekside Way V0E 5N0. Hwy 5, 19.4 mi (31 km) ne on Todd Mountain Rd, follow signs to village. Int corridors. **Pets:** Very small, dogs only. $15 daily fee/pet. Service with restrictions, supervision.
🍽 🛗 ⊗ 🆂 ⊗ 🎬 🔋 🖥

Ⓐ ▼▼▼ The Sun Peaks Grand Hotel & Conference Center 🅷

(250) 578-6000. **$99-$649, 3 day notice.** 3240 Village Way V0E 5N0. Hwy 5, 19.4 mi (31 km) ne on Todd Mountain Rd, follow signs to village. Int corridors. **Pets:** Medium. $35 one-time fee/pet. Designated rooms. 🆂 🅴 🍽 🛗 🏊 ⊗ 📶 ⊗ 🔋 🖥

Ⓐ ▼▼ Best Western Peace Arch Inn 🅷

(604) 541-8100. **$109-$199.** 2293 King George Blvd V4A 5A4. Hwy 99 exit 10 southbound, 2.8 mi (4.5 km) s; exit 2 northbound, 2.1 mi (3.5 km) n. Int corridors. **Pets:** Small. $10 daily fee/pet. Designated rooms, supervision. 🆂 🅴 🛗 🏊 ⊗ 📶 ⊗ 🔋 🖥

▼▼ Comfort Inn & Suites Surrey 🅷

(604) 576-8888. **$104-$239.** 8255 166th St V4N 5R8. Trans-Canada Hwy 1 exit 53 (176th St/Hwy 15), 2.9 mi (4.8 km) s to Fraser Hwy (Hwy 1A), then 1.6 mi (2.6 km) nw. Int corridors. **Pets:** Accepted.
🛗 📶 ⊗ 🔋 🖥

Ⓐ ▼▼ Ramada Langley-Surrey 🅷 🐾

(604) 576-8388. **$110-$230.** 19225 Hwy 10 (56 Ave) V3S 8V9. Trans-Canada Hwy 1 exit 58 (200th St/Langley City), 3.1 mi (5 km) s on 200th St, then 1.2 mi (2 km) w on Hwy 10 (56th Ave); corner of 192nd St and Hwy 10. Int corridors. **Pets:** Dogs only. $300 deposit/room, $15 daily fee/pet. Designated rooms, service with restrictions, crate.
🆂 🍽 🛗 🏊 📶 ⊗ 🔋 🖥

Ⓐ ▼▼▼ Sheraton Vancouver Guildford Hotel 🅷

(604) 582-9288. **$139-$249.** 15269 104th Ave V3R 1N5. Trans-Canada Hwy 1 exit 48 eastbound, 0.6 mi (1 km) s on 152nd St, then just e; exit 50 westbound, just w. Int corridors. **Pets:** Accepted.
🆂 🅴 🍽 🛗 🏊 ⊗ 📶 ⊗ 🔋 🖥

TOFINO

Ⓐ ▼▼▼ Best Western Tin Wis Resort Lodge 🅷 🐾

(250) 725-4445. **$119-$406.** 1119 Pacific Rim Hwy V0R 2Z0. 1.8 mi (3.5 km) s on Hwy 4. Ext/int corridors. **Pets:** Dogs only. $20 daily fee/pet. Designated rooms, service with restrictions, supervision.
🆂 🅴 🍽 🛗 ⊗ 📶 ⊗ 🎬 🔋 🖥

▼▼ Long Beach Lodge Resort 🅷

(250) 725-2442. **$199-$639, 7 day notice.** 1441 Pacific Rim Hwy V0R 2Z0. 4.7 mi (7.5 km) s on Hwy 4. Ext/int corridors. **Pets:** Accepted.
🍽 🛗 ⊗ 📶 ⊗ 🎬 🔋 🖥

▼▼ Pacific Sands Beach Resort 🅷

(250) 725-3322. **Call for rates.** 1421 Pacific Rim Hwy V0R 2Z0. 4.7 mi (7.5 km) s on Hwy 4. Ext corridors. **Pets:** Accepted.
🛗 📶 ⊗ 🎬 🔋 🖥

▼▼ Tofino Motel Ⓜ 🐾

(250) 725-2055. **$105-$315.** 542 Campbell St V0R 2Z0. Jct Campbell and 4th sts; downtown. Ext corridors. **Pets:** Medium, dogs only. $30 daily fee/room. Designated rooms, service with restrictions.
🛗 📶 ⊗ 🎬 🔋 🖥

Ⓐ ▼▼ ▼▼ Wickaninnish Inn 🅷 🐾

(250) 725-3100. **$340-$600, 14 day notice.** 500 Osprey Ln at Chesterman Beach V0R 2Z0. 2.7 mi (4.3 km) e on Hwy 4. Int corridors. **Pets:** Other species. $40 daily fee/pet. Designated rooms, service with restrictions, crate. 🆂 🅴 🍽 🛗 ⊗ 📶 ⊗ 🎬 🔋 🖥

TUMBLER RIDGE

▼▼▼ Trend Mountain Hotel & Conference Centre 🅷

(250) 242-2000. **Call for rates.** 375 Southgate St V0C 2W0. Hwy 29, just n on Monkman Way, 0.5 mi (0.9 km) ne. Int corridors.
Pets: Accepted. 🍽 🛗 📶 ⊗ 🔋 🖥

UCLUELET

▼▼▼ Black Rock Oceanfront Resort 🅷

(250) 726-4800. **$159-$725, 7 day notice.** 596 Marine Dr V0R 3A0. 1 mi (1.6 km) e on Peninsula Rd, just s on Matterson Rd, just w. Ext/int corridors. **Pets:** Accepted.
🅴 🍽 🛗 🏊 ⊗ 📶 ⊗ 🎬 🔋 🖥

▼▼ ▼▼ **Thornton Motel** Ⓜ ❖

(250) 726-7725. **$74-$200.** 1861 Peninsula Rd V0R 3A0. E on Peninsula Rd; at Bay St. Ext corridors. **Pets:** $25 one-time fee/pet. Designated rooms, service with restrictions, supervision.

🛜 ✕ 🅰 🚪 🖥

VALEMOUNT

Ⓒ ▼▼▼▼ **Best Western Plus Valemount Inn &**
    Suites 🏨 ❖

(250) 566-0086. **$170-$220.** 1950 Hwy 5 S V0E 2Z0. 0.9 mi (1.5 km) s on Hwy 5 (Yellowhead Hwy). Int corridors. **Pets:** Medium. $20 one-time fee/room. Designated rooms, service with restrictions, crate.

🆂🅰🆅🅴 ⏹ ➔ 🛜 ✕ 🚪 🖥

VANCOUVER

Ⓒ ▼▼▼▼ **Best Western Plus Chateau Granville Hotel &**
    Suites & Conference Centre 🏨 ❖

(604) 669-7070. **$139-$350.** 1100 Granville St V6Z 2B6. Between Davie and Helmcken sts. Int corridors. **Pets:** Medium, dogs only. $20 daily fee/pet. Service with restrictions, supervision.

🆂🅰🆅🅴 🅴🅲🅾 ⏹ 🄼 🛜 ✕ 🚪 🖥

Ⓒ ▼▼▼▼ **Best Western Plus Sands** 🏨

(604) 682-1831. **$99-$450.** 1755 Davie St V6G 1W5. Between Bidwell and Denman sts. Int corridors. **Pets:** Accepted.

🆂🅰🆅🅴 🅴🅲🅾 ⏹ 🄼 🛜 ✕ 🚪 🖥

▼▼ ▼▼ **The Burrard** 🏨 ❖

(604) 681-2331. **$150-$350.** 1100 Burrard St V6Z 1Y7. Between Helmcken and Davie sts. Ext corridors. **Pets:** Other species. $25 daily fee/room. Service with restrictions, supervision. ⏹ 🛜 ✕ 🚪 🖥

▼▼▼▼ **The Coast Coal Harbour Hotel by APA** 🏨

(604) 697-0202. **$194-$484.** 1180 W Hastings St V6E 4R5. Between Thurlow and Bute sts. Int corridors. **Pets:** Accepted.

⏹ 🄼 🛜 ✕ 🚪 🖥

Ⓒ ▼▼▼▼ **Delta Vancouver Suites** 🏨

(604) 684-8188. **$85-$312.** 550 W Hastings St V6B 1L6. Between Seymour and Richards sts; entrance in alley way. Int corridors.
Pets: Accepted. 🆂🅰🆅🅴 🅴🅲🅾 ⏹ 🄼 🛜 ✕ 🖥

Ⓒ ▼▼▼▼ **Executive Hotel Le Soleil** 🏨 ❖

(604) 632-3000. **Call for rates.** 567 Hornby St V6C 2E8. Between Dunsmuir and Pender sts. Int corridors. **Pets:** $25 daily fee/pet. Designated rooms, service with restrictions.

🆂🅰🆅🅴 🅴🅲🅾 ⏹ 🄼 🛜 ✕ 🖥

Ⓒ ▼▼▼▼ **The Fairmont Hotel Vancouver** 🏨

(604) 684-3131. **$269-$999.** 900 W Georgia St V6C 2W6. Corner of Burrard at W Georgia St; enter from Hornby St. Int corridors.
Pets: Accepted. 🆂🅰🆅🅴 🅴🅲🅾 ⏹ ➔ ✕ 📶 🖥

Ⓒ ▼▼▼▼ **Fairmont Pacific Rim** 🏨

(604) 695-5300. **$349-$1199, 3 day notice.** 1038 Canada Pl V6C 0B9. Between Burrard and Thurlow sts. Int corridors. **Pets:** Accepted.

🆂🅰🆅🅴 🅴🅲🅾 ⏹ 🄼 ➔ ✕ 📶 ✕ 🚪 🖥

Ⓒ ▼▼▼▼ **The Fairmont Waterfront** 🏨

(604) 691-1991. **$239-$999.** 900 Canada Place Way V6C 3L5. Between Howe and Burrard sts. Int corridors. **Pets:** Accepted.

🆂🅰🆅🅴 🅴🅲🅾 ⏹ ⏹ 🄼 ➔ ✕ 📶 ✕ 🖥

Ⓒ ▼▼▼▼ **Four Seasons Hotel Vancouver** 🏨

(604) 689-9333. **$315-$775.** 791 W Georgia St V6C 2T4. Between Howe and Granville sts. Int corridors. **Pets:** Accepted.

🆂🅰🆅🅴 🅴🅲🅾 ⏹ 🄼 ➔ ✕ 🛜 ✕ 🚪 🖥

Ⓒ ▼▼▼▼ **Georgian Court Hotel** 🏨

(604) 682-5555. **$199-$599.** 773 Beatty St V6B 2M4. Between Georgia and Robson sts. Int corridors. **Pets:** Accepted.

🆂🅰🆅🅴 ⏹ 🄼 ✕ 🛜 ✕ 🚪 🖥

Ⓒ ▼▼▼▼ **Granville Island Hotel** 🏨 ❖

(604) 683-7373. **$209-$650.** 1253 Johnston St V6H 3R9. Granville Island; below the bridge, follow signs. Int corridors. **Pets:** Other species. $25 daily fee/room. Designated rooms, service with restrictions.

🆂🅰🆅🅴 ⏹ 🄼 ✕ 🛜 ✕ 🖥

Ⓒ ▼▼▼▼ **Hampton Inn & Suites by Hilton Downtown**
    Vancouver 🏨 ❖

(604) 602-1008. **$169-$249.** 111 Robson St V6B 2A8. Between Cambie and Beatty sts. Int corridors. **Pets:** Small, dogs only. $25 daily fee/pet. Designated rooms, service with restrictions, supervision.

🆂🅰🆅🅴 🅴🅲🅾 ⏹ 🄼 ✕ 🛜 ✕ 🚪 🖥

Ⓒ ▼▼▼▼ **Hotel BLU Vancouver** 🏨

(604) 620-6200. **$230-$600.** 177 Robson St V6B 0N3. Jct Cambie St. Int corridors. **Pets:** Accepted. 🆂🅰🆅🅴 ⏹ 🄼 ✕ 🛜 ✕ 🚪 🖥

Ⓒ ▼▼▼▼ **Hyatt Regency Vancouver** 🏨

(604) 683-1234. **$199-$559.** 655 Burrard St V6C 2R7. Between W Georgia and Melville sts. Int corridors. **Pets:** Accepted.

🆂🅰🆅🅴 🅴🅲🅾 ⏹ 🄼 🛜 ✕ 🚪 🖥

▼▼▼▼ **L'Hermitage Hotel** 🏨

(778) 327-4100. **Call for rates.** 788 Richards St V6B 3A4. Between Robson and W Georgia sts. Int corridors. **Pets:** Accepted.

🄼 ✕ 🛜 ✕ 🚪 🖥

Ⓒ ▼▼▼▼ **Pan Pacific Vancouver** 🏨 ❖

(604) 662-8111. **$219-$729.** 300-999 Canada Pl V6C 3B5. Between Howe and Burrard sts. Int corridors. **Pets:** Large. $30 one-time fee/pet. Service with restrictions, supervision.

🆂🅰🆅🅴 🅴🅲🅾 ⏹ 🄼 ➔ ✕ 📶 ✕ 🚪 🖥

Ⓒ ▼▼▼▼ **Pinnacle Vancouver Harbourfront Hotel** 🏨

(604) 689-9211. **$159-$699.** 1133 W Hastings St V6E 3T3. Between Thurlow and Bute sts. Int corridors. **Pets:** Accepted.

🆂🅰🆅🅴 🅴🅲🅾 ⏹ 🄼 ➔ ✕ 🛜 ✕ 🚪 🖥

Ⓒ ▼▼▼▼ **Residence Inn by Marriott Vancouver**
    Downtown 🏨

(604) 688-1234. **$128-$367.** 1234 Hornby St V6Z 1W2. Between Drake and Davie sts. Int corridors. **Pets:** Accepted.

🆂🅰🆅🅴 🅴🅲🅾 🄼 ➔ 🛜 ✕ 🚪 🖥

Ⓒ ▼▼▼▼ **Rosewood Hotel Georgia** 🏨

(604) 682-5566. **$329-$834.** 801 W Georgia St V6C 1P7. Between Hornby and Howe sts, entrance on Howe St. Int corridors.
Pets: Accepted. 🆂🅰🆅🅴 ⏹ 🄼 ➔ 🛜 ✕ 🖥

Ⓒ ▼▼▼▼ **Shangri-La Hotel Vancouver** 🏨 ❖

(604) 689-1120. **$320-$800.** 1128 W Georgia St V6E 0A8. Between Thurlow and Bute sts. Int corridors. **Pets:** Medium. $50 one-time fee/pet. Service with restrictions, supervision.

🆂🅰🆅🅴 🅴🅲🅾 ⏹ 🄼 ➔ 🛜 ✕ 🖥

Ⓒ ▼▼▼▼ **Sheraton Vancouver Wall Centre Hotel** 🏨

(604) 331-1000. **$169-$649.** 1088 Burrard St V6Z 2R9. Between Helmcken and Nelson sts. Int corridors. **Pets:** Accepted.

🆂🅰🆅🅴 🅴🅲🅾 ⏹ 🄼 ➔ ✕ 🛜 ✕ 🚪 🖥

Ⓒ ▼▼▼▼ **The Sutton Place Hotel** 🏨

(604) 682-5511. **$164-$495.** 845 Burrard St V6Z 2K6. Between Smithe and Robson sts. Int corridors. **Pets:** Accepted.

🆂🅰🆅🅴 🅴🅲🅾 ⏹ 🄼 ➔ ✕ 📶 ✕ 🖥

▼▼ ▼▼ **Sylvia Hotel** 🏨 ❖

(604) 681-9321. **$120-$350.** 1154 Gilford St V6G 2P6. Between Pendrell St and Beach Ave. Int corridors. **Pets:** Other species. Designated rooms, service with restrictions. ⏹ 🛜 ✕ 🅰 🚪 🖥

(AAA) ▼▼▼ **Vancouver Marriott Pinnacle Downtown** H

(604) 684-1128. **$115-$477.** 1128 W Hastings St V6E 4R5. Between Thurlow and Bute sts. Int corridors. **Pets:** Accepted.

[icons]

(AAA) ▼▼▼▼ **The Westin Bayshore Vancouver** H ✿

(604) 682-3377. **$199-$549.** 1601 Bayshore Dr V6G 2V4. Jct W Georgia and Cardero sts. Int corridors. **Pets:** Dogs only. Supervision.

[icons]

(AAA) ▼▼▼ **The Westin Grand, Vancouver** H ✿

(604) 602-1999. **$299-$499.** 433 Robson St V6B 6L9. Between Homer and Richards sts. Int corridors. **Pets:** Dogs only. No service, supervision. [icons]

VERNON

(AAA) ▼▼▼ **Best Western Pacific Inn** H ✿

(250) 558-1800. **$99-$229.** 4790 34th St V1T 5Y9. Hwy 97 (32nd St); corner of 48th Ave. Int corridors. **Pets:** Large, dogs only. $20 daily fee/room. Designated rooms, service with restrictions, supervision.

[icons]

(AAA) ▼▼▼ **Days Inn Vernon** M

(250) 549-2224. **$85-$165.** 5121 26th St V1T 8G4. Hwy 97 (32nd St), 0.4 mi (0.7 km) e, just n on 27th St. Ext corridors. **Pets:** Other species. $15 daily fee/pet. Designated rooms, service with restrictions, crate.

[icons]

(AAA) ▼▼▼ **Holiday Inn Express Hotel & Suites Vernon** H ✿

(250) 550-7777. **Call for rates.** 4716 34th St V1T 5Y9. Hwy 97 (32nd St); corner of 48th Ave. Int corridors. **Pets:** $20 daily fee/pet. Designated rooms, service with restrictions, supervision.

[icons]

(AAA) ▼▼▼▼ **Sparkling Hill Resort** H ✿

(250) 275-1556. **Call for rates.** 888 Sparkling Pl V1H 2K7. 6 mi (10 km) s on Hwy 97, 1.1 mi (1.9 km) n on Bailey Rd, 2.4 mi (4 km) nw on Commonage Rd, then 1.8 mi (3 km) w on Predator Ridge Dr, follow signs. Int corridors. **Pets:** Small. $25 daily fee/pet. Designated rooms, service with restrictions, supervision.

[icons]

▼▼ **Super 8 Vernon** H

(250) 542-4434. **$79-$149.** 4204 32nd St V1T 5P4. Hwy 97 (32nd St); jct 43rd Ave. Int corridors. **Pets:** Accepted. [icons]

(AAA) ▼▼▼ **Vernon Lodge & Conference Centre** H ✿

(250) 545-3385. **$124-$249.** 3914 32nd St V1T 5P1. 1 mi (1.6 km) n on Hwy 97 (32nd St). Int corridors. **Pets:** Other species. $15 daily fee/room. Designated rooms, service with restrictions, supervision.

[icons]

(AAA) ▼▼▼ **Village Green Hotel** H ✿

(250) 542-3321. **$79-$159, 3 day notice.** 4801 27th St V1T 4Z1. Hwy 97 (32nd St), 0.4 mi (0.7 km) e on 48th Ave. Int corridors. **Pets:** Other species. $100 deposit/room, $17 daily fee/pet. Designated rooms, supervision. [icons]

VICTORIA

▼▼ **Accent Inns** H ✿

(250) 475-7500. **Call for rates.** 3233 Maple St V8X 4Y9. 1.9 mi (3 km) n on Blanshard St (Hwy 17); corner of Blanshard St and Cloverdale Ave. Ext corridors. **Pets:** Medium. $20 daily fee/room. Designated rooms, service with restrictions, supervision.

[icons]

▼▼▼ **Chateau Victoria Hotel and Suites** H ✿

(250) 382-4221. **$125-$259, 3 day notice.** 740 Burdett Ave V8W 1B2. Between Douglas and Blanshard (Hwy 17) sts. Int corridors. **Pets:** Dogs only. $20 daily fee/pet. Designated rooms, service with restrictions, supervision. [icons]

(AAA) ▼▼▼ **Comfort Inn & Suites Victoria** H

(250) 382-4400. **$129-$229.** 3020 Blanshard St V8T 5C7. 1.6 mi (2.6 km) n on Hwy 17 (Blanshard St), just s of Finlayson St. Ext/int corridors. **Pets:** Accepted. [icons]

(AAA) ▼▼▼ **Days Inn Victoria on the Harbour** H ✿

(250) 386-3451. **$93-$200.** 427 Belleville St V8V 1X3. Between Oswego and Menzies sts. Int corridors. **Pets:** Other species. $15 daily fee/room. Designated rooms, service with restrictions.

[icons]

(AAA) ▼▼▼ **Days Inn Victoria Uptown** H ✿

(250) 388-6611. **$65-$230.** 229 Gorge Rd E V9A 1L1. From Douglas St, 1.2 mi (2 km) w at Washington Ave. Ext corridors. **Pets:** $15 daily fee/pet. Service with restrictions, supervision.

[icons]

(AAA) ▼▼▼ **Delta Victoria Ocean Pointe Resort and Spa** H

(250) 360-2999. **$99-$340.** 100 Harbour Rd V9A 0G1. Just w of Johnson St Bridge; jct Esquimalt and Harbour rds. Int corridors.
Pets: Accepted. [icons]

(AAA) ▼▼▼ **DoubleTree by Hilton Hotel & Suites Victoria** H ✿

(250) 940-3100. **$139-$269.** 777 Douglas St V8W 2B5. Between Blanshard (Hwy 17) and Douglas sts; downtown. Int corridors. **Pets:** Small. $25 daily fee/room. Designated rooms, service with restrictions.

[icons]

▼▼ **Embassy Inn** H ✿

(250) 382-8161. **$99-$379.** 520 Menzies St V8V 2H4. Corner of Quebec St. Int corridors. **Pets:** Medium. $20 daily fee/pet. Designated rooms, service with restrictions, supervision.

[icons]

(AAA) ▼▼▼ **The Fairmont Empress** H

(250) 384-8111. **$239-$699, 3 day notice.** 721 Government St V8W 1W5. Between Belleville and Humboldt sts. Int corridors.
Pets: Accepted. [icons]

(AAA) ▼▼▼ **Harbour Towers Hotel & Suites** H ✿

(250) 385-2405. **$100-$450.** 345 Quebec St V8V 1W4. Between Oswego and Pendray sts. Int corridors. **Pets:** $35 one-time fee/room. Designated rooms.

[icons]

▼▼▼ **Hotel Zed** H

(250) 388-4345. **Call for rates.** 3110 Douglas St V8Z 3K4. Between Finlayson St and Speed Ave. Ext corridors. **Pets:** Accepted.

[icons]

(AAA) ▼▼▼▼ **The Magnolia Hotel & Spa** H

(250) 381-0999. **Call for rates.** 623 Courtney St V8W 1B8. Corner of Courtney and Gordon sts. Int corridors. **Pets:** Accepted.

[icons]

(AAA) ▼▼▼ **Quality Inn Downtown Inner Harbour Victoria** H ✿

(250) 385-6787. **$119-$299.** 850 Blanshard St V8W 2H2. Between Courtney St and Burdett St. Int corridors. **Pets:** Small, dogs only. $20 one-time fee/room. Designated rooms, crate.

[icons]

▼▼▼ **Robin Hood Motel** 🅜 ❄
(250) 388-4302. **$70-$179.** 136 Gorge Rd E V9A 1L4. From Douglas St, 1.2 mi (2 km) w. Ext corridors. **Pets:** Dogs only. $10 daily fee/pet. Designated rooms, service with restrictions, supervision. 📶 🅗 🖵

Ⓐ ▼▼▼ **Royal Scot Hotel & Suites** 🅗
(250) 388-5463. **$99-$399.** 425 Quebec St V8V 1W7. Between Menzies and Oswego sts. Int corridors. **Pets:** Dogs only. $50 one-time fee/pet. Designated rooms, service with restrictions, crate.
🆂🅰🆅🅴 🅴🅲🅾 🍽 🏊 ⊠ 📶 ⊠ 🅺 🅗 🖵

▼▼▼ **Spinnakers Gastro Brewpub & Guesthouses** 🅑🅑
(250) 386-2739. **Call for rates.** 308 Catherine St V9A 3S8. 1.3 mi (2 km) nw over Esquimalt Rd from jct Johnson St Bridge, just s. Ext/int corridors. **Pets:** Accepted. 🍽 📶 ⊠ 🅺 🅗 🖵

▼▼▼ **Swans Hotel and Brewpub** 🅗
(250) 361-3310. **Call for rates.** 506 Pandora Ave V8W 1N6. Corner of Pandora Ave and Store St. Int corridors. **Pets:** Accepted.
🍽 📶 ⊠ 🅺 🅗 🖵

Ⓐ ▼▼▼ **Victoria Marriott Inner Harbour** 🅗
(250) 480-3800. **$112-$306.** 728 Humboldt St V8W 3Z5. Between Blanshard (Hwy 17) and Douglas sts. Int corridors. **Pets:** Accepted.
🆂🅰🆅🅴 🍽 🅼 🏊 ⊠ 📶 ⊠ 🅗 🖵

Ⓐ ▼▼▼ **Westin Bear Mountain Golf Resort & Spa** 🅗 ❄
(250) 391-7160. **$149-$589.** 1999 Country Club Way V9B 6R3. Trans-Canada Hwy 1 exit 14 (Langford/Highlands), 1.1 mi (1.7 km) n on Millstream Rd, then 1.9 mi (3 km) ne on Bear Mountain Pkwy, follow signs. Int corridors. **Pets:** Medium, dogs only. $20 daily fee/room. Designated rooms, service with restrictions, supervision.
🆂🅰🆅🅴 🅴🅲🅾 🍽 🅼 🏊 ⊠ 📶 ⊠ 🅗 🖵

WEST KELOWNA

Ⓐ ▼▼▼ **Best Western Plus Wine Country Hotel & Suites** 🅗
(250) 707-1637. **$149-$259.** 3460 Carrington Rd V4T 3C1. Hwy 97 (Okanagan Hwy), just e on Elk Rd. Int corridors. **Pets:** Accepted.
🆂🅰🆅🅴 🅴🅲🅾 🅼 🏊 📶 ⊠ 🅗 🖵

▼▼▼ **The Cove Lakeside Resort** 🅗
(250) 707-1800. **Call for rates.** 4205 Gellatly Rd V4T 2K2. Hwy 97 (Okanagan Hwy), 1.5 mi (2.5 km) s, follow signs. Int corridors. **Pets:** Other species. $20 daily fee/room. Service with restrictions, crate.
🅴🅲🅾 🍽 🅼 🏊 📶 ⊠ 🅗 🖵

WHISTLER

▼▼▼ **Aava Whistler Hotel** 🅗
(604) 932-2522. **Call for rates.** 4005 Whistler Way V0N 1B4. Hwy 99, just e on Village Gate Blvd, just s. Int corridors. **Pets:** Accepted.
🍽 🅼 🏊 ⊠ 📶 ⊠ 🅗 🖵

▼▼▼ **The Coast Blackcomb Suites at Whistler** 🅒🅞
(604) 905-3400. **$169-$365, 30 day notice.** 4899 Painted Cliff Rd V0N 1B4. Hwy 99, 0.6 mi (1 km) e on Lorimer Rd (Upper Village), just ne on Blackcomb Way, then just e. Int corridors. **Pets:** Accepted.
🅴🅲🅾 🍽 🅼 🏊 ⊠ 📶 ⊠ 🅺 🅗 🖵

▼▼▼ **Crystal Lodge & Suites** 🅗
(604) 932-2221. **Call for rates.** 4154 Village Green V0N 1B4. Hwy 99, just e on Village Gate Blvd, just s on Whistler Way then just e. Int corridors. **Pets:** Accepted. 🅴🅲🅾 🍽 🅼 🏊 ⊠ 📶 ⊠ 🅗 🖵

Ⓐ ▼▼▼ **Delta Whistler Village Suites** 🅗
(604) 905-3987. **$135-$534.** 4308 Main St V0N 1B4. Hwy 99, just e on Village Gate Blvd, just n on Northlands Blvd, then just e. Int corridors. **Pets:** Medium, other species. $35 one-time fee/room. Designated rooms, service with restrictions, supervision.
🆂🅰🆅🅴 🅴🅲🅾 🍽 🅼 🏊 ⊠ 📶 ⊠ 🅗 🖵

Ⓐ ▼▼▼▼ **The Fairmont Chateau Whistler** 🅗
(604) 938-8000. **$199-$1049, 3 day notice.** 4599 Chateau Blvd V0N 1B4. Hwy 99, 0.6 mi (1 km) e on Lorimer Rd (Upper Village), just s on Blackcomb Way, then just e. Int corridors. **Pets:** Accepted.
🆂🅰🆅🅴 🅴🅲🅾 🍽 🅼 🏊 ⊠ 📶 ⊠ 🅗 🖵

Ⓐ ▼▼▼▼ **Four Seasons Resort and Residences Whistler** 🅗
(604) 935-3400. **$239-$1250.** 4591 Blackcomb Way V0N 1B4. Hwy 99, 0.6 mi (1 km) e on Lorimer Rd (Upper Village), just n. Int corridors.
Pets: Accepted. 🆂🅰🆅🅴 🍽 🅼 🏊 ⊠ 📶 ⊠ 🅗 🖵

Ⓐ ▼▼▼▼ **Hilton Whistler Resort & Spa** 🅗 ❄
(604) 932-1982. **Call for rates.** 4050 Whistler Way V0N 1B4. Hwy 99, just e on Village Gate Blvd, just s. Int corridors. **Pets:** Medium. $25 daily fee/room. Designated rooms, service with restrictions, supervision.
🆂🅰🆅🅴 🅴🅲🅾 🍽 🅼 🏊 ⊠ 📶 ⊠ 🅗 🖵

▼▼▼▼ **The Listel Hotel Whistler** 🅗
(604) 932-1133. **$89-$629, 14 day notice.** 4121 Village Green V0N 1B4. Hwy 99, just e on Village Gate Blvd, just s on Whistler Way, then just e. Int corridors. **Pets:** Accepted. 🍽 🅼 📶 ⊠ 🅗 🖵

Ⓐ ▼▼▼▼ **Nita Lake Lodge** 🅗 ❄
(604) 966-5700. **$159-$650, 14 day notice.** 2131 Lake Placid Rd V0N 1B2. 1.8 mi (3 km) s on Hwy 99, just w. Int corridors. **Pets:** $25 daily fee/pet. Designated rooms, service with restrictions.
🆂🅰🆅🅴 🅴🅲🅾 🍽 🅼 🏊 ⊠ 📶 ⊠ 🅗 🖵

▼▼▼▼ **Pan Pacific Whistler Village Centre** 🅗
(604) 966-5500. **Call for rates.** 4299 Blackcomb Way V0N 1B4. Hwy 99, just e on Village Gate Blvd, just s. Int corridors. **Pets:** Accepted.
🅴🅲🅾 🍽 🅼 🏊 ⊠ 📶 ⊠ 🅗 🖵

Ⓐ ▼▼▼▼ **The Westin Resort & Spa, Whistler** 🅗
(604) 905-5000. **$189-$1299.** 4090 Whistler Way V0N 1B4. Hwy 99, just e on Village Gate Blvd, just s. Int corridors. **Pets:** Accepted.
🆂🅰🆅🅴 🅴🅲🅾 🍽 🅼 🏊 ⊠ 📶 🄢 ⊠ 🅗 🖵

Ⓐ ▼▼▼ **Whistler Pinnacle Hotel** 🅗
(604) 938-3218. **$129-$779, 14 day notice.** 4319 Main St V0N 1B4. Hwy 99, just e on Village Gate Blvd, just n on Northlands Blvd, then just e. Int corridors. **Pets:** Accepted.
🆂🅰🆅🅴 🍽 🅼 🏊 ⊠ 📶 ⊠ 🅗 🖵

▼▼▼ **Whistler Village Inn & Suites** 🅗
(604) 932-4004. **Call for rates.** 4429 Sundial Pl V0N 1B4. Hwy 99, just e on Village Gate Blvd, just s on Blackcomb Way. Int corridors.
Pets: Accepted. 🏊 ⊠ 📶 ⊠ 🅗 🖵

WHITE ROCK

▼▼▼ **Ocean Promenade Hotel** 🅗
(604) 542-0102. **Call for rates.** 15611 Marine Dr V4B 1E1. Hwy 99 exit 2B southbound; exit 2 (White Rock/8th Ave) northbound, 1.3 mi (2 km) w. Ext/int corridors. **Pets:** Accepted. 📶 ⊠ 🅗 🖵

WILLIAMS LAKE

Ⓐ ▼▼▼ **Best Western Williams Lake Hotel** 🅗
(778) 412-9000. **$115-$143.** 1850 S Broadway Ave V2G 5G8. 1.3 mi (2.1 km) s on Hwy 97. Int corridors. **Pets:** Accepted.
🆂🅰🆅🅴 📶 ⊠ 🅗 🖵

▼▼ **Drummond Lodge Motel** 🅜
(250) 392-5334. **Call for rates.** 1405 Cariboo Hwy V2G 2W3. 0.6 mi (1 km) s on Hwy 97. Ext corridors. **Pets:** Accepted. 📶 🅗 🖵

▼▼ **Ramada Williams Lake** 🅗
(250) 392-3321. **$100-$159.** 1118 Lakeview Cres V2G 1A3. Jct Hwy 97 and 20, just e. Int corridors. **Pets:** Accepted. 🍽 📶 ⊠ 🅗 🖵

(AA) ▼▼ **Super 8 Williams Lake** [M]

(250) 398-8884. **$105-$120.** 1712 Broadway Ave S V2G 2W4. 1.2 mi (2 km) s on Hwy 97. Int corridors. **Pets:** Other species. $10 daily fee/pet. Designated rooms, service with restrictions, supervision.

[SAVE] 🛜 ✕ 🖥 💻

MANITOBA

BRANDON

(AA) ▼▼▼ **Best Western Plus Brandon Inn** [H] ❀

(204) 727-7997. **$150-$205.** 205 Middleton Ave R7A 1A8. Jct Trans-Canada Hwy 1 and 10; access via north service road. Int corridors. **Pets:** Other species. $10 daily fee/room. Designated rooms, service with restrictions, supervision. [SAVE] [♿M] 🏊 🛜 ✕ 🖥 💻

(AA) ▼▼ **Canad Inns Destination Centre Brandon** [H]

(204) 727-1422. **$122-$259.** 1125 18th St R7A 7C5. On Hwy 10 (18th St); jct Brandon Ave. Int corridors. **Pets:** Accepted.

[SAVE] [ECO] [¶] [♿M] 🏊 🛜 ✕ 🖥 💻

(AA) ▼▼ **Comfort Inn Brandon** [M]

(204) 727-6232. **$105-$190.** 925 Middleton Ave R7C 1A8. Trans-Canada Hwy 1; between Hwy 10 (18th St) N and 10 S; on north side of service road. Int corridors. **Pets:** Accepted.

[SAVE] [ECO] [♿M] 🛜 ✕ 🖥 💻

▼▼ **Days Inn & Suites Brandon** [H]

(204) 727-3600. **$89-$159.** 2130 Currie Blvd R7B 4E7. Jct Trans-Canada Hwy 1, 4.9 mi (7.9 km) s on Hwy 10 (18th St). Int corridors. **Pets:** $15 daily fee/pet. Designated rooms, service with restrictions, crate. [ECO] [♿M] 🏊 🛜 ✕ 🖥 💻

CHURCHILL

▼▼ **Polar Inn & Suites** [H]

(204) 675-8878. **Call for rates.** 153 Kelsey Blvd R0B 0E0. Corner of Franklin St; center. Int corridors. **Pets:** Large. Service with restrictions, crate. 🛜 ✕ [♿] 🖥 💻

▼▼ **The Tundra Inn** [H]

(204) 675-8831. **$139-$265, 30 day notice.** 34 Franklin St R0B 0E0. Just n on Kelsey Blvd; center. Int corridors. **Pets:** Other species. $15 daily fee/pet. Designated rooms, service with restrictions, crate.

[¶] 🛜 ✕ [♿] 🖥 💻

DAUPHIN

▼▼ **Super 8 Dauphin** [H]

(204) 638-0800. **$128-$136.** 1457 Main St S R7N 3B3. Jct Hwy 10 and 5, 3.5 (5.9 km) n. Int corridors. **Pets:** Other species. $15 daily fee/pet. Supervision. 🛜 ✕ 🖥 💻

HEADINGLEY

(AA) ▼▼▼ **Best Western Plus Winnipeg West** [H] ❀

(204) 594-2200. **$120-$140.** 4140 Portage Ave R4H 1C5. Jct Trans-Canada Hwy 1 (Portage Ave) and 101 just w; entrance through travel plaza. Int corridors. **Pets:** $20 daily fee/pet. Service with restrictions, supervision. [SAVE] [♿M] 🛜 ✕ 🖥 💻

HECLA

▼▼▼ **Lakeview Hecla Resort** [H]

(204) 279-2041. **Call for rates.** Hwy 8 R0C 2R0. 5 mi (8.3 km) n of Hecla Village. Int corridors. **Pets:** Accepted.

[¶] 🏊 ✕ 🛜 ✕ 🖥 💻

RUSSELL

▼ **The Russell Inn Hotel & Conference Centre** [H] ❀

(204) 773-2186. **$96-$141, 14 day notice.** Hwy 16 R0J 1W0. 0.8 mi (1.2 km) se on Hwy 16 and 83. Ext/int corridors. **Pets:** Small, other species. Designated rooms, service with restrictions, crate.

[¶] 🏊 ✕ 🛜 ✕ 🖥 💻

STEINBACH

▼▼ **Days Inn** [H]

(204) 320-9200. **$110-$118.** 75 Hwy 12 N R5G 1T3. 0.5 mi (0.8 km) n of jct Hwy 52. Int corridors. **Pets:** Accepted.

[¶] [♿M] 🏊 🛜 ✕ 🖥 💻

SWAN RIVER

▼▼ **Swan Valley Super 8** [H]

(204) 734-7888. **$109-$129.** 115 Kelsey Tr R0L 1Z0. Corner of Hwy 10 and 83. Int corridors. **Pets:** Large, other species. $15 daily fee/room. Designated rooms, service with restrictions, supervision.

[ECO] [♿M] 🛜 ✕ 🖥 💻

THE PAS

▼▼ **Andersen Inn & Suites** [H]

(204) 623-1888. **$120-$130.** 1717 Gordon Ave R9A 1K3. At southern approach to town. Int corridors. **Pets:** Accepted.

🏊 🛜 ✕ 🖥 💻

▼▼ **Kikiwak Inn** [H]

(204) 623-1800. **Call for rates.** Hwy 10 N R0B 2J0. On Hwy 10, 0.4 mi (0.6 km) n. Int corridors. **Pets:** Accepted.

[¶] [♿M] 🏊 🛜 ✕ 🖥 💻

WINNIPEG

(AA) ▼▼▼ **Best Western Plus Pembina Inn & Suites** [H] ❀

(204) 269-8888. **$130-$189.** 1714 Pembina Hwy R3T 2G2. 0.6 mi (1 km) n of jct Bishop Grandin Blvd. Int corridors. **Pets:** $20 daily fee/pet. Designated rooms, supervision.

[SAVE] [ECO] [♿M] 🏊 🛜 ✕ 🖥 💻

(AA) ▼▼▼ **Best Western Plus Winnipeg Airport Hotel** [H]

(204) 775-9889. **$99-$209.** 1715 Wellington Ave R3H 0G1. Jct Century St. Int corridors. **Pets:** Accepted.

[SAVE] [ECO] [¶] [♿M] 🏊 🛜 ✕ 🖥 💻

(AA) ▼▼ **Canad Inns Destination Centre Fort Garry** [H]

(204) 261-7450. **$115-$234.** 1824 Pembina Hwy R3T 2G2. Just n of Bishop Grandin Blvd. Int corridors. **Pets:** $10 daily fee/pet. Service with restrictions, crate. [SAVE] [ECO] [¶] [♿M] 🏊 🛜 ✕ 🖥 💻

(AA) ▼▼ **Canad Inns Destination Centre Polo Park** [H]

(204) 775-8791. **$115-$259.** 1405 St. Matthews Ave R3G 0K5. Just e of St James St. Int corridors. **Pets:** Accepted.

[SAVE] [ECO] [¶] [♿M] 🏊 🛜 ✕ 🖥 💻

▼▼▼ **Clarion Hotel & Suites** [H] ❀

(204) 774-5110. **$151-$269.** 1445 Portage Ave R3G 3P4. Jct Empress St. Int corridors. **Pets:** Medium, other species. $15 daily fee/pet. Designated rooms, service with restrictions, crate.

[ECO] [¶] [♿M] 🏊 ✕ 🛜 ✕ 🖥 💻

(AA) ▼▼ **Comfort Inn Airport** [H]

(204) 783-5627. **$99-$145.** 1770 Sargent Ave R3H 0C8. At King Edward St. Int corridors. **Pets:** Accepted.

[SAVE] [ECO] [♿M] 🛜 ✕ 🖥 💻

(AA) ⬦⬦ **Comfort Inn Winnipeg South** H
(204) 269-7390. **$107-$180.** 3109 Pembina Hwy R3T 4R6. Just n of jct Perimeter Hwy 100 and 75. Int corridors. **Pets:** Medium. $15 daily fee/room. Designated rooms, service with restrictions, supervision.
[SAVE] [ECO] ⊞ ⌖ ⚏ ⌧ ⛉ ▭

⬦⬦⬦ **Days Inn & Suites Winnipeg Airport** H
(204) 505-1500. **$130-$200.** 695 Berry St R3H 0S4. Jct Sargent Ave. Int corridors. **Pets:** Accepted. ⌖ ⚏ ⌧ ⛉ ▭

⬦⬦⬦ **Delta Winnipeg** H 🐾
(204) 942-0551. **$120-$239, 7 day notice.** 350 St. Mary Ave R3C 3J2. Jct Hargrave St. Int corridors. **Pets:** $35 one-time fee/pet, $7 daily fee/pet. Service with restrictions.
[ECO] ⊞ ⌖ ≋ ⌧ ⚏ ⌧ ⛉ ▭

(AA) ⬦⬦ **Express by Canad Inns** H
(204) 269-6955. **$105-$165.** 1792 Pembina Hwy R3T 2G2. Just n of Bishop Grandin Blvd. Int corridors. **Pets:** Accepted.
[SAVE] [ECO] ⊞ ⚏ ⌧ ⛉ ▭

⬦⬦⬦ **Fairfield Inn & Suites by Marriott** H
(204) 783-7900. **$103-$166.** 1301 Ellice Ave R3G 0N5. Between Empress and Strathcona sts. Int corridors. **Pets:** Accepted.
≋ ⚏ ⌧ ⛉ ▭

(AA) ⬦⬦⬦ **The Fairmont Winnipeg** H 🐾
(204) 957-1350. **$129-$309.** 2 Lombard Pl R3B 0Y3. Just e of Portage Ave and Main St. Int corridors. **Pets:** Medium, other species. $25 daily fee/pet. Supervision. [SAVE] [ECO] ⊞ ⌖ ≋ ⌧ 🔊 ⌧ ▭

(AA) ⬦⬦⬦ **Four Points by Sheraton Hotel Winnipeg Airport** H
(204) 775-5222. **$97-$153.** 1999 Wellington Ave R3H 1H5. At Winnipeg James Armstrong Richardson International Airport. Int corridors. **Pets:** Other species. $15 one-time fee/room. Designated rooms, service with restrictions, crate. [SAVE] [ECO] ⊞ ⚏ ⌧ ⛉ ▭

⬦⬦⬦ **Hilton Winnipeg Airport Suites** H
(204) 783-1700. **$129-$199.** 1800 Wellington Ave R3H 1B2. At Berry St. Int corridors. **Pets:** Accepted.
[ECO] ⊞ ⌖ ≋ ⌧ ⚏ ⌧ ⛉ ▭

⬦⬦⬦ **Holiday Inn Winnipeg South** H
(204) 452-4747. **Call for rates.** 1330 Pembina Hwy R3T 2B4. At McGillivray Blvd. Int corridors. **Pets:** Accepted.
[ECO] ⊞ ⌖ ≋ ⚏ ⌧ ⛉ ▭

⬦⬦⬦ **Homewood Suites by Hilton Winnipeg Airport-Polo Park** H
(204) 515-1941. **$149-$209.** 1295 Ellice Ave R3G 0N5. Between Empress and Strathcona sts. Int corridors. **Pets:** Accepted.
⚏ ⌧ ⛉ ▭

⬦⬦⬦ **MainStay Suites Winnipeg** H
(204) 594-0500. **$120-$220.** 670 King Edward St R3H 0P2. Between Sargent and Ellice aves. Int corridors. **Pets:** Accepted.
⊞ ⌖ ⚏ ≋ ⌧ ⛉ ▭

⬦⬦⬦ **Mere Hotel** H
(204) 594-0333. **Call for rates.** 333 Waterfront Dr R3C 0A2. Between Pacific and Bannatyne aves. Int corridors. **Pets:** Accepted.
⊞ ⌖ ≋ ⌧ ⛉ ▭

(AA) ⬦⬦ **Quality Inn & Suites** H 🐾
(204) 453-8247. **$103-$220.** 635 Pembina Hwy R3M 2L4. Just s of Grant Ave. Int corridors. **Pets:** Other species. $15 daily fee/pet. Service with restrictions, crate. [SAVE] ⊞ ≋ ⛉ ▭

(AA) ⬦⬦⬦ **Radisson Hotel Winnipeg Downtown** H
(204) 956-0410. **$160-$265.** 288 Portage Ave R3C 0B8. At Smith St. Int corridors. **Pets:** Accepted. [SAVE] [ECO] ⊞ ≋ ⌧ ⛉ ▭

⬦⬦⬦ **Sandman Hotel & Suites Winnipeg Airport** H
(204) 775-7263. **$151.** 1750 Sargent Ave R3H 0C7. Between King Edward and Century sts. Int corridors. **Pets:** Accepted.
[ECO] ⊞ ⌖ ⚏ ≋ ⌧ ⛉ ▭

⬦⬦ **Viscount Gort Hotel** H
(204) 775-0451. **$117-$149.** 1670 Portage Ave R3J 0C9. Jct Rt 90. Int corridors. **Pets:** Accepted. ⊞ ⌖ ⚏ ⌧ ≋ ⌧ ⛉ ▭

NEW BRUNSWICK

BATHURST
⬦⬦ **Atlantic Host Hotel** H
(506) 548-3335. **Call for rates.** 1450 Vanier Blvd E2A 4H7. Rt 11 exit 310 (Vanier Blvd). Ext/int corridors. **Pets:** Accepted.
⊞ ⌖ ⚏ ⌧ ≋ ⌧ ⛉ ▭

⬦⬦ **Comfort Inn Bathurst** H
(506) 547-8000. **$98-$193.** 1170 St. Peter Ave E2A 2Z9. 2.1 mi (3.4 km) n on Rt 134 (St. Peter Ave). Ext/int corridors. **Pets:** Accepted.
≋ ⌧ ⛉ ▭

⬦⬦ **Danny's Hotel Suites Events Centre** H
(506) 546-6621. **$139-$159.** 1223 rue Principale E2A 3Z2. Rt 11 exit 310 (Vanier Blvd) northbound to Rt 134 (St. Peter Ave), 2.3 mi (3.7 km) n; exit 318 southbound to Rt 134 (St. Peter Ave), 2.3 mi (3.7 km) s. Ext/int corridors. **Pets:** Accepted. ⊞ ⚏ ≋ ⌧ ⛉ ▭

⬦⬦ **Lakeview Inns & Suites** H
(506) 548-4949. **$99-$117.** 777 St. Peter Ave E2A 2Y9. 1.8 mi (3 km) n on Rt 134 (St. Peter Ave). Ext/int corridors. **Pets:** Accepted.
[ECO] ⌖ ≋ ⌧ ⛉ ▭

BOUCTOUCHE
⬦⬦ **Auberge Bouctouche Inn & Suites** H
(506) 743-5003. **$95-$175.** 50 Industrielle St E4S 3H9. Rt 11 exit 32A/B. Int corridors. **Pets:** $10 daily fee/pet. Designated rooms, service with restrictions, supervision. ⌖ ≋ ⌧ ⛉ ▭

CAMPBELLTON
⬦⬦ **Comfort Inn** H
(506) 753-4121. **$99-$150.** 111 chemin Val D'Amour Rd E3N 5B9. Hwy 11 exit 415, 0.6 mi (1 km) e on Sugarloaf St W. Ext/int corridors.
Pets: Accepted. [ECO] ≋ ⌧ ⛉ ▭

(AA) ⬦⬦ **Quality Hotel & Conference Centre** H
(506) 753-4133. **$99-$144.** 157 Water St E3N 3H2. Hwy 134; in City Centre Complex. Ext/int corridors. **Pets:** Accepted.
[SAVE] ⊞ ⌖ ≋ ⌧ ⛉ ▭

⬦⬦ **Super 8-Campbellton** H
(506) 753-8080. **$100-$118.** 26 Duke St E3N 2K3. Just s of Roseberry St; jct George and Duke sts; downtown. Ext/int corridors.
Pets: Accepted. [ECO] ⌖ ⚏ ⌧ ≋ ⌧ ⛉ ▭

DIEPPE
⬦⬦ **Coastal Inn Dieppe** H
(506) 857-9686. **$99-$152.** 502 Kennedy St E1A 5Y7. At Paul St. Ext/int corridors. **Pets:** Accepted. [ECO] ⊞ ⚏ ≋ ⌧ ⛉ ▭

⬦⬦ **Quality Inn Airport Moncton** H
(506) 850-0080. **$99-$199.** 370 Dieppe Blvd E1A 8H4. Hwy 15 exit 16, 0.6 mi (1 km) s. Int corridors. **Pets:** Accepted.
[ECO] ⌖ ⚏ ≋ ⌧ ⛉ ▭

DOAKTOWN

◆◆◆ The Ledges Inn CI
(506) 365-1820. **Call for rates.** 30 Ledges Inn Ln E9C 1A7. On Rt 8; just w of center. Ext/int corridors. **Pets:** Accepted. ⊞ ⊠ 🛜 ⊠

EDMUNDSTON

⟨AA⟩ ◆◆◆ Best Western Plus Edmundston Hotel H
(506) 739-0000. **$150-$200.** 280 Hebert Blvd E3V 0A3. Trans-Canada Hwy 2 exit 18 (Hebert Blvd). Ext/int corridors. **Pets:** Accepted.
⟨SAVE⟩ ⟨ECO⟩ 🛗 ⇆ 🛜 ⊠ 🖪 🖵

⟨AA⟩ ◆◆ Comfort Inn H
(506) 739-8361. **$114-$200.** 5 Bateman Ave E3V 3L1. Trans-Canada Hwy 2 exit 18 (Hebert Blvd). Ext/int corridors. **Pets:** Accepted.
⟨SAVE⟩ ⟨ECO⟩ 🛜 ⊠ 🖪 🖵

◆◆ Days Inn Edmundston H
(506) 263-0000. **Call for rates.** 10 rue Mathieu E7C 3E1. Trans-Canada Hwy 2 exit 26. Ext/int corridors. **Pets:** Accepted. ⊞ 🛜 🖪 🖵

⟨AA⟩ ◆◆◆◆ Four Points by Sheraton Edmundston H
(506) 739-7321. **Call for rates.** 100 rue Rice E3V 1T4. Trans-Canada Hwy 2 exit 18 (Hebert Blvd), 1 mi (1.6 km) sw, then just w on Church Rd. Int corridors. **Pets:** Accepted.
⟨SAVE⟩ ⊞ 🛗 ⇆ 🛜 ⊠ 🖪 🖵

◆◆ Travelodge Edmundston H
(506) 735-5525. **$90-$175.** 919 chemin Canada E3V 3X2. Trans-Canada Hwy 2 exit 13A-B. Ext/int corridors. **Pets:** Accepted.
⊞ 🛗 ⇆ ⊠ 🛜 🖪

FREDERICTON

⟨AA⟩ ◆◆◆◆ Best Western Plus Fredericton Hotel & Suites H 🐾
(506) 455-8448. **$119-$299.** 333 Bishop Dr E3C 2M6. Rt 8 exit 6A eastbound; exit 6B westbound, just w of Regent Mall. Int corridors. **Pets:** Medium, other species. $20 daily fee/room. Designated rooms, service with restrictions, supervision.
⟨SAVE⟩ 🛗 ⇆ 🛜 ⊠ 🖪 🖵

◆ City Motel H
(506) 450-9900. **$79-$99.** 1216 Regent St E3B 3Z4. Trans-Canada Hwy 2 exit 285A eastbound; exit 285B westbound, 2 mi (3.3 km) n on Rt 101 (Regent St). Int corridors. **Pets:** $10 daily fee/pet. Designated rooms, service with restrictions, crate. ⊞ 🛜 🖪 🖵

⟨AA⟩ ◆◆ Comfort Inn H 🐾
(506) 453-0800. **$109-$200.** 797 Prospect St E3B 5Y4. Trans-Canada Hwy 2 exit 281, 2.5 mi (4 km) ne on Rt 640 (Hanwell Rd), then right. Ext/int corridors. **Pets:** Other species. Service with restrictions.
⟨SAVE⟩ ⟨ECO⟩ 🛗 🛜 ⊠ 🖪 🖵

◆◆◆ Crowne Plaza Fredericton Lord Beaverbrook H
(506) 455-3371. **$140-$260.** 659 Queen St E3B 5A6. Corner of Regent St. Int corridors. **Pets:** Accepted.
⟨ECO⟩ ⊞ ⇆ ⊠ 🛜 ⊠ 🖪 🖵

⟨AA⟩ ◆◆◆◆ Delta Fredericton H
(506) 457-7000. **$139-$279.** 225 Woodstock Rd E3B 2H8. 1 mi (1.6 km) n on Rt 102; downtown. Int corridors. **Pets:** Accepted.
⟨SAVE⟩ ⟨ECO⟩ ⊞ 🛗 ⇆ ⊠ 🛜 ⊠ 🖪 🖵

◆◆◆ Hampton Inn & Suites by Hilton H 🐾
(506) 300-1818. **Call for rates.** 470 Bishop Dr E3C 0B4. Rt 8 exit 6A eastbound; exit 6B westbound, just w of Regent Mall. Int corridors. **Pets:** Designated rooms, service with restrictions, crate.
⊞ 🛗 🛜 ⊠ 🖪 🖵

◆◆◆ Holiday Inn Express & Suites H
(506) 459-0035. **$129-$214.** 665 Prospect St E3B 6B8. Rt 8 exit 3 (Hanwell Rd) eastbound; exit 5 (Smythe St) westbound. Int corridors. **Pets:** Accepted. ⟨ECO⟩ 🛜 ⊠ 🖪 🖵

◆◆◆ Knights Inn M
(506) 458-8784. **$55-$82.** 1214 Lincoln Rd E3B 8C8. 1.2 mi (2 km) n on Rt 102 from airport. Ext corridors. **Pets:** Accepted. 🛜 ⊠ 🖪

◆◆ Ramada Hotel Fredericton H
(506) 460-5500. **$89-$149.** 480 Riverside Dr E3A 8C2. On Rt 105; at north end of Princess Margaret Bridge. Int corridors. **Pets:** Accepted.
⟨ECO⟩ ⊞ ⇆ ⊠ 🛜 ⊠ 🖪 🖵

GRAND FALLS

⟨AA⟩ ◆◆◆ Best Western Plus Grand-Sault Hotel & Suites H 🐾
(506) 473-6200. **$150-$250.** 187 Ouellette St E3Z 3E8. Trans-Canada Hwy 2 exit 79. Int corridors. **Pets:** Other species. $20 one-time fee/ room. Designated rooms, crate.
⟨SAVE⟩ ⟨ECO⟩ 🛗 ⇆ 🛜 ⊠ 🖪 🖵

◆◆ Quality Inn Grand Falls H
(506) 473-1300. **$115-$199.** 10039 Rt 144 E3Y 3H5. Trans-Canada Hwy 2 exit 75, just w. Ext/int corridors. **Pets:** Accepted.
⊞ 🛗 ⇆ ⊠ 🛜 ⊠ 🖪 🖵

MIRAMICHI

◆◆◆ Days Inn Miramichi H
(506) 622-1215. **$89-$126.** 201 Edward St E1V 2Y7. 0.6 mi (1 km) w of center. Int corridors. **Pets:** Small. $10 daily fee/pet. Designated rooms, service with restrictions, supervision. ⟨ECO⟩ 🛜 ⊠ 🖪 🖵

◆◆◆ Lakeview Inns & Suites H
(506) 627-1999. **Call for rates.** 333 King George Hwy E1V 1L2. 1.1 mi (1.8 km) w from center. Ext/int corridors. **Pets:** Accepted.
⟨ECO⟩ 🛗 🛜 🖪 🖵

◆◆◆ Rodd Miramichi River Hotel H
(506) 773-3111. **$135-$195.** 1809 Water St E1N 1B2. Hwy 11 exit 120, 1 mi (1.6 km) e. Ext/int corridors. **Pets:** Accepted.
⟨ECO⟩ ⊞ 🛗 ⇆ ⊠ 🛜 ⊠ 🖪 🖵

MONCTON

⟨AA⟩ ◆◆◆◆ Casino New Brunswick H
(506) 861-4661. **$119-$999.** 21 Casino Dr E1G 0R7. Trans-Canada Hwy 2 exit 450. Int corridors. **Pets:** Large, other species. $30 one-time fee/room. Service with restrictions, supervision.
⟨SAVE⟩ ⊞ 🛗 ⇆ ⊠ 🛜 ⊠ 🖪 🖵

⟨AA⟩ ◆◆ Comfort Inn H
(506) 859-6868. **$109-$219.** 20 Maplewood Dr E1A 6P9. Trans-Canada Hwy 2 exit 459A on Hwy 115 S, left on Rt 134 E (Lewisville Rd). Ext/int corridors. **Pets:** Accepted. ⟨SAVE⟩ ⟨ECO⟩ 🛜 ⊠ 🖪 🖵

⟨AA⟩ ◆◆ Comfort Inn-Magnetic Hill H
(506) 384-3175. **$109-$209.** 2495 Mountain Rd E1G 2W4. Trans-Canada Hwy 2 exit 450. Ext/int corridors. **Pets:** Accepted.
⟨SAVE⟩ ⟨ECO⟩ 🛜 ⊠ 🖪 🖵

⟨AA⟩ ◆◆◆◆ Crowne Plaza Moncton Downtown H 🐾
(506) 854-6340. **$129-$209.** 1005 Main St E1C 1G9. At Highfield and Main sts; downtown. Int corridors. **Pets:** Other species. Designated rooms, service with restrictions, supervision.
⟨SAVE⟩ ⟨ECO⟩ ⊞ ⇆ ⊠ 🛜 ⊠ 🖪 🖵

◆◆ Days Inn & Suites H
(506) 384-1050. **$85-$125.** 2515 Mountain Rd E1G 2W4. Trans-Canada Hwy 2 exit 450. Ext/int corridors. **Pets:** Accepted.
⟨ECO⟩ 🛗 ⇆ ⊠ 🛜 ⊠ 🖪 🖵

◆◆◆ Delta Beauséjour H
(506) 854-4344. **$129-$329.** 750 Main St E1C 1E6. Jct Main St and Sommet Ln; downtown. Int corridors. **Pets:** Accepted.
⟨ECO⟩ ⊞ ⇆ ⊠ 🛜 ⊠ 🖪 🖵

▼▼▼▼ Fairfield Inn & Suites by Marriott Moncton H
(506) 855-0033. **$71-$183.** 26 Marriott Dr E1A 7S4. Rt 15 exit 11 westbound; exit 16 eastbound, just nw. Int corridors. **Pets:** Other species. $25 one-time fee/room. Designated rooms, service with restrictions, crate. 🔥📶✖️📱💻

ⓐ ▼▼▼▼ Four Points by Sheraton Moncton H 🐾
(506) 852-9600. **$139-$199.** 40 Lady Ada Blvd E1G 0E3. Trans-Canada Hwy 2 exit 454. Int corridors. **Pets:** Designated rooms, service with restrictions, supervision. 🅢🅐🅥🅔 🍴🔥📶✖️📱💻

ⓐ ▼▼▼▼ Hampton Inn & Suites Moncton H
(506) 855-4819. **$144-$189.** 700 Mapleton Rd E1G 0L7. Trans-Canada Hwy 2 exit 454. Int corridors. **Pets:** Accepted.
🅢🅐🅥🅔🔥🐾📶✖️📱💻

▼▼▼ Hotel St. James H
(506) 388-4283. **$169-$289.** 14 Church St E1C 4Y9. Corner of Main and Church sts. Int corridors. **Pets:** Accepted. 🍴📶✖️📱

ⓐ ▼▼▼ Quality Inn H
(506) 386-6749. **$94-$270.** 2530 Mountain Rd E1G 1B4. Trans-Canada Hwy 2 exit 450. Int corridors. **Pets:** Medium, other species. $10 daily fee/pet. Designated rooms, service with restrictions, supervision.
🅢🅐🅥🅔🔥🐾📶✖️📱💻

ⓐ ▼▼▼▼ Residence Inn by Marriott Moncton H 🐾
(506) 854-7100. **$88-$331.** 600 Main St E1C 0M6. At Assomption Blvd. Int corridors. **Pets:** Medium, other species. $75 one-time fee/room. Designated rooms, service with restrictions, supervision.
🅢🅐🅥🅔 🅔🅒🅞 🍴🔥🐾📶✖️📱💻

▼▼▼ Rodd Moncton H
(506) 382-1664. **$115-$169.** 434 Main St E1C 1B9. On Rt 106 (Main St) at King St. Ext/int corridors. **Pets:** Large, other species. Designated rooms, service with restrictions, supervision.
🅔🅒🅞🐾📶✖️📱💻

▼▼▼ Travelodge Suites Moncton H
(506) 852-7000. **$89-$174.** 2475 Mountain Rd E1G 2J5. Trans-Canada Hwy 2 exit 450. Ext/int corridors. **Pets:** $10 one-time fee/room. Service with restrictions, crate. 🅔🅒🅞📶✖️📱💻

▼▼▼ V Hotel & Suites H
(506) 382-3395. **$89-$200.** 42 Highfield St E1C 5N3. Center; 1 blk n of Main St. Ext/int corridors. **Pets:** Small. $25 one-time fee/room. Service with restrictions, supervision. 🍴🐾📶✖️📱💻

OROMOCTO

ⓐ ▼▼▼ Days Inn & Conference Centre Oromocto H
(506) 357-5657. **$105-$125.** 60 Brayson Blvd E2V 4T9. Trans-Canada Hwy 2 exit 301 eastbound; exit 303 northbound, just s to Pioneer Ave, then 1 mi (1.6 km) w. Int corridors. **Pets:** Other species. $10 daily fee/pet. Designated rooms, service with restrictions, supervision.
🅢🅐🅥🅔 🅔🅒🅞 🍴🔥🐾📶✖️📱💻

PENOBSQUIS

▼ Pine Cone Motel M
(506) 433-3958. **Call for rates.** 12808 Rt 114 E4G 2Y8. Hwy 1 exit 198, 1.2 mi (2 km) e. Ext corridors. **Pets:** Accepted.
📶✖️🐾📱

PERTH-ANDOVER

ⓐ ▼▼▼▼ The Castle Inn CI
(506) 273-9495. **$119-$229.** 21 Brentwood Dr E7H 1P1. Trans-Canada Hwy 2 exit 115, follow signs over Saint John River, then s on Station Rd. Int corridors. **Pets:** Accepted.
🅢🅐🅥🅔 🍴🐾✖️📶✖️📱💻

POINTE-VERTE

▼▼▼ Gite Toutes Saisons Bed & Breakfast BB
(506) 783-3122. **$139-$189, 7 day notice.** 10 rue des Oiseaux E8J 2V6. Rt 11 exit 333 to Rt 134, 0.8 mi (1.3 km) nw. Int corridors. **Pets:** Dogs only. $200 deposit/room. No service, crate.
🍴🔥📶✖️✖️✖️✖️

SACKVILLE

▼▼ Coastal Inn Sackville H
(506) 536-0000. **$99-$155.** 15 Wright St E4L 4P8. Trans-Canada Hwy 2 exit 504. Ext/int corridors. **Pets:** Accepted. 🅔🅒🅞📶✖️📱

ⓐ ▼▼▼▼ Marshlands Inn CI
(506) 536-0170. **$94-$225.** 55 Bridge St E4L 3N8. On Hwy 106; center. Int corridors. **Pets:** Accepted. 🅢🅐🅥🅔 🍴📶✖️

ST. ANDREWS *(Restaurants p. 630)*

ⓐ ▼▼▼▼▼ The Algonquin Resort, Autograph Collection H 🐾
(506) 529-8823. **$79-$243, 3 day notice.** 184 Adolphus St E5B 1T7. Off Hwy 127. Int corridors. **Pets:** Other species. $35 one-time fee/room. Designated rooms, service with restrictions, supervision.
🅢🅐🅥🅔 🅔🅒🅞 🍴🐾✖️📶✖️📱💻

ⓐ ▼▼▼ Tara Manor Historic Inn M
(506) 529-3304. **Call for rates.** 559 Mowat Dr E5B 2P2. 1.7 mi (2.8 km) n on Hwy 127. Ext corridors. **Pets:** Accepted.
🅢🅐🅥🅔 🍴🐾📶✖️📱💻

ST. GEORGE

ⓐ ▼▼▼ The Granite Town Hotel H
(506) 755-6415. **$99-$140.** 79 Main St E5C 3J4. Hwy 1 exit 56, 1.8 mi (3 km) w. Int corridors. **Pets:** Accepted. 🅢🅐🅥🅔 🍴📶✖️📱💻

ST-JACQUES

▼▼ Auberge Les Jardins Inn H
(506) 739-5514. **$89-$179.** 60 Principale St E7B 1V7. Trans-Canada Hwy 2 exit 8, just e. Ext/int corridors. **Pets:** Designated rooms, service with restrictions, crate. 🍴🐾📶📱💻

SAINT JOHN *(Restaurants p. 630)*

ⓐ ▼▼▼▼ Best Western Plus Saint John Hotel & Suites H 🐾
(506) 657-9966. **$99-$249.** 55 Majors Brook Dr E2J 0B2. Hwy 1 exit 129 westbound, 1 mi (1.6 km) s on Rt 100 (Rothesay Ave) to McAllister Dr, just e; exit 128 eastbound, 1 mi (1.6 km) n on Rt 100 (Rothesay Ave), just n to McAllister Dr, then just e. Int corridors. **Pets:** Medium. $100 deposit/room, $15 daily fee/room. Designated rooms, service with restrictions, supervision. 🅢🅐🅥🅔 🔥🐾📶✖️📱💻

▼▼ Comfort Inn H
(506) 674-1873. **$100-$150.** 1155 Fairville Blvd E2M 5T9. Hwy 1 exit 117 westbound; exit 119 eastbound, then left. Ext/int corridors.
Pets: Accepted. 🅔🅒🅞📶📱💻

ⓐ ▼▼▼▼ Delta Brunswick H
(506) 648-1981. **$90-$234.** 39 King St E2L 4W3. Center of downtown; in Brunswick Square Mall. Int corridors. **Pets:** Accepted.
🅢🅐🅥🅔 🅔🅒🅞 🍴🔥🐾📶✖️📱💻

ⓐ ▼▼▼▼ Hampton Inn & Suites H
(506) 657-4600. **$116-$166.** 51 Fashion Dr E2J 0A7. Hwy 1 exit 129, 1.5 mi (2.4 km) s on Rothesay Ave to Retail Dr; behind Home Depot. Int corridors. **Pets:** Medium. Service with restrictions, supervision.
🅢🅐🅥🅔 🔥🐾📶✖️📱💻

ⓐ ▼▼▼▼ Hilton Saint John H
(506) 693-8484. **$129-$229.** 1 Market Square E2L 4Z6. Hwy 1 exit 122; at Market Square. Int corridors. **Pets:** Accepted.
🅢🅐🅥🅔 🅔🅒🅞 🍴🐾📶✖️📱💻

(CAA) ▽▽▽▽ **Holiday Inn Express & Suites** [H]
(506) 642-2622. **$129-$179.** 400 Main St/Chesley Dr E2K 4N5. 0.6 mi (1 km) w on Hwy 1; north end of Chesley Dr exit 121; off Harbour Bridge. Int corridors. **Pets:** Accepted.
[SAVE] [ECO] 🏊 🛜 ✕ 🛏 🖥

▽▽▽ **Homeport Historic Inn Circa 1858** [BB] 🐾
(506) 672-7255. **$129-$175, 7 day notice.** 80 Douglas Ave E2K 1E4. Hwy 1 exit 121 eastbound; exit 123 westbound. Int corridors. **Pets:** Dogs only. Service with restrictions, supervision. 🛜 ✕ 🛏

▽▽▽ **Travelodge Suites Saint John** [H]
(506) 635-0400. **$95-$114.** 1011 Fairville Blvd E2M 5T9. Hwy 1 exit 119A westbound; exit 119B eastbound, left on Catherwood Dr, then left at lights. Int corridors. **Pets:** Accepted. [ECO] 🛜 🛏 🖥

ST-LEONARD

(CAA) ▽▽▽ **Daigle's Motel** [M]
(506) 423-6351. **$89-$129.** 68 rue DuPont E7E 1Y1. Hwy 17, 0.6 mi (1 km) s of Trans-Canada Hwy 2 exit 58. Ext corridors. **Pets:** Accepted.
[SAVE] 🍴 🏊 🛜 ✕ 🛏 🖥

ST. STEPHEN

▽▽ **St. Stephen Inn** [M]
(506) 466-1814. **Call for rates.** 99 King St E3L 2C6. Just n of Prince William St; center. Ext/int corridors. **Pets:** Accepted. 🛜 🛏

(CAA) ▽▽▽ **Winsome Inn** [M]
(506) 466-2130. **$94-$140.** 198 King St E3L 2E2. Hwy 1 exit King St, just s on Rt 3. Ext corridors. **Pets:** Other species. $10 daily fee/pet. Designated rooms, supervision. [SAVE] 🍴 🏊 🛜 ✕ 🛏

SHEDIAC

(CAA) ▽▽▽▽ **Hotel Shediac** [H]
(506) 532-6100. **$139-$229.** 222 Belliveau St E4P 0M2. Rt 133 at Weldon St, just n. Int corridors. **Pets:** Accepted.
[SAVE] 🍴 ♿M ✕ 🛜 ✕ 🛏 🖥

SUSSEX

▽▽ **All Seasons Inn** [M]
(506) 433-2220. **$64-$154.** 1015 Main St E4E 2M6. Hwy 1 exit 192 eastbound; exit 198 westbound, left towards Sussex Corner; center. Ext corridors. **Pets:** Medium, dogs only. $15 daily fee/pet. Designated rooms, service with restrictions, crate. 🍴 🛜 🛏 🖥

▽▽ **Fairway Inn** [H]
(506) 433-3470. **$135-$185.** 216 Roachville Rd E4E 5L6. Hwy 1 exit 193. Ext/int corridors. **Pets:** Medium. $10 daily fee/pet. Designated rooms, service with restrictions, supervision.
🍴 🏊 🛜 ✕ 🛏 🖥

TRACADIE-SHEILA

▽▽ **Deux Rivieres Resort** [CA]
(506) 394-4050. **Call for rates.** 100 rue Deux Rivieres E1X 1C9. Just e of Rt 11; center. Ext/int corridors. **Pets:** Accepted.
🍴 ♿M 🏊 ✕ 🛜 🛏 🖥

WAASIS

▽▽ **Travelodge Fredericton** [M]
(506) 446-9077. **$80-$120.** 42 Chaparral Rd E3B 0G9. Trans-Canada Hwy 2 exit 297. Ext/int corridors. **Pets:** Other species. $10 daily fee/room. Designated rooms, service with restrictions, supervision.
🛜 🛏 🖥

WOODSTOCK

(CAA) ▽▽▽▽ **Best Western Plus Woodstock Hotel & Conference Centre** [H]
(506) 328-2378. **$135-$160.** 123 Gallop Ct E7M 3P7. Trans-Canada Hwy 2 exit 185. Int corridors. **Pets:** Large. $20 one-time fee/room. Designated rooms, service with restrictions, supervision.
[SAVE] ♿M 🏊 🛜 ✕ 🛏 🖥

NEWFOUNDLAND AND LABRADOR

CHANNEL-PORT AUX BASQUES

▽▽ **St. Christopher's Hotel** [H]
(709) 695-7034. **$123-$138.** 146 Caribou Rd A0M 1C0. Trans-Canada Hwy 1 exit Port aux Basques, follow signs 1.2 mi (2 km); downtown. Int corridors. **Pets:** Accepted. 🍴 🛜 ✕ 🛏 🖥

CLARENVILLE

▽▽ **Clarenville Inn** [H]
(709) 466-7911. **Call for rates.** 134 Trans-Canada Hwy A5A 1Y3. Center. Int corridors. **Pets:** Accepted. 🍴 🏊 ✕ 🛜 ✕ 🛏 🖥

▽ **Restland Motel** [H]
(709) 466-7636. **$120-$130.** 262 Memorial Dr A5A 1N9. Just w of jct Manitoba Dr; center. Ext/int corridors. **Pets:** $300 deposit/room. Designated rooms, service with restrictions, crate. 🍴 🛜 ✕ 🛏 🖥

CORNER BROOK

▽▽ **Comfort Inn** [H] 🐾
(709) 639-1980. **$139-$250.** 41 Maple Valley Rd A2H 6T2. Trans-Canada Hwy 1 exit 5 eastbound; exit 6 westbound, via Confederation Ave. Int corridors. **Pets:** Large, other species. Designated rooms, service with restrictions, supervision. [ECO] 🍴 🛜 ✕ 🛏 🖥

▽▽▽ **Glynmill Inn** [H]
(709) 634-5181. **$125-$210, 3 day notice.** 1B Cobb Ln A2H 2V3. Just w of W Valley Rd; center. Int corridors. **Pets:** Designated rooms, service with restrictions, supervision. 🍴 🛜 ✕ 🛏 🖥

COW HEAD

▽▽ **Shallow Bay Motel & Cabins** [H]
(709) 243-2471. **$135-$150.** 193 Main St A0K 2A0. Rt 430 (Viking Trail) 2.5 mi (4 km) w towards the ocean, follow signs. Ext/int corridors. **Pets:** Medium. $15 daily fee/room. Designated rooms, no service, supervision. 🍴 🏊 ✕ 🛜 ✕ 🛏 🖥

DEER LAKE

▽▽ **Deer Lake Motel** [H]
(709) 635-2108. **Call for rates.** 15 Trans-Canada Hwy 1 A8A 2E5. on T.C.H. 1 at jct Rt 430 (Viking Trail). Ext/int corridors. **Pets:** Accepted.
🍴 🛜 ✕ 🛏 🖥

▽▽▽ **Holiday Inn Express** [H]
(709) 635-3232. **Call for rates.** 38 Bennett Ave A8A 1A9. Trans-Canada Hwy 1 exit 15, just n on Nicholsville Rd, then just s. Int corridors. **Pets:** Accepted. 🍴 🛜 ✕ 🛏 🖥

GANDER

▽▽ **Comfort Inn** [H]
(709) 256-3535. **$129-$219.** 112 Trans-Canada Hwy 1 A1V 1P8. Center. Ext/int corridors. **Pets:** Accepted. 🍴 🛜 ✕ 🛏 🖥

PORTLAND CREEK

▽ **Mountain Waters Resort** [CA]
(709) 898-2490. **Call for rates.** Viking Tr A0K 4G0. 3 mi (5 km) n on Rt 430, then 1 mi (1.6 km) e on gravel entry road. Ext corridors. **Pets:** Accepted. 🍴 🛜 ✕ 🎿 🐾 🛏 🖥

ROCKY HARBOUR

▼▼ Fisherman's Landing Inn **M**
(709) 458-2711. **$139-$189.** 21-29 W Link Rd A0K 4N0. Rt 430 (Viking Trail), first entrance to Rocky Harbour, just w. Ext/int corridors. **Pets:** Small. $25 one-time fee/pet. Service with restrictions, supervision.
🛜 ✕ 🛄 ▣

▼▼ Ocean View Hotel **H**
(709) 458-2730. **Call for rates.** 38-42 Main St A0K 4N0. Rt 430 (Viking Trail), 2nd Rocky Harbor exit, just w on Harbour Dr. Ext/int corridors. **Pets:** Accepted. 🍴 🛜 ✕ 🛄 ▣

ST. JOHN'S

▼▼ Capital Hotel **H**
(709) 738-4480. **Call for rates.** 208 Kenmount Rd A1B 3P9. Trans-Canada Hwy 1 exit 45, 4 mi (6.4 km) s on Team Gushue Hwy to Kenmount Rd. Int corridors. **Pets:** Accepted. 🍴 🛜 ✕ 🛄 ▣

▼▼ Comfort Inn Airport **H**
(709) 753-3500. **$95-$200.** 106 Airport Rd A1A 4Y3. Trans-Canada Hwy 1 exit 47B, 0.6 mi (1 km) n on Rt 40 (Portugal Cove Rd). Int corridors. **Pets:** Accepted. 🍴 🛜 ✕ 🛄 ▣

▼▼▼ Compton House Heritage Inn **BB**
(709) 722-0387. **Call for rates.** 26 Waterford Bridge Rd A1E 1C6. Just s of jct Water St. Ext/int corridors. **Pets:** Accepted.
🍴 🛜 ✕ 🛄 ▣

▼▼▼ Delta St. John's Hotel and Conference Centre **H**
(709) 739-6404. **$169-$299.** 120 New Gower St A1C 6K4. At Barter's Hill Rd; center. Int corridors. **Pets:** Accepted.
ECO 🍴 ♿ 🏊 ✕ 🛜 ✕ 🛄 ▣

▼▼ Extended Stay Canada **H**
(709) 754-7888. **$120-$170.** 222 LeMarchant Rd A1C 2H9. Corner of Pleasant St. Int corridors. **Pets:** $25 daily fee/pet. Service with restrictions, crate. 🍴 ♿ 🛜 ✕ 🛄 ▣

CAA ▼▼▼ Quality Hotel-Harbourview **H**
(709) 754-7888. **$105-$269.** 2 Hill O' Chips A1C 6B1. At Cavendish Square; downtown. Int corridors. **Pets:** Accepted.
SAVE ECO 🍴 🛜 ✕ 🛄 ▣

CAA ▼▼▼ Sheraton Hotel Newfoundland **H** 🐾
(709) 726-4980. **$139-$360.** 115 Cavendish Square A1C 3K2. At Duckworth and Ordnance sts. Int corridors. **Pets:** Medium. Service with restrictions, supervision.
SAVE ECO 🍴 ♿ 🏊 ✕ 🛜 ✕ 🛄 ▣

▼▼ Super 8 **H**
(709) 739-8888. **$126-$200.** 175 Higgins Line A1B 4N4. Trans-Canada Hwy 1 exit 47A, just s on Rt 40 (Portugal Cove Rd). Int corridors. **Pets:** $20 one-time fee/room. Designated rooms, service with restrictions, supervision. ECO ♿ 🏊 🛜 ✕ 🛄 ▣

STEPHENVILLE

▼▼ Days Inn Stephenville **H**
(709) 643-6666. **$106-$170.** 44 Queen St A2N 2M5. Center. Int corridors. **Pets:** Accepted. ECO 🍴 🛜 ✕ 🛄 ▣

TRAYTOWN

▼▼ Pinetree Lodge & Cabins **CA**
(709) 533-6601. **Call for rates.** 62-64 Main St A0G 4K0. On Rt 310. Ext corridors. **Pets:** Accepted. 🍴 🏊 ✕ 🛜 ✕ 🛄 ▣

NORTHWEST TERRITORIES

YELLOWKNIFE

CAA ▼▼▼▼ Coast Fraser Tower **H** 🐾
(867) 873-8700. **$185-$250.** 5303 52nd St X1A 1V1. Corner of 52nd St and 53rd Ave. Int corridors. **Pets:** Large. $15 daily fee/pet. Designated rooms, service with restrictions, crate.
SAVE ECO 🍴 🛜 ♿ 🛄 ▣

▼▼ Days Inn & Suites Yellowknife **H**
(867) 873-9700. **$170-$199.** 4401 50th Ave X1A 2N2. Downtown. Int corridors. **Pets:** Accepted. 🍴 🛜 ✕ 🛄 ▣

▼▼ The Explorer Hotel **H**
(867) 873-3531. **Call for rates.** 4825 49th Ave X1A 2R3. Downtown. Int corridors. **Pets:** Accepted. 🍴 🛜 ✕ 🛄 ▣

▼▼ Super 8 Yellowknife **M**
(867) 669-8888. **$160-$188.** 308 Old Airport Rd X1A 3G3. 1.2 mi (2 km) s on Franklin Ave, 0.6 mi (1 km) w; in Walmart Plaza. Int corridors. **Pets:** Large, other species. $30 one-time fee/room. Designated rooms, service with restrictions, crate. ECO 🛜 ✕ 🛄 ▣

NOVA SCOTIA

AMHERST

▼▼ Comfort Inn Amherst **H**
(902) 667-0404. **$115-$200.** 143 S Albion St B4H 2X2. Trans-Canada Hwy 104 exit 4, 1 mi (1.6 km) n on Rt 2. Int corridors. **Pets:** Other species. $10 deposit/room. Designated rooms, service with restrictions, supervision. ECO 🛜 ✕ 🛄 ▣

▼▼ Super 8 Amherst **H**
(902) 660-8888. **$101-$153.** 40 Lord Amherst Dr B4H 4W6. Trans-Canada Hwy 104 exit 4. Int corridors. **Pets:** Accepted.
ECO ♿ 🏊 🛜 🛄 ▣

ANNAPOLIS ROYAL

▼▼ The Garrison House Inn **CI**
(902) 532-5750. **$99-$169.** 350 St. George St B0S 1A0. Jct Rt 1 and 8. Int corridors. **Pets:** Accepted. 🍴 🛜 ✕ 🐾 ▣

▼▼▼ Hillsdale House Inn **BB**
(902) 532-2345. **$89-$169.** 519 St. George St B0S 1A0. Just e of Rt 1; center. Int corridors. **Pets:** Accepted. 🛜 ✕ ▣

ANTIGONISH

▼▼ Maritime Inn Antigonish **H**
(902) 863-4001. **Call for rates.** 158 Main St B2G 2B7. Between St. Mary's and Court sts; center. Ext/int corridors. **Pets:** Accepted.
🍴 ♿ 🛜 ✕ 🛄 ▣

AULD

CAA ▼▼▼ Cove Motel & Restaurant/Gift Shop **M**
(902) 747-2700. **$99-$130.** 227 D-31 Rd B0H 1K0. 0.6 mi (1 km) n off Trans-Canada Hwy 104; 1.9 mi (3 km) w of Canso Cswy. Ext corridors. **Pets:** Accepted. SAVE 🍴 🛜 🛄 ▣

BADDECK

▼▼ **Hunter's Mountain Chalets** CA
(902) 295-3392. **$95-$142, 7 day notice.** 562 Cabot Tr B0E 1B0. Trans-Canada Hwy 105 exit 7, 1.6 mi (2.6 km) n. Ext corridors. **Pets:** Accepted. 🛠M 🛜 ✖ 🐾 🔀 🔋 💻

▼▼ **McIntyre's Housekeeping Cottages** CA
(902) 295-1133. **$90-$350, 4 day notice.** 8908 Hwy 105 B0E 1B0. Trans-Canada Hwy 105, 3 mi (5 km) w. Ext corridors. **Pets:** Other species. $20 daily fee/pet. Designated rooms, service with restrictions, supervision. 🍴 🛠M 🛜 ✖ 🔋 💻

▼▼ **Silver Dart Lodge & MacNeil House Suites** H
(902) 295-2340. **Call for rates.** 257 Shore Rd B0E 1B0. Trans-Canada Hwy 105 exit 8, 0.6 mi (1 km) e on Rt 205 (Shore Rd). Ext/int corridors. **Pets:** Accepted. 🍴 🛠M 🏊 ✖ 🛜 ✖ 🔋 💻

BRIDGEWATER

CAA ▼▼▼▼ **Best Western Plus Bridgewater Hotel & Convention Centre** H
(902) 530-0101. **$140-$150.** 527 Hwy 10 B4V 7P4. Hwy 103 exit 12, just n. Int corridors. **Pets:** Accepted.
SAVE 🍴 🛠M 🏊 🛜 ✖ 🔋 💻

▼▼▼▼ **Days Inn & Conference Centre Bridgewater** H
(902) 543-7131. **$86-$126.** 50 North St B4V 2V6. Hwy 103 exit 12, 1.1 mi (1.8 km) s on Rt 10. Ext/int corridors. **Pets:** Accepted.
🍴 🏊 🛜 ✖ 🔋 💻

CANNING

▼▼▼▼ **The Farmhouse Inn** BB 🐾
(902) 582-7900. **$129-$169, 3 day notice.** 9757 Main St B0P 1H0. Hwy 101 exit 11, follow signs to town, 5 mi (8 km) n on Rt 358. Ext/int corridors. **Pets:** Medium. $20 daily fee/room. Designated rooms, service with restrictions, crate. 🛜 ✖ 🐾 🔋

CHARLOS COVE

▼▼ **Seawind Landing Country Inn** CI 🐾
(902) 525-2108. **$99-$179.** 159 Wharf Rd B0H 1T0. Rt 316, 0.5 mi (0.8 km) se on gravel road. Ext/int corridors. **Pets:** Designated rooms, service with restrictions, supervision. 🍴 🛠M 🛜 ✖ 🐾

CHESTER

▼ **Windjammer Motel** M
(902) 275-3567. **$85-$95.** 4070 Rt 3 B0J 1J0. 0.6 mi (1 km) w. Ext corridors. **Pets:** Medium. Designated rooms, service with restrictions, supervision. 🛜 ✖ 🔋

CHÉTICAMP

▼▼ **Cabot Trail Sea & Golf Chalets** CA
(902) 224-1777. **$139-$179, 7 day notice.** 71 Fraser Doucet Ln B0E 1H0. Center. Ext corridors. **Pets:** Accepted.
🍴 🛠M 🛜 ✖ 🐾 🔀 🔋 💻

▼▼ **Laurie's Motor Inn** H
(902) 224-2400. **$99-$164.** 15456 Cabot Tr B0E 1H0. Center. Ext/int corridors. **Pets:** Accepted. 🍴 🛜 ✖ 🔋 💻

DARTMOUTH

▼▼ **Comfort Inn** H
(902) 463-9900. **$101-$152.** 456 Windmill Rd B3A 1J7. Hwy 111 exit Shannon Park. Ext/int corridors. **Pets:** Other species. Service with restrictions, supervision. ECO 🛜 ✖ 🔋 💻

CAA ▼▼▼▼ **Hampton Inn & Suites by Hilton-Halifax/Dartmouth** H
(902) 406-7700. **Call for rates.** 65 Cromarty Dr B3B 0G2. Hwy 118 (Lakeview Dr) exit Wright Ave; in Dartmouth Crossing Outlet Mall. Int corridors. **Pets:** Accepted. SAVE ECO 🛠M 🏊 🛜 ✖ 🔋 💻

▼▼ **Hearthstone Inn Dartmouth** H
(902) 469-5850. **Call for rates.** 313 Prince Albert Rd B2Y 1N3. Hwy 111 exit 6A, 1 blk s. Int corridors. **Pets:** Accepted.
🍴 🛜 ✖ 🔋 💻

▼▼ **Holiday Inn Halifax-Harbourview** H
(902) 463-1100. **Call for rates.** 101 Wyse Rd B3A 1L9. Adjacent to Angus L MacDonald Bridge. Ext/int corridors. **Pets:** Accepted.
ECO 🍴 🛠M 🏊 🛜 ✖ 🔋 💻

▼▼ **Park Place Hotel & Conference Centre Ramada Plaza** H
(902) 468-8888. **$100-$180.** 240 Brownlow Ave B3B 1X6. From A. Murray MacKay Bridge, 0.7 mi (1.2 km) n on Hwy 111 exit 3 (Burnside Dr). Int corridors. **Pets:** Accepted. ECO 🍴 🛠M 🏊 ✖ 🛜 🔋 💻

▼▼ **Travelodge Suites Dartmouth** H
(902) 465-4000. **$95-$145.** 101 Yorkshire Ave Ext B3A 0C5. Hwy 111 exit Princess Margaret Blvd; at toll booth for A. Murray MacKay Bridge. Ext/int corridors. **Pets:** Accepted. ECO 🛜 🔋 💻

DAYTON

▼▼ **Voyageur Motel** M
(902) 742-7157. **$89-$189, 3 day notice.** 518 Hwy 1 B5A 5A2. 3 mi (4.8 km) ne on Hwy 1. Ext corridors. **Pets:** $10 daily fee/pet. Designated rooms, service with restrictions, crate. 🍴 🛜 🔋

DIGBY

CAA ▼▼▼▼ **Digby Pines Golf Resort & Spa, an Ascend Hotel Collection Member** H
(902) 245-2511. **$105-$545.** 103 Shore Rd B0V 1A0. Hwy 101 exit 26, 1.5 mi (2.5 km) n, follow Saint John Ferry signs, then 1.5 mi (2.5 km) w on Victoria Rd, follow signs; 1.2 mi (2 km) e of ferry terminal. Ext/int corridors. **Pets:** Accepted.
SAVE ECO 🍴 🛠M 🏊 ✖ 🛜 ✖ 🔋 💻

▼▼▼▼ **Dockside Suites** H
(902) 245-4950. **$109-$179.** 34 Water St B0V 1A0. Center; in Fundy Complex. Ext/int corridors. **Pets:** $15 daily fee/pet. Designated rooms, service with restrictions, supervision. 🍴 🛜 🔋 💻

ENFIELD

▼▼▼▼ **ALT Hotel-Halifax Airport** H
(902) 334-0136. **$164-$184.** 40 Silver Dart Dr B2T 1K2. 1 mi (1.6 km) e of Hwy 102, exit 6; opposite the Halifax Stanfield International Airport terminal. Int corridors. **Pets:** Accepted. 🍴 🛠M 🛜 ✖ 💻

▼▼▼▼ **Holiday Inn Express Hotel & Suites Halifax Airport** H
(902) 576-7600. **$139-$229.** 180 Pratt & Whitney Dr B2T 0C8. Hwy 102 exit 5A, 0.8 mi (1.2 km) e, then just n. Int corridors. **Pets:** Accepted.
🛠M 🏊 🛜 ✖ 🔋 💻

FALL RIVER

▼▼▼▼ **Inn on the Lake, an Ascend Hotel Collection Member** H
(902) 861-3480. **$129-$290.** 3009 Hwy 2 B2T 1J5. Hwy 102 exit 5, right off exit ramp. Ext/int corridors. **Pets:** Accepted.
🍴 🏊 🛜 ✖ 🔋 💻

HALIFAX

CAA ▼▼▼▼ **Atlantica Hotel Halifax** H 🐾
(902) 423-1161. **$119-$289.** 1980 Robie St B3H 3G5. Jct Quinpool St. Int corridors. **Pets:** Other species. $100 deposit/room. Supervision.
SAVE ECO 🍴 🏊 ✖ 🛜 🔋 💻

CAA ▼▼▼▼ **Best Western Plus Chocolate Lake Hotel** H 🐾
(902) 477-5611. **$129-$189.** 250 St. Margaret's Bay Rd B3N 1J4. 0.4 mi (0.7 km) e of Armdale Rotary. Ext/int corridors. **Pets:** Designated rooms, supervision. SAVE ECO 🍴 🏊 ✖ 🛜 ✖ 🔋 💻

⬙⬙⬙⬙ Cambridge Suites Hotel 🅷
(902) 420-0555. **Call for rates.** 1583 Brunswick St B3J 3P5. Corner of Brunswick and Sackville sts. Int corridors. **Pets:** Accepted.
[SAVE] [ECO] [🍴] [♿] [✕] [📶] [✕] [🔌] [🖥]

⬙⬙⬙⬙ Château Bedford, an Ascend Hotel Collection
Member 🅷 ❀
(902) 445-1100. **$130-$200.** 133 Kearney Lake Rd B3M 4P3. Hwy 102 exit 2, just e. Int corridors. **Pets:** Large, other species. $25 one-time fee/room. Designated rooms, service with restrictions, crate.
[SAVE] [ECO] [♿] [≈] [📶] [✕] [🔌] [🖥]

⬙ Chebucto Inn Ⓜ
(902) 453-4330. **$85-$145.** 6151 Lady Hammond Rd B3K 2R9. Jct Hwy 111 and Rt 2 (Bedford Hwy), 0.4 mi (0.7 km) e. Ext corridors.
Pets: Accepted. [🍴] [📶] [🔌] [🖥]

⬙⬙ Coastal Inn Halifax 🅷
(902) 450-3020. **$104-$159.** 98 Chain Lake Dr B3S 1A2. Hwy 102 exit 2A eastbound; Hwy 103 exit 2. Ext/int corridors. **Pets:** Accepted.
[ECO] [♿] [≈] [📶] [✕] [🔌] [🖥]

⬙⬙ Comfort Inn Halifax 🅷 ❀
(902) 443-0303. **$104-$189.** 560 Bedford Hwy B3M 2L8. On Rt 2 (Bedford Hwy), 6 mi (9.6 km) w. Ext/int corridors. **Pets:** $20 one-time fee/pet. Service with restrictions, crate. [SAVE] [♿] [≈] [📶] [✕] [🔌] [🖥]

⬙⬙ Delta Barrington 🅷 ❀
(902) 429-7410. **$149-$239.** 1875 Barrington St B3J 3L6. Between Cogswell and Duke sts. Int corridors. **Pets:** Medium. $35 one-time fee/room. Service with restrictions.
[SAVE] [ECO] [🍴] [≈] [📶] [✕] [🔌] [🖥]

⬙⬙ Delta Halifax 🅷 ❀
(902) 425-6700. **$149-$239.** 1990 Barrington St B3J 1P2. At Cogswell St. Int corridors. **Pets:** Medium. $35 one-time fee/room. Service with restrictions. [SAVE] [ECO] [🍴] [≈] [✕] [📶] [✕] [🔌] [🖥]

⬙⬙⬙⬙ Four Points by Sheraton Halifax 🅷
(902) 423-4444. **Call for rates.** 1496 Hollis St B3J 3Z1. Between Salter and Bishop sts. Int corridors. **Pets:** Accepted.
[SAVE] [ECO] [🍴] [♿] [≈] [📶] [✕] [🔌] [🖥]

⬙⬙ Future Inns Halifax Hotel & Conference
Centre 🅷 ❀
(902) 443-4333. **$121-$171.** 30 Fairfax Dr B3S 1P1. Hwy 102 exit 2A. Int corridors. **Pets:** Other species. Designated rooms.
[🍴] [♿] [📶] [✕] [🔌] [🖥]

⬙⬙⬙⬙ Halifax Marriott Harbourfront 🅷
(902) 421-1700. **$82-$289.** 1919 Upper Water St B3J 3J5. Adjacent to historic properties and Casino Nova Scotia. Int corridors.
Pets: Accepted. [SAVE] [ECO] [🍴] [♿] [≈] [✕] [📶] [✕] [🔌] [🖥]

⬙⬙⬙⬙ Hampton Inn by Hilton
Halifax-Downtown 🅷
(902) 422-1391. **Call for rates.** 1960 Brunswick St B3J 2G7. Between Cogswell St and Rainnie Dr. Int corridors. **Pets:** Medium. $35 one-time fee/room. Service with restrictions, supervision.
[SAVE] [♿] [📶] [✕] [🔌] [🖥]

⬙⬙⬙⬙ Homewood Suites by Hilton
Halifax-Downtown 🅷
(902) 429-6620. **Call for rates.** 1960 Brunswick St B3J 2G7. Between Cogswell St and Rainnie Dr. Int corridors. **Pets:** Medium. $35 one-time fee/room. Service with restrictions, supervision.
[SAVE] [♿] [📶] [✕] [🔌] [🖥]

⬙⬙⬙⬙ The Lord Nelson Hotel & Suites 🅷
(902) 423-6331. **$139-$199, 3 day notice.** 1515 S Park St B3J 2L2. Corner of Park St and Spring Garden Rd. Int corridors. **Pets:** Accepted.
[SAVE] [ECO] [🍴] [♿] [📶] [✕] [🔌] [🖥]

⬙⬙⬙⬙ The Prince George Hotel 🅷
(902) 425-1986. **Call for rates.** 1725 Market St B3J 3N9. Between Prince and Carmichael sts. Int corridors. **Pets:** Accepted.
[SAVE] [ECO] [🍴] [≈] [✕] [📶] [✕] [🔌] [🖥]

⬙⬙ Quality Inn Halifax Airport 🅷
(902) 873-3000. **$126-$206.** 60 Sky Blvd B2T 1K3. Hwy 102 exit 6, just s. Int corridors. **Pets:** Accepted. [ECO] [🍴] [≈] [📶] [✕] [🔌] [🖥]

⬙⬙⬙⬙ Residence Inn by Marriott Halifax
Downtown 🅷
(902) 422-0493. **$73-$314.** 1599 Grafton St B3J 2C3. Corner of Sackville St. Int corridors. **Pets:** Other species. $50 one-time fee/room. Service with restrictions. [SAVE] [ECO] [♿] [📶] [✕] [🔌] [🖥]

⬙⬙⬙⬙ The Westin Nova Scotian 🅷
(902) 421-1000. **$99-$249.** 1181 Hollis St B3H 2P6. Between Barrington and Lower Water sts. Int corridors. **Pets:** Accepted.
[SAVE] [ECO] [🍴] [♿] [≈] [✕] [📶] [✕] [🔌] [🖥]

INGONISH BEACH

⬙⬙⬙ Keltic Lodge Resort & Spa 🅷
(902) 285-2880. **Call for rates.** 383 Keltic In Rd B0C 1L0. In Cape Breton Highlands National Park; off Cabot Tr. Ext/int corridors.
Pets: Accepted. [SAVE] [🍴] [♿] [≈] [✕] [📶] [✕] [🔌] [🖥]

KEMPTVILLE

⬙⬙⬙ Trout Point Lodge of Nova Scotia 🅲🅸
(902) 761-2142. **$299-$479, 21 day notice.** 189 Trout Point Rd B0W 1Y0. 6.6 mi (11 km) e on Rt 203, 2.1 mi (3.5 km) n on gravel entry road. Ext corridors. **Pets:** Accepted.
[🍴] [✕] [📶] [✕] [📺] [🔌] [🖥]

KINGSTON

⬙⬙ Aurora Inn 🅷
(902) 765-3306. **$120-$169.** 831 Main St B0P 1R0. Hwy 101 exit 17 to Rt 1, follow signs. Ext corridors. **Pets:** Accepted.
[🍴] [📶] [✕] [🔌] [🖥]

LISCOMB

⬙⬙⬙ Liscombe Lodge Resort & Conference
Centre 🅷
(902) 779-2307. **Call for rates.** 2884 Hwy 7 B0J 2A0. On Hwy 7. Ext/int corridors. **Pets:** Other species. Designated rooms, service with restrictions, crate. [SAVE] [🍴] [♿] [≈] [✕] [📶] [✕] [🔌] [🖥]

LIVERPOOL

⬙⬙⬙ Best Western Plus Liverpool Hotel &
Conference Centre 🅷
(902) 354-2377. **$136-$160.** 63 Queens Place Dr B0T 1K0. Hwy 103 exit 19 (Hwy 8), just e. Int corridors. **Pets:** Accepted.
[SAVE] [ECO] [♿] [≈] [📶] [✕] [🔌] [🖥]

LOWER ARGYLE

⬙⬙⬙ Argyler Lodge 🅲🅸
(902) 643-2500. **Call for rates.** 52 Rt 3, 52 Ye Olde Argyler Rd B0W 1W0. Hwy 103 exit 32, 4.5 mi (7.5 km) e. Int corridors. **Pets:** Accepted.
[🍴] [✕] [📶] [✕] [🔌]

LUNENBURG

⬙⬙ The Homeport Motel Ⓜ
(902) 634-8234. **Call for rates.** 167 Victoria Rd B0J 2C0. 0.6 mi (1 km) w on Rt 3. Ext corridors. **Pets:** Accepted.
[🍴] [📶] [✕] [📺] [🔌] [🖥]

Lunenburg Arms Hotel & Spa 🅗 ❀
(902) 640-4040. **$129-$139.** 94 Pelham St B0J 2C0. At Duke St; center.
Int corridors. **Pets:** Other species. $25 one-time fee/room.
🍴 📶 ❌ 🛎 ▭

MILLBROOK

🅐 **Hampton Inn & Suites by Hilton
        Truro** 🅗 ❀
(902) 843-4343. **Call for rates.** 35 Legends Ave B6L 0C9. Hwy 102 exit
13A. Int corridors. **Pets:** Large. $15 daily fee/pet. Designated rooms,
service with restrictions. 🆂🅰🆅🅴 🍴 ♿ 📶 ❌ 🛎 ▭

Super 8 🅗
(902) 895-8884. **$130-$180.** 85 Treaty Tr B2N 5A9. Hwy 102 exit 13A.
Int corridors. **Pets:** Medium. $20 one-time fee/room. Designated rooms,
service with restrictions, supervision.
🅴🅲🅾 ♿ 🏊 📶 ❌ 🛎 ▭

NEW GLASGOW

Comfort Inn 🅗 ❀
(902) 755-6450. **$124-$190.** 740 Westville Rd B2H 2J8. On Hwy 289,
just e of jct Trans-Canada Hwy 104 exit 23. Ext/int corridors. **Pets:** $10
one-time fee/pet. Designated rooms, service with restrictions, crate.
🅴🅲🅾 📶 ❌ 🛎 ▭

Travelodge Suites New Glasgow 🅗
(902) 928-1333. **$90-$165.** 700 Westville Rd B2H 2J8. On Hwy 289,
just e of jct Trans-Canada Hwy 104 exit 23. Ext/int corridors.
Pets: Accepted. 🅴🅲🅾 📶 🛎 ▭

NEW HARBOUR

Lonely Rock Seaside Bungalows 🅒🅐
(902) 387-2668. **$99-$259, 14 day notice.** 150 New Harbour Rd B0H
1T0. Rt 316, 0.4 mi (0.7 km) s. Ext corridors. **Pets:** Dogs only. $15
daily fee/pet. Designated rooms, supervision.
🍴 ♿ 📶 ❌ ♨ ⛢ 🛎 ▭

NORTH SYDNEY

🅐 **Clansman Motel** 🅜 ❀
(902) 794-7226. **$95-$125.** 9 Baird St B2A 0A9. Hwy 125 exit 2, just e
on King St. Ext/int corridors. **Pets:** Other species. $10 one-time fee/
room. Designated rooms, service with restrictions.
🆂🅰🆅🅴 🍴 ♿ 🏊 📶 🛎 ▭

PARRSBORO

Gillespie House Inn 🅑🅑
(902) 254-3196. **$139-$149.** 358 Main St B0M 1S0. On Rt 2; center. Int
corridors. **Pets:** Dogs only. Designated rooms, service with restrictions,
supervision. 📶 ❌ ♨ ⛱ ⛢

PICTOU

Caribou River Cottage 🅒🅐
(902) 485-6352. **$120-$140, 3 day notice.** 1308 Shore Rd B0K 1H0.
PEI ferry terminal, 3 mi (4.8 km) w on Three Brooks Rd. Ext corridors.
Pets: Accepted. 🍴 ♿ 📶 ❌ ♨ ⛢ 🛎 ▭

Pictou Lodge Beach Resort 🅗
(902) 485-4322. **Call for rates.** 172 Lodge Rd B0K 1H0. 4.3 mi (7 km)
nw on Braeshore Rd; midway between Pictou and PEI ferry terminal; at
Caribou and Munroe's Island Provincial Park. Ext corridors.
Pets: Accepted. 🍴 🏊 ♿ 📶 ❌ 🛎 ▭

Willow House Inn 🅑🅑
(902) 485-5740. **$60-$130.** 11 Willow St B0K 1H0. Corner of Willow and
Church sts; center. Int corridors. **Pets:** Dogs only. $15 one-time fee/
room. Supervision. 📶 ❌

PORT HAWKESBURY

Maritime Inn Port Hawkesbury 🅗
(902) 625-0320. **Call for rates.** 717 Reeves St B9A 2S2. 4.2 mi (6.4
km) e of Canso Cswy on Hwy 4. Ext/int corridors. **Pets:** Accepted.
🍴 🏊 📶 ❌ 🛎 ▭

ST. PETER'S

Bras d'Or Lakes Inn 🅗
(902) 535-2200. **Call for rates.** 10095 Grenville St B0E 3B0. Rt 104,
just w of St. Peter's Bay Bridge. Int corridors. **Pets:** $15 daily fee/room.
Designated rooms, service with restrictions, supervision.
🍴 ♿ 📶 ❌ 🛎 ▭

SHELBURNE

Wildwood Motel 🅜
(902) 875-2964. **Call for rates.** 242 Minto St B0T 1W0. Hwy 103 exit
26, 1.1 mi (1.8 km) e on Rt 3. Ext corridors. **Pets:** Other species. $10
deposit/pet. Designated rooms, service with restrictions.
🍴 📶 ❌ 🛎 ▭

SMITHS COVE

Harbourview Inn 🅑🅑
(902) 245-5686. **Call for rates.** 25 Harbourview Rd B0S 1S0. Hwy 101
exit 25 eastbound; exit 24 westbound. Ext/int corridors. **Pets:** Accepted.
🍴 ♨ 📶 ❌ 🛎 ▭

Hedley House Inn By The Sea 🅜
(902) 245-2500. **$95-$149.** 375 Hwy 1 B0S 1S0. Hwy 101 exit 25 eastbound; exit 24 westbound. Ext corridors. **Pets:** Accepted.
🍴 📶 ❌ ⛢ 🛎 ▭

STELLARTON

Holiday Inn Express Stellarton-New Glasgow 🅗
(902) 755-1020. **Call for rates.** 86 Lawrence Blvd B0K 1S0. Hwy 104
exit 24, just s, then 0.6 mi (1 km) w. Int corridors. **Pets:** Accepted.
🍴 ♿ 🏊 📶 ❌ 🛎 ▭

SYDNEY

🅐 **Cambridge Suites Hotel Sydney** 🅗
(902) 562-6500. **$119-$169.** 380 Esplanade B1P 1B1. Hwy 4, 3.1 mi (5
km) e of jct Hwy 125 exit 6E; downtown. Int corridors. **Pets:** Accepted.
🆂🅰🆅🅴 🅴🅲🅾 🍴 ♿ 📶 ❌ 🛎 ▭

🅐 **Hampton Inn by Hilton Sydney** 🅗
(902) 564-6555. **Call for rates.** 60 Maillard St B1S 3W3. Hwy 125 exit
7, 1.2 mi (2 km) n on Rt 327 to Membertou St, then just s. Int corridors. **Pets:** Accepted. 🆂🅰🆅🅴 ♿ ♨ 📶 ❌ 🛎 ▭

Holiday Inn Sydney-Waterfront 🅗
(902) 562-7500. **Call for rates.** 300 Esplanade B1P 1A7. At Prince St;
center. Int corridors. **Pets:** $50 one-time fee/pet. Service with restric-
tions, supervision. 🅴🅲🅾 🍴 ♨ 📶 ❌ 🛎 ▭

Sydney Comfort Inn 🅗
(902) 562-0200. **$119-$199.** 368 Kings Rd B1S 1A8. Hwy 4, 2.1 mi (3.5
km) e of jct Hwy 125 exit 6E. Ext/int corridors. **Pets:** Accepted.
🅴🅲🅾 🍴 📶 ❌ 🛎 ▭

TRURO

🅐 **Best Western Glengarry Hotel** 🅗
(902) 893-4311. **$140-$170.** 150 Willow St B2N 4Z6. 0.6 mi (1 km) se
on Hwy 2. Ext/int corridors. **Pets:** Accepted.
🆂🅰🆅🅴 🅴🅲🅾 🍴 ♿ ♨ 📶 ❌ 🛎 ▭

Comfort Inn 🅗
(902) 893-0330. **$114-$190.** 12 Meadow Dr B2N 5V4. Hwy 102 exit 14.
Ext/int corridors. **Pets:** Accepted. 🅴🅲🅾 📶 ❌ 🛎 ▭

▼▼▼▼ Holiday Inn Hotel & Conference Centre Truro 🅷
(902) 895-1651. **$109-$159.** 437 Prince St B2N 1E6. On Old Hwy 2, just e of Willow St; center. Int corridors. **Pets:** Accepted.
ECO 🍽 🔥M 🛏 🛜 ✖ 🔌 🖥

WALLACE

🅐🅐 ▼▼▼ ▼▼▼ Fox Harb'r Golf Resort & Spa 🅷
(902) 257-1801. **$219-$495.** 1337 Fox Harbour Rd B0K 1Y0. Hwy 6, 3.6 mi (6 km) w, 3.6 mi (6 km) n on Ferry Rd, then 1.2 mi (2 km) e. Ext/int corridors. **Pets:** Accepted.
SAVE 🍽 🔥M 🛏 ✖ 🛜 ✖ 🔌 🖥

WESTERN SHORE

🅐🅐 ▼▼▼ Atlantica Oak Island Resort and Conference Centre 🅷 ❀
(902) 627-2600. **Call for rates.** 36 Treasure Dr B0J 3M0. Hwy 103 exit 9 or 10, follow signs on Rt 3; 6 mi (10 km) e of Mahone Bay. Int corridors. **Pets:** Large, other species. Designated rooms, service with restrictions, supervision. SAVE ECO 🍽 🛏 ✖ 🛜 ✖ 🔌 🖥

WHITE POINT

▼▼▼▼ White Point Beach Resort 🅷
(902) 354-2711. **Call for rates.** 75 White Point Beach Resort Rd B0T 1G0. Hwy 103 exit 20A westbound, 5 mi (8 km) w on Rt 3; exit 20 eastbound, 6 ml (10 km) e on Rt 3. Ext/int corridors. **Pets:** Accepted.
ECO 🍽 🛏 ✖ 🛜 ✖ 🔌 🖥

WINDSOR

▼▼▼ Super 8 Windsor 🅷 ❀
(902) 792-8888. **$120-$145.** 63 Cole Dr B0N 2T0. Hwy 101 exit 5A, just s. Int corridors. **Pets:** Other species. $20 one-time fee/room. Designated rooms, service with restrictions, supervision.
ECO 🔥M 🛏 🛜 ✖ 🔌 🖥

WOLFVILLE

▼▼▼▼ Tattingstone Inn 🅱🅱
(902) 542-7696. **Call for rates.** 620 Main St B4P 1E8. 0.4 mi (0.6 km) w on Rt 1. Ext/int corridors. **Pets:** Accepted. 🛏 🛜 ✖

YARMOUTH

🅐🅐 ▼▼▼ Best Western Mermaid Yarmouth 🅼
(902) 742-7821. **Call for rates.** 545 Main St B5A 1J6. Corner of Main St and Starrs Rd. Ext corridors. **Pets:** Accepted.
SAVE 🛏 🛜 ✖ 🔌 🖥

🅐🅐 ▼▼▼ Comfort Inn 🅷
(902) 742-1119. **$119-$190.** 96 Starrs Rd B5A 2T5. Jct Hwy 101 E and 3. Ext/int corridors. **Pets:** Accepted. SAVE ECO 🛜 ✖ 🔌 🖥

▼▼ ▼▼ Rodd Grand Yarmouth 🅷
(902) 742-2446. **$99-$179.** 417 Main St B5A 1G3. Corner of Grand St. Int corridors. **Pets:** Accepted. ECO 🍽 🛏 ✖ 🛜 ✖ 🔌 🖥

ONTARIO

AJAX

▼▼▼ Super 8-Ajax 🅷
(905) 428-6884. **$99-$134.** 210 Westney Rd S L1S 7P9. Hwy 401 exit Westney Rd, 0.6 mi (1 km) s; jct Bayly St. Int corridors.
Pets: Accepted. 🛏 🛜 ✖ 🔌 🖥

ALGONQUIN PROVINCIAL PARK

🅐🅐 ▼▼▼▼ Killarney Lodge 🅲🅰
(705) 633-5551. **$438-$898, 3 day notice.** Hwy 60-Lake of Two Rivers-Algonquin P1H 2G9. 21 mi (33 km) into park from West Gate; 14 mi (23 km) from East Gate. Ext corridors. **Pets:** Large, dogs only. $25 daily fee/pet. Designated rooms, service with restrictions, crate.
SAVE 🍽 ✖ 🛜 ✖ 🅰🅲 🅿🅽 ✖

ALLISTON

▼▼▼ Red Pine Inn & Conference Centre 🅼
(705) 435-4381. **Call for rates.** 497 Victoria St E L9R 1T9. 1.8 mi (3 km) e of King St. Ext/int corridors. **Pets:** Accepted.
🍽 🛏 ✖ 🛜 ✖ 🔌 🖥

ALTON

🅐🅐 ▼▼▼ ▼▼▼ Millcroft Inn & Spa 🅲🅸
(519) 941-8111. **$220-$500, 3 day notice.** 55 John St L7K 0C4. 2.5 mi (4 km) n off Hwy 136 from Hwy 24, 0.6 mi (1 km) w on Queen St E, then just n. Ext/int corridors. **Pets:** Accepted.
SAVE 🍽 🛏 ✖ 🛜 ✖ 🔌 🖥

ARNPRIOR

🅐🅐 ▼▼▼ Quality Inn 🅷
(613) 623-7991. **$120-$175.** 70 Madawaska Blvd K7S 1S5. Hwy 417 exit 180, 0.4 mi (0.7 km) n on CR 29, then 1.4 mi (2.3 km) w. Int corridors. **Pets:** $10 daily fee/room. Service with restrictions, supervision.
SAVE 🍽 🛜 ✖ 🔌 🖥

BANCROFT

▼▼▼ Sword Inn Bancroft 🅼
(613) 332-2474. **$160-$165.** 146 Hastings St K0L 1C0. On Hwy 62 N; center. Ext/int corridors. **Pets:** Dogs only. $10 deposit/pet. Designated rooms, no service, supervision. 🍽 🛏 ✖ 🛜 ✖ 🔌 🖥

BARRIE

▼▼▼ Comfort Inn 🅷
(705) 722-3600. **$90-$195.** 75 Hart Dr L4N 5M3. Hwy 400 exit 96A (Dunlop St E). Int corridors. **Pets:** $10 daily fee/pet. Designated rooms, service with restrictions, supervision. ECO 🍽 🛜 ✖ 🔌 🖥

🅐🅐 ▼▼▼▼ Comfort Inn & Suites 🅷
(705) 721-1122. **$80-$200.** 210 Essa Rd L4N 3L1. Hwy 400 exit 94 (Essa Rd), just e. Int corridors. **Pets:** Accepted.
SAVE ECO 🛜 ✖ 🔌 🖥

🅐🅐 ▼▼▼▼ Holiday Inn Barrie-Hotel & Conference Centre 🅷
(705) 722 -0555. **$140-$220.** 20 Fairview Rd L4N 4P3. Hwy 400 exit 94 (Essa Rd), just e. Int corridors. **Pets:** Accepted.
SAVE ECO 🍽 🔥M 🛏 ✖ 🛜 ✖ 🔌 🖥

▼▼▼▼ Horseshoe Resort 🅷
(705) 835-2790. **Call for rates.** 1101 Horseshoe Valley Rd W L4M 4Y8. Hwy 400 exit 117 (Horseshoe Valley Rd), 3.8 mi (6 km) e. Int corridors. **Pets:** Accepted. 🍽 🔥M 🛏 ✖ 🛜 ✖ 🔌 🖥

▼▼ ▼▼ Quality Inn 🅷
(705) 734-9500. **$70-$200.** 55 Hart Dr L4N 5M3. Hwy 400 exit 96A (Dunlop St E). Int corridors. **Pets:** Accepted.
ECO 🍽 🛏 🛜 ✖ 🔌 🖥

▼▼ ▼▼ Super 8 Barrie 🅷
(705) 814-8888. **$100-$110.** 441 Bryne Dr L4N 6C8. Hwy 400 exit 90 (Mapleview Dr), just nw. Int corridors. **Pets:** Accepted.
ECO 🔥M 🛏 🛜 ✖ 🔌 🖥

BARRY'S BAY

◆ **Mountain View Motel** Ⓜ

(613) 756-2757. **$85-$105, 7 day notice.** 18508 Hwy 60 E K0J 1B0. 2.5 mi (4 km) e of town. Ext corridors. **Pets:** Accepted.

〔ｲｌ〕◎ ✕ 🖥 💻

BAYFIELD *(Restaurants p. 630)*

◆◆◆ **The Little Inn of Bayfield** Ⓒ🐾

(519) 565-2611. **$220-$369, 3 day notice.** 26 Main St N0M 1G0. Hwy 21 exit Main St; jct Catherine St. Int corridors. **Pets:** Other species. $35 one-time fee/pet. Designated rooms, service with restrictions, crate.

〔ｲｌ〕&ᴹ ◎ ✕ 🖥 💻

BELLEVILLE

ⒶⒶ ◆◆◆ **Best Western Belleville** Ⓗ

(613) 969-1112. **$140-$226.** 387 N Front St K8P 3C8. Hwy 401 exit 543A, 0.3 mi (0.5 km) s on Hwy 62. Int corridors. **Pets:** Accepted.

🆂🅰🆅🅴 🄴🄲🄾 ➹ ◎ ✕ 🖥 💻

ⒶⒶ ◆◆◆ **Comfort Inn** Ⓗ

(613) 966-7703. **$125-$170.** 200 N Park St K8P 2Y9. Hwy 401 exit 543A, 0.6 mi (1 km) s on Hwy 62. Int corridors. **Pets:** Accepted.

🆂🅰🆅🅴 ◎ ✕ 🖥 💻

◆◆◆ **TownePlace Suites by Marriott** Ⓗ🐾

(613) 779-1212. **$100-$183.** 400 Bell Blvd K8P 5H8. Hwy 401 exit 538, s to Bell Blvd, then 1.2 mi (2 km) e. Int corridors. **Pets:** Medium, dogs only. $75 one-time fee/room. Designated rooms, service with restrictions, supervision. 〔ｲｌ〕&ᴹ ◎ ✕ 🖥 💻

◆◆ **Travelodge Hotel Belleville** Ⓗ

(613) 968-3411. **$99-$130.** 11 Bay Bridge Rd K8P 3P6. 0.3 mi (0.5 km) s of Hwy 2 (Dundas St). Int corridors. **Pets:** Accepted.

🄴🄲🄾 〔ｲｌ〕➹ ✕ ◎ ✕ 🖥 💻

BLIND RIVER

◆◆ **Lakeview Inn** Ⓜ

(705) 356-0800. **Call for rates.** 143 Causley St P0R 1B0. On Hwy 17, just e of Hwy 557. Ext corridors. **Pets:** Accepted.

〔ｲｌ〕◎ ✕ 🖥 💻

BLUE MOUNTAINS

ⒶⒶ ◆◆◆ ◆◆◆ **The Westin Trillium House, Blue Mountain** Ⓗ

(705) 443-8080. **$159-$319, 7 day notice.** 220 Gord Canning Dr L9Y 0V9. Jct Hwy 26 and Mountain Rd, 6.3 mi (10 km) w on Mountain Rd, just w on Jozo Weider Blvd, then just w. Int corridors. **Pets:** Accepted.

🆂🅰🆅🅴 〔ｲｌ〕&ᴹ ➹ ✕ 📠 ✕ 🖥 💻

BOWMANVILLE

ⒶⒶ ◆◆◆ **Best Western Plus Bowmanville** Ⓗ

(905) 623-8500. **$119-$229.** 160 Liberty St S L1C 2W4. Hwy 401 exit 432 (Liberty St), just n. Int corridors. **Pets:** $20 daily fee/pet. Service with restrictions, supervision. 🆂🅰🆅🅴 🄴🄲🄾 &ᴹ ➹ ◎ ✕ 🖥 💻

◆◆◆ **Holiday Inn Express & Suites Bowmanville** Ⓗ

(905) 697-8089. **$129-$219.** 37 Spicer Square L1C 5M2. Jct Hwy 401 and Waverly Rd N. Int corridors. **Pets:** Large, other species. $25 daily fee/pet. Service with restrictions, supervision.

〔ｲｌ〕&ᴹ ➹ ◎ ✕ 🖥 💻

BRACEBRIDGE

◆◆ **Sleep Inn Muskoka** Ⓜ

(705) 645-2519. **$100-$211.** 510 Hwy 118 W P1L 1W8. Just e of Manitoba St. Int corridors. **Pets:** Medium. $15 daily fee/pet. Service with restrictions, supervision. ◎ ✕ 🖥 💻

◆◆ **Travelodge Bracebridge** Ⓜ

(705) 645-2235. **$99-$180.** 320 Taylor Rd P1L 1K1. Hwy 11 exit 189 (Hwy 42/Taylor Rd), 0.6 mi (1 km) w. Ext corridors. **Pets:** Medium, dogs only. $15 daily fee/pet. Designated rooms, service with restrictions, supervision. ➹ ◎ 🖥 💻

BRAMPTON

◆◆ **Motel 6 Brampton #1902** Ⓗ

(905) 451-3313. **$69-$105.** 160 Steelwell Rd L6T 5T3. Hwy 410 exit Steeles Ave E, s on Tomken Rd, then just w. Int corridors.

Pets: Accepted. 🄴🄲🄾 〔ｲｌ〕&ᴹ ◎ 🖥

BRANTFORD

ⒶⒶ ◆◆◆ **Best Western Brantford Hotel & Conference Centre** Ⓗ🐾

(519) 753-8651. **$128-$158.** 19 Holiday Dr N3R 7J4. Jct Hwy 403 and Wayne Gretzky Pkwy. Int corridors. **Pets:** Small. $5 daily fee/room. Designated rooms, service with restrictions, crate.

🆂🅰🆅🅴 🄴🄲🄾 〔ｲｌ〕&ᴹ ➹ ✕ ◎ ✕ 🖥 💻

ⒶⒶ ◆◆◆ **Comfort Inn** Ⓗ

(519) 753-3100. **$100-$140.** 58 King George Rd N3R 5K4. Just s of jct Hwy 403 and 24. Int corridors. **Pets:** Accepted.

🆂🅰🆅🅴 〔ｲｌ〕◎ ✕ 🖥 💻

◆◆◆ **Days Inn** Ⓗ

(519) 759-2700. **$80-$125.** 460 Fairview Dr N3R 7A9. Hwy 403 exit Wayne Gretzky Pkwy, 0.5 mi (0.8 km) n. Int corridors. **Pets:** Accepted.

🄴🄲🄾 ◎ ✕ 🖥 💻

BRIGHTON

◆◆◆ **Timber House Resort** Ⓒ

(613) 475-3304. **Call for rates.** 116 Cedardale Rd K0K 1H0. Jct Hwy 2 and 64, just w over swing bridge, follow signs. Int corridors.

Pets: Accepted. 〔ｲｌ〕➹ ◎ ✕

BROCKVILLE

ⒶⒶ ◆◆◆ **Comfort Inn** Ⓗ

(613) 345-0042. **$110-$180.** 7777 Kent Blvd K6V 6N7. Hwy 401 exit 696, just nw. Int corridors. **Pets:** Accepted. 🆂🅰🆅🅴 ◎ 🖥 💻

◆◆ **Super 8 Brockville** Ⓜ

(613) 345-1622. **$89-$147.** 1843 Hwy 2 E K6V 5T1. Hwy 401 exit 698, 1.2 mi (1.9 km) s on N Augusta Rd, then 0.9 mi (1.5 km) e. Ext corridors. **Pets:** Accepted. ➹ ◎ 💻

BURLINGTON

ⒶⒶ ◆◆◆ **Admiral Inn** Ⓗ

(905) 639-4780. **$95-$105.** 3500 Billings Ct L7N 3N6. QEW exit Walkers Line westbound, just s to Harvester Rd, then just w to S Service Rd; exit Guelph Line Rd eastbound, just s to Harvester Rd, then just e to S Service Rd. Int corridors. **Pets:** Accepted.

🆂🅰🆅🅴 ◎ ✕ 🖥 💻

◆◆◆ **Comfort Inn** Ⓗ

(905) 639-1700. **$90-$190.** 3290 S Service Rd L7N 3M6. QEW exit Walkers Line westbound, just s to Harvester Rd, then just w; exit Guelph Line Rd eastbound, just s to Harvester Rd, then just e. Int corridors. **Pets:** Medium. $25 daily fee/room. Designated rooms, service with restrictions, supervision. 🄴🄲🄾 ◎ ✕ 🖥 💻

ⒶⒶ ◆◆◆ **Homewood Suites by Hilton** Ⓗ

(905) 631-8300. **$129-$219.** 975 Syscon Rd L7L 5S3. QEW exit Burloak Dr, s to Harvester Rd, then w. Int corridors. **Pets:** Medium. $75 one-time fee/room. Designated rooms, service with restrictions, supervision. 🆂🅰🆅🅴 &ᴹ ➹ ◎ 🖥 💻

◆◆ **Motel 6 Burlington #1900** Ⓗ

(905) 331-1955. **$71-$99.** 4345 N Service Rd L7L 4X7. QEW exit Walkers Line N to N Service Rd, 0.9 mi (1.4 km) e. Int corridors.

Pets: Accepted. 🄴🄲🄾 〔ｲｌ〕&ᴹ ◎ 🖥

▼▼▼ Quality Hotel Burlington 🄷

(905) 639-9290. **$99-$179.** 950 Walkers Line L7N 2G2. QEW exit Walkers Line, just s. Int corridors. **Pets:** Small. $25 daily fee/pet. Designated rooms, service with restrictions, supervision.

🄴🄲🄾 �🍴 🛍 🛜 🖂 🛗 🖵

Ⓐ **▼▼▼ Waterfront Hotel Downtown Burlington** 🄷 🐾

(905) 681-5400. **Call for rates.** 2020 Lakeshore Rd L7R 4G8. Corner of Brant St; downtown. Int corridors. **Pets:** Other species. $15 one-time fee/pet. Designated rooms, service with restrictions.

🅂🄰🅅🄴 🄴🄲🄾 ⍾ 🍴 ⚿ 🛍 🛜 🖂 🛗 🖵

CAMBRIDGE

Ⓐ **▼▼▼▼ Cambridge Hotel Conference Centre** 🄷

(519) 622-1505. **$119-$154, 14 day notice.** 700 Hespeler Rd N3H 5L8. Hwy 401 exit 282, just s. Int corridors. **Pets:** Accepted.

🅂🄰🅅🄴 🍴 🛜 🖂 🛗 🖵

Ⓐ **▼▼▼ Comfort Inn** 🄷

(519) 658-1100. **$105-$140.** 220 Holiday Inn Dr N3C 1Z4. Hwy 401 exit 282, just n to Groh Ave. Int corridors. **Pets:** Accepted.

🅂🄰🅅🄴 🄴🄲🄾 🛜 🖂 🛗 🖵

▼▼▼ Holiday Inn Cambridge 🄷

(519) 658-4601. **Call for rates.** 200 Holiday Inn Dr N3C 1Z4. Hwy 401 exit 282, just n to Groh Ave. Int corridors. **Pets:** Accepted.

🄴🄲🄾 🍴 🛍 🖂 🛜 🛗 🖵

▼▼▼ Homewood Suites by Hilton Cambridge/Waterloo 🄷

(519) 651-2888. **$169-$209.** 800 Jamieson Pkwy N3C 4N6. Hwy 401 exit 286 (Townline Rd), just n. Int corridors. **Pets:** Large. $75 one-time fee/room. Designated rooms, service with restrictions, supervision.

⚿ 🛍 🛜 🛗 🖵

Ⓐ **▼▼▼ ▼▼▼ Langdon Hall Country House Hotel & Spa** 🄲🄸

(519) 740-2100. **$325-$800, 3 day notice.** 1 Langdon Dr N3H 4R8. Hwy 401 exit 275, 0.8 mi (1.3 km) se on Fountain St, 0.6 mi (1 km) s on Blair Rd, follow signs. Ext/int corridors. **Pets:** Accepted.

🅂🄰🅅🄴 🍴 🛍 🖂 🛜 🖂 🛗 🖵

▼▼▼ Super 8 Cambridge 🄷

(519) 622-1070. **$90.** 650 Hespeler Rd N1R 6J8. Hwy 401 exit 282, 0.6 mi (1 km) s. Int corridors. **Pets:** Accepted. 🍴 🛍 🛜 🛗 🖵

CHATHAM

Ⓐ **▼▼ Comfort Inn** 🄷

(519) 352-5500. **$86-$155.** 1100 Richmond St N7M 5J5. Hwy 401 exit 81 (Bloomfield Rd), 3.1 mi (5 km) n. Int corridors. **Pets:** Accepted.

🅂🄰🅅🄴 🄴🄲🄾 🛜 🖂 🛗 🖵

▼▼▼ Holiday Inn Express & Suites 🄷

(519) 351-1100. **Call for rates.** 575 Richmond St N7M 1R2. Hwy 401 exit 81 (Bloomfield Rd) to jct Hwy 2, 0.9 mi (1.5 km) e, then 0.9 mi (1.5 km) w. Int corridors. **Pets:** Accepted.

⚿ 🛍 🛜 🖂 🛗 🖵

▼▼ Travelodge Chatham 🄷

(519) 436-1200. **$87-$150.** 555 Bloomfield Rd N7M 5J5. Hwy 401 exit 81 (Bloomfield Rd), 3 mi (5 km) n. Int corridors. **Pets:** $15 daily fee/pet. Designated rooms, service with restrictions, supervision.

🄴🄲🄾 🛜 🛗 🖵

CHATSWORTH

▼▼ Key Motel 🄼

(519) 794-2350. **Call for rates.** 317051 Hwy 6/10 N0H 1G0. On SR 6 and 10. Ext/int corridors. **Pets:** $50 deposit/room. Designated rooms, service with restrictions, supervision. 🛍 🛜 🛗

COBOURG

Ⓐ **▼▼▼▼ Best Western Plus Cobourg Inn & Convention Centre** 🄷

(905) 372-2105. **$160-$340.** 930 Burnham St K9A 2X9. Hwy 401 exit 472 (Burnham St S). Int corridors. **Pets:** Accepted.

🅂🄰🅅🄴 🄴🄲🄾 🍴 🛍 🛜 🖂 🛗 🖵

▼▼ Comfort Inn 🄷

(905) 372-7007. **$110-$145.** 121 Densmore Rd K9A 4J9. Hwy 401 exit 474, just se. Int corridors. **Pets:** Accepted.

🄴🄲🄾 🍴 🛜 🖂 🛗 🖵

COLLINGWOOD

Ⓐ **▼▼▼▼ Living Water Resort & Spa** 🄷

(705) 446-3282. **$149-$799.** 9 Harbour St E L9Y 5C5. 1.5 mi (2.4 km) nw of jct Hwy 26 and 24. Int corridors. **Pets:** Accepted.

🅂🄰🅅🄴 🍴 🖂 🛜 🖂 🛗 🖵

CORNWALL *(Restaurants p. 630)*

Ⓐ **▼▼▼ Best Western Parkway Inn & Conference Centre** 🄷

(613) 932-0451. **$160-$200.** 1515 Vincent Massey Dr K6H 5R6. Hwy 401 exit 789 (Brookdale Ave), 1.8 mi (2.8 km) s, then just w. Int corridors. **Pets:** Accepted. 🅂🄰🅅🄴 🄴🄲🄾 🍴 🛍 🛜 🖂 🛗 🖵

▼▼▼ Comfort Inn-Cornwall 🄷

(613) 937-0111. **$96-$179.** 1625 Vincent Massey Dr K6H 5R6. Hwy 401 exit 789 (Brookdale Ave), 1.8 mi (2.8 km) s, then 0.4 mi (0.7 km) w. Int corridors. **Pets:** Accepted. 🛍 🛜 🛗 🖵

DRYDEN

Ⓐ **▼▼▼ Best Western Plus Dryden Hotel & Conference Centre** 🄷

(807) 223-3201. **$129-$200.** 349 Government St P8N 2P4. On Hwy 17. Int corridors. **Pets:** Accepted. 🅂🄰🅅🄴 🍴 🛍 🖂 🛜 🖂 🛗 🖵

▼▼ Comfort Inn 🄷

(807) 223-3893. **$120-$230.** 522 Government St P8N 2P7. On Hwy 17. Int corridors. **Pets:** Accepted. 🄴🄲🄾 🍴 🛜 🖂 🛗 🖵

▼▼▼ Holiday Inn Express Dryden 🄷

(807) 223-3000. **Call for rates.** 585 Government St P8N 2Z4. On Hwy 17. Int corridors. **Pets:** Accepted. 🍴 ⚿ 🛍 🛜 🖂 🛗 🖵

FONTHILL

▼ Hipwell's Motel 🄼

(905) 892-3588. **$50-$95.** 299 Reg Rd 20 W L0S 1E0. 1 mi (1.6 km) w; center. Ext corridors. **Pets:** Dogs only. $10 daily fee/pet. Service with restrictions, supervision. 🍴 🛜 🛗

FORT ERIE

Ⓐ **▼▼▼ Clarion Hotel & Conference Centre** 🄷

(905) 871-8333. **$95-$280.** 1485 Garrison Rd L2A 1P8. QEW exit Gilmore Rd. Int corridors. **Pets:** Medium. $30 daily fee/room. Designated rooms, service with restrictions, crate.

🅂🄰🅅🄴 🄴🄲🄾 🍴 🛍 🖂 🛜 🖂 🛗 🖵

FORT FRANCES

Ⓐ **▼▼▼ La Place Rendez-Vous** 🄷

(807) 274-9811. **$114-$127.** 1201 Idylwild Dr, B2-RR 2 P9A 3M3. Hwy 11, just e on Lake Rd; east end of town. Int corridors. **Pets:** Other species. $10 one-time fee/pet. Service with restrictions, supervision.

🅂🄰🅅🄴 🍴 🛜 🖂 🛗 🖵

▼▼▼ Super 8 🄷

(807) 274-4945. **$106-$150.** 810 Kings Hwy P9A 2X4. On Hwy 11. Int corridors. **Pets:** Accepted. ⚿ 🛍 🛜 🖂 🛗 🖵

GANANOQUE

⚠ ▼▼▼ Comfort Inn & Suites Thousand Islands Harbour District 🅷

(613) 382-7272. **$99-$400.** 22 Main St K7G 2L7. Corner of Hwy 2 (King St); center. Int corridors. **Pets:** Medium. $15 daily fee/pet. Designated rooms, supervision. 🅂🄰🅅🄴 🄼 ⓐ 🛜 ✕ 🅸 🖵

⚠ ▼▼▼ Country Squire Resort & Spa 🅷

(613) 382-3511. **Call for rates.** 715 King St E K7G 1H4. Hwy 401 exit 647 eastbound; exit 648 westbound, 0.6 mi (1 km) w on Hwy 2 (King St). Ext/int corridors. **Pets:** $20 daily fee/room. Designated rooms, service with restrictions, supervision.
🅂🄰🅅🄴 🍴 🄰 ✕ 🛜 ✕ 🅸 🖵

⚠ ▼▼▼ Holiday Inn Express & Suites 1000 Islands 🅷

(613) 382-8338. **$99-$399.** 777 King St E K7G 1H4. Just w of jct Hwy 2 (King St), 401 and 1000 Islands Pkwy. Int corridors. **Pets:** Accepted.
🅂🄰🅅🄴 🄴🄲🄾 🄼 🄰 🛜 ✕ 🅸 🖵

⚠ ▼▼ Quality Inn & Suites 1000 Islands 🄼

(613) 382-1453. **$78-$289.** 650 King St E K7G 1H3. Hwy 401 exit 647 eastbound; exit 648 westbound, 0.6 mi (1 km) w on Hwy 2 (King St). Ext corridors. **Pets:** Small, dogs only. $15 daily fee/pet. Designated rooms, no service, supervision. 🅂🄰🅅🄴 🍴 🄰 🛜 🅸 🖵

▼▼ Ramada Provincial Inn 🄼

(613) 382-2038. **$99-$275.** 846 King St E K7G 1H3. Hwy 401 exit 647 eastbound; exit 648 westbound, 0.3 mi (0.5 km) w on Hwy 2 (King St). Ext corridors. **Pets:** Accepted. 🍴 🄰 🛜 ✕ 🅸 🖵

⚠ ▼▼ Travelodge 1000 Islands 🄼

(613) 382-4728. **$67-$230.** 785 King St E K7G 1H4. Hwy 401 exit 647 eastbound; exit 648 westbound, 0.3 mi (0.5 km) w on Hwy 2 (King St). Ext/int corridors. **Pets:** Large. $20 daily fee/room. Service with restrictions. 🅂🄰🅅🄴 🄰 🛜 ✕ 🅸 🖵

▼▼▼ Trinity House Inn 🄲🅸

(613) 382-8383. **$99-$250, 7 day notice.** 90 Stone St S K7G 1Z8. Corner of Pine St; center. Int corridors. **Pets:** Accepted.
🛜 ✕ 🄩 🅸 🖵

GEORGETOWN

⚠ ▼▼ Best Western Inn On The Hill 🅷

(905) 877-6986. **$99-$199.** 365 Guelph St (Hwy 7) L7G 4B6. At Delrex Blvd. Ext corridors. **Pets:** $150 one-time fee/room. Designated rooms, service with restrictions, supervision. 🅂🄰🅅🄴 🛜 🅸 🖵

GODERICH

⚠ ▼▼▼ ▼▼ Benmiller Inn & Spa 🄲🅸

(519) 524-2191. **$155-$378, 7 day notice.** 81175 Benmiller Line N7A 3Y1. 5 mi (8 km) on Hwy 8 E to Huron Rd 1 (Benmiller Line), 1.9 mi (3 km) e. Ext/int corridors. **Pets:** Accepted.
🅂🄰🅅🄴 🍴 🄰 ✕ 🛜 ✕ 🅸 🖵

GRAFTON

⚠ ▼▼▼ ▼▼ Ste. Anne's Spa 🄲🅸

(905) 349-3704. **$329-$545, 21 day notice.** 1009 Massey Rd, RR 1 K0K 2G0. Hwy 401 exit 487, 1.8 mi (3 km) n. Int corridors.
Pets: Accepted. 🅂🄰🅅🄴 🍴 🄰 ✕ 🛜 ✕ 🅆 🅸 🖵

GRAVENHURST

⚠ ▼▼▼ Residence Inn by Marriott Gravenhurst Muskoka Wharf 🅷

(705) 687-6600. **$83-$411.** 285 Steamship Bay Rd P1P 1Z9. Hwy 11 exit 169 (Bethune Dr); at Muskoka Wharf, follow signs. Int corridors.
Pets: Accepted. 🅂🄰🅅🄴 🄼 🄰 🛜 ✕ 🅸 🖵

GRIMSBY

⚠ ▼▼▼ Super 8-Grimsby 🅷

(905) 309-8800. **$106-$166.** 11 Windward Dr L3M 4E9. QEW exit 74 (Casablanca Blvd N). Int corridors. **Pets:** Medium, other species. $10 daily fee/pet. Service with restrictions, crate.
🅂🄰🅅🄴 🄰 🛜 ✕ 🅸 🖵

GUELPH

⚠ ▼▼▼ Comfort Inn Guelph 🅷

(519) 763-1900. **$90-$195.** 480 Silvercreek Pkwy N1H 7R5. Jct Hwy 6 and 7. Int corridors. **Pets:** Dogs only. $20 daily fee/pet. Designated rooms, service with restrictions, supervision.
🅂🄰🅅🄴 🄴🄲🄾 🛜 ✕ 🅸 🖵

⚠ ▼▼ Days Inn-Guelph 🅷

(519) 822-9112. **$92-$102.** 785 Gordon St N1G 1Y8. Hwy 401 exit 299 (Brock Rd), 7 mi (11.5 km) n. Int corridors. **Pets:** Accepted.
🅂🄰🅅🄴 🄴🄲🄾 🛜 ✕ 🅸 🖵

▼▼▼ Delta Guelph Hotel and Conference Centre 🅷

(519) 780-3700. **$71-$196.** 50 Stone Rd W N1G 0A9. Jct Gordon St. Int corridors. **Pets:** Accepted. 🄴🄲🄾 🍴 🄼 🛜 ✕ 🅸 🖵

⚠ ▼▼▼▼ Holiday Inn Guelph Hotel & Conference Centre 🅷

(519) 836-0231. **$109-$200.** 601 Scottsdale Dr N1G 3E7. Jct Hwy 6 N and Stone Rd E; 5 mi (8 km) n of jct Hwy 401. Int corridors.
Pets: Accepted. 🅂🄰🅅🄴 🄴🄲🄾 🍴 🄼 ✕ 🛜 ✕ 🅸 🖵

▼▼▼ Staybridge Suites 🅷

(519) 767-3300. **$143-$223, 3 day notice.** 11 Corporate Ct N1G 5G5. Jct Hwy 6 and Laird St, just e. Int corridors. **Pets:** Large, other species. $35 one-time fee/room. Service with restrictions, crate.
🄴🄲🄾 🍴 🄼 🄰 🛜 🅸 🖵

HALIBURTON

▼ Lakeview Motel 🄼

(705) 457-1027. **$147-$265, 5 day notice.** 4951 CR 21 K0M 1S0. Jct Hwy 118, 1.6 mi (2.5 km) w. Ext corridors. **Pets:** $12 daily fee/pet. Designated rooms, service with restrictions. 🍴 🄰 🛜 ✕ 🅸 🖵

HAMILTON

⚠ ▼▼▼ Admiral Inn 🅷

(905) 529-2311. **$99-$129, 3 day notice.** 149 Dundurn St N L8R 3E7. Hwy 403 exit York Blvd. Int corridors. **Pets:** Accepted.
🅂🄰🅅🄴 🍴 🛜 ✕ 🅸 🖵

⚠ ▼▼▼ Comfort Inn 🅷

(905) 560-4500. **$105-$180.** 183 Centennial Pkwy N L8E 1H8. QEW exit 88 (Hwy 20), 0.6 mi (1 km) s. Int corridors. **Pets:** Accepted.
🅂🄰🅅🄴 🄴🄲🄾 🛜 ✕ 🅸 🖵

▼▼▼ Homewood Suites by Hilton Hamilton 🅷

(905) 667-1200. **Call for rates.** 40 Bay St S L8P 0B3. Jct George St; downtown. Int corridors. **Pets:** Accepted. 🄼 🛜 ✕ 🅸 🖵

⚠ ▼▼▼ Sheraton Hamilton Hotel 🅷

(905) 529-5515. **$129-$349.** 116 King St W L8P 4V3. Between Bay and James sts; downtown. Int corridors. **Pets:** Accepted.
🅂🄰🅅🄴 🍴 🄼 🄰 🛜 ✕ 🅸 🖵

▼▼▼ Staybridge Suites - Hamilton Downtown 🅷

(905) 527-1001. **Call for rates.** 20 Caroline St S L8P 0B1. Between Main and King sts. Int corridors. **Pets:** Accepted.
🄼 🄰 🛜 ✕ 🅸 🖵

▼▼ Super 8-Hamilton Airport/Mount Hope 🅷

(905) 679-3355. **$95.** 2975 Homestead Dr L0R 1W0. Jct Hwy 6 S (Upper James St) and Homestead Dr. Int corridors. **Pets:** Accepted.
🛜 ✕ 🅸 🖵

HUNTSVILLE

▼▼ Comfort Inn **H** ❀
(705) 789-1701. **$105-$190.** 86 King William St P1H 1E4. Jct Hwy 60. Int corridors. **Pets:** Medium. $20 daily fee/pet. Designated rooms, service with restrictions, supervision. ▣ 🛜 ✕ 🖥 🖵

▼▼▼ Deerhurst Resort **H**
(705) 789-6411. **Call for rates.** 1235 Deerhurst Dr P1H 2E8. Jct Hwy 11, 4.3 mi (7 km) e on Hwy 60 to Deerhurst Canal Rd (CR 23), then 1.2 mi (2 km), follow signs. Ext/int corridors. **Pets:** Accepted.
▣ 🍴 ⚙ 🏊 ✕ 🛜 ✕ 🖥 🖵

▼▼▼ Hidden Valley Resort, an Ascend Hotel Collection Member **H**
(705) 789-2301. **$109-$279, 3 day notice.** 1755 Valley Rd P1H 1Z8. Jct Hwy 11, 4 mi (6.5 km) e on Hwy 60 to Canal Rd, follow signs. Int corridors. **Pets:** Accepted. 🍴 ⚙ 🏊 ✕ 🛜 ✕ 🖥 🖵

▼▼▼ Holiday Inn Express Hotel & Suites **H**
(705) 788-9500. **Call for rates.** 100 Howland Dr P1H 2P9. Jct Hwy 11 and 60, just se. Int corridors. **Pets:** Accepted. 🏊 🛜 ✕ 🖥 🖵

▼▼ Motel 6-Huntsville **H**
(705) 787-0118. **Call for rates.** 70 Howland Dr P1H 2P9. Jct Hwy 11 and 60, just se. Int corridors. **Pets:** Accepted.
▣ ⚙ 🏊 🛜 ✕ 🖥

INGERSOLL

▼▼▼ Comfort Inn & Suites **H** ❀
(519) 425-1100. **$96-$200.** 20 Samnah Cres N5C 3J7. Hwy 401 exit 216 (Culloden Rd). Int corridors. **Pets:** Medium, dogs only. $20 one-time fee/room. Designated rooms, service with restrictions, supervision.
🏊 🛜 ✕ 🖥 🖵

JACKSONS POINT

Ⓐ ▼▼▼ The Briars Resort and Spa **H**
(905) 722-3271. **$169-$479, 21 day notice.** 55 Hedge Rd, RR 1 L0E 1L0. Hwy 48, through Sutton to Jacksons Point, 0.6 mi (1 km) e. Ext/int corridors. **Pets:** Accepted. 🅂🅰🅅🅴 🍴 🏊 ✕ 🛜 ✕ 🖥 🖵

KANATA

Ⓐ ▼▼▼ ▼▼▼ Brookstreet Hotel **H**
(613) 271-1800. **$139-$599.** 525 Legget Dr K2K 2W2. Hwy 417 exit 138 (March Rd), 2.3 mi (3.7 km) n, just e on Solandt Dr to Legget Dr, then just n. Int corridors. **Pets:** Medium. $250 deposit/pet, $25 daily fee/pet. Designated rooms, service with restrictions, crate.
🅂🅰🅅🅴 ▣ 🍴 🏊 ✕ 🛜 ✕ 🖥 🖵

Ⓐ ▼▼ Comfort Inn Ottawa West Kanata **H**
(613) 592-2200. **$120-$200.** 222 Hearst Way K2L 3A2. Hwy 417 exit 138 (Eagleson Rd), 0.4 mi (0.6 km) s, just w on Katimavik Rd, then 0.5 mi (0.8 km) n. Int corridors. **Pets:** Accepted.
🅂🅰🅅🅴 ▣ 🛜 ✕ 🖥 🖵

KAPUSKASING

Ⓐ ▼▼ Comfort Inn **H**
(705) 335-8583. **$110-$160.** 172 Government Rd E P5N 2W9. Hwy 11; corner of Brunelle Rd. Int corridors. **Pets:** Accepted.
🅂🅰🅅🅴 ▣ 🛜 ✕ 🖥 🖵

Ⓐ ▼▼▼ Super 8 **H**
(705) 335-8887. **$120-$139.** 430 Government Rd P5N 2X7. Hwy 11. Int corridors. **Pets:** $20 one-time fee/room. Designated rooms, service with restrictions, supervision. 🅂🅰🅅🅴 ⚙ 🏊 ✕ 🛜 ✕ 🖥 🖵

KENORA

▼▼ Clarion Lakeside Inn and Conference Centre **H**
(807) 468-5521. **$120-$400.** 470 1st Ave S P9N 1W5. Just s on 4th Ave S from jct Hwy 17. Int corridors. **Pets:** Accepted.
▣ 🍴 🏊 🛜 ✕ 🖥 🖵

▼▼ Comfort Inn **H** ❀
(807) 468-8845. **$120-$239.** 1230 Hwy 17 E P9N 1L9. 0.9 mi (1.5 km) e of town. Int corridors. **Pets:** Other species. $15 daily fee/pet. Designated rooms, service with restrictions, supervision.
🍴 🛜 ✕ 🖥 🖵

▼▼ Super 8 Kenora **H**
(807) 468-8016. **Call for rates.** 240 Lakeview Dr P9N 0H2. Just w on Hwy 17. Int corridors. **Pets:** Other species. $15 deposit/pet. Designated rooms, service with restrictions, crate. 🍴 🛜 ✕ 🖥 🖵

KILLALOE

▼▼▼ Annie's Inn Bed & Breakfast ▣▣
(613) 757-0950. **$90-$225, 7 day notice.** 67 Roche St K0J 2A0. Hwy 60 exit Maple St, 1 blk to Roche St, then w; driveway entrance is at the end of the street. Int corridors. **Pets:** Accepted.
🍴 🛜 ✕ ⚙ 🖥 🖵

KINCARDINE

Ⓐ ▼▼▼ Best Western Plus Governor's Inn **H**
(519) 396-8242. **$160-$200.** 791 Durham St N2Z 1M4. Jct Hwy 21. Int corridors. **Pets:** Accepted. 🅂🅰🅅🅴 🍴 ✕ 🛜 ✕ 🖥 🖵

▼▼▼ Holiday Inn Express and Suites-Kincardine **H**
(519) 395-3545. **$165-$195.** 2 Millenium Way N2Z 0B5. Jct Hwy 21. Int corridors. **Pets:** Other species. $20 one-time fee/room. Service with restrictions, crate. ⚙ 🏊 🛜 ✕ 🖥 🖵

▼▼▼ TownePlace Suites by Marriott **H**
(519) 395-2665. **$106-$201.** 19 Millenium Way N2Z 0B5. Jct Hwy 21. Int corridors. **Pets:** Accepted. ⚙ 🛜 ✕ 🖥 🖵

KINGSTON

Ⓐ ▼▼▼ Ambassador Hotel & Conference Centre **H**
(613) 548-3605. **$109-$299.** 1550 Princess St K7M 9E3. Hwy 401 exit 613 (Sydenham Rd), 1.8 mi (3 km) se. Int corridors. **Pets:** Medium. $25 daily fee/room. Designated rooms, service with restrictions, crate.
🅂🅰🅅🅴 ▣ 🍴 ⚙ 🏊 ✕ 🛜 ✕ 🖥 🖵

Ⓐ ▼▼▼ Best Western Fireside Inn **H**
(613) 549-2211. **$139-$219.** 1217 Princess St K7M 3E1. Hwy 401 exit 615 (Sir John A MacDonald Blvd), 2.5 mi (4 km) sw. Int corridors. **Pets:** Large. $20 daily fee/pet. Designated rooms, service with restrictions, supervision. 🅂🅰🅅🅴 🍴 🏊 ✕ 🛜 ✕ 🖥 🖵

Ⓐ ▼▼ Comfort Inn Hwy 401 **H** ❀
(613) 546-9500. **$108-$240.** 55 Warne Cres K7K 6Z5. Hwy 401 exit 617 (Division St), just s to Dalton Ave. Int corridors. **Pets:** Large. $10 daily fee/room. Service with restrictions, crate.
🅂🅰🅅🅴 ▣ 🛜 ✕ 🖥 🖵

Ⓐ ▼▼▼ Comfort Inn Midtown **H**
(613) 549-5550. **$102-$146.** 1454 Princess St K7M 3E5. Hwy 401 exit 613 (Sydenham Rd), 2.5 mi (4 km) se. Int corridors. **Pets:** Medium. $10 daily fee/room. Service with restrictions, supervision.
🅂🅰🅅🅴 ▣ 🛜 ✕ 🖥 🖵

▼▼ Confederation Place Hotel **H**
(613) 549-6300. **Call for rates.** 237 Ontario St K7L 2Z4. Center of downtown. Int corridors. **Pets:** Accepted. 🏊 🛜 ✕ 🖥 🖵

Ⓐ ▼▼▼▼ Delta Kingston Waterfront Hotel **H**
(613) 549-8100. **$179-$499.** 1 Johnson St K7L 5H7. At foot of Johnson St; downtown. Int corridors. **Pets:** Accepted.
🅂🅰🅅🅴 ▣ 🍴 ⚙ 🏊 🛜 ✕ 🖥 🖵

Ⓐ ▼▼▼▼ Four Points by Sheraton Kingston **H**
(613) 544-4434. **Call for rates.** 285 King St E K7L 3B1. Hwy 401 exit 615 (Sir John A MacDonald Blvd), e on King St, then s on Clarence St; downtown. Int corridors. **Pets:** Accepted.
🅂🅰🅅🅴 ▣ 🍴 ⚙ 🏊 🛜 ✕ 🖥 🖵

(AA) ▼▼▼ Green Acres Inn M ❀
(613) 546-1796. **$139-$199.** 2480 Princess St K7M 3G4. Hwy 401 exit 611 (Hwy 38), 1.9 mi (3 km) s, then 0.3 mi (0.5 km) e. Ext corridors. **Pets:** $200 deposit/room. Designated rooms, service with restrictions, crate. SAVE 🛆 🛜 ✕ 🖥 🖵

(AA) ▼▼▼ Holiday Inn Kingston-Waterfront H
(613) 549-8400. **$150-$250, 3 day notice.** 2 Princess St K7L 1A2. Corner of Ontario St; center of downtown. Int corridors. **Pets:** $80 one-time fee/room. Designated rooms, service with restrictions, supervision.
SAVE ECO ¶¶ 🛆M 🛆 ✕ 🛜 ✕ 🖥 🖵

▼▼ Motel 6 Kingston H
(613) 507-6666. **Call for rates.** 1542 Robinson Ct K7L 4V2. Hwy 401 exit 611, just s. Int corridors. **Pets:** Accepted.
ECO ¶¶ 🛆M 🛜 ✕ 🖥

(AA) ▼▼▼ Quality Inn & Suites H
(613) 389-9998. **$109-$179.** 1530 Robinson Ct K7P 0K4. Hwy 401 exit 611, just s. Int corridors. **Pets:** Accepted.
SAVE ¶¶ 🛆M 🛜 ✕ 🖥 🖵

(AA) ▼▼▼ Ramada Kingston Hotel & Conference Centre H
(613) 546-3661. **$98-$179.** 33 Benson St K7K 5W2. Hwy 401 exit 617, s on Division St, then just e. Ext/int corridors. **Pets:** Accepted.
SAVE ¶¶ 🛜 ✕ 🖥 🖵

▼▼▼ Residence Inn by Marriott Kingston Water's Edge H
(613) 544-4888. **$92-$306.** 7 Earl St K7L 0A4. Hwy 401 exit 617 (Division St) to Princess St, right on King St, then left, 2 blks w of city hall. Int corridors. **Pets:** Accepted. 🛆M 🛆 ✕ 🛜 🖥 🖵

(AA) ▼▼▼ Super 8 Kingston M
(613) 549-1620. **$99-$169, 3 day notice.** 794 Hwy 2 K7L 4V1. Hwy 401 exit 623, 5 mi (8 km) s, then 1.3 mi (2 km) e. Ext corridors. **Pets:** Accepted. SAVE ¶¶ 🛆 🛜 ✕ 🖥 🖵

KIRKLAND LAKE
▼▼ Comfort Inn H
(705) 567-4909. **$114-$179.** 455 Government Rd W P0K 1A0. On Hwy 66. Int corridors. **Pets:** Other species. Service with restrictions, crate.
ECO 🛜 ✕ 🖥 🖵

(AA) ▼▼ Microtel Inn & Suites by Wyndham-Kirkland Lake H ❀
(705) 462-2401. **$119-$165.** 350 Government Rd W P2N 3L1. On Hwy 66. Int corridors. **Pets:** Other species. $25 one-time fee/pet. Service with restrictions. SAVE ¶¶ 🛆M 🛜 ✕ 🖥 🖵

KITCHENER
(AA) ▼▼▼ Radisson Hotel Kitchener Waterloo H ❀
(519) 894-9500. **$144-$229.** 2960 King St E N2A 1A9. Hwy 401 exit 278, 3.8 mi (6 km) w on Hwy 8 exit Weber St. Int corridors. **Pets:** Medium. $35 daily fee/room. Designated rooms, service with restrictions, crate. SAVE ECO ¶¶ 🛆 🛜 ✕ 🖥 🖵

LEAMINGTON
(AA) ▼▼▼ Best Western Plus Leamington Hotel and Conference Centre H
(519) 326-8646. **$116-$189, 3 day notice.** 566 Bevel Line Rd N8H 3V4. 0.6 mi (1 km) s of jct Talbot and Erie sts, then 1.2 mi (2 km) w to signs following the direct route to Point Pelee National Park. Int corridors. **Pets:** Accepted. SAVE ¶¶ ✕ 🛜 ✕ 🖥 🖵

LINCOLN
▼▼▼ Inn on the Twenty CI
(905) 562-5336. **$159-$389, 7 day notice.** 3845 Main St L0R 1S0. QEW exit 57 (Victoria Ave/Reg Rd 24), 1.9 mi (3 km) s, 1.9 mi (3 km) e on Reg Rd 81, then just n. Ext/int corridors. **Pets:** Accepted.
¶¶ 🛜 ✕ 🖥 🖵

▼▼▼ Ramada Jordan Beacon Harbourside Hotel & Suites H
(905) 562-4155. **$69-$200.** 2793 Beacon Blvd L0R 1S0. QEW exit 55. Int corridors. **Pets:** Accepted. ¶¶ 🛆 ✕ 🛜 ✕ 🖥 🖵

LINDSAY
(AA) ▼▼▼ Days Inn & Suites Lindsay H ❀
(705) 328-0100. **$114-$135.** 134 Angeline St S K9V 3L6. 1 mi (1.6 km) n of jct Hwy 7. Int corridors. **Pets:** Other species. $25 one-time fee/room. Designated rooms, service with restrictions, crate.
SAVE ¶¶ 🛆M 🛜 🖥 🖵

LONDON
(AA) ▼▼▼ Best Western London Airport Inn & Suites H ❀
(519) 457-1200. **$119-$290.** 2230 Dundas St N5V 1R5. Hwy 401 exit Veteran's Memorial Pkwy, 4.8 mi (7.7 km) n; corner of Airport Rd and Dundas St E. Int corridors. **Pets:** Medium, dogs only. $20 daily fee/pet. Designated rooms, no service, supervision.
SAVE ¶¶ 🛆M 🛜 ✕ 🖥 🖵

(AA) ▼▼▼ Best Western Plus Lamplighter Inn & Conference Centre H ❀
(519) 681-7151. **$129-$179.** 591 Wellington Rd S N6C 4R3. Hwy 401 exit 186 (Wellington Rd), 2.3 mi (3.7 km) n. Int corridors. **Pets:** Large, other species. $10 daily fee/room. Designated rooms, service with restrictions, supervision. SAVE ECO ¶¶ 🛆 ✕ 🛜 ✕ 🖥 🖵

▼▼▼ Comfort Inn H
(519) 685-9300. **$93-$130.** 1156 Wellington Rd N6E 1M3. Hwy 401 exit 186B (Wellington Rd), just n. Int corridors. **Pets:** Accepted.
ECO 🛜 ✕ 🖥 🖵

(AA) ▼▼▼ Delta London Armouries H
(519) 679-6111. **$169-$269.** 325 Dundas St N6B 1T9. Between Wellington and Waterloo sts. Int corridors. **Pets:** Accepted.
SAVE ECO ¶¶ 🛆 ✕ 🛜 ✕ 🖥 🖵

(AA) ▼▼▼ Four Points by Sheraton London H
(519) 681-0600. **$109-$199.** 1150 Wellington Rd S N6E 1M3. Hwy 401 exit 186B (Wellington Rd), 1 mi (1.5 km) n. Int corridors. **Pets:** Medium. $50 one-time fee/pet. Designated rooms, service with restrictions, supervision. SAVE ¶¶ 🛆M 🛆 🛜 ✕ 🖥 🖵

▼▼▼ Holiday Inn Hotel & Suites London H
(519) 668-7900. **Call for rates.** 855 Wellington Rd S N6E 3N5. Jct Wellington and Southdale rds. Int corridors. **Pets:** Accepted.
ECO ¶¶ 🛆 🛜 ✕ 🖥 🖵

▼▼▼ Homewood Suites by Hilton London H
(519) 686-7700. **$99-$209.** 45 Bessemer Rd N6E 0A2. Hwy 401 exit 186B (Wellington Rd), just n. Int corridors. **Pets:** Accepted.
🛆M 🛆 🛜 🖥 🖵

▼▼▼ Hotel Metro-London H
(519) 518-9000. **$149-$229.** 32 Covent Market Pl N6A 1E8. Jct Talbot St. Int corridors. **Pets:** Accepted. ¶¶ 🛜 ✕ 🖥 🖵

▼▼ Motel 6 London #5703 H
(519) 680-0900. **Call for rates.** 810 Exeter Rd N6E 1L5. Hwy 401 exit 186 (Wellington Rd), just n. Int corridors. **Pets:** Accepted.
ECO 🛆M 🛆 🛜 🖥

◆◆ Ramada London H
(519) 681-4900. $79-$170. 817 Exeter Rd N6E 1W1. Hwy 401 exit 186B (Wellington Rd), just n. Int corridors. Pets: Accepted.
🍴 🏊 🛜 🛅 💻

CAA ◆◆◆ Residence Inn by Marriott London H
(519) 433-7222. $82-$193. 383 Colborne St N6B 3P5. Jct King St. Int corridors. Pets: Accepted. SAVE ECO &M 🛜 ✕ 🛅 💻

CAA ◆◆◆ StationPark All Suite Hotel H
(519) 642-4444. $149-$239. 242 Pall Mall St N6A 5P6. Hwy 401 exit 186B (Wellington Rd), 5.6 mi (9 km) n. Int corridors. Pets: Accepted.
SAVE ✕ 🛜 ✕ 🛅 💻

◆◆◆ Staybridge Suites H
(519) 649-4500. $129-$399. 824 Exeter Rd N6E 1L5. Hwy 401 exit 186B (Wellington Rd), just n. Int corridors. Pets: Other species. $40 one-time fee/room. Service with restrictions, crate.
ECO &M 🏊 🛜 🛅 💻

CAA ◆◆◆ TownePlace Suites by Marriott H
(519) 681-1200. $54-$147. 800 Exeter Rd N6E 1L5. Hwy 401 exit 186B (Wellington Rd), just n. Int corridors. Pets: Accepted.
SAVE ECO &M 🛜 ✕ 🛅 💻

MARKHAM
◆◆◆ Comfort Inn H
(905) 477-6077. $94-$169. 8330 Woodbine Ave L3R 2N8. Hwy 401 exit 375, 5.6 mi (9 km) n; Hwy 404 exit Hwy 7, just e, then s. Int corridors. Pets: Accepted. 🏊 ✕ 🛜 🛅 💻

◆◆◆ Edward Village Markham H
(905) 477-2010. $99-$179. 50 E Valhalla Dr L3R 0A3. Hwy 404 exit Hwy 7, just e. Int corridors. Pets: Accepted.
ECO 🍴 🏊 ✕ 🛜 🛅 💻

CAA ◆◆◆ Hampton Inn & Suites by Hilton Toronto Markham H
(905) 752-5600. Call for rates. 52 Bodrington Court L6G 0A9. Hwy 407 exit 84 (Woodbine Ave), just ne. Int corridors. Pets: Medium. $50 one-time fee/pet. Designated rooms, service with restrictions, supervision.
SAVE &M 🛜 ✕ 🛅 💻

CAA ◆◆◆ ◆◆◆ Hilton Toronto/Markham Suites Conference Centre & Spa H
(905) 470-8500. $125-$250. 8500 Warden Ave L6G 1A5. Hwy 404 exit Hwy 7, 2 mi (3.2 km) e. Int corridors. Pets: Accepted.
SAVE ECO 🍴 &M 🏊 ✕ 🛜 🛅 💻

CAA ◆◆◆ Homewood Suites by Hilton Toronto/Markham H
(905) 477-4663. $179-$199. 50 Bodrington Ct L6G 0A9. Hwy 407 exit 84 (Woodbine Ave), just ne. Int corridors. Pets: Small. $50 one-time fee/pet. Designated rooms, service with restrictions, supervision.
SAVE &M 🏊 🛜 🛅 💻

◆◆◆ Residence Inn by Marriott Toronto-Markham H
(905) 707-7933. $81-$184. 55 Minthorn Blvd L3T 7Y9. Hwy 404 exit Hwy 7, 0.7 mi (1.1 km) w. Int corridors. Pets: Accepted.
&M 🏊 🛜 ✕ 🛅 💻

◆◆◆ Staybridge Suites Toronto-Markham H
(905) 771-9333. Call for rates. 355 S Park Rd L3T 7W2. Hwy 404 exit Hwy 7, 0.9 mi (1.4 km) w, 0.3 mi (0.5 km) s on Commerce Valley Dr W, then just e. Int corridors. Pets: Accepted.
🍴 &M 🏊 🛜 ✕ 🛅 💻

◆◆ TownePlace Suites by Marriott Toronto Northeast/Markham H
(905) 752-0446. $41-$211. 7095 Woodbine Ave L3R 1A3. Hwy 404 exit Steeles Ave, just n. Int corridors. Pets: Medium. $100 one-time fee/room. Service with restrictions. 🍴 &M 🛜 ✕ 🛅 💻

MIDLAND
◆◆◆ Comfort Inn H
(705) 526-2090. $89-$190. 980 King St L4R 4K3. Jct Hwy 12 and King St. Int corridors. Pets: Accepted. ECO 🛜 ✕ 🛅 💻

◆◆◆ Quality Inn & Conference Centre H
(705) 526-9307. $110-$190. 924 King St L4R 0B8. Jct Hwy 12 and King St. Ext/int corridors. Pets: Small. $20 daily fee/pet. Designated rooms, service with restrictions, supervision.
🍴 🏊 ✕ 🛜 🛅 💻

MILTON
CAA ◆◆◆ Best Western Plus Milton H
(905) 875-3818. $129-$199. 161 Chisholm Dr L9T 4A6. Jct Hwy 401 and 25 S. Int corridors. Pets: Accepted.
SAVE 🍴 🏊 🛜 ✕ 🛅 💻

◆◆◆ Home2 Suites by Hilton H
(289) 878-3800. Call for rates. 8490 Parkhill Dr L9T 4A6. Jct Hwy 401 and 25 N. Int corridors. Pets: Accepted. 🍴 &M 🛜 ✕ 🛅 💻

MINDEMOYA
◆ Mindemoya Motel M
(705) 377-4779. Call for rates. 6375 Hwy 542 P0P 1S0. In Mindemoya; 0.6 mi (1 km) w of jct Hwy 551 and 542. Ext corridors. Pets: Accepted.
🛜 🛅 💻

MISSISSAUGA
◆◆◆ Admiral Inn & Suites Mississauga H
(905) 403-9777. Call for rates. 2161 N Sheridan Way L5K 1A3. QEW exit Erin Mills Pkwy, just n to N Sheridan Way, then just w. Int corridors. Pets: Accepted. 🍴 &M 🏊 ✕ 🛜 ✕ 🛅 💻

◆◆ Alt Toronto Airport H
(905) 362-4337. Call for rates. 6080 Viscount Rd L4V 0A1. Just s of Airport Rd; connected to Toronto Pearson International Airport by monorail. Int corridors. Pets: Accepted. 🍴 &M 🛜 ✕ 💻

◆◆ Comfort Inn Airport West H
(905) 624-6900. $79-$200. 1500 Matheson Blvd L4W 3Z4. Hwy 401 exit Dixie Rd, then s. Int corridors. Pets: Accepted.
ECO 🍴 🛜 ✕ 🛅 💻

CAA ◆◆ Comfort Inn Toronto Airport H
(905) 677-7331. $100-$160. 6355 Airport Rd L4V 1E4. 1.3 mi (2 km) s of Derry Rd. Int corridors. Pets: Accepted.
SAVE 🍴 🛜 ✕ 🛅 💻

CAA ◆◆ DoubleTree by Hilton Toronto Airport West H
(905) 624-1144. $99-$239. 5444 Dixie Rd L4W 2L2. 0.6 mi (1 km) s of jct Hwy 401 and Dixie Rd. Int corridors. Pets: $35 daily fee/room. Designated rooms, service with restrictions, supervision.
SAVE ECO 🍴 🏊 ✕ 🛜 ✕ 🛅 💻

CAA ◆◆ Four Points by Sheraton Mississauga Meadowvale H
(905) 858-2424. $99-$199. 2501 Argentia Rd L5N 4G8. Hwy 401 exit 336 (Mississauga Rd), just s on Erin Mills Pkwy, then 1 mi (1.6 km) w. Int corridors. Pets: Medium. $25 daily fee/pet. Designated rooms, service with restrictions, supervision.
SAVE ECO 🍴 &M 🏊 🛜 ✕ 🛅 💻

CAA ◆◆◆ Hilton Mississauga/Meadowvale H
(905) 821-1981. $119-$249. 6750 Mississauga Rd L5N 2L3. Hwy 401 W exit 336 (Mississauga Rd), just s. Int corridors. Pets: Accepted.
SAVE ECO 🍴 &M 🏊 ✕ 🛜 ✕ 🛅 💻

◆◆ Holiday Inn Toronto-Mississauga H
(905) 855-2000. $89-$189, 3 day notice. 2125 N Sheridan Way L5K 1A3. QEW exit Erin Mills Pkwy. Int corridors. Pets: Accepted.
🍴 &M 🏊 🛜 ✕ 🛅 💻

◆◆ Motel 6 Mississauga #1910 H
(905) 814-1664. $75-$105. 2935 Argentia Rd L5N 8G6. Hwy 401 exit
333 (Winston Churchill Blvd), just s. Int corridors. Pets: Accepted.
ECO 🛜 🔲

◆◆◆ Novotel Toronto Mississauga Centre H ❧
(905) 896-1000. Call for rates. 3670 Hurontario St L5B 1P3. Hwy 403
exit 344, 0.8 mi (1.2 km) s on Hwy 10 (Hurontario St); at Burn-
hamthorpe Rd. Int corridors. Pets: Small, other species. Designated
rooms, service with restrictions, crate.
ECO 🍴 ⇆ 🛜 ✕ 🔲 💻

◆◆◆ Residence Inn by Marriott Mississauga Airport
Corporate Centre West H
(905) 602-7777. $89-$259. 5070 Creekbank Rd L4W 5R2. Hwy 401 W
exit Dixie Rd S, 0.9 mi (1.5 km) e to Eglinton Ave, then 0.6 mi (1 km).
Int corridors. Pets: Accepted. ⓖ⊞ ⇆ 🛜 ✕ 🔲 💻

◆◆◆ Residence Inn by Marriott
Toronto-Mississauga/Meadowvale H
(905) 567-2577. $70-$210. 7005 Century Ave L5N 7K2. Hwy 401 exit
Erin Mills Pkwy/Mississauga Rd, s to Argentia Rd. Int corridors.
Pets: Accepted. ⓖ⊞ ⇆ 🛜 ✕ 🔲 💻

◆◆◆ Sandman Signature Mississauga H
(905) 238-0159. Call for rates. 5400 Dixie Rd L4W 4T4. Hwy 401 exit
346 (S Dixie Rd), 0.6 mi (1 km) s. Int corridors. Pets: Accepted.
🍴 ⇆ 🛜 ✕ 🔲 💻

◆◆ ◆◆◆ Sheraton Gateway Hotel in Toronto
International Airport H
(905) 672-7000. $139-$469. Terminal 3, Toronto AMF L5P 1C4. In
Toronto Pearson International Airport. Int corridors. Pets: Accepted.
ⓢ 🍴 ⓖ⊞ ⇆ ✕ 🛰 ✕ 💻

◆◆ ◆◆◆ TownePlace Suites by Marriott Mississauga -
Airport Corporate Centre H
(905) 238-9600. $70-$154. 5050 Orbitor Dr L4W 4X2. Jct Eglinton Ave
and Renforth Dr, 1.4 mi (2.3 km) w on Eglinton Ave. Int corridors.
Pets: Medium. $75 one-time fee/room. Designated rooms, service with
restrictions, crate. ⓢ ECO 🍴 ⇆ 🛜 ✕ 🔲 💻

◆◆◆ The Waterside Inn H
(905) 891-7770. $159-$249. 15 Stavebank Rd S L5G 2T2. QEW exit
Hwy 10 S (Hurontario St S), just w on Lakeshore Blvd. Int corridors.
Pets: Accepted. 🍴 🛜 ✕ 🔲 💻

MONETVILLE

◆◆ Memquisit Lodge CA
(705) 898-2355. Call for rates. 506 Memquisit Rd P0M 2K0. 13 mi
(20.8 km) ne on west arm of Lake Nipissing, on Hwy 64 and Memquisit
Lodge Rd; 23 mi (36.8 km) sw off Hwy 17, on Hwy 64. Ext corridors.
Pets: Accepted. 🍴 ✕ 🛜 ✕ 🎿 🅦 🔲 🔲 💻

MORRISBURG

◆◆ ◆◆ The McIntosh Country Inn & Conference
Centre H
(613) 543-3788. $109-$209. 12495 Hwy 2 E K0C 1X0. Hwy 401 exit
750, 1.2 mi (2 km) s on Rt 31, then 0.6 mi (1 km) e. Int corridors.
Pets: $25 daily fee/pet. Designated rooms, service with restrictions,
crate. ⓢ 🍴 ⇆ ✕ 🛜 🔲 💻

NEWMARKET

◆◆ ◆◆◆ Comfort Inn H
(905) 895-3355. $105-$180. 1230 Journey's End Cir L3Y 8Z6. Hwy 404
exit 51 (Davis Dr), just w, then just n on Harry Walker Pkwy. Int corridors. Pets: Accepted. ⓢ ECO 🍴 🛜 ✕ 🔲 💻

NIAGARA FALLS

◆◆ ◆◆◆ Best Western Plus Cairn Croft Hotel H
(905) 356-1161. $79-$379. 6400 Lundy's Ln L2G 1T6. 1.5 mi (2.4 km)
w on Hwy 20. Ext/int corridors. Pets: Accepted.
ⓢ 🍴 ⇆ ✕ 🛜 ✕ 🔲 💻

◆◆ ◆ Crystal Inn M
(905) 354-9444. $49-$209. 4249 River Rd L2E 3E7. 1.8 mi (2.9 km) n
of the falls on Niagara River Pkwy. Ext corridors. Pets: Accepted.
ⓢ 🍴 ⇆ 🛜 ✕ 🔲 💻

◆◆ ◆◆ Days Inn Lundys Lane H
(905) 358-3621. $55-$205. 7280 Lundys Ln L2G 1W2. QEW exit Hwy
20, 2.4 mi (3.8 km) w. Ext/int corridors. Pets: Accepted.
🍴 ⇆ 🛜 ✕ 🔲 💻

◆◆ ◆◆◆ Falls Manor Resort & Restaurant M
(905) 358-3211. $49-$149. 7104 Lundy's Ln L2G 1W2. On Hwy 20, 2.1
mi (3.4 km) w. Ext corridors. Pets: Dogs only. $100 deposit/room, $20
daily fee/pet. Designated rooms, service with restrictions, supervision.
ⓢ 🍴 ⇆ 🛜 ✕ 🔲

NIAGARA-ON-THE-LAKE
(Restaurants p. 630)

◆◆ ◆◆ ◆◆◆ Harbour House Hotel H
(905) 468-4683. Call for rates. 85 Melville St L0S 1J0. Jct Ricardo St.
Int corridors. Pets: Accepted. ⓢ 🛜 ✕ 🔲 💻

◆◆◆ ◆◆◆ The Oban Inn, Spa and Restaurant H
(905) 468-2165. $150-$495. 160 Front St L0S 1J0. Jct Gate St. Ext/int
corridors. Pets: Accepted. 🍴 ⇆ ✕ 🛜 ✕ 💻

◆◆ ◆◆◆ ◆◆◆ Pillar and Post Hotel CI
(905) 468-2123. Call for rates. 48 John St L0S 1J0. Just n on Hwy 55
(Mississauga St), just e; 13 mi (20.8 km) from QEW. Ext/int corridors.
Pets: Accepted. ⓢ 🍴 ⇆ ✕ 🛜 ✕ 🔲 💻

◆◆ ◆◆◆ ◆◆◆ Prince of Wales Hotel & Spa H ❧
(905) 468-3246. Call for rates. 6 Picton St L0S 1J0. Jct Picton and
King sts; 9 mi (14.4 km) e of jct QEW and Hwy 55 (Mississauga St),
via Hwy 55. Ext/int corridors. Pets: $35 daily fee/room. Designated
rooms, service with restrictions.
ⓢ 🍴 ⇆ ✕ 🛜 ✕ 🔲 💻

◆◆ ◆◆◆ ◆◆◆ Shaw Club Hotel H ❧
(905) 468-5711. Call for rates. 92 Picton St L0S 1J0. Jct Wellington St.
Int corridors. Pets: Dogs only. $25 daily fee/room. Designated rooms,
service with restrictions. ⓢ 🍴 ⓖ⊞ 🛜 ✕ 🔲 💻

NORTH BAY

◆◆ ◆◆◆ Best Western North Bay Hotel & Conference
Centre H
(705) 474-5800. $131-$159. 700 Lakeshore Dr P1A 2G4. Hwy 11 exit
338, 2.5 mi (4 km) w. Int corridors. Pets: Accepted.
ⓢ ECO 🍴 ⇆ ✕ 🛜 ✕ 🔲 💻

◆◆ ◆◆ Comfort Inn-Airport H
(705) 476-5400. $100-$175. 1200 O'Brien St P1B 9B3. On Hwy 11/17;
jct O'Brien St. Int corridors. Pets: Accepted. 🛜 ✕ 🔲 💻

◆◆ ◆◆◆ Holiday Inn Express Hotel & Suites H
(705) 476-7700. Call for rates. 1325 Seymour St P1B 9V6. Jct Hwy
11/17. Int corridors. Pets: Designated rooms, service with restrictions,
crate. ⓢ ECO ⓖ⊞ ⇆ 🛜 ✕ 🔲 💻

◆◆ ◆◆◆ Ramada Pinewood Park Resort - North
Bay H
(705) 472-0810. $95-$999. 201 Pinewood Park Dr P1B 8Z4. Hwy 11
exit 338, just w on Lakeshore Dr, then 0.4 mi (0.7 km) s. Int corridors.
Pets: Other species. Designated rooms, service with restrictions, supervision. ⓢ 🍴 ⇆ ✕ 🛜 ✕ 🔲 💻

(AA) ▼▼ **Super 8 North Bay** H
(705) 495-4551. **$100-$160.** 570 Lakeshore Dr P1A 2E6. Hwy 11 exit 338, 2.8 mi (4.5 km) w. Int corridors. **Pets:** Medium. $10 deposit/pet. Designated rooms, service with restrictions, supervision.
[SAVE] 🛜 ✕ 🛏 💻

(AA) ▼▼ **Travelodge Airport North Bay** H
(705) 495-1133. **$110-$150.** 1525 Seymour St P1B 8G4. Jct Hwy 11/17. Int corridors. **Pets:** Medium. Service with restrictions, supervision.
[SAVE] [ECO] 🛄 🛜 🛏 💻

▼▼ **Travelodge Lakeshore North Bay** H
(705) 472-7171. **$110-$200.** 718 Lakeshore Dr P1A 2G4. Hwy 11 exit 338, 2.5 mi (4 km) w. Int corridors. **Pets:** Accepted.
[ECO] 🛜 🛏 💻

OAKVILLE

▼▼▼ **Holiday Inn Oakville Centre** H
(905) 842-5000. **Call for rates.** 590 Argus Rd L6J 3J3. QEW exit 118 (Trafalgar Rd), just s. Int corridors. **Pets:** Accepted.
[ECO] 🍴 ♿ 🛄 🛜 ✕ 🛏 💻

▼▼▼ **Staybridge Suites Oakville Burlington** H
(905) 847-2600. **$139-$209.** 2511 Wyecroft Rd L6L 6P8. QEW exit 111 (Bronte Rd/Hwy 25), 0.3 mi (0.5 km) s, then just e. Int corridors.
Pets: Accepted. ♿ 🛄 🛜 🛏 💻

ORILLIA

(AA) ▼▼▼ **Best Western Plus Couchiching Inn** H ❀
(705) 325-6505. **$129-$259.** 440 Couchiching Point Rd L3V 6P8. Jct Hwy 12 S and Couchiching Point Rd. Int corridors. **Pets:** Medium. $100 deposit/room, $20 one-time fee/room. Designated rooms, service with restrictions, crate. [SAVE] [ECO] 🍴 ✕ 🛜 ✕ 🛏 💻

(AA) ▼▼▼ **Best Western Plus Mariposa Inn & Conference Centre** H ❀
(705) 325-9511. **$125-$200.** 400 Memorial Ave L3V 6J3. Jct Hwy 12 and Memorial Ave, just s. Int corridors. **Pets:** $20 daily fee/pet. Designated rooms, service with restrictions, supervision.
[SAVE] [ECO] 🍴 🛄 ✕ 🛜 ✕ 🛏 💻

(AA) ▼▼ **Comfort Inn** H
(705) 327-7744. **$110-$190.** 75 Progress Dr L3V 0T7. Hwy 11 N exit Hwy 12, just s on Memorial Ave; corner of Progress Dr and Memorial Ave. Int corridors. **Pets:** Small. $15 daily fee/room. Designated rooms, service with restrictions, crate. [SAVE] [ECO] 🛜 ✕ 🛏 💻

▼▼ **Highwayman Inn & Conference Centre** H
(705) 326-7343. **Call for rates.** 201 Woodside Dr L3V 6T4. Hwy 11 exit Hwy 12 (Coldwater Rd), just e, then just s. Int corridors.
Pets: Accepted. 🍴 🛄 ✕ 🛜 ✕ 🛏 💻

OSHAWA

▼▼▼ **Travelodge Oshawa** H
(905) 436-9500. **$99-$129.** 940 Champlain Ave L1J 7A6. Hwy 401 exit 412 (Thickson Rd N). Int corridors. **Pets:** Accepted.
[ECO] 🍴 🛄 🛜 🛏 💻

OTTAWA (Restaurants p. 630)

(AA) ▼▼▼ **ARC The.Hotel** H
(613) 238-2888. **Call for rates.** 140 Slater St K1P 5H6. Between Metcalfe and O'Connor sts. Int corridors. **Pets:** Accepted.
[SAVE] [ECO] 🍴 🛜 🛏 💻

(AA) ▼▼▼ **Best Western Plus Ottawa/Kanata Hotel & Conference Centre** H
(613) 828-2741. **$124-$165.** 1876 Robertson Rd K2H 5B8. Hwy 417 exit 130, 1.8 mi (2.9 km) s. Int corridors. **Pets:** Accepted.
[SAVE] 🍴 🛄 ✕ 🛜 ✕ 🛏 💻

(AA) ▼▼ **Comfort Inn Ottawa East** H
(613) 744-2900. **$100-$175.** 1252 Michael St K1J 7T1. Hwy 417 exit 115 (St. Laurent Blvd), just ne. Int corridors. **Pets:** Other species. Designated rooms, service with restrictions, crate.
[SAVE] [ECO] 🛜 ✕ 🛏 💻

(AA) ▼▼ **Days Inn-Downtown Ottawa** H
(613) 789-5555. **$100-$205.** 319 Rideau St K1N 5Y4. Between Nelson St and King Edward Ave. Ext/int corridors. **Pets:** Medium, other species. $20 one-time fee/pet. Designated rooms, service with restrictions, crate.
[SAVE] [ECO] 🍴 🛜 ✕ 🛏 💻

(AA) ▼▼ **Days Inn Ottawa West** H
(613) 726-1717. **$130-$135.** 350 Moodie Dr K2H 8G3. Hwy 417 exit 134, 0.9 mi (1.5 km) s. Int corridors. **Pets:** Large. $10 daily fee/room. Designated rooms, service with restrictions, crate.
[SAVE] 🍴 🛜 ✕ 🛏 💻

(AA) ▼▼▼ **Delta Ottawa City Centre** H
(613) 237-3600. **$90-$402.** 101 Lyon St K1R 5T9. Entrance at corner of Albert St. Int corridors. **Pets:** Accepted.
[SAVE] [ECO] 🍴 🛄 🛜 ✕ 🛏 💻

▼▼▼ **Extended Stay Canada - Ottawa Downtown** H
(613) 236-7500. **$125-$180.** 141 Cooper St K2P 0E8. Between Elgin and Cartier sts. Int corridors. **Pets:** $25 daily fee/pet. Service with restrictions, crate. 🍴 🛜 ✕ 🛏 💻

(AA) ▼▼ ▼▼ **Fairmont Château Laurier** H
(613) 241-1414. **$229-$699.** 1 Rideau St K1N 8S7. Just e of Parliament Buildings. Int corridors. **Pets:** Accepted.
[SAVE] [ECO] 🍴 🛄 ✕ 🐾 ✕ 🛏 💻

▼▼▼ **Holiday Inn Express & Suites Ottawa West - Nepean** H
(613) 690-0100. **Call for rates.** 2055 Robertson Rd K2H 5Y9. Hwy 417 exit 134, 0.9 mi (1.5 km) s on Moodie Dr, then just e. Int corridors.
Pets: Accepted. 🛄 ✕ 🛜 ✕ 🛏 💻

(AA) ▼▼▼ **Les Suites Hotel Ottawa** H 🐾
(613) 232-2000. **$149-$499.** 130 Besserer St K1N 9M9. Between Nicholas and Waller sts. Int corridors. **Pets:** $35 one-time fee/room. Designated rooms, service with restrictions, crate.
[SAVE] [ECO] 🍴 🛄 ✕ 🛜 ✕ 🛏 💻

▼▼▼ **Lord Elgin Hotel** H
(613) 235-3333. **Call for rates.** 100 Elgin St K1P 5K8. Between Laurier Ave and Slater St. Int corridors. **Pets:** Accepted.
[ECO] 🍴 ✕ 🐾 ✕ 🛏 💻

(AA) ▼▼▼ **Marriott Ottawa Hotel** H
(613) 238-1122. **$77-$378.** 100 Kent St K1P 5R7. Corner of Queen St. Int corridors. **Pets:** Accepted.
[SAVE] [ECO] 🍴 ✕ 🐾 🛜 ✕ 🛏 💻

▼▼▼ **The Metcalfe Hotel** H 🐾
(613) 231-6555. **Call for rates.** 123 Metcalfe St K1P 5L9. Corner of Laurier Ave W. Int corridors. **Pets:** Medium, other species. $75 one-time fee/room. Service with restrictions, supervision.
[ECO] 🍴 ✕ 🛜 ✕ 🛏 💻

▼▼▼ **Novotel Ottawa Hotel** H 🐾
(613) 230-3033. **Call for rates.** 33 Nicholas St K1N 9M7. Corner of Daly Ave. Int corridors. **Pets:** Other species. Designated rooms, service with restrictions, crate. [ECO] 🍴 ✕ 🛜 ✕ 🛏 💻

(AA) ▼▼▼ **Radisson Hotel Ottawa Parliament Hill** H
(613) 236-1133. **Call for rates.** 402 Queen St K1R 5A7. Corner of Bay and Queen sts. Int corridors. **Pets:** Medium. $25 one-time fee/pet. Designated rooms, service with restrictions. [SAVE] 🍴 🛜 ✕ 🛏 💻

▼▼ **Ramada Ottawa On The Rideau** H
(613) 288-3500. **$79-$239.** 2259 Prince of Wales Dr K2E 6Z8. 0.5 mi (0.8 km) s of Hunt Club Rd. Ext corridors. **Pets:** Accepted.
[ECO] 🍴 ✕ 🛜 ✕ 🛏 💻

▼▼▼ Residence Inn by Marriott Ottawa Downtown ⊞
(613) 231-2020. $91-$311. 161 Laurier Ave W K1P 5J2. Corner of Elgin St. Int corridors. Pets: Accepted. ▣ 🏊 ✖ 📶 ✖ 📋 💻

ⒶⒶ ▼▼ Rideau Heights Inn Ⓜ
(613) 226-4152. $99-$129. 72 Rideau Heights Dr K2E 7A6. Hwy 16 (Prince of Wales Dr), 0.3 mi (0.5 km) n of Hunt Club Rd. Ext corridors. Pets: Small. $20 daily fee/pet. Designated rooms, service with restrictions, supervision. SAVE 🍽 📶 ✖ 📋 💻

ⒶⒶ ▼▼▼ Sheraton Ottawa Hotel ⊞
(613) 238-1500. Call for rates. 150 Albert St K1P 5G2. Corner of O'Connor St. Int corridors. Pets: Accepted.
SAVE ▣ 🍽 🏊 📶 ✖ 📋 💻

ⒶⒶ ▼▼▼ Travelodge Ottawa East ⊞
(613) 745-1133. $105-$160. 1486 Innes Rd K1B 3V5. Hwy 417 exit 112 (Innes Rd), just e. Int corridors. Pets: Accepted.
SAVE ▣ 🍽 🏊 📶 📋 💻

ⒶⒶ ▼▼▼ WelcomINNS Hotel Ottawa ⊞
(613) 748-7800. $119-$150. 1220 Michael St K1J 7T1. Just ne off Hwy 417; just e of St. Laurent Blvd. Int corridors. Pets: Medium. $25 daily fee/pet. Designated rooms, service with restrictions, supervision.
SAVE ▣ 📶 ✖ 📋 💻

ⒶⒶ ▼▼▼▼ The Westin Ottawa ⊞
(613) 560-7000. $159-$1000. 11 Colonel By Dr K1N 9H4. Corner of Rideau St. Int corridors. Pets: Accepted.
SAVE ▣ 🍽 🏊 ✖ 📶 ✖ 📋 💻

OWEN SOUND (Restaurants p. 630)

ⒶⒶ ▼▼▼▼ Best Western Inn On The Bay & Conference Centre ⊞
(519) 371-9200. $170-$230. 1800 2nd Ave E N4K 5R1. 1 mi (1.5 km) n of 10th St E. Int corridors. Pets: Accepted.
SAVE ▣ 🍽 ♿ ✖ 📶 ✖ 📋 💻

▼▼ Comfort Inn ⊞
(519) 371-5500. $109-$192. 955 9th Ave E N4K 6N4. Jct Hwy 6, 10, 21 and 26. Int corridors. Pets: Accepted. ▣ 📶 ✖ 📋 💻

ⒶⒶ ▼▼▼ Quality Inn Owen Sound ⊞
(519) 376-1551. Call for rates. 950 6th St E N4K 1H1. Just off Hwy 6 and 10. Int corridors. Pets: Accepted.
SAVE ▣ 🍽 🏊 ✖ 📶 ✖ 📋 💻

PARRY SOUND

▼▼ Comfort Inn ⊞
(705) 746-6221. $100-$205. 120 Bowes St P2A 2L7. Hwy 69 exit 224 (Bowes St), just w. Int corridors. Pets: Accepted.
▣ 📶 ✖ 📋 💻

▼▼ Parry Sound Inn & Suites ⊞
(705) 746-2700. Call for rates. 292 Louisa St P2A 0A1. Hwy 69 exit 224 (Bowes St), just w. Int corridors. Pets: Accepted.
📶 ✖ 📋 💻

PEMBROKE

▼ Colonial Fireside Inn Ⓜ
(613) 732-3623. $72-$120. 1350 Pembroke St W K8A 7A3. 2.7 mi (4.3 km) n on Forest Lea Rd (CR 42) from jct Hwy 17, just e. Ext corridors. Pets: Small, dogs only. $10 daily fee/pet. Designated rooms, no service, supervision. 🏊 📶 📋 💻

ⒶⒶ ▼▼▼ Comfort Inn ⊞
(613) 735-1057. $120-$170. 959 Pembroke St E K8A 3M3. 1 mi (1.6 km) e of town center. Int corridors. Pets: Other species. $15 daily fee/room. Designated rooms, service with restrictions, supervision.
SAVE ▣ 📶 📋 💻

PETAWAWA

▼▼ Petawawa River Inn & Suites ⊞
(613) 687-4686. Call for rates. 3520 Petawawa Blvd K8H 1W9. Hwy 17 exit Paquette Rd, 1.5 mi (2.4 km) e, then just s. Int corridors.
Pets: Accepted. 🍽 📶 📋 💻

ⒶⒶ ▼▼▼ Quality Inn & Suites Petawawa ⊞
(613) 687-2855. $139-$212. 3119-B Petawawa Blvd K8H 1X9. Hwy 17 exit Murphy Rd (Hwy 37), 1.8 mi (3 km) ne. Int corridors.
Pets: Accepted. SAVE ♿ 🏊 ✖ 📶 ✖ 📋 💻

PETERBOROUGH

ⒶⒶ ▼▼▼ Comfort Hotel & Suites ⊞
(705) 740-7000. $108-$183. 1209 Lansdowne St W K9J 7M2. 0.4 mi (0.6 km) w of jct Hwy 28. Int corridors. Pets: Other species. Service with restrictions, supervision. SAVE ▣ 🍽 🏊 📶 ✖ 📋 💻

▼▼ Motel 6 - Peterborough ⊞
(705) 748-0550. Call for rates. 133 Landsdowne St E K9J 7P7. 1.6 mi (2.6 km) e of The Parkway. Int corridors. Pets: Accepted.
▣ 📶 ✖ 📋

▼▼ Quality Inn ⊞
(705) 748-6801. $92-$175. 1074 Lansdowne St W K9J 1Z9. 1.9 mi (3 km) from jct Hwy 115. Int corridors. Pets: Accepted.
▣ 📶 ✖ 📋 💻

▼▼▼▼ Super 8 Peterborough ⊞ 🐾
(705) 876-8898. $89-$137. 1257 Lansdowne St W K9J 7M2. 0.3 mi (0.5 km) e from jct Hwy 28. Int corridors. Pets: Medium, other species. $25 one-time fee/room. Designated rooms, service with restrictions.
▣ 🏊 📶 ✖ 📋 💻

PICKERING

ⒶⒶ ▼▼▼ Comfort Inn ⊞
(905) 831-6200. $100-$160. 533 Kingston Rd L1V 3N7. Hwy 401 exit 394N (Whites Rd) to Hwy 2, 0.3 mi (0.5 km) w. Int corridors. Pets: $10 one-time fee/pet. Designated rooms, service with restrictions.
SAVE ▣ 📶 ✖ 📋 💻

PLANTAGENET

▼▼ Place 19-67 Ⓜ
(613) 673-5220. $80-$110. 5999 Hwy 17 K0B 1L0. Jct CR 9. Ext/int corridors. Pets: Accepted. 🍽 📶 ✖ 📋

PORT COLBORNE

▼ Knights Inn Ⓜ
(905) 835-5202. $60-$129. 10134 Hwy 3 W L3K 5V4. 0.6 mi (1 km) w of jct Rt 58 and 3. Ext/int corridors. Pets: Accepted.
🍽 🏊 📶 📋 💻

PORT HOPE

▼▼ Comfort Inn ⊞
(905) 885-7000. $104-$169. 2211 County Rd 28 L1A 3V6. Hwy 401 exit 464 (Hwy 28), just n. Int corridors. Pets: Accepted. 📶 ✖ 📋 💻

PROVIDENCE BAY

▼ Aux Huron Sands Motel Ⓜ
(705) 377-4616. $80-$160, 3 day notice. 5216 Hwy 551 P0P 1T0. In Providence Bay; center. Ext corridors. Pets: Other species. $10 one-time fee/pet. Service with restrictions, supervision. 📶 🏊 📋 💻

RENFREW

▼▼ Days Inn & Conference Centre Renfrew ⊞
(613) 432-8109. $110-$149. 760 Gibbons Rd K7V 0B7. Hwy 17 exit O'Brien Rd, just s to Wrangler Rd, then just w. Int corridors.
Pets: Accepted. 🍽 🏊 📶 ✖ 📋 💻

▼ The Rocky Mountain Lodge **M**
(613) 432-5801. **Call for rates.** 409 Stewart St N K7V 1Y4. Hwy 17 exit Bruce St, 1.9 mi (3.1 km) s, then just w. Ext corridors.
Pets: Accepted. 🍴 📶 🛗 💻

RICHMOND HILL

Ⓐ ▼▼▼ Holiday Inn Express & Suites
Toronto-Markham **H**
(905) 695-5990. **Call for rates.** 10 E Pearce St L4B 0A8. Just n of jct Leslie St and Hwy 7. Int corridors. **Pets:** Accepted.
🆂🅰🆅🅴 🅴🅲🅾 🍴 🕹M 🛟 📶 ✕ 🛗 💻

Ⓐ ▼▼▼ Sheraton Parkway Toronto North Hotel and
Suites **H**
(905) 881-2121. **Call for rates.** 9005 Leslie St L4B 1B2. Hwy 404 exit 27, 0.6 mi (1 km) w. Int corridors. **Pets:** Accepted.
🆂🅰🆅🅴 🅴🅲🅾 🍴 🛟 ✕ 🅂📶 ✕ 🛗 💻

ST. CATHARINES

Ⓐ ▼▼▼ Best Western St. Catharines Hotel &
Conference Centre **H** 🐾
(905) 934-8000. **$130-$270.** 2 N Service Rd L2N 4G9. QEW exit 46 (Lake St), just e. Int corridors. **Pets:** Dogs only. $20 daily fee/room. Designated rooms, service with restrictions, crate.
🆂🅰🆅🅴 🍴 🕹M 🛟 ✕ 📶 ✕ 🛗 💻

▼▼ Comfort Inn **H**
(905) 687-8890. **$95-$180.** 2 Dunlop Dr L2R 1A2. QEW exit 46 (Lake St); between Lake and Geneva sts. Int corridors. **Pets:** Accepted.
🅴🅲🅾 🍴 📶 ✕ 🛗 💻

Ⓐ ▼▼ Days Inn St. Catharines Niagara **H**
(905) 934-5400. **$119-$199.** 89 Meadowvale Dr L2N 3Z8. QEW exit 46 (Lake St). Int corridors. **Pets:** $15 daily fee/pet. Designated rooms, service with restrictions, supervision. 🆂🅰🆅🅴 🍴 🛟 📶 ✕ 🛗 💻

Ⓐ ▼▼▼ Holiday Inn & Suites Parkway Conference
Center **H** 🐾
(905) 688-2324. **Call for rates.** 327 Ontario St L2R 5L3. QEW exit 47 (Ontario St), 0.5 mi (0.8 km) s. Int corridors. **Pets:** Large. $35 daily fee/pet. Designated rooms, service with restrictions.
🆂🅰🆅🅴 🍴 🕹M 🛟 ✕ 📶 ✕ 🛗 💻

ST. THOMAS

Ⓐ ▼▼ Cardinal Court Motel **M**
(519) 633-0740. **$89-$109.** 10401 Sunset Rd, RR 7 N5P 3T2. Hwy 4, 4.1 mi (6.5 km) s of jct Hwy 4 and 401 exit 177A. Ext corridors. **Pets:** Small, dogs only. $10 daily fee/pet. Service with restrictions, crate. 🆂🅰🆅🅴 🍴 📶 ✕ 🛗 💻

▼▼ Comfort Inn **H** 🐾
(519) 633-4082. **$87-$176.** 100 Centennial Ave N5R 5B2. On Hwy 3, 4.1 mi (6.5 km) e. Int corridors. **Pets:** Small, dogs only. $25 one-time fee/room. Designated rooms, service with restrictions, supervision.
🍴 📶 ✕ 🛗 💻

SARNIA

Ⓐ ▼▼▼ Best Western Plus Guildwood Inn **H** 🐾
(519) 337-7577. **$124-$134.** 1400 Venetian Blvd N7T 7W6. 0.6 mi (1 km) e of Bluewater Bridge. Ext/int corridors. **Pets:** Small. $10 deposit/pet. Designated rooms, service with restrictions, supervision.
🆂🅰🆅🅴 🍴 🛟 ✕ 🛗 💻

▼▼ Comfort Inn **H**
(519) 383-6767. **$100-$145.** 815 Mara St N N7V 0A2. Jct Church St. Int corridors. **Pets:** Accepted. 📶 ✕ 🛗 💻

▼▼ Super 8-Sarnia **H**
(519) 337-3767. **$80-$130.** 420 Christina St N N7T 5W1. Between Exmouth St and London Rd. Ext/int corridors. **Pets:** Accepted.
🍴 📶 ✕ 🛗 💻

SAULT STE. MARIE

▼ Adams Motel **M**
(705) 254-4345. **Call for rates.** 647 Great Northern Rd (Hwy 17) P6B 5A1. Hwy 17, 2.8 mi (4.4 km) n. Ext corridors. **Pets:** Accepted.
📶 🛗 💻

Ⓐ ▼▼▼ Algoma's Water Tower Inn &
Suites **H** 🐾
(705) 949-8111. **$119-$179.** 360 Great Northern Rd P6B 4Z7. Jct Hwy 17 and Second Line. Int corridors. **Pets:** Medium. $25 one-time fee/room. Designated rooms, service with restrictions, crate.
🆂🅰🆅🅴 🅴🅲🅾 🍴 🛟 ✕ 📶 ✕ 🛗 💻

▼▼ Ambassador Motel **M**
(705) 759-6199. **$74-$99.** 1275 Great Northern Rd P6B 0B9. 4 mi (6.4 km) n on Hwy 17. Ext corridors. **Pets:** Other species. $10 daily fee/pet. Designated rooms, service with restrictions, supervision.
🛟 ✕ 📶 🛗 💻

Ⓐ ▼▼ Catalina Motel **M**
(705) 945-9260. **Call for rates.** 259 Great Northern Rd P6B 4Z2. 2 mi (3.2 km) n on Hwy 17. Ext corridors. **Pets:** Large. $10 daily fee/room. Designated rooms, no service, crate. 🆂🅰🆅🅴 📶 ✕ 🛗 💻

Ⓐ ▼▼ Comfort Inn **H**
(705) 759-8000. **$98-$179.** 333 Great Northern Rd P6B 4Z8. 2.3 mi (3.6 km) n on Hwy 17. Int corridors. **Pets:** Medium. $15 daily fee/pet. Designated rooms, service with restrictions, supervision.
🆂🅰🆅🅴 🅴🅲🅾 📶 ✕ 🛗 💻

▼▼ Delta Sault Ste. Marie Waterfront Hotel and
Conference Centre **H**
(705) 949-0611. **$64-$178.** 208 St. Marys River Dr P6A 5V4. Just sw of Bay St. Int corridors. **Pets:** Accepted.
🅴🅲🅾 🍴 🕹M 🛟 ✕ 📶 ✕ 🛗 💻

▼▼ Glenview Cottages **CA**
(705) 759-3436. **Call for rates.** 2611 Great Northern Rd P6A 5K7. 6 mi (9.6 km) n on Hwy 17. Ext corridors. **Pets:** Accepted.
🅴🅲🅾 🍴 🛟 ✕ 📶 🛗 💻

▼ Holiday Motel **M**
(705) 759-8608. **$65-$100.** 435 Trunk Rd P6A 3T1. On Hwy 17, just e of jct Hwy 17B. Ext corridors. **Pets:** Other species. $5 one-time fee/pet. Service with restrictions, supervision. 📶 🛗 💻

▼ Northlander Motel **M**
(705) 254-6452. **Call for rates.** 243 Great Northern Rd P6B 4Z2. 1.9 mi (2 km) n on Hwy 17. Ext corridors. **Pets:** Other species. $10 one-time fee/room. Service with restrictions, supervision. 📶 🛗 💻

▼▼ Sleep Inn **H**
(705) 253-7533. **$79-$154.** 727 Bay St P6A 6Y3. Between East and Church sts; downtown. Int corridors. **Pets:** Accepted.
📶 ✕ 🛗 💻

▼▼ Super 8 **H**
(705) 254-6441. **$95-$119.** 184 Great Northern Rd P6B 4Z3. 1.3 mi (2 km) n on Hwy 17. Int corridors. **Pets:** Accepted. 📶 🛗 💻

SIMCOE

Ⓐ ▼▼▼ Best Western Little River Inn **H**
(519) 426-2125. **$110-$122.** 203 Queensway W (Hwy 3) N3Y 2M9. Jct Hwy 24, just w on Hwy 3. Int corridors. **Pets:** Medium. $20 one-time fee/pet. Designated rooms, service with restrictions, supervision.
🆂🅰🆅🅴 🍴 🛟 📶 ✕ 🛗 💻

▼▼ Comfort Inn **H**
(519) 426-2611. **$110-$157.** 85 Queensway E N3Y 4M5. 0.3 mi (0.5 km) e on Hwy 3. Int corridors. **Pets:** Accepted.
🅴🅲🅾 📶 ✕ 🛗 💻

SMITHS FALLS

ⒸⒶ ▼▼▼ **Best Western Colonel By Inn** 🏨
(613) 284-0001. **$190-$199.** 88 Lombard St K7A 4G5. On Hwy 15, just w of jct Hwy 29. Int corridors. **Pets:** Accepted.
SAVE 〓 ∂ ✕ 🔌 🖥

SOUTH BAYMOUTH

ⒸⒶ ▼ **Huron Motor Lodge** Ⓜ
(705) 859-3131. **Call for rates.** 24 Water St N P0P 1Z0. In South Baymouth; center. Ext/int corridors. **Pets:** Medium, other species. $10 daily fee/pet. Designated rooms, service with restrictions, supervision.
SAVE 〓 ∂ ✕ 🎮 ⊠ 🔌

STRATFORD *(Restaurants p. 630)*

ⒸⒶ ▼▼▼ **Best Western Plus The Arden Park Hotel** 🏨
(519) 275-2936. **$159-$329.** 552 Ontario St (Hwy 7 & 8) N5A 3J3. Jct Romeo St. Int corridors. **Pets:** Large. $20 daily fee/room. Designated rooms, service with restrictions.
SAVE ¶¶ ⤒M 〓 ∂ ✕ 🔌 🖥

STURGEON FALLS

▼▼▼ **Comfort Inn** 🏨
(705) 753-5665. **$109-$169.** 11 Front St P2B 3L3. On Hwy 17 at western approach to town. Int corridors. **Pets:** Accepted.
¶¶ ⤒M 〓 ∂ ✕ 🔌 🖥

SUDBURY

ⒸⒶ ▼▼▼ **Best Western Downtown Sudbury Centreville** 🏨 🐾
(705) 673-7801. **$116-$166.** 151 Larch St P3E 1C3. Just w of Paris St; center. Int corridors. **Pets:** Medium, other species. $20 daily fee/pet. Designated rooms, service with restrictions, supervision.
SAVE ¶¶ ∂ ✕ 🔌 🖥

▼▼ **Clarion Hotel** 🏨
(705) 674-7517. **$110-$180.** 117 Elm St P3C 1T3. Corner of Lorne St; downtown. Int corridors. **Pets:** Small. $20 one-time fee/pet. Designated rooms, service with restrictions. ¶¶ 〓 ∂ ✕ 🔌 🖥

ⒸⒶ ▼▼ **Comfort Inn** 🏨
(705) 522-1101. **$99-$180.** 2171 Regent St P3E 5V3. Trans-Canada Hwy 17 exit Hwy 69/RR 46, 1.8 mi (2.8 km) n. Int corridors.
Pets: Accepted. SAVE ECO ∂ ✕ 🔌 🖥

ⒸⒶ ▼▼ **Comfort Inn East** 🏨
(705) 560-4502. **$110-$195.** 440 2nd Ave N P3B 4A4. Just s of Kingsway Rd. Int corridors. **Pets:** Accepted. SAVE ECO ∂ ✕ 🔌 🖥

▼▼▼ **Holiday Inn Hotel Sudbury** 🏨
(705) 522-3000. **Call for rates.** 1696 Regent St P3E 3Z8. Trans-Canada Hwy 17 exit Hwy 69/RR 46, 2.4 mi (3.9 km) n. Int corridors.
Pets: Accepted. ¶¶ 〓 ∂ ✕ 🔌 🖥

▼▼▼ **Homewood Suites by Hilton Sudbury** 🏨 🐾
(705) 523-8100. **$129-$299.** 2270 Regent St P3E 0B4. Trans-Canada Hwy 17 exit Hwy 69/RR 46, 1.6 mi (2.5 km) n. Int corridors. **Pets:** $50 one-time fee/room. Service with restrictions, crate.
⤒M 〓 ∂ ✕ 🔌 🖥

▼▼▼ **Radisson Hotel Sudbury Downtown** 🏨
(705) 675-1123. **Call for rates.** 85 Ste. Anne Rd P3E 4S4. Jct Notre Dame Ave; downtown. Int corridors. **Pets:** Accepted.
¶¶ 〓 ∂ ✕ 🔌 🖥

ⒸⒶ ▼▼▼ **TownePlace Suites by Marriott Sudbury** 🏨 🐾
(705) 525-7700. **$80-$178.** 1710 Kingsway Rd P3B 0E4. Just e of jct Falconbridge Rd. Int corridors. **Pets:** Other species. $20 daily fee/pet. No service, supervision. SAVE ⤒M 〓 ∂ ✕ 🔌 🖥

ⒸⒶ ▼▼▼ **Travelodge Hotel Sudbury** 🏨 🐾
(705) 522-1100. **$119-$169.** 1401 Paris St P3E 3B6. Trans-Canada Hwy 17 exit Hwy 69/RR 46, 2 mi (3.2 km) n on Regent St, then 0.9 mi (1.5 km) e. Int corridors. **Pets:** Other species. $25 one-time fee/room. Designated rooms, service with restrictions, supervision.
SAVE ECO ¶¶ 〓 ∂ ✕ 🔌 🖥

THOROLD

ⒸⒶ ▼▼▼ **Four Points by Sheraton St. Catharines Niagara Suites** 🏨
(905) 984-8484. **Call for rates.** 3530 Schmon Pkwy L2V 4Y6. Hwy 406 exit St. David's Rd W; just s of Brock University. Int corridors.
Pets: Accepted. SAVE ¶¶ 〓 ✕ ∂ ✕ 🔌 🖥

THUNDER BAY

ⒸⒶ ▼▼▼ **Best Western Plus Nor'Wester Hotel & Conference Centre** 🏨
(807) 473-9123. **$140-$160.** 2080 Hwy 61 P7J 1B8. On Hwy 61 at Loch Lomond Rd. Int corridors. **Pets:** Small, dogs only. $20 daily fee/room. Designated rooms, service with restrictions, crate.
SAVE ¶¶ ⤒M 〓 ✕ ∂ ✕ 🔌 🖥

ⒸⒶ ▼▼▼ **Best Western Thunder Bay Crossroads** 🏨
(807) 577-4241. **$130-$150.** 655 W Arthur St P7E 5R6. Just e of Hwy 61. Ext/int corridors. **Pets:** Medium. $15 daily fee/room. Designated rooms, service with restrictions, supervision. SAVE ∂ ✕ 🔌 🖥

ⒸⒶ ▼▼ **Comfort Inn** 🏨
(807) 475-3155. **$105-$170.** 660 W Arthur St P7E 5R8. Just e of Hwy 61. Int corridors. **Pets:** Other species. $20 daily fee/pet. Service with restrictions, supervision. SAVE ECO ∂ ✕ 🔌 🖥

▼▼▼ **Holiday Inn Express** 🏨
(807) 346-0220. **Call for rates.** 1041 Carrick St P7B 6L9. 1.7 mi (2.9 km) e on Harbour Expwy from jct Hwy 17/61, just s. Int corridors.
Pets: $15 daily fee/pet. Designated rooms, service with restrictions, supervision. ⤒M 〓 ✕ ∂ 🔌 🖥

▼▼▼ **TownePlace Suites by Marriott - Thunder Bay** 🏨
(807) 346-9000. **$86-$152.** 550 Harbour Expwy P7B 6P4. 1.8 mi (3 km) e from jct Hwy 17/61. Int corridors. **Pets:** Other species. $50 one-time fee/room. Designated rooms, service with restrictions, crate.
⤒M 〓 ✕ ∂ 🔌 🖥

▼▼ **Victoria Inn Hotel & Convention Centre** 🏨
(807) 577-8481. **$121-$158.** 555 W Arthur St P7E 5R5. 0.5 mi (0.8 km) e of Hwy 61. Int corridors. **Pets:** Accepted.
¶¶ 〓 ∂ ✕ 🔌 🖥

TILLSONBURG

▼▼ **Howard Johnson/Tillsonburg** 🏨
(519) 842-7366. **$99-$153.** 92 Simcoe St N4G 2J1. Hwy 19, just e. Int corridors. **Pets:** $10 daily fee/pet. Service with restrictions, supervision.
ECO ¶¶ 〓 ✕ 🔌 🖥

TIMMINS

ⒸⒶ ▼▼▼ **Comfort Inn** 🏨
(705) 264-9474. **$105-$170.** 939 Algonquin Blvd E P4N 7J5. Hwy 101, 0.3 mi (0.5 km) e of Hwy 655. Int corridors. **Pets:** Accepted.
SAVE ECO ⤒M 〓 ✕ 🔌 🖥

▼▼ **Days Inn and Conference Center - Timmins** 🏨
(705) 267-6211. **$87-$160.** 14 Mountjoy St S P4N 1S4. Jct Hwy 101. Int corridors. **Pets:** Accepted. ¶¶ 〓 🔌 🖥

▼▼▼ **Holiday Inn Express & Suites Timmins** 🏨 🐾
(705) 531-4000. **$124-$279.** 30 Algonquin Blvd W P4N 2R3. Hwy 101; jct Mountjoy St. Int corridors. **Pets:** Service with restrictions, crate.
⤒M 〓 ✕ ∂ 🔌 🖥

◉ ▼▼▼ **Microtel Inn & Suites by Wyndham Timmins** 🅷

(705) 264-1477. **$99-$139.** 1960 Riverside Dr P4R 0A2. Hwy 101, just e of Government Rd N. Int corridors. **Pets:** $10 one-time fee/room. Service with restrictions, supervision.

SAVE 🅼 ⛴ ✕ 🛜 ✕ 🔋 🖥

TOBERMORY

◈ **Coach House Inn** Ⓜ

(519) 596-2361. **$57-$139.** 7189 Hwy 6 N0H 2R0. 1.2 mi (2 km) s of ferry docks. Ext corridors. **Pets:** Accepted.

🍽 ⛴ 🛜 ✕ 🅣 🔋

TORONTO *(Restaurants p. 630)*

◉ ▼▼▼ **Best Western Premier Toronto Airport Carlingview Hotel** 🅷 ❀

(416) 637-7000. **$108-$190.** 135 Carlingview Dr M9W 5E7. Just n of Dixon Rd. Int corridors. **Pets:** Medium. $250 deposit/room, $35 daily fee/pet. Designated rooms, service with restrictions, crate.

SAVE 🍽 🅼 ⛴ ✕ 🛜 ✕ 🔋 🖥

◉ ▼▼▼ **Best Western Roehampton Hotel & Suites** 🅷

(416) 487-5101. **$150-$290.** 808 Mt. Pleasant Rd M4P 2L2. Just n of Eglinton Ave. Int corridors. **Pets:** Small. $50 one-time fee/pet. Service with restrictions, supervision. SAVE ECO ⛴ 🛜 🔋 🖥

▼▼ **Bond Place Hotel** 🅷

(416) 362-6061. **Call for rates.** 65 Dundas St E M5B 2G8. Corner of Yonge and Dundas sts, just e. Int corridors. **Pets:** Accepted.

ECO 🍽 🅼 🛜 ✕ 🔋 🖥

◉ ▼▼▼ **Chelsea Hotel, Toronto** 🅷

(416) 595-1975. **$130-$350.** 33 Gerrard St W M5G 1Z4. Just w of Yonge St; just s of College St. Int corridors. **Pets:** Medium. $35 one-time fee/room. Service with restrictions, supervision.

SAVE ECO 🍽 🅼 ⛴ ✕ 🛜 ✕ 🔋 🖥

▼▼▼ **Comfort Inn** 🅷

(416) 967-6781. **$139-$349.** 321 Jarvis St M5B 2C2. Just s of Gerrard St. Int corridors. **Pets:** Accepted. 🛜 ✕ 🔋 🖥

▼▼▼ **Crowne Plaza Toronto Airport** 🅷

(416) 675-1234. **$94-$294.** 33 Carlson Ct M9W 6H5. Just w of jct Hwy 27, just n of Dixon Rd. Int corridors. **Pets:** Small. $35 one-time fee/ room. Designated rooms, service with restrictions, supervision.

ECO 🍽 🅼 ⛴ ✕ 🛜 ✕ 🖥

◉ ▼▼▼ **Delta Hotels by Marriott Toronto Airport & Conference Centre** 🅷

(416) 244-1711. **Call for rates.** 655 Dixon Rd M9W 1J3. Jct Hwy 27 N, just w of jct Hwy 401. Int corridors. **Pets:** Medium. $30 one-time fee/ pet. Service with restrictions, supervision.

SAVE ECO 🍽 🅼 ⛴ ✕ 🛜 ✕ 🖥

◉ ▼▼▼ **Delta Hotels by Marriott Toronto East** 🅷

(416) 299-1500. **$75-$184.** 2035 Kennedy Rd M1T 3G2. Hwy 401 exit 379 (Kennedy Rd), just ne. Int corridors. **Pets:** Accepted.

SAVE ECO 🍽 ⛴ ✕ 🛜 ✕ 🔋 🖥

▼▼▼ **Delta Toronto** 🅷

(416) 849-1200. **$203-$999.** 75 Lower Simcoe St M5J 3A6. Jct Bremner Blvd; between the CN Tower and Air Canada Center. Int corridors. **Pets:** Medium. $35 one-time fee/pet. Designated rooms, service with restrictions, supervision. 🍽 🅼 ✕ 🛜 ✕ 🔋 🖥

▼▼▼ **Executive Hotel Cosmopolitan Toronto** 🅷

(416) 350-2000. **Call for rates.** 8 Colborne St M5E 1E1. Between King and Wellington sts. Int corridors. **Pets:** Accepted.

🍽 ✕ 🛜 ✕ 🔋 🖥

◉ ▼▼▼ **Fairmont Royal York** 🅷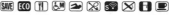

(416) 368-2511. **$239-$619.** 100 Front St W M5J 1E3. QEW/Gardiner Expwy, exit n on York or Bay sts; entrance on Wellington St. Int corridors. **Pets:** Accepted.

SAVE ECO 🍽 🅼 ⛴ ✕ 🛜 ✕ 🔋 🖥

◉ ▼▼▼ **Four Seasons Hotel Toronto** 🅷

(416) 964-0411. **$445-$770.** 60 Yorkville Ave M4W 0A4. Jct Bay St. Int corridors. **Pets:** Accepted.

SAVE 🍽 🅼 ⛴ ✕ 🛜 ✕ 🔋 🖥

▼▼▼ **The Grand Hotel & Suites Toronto** 🅷

(416) 863-9000. **Call for rates.** 225 Jarvis St M5B 2C1. Jct Dundas St. Int corridors. **Pets:** Accepted. 🍽 🅼 ⛴ ✕ 🛜 ✕ 🔋 🖥

◉ ▼▼▼ **The Hazelton Hotel** 🅷

(416) 963-6300. **Call for rates.** 118 Yorkville Ave M5R 1C2. Jct Avenue Rd. Int corridors. **Pets:** Accepted.

SAVE 🍽 🅼 ✕ 🛜 ✕ 🔋 🖥

◉ ▼▼▼ **Holiday Inn Express Toronto-North York** 🅷

(416) 665-3500. **$109-$169.** 30 Norfinch Dr M3N 1X1. Hwy 400 exit Finch Ave E. Int corridors. **Pets:** Large. $25 daily fee/pet. Designated rooms, service with restrictions, crate. SAVE 🛜 ✕ 🔋 🖥

▼▼▼ **Holiday Inn Toronto Yorkdale** 🅷

(416) 789-5161. **$159-$239.** 3450 Dufferin St M6A 2V1. Just s of jct Hwy 401 and Dufferin St; Hwy 401 W exit 365 (Allen Rd S/Yorkdale Rd). Int corridors. **Pets:** Accepted.

ECO 🍽 🅼 ⛴ ✕ 🛜 ✕ 🔋 🖥

◉ ▼▼ **Hotel Carlingview Toronto Airport** 🅷

(416) 675-3303. **Call for rates.** 221 Carlingview Dr M9W 5E8. QEW exit Hwy 427 N to Dixon Rd E, 0.6 mi (1 km) to Carlingview Dr, then just s. Ext/int corridors. **Pets:** Accepted. SAVE ECO 🛜 🔋 🖥

▼▼▼ **Hotel Le Germain Maple Leaf Square** 🅷

(416) 649-7575. **$309-$629.** 75 Bremner Blvd M5J 0A1. Jct York St, just w of Air Canada Centre. Int corridors. **Pets:** Accepted.

🍽 🅼 🛜 ✕ 🔋 🖥

▼▼▼ **Hotel Le Germain Toronto** 🅷

(416) 345-9500. **Call for rates.** 30 Mercer St M5V 1H3. Between John St and Blue Jays Way. Int corridors. **Pets:** Accepted.

🍽 🅼 🛜 ✕ 🔋 🖥

◉ ▼▼▼ **Hyatt Regency Toronto** 🅷 ❀

(416) 343-1234. **$99-$499.** 370 King St W M5V 1J9. Just e of Peter St. Int corridors. **Pets:** Medium, dogs only. $100 one-time fee/room. Designated rooms, service with restrictions, supervision.

SAVE 🍽 🅼 ⛴ ✕ 🛜 ✕ 🔋 🖥

◉ ▼▼▼ **InterContinental Toronto Centre** 🅷 ❀

(416) 597-1400. **Call for rates.** 225 Front St W M5V 2X3. Between Spadina and University aves. Int corridors. **Pets:** Medium, dogs only. $50 one-time fee/pet. Designated rooms, service with restrictions, supervision. SAVE ECO 🍽 🅼 ⛴ ✕ 🛜 ✕ 🔋 🖥

▼▼▼ **InterContinental Toronto Yorkville** 🅷

(416) 960-5200. **Call for rates.** 220 Bloor St W M5S 1T8. Just w of Avenue Rd. Int corridors. **Pets:** Accepted.

ECO 🍽 🅼 ⛴ ✕ 🛜 ✕ 🔋 🖥

◉ ▼▼▼ **Novotel Toronto Centre** 🅷

(416) 367-8900. **Call for rates.** 45 The Esplanade M5E 1W2. Just ne of Gardiner Expwy via Yonge St. Int corridors. **Pets:** Accepted.

SAVE ECO 🍽 🅼 ⛴ ✕ 🔋 🖥

▼▼▼ **Novotel Toronto North York** 🅷

(416) 733-2929. **$109-$399.** 3 Park Home Ave M2N 6L3. Hwy 401 exit Yonge St, 1.1 mi (1.7 km) n, then just w. Int corridors. **Pets:** Accepted.

ECO 🍽 🅼 ⛴ 🛜 ✕ 🔋 🖥

▼▼▼ ▼▼▼ The Omni King Edward Hotel H
(416) 863-9700. Call for rates. 37 King St E M5C 1E9. Just e of Yonge St. Int corridors. Pets: Accepted.

▼▼▼ Pantages Hotel Toronto Centre H
(416) 362-1777. $179-$399. 200 Victoria St M5B 1V8. Jct Shuter St. Int corridors. Pets: Accepted.

(CAA) ▼▼▼ ▼▼▼ Park Hyatt Toronto H ❧
(416) 925-1234. $199-$449, 3 day notice. 4 Avenue Rd M5R 2E8. Corner of Bloor St W. Int corridors. Pets: Medium, dogs only. $100 one-time fee/pet, $100 daily fee/pet. Service with restrictions, supervision.

(CAA) ▼▼▼ Quality Hotel & Suites Toronto Airport East H
(416) 240-9090. $89-$189. 2180 Islington Ave M9P 3P1. Hwy 401 exit 356, just s. Int corridors. Pets: Small. $15 daily fee/pet. Designated rooms, service with restrictions, supervision.

▼▼▼ Quality Suites Toronto Airport H
(416) 674-8442. $100-$180. 262 Carlingview Dr M9W 5G1. 0.6 mi (1 km) w of jct Hwy 27 N and Dixon Rd. Int corridors. Pets: Accepted.

(CAA) ▼▼▼ Radisson Hotel Toronto East H
(416) 493-7000. $119-$259. 55 Hallcrown Pl M2J 4R1. Hwy 401 exit Victoria Park N to Consumers Rd, then w. Int corridors. Pets: Accepted.

(CAA) ▼▼▼ Renaissance Toronto Downtown Hotel H
(416) 341-7100. $92-$408. 1 Blue Jays Way M5V 1J4. Jct Front St. Int corridors. Pets: Medium, dogs only. $50 one-time fee/room. Service with restrictions.

(CAA) ▼▼▼ Residence Inn by Marriott Toronto Airport H
(416) 798-2900. $76-$208. 17 Reading Ct M9W 7K7. Just w of jct Hwy 27 and Dixon Rd. Int corridors. Pets: Accepted.

▼▼▼ Residence Inn by Marriott Toronto Downtown/ Entertainment District H
(416) 581-1800. $98-$469. 255 Wellington St W M5V 3P9. Jct Blue Jays Way. Int corridors. Pets: Large, other species. $100 one-time fee/ room. Service with restrictions, crate.

(CAA) ▼▼▼ ▼▼▼ The Ritz-Carlton, Toronto H ❧
(416) 585-2500. $499-$1300. 181 Wellington St W M5V 3G7. Between Simcoe and John sts. Int corridors. Pets: Small, dogs only. $150 one-time fee/room. Service with restrictions, supervision.

(CAA) ▼▼▼ ▼▼▼ Shangri-La Hotel Toronto H
(647) 788-8888. $410-$700. 188 University Ave M5H 0A3. Between Adelaide and Richmond sts. Int corridors. Pets: Accepted.

(CAA) ▼▼▼ Sheraton Centre Toronto Hotel H ❧
(416) 361-1000. $159-$800. 123 Queen St W M5H 2M9. Opposite Toronto Civic Centre and City Hall. Int corridors. Pets: Other species. Service with restrictions, supervision.

(CAA) ▼▼▼ ▼▼▼ Sheraton Toronto Airport Hotel & Conference Centre H
(416) 675-6100. $109-$409. 801 Dixon Rd M9W 1J5. Jct Hwy 27 N and Dixon Rd. Int corridors. Pets: Accepted.

(CAA) ▼▼▼ ▼▼▼ SoHo Metropolitan Hotel H
(416) 599-8800. $250-$895. 318 Wellington St W M5V 3T4. Jct Blue Jays Way. Int corridors. Pets: Accepted.

(CAA) ▼▼▼ Super 8 Downtown Toronto H
(647) 426-8118. $88-$200. 222 Spadina Ave M5T 3B3. At Dundas St; at Chinatown Centre. Int corridors. Pets: Accepted.

▼▼▼ ▼▼▼ Thompson Hotel Toronto H
(416) 640-7778. Call for rates. 550 Wellington St W M5V 2V4. Jct Bathurst St. Int corridors. Pets: Accepted.

(CAA) ▼▼▼ ▼▼▼ Toronto Don Valley Hotel & Suites H ❧
(416) 449-4111. $109-$189. 175 Wynford Dr M3C 1J3. Don Valley Pkwy exit 375 (Wynford Dr); jct Don Valley Pkwy and Eglinton Ave E. Int corridors. Pets: Small. $20 one-time fee/pet. Designated rooms, service with restrictions, supervision.

(CAA) ▼▼▼ ▼▼▼ Toronto Marriott Bloor Yorkville H ❧
(416) 961-8000. $69-$358. 90 Bloor St E M4W 1A7. Just e of Yonge St. Int corridors. Pets: Medium. $50 one-time fee/room. Designated rooms, service with restrictions, supervision.

(CAA) ▼▼▼ Trump International Hotel & Tower Toronto® H
(416) 306-5800. $350-$1245. 325 Bay St M5H 4G3. Jct Adelaide St. Int corridors. Pets: Accepted.

(CAA) ▼▼▼ ▼▼▼ The Westin Bristol Place Toronto Airport H
(416) 675-9444. $100-$399. 950 Dixon Rd M9W 5N4. 1.6 mi (2.6 km) w of jct Hwy 401. Int corridors. Pets: Accepted.

(CAA) ▼▼▼ ▼▼▼ The Westin Harbour Castle H
(416) 869-1600. $159-$800. One Harbour Sq M5J 1A6. At the foot of Bay St. Int corridors. Pets: Accepted.

(CAA) ▼▼▼ ▼▼▼ The Westin Prince Toronto H
(416) 444-2511. Call for rates. 900 York Mills Rd M3B 3H2. Just s of Hwy 401 via Leslie St exit to York Mills Rd E. Int corridors.
Pets: Accepted.

▼▼▼ ▼▼▼ Windsor Arms Hotel H
(416) 971-9666. Call for rates. 18 St. Thomas St M5S 3E7. Just s of Bloor St. Int corridors. Pets: Accepted.

TRENTON
▼▼▼ Comfort Inn H
(613) 965-6660. $115-$200. 68 Monogram Pl K8V 5P8. Hwy 401 exit 526 (Glen Miller Rd), just s, then just e. Int corridors. Pets: Medium. $15 daily fee/pet. Designated rooms, service with restrictions, supervision.

(CAA) ▼▼▼ Ramada Trenton Hotel H
(613) 394-4855. $99-$140. 99 Glen Miller Rd K8V 5P8. Hwy 401 exit 526 (Glen Miller Rd), just s. Int corridors. Pets: Medium. $20 daily fee/ room. Designated rooms, service with restrictions, supervision.

(CAA) ▼▼▼ Travelodge Trenton H
(613) 965-6789. $89-$180. 598 Old Hwy 2 K8V 5P5. Hwy 401 exit 538, 1.3 mi (2 km) s to Old Hwy 2, then 3.8 mi (6 km) w; 3.1 mi (4.9 km) e of jct Hwy 33. Int corridors. Pets: Medium. $15 daily fee/pet. Designated rooms, service with restrictions, crate.

TWEED

▼ **Park Place Motel** Ⓜ
(613) 478-3134. **$105-$150, 3 day notice.** 43 Victoria St S K0K 3J0.
Hwy 37, 0.3 mi (0.5 km) s of center. Ext corridors. **Pets:** Small, dogs
only. $15 daily fee/pet. Designated rooms, service with restrictions,
supervision. 🛰 ✕ 🛏 🖥

VAUGHAN

Ⓐ ▼▼▼ **Aloft Vaughan Mills** Ⓗ ❀
(905) 695-0500. **$149-$229.** 151 Bass Pro Mills Dr L4K 0E6. Hwy 400
exit 33 (Rutherford Rd) southbound; exit 32 (Bass Pro Mills Dr) northbound. Int corridors. **Pets:** Medium, dogs only. Service with restrictions,
supervision. 🆂 ㏌ Ⓜ 🏊 🛰 ✕ 🛏 🖥

Ⓐ ▼▼▼ **Element Vaughan Southwest** Ⓗ
(905) 264-6474. **$179-$259.** 6170 Hwy 7 L4H 0R2. Jct Hwy 27. Int
corridors. **Pets:** Accepted. 🆂 ㏌ 🛰 ✕ 🛏 🖥

▼▼▼ **Holiday Inn Express & Suites
Vaughan-Southwest** Ⓗ
(905) 851-1510. **Call for rates.** 6100 Hwy 7 L4H 0R2. Jct Hwy 27. Int
corridors. **Pets:** Accepted. 🅴🅲🅾 🏊 🛰 ✕ 🛏 🖥

Ⓐ ▼▼▼ **Novotel Toronto Vaughan Centre** Ⓗ
(905) 660-0212. **$99-$399.** 200 Bass Pro Mills Dr L4K 0B9. Hwy 400 S
exit 33 (Rutherford Rd); Hwy 400 N exit 32 (Bass Pro Mills Dr). Int
corridors. **Pets:** Service with restrictions, crate.
🆂 🅴🅲🅾 ㏌ Ⓜ 🏊 🛰 ✕ 🛏 🖥

▼▼▼ **Residence Inn by Marriott Toronto/Vaughan** Ⓗ
(905) 695-4002. **$57-$217.** 11 Interchange Way L4K 5W3. Hwy 400 exit
29 (Hwy 7), 0.6 mi (1 km) e. Int corridors. **Pets:** Other species. $100
one-time fee/room. Service with restrictions.
Ⓜ 🏊 🛰 ✕ 🛏 🖥

WATERLOO

Ⓐ ▼▼ **Comfort Inn** Ⓗ
(519) 747-9400. **$110-$165.** 190 Weber St N N2J 3H4. Jct University
Ave, just s. Int corridors. **Pets:** Accepted.
🆂 🅴🅲🅾 ㏌ 🛰 ✕ 🛏 🖥

Ⓐ ▼▼▼ **Delta Waterloo** Ⓗ
(519) 514-0404. **$149-$249.** 110 Erb St W N2L 0C6. At Father David
Bauer Dr. Int corridors. **Pets:** Accepted.
🆂 ㏌ Ⓜ 🛰 ✕ 🛏 🖥

▼▼▼ **The Inn of Waterloo and Conference
Centre** Ⓗ ❀
(519) 804-1130. **$124-$204.** 475 King St N N2J 2Z5. 1.9 mi (3 km) n
on King St, jct Hwy 85. Int corridors. **Pets:** Large. $20 daily fee/pet.
Designated rooms, service with restrictions, crate.
㏌ Ⓜ 🏊 ✕ 🛰 ✕ 🛏 🖥

▼▼▼ **Les Diplomates B & B (Executive Guest
House)** ㏗
(519) 725-3184. **Call for rates.** 100 Blythwood Rd N2L 4A2. Hwy 85 N
exit King St, s to Columbia St, w to Hazel St, then just n. Ext/int corridors. **Pets:** Accepted. 🛰 ✕ 🛏 🖥

WAWA *(Restaurants p. 630)*

▼▼ **Best Northern Motel & Restaurant** Ⓜ
(705) 856-7302. **$95-$190.** 150 Hwy 17 S P0S 1K0. On Hwy 17, 3.3 mi
(5.3 km) s of jct Hwy 101. Ext corridors. **Pets:** Small, other species.
$15 daily fee/pet. Designated rooms, service with restrictions, supervi-
sion. ㏌ 🛰 ✕ 🎿 🛏 🖥

Ⓐ ▼▼▼ **Parkway Motel** Ⓜ
(705) 856-7020. **Call for rates.** 232 Hwy 17 S P0S 1K0. On Hwy 17,
2.5 mi (4 km) s of jct Hwy 101. Ext corridors. **Pets:** Accepted.
🆂 🛰 ✕ 🎿 🛏 🖥

WHITBY

▼▼ **Canadiana Inn** Ⓜ
(905) 668-3686. **Call for rates.** 732 Dundas St E (Hwy 2) L1N 2J7.
Hwy 401 exit 410 (Brock St/Hwy 12), 1 mi (1.6 km) n to Dundas St,
then 0.6 mi (1 km) e. Ext corridors. **Pets:** Accepted.
🏊 🛰 🛏 🖥

▼▼ **Motel 6 Whitby #1907** Ⓗ
(905) 665-8883. **$75-$105.** 165 Consumers Dr L1N 1C4. Hwy 401 exit
410 (Brock St/Hwy 12), just ne. Int corridors. **Pets:** Accepted.
🅴🅲🅾 🛰 🛏

Ⓐ ▼▼ **Quality Suites** Ⓗ
(905) 432-8800. **$100-$200.** 1700 Champlain Ave L1N 6A7. Hwy 401
exit 412 (Thickson Rd), 0.3 mi (0.5 km) n to Champlain Ave, then 0.6
mi (1 km) e. Int corridors. **Pets:** Accepted.
🆂 🅴🅲🅾 ㏌ 🛰 🛏 🖥

▼▼▼ **Residence Inn by Marriott Whitby** Ⓗ
(905) 444-9756. **$60-$204.** 160 Consumers Dr L1N 9S3. Hwy 401 exit
410 (Brock St/Hwy 12). Int corridors. **Pets:** Accepted.
Ⓜ 🏊 🛰 ✕ 🛏 🖥

WINDSOR

Ⓐ ▼▼▼ **Best Western Plus Waterfront Hotel
Windsor** Ⓗ
(519) 973-5555. **$139-$299.** 277 Riverside Dr W N9A 5K4. 0.6 mi (1
km) w of Detroit-Windsor Tunnel; 0.6 mi (1 km) e of Ambassador
Bridge; downtown. Int corridors. **Pets:** Accepted.
🆂 🅴🅲🅾 🏊 🛰 ✕ 🛏 🖥

▼▼ **Cadillac Inn** Ⓜ
(519) 969-9340. **$89-$120, 7 day notice.** 2498 Dougall Ave N8X 1T2.
2.5 mi (4 km) s on Hwy 3B from Detroit-Windsor Tunnel, just w on
Eugenie St, then just n. Ext corridors. **Pets:** Accepted.
㏌ 🏊 🛰 🛏

Ⓐ ▼▼▼ **Comfort Inn** Ⓗ
(519) 966-7800. **$105-$220.** 2955 Dougall Ave N9E 1S1. 3.3 mi (5.3
km) s on Hwy 3B, off Hwy 401 via Detroit-Windsor Tunnel exit. Int corridors. **Pets:** Accepted. 🆂 🅴🅲🅾 ㏌ 🛰 🛏 🖥

▼▼ **Comfort Inn & Suites Ambassador Bridge** Ⓗ
(519) 972-1100. **$115-$221.** 2330 Huron Church Rd N9E 3S6. North of
EC Row Expwy. Int corridors. **Pets:** Accepted.
㏌ 🏊 🛰 ✕ 🛏 🖥

▼▼ **Hampton Inn & Suites by Hilton Windsor** Ⓗ
(519) 972-0770. **$154-$199.** 1840 Huron Church Rd N9C 2L5. 0.9 mi
(1.5 km) n of EC Row Expwy. Int corridors. **Pets:** Accepted.
Ⓜ 🏊 🛰 ✕ 🛏 🖥

Ⓐ ▼▼▼ **Holiday Inn Downtown Windsor** Ⓗ
(519) 256-4656. **$139-$249, 10 day notice.** 430 Ouellette Ave N9A
1B2. 0.3 mi (0.5 km) s of Riverside Dr at Park St W. Int corridors.
Pets: Accepted. 🆂 ㏌ Ⓜ 🏊 🛰 ✕ 🛏 🖥

▼▼ **Holiday Inn Express Windsor Waterfront Hotel** Ⓗ
(519) 258-7774. **$95-$140.** 33 Riverside Dr E N9A 2S4. Jct Ouellette
Ave; downtown. Int corridors. **Pets:** Accepted.
🅴🅲🅾 ㏌ 🏊 🛰 ✕ 🛏 🖥

▼▼ **Howard Johnson Plaza Hotel - Windsor
Central** Ⓗ
(519) 966-1860. **$60-$95.** 2530 Ouellette Ave N8X 1L7. Jct Eugenie St.
Int corridors. **Pets:** Accepted. ㏌ 🛰 ✕ 🛏

▼ **Ivy Rose Motor Inn** Ⓜ
(519) 966-1700. **$69-$89.** 2885 Howard Ave N8X 3Y4. 3 mi (4.8 km) s
of downtown; just n of Devonshire Mall. Ext corridors. **Pets:** Accepted.
㏌ 🏊 🛰 🛏

▼▼ Motel 6 Windsor Ⓜ

(519) 966-8811. **Call for rates.** 2000 Huron Church Rd N9C 2L5. 0.6 mi (1 km) n of EC Row Expwy. Ext corridors. **Pets:** Accepted.

🍴 ♿ 📶 ✕ 🛎 💻

WOODSTOCK

Ⓐ **▼▼▼ Days Inn** Ⓗ 🐾

(519) 421-4588. **$70-$165.** 560 Norwich Ave N4V 1C6. Hwy 401 exit 232, just n; w of Hwy 59. Int corridors. **Pets:** $25 one-time fee/room. Designated rooms, service with restrictions, supervision.

💲 📶 ✕ 🛎 💻

Ⓐ **▼▼▼ Quality Hotel and Suites** Ⓗ 🐾

(519) 537-5586. **$120-$200.** 580 Bruin Blvd N4V 1E5. Hwy 401 exit 232, just n; w of Hwy 59. Int corridors. **Pets:** $25 one-time fee/room. Designated rooms, service with restrictions, supervision.

💲 🌿 🍴 🏊 📶 🛎 💻

PRINCE EDWARD ISLAND

CAVENDISH

▼▼ Bay Vista Ⓜ

(902) 963-2225. **Call for rates.** 9517 Cavendish Rd W C0A 1E0. Jct Rt 13, 2.8 mi (4.8 km) w on Rt 6. Ext corridors. **Pets:** Accepted.

🍴 🏊 📶 ✕ 🛎 💻

▼▼ Cavendish Bosom Buddies Cottages & Suites Ⓒ🅰

(902) 963-3449. **Call for rates.** 84 MacCoubrey Ln C0A 1N0. Jct Rt 6 and 13, 0.4 mi (0.7 km) e on Rt 6. Ext corridors. **Pets:** Accepted.

🍴 📶 ✕ 🏖 🛎 💻

▼▼ Silverwood Motel Ⓜ

(902) 963-2439. **Call for rates.** 8933 Cavendish Rd (Rt 6) C0A 1M0. Jct Rt 6, 1 mi (1.6 km) w of jct Rt 13. Ext corridors. **Pets:** Accepted.

🏊 📶 ✕ 🛎 💻

▼▼ Sundance Cottages Ⓒ🅰

(902) 963-2149. **Call for rates.** 42 MacCoubrey Ln C0A 1N0. Jct Rt 13, 0.4 mi (0.6 km) e on Rt 6. Ext corridors. **Pets:** Accepted.

🏊 ✕ 📶 ✕ 🛎 💻

CHARLOTTETOWN

Ⓐ **▼▼▼ Charlottetown Inn & Conference Centre** Ⓗ

(902) 892-2461. **$99-$239.** 238 Grafton St C1A 1L5. Between Hillsborough and Weymouth sts; center. Int corridors. **Pets:** Accepted.

💲 🌿 ♿ 🏊 📶 ✕ 🛎 💻

Ⓐ **▼▼▼ Comfort Inn Charlottetown** Ⓗ

(902) 566-4424. **$114-$226.** 112 Capital Dr C1E 1E7. Trans-Canada Hwy 1, 2.8 mi (4.5 km) w. Ext/int corridors. **Pets:** Accepted.

💲 🌿 📶 ✕ 🛎 💻

Ⓐ **▼▼▼▼ Delta Prince Edward** Ⓗ 🐾

(902) 566-2222. **$129-$399.** 18 Queen St C1A 4A1. At Water and Queen sts. Int corridors. **Pets:** Medium. $35 one-time fee/room. Designated rooms, service with restrictions, supervision.

💲 🌿 🍴 ♿ 🏊 ✕ 📶 ✕ 🛎 💻

Ⓐ **▼▼▼ Holiday Inn Express & Suites Charlottetown** Ⓗ

(902) 892-1201. **$129-$210.** 200 Capital Dr C1E 2E8. On Trans-Canada Hwy 1, 3 mi (5 km) w. **Pets:** Designated rooms, service with restrictions, crate. 💲 🌿 ♿ 🏊 📶 ✕ 🛎 💻

Ⓐ **▼▼▼▼ The Holman Grand Hotel** Ⓗ

(902) 367-7777. **$164-$479.** 123 Grafton St C1A 1K9. Between University Ave and Queen St. Int corridors. **Pets:** Accepted.

💲 🍴 ♿ 🏊 ✕ 📶 ✕ 🛎 💻

▼▼ Quality Inn & Suites Downtown Ⓗ 🐾

(902) 894-8572. **$110-$246.** 150 Euston St C1A 1W5. Just e of University Ave. Int corridors. **Pets:** Medium. Designated rooms, service with restrictions, supervision. 🍴 📶 ✕ 🛎 💻

▼▼▼ Rodd Charlottetown Ⓗ

(902) 894-7371. **$119-$269.** 75 Kent St C1A 7K4. Corner of Kent and Pownal sts. Int corridors. **Pets:** Accepted.

🌿 🍴 🏊 📶 ✕ 🛎 💻

▼▼▼ Rodd Royalty Ⓗ

(902) 894-8566. **$119-$231.** 14 Capital Dr C1A 8C2. 2.5 mi (4 km) w on Trans-Canada Hwy 1. Ext/int corridors. **Pets:** Accepted.

🌿 🍴 🏊 📶 ✕ 🛎 💻

CORNWALL

Ⓐ **▼▼▼ Super 8 Charlottetown** Ⓗ

(902) 892-7900. **$99-$180.** 15 York Point Rd C0A 1H0. On Hwy 1, 3.7 mi (6 km) w of Charlottetown. Int corridors. **Pets:** Medium, other species. $15 one-time fee/pet. Service with restrictions, supervision.

💲 🏊 📶 ✕ 🛎 💻

DALVAY BEACH

Ⓐ **▼▼▼ Dalvay by-the-Sea** ⒸⒾ

(902) 672-2048. **$169-$299, 3 day notice.** 16 Cottage Cres PEI National Pkwy C0A 1P0. Off Rt 6; at east end of PEI National Park. Ext/int corridors. **Pets:** Accepted.

💲 🍴 ♿ ✕ 📶 ✕ 🎾 🏖 🛎 💻

FRENCH RIVER

▼▼▼ The Beach House Inn Ⓑ🅱

(902) 886-2145. **$89-$219, 14 day notice.** 712 Cape Rd C0B 1M0. 0.8 mi n on River Rd, 0.9 mi e. Ext/int corridors. **Pets:** Medium, dogs only. $10 daily fee/room. Designated rooms, service with restrictions, supervision. 📶 ✕ 🎾 🛎 💻

MAYFIELD

▼▼ Cavendish Gateway Resort Ⓗ

(902) 963-2213. **$80-$250, 21 day notice.** 6596 Rt 13 C0A 1N0. On Rt 13, 3.6 mi (6 km) w of Cavendish; center. Ext/int corridors. **Pets:** Accepted. 🏊 ✕ 📶 ✕ 🛎 💻

MORELL

▼▼▼ Rodd Crowbush Golf & Beach Resort Ⓗ 🐾

(902) 961-5600. **$159-$349, 3 day notice.** 632 Rt 350 Lakeside Rd C0A 1S0. 3 mi (5 km) w on Rt 2, follow signs. Ext/int corridors. **Pets:** $10 daily fee/pet. Designated rooms, service with restrictions, supervision. 🍴 ♿ 🏊 ✕ 📶 ✕ 🛎 💻

NORTH RUSTICO *(Restaurants p. 630)*

▼▼ Gulf View Cottages Ⓒ🅰

(902) 963-2052. **$95-$175, 14 day notice.** 36 MacNeill Ln C0A 1X0. Hwy 6, 0.6 mi (1 km) ne on Church Hill Ave, then 0.6 mi (1 km) n; in PEI National Park. Ext corridors. **Pets:** Accepted.

📶 ✕ 🏖 🛎 💻

ROSENEATH

▼▼ ▼▼ **Brudenell Chalets** 🅲🅰
(902) 652-2900. **Call for rates.** 1068 Georgetown Rd C0A 1L0. Jct Rt 4 and 3, 4 mi (6.4 km) e on Rt 3. Ext corridors. **Pets:** Accepted.
🍴 🛏 🛜 ✕ 🔋 🖵

▼▼▼ **Rodd Brudenell River Resort** 🅷
(902) 652-2332. **$110-$199, 3 day notice.** 86 Dewars Ln, Rt 3 C0A 1L0. Jct Rt 4, 3.3 mi (5.5 km) e; in Brudenell River Provincial Park. Ext/int corridors. **Pets:** Accepted.
🍴 ♿ 🛏 ✕ 🛜 ✕ 🔋 🖵

ST. PETERS

▼▼▼ **The Inn at St. Peters** 🅲🅸
(902) 961-2135. **$215-$300, 7 day notice.** 1668 Greenwich Rd C0A 2A0. Jct Rt 16 and 313, 0.6 mi (1 km) w on Rt 313. Ext corridors. **Pets:** $10 daily fee/room. Designated rooms, service with restrictions.
🍴 🛜 ✕ 🔋 🖵

STANLEY BRIDGE

▼▼ ▼▼ **Inn at the Pier** 🅲🅸
(902) 886-3126. **$115-$259, 14 day notice.** 9796 Cavendish Rd C0A 1E0. Rt 6, 3.6 mi (6 km) w of Cavendish; center. Ext/int corridors.
Pets: Accepted. 🍴 🛏 🛜 ✕ 🔋 🖵

SUMMERSIDE *(Restaurants p. 630)*

🅐🅐 ▼▼ ▼▼ **Quality Inn & Suites** 🅷 🐾
(902) 436-2295. **$120-$275.** 618 Water St E C1N 2V5. 1 mi (1.6 km) e on Hwy 11. Ext/int corridors. **Pets:** Large, other species. $10 one-time fee/pet. Designated rooms, service with restrictions, supervision.
🆂🅰🆅🅴 🍴 🛏 ✕ 🛜 ✕ 🔋 🖵

WOODSTOCK

▼▼ ▼▼ **Rodd Mill River Resort** 🅷
(902) 859-3555. **$100-$181, 3 day notice.** 180 Mill River Resort Rd, Rt 136 C0B 1V0. On Rt 136, just e of jct Rt 2; in Mill River Provincial Park. Int corridors. **Pets:** Accepted.
🍴 🛏 ✕ 🛜 ✕ 🔋 🖵

QUEBEC

ALMA

▼▼ ▼▼ **Comfort Inn** 🅷
(418) 668-9221. **$110-$152.** 870 ave du Pont S G8B 2V8. On Hwy 169; center. Int corridors. **Pets:** Accepted. 🛜 ✕ 🔋 🖵

AMOS

▼▼ ▼▼ **Amosphere Complexe Hotelier** 🅷
(819) 732-7777. **$110-$190.** 1031 Rt 111 est J9T 1N2. Center. Ext/int corridors. **Pets:** Service with restrictions, crate.
🍴 ✕ 🛜 ✕ 🔋 🖵

ANJOU

🅐🅐 ▼▼ ▼▼ **Quality Hotel East** 🅷
(514) 493-6363. **$115-$170.** 8100 ave Neuville H1J 2T2. Hwy 40 exit 78, just n on boul Langelier, 0.4 mi (0.7 km) e on rue Jarry, then s. Int corridors. **Pets:** Medium, dogs only. $35 one-time fee/pet. Designated rooms, service with restrictions, supervision.
🆂🅰🆅🅴 🅴🅲🅾 🍴 🛜 🔋 🖵

AYER'S CLIFF

🅐🅐 ▼▼ ▼▼ ▼▼ **Ripplecove Hotel & Spa** 🅲🅸
(819) 838-4296. **$176-$555, 7 day notice.** 700 Ripplecove Rd J0B 1C0. Hwy 55 exit 21, 5 mi (8 km) s on Rt 141. Int corridors. **Pets:** Accepted.
🆂🅰🆅🅴 🍴 🛏 ✕ 🛜 ✕ 🔋 🖵

BAIE-COMEAU

▼▼ ▼▼ **Comfort Inn** 🅷
(418) 589-8252. **$122-$168.** 745 boul Lafleche G5C 1C6. On Rt 138. Ext/int corridors. **Pets:** Accepted. 🅴🅲🅾 🛜 ✕ 🔋 🖵

▼▼ ▼▼ **Hotel Le Manoir** 🅷
(418) 296-3391. **Call for rates.** 8 ave Cabot G4Z 1L8. Jct Rt 138 and boul LaSalle, 2.6 mi (4.4 km) e, follow signs. Int corridors.
Pets: Accepted. 🍴 ✕ 🛜 ✕ 🔋 🖵

BAIE-ST-PAUL

▼▼ ▼▼ **Le Hotel Germain Charlevoix** 🅷 🐾
(418) 240-4100. **Call for rates.** 50 Rue de la Ferme G3Z 0G2. Just se from jct Rt 362. Int corridors. **Pets:** Dogs only. $30 one-time fee/room. Designated rooms, service with restrictions, supervision.
🍴 ♿ ✕ 🛜 ✕ 🔋 🖵

BELOEIL

🅐🅐 ▼▼▼ **Hotel Rive Gauche** 🅷
(450) 467-4477. **$144-$164.** 1810 rue Richelieu J3G 4S4. Hwy 20 exit 112, 0.6 mi (1 km) s on rue Serge-Pepin, just sw on Rt 223, follow signs. Int corridors. **Pets:** Accepted. 🆂🅰🆅🅴 🍴 🛜 ✕ 🔋 🖵

BOISCHATEL

🅐🅐 ▼▼ ▼▼ **Econo Lodge Montmorency** 🅷
(418) 822-4777. **$76-$150.** 5490 boul Ste-Anne G0A 1H0. On Hwy 138. Int corridors. **Pets:** Accepted. 🆂🅰🆅🅴 🛜 🔋

BROMONT

▼▼▼ **Hotel Chateau-Bromont** 🅷
(450) 534-3433. **$169-$249.** 90 Stanstead St J2L 1K6. Hwy 10 exit 78, 1.8 mi (2.9 km) se on boul Bromont, 0.8 mi (1.2 km) s on rue Champlain. Int corridors. **Pets:** Accepted.
🍴 🛏 ✕ 🛜 ✕ 🔋 🖵

▼▼▼ **Le St-Martin Bromont Hotel & Suites** 🅷
(450) 534-0044. **Call for rates.** 111 boul du Carrefour J2L 3L1. Hwy 10 exit 78, just s on boul de Bromont, then just w. Int corridors.
Pets: Accepted. ♿ 🛜 ✕ 🔋 🖵

BROSSARD

▼▼▼ **Alt Hotel Quartier Dix 30** 🅷
(450) 443-1030. **Call for rates.** 6500 boul de Rome J4Y 0B6. Jct Hwy 10 and 30, just w on Hwy 30 exit boul de Rome; in Quartier Dix 30 Mall. Int corridors. **Pets:** Accepted. 🅴🅲🅾 🛜 ✕ 🖵

🅐🅐 ▼▼ ▼▼ **Best Western Hotel Brossard** 🅷
(450) 466-6756. **$140-$160.** 7746 boul Taschereau J4X 1C2. Rt 134, 0.8 mi (1.3 km) w of Hwy 10 exit boul Taschereau ouest. Ext/int corridors. **Pets:** $35 daily fee/pet. Service with restrictions, supervision.
🆂🅰🆅🅴 🅴🅲🅾 🛏 🛜 ✕ 🔋 🖵

▼▼ ▼▼ **Comfort Inn** 🅷
(450) 678-9350. **$117-$369.** 7863 boul Taschereau J4Y 1A4. Rt 134, 0.9 mi (1.5 km) w of Hwy 10 exit boul Taschereau. Int corridors.
Pets: Accepted. 🅴🅲🅾 🛜 ✕ 🔋 🖵

CHICOUTIMI

▼▼ ▼▼ **Comfort Inn** 🅷
(418) 693-8686. **$112-$167.** 1595 boul Talbot G7H 4C3. Jct Rt 170, 1.8 mi (2.8 km) n. Ext/int corridors. **Pets:** Accepted. 🛜 ✕ 🔋 🖵

DORVAL

(AA) ▼▼▼ Aloft Montréal Airport 🏨 ❀
(514) 633-0900. **$119-$349.** 500 ave McMillan H9P 0A2. Just n of Hwy 520 on north side service road at airport entrance. Int corridors. **Pets:** Small. Designated rooms, service with restrictions, supervision.
🆘 🍴 ⛎ 📶 ✖ 🖥 📲

(AA) ▼▼▼ Comfort Inn Dorval 🏨
(514) 636-3391. **$92-$179.** 340 ave Michel-Jasmin H9P 1C1. Hwy 520 exit 2 eastbound; exit 1 westbound, just e along service road to ave Marshall, follow to ave Michel-Jasmin. Int corridors. **Pets:** Accepted.
🆘 ⭕ 📶 🖥 📲

(AA) ▼▼▼ Hampton Inn & Suites by Hilton Montreal (Dorval) 🏨 ❀
(514) 633-8243. **$129-$229.** 1900 Rt Transcanadienne (Hwy 40) H9P 2N4. Hwy 40 exit 55, 0.5 mi (0.8 km) e of boul des Sources; on south side service road. Int corridors. **Pets:** Medium, other species. $50 one-time fee/pet. Designated rooms, service with restrictions, supervision.
🆘 🍴 ⛎ 📶 🖥 📲

(AA) ▼▼▼ ▼▼▼ Sheraton Montreal Airport Hotel 🏨
(514) 631-2411. **Call for rates.** 555 boul McMillan H9P 1B7. Just n of Hwy 520 on north side service road; at airport entrance. Int corridors. **Pets:** Accepted. 🆘 🍴 ⛎ ⛎ ✖ 📶 🖥 📲

DRUMMONDVILLE

(AA) ▼▼▼ Best Western Hotel Universel Drummondville 🏨
(819) 478-4971. **$89-$299.** 915 rue Hains J2C 3A1. Hwy 20 exit 177, just s on boul St-Joseph, then just e. Int corridors. **Pets:** Accepted.
🆘 🍴 ⛎ 📶 ✖ 🖥 📲

(AA) ▼▼▼ Comfort Inn 🏨
(819) 477-4000. **$102-$162.** 1055 rue Hains J2C 6G6. Hwy 20 exit 177, 0.3 mi (0.5 km) s on boul St-Joseph, then just w. Int corridors. **Pets:** Accepted. 🆘 ⭕ 📶 ✖ 🖥 📲

▼▼▼ Hotel & Suites Le Dauphin 🏨
(819) 478-4141. **$99-$225.** 600 boul St-Joseph J2C 2C1. Hwy 20 exit 177, 0.8 mi (1.3 km) s. Ext/int corridors. **Pets:** Accepted.
⭕ 🍴 ⛎ 📶 ✖ 🖥 📲

▼▼▼ Hotel-Motel Drummond 🏍
(819) 478-4614. **Call for rates.** 105 boul St-Joseph ouest J2E 1A4. Hwy 20 exit 177, just n on boul St-Joseph, then just w on rue St-Roch. Ext corridors. **Pets:** Accepted. 🍴 📶 🖥 📲

▼▼▼ Quality Suites Drummondville 🏨
(819) 472-2700. **$100-$259.** 2125 rue Canadien J2C 7V8. Hwy 20 exit 175, just s. Int corridors. **Pets:** Accepted.
⭕ ⛎ 📶 ✖ 🖥 📲

GATINEAU

(AA) ▼▼▼ Comfort Inn Gatineau 🏨
(819) 243-6010. **$119-$171.** 630 boul La Gappe J8T 7S8. Hwy 50 exit 140, 1.1 mi (1.9 km) e; in Hull sector. Int corridors. **Pets:** Accepted.
🆘 ⭕ 📶 ✖ 🖥 📲

(AA) ▼▼▼▼ Four Points by Sheraton Hotel & Conference Centre Gatineau-Ottawa 🏨
(819) 778-6111. **$149-$249.** 35 rue Laurier J8X 4E9. Corner of rue Victoria; across from Canadian Museum of Civilization; in Hull sector. Int corridors. **Pets:** Accepted. 🆘 ⭕ 🍴 ⛎ 📶 ✖ 📲

(AA) ▼▼▼ ▼▼▼ Hilton Lac-Leamy 🏨
(819) 790-6444. **$209-$539.** 3 boul du Casino J8Y 6X4. In Casino du Lac Leamy; in Hull sector. Int corridors. **Pets:** Accepted.
🆘 ⭕ 🍴 ⛎ ✖ 📶 🖥 📲

ISLE-AUX-COUDRES

▼▼▼ Hotel Motel La Roche Pleureuse 🏨
(418) 438-2734. **Call for rates.** 2901 chemin des Coudriers G0A 2A0. On Isle-aux-Coudres, 4.8 mi (8 km) e of ferry dock, follow signs; in la Baleine sector; access by ferry. Ext/int corridors. **Pets:** Accepted.
🍴 ⛎ ✖ 📶 ✖

JONQUIÈRE

▼▼▼ Delta Saguenay Hotel 🏨
(418) 548-3124. **$82-$135.** 2675 boul du Royaume G7S 5B8. Hwy 70 exit 39, just ne, follow signs. Int corridors. **Pets:** Accepted.
🍴 ⛎ ⛎ ✖ 📶 ✖ 🖥 📲

LAC-BROME (KNOWLTON)

(AA) ▼▼▼▼ Hôtel Suites Lac-Brome 🏩
(450) 243-0404. **$139-$359.** 572 chemin Lakeside J0E 1R0. Hwy 10 exit 90, 3.1 mi (4.9 km) s on Rt 243. Int corridors. **Pets:** Small, dogs only. $40 daily fee/pet. Designated rooms, supervision.
🆘 🍴 ⛎ ✖ 📶 ✖ 🖥 📲

L'ANCIENNE-LORETTE

▼▼▼ Comfort Inn 🏨
(418) 872-5900. **$107-$149.** 1255 boul Duplessis G2G 2B4. Jct boul Wilfrid-Hamel (Hwy 138). Ext/int corridors. **Pets:** Medium. $25 one-time fee/pet. Designated rooms, supervision. ⭕ 📶 ✖ 🖥 📲

LAVAL

(AA) ▼▼▼ Best Western Plus Laval-Montreal 🏨
(450) 681-9000. **$100-$200.** 3655 Autoroute des Laurentides H7L 3H7. Hwy 15 exit 10, just n on east side service road. Int corridors. **Pets:** Accepted. 🆘 🍴 ⛎ 📶 ✖ 🖥 📲

(AA) ▼▼▼ Comfort Inn 🏨
(450) 686-0600. **$104-$276.** 2055 Autoroute des Laurentides H7S 1Z6. Hwy 15 exit 8 (boul St-Martin), e on boul St-Martin, 0.4 mi (0.7 km) n on boul Le Corbusier, then just w on boul Tessier. Int corridors. **Pets:** Accepted. 🆘 ⭕ 📶 ✖ 🖥 📲

(AA) ▼▼▼ Quality Suites Laval 🏨
(450) 686-6777. **$106-$250.** 2035 Autoroute des Laurentides H7S 1Z6. Hwy 15 exit 8 (boul St-Martin), 0.4 mi (0.7 km) n on boul Le Corbusier, then just w on boul Tessier. Int corridors. **Pets:** Accepted.
🆘 ⭕ 📶 ✖ 🖥 📲

LÉVIS

▼▼▼ Comfort Inn & Suites Rive-Sud Québec 🏨
(418) 836-3336. **$111-$143.** 1394 Route des Rivières G7A 2N9. Trans-Canada Hwy 20 exit 311, just ne on Rt 116. Int corridors. **Pets:** Accepted. ⛎ ⛎ 📶 ✖ 🖥 📲

▼▼▼ Comfort Inn Levis 🏨
(418) 835-5605. **$91-$161.** 10 rue du Terroir G6V 9J3. Trans-Canada Hwy 20 exit 325S eastbound; exit 325 westbound, just s. Ext/int corridors. **Pets:** Small. $35 one-time fee/room. Designated rooms, service with restrictions, supervision. ⭕ 📶 ✖ 🖥 📲

(AA) ▼▼▼ Hotel-Motel Hospitalite 🏍
(418) 837-6664. **$70-$130.** 3500 boul Guillaume-Couture G6W 6N7. Trans-Canada Hwy 20 exit 321 (chemin des Iles), 1.4 mi (2.3 km) n, then just w on Rt 132. Ext/int corridors. **Pets:** $20 one-time fee/room. Designated rooms, supervision. 🆘 🍴 📶 ✖ 🖥

▼▼▼ Quality Inn & Suites Levis 🏨 ❀
(418) 833-1212. **$106-$249.** 5800 rue des Arpents G6V 0B5. Trans-Canada Hwy 20 exit 325N eastbound; exit 325 westbound, just n, then just e. Int corridors. **Pets:** $25 one-time fee/room. Designated rooms, service with restrictions, supervision. ⛎ 📶 ✖ 🖥 📲

LOUISEVILLE

▼▼▼ **Gîte du Carrefour et Maison historique J.L.L. Hamelin** BB

(819) 228-4932. **Call for rates.** 11 ave St-Laurent ouest J5V 1J3. Jct rts 138 and 349; center. Int corridors. **Pets:** No service, supervision.

⒯ 🛜 ✕ 🅇 🅦 🇿 🖵

MONTEBELLO

(AA) ▼▼▼▼ **Fairmont Le Château Montebello** H ❀

(819) 423-6341. **$199-$649, 3 day notice.** 392 rue Notre-Dame J0V 1L0. On Rt 148, just w of Rt 323. Int corridors. **Pets:** Dogs only. $45 daily fee/room. Designated rooms, service with restrictions, crate.

SAVE ECO ⒯ ⇌ ✕ 🖥 ✕ 🇶 🖵

MONT-LAURIER

(AA) ▼▼▼ **Best Western Plus Mont-Laurier** H

(819) 623-5252. **$118-$128.** 1231 boul Albiny-Paquette J9L 1M6. On Rt 117; center. Ext/int corridors. **Pets:** Accepted.

SAVE ⒯ 🅼 ⇌ 🛜 ✕ 🇶 🖵

▼▼ **Comfort Inn** H

(819) 623-6465. **$114-$132.** 700 boul Albiny-Paquette J9L 1L4. On Rt 117; center. Int/ext corridors. **Pets:** Accepted.

⒯ ✕ 🛜 ✕ 🇶 🖵

MONTRÉAL *(Restaurants p. 631)*

▼▼▼ **ALT Hotel Montreal Griftintown** H

(514) 375-0220. **$179-$199.** 120 Peel St H3C 0L8. Jct Wellington St. Int corridors. **Pets:** Accepted. ⒯ 🅼 🛜 ✕ 🖵

(AA) ▼▼▼ **Château Versailles Hotel** H

(514) 933-3611. **Call for rates.** 1659 rue Sherbrooke ouest H3H 1E3. Corner of rue St-Mathieu. Int corridors. **Pets:** Accepted.

SAVE 🛜 ✕ 🇶 🖵

(AA) ▼▼▼ **Delta Montreal** H ❀

(514) 286-1986. **$159-$499.** 475 ave du President-Kennedy H3A 1J7. Corner of rue City Councillors. Int corridors. **Pets:** Medium, dogs only. $35 one-time fee/room. Designated rooms, service with restrictions, supervision. SAVE ECO ⒯ ⇌ ✕ 🛜 ✕ 🇶 🖵

(AA) ▼▼▼ **Hotel 10 Montreal** H

(514) 843-6000. **$149-$609, 3 day notice.** 10 rue Sherbrooke ouest H2X 4C9. Corner of boul St-Laurent. Int corridors. **Pets:** Dogs only. $50 one-time fee/room. Service with restrictions, supervision.

SAVE ⒯ 🛜 ✕ 🇶 🖵

(AA) ▼▼▼▼ **Hotel Bonaventure Montreal** H

(514) 878-2332. **$199-$999, 3 day notice.** 900 rue de la Gauchetiere ouest H5A 1E4. Corner of rue Mansfield. Int corridors. **Pets:** Small. $50 one-time fee/pet. Designated rooms, supervision.

SAVE ECO ⒯ 🅼 ⇌ 🛜 ✕ 🇶 🖵

▼▼ **Hôtel Chrome** H

(514) 393-3388. **$95-$399.** 215 boul Rene-Levesque est H2X 1N7. Corner of Hotel-de-ville Ave. Int corridors. **Pets:** Accepted.

ECO ⒯ 🅼 🛜 ✕ 🇶 🖵

▼▼ **Hôtel Faubourg Montréal** H

(514) 448-7100. **$99-$475.** 155 boul Rene-Levesque est H2X 3Z8. Corner of rue de Bullion. Int corridors. **Pets:** Accepted.

ECO 🅼 🛜 ✕ 🇶 🖵

(AA) ▼▼▼ **Hotel Gault** H ❀

(514) 904-1616. **$240-$980.** 449 rue Ste-Helene H2Y 2K9. Just s of rue Notre-Dame. Int corridors. **Pets:** $60 daily fee/pet. Supervision.

SAVE ⒯ 🅼 🛜 ✕ 🇶 🖵

▼▼▼ **Hotel Gouverneur Place Dupuis** H

(514) 842-4881. **Call for rates.** 1415 rue St-Hubert H2L 3Y9. Between boul de Maisonneuve and rue Ste-Catherine. Int corridors. **Pets:** Accepted. ECO ⒯ ⇌ 🛜 ✕ 🇶 🖵

(AA) ▼▼▼▼ **Hôtel Le Crystal** H ❀

(514) 861-5550. **Call for rates.** 1100 rue de la Montagne H3G 0A1. Corner of boul Rene-Levesque. Int corridors. **Pets:** Medium, other species. $75 one-time fee/room. Service with restrictions, crate.

SAVE ECO ⒯ 🅼 ⇌ ✕ 🛜 ✕ 🇶 🖵

▼▼▼ **Hôtel Le Germain Montréal** H

(514) 849-2050. **Call for rates.** 2050 rue Mansfield H3A 1Y9. Corner of ave du President-Kennedy. Int corridors. **Pets:** Accepted.

⒯ 🅼 🛜 ✕ 🇶 🖵

▼▼▼ **Hôtel Le St-James** H

(514) 841-3111. **Call for rates.** 355 rue St-Jacques H2Y 1N9. Corner of rue St-Pierre. Int corridors. **Pets:** Accepted.

⒯ ✕ 🛜 ✕ 🇶 🖵

(AA) ▼▼▼▼ **Hôtel Omni Mont-Royal** H ❀

(514) 284-1110. **Call for rates.** 1050 rue Sherbrooke ouest H3A 2R6. Corner of rue Peel. Int corridors. **Pets:** Small, dogs only. $50 one-time fee/room. Designated rooms, service with restrictions, supervision.

SAVE ⒯ 🅼 ⇌ ✕ 🛜 ✕ 🇶 🖵

▼▼▼ **Hotel St-Paul** H

(514) 380-2222. **$205-$330.** 355 rue McGill H2Y 2E8. Corner of rue St-Paul. Int corridors. **Pets:** Medium, dogs only. $75 one-time fee/pet. Service with restrictions, crate. ⒯ 🅼 🛜 ✕ 🖵

(AA) ▼▼▼ **Hôtel Travelodge Montreal Centre** H

(514) 874-9090. **$84-$309.** 50 boul Rene-Levesque ouest H2Z 1A2. Between rues Clark and St-Urbain. Int corridors. **Pets:** Accepted.

SAVE ECO 🅼 🛜 ✕ 🇶 🖵

(AA) ▼▼▼▼ **Hyatt Regency Montreal** H

(514) 982-1234. **$89-$429.** 1255 rue Jeanne-Mance H5B 1E5. Corner of rue Ste-Catherine. Int corridors. **Pets:** Accepted.

SAVE ⒯ 🅼 ⇌ ✕ 🛜 ✕ 🇶 🖵

(AA) ▼▼▼▼ **InterContinental Montréal** H

(514) 987-9900. **$199-$1099.** 360 rue St-Antoine ouest H2Y 3X4. Corner of rue St-Pierre. Int corridors. **Pets:** Accepted.

SAVE ECO ⒯ 🅼 ⇌ ✕ 🖥 ✕ 🇶 🖵

(AA) ▼▼▼ **L'Appartement Hôtel** H

(514) 284-3634. **$119-$234.** 455 rue Sherbrooke ouest H3A 1B7. Corner of rue Durocher. Int corridors. **Pets:** Designated rooms, service with restrictions, crate. SAVE ECO ⇌ 🛜 ✕ 🇶 🖵

(AA) ▼▼▼ **Le Centre Sheraton** H ❀

(514) 878-2000. **$159-$549.** 1201 boul Rene-Levesque ouest H3B 2L7. Between rues Drummond and Stanley. Int corridors. **Pets:** Medium. Service with restrictions, supervision.

SAVE ECO ⒯ ⇌ ✕ 🖥 ✕ 🇶 🖵

(AA) ▼▼▼ **Le Meridien Versailles-Montreal** H

(514) 933-8111. **$109-$1200.** 1808 rue Sherbrooke ouest H3H 1E5. Corner of rue St-Mathieu. Int corridors. **Pets:** Accepted.

SAVE ⒯ 🛜 ✕ 🇶 🖵

(AA) ▼▼▼▼ **Le Saint-Sulpice Hôtel & Suites Montréal** H

(514) 288-1000. **$189-$699.** 414 rue St-Sulpice H2Y 2V5. Just n of rue St-Paul. Int corridors. **Pets:** Accepted. SAVE ⒯ 🛜 ✕ 🇶 🖵

(AA) ▼▼▼ **Le Square Phillips Hotel & Suites** H

(514) 393-1193. **$149-$399.** 1193 Place Phillips H3B 3C9. Between rue Ste-Catherine and boul Rene-Levesque. Int corridors. **Pets:** Designated rooms, service with restrictions, crate.

SAVE ECO ⒯ ⇌ 🛜 ✕ 🇶 🖵

(AA) ▽▽▽ **Le Westin Montréal** H
(514) 380-3333. **$199-$499.** 270 rue St-Antoine ouest H2Y 0A3. Corner of rue Jeanne-Mance. Int corridors. **Pets:** Accepted.
[SAVE] [⛔] [⛔] [⛔] [⛔] [⛔] [⛔] [⛔] [⛔]

(AA) ▽▽▽ **Loews Hôtel Vogue** H ✻
(514) 285-5555. **$169-$1749.** 1425 rue de la Montagne H3G 1Z3. Between rue Ste-Catherine and boul de Maisonneuve. Int corridors. **Pets:** Other species. $25 one-time fee/room. Service with restrictions, supervision. [SAVE] [⛔] [⛔] [⛔] [⛔]

▽▽▽ **Novotel Montreal Centre** H
(514) 861-6000. **$119-$499.** 1180 rue de la Montagne H3G 1Z1. Between rue Ste-Catherine and boul Rene-Levesque. Int corridors. **Pets:** Accepted. [ECO] [⛔] [⛔] [⛔] [⛔]

▽▽▽ **Parc Suites Hotel** H
(514) 985-5656. **$119-$239, 3 day notice.** 3463 ave du Parc H2X 2H6. Between rues Sherbrooke and Milton. Int corridors. **Pets:** Medium, other species. $20 daily fee/pet. Designated rooms. [⛔] [⛔] [⛔] [⛔]

(AA) ▽▽▽ **Renaissance Montréal Centre-Ville** H
(514) 657-5000. **$64-$382.** 1250 boul Robert-Bourassa H3B 3B8. Just s of rue St-Catherine; corner of rue Cathcart. Int corridors. **Pets:** Accepted. [SAVE] [⛔] [⛔] [⛔] [⛔] [⛔] [⛔]

▽▽▽ **Residence Inn by Marriott Montreal Airport** H
(514) 336-9333. **$83-$248.** 6500 Place Robert-Joncas H4M 2Z5. Hwy 40 exit 64 (boul Cavendish), 0.3 mi (0.5 km) w on north side service road, then just n on rue Beaulac. Int corridors. **Pets:** Accepted.
[ECO] [⛔] [⛔] [⛔] [⛔] [⛔] [⛔] [⛔]

(AA) ▽▽▽ **Residence Inn by Marriott Montreal-Downtown** H
(514) 982-6064. **$89-$371.** 2045 rue Peel H3A 1T6. Between rue Sherbrooke and boul de Maisonneuve. Int corridors. **Pets:** Other species. $100 one-time fee/room. Service with restrictions, crate.
[SAVE] [ECO] [⛔] [⛔] [⛔] [⛔] [⛔]

(AA) ▽▽▽ **Residence Inn by Marriott Montreal Westmount** H
(514) 935-9224. **$68-$294.** 2170 ave Lincoln H3H 2N5. Just e of rue Atwater. Int corridors. **Pets:** Accepted.
[SAVE] [ECO] [⛔] [⛔] [⛔] [⛔] [⛔] [⛔]

(AA) ▽▽▽ **The Ritz-Carlton Montréal** H
(514) 842-4212. **$575-$695.** 1228 rue Sherbrooke ouest H3G 1H6. Corner of rue de la Montagne. Int corridors. **Pets:** Accepted.
[SAVE] [⛔] [⛔] [⛔] [⛔] [⛔] [⛔] [⛔] [⛔]

(AA) ▽▽▽ **Sofitel Montréal Le Carré Doré** H ✻
(514) 285-9000. **$189-$579.** 1155 rue Sherbrooke ouest H3A 2N3. Corner of rue Stanley. Int corridors. **Pets:** Other species. Designated rooms, supervision. [SAVE] [ECO] [⛔] [⛔] [⛔] [⛔] [⛔] [⛔]

(AA) ▽▽▽ **W Montréal** H ✻
(514) 395-3100. **$189-$999.** 901 Square Victoria H2Z 1R1. Corner of rue St-Antoine. Int corridors. **Pets:** Other species. $100 one-time fee/room. Designated rooms, supervision.
[SAVE] [⛔] [⛔] [⛔] [⛔] [⛔] [⛔]

MONT-TREMBLANT

(AA) ▽▽▽ **Fairmont Tremblant** H
(819) 681-7000. **$199-$639, 7 day notice.** 3045 chemin de la Chapelle J8E 1E1. In Mont-Tremblant Resort Centre. Int corridors.
Pets: Accepted. [SAVE] [ECO] [⛔] [⛔] [⛔] [⛔] [⛔] [⛔] [⛔]

▽▽▽ **Le Grand Lodge Mont-Tremblant** H
(819) 425-2734. **Call for rates.** 2396 rue Labelle J8E 1T8. On Rt 327, 0.3 mi (0.4 km) s of Montée Ryan. Int corridors. **Pets:** Accepted.
[⛔] [⛔] [⛔] [⛔] [⛔] [⛔] [⛔]

(AA) ▽▽▽ **Le Westin Resort & Spa, Tremblant** H ✻
(819) 681-8000. **Call for rates.** 100 chemin Kandahar J8E 1E2. Hwy 117 N exit 119 (Montee Ryan), 6 mi (10 km) e, follow signs. Int corridors. **Pets:** Medium, dogs only. Designated rooms, service with restrictions, supervision. [SAVE] [⛔] [⛔] [⛔] [⛔] [⛔] [⛔] [⛔]

NORTH HATLEY

(AA) ▽▽▽ **Manoir Hovey Relais & Châteaux** CI
(819) 842-2421. **$200-$1090, 14 day notice.** 575 rue Hovey J0B 2C0. Hwy 55 exit 29, 7.5 mi (12 km) e on Rt 108 E. Ext/int corridors.
Pets: Accepted. [SAVE] [⛔] [⛔] [⛔] [⛔] [⛔] [⛔] [⛔]

ORFORD

▽▽▽ **Hotel Cheribourg** H
(819) 843-3308. **Call for rates.** 2603 chemin du Parc J1X 8C8. Hwy 10 exit 118, 1.9 mi (3 km) n on Hwy 141. Ext/int corridors. **Pets:** Accepted.
[⛔] [⛔] [⛔] [⛔] [⛔] [⛔] [⛔] [⛔]

▽▽▽ **Manoir des Sables Hotel & Golf** H
(819) 847-4747. **Call for rates.** 90 ave des Jardins J1X 6M6. Hwy 10 exit 118, 1.3 mi (2 km) n on Rt 141. Int corridors. **Pets:** Accepted.
[⛔] [⛔] [⛔] [⛔] [⛔] [⛔] [⛔] [⛔]

PERCÉ

▽▽ **Au Pic de l'Aurore** M
(418) 782-2151. **$79-$149, 3 day notice.** 1 Rt 132 W G0C 2L0. 1.2 mi (2 km) w from village. Ext corridors. **Pets:** Medium, dogs only. $25 one-time fee/pet. Designated rooms, service with restrictions, supervision.
[⛔] [⛔] [⛔] [⛔] [⛔]

▽▽▽ **Hotel La Normandie** H
(418) 782-2112. **Call for rates.** 221 Rt 132 ouest G0C 2L0. Center. Ext/int corridors. **Pets:** Small. $30 one-time fee/pet. Designated rooms, service with restrictions, crate. [⛔] [⛔] [⛔] [⛔] [⛔] [⛔]

▽▽▽ **Hotel/Motel Le Mirage** M
(418) 782-5151. **$89-$198.** 288 Rt 132 ouest G0C 2L0. On Rt 132. Ext corridors. **Pets:** Accepted. [⛔] [⛔] [⛔] [⛔] [⛔]

▽▽▽ **Hotel Motel Manoir de Percé** H
(418) 782-2022. **$79-$188, 3 day notice.** 212 Rt 132 G0C 2L0. Center. Ext/int corridors. **Pets:** $25 one-time fee/room. Service with restrictions, supervision. [⛔] [⛔] [⛔] [⛔]

POINTE-CLAIRE

▽▽ **Quality Suites Montreal Aeroport, Pointe-Claire** H ✻
(514) 426-5060. **$110-$215.** 6300 Rt Transcanadienne H9R 1B9. Hwy 40 exit 52 eastbound, south side service road; exit westbound, follow signs for boul St-Jean sud and Hwy 40 est to access south side service road. Int corridors. **Pets:** Medium. $50 one-time fee/room. Designated rooms, service with restrictions, supervision.
[ECO] [⛔] [⛔] [⛔] [⛔] [⛔]

QUÉBEC (Restaurants p. 631)

▽▽▽ **ALT Hotel-Québec** H ✻
(418) 658-1224. **$169-$209.** 1200 ave Germain-des-Pres G1V 3M7. Just n of boul Laurier; facing Laurier Québec. Int corridors. **Pets:** Medium, dogs only. $30 one-time fee/room. Designated rooms, service with restrictions, supervision. [⛔] [⛔] [⛔] [⛔] [⛔]

▽▽▽ **Auberge Place d'Armes** H
(418) 694-9485. **Call for rates.** 24 rue Ste-Anne G1R 3X3. Just w of rue du Trésor. Int corridors. **Pets:** Accepted. [⛔] [⛔] [⛔] [⛔] [⛔]

(AA) ▽▽▽ **Best Western Plus City Centre/Centre-Ville** H ✻
(418) 649-1919. **$169-$899.** 330 rue de la Couronne G1K 6E6. Corner of rue du Roi. Int corridors. **Pets:** Medium. $15 daily fee/pet. Service with restrictions. [SAVE] [⛔] [⛔] [⛔] [⛔] [⛔] [⛔]

(AA) ▼▼▼▼ **Delta Québec** H ❖

(418) 647-1717. **$149-$369.** 690 boul Rene-Levesque est G1R 5A8. Just w of boul Honore-Mercier. Int corridors. **Pets:** Medium. $50 one-time fee/room. Designated rooms, service with restrictions, supervision.

SAVE ECO ❙❙ ➥ ❐ 🛜 ✕ 🖥

(AA) ▼▼▼▼ ▼▼▼▼ **Fairmont Le Château Frontenac** H ❖

(418) 692-3861. **$199-$599, 3 day notice.** 1 rue des Carrieres G1R 4P5. In Old Québec. Int corridors. **Pets:** $50 daily fee/room. Designated rooms, supervision. SAVE ECO ❙❙ ➥ ✕ 🆂🅰 ✕ 🖥 🖳

(AA) ▼▼▼▼ **Hilton Québec** H

(418) 647-2411. **Call for rates.** 1100 boul Rene-Levesque est G1R 4P3. Corner of ave Honore-Mercier. Int corridors. **Pets:** Other species. $50 one-time fee/pet. Supervision.

SAVE ❙❙ ➥ ✕ 🛜 ✕ 🖥 🖳

▼▼▼▼ **Hotel & Suites Dauphin Québec City** H ❖

(418) 688-3888. **$99-$259.** 400 rue du Marais G1M 3R1. Hwy 40 exit 312S, westbound just s on boul Pierre-Bertrand, eastbound, just w. Int corridors. **Pets:** $15 daily fee/room. Designated rooms, service with restrictions, supervision. ECO 🆖M 🛜 ✕ 🖥 🖳

▼▼▼▼ **Hotel & Suites Normandin** H ❖

(418) 622-1611. **$125-$249.** 4700 boul Pierre-Bertrand G2J 1A4. Hwy 40 exit 312N eastbound, just w on rue Marais, then just n; exit 312N westbound, just w on rue Bouvier, then just n. Int corridors. **Pets:** Medium. $15 daily fee/room. Designated rooms, service with restrictions, crate. ❙❙ 🆖M 🛜 ✕ 🖥 🖳

▼▼▼▼ **Hotel Champlain Vieux-Québec** H

(418) 694-0106. **Call for rates.** 115 rue Ste-Anne G1R 3X6. Between rue Ste-Angele and St-Stanislas; in Old Québec. Int corridors. **Pets:** Accepted. 🛜 ✕ 🖳

(AA) ▼▼▼ **Hôtel Château Bellevue** H

(418) 692-2573. **$99-$399.** 16 rue de la Porte G1R 4M9. Corner of ave Ste-Genevieve. Int corridors. **Pets:** Accepted. SAVE ECO 🛜 ✕

▼▼▼ **Hôtel Citadelle** H

(418) 871-3938. **Call for rates.** 4800 boul Wilfrid-Hamel G1P 2J9. Hwy 73 exit 141, just e. Ext/int corridors. **Pets:** Accepted. 🛜 🖥 🖳

(AA) ▼▼▼ **Hotel Clarion Québec** H

(418) 653-4901. **$99-$269.** 3125 boul Hochelaga G1V 4A8. Hwy 73 exit 136 (boul Hochelaga ouest). Int corridors. **Pets:** Dogs only. $20 daily fee/pet. Designated rooms, service with restrictions, crate.

SAVE ❙❙ 🆖M ➥ ✕ 🛜 ✕ 🖥 🖳

▼▼▼ ▼▼▼ **Hôtel Le Germain Québec** H

(418) 692-2224. **Call for rates.** 126 rue St-Pierre G1K 4A8. Corner of rue St-Paul. Int corridors. **Pets:** Accepted. ✕ 🛜 ✕ 🖳

(AA) ▼▼▼▼ **Hotel Pur Québec** H

(418) 647-2611. **$109-$209.** 395 rue de la Couronne G1K 7X4. Corner of rue St-Joseph est. Int corridors. **Pets:** Medium. $25 daily fee/room. Designated rooms, service with restrictions, supervision.

SAVE ❙❙ 🆖M ➥ 🛜 ✕ 🖥 🖳

▼▼▼ **Hotel Super 8 Québec Ste-Foy** H

(418) 877-6888. **$80-$151.** 7286 boul Wilfred-Hamel G2G 1C1. Hwy 138, 0.7 mi (1.1 km) w of Hwy 540 (Autoroute Duplessis). **Pets:** Medium. $20 daily fee/room. Designated rooms, service with restrictions, supervision. ECO ➥ 🛜 ✕ 🖥 🖳

(AA) ▼▼▼ ▼▼▼ **Le Bonne Entente** H

(418) 653-5221. **$159-$599.** 3400 chemin Ste-Foy G1X 1S6. Hwy 540 (Autoroute Duplessis) exit chemin Ste-Foy, just w. Int corridors. **Pets:** Accepted. SAVE ❙❙ 🆖M ➥ ✕ 🛜 ✕ 🖳

▼▼▼ **L'Hôtel du Vieux-Québec** H

(418) 692-1850. **Call for rates.** 1190 rue St-Jean G1R 1S6. Corner of rue de l'Hotel-Dieu. Int corridors. **Pets:** Accepted.

ECO ❙❙ 🛜 ✕ 🖥 🖳

▼▼▼ **N Hôtel** H ❖

(418) 666-1226. **Call for rates.** 3390 boul Ste-Anne G1E 3L7. Hwy 440 exit Francois-de-Laval, then just e. Int corridors. **Pets:** Medium. $15 daily fee/room. Service with restrictions, crate.

🛜 ✕ 🖥 🖳

(AA) ▼▼▼ ▼▼▼ **Relais & Châteaux Auberge Saint-Antoine** H

(418) 692-2211. **$229-$1450.** 8 rue St-Antoine G1K 4C9. Corner of rue Dalhousie. Int corridors. **Pets:** Accepted.

SAVE ❙❙ ✕ 🛜 ✕ 🖥 🖳

RIGAUD

▼▼▼ **orcaSound Hotel** H

(450) 458-7779. **Call for rates.** 93 Montee Lavigne (Rt 201) J0P 1P0. Hwy 40 exit 17, just ne. Int corridors. **Pets:** Accepted.

🛜 ✕ 🖥 🖳

RIMOUSKI

▼▼▼ **Comfort Inn** H

(418) 724-2500. **$112-$167.** 455 boul St-Germain ouest G5L 3P2. On Rt 132. Ext/int corridors. **Pets:** $25 one-time fee/room. Service with restrictions, supervision. ECO 🛜 ✕ 🖥 🖳

(AA) ▼▼▼ **Hotel Gouverneur Rimouski** H

(418) 723-4422. **$89-$169.** 155 boul Rene-Lepage E G5L 1P2. On Rt 132. Int corridors. **Pets:** Medium. $40 daily fee/pet. Designated rooms, supervision. SAVE ❙❙ ➥ 🛜 ✕ 🖥 🖳

▼▼▼ **Hotel L'Empress** H

(418) 723-6944. **Call for rates.** 360 Montee Industrielle & Commerciale G5M 1X1. Hwy 20 exit 614, 2.1 mi (3.4 km) n. Int corridors. **Pets:** Accepted. ❙❙ 🛜 ✕ 🖥 🖳

RIVIÈRE-DU-LOUP

▼▼▼ **Comfort Inn** H

(418) 867-4162. **$100-$189.** 85 boul Cartier G5R 4X4. Hwy 20 exit 507, just se; Hwy 85 exit 96 (Fraserville), follow signs. Ext/int corridors. **Pets:** Other species. $25 one-time fee/room. Service with restrictions, supervision. ECO 🛜 ✕ 🖥 🖳

(AA) ▼▼▼ ▼▼▼ **Hotel Universel Riviere-du-Loup** H

(418) 862-9520. **$119-$199.** 311 boul Hotel-de-Ville G5R 5S4. At Rt 132. Ext/int corridors. **Pets:** Accepted.

SAVE ❙❙ 🆖M ✕ 🛜 ✕ 🖥 🖳

▼▼▼ **Motel Au Vieux Piloteux** M

(418) 867-2635. **Call for rates.** 185 rue Fraser G5R 1E2. Hwy 20 exit 503, 0.6 mi (1 km) e on Rt 132. Ext corridors. **Pets:** Accepted.

➥ ✕ 🛜 ✕ 🖥 🖳

ROUYN-NORANDA

(AA) ▼▼▼▼ **Best Western Plus Albert Centre-Ville** H

(819) 762-3545. **$145-$152.** 84 Ave Principale J9X 4P2. Center. Int corridors. **Pets:** Medium, dogs only. $25 daily fee/pet. Supervision.

SAVE ❙❙ 🆖M 🛜 ✕ 🖥 🖳

▼▼▼ **Comfort Inn** H

(819) 797-1313. **$111-$147.** 1295 ave Lariviere J9X 6M6. On Rt 117, 2.5 mi (4 km) s from town center. Int corridors. **Pets:** Small. $25 one-time fee/pet. Designated rooms, service with restrictions, supervision.

ECO 🆖M 🛜 ✕ 🖥 🖳

▼▼▼▼ **Hôtel Gouverneur le Noranda** H

(819) 762-2341. **Call for rates.** 41 6ieme rue J9X 1Y8. Corner of rue Murdoch; center. Ext/int corridors. **Pets:** Other species. $30 one-time fee/room. Service with restrictions, supervision.

❙❙ ✕ 🛜 ✕ 🖥 🖳

ST-APOLLINAIRE

◆◆ Econo Lodge H

(418) 881-3335. **$90-$168.** 372 rue Laurier G0S 2E0. Hwy 20 exit 291, just ne. Ext/int corridors. **Pets:** Other species. $20 daily fee/room. Service with restrictions, crate. 🍴 📶 ✕ 🔒 💻

ST-FAUSTIN-LAC-CARRÉ

◆ Motel Tremblant M

(819) 688-2102. **Call for rates.** 357 Rt 117 J0T 1J2. On Rt 117, 1.6 mi (2.5 km) e of city exit. Ext/int corridors. **Pets:** Accepted. 🍴 📶 ✕ 🔒 💻

ST-HYACINTHE

◆◆◆ Holiday Inn Express & Suites H

(450) 251-1111. **Call for rates.** 1500 rue Johnson est J2S 8W5. Hwy 20 exit 133, 0.3 mi (0.5 km) s on boul Laframboise, 1 mi (1.6 km) e on boul Casavant. Int corridors. **Pets:** Accepted. 📶 ✕ 🔒 💻

ST-JEAN-PORT-JOLI

◆◆ Faubourg ô fleuve M

(418) 598-6455. **Call for rates.** 280 ave de Gaspe (Rt 132) ouest G0R 3G0. Trans-Canadian Hwy 20 exit 414, 0.5 mi (0.8 km) n on Rt 204, then 1.4 mi (2.4 km) w. Ext corridors. **Pets:** Accepted. 🍴 📶 ✕ 🔒 💻

ST-JEAN-SUR-RICHELIEU

◆◆◆ Holiday Inn Express H ❀

(450) 359-4466. **Call for rates.** 700 rue Gadbois J3A 1V1. Hwy 35 exit 45, e on rue Pierre-Caisse. Int corridors. **Pets:** Small. $15 daily fee/room. Designated rooms, service with restrictions, crate. 📶 ✕ 🔒 💻

ST-JÉRÔME

◆◆ Super 8 St-Jerome H

(450) 438-4388. **$99-$134.** 3 boul J. F. Kennedy J7Y 4B4. Hwy 15 exit 41 southbound, just n; on west side of autoroute. Int corridors. **Pets:** Accepted. 🍴 ♿ 📶 ✕ 🔒 💻

ST-LAURENT

CAA ◆◆◆◆ Crowne Plaza Montréal Airport H

(514) 344-1999. **$99-$250.** 6600 Côte de Liesse Expwy H4T 1E3. Hwy 520 exit 3E eastbound on south side service road; exit westbound to rue Ness, follow signs for rue Hickmore and Hwy 520 E. Int corridors. **Pets:** Medium. $75 one-time fee/room. Service with restrictions, crate. SAVE 🍴 📶 ✕ 🔒 💻

CAA ◆◆◆ Holiday Inn Montreal-Airport H

(514) 739-3391. **$109-$209.** 6500 Côte-de-Liesse H4T 1E3. Hwy 520 exit 5 eastbound on south side service road; exit westbound to rue Ness, follow signs for rue Hickmore and Hwy 520 E. Ext/int corridors. **Pets:** Accepted. SAVE 🍴 ♿ 📶 ✕ 🔒 💻

◆◆◆ Novotel Montreal Airport H

(514) 337-3222. **Call for rates.** 2599 boul Alfred-Nobel H4S 2G1. Hwy 40 exit 60 (boul Alfred-Nobel); in St-Laurent Technoparc, just s of south side service road. Int corridors. **Pets:** Accepted. 🍴 📶 ✕ 🔒 💻

STE-AGATHE-DES-MONTS

◆ Super 8 Ste-Agathe H

(819) 324-8880. **$89-$129.** 500 rue Leonard J8C 0A3. Hwy 15 exit 86, just w on Rt 117 to rue Leonard, 0.3 mi (0.5 km) s. Int corridors. **Pets:** Medium. $15 daily fee/pet. Designated rooms, service with restrictions, supervision. 🍴 ♿ 📶 ✕ 🔒 💻

STE-ANNE-DE-BEAUPRÉ

CAA ◆◆◆ Quality Suites Mont Sainte-Anne H

(418) 827-1570. **$96-$170.** 9800 boul Ste-Anne G0A 3C0. On Hwy 138. Int corridors. **Pets:** Accepted. SAVE 📶 ✕ 🔒 💻

STE-EULALIE

◆◆ Motel Marie-Dan M

(819) 225-4604. **Call for rates.** 311 rue des Bouleaux (Rt 161) G0Z 1E0. Hwy 20 exit 210, follow signs to Rt 161, just s. Ext corridors. **Pets:** Very small. $10 daily fee/pet. Supervision. 🍴 📶 ✕ 🔒

STE-MARTHE

◆◆◆ Auberge des Gallant H 🐾

(450) 459-4241. **$129-$250.** 1171 Chemin St-Henri J0P 1W0. From Hwy 201, 5.3 mi (8.5 km) w. Int corridors. **Pets:** $15 daily fee/room. Designated rooms, crate. 🍴 ♿ 📶 ✕ 📶 ✕ 🔒 💻

SEPT-ÎLES

◆◆ Comfort Inn H

(418) 968-6005. **$114-$157.** 854 boul Laure G4R 1Y7. 2.8 mi (4.5 km) w on Rt 138. Ext/int corridors. **Pets:** Medium. $25 one-time fee/pet. Service with restrictions, supervision. ECO 📶 ✕ 🔒 💻

SHAWINIGAN

◆◆ Auberge Escapade Inn H

(819) 539-6911. **Call for rates.** 3383 rue Trudel G9N 6R4. Hwy 55 exit 217, 0.3 mi (0.5 km) n on Rt 351. Ext/int corridors. **Pets:** Accepted. 🍴 📶 ✕ 🔒

◆◆ Auberge Gouverneur & Centre de Congrès Shawinigan H

(819) 537-6000. **Call for rates.** 1100 Promenade-du-St-Maurice G9N 1L8. Hwy 55 N exit 211, 2.8 mi (4.4 km) n on Hwy 153, follow signs. Int corridors. **Pets:** Accepted. 🍴 📶 ✕ 📶 🔒 💻

◆◆ Comfort Inn & Suites H

(819) 536-2000. **$90-$165.** 705 ave du Capitaine Veilleux G9P 5J6. Hwy 55 N exit 211, 2.8 mi (4.4 km) n on Hwy 153, then 1.3 mi (2 km) s on Rt 157. Int corridors. **Pets:** Accepted. ECO 🍴 📶 ✕ 🔒 💻

SHERBROOKE

◆◆ Comfort Inn H

(819) 564-4400. **$107-$149.** 4295 boul Bourque J1N 1S4. Hwy 410 exit 4W, 0.9 mi (1.5 km) w on Rt 112. Ext/int corridors. **Pets:** Medium. $30 one-time fee/room. Designated rooms, service with restrictions, supervision. ECO 📶 ✕ 🔒 💻

◆◆◆ Delta Sherbrooke Hotel and Conference Centre H

(819) 822-1989. **$126-$246.** 2685 rue King ouest J1L 1C1. Hwy 410 exit 4W, 0.6 mi (1 km) e on Rt 112. Int corridors. **Pets:** Accepted. ECO 🍴 ♿ 📶 📶 ✕ 🔒 💻

CAA ◆◆◆ Quality Hotel & Suites Sherbrooke H

(819) 563-4755. **$99-$164.** 4206 rue King ouest J1L 1V5. Hwy 410 exit 4W, 0.4 mi (0.6 km) w. Ext/int corridors. **Pets:** $15 daily fee/pet. Designated rooms, service with restrictions, supervision. SAVE 🍴 📶 📶 ✕ 🔒 💻

TERREBONNE

◆◆ Super 8 Hotel Lachenaie Terrebonne H

(450) 582-8288. **$161-$180.** 1155 ave Yves-Blais J6V 0A9. Hwy 640 exit 50, just s on Montee des Pionniers, then just e; in Lachenaie sector. Int corridors. **Pets:** Accepted. ECO 📶 📶 ✕ 🔒 💻

THETFORD MINES

◆◆ Hotel Comfort Inn Thetford Mines H

(418) 338-0171. **$123-$152.** 123 boul Frontenac ouest G6G 7S7. On Rt 112. Int corridors. **Pets:** Accepted. ECO 🍴 📶 ✕ 🔒 💻

TROIS-RIVIÈRES

▼▼▼ Comfort Inn H

(819) 371-3566. **$93-$180.** 6255 rue Corbeil G8Z 4P9. Hwy 55 exit 183 (boul Jean XXIII); 1.3 mi (2 km) n of Laviolette Bridge, 0.3 mi (0.5 km) e. Int corridors. **Pets:** Medium. $25 one-time fee/pet. Designated rooms, service with restrictions, supervision. ⬛ 📶 ⊠ 🛄 💻

CAA ▼▼▼▼ Delta Trois-Rivieres Hotel and Conference Centre H

(819) 376-1991. **$119-$286.** 1620 rue Notre-Dame Centre G9A 6E5. Corner of rue St-Roch; center. Int corridors. **Pets:** Medium. $35 one-time fee/room. Service with restrictions, crate.

SAVE ⬛ 🍽 🛋 ⊠ 📶 🛄 💻

▼▼ Hotel Gouverneur Trois-Rivieres H

(819) 379-4550. **Call for rates.** 975 rue Hart G9A 4S3. Jct rue Laviolette; center. Int corridors. **Pets:** Accepted.

🍽 🛋 📶 ⊠ 🛄 💻

▼▼ Super 8 Trois-Rivieres H

(819) 377-5881. **$110-$160.** 3185 boul St-Jean G9B 2M4. Hwy 55 exit 183 (boul Jean XXIII), just nw. Int corridors. **Pets:** $15 daily fee/pet. Designated rooms, service with restrictions, supervision.

⬛ 🛋 📶 ⊠ 🛄 💻

VAL-D'OR

▼▼ Comfort Inn H

(819) 825-9360. **$120-$157.** 1665 3ieme Ave J9P 1V9. In town center. Int corridors. **Pets:** Accepted. ⬛ 📶 ⊠ 🛄 💻

▼▼▼ L'Escale Hotel Suites H

(819) 824-2711. **$130-$165.** 1100 rue L'Escale J9P 4G8. In town center. Ext/int corridors. **Pets:** Designated rooms, service with restrictions, supervision. 🍽 🛋M 📶 ⊠ 🛄 💻

VAUDREUIL-DORION

▼▼▼ Holiday Inn Express & Suites Vaudreuil-Dorion H

(450) 455-5522. **$139-$199.** 33 de la Cité-des-Jeunes E J7V 0N3. Hwy 40 exit 35, just e; at roundabout take 3rd exit, just e. Int corridors. **Pets:** Other species. $50 one-time fee/room. Service with restrictions, supervision. 🛋M 📶 ⊠ 🛄 💻

VICTORIAVILLE

▼▼▼ Quality Inn & Suites Victoriaville H

(819) 330-8888. **$120-$190.** 1 boul Arthabaska est G6T 0S4. Jct rue Notre-Dame est. Int corridors. **Pets:** Small. $15 daily fee/pet. Designated rooms, service with restrictions, supervision.

🛋 ⊠ 📶 ⊠ 🛄 💻

WAKEFIELD

▼▼▼ Moulin Wakefield Mill Hotel & Spa H

(819) 459-1838. **$199-$279, 3 day notice.** 60 chemin Mill J0X 3G0. 0.6 mi (1 km) w of Riverside Dr; center. Int corridors. **Pets:** Accepted.

⬛ 🍽 🛋 ⊠ 📶 ⊠ 🛄 💻

SASKATCHEWAN

CARLYLE

▼▼▼ Ramada Inn Carlyle Hotel H

(306) 453-2686. **$140-$215.** 110 Turriff Ave E S0C 0R0. Jct Hwy 9 and Main St, just e. Ext/int corridors. **Pets:** Accepted.

🍽 🛋M 📶 ⊠ 🛄 💻

ESTEVAN

CAA ▼▼▼▼ Best Western Plus Estevan Inn & Suites H 🐾

(306) 634-7447. **$129-$199.** 92 King St S4A 2T5. Hwy 39, 1 mi (1.6 km) n at Kensington Ave. Int corridors. **Pets:** $20 one-time fee/pet. Designated rooms, no service, supervision.

SAVE 🛋M 🛋 📶 ⊠ 🛄 💻

▼▼ Microtel Inn & Suites by Wyndham Estevan H 🐾

(306) 634-7474. **$99-$189.** 120 King St S4A 2T5. Hwy 39, 1 mi (1.7 km) n at Kensington Ave, just w. Int corridors. **Pets:** Medium. $15 daily fee/pet. Designated rooms, service with restrictions, supervision.

📶 ⊠ 🛄 💻

▼▼ Motel 6 Estevan M

(306) 634-8666. **Call for rates.** 88 King St E S4A 2A4. Hwy 39, 1 mi (1.7 km) n at Kensington Ave, just e. Int corridors. **Pets:** Accepted.

🛋M 📶 🛄

KINDERSLEY

CAA ▼▼▼▼ Best Western Plus Kindersley Hotel H

(306) 463-3600. **$139-$149.** 501 14th Ave E S0L 1S0. Jct Hwy 21 and 7, 0.7 mi (1.1 km) e, then just n. Int corridors. **Pets:** Accepted.

SAVE 🍽 🛋M 📶 ⊠ 🛄 💻

LLOYDMINSTER

▼▼ Microtel Inn & Suites by Wyndham H 🐾

(306) 825-3820. **$109-$229.** 4257 44th St S9V 2H1. Jct Hwy 16 and 45th Ave, just e on Hwy 16. Int corridors. **Pets:** $20 daily fee/room. Service with restrictions, supervision. 🍽 🛋M 📶 ⊠ 🛄 💻

▼▼ Super 8 Lloydminster H

(306) 825-7988. **$75-$140.** 4351 41st Ave S9V 2H1. Jct Hwy 16 and 45th Ave, just e on Hwy 16. Int corridors. **Pets:** Accepted.

🍽 🛋M 📶 ⊠ 🛄 💻

MOOSE JAW

▼▼ Comfort Inn H

(306) 692-2100. **$120-$170.** 155 Thatcher Dr W S6J 1M1. 0.8 mi (1.2 km) s on Hwy 2 from jct Trans-Canada Hwy 1, just w. Int corridors. **Pets:** Other species. $15 one-time fee/room. Designated rooms, service with restrictions, crate. 🛋M 📶 ⊠ 🛄 💻

▼▼ Heritage Inn Hotel & Convention Centre H

(306) 693-7550. **$130-$200.** 1590 Main St N S6J 1L3. On Hwy 2, 0.9 mi (1.4 km) s of jct Trans-Canada Hwy 1. Int corridors. **Pets:** Medium, dogs only. $20 daily fee/pet. Designated rooms, service with restrictions, supervision. 🍽 🛋M 🛋 📶 ⊠ 🛄 💻

▼▼ Super 8-Moose Jaw H

(306) 692-8888. **$117-$120.** 1706 Main St N S6J 1L4. On Hwy 2, 0.7 mi (1.1 km) s of jct Trans-Canada Hwy 1. Int corridors. **Pets:** Other species. $15 one-time fee/room, $10 daily fee/room. Designated rooms, service with restrictions, supervision. 🛋M 📶 ⊠ 🛄 💻

MOOSOMIN

CAA ▼▼▼▼ Best Western Plus Moosomin Hotel H

(306) 435-4700. **$149-$179.** 405 Moose St S0G 3N0. Jct Trans-Canada Hwy 1 and Main St, just s. Int corridors. **Pets:** Accepted.

SAVE 🍽 🛋M 📶 ⊠ 🛄 💻

NORTH BATTLEFORD

▼▼ Lone Star Hotel H

(306) 446-8888. **$85-$150.** 1006 Hwy 16 S9A 3W2. 0.3 mi (0.5 km) nw of jct Hwy 16 (Yellowhead Hwy). Int corridors. **Pets:** Accepted.

🛋M 📶 🛄 💻

PRINCE ALBERT

Ⓐ ▼▼▼▼ Best Western Marquis Inn & Suites H
(306) 922-9595. **$109-$150.** 602 Marquis Rd E S6V 7P2. Jct Hwy 3 (6th Ave E). Int corridors. **Pets:** Accepted.
[SAVE] 🍴 ♿ 🛜 ✕ 🔌 💻

Ⓐ ▼▼▼ Comfort Inn Prince Albert H
(306) 763-4466. **$119-$159.** 3863 2nd Ave W S6W 1A1. On Hwy 2, 1.6 mi (2.6 km) s. Int corridors. **Pets:** Accepted.
[SAVE] [ECO] 🛜 ✕ 🔌 💻

▼▼ Super 8-Prince Albert H
(306) 953-0088. **$119-$139.** 4444 2nd Ave W S6V 5R7. On Hwy 2, 1.7 mi (2.7 km) s. Int corridors. **Pets:** Accepted. ♿ 🛜 ✕ 🔌 💻

▼▼ Travelodge Prince Albert M
(306) 764-6441. **$104-$128.** 3551 2nd Ave W S6V 5G1. On Hwy 2, 1.4 mi (2.2 km) s. Ext/int corridors. **Pets:** Other species. Service with restrictions, supervision. [ECO] 🍴 🛜 🔌 💻

REGINA (Restaurants p. 631)

Ⓐ ▼▼▼▼ Best Western Plus Eastgate Inn & Suites H 🐾
(306) 352-7587. **$160-$209.** 3840 Eastgate Dr S4Z 1A5. Trans-Canada Hwy 1, 1.5 mi (2.4 km) e of Ring Rd, just n. Int corridors. **Pets:** Other species. $20 daily fee/pet. Designated rooms, service with restrictions, supervision. [SAVE] ♿ 🛜 ✕ 🔌 💻

Ⓐ ▼▼▼ Best Western Seven Oaks Inn H
(306) 757-0121. **$160-$170.** 777 Albert St S4R 2P6. On Hwy 6; jct 2nd Ave. Int corridors. **Pets:** Other species. $15 daily fee/pet. Designated rooms, supervision. [SAVE] 🍴 🏊 🛜 ✕ 🔌 💻

▼▼▼ Country Inn & Suites By Carlson H
(306) 789-9117. **$115-$199, 3 day notice.** 3321 Eastgate Bay S4Z 1A4. Trans-Canada Hwy 1, 1.2 mi (2 km) e of Ring Rd; at eastern approach to city. Int corridors. **Pets:** Accepted. [ECO] ♿ 🛜 ✕ 🔌 💻

Ⓐ ▼▼▼ Delta Regina H
(306) 525-5255. **$85-$207.** 1919 Saskatchewan Dr S4P 4H2. At Rose St; center. Int corridors. **Pets:** Accepted.
[SAVE] [ECO] 🍴 ♿ 🏊 ✕ 🛜 ✕ 🔌 💻

▼▼▼ DoubleTree by Hilton Hotel & Conference Centre Regina H
(306) 525-6767. **$119-$189.** 1975 Broad St S4P 1Y2. Jct Victoria Ave; center. Int corridors. **Pets:** Medium, dogs only. $35 one-time fee/room. Service with restrictions, crate. [ECO] 🍴 🛜 ✕ 🔌 💻

▼▼▼ Executive Royal Hotel Regina H 🐾
(306) 586-6755. **Call for rates.** 4025 Albert St S S4S 3R6. On Hwy 6, 1.2 mi (2 km) n of jct Trans-Canada Hwy 1. Int corridors. **Pets:** Other species. $25 daily fee/room. Designated rooms, service with restrictions, supervision. 🍴 🛜 ✕ 🔌 💻

Ⓐ ▼▼▼▼ The Hotel Saskatchewan, Autograph Collection H
(306) 522-7691. **$152-$237, 3 day notice.** 2125 Victoria Ave S4P 0S3. At Scarth St; center. Int corridors. **Pets:** Dogs only. $50 one-time fee/room. Crate. [SAVE] [ECO] 🍴 ✕ 🛜 ✕ 🔌 💻

Ⓐ ▼▼▼ Quality Hotel H
(306) 569-4656. **$99-$219.** 1717 Victoria Ave S4P 0P9. Just e of Broad St; downtown. Int corridors. **Pets:** Accepted.
[SAVE] [ECO] 🍴 🛜 🔌 💻

▼▼▼ Sandman Hotel Suites & Spa Regina H
(306) 757-2444. **Call for rates.** 1800 Victoria Ave E S4N 7K3. On Trans-Canada Hwy 1, just e of Ring Rd. Int corridors. **Pets:** Accepted.
[ECO] 🍴 ♿ 🛜 🔌 💻

▼▼ Super 8 Regina H
(306) 789-8833. **$115-$140.** 2730 Victoria Ave E S4N 6M5. On Trans-Canada Hwy 1, 1 mi (1.6 km) e of Ring Rd; at eastern approach to city. Int corridors. **Pets:** Medium. $20 daily fee/room. Designated rooms, service with restrictions, supervision. ♿ 🛜 ✕ 🔌 💻

▼▼▼ Wingate by Wyndham Regina H
(306) 584-7400. **$149-$189.** 1700 Broad St S4P 1X4. Jct Saskatchewan Dr; center. Int corridors. **Pets:** Other species. $30 one-time fee/room. Service with restrictions. [ECO] 🍴 ♿ 🛜 ✕ 🔌 💻

SASKATOON (Restaurants p. 631)

Ⓐ ▼▼▼▼ Best Western Plus Blairmore H
(306) 242-2299. **$150-$173.** 306 Shillington Crescent S7M 1L2. Jct Hwy 7 and 14. Int corridors. **Pets:** Accepted.
[SAVE] ♿ 🏊 🛜 ✕ 🔌 💻

Ⓐ ▼▼▼ Best Western Plus East Side H
(306) 986-2400. **$160-$175.** 3331 8th St E S7H 4K1. Hwy 16 exit 8th St E, just e. Int corridors. **Pets:** Accepted.
[SAVE] 🍴 ♿ 🛜 ✕ 🔌 💻

Ⓐ ▼▼▼ Colonial Square Inn & Suites H
(306) 343-1676. **$109-$129.** 1301 8th St E S7H 0S7. 1.5 mi (2.4 km) e of jct Hwy 11 (Idylwyld Dr S); 1.4 mi (2.3 km) w of jct Circle Dr. Ext/int corridors. **Pets:** Accepted. [SAVE] 🍴 🛜 ✕ 🔌 💻

Ⓐ ▼▼▼ Comfort Inn M
(306) 934-1122. **$99-$270.** 2155 Northridge Dr S7L 6X6. Just ne of jct Hwy 11 (Idylwyld Dr N) and Circle Dr. Int corridors. **Pets:** Medium. $15 daily fee/room. Designated rooms, service with restrictions, supervision.
[SAVE] [ECO] 🛜 ✕ 🔌 💻

Ⓐ ▼▼▼ Country Inn & Suites By Carlson H
(306) 934-3900. **$110-$160.** 617 Cynthia St S7L 6B7. Just w on Circle Dr from jct Hwy 11 (Idylwyld Dr N), just n on Ave CN. Int corridors. **Pets:** Accepted. [ECO] ♿ 🛜 ✕ 🔌 💻

Ⓐ ▼▼▼▼ Delta Bessborough H
(306) 244-5521. **$139-$229.** 601 Spadina Crescent E S7K 3G8. Jct 21st St E; center. Int corridors. **Pets:** Accepted.
[SAVE] [ECO] 🍴 ♿ 🏊 ✕ 🛜 ✕ 🔌 💻

▼▼▼▼ Hilton Garden Inn Saskatoon Downtown H
(306) 244-2311. **$144-$219.** 90 22nd St E S7K 3X6. Just e of jct Hwy 11 (Idylwyld Dr N); at 1st Ave. Int corridors. **Pets:** Accepted.
[ECO] 🍴 🏊 🛜 ✕ 🔌 💻

▼▼▼ Holiday Inn Express Hotel & Suites Saskatoon H
(306) 384-8844. **Call for rates.** 315 Idylwyld Dr N S7L 0Z1. On Hwy 11 (Idylwyld Dr), just n of jct 23rd St. Int corridors. **Pets:** Accepted.
[ECO] ♿ 🏊 🛜 ✕ 🔌 💻

▼▼ Motel 6 Saskatoon H
(306) 665-6688. **Call for rates.** 231 Marquis Dr S7R 1B7. Just e of jct Trans-Canada Hwy 16; 0.4 mi (0.7 km) w of Hwy 11 (Idylwyld Dr N). Int corridors. **Pets:** Accepted. ♿ 🏊 🛜 ✕ 🔌 💻

Ⓐ ▼▼▼▼ Quality Inn & Suites H 🐾
(306) 244-5552. **Call for rates.** 1715 Idylwyld Dr N S7L 1B4. On Hwy 11 (Idylwyld Dr), 0.4 mi (0.7 km) s of jct Circle Dr. Ext/int corridors. **Pets:** Other species. $15 daily fee/room. Designated rooms, service with restrictions, supervision. [SAVE] [ECO] 🍴 ♿ 🛜 ✕ 🔌 💻

Ⓐ ▼▼▼ Radisson Hotel Saskatoon H
(306) 665-3322. **Call for rates.** 405 20th St E S7K 6X6. At 4th Ave S; center. Int corridors. **Pets:** Designated rooms, service with restrictions, supervision. [SAVE] [ECO] 🍴 ♿ 🏊 🛜 ✕ 🔌 💻

(AA) ▼▼▼ **Ramada Hotel-Saskatoon** H

(306) 665-6500. **$119-$139.** 806 Idylwyld Dr N S7L 0Z6. On Hwy 11 (Idylwyld Dr), 2.5 mi (4 km) s of jct Circle Dr. Int corridors. **Pets:** Large, other species. $25 one-time fee/room. Designated rooms, service with restrictions, crate. [SAVE] [ECO] [¶] [&M] [🛏] [🛜] [🖥] [💻]

▼▼▼ **Sandman Hotel Saskatoon** H

(306) 477-4844. **Call for rates.** 310 Circle Dr W S7L 2Y5. Just w of Hwy 11 (Idylwyld Dr). Int corridors. **Pets:** Accepted.
[ECO] [¶] [&M] [🛏] [🛜] [✕] [🖥] [💻]

(AA) ▼▼▼ **Sheraton Cavalier Saskatoon Hotel** H

(306) 652-6770. **$139-$289.** 612 Spadina Crescent E S7K 3G9. Jct 21st St E; center. Int corridors. **Pets:** Accepted.
[SAVE] [ECO] [¶] [&M] [🛏] [🛜] [✕] [🖥] [💻]

▼▼ **Super 8 East-Saskatoon** H

(306) 384-8989. **$127-$139.** 706 Circle Dr E S7K 3T7. 1.3 mi (2 km) e of jct Hwy 11 (Idylwyld Dr N). Ext/int corridors. **Pets:** Accepted.
[&M] [🛜] [✕] [🖥] [💻]

SWIFT CURRENT

(AA) ▼▼▼ **Comfort Inn Swift Current** H

(306) 778-3994. **$88-$150.** 1510 S Service Rd E S9H 3X6. Trans-Canada Hwy 1, just w of 22nd Ave NE. Int corridors. **Pets:** Accepted.
[SAVE] [ECO] [&M] [🛜] [✕] [🖥] [💻]

▼▼ **Motel 6 Swift Current** H

(306) 778-6060. **$90-$110.** 1185 5th Ave NE S9H 5N7. Trans-Canada Hwy 1, just e of Central Ave N, on N Service Rd W, then just n. Int corridors. **Pets:** Accepted. [&M] [🛜] [✕] [🖥]

WEYBURN

▼▼▼ **Canalta Hotel** H

(306) 842-8000. **$129-$139.** 1360 Sims Ave S4H 3N9. On Hwy 39, just w of Hwy 35. Ext/int corridors. **Pets:** Accepted.
[ECO] [&M] [✕] [🛜] [✕] [🖥] [💻]

▼▼ **Microtel Inn & Suites by Wyndham Weyburn** H 🐾

(306) 842-5700. **$101-$189.** 88 Grace St S4H 3N9. On Hwy 39, just w of Hwy 35, then just s. Int corridors. **Pets:** Small. $15 daily fee/pet. Designated rooms, service with restrictions, supervision.
[&M] [✕] [🛜] [✕] [🖥] [💻]

▼▼▼ **Ramada Inn & Suites** H

(306) 842-4994. **$139-$169.** 1420 Sims Ave S4H 3N9. On Hwy 39, just w of Hwy 35. Ext/int corridors. **Pets:** Accepted.
[ECO] [&M] [🛏] [🛜] [✕] [🖥] [💻]

▼▼ **Travelodge Hotel Weyburn** M

(306) 842-1411. **$65-$199.** 53 Government Rd S S4H 2A2. Jct Simms Ave. Ext/int corridors. **Pets:** $10 daily fee/pet. Designated rooms, service with restrictions, supervision. [ECO] [¶] [&M] [🛜] [🖥] [💻]

YORKTON

▼▼▼ **Days Inn & Suites Yorkton** H

(306) 782-3112. **$80-$205.** 1-275 Broadway St E S3N 0N5. Just w of jct Hwy 9, 10 and 16 (Yellowhead Hwy). Int corridors. **Pets:** Accepted.
[&M] [🛜] [✕] [🖥] [💻]

YUKON

DAWSON CITY

▼▼ **Klondike Kate's Cabins** CA

(867) 993-6527. **$140-$200.** 1102 3rd Ave Y0B 1G0. Corner of 3rd Ave and King St; center. Ext corridors. **Pets:** Other species. $25 daily fee/ pet. Service with restrictions. [¶] [🛜] [✕] [🅺] [🖥] [💻]

WHITEHORSE

(AA) ▼▼▼ **Best Western Gold Rush Inn** H 🐾

(867) 668-4500. **$150-$185.** 411 Main St Y1A 2B6. Between 4th and 5th aves; center. Int corridors. **Pets:** Medium, other species. $20 daily fee/room. Designated rooms, service with restrictions.
[SAVE] [ECO] [¶] [🛜] [✕] [🖥] [💻]

(AA) ▼▼▼ **Coast High Country Inn** H

(867) 667-4471. **$150-$185.** 4051 4th Ave Y1A 1H1. 0.4 mi (0.6 km) e of Main St. Int corridors. **Pets:** Accepted.
[SAVE] [ECO] [¶] [🛜] [✕] [🖥] [💻]

▼▼ **Westmark Whitehorse Hotel & Conference Center** H 🐾

(867) 393-9700. **Call for rates.** 201 Wood St Y1A 2E4. At 2nd Ave; center. Int corridors. **Pets:** $20 one-time fee/room. Designated rooms, service with restrictions, supervision.
[¶] [&M] [📶] [✕] [🅺] [🖥] [💻]

Pet-Friendly Restaurants

United States
Canada

United States

Alabama

BIRMINGHAM

▼▼▼ FLIP burger Boutique
(205) 968-2000. New American. Casual Dining. **$7-$21.** 220 Summit Blvd, Suite 140 35243. Just n of jct US 280 and I-459; in The Summit shopping center. L D &M

▼▼ Fuego Cantina and Saloon
(205) 933-1544. Tex-Mex. Casual Dining. **$8-$17.** 1101 20th St S 35205. Jct 20th St S and 11th Ave S; just se of University Blvd; in Five Points South. L D LATE &M ✎

▼▼ Little Savannah
(205) 591-1119. Southern Natural/Organic. Casual Dining. **$13-$38.** 3811 Clairmont Ave 35222. Between 38th and 39th sts S; near Highland Golf Course. D

CULLMAN

▼▼ Rumors Deli & Coffee House
(256) 737-0911. Sandwiches. Quick Serve. **$5-$9.** 105 1st Ave NE 35055. Across from Clark St NE; downtown. B L

DECATUR

▼▼ Simp McGhee's
(256) 353-6284. American. Casual Dining. **$18-$36.** 725 Bank St 35601. Jct Lafayette St NW; in historic downtown. D

EUFAULA

▼▼ The Cajun Corner
(334) 616-0816. Cajun. Casual Dining. **$8-$23.** 114 N Eufaula Ave 36027. Corner of W Broad St and US 431; in historic downtown area. L D

FAIRHOPE

▼ Mary Ann's
(251) 928-3663. Deli. Casual Dining. **$6-$17.** 85 N Bancroft St 36532. Corner of Equality St; downtown; in Windmill Market. L

HOMEWOOD

▼ Dave's Pizza
(205) 871-3283. Pizza. Casual Dining. **$8-$35.** 1819 29th Ave S 35209. Jct US 31, just w. L D

▼▼ Nabeel's Cafe and Market
(205) 879-9292. Greek. Casual Dining. **$7-$19.** 1706 Oxmoor Rd 35209. Jct Central Ave and Oxmoor Rd. L D

HUNTSVILLE

▼▼ Cantina Laredo
(256) 327-8580. Mexican. Casual Dining. **$9-$30.** 300 The Bridge St NW, Suite 110 35806. I-565 exit 14A, 0.5 mi n on SR 255 (Research Park Blvd), then w on Old Madison Pike; in Bridge Street Town Centre. L D &M

▼ Main St Cafe & Bakery
(256) 881-0044. Sandwiches Desserts. Quick Serve. **$6-$9.** 7500 S Memorial Pkwy 35802. I-565 exit 19A, 5 mi s on US 231/431/Memorial Pkwy. B L

▼▼ Pane e Vino Pizzeria
(256) 533-1180. Italian Pizza. Casual Dining. **$9-$14.** 300 Church St 35801. Corner of Williams Ave; downtown. L D

▼▼▼ Sage Grille
(256) 428-5424. Mediterranean. Fine Dining. **$9-$30.** 6800 Governors West NW 35806. I-565 exit 14A, 0.5 mi n on SR 255 (Research Park Blvd), just w on Old Madison Pike, then 0.5 mi n; in The Westin Huntsville. B L D &M

▼ Sam & Greg's Pizzeria - Gelateria
(256) 533-9030. Pizza. Casual Dining. **$6-$25.** 119 North Side Square 35801. Between Jefferson and Washington sts; downtown; across from courthouse. L D

IRONDALE

▼ Hamburger Heaven
(205) 951-3570. Burgers. Quick Serve. **$2-$7.** 1703 Crestwood Blvd 35210. I-20 exit 132B, just s on Montevallo Rd, then 0.5 mi e. L D &M

MOBILE

▼▼ Jerusalem Cafe
(251) 304-1155. Middle Eastern. Casual Dining. **$6-$17.** 4715 Airport Blvd, Suite 330 36608. I-65 exit 3 (Airport Blvd), 3 mi w; in Regency Square Shopping Center; behind Applebee's. L D

MONTGOMERY

▼▼ Sinclair's Cloverdale
(334) 834-7462. American. Casual Dining. **$8-$27.** 1051 E Fairview Ave 36106. I-65 exit 170, 1.7 mi e; corner of Boultier St. L D

MOUNTAIN BROOK

▼▼ La Paz Restaurant
(205) 879-2225. Mexican. Casual Dining. **$7-$17.** 99 Euclid Ave 35213. Just w of Church St. L D

ORANGE BEACH

▼▼ Cosmo's Restaurant
(251) 948-9663. Seafood. Casual Dining. **$8-$28.** 25753 Canal Rd 36561. On SR 180, just w of jct SR 161. L D &M

PRATTVILLE

▼▼ Chappy's Deli
(334) 290-3313. Sandwiches. Casual Dining. **$5-$11.** 585 Pinnacle Pl 36066. I-65 exit 179, just w. B L D &M ✎

TUSCALOOSA

▼▼▼ Epiphany Farm-to-Fork
(205) 344-5583. Southern American. Fine Dining. **$14-$25.** 519 Greensboro Ave 35401. Between University Blvd and 6th St; downtown. D

VESTAVIA HILLS

▼▼ Diplomat Deli
(205) 979-1515. Sandwiches Deli. Quick Serve. **$6-$20.** 1425 Montgomery Hwy 35216. I-65 exit 252, 1 mi n; in Park South Plaza. L D &M

▼▼ Mudtown Eat & Drink
(205) 967-3300. American. Casual Dining. **$9-$29.** 3144 Green Valley Rd 35243. Just e of US 280. L D

Arizona

GOLD CANYON

▼▼▼ Kokopelli's
(480) 671-5517. American. Fine Dining. **$8-$33.** 6100 S Kings Ranch Rd 85219. US 60 exit Kings Ranch Rd, 1 mi n; in Gold Canyon Golf Resort.
[B] [L] [D]

LAKE HAVASU CITY

▼▼ The Turtle Grill
(928) 855-1897. American. Casual Dining. **$9-$38.** 1000 McCulloch Blvd N 86403. 1.4 mi w of London Bridge, follow signs; in The Nautical Beachfront Resort. [B] [L] [D]

PHOENIX

▼▼▼ Alexi's Grill
(602) 279-0982. Northern Italian. Casual Dining. **$7-$29.** 3550 N Central Ave 85012. Just n of Osborn Rd. [L] [D]

▼▼▼ The Arrogant Butcher
(602) 324-8502. American. Gastropub. **$12-$34.** 2 E Jefferson St, #150 85004. Northwest corner of Jefferson and 1st sts; in CityScape. [L] [D]

▼▼ Aunt Chilada's Hideaway
(602) 944-1286. Mexican. Casual Dining. **$6-$18.** 7330 N Dreamy Draw Dr 85020. SR 51 exit 5 (Glendale Ave), 0.4 mi w to 16th St, 0.6 mi to Morten Ave, then just e. [L] [D]

▼▼ Cibo Urban Pizzeria Cafe
(602) 441-2697. Italian. Casual Dining. **$9-$17.** 603 N 5th Ave 85003. Corner of Fillmore St; downtown. [L] [D]

▼▼▼ North Italia
(602) 324-5600. Italian. Casual Dining. **$12-$34.** 4925 N 40th St 85018. Jct Camelback Rd, just s. [L] [D]

▼▼▼ Phoenix City Grille
(602) 266-3001. American. Casual Dining. **$12-$32.** 5816 N 16th St 85016. 0.8 mi n of Camelback Rd. [L] [D]

PINETOP-LAKESIDE

▼ Village Grill
(928) 368-2424. Burgers. Quick Serve. **$4-$12.** 1477 W White Mountain Blvd, Suite 4 85929. Jct Woodland Rd; in Lakeside. [L] [D]

SCOTTSDALE

▼▼▼ The Herb Box
(480) 289-6160. American. Casual Dining. **$15-$32.** 7134 E Stetson Dr 85251. Jct Scottsdale Rd, just w; in Southbridge District. [L] [D]

▼▼▼ NoRTH Italia
(480) 948-2055. New Italian. Casual Dining. **$10-$28.** 15024 N Scottsdale Rd 85254. Just w on Greenway Pkwy; in Kierland Commons.
[L] [D]

▼▼▼ Persian Room
(480) 614-1414. Middle Eastern. Fine Dining. **$9-$35.** 17040 N Scottsdale Rd 85255. Jct Bell Rd, just n. [L] [D]

▼▼▼ Stingray Sushi
(480) 427-2011. Sushi. Casual Dining. **$13-$30.** 15027 N Scottsdale Rd 85260. SR 101 exit 34 (Scottsdale Rd), 2.2 mi s; in Scottsdale Quarter.
[L] [D] [LATE]

▼▼▼ Tommy V's Urban Kitchen and Bar
(480) 427-2264. Italian. Casual Dining. **$15-$26.** 7303 E Indian School Rd 85251. Jct Scottsdale Rd, just e. [L] [D]

▼▼▼ Zinc Bistro
(480) 603-0922. French. Casual Dining. **$10-$36.** 15034 N Scottsdale Rd, Suite 140 85254. Just w of jct N Scottsdale Rd and Greenway-Hayden Loop; in Kierland Commons. [L] [D]

SEDONA

▼▼▼ Creekside Restaurant
(928) 282-1705. American. Casual Dining. **$12-$37.** 251 Hwy 179 86336. Jct SR 89A, just s. [B] [L] [D]

▼▼▼ The Heartline Cafe
(928) 282-0785. American. Fine Dining. **$8-$30.** 1600 W Hwy 89A 86336. On SR 89A, 1.5 mi s of jct SR 179. [D]

▼▼ Judi's Restaurant
(928) 282-4449. American. Casual Dining. **$11-$32.** 40 Soldier's Pass Rd 86336. Jct SR 179, 1 mi w on SR 89A; northeast corner. [L] [D]

▼▼ Mesa Grill
(928) 282-2400. Italian. Casual Dining. **$10-$39.** 1185 Airport Rd 86336. Jct SR 179, 1 mi w on SR 89A, 1 mi s. [B] [L] [D] [🛇M]

🆎🆎🆎 ▼▼▼ Rene At Tlaquepaque
(928) 282-9225. Continental. Fine Dining. **$9-$42.** 336 Hwy 179 86336. SR 89A, 0.3 mi s; in Tlaquepaque Arts & Crafts Village. [L] [D]

▼▼ Spoke & Wheel Tavern and Eatery
(928) 203-5334. American. Casual Dining. **$12-$39.** 160 Portal Ln 86336. Jct SR 89A, just s on SR 179, then just w; in Los Abrigados Resort & Spa. [B] [L] [D]

▼▼ Szechuan Chinese Restaurant & Sushi Bar
(928) 282-9288. Asian. Casual Dining. **$10-$21.** 1350 W Hwy 89A, Suite 21 86336. Jct SR 179, 1.3 mi w. [L] [D]

TEMPE

▼▼ Pita Jungle
(480) 804-0234. Mediterranean. Casual Dining. **$6-$15.** 1250 E Apache Blvd, Suite 113 85282. 0.4 mi e of jct Rural Rd and Apache Blvd.
[L] [D]

TUCSON

▼▼▼ Dakota Bar & Grill
(520) 298-7188. American. Casual Dining. **$11-$30.** 6541 E Tanque Verde Rd 85715. Jct Campbell Ave, 5.6 mi e on Grant Rd, just s.
[L] [D]

▼▼ Ghini's French Caffe
(520) 326-9095. French. Casual Dining. **$8-$13.** 1803 E Prince Rd 85719. Just w of Campbell Ave. [B] [L]

▼▼ Pasco Kitchen & Lounge
(520) 882-8013. New American. Casual Dining. **$11-$21.** 820 E University Blvd 85719. I-10 exit 257 (Speedway Blvd), 1.5 mi e, 0.3 mi s on Euclid Ave, then just e. [L] [D]

WILLIAMS

▼▼ Cruiser's Route 66 Bar & Grill
(928) 635-2445. American. Casual Dining. **$8-$20.** 233 W Route 66 86046. Jct Route 66 and 3rd St. [L] [D]

🆎🆎🆎 ▼▼▼ Western View Steakhouse
(928) 635-4400. Steak. Casual Dining. **$17-$45.** 2600 W Route 66 86046. I-40 exit 161, south on Route 66; in Best Western Plus Inn of Williams. [D] [🛇M]

Arkansas

EUREKA SPRINGS

▼▼▼ **Rogue's Manor at Sweet Spring**
(479) 253-4911. American. Fine Dining. **$14-$70.** 124 Spring St 72632.
Jct US 62, 0.5 mi n on US 62B Historic Loop; in historic district. D

California

AGOURA HILLS

▼▼ ▼▼ **Cronies Sports Bar and Grill**
(818) 889-0889. American. Gastropub. **$8-$15.** 5687 Kanan Rd 91301.
US 101 exit 36 (Kanan Rd), 1 mi n. B L D &M

▼▼ ▼▼ **The Latigo Kid**
(818) 889-1195. Mexican. Casual Dining. **$9-$20.** 5617 Kanan Rd
91301. US 101 N exit 36 (Kanan Rd), just e. L D &M

▼▼ ▼▼ **The Old Place**
(818) 706-9001. Steak Small Plates. Casual Dining. **$14-$20.** 29983
Mulholland Hwy 91301. US 101 N exit 36 (Kanan Rd), 3.1 mi w to Trout-
dale Dr, 0.4 mi s, then just e. L D

▼▼ ▼▼ **Tavern 101 American Grill**
(818) 991-7227. Barbecue. Casual Dining. **$12-$27.** 28434 Roadside Dr
91301. US 101 N exit 36 (Kanan Rd), just w, then just s.
L D &M

▼▼ ▼▼ **Wildflour Bakery and Cafe**
(818) 597-8774. Breakfast. Quick Serve. **$4-$15.** 29105 Canwood St
91301. US 101 N exit 36 (Kanan Rd), just e, then just s. B L &M

ALISO VIEJO

▼▼ ▼▼ **Cosmo's Italian Kitchen**
(949) 448-9040. Italian. Casual Dining. **$10-$19.** 23411 Aliso Viejo Pkwy,
Suite A 92656. I-5 exit 90 (Alicia Pkwy), 1 mi w, 0.4 mi n on Paseo de
Valencia, then 1.4 mi w on Laguna Hills Dr (which becomes Aliso Viejo
Pkwy); in Aliso Viejo Creek Marketplace. L D

ARROYO GRANDE

▼▼ ▼▼ **Alphy's Broiler and Coffee House**
(805) 473-1133. American. Quick Serve. **$6-$10.** 130 W Branch St
93420. US 101 N exit 187A (SR 227/E Grand Ave), just e.
B L D &M

AVILA BEACH

▼▼ ▼▼ **The Custom House**
(805) 595-7555. American. Casual Dining. **$10-$38.** 404 Front St 93424.
US 101 northbound, exit 195 (Avila Beach Dr), 3 mi w, then just s.
B L D

▼▼▼ ▼▼ **The Gardens of Avila**
(805) 595-7302. American. Casual Dining. **$10-$34.** 1215 Avila Beach Dr
93405. US 101 exit 195 (Avila Beach Dr), 1 mi w; in Sycamore Mineral
Springs. B L D

BENICIA

▼▼ ▼▼ **First St Cafe & Catering**
(707) 745-1400. American. Casual Dining. **$10-$25.** 440 First St 94510.
I-780 exit 2nd St/Downtown Benicia W, just n on Military St, then 0.5 mi w;
jct East E St. B L D &M

BERKELEY

(AAA) ▼▼ ▼▼ **Bistro Liaison**
(510) 849-2155. French. Fine Dining. **$14-$28.** 1849 Shattuck Ave
94709. I-80 exit 11 (University Ave), 2 mi e, then just n at Hearst Ave.
L D 🍽

BEVERLY HILLS

▼▼ ▼▼ ▼▼ **Bouchon**
(310) 271-9910. French. Fine Dining. **$18-$49.** 235 N Canon Dr 90210.
I-10 exit 7A (La Cienega Blvd), 0.6 mi w, 2 mi n, 1.2 mi w on Wilshire
Blvd, then just n. L D

BIG BEAR LAKE

▼▼ **Village Pizza**
(909) 866-8505. Italian. Casual Dining. **$11-$30.** 40568 Village Dr 92315.
SR 18, 0.9 mi w of Pine Knot Ave. L D &M

BISHOP

▼▼ ▼▼ **Upper Crust Pizza Company**
(760) 872-8153. Pizza. Casual Dining. **$7-$29.** 1180 N Main St 93514.
On US 395. L D 🛍

BLYTHE

▼▼ ▼▼ **Rosita's**
(760) 922-4090. Mexican. Casual Dining. **$6-$16.** 611 W Hobsonway
92225. I-10 exit 239 (Lovekin Blvd), just n, then just e.
B L D 🛍

BURBANK

▼▼ ▼▼ **Don Cuco Mexican Restaurant**
(818) 955-8895. Mexican. Casual Dining. **$11-$23.** 218 E Orange Grove
Ave 91502. US 5 exit 146A (E Angeleno Ave) 0.3 mi n, then just e.
L D &M

CALABASAS

▼▼ ▼▼ **King's Fish House**
(818) 225-1979. Seafood. Casual Dining. **$13-$45.** 4798 Commons Way
91302. US 101 exit 30 (Pkwy Calabasas) northbound, just e, then just s.
L D

▼▼ ▼▼ **Le Pain Quotidien**
(747) 444-5163. Breakfast Natural/Organic. Casual Dining. **$9-$17.** 4719
Commons Way 91302. US 101 N exit 29 (Valley Circle Blvd), just w, then
0.6 mi n; in Commons Shopping Center. B L D &M

▼▼▼ ▼▼ **Pedaler's Fork**
(818) 225-8231. Natural/Organic Specialty. Casual Dining. **$12-$37.**
23504 Calabasas Rd 91302. US 101 W exit 29 (Valley Circle Blvd), just
s, then just w. B L D &M

CAMARILLO

▼▼▼ ▼▼ **The 805 Pour House**
(805) 383-8800. Specialty Small Plates. Casual Dining. **$11-$20.** 2135 E
Ventura Blvd 93010. US 101 N exit 53B (E Daily Dr) northbound, 0.5 mi,
then just w. L D &M

▼▼▼ ▼▼ **Bistro 13**
(805) 383-3388. Italian. Casual Dining. **$12-$26.** 4910 Verdugo Way
93010. US 101 exit 52 (Pleasant Valley Rd/Santa Rosa Rd) northbound,
just e; in Pardee Plaza. L D

CAMBRIA

▼▼▼ ▼▼ **Cambria Pines Lodge Restaurant**
(805) 927-4200. American. Casual Dining. **$12-$32.** 2905 Burton Dr
93428. SR 1 N, exit Burton Way, 0.3 mi e.
🍸 B L D 🍽

▼▼▼ ▼▼ **La Terraza**
(805) 927-7700. Mexican. Casual Dining. **$7-$17.** 1316 Tamson St
93428. SR 1 N exit Cambria St, just e, then just s.
B L D &M 🍽

▼▼▼ Old Stone Station
(805) 927-4229. American. Casual Dining. **$8-$36.** 713 Main St 93428. SR 1 exit Main St northbound, 2 mi ne; exit Cambria Dr southbound, just se. ⌐L⌐ ⌐D⌐

⟨AAA⟩ ▼▼▼ Robin's
(805) 927-5007. International. Casual Dining. **$18-$32.** 4095 Burton Dr 93428. SR 1 exit Burton Dr, 1 mi ne. ⌐L⌐ ⌐D⌐ ⌐Ⅻ⌐

▼▼ Wild Ginger
(805) 927-1001. Asian. Casual Dining. **$14-$19.** 2380 Main St 93428. SR 1 exit Main St northbound, 1.5 mi nw; in East Village area.
⌐L⌐ ⌐D⌐ ⌐Ⅻ⌐

CAMPBELL

▼▼ Grill 'Em Steakhouse
(408) 371-8729. Steak. Casual Dining. **$8-$24.** 2509 S Bascom Ave 95008. SR 17 exit Hamilton Ave, 0.4 mi e, then 1.1 mi s. ⌐L⌐ ⌐D⌐ ⌐&M⌐

CARLSBAD

▼▼▼ Bistro West
(760) 930-8008. American. Casual Dining. **$11-$29.** 4960 Avenida Encinas 92008. I-5 exit 48 (Cannon Rd), just w, then just n; next to West Inn & Suites. ⌐L⌐ ⌐D⌐ ⌐&M⌐

▼▼ Broken Yolk Cafe
(760) 943-8182. American. Casual Dining. **$6-$13.** 7670 El Camino Real 92009. I-5 exit 44 (La Costa Ave), 1.8 mi e. ⌐B⌐ ⌐L⌐

▼▼ Fresco Trattoria & Bar
(760) 720-3737. Mediterranean. Casual Dining. **$14-$34.** 264 Carlsbad Village Dr 92008. I-5 exit 50 (Carlsbad Village Dr), 0.9 mi w.
⌐L⌐ ⌐D⌐ ⌐&M⌐

▼▼▼ Vigilucci's Cucina Italiana
(760) 434-2500. Italian. Casual Dining. **$15-$39.** 2943 State St 92008. I-5 exit 50 (Carlsbad Village Dr), just w, then just n. ⌐L⌐ ⌐D⌐ ⌐&M⌐

CARMEL-BY-THE-SEA

▼▼▼ Casanova
(831) 625-0501. French. Fine Dining. **$14-$52.** 5th Ave between Mission St & San Carlos St 93922. Just n of Ocean Ave. ⌐L⌐ ⌐D⌐ ⌐&M⌐

CATHEDRAL CITY

▼▼ Don & Sweet Sue's Cafe
(760) 770-2760. American. Casual Dining. **$10-$17.** 68-955 Ramon Rd 92234. I-10 exit 126 (Date Palm Dr), 2.2 mi s, then just w.
⌐B⌐ ⌐L⌐ ⌐D⌐ ⌐◥⌐

CHULA VISTA

▼▼ La Bella Pizza Garden - La Bella Cafe & Games
(619) 426-8820. Pizza. Casual Dining. **$5-$24.** 373 3rd Ave 91910. I-805 exit 7B (H Street W), 1.5 mi w, then just 0.3 mi nw. ⌐B⌐ ⌐L⌐ ⌐D⌐ ⌐&M⌐

CLAREMONT

▼▼ Union on Yale
(909) 833-5104. Italian. Casual Dining. **$10-$48.** 232 Yale Ave 91711. I-10 exit 47 (Indian Hill Blvd), just n, just e on Bonita Ave, then just s.
⌐L⌐ ⌐D⌐ ⌐&M⌐

CORONA

▼▼ Hunny's Cafe
(951) 735-7020. American. Casual Dining. **$7-$18.** 402 S Corona Mall 92879. SR 91 exit 50B (S Main St) eastbound; exit 50 westbound, just s, then just e. ⌐B⌐ ⌐L⌐ ⌐D⌐ ⌐◥⌐

CORONADO

▼▼▼ Chez Loma French Bistro
(619) 435-0661. French. Casual Dining. **$10-$33.** 1132 Loma Ave 92118. I-5 exit 14A (Coronado Bridge), 2.4 mi nw, 1 mi sw on Orange Ave, then just n. ⌐L⌐ ⌐D⌐ ⌐◥⌐

▼▼ Village Pizzeria
(619) 522-0449. Italian. Casual Dining. **$12-$52.** 1206 Orange Ave 92118. I-15 exit 14A (Coronado Bridge), 2.3 mi nw, then 0.9 mi sw.
⌐L⌐ ⌐D⌐ ⌐&M⌐

COSTA MESA

▼▼ Nello Cucina
(714) 540-3365. Italian. Casual Dining. **$11-$28.** 3333 Bear St, Suite 118 92626. SR 73 exit 17B (Bear St), 0.5 mi n. ⌐L⌐ ⌐D⌐ ⌐◥⌐

DAVIS

▼▼ Paesanos
(530) 758-8646. Italian Pizza. Casual Dining. **$10-$14.** 139 G St 95616. I-80 exit 72B (Richards Blvd) westbound; exit 72 eastbound, just nw to 1st St, just e, then just n. ⌐L⌐ ⌐D⌐ ⌐&M⌐

DEL MAR

▼▼▼ Pacifica Del Mar
(858) 792-0476. Seafood. Casual Dining. **$12-$36.** 1555 Camino Del Mar, Suite 321 92014. I-5 exit 34 (Del Mar Heights Rd), 1 mi w, then 1 mi. ⌐L⌐ ⌐D⌐ ⌐&M⌐

▼▼▼ Sbicca
(858) 481-1001. California. Casual Dining. **$9-$34.** 215 15th St 92014. I-5 exit 34 (Del Mar Heights Rd), 1 mi w, 1 mi n, then just w.
⌐L⌐ ⌐D⌐ ⌐Ⅻ⌐

DIAMOND BAR

▼▼ Boulevard 574
(909) 861-1517. American. Gastropub. **$9-$12.** 574 N Diamond Bar Blvd 91765. I-60 exit 26 (Diamond Bar Blvd), just ne. ⌐B⌐ ⌐L⌐ ⌐D⌐ ⌐&M⌐

EL DORADO HILLS

▼ Hop House
(916) 960-3057. American. Quick Serve. **$10-$16.** 4364 Town Center Blvd 95762. US 50 exit 30A (Latrobe Rd) eastbound; exit 30 westbound, just s, just e on Town Center Blvd; in Town Center Shopping Center; adjacent to Bistro 33. ⌐L⌐ ⌐D⌐ ⌐&M⌐

▼▼ Selland's Market Cafe
(916) 932-5025. American. Quick Serve. **$9-$21.** 4370 Town Center Blvd, Suite 120 95762. US 50 exit 30A (Latrobe Rd) eastbound; exit 30 westbound, just se, then just e; in Town Center Shopping Center.
⌐L⌐ ⌐D⌐ ⌐&M⌐

EL SEGUNDO

▼▼ Marmalade Cafe
(310) 648-7200. American. Casual Dining. **$10-$25.** 2014 Park Pl 90245. I-405 exit 43 (Rosecrans Ave), 1.5 mi w, then just n; in Plaza El Segundo. ⌐B⌐ ⌐L⌐ ⌐D⌐ ⌐&M⌐

ENCINITAS

▼▼ Le Papagayo
(760) 944-8252. American Fusion. Casual Dining. **$9-$25.** 1002 N Coast Hwy 101 92024. I-5 exit 42 (Encinitas Blvd), just e, 0.3 mi n on N Coast Hwy 101, then 1.3 mi. ⌐B⌐ ⌐L⌐ ⌐D⌐ ⌐&M⌐

ESCONDIDO

▼▼▼ Vincent's
(760) 745-3835. French. Casual Dining. **$10-$36.** 113 W Grand Ave 92025. I-15 exit 31 (Valley Pkwy), 0.6 mi se, then 0.5 mi e. ⌐D⌐

FALLBROOK

▼▼ **Aqua Terra**
(760) 728-5881. American. Casual Dining. **$8-$38.** 2001 Old Hwy 395 92028. I-15 exit 46 (SR 76/Pala Rd/Oceanside), just w, then 2 mi n; in Pala Mesa Resort. ⃞B⃞ ⃞L⃞ ⃞D⃞ ⃞◥⃞

▼▼ **La Caseta Fine Mexican Food**
(760) 728-9737. Mexican. Casual Dining. **$9-$16.** 111 N Vine St 92028. I-15 exit 51 (Mission Rd), 4.9 mi w, then just s. ⃞L⃞ ⃞D⃞ ⃞◥⃞

FOLSOM

▼ **Karen's Bakery Cafe & Catering**
(916) 985-2665. Breads/Pastries Sandwiches. Quick Serve. **$12-$15.** 705 Gold Lake Dr, Suite 340 95630. Jct Leidesdorf St; downtown; near American River Bridge. ⃞B⃞ ⃞L⃞ ⃞&M⃞

FOOTHILL RANCH

▼▼ **California Fish Grill**
(949) 470-9600. Seafood. Quick Serve. **$7-$14.** 41 Auto Center Dr, Suite 113 92610. I-5 exit 92A (Lake Forest Dr) northbound exit 92 (Bake Pkwy/Lake Forest Dr); southbound, 5 mi e on Lake Forest Dr, just n on Towne Center, then just e. ⃞L⃞ ⃞D⃞

FORESTVILLE

▼ **Russian River Pub**
(707) 887-7932. Burgers Sandwiches. Casual Dining. **$8-$14.** 11829 River Rd 95436. 7 mi w of jct SR 101. ⃞L⃞ ⃞D⃞

FORT BRAGG

▼▼ **Piaci Pub & Pizzeria**
(707) 961-1133. Italian Pizza. Casual Dining. **$9-$20.** 120 W Redwood Ave 95437. SR 1 (N Main St), just w; downtown. ⃞L⃞ ⃞D⃞

FREMONT

▼ **Falafel, Etc.**
(510) 795-7170. Middle Eastern. Quick Serve. **$8-$15.** 39200 Fremont Blvd 94538. I-880 exit Mowry Ave, 1.5 mi e, then just s at Beacon Ave; in Fremont Plaza Shopping Center. ⃞L⃞ ⃞D⃞ ⃞&M⃞

GARBERVILLE

▲▲▲◢ ▼▼▼ **Benbow Inn Restaurant**
(707) 923-2124. Regional California. Fine Dining. **$21-$46.** 445 Lake Benbow Dr 95542. US 101 exit 636 (Benbow Lake Rd), just w; in Benbow Historic Inn. ⃞B⃞ ⃞L⃞ ⃞D⃞

GOLETA

▼▼ **Hollister Brewing Company**
(805) 968-2810. American. Gastropub. **$7-$14.** 6980 Marketplace Dr 93117. US 101 N exit 108 (Glen Annie Rd), just w, then just n. ⃞L⃞ ⃞D⃞

HALF MOON BAY

▼▼ **Half Moon Bay Brewing Company**
(650) 728-2739. American. Casual Dining. **$10-$24.** 390 Capistrano Rd 94018. SR 1, just w. ⃞L⃞ ⃞D⃞ ⃞◢⃞

HEALDSBURG

▼▼▼ **Spoonbar**
(707) 433-7222. Mediterranean. Casual Dining. **$15-$50.** 219 Healdsburg Ave 95448. Between Matheson and Mill sts; in H2 Hotel. ⃞D⃞

HEMET

▼▼ **Sweet Baby Jane's BBQ Bar & Grill**
(951) 652-4227. Barbecue. Casual Dining. **$8-$30.** 124 S Harvard St 92543. SR 74, just e of State St, just s. ⃞L⃞ ⃞D⃞ ⃞◥⃞

HESPERIA

▼▼ **Cancun Mexican Seafood Restaurant**
(760) 956-7720. Mexican Seafood. Casual Dining. **$9-$20.** 15550 Main St, Suite A-1 92345. I-15 exit 143 (Hesperia/Main St), 3.4 mi e; in The Plaza on Main Street Shopping Center. ⃞L⃞ ⃞D⃞ ⃞◥⃞

HIGHLAND

▼▼ **Mi Cocina Restaurant**
(909) 425-0393. Mexican. Casual Dining. **$6-$19.** 27961 Highland Ave 92346. SR 330 exit Highland Ave, just w; in San Manuel Village. ⃞L⃞ ⃞D⃞

IDYLLWILD

▼▼ **Gastrognome Restaurant**
(951) 659-5055. American. Casual Dining. **$8-$32.** 54381 Ridgeview Dr 92549. Just e of SR 243; in Village Center. ⃞B⃞ ⃞L⃞ ⃞D⃞

INDIAN WELLS

▼▼▼ **The Nest**
(760) 346-2314. Continental. Casual Dining. **$13-$38.** 75-188 Hwy 111 92210. I-10 exit 134 (Cook St), 4.4 mi s, then just e. ⃞D⃞ ⃞&M⃞ ⃞◥⃞

INDUSTRY

▼▼▼ **Red**
(626) 854-2509. California Steak Seafood. Casual Dining. **$20-$42.** 1 Industry Hills Pkwy 91744. SR 60 exit 18 (Azusa Ave), 1.3 mi n, then 0.5 mi w; in Pacific Palms Resort. ⃞◼⃞ ⃞L⃞ ⃞D⃞ ⃞LATE⃞ ⃞&M⃞

IRVINE

▼▼▼ **Gulliver's**
(949) 833-8411. American. Gastropub. **$10-$50.** 18482 MacArthur Blvd 92612. I-405 exit 8 (MacArthur Blvd/John Wayne Airport), just sw. ⃞L⃞ ⃞D⃞ ⃞◥⃞

JULIAN

▼▼ **Julian Grille**
(760) 765-0173. American. Casual Dining. **$8-$32.** 2224 Main St 92036. Just w of SR 78 and 79. ⃞L⃞ ⃞D⃞

▼▼ **Romano's Restaurant**
(760) 765-1003. Italian. Casual Dining. **$8-$25.** 2718 B St 92036. Just s of SR 78 and 79. ⃞L⃞ ⃞D⃞ ⃞◢⃞ ⃞◥⃞

KERNVILLE

▼ **Cheryl's Diner**
(760) 376-6131. American. Casual Dining. **$6-$20.** 11030 Kernville Rd 93238. SR 155 (Kernville Rd/Wofford Heights Blvd) westbound 10.8 mi, just e. Adjacent to Riverside Park. ⃞B⃞ ⃞L⃞ ⃞D⃞ ⃞◥⃞

▼▼ **Kern River Brewing Company**
(760) 376-2337. Burgers. Gastropub. **$8-$12.** 13415 Sierra Way 93238. At Sierra Way; just n of Kernville Rd. ⃞L⃞ ⃞D⃞

LA CAÑADA FLINTRIDGE

▼▼ **Cafe Sole**
(818) 790-6062. Italian. Casual Dining. **$11-$22.** 1929 Verdugo Blvd 91011. I-210 exit 20 (SR 2/Angeles Crest Hwy), just s, just w on Foothill Blvd, then just sw. ⃞L⃞ ⃞D⃞

LAGUNA BEACH

▼▼ **Ristorante Rumari**
(949) 494-0400. Italian. Casual Dining. **$16-$46.** 1826 S Coast Hwy 92651. SR 133, 1 mi s on SR 1. ⃞D⃞

LA HABRA

▼▼ El Cholo Cafe

(562) 691-4618. Mexican. Casual Dining. $8-$18. 840 E Whittier Blvd 90631. 1.5 mi e of SR 39 (Beach Blvd). [L] [D]

LA JOLLA

▼▼▼▼ Cafe Japengo

(858) 450-3355. Pacific Rim. Casual Dining. $16-$42. 8960 University Center Ln 92122. I-5 exit 28 (La Jolla Village Dr), just e; across from Hyatt Regency La Jolla. [L] [D] [&M]

▼▼▼▼ Nine-Ten

(858) 964-5400. California. Fine Dining. $12-$39. 910 Prospect St 92037. I-5 exit 28 (La Jolla Village Dr) southbound, 0.7 mi w to Torrey Pines Rd, 2.5 mi sw to Prospect St, then 0.6 mi w; exit 26A (La Jolla Pkwy) northbound, 1.5 mi n to Torrey Pines Rd, 1 mi sw, then 0.6 mi w; in The Grande Colonial. [B] [L] [D] [N]

▼▼▼▼ Tapenade

(858) 551-7500. French. Fine Dining. $14-$38. 7612 Fay Ave 92037. I-5 exit 28 (La Jolla Village Dr) southbound; 1 mi w to Torrey Pines Rd, 2.5 mi sw to Prospect St, 1 mi sw, then 0.3 mi se; exit 26A (La Jolla Pkwy) northbound, 1.5 mi n to Torrey Pines Rd, 1.2 mi w to Prospect St, 1 mi sw, then 0.3 mi se. [L] [D] [&M] [N]

LAKE ELSINORE

▼▼▼▼ Vincenzo's Olive Tree

(951) 674-8941. Southern Italian. Casual Dining. $8-$25. 31712 Casino Dr, Suite 3B 92530. I-15 exit 73 (Diamond Dr/Railroad Canyon Rd), just w, then just s. [L] [D] [N]

LAKE FOREST

▼▼ The Original Peppino's Italian Family Restaurant

(949) 951-2611. Traditional Italian Pizza. Casual Dining. $8-$23. 23600 Rockfield Blvd 92630. I-5 exit 92A (Lake Forest Dr) northbound; exit 92 (Bake Pkwy/Lake Forest Dr) southbound, 0.5 mi e, then just n. [L] [D]

LA MESA

▼▼ Anthony's Fish Grotto

(619) 463-0368. Seafood. Casual Dining. $9-$50. 9530 Murray Dr 91942. I-8 exit 14C (Severin Dr), just n. [L] [D] [&M]

LARKSPUR

▼▼▼▼ Left Bank

(415) 927-3331. French. Casual Dining. $10-$32. 507 Magnolia Ave 94939. At Ward St; downtown. [L] [D]

LEE VINING

▼▼ Whoa Nellie Deli

(760) 647-1088. American. Casual Dining. $9-$25. 22 Vista Point Dr 93541. Jct US 395, at SR 120; in Tioga Mobil Gas Mart.

[B] [L] [D] [𝕏]

LITTLE RIVER

▼▼▼▼ Little River Inn Restaurant

(707) 937-5942. California. Fine Dining. $15-$32. 7901 N SR 1 95456. On SR 1, just s of Van Damme State Park entrance; in Little River Inn.

[⊟] [B] [D]

LONG BEACH

▼▼ The Attic

(562) 433-0153. Southern American. Casual Dining. $10-$28. 3441 E Broadway 90803. Jct Ocean Blvd and Newport Ave, 0.7 mi n.

[B] [L] [D]

LOS ANGELES

▼▼▼▼ Ca' Brea Italian Country Cuisine

(323) 938-2863. Northern Italian. Fine Dining. $13-$26. 346 S La Brea Ave 90036. I-10 exit 8 (La Brea Ave), 2.6 mi n. [B] [L] [D] [N]

▼▼▼▼ Chaya Brasserie

(310) 859-8833. Continental. Casual Dining. $18-$35. 8741 Alden Dr 90048. I-10 exit 7A (La Cienega Blvd), 2.2 mi n to San Vincentes Blvd, just ne, then just w. [L] [D]

▼▼▼▼ Napa Valley Grille

(310) 824-3322. American. Fine Dining. $14-$44. 1100 Glendon Ave 90024. I-405 exit 55B (Wilshire Blvd), 0.6 mi e, then just n; in Westwood Village. [L] [D]

▼▼ Pizzicotto

(310) 442-7188. Italian. Casual Dining. $11-$18. 11758 San Vicente Blvd 90049. I-405 exit 55A (Wilshire Blvd), 0.6 mi w, then 0.6 mi nw; in Brentwood area. [L] [D]

▼▼ Rockwell Table & Stage

(323) 661-6163. California. Casual Dining. $18-$36. 1714 N Vermont Ave 90027. US 101 exit 6A (Vermont Ave), 1.5 mi n; in Los Felix area. [L] [D] [N]

▼▼ Tanino Ristorante

(310) 208-0444. Italian. Casual Dining. $13-$40. 1043 Westwood Blvd 90024. I-405 exit 55B (Wilshire Blvd), 0.5 mi e, then just n; in Westwood Village. [L] [D]

MAMMOTH LAKES

▼▼ Base Camp

(760) 934-3900. American. Casual Dining. $9-$18. 3325 Main St 93546. On SR 203, 0.3 mi w of Sierra Park Rd. [B] [L] [𝕏]

▼▼ Toomey's

(760) 924-4408. American. Quick Serve. $9-$33. 6085 Minaret Rd 93546. Just n of SR 203; in the Village Center. [B] [L] [D] [&M] [𝕏]

MARINA DEL REY

▼▼ The Warehouse Restaurant

(310) 823-5451. Seafood Steak. Casual Dining. $19-$39. 4499 Admiralty Way 90292. SR 90 (Marina Frwy) exit Lincoln Blvd (SR 1), just s, then just w on Bali Way. [L] [D] [&M]

MARYSVILLE

▼ The Brick Coffee House Cafe

(530) 743-5283. American. Quick Serve. $6-$11. 316 D St 95901. Between 3rd and 4th sts; center; in historic downtown. [B] [L]

MENDOCINO

🆔 ▼▼▼▼ The Ravens'

(707) 937-5615. Vegan. Fine Dining. $15-$27. 44850 Comptche-Ukiah Rd 95460. SR 1 exit Comptche-Ukiah Rd, just e; in Stanford Inn by the Sea Eco-Resort. [⊟] [B] [D] [𝕏]

MONROVIA

▼▼ Sunday's Old Town Bistro

(626) 303-7100. French Sandwiches Soup. Casual Dining. $9-$15. 520 S Myrtle Ave 91016. I-210 exit 34 (Myrtle Ave), just n. [B] [L] [D] [&M]

MONTEREY

▼▼▼▼ Cafe Fina
(831) 372-5200. Seafood. Fine Dining. **$10-$30.** 47 Fishermans Wharf #1 93940. On Fisherman's Wharf. ⒧ ⒟

▼▼▼▼ The C Restaurant + Bar
(831) 375-4800. California Seafood. Casual Dining. **$12-$58.** 750 Cannery Row 93940. Between Prescott and David aves; in InterContinental The Clement Monterey. ⒝ ⒧ ⒟ 🅰Ⓜ

▼▼▼▼ Tarpy's Roadhouse
(831) 647-1444. Regional American. Fine Dining. **$12-$79.** 2999 Monterey Salinas Hwy 93940. On SR 68, 2.5 mi e of jct SR 1.
⒧ ⒟ 🅰Ⓜ ⒜

MONTROSE

▼▼▼▼ New Moon Restaurant
(818) 249-4393. Chinese. Casual Dining. **$10-$16.** 2138 Verdugo Blvd 91020. I-210 exit 18 (Oceanview Blvd), just s to Honolulu Ave, just e, then just ne. ⒧ ⒟

▼▼▼▼ Oceanview Restaurant
(818) 248-2722. American. Casual Dining. **$8-$30.** 3826 Oceanview Blvd 91020. I-210 exit 18 (Oceanview Blvd), 0.4 mi s. ⒝ ⒧ ⒟ 🅰Ⓜ

MORRO BAY

▼▼▼ Blue Skye Coastal Cafe
(805) 772-8988. Seafood. Casual Dining. **$7-$19.** 699 Embarcadero #6 93442. SR 1 exit Main St southbound, 0.5 mi s to Harbor Blvd, 0.3 mi w, then just s; exit Morro Bay Blvd northbound, just w, 0.7 mi w on Harbor Blvd, then just s. ⒝ ⒧ ⒟ 🅰Ⓜ ⒜

▼▼▼▼ Dorn's Breakers Cafe
(805) 772-4415. Seafood. Casual Dining. **$10-$40.** 801 Market Ave 93442. SR 1 N exit 278 (Morro Bay Blvd), 0.5 mi w; corner of Morro Bay Blvd. ⒝ ⒧ ⒟ ⒜

▼▼▼ Harbor Hut Restaurant
(805) 772-2255. Seafood. Casual Dining. **$9-$35.** 1205 Embarcadero 93442. From Main St, just w on Harbor Dr. ⒧ ⒟ 🅰Ⓜ ⒜

MOSS BEACH

🅰🅰🅰⟋ ▼▼▼ Moss Beach Distillery
(650) 728-5595. Seafood. Casual Dining. **$13-$39.** 140 Beach Way 94038. SR 1 exit Cypress St, 6 mi n of jct SR 92. ⒧ ⒟

MOUNTAIN VIEW

▼▼▼▼ Cascal
(650) 940-9500. Latin American Small Plates. Casual Dining. **$13-$29.** 400 Castro St 94041. Corner of Castro and California sts; downtown.
⒧ ⒟

MURPHYS

▼▼▼▼ Rob's Place
(209) 813-7003. New American. Casual Dining. **$12-$26.** 140 Main St 95247. Jct Main St and Big Trees Rd; downtown. ⒧ ⒟

NEEDLES

▼▼▼▼ Juicy's Famous River Cafe
(760) 326-2233. Breakfast Burgers. Casual Dining. **$10-$20.** 2411 W Broadway 92363. I-40 exit 141 (W Broadway/River Rd), just se; on Business Loop I-40. ⒝ ⒧ ⒟

▼▼▼▼ River City Pizza Co.
(760) 326-9191. Italian. Casual Dining. **$6-$13.** 1901 Needles Hwy 92363. I-40 exit 141 (W Broadway/River Rd), 0.7 mi se on Business Loop I-40. ⒧ ⒟ ⓢ

NEWPORT BEACH

▼▼▼▼ Bayside Restaurant
(949) 721-1222. American. Casual Dining. **$14-$36.** 900 Bayside Dr 92660. SR 73 exit 15 (Jamboree Rd), 3.5 mi s to Pacific Coast Hwy, then just nw. ⒧ ⒟

OAKHURST

🅰🅰🅰⟋ ▼▼▼ Crab Cakes
(559) 641-7667. Seafood. Casual Dining. **$10-$40.** 49271 Golden Oak Loop 93644. Just off SR 41; center. ⒧ ⒟

OCEANO

▼▼▼ Old Juan's Cantina
(805) 489-5680. Mexican. Casual Dining. **$8-$18.** 649 Pier Ave 93445. SR 1, just w. ⒧ ⒟

▼▼▼ Rock & Roll Diner
(805) 473-2040. American. Casual Dining. **$6-$18.** 1300 Railroad St 93445. On SR 1; jct Mendel Dr. ⒝ ⒧ ⒟ ⓢ

OCEANSIDE

▼▼▼ Fratelli's Italian Kitchen
(760) 696-9007. Italian. Casual Dining. **$12-$28.** 3915 Mission Ave, Suite 12 92058. I-5 exit 53 (Mission Ave), 3.5 mi e; in Mission Douglas Plaza.
⒧ ⒟ 🅰Ⓜ

OJAI

▼▼▼ The Deer Lodge
(805) 646-4256. Steak Barbecue. Casual Dining. **$15-$48.** 2261 Maricopa Hwy 93023. SR 33, 1 mi n. ⒧ ⒟ ⓁⒶⓉⒺ ⓢ

🅰🅰🅰⟋ ▼▼▼ ▼▼▼ Olivella
(805) 640-2100. California. Fine Dining. **$20-$50.** 905 Country Club Dr 93023. 1 mi w on SR 150, just s; in Ojai Valley Inn & Spa. ⒟ 🅰Ⓜ

▼▼▼ Sea Fresh
(805) 646-7747. Seafood. Casual Dining. **$7-$17.** 533 E Ojai Ave 93023. On SR 150; center of downtown. ⒝ ⒧ ⒟ 🅰Ⓜ

OXNARD

▼ PizzaRev
(805) 278-1727. Pizza. Quick Serve. **$10-$12.** 1831 N Rose Ave 93030. US 101 exit 61 (Rose Ave), 0.3 mi w. ⒧ ⒟ 🅰Ⓜ

▼▼▼▼ Waterside Restaurant and Wine Bar
(805) 985-4677. American. Casual Dining. **$12-$38.** 3500 S Harbor Blvd 93035. US 101 N exit 64 (Victoria Ave), 5.5 mi sw, 0.5 mi w on W Channel Islands Blvd, then just s. ⒧ ⒟ 🅰Ⓜ

PALM DESERT

▼▼▼ Cafe Des Beaux Arts
(760) 346-0669. Provincial French. Casual Dining. **$13-$30.** 73-640 El Paseo 92260. Just s of SR 111; corner of Larkspur Ln.
⒝ ⒧ ⒟ 🅰Ⓜ

▼▼▼ Cuistot
(760) 340-1000. French. Fine Dining. **$15-$45.** 72-595 El Paseo 92260. I-10 exit 131 (Monterey Ave), 5.7 mi s, then 0.6 mi w. ⒧ ⒟ ⓢ

▼▼▼ Daily Grill
(760) 779-9911. American. Casual Dining. **$9-$33.** 73061 El Paseo 92260. On SR 74, just s of SR 111, just e. ⒧ ⒟ 🅰Ⓜ

▼ Fisherman's Market & Grill
(760) 776-6533. Seafood. Quick Serve. **$8-$24.** 44-250 Town Center Way, Suite C-2 92260. I-10 exit 131 (Monterey Ave), 5.7 mi s, 0.4 mi w on SR 111, then 0.3 mi n on Village Center Dr. ⒧ ⒟ 🅰Ⓜ ⓢ

▽▽ Roc's Firehouse Grille
(760) 340-3222. American. Casual Dining. **$9-$35.** 36-891 Cook St, Suite 10 92211. I-10 exit 134 (Cook St), just s; in The Village at University Park. [L] [D] [LATE] [◨]

PALM SPRINGS

▽▽ Blue Coyote Bar & Grill
(760) 327-1196. Southwestern. Casual Dining. **$9-$25.** 445 N Palm Canyon Dr 92262. 0.4 mi n of Tahquitz Canyon Way; downtown.
[L] [D] [&M]

▽▽ El Mirasol at Los Arboles
(760) 459-3136. Regional Mexican. Casual Dining. **$14-$20.** 784 N Indian Canyon Dr 92262. 0.6 mi n of Tahquitz Canyon Way.
[L] [D] [&M]

▽▽ ▽▽ Europa Restaurant at the Villa Royale Inn
(760) 327-2314. Continental. Fine Dining. **$25-$39.** 1620 S Indian Tr 92264. 2 mi se of Tahquitz Canyon Way on Palm Canyon Dr, just n; in Villa Royale Inn. [D]

▽▽ Fisherman's Market & Grill
(760) 327-1766. Seafood. Quick Serve. **$9-$30.** 235 S Indian Canyon Dr 92262. From Tahquitz Canyon Way, just s; downtown.
[L] [D] [&M] [◨]

▽▽ Sherman's Deli & Bakery
(760) 325-1199. Deli. Casual Dining. **$11-$17.** 401 E Tahquitz Canyon Way 92262. Just e of downtown. [B] [L] [D]

▽▽▽ Spencer's Restaurant
(760) 327-3446. American. Fine Dining. **$19-$55.** 701 W Baristo Rd 92262. Just s of Tahquitz Canyon Way; just w of Palm Canyon Dr; at west end of Baristo Rd. [B] [L] [D]

PASADENA

▽▽▽ Bistro 45
(626) 795-2478. French. Fine Dining. **$17-$40.** 45 S Mentor Ave 91106. I-210 exit 26B (Lake Ave), 0.5 mi s to Colorado Blvd, just e, then just s.
[L] [D]

▽▽ Mi Piace
(626) 795-3131. Italian. Casual Dining. **$15-$40.** 25 E Colorado Blvd 91105. I-210 exit 25A (Fair Oaks Ave), just s, then just w; exit Colorado Blvd eastbound, 0.5 mi e; in Old Town. [B] [L] [D] [LATE]

PISMO BEACH

▽▽ Spyglass Inn Restaurant
(805) 773-1222. Seafood. Casual Dining. **$8-$40.** 2703 Spyglass Dr 93449. US 101 exit 193 (Spyglass Dr) northbound, just w; exit 193 (Shell Beach Rd) southbound, just w; in Spyglass Inn. [B] [L] [D]

▽▽▽ Ventana Grill
(805) 773-0000. Latin American. Fine Dining. **$10-$34.** 2575 Price St 93449. US 101 exit 191 B (Shell Beach Rd), SR 1 N, just w, then just s.
[L] [D] [&M] [Ⓐ]

RANCHO CUCAMONGA

▽▽▽ P.F. Chang's China Bistro
(909) 463-4095. Chinese Noodles. Fine Dining. **$10-$25.** 7870 Monticello Ave 91739. I-15 exit 112 (Foothill Blvd), just w to Dry Creek Blvd, just n to Victoria Park Ln, just e, then just n. [L] [D]

RANCHO MIRAGE

▽▽ Babe's Bar-B-Que Grill & Brewhouse
(760) 346-8738. Barbecue. Casual Dining. **$8-$33.** 71-800 Hwy 111, Bldg A176 92270. I-10 exit 130 (Bob Hope Dr), 5.9 mi s, then just w; at west end of The River Shopping/Dining Center. [L] [D] [&M]

RANCHO SANTA FE

▽▽▽ ▽▽▽ Mille Fleurs
(858) 756-3085. French. Fine Dining. **$13-$54.** 6009 Paseo Delicias 92067. I-5 exit 37 (Lomas Santa Fe Dr), 4 mi e on CR S-8; in Village area. [L] [D] [&M]

REDDING

▽ The Habit Burger Grill
(530) 223-1027. Burgers. Quick Serve. **$5-$10.** 1020 E Cypress Ave 96002. I-5 exit 677 (Cypress Ave), just e. [L] [D] [&M]

RIVERSIDE

▽▽▽ Mario's Place
(951) 684-7755. Northern Italian. Fine Dining. **$12-$36.** 3646 Mission Inn Ave 92501. SR 91 exit 64 (University Ave) eastbound; exit 64 (Mission Inn Ave) westbound, just w. [D]

ROCKLIN

▽▽ Lucille's Smokehouse Bar-B-Que & Catering
(916) 780-7427. Barbecue. Casual Dining. **$10-$31.** 6628 Lonetree Blvd 95765. SR 65 exit Blue Oaks Blvd, just e, then just n; in Blue Oaks Town Center. [L] [D]

SACRAMENTO

▽▽ Bella Bru Cafe
(916) 928-1770. American. Casual Dining. **$10-$25.** 4680 Natomas Blvd 95835. I-5 exit 525A (Del Paso Rd), 1 mi e, then just n; in Park Place Shopping Center. [B] [L] [D] [&M]

▽▽ Pizza Rock
(916) 737-5777. Pizza. Casual Dining. **$11-$30.** 1020 K St 95814. Between 10th and 11th sts. [L] [D] [&M]

▽▽ Selland's Market - Cafe
(916) 736-3333. American. Casual Dining. **$5-$23.** 5340 H St 95819. Business Rt I-80 (Capital City Frwy) exit J St, 1.7 mi e, then just n on El Dorado Way; jct El Dorado Way. [L] [D] [&M]

ST. HELENA

▽ Gott's Roadside
(707) 963-3486. American. Quick Serve. **$7-$17.** 933 Main St 94574. On SR 29; between Mitchell Dr and McCorkle Ave. [B] [L] [D] [Ⓐ]

▽▽ Himalayan Sherpa Kitchen
(707) 963-4439. Indian. Casual Dining. **$12-$26.** 1148 Main St 94574. On SR 29; center. [L] [D]

SAN CARLOS

▽▽▽ Locanda Positano
(650) 591-5700. Italian. Casual Dining. **$13-$28.** 617 Laurel St 94070. US 101 exit Holly St, 0.3 mi w, then just s. [L] [D]

▽▽▽ Piacere Ristorante
(650) 592-3536. Italian. Casual Dining. **$12-$39.** 727 Laurel St 94070. SR 82, just w on San Carlos Ave, 0.3 mi s. [L] [D]

SAN DIEGO

▽▽ Brazen BBQ Smokehouse & Bar
(629) 816-1990. Barbecue. Casual Dining. **$10-$30.** 441 Washington St 92103. SR 163 exit 2B (Washington St W), then just s. [L] [D] [&M]

▽ Cocina 35
(858) 309-5461. Mexican. Buffet Style. **$4-$13.** 1435 6th Ave 92101. I-5 exit 17 (Front St towards Civic Center) southbound, just e on Cedar St, then just s; exit 16B (onto 6th Ave) northbound, just s. [B] [L] [&M]

W W Edgewater Grill
(619) 232-7581. Seafood. Casual Dining. **$12-$36.** 861 W Harbor Dr 92101. I-5 exit 16B (6th Ave/Downtown) northbound, just n, then 2.5 mi w on Market St; exit 17 (Front St/Civic Center) southbound, 1.5 mi s, then 5 mi w on Market St; in Seaport Village. `B` `L` `D` `&M`

W W El Charko Grill & Bar
(619) 795-0908. Mexican. Casual Dining. **$9-$18.** 2415 San Diego Ave 92110. I-5 exit 19 (Old Town Ave), just nw on San Diego Ave, just nw on Congress St, then just ne on Conde St. `L` `D` `&M` `K` `N`

W W W Farmer's Bottega Restaurant
(619) 458-9929. Italian. Casual Dining. **$13-$34.** 860 W Washington St 92103. SR 163 exit 2B (Washington St), the just w. `B` `L` `D` `&M`

AAA W W W W Grant Grill
(619) 744-2077. California. Fine Dining. **$20-$58.** 326 Broadway 92101. I-5 exit 17 (Front St/Civic Center) southbound, 0.9 mi s to Broadway, then just e; exit 16B (6th Ave/Downtown) northbound, 0.6 mi s, then just w; in The US Grant, a Luxury Collection Hotel, San Diego. `B` `L` `D` `&M`

W W King's Fish House
(619) 574-1230. Seafood. Casual Dining. **$12-$45.** 825 Camino de La Reina 92108. I-8 exit 5 (Mission Center Rd), just n; in Mission Valley West Center. `L` `D`

W W W The Prado At Balboa Park
(619) 557-9441. California. Casual Dining. **$10-$35.** 1549 El Prado 92101. I-5 exit 15B (Pershing Dr/Civic Center) northbound, just e, just n on Florida St, just w on Zoo St, just s on Park Blvd, just e on Presidents Way, just n on Pan American Rd, then just e; SR 163 exit 1B (Via de San Ysidro Blvd) southbound, just n, just w on Presidents Way, just n on Pan American Rd, then just e. `L` `D`

W W W Restaurant Vallarta Mexican & Seafood
(619) 661-1826. Mexican. Casual Dining. **$8-$20.** 2335 Roll Dr, Suite 11 92154. I-905 exit 9 (Siempre Viva), just e, then just s; in Roll Drive Center, just n of Otay Mesa International Border Crossing. `B` `L` `D` `N`

W W W Rustic Root
(619) 702-5595. American. Casual Dining. **$14-$37.** 535 Fifth Ave 92101. I-5 exit 17 (Front St/Civic Center) southbound, 1.4 mi s to Broadway, then e on Island Ave, then just n; exit 16B (6th Ave/Downtown) northbound, 1.1 mi s, w on Island Ave, then just n. `B` `L` `D` `LATE` `&M`

W W W Sally's Seafood on the Water
(619) 358-6740. Seafood. Fine Dining. **$15-$40.** 1 Market Pl 92101. I-5 exit 17 (Front St/Civic Center), 1.3 mi s, then just w; in Manchester Grand Hyatt San Diego. `L` `D` `N`

SAN FRANCISCO

W W W 54 Mint
(415) 543-5100. Italian. Casual Dining. **$14-$31.** 16 Mint Plaza 94103. On the Plaza; enter on 5th or Mission sts. `L` `D` `K`

W W Boulettes Larder
(415) 399-1155. California. Casual Dining. **$17-$32.** 1 Ferry Building Marketplace 94111. In northeast corner of Ferry Building Marketplace. `B` `L`

W W La Mediterranee
(415) 921-2956. Mediterranean. Casual Dining. **$12-$17.** 2210 Fillmore St 94115. Between Sacramento and Clay sts. `L` `D` `K`

W W Padrecito
(415) 742-5505. Mexican Small Plates. Casual Dining. **$13-$18.** 901 Cole St 94117. At Carl St. `D` `K`

W W W Rose Pistola
(415) 399-0499. Italian. Casual Dining. **$13-$38.** 532 Columbus Ave 94133. Between Green and Union sts. `L` `D`

W W Rose's Cafe
(415) 775-2200. Italian. Casual Dining. **$13-$27.** 2298 Union St 94123. At Steiner St. `B` `L` `D`

W W Tal-Y-Tara Tea & Polo Shoppe
(415) 751-9275. Specialty. Casual Dining. **$8-$12.** 6439 California St 94121. Between 26th and 27th aves. `L` `K`

W W Universal Cafe
(415) 821-4608. California. Casual Dining. **$9-$28.** 2814 19th St 94110. Between Bryant and Florida sts. `L` `D` `K`

W W W The Waterfront Restaurant
(415) 391-2696. California Seafood. Fine Dining. **$16-$35.** Pier 7 94111. Just n of the Ferry Building; on The Embarcadero at Broadway St. `L` `D` `&M`

W W Zazie
(415) 564-5332. French. Casual Dining. **$11-$30.** 941 Cole St 94117. Between Carl St and Parnassus Ave. `B` `L` `D` `K`

SAN JOSE

W W W The Grill on the Alley
(408) 294-2244. Steak. Fine Dining. **$15-$52.** 172 S Market St 95113. At Fairmont Plaza; in The Fairmont San Jose. `L` `D` `&M`

W W Habana Cuba
(408) 998-2822. Cuban. Casual Dining. **$10-$32.** 238 Race St 95126. I-280 exit Race St, just n; at San Carlos St. `L` `D` `&M`

W W W Three Flames Restaurant
(408) 269-3133. Continental. Fine Dining. **$15-$30.** 1547 Meridian Ave 95125. Just n of Hamilton Ave; in Carriage Square Shopping Center. `L` `D` `&M`

SAN JUAN CAPISTRANO

W W Cafe Mozart
(949) 496-0212. Continental. Casual Dining. **$9-$33.** 31952 Camino Capistrano, Suite A1 92675. I-5 exit 82 (SR 74/Ortega Hwy), 0.3 mi s, then just s; in Mercado Village. `L` `D` `N`

W W W Cedar Creek Inn
(949) 240-2229. American. Casual Dining. **$10-$31.** 26860 Ortega Hwy 92675. I-5 exit 82 (SR 74/Ortega Hwy), 0.5 mi w; in Mission Promenade. `L` `D`

W W W Sundried Tomato Cafe
(949) 661-1167. American. Casual Dining. **$12-$28.** 31781 Camino Capistrano 92675. I-5 exit 82 (SR 74/Ortega Hwy), 0.3 mi w, then just s. `L` `D`

W W The Tea House on Los Rios
(949) 443-3914. English Coffee/Tea Breads/Pastries. Casual Dining. **$15-$18.** 31731 Los Rios St 92675. I-5 exit 82 (SR 74/Ortega Hwy), just w, 0.4 mi sw on Del Obispo St, then just n. `L`

SAN LUIS OBISPO

W W W Luna Red Restaurant
(805) 540-5243. Small Plates Wild Game. Fine Dining. **$8-$26.** 1023 Chorro St 93401. US 101 exit 202 (Broad St), nw on Palm St, then just e; next to Mission Church. `B` `L` `D` `LATE`

W Splash Cafe
(805) 544-7567. American. Quick Serve. **$5-$13.** 1491 Monterey St 93401. US 101 N exit 203C (California Blvd), 0.4 mi e, then just n. `B` `L` `D` `&M`

SAN MATEO

W W W Spiedo Ristorante
(650) 375-0818. Italian. Casual Dining. **$10-$30.** 223 E 4th Ave 94401. US 101 exit E 3rd Ave, 0.5 mi w. `L` `D` `&M`

SANTA ANA

◆◆◆◆ Darya
(714) 557-6600. Persian. Casual Dining. **$13-$20.** 3800 S Plaza Dr 92704. I-405 exit 9B (Bristol St), just n to Sunflower Ave, just w, then just n; in South Coast Plaza Village. [L] [D]

SANTA BARBARA

◆◆◆◆ Carlito's Cafe y Cantina
(805) 962-7117. Mexican. Casual Dining. **$10-$20.** 1324 State St 93101. US 101 exit 98 (Carrillo St), 0.5 mi e, then just n. [L] [D]

◆◆ C'est Cheese
(805) 965-0318. Sandwiches Breads/Pastries. Casual Dining. **$6-$20.** 825 Santa Barbara St 93101. US 101 exit (Garden St), 0.3 mi e, then just s. [B] [L] [&M] [丒]

◆ Madam Lu Chinese Restaurant
(805) 898-9289. Chinese. Casual Dining. **$9-$20.** 3524 State St 93105. US 101 exit 101A (La Cumbre Rd/Hope Ave) northbound, just n, then 0.4 mi w; exit 101B (State St) southbound, 0.6 mi w. [L] [D]

◆◆ Pascucci
(805) 963-8123. Italian. Casual Dining. **$10-$15.** 729 State St 93101. US 101 exit 98 (Carrillo St), just e, then 0.5 mi s; in Paseo Nuevo.
[L] [D] [丒]

◆◆ Sambo's on the Beach
(805) 965-3269. American. Casual Dining. **$7-$13.** 216 W Cabrillo Blvd 93101. US 101 northbound exit 96B (Garden St), 0.4 mi w, then just n.
[B] [L] [&M] [丒]

◆ Shoreline Cafe
(805) 568-0064. American. Casual Dining. **$7-$16.** 801 Shoreline Dr 93109. US 101 exit 97 (Castillo St) northbound, 0.5 mi w, then 0.7 mi n.
[B] [L] [D] [丒]

◆◆◆ Stella Mare's
(805) 969-6705. French. Fine Dining. **$12-$30.** 50 Los Patos Way 93108. US 101 exit 94B (Cabrillo Blvd), just sw, then just nw; opposite Andre Clark Bird Refuge. [L] [D]

◆◆ Via Maestra 42
(805) 569-6522. Italian. Casual Dining. **$11-$30.** 3343 State St 93105. US 101 exit 100 (Las Positas Rd), 0.8 mi n to State St, then just w; in San Roque Plaza. [B] [L] [D] [◥]

◆ Wildwood Kitchen
(805) 845-3995. Barbecue Sandwiches. Casual Dining. **$11-$26.** 410 E Haley St 93101. US 101 N exit 96B (Laguna St), 0.3 mi e, then just s.
[L] [D] [&M]

SANTA CLARITA

◆◆◆ Bricks
(661) 286-1091. Burgers Sandwiches. Casual Dining. **$8-$15.** 23820 Lyons Ave 91321. US 5 N exit 167 (Lyons Ave), just e. [L] [D] [&M]

SANTA MARIA

◆◆◆ Garden Room at Historic Santa Maria Inn
(805) 346-7908. American. Casual Dining. **$12-$39.** 801 S Broadway 93454. US 101 exit 171 (Main St), 1 mi w, then 0.5 mi s; in Historic Santa Maria Inn. [B] [L] [D]

SANTA ROSA

◆◆ Third Street AleWorks
(707) 523-3060. American. Casual Dining. **$11-$20.** 610 3rd St 95404. Between D St and Mendocino Ave. [L] [D] [&M]

SANTEE

◆◆ Oggi's Pizza & Brewing Co.
(619) 449-6441. American. Gastropub. **$8-$14.** 9828 Mission Gorge Rd, Suite A 92071. SR 52 exit 17 (Cuyamaca St), 0.4 mi n, then 0.3 mi e; at Trolley Square at Santee Town Center. [L] [D]

SAUSALITO

◆◆ Fish
(415) 331-3474. Seafood. Quick Serve. **$15-$36.** 350 Harbor Dr 94965. US 101 exit Sausalito/Marin City, s on Bridgeway Blvd, then just e.
[L] [D] [丒]

◆◆◆ Poggio
(415) 332-7771. Italian. Casual Dining. **$11-$69.** 777 Bridgeway 94965. US 101 exit Alexander Ave, 1.5 mi e; in Casa Madrona Hotel & Spa.
[B] [L] [D]

SEAL BEACH

◆◆◆ Spaghettini Grill & Jazz Club
(562) 596-2199. Northern Italian. Casual Dining. **$14-$45.** 3005 Old Ranch Pkwy 90740. I-405 exit 22 (Seal Beach Blvd/Los Alamitos), just n.
[L] [D] [◥]

SHERMAN OAKS

◆◆◆ P.F. Chang's China Bistro
(818) 784-1694. Chinese. Fine Dining. **$10-$27.** 15301 Ventura Blvd, Suite P-22 91403. US 101 exit 18 (Sepulveda Blvd) northbound, just s, then just w; exit 19B (Haskell Ave) southbound, just s, then just w; in Sherman Oaks Galleria. [L] [D]

SIMI VALLEY

◆◆ Limon Latin Grill
(805) 955-9277. Latin American Burgers. Gastropub. **$11-$32.** 1555 Simi Town Center Way 93065. SR 23 7.8 mi n, SR 118 6.3 mi e exit 24 (Erringer Rd), just n, then just w; in Simi Valley Town Shopping Center.
[L] [D] [LATE] [&M]

SOLANA BEACH

◆◆ Parioli Italian Bistro
(858) 755-2525. Italian. Casual Dining. **$9-$28.** 647 S Hwy 101 92075. I-5 exit 36 (Via de la Valle), 1 mi w, then just n. [L] [D] [&M]

SOLVANG

◆◆◆ Cecco Ristorante
(805) 688-8880. Italian. Casual Dining. **$11-$28.** 475 1st St 93463. On SR 246, 5.1 mi w. [L] [D] [&M]

◆◆ Chomp
(805) 688-7733. Burgers. Casual Dining. **$7-$10.** 1693 Mission Dr 93463. SR 154 NW exit 246 (Mission Dr), 5 mi w. [L] [D]

◆◆ Fresco Valley Cafe
(805) 688-8857. California. Casual Dining. **$11-$25.** 442 Atterdag Rd 93463. Just w of SR 246. [L] [D] [&M]

◆◆ Mandarin Touch
(805) 686-0222. Mandarin. Casual Dining. **$8-$29.** 1635 Mission Dr 93463. SR 154 nw exit 246 (Mission Dr), 5.3 mi w. [L] [D] [LATE]

◆◆◆ Paula's Pancake House
(805) 688-2867. American. Casual Dining. **$8-$14.** 1531 Mission Dr 93463. On SR 246. [B] [L] [&M]

◆◆◆ Succulent Cafe
(805) 691-9444. California. Fine Dining. **$10-$36.** 1555 Mission Dr 93463. On SR 246; center of downtown. [B] [L] [D] [&M]

SONOMA

▼▼▼ the girl & the fig
(707) 938-3634. French. Casual Dining. **$12-$24.** 110 W Spain St 95476. In historic Sonoma Plaza; in Sonoma Hotel. [L] [D]

▼▼ HopMonk Tavern Sonoma
(707) 935-9100. American. Casual Dining. **$11-$23.** 691 Broadway St 95476. SR 12, just s. [L] [D]

▼▼ Swiss Hotel Restaurant
(707) 938-2884. Swiss. Casual Dining. **$9-$30.** 18 W Spain St 95476. In Sonoma Plaza. [L] [D]

SOUTH LAKE TAHOE

▼▼▼ Nepheles
(530) 544-8130. California. Fine Dining. **$22-$37.** 1169 Ski Run Blvd 96150. 1.1 mi s of casino area to Ski Run Blvd, 0.3 mi w. [D] [LATE] [AC]

SUMMERLAND

▼▼ Summerland Beach Cafe
(805) 969-1019. Breakfast Sandwiches. Casual Dining. **$7-$16.** 2294 Lillie Ave 93067. US 101 N exit 91 (Evans Ave) just e, then just n. [B] [L]

TAHOE CITY

▼▼ The Blue Agave Mexican Restaurant & Cantina
(530) 583-8113. Mexican. Casual Dining. **$8-$26.** 425 N Lake Blvd 96145. SR 28 (N Lake Blvd), 0.3 mi e of jct SR 89. [L] [D]

▼▼ Dockside 700 Wine Bar & Grill
(530) 581-0303. American. Casual Dining. **$8-$32.** 700 N Lake Tahoe Blvd 96145. Jct SR 89 and 28 (N Lake Blvd), just ne; at Tahoe City Marina. [L] [D] [&M]

▼▼ Rosie's Cafe
(530) 583-8504. American. Casual Dining. **$10-$20.** 571 N Lake Blvd 96145. SR 28 (N Lake Blvd), 0.5 mi e of jct SR 89. [B] [L] [D] [AC]

TEHACHAPI

▼▼▼ Jake's Steakhouse
(661) 822-6015. Steak. Casual Dining. **$9-$26.** 213 S Curry St 93561. SR 58 northbound exit 151 (E Tehachapi Blvd), 2.3 mi w, then just s; SR 58 southbound exit 24 (Tucker Rd) just e, then just s; downtown. [L] [D]

TEMECULA

▼▼▼ Cafe Champagne
(951) 699-0088. California. Casual Dining. **$17-$39.** 32575 Rancho California Rd 92591. I-15 exit 59 (Rancho California Rd), 4 mi e; at Thornton Winery. [L] [D]

▼▼▼ Pinnacle Restaurant
(951) 676-8231. Mediterranean. Casual Dining. **$15-$24.** 40620 Calle Contento 92591. I-15 exit 59 (Rancho California Rd), 5 mi e, then 0.3 mi n; at Falkner Winery. [L]

▼▼ Texas Lil's Mesquite Grill
(951) 699-5457. Barbecue. Casual Dining. **$9-$27.** 28495 Old Town Front St 92590. I-15 exit 59 (Rancho California Rd), just w, then 0.5 mi s. [L] [D] [N]

TEMPLETON

▼▼ Griff's Bistro and Pizzeria
(805) 434-1760. Italian. Casual Dining. **$8-$30.** 105 N Main St 93465. US 101 N, exit 224 (Vineyard Dr), just e, then 0.9 mi n; in shopping center. [L] [D] [&M]

THOUSAND OAKS

▼▼▼ Lazy Dog Restaurant and Bar
(805) 449-5206. American. Casual Dining. **$9-$18.** 172 W Hillcrest Dr 91360. US 101 exit 44 (Moorpark Rd), just n; next to The Oaks Mall. [L] [D] [LATE] [&M]

THREE RIVERS

▼▼ Gateway Restaurant
(559) 561-4133. American. Casual Dining. **$12-$41.** 45978 Sierra Dr 93271. SR 198, 6 mi ne of town center; 0.5 mi sw of entrance to Sequoia National Park; in Gateway Lodge. [🍴] [L] [D] [N]

▼▼ River View Restaurant and Lounge
(559) 561-2211. American. Casual Dining. **$7-$23.** 42323 Sierra Dr 93271. On SR 198/Sierra Dr; east side of downtown. [B] [L] [D] [LATE] [&M] [N]

▼▼ Sequoia Cider Mill Restaurant
(559) 561-4157. American. Casual Dining. **$8-$20.** 40311 Sierra Dr 93271. On SR 198; center of downtown. [B] [L] [D] [&M]

TWENTYNINE PALMS

🔷 ▼▼ The Rib Co.
(760) 367-1663. Barbecue. Casual Dining. **$10-$32.** 72183 Twentynine Palms Hwy 92277. SR 62, 1.8 mi w of Adobe Rd. [L] [D]

UPPER LAKE

▼▼ Blue Wing Saloon Restaurant
(707) 275-2233. American. Gastropub. **$12-$29.** 9520 Main St 95485. Just n of SR 20; downtown. [L] [D]

VENTURA

▼▼ Greek at the Harbor
(805) 650-5350. Greek. Casual Dining. **$12-$30.** 1583 Spinnaker Dr, Suite 101 93001. US 101 exit 68 (Seaward Ave), just w, 1.8 mi sw on Harbor Blvd, then 0.8 mi w; in Ventura Harbor Village. [B] [L] [D] [AC]

▼▼ Social Tap
(805) 667-8485. Burgers Wings. Gastropub. **$8-$14.** 1105 S Seaward Ave 93001. US 101 N exit Seaward Ave, just w. [L] [D] [LATE] [&M] [AC]

VISALIA

▼▼▼ The Vintage Press
(559) 733-3033. California. Fine Dining. **$12-$38.** 216 N Willis St 93291. SR 198 exit 105A (Central Visalia E), just n to Center St, then just w; downtown. [L] [D]

WALNUT CREEK

▼▼▼ Va de Vi Bistro & Wine Bar
(925) 979-0100. International Small Plates. Casual Dining. **$9-$17.** 1511 Mt. Diablo Blvd 94596. Jct Mt Diablo Blvd and S Main St; downtown. [L] [D]

WESTLAKE VILLAGE

▼▼ Figueroa Mountain Brewing Company
(805) 694-2252. Small Plates. Gastropub. **$7-$16.** 30770 Russell Ranch Rd 91362. US 101 N exit 39 (Lindero Canyon Rd), 0.5 mi e, then just s. [L] [D] [&M]

▼▼ Marmalade Cafe
(805) 370-1331. American. Casual Dining. **$12-$23.** 140 Promenade Way, Suite 1 91362. US 101 exit 40 (Westlake Blvd), just n; in Westlake Promenade. [B] [L] [D]

▼▼▼ **Mediterraneo**
(818) 889-9105. Mediterranean. Fine Dining. **$16-$55.** 32037 Agoura Rd 91361. US 101 exit 40 (Westlake Blvd), 1.3 mi se; in Westlake Village Inn.
[L] [D] [🅂]

▼▼▼ **Public School 805**
(805) 379-3909. New American. Gastropub. **$10-$27.** 120 Promenade Way 91362. US 101 N exit 40 (SR 23/Westlake Blvd), just e, then just s.
[L] [D] [&M]

▼▼▼ **Tuscany II Ristorante**
(805) 495-2768. Italian. Fine Dining. **$13-$42.** 968 S Westlake Blvd 91361. US 101 exit 40 (Westlake Blvd) northbound, 0.3 mi w; in Westlake Plaza Shopping Center. [L] [D]

WOODLAND HILLS

▼▼ **Angel City Cafe**
(818) 713-9500. American. Casual Dining. **$11-$27.** 21136 Ventura Blvd 91364. US 101 N exit 26B (Canoga Ave), just w, then just s.
[L] [D] [&M]

▼▼ **Blu Jam Cafe**
(818) 222-1044. California. Casual Dining. **$11-$20.** 23311 Mulholland Dr 91364. US 101 N exit 29 (Valley Circle/Mulholland Dr), just e.
[B] [L] [&M]

▼▼ **Jerry's Famous Deli and Restaurant**
(818) 340-0810. Deli. Casual Dining. **$10-$19.** 21857 Ventura Blvd 91307. US 101 exit 26 (Ventura Blvd) northbound, just w.
[B] [L] [D] [LATE]

YERMO

(AAA) ▼ **Peggy Sue's Diner**
(760) 254-3370. American. Casual Dining. **$7-$13.** 35654 Yermo Rd 92398. I-15 exit 191 (Ghost Town Rd), just ne. [B] [L] [D]

Colorado

BOULDER

▼▼▼ **The Greenbriar Inn**
(303) 440-7979. American. Fine Dining. **$23-$39.** 8735 N Foothills Hwy 80302. North of town on US 36 (28th St), west side of highway. [D]

BROOMFIELD

▼▼▼ **Village Tavern**
(720) 887-6900. American. Casual Dining. **$11-$32.** 100 W Flatiron Crossing Dr 80021. US 36 (Boulder Tpke) exit Interlocken Loop/Storagetek Dr; in Flatiron Shopping District. [L] [D] [&M]

CRESTED BUTTE

▼▼▼ **Django's Restaurant & Wine Bar**
(970) 349-7574. Small Plates. Fine Dining. **$15-$27.** 620 Gothic Rd 81224. 3 mi n of Elk Ave; in The Lodge at Mountaineer Square. [D]

DEL NORTE

▼▼ **Three Barrel Brewing**
(719) 657-0681. Italian. Casual Dining. **$8-$12.** 475 Grand Ave 81132. Just s of US 160. [L] [D]

DENVER

▼▼▼ **Bistro Vendome**
(303) 825-3232. French. Casual Dining. **$17-$26.** 1420 Larimer St 80202. Between 14th and 15th sts. [D]

HESPERUS

▼▼▼ **Kennebec Cafe**
(970) 247-5674. Mediterranean. Casual Dining. **$12-$36.** 4 CR 124 81326. 10 mi w on US 160 (north side). [L] [D]

LITTLETON

▼▼ **NoNo's Cafe**
(303) 738-8330. Cajun. Casual Dining. **$10-$20.** 3005 W County Line Rd 80129. SR 470 exit Santa Fe, just n, then just e. [B] [L] [D]

VAIL

▼▼▼ **Bol Vail**
(970) 476-5300. American. Casual Dining. **$16-$36.** 141 E Meadow Dr 81657. I-70 exit 176, just s, 3rd exit at roundabout, 0.3 mi e to Vail Center Rd, just s, then just w; in Solaris Residences. [D]

Connecticut

HARTFORD

▼▼▼ **Trumbull Kitchen**
(860) 493-7417. International. Fine Dining. **$11-$29.** 150 Trumbull St 06103. Between Asylum and Pearl sts; downtown. [L] [D]

MANCHESTER

▼▼▼ **Cavey's Restaurant-Italian**
(860) 643-2751. Northern Italian. Fine Dining. **$9-$44.** 45 E Center St 06040. On US 6 and 44, just e of jct SR 83; downtown. [D]

MYSTIC

▼▼▼ **Anthony J's Bistro**
(860) 536-0448. New Italian. Casual Dining. **$9-$32.** 6 Holmes St 06355. I-95 exit 90, 1.1 mi s on SR 27, then just w. [L] [D]

NEW CANAAN

▼▼▼ **Solé**
(203) 972-8887. Italian. Fine Dining. **$16-$40.** 105 Elm St 06840. Between Park St and South Ave; downtown. [L] [D]

NEW HAVEN

▼▼▼ **John Davenport's at the Top of the Park**
(203) 974-6858. New England. Fine Dining. **$12-$32.** 155 Temple St 06510. Between Chapel and Crown sts; downtown; in Omni New Haven Hotel at Yale. [◀] [B] [L] [D]

SOUTH NORWALK

▼▼▼ **Match**
(203) 852-1088. New American. Casual Dining. **$22-$38.** 98 Washington St 06854. I-95 exit 14 northbound, 0.3 mi nw on Fairfield Ave, then just e; exit 16 southbound, 0.4 mi se on East Ave, then 0.7 mi w to SR 136. [D]

▼▼▼ **Strada 18**
(203) 853-4546. Italian. Casual Dining. **$11-$26.** 122 Washington St 06854. I-95 exit 14 northbound, 0.3 mi nw on Fairfield Ave, then just e; exit 16 southbound, 0.4 mi se on East Ave, then 0.7 mi w to SR 136. [L] [D]

STAMFORD

▼▼▼ **Barcelona Restaurant and Wine Bar**
(203) 348-4800. Spanish Small Plates. Casual Dining. **$6-$28.** 222 Summer St 06901. Between Broad and Main sts; downtown. [L] [D] [&M]

STONINGTON

▼▼ **Dog Watch Cafe**
(860) 415-4510. American. Casual Dining. **$10-$26.** 194 Water St 06378. Jct US 1A, just sw on Alpha Ave, then just n. Ⓛ Ⓓ Ⓜ

WEST HARTFORD

▼▼▼ **Max's Oyster Bar**
(860) 236-6299. Seafood. Fine Dining. **$15-$35.** 964 Farmington Ave 06107. On SR 4; between S Main St and Lasalle Rd; center.
Ⓛ Ⓓ Ⓜ

WESTPORT

▼ **Shake Shack**
(203) 682-6570. Burgers Hot Dogs. Quick Serve. **$3-$9.** 1849 Post Rd E 06880. I-95 exit 19, just e on US 1. Ⓛ Ⓓ Ⓜ

WOODSTOCK

▼▼▼ **Inn at Woodstock Hill**
(860) 928-0528. Continental. Fine Dining. **$11-$50.** 94 Plaine Hill Rd 06281. 0.8 mi n on SR 169. Ⓛ Ⓓ

Delaware

LEWES

▼▼▼ **The Buttery**
(302) 645-7755. American. Fine Dining. **$12-$38.** 102 2nd St 19958. Jct 2nd St and Savannah Rd (US 9 business route). Ⓛ Ⓓ

REHOBOTH BEACH

🆎 ▼▼▼ **Victoria's**
(302) 227-0615. American. Fine Dining. **$10-$36.** 2 Olive Ave 19971. Just n of Rehoboth Ave; in Boardwalk Plaza Hotel. Ⓑ Ⓛ Ⓓ

District of Columbia

WASHINGTON, D.C.

▼ **100 Montaditos**
(202) 488-8500. Spanish Sandwiches Small Plates. Quick Serve. **$2-$22.** 300 Tingey St SE 20003. Between 3rd and 4th sts SE; in Navy Yard area. Ⓛ Ⓓ Ⓜ

▼▼▼ **14K Restaurant & Lounge**
(202) 218-7575. American. Casual Dining. **$15-$36.** 1001 14th St NW 20005. At 14th and K sts NW; in Hamilton Crowne Plaza, Washington DC.
Ⓑ Ⓛ Ⓓ Ⓜ

▼▼▼ **Acadiana**
(202) 408-8848. Southern American Seafood. Casual Dining. **$13-$35.** 901 New York Ave NW 20001. Between 9th and 10th sts. Ⓛ Ⓓ

▼▼▼ **Art and Soul**
(202) 393-7777. Regional American. Casual Dining. **$15-$39.** 415 New Jersey Ave NW 20001. On Capitol Hill, just n of Capitol grounds; in The Liaison Capitol Hill, a Joie de Vivre Hotel. Ⓛ Ⓓ Ⓜ

▼▼ **Bayou on Penn**
(202) 223-6941. Regional American. Casual Dining. **$14-$29.** 2519 Pennsylvania Ave NW 20037. Between 25th and 26th sts NW. Ⓛ Ⓓ

▼▼▼ **Bobby Van's Grill**
(202) 589-1504. Steak. Fine Dining. **$15-$50.** 1201 New York Ave NW 20005. 12th St and New York Ave NW. Ⓛ Ⓓ Ⓜ

▼▼▼ **Bourbon Steak**
(202) 944-2026. American. Fine Dining. **$19-$65.** 2800 Pennsylvania Ave NW 20007. Jct M St NW and Pennsylvania Ave NW; in Four Seasons Hotel Washington, D.C. Ⓛ Ⓓ Ⓜ

▼▼▼ **Brasserie Beck**
(202) 408-1717. Belgian. Casual Dining. **$18-$37.** 1101 K St NW 20005. Jct K and 11th sts NW. Ⓛ Ⓓ ⓁⒶⓉⒺ

▼▼ **Cafe Divan**
(202) 338-1747. Turkish. Casual Dining. **$7-$20.** 1834 Wisconsin Ave NW 20007. Jct 34th St NW; in upper Georgetown. Ⓛ Ⓓ Ⓜ

▼▼▼ **Cafe du Parc**
(202) 942-7000. French. Casual Dining. **$15-$45.** 1401 Pennsylvania Ave NW 20004. Just e of the White House; jct 14th St NW; in The Willard InterContinental. Ⓑ Ⓛ Ⓓ Ⓜ

▼▼ **Café Olé**
(202) 244-1330. Mediterranean Small Plates. Casual Dining. **$5-$16.** 4000 Wisconsin Ave NW 20016. Jct Upton St; in Tenleytown area.
Ⓛ Ⓓ

▼▼▼ **Casa Luca**
(202) 628-1099. Regional Italian. Fine Dining. **$20-$38.** 1099 New York Ave NW 20001. At 11th St NW; entrance on 11th St NW. Ⓛ Ⓓ

▼▼▼ **Cashion's Eat Place**
(202) 797-1819. American. Fine Dining. **$15-$31.** 1819 Columbia Rd NW 20009. Between 18th St and Belmont Rd NW; in Adams Morgan area.
Ⓓ

▼▼▼ **Charlie Palmer Steak**
(202) 547-8100. Steak. Fine Dining. **$15-$60.** 101 Constitution Ave NW 20001. On Capitol Hill; jct 1st St and Constitution Ave NW. Ⓛ Ⓓ Ⓜ

▼▼▼ **Doi Moi**
(202) 733-5131. Asian Small Plates. Casual Dining. **$15-$31.** 1800 14th St NW 20009. At 14th and S sts NW. Ⓓ Ⓜ

▼▼▼ **Garrison**
(202) 506-2445. New American. Casual Dining. **$25-$30.** 524 8th St SE 20003. Between E and G sts SE; Barracks Row on Capitol Hill. Ⓓ Ⓜ

▼▼ **The Grill from Ipanema**
(202) 986-0757. Brazilian. Casual Dining. **$16-$32.** 1858 Columbia Rd NW 20009. Between 18th St and Belmont Rd; in Adam's Morgan area.
Ⓓ

▼▼▼ **Jaleo**
(202) 628-7949. Spanish Small Plates. Casual Dining. **$9-$95.** 480 7th St NW 20004. Jct 7th and E St NW; 1 blk s of Verizon Center; in Penn Quarter. Ⓛ Ⓓ Ⓜ

▼▼▼ **Juniper**
(202) 457-5020. American. Fine Dining. **$15-$36.** 2401 M St NW 20037. 24th and M sts NW; in Fairmont Washington, D.C., Georgetown.
Ⓑ Ⓛ Ⓓ Ⓜ

▼▼ **Lauriol Plaza**
(202) 387-0035. Latin American. Casual Dining. **$9-$22.** 1835 18th St NW 20009. Jct 18th and T sts NW. Ⓛ Ⓓ

▼▼ **Mai Thai of Georgetown**
(202) 337-2424. Thai. Casual Dining. **$11-$24.** 3251 Prospect St NW 20007. Between 33rd St and Wisconsin Ave; in Georgetown. Ⓛ Ⓓ

▼▼ **Meiwah Restaurant**
(202) 833-2888. Chinese. Casual Dining. **$12-$28.** 1200 New Hampshire Ave NW 20036. Jct M St and New Hampshire Ave NW. Ⓛ Ⓓ Ⓜ

▼ **Menomale**
(202) 248-3946. Pizza. Casual Dining. **$9-$19.** 2711 12th St NE 20018. Just n of Rhode Island Ave NE. Ⓛ Ⓓ Ⓜ

▼▼ **Peacock Cafe**
(202) 625-2740. American. Casual Dining. **$13-$33.** 3251 Prospect St NW 20007. Jct Prospect and Wisconsin sts; in Georgetown. Ⓛ Ⓓ

◆◆ Petits Plats
(202) 518-0018. French. Casual Dining. $11-$32. 2653 Connecticut Ave NW 20008. At Calvert St. L D

◆◆◆ Robert's Restaurant
(202) 756-5300. American. Fine Dining. $14-$46. 2500 Calvert St NW 20008. Just w of Connecticut Ave; in Omni Shoreham Hotel.
B L D &M

◆◆◆ Urbana
(202) 956-6650. Italian. Casual Dining. $10-$34. 2121 P St NW 20037. Between 21st and 22nd sts NW, just w of Dupont Circle; in Kimpton Hotel Palomar Washington DC. B D LATE

◆◆◆◆ Westend Bistro
(202) 974-4900. New American. Casual Dining. $12-$36. 1150 22nd St NW 20037. At 22nd and M sts NW; in The Ritz-Carlton, Washington, D.C.
B L D &M

Florida

BOCA RATON

◆◆◆ Rocco's Tacos & Tequila Bar
(561) 416-2131. Mexican. Casual Dining. $4-$24. 5250 Town Center Cir 33486. I-95 exit 44 (Palmetto Park Rd), 0.7 mi w to Military Tr, then 1.1 mi n; in The Shops at Boca Center. L D LATE &M ◣

◆◆ Tucker Duke's Lunchbox
(561) 717-8153. Southern Comfort Food Burgers. Gastropub. $8-$35. 1658 N Federal Hwy 33432. I-95 exit 45 (Glades Rd), 2.5 mi e to US 1 (Federal Hwy), then 0.3 mi n. L D &M ◣

BOYNTON BEACH

◆◆ Hurricane Alley Raw Bar & Restaurant
(561) 364-4008. Seafood Sandwiches. Casual Dining. $9-$19. 529 E Ocean Ave 33435. I-95 exit 57 (Boynton Beach Blvd), 1 mi e to US 1 (Federal Hwy), just s to Ocean Ave, then just w. L D ◣

CAPE HAZE

◆◆ Johnny Leverock's Seafood House
(941) 698-6900. Seafood. Casual Dining. $7-$30. 7092 Placida Rd 33946. Jct CR 771/775/776, 5 mi s to Panama Blvd, just w to Ferry Landing (Gulf Blvd), then 1.1 mi w. L D

CAPTIVA

◆◆ The Green Flash Bayside Restaurant
(239) 472-3337. Seafood. Casual Dining. $7-$47. 15183 Captiva Dr 33924. Jct Murmond Ln. L D

◆◆ The Mucky Duck
(239) 472-3434. Seafood. Casual Dining. $8-$39. 11546 Andy Rosse Ln 33924. Just w of jct Captiva Dr. L D

◆◆ R C Otter's Island Eats
(239) 395-1142. American. Casual Dining. $7-$29. 11506 Andy Rosse Ln 33924. Jct Captiva Dr. B L D

CELEBRATION

◆◆ Market Street Cafe
(407) 566-1144. American. Casual Dining. $8-$18. 701 Front St 34747. Just e of jct Celebration Ave on Mulberry Ave, then just se to Front; downtown. B L D

CLEARWATER

◆ Pickles Plus Deli
(727) 725-3325. Sandwiches Breakfast. Casual Dining. $7-$11. 2530 N McMullen Booth Rd 33761. On CR 611 at Enterprise Rd; in Northwood Plaza. B L D

COCONUT GROVE

◆◆ Berries in the Grove
(305) 448-2111. International. Casual Dining. $11-$25. 2884 SW 27th Ave 33133. Just e of US 1. B L D

◆◆ Calamari Restaurant
(305) 441-0219. Italian. Casual Dining. $12-$36. 3540 Main Hwy 33133. Between Franklin and Charles aves; downtown. L D

◆◆ LoKal Beer & Burger
(305) 442-3377. American. Casual Dining. $9-$15. 3190 Commodore Plaza 33133. Between Grand and Thomas aves. L D LATE &M

CORAL GABLES

◆◆ Angelique Euro Cafe
(305) 529-9922. International. Casual Dining. $14-$29. 117 Miracle Mile 33134. Between Ponce de Leon Blvd and Galiano St; downtown.
L D

◆◆ Caffe Abbracci
(305) 441-0700. Italian. Casual Dining. $16-$42. 318 Aragon Ave 33134. At Aragon Ave and Salzedo St; just e of SR 953 (LeJeune Rd); downtown.
L D &M

◆◆ Ortanique Cuisine of the Sun
(305) 446-7710. New Caribbean Fusion. Fine Dining. $13-$55. 278 Miracle Mile 33134. Between SR 953 (LeJeune Rd) and Ponce de Leon Blvd; next to theater. L D &M

◆◆ Sawa Restaurant and Lounge
(305) 447-6555. International Fusion. Casual Dining. $8-$60. 360 San Lorenzo Ave, Suite 1500 33146. In Village of Merrick Park.
L D &M

◆◆ Spritz of Coral Gables
(305) 444-3388. Italian. Casual Dining. $11-$20. 2305 Ponce de Leon Blvd 33134. Just s of Giralda Ave; between Aragon and Giralda aves.
L D &M

◆◆ Tarpon Bend Raw Bar & Grill
(305) 444-3210. International. Casual Dining. $12-$37. 65 Miracle Mile 33134. On Miracle Mile; just w of Douglas Rd; between Galiano St and S Douglas Rd. L D &M

CORAL SPRINGS

◆◆ Big Bear Brewing Company
(954) 341-5545. American. Gastropub. $11-$28. 1800 N University Dr 33071. From SR 814 (Atlantic Blvd), 0.9 mi n. L D &M

◆◆ Runyon's
(954) 752-2333. Continental. Fine Dining. $11-$50. 9810 W Sample Rd 33065. Florida Tpke exit 69 (SR 834), 5.7 mi w. L D ◣

CRESTVIEW

◆◆ The Wild Olive
(850) 682-4455. American. Casual Dining. $9-$29. 797 N Pearl St 32536. Corner of Hickory Ave; downtown. B L D &M

DAVIE

◆ Char-Hut 84
(954) 474-9312. American. Quick Serve. $4-$13. 9000 W SR 84 33324. I-595 exit 4, just w; in Pine Island Ridge Plaza. L D &M

DAYTONA BEACH SHORES

◆◆ Boondocks Restaurant
(386) 760-9001. Seafood. Casual Dining. $6-$24. 3948 S Peninsula Dr 32127. I-95 exit 256 (SR 421), 5 mi e to SR A1A (Atlantic Ave), 1.5 mi s to Mallard St, then just w; in Adventure Yacht Harbor. L D ꝏ ◣

DEERFIELD BEACH

◇ Crepe Cafe
(954) 419-9620. French Desserts. Quick Serve. **$7-$11.** 123 NE 20th Ave 33441. I-95 exit 42A (Hillsboro Blvd), 2.8 mi e to 20th Ave (A1A), then just n. [B] [L] [D] [\]

◇◇ Tucker Duke's Lunchbox
(954) 708-2035. Southern Comfort Food Burgers. Casual Dining. **$8-$35.** 1101 S Powerline Rd 33442. I-95 exit 41 (SW 10th St), 2 mi w to Powerline Rd, then just s. [L] [D] [&M] [\]

DELRAY BEACH

◇◇ Boston's on the Beach
(561) 278-3364. American. Casual Dining. **$8-$27.** 40 S Ocean Blvd 33483. I-95 exit 52 (Atlantic Ave), 2 mi e to SR A1A (Ocean Blvd), then just s. [L] [D] [LATE]

DESTIN

◇◇ Graffiti
(850) 424-7514. American. Casual Dining. **$15-$29.** 707 Harbor Blvd 32541. On US 98, 2.9 mi w of bridge. [D]

◇◇ Hog's Breath Saloon & Cafe
(850) 837-5991. American. Casual Dining. **$7-$22.** 541 Harbor Blvd 32541. On US 98, 1 mi e of Destin Bridge. [L] [D] [LATE]

FORT LAUDERDALE

◇◇◇ Big City Tavern Restaurant & Bar
(954) 727-0307. American. Casual Dining. **$12-$35.** 609 E Las Olas Blvd 33301. I-95 exit 27 (Broward Blvd), 2.4 mi e to US 1, just s to Las Olas Blvd, then just e; downtown. [L] [D] [LATE]

FORT MYERS

◇◇ The Prawnbroker Restaurant & Fish Market
(239) 489-2226. Seafood. Casual Dining. **$12-$25.** 13451-16 McGregor Blvd 33919. 0.7 mi s of jct College Pkwy at Cypress Lake Dr; in Cypress Square. [D]

GULF BREEZE

◇◇ Aegean Breeze
(850) 916-0430. Greek. Casual Dining. **$7-$25.** 913 Gulf Breeze Pkwy, Unit 20 32561. Just e of jct SR 399; in Harbour Town Village Plaza. [L] [D]

HUDSON

◇◇ Sam's Hudson Beach Restaurant
(727) 868-1971. Seafood. Casual Dining. **$8-$19.** 6325 Clark St 34667. 0.8 mi w of jct US 19, just s; at Armand Way; at Hudson Beach. [L] [D] [JC]

ISLAMORADA

◇◇◇ Lorelei Restaurant & Cabana Bar
(305) 664-2692. American. Casual Dining. **$9-$24.** 96 Mile Marker 82 Rd 33036. MM 82 bayside; center. [B] [L] [D] [&M] [JC] [\]

◇◇ Marker 88 Restaurant
(305) 852-9315. Seafood. Casual Dining. **$12-$42.** 88000 Overseas Hwy 33036. US 1 at MM 88. [◁] [L] [D] [\]

JACKSONVILLE

◇◇ Seven Bridges Grille & Brewery
(904) 997-1999. International. Casual Dining. **$10-$30.** 9735 Gate Pkwy N 32246. I-95 exit 344 (SR 202), 2.5 mi e on J Turner Butler Blvd, 0.8 mi n on SR 115, then just e. [L] [D] [&M]

JACKSONVILLE BEACH

◇ Graffiti Junktion
(904) 372-9985. Burgers. Casual Dining. **$10-$14.** 265 5th Ave N 32250. Corner of 3rd St N and 5th Ave N. [L] [D] [LATE] [\]

◇◇ Metro Diner
(904) 853-6817. American. Casual Dining. **$8-$15.** 1534 3rd St N 32250. On SR A1A/3rd St; between 14th and 15th aves N. [B] [L]

JUPITER

◇◇ Berry Fresh Cafe
(561) 401-5693. American. Casual Dining. **$8-$13.** 3755 Military Tr 33458. I-95 exit 83 (Donald Ross Rd), 1.6 mi w to Military Tr, then 1.1 mi n; in Admirals Crossing Plaza. [B] [L] [&M]

KEY BISCAYNE

◇◇ Sushi Siam
(305) 361-7768. Asian. Casual Dining. **$13-$33.** 632 Crandon Blvd 33149. Just s of jct Crandon Blvd and McIntyre St. [L] [D]

KEY LARGO

◇◇ Ballyhoo's Historic Seafood Grille
(305) 852-0822. Seafood. Casual Dining. **$10-$36.** 97860 Overseas Hwy 33037. US 1 at MM 97.8; in median. [L] [D]

⊛ ◇◇ The Fish House Restaurant & Seafood Market
(305) 451-4665. Seafood. Casual Dining. **$12-$31.** 102401 Overseas Hwy 33037. US 1 at MM 102.4. [L] [D]

◇◇ Key Largo Conch House
(305) 453-4844. International Seafood. Casual Dining. **$13-$32.** 100211 Overseas Hwy 33037. US 1 at MM 100.2. [B] [L] [D]

KEY WEST

◇ Amigo's Tortilla Bar
(305) 292-2009. Mexican. Quick Serve. **$8-$15.** 425 Greene St 33040. Between Duval St and Telegraph Ln. [B] [L] [D]

◇◇◇ Blackfin Bistro
(305) 509-7408. International. Casual Dining. **$14-$31.** 918 Duval St 33040. Between Truman and Olivia sts. [L] [D]

◇◇ Blue Heaven Restaurant & Bar
(305) 296-8666. Caribbean. Casual Dining. **$15-$35.** 729 Thomas St 33040. Just s of Duval St; corner of Petronia and Thomas sts. [B] [L] [D] [JC] [\]

◇ Half Shell Raw Bar
(305) 294-7496. Seafood. Casual Dining. **$12-$40.** 231 Margaret St 33040. West end of Margaret St; at Lands End Village in Historic Seaport District; at Key West Bight Ferry Terminal. [L] [D] [&M] [JC] [\]

◇ Harpoon Harry's
(305) 294-8744. Comfort Food. Casual Dining. **$7-$16.** 832 Caroline St 33040. Corner of Margaret and Caroline sts; across from Key West Historic Seaport. [B] [L] [D]

◇◇◇ Louie's Backyard
(305) 294-1061. International. Fine Dining. **$12-$40.** 700 Waddell Ave 33040. Just s of Truman Ave via Simonton St to South St, just e to Vernon, then s. [L] [D] [&M]

◇ Pepe's Cafe
(305) 294-7192. American. Casual Dining. **$12-$31.** 806 Caroline St 33040. Between Margaret and William sts; just e of Duval St. [B] [L] [D]

SHOR American Seafood Grill
(305) 809-4000. American. Casual Dining. **$13-$41.** 601 Front St 33040. Corner of Simonton and Front sts; just n of Mallory Square; in Old Town; in Hyatt Key West Resort & Spa. (B) (L) (D)

SQ1 Restaurant
(305) 296-4300. New American. Casual Dining. **$13-$30.** 1075 Duval St 33040. At Duval Square, just e of Truman Ave. (L) (D) (&M)

LAKE MARY

Cozee Cafe, The Corner Bistro
(407) 804-0066. American. Casual Dining. **$7-$33.** 1145 TownPark Ave, Suite 1221 32746. I-4 exit 101C, just w; in Colonial TownPark.
(B) (L) (D) (N)

Liam Fitzpatrick's Irish Restaurant & Pub
(407) 936-3782. Irish. Gastropub. **$10-$30.** 951 Market Promenade Ave, Suite 1115 32746. I-4 exit 101A, just w; in Colonial TownPark.
(L) (D) (LATE) (&M) (N)

LAKE WORTH

Brogues Downunder
(561) 585-1885. Continental. Casual Dining. **$9-$22.** 621 Lake Ave 33460. I-95 exit 64 (10th Ave), 0.7 mi e to US 1 (Dixie Hwy), 0.8 mi s to Lake Ave, then just e; downtown. (L) (D) (LATE) (N)

Dave's Last Resort & Raw Bar
(561) 588-5208. American. Casual Dining. **$9-$23.** 632 Lake Ave 33460. Jct K St and Lake Ave; downtown. (L) (D) (LATE) (N)

Havana Hideout
(561) 585-8444. Latin American. Casual Dining. **$5-$12.** 509 Lake Ave 33460. I-95 exit 64 (10th Ave), 0.7 mi e to US 1 (Dixie Hwy), 0.8 mi s to Lake Ave, then just e; downtown. (L) (D) (X) (N)

MAITLAND

Antonio's Market & Cafe Downstairs
(407) 645-1039. Italian. Casual Dining. **$8-$18.** 611 S Orlando Ave 32751. On US 17-92, 1.3 mi n of jct SR 423 (Lee Rd). (L) (D)

MARCO ISLAND

CJ's on the Bay
(239) 389-4511. American. Casual Dining. **$10-$36.** 740 N Collier Blvd, Suite 105 34145. Jct SR 951 (N Collier Blvd) and W Elkcam Cir; in Esplanade Complex; on Smokehouse Bay. (L) (D) (&M) (N)

MELBOURNE

El Chico
(321) 722-4622. Tex-Mex. Casual Dining. **$9-$20.** 1751 Evans Rd 32904. I-95 exit 180 (US 192/New Haven Ave), 3.2 mi e to Evans Rd, then just n; in front of Melbourne Square Mall. (L) (D) (&M) (N)

MIAMI

100 Montaditos from Spain
(786) 409-3107. Spanish Small Plates. Quick Serve. **$8-$12.** 1401 Brickell Ave 33131. Corner of SE 14th St and Brickell Ave; in Banco Santander Building. (L) (D)

Blue Collar
(305) 756-0366. New Comfort Food. Casual Dining. **$15-$25.** 6730 Biscayne Blvd 33138. Between NE 68th and NE 67th sts; in MiMo District.
(L) (D)

Buena Vista Bistro
(305) 456-5909. International. Casual Dining. **$12-$33.** 4582 NE 2nd Ave 33137. I-195 exit 2B, just w to NE 2nd Ave, then 0.5 mi n. (L) (D) (LATE)

Burger & Beer Joint
(305) 523-2244. Burgers. Casual Dining. **$12-$32.** 900 S Miami Ave, Suite 130 33130. Corner of SW 9th St and S Miami Ave; in The Shops at Mary Brickell Village. (L) (D) (LATE)

Fratelli Milano
(305) 373-2300. Italian. Casual Dining. **$10-$28.** 213 SE 1st St 33131. Between SE 3rd and NE 2nd aves; in Ingraham Building. (L) (D)

La Riviera
(305) 264-4888. New Continental. Fine Dining. **$13-$32.** 5800 Blue Lagoon Dr 33126. SR 836 (Dolphin Expwy) exit NW 57th Ave/Red Rd/SR 959, just s to Blue Lagoon Dr, then just w; in Sofitel Miami.
(B) (L) (D) (&M) (N)

Morgan's
(305) 573-9678. International. Casual Dining. **$14-$27.** 28 NE 29th St 33132. Corner of N Miami Ave and NE 29th St. (B) (L) (D) (&M)

PM Fish & Steak House
(305) 200-5606. Argentine. Fine Dining. **$22-$65.** 1453 S Miami Ave 33130. Corner of SW 14th Terrace and S Miami Ave; in One Broadway complex. (L) (D) (&M)

Sugarcane Raw Bar Grill
(786) 369-0353. International Small Plates Sushi. Casual Dining. **$16-$46.** 3250 NE 1st Ave 33137. I-195 exit 2A (N Miami Ave), just s to NE 34th St, just e to NE 1st Ave, then just s. (L) (D) (LATE) (N)

MIAMI BEACH

Alta Mare
(305) 532-3061. International. Casual Dining. **$22-$48.** 1233 Lincoln Rd 33139. Between Alton Rd and Alton Ct; far west end of Lincoln Road Mall.
(D) (&M)

Aura
(305) 695-1100. International. Casual Dining. **$12-$36.** 613 Lincoln Rd 33139. Between Pennsylvania and Euclid aves. (L) (D) (N)

Balans
(305) 534-9191. International. Casual Dining. **$9-$30.** 1022 Lincoln Rd 33139. Between Michigan and Lenox aves. (B) (L) (D) (N)

Big Pink
(305) 532-4700. American. Casual Dining. **$10-$23.** 157 Collins Ave 33139. Jct 2nd St. (B) (L) (D) (LATE)

The Cafe at Books and Books
(305) 695-8898. International. Casual Dining. **$10-$23.** 933 Lincoln Rd 33139. Between Michigan and Jefferson aves; in Lincoln Road Mall.
(L) (D) (&M) (X)

Doraku
(305) 695-8383. Japanese Sushi. Casual Dining. **$12-$30.** 1104 Lincoln Rd 33139. Between Lenox and Alton rds; in Lincoln Road Mall.
(L) (D) (&M)

Icebox Cafe
(305) 538-8448. International. Casual Dining. **$14-$36.** 1855 Purdy Ave 33139. Just w of Bay Rd; between 20th and 18th sts. (B) (L) (D)

News Cafe
(305) 538-6397. International. Casual Dining. **$11-$20.** 800 Ocean Dr 33139. Corner of 8th St and Ocean Dr. (B) (L) (D) (24) (N)

Nexxt Cafe
(305) 532-6643. International. Casual Dining. **$14-$35.** 700 Lincoln Rd 33139. Between Euclid and Meridian aves; on Lincoln Road pedestrian mall. (L) (D) (&M) (N)

Pelican Restcafé
(305) 673-3373. International. Casual Dining. **$11-$46.** 826 Ocean Dr 33139. Between 8th and 9th sts; just e of SR A1A (Collins Ave).
(B) (L) (D) (LATE)

♦♦♦♦ Prime 112
(305) 532-8112. Steak Seafood. Fine Dining. **$15-$98.** 112 Ocean Dr
33139. Just e of SR A1A (Collins Ave); jct 1st St and Ocean Dr. L D

♦♦♦♦ Sardinia Ristorante
(305) 531-2228. Italian. Fine Dining. **$15-$40.** 1801 Purdy Ave 33139.
Corner of Purdy Ave and 18th St; across from Island View Park.
L D LATE &M

♦ Shake Shack
(305) 434-7787. Hot Dogs Burgers. Quick Serve. **$4-$13.** 1111 Lincoln
Rd 33139. Between Alton Rd and Lenox Ave. ◄█ L D

♦♦♦♦ Sushi Samba Dromo
(305) 673-5337. International Fusion. Casual Dining. **$20-$44.** 600 Lincoln Rd 33139. Corner of Pennsylvania Ave; in Lincoln Road Mall.
L D LATE &M

♦♦♦ Tapelia Spanish Cuisine
(786) 522-0623. Spanish Small Plates. Casual Dining. **$10-$30.** 551
Lincoln Rd 33139. Between Pennsylvania and Drexel aves.
◄█ L D LATE ◥

♦♦♦♦ Tongue and Cheek
(305) 704-2900. New American. Casual Dining. **$16-$42.** 431 Washington Ave 33139. Corner of Washington Ave and 5th St. L D

MILTON

♦♦ Blackwater Bistro
(850) 623-1105. American. Casual Dining. **$9-$24.** 5147 Elmira St
32570. Jct US 90 (Caroline St), just s; in historic downtown district.
L D &M

MOUNT DORA

♦ One Flight Up Café
(407) 758-9818. Sandwiches. Quick Serve. **$9-$14.** 440 N Donnelly St
32757. Jct 5th Ave, just s; downtown. B L D LATE

NAPLES

♦♦♦♦ M Waterfront Grille
(239) 263-4421. New Continental. Fine Dining. **$14-$43.** 4300 Gulf
Shore Blvd 34103. 1.2 mi w of US 41 (9th St N); corner of Park Shore Dr
and Gulf Shore Blvd; in The Village on Venetian Bay. L D &M ◥

♦♦♦ Noodles Italian Cafe & Sushi Bar
(239) 592-0050. Italian Noodles Sushi. Casual Dining. **$10-$33.** 1585
Pine Ridge Rd, Suite 5 34109. I-75 exit 107, 3 mi w on Pine Ridge Rd
(CR 896); in Mission Square Plaza. L D

♦♦♦♦ Sea Salt
(239) 434-7258. New Seafood. Fine Dining. **$15-$65.** 1186 3rd St S
34102. Downtown; in Old Naples. L D &M

♦♦♦♦ Yabba Island Grill
(239) 262-5787. Caribbean. Casual Dining. **$13-$32.** 711 5th Ave S
34102. Just w of US 41 (Tamiami Tr); downtown. D &M

NEPTUNE BEACH

♦♦ North Beach Fish Camp
(904) 249-3474. Southern Seafood. Casual Dining. **$10-$24.** 100 1st St
32266. Corner of Ocean Blvd and 1st St. L D

NEW SMYRNA BEACH

♦ Cafe Heavenly
(386) 427-7475. American. Quick Serve. **$8-$23.** 115 Flagler Ave 32169.
East end of North Causeway Bridge. L D ◥

♦♦♦♦ Gnarly Surf Bar & Grill
(386) 957-3844. Fusion. Casual Dining. **$9-$22.** 114 Flagler Ave 32169.
Jct Flagler and N Peninsula aves; at base of draw bridge. L D

♦ Yellow Dog Eats Kitchen & Bar
(386) 410-4824. Barbecue Sandwiches. Casual Dining. **$10-$14.** 147
Canal St 32168. I-95 exit 249, 4.1 mi e to Live Oak St, just n to Canal St,
then just e; in Canal Street district. L D ◥

NORTH BAY VILLAGE

♦♦♦ Oggi Ristorante Italiano
(305) 866-1238. Italian. Casual Dining. **$9-$33.** 1666 79th St Cswy
33141. 2 mi w of SR A1A (Collins Ave). L D

ORLANDO

♦♦♦ 310 Lakeside
(407) 373-0310. New American. Fine Dining. **$10-$33.** 301 E Pine St
32801. Jct Rosalind and Central aves, just e. L D LATE

♦ Dandelion Communitea Cafe
(407) 362-1864. Vegetarian. Casual Dining. **$6-$10.** 618 N Thornton Ave
32803. Just s of jct SR 50 (Colonial Dr). L D

♦ Graffiti Junktion
(407) 426-9503. American. Casual Dining. **$9-$13.** 900 E Washington
Ave 32801. Jct E Washington and S Hyer aves. L D LATE

♦♦♦ Santiago's Bodega
(407) 412-6979. International Small Plates. Casual Dining. **$7-$17.** 802
Virginia Dr 32803. I-4 exit 85 (Princeton St), just e to Orange Ave, 0.5 mi
s to Virginia Dr, then 0.4 mi e. L D &M

PALM BEACH

♦♦♦ Polo Restaurant
(561) 659-8154. Steak Seafood. Fine Dining. **$14-$68.** 155 Hammon
Ave 33480. 1 blk s of Worth Ave; between S County Rd and SR A1A
(Ocean Blvd); in The Colony Palm Beach. B L D ◥

◉◗ ♦♦♦♦ Testa's Palm Beach
(561) 832-0992. Continental. Casual Dining. **$13-$42.** 221 Royal Poinci-
ana Way 33480. 0.3 mi e of Flagler Memorial Bridge. B L D

PALM BEACH SHORES

♦♦ Johnny Longboats Tropical Grill on the Beach
(561) 249-2795. Caribbean. Casual Dining. **$11-$35.** 2401 N Ocean Dr
33404. On Singer Island; just s of SR A1A. B L D &M ◥

PALM HARBOR

♦♦ East Lake Cafe
(727) 772-0707. Breakfast Sandwiches. Casual Dining. **$8-$12.** 3430 E
Lake Rd 34685. 1.9 mi e of jct US 19 on Tampa Rd (CR 752); in East
Lake Woodlands Shopping Center. B L

♦♦ Thirsty Marlin Grill & Bar
(727) 784-3469. Seafood. Casual Dining. **$8-$26.** 1023 Florida Ave
34683. Just e of jct US 19. L D LATE

PANAMA CITY BEACH

♦♦ Hofbrau Beer Garden
(850) 235-4632. German. Casual Dining. **$8-$18.** 701 Pier Park Dr,
Suite 155 32413. 1.2 mi e of jct SR 79 and 30, just n. L D &M

♦♦ Triple "J" Steak & Seafood
(850) 233-9514. Steak Seafood. Casual Dining. **$11-$34.** 2218 Thomas
Dr 32408. 1 mi s of US 98. L D

PENSACOLA

♦♦ The Oar House on Bayou Chico
(850) 549-4444. American. Casual Dining. **$8-$23.** 1000 S Pace Blvd
32502. I-110 exit 4, 1.1 mi w on SR 295 (Fairfield Dr), then 3 mi s on SR
292. L D LATE &M ◢

▼▼▼ **O'Briens Bistro**
(850) 477-9120. American. Casual Dining. **$9-$25.** 4350 Bayou Blvd, Suite 8 32503. Jct N 12th Ave and SR 296, just n. ⌐L⌐ ⌐D⌐ ⌐&M⌐

PENSACOLA BEACH

▼▼▼ **Hemingway's Island Grill**
(850) 934-4747. American. Casual Dining. **$8-$34.** 400 Quietwater Beach, Suite 16 32561. On Quietwater Beach boardwalk. ⌐L⌐ ⌐D⌐

PORT ST. LUCIE

▼▼ **Berry Fresh Cafe**
(772) 336-5291. American. Casual Dining. **$9-$13.** 1718 SW St. Lucie West Blvd 34986. I-95 exit 121 (St. Lucie West Blvd), 0.4 mi e; in The Village Shoppes at St. Lucie West. ⌐B⌐ ⌐L⌐ ⌐&M⌐

QUINCY

▼▼ **The Whip Waterfront Pub & Grub**
(850) 336-2605. Seafood Steak. Casual Dining. **$8-$24.** 3129 Cooks Landing Rd 32351. 3 mi se of jct SR 267. ⌐L⌐ ⌐D⌐

RAMROD KEY

▼▼ **Boondocks Grille & Draft House**
(305) 872-4094. American. Casual Dining. **$10-$25.** 27205 Overseas Hwy 33042. Between Summerland Key and Little Torch Key; at MM 27.5. ⌐L⌐ ⌐D⌐ ⌐&M⌐ ⌐K⌐ ⌐N⌐

ST. AUGUSTINE

▼▼ **Columbia Restaurant**
(904) 824-3341. Spanish. Casual Dining. **$10-$39.** 98 St. George St 32084. Jct St. George and Hypolita sts; center. ⌐L⌐ ⌐D⌐

▼▼ **Florida Cracker Cafe**
(904) 829-0397. Regional American. Casual Dining. **$10-$18.** 81 St. George St 32084. Between Cuna and Hypolita sts; in historic district. ⌐L⌐ ⌐D⌐

▼▼ **Hoptinger Bier Garden & Sausage House**
(904) 674-4767. Burgers Hot Dogs. Casual Dining. **$8-$17.** 200 Anastasia Blvd 32080. Just e of the Bridge of Lions; corner of Anastasia Blvd/SR A1A and Zorayda Ave. ⌐L⌐ ⌐D⌐ ⌐LATE⌐

ST. PETE BEACH

▼▼ **Sea Critters Cafe**
(727) 360-3706. Seafood. Casual Dining. **$8-$25.** 2007 Pass-A-Grille Way 33706. On SR 699, 0.8 mi s of Pinellas Bayway, jct 21st Ave; in Historic Pass-A-Grille. ⌐L⌐ ⌐D⌐

ST. PETERSBURG

▼▼ **Babalu Restaurant & Bar**
(727) 576-7414. Comfort Food. Casual Dining. **$8-$19.** 9246 4th St N 33702. Jct 92nd Ave N. ⌐L⌐ ⌐D⌐

▼▼ **Casual Clam**
(727) 895-2526. Seafood. Casual Dining. **$7-$31.** 3336 Dr. Martin Luther King St N (9th St N) 33704. I-275 exit 25, 0.9 mi e or on 38th Ave N, then 0.3 mi s. ⌐B⌐ ⌐L⌐ ⌐D⌐

SANFORD

▼▼ **Riverwalk Pizzeria**
(407) 915-5559. Italian Pizza. Casual Dining. **$6-$21.** 5040 W SR 46 32771. I-4 exit 101C, 0.4 mi w; in Dunwoody Plaza. ⌐L⌐ ⌐D⌐

SARASOTA

▼▼ **Mattison's City Grille**
(941) 330-0440. Continental. Casual Dining. **$10-$34.** 1 N Lemon Ave 34236. Jct Main St; downtown. ⌐L⌐ ⌐D⌐ ⌐LATE⌐ ⌐K⌐

SIESTA KEY

▼▼ **The Old Salty Dog**
(941) 349-0158. American. Casual Dining. **$8-$30.** 5023 Ocean Blvd 34242. Just n; in Siesta Village. ⌐L⌐ ⌐D⌐ ⌐LATE⌐

▼▼ **Village Cafe**
(941) 349-2822. Breakfast Sandwiches. Casual Dining. **$8-$13.** 5133 Ocean Blvd 34242. Jct Avenida Madera; center; in Siesta Village. ⌐B⌐ ⌐L⌐

SOUTH MIAMI

▼▼ **Blu by Best Friends**
(305) 666-9285. Italian Pizza. Casual Dining. **$11-$17.** 7201 SW 59th Ave 33143. Just se of US 1 exit Sunset Dr. ⌐L⌐ ⌐D⌐

▼ **Khoury's Restaurant**
(305) 662-7707. Mediterranean. Casual Dining. **$9-$30.** 5887 SW 73rd St 33143. Just e off US 1. ⌐L⌐ ⌐D⌐

▼▼ **Marhaba Mediterranean Cuisine**
(305) 666-9600. Lebanese. Casual Dining. **$12-$35.** 5861 Sunset Dr 33143. Just e of S Dixie Hwy; corner of Sunset Dr and SW 58th Ct; in the Shops at Sunset Place. ⌐L⌐ ⌐D⌐

SUNNY ISLES BEACH

▼ **Epicure Market and Cafe**
(305) 947-4581. Sandwiches Breads/Pastries. Quick Serve. **$14-$35.** 17190 Collins Ave 33160. On SR A1A, just s of 172nd St; just s of SR 826. ⌐B⌐ ⌐L⌐ ⌐D⌐ ⌐&M⌐

SURFSIDE

▼▼▼ **26 Sushi & Tapas**
(305) 570-2626. Asian Kosher Fusion. Casual Dining. **$16-$38.** 9487 Harding Ave 33154. Between 94th and 95th sts; just w of Collins Ave. ⌐L⌐ ⌐D⌐

TALLAHASSEE

▼▼ **Rummy's Pizza, Pasta & Grill**
(850) 878-8669. Pizza. Casual Dining. **$7-$23.** 2887 Kerry Forest Pkwy 32312. 3 mi n on Thomasville Rd. ⌐L⌐ ⌐D⌐ ⌐&M⌐

▼ **Taco Republik**
(850) 765-3314. Mexican. Quick Serve. **$3-$8.** 1122-8 Thomasville Rd 32303. Jct 5th Ave; downtown. ⌐L⌐ ⌐D⌐

TAMPA

▼▼ **SQUARE 1 Burgers & Bar**
(813) 414-0101. Burgers. Casual Dining. **$8-$15.** 3701 Henderson Blvd 33609. I-275 exit 41A, 1.4 mi s on N Dale Mabry Hwy (US 92), then just e. ⌐L⌐ ⌐D⌐ ⌐&M⌐

TAVARES

▼▼ **Hurricane Dockside Grill**
(352) 508-5137. American. Casual Dining. **$5-$18.** 3351 W Burleigh Blvd 32778. On US 441, 2 mi w of SR 19. ⌐L⌐ ⌐D⌐ ⌐LATE⌐

WEST PALM BEACH

▼▼ **Grease Burger, Beer & Whiskey Bar**
(561) 651-1075. Burgers. Casual Dining. **$6-$16.** 213 Clematis St 33401. Just e of Olive Ave; downtown. ⌐L⌐ ⌐D⌐ ⌐LATE⌐ ⌐N⌐

▼▼ **Howley's Restaurant**
(561) 833-5691. Comfort Food. Casual Dining. **$7-$23.** 4700 S Dixie Hwy 33405. I-95 exit 68 (Southern Blvd), 1 mi e to US 1 (Dixie Hwy), then 0.4 mi s. ⌐B⌐ ⌐L⌐ ⌐D⌐ ⌐LATE⌐ ⌐N⌐

▼▼▼ Hullabaloo
(561) 833-1033. New Italian. Gastropub. **$10-$26.** 517 N Clematis St 33401. I-95 exit 70 (Okeechobee Blvd), 0.7 mi e to Tamarind Ave, 0.6 mi n to Clematis St, then 0.6 mi e; downtown. [L] [D] [LATE] [◥]

▼ Relish & More
(561) 629-5377. Burgers. Quick Serve. **$11-$19.** 401 Northwood Rd 33407. I-95 exit 71 (Palm Beach Lakes Blvd), 2.3 mi e to US 1 (Dixie Hwy), then 0.7 mi n; in Northwood Village. [L] [D] [◥]

WINTER PARK

▼▼▼ 310 Park South
(407) 647-7277. American. Casual Dining. **$10-$33.** 310 S Park Ave 32789. Between E Lyman and E New England aves. [L] [D]

▼▼▼ Bosphorous Turkish Cuisine
(407) 644-8609. Turkish. Fine Dining. **$10-$36.** 108 S Park Ave 32789. Just s of Morse Blvd. [L] [D] [◥]

▼▼ The Briarpatch
(407) 628-8651. American. Casual Dining. **$13-$17.** 252 N Park Ave 32789. I-4 exit 87 (Fairbanks Ave), 2 mi e to Park Ave, then 0.5 mi n. [B] [L] [◥]

▼ Bubbalou's Bodacious Bar-B-Que
(407) 628-1212. Barbecue. Casual Dining. **$5-$16.** 1471 Lee Rd 32789. On SR 423, just w of jct US 17-92. [L] [D] [◥]

▼▼▼ Cafe De France
(407) 647-1869. French. Fine Dining. **$9-$34.** 526 S Park Ave 32789. I-4 exit 87, 1.9 mi e, then just n. [L] [D] [◥]

▼▼ Dexter's of Winter Park
(407) 629-1150. New American. Casual Dining. **$7-$25.** 558 W New England Ave 32789. I-4 exit 87 (Fairbanks Ave), 0.7 mi e, 0.3 mi n to Morse Blvd, just e to Pennsylvania Ave, then just s. [L] [D] [◥]

▼▼ Paris Bistro
(407) 671-4424. French. Casual Dining. **$9-$39.** 216 N Park Ave 32789. I-4 exit 87 (Fairbanks Ave), 1.9 mi e to Park Ave, then 0.4 mi n; in Shops on Park. [L] [D] [◥]

Georgia

ATHENS

▼▼ DePalma's Italian Cafe
(706) 552-1237. Italian. Casual Dining. **$6-$20.** 2080 Timothy Rd 30606. SR 8/10 Loop exit US 78 business route (Broad St), just e. [L] [D] [&M]

▼▼▼ Hilltop Grille
(706) 353-7667. American. Casual Dining. **$7-$31.** 2310 W Broad St 30606. Jct SR 10 Loop and US 78 business route (Broad St), 2.9 mi ne on US 78 business route (Broad St). [L] [D] [&M]

▼ Marti's at Midday
(706) 543-3541. Deli. Quick Serve. **$5-$10.** 1280 Prince Ave 30606. SR 10 Loop exit 7 (Prince Ave), 0.7 mi se. [B] [L]

▼▼▼ The National
(706) 549-3450. European. Fine Dining. **$10-$26.** 232 W Hancock Ave 30601. Just w of center; downtown. [L] [D]

ATLANTA

▼ Alon's Bakery & Market
(404) 872-6000. Deli. Quick Serve. **$6-$12.** 1394 N Highland Ave 30306. Jct Virginia and Highland aves, 1.5 mi n. [B] [L] [D]

▼▼▼ C & S Seafood & Oyster Bar
(770) 272-0999. Seafood. Fine Dining. **$10-$40.** 3240 Cobb Pkwy 30339. I-285 exit 20 westbound; exit 19 eastbound, 1.3 mi s; in Riverview Village. [L] [D] [&M]

▼▼ Cowtippers
(404) 874-3751. Steak. Casual Dining. **$6-$23.** 1600 Piedmont Ave NE 30324. Jct Monroe Dr NE, just s. [L] [D]

▼▼ Five Season's Brewing Company
(404) 255-5911. New American. Gastropub. **$8-$27.** 5600 Roswell Rd, Suite 21 30342. I-285 exit 27, just s; in The Prado. [L] [D]

▼▼▼ Food 101
(404) 497-9700. New American. Fine Dining. **$10-$29.** 4969 Roswell Rd, Suite 200 30342. I-285 exit 25, 1.5 mi s; in Belle Isle Shopping Center. [L] [D] [&M]

▼ Grindhouse Killer Burgers
(404) 254-2273. Burgers. Quick Serve. **$3-$9.** 1842 Piedmont Ave NE 30324. I-85 exit 86 northbound, just n to Monroe Dr, just e to Piedmont Rd NE, then just s; exit 88 southbound, just e to Lenox Rd, just e to Cheshire Bridge Rd, 1.5 mi e to Piedmont Rd, then just w. [L] [D] [&M]

▼▼ J. Christopher's
(404) 917-0350. Breakfast. Casual Dining. **$5-$11.** 3050 Peachtree Rd NW 30305. Jct Peachtree and W Paces Ferry rds, just s. [B] [L] [&M]

◍◍◍ ▼▼▼ Max Lager's Wood-Fired Grill & Brewery
(404) 525-4400. American. Casual Dining. **$9-$38.** 320 Peachtree St NW 30308. I-75/85 exit 249A to Baker St, 0.3 mi w to Peachtree St, then just n. [L] [D]

▼ Pig-N-Chik
(404) 255-6368. Barbecue. Quick Serve. **$6-$24.** 4920 Roswell Rd NE 30342. I-285 exit 25, 1.5 mi s; in Fountain Oaks Shopping Center. [L] [D]

▼▼▼ Starfish Restaurant
(404) 350-0799. Japanese. Fine Dining. **$7-$30.** 2255 Peachtree Rd NE 30309. Between Collier Rd and 26th St. [L] [D] [&M]

▼▼▼ Violette
(404) 633-3363. French. Casual Dining. **$9-$29.** 2948 Clairmont Rd NE 30329. I-85 exit 91, just w. [L] [D]

AUGUSTA

▼▼ French Market Grille
(706) 737-4865. Cajun. Casual Dining. **$7-$30.** 425 Highland Ave 30909. Jct SR 28 (Washington Rd), 1.8 mi s on Berckmans Rd; in Surrey Center. [L] [D]

▼▼▼ Oliviana's Pizzeria & Grill
(706) 723-1242. Northern Italian. Fine Dining. **$8-$30.** 399 Highland Ave, Suite A 30909. Jct SR 28 (Washington Rd), 1.8 mi s on Berckmans Rd; in Surrey Center. [L] [D] [&M]

▼▼ Somewhere in Augusta Bar & Grill
(706) 739-0002. Wings Sandwiches. Casual Dining. **$8-$17.** 2820 Washington Rd 30909. I-20 exit 199 (Washington Rd), 0.6 mi e. [L] [D] [LATE] [&M]

COLUMBUS

▼▼ Ben's ChopHouse Steak & Seafood
(706) 256-0466. Steak Seafood. Casual Dining. **$10-$50.** 5300 Sidney Simons Blvd 31904. I-185 exit 8, just w to Sidney Simons Blvd, then just s. [L] [D] [&M]

▼▼ Cannon Brewpub
(706) 653-2337. American. Gastropub. **$10-$30.** 1041 Broadway 31901. In historic uptown district. [L] [D]

DULUTH

▼▼▼ Kurt's Euro Bistro
(770) 623-4128. European. Fine Dining. **$12-$48.** 3305 Peachtree Industrial Blvd, Suite 100 30096. Jct River Green Pkwy; in The Village at River Green. [D]

FORT VALLEY

▼ Peachtree Café
(478) 825-3592. American. Casual Dining. $5-$12. 50 Lane Rd 31030. I-75 exit 142 (SR 96), 4.9 mi w; in Lane Southern Orchard. [L] [D]

HELEN

▼▼ Cafe International
(706) 878-3102. Continental. Casual Dining. $6-$18. 8546 Main St 30545. Downtown. [L] [D]

JEKYLL ISLAND

▼▼ Tortuga Jack's Baja Mexican
(912) 342-2600. Tex-Mex. Casual Dining. $10-$18. 201 N Beachview Dr 31527. Jct Jekyll Island Cswy (SR 520) and N Beachview Dr, just n. [L] [D] [&M]

KENNESAW

▼▼ Kuroshio Sushi Bar & Grille
(770) 499-7160. Japanese. Casual Dining. $9-$55. 840 Ernest Barrett Pkwy NW, Suite 500 30144. I-75 exit 69, 0.3 mi w. [L] [D] [&M]

MACON

▼▼ Molly's Cafe
(478) 744-9898. Sandwiches. Casual Dining. $6-$12. 402 Cherry St 31201. I-16 exit 2, 0.5 mi s on Martin Luther King Jr Blvd, then just w; downtown. [L]

▼▼ The Rookery
(478) 746-8658. American. Casual Dining. $8-$17. 543 Cherry St 31201. I-16 exit 2, 0.5 mi s on Martin Luther King Jr Blvd, then just w; downtown. [L] [D]

MADISON

▼▼ Madison Chophouse Grille
(706) 342-0910. American. Casual Dining. $8-$25. 202 S Main St 30650. I-20 exit 114, 3 mi n on US 441; Historic Town Square. [L] [D]

MARIETTA

▼▼▼ Chicken And The Egg
(678) 388-8813. American. Casual Dining. $9-$18. 800 Whitlock Ave, Suite 124 30064. 0.8 mi w of Historic Marietta Square. [L] [D] [&M]

▼ Jack's New Yorker Deli
(770) 424-1402. Sandwiches. Quick Serve. $5-$12. 168 Roswell St 30060. Just off Historic Marietta Square; downtown. [B] [L] [&M]

▼▼ WR Social House
(770) 792-9995. Cajun. Casual Dining. $8-$19. 25 N Park Square 30060. On Historic Marietta Square; downtown. [L] [D]

PLAINS

▼ Buffalo Cafe at The Old Bank
(229) 824-4520. American. Casual Dining. $4-$10. 118 Main St 31780. Center. [L] [D]

PORT WENTWORTH

▼▼ El Ranchito
(912) 965-0270. Mexican. Casual Dining. $6-$15. 7306 Hwy 21, Suite 201 31407. I-95 exit 109 (SR 21), 0.5 mi n to SR 30, then just e; in shopping center. [L] [D] [&M]

ROSWELL

▼▼▼ Brookwood Grill
(770) 587-0102. New American. Fine Dining. $10-$27. 880A Holcomb Bridge Rd 30076. SR 400 exit 7B, 0.8 mi w. [L] [D]

▼▼▼ Pastis
(770) 640-3870. French. Fine Dining. $10-$28. 928 Canton St 30075. Downtown. [L] [D]

ST. SIMONS ISLAND

▼▼ Barbara Jean's Restaurants
(912) 634-6500. Regional Comfort Food. Casual Dining. $9-$25. 214 Mallery St 31522. Between Beachview Dr and Lord Ave; on south side of island. [L] [D]

▼▼ Iguanas Seafood Restaurant
(912) 638-9650. Seafood. Casual Dining. $9-$37. 303 Mallery St 31522. Jct Kings Way, just sw; on southern tip of island; in Pier Village. [L] [D] [&M]

SAVANNAH

▼ Clary's Cafe
(912) 233-0402. Breakfast Sandwiches. Casual Dining. $6-$13. 404 Abercorn St 31401. Jct Jones St. [B] [L]

▼▼ Corleone's Trattoria
(912) 232-2720. Mediterranean. Casual Dining. $6-$28. 44 Martin Luther King Jr Blvd 31401. Jct W Congress Ln. [L] [D]

▼▼ The Distillery
(912) 236-1772. Burgers Sandwiches. Casual Dining. $8-$18. 416 W Liberty St 31401. Jct W Broad St. [L] [D] [&M]

▼▼ Firefly Cafe
(912) 234-1971. American. Casual Dining. $11-$32. 321 Habersham St 31401. S of E Liberty St; at Harris St; on Troup Square. [L] [D]

▼▼ Huey's New Orleans Cafe
(912) 234-7385. Creole. Casual Dining. $10-$32. 115 E River St 31401. On historic riverfront; under River Street Inn. [B] [L] [D]

▼▼ Love's Seafood Restaurant
(912) 925-3616. Seafood. Casual Dining. $11-$30. 6817 Chief O.F. Love Rd 31419. I-95 exit 94 (SR 204/Abercorn St), 1.9 mi e to US 17 S, 2.8 mi sw to Basin Rd; just ne of Ogeechee River at Kings Ferry Bridge. [D] [&M]

▼▼ Moon River Brewing Company
(912) 447-0943. American. Gastropub. $7-$24. 21 W Bay St 31401. Between Bull and Whitaker sts. [L] [D]

▼▼▼ The Olde Pink House
(912) 232-4286. Regional Seafood. Fine Dining. $15-$35. 23 Abercorn St 31401. Between E Bryan and E Saint Julian sts; facing Reynolds Square. [L] [D]

▼▼▼ River House Seafood & Bakery
(912) 234-1900. Seafood. Casual Dining. $10-$30. 125 W River St 31401. On historic riverfront. [B] [L] [D]

▼▼▼ Sam Snead's Oak Grill & Tavern
(912) 963-0797. American. Fine Dining. $10-$29. 7 Sylvester C. Formey Dr 31408. I-95 exit 104, just se to Crossroads Pkwy, then just sw. [L] [D] [&M]

▼▼▼ Vic's on the River Restaurant & Bar
(912) 721-1000. New Southern. Fine Dining. $8-$38. 26 E Bay St 31401. On historic riverfront; alternate entrance at 15 E River St. [L] [D] [&M]

▼ Vinnie Van Go Go
(912) 233-6394. Pizza. Quick Serve. $3-$16. 317 W Bryan St 31401. Between Montgomery and Jefferson sts; at City Market. [D] [LATE]

STATESBORO

▼▼ **Gnats Landing**
(912) 489-8291. American. Casual Dining. **$6-$18.** 470 S Main St 30458. Jct US 301/25 and SR 67, just s. [L] [D] [LATE]

THOMASVILLE

▼ **Granddaddy's Barbeque**
(229) 225-9500. Barbecue. Casual Dining. **$7-$15.** 2128 Smith Ave 31792. Jct US 19 and 84. [B] [L] [D]

TIFTON

▼▼ **El Cazador Mexican Restaurant**
(229) 386-2126. Mexican. Casual Dining. **$5-$19.** 1103 King Rd 31794. I-75 exit 63B, just e. [L] [D]

VALDOSTA

▼▼▼ **306 North**
(229) 249-5333. American. Fine Dining. **$7-$26.** 306 N Patterson St 31601. Jct US 84 and SR 31A, just n on SR 31A (Patterson St). [L] [D]

WOODSTOCK

▼ **Burger Inn**
(770) 926-1308. Sandwiches. Quick Serve. **$2-$8.** 9680 Main St 30188. I-575 exit 7, 0.9 mi e to Main St (Canton Rd), then just s. [B] [L]

▼▼▼ **Century House Tavern**
(770) 693-4552. New American. Fine Dining. **$15-$23.** 125 E Main St 30188. I-575 exit 8, 0.5 mi e to Main St, then just s; downtown. [L] [D] [&M]

▼▼ **Donovan's Irish Cobbler**
(770) 693-8763. Irish. Casual Dining. **$5-$15.** 1025 Rose Creek Dr, Suite 500 30189. I-575 exit 8, 1.3 mi w to Towne Lake Pkwy, then 2.3 mi n. [L] [D] [LATE] [&M]

▼ **Hot Dog Heaven**
(770) 591-5605. Hot Dogs. Quick Serve. **$3-$8.** 8558 Main St 30188. I-575 exit 8, 0.5 mi e; downtown. [L]

Idaho

MCCALL

▼ **Bistro 45 Wine Bar & Cafe**
(208) 634-4515. American. Quick Serve. **$6-$13.** 1101 N 3rd St 83638. Downtown. [B] [L] [D]

WALLACE

🔷 ▼▼ **1313 Club**
(208) 752-9391. American. Casual Dining. **$6-$23.** 608 Bank St 83873. Downtown. [B] [L] [D]

Indiana

CARMEL

▼▼ **Cafe Patachou**
(317) 566-0765. American. Casual Dining. **$8-$18.** 14390 Clay Terrace Blvd 46032. I-465 exit 31, 6 mi n on US 31, then 0.4 mi w; in Simon's Clay Terrace Mall. [B] [L] [&M]

INDIANAPOLIS

▼▼ **Fire by the Monon**
(317) 602-8590. American. Casual Dining. **$10-$17.** 6523 Ferguson St 46220. Jct N College Ave and 66th St, just s. [L] [D]

▼▼ **Flatwater Restaurant**
(317) 257-5466. American. Casual Dining. **$8-$22.** 832 E Westfield Blvd 46220. I-465 exit 31, 4.7 mi s on Meridian St, then 1 mi e. [L] [D]

▼▼ **Indianapolis Colts Grille**
(317) 631-2007. American. Casual Dining. **$10-$29.** 110 W Washington St 46204. Jct Washington and Illinois sts. [L] [D] [LATE] [&M]

▼▼ **Monon Food Company**
(317) 722-0176. American. Casual Dining. **$7-$15.** 6420 Cornell Ave 46220. Jct N College Ave and 64th St, just n on Cornell Ave; in a residential area. [L] [D] [&M]

▼▼ **Patachou on the Park**
(317) 632-0765. Breakfast Sandwiches. Casual Dining. **$8-$18.** 225 W Washington St 46204. Jct Washington St and Capitol Ave. [B] [L] [&M]

▼▼ **Petite Chou Bistro and Champagne Bar**
(317) 259-0765. French. Casual Dining. **$8-$29.** 823 Westfield Blvd 46220. I-465 exit 31, 4.7 mi s on Meridian St, then 1 mi e. [B] [L] [D]

▼▼ **Public Greens Urban Kitchen**
(317) 964-0864. New American. Casual Dining. **$6-$16.** 900 Cornell St 46220. Jct N College Ave and 64th St, just n on Cornell Ave. [B] [L] [D] [&M]

NASHVILLE

▼▼ **Big Woods Brewing Company**
(812) 988-6000. American. Casual Dining. **$10-$21.** 60 Molly Ln 47448. Jct SR 135 and Main St, just w to Molly Ln, then just n. [L] [D]

VALPARAISO

▼▼ **Meditrina Market Cafe**
(219) 707-5271. Mediterranean. Casual Dining. **$7-$20.** 24 Washington St 46383. Jct Jefferson St. [L] [D]

ZIONSVILLE

▼▼▼ **Noah Grant's Grill House & Oyster Bar**
(317) 732-2233. Steak Seafood. Casual Dining. **$8-$44.** 65 S 1st St 46077. Jct W Oak St. [D] [&M]

Kansas

COTTONWOOD FALLS

🔷 ▼▼ **Grand Central Grill**
(620) 273-6763. American. Casual Dining. **$8-$35.** 215 Broadway 66845. US 177, just w on Main St, then just s; center of downtown; in Grand Central Hotel. [L] [D]

Kentucky

BOWLING GREEN

▼▼ **Chaney's Dairy Barn & Restaurant**
(270) 843-5567. Desserts Chicken. Quick Serve. **$6-$10.** 9191 Nashville Rd 42101. I-65 exit 20B (Natcher Pkwy), 3.5 mi nw to exit 6, then 4.8 mi s on SR 3 W. [L] [D] [&M]

▼ **Griffs Deli**
(270) 904-4743. Sandwiches Deli. Quick Serve. **$6-$9.** 1640 Scottsville Rd 42104. I-65 exit 22 (Scottsville Rd), 2.7 mi w. [L] [D] [&M]

CAVE CITY

▼▼ **El Mazatlan**
(270) 773-7448. Mexican. Casual Dining. **$7-$20.** 105 Gardner Ln 42127. I-65 exit 53, just e. ⃞L ⃞D ⃞&M ⃞↘

GRAND RIVERS

▼▼ **Lite Side Cafe & Bakery**
(270) 362-4586. Breakfast Burgers. Quick Serve. **$6-$9.** 2115 Dover Rd 42045. I-24/69 exit 31 (SR 453), 3.5 mi s. ⃞B ⃞L

PADUCAH

▼▼▼ **Max's Brick Oven Cafe**
(270) 575-3473. Mediterranean. Casual Dining. **$10-$26.** 112 Market House Square 42001. Between Broadway St and Kentucky Ave, on 2nd St; in historic downtown. ⃞D ⃞↘

▼▼▼ **Tribeca Mexican Cuisine**
(270) 444-3960. Mexican. Casual Dining. **$8-$16.** 127 Market House Square 42001. Between Kentucky Ave and Broadway St, on 2nd St; in historic downtown. ⃞L ⃞D

Louisiana

ABITA SPRINGS

▼▼ **Abita Brew Pub**
(985) 892-5837. Regional American. Casual Dining. **$9-$20.** 72011 Holly St 70420. Center; just w of traffic circle. ⃞L ⃞D

BATON ROUGE

▼ **Red Zeppelin Pizza**
(225) 302-7153. Pizza. Casual Dining. **$8-$20.** 4395 Perkins Rd 70808. Just w of College Rd. ⃞L ⃞D

COVINGTON

▼▼▼ **Del Porto Ristorante**
(985) 875-1006. Italian. Fine Dining. **$12-$36.** 501 E Boston St 70433. Jct New Hampshire St; downtown. ⃞L ⃞D ⃞&M

HAMMOND

▼▼ **Tope la'**
(985) 542-7600. Regional American. Casual Dining. **$10-$32.** 104 N Cate St 70401. I-12 exit 40 (US 51), 1.9 mi n, just e on W Morris St, then just n. ⃞L ⃞D

LAFAYETTE

▼▼ **Blue Dog Cafe**
(337) 237-0005. Cajun. Casual Dining. **$8-$32.** 1211 W Pinhook Rd 70503. SR 182, 1.1 mi w of jct US 90 (Evangeline Thruway). ⃞L ⃞D

LAKE CHARLES

▼▼ **Pujo Street Cafe**
(337) 439-2054. American. Casual Dining. **$10-$35.** 901 Ryan St 70601. I-10 exit 30B (Ryan St) westbound; exit 29 (downtown) eastbound, 0.7 mi se on Lakeshore/Broad St to Ryan St, then just s to Pujo St. ⃞L ⃞D

NEW ORLEANS

▼ **Cafe Beignet**
(504) 525-2611. American. Quick Serve. **$5-$13.** 311 Bourbon St 70130. Between Bienville and Conti sts. ⃞B ⃞L ⃞D ⃞Ⓜ ⃞↘

▼▼ **Feelings Cafe**
(504) 945-2222. Regional American. Casual Dining. **$13-$31.** 2600 Chartres St 70117. Just se of jct Elysian Fields; east end of town. ⃞D

▼▼ **Green Goddess**
(504) 301-3347. New International. Casual Dining. **$12-$22.** 307 Exchange Pl 70130. Between Bienville and Conti sts, just sw of Supreme Court Building. ⃞L ⃞D

▼▼ **The Marigny Brasserie**
(504) 945-4472. Regional American. Casual Dining. **$12-$24.** 640 Frenchmen St 70116. Jct Royal St. ⃞L ⃞D

▼▼ **Palace Cafe**
(504) 523-1661. Creole. Fine Dining. **$13-$45.** 605 Canal St 70130. Between Royal and Chartres sts. ⃞B ⃞L ⃞D

▼ **Voo Doo BBQ & Grill**
(504) 522-4647. Barbecue. Quick Serve. **$6-$25.** 1501 St. Charles Ave 70130. Between Melpomene Ave and Terpsichore St. ⃞L ⃞D

▼▼ **Wood, Pizza Bistro and Taphouse**
(504) 281-4893. Pizza Small Plates. Casual Dining. **$9-$16.** 404 Andrew Higgins Dr 70130. Jct Annunciation St. ⃞L ⃞D

Maine

BAR HARBOR

▼▼ **Fish House Grill & Oyster Bar**
(207) 288-3070. Seafood. Casual Dining. **$12-$35.** 1 West St 04609. Center; at Town Pier. ⃞L ⃞D ⃞Ⓜ

▼▼ **Jack Russell's Steakhouse & Brewery**
(207) 288-5214. American. Casual Dining. **$11-$38.** 102 Eden St 04609. 1.8 mi w on SR 3. ⃞D

▼▼ **The Looking Glass Restaurant**
(207) 288-5663. American. Casual Dining. **$16-$42.** 50 Eden St 04609. 0.5 mi w on SR 3; in A Wonder View Inn. ⃞B ⃞D

▼▼▼ **McKay's Public House**
(207) 288-2002. American. Gastropub. **$12-$30.** 231 Main St 04609. Just s of Newton Way; center. ⃞D

CAPE ELIZABETH

▼▼▼ **Sea Glass**
(207) 799-3134. American. Casual Dining. **$12-$42.** 40 Bowery Beach Rd 04107. On SR 77, 7 mi s; in Inn by the Sea. ⃞⊟ ⃞B ⃞L ⃞D ⃞&M

WATERVILLE

▼▼ **The Last Unicorn Restaurant**
(207) 873-9363. American. Casual Dining. **$9-$23.** 8 Silver St 04901. Between Main St and Concourse W. ⃞L ⃞D

Maryland

ANNAPOLIS

▼▼ **Buddy's Crabs & Ribs**
(410) 626-1100. Seafood. Casual Dining. **$8-$25.** 100 Main St 21401. Just nw of State Circle. ⃞L ⃞D

▼▼▼ **Harry Browne's**
(410) 263-4332. Continental. Fine Dining. **$10-$35.** 66 State Circle 21401. In historic district facing the State Capitol. ⃞L ⃞D

▼▼▼ **India's Restaurant**
(410) 263-7900. Indian. Casual Dining. **$12-$25.** 257 West St 21401. 0.5 mi w of Church Circle. ⃞L ⃞D

▼ **Mission BBQ**
(443) 569-4700. Barbecue. Quick Serve. **$7-$19.** 2101 Somerville Rd 21401. 2.3 mi sw on US 50 and 301 exit 22 to Riva Rd, 0.5 mi n. ⃞L ⃞D ⃞&M

BALTIMORE

▼▼▼ Ambassador Dining Room
(410) 366-1484. Indian Vegetarian. Fine Dining. **$15-$27.** 3811 Canterbury Rd 21218. Jct Canterbury Rd and 39th St; 1 blk from Johns Hopkins University Homewood Campus; in Ambassador Apartments. [L] [D]

▼▼ Amicci's
(410) 528-1096. Italian. Casual Dining. **$8-$19.** 231 S High St 21202. In Little Italy area. [L] [D]

▼▼▼ b-A Bolton Hill Bistro
(410) 383-8600. American. Casual Dining. **$13-$33.** 1501 Bolton St 21217. Jct Bolton and Mosher sts; in Bolton Hill area. [D]

▼▼ Blue Agave Restaurant
(410) 576-3938. Mexican. Casual Dining. **$12-$25.** 1032 Light St 21230. Between Poultney and Cross sts; in historic Federal Hill area. [L] [D] [LATE]

▼▼▼ Cinghiale
(410) 547-8282. Regional Italian. Fine Dining. **$20-$35.** 822 Lancaster St 21202. In Harbor East; jct S Exeter and Lancaster sts. [D] [&M]

▼▼ Donna's Cross Keys
(410) 532-7611. Mediterranean. Casual Dining. **$12-$27.** 40 Village Square 21210. I-83 exit 10A (Northern Pkwy), just e, then 0.4 mi s on Falls Rd; in Village of Cross Keys. [B] [L] [D] [&M]

▼▼ Fleet Street Kitchen
(410) 244-5830. New American. Fine Dining. **$25-$34.** 1012 Fleet St 21202. Between Central Ave and S Exeter St. [D] [&M]

▼▼▼ Germano's Piattini
(410) 752-4515. Regional Italian Small Plates. Casual Dining. **$6-$22.** 300 S High St 21202. At S High and Fawn sts; in Little Italy area. [L] [D]

▼▼ Ikaros Restaurant
(410) 633-3750. Greek. Casual Dining. **$7-$35.** 4901 Eastern Ave 21224. I-95 exit 59, 1.2 mi w; jct Ponca St. [L] [D]

▼▼ James Joyce Irish Pub & Restaurant
(410) 727-5107. Irish. Gastropub. **$9-$31.** 616 S President St 21202. Jct President St and Eastern Ave; in Harbor East. [L] [D] [LATE] [&M]

▼▼ Lebanese Taverna
(410) 244-5533. Lebanese. Casual Dining. **$11-$28.** 719 S President St 21202. Jct President and Lancaster sts; in Harbor East. [L] [D] [&M]

▼▼ Regi's American Bistro
(410) 539-7344. American. Casual Dining. **$13-$31.** 1002 Light St 21230. Corner of E Hamburg and Light sts; in historic Federal Hill area. [L] [D]

▼▼ Tapas Teatro
(410) 332-0110. Spanish Small Plates. Casual Dining. **$7-$21.** 1711 N Charles St 21201. Jct E Lanvale St. [D] [LATE]

▼▼▼▼ Wit & Wisdom
(410) 223-1456. American. Fine Dining. **$19-$59.** 200 International Dr 21202. In Harbor East; in Four Seasons Hotel Baltimore. [B] [L] [D] [&M]

BETHESDA

▼ Bethesda Crab House
(301) 652-3382. Seafood. Casual Dining. **$15-$59.** 4958 Bethesda Ave 20814. Jct Arlington Rd and Bethesda Ave, just w. [L] [D]

▼▼▼ Black's Bar & Kitchen
(301) 652-6278. Seafood. Fine Dining. **$13-$39.** 7750 Woodmont Ave 20814. 1 blk w of Wisconsin Ave (SR 355). [L] [D] [&M]

▼▼▼ Cesco Osteria
(301) 654-8333. Northern Italian. Fine Dining. **$11-$33.** 7401 Woodmont Ave 20814. Jct Montgomery Ln; 2 blks w of Wisconsin Ave. [L] [D]

▼▼▼ Jaleo
(301) 913-0003. Spanish Small Plates. Casual Dining. **$9-$65.** 7271 Woodmont Ave 20814. I-495 exit 34, 2.2 mi s on SR 355, just w on Elm St, then just n. [L] [D] [&M]

▼▼▼ Persimmon-An American Bistro
(301) 654-9860. American. Casual Dining. **$12-$36.** 7003 Wisconsin Ave 20815. I-495 exit 34, 2.8 mi s on SR 355. [L] [D] [&M]

▼▼ Uncle Julio's
(301) 656-2981. Mexican. Casual Dining. **$10-$26.** 4870 Bethesda Ave 20814. 2 blks w of SR 355; downtown. [L] [D]

BOWIE

▼▼ TJ Elliott's Restaurant
(301) 262-6282. American. Casual Dining. **$9-$45.** 6814 Laurel Bowie Rd 20715. On SR 197, 2.3 mi n of jct US 50 exit 11; in Bowie Plaza Shopping Center. [L] [D]

CATONSVILLE

▼ Chef Paolino Cafe
(410) 747-4949. Italian. Casual Dining. **$6-$19.** 726 Frederick Rd 21228. I-695 exit 13, 0.4 mi w; just n of jct Bloomsbury Ave. [L] [D] [&M]

COLUMBIA

▼ Mission BBQ
(443) 832-6180. Barbecue. Quick Serve. **$7-$19.** 6270 Columbia Crossing Cir 21045. I-95 exit 41B, 2.1 mi w on SR 175, just n on Dobbin Rd; in Columbia Crossing Shopping Center. [L] [D] [&M]

▼ The Tomato Palace
(410) 715-0211. Italian. Casual Dining. **$10-$27.** 10221 Wincopin Cir 21044. Off SR 175 (Little Patuxent Pkwy), 1.5 mi w of jct US 29; center. [L] [D]

FREDERICK

▼▼▼ Ayse Meze Lounge
(240) 651-5155. Middle Eastern Small Plates. Fine Dining. **$10-$20.** 6 N East St 21701. Jct E Patrick St; in Everedy Square; in historic district. [L] [D] [&M]

▼ Black Hog
(301) 662-9090. Barbecue. Casual Dining. **$7-$26.** 118 S Market St 21701. Between South and All Saints sts; in historic district. [L] [D]

▼▼▼ Isabella's Taverna & Tapas Bar
(301) 698-8922. Spanish Small Plates. Casual Dining. **$11-$30.** 44 N Market St 21701. Between Church and Patrick sts; in historic district. [L] [D] [&M]

▼▼▼ Reina
(301) 694-3015. Latin American. Casual Dining. **$10-$18.** 129 N Market St 21701. Between Church and 2nd sts; in historic district. [L] [D]

▼▼ Sabor de Cuba
(301) 663-1036. Cuban. Casual Dining. **$9-$18.** 9 E Patrick St 21701. Just e of Market St; in historic district. [L] [D]

GLEN BURNIE

▼ Mission BBQ
(410) 773-9888. Barbecue. Casual Dining. **$7-$19.** 7748 Ritchie Hwy 21061. I-695 exit 3B eastbound; exit 2 westbound, 4.3 mi s on SR 2; in Harundale Plaza. [L] [D] [&M]

HANOVER

▼ **Cantina Mamma Lucia**
(410) 684-2900. Italian Pizza. Casual Dining. **$9-$18.** 1350 Dorsey Rd 21076. SR 100 exit 10B, 0.3 mi n on SR 713, then 0.5 mi e on SR 176; in shopping center. Ⓛ Ⓓ &M

▼▼ **Grillfire**
(410) 799-2883. American. Casual Dining. **$11-$45.** 7793-A Arundel Mills Blvd 21076. SR 295 (Baltimore-Washington Pkwy) exit Arundel Mills Blvd, just e; in The Hotel at Arundel Preserve. Ⓑ Ⓛ Ⓓ &M

▼▼ **Rangoli**
(410) 799-5650. Indian. Casual Dining. **$13-$25.** 7791-C Arundel Mills Blvd 21076. SR 295 (Baltimore-Washington Pkwy) exit Arundel Mills Blvd, just e. Ⓛ Ⓓ &M

LA PLATA

▼▼▼ **The Crossing at Casey Jones**
(301) 392-5116. American. Casual Dining. **$10-$30.** 417 E Charles St 20646. Just e of US 301. Ⓛ Ⓓ

LEXINGTON PARK

▼ **Smokey Joe's Restaurant & Pit BBQ**
(301) 866-0995. Barbecue. Quick Serve. **$6-$12.** 22380 Three Notch Rd 20653. On SR 235, 0.6 mi n of Naval Air Station Patuxent River, Gate 1.
Ⓛ Ⓓ

LINTHICUM HEIGHTS

▼ **Urban Bar-B-Que Company**
(410) 636-0850. Barbecue. Quick Serve. **$7-$23.** 802 Pinnacle Dr 21090. I-695 exit 7A, 1 mi s on SR 295, then just nw on Nursery Rd.
Ⓛ Ⓓ &M

NORTH EAST

🅰🅰🅰 ▼▼ **Woody's Crab House**
(410) 287-3541. Seafood. Casual Dining. **$9-$35.** 29 S Main St 21901. I-95 exit 100, 2 mi e on SR 272. Ⓛ Ⓓ

OCEAN CITY

▼▼ **Crab Alley**
(410) 213-7800. Seafood. Casual Dining. **$9-$42.** 9703 Golf Course Rd 21842. On SR 626, 0.5 mi s of jct US 50; in West Ocean City.
Ⓛ Ⓓ &M

▼▼▼ **Hooked**
(410) 723-4665. American. Casual Dining. **$9-$35.** 8003 Coastal Hwy 21842. Jct 80th St. Ⓛ Ⓓ &M

▼▼ **Malia's Cafe**
(443) 664-2420. Breakfast Sandwiches. Casual Dining. **$5-$12.** 1800 N Baltimore Ave 21842. Jct 18th St. Ⓑ Ⓛ

▼▼▼ **Sunset Grille**
(410) 213-8110. Seafood. Casual Dining. **$10-$34.** 12933 Sunset Ave 21842. In West Ocean City; 0.6 mi s on Golf Course Rd from jct US 50, just e; at Sunset Marina. Ⓛ Ⓓ &M

ROCKVILLE

▼▼ **Mykonos Grill**
(301) 770-5999. Greek. Casual Dining. **$12-$31.** 121 Congressional Ln 20852. Jct SR 28, 2 mi s on SR 355; in Congressional Shopping Plaza.
Ⓛ Ⓓ

▼▼▼ **Nick's Chophouse**
(301) 926-8869. Steak Seafood. Fine Dining. **$8-$46.** 700 King Farm Blvd 20850. I-270 exit 8 (Shady Grove Rd), 0.5 mi e, then 0.6 mi s on Gaither Rd. Ⓛ Ⓓ

SYKESVILLE

▼▼▼ **Baldwin's Station**
(410) 795-1041. American. Casual Dining. **$8-$36.** 7618 Main St 21784. I-70 exit 80 (SR 32), 7.6 mi n. Ⓛ Ⓓ

WHITE MARSH

▼▼ **Red Brick Station**
(410) 931-7827. American. Gastropub. **$8-$26.** 8149 Honeygo Blvd 21236. I-95 exit 67, 0.5 mi w on SR 43 (White Marsh Blvd), then 0.6 mi s; in The Avenue at White Marsh. Ⓛ Ⓓ &M

Massachusetts

BOSTON

▼▼ **Masa**
(617) 338-8884. Southwestern. Casual Dining. **$8-$30.** 439 Tremont St 02116. Between Arlington and E Berkeley sts. Ⓓ

CAMBRIDGE

▼▼▼ **Henrietta's Table**
(617) 661-5005. Regional American. Casual Dining. **$6-$37.** 1 Bennett St 02138. Just s of Harvard Square; at Eliot St; in The Charles Hotel, Harvard Square. 🍴 Ⓑ Ⓛ Ⓓ &M

CHELMSFORD

▼▼▼ **moonstones**
(978) 256-7777. Mediterranean. Casual Dining. **$8-$36.** 185 Chelmsford Rd 01824. I-495 exit 34, just s on SR 110. Ⓛ Ⓓ &M

HYANNIS

▼▼▼ **Alberto's Ristorante**
(508) 778-1770. Northern Italian. Casual Dining. **$8-$36.** 360 Main St 02601. Just w of jct Barnstable Rd; downtown. Ⓛ Ⓓ

NANTUCKET

▼▼ **The Tavern Restaurant**
(508) 228-1266. American. Casual Dining. **$10-$29.** 1 Straight Wharf 02554. Just w of Hy-Line ferry terminal. Ⓛ Ⓓ

WELLESLEY

▼▼▼ **Blue Ginger, an East-West Bistro**
(781) 283-5790. Pacific Rim. Casual Dining. **$11-$41.** 583 Washington St 02482. SR 16, just se of SR 135. Ⓛ Ⓓ &M

WELLFLEET

▼▼▼ **Winslow's Tavern**
(508) 349-6450. New American. Casual Dining. **$13-$28.** 316 Main St 02667. US 6 exit Wellfleet Center, just e to town center. Ⓛ Ⓓ

Michigan

ANN ARBOR

▼▼▼ **Real Seafood Co.**
(734) 769-7738. Seafood. Casual Dining. **$11-$34.** 341 S Main St 48104. Jct Huron St, just s; downtown. Ⓛ Ⓓ

BAY CITY

▼ **BJay's Pizza & Coneys**
(989) 686-2499. Pizza Hot Dogs. Quick Serve. **$2-$18.** 363 State Park Dr 48706. I-75 exit 164 (Wilder Rd), 1.5 mi e to N Euclid, then 3 mi n.
Ⓛ Ⓓ &M 🍴

GRAND RAPIDS

▼▼ HopCat
(616) 451-4677. American. Casual Dining. **$10-$12.** 25 Ionia Ave NW 49503. Jct Weston St SW; downtown. ⬡L ⬡D ⬡LATE

PETOSKEY

▼▼▼ Chandler's - A Restaurant
(231) 347-2981. American. Fine Dining. **$10-$48.** 215 1/2 Howard St 49770. Jct E Lake St; downtown. ⬡L ⬡D

PLYMOUTH

▼▼ Crawford's Kitchen
(734) 454-5724. Breakfast Sandwiches. Casual Dining. **$5-$9.** 542 Starkweather St 48170. I-275 exit 28 (Ann Arbor Rd), 1 mi w, 1.3 mi n on Mill St, just w on Farmer St, then just n. ⬡B ⬡L

SUTTONS BAY

▼▼▼▼ Martha's Leelanau Table
(231) 271-2344. Regional American. Casual Dining. **$9-$30.** 413 N St. Joseph St 49682. Downtown. ⬡B ⬡L ⬡D ⬡LATE ⬡&M

Minnesota

MINNEAPOLIS

▼▼ Birchwood Cafe
(612) 722-4474. Natural/Organic. Casual Dining. **$12-$28.** 3311 E 25th St 55406. At S 33rd Ave. ⬡B ⬡L ⬡D

▼▼▼ Cafe & Bar Lurcat
(612) 486-5500. New American. Fine Dining. **$19-$38.** 1624 Harmon Pl 55403. Just sw of Hennepin Ave. ⬡D ⬡LATE

▼▼ The Freehouse
(612) 339-7011. American. Brewpub. **$12-$23.** 701 Washington Ave 55401. At N 7th Ave. ⬡B ⬡L ⬡D ⬡LATE

▼▼ The Lowry
(612) 341-2112. American. Casual Dining. **$10-$14.** 2112 Hennepin Ave 55405. Between W Franklin Ave and W 22nd St. ⬡B ⬡L ⬡D ⬡LATE

▼▼▼ Sanctuary
(612) 339-5058. New American. Fine Dining. **$18-$32.** 903 Washington Ave S 55415. At 9th St. ⬡D

▼▼ Sea Salt Eatery
(612) 721-8990. Seafood. Casual Dining. **$5-$19.** 4825 Minnehaha Ave 55417. In Refectory Building; in Minnehaha Park. ⬡L ⬡D

Mississippi

COLUMBUS

▼ Sweet Peppers Deli
(662) 328-6889. Sandwiches Soup. Quick Serve. **$6-$14.** 2017 Hwy 45 N 39705. On US 45, 0.9 mi n of jct US 82; in Jackson Square. ⬡L ⬡D ⬡&M

HATTIESBURG

▼ Ed's Burger Joint
(601) 602-2601. Burgers. Quick Serve. **$6-$8.** 3800 Hardy St 39402. I-59 exit 65, 0.5 mi e. ⬡L ⬡D

TUPELO

▼ Crossroads Rib Shack
(662) 840-1700. Barbecue. Casual Dining. **$5-$18.** 3061 Tupelo Commons 38804. US 45 exit Barnes Crossing, 0.5 mi sw, then 1 mi e; behind Best Western Plus Tupelo Inn & Suites. ⬡L ⬡D ⬡&M

Missouri

KANSAS CITY

▼▼▼ Bristol Seafood Grill
(816) 448-6007. Seafood. Casual Dining. **$10-$39.** 51 E 14th St 64106. Jct 14th and Main sts. ⬡L ⬡D ⬡&M

ST. LOUIS

▼▼ Bar Italia Ristorante
(314) 361-7010. Italian. Casual Dining. **$7-$30.** 13 Maryland Plaza 63108. I-64/US 40 exit 36A (Kingshighway Blvd), 1 mi n, then just e. ⬡L ⬡D

▼▼ Boathouse Forest Park
(314) 367-2224. American. Casual Dining. **$8-$11.** 6101 Government Dr 63110. I-64/US 40 exit 34D (Hampton Ave), just n, just w on Wells Dr, then just n; in Forest Park. ⬡L ⬡D

Montana

BOZEMAN

▼▼ Cafe Francais Des Arts
(406) 209-7490. French. Casual Dining. **$5-$10.** 24 S Tracy Ave 59715. Between Main and Babcock sts; downtown. ⬡B ⬡L ⬡&M

POLSON

▼ Cherries BBQ Pit
(406) 571-2227. Barbecue. Quick Serve. **$8-$25.** 105 2nd St E 59860. Just s; downtown. ⬡L ⬡D ⬡&M

Nebraska

OMAHA

▼▼ Black Oak Grill
(402) 341-0622. American. Casual Dining. **$8-$22.** 220 S 31st Ave, Suite 3107 68131. I-480 exit 2B westbound; exit 2A northbound, just w; in Midtown Crossing. ⬡L ⬡D ⬡&M

Nevada

BEATTY

▼ KC's Outpost Saloon & Eatery
(775) 553-9175. Sandwiches. Quick Serve. **$4-$8.** 100 E Main St 89003. Center. ⬡L ⬡D ⬡◣

BOULDER CITY

▼▼ The Dillinger
(702) 293-4001. Burgers Sandwiches. Gastropub. **$8-$12.** 1224 Arizona St 89005. Center. ⬡L ⬡D

▼ Milo's Cellar
(702) 293-9540. Sandwiches. Gastropub. **$9-$13.** 538 Nevada Way 89005. Downtown. ⬡L ⬡D

HENDERSON

▼ Rachel's Kitchen
(702) 522-7887. Sandwiches. Quick Serve. **$8-$12.** 2265 Village Walk Dr 89052. I-215 exit 5 (Green Valley Pkwy), just s; in The District Shopping Center. ⬡B ⬡L

LAS VEGAS

▼▼▼ **Grape Street Cafe**
(702) 228-9463. Italian. Fine Dining. **$12-$47.** 7501 W Lake Mead Blvd, Suite 120 89128. US 95 exit 82 (W Lake Mead Blvd), 0.5 mi w. [L] [D]

▼▼▼ **Herringbone**
(702) 590-9898. California Seafood. Fine Dining. **$18-$56.** 3730 Las Vegas Blvd S 89109. Between Flamingo Rd and Tropicana Ave; on the Strip; in ARIA Resort & Casino. [L] [D] [LATE] [&M]

▼▼ **John Cutter**
(702) 309-6200. American. Casual Dining. **$12-$32.** 11770 W Charleston Blvd 89135. I-215 exit 26 (Charleston Blvd), 0.7 mi w. [L] [D] [LATE]

▼▼ **Lazy Dog Restaurant & Bar**
(702) 727-4784. American. Casual Dining. **$10-$26.** 1725 Festival Plaza Dr 89135. I-215 exit 25 (W Sahara Ave), just n; in Downtown Summerlin. [L] [D] [&M]

▼▼ **Market Grille Cafe**
(702) 396-0070. Greek. Casual Dining. **$7-$13.** 7070 N Durango Dr 89149. US 95 exit 93 (Durango Dr), 1 mi w. [L] [D]

▼▼ **Satay Thai Bistro & Bar**
(702) 369-8788. Asian. Casual Dining. **$7-$26.** 3900 Paradise Rd, Suite N 89169. Just n of jct Flamingo and Paradise rds; between Twain Ave and Flamingo Rd. [L] [D]

RENO

▼▼▼ **Rapscallion Seafood House & Bar**
(775) 323-1211. Seafood. Casual Dining. **$16-$60.** 1555 S Wells Ave 89502. I-80 exit Wells Ave, 1 mi s. [L] [D]

VIRGINIA CITY

▼ **Firehouse Saloon & Grill**
(775) 847-7744. Barbecue. Quick Serve. **$5-$10.** 171 S C St 89440. Center. [L]

New Hampshire

CAMPTON

▼▼ **The Country Cow Restaurant at Blair Bridge**
(603) 536-1331. American. Casual Dining. **$8-$23.** 57 Blair Rd 03223. I-93 exit 27, just ne. [L] [D] [&M]

MANCHESTER

▼▼▼ **XO on Elm**
(603) 560-7998. Northern American. Casual Dining. **$11-$31.** 827 Elm St 03101. At Manchester St; downtown. [D]

New Jersey

HOBOKEN

▼▼▼ **The Brass Rail Restaurant & Bar**
(201) 659-7074. Continental. Fine Dining. **$10-$32.** 135 Washington St 07030. Corner of Washington and 2nd sts; downtown. [L] [D]

NORTH BERGEN

▼▼ **Sabor Latin Bistro**
(201) 943-6366. Latin American. Casual Dining. **$10-$36.** 8809 River Rd 07047. I-95 exit 16E (Lincoln Tunnel) to SR 495, 1.2 mi e to Weehawken/Hoboken exit, 1.5 mi n on JFK Blvd, just e on Hillside Rd (CR 505), then 1.6 mi n. [L] [D]

PISCATAWAY

▼▼▼ **Al Dente**
(732) 985-8220. Italian. Casual Dining. **$16-$30.** 1665 Stelton Rd 08854. I-287 exit 5, 1.7 mi s; jct US 1 and Plainfield Ave, 3 mi nw. [L] [D] [&M]

New Mexico

ALBUQUERQUE

▼▼▼ **Flying Star Cafe**
(505) 275-8311. American. Casual Dining. **$9-$13.** 4501 Juan Tabo Blvd NE 87111. Just n of jct Montgomery Blvd. [B] [L] [D]

▼▼▼ **Marcello's Chophouse**
(505) 837-2467. Steak. Fine Dining. **$8-$65.** 2201 Q St, Suite B 87110. I-40 exit 162, 0.5 mi n; in Uptown Center. [L] [D] [&M]

▼▼ **Nob Hill Bar & Grill**
(505) 266-4455. American. Casual Dining. **$11-$25.** 3128 Central Ave SE 87106. Jct Girard Blvd, southwest corner. [L] [D]

▼▼▼ **Pars Cuisine**
(505) 345-5156. Mediterranean. Casual Dining. **$10-$28.** 4320 The 25 Way NE, Suite 100 87109. I-25 exit 229 (Jefferson St), just e. [L] [D]

▼▼▼ **Savoy Bar & Grill**
(505) 294-9463. American. Fine Dining. **$9-$38.** 10601 Montgomery Blvd NE 87111. Between Juan Tabo Blvd and Morris St. [L] [D]

CHIMAYÓ

▼▼ **Rancho de Chimayo**
(505) 351-4444. Regional Mexican. Casual Dining. **$7-$21.** 300 CR 98 87522. 0.6 mi s on CR 98 from jct SR 76. [L] [D]

ESPAÑOLA

▼▼ **La Cocina Restaurant & Cantina**
(505) 753-3016. Mexican. Casual Dining. **$7-$14.** 415 Santa Clara Bridge Rd 87532. Just e of jct SR 30 and US 84. [B] [L] [D]

LAS CRUCES

▼▼▼ **Pecan Grill & Brewery**
(575) 521-1099. American. Casual Dining. **$7-$35.** 500 S Telshor Blvd 88011. I-25 exit 3 (Lohman Ave), just e. [L] [D] [LATE] [&M]

▼▼ **St. Clair Winery & Bistro**
(575) 524-0390. American. Casual Dining. **$7-$22.** 1720 Avenida de Mesilla 88004. I-10 exit 135, just w. [L] [D] [&M]

LOS ALAMOS

▼▼ **The Blue Window Bistro**
(505) 662-6305. International. Casual Dining. **$9-$29.** 813 Central Ave 87544. 0.5 mi w of jct SR 502 and Central Ave. [L] [D]

MESILLA

▼▼▼ **Savoy de Mesilla**
(575) 527-2869. International. Casual Dining. **$8-$26.** 1800 Avenida de Mesilla 88005. I-10 exit 140, 1 mi sw on SR 28. [L] [D]

RUIDOSO

▼▼▼ **Grill Caliente**
(575) 630-0224. Southwestern. Casual Dining. **$16-$30.** 2800 Sudderth Dr 88345. Just e of Mechem Dr; downtown. [L] [D]

▼▼ **The Village Buttery**
(575) 257-9251. Sandwiches Soup. Quick Serve. **$6-$9.** 2107 Sudderth Dr 88345. Center. [L]

SANTA FE

▼▼▼ **Restaurant Martin**
(505) 820-0919. New American. Fine Dining. **$10-$36.** 526 Galisteo St 87501. Jct Paseo de Peralta and Galisteo St; center. Ⓛ Ⓓ

▼▼▼ **Santa Fe Capitol Grill**
(505) 471-6800. International. Casual Dining. **$8-$27.** 3462 Zafarano Dr 87507. Northwest of jct Cerrillos Rd; in San Isidro Plaza. Ⓛ Ⓓ

▼▼ **Saveur**
(505) 989-4200. French. Casual Dining. **$6-$16.** 204 Montezuma Ave 87501. Jct Galisteo St, Cerrillos Rd and Montezuma Ave; downtown. Ⓑ Ⓛ

▼▼ **Vinaigrette**
(505) 820-9205. Natural/Organic. Casual Dining. **$10-$19.** 709 Don Cubero Alley 87505. Just e of jct Cerrillos Rd and Guadalupe St, just w of jct Cerrillos Rd and Paseo de Peralta. Ⓛ Ⓓ ⒼⓂ

TAOS

▼▼▼ **El Meze Restaurant**
(575) 751-3337. Regional Spanish. Casual Dining. **$16-$28.** 1017 Paseo del Pueblo Norte 87571. 1.2 mi n of plaza. Ⓓ

TRUTH OR CONSEQUENCES

▼▼▼ **Cafe BellaLuca**
(575) 894-9866. Italian. Casual Dining. **$8-$38.** 303 Jones St 87901. Center. Ⓛ Ⓓ

New York

ALBANY

▼▼ **Bountiful Bread**
(518) 438-3540. Sandwiches. Quick Serve. **$7-$11.** 1475 Western Ave 12203. Jct US 20 (Western Ave); in Stuyvesant Plaza. Ⓑ Ⓛ Ⓓ ⒼⓂ

BROOKLYN

▼▼ **Talde**
(347) 916-0031. Asian. Casual Dining. **$14-$31.** 369 7th Ave 11215. Between 11th and 12th sts. Ⓛ Ⓓ ⒼⓂ

CARLE PLACE

▼▼▼ **West End Cafe & Bar**
(516) 294-5608. New American. Casual Dining. **$10-$34.** 187 Glen Cove Rd 11514. Meadow Brook Pkwy exit 31, 0.5 mi s; in shopping center. Ⓛ Ⓓ

EAST HAMPTON

▼▼▼ **The Living Room Restaurant**
(631) 324-5006. Natural/Organic. Fine Dining. **$20-$45.** 207 Main St 11937. Jct SR 114, just s on SR 27; in c/o The Maidstone. Ⓒ Ⓑ Ⓛ Ⓓ

FLY CREEK

▼▼▼ **Portabello's**
(607) 547-5145. American. Casual Dining. **$17-$34.** 6207 State Hwy 28 13337. Center. Ⓓ

ITHACA

▼▼▼ **Madeline's Patisserie**
(607) 277-2253. New Fusion. Casual Dining. **$15-$30.** 215 E State St, Suite 10 14850. Downtown; on The Commons. Ⓓ

MIDDLETOWN

▼▼▼ **Nina**
(845) 344-6800. American. Fine Dining. **$8-$33.** 27 W Main St 10940. Just w of North St; downtown. Ⓛ Ⓓ

MONTAUK

▼▼▼ **Swallow East**
(631) 668-8344. New American Small Plates. Casual Dining. **$8-$22.** 474 W Lake Dr 11954. Jct SR 27, 2.3 mi n. Ⓓ

MOUNT KISCO

▼▼▼ **Cafe of Love**
(914) 242-1002. French. Casual Dining. **$15-$42.** 38 E Main St 10549. Jct SR 117, just nw on SR 133. Ⓛ Ⓓ

NEW YORK

▼▼▼ **Circo**
(212) 265-3636. Italian. Casual Dining. **$17-$60.** 120 W 55th St 10019. Between 6th (Ave of the Americas) and 7th aves. Ⓛ Ⓓ

▼▼▼ **Da Nico Ristorante**
(212) 343-1212. Italian. Fine Dining. **$9-$40.** 164 Mulberry St 10013. In Little Italy; between Broome and Grand sts. Ⓛ Ⓓ

ROMULUS

▼▼ **Knapp Winery & Vineyard Restaurant**
(607) 869-9271. Continental. Casual Dining. **$8-$14.** 2770 Ernsberger Rd 14541. Off SR 414, just e on CR 128 (Ernsberger Rd). Ⓛ

SLINGERLANDS

▼▼▼ **Mangia**
(518) 439-5555. Italian. Casual Dining. **$9-$22.** 1562 New Scotland Rd 12159. I-90 exit 4; center of village; on US 85. Ⓛ Ⓓ ⒼⓂ

SYRACUSE

▼ **The Blue Tusk Pub & Wine Bar**
(315) 472-1934. American. Casual Dining. **$8-$18.** 165 Walton St 13202. Center; in Armory Square. Ⓛ Ⓓ

TANNERSVILLE

▼▼ **Last Chance Antiques & Cheese Cafe**
(518) 589-6424. American. Casual Dining. **$6-$20.** 6009 Main St 12485. Center. Ⓛ Ⓓ

North Carolina

ASHEVILLE

▼▼ **Gan Shan Station**
(828) 774-5280. Asian Fusion. Casual Dining. **$8-$18.** 143 Charlotte St 28801. I-240 exit 5B (US 70/Charlotte St), 0.5 mi n. Ⓛ Ⓓ ⒼⓂ

▼▼ **Plant**
(828) 258-7500. Vegan. Casual Dining. **$15-$21.** 165 Merrimon Ave 28801. I-240 exit 5A (Merrimon Ave), just n. Ⓓ

▼ **Westville Pub**
(828) 225-9782. American. Casual Dining. **$8-$15.** 777 Haywood Rd 28806. I-240 eastbound exit 3A; westbound exit straight onto US 19/23, 1 mi w, just s on Louisiana Ave, just w on Pruett St, just s on Mildred Ave, then just e on US 19 business route. Ⓛ Ⓓ ⒧ᴬᵀᴱ

▼ **White Duck Taco Shop**
(828) 258-1660. Mexican. Quick Serve. **$4-$8.** 1 Roberts St 28801. From Pack Square just s on Market St, 0.8 mi w on Hilliard Ave, just w on W Haywood St, then just n; in River Arts District. Ⓛ Ⓓ

BLOWING ROCK

▼▼▼ **Bistro Roca**
(828) 295-4008. American. Fine Dining. **$9-$28.** 143 Wonderland Tr 28605. Just s on Laurel Ln, bear right, then just w; center. L D &M

CAROLINA BEACH

▼▼ **Michael's Seafood Restaurant & Catering**
(910) 458-7761. Seafood. Casual Dining. **$10-$36.** 1206 N Lake Park Blvd 28428. From Snow's Cut Bridge, just e; in Cross Bridge Shopping Center. L D

CARRBORO

▼▼ **Spotted Dog Restaurant & Bar**
(919) 933-1117. American. Casual Dining. **$7-$13.** 111 E Main St 27510. Just e; center. L D

CASHIERS

▼▼ **Cornucopia Restaurant**
(828) 743-3750. American. Casual Dining. **$12-$28.** Hwy 107 S 28717. Jct US 64, 0.5 mi s. L D &M Ⓚ

CHARLOTTE

▼▼ **Lebowski's Neighborhood Grill**
(704) 370-1177. American. Casual Dining. **$9-$16.** 1524 East Blvd 28203. I-77 exit 7 (Clanton Rd), 0.5 mi e, 1.5 mi n on South Blvd, then 1.9 mi e. L D LATE

COROLLA

▼▼ **Agave Roja, Modern Mexican**
(252) 453-0446. Mexican. Casual Dining. **$9-$18.** 807 B Ocean Tr 27927. On SR 12; in Monterey Plaza. L D &M

DURHAM

▼ **Parker & Otis**
(919) 683-3200. Sandwiches. Quick Serve. **$7-$12.** 112 S Duke St 27701. SR 147 (Durham Frwy) exit 12C, 0.4 mi n. B L

FLETCHER

▼▼ **Sierra Nevada Brewing Co**
(828) 651-5300. Small Plates. Brewpub. **$8-$16.** 100 Sierra Nevada Way 28732. I-26 exit 40, 1.4 mi w on SR 280 W (Airport Rd), 0.6 mi n on Ferncliff Park Dr, at traffic circle, take second exit, then just n.
L D &M

GREENSBORO

▼▼ **Europa Bar & Cafe**
(336) 389-1010. Comfort Food. Casual Dining. **$8-$15.** 200 N Davie St 27401. Jct Friendly Ave, just n; downtown. L D

OCRACOKE

▼▼ **Gaffer's Sports Pub**
(252) 928-3456. American. Casual Dining. **$8-$20.** 1050 Irvin Garrish Hwy 27960. From Cedar Island Ferry, 1 mi n on SR 12. L D &M

RALEIGH

▼▼ **Ajisai Japanese Fusion**
(919) 831-9907. Japanese. Casual Dining. **$8-$20.** 427 Woodburn Rd 27605. I-440 exit 3, 2.2 mi e on Hillsborough St, 0.4 mi n on Oberlin Rd, just e on Clark Ave, then just n; in Cameron Village. L D

SOUTHPORT

▼▼ **Loco Jo's Grill**
(910) 457-9009. American. Casual Dining. **$7-$13.** 602 N Howe St 28461. Just n on SR 211 from waterfront. L D &M

WAYNESVILLE

▼▼ **Pasquale's Italian Restaurant**
(828) 454-5002. Italian. Casual Dining. **$7-$23.** 1863 S Main St 28786. 2 mi s on US 23 business route. L D

Ohio

CLEVELAND

▼▼▼ **Bar Cento**
(216) 274-1010. Continental. Casual Dining. **$7-$28.** 1948 25th St 44113. Corner of Lorain Blvd and 25th St; in west side of downtown.
D LATE

Oklahoma

MOORE

▼▼ **Royal Bavaria Restaurant & Brewery**
(405) 799-7666. German. Casual Dining. **$12-$28.** 3401 S Sooner Rd 73165. I-240 exit 8, 6 mi s. D

TULSA

▼▼▼ **The Bistro At Seville**
(918) 296-3000. American. Fine Dining. **$10-$31.** 10021 S Yale Ave 74145. Jct 101st St. L D

Oregon

ASTORIA

▼▼ **Rogue Ales Public House**
(503) 468-0923. American. Casual Dining. **$10-$28.** 100 39th St, Pier 39 97103. 3 mi e of Astoria Bridge on US 30. L D Ⓚ

▼▼ **Wet Dog Cafe & Brewery**
(503) 325-6975. American. Casual Dining. **$10-$21.** 144 11th St 97103. Corner of 11th and Astor sts; downtown. L D Ⓚ

BEND

▼▼▼ **Cascade Lakes Lodge Brewing Company**
(541) 388-4998. American. Casual Dining. **$10-$17.** 1441 SW Chandler Ave, Suite 100 97702. US 97 exit 138 (Downtown/Mt Bachelor Dr), 1.7 mi sw on NW Colorado Ave, then just w. L D

▼▼ **Chow**
(541) 728-0256. Breakfast Small Plates. Casual Dining. **$9-$15.** 1110 NW Newport Ave 97701. Jct NW 11th St and NW Newport Ave.
B L

▼ **Sparrow Bakery Scott Street**
(541) 330-6321. Breads/Pastries Sandwiches. Quick Serve. **$8-$10.** 50 SE Scott St 97701. 0.5 mi s to Arizona Ave, 0.4 mi e to Colorado Ave, just e, then just s. B L Ⓚ

ENTERPRISE

▼ **Terminal Gravity Brew Pub**
(541) 426-0158. American. Casual Dining. **$7-$15.** 803 SE School St 97828. 0.7 mi se of jct North and River sts (SR 82), just s, follow signs.
L D Ⓚ

EUGENE

▼▼ **Studio One Cafe**
(541) 342-8596. Breakfast. Casual Dining. **$7-$13.** 1473 E 19th Ave 97403. 0.6 mi e from jct SR 99 and 126 (Franklin Blvd), 0.5 mi s on Agate St, just w. B L

GEARHART

▼▼ **McMenamins Sand Trap**
(503) 717-8150. American. Casual Dining. **$11-$27.** 1157 N Marion Ave 97138. US 101 exit City Center, 1 mi w; in Gearhart By The Sea.
[B] [L] [D] [&M]

GRANTS PASS

▼▼ **Wild River Brewing & Pizza Co.**
(541) 471-7487. American. Casual Dining. **$8-$33.** 595 NE E St 97526. I-5 exit 58, 1.7 mi s on SR 99, then 0.4 mi e on NE F St. [L] [D]

MCMINNVILLE

▼▼ **McMenamins Hotel Oregon Pub**
(503) 472-8427. American. Casual Dining. **$11-$27.** 310 NE Evans St 97128. At NE 3rd and Evans sts; downtown; in McMenamins Hotel Oregon. [B] [L] [D] [LATE] [&M]

MEDFORD

▼ **Downtown Market Co**
(541) 973-2233. American. Quick Serve. **$9-$13.** 231 E Main St 97501. Jct E Main St and S Bartlett St; downtown. [L]

▼▼ **Misoya Bistro**
(541) 772-4120. Asian Fusion Sushi. Casual Dining. **$8-$17.** 235 Theater Alley 97501. At Central St and Theater Alley; downtown.
[L] [D] [&M]

NEWPORT

⟨AAA⟩ ▼▼ **Canyon Way Restaurant & Bookstore**
(541) 265-8319. American. Casual Dining. **$8-$16.** 1216 SW Canyon Way 97365. 4 blks e of jct US 101 and SW Hurbert St; 1 blk from bayfront. [L] [Ⓚ]

PORTLAND

▼▼ **McMenamins Kennedy School Courtyard Restaurant**
(503) 288-2192. American. Casual Dining. **$5-$29.** 5736 NE 33rd Ave 97211. I-84 exit 33rd Ave eastbound, 2 mi n; exit 43rd Ave westbound, follow signs to Broadway, 1 mi w on Broadway, then 2 mi n.
[B] [L] [D] [LATE]

▼▼ **McMenamins Mall 205**
(503) 254-5411. American. Casual Dining. **$9-$14.** 9710 SE Washington St 97216. I-205 exit 21A southbound; exit 20 northbound, just e on Washington St, then just s. [L] [D]

▼▼ **McMenamins Market Street Pub**
(503) 497-0160. American. Casual Dining. **$7-$13.** 1526 SW 10th Ave 97201. Corner of SW 10th Ave and Market St. [L] [D] [LATE]

▼▼ **McMenamins White Eagle Cafe & Saloon**
(503) 282-6810. American. Casual Dining. **$9-$14.** 836 N Russell St 97227. Just e of N Interstate Ave. [L] [D] [LATE]

PRINEVILLE

▼ **Dawg House**
(541) 447-2878. Hot Dogs Burgers. Quick Serve. **$4-$11.** 318 NW 3rd St 97754. Jct N Main and NW 3rd sts, just w. [L] [D]

REEDSPORT

▼▼ **Schooner Cafe**
(541) 271-3945. Sandwiches Seafood. Casual Dining. **$6-$16.** 423 Riverfront Way 97467. Jct US 101/SR 38, just e on SR 38, just n on 3rd St (at post office), just e on Water Ave, then just nw; adjacent to Umpqua Discovery Center. [L] [&M] [◥]

ROSEBURG

▼▼ **McMenamins Roseburg Station Pub & Brewery**
(541) 672-1934. American. Casual Dining. **$10-$18.** 700 SE Sheridan St 97470. I-5 exit 124, 0.5 mi e, then just s; in Village Station.
[L] [D] [LATE]

SALEM

▼▼ **McMenamins Boon's Treasury**
(503) 399-9062. American. Casual Dining. **$6-$16.** 888 Liberty St NE 97301. I-5 exit 256, 2 mi w on Market St NE, then just s; 0.6 mi n of downtown. [L] [D] [LATE]

SISTERS

▼▼ **The Open Door & Wine Bar**
(541) 549-4994. New American. Casual Dining. **$11-$19.** 303 W Hood Ave 97759. Just s of SR 20 (Cascade Ave), jct S Oak St and Hood Ave.
[L] [D] [&M]

WILSONVILLE

▼▼ **McMenamins Old Church & Pub**
(503) 427-2500. American. Casual Dining. **$10-$20.** 30340 SW Boones Ferry Rd 97070. I-5 exit 283, just sw. [B] [L] [D] [LATE] [&M]

Pennsylvania

ERIE

▼▼▼ **Cloud 9 Wine Bar**
(814) 870-9007. New American. Casual Dining. **$10-$29.** 25 E 10th St, Suite 1 16501. I-79 exit 183A, 2.3 mi e on 12th St, just n on State St, then just e. [L] [D] [&M]

GETTYSBURG

▼▼ **Appalachian Brewing Co.**
(717) 398-2419. American. Brewpub. **$9-$18.** 70 Presidential Cir 17325. US 15 exit York St, just e on US 30. [L] [D] [&M]

▼▼ **La Bella Italia**
(717) 334-1978. Italian. Casual Dining. **$8-$24.** 402 York St 17325. Just e on US 30; jct Fourth St. [L] [D] [&M]

PHILADELPHIA

▼▼▼ **a.kitchen**
(215) 825-7030. American. Casual Dining. **$15-$31.** 135 S 18th St 19103. Between Walnut and Sansom sts. [L] [D]

⟨AAA⟩ ▼▼▼ **City Tavern**
(215) 413-1443. American. Casual Dining. **$9-$27.** 138 S 2nd St 19106. Corner of 2nd and Walnut sts. [L] [D]

▼▼▼ **The Dandelion**
(215) 558-2500. American. Gastropub. **$13-$28.** 124 S 18th St 19103. Corner of 18th and Samson sts. [L] [D]

▼▼▼ **Lolita**
(215) 546-7100. Mexican. Casual Dining. **$10-$24.** 106 S 13th St 19107. Between Sansom and Chestnut sts. [L] [D]

▼▼ **The Plough and The Stars Irish Restaurant & Bar**
(215) 733-0300. Irish. Casual Dining. **$8-$24.** 123 Chestnut St 19106. Just n of jct 2nd and Chestnut sts; entrance on 2nd St. [L] [D] [&M]

▼▼▼ **Pub and Kitchen**
(215) 545-0350. American. Gastropub. **$9-$26.** 1946 Lombard St 19146. Corner of Lombard and 20th sts. [D] [LATE]

▼▼▼ **Serafina Rittenhouse**
(215) 977-7755. Italian. Casual Dining. **$9-$29.** 130 S 18th St 19103. At 18th and Samson sts. [L] [D]

SHIPPENSBURG

▼▼▼ **University Grille**
(717) 530-1148. American. Casual Dining. **$8-$34.** 32 E King St 17257.
I-81 exit 29, 1.5 mi w on SR 174, then 0.8 mi s on US 11; just n of jct SR
696; downtown; in Shippen Place Hotel. ⬜L ⬜D ⬜&M

SLIPPERY ROCK

▼▼ **North Country Brewing Company**
(724) 794-2337. American. Brewpub. **$7-$19.** 141 S Main St 16057. I-79
exit 105, 4 mi e, then just s. ⬜L ⬜D ⬜&M

WEST CHESTER

▼▼▼ **Limoncello**
(610) 436-6230. Italian. Fine Dining. **$8-$30.** 9 N Walnut St 19380.
Between E Market and E Gay sts; downtown. ⬜L ⬜D

Rhode Island

NEWPORT

▼▼▼ **Bouchard Restaurant & Inn**
(401) 846-0123. French. Fine Dining. **$12-$38.** 505 Thames St 02840.
Jct SR 138A, 0.5 mi s. ⬜D

PROVIDENCE

▼▼▼ **Red Stripe**
(401) 437-6950. French. Casual Dining. **$10-$25.** 465 Angell St 02906.
Between Wayland and Elmgrove aves. ⬜L ⬜D ⬜&M

▼▼▼ **Trattoria Zooma**
(401) 383-2002. Southern Italian. Casual Dining. **$10-$34.** 245 Atwells
Ave 02903. I-95 exit 21, 0.3 mi w. ⬜L ⬜D

TIVERTON

▼ **Coastal Roasters**
(401) 624-2343. Coffee/Tea. Quick Serve. **$2-$5.** 1791 Main Rd 02878.
SR 24 exit 5, 1 mi s on SR 77. ⬜B ⬜L ⬜✗

WARWICK

▼▼▼ **Eleven Forty Nine**
(401) 884-1149. New American. Fine Dining. **$12-$30.** 1149 Division St
02818. On SR 401, just e of jct SR 2. ⬜L ⬜D ⬜&M

South Carolina

BLUFFTON

▼▼ **Okatie Ale House**
(843) 706-2584. American. Casual Dining. **$8-$23.** 25 William Pope Ct
29909. I-95 exit 8 (US 278), 7.2 mi e, then just s; adjacent to Sun City.
⬜L ⬜D ⬜&M ⬜◥

CHARLESTON

▼▼ **Brown Dog Deli**
(843) 853-8081. Deli. Quick Serve. **$8-$14.** 40 Broad St 29401. Between
Church and State sts. ⬜L ⬜D

▼▼ **Triangle Char & Bar**
(843) 377-1300. Burgers Sandwiches. Casual Dining. **$9-$16.** 828
Savannah Hwy 29407. Jct US 17/SR 171 (Folly Rd), 0.7 mi w on US 17;
in West Ashley. ⬜L ⬜D ⬜LATE

COLUMBIA

▼▼▼ **Hampton Street Vineyard**
(803) 252-0850. American. Fine Dining. **$10-$33.** 1201 Hampton St
29201. Between Main and Sumter sts; downtown. ⬜L ⬜D

▼▼▼ **Villa Tronco**
(803) 256-7677. Traditional Italian. Casual Dining. **$9-$25.** 1213 Blanding
St 29201. Between Sumter and Main sts; downtown. ⬜L ⬜D ⬜&M

▼▼ **Yesterdays Restaurant & Tavern**
(803) 799-0196. American. Casual Dining. **$7-$15.** 2030 Devine St
29205. Corner of Devine and Harden sts; in Five Points. ⬜L ⬜D ⬜LATE

FOLLY BEACH

▼▼ **Rita's Seaside Grille**
(843) 588-2525. Burgers Seafood. Casual Dining. **$10-$22.** 2 Center St
29439. Center. ⬜L ⬜D ⬜LATE

▼ **Taco Boy**
(843) 588-9761. Mexican. Casual Dining. **$4-$16.** 15 Center St 29439.
Center. ⬜L ⬜D

GREENVILLE

▼▼ **JP's 4 Corners**
(864) 281-7777. Southwestern. Casual Dining. **$9-$30.** 1298 Woodruff
Rd 29607. I-385 exit 35, 0.3 mi se; in The Shops at Merovan.
⬜L ⬜D ⬜&M

▼▼▼ **Soby's**
(864) 232-7007. New Southern. Casual Dining. **$18-$31.** 207 S Main St
29601. Corner of E Court St; downtown. ⬜D ⬜&M

HILTON HEAD ISLAND

▼ **Amigos Café y Cantina**
(843) 785-8226. Mexican. Quick Serve. **$4-$10.** 70 Pope Ave 29928.
Sea Pines Cir, 0.8 mi se; in The Circle Center. ⬜L ⬜D

▼▼ **Bella Italia Bistro & Pizzeria**
(843) 689-5560. Italian Pizza. Casual Dining. **$3-$18.** 95 Matthews Dr,
Suite D-13 29928. 5 mi e of J Wilton Graves Bridge on US 278 business
route; in Port Royal Plaza. ⬜L ⬜D

▼▼ **Giuseppi's Pizza & Pasta**
(843) 785-4144. Italian Pizza. Casual Dining. **$7-$14.** 32 D Shelter Cove
Ln 29928. 8.2 mi e of J Wilton Graves Bridge on US 278 business route;
in Plaza at Shelter Cove. ⬜L ⬜D ⬜&M

▼▼▼ **HogsHead Kitchen & Wine Bar**
(843) 837-4647. Regional Southern. Fine Dining. **$11-$25.** 1555 Fording
Island Rd, Suite D 29926. 0.9 mi nw of J Wilton Graves Bridge on US
278; on the mainland; in Moss Creek Village. ⬜L ⬜D

▼▼ **Kenny B's Cajun Seafood Hut**
(843) 785-3315. Cajun. Casual Dining. **$8-$15.** 70 A Pope Ave, Circle
Bi-Lo Center 29928. Jct Coligny Cir and Pope Ave, just nw on Pope Ave
to Nassau St, just sw. ⬜B ⬜L ⬜D

▼▼ **Main Street Café and Pub**
(843) 689-3999. Sandwiches Seafood. Casual Dining. **$9-$24.** 1411 Main
St 29928. 3.5 mi e of J Wilton Graves Bridge on US 278 business route,
just n; in Main Street Village. ⬜L ⬜D ⬜&M

◉◉◉ ▼▼▼ ▼▼▼ **Old Fort Pub**
(843) 681-2386. Continental. Fine Dining. **$27-$40.** 65 Skull Creek Dr
29926. 1.8 mi e of J. Wilton Graves Bridge on US 278 to Squire Pope Rd,
2.2 mi n; in Hilton Head Plantation. ⬜D

▼▼ **Reilley's Grill & Bar**
(843) 842-4414. American. Gastropub. **$9-$26.** 7D Greenwood Dr
29928. Jct Sea Pines Cir, just w; in Hilton Head Plaza. ⬜L ⬜D ⬜&M

♦♦ **The Salty Dog Cafe**
(843) 671-5199. Regional Seafood. Casual Dining. **$9-$30.** 232 S Sea Pines Dr 29928. Coligny Plaza, 5.2 mi sw on S Forest Beach/Sea Pines drs; at South Beach Marina; in The Sea Pines Resort. L D

♦♦ **San Miguel's - Mexican Cafe**
(843) 842-4555. Mexican. Casual Dining. **$9-$17.** 9 Shelter Cove Ln 29928. 8.5 mi from J Wilton Graves Bridge on US 278 business route to Shelter Cove Ln, just w; in Harbourside II; at Shelter Cove. L D

ISLE OF PALMS

♦♦♦ **The Boathouse at Breach Inlet**
(843) 886-8000. Seafood. Casual Dining. **$18-$30.** 101 Palm Blvd (SR 703) 29451. At south end of island; at Breach Inlet Bridge. D &M

♦♦♦ **Morgan Creek Grill**
(843) 886-8980. American. Casual Dining. **$10-$26.** 80 41st Ave 29451. Jct SR 517 (Isle of Palms Connector)/703 (Palm Blvd), 1.8 mi ne of SR 703 (Palm Blvd), just n; in Isle of Palms Marina. L D &M

JOHNS ISLAND

♦♦ **King Street Grille**
(843) 768-5444. Burgers Sandwiches. Casual Dining. **$10-$25.** 679 Freshfields Dr 29455. Jct Kiawah Island Pkwy, Seabrook Island Rd and Betsy Kerrison Pkwy; in Freshfields Village. L D LATE &M

MOUNT PLEASANT

♦♦ **Another Broken Egg Cafe**
(843) 352-9833. Breakfast Sandwiches. Casual Dining. **$5-$15.** 608-A Long Point Rd 29464. I-526 exit 28 (Long Point Rd), just ne; in Belle Hall Shopping Center. B L &M

♦♦ **Charleston's Cafe**
(843) 856-7796. Regional Breakfast Sandwiches. Casual Dining. **$6-$11.** 1039 Johnnie Dodds Blvd 29464. 2.2 mi ne of Arthur Ravenel Jr Bridge on US 17 (Johnnie Dodds Blvd); in Anna Knapp Plaza. B L &M

♦♦ **Crave Kitchen & Cocktails**
(843) 884-1177. New American. Casual Dining. **$10-$40.** 1968 Riviera Dr, Suite O 29464. I-526 exit 29 (Georgetown/US 17 N), 1.4 mi ne on US 17 to jct SR 517 (Isle of Palms Connector), then 1 mi se on SR 517; in Seaside Farms. L D &M

♦♦ **The Dog & Duck**
(843) 881-3056. Sandwiches Wings. Gastropub. **$5-$14.** 624-A Long Point Rd 29464. I-526 exit 28 (Long Point Rd), just ne; in Belle Hall Shopping Center. L D &M

♦ **East Bay Deli**
(843) 216-5423. Deli. Quick Serve. **$5-$10.** 1120 Oakland Market Rd 29466. Jct US 17 N and SR 41, just ne on US 17 N; in The Market at Oakland. B L D &M

♦♦ **Finn's Brick Oven**
(843) 881-3467. Pizza. Casual Dining. **$9-$14.** 656 Long Point Rd, Suite G 29464. I-526 exit 28 (Long Point Rd), just ne; in Belle Hall Shopping Center. L D &M

♦♦ **Juanita Greenberg's Nacho Royale**
(843) 329-6224. Mexican. Casual Dining. **$3-$10.** 410 W Coleman Blvd 29464. 1 mi e of Arthur Ravenel Jr Bridge on SR 703 (Coleman Blvd). L D LATE &M

♦ **Sawyers on the Boulevard**
(843) 388-5270. American. Casual Dining. **$8-$24.** 1528 Ben Sawyer Blvd 29464. Jct US 17 business/SR 701/703 (Ben Sawyer Blvd), 0.4 mi e on SR 703 (Ben Sawyer Blvd). L D LATE &M

♦♦ **Stack's Evening Eats**
(843) 388-6968. New Southern. Casual Dining. **$12-$25.** 1440 Ben Sawyer Blvd, Suite 1107 29464. Jct US 17 business route/SR 701/703, just e on SR 703 (Ben Sawyer Blvd); in Mount Pleasant Square Shopping Center. D &M

MURRELLS INLET

♦♦ **Graham's Landing**
(843) 947-0520. Regional Seafood. Casual Dining. **$8-$29.** 5225 US 17 Business Rt 29576. Jct US 17 and US 17 business (south end), just ne on US 17 business route. L D &M

MYRTLE BEACH

♦♦♦ **Banditos Restaurant & Cantina**
(843) 808-9800. Mexican. Casual Dining. **$4-$19.** 1410 N Ocean Blvd 29577. Jct 14th Ave N. L D &M

♦♦ **Beach House Bar & Grill**
(843) 839-4705. American. Casual Dining. **$9-$29.** 1205 N Ocean Blvd 29572. Jct 12th Ave N. L D LATE &M ✎

♦♦ **Landshark Bar & Grill**
(843) 788-0001. Burgers Sandwiches. Casual Dining. **$8-$17.** 1110 N Ocean Blvd, Suite B 29577. Jct 11th Ave N; at SkyWheel Myrtle Beach. L D &M

NORTH CHARLESTON

♦♦ **Coosaw Creek Crab Shack**
(843) 552-7171. Regional Seafood. Casual Dining. **$7-$25.** 8486 Dorchester Rd 29420. Jct Ashley Phosphate and Dorchester rds, just nw. L D &M

♦ **East Bay Deli**
(843) 553-7374. Deli. Quick Serve. **$5-$9.** 9135 University Blvd 29406. I-26 exit 205B (US 78), 1 mi se. B L D &M

NORTH MYRTLE BEACH

♦ **BurgerFi**
(843) 491-6492. Burgers Hot Dogs. Quick Serve. **$4-$11.** 801 Main St 29582. Jct Hwy 17. L D &M

♦ **East Bay Deli**
(843) 427-7337. Deli. Quick Serve. **$5-$9.** 3914 Hwy 17 S, Suite C-3 29582. Between 39th and 41st aves S; in Barefoot Commons. B L D &M

♦♦ **Midtown Bistro**
(843) 427-4720. Italian. Casual Dining. **$9-$28.** 2004 Hwy 17 S 29582. Jct 20th Ave S. L D &M

PAWLEYS ISLAND

♦♦ **Pawleys Island Tavern**
(843) 237-8465. Sandwiches Pizza. Casual Dining. **$6-$16.** 10635 Ocean Hwy 29585. Just n of center; behind The Island Shops. L D

SEABROOK ISLAND

♦♦ **Lokal Seabar**
(843) 764-9027. Seafood. Casual Dining. **$11-$32.** 1886 Andell Bluff Blvd 29455. On Seabrook Island; in Bohicket Marina Village. L D

SIMPSONVILLE

♦♦ **Arizona Handcrafted Fare & Drink Co**
(864) 962-1700. Regional American. Casual Dining. **$11-$25.** 3952 Grandview Dr 29680. I-385 exit 27, just s on Fairview Rd, then just se on Service Rd. L D &M

SULLIVAN'S ISLAND

♦♦ **Sullivan's**
(843) 883-3222. Seafood. Casual Dining. **$9-$25.** 2019 Middle St 29482. Just sw of center. D

♦♦ **Taco Mamacita**
(843) 789-4107. Mexican. Casual Dining. **$4-$13.** 2213-B Middle St 29482. Just sw of center. L D

SUMMERVILLE

▼▼ The Continental Corner
(843) 871-1160. Greek. Casual Dining. **$7-$20.** 123 W Richardson Ave 29483. Jct US 17 alternate route, just nw; downtown. ⬛L ⬛D

WEST COLUMBIA

▼▼ Nick's House of Pizza Restaurant
(803) 794-9240. Mediterranean Pizza. Casual Dining. **$6-$16.** 1082 Sunset Blvd, Suite A 29169. I-26 exit 110 (US 378), 2 mi e. ⬛L ⬛D

Tennessee

BRENTWOOD

▼ Mediterranean Cuisine
(615) 661-4100. Mediterranean. Quick Serve. **$5-$16.** 214 Ward Cir 37027. I-65 exit 74B, 0.3 mi s on Franklin Rd (US 31), 0.5 mi w on Maryland Way. ⬛L ⬛D

CHATTANOOGA

▼▼ The Terminal Brewhouse
(423) 752-8090. American. Casual Dining. **$7-$14.** 6 E 14th St 37408. I-24 exit 178 (Broad St) eastbound; exit Market St westbound, 0.5 mi n.
⬛L ⬛D ⬛LATE

▼▼ Tony's Pasta Shop and Trattoria
(423) 265-5033. Italian. Casual Dining. **$7-$15.** 212 High St 37403. US 27 exit 1C (4th St), 1 mi e, then just n; in Bluff View Arts District.
⬛L ⬛D

COLUMBIA

▼▼ Puckett's Gro. & Restaurant
(931) 490-4550. Southern Barbecue. Casual Dining. **$7-$26.** 15 Public Square 38401. In historic downtown. ⬛B ⬛L ⬛D ⬛&M

◆◆◆ Square Market & Cafe
(931) 840-3636. American. Casual Dining. **$5-$11.** 36 Public Square 38401. In historic downtown; northwest corner behind courthouse.
⬛B ⬛L ⬛D ⬛&M

COUNCE

▼▼ Freddy T's
(731) 689-3099. American. Casual Dining. **$10-$27.** 12750 Hwy 57 S 38326. SR 57, 4.3 mi se of jct SR 128; at Pickwick Dam. ⬛D

FARRAGUT

▼▼ Seasons Innovative Bar & Grille
(865) 392-1121. American. Casual Dining. **$12-$23.** 11605 Parkside Dr 37934. I-40/75 exit 373 (Campbell Station Rd), 0.5 mi s, then just e.
⬛L ⬛D ⬛&M

JACKSON

▼▼ Old Town Spaghetti Store
(731) 668-4937. Italian. Casual Dining. **$8-$28.** 550 Carriage House Dr 38305. I-40 exit 80A, just s on US 45 Bypass, then just e. ⬛L ⬛D ⬛&M

KNOXVILLE

▼▼ Chesapeake's
(865) 673-3433. Seafood. Casual Dining. **$9-$40.** 500 Henley St 37902. I-40 exit 388, 1 mi s, then just e. ⬛ ⬛L ⬛D

MEMPHIS

◆◆◆ Capriccio Grill
(901) 529-4199. Italian. Fine Dining. **$12-$42.** 149 Union Ave 38103. Jct 2nd St; in Peabody Memphis. ⬛ ⬛B ⬛L ⬛D ⬛&M

▼ Central BBQ in Memphis
(901) 272-9377. Barbecue. Quick Serve. **$4-$25.** 2249 Central Ave 38104. Between S Cooper St and E Parkway S. ⬛L ⬛D

▼▼▼ Napa Cafe
(901) 683-0441. Continental. Fine Dining. **$13-$32.** 5101 Sanderlin Ave, Suite 122 38117. I-240 exit 15 (Poplar Ave), 1 mi w, 0.5 mi n on White Station Rd, then just w; in Sanderlin Centre. ⬛L ⬛D ⬛&M

▼▼ SOB - South of Beale
(901) 526-0388. American. Gastropub. **$9-$21.** 361 S Main St 38103. Jct Beale St, just s. ⬛L ⬛D ⬛LATE

NASHVILLE

▼ Hog Heaven
(615) 329-1234. Barbecue. Quick Serve. **$4-$14.** 115 27th Ave N 37203. I-440 exit West End Ave, 3 mi e; across from Centennial Park. ⬛L ⬛D

▼ McDougal's Chicken Fingers & Wings
(615) 423-0764. Chicken. Quick Serve. **$5-$10.** 2115 Belcourt Ave 37212. I-65 exit 81, 1.5 mi w on Wedgewood Ave, just s on 21st Ave S; across from historic Belcourt Theatre; in Hillsboro Village. ⬛L ⬛D ⬛&M

PIGEON FORGE

▼ Blue Moose Burgers & Wings
(865) 286-0364. Wings Burgers. Casual Dining. **$6-$10.** 2430 Teaster Ln 37863. US 441, just e of traffic light 2; in Teaster Center.
⬛L ⬛D ⬛LATE ⬛&M

SWEETWATER

▼▼ Bradley's Pit BBQ & Grill
(423) 351-7190. American. Casual Dining. **$5-$20.** 517 New Hwy 68 37874. I-75 exit 60, 1.2 mi e. ⬛L ⬛D

Texas

ADDISON

▼▼ The Londoner
(972) 458-2444. English. Casual Dining. **$8-$12.** 14930 Midway Rd 75001. Just s of jct Midway and Belt Line rds. ⬛L ⬛D ⬛LATE ⬛◥

ALVIN

▼▼ Monterey's Little Mexico
(281) 331-1925. Tex-Mex. Casual Dining. **$8-$17.** 410 S Gordon St 77511. Just w of jct SR 6 and 35. ⬛L ⬛D

AUSTIN

▼▼ The ABGB
(512) 298-2242. Pizza. Casual Dining. **$4-$24.** 1305 W Oltorf St 78704. I-35 exit 232A, just w. ⬛L ⬛D ⬛&M

▼▼ Apothecary Cafe and Wine Bar
(512) 371-1600. Small Plates. Casual Dining. **$9-$20.** 4800 Burnet Rd, Suite 450 78757. I-35 exit 237A (Airport Blvd), 1.7 mi w, then just n; in Roseville Village Center. ⬛D ⬛◥

▼▼▼ Central Standard Kitchen & Bar
(512) 942-0823. American. Casual Dining. **$18-$34.** 1603 S Congress Ave 78704. Between E Monroe and E Milton sts. ⬛D ⬛&M

▼▼ **Corner**
(512) 608-4488. Southwestern. Casual Dining. **$14-$34.** 110 E 2nd St 78701. Corner of Congress Ave and 2nd St; in JW Marriott Austin.
L D &M

▼▼▼ **Kona Grill**
(512) 835-5900. Pacific Rim Fusion. Casual Dining. **$11-$30.** 11410 Century Oaks Terr 78758. Loop 1 (Mo-Pac Expwy) and Braker Ln, just n; in The Domain. L D &M

▼▼ **Moonshine Patio Bar & Grill**
(512) 236-9599. American. Casual Dining. **$11-$23.** 303 Red River St 78701. Jct E 3rd and Red River sts. L D

▼▼▼▼ **North by Northwest Restaurant and Brewery**
(512) 467-6969. American. Gastropub. **$9-$24.** 10010 Capital of Texas Hwy N 78759. US 183 N to Capital of Texas Hwy (SR 360), 2 blks e; on northeast corner. L D &M

▼▼▼▼ **No Va**
(512) 382-5651. American. Casual Dining. **$10-$26.** 87 Rainey St 78701. I-35 exit 234A southbound; exit 234B northbound, jct Driskill and Rainey sts, just s. D &M

BASTROP

▼▼ **Baxters on Main**
(512) 321-3577. American. Casual Dining. **$7-$35.** 919 Main St 78602. Between Chestnut and Pine sts; in historic district. L D &M

COLUMBUS

▼▼ **Nancy's Steakhouse**
(979) 732-9700. Steak. Casual Dining. **$9-$27.** 2536 Hwy 71 S 78934. I-10 exit 696 (SR 71), just s. L D ◥

DALLAS

▼▼ **Bread Winners Cafe & Bakery**
(214) 754-4940. American. Casual Dining. **$9-$26.** 3301 McKinney Ave 75204. Corner of Hall St; uptown. B L D

▼▼ **Gloria's Latin Cuisine**
(214) 942-1831. Latin American. Casual Dining. **$11-$21.** 600 N Bishop Ave 75208. I-35E exit 425A (Zang Blvd), 0.8 mi n, then just w. L D

▼▼ **Green Papaya**
(214) 521-4811. Vietnamese. Casual Dining. **$6-$17.** 3211 Oak Lawn Ave, Suite B 75219. I-35 exit 430A (Oak Lawn Ave), 0.9 mi e.
L D ◥

▼ **Rodeo Goat**
(214) 741-4628. Burgers. Casual Dining. **$9-$13.** 1926 Market Center Blvd 75207. I-35E exit 430B (Market Center Blvd), just sw. L D ◥

▼▼ **Ziziki's Restaurant**
(214) 521-2233. Mediterranean. Casual Dining. **$10-$28.** 4514 Travis St, Suite 122 75205. US 75 exit Knox St/Henderson Ave, just w to Travis St, then just s; in Travis Walk Shopping Complex. L D

GEORGETOWN

▼▼ **Milano Trattoria Pizza & Pasta**
(512) 869-0444. Italian. Casual Dining. **$9-$21.** 1015 W University Ave, Suite 420 78628. I-35 exit 261, just w; in southeast section of Wolf Ranch Shopping Center. L D &M

HIGHLAND PARK

▼▼▼ **Cafe Pacific**
(214) 526-1170. Seafood. Fine Dining. **$12-$45.** 24 Highland Park Shopping Village 75205. Just sw of jct Mockingbird Ln and Preston Rd.
L D

HOUSTON

▼ **Amazon Grill**
(713) 522-5888. Latin American. Quick Serve. **$10-$27.** 5114 Kirby Dr 77098. US 59 (Southwest Frwy) exit Kirby Dr, just s. L D

▼▼ **Brasserie Max & Julie**
(713) 524-0070. French. Casual Dining. **$13-$32.** 4315 Montrose Blvd 77006. At Richmond Ave. L D

▼▼ **BRC Gastropub**
(713) 861-2233. American. Gastropub. **$12-$27.** 519 Shepherd Dr 77007. 0.3 mi n of jct Memorial Dr. L D &M

▼▼ **Churrascos**
(713) 527-8300. Latin American. Fine Dining. **$9-$40.** 2055 Westheimer Rd 77098. At Shepherd Dr; in Shepherd Square Shopping Center.
L D

▼▼ **Chuy's**
(281) 970-0341. Tex-Mex. Casual Dining. **$6-$12.** 19827 Northwest Frwy 77065. Jct US 290 and FM 1960; off southbound frontage road. L D

▼▼▼ **The Grove**
(713) 337-7321. American. Fine Dining. **$16-$50.** 1611 Lamar St 77010. In Discovery Green Park. L D &M

▼▼ **Happy Fatz**
(713) 426-3554. American. Casual Dining. **$7-$8.** 3510 White Oak Dr 77007. I-10 exit 766, 0.5 mi n; jct Cortlandt St and White Oak Dr.
B L D &M

▼▼▼ **Hugo's**
(713) 524-7744. Regional Mexican. Casual Dining. **$15-$30.** 1600 Westheimer Rd 77006. Between Dunlavy St and Montrose Blvd. L D

▼▼▼ **Mezza Grille**
(713) 334-2000. Mediterranean. Casual Dining. **$12-$37.** 6100 Westheimer Rd, Suite 154 77057. Between Fountain View Dr and Voss Rd.
L D &M

▼▼ **Mi Luna Tapas Restaurant & Bar**
(713) 520-5025. Small Plates. Casual Dining. **$8-$22.** 2441 University Blvd 77005. US 59 exit Kirby Dr, 1.1 mi s. L D

▼ **The Original Marini's Empanada House**
(713) 266-2729. Argentine. Casual Dining. **$3-$12.** 10001 Westheimer Rd 77042. Jct Westheimer Rd and Briarpark Dr; in Carrillon Shopping Center. L D &M

▼▼ **Russo's New York Coal Fired Pizzeria**
(713) 647-9100. Italian. Casual Dining. **$7-$20.** 9403 Katy Frwy, Suite B 77024. I-10 exit 758B (Blalock Rd/Campbell Rd) eastbound; exit 758B (Echo Ln) westbound; on eastbound service road; in Hedwig Village Shopping Center. L D &M

▼▼ **Tila's Restaurante & Bar**
(713) 522-7654. Mexican. Casual Dining. **$12-$29.** 1111 S Shepherd Dr 77019. I-10 exit 765B (Shepherd Dr), 1.5 mi s. L D

▼▼ **Zelko Bistro**
(713) 880-8691. American. Casual Dining. **$15-$30.** 705 E 11th St 77008. 1 mi n of I-10 on Studewood St, just w; in Houston Heights.
L D

LA GRANGE

▼▼ **Bistro 108**
(979) 968-9108. American. Casual Dining. **$7-$35.** 108 S Main St 78945. Downtown. L D

LAKE JACKSON

▼▼ **Wurst Haus**
(979) 297-3003. German. Casual Dining. **$9-$29.** 102 This Way 77566. Jct SR 288 and This Way St, 2 blks e. B L D

LAKEWAY

▼▼▼ The Grille At Rough Hollow
(512) 261-3444. Steak Seafood. Casual Dining. **$12-$40.** 103 Yacht Club Cove 78738. Jct SR 620 and Lakeway Blvd, 2.4 mi n to Highlands Blvd, 0.7 mi w to Rough Hollow Dr, 1.1 mi n to Rough Hollow Yacht Club, then 0.4 mi w. L D

▼▼ Taqueria Don Mario
(512) 266-3319. Mexican. Casual Dining. **$7-$18.** 1700 Ranch Rd 620 N, Suite 110 78734. Jct FM 620 and Oak Grove Blvd, just n.
B L D ⚑M

ROCKWALL

▼▼ The Londoner
(469) 314-1126. English. Brewpub. **$10-$14.** 308 N Fannin St 75087. Center. L D

ROUND ROCK

▼▼ The Salt Lick Bar-B-Que
(512) 386-1044. Barbecue. Casual Dining. **$10-$25.** 3350 E Palm Valley Blvd 78665. US 79, 2 mi e; at The Dell Diamond. L D ⚑M

SALADO

▼▼ The Shed
(254) 947-1960. American. Casual Dining. **$7-$15.** 220 Royal St 76571. I-35 exit 284, 2 blks e; downtown. L D

TOMBALL

▼▼ Locatelli's
(281) 255-8800. Italian Pizza. Casual Dining. **$4-$20.** 14257 FM 2920, Suite 100 77377. Jct Louetta and Grant rds, just w of SR 249 Access Rd.
L D ⚑M

VICTORIA

▼▼▼ The Pumphouse Riverside Restaurant and Bar
(361) 572-9800. American. Casual Dining. **$7-$25.** 1201 W Stayton St 77902. 1 mi w of jct US 77 and N Main St. L D ⚑M

WEBSTER

▼▼ Barbazzar
(281) 332-1735. American. Casual Dining. **$7-$22.** 702 Bay Area Blvd 77598. I-45 exit 26 (Bay Area Blvd), 0.4 mi e. B L D ⚑M

Utah

MOAB

▼▼▼ Sorrel River Grill
(435) 259-4642. American. Fine Dining. **$14-$39.** Hwy 128, MM 17 84532. 17 mi e of jct US 191 and SR 128; at MM 17; in Sorrel River Ranch Resort & Spa. ⊟ B L D

Vermont

MANCHESTER CENTER

🔺🔺🔺 ▼▼▼ Bistro Henry
(802) 362-4982. American. Casual Dining. **$18-$36.** 1942 Depot St 05255. On SR 11/30, 0.3 mi e of jct US 7. D

Virginia

ALEXANDRIA

▼▼▼ Bastille
(703) 519-3776. French. Casual Dining. **$14-$35.** 606 N Fayette St 22314. Jct Pendleton and N Fayette sts. L D ⚑M

▼▼ Bombay Curry Company
(703) 836-6363. Indian. Casual Dining. **$7-$15.** 2607 Mount Vernon Ave 22301. 0.6 mi s of jct W Glebe Rd; in Delray area. L D

▼▼ Brabo Tasting Room
(703) 894-5253. Belgian. Casual Dining. **$16-$24.** 1600 King St 22314. Between Harvard and Peyton sts; in Lorien Hotel & Spa-A Kimpton Hotel.
⊟ B L D ⚑M

▼▼ Clyde's of Mark Center
(703) 820-8300. American. Casual Dining. **$13-$26.** 1700 N Beauregard St 22311. I-395 exit 4, 0.3 mi w on Seminary Rd, then 0.3 mi s.
L D LATE ⚑M

▼▼ Gadsby's Tavern Restaurant
(703) 548-1288. American. Casual Dining. **$11-$30.** 138 N Royal St 22314. Just n of King St; in Old Town. L D

▼ Holy Cow
(703) 666-8616. Burgers. Quick Serve. **$6-$13.** 2312 Mt. Vernon Ave 22301. Jct E Oxford Ave; in Del Ray area. L D ⚑M

▼ Pork Barrel BBQ
(703) 822-5699. Barbecue. Quick Serve. **$7-$23.** 2312 Mt. Vernon Ave 22301. Jct E Oxford Ave; in Del Ray area. L D

▼▼ Southside 815
(703) 836-6222. Regional American. Casual Dining. **$10-$22.** 815 S Washington St 22314. 0.6 mi s of jct King St. L D

▼▼ Tempo Restaurant
(703) 370-7900. Northern Italian. Casual Dining. **$14-$27.** 4231 Duke St 22304. I-395 exit 3A, 1.9 mi e on SR 236. L D

▼▼▼ Warehouse Bar & Grill
(703) 683-6868. Regional American. Fine Dining. **$12-$39.** 214 King St 22314. Between Fairfax and Lee sts; in Old Town. L D

ARLINGTON

▼ Ben's Chili Bowl
(571) 312-1091. Hot Dogs Burgers. Quick Serve. **$5-$10.** 1725 Wilson Blvd 22209. I-66 exit 73, just s on Fort Myer Dr, then 0.4 mi w; in Colonial Village Shopping Center. L D LATE ⚑M

▼ Cafe Tirolo
(703) 528-7809. Italian. Quick Serve. **$7-$13.** 4001 N Fairfax Dr, Suite 16 22203. I-66 exit 71, 0.4 mi e of jct Glebe Rd (SR 120) and Fairfax Dr (SR 237); along back side of office building. B L D

▼▼ Delhi Club
(703) 527-5666. Indian. Casual Dining. **$11-$29.** 1135 N Highland St 22201. Jct N Highland St and Wilson Blvd; in Clarendon area. L D

▼▼ Fire Works American Pizzeria & Bar
(703) 527-8700. Pizza. Casual Dining. **$10-$21.** 2350 Clarendon Blvd 22201. Jct N Adams St. L D ⚑M

▼▼▼ Lebanese Taverna
(703) 415-8681. Lebanese. Casual Dining. **$11-$29.** 1101 S Joyce St, Suite B30 22202. I-395 exit 8C, just s off Army Navy Dr; in Pentagon Row. L D ⚑M

▼▼ Tara Temple
(703) 908-4999. Asian. Casual Dining. **$8-$30.** 4001 N Fairfax Dr 22203. I-66 exit 71, 0.4 mi e of jct Glebe Rd (SR 120) and Fairfax Dr (SR 237); in Ballston area. L D

ASHBURN

▼▼ At Kaiser's
(571) 291-3981. Austrian. Casual Dining. **$8-$22.** 44110 Ashburn Shopping Plaza, Suite 100 20147. From SR 7, 1.9 mi s on Ashburn Village Blvd; in Ashburn Shopping Plaza. L D &M

▼▼ The V Eatery & Brew House
(703) 723-6500. American. Gastropub. **$9-$24.** 44630 Waxpool Rd 20147. Just w of jct Loudoun County Pkwy (CR 607); from SR 28, 1.3 mi w. L D LATE &M

CAPE CHARLES

▼▼▼ The Oyster Farm At Kings Creek
(757) 331-8660. Seafood. Fine Dining. **$8-$29.** 900 Marina Village Cir 23310. At Kings Creek Resort Marina. L D &M

▼▼ The Shanty
(757) 695-3853. Seafood. Casual Dining. **$8-$25.** 33 Marina Rd 23310. SR 184 (Mason Ave), just s on Old Cape Charles Rd, just w on Bayshore Rd, then just n; just s of downtown. L D &M Æ

CHANTILLY

▼▼ Anita's
(703) 378-1717. Mexican. Casual Dining. **$8-$16.** 13921 Lee Jackson Memorial Hwy 20151. US 50, 0.4 mi e of jct SR 28. B L D

CHINCOTEAGUE

▼ The Farmer's Daughter
(0) 000-0000. American. Quick Serve. **$5-$13.** 6700 Maddox St 23336. Just nw of entrance to Chincoteague National Wildlife Refuge.
L D &M Æ

CLIFTON

▼▼ Rosemary's Thyme Bistro
(703) 502-1084. Mediterranean. Casual Dining. **$10-$22.** 5762 Union Mill Rd 20124. From US 29 (Lee Hwy), 0.4 mi s on Union Mill Rd; in The Colonnade at Union Mill. L D

▼▼▼ Trummer's on Main
(703) 266-1623. American. Fine Dining. **$14-$38.** 7134 Main St 20124. 3.7 mi s of CR 620 on Clifton Rd. D &M

DUMFRIES

▼▼ Giorgio's Family Restaurant
(703) 580-8500. Italian. Casual Dining. **$8-$25.** 4394 Kevin Walker Dr 22025. I-95 exit 152B, 2 mi n on SR 234; in Montclair Shopping Plaza.
L D &M

FAIRFAX

▼▼ Anita's
(703) 385-2965. Mexican. Casual Dining. **$8-$16.** 10880 Lee Hwy 22030. I-66 exit 60, 0.7 mi s on SR 123, then 0.7 mi w on US 50/29.
B L D

▼▼ Blue Iguana
(703) 502-8108. American. Casual Dining. **$10-$26.** 12727 Shoppes Ln 22033. I-66 exit 55 (Fairfax County Pkwy N), 0.3 mi n on SR 286, then just w; in The Shops at Fair Lakes. L D

▼▼ Cantina D'Italia
(703) 631-2752. Italian. Casual Dining. **$9-$30.** 13015 Fair Lakes Shopping Center 22033. I-66 exit 55 (Fairfax County Pkwy N), 0.3 mi n on SR 286, then 0.5 mi w on Fair Lakes Pkwy; in Fair Lakes Shopping Center.
L D &M

▼▼ Glory Days Grill
(703) 204-0900. American. Casual Dining. **$9-$18.** 3059 Nutley St 22031. I-66 exit 62, 0.6 mi s on Nutley St (SR 243); in Pan Am Shopping Center. L D LATE

▼▼ Hard Times Cafe
(703) 267-9590. American. Casual Dining. **$7-$14.** 4069 Chain Bridge Rd 22030. On SR 123, just s of jct SR 236. L D

▼▼ Lebanese Kitchen
(703) 378-5001. Lebanese. Casual Dining. **$7-$16.** 13031 Lee Jackson Memorial Hwy 22033. I-66 exit 57B, 3.2 mi w on US 50; in Greenbriar Town Center. L D &M

▼ Red Apron
(703) 676-3550. Sandwiches Hot Dogs. Quick Serve. **$5-$10.** 8298 Glass Alley 22031. I-495 exit 50A, just w to SR 650, 0.5 mi n on Gallows Rd; in Mosaic District. L D &M

▼▼ Sisters Thai - The Ordinary Cafe
(703) 280-0429. Thai. Casual Dining. **$11-$18.** 2985 District Ave 22031. I-495 exit 50A, just w to SR 650, then 0.5 mi n on Gallows Rd; in Mosaic District. L D

▼ Tony's New York Pizza
(703) 502-0808. Italian Pizza. Casual Dining. **$6-$18.** 13087 Fair Lakes Shopping Center 22033. I-66 exit 55 (Fairfax County Pkwy N), 0.3 mi n on SR 286, then 0.5 mi w on Fair Lakes Pkwy; in Fair Lakes Shopping Center. L D LATE

FALLS CHURCH

▼▼ Four Sisters Restaurant
(703) 539-8566. Vietnamese. Casual Dining. **$10-$25.** 8190 Strawberry Ln, Suite 1 22042. I-495 exit 50A, just w to SR 650, then 0.4 mi n on Gallows Rd: in Mosaic District. L D &M

▼▼ Pistone's Italian Inn
(703) 533-1885. Italian. Casual Dining. **$10-$37.** 6320 Arlington Blvd 22044. I-395 exit 5, 3 mi e on SR 7, then just n; jct SR 7 and US 50; in Seven Corners area. L D

▼▼▼ Sea Pearl
(703) 372-5161. Seafood Sushi. Casual Dining. **$10-$30.** 8191 Strawberry Ln, Suite 2 22042. I-495 exit 50A, just w to SR 650, then 0.4 mi n on Gallows Rd: in Mosaic District. L D &M

FREDERICKSBURG

▼▼▼ The Bavarian Chef
(540) 656-2101. German. Fine Dining. **$8-$36.** 200 Lafayette Blvd 22401. Between Caroline and Princess Anne sts; in Olde Towne; in Amtrak station. L D &M

▼▼▼ Bistro Bethem
(540) 371-9999. American. Fine Dining. **$7-$28.** 309 William St 22401. Jct Caroline St; in Olde Towne. L D

▼▼ Mason-Dixon Cafe
(540) 371-1950. American. Casual Dining. **$18.** 2100 Princess Anne St 22401. Just se of jct US 1 (Jefferson Davis Hwy). B L D

GAINESVILLE

▼▼ El Tio Tex-Mex Grill
(703) 753-0826. Tex-Mex. Casual Dining. **$11-$21.** 7527 Linton Hall Rd 20155. I-66 exit 43A, 1.1 mi w to Linton Hall Rd (CR 619), just se; in Virginia Gateway shopping complex. L D &M

HAMPTON

▼▼▼ The Point at Phoebus
(757) 224-9299. American. Gastropub. **$10-$30.** 30 E Mellen St 23663. I-64 exit 268 (E Mallory St), just n to E Mellen St; in downtown Phoebus.
L D

HERNDON

▼▼ Tara Thai
(703) 481-8999. Thai. Casual Dining. **$11-$16.** 13021 Worldgate Dr 20170. Jct SR 657 and 267 (Dulles Toll Rd) exit 10; in Worldgate Centre.
L D

LEESBURG

▼▼◆ **Fire Works-Wood Fired Pizza**
(703) 779-8400. Pizza. Casual Dining. **$8-$19.** 201 Harrison St 20175. Jct Loudoun and Harrison sts; in Market Station. L D

▼◆ **Lightfoot**
(703) 771-2233. American. Fine Dining. **$12-$33.** 11 N King St 20176. Just n of jct E Market St (SR 7 business route). L D

▼ **MELT gourmet cheeseburgers**
(703) 443-2105. Burgers. Quick Serve. **$7-$16.** 525 E Market St, Suite J 20176. On SR 7 business route, 0.4 mi w from jct US 15; in Bellwood Commons Shopping Center. L D ᕼM

MANASSAS

▼▼ **Mariachis Tequileria & Restaurant**
(703) 369-6022. Mexican. Casual Dining. **$10-$25.** 9428 Battle St 20110. Just s of Center St; in Historic Old Town; opposite train station. L D

▼▼ **Okra's Cajun Creole**
(703) 330-2729. Regional American. Casual Dining. **$8-$35.** 9110 Center St 20110. Jct Battle St; in Historic Old Town. L D

MIDDLEBURG

▼▼◆◆ **Harrimans**
(540) 326-4070. American. Fine Dining. **$26-$40.** 500 N Pendleton St 20117. Off US 50, just n on Pendleton St; in Salamander Resort & Spa.
B D ᕼM

NASSAWADOX

▼▼ **The Great Machipongo Clam Shack**
(757) 442-3800. Seafood. Casual Dining. **$7-$24.** 6468 Lankford Hwy 23413. 0.8 mi n on US 13. L D ᕼM

NEWPORT NEWS

▼ **Aromas**
(757) 244-4650. Coffee/Tea. Casual Dining. **$5-$11.** 706 Town Center Dr, Suite 104 23606. I-64 exit 255A, 2.5 mi s to Thimble Shoals Dr E; in City Center of Oyster Point. B L D

NORFOLK

▼▼◆◆ **219 American Bistro**
(757) 416-6219. New American. Casual Dining. **$7-$28.** 219 Granby St 23510. Jct Brooke Ave; downtown. L D

▼▼ **Bite Restaurant & Catering**
(757) 486-0035. American. Casual Dining. **$8-$12.** 440 Monticello Ave 23510. Jct Charlotte St; downtown; in Wells Fargo Center. B L

▼▼ **Capt. Groovy's Grill & Raw Bar**
(757) 965-4667. Seafood. Casual Dining. **$8-$27.** 8101 Shore Dr 23518. Just n of jct Little Creek Rd; in East Ocean View. L D ᕼM

▼▼◆ **La Bella in Ghent**
(757) 622-6172. Italian. Casual Dining. **$14-$23.** 738 W 22nd St 23517. Just e of Colley Ave; behind Center Shops; in Ghent. L D ᕼM

▼ **Taste Unlimited**
(757) 623-7770. Specialty Sandwiches. Quick Serve. **$5-$10.** 6464 Hampton Blvd 23508. I-64 exit 276 (I-564/Terminal Blvd), 2.5 mi w to Hampton Blvd, then 0.5 mi s. L D ᕼM

🅰🅰🅰 ▼▼◆ **Todd Jurich's Bistro**
(757) 622-3210. New American. Fine Dining. **$9-$42.** 150 W Main St, Suite 100 23510. Downtown; entrance on Boush St; across from Nauticus.
L D ᕼM

ONANCOCK

▼▼ **Bizzotto's Gallery-Caffe**
(757) 787-3103. Continental. Casual Dining. **$7-$34.** 41 Market St 23417. 1 mi w of US 13; center. L D

PETERSBURG

▼▼ **Dixie Restaurant**
(804) 732-7425. Southern Breakfast Comfort Food. Casual Dining. **$5-$10.** 250 N Sycamore St 23803. Jct W Bank St; in Olde Towne Historic District. B L

PORTSMOUTH

▼▼◆ **Cafe Europa**
(757) 399-6652. Continental. Fine Dining. **$10-$18.** 319 High St 23704. Just s of Crawford Pkwy; center. L D

▼▼◆ **Roger Brown's Restaurant & Sports Bar**
(757) 399-5377. American. Casual Dining. **$9-$22.** 316 High St 23704. Between Court and Crawford sts; in Olde Towne. L D

RICHMOND

▼◆▼ **Bistro 27**
(804) 780-0086. European. Fine Dining. **$15-$26.** 27 W Broad St 23219. Jct Adams St. D

▼ **Fresca...on Addison**
(804) 359-8638. Vegetarian Vegan. Quick Serve. **$8-$12.** 22 S Addison St 23220. Jct W Main St; in Historic Fan District. L

▼◆▼ **Rowland**
(804) 257-9885. American. Fine Dining. **$16-$27.** 2132 W Main St 23220. Jct Shields St; in Historic Fan District. D

SPRINGFIELD

▼ **BGR-The Burger Joint**
(703) 451-4651. Burgers. Quick Serve. **$7-$18.** 8420 Old Keene Mill Rd 22152. I-95 exit 169B, 3 mi w on SR 644; jct Rolling Rd; in Old Keene Mill Center. L D

▼ **Sandwich Republic**
(703) 451-1655. Sandwiches. Quick Serve. **$7-$9.** 7320 Old Keene Mill Rd 22150. I-95 exit 169A, just nw of SR 644; jct I-395 and 495, 0.8 mi s.
L D ᕼM

STAFFORD

▼▼ **Vinny's Italian Grill & Pizzeria**
(540) 657-8400. Italian Pizza. Casual Dining. **$7-$16.** 397 Garrisonville Rd 22554. I-95 exit 143B, 1.5 mi w; in Garrison Village Center. L D

VIRGINIA BEACH

▼▼◆ **Eurasia Cafe & Wine Bar**
(757) 422-0184. New American. Fine Dining. **$10-$30.** 960 Laskin Rd 23451. 1 mi w of oceanfront on 31st St (Laskin Rd/US 58); in Linkhorn Shops. L D ᕼM

▼▼ **The Raven**
(757) 425-1200. American. Casual Dining. **$7-$20.** 1200 Atlantic Ave 23451. At 12th St and Atlantic Ave. L D LATE 🍸

🅰🅰🅰 ▼▼ ▼▼ **Terrapin**
(757) 321-6688. New American. Fine Dining. **$21-$34.** 3102 Holly Rd, Suite 514 23451. I-264 terminus, just n on Baltic Ave to Holly Rd; jct 32nd St; in Pinewood Square. D ᕼM

WARRENTON

▼▼ **Black Bear Bistro**
(540) 428-1005. American. Casual Dining. **$8-$24.** 32 Main St 20186. Between Culpepper and 2nd sts; in Old Town area. L D

WILLIAMSBURG

▼▼▼ **Berret's Seafood Restaurant and Taphouse Grill**
(757) 253-1847. Seafood. Casual Dining. **$8-$30.** 199 S Boundary St
23185. Center; in Merchants Square. [L] [D]

▼▼▼ **Blue Talon Bistro**
(757) 476-2583. French. Casual Dining. **$7-$30.** 420 Prince George St
20106. Center; in Merchants Square. [D] [L] [D]

Washington

BELLINGHAM

⬥⬥⬥ ▼▼▼ **Dirty Dan Harris Steakhouse**
(360) 676-1011. Steak. Casual Dining. **$18-$37.** 1211 11th St 98225. I-5
exit 250, 1.5 mi nw; in Fairhaven Historic District. [D]

COUPEVILLE

▼▼▼ **Christopher's on Whidbey**
(360) 678-5480. Seafood. Casual Dining. **$8-$28.** 103 NW Coveland St
98239. Downtown. [L] [D]

EASTSOUND

▼▼ **Rose's Bakery & Cafe**
(360) 376-5805. American. Casual Dining. **$9-$20.** 382 Prune Alley
98245. In Eastsound; downtown. [B] [L]

EVERETT

▼▼▼ **Anthony's Restaurant**
(425) 252-3333. Seafood. Casual Dining. **$15-$35.** 1726 W Marine View
Dr 98201. I-5 exit 193 northbound, 1.2 mi w on Pacific Ave, then 1.4 mi n;
exit 194 southbound, 1.2 mi w on Everett Ave, then 1 mi n; in Everett
Marina Village. [L] [D]

LANGLEY

▼▼ **The Braeburn**
(360) 221-3211. American. Casual Dining. **$7-$13.** 197 2nd St 98260.
South end of town center. [B] [L] [𝒦]

MILL CREEK

▼▼ **McMenamins Mill Creek**
(425) 316-0520. American. Casual Dining. **$8-$16.** 13300 Bothell Everett
Hwy, Suite 304 98012. I-5 exit 186, 1 mi e, then just s. [L] [D] [LATE]

RENTON

▼▼ **Plum Delicious**
(425) 255-8510. American. Casual Dining. **$9-$23.** 3212 NE Sunset Blvd
98056. I-405 exit 5, 1.3 mi e. [B] [L] [D]

SEATTLE

▼▼▼ **Barolo Ristorante**
(206) 770-9000. Italian. Casual Dining. **$31-$50.** 1940 Westlake Ave
98101. Corner of Westlake Ave and Virginia St. [L] [D]

▼▼▼ **Cuoco**
(206) 971-0710. Northern Italian. Casual Dining. **$10-$42.** 310 Terry Ave
N 98109. Jct Harrison St, just s. [L] [D] [&M]

SPOKANE

▼▼ **Latah Bistro**
(509) 838-8338. Regional American. Casual Dining. **$9-$28.** 4241 S
Cheney-Spokane Rd, Suite C 99224. I-90 exit 279 (US 195 S), 2.4 mi s,
then 0.4 mi w. [L] [D] [&M]

▼▼▼ **Santé Restaurant & Charcuterie**
(509) 315-4613. Continental. Casual Dining. **$6-$29.** 404 W Main Ave
99201. Between N Washington and N Stevens sts; downtown.
[B] [L] [D]

SPOKANE VALLEY

▼▼▼ **Ambrosia Bistro & Wine Bar**
(509) 928-3222. International. Casual Dining. **$12-$29.** 9211 E Montgomery Ave 99206. I-90 exit 287 (Argonne Rd), 0.4 mi n on Mullan
Rd/Argonne Rd, then just e. [L] [D] [&M]

VANCOUVER

▼▼▼ **The Grant House**
(360) 906-1101. American. Casual Dining. **$8-$27.** 1101 Officers Row
98661. I-5 exit 1C (E Mill Plain Blvd), just e, just s on Fort Vancouver Way,
then just e. [L] [D]

▼▼ **McMenamins East Vancouver**
(360) 254-3950. American. Casual Dining. **$7-$30.** 1900 NE 162nd Ave
98684. SR 14 exit 8, 2.8 mi n via 164th and 162nd aves.
[L] [D] [LATE] [&M]

Wisconsin

APPLETON

▼▼ **GingeRootz Asian Grille**
(920) 738-9688. Asian. Casual Dining. **$8-$32.** 2920 N Ballard Rd
54911. US 41 exit 144 (Ballard Rd), 0.6 mi s. [L] [D]

DELAFIELD

▼▼▼ **Seven Seas on Nagawicka Lake**
(262) 367-3903. International. Fine Dining. **$19-$48.** 1807 Nagawicka Rd
53029. I-94 exit 287, 1.2 mi n on SR 83, then 0.7 mi w. [D] [&M]

Wyoming

CASPER

▼▼ **Bosco's Italian Restaurante**
(307) 265-9658. Italian. Casual Dining. **$6-$24.** 847 E 'A' St 82601. I-25
exit 188A (Center St), 0.4 mi s to E 'A' St, then 0.5 mi e. [L] [D]

SHERIDAN

▼ **Java Moon**
(307) 673-5991. Coffee/Tea. Casual Dining. **$6-$15.** 170 N Main St
82801. Center. [B] [L] [𝒦]

Canada

Alberta

BANFF

◆◆ **Coyotes Deli & Grill**
(403) 762-3963. New Southwestern. Casual Dining. **$9-$31.** 206 Caribou St T1L 1A2. Just w of Banff Ave; center. [B] [L] [D]

RED DEER

◆◆ **Moxie's Classic Grill**
(403) 340-0111. American. Casual Dining. **$14-$32.** 2828 Gaetz Ave T4R 1M4. 1 mi (1.6 km) n on Hwy 2A (Gaetz Ave); in Sandman Hotel Red Deer. [B] [L] [D] [LATE] [&M]

British Columbia

GIBSONS

◆◆ **Molly's Reach Restaurant**
(604) 886-9710. American. Casual Dining. **$7-$17.** 647 School Rd V0N 1V0. Jct School Rd and Gibsons Way; on waterfront.
[B] [L] [D] [&M] [K]

GOLDEN

◆◆◆ **The Island Restaurant**
(250) 344-2400. New Canadian. Casual Dining. **$11-$33.** 101 Gould's Island, 10th Ave V0A 1H0. Just between the bridges; downtown.
[B] [L] [D] [&M]

New Brunswick

ST. ANDREWS

(AA) ◆◆ **Harbour Front Restaurant**
(506) 529-4887. American. Casual Dining. **$9-$33.** 225 Water St E5B 1B3. Between King and Frederick sts; center. [L] [D] [K]

SAINT JOHN

◆◆ **Billy's Seafood Restaurant**
(506) 672-3474. Seafood. Casual Dining. **$15-$35.** 49-51 Charlotte St E2L 2H8. Center; in City Market. [L] [D]

◆◆ **Bourbon Quarter & Magnolia Cafe**
(506) 642-1885. Creole. Casual Dining. **$10-$30.** 112 Prince William St E2L 2B3. Corner of Princess St. [B] [L] [D]

Nova Scotia

GLENVILLE

◆◆ **Glenora Dining Room & Pub**
(902) 258-2662. Regional Canadian. Casual Dining. **$14-$37.** 13727 Rt 19 B0E 1X0. On Rt 19; in Glenora Inn & Distillery. [B] [L] [D] [&M]

Ontario

BAYFIELD

◆◆◆ **The Red Pump Restaurant**
(519) 565-2576. New American. Fine Dining. **$15-$45.** 21 Main St N0M 1G0. Hwy 21 exit Main St; between Charles and Catherine sts. [L] [D]

CORNWALL

◆◆◆ **Peppermill's Grill & Bakery**
(613) 932-0451. Canadian. Casual Dining. **$9-$35.** 1515 Vincent Massey Dr K6H 5R6. Hwy 401 exit 789 (Brookdale Ave), 1.8 mi (2.8 km) s, then just w; in BEST WESTERN PLUS Parkway Inn & Conference Centre.
[B] [L] [D]

NIAGARA-ON-THE-LAKE

◆◆◆ **The Epicurean**
(905) 468-3408. International. Fine Dining. **$9-$35.** 84 Queen St L0S 1J0. Center. [L] [D]

OTTAWA

◆◆◆ **Métropolitain Brasserie - Restaurant**
(613) 562-1160. French Seafood. Casual Dining. **$14-$38.** 700 Sussex Dr K1N 1K4. Corner Rideau St. [B] [L] [D] [LATE]

OWEN SOUND

◆◆◆ **Norma Jean's**
(519) 376-2232. International. Casual Dining. **$10-$29.** 243 8th St E N4K 1L2. Between 2nd and 3rd aves. [L] [D]

STRATFORD

◆◆◆ **Keystone Alley Cafe**
(519) 271-5645. International. Casual Dining. **$10-$33.** 34 Brunswick St N5A 3L8. Between Downie and Waterloo sts. [L] [D]

TORONTO

◆◆◆ **Bodega Restaurant**
(416) 977-1287. French. Fine Dining. **$12-$35.** 30 Baldwin St M5T 1L3. Between McCaul and Beverley sts. [L] [D]

WAWA

◆◆ **Kinniwabi Pines Restaurant**
(705) 856-7226. Continental. Casual Dining. **$7-$35.** 136 Hwy 17 S P0S 1K0. 3.3 mi (5.3 km) s of jct Hwy 101. [B] [L] [D]

Prince Edward Island

BRACKLEY BEACH

◆◆◆ **The Dunes Cafe & Studio Gallery**
(902) 672-2586. Canadian. Casual Dining. **$15-$40.** 3622 Brackley Point Rd C1E 1Z3. Jct Rt 6 and 15, 0.6 mi (1 km) n. [L] [D] [&M]

NORTH RUSTICO

◆◆◆ **The Pearl & Eclectic Eatery**
(902) 963-2111. Canadian. Casual Dining. **$25-$40.** 7792 Cavendish Rd C0A 1X0. 2 mi (3.2 km) w on Rt 6. [D] [&M] [K]

SUMMERSIDE

◆◆ **Lobster House Restaurant & Oyster Bar**
(902) 436-8439. Seafood. Casual Dining. **$12-$38.** 370 Water St W C1N 1C4. Between Cedar and 1st sts. [L] [D] [&M] [K] [⬧]

Quebec

MONTRÉAL

▼◆▼ **Le Pois Penché Brasserie Parisienne**
(514) 667-5050. French. Casual Dining. **$16-$48.** 1230 boul de Maisonneuve ouest H3G 1M2. Corner of rue Drummond. ⎣L⎦ ⎣D⎦

QUÉBEC

▼◆▼ **Trattoria La Scala**
(418) 529-8457. Italian. Casual Dining. **$14-$45.** 31 boul Rene-Levesque ouest G1R 2A3. Between rue Cartier and de Salaberry. ⎣L⎦ ⎣D⎦

WESTMOUNT

▼◆▼ **Vago Cucina Italiana**
(514) 846-1414. Italian. Casual Dining. **$18-$42.** 1336 ave Greene H3Z 2B1. Just s of rue Sherbrooke. ⎣L⎦ ⎣D⎦

Saskatchewan

REGINA

▼◆▼ **Creek In Cathedral Bistro**
(306) 352-4448. American. Casual Dining. **$13-$31.** 3414 13th Ave S4T 1P7. Just e of Elphinstone St. ⎣L⎦ ⎣D⎦

SASKATOON

▼◆▼ **Calories Bakery & Restaurant**
(306) 665-7991. International Desserts. Casual Dining. **$12-$32.** 721 Broadway Ave S7N 1B3. Just s of Broadway Bridge. ⎣L⎦ ⎣D⎦ ⎣&M⎦

❀ Pet-Friendly Travel Notes ❀

❀ Pet-Friendly Travel Notes ❀

❧ Pet-Friendly Travel Notes ❧

❧ Pet-Friendly Travel Notes ❧

❀ Pet-Friendly Travel Notes ❀

❀ Pet-Friendly Travel Notes ❀

❀ Pet-Friendly Travel Notes ❀